HANDBOOK OF FOOD SCIENCE, TECHNOLOGY, AND ENGINEERING

Volume 1

Edited by

Y. H. HUI

Associate Editors

J. D. Culbertson, S. Duncan, I. Guerrero-Legarreta,
E. C. Y. Li-Chan, C. Y. Ma, C. H. Manley, T. A. McMeekin,
W. K. Nip, L. M. L. Nollet, M. S. Rahman, F. Toldr , Y. L. Xiong

Taylor & Francis
Taylor & Francis Group
Boca Raton London New York

A CRC title, part of the Taylor & Francis imprint, a member of the
Taylor & Francis Group, the academic division of T&F Informa plc.

Published in 2006 by
CRC Press
Taylor & Francis Group
6000 Broken Sound Parkway NW, Suite 300
Boca Raton, FL 33487-2742

International Standard Book Number-10: 0-8493-9847-9 (Set)
International Standard Book Number-10: 1-57444-551-0 (Vol 1)
International Standard Book Number-10: 0-8493-9848-7 (Vol 2)
International Standard Book Number-10: 1-57444-552-9 (Vol 3)
International Standard Book Number-10: 0-8493-9849-5 (Vol 4)
International Standard Book Number-13: 978-0-8493-9847-6 (Set)
International Standard Book Number-13: 978-1-57444-551-0 (Vol 1)
International Standard Book Number-13: 978-0-8493-9848-3 (Vol 2)
International Standard Book Number-13: 978-1-57444-552-7 (Vol 3)
International Standard Book Number-13: 978-0-8493-9849-0 (Vol 4)
Library of Congress Card Number 2005050551

Library of Congress Cataloging-in-Publication Data

Handbook of food science, technology, and engineering / edited by Y.H. Hui.
    p. cm. -- (Food science and technology ; 148)
  Includes bibliographical references and index.
  ISBN 1-57444-551-0 (v. 1 : alk. paper) -- ISBN 0-8493-9848-7 (v. 2 : alk. paper) -- ISBN 1-57444-552-9 (v. 3 : alk. paper) -- ISBN 0-8493-9849-5 (v. 4 : alk. paper)
  1. Food industry and trade--Handbooks, manuals, etc. 2. Food--Analysis--Handbooks, manuals, etc. 3. Food--Composition--Handbooks, manuals, etc. I. Hui, Y. H. (Yiu H.) II. Food science and technology (Taylor & Francis) ; 148.

TP370.4.H38 2005
664--dc22
                                                  2005050551

Taylor & Francis Group is the Academic Division of Informa plc.

Visit the Taylor & Francis Web site at
http://www.taylorandfrancis.com

and the CRC Press Web site at
http://www.crcpress.com

Preface for Volumes 1 and 2

In the last 30 years, progress in food science, food technology, and food engineering has advanced exponentially. As usual, information dissemination for this progress is expressed in many media, both printed and electronic. Books are available for almost every specialty area within these three disciplines, numbering in the hundreds.

Collective works on the disciplines are also available, though in smaller number. Examples are encyclopedias (food science, food engineering, food packaging) and handbooks (nutrition, food processing, food technology). Because handbooks on these topics are limited, this four-volume treatise is released by Taylor & Francis to fill this gap. The title of these four volumes is *Handbook of Food Science, Technology, and Engineering* with individual volume title as follows:

- Volume 1: Food Science: Properties and Products
- Volume 2: Food Science: Ingredients, Health, and Safety
- Volume 3: Food Engineering and Food Processing
- Volume 4: Food Technology and Food Processing

This preface introduces Volumes 1 and 2. Each volume contains about 1,000 printed pages of scientific and technical information. Volume 1 contains 55 chapters and Volume 2 contains 46 chapters. Volume 1 presents the following categories of topics, with the number of chapters indicated:

- Food components and their properties, 14
- Food categories, 26
- Food analysis, 9
- Food microbiology, 6

Volume 2 presents the following categories of topics, with the number of chapters indicated:

- Food attributes, 7
- Food fermentation, 8
- Food and workers safety, food security, 12
- Functional food ingredients, 15
- Nutrition and health, 4

A brief discussion of the coverage for each volume is described below.

In Volume 1, the first group of topics covers the components and properties of food such as carbohydrate, protein, fat, vitamins, water, and pigments. The second group of topics covers the different categories of food products including, but not limited to, beverages, bakery, cereals, legumes, vegetables, fruits, milk, meat, poultry, fats, oils, seafood, and wine. The third group of topics describes the analysis of food such as basic principles and various techniques (chemical method, spectroscopy, chromatography, mass spectrometry, and other analytical methodology). The last group of topics covers food microbiology such as basic considerations, spoilage, land and marine animals, and analytical methodology.

In Volume 2, the first group of topics covers the attributes of food such as sensory science, data base concepts, flavor, texture, and color. The second group of topics covers food fermentation including basic principles, quality, flavor, meat, milk, cultured products, cheese, yeasts, and pickles. The third group of topics covers food from the perspective of safety, workers health, and security, especially in the United States, such as food standards, food protection methods, filth, pathogens, migratory chemicals, food plant sanitation, retail food sanitation, establishment safety, animal feeds and drugs, and bio-terrorism. The fourth group of topics covers major functional food ingredients including, but not limited to, antioxidants, colors, aroma, flavor, spice, enzyme, emulsifiers, phytates, sorbates, artificial sweeteners, eggs, gums. The last group of topics covers special topics in nutrition and health such as food allergy, Chinese edible botanicals, dietary supplements, and health related advertisement in the United States.

When studying the information in this two-volume text, please note two important considerations:

1. Although major topics in the discipline are included, there is no claim that the coverage is comprehensive.
2. Although the scientific information is applicable worldwide, a small number of topics with legal implications are especially pertinent in the United States.

These two volumes are the result of the combined effort of more than 150 professionals from industry, government, and academia. They are from more than 15 countries with diverse expertise and background in the discipline of food science. These experts were led by an international editorial team of 13 members from 8 countries. All these individuals, authors and editors, are responsible for assembling 2,000 printed pages of scientific topics of immense complexity. In sum, the end product is unique, both in depth and breadth, and will serve as an essential reference on food science for professionals in government, industry, and academia.

The editorial team thanks all the contributors for sharing their experience in their fields of expertise. They are the people who make this book possible. We hope you enjoy and benefit from the fruits of their labor.

We know how hard it is to develop the content of a book. However, we believe that the production of a professional book of this nature is even more difficult. We thank the editorial and production teams at Taylor & Francis for their time, effort, advice, and expertise. You are the best judge of the quality of this book.

Y. H. Hui
J. D. Culbertson
S. Duncan
I. Guerrero-Legarreta
E. C. Y. Li-Chan
C. Y. Ma
C. H. Manley
T. A. McMeekin
W. K. Nip
L. M. L. Nollet
M. S. Rahman
F. Toldrá
Y. L. Xiong

The Editor

Dr. Y. H. Hui holds a Ph.D. in food and nutritional biochemistry from the University of California at Berkeley. He is semi-retired and has been a consultant to the food industry since 2000. He is currently a senior scientist with the consultant firm Science Technology System in West Sacramento, CA. He has authored, coauthored, edited, and coedited more than 35 books in food science, food technology, food engineering, food law, nutrition, health, and medicine, including the *Encyclopedia of Food Science and Technology, Bailey's Industrial Oils and Fat Products, Foodborne Disease Handbook, Food Plant Sanitation,* and *Food Processing: Principles and Applications.*

ASSOCIATE EDITORS

Dr. Jeff Culbertson is a professor of food science at the University of Idaho. He earned his B.S. and M.S. degrees at Oregon State University and his Ph.D. at Washington State University—all in Food Science. He previously taught at the University of Wisconsin–River Falls and Central Michigan University. For a number of years he was the manager of Corporate Quality at the Kellogg Corporation. He maintains an active consulting business with many Fortune 500 clients from the food and beverage industry.

Dr. Susan E. Duncan is a professor in the Department of Food Science and Technology, Virginia Polytechnic Institute and State University, Blacksburg, VA. She earned her Ph.D. in food technology and science, The University of Tennessee, Knoxville. She is the director of the Macromolecular Interfaces with Life Sciences Program, a multidisciplinary graduate program integrating polymer chemistry and life sciences. Dr. Duncan is a sensory specialist with a focus on quality issues of dairy, lipids, nutraceutical, and water/beverage products, emphasizing interactions with packaging materials. She has authored 50 peer-reviewed research publications and 7 book chapters. She is a member of the Institute of Food Technologists and American Dairy Science Association.

Dr. Eunice C. Y. Li-Chan is a professor of food science at the University of British Columbia, Faculty of Agricultural Sciences, Food Nutrition & Health Program. Her significant research contributions include pioneering studies that launched the use of Raman spectroscopy and fluorescent hydrophobic probes as tools to study food protein systems, research that established the potential and protocols for using egg yolk antibodies in lieu of mammalian polyclonal antibodies in immunochemistry and immunoaffinity techniques, and the isolation and characterization of value-added proteins and peptides as functional food ingredients. Her publication record includes authorship or coauthorship in over 75 original articles in peer-reviewed scientific journals, more than 25 chapters in books, and a book entitled *Hydrophobic Interactions in Food Systems* (1988, CRC Press).

Dr. Isabel Guerrero Legarreta is a profesor of food science, Department of Biotechnology, Universidad Autónoma Metropolitana, Iztapalapa, México. She received a B.Eng. degree (1972) in chemical engineering from the Universidad Nacional Autónoma de Mexico, Mexico City, an M.Sc. degree (1975) in food science from the University of Reading, England, and a Ph.D. (1983) in food science from the University of Guelph, Canada. Her research and teaching work has been focused on meat and fish preservation and utilization in subtropical areas. She has also studied the obtainment of products from marine resources, stressing the utilization of marine underutilized material and its by-products. Her professional contributions include over 100 papers, book chapters, and a patent on industrial carotenoid pigment separation from shrimp wastes.

Dr. C. Y. Ma obtained his Ph.D. in food chemistry from the University of British Columbia, Canada. After working as a research scientist in Agriculture and Agri-Food Canada for 16 years, he is now a professor of food science at the University of Hong Kong. His current research activities include the study of structure-function relationships of food proteins and bioactive peptides. The molecular structure and conformation of selected proteins with potential uses as food ingredients and peptides possessing biological/pharmaceutical activities are studied by various physical and chemical techniques. Professor Ma also studies the potential uses of under-utilized protein sources from cereal and legume seeds, and the improvements of functional properties of these proteins by various chemical and physical methods.

Dr. Charles Manley received his Ph.D. from the University of Massachusetts–Amherst for research in the area of food and flavor chemistry. He received a B.S. degree in chemistry at University of Massachusetts–Dartmouth. He has worked as a research chemist for the Givaudan Company, and in various research and management positions within a number of Unilever Companies, including manager of Beverage Development and Technology for Thomas J. Lipton, director of Flavor Operations for the National Starch and Chemical Company, and as vice president, International Business Development for Quest International. Currently he serves as vice president of science and technology for Takasago International Corporation (U.S.A.). Takasago is one of the leading Global Flavor and Fragrance Companies with sales volumes in the top five. His major corporate responsibilities have been in managing commercialization of scientific research efforts and departments at both Unilever and Takasago. He has made major professional contributions, including over 150 publications, patents, and presentations in the field of flavor ingredient safety, food processing and science, and natural product chemistry. He has served as the president of the Institute of Food Technologists (IFT) and the Flavor and Extract Manufacturers' Association (FEMA).

Professor Tom McMeekin holds a personal Chair of Microbiology at the University of Tasmania and is co-director of the Australian Food Safety Centre of Excellence. He is a Fellow of the Australian Academy of Technological Sciences and Engineering, Scientific Fellow of Food Standards Australia New Zealand, and Chair of the Food Safety Information Council. Professor McMeekin has contributed to more than 200 publications, including the monograph "Predictive Microbiology: Theory and Application," and has made greater than 30 invited international conference and workshop presentations. He is an executive board member of the International Committee of Food Microbiology and Hygiene and an editor of the *International Journal of Food Microbiology*. Awards include the JR Vickery Medal (International Institute of Refrigeration, 1987), the Annual Award of Merit (Australian Institute of Food Science and Technology, 1998), and International Leadership Award (International Association of Food Professionals, 2002).

Dr. Wai-Kit Nip is a food technologist emeritus from the Department of Molecular Biosciences and Bioengineering, University of Hawaii at Manoa, Honolulu. Dr. Nip received his B.S. degree (Food Technology, 1962) from National Chung-Hsing University, Taiwan, and an M.S. degree (Food Technology, 1965) and Ph.D. (1969) from Texas A&M University, College Station, Texas, U.S.A. He has taught classes in food processing, food safety, and experimental foods. Research activities include handling and processing of tropical fruits and vegetables, and aquatic foods. He has published numerous refereed articles, proceeding papers, and book chapters, and coedited several books in the food science and techology area. He is also the senior contributor of a patent. He has served at various capacities in local and national scientific organizations.

Dr. Leo M. L. Nollet is a professor of biotechnology at Hogeschool Ghent, Ghent, Belgium. The author and coauthor of numerous articles, abstracts, and presentations, Dr. Nollet is the editor of the *Handbook of Water Analysis*, *Food Analysis by HPLC*, and *Handbook of Food Analysis (3 volumes)* (all titles Marcel Dekker). His research interests include food analysis techniques, HPLC, and environmental analysis techniques. He received an M.S. degree (1973) and a Ph.D. (1978) in biology from the Katholieke Universiteit, Leuven, Blegium.

Dr. Mohammad Shafiur Rahman is an associate professor at the Sultan Qaboos University, Sultanate of Oman. He is the author or coauthor of over 150 technical articles and the author of the internationally acclaimed and award-winning *Food Properties Handbook* published by CRC Press, Boca Raton, FL. He is editor of the *Handbook of Food Preservation* published by Marcel Dekker, New York, which was translated into Spanish by Acribia, Spain in 2003. He is one of the editors for the *Handbook of Food and Bioprocess Modeling Techniques*, which will be published by Taylor & Francis. Dr. Rahman has initiated the *International Journal of Food Properties* (Marcel Dekker) and has been serving as the founding editor for more than 6 years. He is one of the section editors for the Sultan Qaboos University *Journal of Agricultural Sciences* (1999). In 1998 he was invited to serve as a food science adviser for the International Foundation for Science (IFS) in Sweden. He received B.Sc.Eng. (chemical) (1983) and M.Sc.Eng. (chemical) (1984) degrees from Bangladesh University of Engineering and Technology, Dhaka, an M.Sc. degree (1985) from Leeds University, England, and a Ph.D. (1992) in food engineering from the University of New South Wales, Sydney, Australia. Dr. Rahman has received numerous awards and fellowships in recognition of research/teaching achievements, including the HortResearch Chairman's Award, the Bilateral Research Activities Program (BRAP) Award, CAMS Outstanding Researcher Award 2003, and the British Council Fellowship.

Dr. Fidel Toldrá holds a B.Sc. degree in chemistry (1980), M.Sc. degree in food technology (1981), and a Ph.D. in chemistry (1984). Currently, he is research professor and head of the Laboratory of Meat Science, Department of Food Science, at the Instituto de Agroquímica y Tecnología de Alimentos (CSIC) in Burjassot, Valencia (Spain). He is also an associate professor of food technology at the Polytechnical University of Valencia. Professor Toldrá has received several awards such as the 2002 International Prize for Meat Science and Technology, given by the International Meat Secretariat during the 14th World Meat Congress held in Berlin. Professor Toldrá has filed 7 patents, authored 1 book and 45 chapters of books, coedited 9 books, and published more than 121 manuscripts in worldwide recognized scientific journals. His research interests are based on food chemistry and biochemistry with special focus on muscle foods. He has served in several committees for international societies and, since May 2003, is also a member of the Scientific Commission on Food Additives, Flavorings, Processing Aids and Materials in contact with foods of the European Food Safety Authority (EFSA).

Dr. Youling L. Xiong is professor of food chemistry at the Department of Animal and Food Sciences, University of Kentucky. He obtained a Ph.D. from Washington State University (1989) and received postdoctoral training at Cornell University. Professor Xiong also holds joint appointments with the Graduate Center for Nutritional Sciences and the Center for Membrane Sciences at the university. Dr. Xiong's research focuses primarily on food protein chemistry and biochemistry, functionality, and applications, with an emphasis on muscle food processing. His fundamental work in food protein oxidation and the study of enzymic modification of soy, whey, wheat, and potato proteins to obtain physicochemically and biologically functional peptides has earned him several prestigious national awards. Dr. Xiong has published more than 130 research papers, contributed to 18 book chapters, and coedited two food science books. He also teaches undergraduate and graduate food chemistry, food protein, and meat science courses.

Contributors

Sufian F. Al-Khaldi
Center for Food Safety and Applied
  Nutrition
U.S. Food and Drug Administration
College Park, Maryland

Christine Z. Alvarado
Department of Animal and Food
  Sciences
Texas Tech University
Lubbock, Texas

Pedro Alvarez
Department of Food Science and
  Agricultural Chemistry
McGill University
Quebec, Canada

Sameer F. Al-Zenki
Department of Biotechnology
Kuwait Institute for Scientific
  Research
Safat, Kuwait

Fletcher M. Arritt III
Department of Food Science and
  Technology
Virginia Polytechnic Institute and
  State University
Blacksburg, Virginia

Eveline J. Bartowsky
The Australian Wine Research
  Institute
Adelaide, Australia

James N. BeMiller
Whistler Center for Carbohydrate
  Research
Purdue University
West Lafayette, Indiana

Daniel W. Bena
PepsiCo International
Purchase, New York

Yizhong Cai
Cereal Science Laboratory
Department of Botany
The University of Hong Kong
Hong Kong, China

C.G. Carter
Tasmanian Aquaculture and
  Fisheries Institute
University of Tasmania
Tasmania, Australia

Chung Chieh
Department of Chemistry
University of Waterloo
Waterloo, Ontario, Canada

Robert Cocciardi
Department of Food Science and
  Agricultural Chemistry
McGill University
Quebec, Canada

Harold Corke
Cereal Science Laboratory
Department of Botany
The University of Hong Kong
Hong Kong, China

Nanna Cross
Consultant
Chicago, Illinois

Steve W. Cui
Food Research Program
Agriculture and Agri-Food
  Canada
Guelph, Ontario, Canada

Jeff D. Culbertson
Department of Food Science and
  Toxicology
University of Idaho
Moscow, Idaho

Paw Dalgaard
Danish Institute for Fisheries
  Research
Technical University of Denmark
Lyngby, Denmark

Srinivasan Damodaran
Department of Food Science
University of Wisconsin–Madison
Madison, Wisconsin

Johan Debevere
Department of Food Technology,
  Chemistry, Microbiology and
  Human Nutrition
Ghent University
Ghent, Belgium

Joannie Dobbs
Department of Human Nutrition
  Food and Animal Sciences
University of Hawaii at Manoa
Honolulu, Hawaii

Joseph D. Eifert
Department of Food Science and
  Technology
Virginia Polytechnic Institute and
  State University
Blacksburg, Virginia

Ronald R. Eitenmiller
Department of Food Science and
  Technology
University of Georgia
Athens, Georgia

John Flanagan
Riddet Centre
Massey University
Palmerston North, New Zealand

Frederick S. Fry
Center for Food Safety and Applied
  Nutrition
U.S. Food and Drug Administration
College Park, Maryland

Ifigenia Geornaras
Center for Red Meat Safety
Department of Animal Sciences
Colorado State University
Fort Collins, Colorado

Maria Beatriz Abreu Glória
Departamento de Alimentos
Universidade Federal de Minas
  Gerais
Belo Horizonte, MG Brazil

Lone Gram
Danish Institute for Fisheries
  Research
Technical University of Denmark
Lyngby, Denmark

Douglas G. Hayward
Center for Food Safety and Applied
  Nutrition
U.S. Food and Drug Administration
College Park, Maryland

Francisco J. Hidalgo
Instituto de la Grasa y sus Derivados
Consejo Superor de Investigaciones
  Cientificas
Sevilla, Spain

Y.-H. Peggy Hsieh
Department of Nutrition, Food and
  Exercise Sciences
Florida State University
Tallahassee, Florida

Kerry C. Huber
Department of Food Science and
  Toxicology
University of Idaho
Moscow, Idaho

Ashraf A. Ismail
Department of Food Science and
  Agricultural Chemistry
McGill University
Quebec, Canada

Shann-Tzong Jiang
Department of Food Science
National Taiwan Ocean University
Keelung, Taiwan, R.O.C.

David Kang
Department of Food Science and
  Technology
Virginia Polytechnic Institute and
  State University
Blacksburg, Virginia

A.L. Kelly
Department of Food and Nutritional
  Sciences
University College Cork
Cork, Ireland

Konstantinos P. Koutsoumanis
Department of Food Science and
  Technology
Aristotle University of Thessaloniki
Thessaloniki, Greece

JaeHwan Lee
Department of Food Science and
  Technology
Seoul National University of
  Technology
Seoul, Korea

Tung-Ching Lee
Department of Food Science
Rutgers University
New Brunswick, New Jersey

Tomasz Lesiów
Department of Quality Analysis
University of Economics
Wroclaw, Poland

Eunice C.Y. Li-Chan
Food, Nutrition and Health Program
Faculty of Agricultural Sciences
The University of British Columbia
Vancouver, British Columbia, Canada

Li Lite
Department of Food Science and
  Nutritional Engineering
China Agricultural University
Beijing, China

Hsiao-Feng Lo
Department of Horticulture
Chinese Culture University
Taipei, Taiwan, R.O.C.

Miguel A. de Barros Lopes
The Australian Wine Research
  Institute
Adelaide, Australia

R. Malcolm Love
Consultant
East Silverburn, Kingswells
Aberdeen, Scotland

Ching-Yung Ma
Department of Botany
The University of Hong Kong
Hong Kong, China

Armando McDonald
Department of Forest Products
University of Idaho
Moscow, Idaho

P.L.H. McSweeney
Department of Food and Nutritional
  Sciences
University College Cork
Cork, Ireland

Natalie A. Moltschaniwskyj
Tasmanian Aquaculture and
  Fisheries Institute
University of Tasmania
Tasmania, Australia

Magdi M. Mossoba
Center for Food Safety and Applied
  Nutrition
U.S. Food and Drug Administration
College Park, Maryland

Lorraine L. Niba
Department of Human Nutrition,
  Foods and Exercise
Virginia Polytechnic Institute and
  State University
Blacksburg, Virgina

S. Suzanne Nielsen
Department of Food Science
Purdue University
West Lafayette, Indiana

Gregory O. Noonan
Center for Food Safety and Applied
   Nutrition
U.S. Food and Drug Administration
College Park, Maryland

Casey M. Owens
Department of Poultry Science
University of Arkansas
Fayetteville, Arkansas

Richard Owusu-Apenten
Department of Food Science
Pennsylvania State University
University Park, Pennsylvania

Jan Pokorný
Department of Food Chemistry and
   Analysis
Prague Institute of Chemical
   Technology
Prague, Czech Republic

Isak S. Pretorius
The Australian Wine Research
   Institute
Adelaide, Australia

Mark P. Richards
Muscle Biology & Meat Science
   Laboratory
University of Wisconsin–Madison
Madison, Wisconsin

Manoj K. Rout
Department of Botany
The University of Hong Kong
Hong Kong, China

Robert B. Rucker
Department of Agricultural and
   Environmental Science and
   Nutrition
University of California
Davis, California

Christine H. Scaman
Food, Nutrition and Health Program
Faculty of Agricultural Sciences
The University of British Columbia
Vancouver, British Columbia, Canada

Steven J. Schwartz
Department of Food Science and
   Technology
The Ohio State University
Columbus, Ohio

Jacqueline Sedman
Department of Food Science and
   Agricultural Chemistry
McGill University
Quebec, Canada

Jiwan S. Sidhu
College for Women
Kuwait University
Safat, Kuwait

Harjinder Singh
Riddet Center
Massey University
Palmerston North, New Zealand

Antoine-Michel Siouffi
Université Paul Cezanne
Campus St. Jerôme
Marseille, France

John N. Sofos
Center for Red Meat Safety
Department of Animal Sciences
Colorado State University
Fort Collins, Colorado

Frank W. Sosulski
GrainTech Consulting Inc.
Saskatoon, Canada

Krystyna Sosulski
GrainTech Consulting Inc.
Saskatoon, Canada

Bernd Spangenberg
Umweltanalytik
   Fachhochschule Offenburg
Offenburg, Germany

Peggy Stanfield
Dietetic Resources
Twin Falls, Idaho

Francene Steinberg
Department of Agricultural and
   Environmental Science and
   Nutrition
University of California
Davis, California

C. Alan Titchenal
Department of Human Nutrition,
   Food and Animal Sciences
University of Hawaii at Manoa
Honolulu, Hawaii

Fidel Toldrá
Instituto de Agroquímica y
   Tecnología de Alimentos (CSIC)
Burjassot (Valencia), Spain

Jocelyn Shing-Jy Tsao
Department of Horticulture
National Taiwan University
Taipei, Taiwan, R.O.C.

Sherri B. Turnipseed
Animal Drug Research Center
U.S. Food and Drug Administration
Denver, Colorado

Mieke Uyttendaele
Department of Food Technology,
   Chemistry, Microbiology and
   Human Nutrition
Ghent University
Ghent, Belgium

Baowu Wang
Department of Food and Nutritional
   Sciences
Tuskegee University
Tuskegee, Alabama

Qi Wang
Food Research Program
Agriculture and Agri-Food Canada
Guelph, Ontario, Canada

P. J. Wood
Food Research Program
Agriculture and Agri-Food
  Canada
Guelph, Ontario, Canada

Lin Ye
Department of Food Science and
  Technology
University of Georgia
Athens, Georgia

Rosario Zamora
Instituto de la Grasa y sus Derivados
Consejo Superor de Investigaciones
  Cientificas
Sevilla, Spain

Contents

Part A

Components

1 Carbohydrate Chemistry

Kerry C. Huber
Department of Food Science and Toxicology, University of Idaho

Armando McDonald
Department of Forest Products, University of Idaho

James N. BeMiller
Whistler Center for Carbohydrate Research, Purdue University

CONTENTS

I. INTRODUCTION TO CARBOHYDRATES

Carbohydrates, which in their basic form exhibit the general chemical formula $C_n(H_2O)_n$, are a class of organic compounds that were historically designated "hydrates of carbon" due to their observed elemental composition. As the most abundant class of organic compounds on Earth, carbohydrates are the primary constituents of plants and exoskeletons of crustaceans and insects. Therefore, carbohydrates are virtually an unavoidable element of daily life, as they are encountered in food (glucose, sucrose, starch, etc.), wood, paper, and cotton (cellulose). Carbohydrates themselves can be sub-grouped according to the number of sugar building blocks comprising their respective structures from monomers (monosaccharides) right through to polymers (polysaccharides). In addition, the diversity of carbohydrates occurring within nature arises from the number of carbon atoms comprising sugar monomer units (monosaccharides of 3 to 9 carbon atoms), the varied chemical structure of monosaccharides (including substituent groups), and the nature of linkages joining monosaccharide units.

II. MONOSACCHARIDES

Monosaccharides, which represent the most basic carbohydrate elements, are polyhydroxy aldehydes and ketones commonly referred to as aldoses and ketoses, respectively. In addition, the number of carbon atoms present in the molecule also aids classification of monosaccharides. For sugars comprised of 3, 4, 5, 6, and 7 carbon atoms, the analogous aldose sugars are referred to as *trioses*, *tetroses*, *pentoses*, *hexoses*, and *heptoses*, respectively, while the same ketoses are correspondingly and officially named *triuloses*, *tertruloses*, *pentuloses*, *hexuloses*, and *heptuloses*, respectively. They may also be unofficially grouped with names such as ketopentose and ketohexose. The simplest aldose and ketose monosaccharides are the two entantiomers of glyceraldehyde (D and L) (Figure 1.1) and 1,3-dihydroxyacetone (Figure 1.2), respectively. Aldoses exhibit one additional chiral center compared to ketoses for the same number of carbon atoms. With the addition of an extra carbon atom to a growing monosaccharide chain, the number of possible stereoisomers increases. For the total number of chiral or asymmetric centers (n) possessed by a

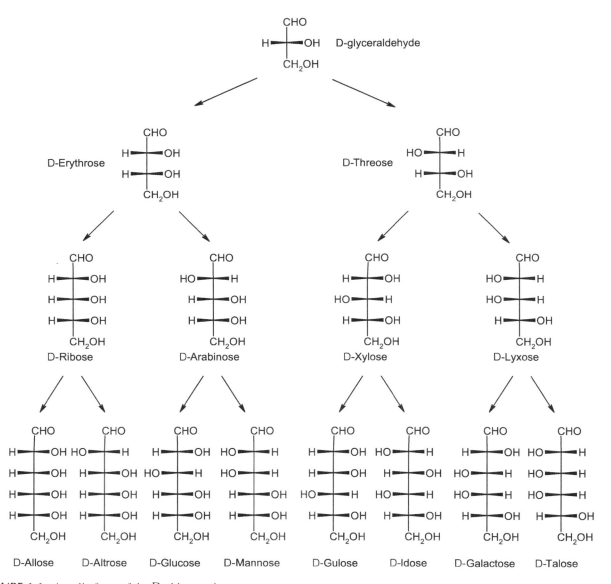

FIGURE 1.1 Acyclic form of the D-aldose series.

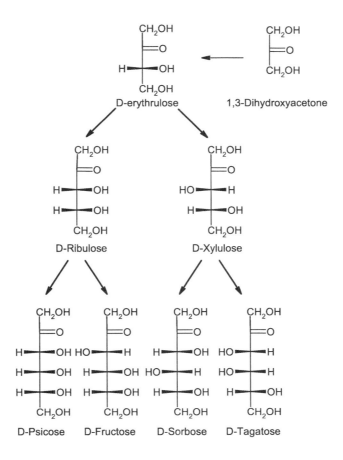

FIGURE 1.2 Acyclic form of the D-ketose series.

monosaccharide, there are 2^n possible arrangements. The reference monosaccharide is considered to be D-glyceraldehyde, which provides a template for generation of acyclic carbon skeletons (from 3 to 6 carbon atoms) as outlined in Figure 1.1 (Fischer projection format). For D-sugars, the hydroxyl group of the highest numbered asymmetric carbon atom (the one furthest from the carbonyl group) is situated on the right-hand side of the Fischer projection, while for L-sugars, the same hydroxyl group is positioned on the left. Thus, the analogous L-aldose series (for brevity not shown) is represented by the exact mirror image structures presented for the D-aldose series. Most sugars found in nature are of the D-configuration, though some common exceptions include L-arabinose, L-rhamnose, L-fucose, L-guluronic acid and L-iduronic acid. Monosaccharide units that differ only in the configuration about a single chiral carbon atom are referred to as epimers (diastereomers). For example, D-glucose and D-galactose are C-4 epimers. Similar to the pattern previously presented for the aldoses, the ketose acyclic series begins with 1,3-dihydroxyacetone; however, the chiral template series starts at D-erythrulose (Figure 1.2) [1,2].

The carbonyl group of aldoses and ketoses is reactive and readily forms an intramolecular cyclic hemiacetal.

Therefore, most monosaccharides (except glyceraldehydes, 1,3-dihydroxyacetone and tetrulose) form energetically stable 5- (furan) and 6- (pyran) membered ring structures. Through cyclization, an additional chiral center is formed (compared to the acyclic form) at C-1 (aldoses) or C-2 (ketoses), which is designated the anomeric carbon atom. At the new chiral center, there are two possible anomeric configurations, α and β, which denote the hydroxyl group below and above the ring plane, respectively (true for D-sugars, while the opposite designation is true for L-sugars). The cyclic hemiacetal formation for both pyranose and furanose ring structures (Haworth projections) is illustrated in Figure 1.3 for D-glucose. The actual conformation of the glucopyranosyl structure exists predominantly in the form of a chair-shaped ring (not all ring atoms within the same plane) with the bulky hydroxyl groups in an equatorial arrangement to minimize steric (1,3-*syn*-diaxial) interactions and lessen bond angle strain. For example, β-D-glucopyranose is shown in the $^4C_1$ conformation (Figure 1.3). The superscript and subscript numbers of the conformational notation denote the numbers of the carbon atoms above and below the plane of the ring, respectively [1,2].

Aldoses and ketoses (both hemiacetals) can readily react with alcohols to produce acetals called glycosides. The

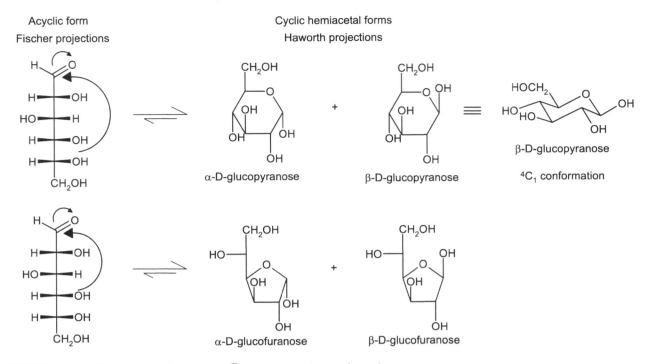

Acyclic form
Fischer projections

Cyclic hemiacetal forms
Haworth projections

α-D-glucopyranose   +   β-D-glucopyranose ≡ β-D-glucopyranose $^4C_1$ conformation

α-D-glucofuranose   +   β-D-glucofuranose

FIGURE 1.3 Cyclic hemiacetal formation of D-glucose and ring conformation.

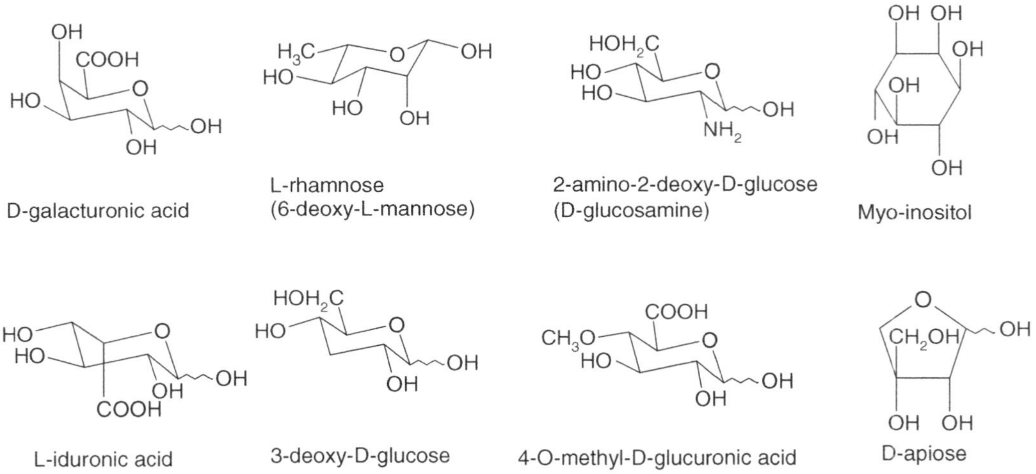

D-galacturonic acid   L-rhamnose (6-deoxy-L-mannose)   2-amino-2-deoxy-D-glucose (D-glucosamine)   Myo-inositol

L-iduronic acid   3-deoxy-D-glucose   4-O-methyl-D-glucuronic acid   D-apiose

FIGURE 1.4 Structures of other common monosaccharides and inositol.

suffix -*ide* indicates an acetal linkage. For example, D-xylose reacting with methanol produces a mixure of methyl α-D-xylopyranoside and methyl β-D-xylopyranoside [1]. The alcohol (methanol in the above example) portion of the glycoside is called the *aglycon*. In nature, the aglycon (alcohol) is most often another monosaccharide unit, and the covalent bond joining two monosaccharide units is termed a glycosidic bond. This concept can be used to describe two (disaccharide) or more monosaccharide units attached through glycosidic linkages, including extensive polymeric chains (e.g., polysaccharides) comprised of many monosaccharide units.

In addition to the stereoisomeric configurations of sugars, the chemical diversity of monosaccharides can include chemical functionalities such as: carboxyl groups at the primary hydroxyl group position (uronic acids), amino groups in place of hydroxyl groups (amino sugars), hydroxyl groups replaced with hydrogen atoms (deoxy sugars), double bonds (unsaturated derivatives), branch chain sugars, ether substituents, and ester substituents. Examples of these diverse structures are shown in Figure 1.4. A uronic acid is an aldose in which the primary alcohol group (e.g., C-6) has been converted to a carboxylic acid (e.g., α-D-galacturonic acid). A deoxy monosaccharide involves the replacement of a hydroxyl group with a substituent such as a hydrogen atom (e.g., 6-deoxy-L-mannopyranose, commonly known as L-rhamnose; 2-deoxy-D-*erythro*-pentose, also known as 2-deoxy-D-ribose; 3-deoxyl-D-*ribo*-hexose, also known as 3-deoxy-D-glucose). An amino sugar is a monosaccharide, in which a hydroxyl group is replaced by an amino group (e.g., 2-amino-2-deoxy-β-D-glucopyranose). A branch chain sugar is C-substituted at a non-terminal carbon (e.g., 3-C-hydroxymethyl-D-*erythro*-tetrose, also known as D-apiose). Ether and ester carbohydrate derivatives will be discussed later.

Polyhydroxycyclohexanes, also known as cyclitols or inositols, are discussed here due to their similarities to pyranoses. Nine stereoisomers are possible, and the most widespread in nature is *myo*-inositol (Figure 1.4). Methyl ether derivatives of inositols are also common.

III. REACTIONS OF CARBOHYDRATES

A. HYDROLYSIS

Glycosides, including disaccharides and polymeric chains (oligosaccharides and polysaccharides), undergo hydrolysis in aqueous acids to yield free sugars. The process somewhat randomly cleaves glycosidic bonds to reduce large carbohydrate chains into smaller fragments, which can in turn be further depolymerized to monosaccharide units. Hydrolysis is initiated in glycosides by protonation of the *exocyclic* oxygen atom followed by breakdown of the conjugate acid (cleavage of the bond between the anomeric carbon atom and the *glycosidic* oxygen atom) resulting in the formation of a cyclic carbocation, which is attacked by water to yield the hemiacetal product (Figure 1.5). Glycosidic bonds can also be cleaved by enzymes, which are very specific to the

type of sugar residue (e.g., D-galactosyl vs. D-glucosyl), anomeric configuration (α or β), and the glycosidic linkage site (e.g., 1→3). Both acid- and enzyme-catalyzed hydrolysis are commonly employed in the manufacture of maltodextrins and corn syrups, as well as in the commercial production schemes of polysaccharides.

B. OXIDATION/REDUCTION

Aldoses can be readily oxidized to aldonic acids. Because during the oxidation there is a concurrent reduction of the oxidizing agent, aldoses are called reducing sugars (Figure 1.6). Aldonic acids can readily cyclize to form a stable lactone under neutral or acidic conditions. This oxidation reaction has been successfully exploited either chemically (Fehling solution, $Cu(OH)_2$; bromine solution; Tollens reagent) or enzymatically (glucose oxidase) to quantitatively determine sugars [1,2]. In contrast, ketoses must first be isomerized to an aldose (under alkaline conditions), which can then undergo oxidation.

Reduction of an aldose or ketose results in the formation of an alditol or sugar alcohol (denoted by the *-itol* suffix). Commercial-scale operations typically use high-pressure hydrogenation in conjunction with nickel catalyst for such reductions. Sorbitol (D-glucitol) is a commonly occurring alditol in fruits, and is 50% as sweet as sucrose. Sugar alcohols, such as D-glucitol, D-mannitol, and D-xylitol, are frequently used as alternative sweeteners (noncariogenic) in chewing gum and confectionary applications.

C. THERMAL REACTIONS

Heating of reducing sugars results in a complex series of reactions called caramelization. The process is a cascade of

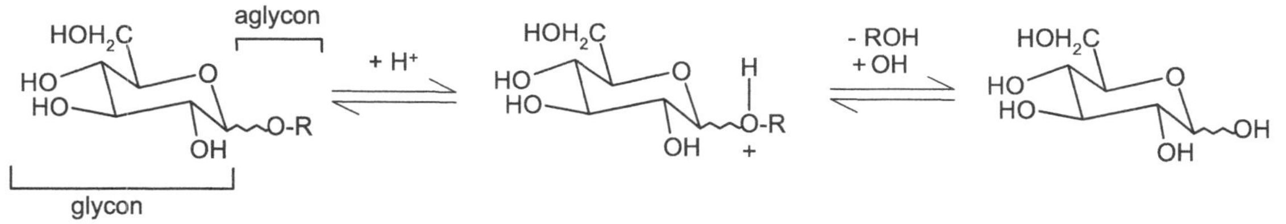

FIGURE 1.5 Abbreviated mechanism of acid-catalyzed hydrolysis of a glycoside.

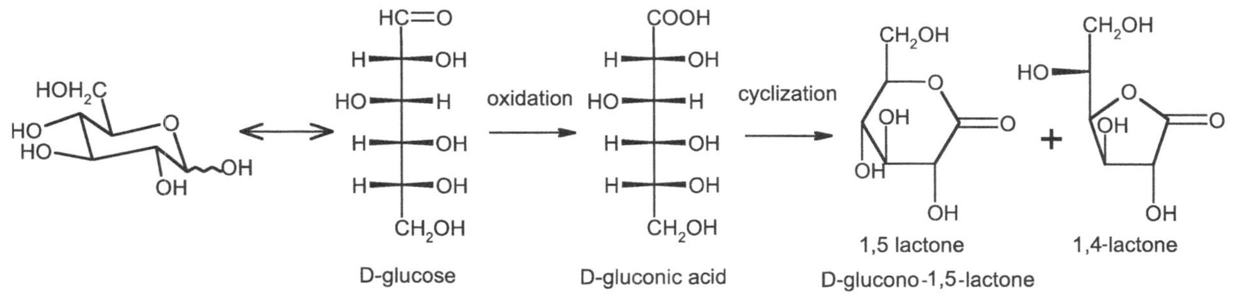

FIGURE 1.6 Oxidation of an aldose to an aldonic acid with subsequent formation of D-gluconolactone.

dehydration reactions that form semi-volatile anhydrides (e.g., 1,6-anhydro-β-D-glucopyranose (levo-glucosan)) and unsaturated compounds (e.g., 5-hydroxy-methyl-furaldehyde (HMF) and furaldehyde) as shown in Figure 1.7 [1]. Catalysts such as salts and acids are added to promote the reaction.

Reducing sugars in the presence of amines (such as proteins and amino acids) undergo a thermal reaction called the Amadori rearrangement. In the case of D-glucose, reaction with an amine (R-NH$_2$) will form a derivative of 1-amino-1-deoxy-D-fructose and D-glucosylamine (Figure 1.8a). If the reaction continues under acidic conditions, it will undergo dehydration reactions to form HMF. Above pH 5, reactive Amadori intermediates yield complex polymerized dark-colored products via the poorly understood non-enzymatic browning or Maillard reaction, which contributes both color and flavor components to a wide range of food systems (e.g., bread crust, chocolate, caramels, etc.) Recently, acrylamide has been detected in a myriad of high-temperature processed foods (French fries, bread, breakfast cereal, popcorn, etc.), and seems to be primarily derived by the reaction between D-glucose and asparagine. The reaction likely proceeds via the glucosyl-asparagine derivative, and then undergoes decarboxylative deamination to form acrylamide (Figure 1.8b) [4]. To date, it is not known whether the low levels (ppb) detected in food pose any significant health risk to humans.

D. ESTER/ETHER FORMATION

Hydroxyl groups of sugars can form esters with organic and inorganic acids. Reaction of hydroxyl groups with acyl chlorides or acid anhydrides in the presence of a catalyst (base) produces esters. Industrially, starches are esterified (acetates, phosphates, succinates, adipates, etc.) to improve their food-use properties. Acetates, sulfates, and phosphates are commonly found as native constituents of carbohydrates. For example, acetyl groups are present in certain polysaccharides such as the plant hemicelluloses (xylan and glucomannan), certain pectins, and xanthan, while sugar phosphates are common intermediates in the biosynthesis of monosaccharides and polysaccharides. The polysaccharide carrageenan contains sulfate half-ester substituents. In addition to esters from sugar hydroxyl groups, esterified uronic acid units are found in polysaccharides. The best example is pectin, in which some of its D-galacturonic acid units exist in the methyl ester form.

The hydroxyl groups of carbohydrates can also form ethers. In nature, ether groups are not common, though some D-glucuronic acid units, particularly in hemicelluloses, such as glucuronoxylan, are methylated at the O-4 position (4-O-methyl-D-glucuronic acid). Industrially, starches and celluloses are methylated (cellulose), hydroxypropylated (starch, cellulose), and carboxymethylated (cellulose) to improve the properties of these polysaccharides for a variety of food applications.

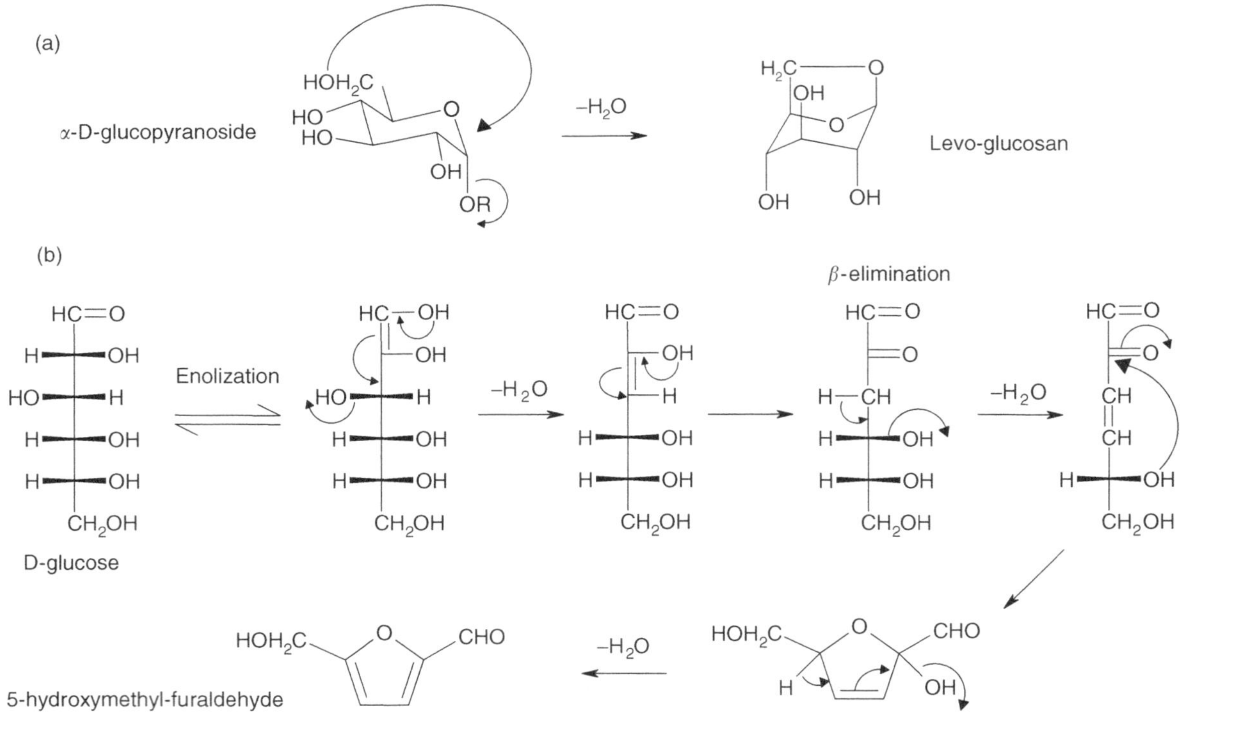

FIGURE 1.7 Reaction mechanism for the formation of (a) levo-glucosan and (b) HMF.

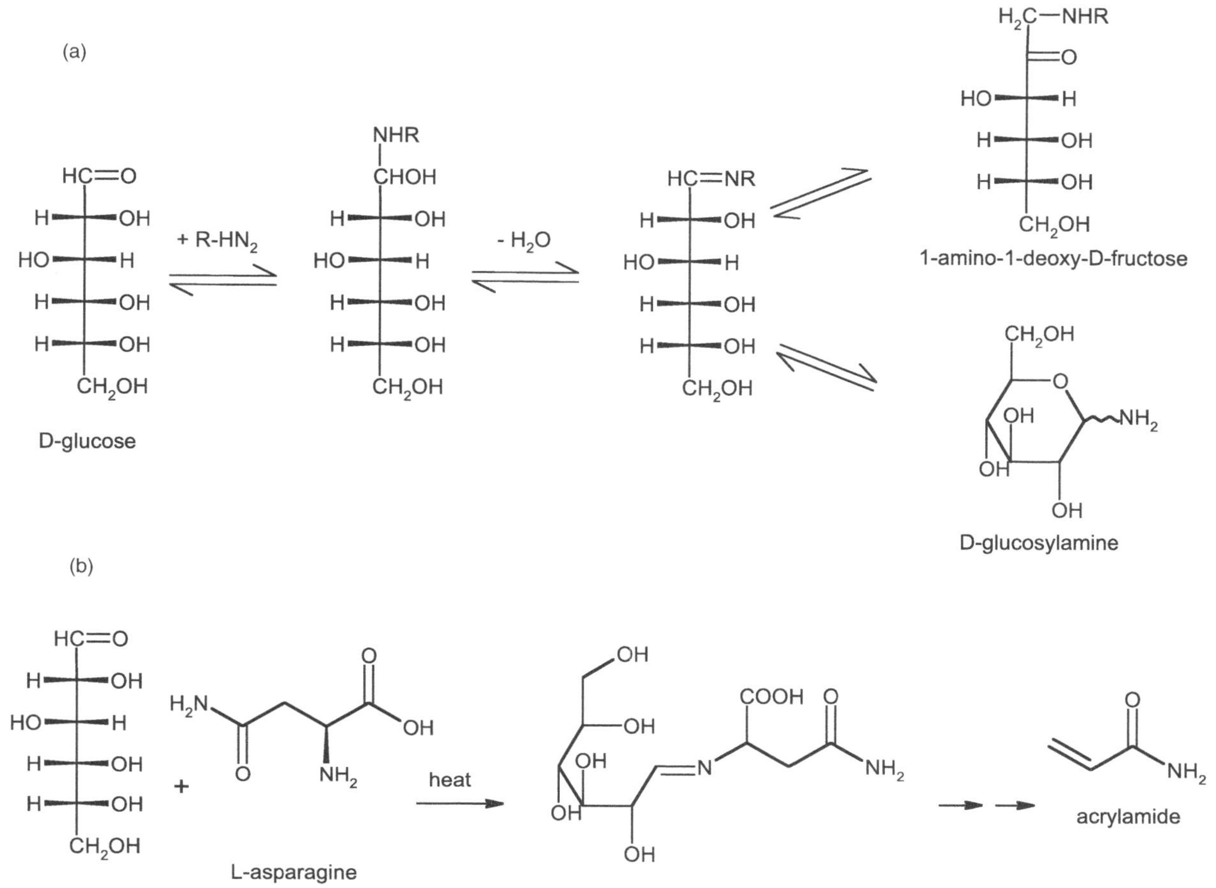

(a)

(b)

FIGURE 1.8   (a) Amadori reaction scheme and (b) formation of acrylamide.

IV.   OLIGOSACCHARIDES

Oligosaccharides are comprised of 2 to 20 glycosidically-linked monosaccharide units [3]. In nature, enzymes called glycosyltransferases catalyze the biosynthesis of both oligosaccharides and larger polymeric carbohydrates (e.g., polysaccharides). These very specific enzymes link specific monosaccharide units together according to a defined anomeric configuration and linkage position (e.g., C-3) on the aglycon sugar. Commercially, oligosaccharides also can be generated through enzyme- or acid-catalyzed hydrolysis of polysaccharides. The following section will briefly discuss common disaccharides, trisaccharides, and fructo-oligosaccharides.

A.   DISACCHARIDES

Disaccharides are composed of two monosaccharide units joined by a glycosidic bond. Disaccharides can either be reducing (e.g., maltose and lactose, Figure 1.9) or non-reducing (e.g., sucrose, Figure 1.10), depending on whether one or both anomeric carbon atoms are involved in the disaccharide glycosidic bond. Maltose (Figure 1.9), a disaccharide formed by enzymatic hydrolysis of starch, is produced commercially from the malting of barley, and

is the primary fermentable sugar used in the production of beer [3]. The structure of maltose (α-D-glucopyranosyl($1\rightarrow4$)-D-glucopyranose) can be written in shorthand notation as αGlc$p$($1\rightarrow4$)Glc$p$. The shorthand abbreviation for a monosaccharide unit is based on its first three letters, except for glucose, which is designated as Glc. The position of the linkage is designated as ($1\rightarrow4$) from carbon atom 1 of the glycosyl unit to carbon atom 4 of the agylcon unit. The sugar ring size is denoted as p for pyranose or f for furanose, while the anomeric configuration is designated as either α or β. In the case of D or L configuration, it is only necessary to stipulate L-sugars (D-sugars are assumed unless noted otherwise). This shorthand notation can be used to define both oligosaccharide and more complex polymeric (polysaccharide) carbohydrate structures.

Lactose (βGal$p$($1\rightarrow4$)Glc$p$; Figure 1.9) is found in milk at concentrations between 4 and 9%, and is the primary carbohydrate source for developing mammals. For energy utilization, it is necessary that lactose be hydrolyzed by the enzyme lactase (β-galactosidase) to D-galactose and D-glucose in the small intestine to facilitate absorption into the bloodstream. In some individuals, lactose is not (or is only partially) hydrolyzed (lactase deficiency), which

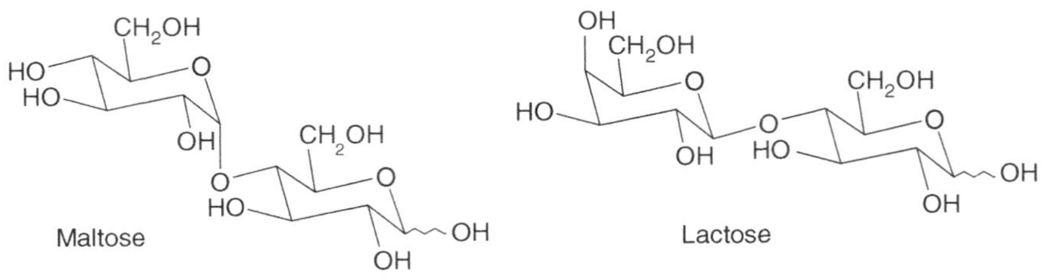

FIGURE 1.9 Structures of maltose and lactose.

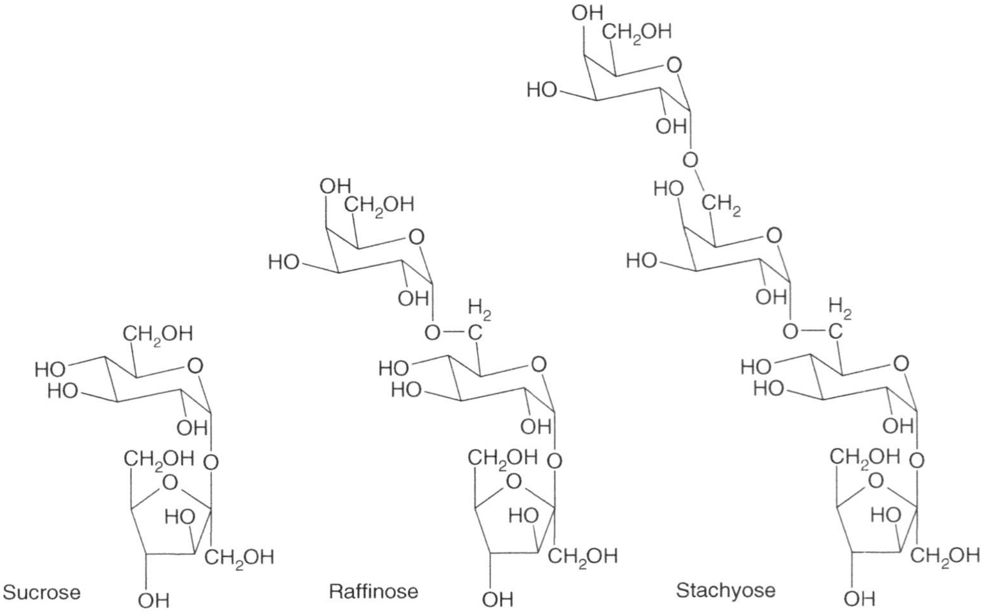

FIGURE 1.10 Structures of sucrose, raffinose, and stachyose.

condition is clinically termed lactose intolerance, and results in the bacterial, anaerobic fermentation of lactose in the large intestine to lactic acid and gaseous products [3].

Sucrose (αGlc$p$(1$\leftrightarrow$2)βFru$f$; Figure 1.10) is composed of an α-D-glucopyranosyl unit linked (reducing end to reducing end) to a β-D-fructofuranosyl unit, and therefore is non-reducing, because it has no free carbonyl (aldehyde) group. Sucrose (table sugar) is one of the most common low-molecular-weight carbohydrates in the human diet. It is found in plants (e.g., sugar beets, sugarcane, and fruit), where it represents an easily transportable energy and carbon source and an intermediate in starch and cellulose biosynthesis. Another attribute of sucrose is its solubility in water to form highly concentrated solutions, which result in the lowering of the freezing point of water (anti-freeze) and resistance against dehydration in plants and fruits [3]. As a food ingredient, sucrose is utilized due to its water-solubility, desirable sweet taste, effects on colligative properties (e.g., boiling and freezing point regulation), preservative function (osmotic effect), and texturizing effects.

In certain plants, some sucrose molecules are α-galactosylated to form the non-reducing trisaccharide, raffinose (αGal$p$(1$\rightarrow$6)αGlc$p$(1$\leftrightarrow$2)βFru$f$), the tetrasaccharide, stachyose (αGal$p$(1$\rightarrow$6)αGal$p$(1$\rightarrow$6)αGlc$p$(1$\leftrightarrow$2)βFru$f$) as shown in Figure 1.10, and the pentasaccharide, verbascose. These oligosaccharides are found especially in beans, onions, and sugarcane. They are non-digestible and are responsible for causing the flatulence (due to microbial fermentation in the colon) associated with the eating of beans and onions [3].

B. FRUCTOOLIGOSACCHARIDES

Fructans, which are polymers (polysaccharides) consisting of β-D-fructofuranosyl units, are found in higher plants, and are composed of two types, inulins and levans (Figure 1.11). Inulins consist of (2$\rightarrow$1)-linked β-D-fructofuranosyl units and are found in Jerusalem artichoke, chicory, and dahlia tubers, while levans, consisting of (2$\rightarrow$6)-linked β-D-fructofuranosyl units, are found in grasses. Both types of fructans are terminated at the reducing end with a sucrose unit [2]. Fructo-oligosaccharides, which are smaller versions of fructans are used in prebiotic food applications, and are believed to serve as a

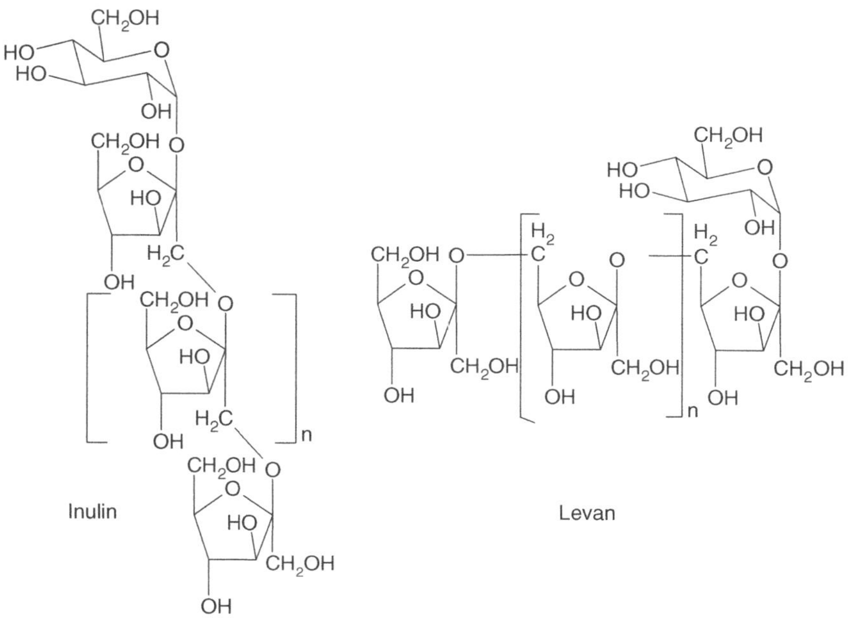

FIGURE 1.11 Structures of inulin and levan oligosaccharides.

TABLE 1.1
Categorization of Select Polysaccharides according to Origin[1]

Origin/Source	Polysaccharide Examples
Higher plants	
Cell wall associated	Cellulose, hemicellulose, pectin
Energy stores (seeds, roots, tubers)	Starch, guar gum, locust bean gum
Exudates	Gum arabic, gum karaya
Marine plants (seaweed extracts)	Carrageenan, alginate, agar
Microorganisms (bacterial fermentation)	Xanthan, gellan
Chemical derviatives (of varied native origin)	Hydroxypropylstarch, starch acetate, starch phosphate, carboxymethylcellulose, hydroxypropylmethylcellulose, methylcellulose
Synthetic	Polydextrose

[1]Adapted from Ref. [3].

preferred substrate to promote colonization of beneficial gut microflora (e.g., bifidobacteria).

V. POLYSACCHARIDES

By definition, polysaccharides (glycans) are long-chain, carbohydrate polymers comprised of, at minimum, 20 glycosidically linked monosaccharide (monomer) units [3]. The number of individual monosaccharide units that comprise a particular polysaccharide is referred to as the *degree of polymerization (DP)*. Most indigenous polysaccharides possess DPs far in excess of the stated minimum (200–3000 DP is typical), though extremes are observed in nature at both ends of the DP spectrum [3]. While polysaccharides are present in a wide range of plant and animal biological systems, most glycans of commercial significance occur in higher plants (though a few are produced by

bacteria). Collectively, polysaccharides from varied origins offer a multitude of structural and functional diversity consistent with their respective intended roles (e.g., structure, energy storage, hydration, etc.) within biological systems. Of the various carbohydrate classes, polysaccharides are by far the most abundant in nature [3], and, as a class of compounds, represent the greatest single component of biomass on the planet. Their relative abundance combined with their diverse structural and functional characteristics make them a superb source of biopolymers for utilization in a wide range of food applications.

A. CLASSIFICATION OF POLYSACCHARIDES

Though commonly classified by source (Table 1.1), polysaccharides may also be categorized according to the number of different monosaccharide types contained

TABLE 1.2

Categorization of Select Polysaccharides according to Multiple Classification Schemes Related to Structure and Behavior[1]

Origin/Source	Polysaccharide Examples
By Shape	
Linear	Cellulose, starch (amylose[2]), pectin,[3] alginate, agar, carrageenan, gellan, cellulose derivatives (carboxymethylcellulose, hydroxypropylmethylcellulose, methylcellulose)
Branched	Guar gum, locust bean gum, xanthan
Branch-on-branch	Starch (amylopectin), gum arabic
By Number of Types of Monomeric Units	
Homoglycan	Cellulose, starch (amylose, amylopectin)
(Di)Heteroglycan	Guar gum, locust bean gum, alginate, agar, carrageenan, pectin[3]
(Tri)Heteroglycan	Xanthan, gellan
(Tetra)Heteroglycan	Gum arabic
By Charge	
Neutral	Cellulose, starch (amylose, amylopectin[4]), agar,[5] guar gum, locust bean gum, methylcellulose, hydroxypropylmethyl-cellulose, hydroxypropylstarch, starch acetate
Anionic	Xanthan, gellan, alginate, carageenan, pectin, gum arabic, gum karaya, carboxymethylcellulose, starch phosphate
By Rheological Properties	
Gelling	Starch and starch derivatives, alginate, agar, carrageenan (κ- and ι-types), pectin, gellan, hydroxypropylmethylcellulose, methylcellulose
Non-gelling	Celulose, xanthan,[6] locust bean gum,[7] guar gum, carrageenan (λ-type), gum arabic,[8] carboxymethylcellulose, polydextrose

[1] Adapted from Ref. [3].

[2] Depending on botanical source, amylose can contain some minor short branches toward the molecular reducing end [3].

[3] Categorization does not account for native pectin hairy regions (regions of extensive branching composed of multiple monosaccharide units), most of which are lost during processing to commercial grade pectin [26].

[4] Some starch amylopectin molecules (i.e., potato) may possess small amounts of native starch monophosphate [3].

[5] Agar does possess small amounts of sulfate [30], but is considered to be largely neutral.

[6] Though xanthan solutions do not gel, xanthan does form synergistic gels with locust bean gum, agar, and κ-carrageenan [3].

[7] Though primarily a thickener, locust bean gum exhibits synergistic gelling behavior with xanthan, agar, and κ-carrageenan [3].

[8] Forms gels at very high concentrations [3].

within their molecular structure (e.g., homoglycan: one type vs. heteroglycan: more than one type), molecular shape (e.g., branched vs. linear), electrostatic charge (e.g., neutral vs. anionic) and properties (e.g., gelling vs. non-gelling) (Table 1.2).

In addition, polysaccharides differ from proteins and nucleic acids in that they are both *polydisperse* and *polymolecular* [3]. With regard to polydispersity, a particular polysaccharide type (e.g., pectin) is not defined by a specific number of monomeric units or a defined molecular weight, but rather possesses a range of DPs and molecular weights. Further, the majority of polysaccharides are not chemically homogeneous (cellulose and bacterial polysaccharides are exceptions); they are polymolecular in the sense that individual molecules within a polysaccharide type (e.g., pectin) may differ from one another with respect

to fine structure (monosaccharide sequence, proportion of monosaccharide constituents, linkage type, branching frequency). Thus, it is important to keep in mind that the described structure of a polysaccharide type often is not absolute; rather it is an idealized, statistical representation for a population of macromolecules. For every polysaccharide, the reported molecular weight is also an average value.

B. STRUCTURAL REGIMES OF POLYSACCHARIDES

Nevertheless, structural aspects of polysaccharides may be defined on several different organizational levels (analogous to protein primary, secondary, tertiary, and quaternary structural regimes) [5]. Polysaccharide *primary structure* refers to the sequence of monosaccharide units and the configuration of accompanying glycosidic linkages. However, it is the glycan primary structure that ultimately dictates the nature and extent of intramolecular and intermolecular associations within a polysaccharide system that lead to development of three-dimensional molecular order (secondary, tertiary, and quaternary structures). Of the two defining elements of primary structure, linkage type generally exerts a greater influence on molecular conformation than monosaccharide type [6]. While there is free rotation about glycosidic bonds, the extent of rotation is limited to a narrow range of thermodynamically favored conformations that coincide with potential energy minima (as a function of hydrogen bonding, van der Waals, polar, and torsional interactions) [5]. These preferred conformations define the proximity of adjacent glycosyl units one to another, and dictate the polysaccharide long-range, three-dimensional shape. This principle is illustrated by the classic comparison of cellulose, amylose, and dextran polysaccharides, which are all linear chains of polyglucose, differing only in the nature of their glycosidic linkages (Figures 1.12a–c) [3].

The equatorial-equatorial β(1→4) glycosidic linkage of cellulose, which facilitates a strong hydrogen bonding interaction between the ring oxygen atom and the C-3 hydroxyl group of adjacent glycosyl units, gives rise to a flat, ribbon-like molecular conformation. On the contrary, the axial-equatorial α(1→4) linkage of amylose leads to a more open, coiled, helical structure, based on favorable

hydrogen bonding between the C-2 and C-3 hydroxyl groups of neighboring glucosyl units. Finally, the α(1→6) glycosidic linkage inherent to dextran introduces an additional bond (C-5–C-6), about which free rotation can occur. This additional bond also increases the distance between adjacent glycosyl units such that hydrogen bonding cannot occur. The resulting consequence is that dextran molecules do not generally possess an ordered three-dimensional conformation, but instead adopt the structure of a random coil (possess no defined shape).

The ability to form ordered secondary structure is favored by a high degree of chain uniformity (regularity of monosaccharide sequence and glycosidic linkage) [3], while a random coil results from the lack thereof. In summary, the *ribbon*, *helix*, and *random coil* conformations described for cellulose, amylose, and dextran, respectively, effectively demonstrate the range of *secondary structure* typical of polysaccharide systems.

An example of polysaccharide *tertiary structure* is observed with starch amylose molecules, which can associate to form sections of ordered, double-helical arrangements [5]. Triple-helical tertiary structures have also been reported to exist for various polysaccharides [7,8]. Most polysaccharide tertiary structures are typically stabilized through intermolecular hydrogen bonds.

Temperature and physical state also influence the tendency for a polysaccharide to adopt an ordered secondary

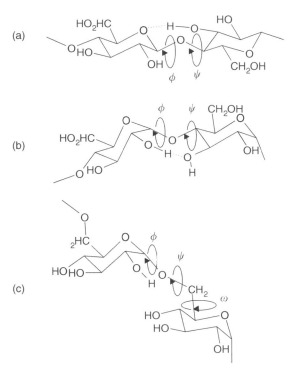

FIGURE 1.12 Rotation about glycosidic bonds (φ and ψ) exhibited by polyglucose chains of (a) cellulose, (b) amylose, and (c) dextran (also exhibits free rotation about C5–C6 bond, ω) that provide the basis for long-range, three-dimensional conformational structure (ribbon, helix, and random coil, respectively). Dotted lines between adjacent glucosyl units depict stabilizing hydrogen bonds.

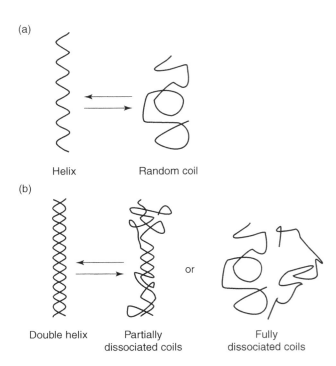

FIGURE 1.13 Depiction of the conformational changes associated with the thermoreversible order to disorder transition for (a) single- and (b) double-helical structures.

or tertiary structure. A polysaccharide in an ordered conformation typically undergoes a reversible order (helix) to disorder (random coil) transition with an increase in temperature sufficient to disrupt hydrogen bonds that stabilize the ordered conformation (Figure 1.13a) [9]. Under these circumstances, double-stranded tertiary structures generally unfold (Figure 1.13b). Upon cooling below the transition temperature, polysaccharide molecules are again able to regain their respective ordered secondary and/or tertiary arrangements. For polysaccharides capable of forming ordered secondary structures, the crystalline state generally favors the existence of the ordered conformation, while the solution state (in water) often results in adoption of a random coil [5]. In the solution state, competing hydrogen bonds between solute (polysaccharide) and solvent (water) molecules tend to minimize the stabilizing effects of intramolecular (solute-solute) hydrogen bonds that would otherwise stabilize an ordered polysaccharide secondary structure. Nevertheless, the solution state does not necessarily impede the formation of double-helical tertiary structures, though solvent conditions necessary for development of such structures may vary with polysaccharide type.

The ability to form some degree of ordered secondary or tertiary structure is generally a prerequisite (but not a guarantee) for polysaccharides to participate in advanced quaternary supramolecular structures. *Quaternary structure* develops through alignment and aggregation of secondary- and/or tertiary-ordered polysaccharide molecules

[5], and is typically stabilized by non-covalent interactions (electrostatic, non-polar, hydrogen bond associations) under requisite solvent conditions. Such quaternary order is responsible for the intermolecular associations that lead to development of both gel (junction zone) and other crystalline structures, which are important to processed foods and native plant cell wall systems. However, in discussing any level of polysaccharide three-dimensional structure, it is important to note that polysaccharide molecules in solution are in a constant state of dynamic flux, and likely exist in a wide range of physical forms (helix, double helix, random coil, etc.) at any point in time (even though a statistically favored conformation may be dominant) [3,5]. Nevertheless, the three-dimensional structures discussed here provide a basis for many of the observed properties of polysaccharide systems. A more detailed description of molecular features impacting polysaccharide conformation and physical properties is presented next.

C. IMPACT OF POLYSACCHARIDE MOLECULAR FEATURES ON PHYSICAL PROPERTIES

While polysaccharides possess ring oxygen and hydroxyl groups capable of interacting with water through hydrogen bonds [3], physical properties such as solubility, viscosity, and gelling capability are additionally influenced by other molecular features inherent to a polysaccharide. Water solubility of a polysaccharide is generally enhanced by molecular features that prevent formation of

TABLE 1.3

General Description[1] of Polysaccharide Molecular Features and Conditions That Promote Water-Solubility, Viscosity Development, Gelling Behavior

Polysaccharide Feature	Water-Solubility	Viscosity Development	Gelling Behavior/Stability
Backbone linkage and/or monosaccharide repeat	Irregular	Regular (rigid structures)	Mixed (both regular and irregular segments)
Backbone shape	Branch-on-branch structure	Linear, extended structures	Linear, extended structures
Degree of branching and/or substitution	Regular, even distribution of sidechains or substituents along polymer chains	Regular, even distribution of short sidechains or substituents along polymer chains	Sporadic or irregular distribution of side chains or substituents along polymer chains
Molecular charge (if charged)	Even distribution of charge (repulsive) along polymer chains	Even distribution of charge (repulsive) along polymer chains	Uneven distribution of charge (repulsive) along polymer chains
Degree of solvation	Maximum	High	Balanced (segments of both polymer-polymer and polymer-water interactions)
Molecular size	Low	Intermediate to high	Low to intermediate

[1] It is important to note that polysaccharides do not necessarily need to possess all suggested molecular features or conditions to exhibit a particular property, though the greater number of molecular features present will increase the likelihood for a particular property to be exhibited. Exceptions do also exist.

an ordered three-dimensional structure (e.g., irregular backbone structure) or that present physical barriers to intermolecular interactions (e.g., uniform sidechains, backbone repulsive charge) (Table 1.3). An irregular polysaccharide glycosidic linkage or monosaccharide repeat tends to promote polymer flexibility, which can reduce opportunity for intermolecular association and aid solubility. The presence of regular sidechains or derivatized polysaccharide hydroxyl groups can introduce steric hindrance and molecular repulsion (if substituents are charged), which minimize polysaccharide intermolecular associations, leading to increased solubility [3].

The basis for the increased viscosity of polysaccharide solutions (relative to pure water) varies according to polysaccharide concentration. The viscosity of a polysaccharide system within the dilute regime arises from the restructuring of water at the polysaccharide-water interface, and represents the collective (additive) effect of individual polysaccharide molecules in solution [10]. At more intermediate concentrations, typical of industrial applications, intermolecular effects become more predominant. As a result of being in constant dynamic motion, a polysaccharide molecule in solution sweeps out or occupies a theoretical volume or domain of spherical shape [10]. With increasing polysaccharide concentration, the probability for individual polysaccharide molecular domains to collide or overlap becomes increasingly likely, leading to entanglements, internal friction, and increased viscosity [3,11]. The polysaccharide concentration at which interpenetration of polymer domains occurs is referred to as the overlap concentration, and coincides with a concurrent

rise in the slope of the viscosity increase in response to an increasing polysaccharide concentration [11].

Aside from concentration effects, molecular characteristics of polysaccharides greatly influence solution viscosity. The greater the theoretical volume swept out by a polysaccharide molecule in motion, the greater the resulting viscosity (assuming a constant concentration). Thus, in principle, the volume swept out by a polysaccharide in solution is a function of both molecular size (DP) and shape (three-dimensional structure) [3]. While a polysaccharide of high molecular weight or DP might generally be expected to sweep out a greater volume compared to a glycan of relatively smaller size, the factor of molecular shape must also be considered. A random coil (highly flexible) structure will occupy a smaller spherical solution domain than that of a stiff, rod-like extended structure of equal molecular size (Figures 1.14a and 1.14b) [3]. Likewise, with the continued assumption of equal molecular weight, a highly branched polysaccharide is anticipated to exhibit a more compact shape and smaller volume in solution compared to that of a highly linear, extended glycan (Figures 1.14b and 1.14c) [3]. Thus, linear, high-molecular-weight polysaccharides capable of forming ordered secondary (helical) and/or tertiary (double-helical) rod-like, extended structures generally produce highly viscous solutions (at relatively low concentrations). As previously described, formation of ordered secondary or tertiary structures is generally favored by extended regions of chain uniformity (regularity of monosaccharide sequence and glycosidic linkage). Nevertheless, some degree of chain disruption (presence of sidechain, charged, or derivatized moieties

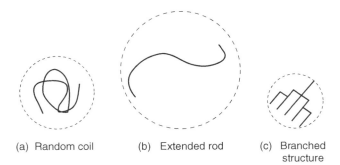

(a) Random coil   (b) Extended rod   (c) Branched
                                                   structure

FIGURE 1.14 Comparison of theoretical solution volumes occupied or swept out by (a) a random coil, (b) a somewhat rigid rod, and (c) a branched macromolecule with the assumption of identical molecular weight.

along backbone, etc.) is often necessary to retain polysaccharide solubility (Table 1.2) [3,5]. In particular, charged groups along the polysaccharide backbone tend to keep

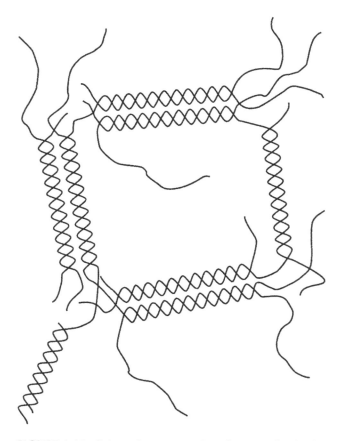

FIGURE 1.15 Schematic representation of a generalized polysaccharide gel structure consisting of segments of aggregated, ordered polysaccharide molecules (double helices) that comprise junction zones (intermolecular cross-links) stabilizing a porous, continuous three-dimensional network or suprastructure. Void spaces are occupied by entrapped solvent (water) and unordered (fully solvated) portions of polysaccharide molecules to yield a viscoelastic material.

polysaccharides in extended form by way of intramolecular repulsion, and enhance solubility and increase viscosity.

The ability to form viscoelastic (combination of both liquid-like (viscous) and solid-like (elastic) behavior) gels represents another significant physical property inherent to many polysaccharide systems. A polysaccharide gel typically consists of some form of an open, continuous, three-dimensional network of aggregated solute macromolecules (polysaccharides) capable of entrapping significant volumes of solvent molecules (water) (Figure 1.15) [3]. The polysaccharide network is generally reinforced through limited aggregation of secondary- and/or tertiary-ordered polysaccharide molecules that form regions of supramolecular quaternary structure termed *junction zones* (intermolecular cross-links) [3,5]. Junction zones may be anchored by a range of stabilizing forces (hydrogen bonds, hydrophobic interactions, electrostatic forces, van der Waals attractions, molecular entanglement, etc.) defined by the polysaccharide structure and solvent conditions. Regions of polysaccharide molecules not involved in junction zone structure maintain strong interaction with water molecules to achieve a delicate balance between the solute-solute (junction zone structure) and solute-solvent (soluble polysaccharide) interactions that constitute a gel.

In general, the polysaccharide structural features that promote gel formation (junction zone development) are similar to those previously described to favor development of secondary- and/or tertiary-ordered structures (characteristics that encourage chain regularity). Nevertheless, to achieve gel stability, most gelling polysaccharides also possess some degree of structural perturbation or disruption that breaks up or limits the formation of the ordered arrangement at sites along the length of polysaccharide chains (Table 1.3) [5]. Such disruptions prevent excessive growth or development of junction zones that would otherwise lead to syneresis (loss of water-holding capacity) and gradual precipitation of polysaccharide molecules [3]. Specific structural features that serve this purpose include: occasional irregularity within the chain primary structure (e.g., carrageenan); occurrence of mixed blocks of monsaccharides within the primary chain (e.g., alginate); and presence of short, sporadic sidechains (e.g., locust bean gum in mixed gel systems with xanthan or carrageenan), substituent groups (e.g., hydroxypropylated starch), or charged moieties (e.g., high-methoxyl pectin). Formation of a stable gel structure also requires manipulation of solvent conditions to meet gelling requirements imposed by the specific structural features of a polysaccharide. Addition of low-molecular-weight solutes (acids, salts, sugar, etc.) or adjustment of temperature may also be used to encourage polysaccharide interaction (reduction of solvation), and regulate the balance of attractive and repulsive forces that coincide with the formation of a stable gel system.

D. POLYSACCHARIDE STABILITY AND REACTIVITY

Polysaccharides are subject to a range of environments and conditions in food systems that have the potential to alter not only their conformations, but also their chemical structures and behaviors. A primary means by which molecular structure is significantly altered occurs through the cleavage of glycosidic bonds (depolymerization), which transpires by two primary means, *hydrolysis* and β-*elimination* reactions. The mechanism of chain cleavage by hydrolysis, which may be initiated by acids or enzymes, was described in an earlier section (Section II, Figure 1.5). While the rate of acid-catalyzed hydrolysis is influenced by pH (lower = faster rate), temperature, and time of exposure, it also varies with the nature of the glycosidic linkage [3]. For example, the rate of acid-catalyzed hydrolysis for uronic acid-based polysaccharides (e.g., alginate) is significantly slower than for corresponding neutral polysaccharides. For enzyme-catalyzed hydrolysis, polysaccharides such as starch can be readily hydrolyzed into maltose and branched oligosaccharides by treatment with β-amylase (*exo*-glucanase), which cleaves terminal maltosyl residues from starch polysaccharides. In contrast, α-amylase (*endo*-glucanase) cleaves α(1→4)-linked bonds at random points along the polysaccharide chain affording oligosaccharide products. Thus, for various polysaccharides, the pattern of enzymatic hydrolysis may differ according to the specific enzymes employed. Lastly, polysaccharide depolymerization by means of beta-elimination is favored under alkaline conditions, and requires oxidation at O-2, O-3, or O-6 for the reaction to proceed as depicted below (Figure 1.16). Aside from conditions encountered within food systems, it is important to note that depolymerization reactions are often intentionally employed in the production schemes of many commercial polysaccharides [3].

The reactivity of polysaccharides is also frequently manipulated to improve and extend their physical properties. The reactions described earlier in relation to monosaccharides (Section II) are also pertinent to polysaccharides, and generally involve derivatization of polysaccharide hydroxyl groups. The extent of chemical modification is most commonly described by the *degree of substitution* (*DS*). Most individual monosaccharide units within a polysaccharide structure possess an average of three hydroxyl groups available for reaction. The DS, which may exhibit a maximum value of three, depicts the average number of modified hydroxyl groups per glycosyl unit [3]. For reactions in which it is possible for a substituent group resulting from reaction with a polysaccharide hydroxyl group to further react with another reagent molecule, the degree of reaction is described in terms of *molar substitution* (*MS*), which is defined as the average number of moles of reactant per glycosyl unit [3].

VI. POLYSACCHARIDE STRUCTURES AND FUNCTIONS

Polysaccharides of commercial significance will be discussed in terms of their structural constituents that are ultimately responsible for their observed properties. The discussion of specific polysaccharides is anticipated to highlight the diversity of structures and functions common to food systems, but is not intended to represent a comprehensive list of polysaccharides present in foods either naturally or as added ingredients.

A. STARCH AND ITS DERIVATIVES

As the primary storage medium in higher plants, *starch* in its simplest form consists of two diverse homopolymers, *amylose* (linear structure) and *amylopectin* (branch-on-branch structure), both of which are comprised exclusively of D-glucosyl units (Figure 1.17a and 1.17b). The linear fraction, amylose, consists of (1→4)-linked α-D-glucopyranosyl units, and has a molecular weight in the range of 30,000 to greater than 10^6, depending on source [3]. While the amylopectin backbone exhibits a primary structure identical to that of amylose, it also possesses sidechains of (1→4)-linked α-D-glucosyl units (average chain length

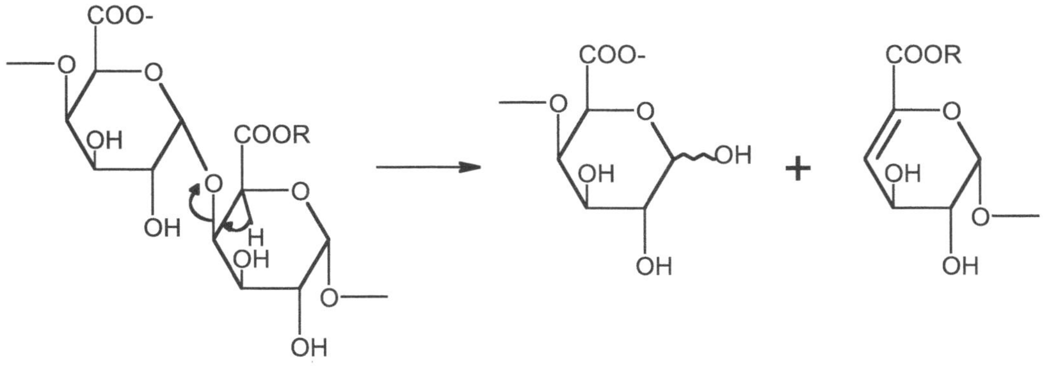

FIGURE 1.16   A possible mechanism for depolymerization of pectin, which possesses native carboxylate and carboxy methyl ester groups, via β-elimination.

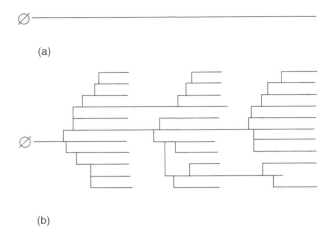

(a)

(b)

FIGURE 1.17 Idealized diagrams depicting the linear and branch-on-branch structures of starch molecules, (a) amylose and (b) amylopectin, respectively ($\varnothing$ depicts the molecular reducing end).

of 20–30 units) attached to the main chain through $\alpha(1\rightarrow6)$ linkages. The sidechains themselves give rise to further branches to yield large, yet compact, branch-on-branch structures of significant molecular weight (approaching 10^9) (Figure 1.17b) [3,12]. Starch is unique in the sense that amylose and amylopectin molecules are biosynthesized and assembled in the form of semi-crystalline aggregates, called *granules*, which vary in size (1–100 μm) and shape (spherical, elliptical, angular, lenticular, etc.) according to the botanical source. Starch granules, which are stabilized by regions of complex molecular order (double-helical association of polymer chains), are insoluble in room temperature water. Slurries of starch granules in water require heating sufficient to

disrupt the native granular structure to achieve solubility and realize the functionality of starch [3].

Heating of starch granules in water brings about *gelatinization* or the irreversible loss of granular order, which is accompanied by increased granule hydration, swelling, and leaching of soluble components (primarily amylose) [3,12–14]. In the presence of shear, the fragile, swollen granules are reduced to a paste composed of granule remnants dispersed within a continuous phase of solubilized starch. As the paste is cooled, the linear amylose molecules *retrograde* (crystallize), adopting regions of double-helical structure, which through aggregation, form junction zones that comprise a continuous three-dimensional gel network (Figure 1.18) [15]. The dispersed phase of a starch gel network consists of amylopectin-rich regions and granule remnants. The branched nature of amylopectin limits its intermolecular association, and favors initial water solubility, though amylopectin chains do slowly interact (crystallize) in time [3,12]. Thus, waxy starches, which contain only amylopectin, lack the ability to form strong gel networks, but are nevertheless capable of generating highly viscous solutions over time at starch levels above the overlap concentration via the development of weak intermolecular associations.

Due to their properties and abundance, starches of varied biological origin are frequently exploited as thickeners, gelling agents, binding agents, texture modifiers, and substrates in diverse food applications. However, most food starch ($\approx$75%) added as an ingredient is first chemically and/or physically modified [16], while yet in the granular form, to enhance the physical properties of starch polymers in accordance with the intended end-use. Several categories of starch derivatives will be discussed briefly, though in reality most commercial starch derivatives undergo multiple modifications.

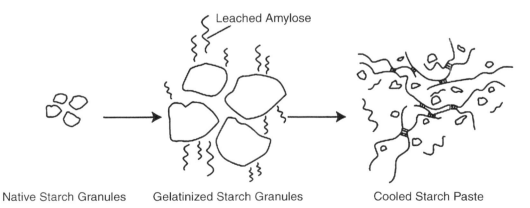

Native Starch Granules   Gelatinized Starch Granules   Cooled Starch Paste

FIGURE 1.18 Schematic representation of the structural changes associated with the gelatinization and pasting of native starch granules. Gelatinization (loss of granular molecular order) is accompanied by granule swelling and leaching of soluble starch components (amylose) during aqueous heating. With the application of shear, swollen granules undergo further disintegration to yield a paste, which is composed of a continuous phase of solubilized starch and a dispersed phase of granule remnants. Upon cooling, amylose retrogradation (depicted by the cross-hatching between molecules within the paste) results in the formation of a gel network.

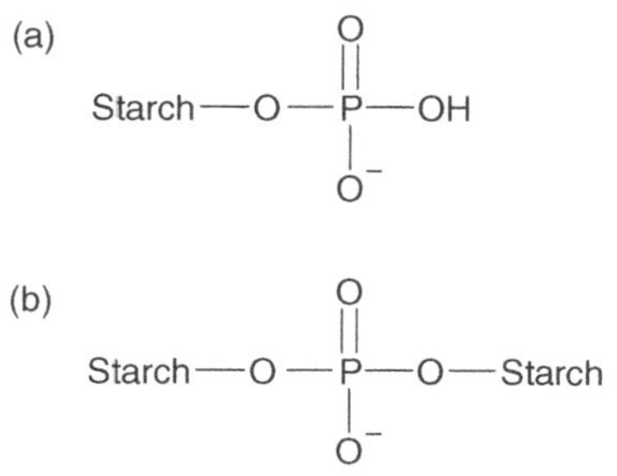

(a)

$$\text{Starch} - \text{O} - \overset{\displaystyle O}{\underset{\displaystyle O^-}{\overset{\|}{P}}} - \text{OH}$$

(b)

$$\text{Starch} - \text{O} - \overset{\displaystyle O}{\underset{\displaystyle O^-}{\overset{\|}{P}}} - \text{O} - \text{Starch}$$

FIGURE 1.19 Chemical structures of a (a) stabilized (starch monophosphate) and (b) cross-linked (distarch phosphate) starch derivatives.

Starch *stabilization* generally involves conversion of starch hydroxyl groups to phosphate monoesters (DS $\leq$ 0.002), acetate esters (DS $\leq$ 0.09), or hydroxypropyl ethers (MS $\leq$ 0.1) [3]. Modification is employed to overcome the tendency for syneresis of native starch pastes, which occurs due to excessive junction zone growth. The periodic incorporation of bulky (hydroxypropyl) and/or charged (phosphate monoester) substituent groups onto starch molecules (particularly amylose) introduces a physical and/or electrostatic impediment to intermolecular association and formation of ordered structures (Figure 1.19a) [3,17]. By regulating junction zone growth, stabilized starches exhibit improved paste clarity and syneresis/freeze-thaw stability in comparison to their native counterparts [3,17].

Cross-linked food starches are most frequently generated through reaction with phosphorus oxychloride or sodium trimetaphosphate, and exhibit of low levels of distarch phosphate ester cross-links (one per 1000–2000 glycosyl units) between adjacent starch molecules and/or chains (Figure 1.19b) [17]. While the presence of cross-links generally reduces the swelling of granules during gelatinization, it also contributes stability and rigidity to the swollen granule structure (less breakdown with shear), leading to a higher ultimate paste viscosity (compared to the unmodified starch) [17]. Due to the reinforced granule structure, cross-linked starches display good stability to shear, acidic conditions, and extended heating, and are utilized in a broad array of food systems (retorted, extruded, frozen, baked, and dehydrated applications) [3].

Acid-modified starch results from treatment of granular starch with dilute acid to effect partial hydrolysis of starch molecules within granule amorphous (disordered) regions [17]. While retaining their granular shape, acid-modified starch granules display minimal swelling and almost complete disintegration upon heating in water. Most importantly, hot pastes of acid-modified starches exhibit very low viscosities (breakdown of swollen granules), and are easily pumped while hot, but form stiff, opaque gels upon cooling [17]. Acid treatment of starch increases the proportion of linear starch molecules (due to hydrolysis of branched starch chains), which facilitate development of tertiary- and quaternary-ordered structures that comprise a gel network. Primary applications of acid-thinned starches involve production of gelled candy products [3].

Generation of *pregelatinized* or *cold-water swelling* starches requires the partial or complete disruption of the native granule structure (molecular order) by pre-processing (heating) a starch slurry under prescribed conditions [3]. The resulting starch products exhibit either ambient temperature solubility (pregelatinized) or granule swelling (cold-water swelling) to achieve viscosity development in aqueous environments without the requirement of additional heating. Pregelatinized and cold-water swelling starches are incorporated as both thickening and gelling agents in dehydrated and/or instant food products that do not require heat preparation.

Lastly, starch is the substrate for an assortment of carbohydrate ingredients classified as starch *hydrolyzate products*, which include maltodextrins, dextrose (commercial name for glucose), corn syrups, and high fructose syrups (HFS) [18]. Generation of these products involves variable degrees of acid and/or enzyme conversion of starch to lower-molecular-weight polysaccharides, oligosaccharides, and glucose. With the exception of some maltodextrins (bulking agent), all other noted starch hydrolyzate products (sweeteners) are reduced in molecular size to the point they are no longer classified as polysaccharides.

B. CELLULOSICS

As the most abundant component of biomass on the planet, *cellulose* is the key structural constituent of plant primary cell walls. It consists of long, linear chains composed solely of (1→4)-linked β-D-glucopyranosyl units (Figure 1.12a) [3]. As previously described, the nature of the cellulose glycosidic linkage, its regular monosaccharide sequence, and its linear backbone causes cellulose molecules to adopt flat, rigid, ribbon-like secondary structures that readily aggregate to form crystalline, water-insoluble superstructures [3]. Thus, in the native state, while cellulose represents a good source of dietary fiber in indigenous whole foods or in isolated form (referred to as *powdered cellulose*), it generally requires further processing or derivatization to enhance functionality for broader food use. Several such cellulose derivatives will be highlighted below.

Microcrystalline cellulose (MCC), which is generated by acid-catalyzed hydrolysis of native crystalline cellulose fibers, can be categorized into two primary types, powdered and colloidal, based on processing scheme and function. Both are insoluble in water. For powdered MCC, hydrolysis is conducted to generate small crystalline fragments, which are spray-dried and agglomerated to yield open, porous, aggregates of crystals of desired size (20–100 μm typical) [3]. Powdered MCC is used as a bulking agent and flow aid in food systems. On the other hand, colloidal MCC is produced by applying mechanical shear to crystalline fragments (obtained by acid hydrolysis) sufficient to further reduce crystallite size to the colloidal range (0.2 μm) [3]. A second polysaccharide (generally one with a backbone negative charge) is added to stabilize the dispersed phase (cellulose crystals) by providing a physical and or electrostatic barrier to aggregation [3,19]. Functioning as a protective colloid, the second polysaccharide interacts with cellulose crystals along uncharged segments of its backbone, while its charged regions provide electrostatic repulsion to prevent excessive association of cellulose particles. The dried dispersion, known as colloidal MCC, functions in food as an emulsion stabilizer, thickener, or fat replacer depending upon the properties of the protective colloid.

Production of *carboxymethylcellulose* (*CMC*) involves reaction of cellulose with chloroacetic acid, and converts native hydroxyl groups to carboxymethyl ethers (Figure 1.20a). For food applications, typical DS levels range from 0.4–0.95 [20]. The introduction of charged substituents along the cellulose backbone greatly enhances solubility (relative to that of native cellulose) by way of intermolecular repulsion [3]. At pH values above the carboxyl pK_a, CMC molecules occur as extended linear structures and sweep out large molecular domains to form high viscosity solutions. Commercially, CMC is available in a range of molecular weights (viscosity grades) as are most food gums. It is utilized primarily as a thickener in a wide range of food applications [20].

Methylcellulose (MC) and *hydroxypropylmethylcellulose (HPMC)* are additional ether derivatives that offer unique properties to food systems. Methylcellulose is achieved through reaction of cellulose with methyl chloride (MS levels 1.6–1.9) (Figure 1.20b), while production of HPMC involves additional derivatization with propylene oxide (DS levels 0.07–0.34) (Figure 1.20c) [3]. Relative to CMC, significantly higher derivatization levels are required to achieve water-solubility of methylcellulose, which is only marginally enabled by the presence of

bulky (but nonpolar) substituent groups distributed along the length of cellulose chains. The marginal solubility of MC becomes further reduced at increased temperatures (due to loss of water molecules of solvation, which facilitates intermolecular association of polymer chains, through hydrophobic interactions). The result is thermoreversible gelation over the temperature range of 50–90°C [3,20]. Due to the ability to form thermal gels, MC may provide a physical barrier against moisture loss and fat uptake during high-temperature frying operations. While HPMC also exhibits thermal gelation behavior, gels are typically weaker (relative to those of MC), and increase in softness with an increasing degree of hydroxypropylation (decreases hydrophobic nature and provides a physical barrier to intermolecular associations) [20]. In addition, HPMC exhibits good surface activity as a foam stabilizer [3].

C. GALACTOMANNANS: LOCUST BEAN AND GUAR GUMS

Galactomannans of significance include *guar* and *locust bean* (carob) gums, which commercially are the ground crude flours of their respective seed endosperm [3]. The primary polysaccharide component of both guar and locust bean gums possesses a backbone structure comprising of (1→4)-linked β-D-mannopyranosyl units with the occurrence of solitary α-D-galactopyranosyl units attached glycosidically at C-6 of main-chain mannosyl units (Figure 1.21) [3,21].

While guar and locust bean gums have only low to moderate molecular weights (200,000 and 80,000, respectively) [21], the mannan backbone (extended ribbon-like structure) contributes molecular rigidity that facilitates a large hydrodynamic volume and development of high viscosity solutions [3]. The presence of sidechains (impede aggregation) enhances the solubility of both guar and locust bean gums relative to unsubstituted mannan, which forms insoluble, crystalline, intermolecular aggregates (akin to native cellulose) [21]. Though the two gums have similar structures, substitution with D-galactosyl units is more frequent in guar gum (about 1 of 2 backbone units substituted) and more evenly distributed over the length of the polysaccharide chains as compared to locust bean gum

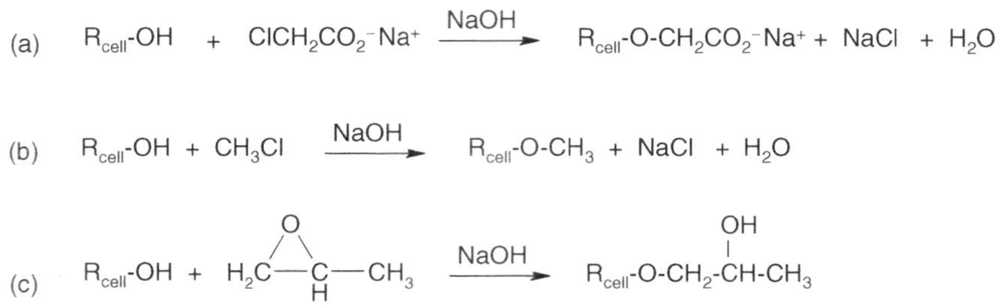

(a) R_{cell}-OH   +   ClCH$_2$CO$_2^-$ Na$^+$ $\xrightarrow{\text{NaOH}}$ R_{cell}-O-CH$_2$CO$_2^-$ Na$^+$ +   NaCl   +   H$_2$O

(b) R_{cell}-OH   +   CH$_3$Cl $\xrightarrow{\text{NaOH}}$ R_{cell}-O-CH$_3$ +   NaCl   +   H$_2$O

(c) R_{cell}-OH   + $H_2C \overset{O}{\overset{\diagup\diagdown}{-\underset{H}{C}-}} CH_3$ $\xrightarrow{\text{NaOH}}$ R_{cell}-O-CH$_2$-$\overset{OH}{\overset{|}{CH}}$-CH$_3$

FIGURE 1.20   Reactions used for generation of (a) carboxymethyl-, (b) methyl-, and (c) hydroxypropylcellulose derivatives.

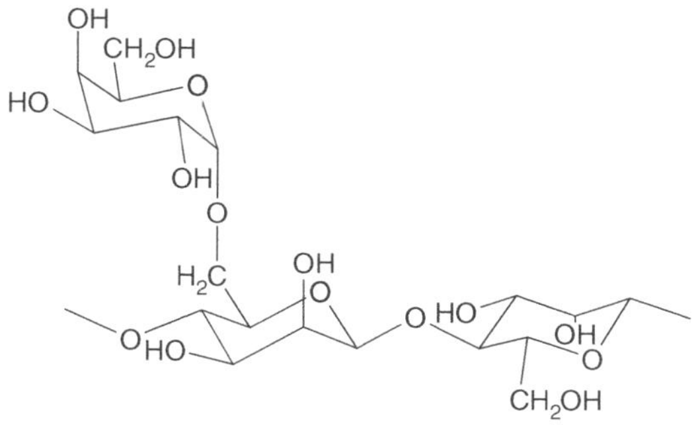

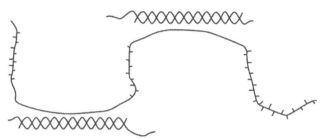

FIGURE 1.21 Generalized structural repeat of galactomannans.

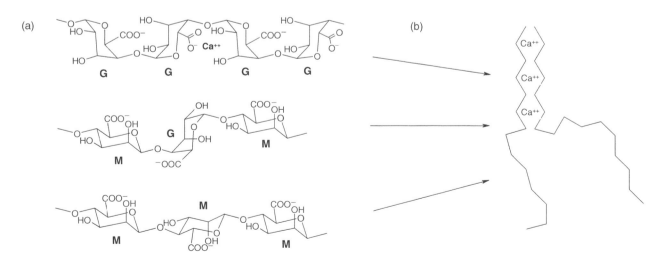

FIGURE 1.22 Schematic representation of the junction zone gel structure between locust bean gum "naked regions" and xanthan or carrageenan double-helical segments.

(about 1 of 4 backbone units substituted with irregular sidechain distribution) [3,21]. The regular substitution pattern of guar gum minimizes intermolecular associations, and explains the excellent water solubility and non-gelling behavior of this polysaccharide. The "naked regions" (large polymer sections devoid of sidechains) of locust bean gum afford open segments of the main chain capable of intermolecular interaction, and account for the gel-forming capabilty with xanthan gum and

κ-carrageenan (Figure 1.22) [3,21]. Thus, it is the differing patterns of sidechain substitution that primarily account for the basic differences in the properties of locust bean and guar gum.

D. Alginate

Extracted from brown seaweeds, *alginates* are complex, linear, block copolymers composed of (1→4)-linked β-D-mannopyranosyluronic acid and α-L-gulopyranosyluronic acid (occurs in $^1C_4$ chair conformation) units [3,5,22]. Three major types of primary structure generally describe the polymer backbone of alginate: 1) uninterrupted sections of D-mannuronate units (M blocks), 2) uninterrupted regions of L-guluronate units (G blocks), and 3) intermingled sequences of D-mannuronate and L-guluronate units (mixed or MG blocks) (Figure 1.23a) [23]. The occurrence of multiple, primary structural regimes within a single molecule has significant consequences on alginate three-dimensional structure and properties. Due to backbone charge, alginate molecules adopt an extended solution structure consisting of sections of M blocks (ribbon-like structure), G blocks (buckled shape), and MG blocks (irregular coil). In the presence of divalent cations, alginate forms gel structures that are described by the *egg-box* model (Figure 1.23b) [24]. In this model, junction zones are stabilized by divalent cations, which provide electrostatic cross-bridges between oriented G block regions of adjacent molecules. While the M and MG blocks do not participate in junction zone formation, they do serve to balance intermolecular associations by breaking up G block regions and limiting excessive junction zone growth. At excessively low pH values (below the pK_a of the carboxylate group), intermolecular electrostatic repulsion is lost, and precipitation can occur [3].

FIGURE 1.23 Depiction of alginate (a) G block, M block, and MG (mixed) block conformational structures and (b) the contribution of each respective conformation to junction zone gel structure characterized by the egg-box model.

E. PECTIN

Pectin, a cell-wall associated polysaccharide of higher plants, is a predominantly linear glycan consisting of α-D-galactopyranosyluronic acid units, some of which are present in a methyl ester form [3,25,26]. The polygalacturonate chain may also be disrupted by the occasional insertion of an α-L-rhamnopyranosyl unit [3,25,26] and the presence of sporadic, highly branched segments (hairy regions) [25,26], both of which introduce backbone irregularity (though hairy regions are mostly removed during preparation of commercial pectin). Commercially, pectins are categorized according to their degree of esterification as either low-methoxyl (LM; <50% esterified) or high-methoxyl (HM; > 50% esterified), which designation also defines the optimum conditions in which they gel [3]. LM pectins form gels in the presence of divalent cations, and align to form an "egg box" junction zone structure similar to that previously depicted for alginate (LM pectin and alginate G blocks possess almost mirror image secondary structures).

For HM pectin, solvent conditions must be adjusted to reduce both polysaccharide solvation and intermolecular repulsion (due to ionized carboxylate groups) to facilitate junction zone development. In food systems, the addition of competing solute (usually sugar; 55% minimum) and acid (to achieve a pH <3.5 and reduce the amount of negative charge) provide conditions that lead to gelation [3]. Junction zones, which are stabilized by a combination of both hydrogen bonds and hydrophobic interactions (between methyl ester groups) on adjacent molecules [27], are also effectively limited in size by occasional backbone irregularity (insertion of rhamnose, presence of hairy regions) to benefit gel stability [3,25].

F. CARRAGEENANS

Carrageenans represent a family of linear polysaccharides isolated from red seaweed species, and are generally categorized into three primary classes (κ-, ι-, and λ-types) according to chemical structure and physical properties [3]. All three classes exhibit a common, idealized, disaccharide repeat consisting of 3-O-substituted β-D-galactopyranosyl and 4-O-substituted α-D-galactopyranosyl units, but differ primarily with respect to their degree of sulfation (at C-6 and C-2), which generally follows the trend $\kappa < \iota < \lambda$ (Figure 1.24a–c) [3,28]. Both κ- and ι-types also possess significant proportions of 3,6-anhydro ring structures.

Due to the charged backbone arising from the presence of sulfate substituents, all classes of carrageenan (only sodium salt forms for κ- and ι-types) are highly soluble in water and adopt rigid, extended coil solution structures [3]. Below a particular transition temperature (40–70°C), both κ- and ι-types form regions of double-helical secondary order at sites along the polymer chain [3,5]. In the presence of K^+ and Ca^{2+} cations (κ- and

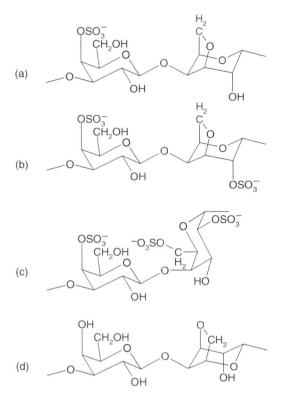

FIGURE 1.24 Idealized structural repeats for (a) κ-carrageenan, (b) ι-carrageenan, (c) λ-carrageenan, and (d) agar that provide insight into the physical properties of each respective polysaccharide.

ι-types, respectively), the shielding of negative charge by counterions facilitates aggregation of double-helical regions of polymer chains to form junction zones and a characteristic gel structure (Figure 1.25) [3,5]. Periodic irregularity (kinks) in the backbone structure limits the length of double-helical segments, which in turn regulate junction zone growth and promote gel stability [3,5].

In contrast, the high degree of negative charge and the different shape of the disaccharide repeat inherent to λ-type carrageenan molecules preclude significant intermolecular association and gel formation under any conditions common to food systems [3]. For carageenans, gel strength decreases in the order $\kappa > \iota > \lambda$ (non-gelling), which is inversely related to the degree of polysaccharide molecular charge.

G. AGAR

Agar, which is also derived from specific species of red seaweed, exhibits a chemical structure similar to that of κ-carrageenan, except that the second unit of the characteristic disaccharide repeat is a 3,6-anhydro-α-L-galactopyranosyl unit (in carrageenans, D-entantiomer is present instead) (Figure 1.24d) [29]. Similar to the carrageenans, the backbone structure is interrupted by an occasional kink (presence of sulfate hemiester at C-6 of the α-L-galactosyl unit),

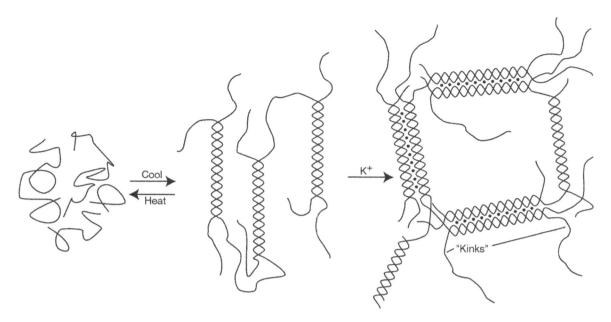

FIGURE 1.25 Representation of the gelation mechanism and junction zone structure for κ-carrageenan gels, in which potassium ions (•) shield backbone negative charges to allow intermolecular interaction of double-helical polysaccharide segments. The presence of "kinks" (occasional backbone structural irregularity) lends stability to the gel by limiting junction zone size and growth. Agar gels are believe to possess a similar gel mechanism and structure, except that potassium ions are not required to bring about gelation.

though the sulfate content of agar is nominal (1.5–2.5%) compared to that of carrageenan (>20%) [30]. While heating (85°C) is required to bring about water solubility, the lack of consistent negative charge along the length of the agar backbone results in a fairly flexible, non-extended polymer chain of relatively low viscosity (in comparison to carrageenan) [29]. However, upon cooling (40°C), agar molecules undergo a transition to an ordered double-helical tertiary structure, which leads to intermolecular aggregation of sections of ordered polymer chains and development of a quaternary gel structure [23]. Agar junction zone and gel structure are thought to mimic that of gelling carrageenans, with the exception that counterions are not required to promote gel formation in agar (lack significant negative charge that would require shielding for intermolecular association to occur) (Figure 1.25). Similar to carrageenan, occasional kinks in backbone structure disrupt the double-helical arrangement, which in turn prevents excessive growth of junction zones and aids gel stability [29].

H. XANTHAN

Xanthan is the common name for the heteroglycan isolated from the bacterium *Xanthomonas campestris*. While xanthan has a backbone primary structure identical to that of cellulose, it differs from cellulose in that it possesses a trisaccharide sidechain glycosidically attached to O-3 of alternating backbone units [3,31]. The sidechain consists of two mannosyl units separated by a glucuronic acid unit (Figure 1.26). Approximately half of the terminal

mannose units of the sidechain contain pyruvic acid, linked at C-4 and C-6 via a cyclic acetal structure, while the nonterminal mannosyl units contain an acetyl substituent attached at C-6.

The presence of the trisaccharide sidechain, which reduces intermolecular associations (due to electrostatic repulsion and steric hindrance), is thought to account for the excellent water solubility of xanthan relative to that of native cellulose (water-insoluble) [32]. Xanthan forms highly viscous, pseudoplastic (shear-thinning) solutions at low concentrations, which solutions are stable to viscosity change over a wide range of pH (1–12), salt concentration (up to 0.7%), and temperature (0–95°C) [3]. The relatively high-viscosity solutions are attributable to a high molecular weight (2–10×10^6) and molecular rigidity derived from its ordered conformation, which is thought to consist of an extended double-stranded helix [33]. At a temperature of 120°C, xanthan solutions lose up to 98% of their original viscosity due to loss of molecular order and rigidity [34]. At reduced temperature, xanthan solutions regain up to 80% of their original viscosity as molecules appear to reform the ordered conformation [34]. Due to its unique solution behavior, xanthan is used as a multipurpose thickener in a wide range of food applications.

I. GUM ARABIC

Gum arabic, also known as acacia gum, is the exudate material of the acacia tree common to the Sahel zone of

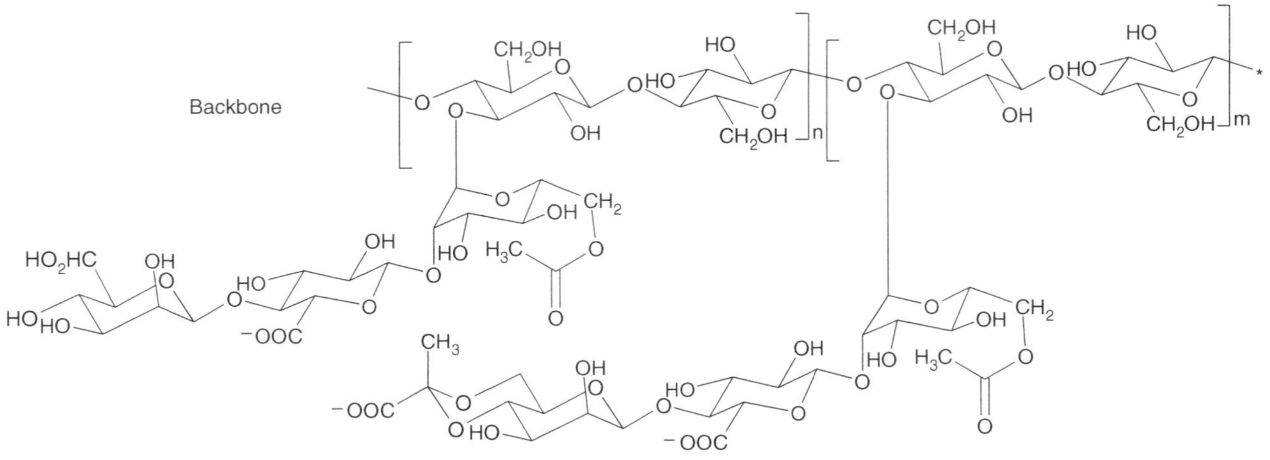

FIGURE 1.26 Chemical structural repeat of xanthan.

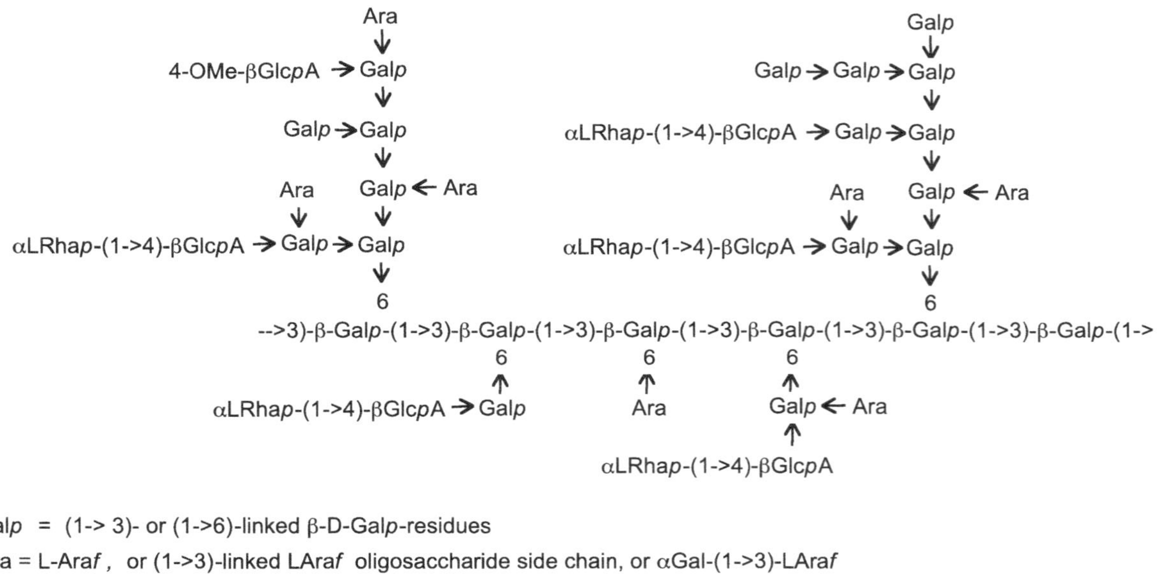

Galp = (1-> 3)- or (1->6)-linked β-D-Galp-residues

Ara = L-Araf , or (1->3)-linked LAraf oligosaccharide side chain, or αGal-(1->3)-LAraf

FIGURE 1.27 Representation of the branched chemical structure and composition of gum arabic.

Africa [35,36]. The gum contains 2–3% protein (gives rise to emulsification capability), which is covalently bound to the polysaccharide component [3]. Chemically, gum arabic has a (1→3)-linked backbone of β-D-galactopyranosyl units, which constitute approximately 40% of the total monosaccharide content of the gum (Figure 1.27) [3,36]. Further, the gum arabic backbone is highly substituted with sidechains (which themselves may give rise to further branching), producing a highly branched structure. It contains at least four additional types of monosaccharide units (L-arabinofuranosyl, L-rhamnopyranosyl, D-glucopyranosyluronic acid, and 4-O-methyl-D-glucopyranosyluronic acid units) attached to the branched backbone [3,35].

Due to its highly branched nature, gum arabic, though of substantial molecular weight (580,000), possesses a very compact three-dimensional structure, which provides the basis for its most unique physical properties, its astronomical solubility, and low viscosity (up to 50% gum solutions may be prepared) [3]. The compact nature of gum arabic molecules is best comprehended by the fact that gum solutions of up to 10% (w/v) display Newtonian flow behavior, and that it is not until 30% (w/v) solutions are achieved that steric overlap of individual molecular domains begins to occur accompanied by a more substantial rise in viscosity as a function of increasing gum concentration [36].

REFERENCES

1. P Collins, R Ferrier. Monosaccharides: Their Chemistry and Their Roles in Natural Products. Chichester: John Wiley & Sons Ltd, 1995.

2. J Lehmann. Carbohydrates Structure and Biology. Stuttgart: Georg Thieme Verlag, 1998.

3. RL Whistler, JN BeMiller. Carbohydrate Chemistry for Food Scientists. St. Paul, MN: Eagan Press, 1997.

4. M Friedman. Chemistry, Biochemistry, and Safety of Acrylamide. A review. J Agric Food Chem 51: 4504–4526, 2003.

5. D Oakenfull. Polysaccharide molecular structures. In: RH Walter. ed. Polysaccharide Association Stuctures in Food. New York: Marcel Dekker, Inc., 1998, pp. 15–36.

6. ER Morris. Polysaccharide structure and conformation in solutions and gels. In: JMV Blanshard, JR Mitchel. eds. Polysaccharides in Food. London: Butterworths, 1979, pp. 15–31.

7. CT Chuah, A Sarko, Y Deslandes, RH Marchessault. Triple helical crystal curdlan and paramylon hydrates. Macromolecules 16:1375–1382, 1983.

8. Y Deslandes, RH Marchessault, A Sarko. Triple helical structure of (1-3)-β-D-glucan. Macromolecules 13:1466–1471, 1980.

9. D Oakenfull. Gelling agents. Crit Rev Food Sci Nutrit 26:1–26, 1987.

10. RH Walter. Origin of polysaccharide supramolecular assemblies. In: RH Walter. ed. Polysaccharide Association Structures in Food. New York: Marcel Dekker, Inc., 1998, pp. 1–13.

11. ER Morris. Polysaccharide rheology and in-mouth perception. In: AM Stephen. ed. Food Polysaccharides and Their Applications. New York: Marcel Dekker, Inc., 1995, pp. 517–546.

12. CG Biliaderis. Structures and phase transitions of starch polymers. In: RH Walter. ed. Polysaccharide Association Structures in Food. New York: Marcel Dekker, Inc., 1998, pp. 57–168.

13. P Colonna, A Buleon. New insight on starch structure and properties. In: P Feillet. ed. Cereal Chemistry and Technology: A Long Past and a Bright Future. Paris: Ninth International Cereal and Bread Congress, 1992, pp. 25–42.

14. DJ Gallant, B Bouchet, PM Baldwin. Microscopy of starch: evidence of a new level of granule organization. Carbohydr Polym 32:177–191, 1997.

15. JJG van Soest, D de Wit, H. Turnois, JFG Vliegenthart. Retrogradation of potato starch as studied by Fourier transform infrared spectroscopy. Starch 46:453–457, 1994.

16. RJ Alexander. Carbohydrates used as fat replacers. In: RJ Alexander, HF Zobel. eds. Developments in Carbohydrate Chemistry. St. Paul, MN: American Association of Cereal Chemists, 1992, pp. 343–370.

17. OB Wurzburg. Modified starches. In: AM Stephen. ed. Food Polysaccharides and Their Applications. New York, Marcel Dekker, Inc., 1995, pp. 67–97.

18. PH Blanchard, FR Katz. Starch hydrolysates. In: AM Stephen. ed. Food Polysaccharides and Their Applications. New York, Marcel Dekker, Inc., 1995, pp. 99–122.

19. GS Buliga, GW, Ayling, GR Krawczyk, EJ McGinley. Microcrystalline cellulose technology. In: RH Walter. ed. Polysaccharide Association Stuctures in Food. New York: Marcel Dekker, Inc., 1998, pp. 169–225.

20. DG Coffey, DA Bell. Cellulose and cellulose derivatives. In: AM Stephen. ed. Food Polysaccharides and Their Applications. New York: Marcel Dekker, Inc., 1995, pp. 123–153.

21. JE Fox. Seed gums. In: A Imeson. ed. Thickening and Gelling Agents for Food. 3rd ed. Gaithersburg, MD: Aspen Publishers, Inc., 1999, pp. 262–283.

22. E Onsoyen. Alginates. In: A Imeson. ed. Thickening and Gelling Agents for Food. 3rd ed. Gaithersburg, MD: Aspen Publishers, Inc., 1999, pp. 22–44.

23. D. Oakenfull. Gelation mechanisms. Food Ingredients J Jpn 167:48–68, 1996.

24. GT Grant, ER Morris, DA Rees, PJC Smith, D Thom. Biological interactions between polysaccharides and divalent cations: The egg-box model. FEBS Lett 32:195–198, 1973.

25. AGJ Voragen, W Pilnik, J-F Thibault, MAV Axelos, CMGC Renard. Pectins. In: AM Stephen. ed. Food Polysaccharides and Their Applications. New York: Marcel Dekker, Inc., 1995, pp. 287–339.

26. CD May. Pectins. In: A Imeson. ed. Thickening and Gelling Agents for Food. 3rd ed. Gaithersburg, MD: Aspen Publishers, Inc., 1999, pp. 230–261.

27. D Oakenfull, A Scott. Hydrophobic interaction in the gelation of high methoxyl pectins. J Food Sci 49:1093, 1984.

28. L Piculell. Gelling carrageenans. In: AM Stephen. ed. Food Polysaccharides and Their Applications. New York: Marcel Dekker, Inc., 1995, pp. 205–244.

29. NF Stanley. Agars. In: AM Stephen. ed. Food Polysaccharides and Their Applications. New York: Marcel Dekker, Inc., 1995, pp. 187–204.

30. R Armisen. Agar. In: A Imeson. ed. Thickening and Gelling Agents for Food. 3rd ed. Gaithersburg, MD: Aspen Publishers, Inc., 1999, pp. 1–21.

31. S Kitamura, K Takeo, T Kuge, BT Stokke. Thermally induced conformational transition of double-stranded xanthan in aqueous salt solutions. Biopolymers 31:1243–1255, 1991.

32. G Robinson, CE Manning, ER Morris, ICM Dea. Sidechain-mainchain interactions in bacterial polysaccharides. In: GO Phillips, DJ Wedlock, PA Williams. eds. Gums and Stabilisers for the Food Industry 4. Washington, DC: IRL Press Ltd, 1987.

33. A Gamini, M Mandel. Physicochemical properties of aqueous xanthan solutions: static light scattering. Biopolymers 34:783–797, 1994.

34. M Glicksman. Food Hydrocolloids, Vol 1. Boca Raton, FL: CRC Press, Inc., 1982.

35. AM Stephen, SC Churms. Gums and mucilages. In: AM Stephen. ed. Food Polysaccharides and Their Applications. New York: Marcel Dekker, Inc., 1995, pp. 377–440.

36. MV Wareing. Exudate gums. In: A Imeson. ed. Thickening and Gelling Agents for Food. 3rd ed. Gaithersburg, MD: Aspen Publishers, Inc., 1999, pp. 86–118.

2 Carbohydrates: Physical Properties

Qi Wang and P.J. Wood
Food Research Program, Agriculture and Agri-Food Canada

CONTENTS

I. INTRODUCTION

Carbohydrates include monosaccharides, oligosaccharides, and polysaccharides as well as substances derived from them by various reactions such as reduction, oxidation, esterification, etc. Monosaccharides are the basic units from which all carbohydrates are built. Linking of monosaccharides via glycosidic bonds leads to the formation of oligosaccharides (2 to 20 monomers) and polysaccharides (more than 20 monomers). The term "sugars" is often used to refer to the monosaccharides and some disaccharides (e.g., sucrose). Polysaccharides are grouped into two major classes: (1) simple polysaccharides, which contain only monosaccharides and their derivatives (esters and ethers), and (2) conjugate polymers made up of a polysaccharide linked to another polymer, such as polypeptide. It is the purpose of this chapter to focus on the physical properties of simple carbohydrates and associated characterization techniques that are important to food sciences.

As one of the three major food components, carbohydrates have enormous functions and applications. They not only supply most of the energy in the diet of humans, but also have various functionalities which are used to confer desired texture in foods. In these latter applications, the physical properties of carbohydrates, such as solubility, water holding capacity, and solution rheology, play important roles. Although containing similar building blocks, mono-, oligo-, and poly-saccharides have different physical properties. An extreme example of this is the contrast between the highly soluble monomeric glucose and the completely insoluble cellulose, which is a polymer of glucose. It has long been known that the configuration and conformation of sugars are the determinants of their chemical and physical properties, and those of oligosaccharides and polysaccharides inevitably depend on the constituent monosaccharide as well as the

intermonomeric linkages. Abundant evidence has shown that most of the physical properties of carbohydrates depend on the size, shape, charge, and polarity of the individual molecules. The study of structure-function relationships has been an important topic of carbohydrate research, and advances in physical techniques continue to improve our understanding and provide more insight into these relationships.

II. CONFORMATION OF CARBOHYDRATES

A. MONOSACCHARIDES

Most monosaccharides and their derivatives encountered in foods are polyhydric alcohols carrying a "reducing" keto or aldehydo unit, and they exist primarily in cyclic tetrahydropyran and tetrahydrofuran forms, with the latter occurring less frequently than the former. However, the common ketosugars are more likely than aldosugars to exist as furanoses. Seven-membered rings occur but are not common in foods. Free reducing sugars in solution may exist in different cyclic forms, which are in equilibrium via the acyclic aldehydo or keto form.

There are three potentially stable shapes for the six-membered saturated sugar rings, namely chair, boat, and skew (Figure 2.1). The chair conformation predominates in most cases because the widest separation of the electronegative oxygen atoms is usually achieved through equatorial orientations of most of the hydroxyl and CH_2OH groups. The anomeric hydroxyl unit differs in that it may adopt two orientations (α or β), which are strongly influenced by the ring oxygen. Similarly, there are two principal conformations for saturated furanoid rings, described as envelope (E) and twist (T) (Figure 2.1), each with four or three coplanar atoms, respectively. Because of the low energy barriers between the E and

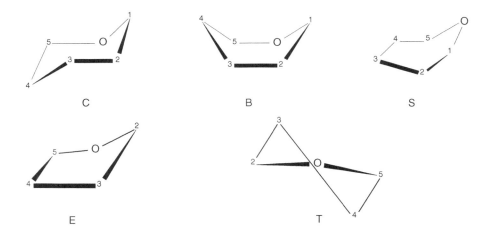

FIGURE 2.1 Examples of chair (C), boat (B), and skew (S) forms for pyranoid rings and envelope (E) and twist (T) forms for furanoid rings.

T conformers, interconversions of these occur more readily than between the pyranoid forms. The shapes of acyclic aldehydo and keto carbohydrates and their reduced forms are usually described as either a linear (zig-zag) or a sickle shape. The advent of diffraction and NMR techniques has allowed the determination of the configuration and conformation of almost all the important monosaccharides (1). In crystals, most molecules adopt a single conformation, whereas in solution there is generally more than one conformation undergoing fast interconversion.

For a more detailed treatment of monosaccharide chemistry and nomenclature, the readers are referred to standard textbooks (2).

B. OLIGOSACCHARIDES

The conformation of oligosaccharides is less well documented than that of monosaccharides, although the naturally occurring common oligosaccharides are well characterized. Most data from x-ray diffraction and NMR analysis are limited to oligosaccharides having less than four monomeric units. There is considerable experimental difficulty encountered when applying these techniques to large oligosaccharides (3). However, although based on limited amount of data, some general features about the conformation of oligosaccharides can be drawn. Once incorporated into an oligosaccharide or polysaccharide chain, the monosaccharide ring is relatively rigid and the ring geometry becomes effectively fixed. Thus, the overall shape of oligosaccharides become more determined by the two torsion (dihedral) angles ϕ and υ across the two single bonds of their connecting glycosidic linkage than by the unit geometries. Wells of minimum potential energy may be calculated, which limit the values adopted by ϕ and ψ but not rigidly so. Generally speaking, disaccharides should have a preference for staggered conformations about the two linkage bonds, unless there are geometric constraints imposed by, for example, a hydrogen bond between the two rings. The crystal structures of many oligosaccharides have been elucidated (3). Monosaccharides and certain oligosaccharides possess definite crystalline structures, and thus have well-defined melting points and solubilities.

C. POLYSACCHARIDES

Similar to polypeptides, polysaccharides also have different levels of structures, although higher level structures are less well defined. The primary structure describes the covalent sequence of monosaccharide units and the respective glycosidic linkages. The secondary structure describes the characteristic shapes of individual chains such as ribbons and helices, which arise from repetition of units adopting a particular average orientation in shape. Polysaccharide chains with well-defined secondary structure (or sufficient areas of such) may interact with each other, leading to further ordered organizations incorporating a group of molecules. This is known as the tertiary structure. Further association of these ordered entities results in large quaternary structures.

1. Ordered Structures in the Solid State

A repeated sequence of monomers or oligomers leads to an ordered and periodic conformation of polysaccharide molecules. The different linkage types, arising from the anomeric nature of glycosidic linkage and the orientation of OH units through which it is attached, impose certain general features on oligosaccharide and polysaccharide conformations because of the limitations placed on the dihedral angles. Fundamentally there are four different types of chain shapes: ribbons, hollow helices, loosely jointed, and crumpled types (4). For example, for β-(1→4) linked D-glucopyranosyl units, the two bonds from the ring to its two bridging oxygens define a zig-zag form, which promotes a tendency to adopt a flat, extended, ribbon-like conformation, in the polymer (Figure 2.2a). In contrast, when the links between the D-glucopyranosyl units are β-(1→3) or α-(1→4), they define a U-turn form (Figure 2.2b); this geometry extended over multiple units often produces a hollow helical conformation, which becomes stabilized in multiple helices. The linkage through the primary hydroxyl units, such as between (1→6) linked hexopyranose units, leads to a loosely jointed type of conformation and marked molecular flexibility in the resultant polysaccharides. This arises from the extra single bond and torsion angle (ω) between the two sugar rings that separates the rings, reducing inter-unit interactions and allowing a greater range of conformational

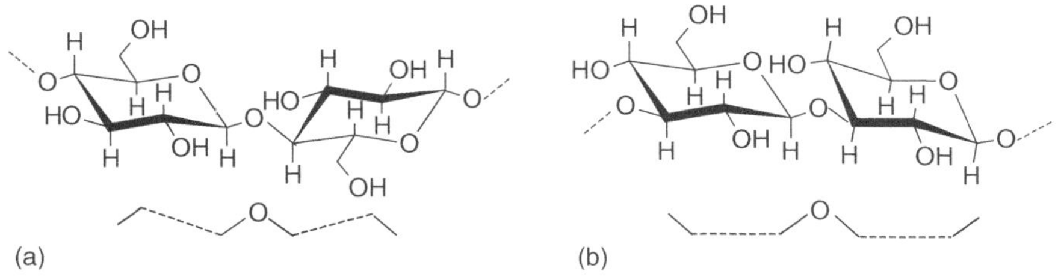

(a)   (b)

FIGURE 2.2 Examples of geometrical relationships across sugar rings. (a) Zig-zag relationship across 1,4-linked β-D-glucopyranose; (b) U-turn relationship across 1,3-linked β-D-glucopyranose.

possibilities. A further type of conformation known as "crumpled," such as in β-(1→2) linked glucopyranoxyl units, is less common in food carbohydrates.

The regular conformation of polysaccharides can always be described as a helix, which may be defined by just two parameters, the number of units per turn of the helix, and the translation of each repeating residue along the helical axis. The resultant single helix may associate to form multiple helices, which are then further packed in various ways to form higher ordered structures in the solid state. The majority of polysaccharides in their native form exist in an amorphous structure, examples being the antiparallel, extended twofold ribbon-like organized chain structure in the family of mannans and galactomannans (5). A relatively small number of polysaccharides are organized into a repeating crystalline or partly crystalline structure, examples being cellulose, starches, chitin, and some β-D-glucans. The crystalline element is usually capable of existing in different polymorphic forms. The ordered structures of polysaccharides have been extensively studied by x-ray and electron diffraction (6), and the x-ray structures of more than 50 well-defined polysaccharides are known (7).

2. Secondary and Tertiary Structures in Solutions and Gels

The extensively ordered conformation of a polysaccharide in the solid state may not be retained following hydration in solutions and gels. Polysaccharide chains tend to adopt a more or less coiled shape in solutions and fluctuate continuously between different local and overall conformations. A large group of non-gelling polysaccharides, or gelling polysaccharides in non-gelling conditions, exist in solutions with a conformation known as disordered random coils. Since polysaccharide molecules contain a large number of hydroxyl groups, they have a high tendency to associate into supramolecular aggregates through hydrogen bonding in aqueous solutions. For example, combining static and dynamic light scattering, a fringed micelle model was proposed for the aggregates formed in solutions by a number of neutral polysaccharides including tamarind xyloglucan (8) and cereal (1→3)(1→4)-β-glucans (9). The association of molecules in such a form markedly increases the stiffness of the single chains, leading to enhanced solution viscosity. More ordered structures may be developed, in solution through the so-called cooperative interactions, especially for polysaccharides in which identical repeat units result in a regularity of sequence. Conformational transitions in solution between random coils and helices have been well recognized and characterized for a number of polysaccharides such as curdlan, xanthan, and gellan (10). Under favorable conditions, these ordered structures may further associate, leading to the formation of three-dimensional gel networks.

D. PHYSICAL TECHNIQUES USED TO STUDY CARBOHYDRATE CONFORMATION

A wide range of physical techniques has been used to study the structures of carbohydrates at different levels, i.e., molecular, macromolecular, and supramolecular structures (11). The use of such means as mass spectroscopy and molecular spectroscopy to elucidate the primary structure of carbohydrates will not be covered in this chapter. The purpose is to include only those physical techniques used for studying the conformation of carbohydrates in general, and for probing the higher level structures of polysaccharides. Generally there is a need to combine several physical techniques to provide complementary information about the structure of carbohydrates.

1. X-Ray Diffraction

a. Background
X-ray diffraction and other types of diffraction methods (electron and neutron) have contributed to our understanding of the molecular geometry of carbohydrates. Diffraction is essentially a scattering phenomenon. When a monochromatic x-ray beam travels through a test specimen, a small proportion of the radiation is scattered with mutual reinforcement of a large number of scattered rays, and the resultant x-ray intensity in specific directions depends on the arrangement of the scattering atoms within the sample. X-ray scattering techniques are divided into two categories: wide-angle x-ray scattering (WAXS) and small-angle x-ray scattering (SAXS). Typically, SAXS gives information on a scale of ~ a few nanometers and smaller, while WAXS gives information on a scale of 1–1000 nm. WAXS is used to measure crystal structure and related parameters, which is the topic of this section. SAXS will be discussed in the next section together with light and neutron scattering techniques.

The diffraction pattern, commonly recorded on photographic film, consists of an array of spots (reflections) of varying intensities, from which structural information for a chemical repeat may be deduced. If a large enough size of crystal can be prepared, it is usually possible to determine the crystal structure and hydrogen bonding to a high degree of accuracy. Information such as repeating unit cell dimensions, lattice type, space group symmetry and bond lengths, and valence angles can be derived from the analysis.

b. Monosaccharides and oligosaccharides
For almost all monosaccharides and many oligosaccharides with low degrees of polymerization, it is not a major problem to prepare single crystals for x-ray measurement. X-ray characterized structures are available for most of these molecules (3, 12–16). As an example, in the study of mannotriose (O-β-D-mannopyranosyl-(1→4)-O-β-D-mannopyranosyl-(1→4)-O-α-D-mannopyranose) (14), the unit cell was determined as monoclinic with dimensions of

$a = 0.1183$ nm, $b = 0.1222$ nm, and $c = 0.9223$ nm, and $\beta = 112.34°$; the space group was $P2_1$. The crystal structure includes three water molecules, two of which are involved in hydrogen bonding such that the mannotriose molecules occur effectively as sheets of long parallel chains, with each consecutive sheet having chains lying at approximately right angle to those in a neighboring sheet.

c. Polysaccharides

Large oligosaccharides rarely and polysaccharides never form single crystals that are good enough for classical x-ray crystallography. They tend to form fibers that are amorphous, or at best only partly crystalline, starch being a typical example of the latter. X-ray study of starches mostly measures the degree of crystallinity and identifies different polymorphic forms. To obtain useful x-ray diffraction data from other more amorphous non-starch polysaccharides, oriented fibers or films are used (6). These polycrystalline fibers or films are prepared in such a way that the polysaccharide helices are preferentially oriented with their long axes nearly parallel. The x-ray diffraction intensities then provide information about the helical structures such as repeat spacing of the helix and helix screw symmetry, and if the diffraction pattern is sufficiently "crystalline," the unit cell dimensions and lattice type. However, the x-ray data alone are inadequate to solve a fiber structure, and interpretation requires supplementation with molecular modeling analysis using existing stereochemical information derived from surveys of crystal structures of related mono- or oligosaccharides (7, 17).

X-ray fiber diffraction is of great value in the determination of the conformations of polysaccharides. Studies of the $(1\to3)$-β-D-glucan family, curdlan, schizophyllan, and scleroglucan, are good examples. Curdlan is a linear $(1\to3)$-β-D-glucan, whereas schizophyllan and scleroglucan also contain some β-$(1\to6)$-glucosyl branches. These $(1\to3)$-β-D-glucans usually form triple-stranded helices (18). The structure of curdlan (in both hydrated and anhydrous forms), determined from oriented fibers, assume a right-handed, parallel, six-fold triple-helical conformation. There are interstrand $O2\cdots O2$ hydrogen bonds in the hexagonal unit cell, with parameters $a = b = 1.441$ nm and $c = 0.587$ nm. The space group is $P6_3$ and there is one helix per unit cell (19). The short-branch substitutions on the main chain primary hydroxyls in schizophyllan and scleroglucan do not seem to affect the fundamental triple-helical structure (20).

2. Light, X-Ray, and Neutron Scattering

a. Background

The principles on which light, x-ray, and neutron scattering depend are basically similar and can be treated by the same fundamental sets of equations. For all three modes of scattering, angular dependence of the normalized scattering intensity provides information on the size and shape of the macromolecules. The resolving power of scattering techniques is related to the wavelength of the scattered radiation (21). The wavelengths are 0.1–0.3 nm for SAXS, 0.2–1.0 nm for small angle neutron scattering (SANS), and ~500 nm for light scattering. Conventional light scattering typically reveals only the global dimensions of a macromolecule, which may be tens to hundreds of nanometers for a typical polysaccharide. SAXS and SANS can probe molecular structures at closer ranges of about 2–25 nm (22). SANS may additionally observe the Gaussian behavior of polymer chains in their own bulk (solid), which conventional light scattering cannot. Light scattering is effective in measuring the angular dependence of intensity typically in the range 30° to 135°. SAXS can be carried out at very small angles, typically less than 1°, and is thus superior for the determination of the size and shape of macromolecules, but it is less convenient for the determination of molecular weight and second virial coefficient.

b. Application to polysaccharides

Scattering measurements can be carried out in two modes, static and dynamic. The former measures the average scattering intensity within a selected time period, whereas the latter measures the fluctuation of the intensity over time. From static measurements, the weight average molecular weight (M_w), z-average radius of gyration (R_g), and the second virial coefficient can be extracted. From dynamic measurement, the translational diffusion coefficient is obtained from which the hydrodynamic radius (R_h) can be determined. The parameter, $\rho = R_g/R_h$, may provide information on the architecture of the macromolecules and their aggregates (23). From the combination of static and dynamic scattering data, other information may be derived including the linear mass density, Kuhn segment length, and polydispersity index. To obtain as much structural information as possible, experimental data from scattering are usually processed and presented through various plots, and need to be interpreted using molecular model such as the worm-like chain model (23).

Light scattering was applied to study the solution properties of amyloses and the retrogradation of amyloses as early as the 1960s (24–26). A typical flexible chain behavior was observed for high-molecular-weight amyloses in freshly prepared aqueous solutions. With decreasing molecular weight, the tendency to aggregate increased considerably so that a stable aqueous solution could not be prepared. The many studies on amylopectin and glycogen demonstrated how scattering techniques may be used for investigating the branching behavior of polysaccharides (27). The branching nature of amylopectin and glycogen can be detected clearly by light scattering from the Zimm plot, which shows an upturn (28, 29).

Scattering techniques can be used to probe the conformational transition of polysaccharides in solution. For example, the thermal transition evident in low ionic strength xanthan solutions was followed by light scattering (30). It was observed that the apparent hydrodynamic radius significantly decreases with increasing temperature in the vicinity of the helix-coil transition temperature. As discussed above (Section II.C.2), light scattering is also useful in investigating aggregation properties of polysaccharides.

3. Chiroptical Methods

a. Background

Optical activity is one of the most readily and often measured physical properties of carbohydrates. Carbohydrates contain several similarly substituted asymmetric carbon atoms and are therefore all optically active. The optical activity can be determined by optical rotation (OR), optical rotatory dispersion (ORD), and circular dichroism (CD). OR is measured by a polarimeter at a single wavelength, usually the sodium D line (589 nm), and expressed as specific (or molecular) rotations $[\alpha]_D$. A number of approaches, all of them empirical in nature, have been devised to interpret the relationship between the measured optical rotations and structural features of carbohydrates (31). Specific rotations are used extensively to characterize new derivatives and to recognize known ones. Instead of using a single wavelength, optical rotatory dispersion measures the optical rotation angle (φ) over a wide range of wavelengths, and circular dichroism measures the differential absorption of right- and left-circularly polarized light as a function of wavelength. Both ORD and CD spectra can exhibit marked changes in slope in the vicinity of the absorption maximum of a chromophore attached to the chiral center, known as the Cotton effect.

b. Optical rotation

In a monosaccharide molecule, several chiral carbons contribute to the overall optical rotation, but the configuration of the carbon atoms attached to the ring oxygen atom have the greatest influence on the overall rotation value. For many monosaccharides and reducing oligosaccharides, the initial optical rotation in aqueous solutions changes with time until reaching a constant value. This phenomenon is known as mutarotation, most often the outcome of interconversion between α and β ring isomers, until reaching an equilibrium.

Similar to monosaccharides, oligo- and polysaccharides have optical activity. With advances in the understanding of carbohydrate stereochemistry, it has become generally recognized that the overall optical rotation is determined more by the relative orientation of adjacent monosaccharide residues (defined by dihedral angles) than by the additive contributions from each asymmetric center. The optical activity of these is therefore beyond those arising from the simple monosaccharides, but is rather associated with the conformation of larger molecules or macromolecules. Stevens and co-workers developed a chiroptical technique to investigate disaccharide conformation (32), based upon the estimates of variation in the optical activity of a particular disaccharide as a function of its glycosidic conformation. A number of disaccharides, including sucrose, maltose and cellobiose, have been characterized using this method (33).

The optical rotation of polysaccharides at long wavelengths is usually dominated by the optical activity of the polymer backbone. Measurement of optical rotation at long wavelengths remains a standard and practical technique for polysaccharide systems despite the advent of ORD and CD instruments. For example, OR is used frequently for monitoring the progress of cooperative conformational transitions of polysaccharides (34).

c. Circular dichroism and optical rotatary dispersion

Monosaccharides of most food carbohydrates exist in cyclic forms, thus do not possess the unsaturated chromophores necessary to display a Cotton effect at long wavelengths. In the absence of unsaturated chromophores, two very short wavelength transitions associated with conformational transitions of carbohydrate backbone may be used (35–37). These can be observed by modern vacuum UV polarimetry. One such transition is centered near 175 nm, attributed to the n→σ* transitions of the acetal oxygen atoms. The second is usually found around 150 nm and is closely related to the optical rotation at long wavelengths. CD and ORD experiments show that the variation in intensity of these two bands in polysaccharides is correlated to their composition and conformation (38). Thus, CD and ORD offer powerful tools to study structural and conformational transitions.

Some polysaccharides contain chromophores that absorb at substantially longer wavelengths than the polymeric backbone and thus give significant CD and ORD bands at wavelengths above ~185 nm. Examples are acyl and pyruvate ketal constituents and the carboxyl groups. In these cases, the CD spectra are close to those of the isolated monosaccharides, with little direct influence from the chain geometry. Since CD is very sensitive to the local environment of chromophores, conformational changes caused by, for example, specific site binding of uronate segments are usually accompanied by dramatic changes in CD spectra (39). This provides an alternative approach to study the gelation mechanisms of polysaccharides containing carboxyl groups such as alginate, pectin, xanthan, and gellan (40, 41).

4. Microscopy Techniques

a. Background

Direct imaging of polysaccharides using microscopy provides an important additional method for physical characterization of polysaccharides. Two types of microscopy are especially of interest. First, electron microscopy (EM) is the traditional type, like light microscopy, but instead uses an electron beam to probe smaller structures than possible with light. Atomic force microscopy (AFM) senses forces such as electrostatic, magnetic, capillary, or van der Waals forces, as the molecular surface is approached by a probe. EM has considerable power to study supramolecular assemblies such as starch granules and mixed structures such as composite gels, whereas AFM has wide potential applications in investigating the structures of single molecules, as well as supramolecular assemblies and gel networks.

b. Electron microscopy

In EM, an electron beam produced from an electron gun is employed as an illuminating source instead of visible light. In transmission electron microscopy (TEM), when a fine electron beam hits the specimen, the electrons are transmitted after a series of interactions with the specimen, and then magnified to produce the image on a fluorescent screen or a photographic film. In scanning electron microscopy (SEM), the secondary electrons originating from ionization of the specimen atoms by the incident primary electrons are collected by an electron detector. The incident beam is scanned over a small area corresponding to the area of the micrograph. EM gives a better resolution than light microscopy because the wavelength of an electron beam is shorter than that of visible light.

A critical part of electron microscopy is adequate preparation of the specimen to minimize structural changes and to avoid artifacts. In most cases, the samples are exposed to a series of treatments prior to observation such as dehydration (or solidification), sectioning, and coating with electrical conducting materials. Thus, the image shapes obtained from the specimens may differ from their true shapes in the hydrated state.

Information can be obtained from EM on how macromolecules associate into supramolecular assemblies, and under favorable conditions, form gel networks (42). EM was used to monitor the conformational changes of polysaccharides that often initiate gelation such as coil-helix transitions (42). Direct visualizing of the structure of gel networks using EM has helped the understanding of structure-function relationships of polysaccharide gelation. In addition to these qualitative assessments of structural features, it is also possible to quantify properties like contour length, persistence length, linear mass density, and thickness of strands, using advanced image analysis systems (42, 43). Polysaccharides like xanthan and various β-D-glucans, all with a persistence length in the order of 100 nm, are ideally suited for such EM investigations. Since EM only provides a two-dimensional projection of the specimen, it is important to compare the parameters derived from EM with those obtained from other physical techniques, or from specimens prepared by different techniques.

c. Atomic force microscopy

AFM is still a relatively new form of microscopy and has only been applied to the study of biopolymers since the late 1990s. It generates images by sensing the changes in force between a probe and the sample surface as the sample is scanned. Using a variety of probing methods (44), a three-dimensional image with sub-nanometer resolution of the surface topography of tested samples can be produced (45). Thus, AFM affords an opportunity to directly image individual molecules and the helical structures of polysaccharides with minimal sample preparation (44, 46, 47). The polysaccharides are simply deposited from aqueous solution onto the surface of freshly cleaved mica, air dried, and then imaged directly under appropriate liquid (45).

For highly flexible polysaccharides such as dextrans, the AFM images show globular structures representing time-averaged pictures of the random coil structure. For more extended polysaccharides, such as xanthan and β-D-glucans, the AFM images may be quantified to yield persistence length, contour length, and its distributions (48). The dimensions observed by AFM are often larger than those derived from conventional techniques (44). This is believed to be due to the polymer-surface interactions which occur when the molecules are absorbed onto the mica surface prior to observation. AFM can be used to investigate the nature of association in junction zones, and also the overall structure of gel networks (49–51).

The use of EM and AFM has led to an improved understanding of the functional properties of polysaccharides at a molecular level. Furthermore, the ability to provide direct information about heterogeneity makes microscopy not simply complementary to other physical techniques, but also indispensable for obtaining additional detailed structural information.

5. Nuclear Magnetic Resonance

a. Background

Nuclear magnetic resonance (NMR) spectroscopy provides detailed structural information of carbohydrates, such as identification of monosaccharide composition, elucidation of α or β configurations, and establishment of linkage patterns and sequence of the sugar units in oligosaccharides and polysaccharides. Recent advances in two-dimensional NMR techniques allow the elucidation of some polysaccharides without chemical analysis (52). NMR can also be used to determine the conformation and chain stiffness/mobility of oligosaccharides and some polysaccharides in solution and to monitor coil-helix transitions and gel formation (53).

The principle of NMR spectroscopy is based on the magnetic property of the nucleus in atoms associated with spins. The most useful nuclei in carbohydrate research are ^1H and ^{13}C, which by absorbing radio frequency energy in a strong magnetic field, jump to higher energy levels. Spins at the higher energy levels tend to relax to lower energy levels, and the transitions are dependent on the magnetic field strength in the local environment of the nucleus. Therefore, every nuclear spin in a molecule is influenced by the small magnetic fields of the nuclei of its nearest neighbors. Hence, the signal released by the nucleus reveals structural information of the nucleus in specific environment. The analysis of these individual signals relative to a standard, expressed by chemical shift and spin-coupling between nuclei, can yield detailed information on the structure and shape of molecules.

One-dimensional NMR experiments are limited to the portrayal of response intensity as a function of the observation frequency under the applied field. Two-dimensional NMR techniques utilize a second frequency domain, which greatly expands the information contained in the spectrum. The introduction of this second domain allows correlations to be established and hence connectivity information can be obtained. These are very useful in determining molecular structures, particularly of complex oligosaccharides and polysaccharides. For example, COSY (COrrelation SpectroscopY) and TOCSY (TOtal Correlation SpectroscopY) are used to establish connectivities around monosaccharide rings. Long-range correlation experiments, such as Nuclear Overhauser Effect (NOE), a through-space phenomenon, can be used in the study of shape and conformation. Long-range heteronuclear correlation experiments can establish inter-residue connectivity, and the sequences of complex oligosaccharides and polysaccharides can therefore be determined.

b. NMR in molecular dynamics and conformational analysis

NMR relaxation data (T_1 and T_2^*) provide information on the dynamics of oligosaccharides and polysaccharides involving several different types of internal motion (53). NOESY provides information on inter-glycosidic spatial constraints, which helps define linkage conformations. Since they are able to provide conformational analysis of oligosaccharides in solution, NMR techniques are important means to obtain information on the three-dimensional structures free of crystal lattice constraints. NMR measurements of vicinal long-range homonuclear couplings

($^3J_{H,H}$) and long-range heteronuclear couplings ($^3J_{C,H}$) provide information on both intra- and inter-residue conformation(s) by measuring the parameters controlled by the dihedral angles between constituent monosaccharides of oligosaccharides and polysaccharides. In a recent application of NMR spectroscopy, long-range heteronuclear coupling constants were measured across the glycosidic linkages of a series of eight α- or β-linked disaccharides in solution (54). The $^3J_{C,H}$ values were determined by multiple ^{13}C site-selective excitation experiments using ^1H decoupling under pulsed field gradient-enhanced spectroscopy. The experimentally determined long-range three-bond heteronuclear coupling constants were converted to calculate values of the glycosidic dihedral angles of each disaccharide using a Karplus-type equation. Wide applications of NMR in solution dynamics, conformational analysis, and prediction of helical structure of oligosaccharides and polysaccharides can be found in the literature (55–57).

In summary, NMR spectroscopy is a very powerful tool not only for analyzing the primary structures of carbohydrates to provide information such as anomeric configuration, linkage sites, and sequences of monosaccharides, but also to determine the dynamics and shape of carbohydrates in solutions. The information can be further enhanced by combining with molecular modeling techniques. In this way, a deeper understanding of the dynamic properties and three-dimensional conformation of oligosaccharides and polysaccharides, and hence, the structure-property relationships, are obtained.

III. MOLECULAR WEIGHT AND MOLECULAR WEIGHT DISTRIBUTION

A. POLYDISPERSITY AND MOLECULAR WEIGHT AVERAGES

Monosaccharides and oligosaccharides have well-defined chemical structures, and specific molecular weights. However, polysaccharides contain molecules with different numbers of monosaccharide units (thus different molecular weights) and are said to be polydisperse. The distribution of molecular weight (MWD) varies, depending on the synthetic pathway and environments, as well as the extraction conditions to isolate the polysaccharides. The distribution may be described as mono-, bi-, or polymodal. Before we discuss how to quantitatively describe this polydispersity in molecular weight, we have to introduce the concept of molecular weight averages.

There are four statistically described molecular weight averages in common use, number average molecular weight (M_n), weight average molecular weight (M_w), z-average molecular weight (M_z), and viscosity average molecular weight (M_v). The mathematical descriptions of

---

* T_1 relaxation, or spin-lattice relaxation, is characterized by the longitudinal return of the net magnetization to its ground state of maximum length in the direction of the main magnetic field through energy loss to the surrounding lattice. T_2 relaxation, or spin-spin relaxation, is characterized by the exchange of energy of spins at different energy levels, and does not lose the energy to the surrounding lattice.

these averages in terms of the numbers of molecules N_i having molecular weight M_i are:

$$M_n = \frac{\sum_{i=1}^{\infty} M_i N_i}{\sum_{i=1}^{\infty} N_i} \qquad (2.1)$$

$$M_w = \frac{\sum_{i=1}^{\infty} M_i^2 N_i}{\sum_{i=1}^{\infty} M_i N_i} \qquad (2.2)$$

$$M_z = \frac{\sum_{i=1}^{\infty} M_i^3 N_i}{\sum_{i=1}^{\infty} M_i^2 N_i} \qquad (2.3)$$

$$M_v = \left[\frac{\sum_{i=1}^{\infty} M_i^{1+\alpha} N_i}{\sum_{i=1}^{\infty} M_i N_i} \right]^{1/\alpha} \qquad (2.4)$$

In Equation 2.4, α is the Mark Houwink exponent (Section V.B.2). Most of the thermodynamic properties are dependent on M_n and bulk properties such as viscosity are particularly affected by M_w. M_w and M_z emphasize the heavier molecules to a greater extent than does M_n. M_v is usually between M_w and M_n and closer to M_w; when $\alpha = 1$, $M_w = M_v$. For very stiff polysaccharides with $\alpha > 1$, M_v exceeds M_w.

A convenient measure of the range of molecular weights present in a distribution is the ratio M_w/M_n, called the polydispersity index (PI). In a random MWD produced by condensation syntheses, as with polysaccharides, PI is typically around 1.5~2.

B. PHYSICAL METHODS FOR MOLECULAR WEIGHT DETERMINATION

Absolute techniques for MW determination include membrane osmometry, static light scattering and equilibrium sedimentation. These techniques require no assumptions about molecular conformation and do not require calibration employing standards of known MW. Relative techniques include gel permeation chromatography (GPC), dynamic light scattering, velocity sedimentation and viscometry, and require either knowledge/assumptions concerning macromolecular conformation or calibration using standards of known MW. Combined techniques use information from two or more methods, such as velocity sedimentation combined with dynamic light scattering, velocity sedimentation combined with intrinsic viscosity measurements, and GPC combined with on-line (or off-line) static light scattering or equilibrium sedimentation.

1. Osmometry

Polymer solutions exert osmotic pressure across a porous boundary because the chemical potentials of a pure solvent and the solvent in a polymer solution are unequal. There is a thermodynamic drive toward dilution of the polymer-containing solution with a net flow of solvent through a separating membrane, toward the side containing the polymer. When sufficient pressure is built up on the solution side of the membrane, equilibrium is restored. The osmotic pressure π depends on M_n and polymer concentration c as follows (58):

$$\pi = RT \left(\frac{c}{M_n} + A_2 c^2 + A_3 c^3 + \cdots \right) \qquad (2.5)$$

where R is the molar universal gas constant, T is the absolute temperature, and A_2 and A_3 are the second and the third virial coefficients, respectively. In very dilute solutions, it is usually sufficient to consider only the first two terms in the equation, which can then be rearranged as:

$$\frac{\pi}{c} = \frac{RT}{M_n} + RTA_2 c \qquad (2.6)$$

where π/c is called the reduced osmotic pressure. According to the above equation, M_n may be determined by a plot of π/c versus c extrapolated to zero concentration. The intercept gives RT/M_n, and the slope of the plot yields A_2.

For neutral polysaccharides, osmotic pressure measurements can be made in water. However, for charged polysaccharides, salt solutions should be used to suppress the charge effects on apparent molecular weights. Usually 0.1–1 M NaCl or LiI is of sufficient ionic strength. Since osmotic pressure is dependent on the number of molecules present in solution, it is less sensitive to high MW polysaccharides. In practice, this method is only useful for polysaccharides having MW less than 500,000 g/mol (59).

2. Static Light Scattering

Static light scattering is widely used for determining the MW of macromolecules and measures M_w. For a highly dilute solution, the normalized intensity of scattered light R(q) as a function of scattering wave vector (q) and concentration (c) is given as (60):

$$\frac{Kc}{R(q)} = \frac{1}{M_w P(q)} + 2A_2 c \qquad (2.7)$$

where K is a contrast constant and P(q) is the particle scattering factor. For a random coil, P(q) is expressed by:

$$P(q) = 1 - \frac{q^2 R_g^2}{3} + \cdots \qquad (2.8)$$

$$\text{and } q = \frac{4\pi}{\lambda} \sin\left(\frac{\theta}{2} \right) \qquad (2.9)$$

where λ is the wavelength, θ is the scattering angle, and R_g is the radius of gyration. Equations 2.7–2.9 form the

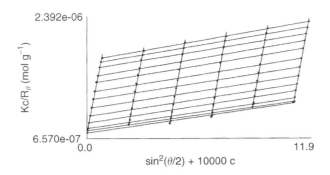

FIGURE 2.3 Zimm plot of tricarbanilate of β-D-(1→3) (1→4)-glucan measured in dioxan.

basic theory for MW determination using static light scattering. In practice, this is done by measuring the angular dependence of scattered light from a series of dilute solutions. The scattering data are then processed in the form of a Zimm plot or other associated plots (Berry and Gunniur plots). In a typical Zimm plot, $Kc/R(q, c)$ is plotted against $q^2 + kc$, where k is an arbitrary constant to separate the angle-dependent curves from different concentrations. The double extrapolation to c = 0 and q = 0 (i.e., $\theta=0$) results in two limiting curves intersecting the ordinate at the same point. This point gives $1/M_w$. The initial slope of the curve at $\theta = 0$ is $2A_2$, and from the initial slope of the curve at c = 0, R_g is obtained. Figure 2.3 is a Zimm plot of (1→3) (1→4)-β-D-glucan tricarbanilate measured in dioxan by static light scattering.

The measurement of the MW of polysaccharides by light scattering has not been an easy task when compared to many other macromolecules. The major difficulty is the preparation of optically clear solutions that are free of dust and molecular aggregates. A detailed procedure for the preparation and clarification of polymer solutions is given by Tabor (61) and Harding *et al.* (59). The measurement of MW is especially complicated by the existence of aggregates. Extreme caution has to be taken in interpreting the data. Poor reproducibility is often an indication of the presence of aggregates. Extensive efforts have been made to eliminate aggregates by the selection of appropriate solvents (9, 62, 63) or by chemically transforming the polysaccharides to reduce H-bonding, using derivatives such as carbanilates (64).

3. Sedimentation

Sedimentation methods are of two types, sedimentation equilibrium and sedimentation velocity. The equilibrium technique employs a centrifugal field to create concentration gradients in a polymer solution contained in a special centrifuge cell. For a solute under appropriate conditions (sedimentation equilibrium), sedimentation and diffusion become comparable so that there is no net transport of the solute. Analysis of the distribution of the solute concentration along the centrifugal field at such an equilibrium provides a means to study the MWD and the average MW. For polysaccharides, such an equilibrium distribution is generally achieved in 24–48 hours depending on the nature of the solute and experimental conditions (59).

The basic equation describing the distribution of solute concentration J(r) at sedimentation equilibrium is given for an ideal system as (65):

$$\frac{d\ln J(r)}{d(r^2)} = \frac{M_w(r)(1 - \upsilon\rho)\omega^2}{2RT} \quad (2.10)$$

where r is the distance of a given point in the cell from the center of the rotor, ω is the rotor speed (rad/s), υ is the partial specific volume (ml/g), and ρ is the solution density. The solute concentration profile is recorded, usually by a Rayleigh interference optical system, and transformed into plots of log J(r) versus r^2, from which the (point) weight average molecular weight can be obtained. The whole-cell M_w can then be calculated as

$$M_w = \frac{J(b) - J(a)}{J_0(b^2 - a^2)} \frac{2RT}{\omega^2(1 - \upsilon\rho)} \quad (2.11)$$

where a and b are the distance from the center of the rotor to the cell meniscus and cell bottom, respectively, and J_0 is the initial loading concentration.

Sedimentation equilibrium can cover a very wide range of molecular weights compared to light scattering and osmotic pressure methods. However, since the procedure is inherently time consuming and the thermodynamic non-ideality of polysaccharides can complicate interpretation of the measurements, the technique is not frequently applied in polysaccharide research.

As with equilibrium sedimentation, velocity sedimentation is based on the principle that the sedimentation rate of a polymer under a centrifugal field is directly proportional to its MW and shape. Velocity sedimentation monitors the boundary movement during ultracentrifugation by an optical method, from which the sedimentation coefficient, and hence MW, can be estimated provided the conformation of the molecule is known. By the use of high angular velocities, initial sedimentation may occur before diffusion effects become important. Compared to equilibrium sedimentation, velocity sedimentation is less time consuming, but can only provide qualitative information on average MW and MWD.

4. Viscometry

Because of the simple experimental setup and ease of operation, viscometry is extensively used to determine the MW of polysaccharides. The method simply requires the measurement of the relative viscosity η_r and polymer concentration of dilute solutions. Experimentally, η_r can be measured either by a capillary viscometer, a rotational viscometer, or a differential viscometer (66). The MW of the polysaccharides is then calculated via the Mark-Houwink relationship (Equation 2.18). The Mark-Houwink constants K and α are usually determined experimentally using a series of ideally monodisperse substances with known molecular weights. More discussion of this method will follow (Section V.B).

Caution is needed when applying this relative method to polysaccharides with chemical heterogeneity. Any factors that may change chain extension lead to changes in K and α values; examples are degree of branching (as with amylopectin and dextrans) and the distribution and/or substitution of certain monosaccharide units (as with alginates and galactomannans). The chemical composition and structure of the material under test should resemble those of the calibration substances.

5. Gel Permeation Chromatography

Gel permeation chromatography (GPC) or size exclusion chromatography (SEC) is widely used for the determination of MW and MWD of polysaccharides. In GPC, the polymer chains are separated according to differences in hydrodynamic volume by the column packing material. Separation is achieved by partitioning the polymer chains between the mobile phase flowing through the column and the static liquid phase that is present in the interior of the packing material, which is constructed to allow access of smaller molecules and exclude larger ones. Thus, larger molecules are eluted before smaller ones.

Conversion of the retention (or elution) volume of a polymer solute on a given column to MW can be accomplished in a number of ways. Narrow MWD standards with known MW, such as pullulan and dextran, may be used to calibrate the column. As with viscometry, the difference in structure between the calibration standards and the tested sample may lead to over- or underestimating the MW. To overcome this, a universal calibration approach may be applied in which the product of intrinsic viscosity $[\eta]$ and MW, being proportional to hydrodynamic volume, is used (67). For different polysaccharides, a plot of log $[\eta]$ MW versus elution volume emerges to a common line, the so-called "universal calibration curve." The calibration is usually obtained using narrow MWD standards from which the MW of a test sample can be read, provided the intrinsic viscosity is known.

In the last two decades or so, methods for the determination of MWD have been facilitated by combining GPC with a laser light scattering detector (68, 69). These methods provide absolute measurement of average MW and information on MWD and molecular conformations.

6. Other Methods

There are a number of other less frequently used methods for MW determination of carbohydrates, such as mass spectrometry, end group analysis, and NMR. The readers

are referred to the review by Harding (59) for a detailed discussion of alternative methods on MW determination of carbohydrates. In addition, recent development in AFM has shown that it is a potential means for MW determination of polysaccharides. The power of this approach is that it permits MW measurements of single polysaccharide molecules rather than mixtures of single molecules and aggregates. All the other methods described above determine the apparent MW of samples that often include molecular aggregates. Round *et al.* (46) found that M_n and M_w obtained from AFM is 2–3 times smaller than that for similar samples measured by conventional techniques.

IV. HYDRATION AND SOLUBILITY OF CARBOHYDRATES

A. LOW-MOLECULAR-WEIGHT CARBOHYDRATES

Carbohydrates contain both polar -OH groups and non-polar -CH groups. In an aqueous system, the numerous hydroxyl groups of carbohydrates may hydrogen bond strongly with water molecules. Also, the ring oxygen atom and the glycosidic bridging oxygen atom can form hydrogen bonds with water. Franks and coworkers discussed the thermodynamic data of small carbohydrates in the context of NMR and dielectric relaxation data (70). They found no solute-solute interactions in aqueous solutions even at fairly high concentrations. Both the sites of hydration and their relative conformations are important factors in the resultant hydration properties. Molecular dynamics studies have revealed that hydroxyl groups make on average between two and three hydrogen bonds with solvent (71, 72). Because of the proximity of adjacent hydroxyl groups, many water molecules were found to simultaneously hydrogen bond to two hydroxyl groups (71). The geometric requirements of these solute-solvent hydrogen bonds favor one conformation over another, leading to some solutes experiencing less favorable interactions with water, and hence being less soluble (73, 74). Nevertheless, low-molecular-weight carbohydrates, with degrees of polymerization less than 15~20, are generally very soluble in water and other polar solvents (75). The solubility decreases with increasing degree of polymerization because of increased solute-solute interactions.

Addition of polar organic solvents to solutions of carbohydrates results in the precipitation of an amorphous or crystalline form of the carbohydrates. Increasing the concentration of alcohol decreases the solubility of mono- and oligosaccharides, and they are only slightly soluble when the alcohol concentration is higher than 80% (76).

B. POLYSACCHARIDES

Polysaccharides display a wide range of solubilities conventionally described as easily soluble, intermediately soluble, and insoluble. There is no clear boundary between the three groups but the general consensus is: easily soluble polysaccharides are readily dissolved in cold water; intermediately soluble ones are only soluble in hot water; and insoluble ones cannot be dissolved even in boiling water. Structure and molecular weight are the two primary factors that determine solubility. Polysaccharides with a highly regular conformation that can form crystalline or partial crystalline structures (Section II.C.1) are usually insoluble in water. Linear polysaccharides with high regularity in structure, such as 1→4 or 1→3 linked β-D-glucans, and 1→4 linked β-D-mannans, are examples of this group. Although (1→4)-β-D-mannan can be dissolved in 5% alkaline solution, neutralization leads to reassociation and precipitation. Cellulose is insoluble, but swells in strong alkaline solutions such as 18% sodium hydroxide (77). Only cellodextrins with DP of about 15–80 can be dissolved or dispersed in such alkaline solutions; for DP less than 15, there is solubility in neutral aqueous solutions (75). Amylose, an α-(1→4)-homoglycan, is insoluble in cold water but can be dissolved in hot water.

A decrease in uniformity/regularity of molecular structure is always accompanied by an increase in solubility. The irregularity of the molecular chains prevents the formation of a closely packed structure, allowing many polysaccharides to readily hydrate and dissolve when water is available. The mixed linkage (1→3) (1→4)-β-D-glucans from cereals differ from cellulose only by the introduction of occasional single (1→3) linkages. The insertion of these linkages introduces "kink" points into the otherwise stiff cellulosic backbone, rendering the polymer soluble in water. Branching or substitution of the polysaccharide chain also reduces the possibility of intermolecular association and usually increases solubility. Examples are easily seen by comparing the solubility of galactomannans with that of (1→4)-β-D-mannan. By introducing single α-D-galactopyranosyl constituents (1→6) linked to the mannan backbone, the resulting galactomannans are fairly soluble in water. Any structures which contain especially flexible units such as (1→6) linkages will lead to higher solubility because of a larger favorable entropy of solution. Highly branched polysaccharides are almost always very soluble in water as in the case of amylopectin which has a much better solubility compared to its linear counterpart, amylose.

C. DISSOLUTION KINETICS

The ability of a substance to be solvated is governed by the fundamental thermodynamic equation:

$$\Delta G = \Delta H - T\Delta S \qquad (2.12)$$

where ΔG, ΔH, and ΔS are the changes of Gibbs free energy, enthalpy, and entropy of mixing, respectively. T is the absolute temperature of the system. A homogeneous solution is obtained when the Gibbs free energy is negative. For an ideal system, ΔH is usually small, so dissolution is an entropically driven process.

For low-molecular-weight carbohydrates, dissolution of the molecules is promoted by a large increase in entropy on mixing. The dissolution rate is mainly controlled by the diffusion or convective transport of solute from the interfacial boundaries to the bulk solution, which in turn is determined by the difference between the solute concentration and the saturated concentration at a given temperature. The dissolution process is generally fast as long as the solution is not close to the saturation point. Increase in the hydrodynamic field, such as stirring, promotes dissolution.

For polysaccharides, the contribution of entropy changes during dissolution is limited because of conformational constraints of the polymer chains. Most linear polysaccharides only form colloidal dispersions in aqueous systems that are not in thermodynamic equilibrium. In the initial stage of dissolution, amorphous polymer starts to swell as a result of water diffusing into the particle with a simultaneous transition from a glassy state to a rubbery gel-like state. Consequently, a gel layer forms on the surface of the polymer particle. The dissolution rate may be determined by a number of factors, either individually or combined together, including the rate of water penetration into the polymer, the rate of disentanglement of the polymer from the gel layer, and the diffusion or convective transport of solute from the interfacial boundaries to the bulk solution. In the case of high MW polysaccharides, the disentanglement of molecules is often the limiting step of dissolution. Thus the dissolution rate is expected to decrease with increasing MW because disentanglement of large molecules from the gel layer takes a longer time. The dissolution rate of guar gum was shown to be inversely related to the MW of the galactomannan (78). Diffusion or transport of solutes may also be the controlling factor in combination with disentanglements, such as in the case of a low MW polymer in low hydrodynamic environment (low temperature, low agitation), or when the viscosity of the solvent phase has built up significantly (78). The initial solvent content may also affect the dissolution of certain polysaccharides, but in various ways. Theoretical work and experiments suggest that dissolution rate increases with the level of residual solvent in the solid polymer (79, 80). However, if the presence of low levels of solvent leads to an increase in structure ordering, the suggested enhanced dissolution may not occur. For example, it has been observed that purified (1→3) (1→4)-β-D-glucan is very difficult to dissolve in water when it is precipitated from an aqueous solution and air dried. Solvent exchange using isopropanol before drying greatly improves solubility and dissolution. This is presumably due to the presence of water in the polymer, resulting in increased ordering of the polymer and poorer solubility. Other factors such as particle size and porosity of the polymer may also influence dissolution rate.

V. RHEOLOGICAL PROPERTIES OF POLYSACCHARIDES

A. CONCENTRATION REGIME

Rheology is the study of flow and deformation of materials, and for any given polysaccharide, concentration is of course of primary importance. A dilute polymer solution is one in which each polymer coil and the solvent associated with it occupies a discrete hydrodynamic domain within the solution. The isolated macromolecules provide their individual contribution to the rheological properties of the system almost independently of the imposed shear rate. As the concentration of polymer increases, a stage is reached at which the individual molecular domains begin to touch one another frequently. The corresponding concentration is called the overlap concentration c*. At polymer concentration $c > c^*$, the solution is called semi-dilute and when $c >> c^*$ the solution is concentrated.

B. DILUTE SOLUTIONS

1. Steady Shear Viscosity

The ratio of applied shearing stress (τ) to rate of shear ($\dot{\gamma}$) for an ideal viscous fluid is called the coefficient of viscosity, or simply viscosity (η), which is a measure of the resistance to flow. The term "fluidity," which is the reciprocal of viscosity, is sometimes used in the food industry. The viscosity increase due to the contribution of dissolved or dispersed solutes over the solvent is described by the relative viscosity (η_r) and specific viscosity (η_{sp}):

$$\eta_r = \frac{\eta}{\eta_s} \tag{2.13}$$

$$\eta_{sp} = \frac{\eta - \eta_s}{\eta_s} = \eta_r - 1 \tag{2.14}$$

where η_s is the solvent viscosity and η the overall solution viscosity. For most polysaccharides, especially of the random coil type, dilute solutions under shear flow show essentially Newtonian behavior. That means the viscosity of the solution is a constant independent of share rate. However, non-Newtonian flow behavior is observed for dilute solutions of some rigid polysaccharides, such as xanthan and some other β-glucans (81). For these systems, the apparent viscosity falls as the shear rate increases — a phenomenon called shear thinning. The shear thinning behavior of such polysaccharide solutions is a result of progressive orientation of the stiff molecules in increasing field of shear.

2. Intrinsic Viscosity

In dilute solutions, viscosity usually increases with concentration according to the Huggins and the Kramer equations:

$$\eta_{sp} = [\eta]c + K'[\eta]^2 c^2 \tag{2.15}$$

$$\ln(\eta_r) = [\eta]c + (K' - 0.5)[\eta]^2 c^2 \tag{2.16}$$

where K' is the Huggins coefficient. [η] is known as intrinsic viscosity and is the limit of reduced viscosity (η_{sp}/c) as $c \rightarrow 0$:

$$[\eta] = \lim_{c \rightarrow 0}(\eta_{sp}/c) \tag{2.17}$$

Experimentally, [η] is usually determined from the measurement of η_r or η_{sp} over a series of dilute solutions. By plotting η_{sp}/c or ln $(\eta_r)/c$ versus c, [η] is obtained as the average of the two intercepts at the ordinate via graphic extrapolations of $c \rightarrow 0$.

Intrinsic viscosity is not actually a viscosity but is a characteristic property of an isolated polymeric molecule in a given solvent, and is a measure of its hydrodynamic volume. It has a unit of volume per unit weight. Mark (82) and Houwink (83) independently correlated the intrinsic viscosity with the viscosity average molecular weight M_v

$$[\eta] = KM_v^\alpha \tag{2.18}$$

where both K and α are constants for a given polysaccharide-solvent pair at a given temperature. The exponent α is a conformation-sensitive parameter and usually lies in the range of 0.5–0.8 for random coil polymers, and increases with increasing chain stiffness. It can be as high as 1.8 for polysaccharides with a stiff rod conformation. Low values of α (<0.5) tend to indicate significant branching or a compact structure. Values of K and α for some food polysaccharides have been documented by Harding (66).

C. SEMI-DILUTE AND CONCENTRATED SOLUTIONS

1. Steady Shear Viscosity

Polysaccharides of sufficiently high molecular weights and concentrations can form an entangled network in solution which impedes flow. Such a system usually shows strong shear thinning behavior. Unlike dilute solutions, the shear thinning behavior of a semi-dilute or concentrated solution is associated with the continuous interchange between entanglement and disentanglement. At high shear rates, the newly formed entanglements cannot compensate for those being disentangled, which leads to a decrease in viscosity. A typical viscosity-shear rate flow curve consists of a low shear rate Newtonian plateau, followed by a shear thinning region where viscosity decreases as shear rate increases (Figure 2.4). In theory, there exists an upper Newtonian plateau at very high shear rates, but this is not accessible for most polysaccharide solutions using current instrumentation. As shown in Figure 2.4, the increase in viscosity with concentration is more pronounced at low shear rates. Therefore, for meaningful comparison of different systems, zero-shear rate viscosity (η_0) should be used. η_0 is obtained by measuring viscosity at a range of low shear rates and extrapolating to zero concentration, as illustrated in Figure 2.4 (84).

Shear thickening of polysaccharide solution, although rare, is observed occasionally. This phenomenon usually results from a shear-induced formation of ordered structures (10).

2. Concentration and Molecular Weight Effects

As with dilute solutions, the viscosity of semi-dilute or concentrated polysaccharide solutions also increases with increasing concentration. The relationship normally can be described by the power-law type correlation:

$$\eta_{sp} = ac^n \tag{2.19}$$

where η_{sp} is zero-shear specific viscosity. At a concentration above the overlap concentration c*, a more pronounced increase in both the zero-shear viscosity and the shear rate dependence of viscosity develops. For most random coil systems, the exponent n lies between 1~1.5 when c < c*, and 3.5~5 at c > c* (85).

Precisely, the viscosity generated by disordered polymer coils is dependent on the degree of space-occupancy by the polymer, which is determined by both concentration and molecular weight. In general, for linear polysaccharides in

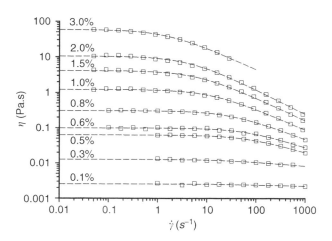

FIGURE 2.4 Shear rate ($\dot{\gamma}$) dependence of viscosity (η) for xyloglucan from *Detarium senegalense* Gmelin in aqueous solutions at different concentrations. From Wang *et al.*, 1997 (84).

a given solvent, solution viscosity increases proportionally to their molecular weight and concentration. The space occupancy is characterized by the dimensionless product of concentration and intrinsic viscosity c[η], since [η] is a measure of volume occupancy of the isolated coil in the solvent. Morris *et al.* (86) found that the double-logarithmic plots of η_{sp} vs. c[η] for a number of different disordered polysaccharides and the same polysaccharides with different molecular weights are virtually identical.

3. Temperature and Ionic Strength Effects

Another important factor that may affect the viscosity values and the profile of flow curves is temperature. In the absence of temperature-induced conformational changes, increasing the temperature leads to a monotonical decrease of solution viscosity and an increase of the shear rate of onset of the non-Newtonian region. For polysaccharides with charged groups, the shear viscosity is also sensitive to ionic strength and pH. Due to an expanded chain conformation caused by like-charge repulsions, a higher viscosity is normally obtained at lower ionic strength. Electrostatic repulsions are suppressed at higher ionic strength, leading to a less extended chain conformation and hence lower viscosity.

4. Dynamic Properties

Polysaccharide solutions are viscoelastic substances, i.e., have both solid and liquid characteristics. An important experimental approach to the study of the viscoelasticity of a polymer solution is to use a dynamic oscillatory measurement. A sample is subjected to a small sinusoidal oscillating strain (γ); this generates two stress components in viscoelastic materials, an elastic component which is in phase with the applied strain and a viscous component which is 90° out of phase with the strain:

$$\sigma_0 = G'\gamma_0 \sin\omega t + G''\gamma_0 \cos\omega t \tag{2.20}$$

$$\tan\delta = \frac{G''}{G'} \tag{2.21}$$

where G' is the elastic or storage modulus, G'' is the viscous or loss modulus, $\tan\delta$ is the loss tangent, and ω is the frequency of oscillation. The loss tangent is the ratio of the energy dissipated to that stored per cycle of deformation. The frequency dependency of these viscoelastic quantities allows specific features of different classes of polysaccharides to be distinguished. Based on the relative magnitudes of G' and G'' in a frequency sweep experiment within the linear viscoelastic strain range, three types of polysaccharide systems may be distinguished: solutions, weak gels, and gels (85). For dilute solutions of polysaccharides, G'' values are higher than G', with $G'' \propto \omega$ and $G' \propto \omega^2$ at low frequency. When the frequency or concentration is increased, there is a crossover between G' and G'', implying that the system passes from being a more and more viscous liquid to being a viscoelastic solid. Also, both G′ and G″ become less frequency dependent as the frequency is increased; a "rubbery" plateau of G′ is seen at high frequencies. Gels have a very different spectrum, with G′ remaining almost constant and G″ only increasing slightly as frequency increases; and G′ values are higher than G″ at all frequencies, with tan δ around 10^{-1} for a weak gel and 10^{-2} for a true gel.

D. POLYSACCHARIDE GELS

1. Gelation Mechanism

Under certain conditions, the association of hydrated polysaccharides results in a three-dimensional polymeric network (a gel) that fills the liquid available rather than precipitation of the polysaccharide. In these resultant gels, polysaccharide molecules or portions of these are aggregated in the junction zones through interactions such as hydrogen bonding, hydrophobic association, and cation-mediated cross-linking. To induce gelation, polysaccharides usually have to be first dissolved or dispersed in a solution, in order to disrupt mostly the hydrogen bonds from the solid state. The subsequent transformation of sols to gels is achieved by treatments such as heating and cooling, addition of cations, and change of pH.

The adoption of an ordered secondary and tertiary structure such as a helix or flat ribbon is a primary mechanism for the gelation of polysaccharides. The familiar gelation of algal polysaccharides agarose and κ-carrageenan, and bacterial polysaccharide gellan, involves the formation of helices (87). These helices may further associate to form a quaternary structure (gel network) through intermolecular hydrogen bonding or incorporation of counterions in the case of some charged polymers. The gelation of some other polysaccharides is through the formation of pleated sheets, sometimes described as an egg-box structure. Familiar examples of this are gels of low-methoxyl pectin and alginate. In this structure, the polysaccharides associate into matched aggregates in a twofold ribbon-like conformation, with the metal ions cooperatively bound during the process, sitting inside the electronegative cavities like eggs in an egg box.

2. Physical Properties of Polysaccharide Gels

Polysaccharides are able to form a vast range of gel structures which can be controlled by the properties of polysaccharides themselves and by the gelling conditions. A list of gelling food polysaccharides and a comparison of their relative textural characteristics are given by Williams and Phillips (88). Some polysaccharides form thermo-reversible gels and examples exist where gelation occurs on either the cooling or heating cycle. Thermal hysteresis may exist in some of the thermo-reversible gels; the melting temperature of the gel is significantly higher than the setting temperature. Thus, gelation occurs when hot agarose

solutions are cooled to below 40°C, but this gel does not melt until the temperature is raised to above ~90°C. Some polysaccharides form thermally irreversible gels, which are usually formed by cross-linking polysaccharide chains with divalent cations.

Gel formation occurs above a critical minimum concentration for each polysaccharide, and gel strength normally increases with increasing concentration. Molecular weight is also important. Intermolecular associations of polysaccharides are stable only above a minimum critical chain length necessary for the cooperative nature of the interaction, typically in the range of 15–20 residues (75). Gel strength normally increases significantly as MW increases up to a certain point, then becomes MW independent at higher values.

The gelation of anionic polysaccharides is also dependent on the type and concentration of associated cations because the association of the charged tertiary structures may be promoted by specific counterions whose radii and charges are suitable for incorporation into the structure of the junction zones.

Mixed gels from two or three polysaccharides may impart novel and improved rheological characteristics to food products. Synergy is observed for a number of binary systems including pectin-alginate, xanthan-galactomannan or glucomannan, and agarose or carrageenan–galactomannan or glucomannan. In these mixtures, synergism confers either enhanced gelling properties at a given polysaccharide concentration, or gelation under conditions in which the individual components will not gel. Although the gelation mechanisms for mixed polysaccharides are still controversial, there is evidence that some form of binding and structure compatibility has to be present between the two polysaccharides (87).

REFERENCES

1. GA Jeffrey, M Sundaralingam. Bibliography of crystal structures of carbohydrates, nucleosides, and nucleotides. Adv Carbohydr Chem Biochem 43: 203–421, 1985.
2. RL Whistler, JN BeMiller. Carbohydrate Chemistry for Food Scientists. St. Paul, MN: Eagan Press, 1997, pp. 1–17.
3. J Brady. Oligosaccharides geometry and dynamics. In: P Finch. ed. Carbohydrates: Structures, Syntheses and Dynamics. London: Kluwer Academic Publishers, 1999, pp. 228–257.
4. DA Rees. Polysaccharides Shapes. New York: John Wiley & Sons, 1977, pp. 42–43.
5. RH Marchessault, A Buleon, Y Deslandes, T Goto. Comparison of x-ray diffraction data of galactomannans. J Colloid Interface Sci 71: 375–382, 1979.
6. AH Clark. X-ray scattering and diffraction. In: SB Ross-Murphy. ed. Physical Techniques for the Study of Food Biopolymers. New York: Blackie Academic & Professional, 1994, pp. 65–150.

7. R Chandrasekharan. Molecular architecture of polysaccharide helices in oriented fibres. Adv Carbohydr Chem Biochem 52: 311–439, 1997.

8. P Lang, W Burchard. Structure and aggregation behaviour of tamarind seed polysaccharide in aqueous solution. Makromol Chem Macromol Chem Phys 194: 3157–3166, 1993.

9. A Grimm, E Kruger, W Burchard. Solution properties of β-D-(1,3) (1,4)-glucan isolated from beer. Carbohydr Polym 27: 205–214, 1995.

10. R Lapasin, S Pricl. Rheology of Industrial Polysaccharides. London: Blackie Academic and Professional, 1995, pp. 250–494.

11. SB Ross-Murphy. Introduction. In: SB Ross-Murphy. ed. Physical Techniques for the Study of Food Biopolymers. New York: Blackie Academic & Professional, 1994, pp. 1–12.

12. GA Jeffrey, M Sundaralingam. Bibliography of crystal structures of carbohydrates, nucleosides, and nucleotides. Adv Carbohydr Chem Biochem 43: 203–421, 1985.

13. GA Jeffrey, D Huang. The hydrogen bonding in the crystal structure of raffinose pentahydrate. Carbohydr Res 206: 173–182, 1990.

14. W Mackie, B Sheldrick, D Akrigg, S Perez. Crystal and molecular structure of mannotriose and its relationship to the conformations and packing of mannan and glucomannan chains and mannobiose. Int J Bio Macromol 8: 43–51, 1986.

15. R Gilardi, JL Flippen-Anderson. The tetrasaccharide stachyose. Acta Crys C43: 806–808, 1986.

16. S Raymond, A Heyraud, DT Qui, A Kvick, H Chanzy. Crystal and molecular structure of β-D-cellotetraose hemihydrate as a model of cellulose II. Macromol 28: 2096–2100, 1995.

17. S Arnott, WE Scott. Accurate x-ray diffraction analysis of fibrous polysaccharides containing pyranose rings. l. linked-atom approach. J Chem Soc Perkin Trans 2: 324–335, 1972.

18. RH Marchessault, Y Deslandes, K Ogawa, PR Sundarajan. X-Ray diffraction data for β-(1,3)-D-glucan. Can J Chem 55: 300–303, 1977.

19. Y Deslandes, RH Marchessault, A Sarko. Triple-helical structure of (1,3)-β-D-glucan. Macromolecules 13: 1466–1471, 1980.

20. T Yanaki, T Norisuye, H Fujita. Triple helix of schizophyllum commune polysaccharide in dilute solution. 3. Hydrodynamic properties in water. Macromolecules 13: 1462–1466, 1980.

21. K Kajiwara, T Miyamoto. Progress in structural characterization of functional polysaccharides. In: S Dumitriu. ed. Polysaccharides: Structural Diversity and Functional Versatility. New York: Marcel Dekker, 1998, pp. 1–55.

22. DA Brant. Novel approaches to the analysis of polysaccharide structures. Current Opinion in Structural Biology 9: 556–562, 1999.

23. W Burchard. Light scattering. In: SB Russ-Murphy. ed. Physical Techniques for the Study of Food Biopolymers. New York: Blackie Academic & Professional, 1994, pp. 151–214.

24. E Husemann, B Pfannemüller, W Burchard. Streulichtmessungen und Viskositätsmessungen an wässrigen Amyloselösungen, I and II. Makromol Chem 59: 1–27, 1963.

25. HL Doppert, AJ Staverman. Kinetics of amylose retrogradation. J Polym Sci A-1 4: 2353–2366, 1966.

26. M Kodama, H Noda, T Kamata. Conformation of amylose in water. I. Light scattering and sedimentation-equilibrium measurements. Biopolymers 17: 985–1002, 1978.

27. W Burchard. Static and dynamic light scattering from branched polymers and biopolymers. Adv Polym Sci 48: 1–120, 1983.

28. A Thurn, W Burchard. Heterogeneity in branching of amylopectin. Carbohydr Polym 5: 441–460, 1985.

29. W Burchard, JMG Cowie. Selected topics in biopolymeric systems. In: Light Scattering from Polymer Solutions. New York: Academic Press, 1972, pp. 725–787.

30. JG Southwick, AM Jamieson, J Blackwell. Quasielastic light scattering studies of xanthan in solution. In: DA Brant. ed. Solution Properties of Polysaccharides. Washington, D.C.: American Chemical Society, 1980, pp 1–13.

31. ES Stevens, CA Duda. Solution conformation of sucrose from optical rotation. J Am Chem Soc 113: 8622–8627, 1991.

32. ES Stevens, BK Sathyanarayana. A semiempirical theory of the optical activity of saccharides. Carbohydr Res 166: 181–193, 1987.

33. ES Stevens. The potential energy surface of methyl 3-O-(alpha-D-mannopyranosyl)-alpha-D-mannopyranoside in aqueous solution: Conclusions derived from optical rotation. Biopolymers 34: 1395–1401, 1994.

34. DA Rees, ER Morris, D Thom, JK Madden. Shapes and interactions of carbohydrate chains. In: GO Aspinall. ed. The Polysaccharides. Vol. 1. Toronto: Academic Press, 1982, pp 195–290.

35. RG Nelson, WC Johnson Jr. Optical properties of sugars. I. Circular dichroism of monomers at equilibrium. J Am Chem Soc 94: 3343–3345, 1972.

36. RG Nelson, WC Johnson Jr. Optical properties of sugars. 3. Circular dichroism of aldo- and ketopyranose anomers. J Am Chem Soc 98: 4290–4295, 1976.

37. JS Balcerski, ES Pysh, GC Chen, JT Yang. Optical rotatory dispersion and vacuum ultraviolet circular dichroism of a polysaccharide, ι-Carrageenan. J Am Chem Soc 97: 6274–6275, 1975.

38. WC Johnson Jr. The circular dichroism of carbohydrates. Adv Carbohydr Chem Biochem 45: 73–124, 1987.

39. I Listowsky, S Englard, G Avigad. Conformational aspects of acidic sugars: circular dichroism studies. Trans NY Acad Sci 34: 218–226, 1972.

40. ER Morris, DA Rees, GR Sanderson, D Thom. Conformation and critical dichroism of uronic acid residues in glycosides and polysaccharides. J Chem Soc Perkin Trans II: 1418–1425, 1975.

41. D Thom, GT Grant, ER Morris, DA Rees. Characterisation of cation binding and gelation of polyuronates by circular dichroism. Carbohydr Res 100: 29–42, 1982.

42. BT Stokke, A Elgsaeter. Conformation, order-disorder conformational transitions and gelation of non-crystalline polysaccharides studied using electron microscopy. Micron 25: 469–491, 1994.

43. AM Hermansson, M Langton. Electron microscopy. In: SB Ross-Murphy. ed. Physical Techniques for the Study of Food Biopolymers. New York: Blackie Academic & Professional, 1994, pp. 277–341.

44. VJ Morris, AR Kirby, AP Gunning. Atomic Force Microscopy for Biologists. London: Imperial College Press, 1999.

45. AR Kirby, AP Gunning, VJ Morris. Imaging polysaccharides by atomic force microscopy. Biopolymers 38: 355–366, 1996.

46. AN Round, AJ MacDougall, SG Ring, VJ Morris. Unexpected branching in pectin observed by atomic force microscopy. Carbohydr Res 303: 251–253, 1997.

47. AW Decho. Imaging an alginate polymer gel matrix using atomic force microscopy. Carbohydr Res 315: 330–333, 1999.

48. MJ Ridout, GJ Brownsey, AP Gunning, VJ Morris. Characterisation of the polysaccharide produced by Acetobacter xylinum strain CR1/4 by light scattering and atomic force microscopy. Int J Bio Macromol 23: 287–293, 1998.

49. AP Gunning, AR Kirby, MJ Ridout, GJ Brownsey, VJ Morris. Investigation of gellan networks and gels by atomic force microscopy. Macromolecules 29: 6791–6796, 1996.

50. AP Gunning, AR Kirby, MJ Ridout, GJ Brownsey, VJ Morris. 'Investigation of gellan networks and gels by atomic force microscopy vol. 29, pp. 6791–6796, 1996.' Macromolecules 30: 163–164, 1997.

51. VJ Morris, AR Mackie, PJ Wilde, AR Kirby, ECN Mills, PA Gunning. Atomic force microscopy as a tool for interpreting the rheology of food biopolymers at the molecular level. Lebensm-Wiss Technol 34: 3–10, 2001.

52. W Cui. Application of two dimensional (2D) NMR spectroscopy in the structural analysis of selected polysaccharides. In: PA Williams, GO Phillips. eds. Gums and Stabilizers for the Food Industry. Vol. 11, Cambridge: Royal Chemical Society, 2001, pp. 27–38.

53. CA Bush, M Martin-Pastor, A Imberty. Structure and conformation of complex carbohydrates of glycoproteins, glycolipids, and bacterial polysaccharides. Ann Rev Biophys Biomol Struct 28: 269–293, 1999.

54. NWH Cheetham, P Dasgupta, GE Ball. NMR and modelling studies of disaccharide conformation. Carbohydr Res 338: 955–962, 2003.

55. P Dais. Carbon-13 nuclear magnetic relaxation and motional behavior of carbohydrate molecules in solution. Adv Carbohydr Chem Biochem 51: 63–131, 1995.

56. L Catoire, C Derouet, AM Redon, R Goldberg, CH du Penhoat. An NMR study of the dynamic single-stranded conformation of sodium pectate. Carbohydr Res 300: 19–29, 1997.

57. B Coxon, N Sari, G Batta, V Pozsgay. NMR spectroscopy, molecular dynamics, and conformation of a synthetic octasaccharide fragment of the O-Specific polysaccharide of Shigella dysenteriae type 1. Carbohydr Res 324: 53–65, 2000.

58. C Tanford. Physical Chemistry of Macromolecules. New York: John Wiley & Sons, 1961.

59. SE Harding, KM Vårum, BT Stokke, O Smidsrød. Molecular weight determination of polysaccharides. Adv Carbohydr Anal 1: 63–144, 1991.

60. BH Zimm. The scattering of light and the radial distribution function of high polymer solutions. J Chem Phys 16: 1093–1099, 1948.

61. BE Tabor. Preparation and clarification of solutions. In: MB Huglin. ed. Light Scattering from Polymer Solutions. London: Academic Press, 1972, pp. 1–25.

62. ML Fishman, HK Chau, F Kolpak, P Brady. Solvent effects on the molecular properties of pectins. J Agric Food Chem 49: 4494–4501, 2001.

63. B Seger, T Aberle, W Burchard. Solution behaviour of cellulose and amylose in iron sodium tartrate. Carbohydr Polym 31: 105–112, 1996.

64. W Burchard, E Husemann. Eine vergleichende Strukturanalyse von Cellulose und Amylose-tricarbanilaten. Makromol Chem 44–46: 358–387, 1961.

65. JM Creeth, RH Pain. The determination of molecular weights of biological macromolecules by ultracentrifuge methods. Prog Biophys Mol Biol 17: 217–287, 1967.

66. SE Harding. Dilute solution viscometry of food biopolymers. In: SE Hill, DA Ledward, JR Mitchell. eds. Functional Properties of Food Macromolecules. Gaithersburg, MD: Aspen Publishers, 1998, pp. 1–49.

67. H Benoit, Z Grubisic, P Rempp, D Decker, JG Zilliox. Liquid-phase chromatographic study of branched and linear polystyrenes of known structure. J Chem Phys 63: 1507–1514, 1966.

68. ML Fishman, L Pepper, WC Damert, JG Phillips, RA Barford. A critical reexamination of molecular weight and dimensions of citrus pectins. In: ML Fishman, JJ Jen. eds. Chemistry and Functions of Pectins. Washington, DC: American Chemical Society, 1986, pp. 22–37.

69. MG Kontominas, JL Kokini. Measurement of molecular parameters of water soluble apple pectin using low angle laser light scattering. Lebensm-Wiss Technol 23: 174–177, 1990.

70. F Franks, JR Ravenhill, DS Reid. Thermodynamic studies of dilute aqueous solutions of cyclic ethers and simple carbohydrates. J Solution Chem 1: 3–16, 1972.

71. Q Liu, JW Brady. Anisotropic solvent structuring in aqueous sugar solutions. J Am Chem Soc 118: 12276–12286, 1996.

72. RK Schmidt, M Karplus, JW Brady. The anomeric equilibrium in D-xylose: Free energy and the role of solvent structuring. J Am Chem Soc 118: 541–546, 1996.

73. H Shiio. Ultrasonic interferometer measurements of the amount of bound water, saccharides. J Am Chem Soc 80: 70–73, 1958.

74. H Høiland. Partial molar compressibilities of organic solutes in water. In: H Hinz. ed. Thermodynamic Data for Biochemistry and Biotechnology. New York: Springer-Verlag, 1986, pp. 129–147.

75. RL Whistler. Solubility of polysaccharides and their behavior in solution. Adv Chem Series 117: 242–255, 1973.

76. M Levine, JF Foster, RM Hixon. Structure of the dextrins isolated from corn sirup. J Am Chem Soc 64: 2331–2337, 1942.

77. JO Warwicker, AC Wright. Function of sheets of cellulose chains in swelling reactions on cellulose. J Appl Polym Sci 11: 659–671, 1967.

78. Q Wang, PR Ellis, SR Ross-Murphy. Dissolution kinetics of guar gum powders, II. Effects of concentration and molecular weight. Carbohydr Polym 53: 75–83, 2003.

79. I Devotta, MV Badiger, PR Rajamohanan, S Ganapathy, RA Mashelkar. Unusual retardation and enhancement in polymer dissolution: Role of disengagement dynamics. Chem Eng Sci 50: 2557–2569, 1995.

80. AA Ouano. Solvent-property relationships in polymers. In: RB Seymour, GA Stahl. eds. Macromolecular Solutions. New York: Pergamon Press, 1992, pp. 208–219.

81. E Steiner, H Divjak, W Steiner, RM Lafferty, H Esterbauer. Rheological properties of solutions of a colloid-disperse homoglucan from *Schizohyicum commune*. Progr Coll Polym Sci 77: 217–220, 1988.

82. H Mark. Der Feste Korper. Leipzig, Germany: Hirzel, 1938.

83. R Houwink. Relation between the polymerization degree determined by osmotic and viscometric methods. J Prakt Chem 157: 15–18, 1940.

84. Q Wang, PR Ellis, SB Ross-Murphy, W Burchard. Solution characteristics of the xyloglucan extracted from *Detarium senegalense* Gmelin. Carbohydr Polym 33: 115–124, 1997.

85. SB Ross-Murphy. Rheological methods. In: HS Chan. ed. Biophysical Methods in Food Research. Critical Reports on Applied Chemistry, Vol. 5. Oxford: Blackwell Scientific Publications, 1984, pp. 138–199.

86. ER Morris, AN Cutler, SB Ross-Murphy, DA Rees, J Price. Concentration and shear rate dependence of viscosity in random coil polysaccharide solutions. Carbohydr Polym 1: 5–21, 1981.

87. VJ Morris. Gelation of polysaccharides. In: SE Hill, DA Ledward, JR Mitchell. eds. Functional Properties of Food Macromolecules. Gaithersburg, MD: Aspen Publishers, 1998, pp. 143–226.

88. PA Williams, GO Phillips. Introduction to food hydrocolloids. In: PA Williams, GO Phillips. ed. Handbook of Hydrocolloids. Boca Raton, FL: CRC Press, 2000, pp. 1–20.

3 Carbohydrates: Starch

Lorraine L. Niba
Department of Human Nutrition, Foods and Exercise,
Virginia Polytechnic Institute and State University

CONTENTS

Starch is the major source of calories and dietary energy in most human food systems. As the primary human metabolic substrate, starch is preferentially digested, absorbed and metabolized. Most diets worldwide have a substantial starchy component as a main or side item. For instance, potatoes are a major item in most northern European diets, rice is popular in Asian diets, maize-based foods are common in Latin America, and starchy root and tuber crops constitute a significant part of the diet in most tropical areas.

Starch occurs naturally in plants and is the storage polysaccharide of plants. It is heterogeneous, consisting of two glucose polymers: amylose and amylopectin. It is a polymer of glucose and a complex carbohydrate, which finds multiple applications in various industries such as pharmaceuticals, textiles, paper, and the food industry.

Starch performs various functions in food systems. It is used as a carrier in various products, as a texture modifier, as a thickener, and as a raw material for the production of other valuable food ingredients and products. Physiologically, it is a source of energy. In addition, starches that are resistant to amylase digestion have properties similar to soluble fiber.

I. STARCH COMPOSITION AND STRUCTURE

Starch is composed of two basic molecular components: amylose and amylopectin. These are identical in their constituent basic units (glucose), but differ in their structural organization (linkages). These variations in the linkages in turn affect their functionality in food applications. Amylose is a straight chain molecule, while amylopectin is a branched molecule. In addition, each is hydrolyzed, digested, and absorbed differently. Amylose is hydrolyzed mainly by amylases, while amylopectin requires debranching enzymes such as pullulanase for complete hydrolysis. As a result of their structure, the nature and products of hydrolysis of amylose and amylopectin differ. The proportions of amylose and amylopectin in foods therefore influence the extent of digestibility of the starch.

The ratios of amylose to amylopectin vary among starch sources and play a considerable role in determining reactions and physicochemical properties of starches in processing and food applications (1–6). Most tuber starches contain high levels of amylopectin, imparting a "waxy" texture.

Amylose and amylopectin are the polymers which constitute the starch granule (Table 3.1).

A. AMYLOSE

Amylose is composed of D-glucose molecules, which are linked in an α-1$\rightarrow$4 conformation. The glucose monomers therefore form a linear straight chain polymer.

Amylose is less predominant (about 20%) and typically constitutes about 20–40% in proportion (7).

Amylose contains α-1$\rightarrow$4 glycosidic bonds and is slightly soluble in water. Amylose molecules are arranged in a helical conformation. This facilitates formation of complexes with iodine, lipids, and other polar substances (2,8,9). The iodide ions are sequestered in the central tunnel of the helix. Amylose forms a blue complex with iodine, which can be read at about 650 nm.

The starch iodine test is often used to determine amylose content of various starches and starch types (4,10). Amylose is more suitable for the starch-iodine test. The affinity of pure amylose for iodine is 19–20% compared to only about 1% for amylopectin (1,2,6). Amylose would adsorb 19–20.5 g of iodine per 100 g compared to only about 1.2 g for amylopectin. The starch iodine test is often considered to be a measure of apparent amylose content of the starch.

Amylose is the key component involved in water absorption, swelling, and gelation of starch in food processing. High amylose starches are therefore most commonly applied in food products that require quick-setting gels such as candies and confectionery. Amylose is more susceptible to gelatinization and retrogradation, and hence is most commonly involved in resistant starch formation.

TABLE 3.1
Properties of Amylose and Amylopectin (1–6,9)

Property	Amylose	Amylopectin
Structure	Linear (branched chains isolated from some starches)	Branched chains (long segments of linear chains in some starches)
Molecular weight	Up to 1 000 000	Up to 5 000 000
Glycosidic linkage	α-1$\rightarrow$4	α-1$\rightarrow$4 and α-1$\rightarrow$6
Iodine complex	Blue	Purple
Iodine affinity	19–20.5%	0–1.2%
Blue value	1.2–1.6	0–0.05
Polar agents	Complexes with polar agents	Does not complex with polar agents
X-ray diffraction pattern	Crystalline	Amorphous
Phosphorus	Phosphorus-free	0.06–0.9% phosphorus (mostly in root/tuber starches)
Association with lipids	High	Low
α-Amylase hydrolysis products	Glucose, maltose, maltotriose, mainly oligosaccharides	Small amounts of reducing sugars, mainly oligosaccharides
Hydrolysis to maltose	100%	55–60 (100% with limit dextrinase and β-amylase)
Pullulanase	No effect	Debranches α-1$\rightarrow$6 linkages
Gel stability	Firm, translucent, quick-setting gels	Clear viscous gels
Susceptibility to retrogradation	Retrogrades readily	Mostly stable
Common sources	Typically higher in cereal starches (e.g., corn starch)	Typically high in tubers and root starches (e.g., tapioca starch)

B. AMYLOPECTIN

Amylopectin consists of D-glucose units which are linked in an α-1$\rightarrow$4 conformation as is the case with amylose, as well as D-glucose units in an α-1$\rightarrow$6 conformation. Amylopectin is therefore highly branched as the α-1$\rightarrow$4 linear chains are punctuated with the α-1$\rightarrow$6 linkages. The α-1$\rightarrow$6 constitute about 5% of the structure of amylopectin and gives rise to the branching (11). The amylopectin molecule therefore is much larger than the amylose molecule. The larger molecular size of amylopectin from amylose facilitates separation of these two polymers by size exclusion chromatography (2,7). Negligible amounts of unbranched amylopectin (A chains) in some starches have also been reported. In addition, there are long unbranched portions of the glucose polymer in some amylopectin molecules. While the straight chain of amylose is readily hydrolyzed by β-amylases, de-branching enzymes have to be used to obtain full hydrolysis of amylopectin (2,3,8).

Amylopectin has short branched chains and branch linkages, and thus cannot form the helical complex with iodine. The branched dextrin of amylopectin, however, gives a purple color with the iodine complex, identifiable at about 550 nm (3,9).

The enzymes required for amylopectin hydrolysis vary from those required for hydrolysis of amylose. Pullulanase, an enzyme which is specific for the α-1$\rightarrow$6 glycosidic linkage, and other debranching enzymes are needed to hydrolyze amylopectin.

The properties of amylopectin in food applications differ considerably from those of amylose. Amylopectin gels are more flexible and resistant. Amylopectin also is much more resistant to retrogradation than amylose. High amylopectin starches (waxy starches) are therefore commonly used in noodle processing and in some baked products to extend shelf-life. They also are used to improve freeze-thaw stability due to their resistance to retrogradation.

C. THE STARCH GRANULE

The basic components of starch, amylose and amylopectin, are located in granules. The size, shape, and characteristics of the granules are specific to the plant source. The growth and development of the granule originates at the center of the granule, which is known as the hilum. Under magnification and polarized light, native starch granules typically appear to have a cross-like structure, similar to a maltese cross, exhibiting birefringence. The size and shape of this cross-like shape varies among botanical starch sources. For instance, starch from pinto bean has elliptical shaped lobes, while some starches have more than four lobes (12).

The ordered arrangement of amylopectin molecules intertwines to form three-dimensional double helices between adjacent branches of the same amylopectin molecule or between adjacent clusters. The double helices are

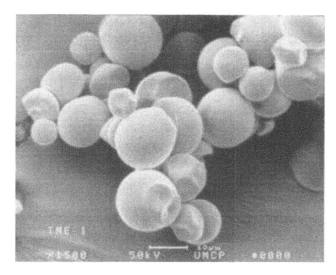

FIGURE 3.1 Tapioca starch granules.

stabilized by weak van der Waals and hydrogen bonds. The various arrangements of the helices result in the presence of crystalline regions on the granule (11,13,14). The nature of these regions becomes clear by their X-ray diffraction patterns. The crystalline patterns vary under X-ray diffraction patterns. These polymorphic arrangements occur in two patterns, which are classified as A or B, and an intermediate form or mixture of A and B forms, known as C type (11,14,15). Most cereal starches have A type patterns. Root and tuber starches such as potato starch contain mostly B type patterns, while legume starches have a combination of both polymorphic A and B forms, and hence are classified as C forms (11,14,15). The crystalline nature and diffraction of starch is greatly altered by processing (16).

Natural starch granules are insoluble in water, which is why starch is separated by sedimentation. This shape is disfigured and lost as starch loses its structure with modification such as heat and moisture.

Granules vary in shape and size and are characteristic of the starch sources. These shapes may be round, lenticular, or oval (11,17). Starch granule properties are used as diagnostic characteristics for identification and characterization of starches, based on structure and shape (Figure 3.1).

D. NON-STARCH COMPONENTS

Various non-starch components are covalently linked to amylose or amylopectin in starch. Structural and functional proteins are present which surround the starch granule. The protein friabilin, responsible for hardness of the endosperm in most cereals, is located on the granule. In addition, the enzyme responsible for starch synthesis, granule-bound starch synthase (GBSS), is located on the granule (18,19). Wheat starch characteristics are especially influenced by the presence of proteins. The proportion of protein in starches could be up to 0.5%.

Most starches contain glycolipids, complexed to amylose or amylopectin. Wheat starch, for instance, contains amylose-lipid complexes. The nature of lipids present in starches differs depending on the origin and nature of the starch. Lipids such as monoglycerides and lysophosphatidyl choline form complexes with amylose and amylopectin. Lipids may occur on the surface of the starch granule as well as in the interior of the granule. Lipids that occur within the starch granule are typically monoacyl lipids which could either be mostly free fatty acids or lysophospholipids (20). In addition, most of the lipids on the surface of the granules are monoacyl lipids. Some lipids are non-starch lipids and not associated with starch, but rather occur in the endosperm (21).

Phosphorus is a common constituent of many starches, occurring primarily as phosphate monoesters on amylose and amylopectin. Rice starch, corn starch, wheat starch, and potato starch contain various proportions of organic phosphorus or phosphate groups (22,23). Banana starches are reported to contain potassium and magnesium (24).

Non-starch components such as protein and lipids influence starch behavior in food applications. Functional properties such as water absorption, gelatinization, and starch hydrolysis are influenced by the presence of these components. The presence of lipids, for instance, affects water absorption and hence gelatinization properties. This in turn influences the formation of resistant starch and starch susceptibility to enzymatic digestion.

II. STARCH SOURCES

Starch is obtained from various plant sources. The most common sources of dietary and industrial starch are grains, such as maize and wheat, and roots such as potato and cassava (tapioca). Roots and tubers are significant sources of dietary starch (25).

A. GRAIN STARCHES

The grains primarily used as dietary and industrial starch sources include various cereal grains, mainly maize, wheat, and rice. Legumes and pulses also contribute considerably to dietary starch consumption. Corn starch, from maize (*Zea mays*), is the most commonly used source of industrial starch. Corn contains about 86% starch on a dry weight basis. As a high amylose starch, it forms heavy and easy setting gels, and therefore is commonly used for thickening. Corn starch is also used as a carrier, as an ingredient for various applications, and as raw material for other industrial products. For instance, it is hydrolyzed in various ways to obtain sweeteners and glucose. Starch from wheat (*Triticale aestivum*) and rice (*Oryza sativa*) is also a predominant ingredient in food industry applications. Other cereal grains such as sorghum (*Sorghum bicolor*) and barley (*Hordeum distichon*) are sources of starch, less commonly used than maize or wheat starch (Figure 3.2).

Grain starches tend to have high levels of amylose. Furthermore, these starches typically contain amylopectin in the crystalline regions. The amylose of these starches meanwhile may form complexes with glycolipids (26). Most cereal starch sources such as maize and wheat starches are A-type starches (15).

Various legumes contain up to 45% starch (12). Legumes commonly used as sources of starch include pinto bean, faba bean, moth bean, chickpea, and mung bean. As a result of their high amylopectin content, some legume starches such as mung bean starch have restricted swelling and increased overall stability during processing. They are therefore of high suitable quality for application in food products such as starch noodles (27).

Most legumes contain B-type starches that are generally more resistant to digestion (28,29). In addition, other legume starches such as pea starch meanwhile contain C-type starches. Legume starches have lower digestibility than other starches and hence result in a lower post-prandial glycemic and insulin response (30) (Figure 3.3).

B. ROOT AND TUBER STARCHES

Among the root starches, potato (*Solanum tuberosum*) starch and tapioca (*Manihot esculenta*) or cassava starch are the most predominant industrial starch sources. Root starches have high amylopectin content and therefore have greater clarity, minimal flavor, and acceptable water absorption, and subsequently swelling capacity. Tapioca (cassava) starch is a major ingredient in dietary and industrial starch application. Also known as yucca or manioc, this root crop is the primary source of dietary energy in various tropical regions of the world. Tapioca starch has unique attributes that make it particularly desirable in food applications.

Potato is a dietary staple of most European and Scandinavian diets. Potato starch has high water-binding capacity and a bland taste, and is commonly used in the food industry in many applications for thickening and texture modification.

Other dietary and industrially important root and tuber starch sources include banana and plantain (*Musa* spp.), taro (*Colocasia esculenta*), cocoyams (*Xanthosoma* spp.), and various yams (*Dioscorea* spp.), sweet potato (*Ipomea batatas*) (31,32). Even though there are multiple sources of dietary starch in the tropics, including grains and legumes, roots and tubers constitute dietary staples in most areas as their cultivation is suited to the hot humid tropics. When freshly harvested, they are high in moisture, containing about 70–80% moisture and between 16–24% starch (32). Starchy foods are generally processed in some manner prior to utilization in food preparation. In addition, they are processed into raw material for secondary products. These therefore satisfy needs for calories, food preferences, and convenience foods (Figure 3.4).

Some of these find limited use in industrial applications such as is the case with yam starches (32). Root starches contain amylopectin in the crystalline regions, while amylose is more common in the amorphous regions of the starch granule (26).

C. OTHER SOURCES OF STARCH

In addition to the major sources of dietary and industrial starch such as maize and tapioca starch, other starch-containing plants find considerable application as dietary and commercial sources of starch. These include lesser known sources of starch such as sago (*Metroxylon sagu*),

arrow root (*Maranta arundinacea*), and edible canna (*Canna edulis*). Sago starch is obtained from the trunk of the plant *Metroxylon sagu*. The starch is used in various food products as it has high storage stability. Refined sago starch finds application in noodles, as well as raw material in industry for monosodium glutamate (MSG), glucose, and caramel (33). It is susceptible to enzymatic hydrolysis to glucose, which can then be fermented to produce fermentation products.

Arrowroot starch contains up to 23% amylose and is used in dietary applications as a thickener in various

FIGURE 3.2 Some common cereal grain starch sources: (a) wheat, (b) barley, (c) maize.

FIGURE 3.3 Some legume starch sources: (a) pinto bean, (b) black-eye pea.

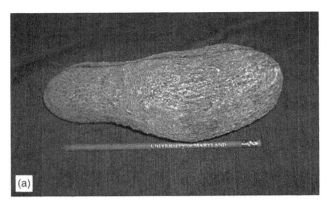
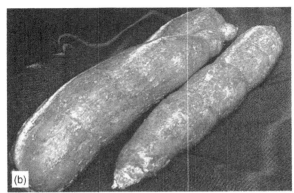

FIGURE 3.4   (a) Brazil yam, (b) cassava (tapioca) root, (c) plantain.

sauces. Another lesser known root crop commonly used in starch production for food application is edible canna, obtained from *Canna edulis* (34). The root contains up to 16% high amylose starch. The separated starch is used in production of noodles in various parts of Asia, particularly Vietnam. The properties of the canna starch are desirable for noodle production.

III. STARCH PHYSICOCHEMICAL PROPERTIES AND FUNCTIONALITY

The application of starch in food products is greatly influenced by its physicochemical properties and interactions with various components. The reaction of starch molecules in foods is essential for the multiple properties that they contribute to the quality of food products. For instance, water absorption and gel formation are extremely essential for the thickening properties of starch. In addition, hydrolysis and digestion of starch, for instance, are not feasible if starch is not gelatinized as the amylases and starch hydrolysis enzymes do not interact with intact, ungelatinized granules.

Characteristics such as gelatinization temperature, granule size, and shape are specific to the type of starch. They are diagnostic properties characteristic of native starches and can therefore be used for identification. The quality of products formulated with starch, such as carriers and thickeners, is largely affected by its functional and pasting properties (35,36).

Water-holding capacity, solubility, and paste viscosity are important parameters that influence the quality of products such as carbohydrate-based fat substitutes (37). These in turn influence gelling ability, water- and fat-binding ability, slicing ability, and hence textural quality of food products. Functionality and physicochemical properties vary among starches as they are influenced by the ratios of amylose to amylopectin. High amylopectin starches for instance are preferred for high viscosity products. In addition, the presence of phosphate esters in some starches such as potato starch may influence starch water-binding capacity by weakening the bonds between starch molecules due to ionic repulsion.

A. STARCH GELATINIZATION

Gelatinization occurs when the ordered structure of the starch granule is disrupted and reorganized in the presence of heat and sufficient moisture. The granules are disrupted with absorption of water, losing their organized molecular structure, to facilitate swelling (29,38).

Starch gelatinization is critical in the utilization of starch in food applications. Native starch granules are insoluble in cold water and gelatinization is essential to facilitate water absorption and enhances the chemical and physical reactivity of inert starch granules in food processing (11). Granular characteristics of starches are characteristic of the plant source. The structure of the granule in turn influences the structure of the gels or pastes formed on heating.

Gelatinization results in starch swelling, and formation of a viscous paste that may be opaque or translucent depending on the nature of the starch (12). Gelatinization is followed by gelation, a process in which the swollen granules are disrupted and amylose is released into the starch-water medium. The leaching of amylose from gelatinized granules contributes to the thickening characteristics of starch and gel formation, a colloidal dispersion of starch in water. The leached amylose in the starch-water system associates to form a structural network to entrap the granules, resulting in the formation of a gel.

Viscosity of starches such as maize and tapioca starch are greatly influenced by ratios of amylose to amylopectin (10). Genetically modified high amylose starches form highly resistant and firmer gels (39). Increasing amylose content also increases early onset of gelation. Starches with low levels of amylose such as waxy maize — less than 1% amylose — do not form gels effectively. Instead, they form clear pastes that are generally resistant to syneresis (11).

The strength of the starch gel is influenced by the presence of ionic components which may interact with the negatively charged starch molecules. Water absorption and swelling of starch is limited by the presence of amylose-lipid complexes (20).

B. STARCH RETROGRADATION

Cooling of gelatinized starch results in the re-association of the leached amylose from gelatinized granules. This is the process of retrogradation. Retrogradation is also referred to as setback, and occurs with re-crystallization of amylose. Amylose is much more susceptible to retrogradation and amylopectin is only minimally involved in starch retrogradation even though amylopectin has been shown to influence retrogradation and syneresis in corn starch gels (5). This re-association and re-crystallization of amylose causes release of the water absorbed and bound during gelatinization, leading to the phenomenon known as syneresis.

Retrogradation of starch in food products is a concern as it affects product quality. The stability of starch-containing products during cold storage in particular is greatly affected by the extent of retrogradation. Freeze-thaw cycles result in extensive retrogradation and syneresis.

Retrogradation of starch in some instances enhances quality as such starches are resistant to enzyme hydrolysis

and hence more stable. Cooling retrograded starches at room temperature prior to freezing at −20°C results in the formation of resistant starch as the retrograded starch is no longer susceptible to enzyme hydrolysis (29). This procedure is used in the production of industrial resistant starch.

C. STARCH DAMAGE

Starch damage is the modification or destruction of starch granule structure to the extent that it affects physicochemical properties such as water absorption. This in turn influences functionality of damaged starch in food applications, and subsequently, the quality of the final product. Starch damage results from various processes such as milling of grains. Starch damage affects the susceptibility of starch to hydrolysis and reactions as enzymes do not properly interact with the restructured granules.

Starch damage by processing or mechanical action causes a cracked appearance to granules. Extensive starch damage causes disruptions in the molecular structure of the starch. Modification to the starch granule therefore results in increased swelling ability and is more susceptible to enzymatic hydrolysis (19). In addition, cold water solubility of starch is enhanced. This affects the applicability in baking and food applications.

D. INTERACTIONS WITH ACIDS, SUGAR, AND SALTS

The presence of chemical components such as sugar and salts has a great effect on the characteristics of starch in food systems. The granule surface structure is affected and restructured in the presence of acid, as there is de-polymerization and hydrolysis of amylose and amylopectin (40). This results in lower viscosities of starch pastes. Solubility of starch is enhanced by acid. These effects are due to the disintegration of the component amylose and amylopectin at the low pHs typical of highly acidic solutions.

Starch competes with sugars such as glucose, fructose, and sucrose for water absorption. Gelling and swelling of a starch is therefore modified in the presence of sugars. This is because sugars contain hydrophilic hydroxyl groups identical to the glucose monomers of starch. As a result they decrease the water activity of the starch-water system. There is an overall increase in the free volume of water, reducing its effectiveness as a desirable plasticizer required to facilitate starch gelatinization (41,42). Slade and Levine (1988) report that sugar has an anti-plasticization effect on starch. The sugars bind the water, reducing its availability for starch gelatinization (43). Consequently, sugars elevate the temperature at which the gelatinization of various starches occurs.

The ionic nature of salts is responsible for their interaction with starch and the subsequent effects on starch physicochemical properties. Starch molecules possess a weakly charged ionic structure. In the presence of cations, the granules are stabilized and protected, whereas in the presence of anions, the hydrogen bonds are ruptured. This destabilizes the granules, enhancing and facilitating gelatinization (44,45).

Various salts such as phosphates form complexes with the amylose and amylopectin, a property exploited for use in industrial in starch modification. Salts overall delay loss of birefringence and depress overall extent of gelatinization.

Sodium chloride has great influence on starch physicochemical properties. Sodium chloride increases the gelatinization temperature of various starches. At concentrations of 6–9%, sodium chloride solution inhibits starch gelatinization (46). Various procedures for starch pre-treatment are commonly used in food processing. A common procedure is alkalization, in which alkalizing agents are added to maize, wheat, or rice in the preparation of tortillas, Chinese wheat noodles or rice dumplings, respectively. Common alkalizing agents include sodium hydroxide, or sodium and potassium carbonate (47).

Addition of alkali contributes to improving starch swelling capacity. The presence of lime (calcium hydroxide) has been shown to decrease starch crystallinity in corn (48). Gelatinization temperature of corn starch is also increased by the presence of lime, attributed to cross linking of calcium with the starch, as well as due to ionic interactions with hydroxyl groups on the starches (47). It is expected that these would in turn lead to variations in gelatinized starch quality characteristics — color, gelation, and retrogradation tendency.

IV. STARCH HYDROLYSIS

Starch hydrolysis is the cleaving of the starch polymer to short chain fragments such as dextrins and maltose, or to the glucose monomers. Starch hydrolysis is essential in many aspects of the application of starch. For instance, starch is hydrolyzed by various means for the production of sweeteners. Hydrolysis products of starch are multifold and include products such as dextrins and simple sugars. Starch hydrolysis is carried out primarily by the use of enzymes or chemicals, or in combination.

A. ENZYME HYDROLYSIS

Enzymatic hydrolysis of starch is carried out for various purposes, but most notably for the industrial production of maltose syrup (49). The key enzymes used for starch hydrolysis are β-glucosidases, which hydrolyze the amylose and amylopectin in starch. These include α-amylase, amyloglucosidase, and pullulanase.

The extent of starch hydrolysis is quantified by various parameters. This could be the hydrolysis index (HI), or by the dextrose equivalent (DE). The hydrolysis index

quantifies the proportion of starch hydrolyzed. Dextrose equivalent describes the potential for starch conversion to dextrose (glucose) and is defined as the sum of reducing sugars expressed as dextrose. This is because starch in its native form has few reducing sugar ends. The number of reducing ends is influenced by the proportion of amylopectin. Degree of polymerization is indicative of the number of glucose residues. Amylose from starches such as maize or wheat have DP of 200–1200, while amylose from potato or tapioca starch have DP of about 1000–6000.

Hydrolysis of starch to maltodextrins is achieved by use of α-amylase enzymes. These enzymes are categorized either as endoamylases, exoamylases, debranching enzymes, or transferases (26). The endoamylases, the most common being α-amylase (EC 3.2.1.1), are specific for the α-1→4 linkage in amylose and amylopectin. Their hydrolysis products from starch hydrolysis are mainly oligosaccharides and dextrins (26). Exoamylases, on the other hand, have the ability to hydrolyze both the α-1→4 and α-1→6 bonds of amylose and amylopectin. A common example is amyloglucosidase (EC 3.2.1.20). β-Amylase is an exoamylase that has the ability to hydrolyze the α-1→4 bond of amylose.

Debranching enzymes used in starch hydrolysis are targeted at hydrolyzing the α-1→6 bonds in amylopectin. These include pullulanases. Hydrolysis products of these are mainly maltose and maltotriose. The transferases have low activity with regard to starch hydrolysis but are involved in formation of new glycosidic linkages (26).

Enzymatic hydrolysis of starch is influenced by the presence of non-starch components such as lipids, particularly lipids bound to amylose. This is because the presence of these complexes renders the amylose less susceptible to hydrolysis enzymes (20). Additional enzymes such as lysophospholipase are therefore sometimes required for complete hydrolysis of starch in the production of glucose from starch.

Amylase enzymes produced by lactic acid bacteria — *Lactobacillus plantarum*, *Lactobacillus amylophilus*, and *Lactobacillus delbruecki*, in particular — are used for industrial hydrolysis of starch for conversation of starch to glucose. This is a process known as saccharification (50). Yeasts such as *Saccharomyces cerevisiae*, which produce α-amylase, are also used in bioreactors for enzymatic hydrolysis of starch and subsequent fermentation of the hydrolysis product (glucose) by the yeast strains (33). These micro-organisms produce heat-stable amylase which can survive the high bioreactor process temperatures required for gelatinization and hydrolysis of the starch. The lactobacilli produce enzymes that hydrolyze the starch to glucose, and then the bacteria ferment the starch of the industrial production of lactic acid.

Immobilized enzymes also are used in industrial hydrolysis of starch. The enzymes are extracted from an industrial source, usually microorganisms such as *Aspergillus*, and then immobilized on inert particles such as silica (51). This ensures that the enzyme has optimum activity and access for starch hydrolysis. Co-enzymes and ionic particles such as calcium are required for starch hydrolysis.

While traditionally acids (mainly hydrochloric acid) have been used for hydrolysis of starch, there has been an increase in use of industrial enzymes for starch hydrolysis. Most of these convert starches for the production of maltodextrin, modified starches, glucose syrup, or fructose syrup. Hydrolysis of starch in foods is increased by processing. Enzymatic hydrolysis of starch in various legumes for instance is enhanced by soaking and sprouting. Gelatinization of starch is required prior to enzymatic hydrolysis.

B. ACID HYDROLYSIS

Acids are used to facilitate the hydrolysis of starch. The α-1→4 linkages in amylose and amylopectin are susceptible to hydrolysis at the low pH typical of acids. Hydrochloric acid at low concentrations (0.36% w/v) hydrolyzes starch (52).

The use of acids in combination of alcohols has been suggested for starch hydrolysis. Formation of limit-dextrins with varying degrees of polymerization occurs in the presence of various alcohols such as methanol, ethanol, and propanol. These alcohols are possibly involved in disrupting the hydrophobic and hydrogen bonds of the starch helical structure in the granule. Increase in temperature further increases the susceptibility of starch to acid hydrolysis in alcohol (52).

C. ALKALINE HYDROLYSIS

Alkaline hydrolysis of starch is enhanced and influenced in the presence of heat and inorganic salts. There is complete hydrolysis of starch with microwave heating in the presence of metal chlorides (53). The theoretical yield of glucose (111%) is obtained in the presence of chloride salts such as lithium chloride, barium chloride, and iron trichloride. On the other hand, acid hydrolysis of starch is greatly limited in the presence of sulfate salts. In the presence of sulfate salts — sodium sulfate, magnesium sulfate and or zinc sulfate — acid hydrolysis is actually greatly impeded (53).

D. HEAT-INDUCED HYDROLYSIS

Extrusion of starch is used in combination with enzymes for effective starch hydrolysis. The starch is treated under conditions of high temperature, high pressure, shear, and moisture (54). Heat stable amylase is used for starch hydrolysis. Extrusion cooking facilitates disruption of the granule structure and the crystallinity. This renders the amylose and amylopectin susceptible to gelatinization (55). Application of extrusion in starch hydrolysis has the advantage in that the process conditions can be modified such that the extent of hydrolysis is controlled for desired end products and dextrins (55).

V. STARCH MODIFICATION

Native starches such as tapioca starch often require considerable modification to enhance quality and versatility in food applications, and for storage stability. The components of starch — amylose and amylopectin — are highly sensitive to shear, stress, acidity, and high temperatures, and are typically altered by heat-moisture conditions of processing (15). Most native starches such as tapioca starch have limited swelling power and solubility. Modification is essential to improve paste clarity, paste stability, resistance to degradation, and freeze-thaw stability. Modification of starch is important to improve the reactivity of glucose, as well as introduce reactive side chains (56). The integrity and structure of the granule is also enhanced by modification. Additional side chains interfere with potentially deleterious post-process starch properties such as retrogradation. Most starches used in food applications are modified starches.

Modification of starches is by physical and chemical procedures. Modification procedures include acetylation, hydroxypropylation, and a combination of hydroxypropylation and cross-linking (57). Hydroxypropylated starches are most commonly used in the food industry (57). Stabilization of starch is facilitated by use of acetates and hydroxypropyl esters (58). These modification procedures greatly increase freeze-thaw stabilization and increase resistance to process conditions such as heat and shear.

Cross-linking is commonly carried out with various chemical agents such as phosphorus oxychloride, sodium trimetaphosphate, and anhydrides (58). Cross-linked starches are more resistant to process conditions such as temperature and acidity as a result of the fact that the hydrogen bonds have been reinforced and act as bridges. These are useful in preventing re-crystallization of amylose and the subsequent retrogradation in processed starchy foods.

Some procedures that have been shown to be effective in modification of banana starch include cross-linking with sodium trimetaphosphate, formation of starch phosphate with sodium tripolyphosphate, and hydroxypropylation using a combination of sodium hydroxide and sodium sulphate (24). These procedures result in starches with enhanced water-binding capacity, and in most cases, increased solubility. Starch phosphates in particular have increased freeze-thaw stability.

Acid-thinned starches are obtained by reducing the concentration of concentrated starch slurry with a mineral acid at 40–60°C, to obtain a desirable viscosity. The starch is recovered after the acid is neutralized (59). The granule structure of the starch is not destroyed in the process, but various changes to the properties of the starches occur. Starch solubility and gel strength for instance are increased, while starch viscosity is decreased (60). Rate of starch hydrolysis is increased with increasing concentration of acid (59).

Physical modification procedures that have been used include pre-gelatinization. Pre-gelatinization increases swelling power and paste clarity of banana starch (24). Extrusion cooking of starch is used to improve quality and characteristics of starch.

VI. STARCH IN FOOD APPLICATIONS

Starch is a functional ingredient in many food products. There are multiple functions of starch in food products. Most commonly, starch is used as a bulking agent, binder, carrier, in fat-replacers, as a texture-modifier, and as raw material for other starch-related products. It is a basic ingredient in products such as breads, puddings, marinades, and sauces, and also serves a considerable function in other products such as powdered spices and beverages. The applicability and utility of a starch in food products is enhanced by factors such as its composition and functionality. Starch is a substrate for lactic acid bacteria in fermentation to produce lactic acid (61).

Starch-based foods play a major role in the diet in various areas because of their bulking quality, and ability to contribute to satiety. Fermentation of cassava for instance imparts a sour taste that is sometimes highly desirable.

A. FUNCTIONAL PROPERTIES

Starch is used as to facilitate thickening and gel formation in various food products such as fruit preparations (62). The consistency of products such as tapioca pudding and many custards would not be attainable without the thickening and stabilizing properties of starch.

High amylose starches have high viscosity, and form thick gels. This enhances their properties as thickeners in food products. Starches with lower amylose content are better suited for use in certain types of noodles, such as Japanese noodles (23). High amylose starches are desirable for application in fried products as they have minimal fat absorption. High amylose starches are also applicable as thickeners and for use as gelling agents in foods such as jellies. High amylose starch gels set rapidly hence are desirable in production of confectionary and candies (56). Other desirable properties of high amylose starches include their flexibility, water resistance, and tensile strength (63).

Starches with high swelling ability and high viscosity are desirable for various types of Asian noodles (18).

Starches high in amylopectin and low in amylose (waxy starches) such as waxy wheat are produced for use in such products. The higher levels of amylopectin further contribute to extending shelf-life, by reducing retrogradation and staling in baked products. High amylopectin starches are less susceptible to retrogradation, and hence very applicable in improving freeze-thaw stability (63).

Modified starches are highly effective as stabilizers in products such as yogurt (57). The presence of side groups such as acetyl and hydroxyl groups in modified starches, however, results in interactions with amylose and amylopectin, improving overall stabilizing ability.

Fermented, sun-dried cassava starch is commonly used in baked products in various parts of South America and Brazil. This is unique in that the fermentation facilitates expansion which is desirable in the baked products (64). Viscosity of sour starch pastes is lower than for nonfermented starch, attributable to the solubilization of amylopectin.

Starch is used to improve quality of extruded food products. Addition of cassava starch to cassava flour prior to extrusion increases water solubility, but decreases water absorption and bulk density properties (65).

Shear thinning of starch is an important characteristic with regards to stability of starch pastes during processing, particular in food products that require extensive stirring and agitation. Removal of lipids (defatting) in sorghum starch has been associated with increased shear-thinning characteristics (66). Starches that are resistant to shear thinning are generally highly desirable to ensure product stability and suitable consistency.

Products of starch hydrolysis find considerable application in food products. Maltodextrins, for instance, are commonly used in heat-stable gels (67).

B. VALUE-ADDED FOOD APPLICATIONS

Starch is used as a basic ingredient in starch-based fat substitutes. These simulate the functional properties of fats, particularly texture modification, but with less caloric value. Various starch-based fat substitutes are commonly used in industry. Some examples of these include TrimChoice™ (Specialty Grain products, NE) made from hydrolyzed oat starch, Amalean™ (American Maize Products, IN) made from modified high-amylose corn starch, and SlenderLean™ (National Starch, NJ) made from tapioca starch (37).

Starch-based fat substitutes are especially applicable in baked products and value-added foods.

Resistant and minimally digestible starches are used in value-added food products. Most of these products are targeted at the management of diet-related diseases such as obesity and type II diabetes. An example of such a product is Extend™, a snack bar formulated with resistant starch (corn and rice starch), which has been formulated for the

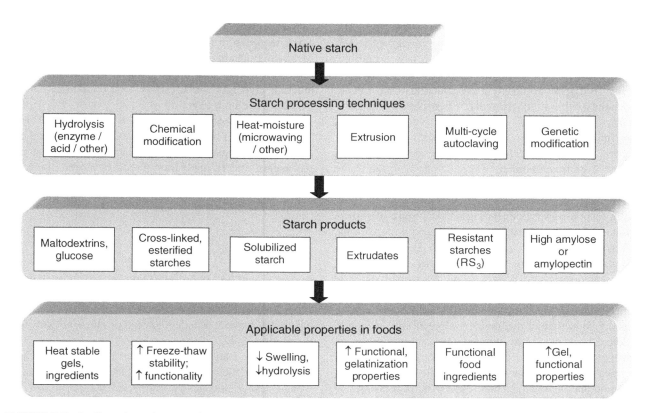

FIGURE 3.5 Outline of starch processing and applications in foods.

management of type II diabetes. The product ensures a slow and sustained digestion of the resistant starch, and minimal absorption of glucose, mitigating the problems of high post-prandial blood glucose levels (Figure 3.5).

VII. STARCH NUTRITIONAL QUALITY

Starch is the primary nutrient involved in energy intake and regulation. Typically, most adults require about 200 g carbohydrate daily to facilitate brain and muscle function. The digestibility and absorption of starch has significant nutritional and physiological implications. As the primary source of energy, starch is rapidly metabolized and absorbed. The extent of starch digestibility is influenced by the nature of the starch, food processing, and physiological status.

There is a dichotomy of starch functionality as a nutrient. On the one hand, it is a source of glucose, the primary substrate for cell metabolism. On the other hand, starch resistant to digestion (resistant starch) is minimally digestible and only minimally absorbed, and therefore is not physiologically available.

A. STARCH AND GLYCEMIC INDEX

Starch is the primary source of metabolizable energy, and therefore its availability and digestion are important. High

starch foods are rapidly digested and metabolized. Glycemic index (GI), the post-prandial blood glucose response to a particular food, has been used to differentiate the metabolic response to dietary carbohydrates (68). Glycemic index is indicative of the relationship between a food and the implications of starch digestibility, absorption, and metabolism. Foods that are high in readily digestible starch result in high levels of glucose in the blood. These are classified as high GI foods. Typically, most tropical root starchy staples such as cassava and yams have high levels of readily digestible waxy starches (high amylopectin). These are rapidly and readily absorbed, resulting in elevated levels of glucose in the blood. This is, however, modified to a large extent by other factors associated with the nature of the starch, its processing, preparation, and consumption.

Starch is hydrolyzed by salivary and pancreatic amylases to yield monosaccharides such as glucose and fructose, and maltodextrins. These are transported via the hepatic portal vein and available for metabolism. Starch digestion and metabolism has been classified into three categories: rapidly digestible starch, slowly digestible starch, and resistant starch (69). Rapidly digestible starch, which typically is completely digested, is associated with post-prandial glucose response, and hence has effect on insulin levels. Rapidly available glucose meanwhile describes glucose and sucrose obtained as hydrolysis products of rapidly digestible starch. Rapidly digestible starch occurs most commonly in highly processed foods such as puffed wheat cereal, while slowly digestible starch occurs in foods such as legumes and pasta (69).

Starch digestion and glycemic index also have been associated with satiety. Rapidly digestible starches are quickly absorbed and metabolized, whereas slower digesting starches are only slowly absorbed and therefore improve satiety (70). These have also been shown to improve exercise endurance (71).

There are differences in the metabolic response to dietary carbohydrates. Post-prandial blood glucose and insulin responses vary depending on the nature of carbohydrates, particularly starch. Physiological conditions such as type II diabetes and obesity have been associated with starch metabolism. Other conditions such as coronary heart disease are linked to metabolism of glucose derived from dietary starch. The physiological consequence of starch consumption is influenced by the extent of its digestibility and metabolism. Digestibility of starch is determined by its availability and susceptibility to digestive enzymes. Susceptibility of starch to digestive enzymes is in turn influenced by the chemical nature of the starch and the changes that result from processing.

Starch digestibility is influenced by various factors such as processing, storage, amylose content, and presence of dietary fiber (72). The ratios of amylose to amylopectin are important in starch digestion and metabolism. Consumption of modified high amylopectin starches have been shown to result in an increase in serum free fatty acids and serum glucose levels. This is probably as a result of gluconeogenesis. Conversely, modified amylose cornstarch is highly digestible, and results in lower insulin levels. Starch that is digested and absorbed, however, has physiological effects, some of which have been linked to disease conditions.

Researchers have demonstrated that the consumption of high starch diets in human test subjects apparently leads to an overall decrease in overall energy intake, compared to a high-sucrose (simple sugar) or high fat meals (70,73). This indicates that high starch may have potential for a high satiety value, but with low caloric density, and hence the lowered energy intake.

Type II diabetes, a condition that results from inadequate production of insulin to facilitate glucose uptake, is exacerbated by the presence of glucose in the blood. Clinical manifestations of Type II diabetes include fainting and dizzy spells as a result of low brain glucose levels. Starch and glucose metabolism have been also associated with obesity and accumulation of fat, as glucose is involved in fat metabolism.

The nature of starch and the level of amylose in the starch play a considerable role in the diabetic process and insulin response. Long-term consumption of a high amylose corn starch (70% amylose) by hyper-insulinemic subjects results in a normal insulin response (74). High amylose starch in the diet reduces insulin response (75). Meanwhile legume starches such as pure pea starch have been shown to be even more effective than corn starch in reducing hyperglycemia, as has been demonstrated with purified pea starch (76).

The conversion of sugars, which are starch hydrolysis products, into fat has been implicated in diabetes and cardiovascular disease and obesity. The consumption of simple sugars and refined grain foods has been linked to higher rates of cardiovascular disease and Type II diabetes, particularly in instances of insulin resistance (68,77).

B. RESISTANT STARCH

Resistant starch is non-digestible starch which occurs in foods in various forms.

Resistant starch is described in various ways, including as starch and starch degradation products not absorbed in the gut (78,79).

Resistant starch occurs in four categories, primarily dependent on their mode of origin. These are described as: type 1 (RS_1): physically entrapped starch in the cell matrix of whole or partially milled grains, hence is inaccessible; type 2 (RS_2): native granular starch, mostly B-type legume starches which are may be ungelatinized during processing; type 3 (RS_3): retrograded starch, particularly from food processing; and type 4 (RS_4): chemically modified starch (29,79–82).

Resistant starch levels in food products are influenced by various factors including the nature of the starch, the mode of food processing and preparation, and storage conditions (83). Physical inaccessibility such as cell wall structure and the presence of dietary fiber influences levels of resistant starch, particularly in legumes (72).

Type 3 resistant starch (RS_3), which is retrograded starch, is the most commonly occurring form of resistant starch in processed foods. Starch in cooked then cooled foods such as pasta, rice, and lentils exhibits considerably reduced susceptibility to enzymatic digestion, indicating the formation of resistant starch (72). This is attributable to the retrogradation which occurs following cooling of gelatinized starch. Amylose is more susceptible to retrogradation than amylopectin. Resistant starch formation is therefore influenced by ratios of amylose to amylopectin.

Processing of starchy foods, in addition to factors such as starch amylose: amylopectin ratios and chemical modification, influences their digestibility. This is as a consequence of the disruption of the physical and chemical structure of the starch (84,85). Retrogradation of amylose with processing is mainly thought to be responsible for this alteration in susceptibility to digestive enzymes. In some cases, however, partial damage to starch molecules which would otherwise be physically entrapped by the cell wall and inaccessible to digestive enzymes, may improve their susceptibility to digestion (86).

Consumption of resistant starch yields physiological effects similar to soluble fiber (82). Fermentation products include short chain fatty acids such as acetate, propionate, and butyrate, which facilitate absorption of minerals, excretion of bile acids, and consequently protect against colorectal cancer.

Resistant starch-containing foods such as legumes, and retrograded starches, however, have been associated with disease prevention. Fermented corn porridge, commonly consumed among some indigenous populations, has been shown to contain considerable amounts of starch that is resistant to digestion and subsequently is protective against various colon conditions (87). Experimental evidence using high resistant starch breakfast cereals in humans shows an improved glucose tolerance (88). In rural South Africa, however, consumption of cold maize porridge, which is high in retrograded starch and has rather low starch digestibility and a low glycemic index, has been associated with low levels of diabetes mellitus (87,89).

High resistant starch foods which have low glycemic index are effective in lowering the concentrations of high-density-lipoprotein (HDL) cholesterol and in improving glucose tolerance in incidence of diabetes and insulin resistance (77,88,90).

Root and tuber starches, unlike grain starches, are high in amylopectin and do not have the same restricting nature of the cell wall. They are, therefore, generally more digestible. Processing techniques such as autoclaving to reduce starch digestibility by increasing resistant starch levels have been suggested in foods (91). Digestibility of legume starch is increased by processes such as soaking and sprouting (30).

VIII. NEW STARCH TECHNOLOGIES

The functionality and applicability of starch in so many food applications and its importance as a food ingredient have led to continuous efforts to improve and optimize properties and versatility of starch. Some techniques currently used include genetic modification to modify starch yields and quality, multi-cycle autoclaving for production of resistant starch, and new processes such as microwave hydrolysis of starch.

A. GENETIC MODIFICATION

Genetic modification of starch most commonly targets the enzymes of the starch biosynthetic pathway. The activities of these enzymes dictate and determine the quantities of starch synthesized as well as specific characteristics such as ratios of amylose to amylopectin. Their activity therefore influences starch properties: its reactivity, functionality, and applicability in food processing and in food applications.

Genetic modification of cereal starch is commonly employed to modify ratios of amylose to amylopectin, and hence improve functionality and nutritional quality of starch.

The primary enzymes involved in starch synthesis include the starch synthases, starch branching enzymes and adenosine diphosphate-glucose pyrophosphorylase (ADP-glucose-phosphorylase). The starch synthases occur both as a granule-bound synthase (GBSS) or located in the soluble phase, and catalyze the formation of the α-1$\rightarrow$4 glucan chains by adding ADP-glucose to the non-reducing end of the primer. The starch branching enzyme catalyzes formation of the α-1$\rightarrow$6 branches of amylopectin molecules. The ADP-glucose pyrophosphorylase catalyzes the formation of ADP-glucose (56). Other important enzymes are starch debranching enzymes and phosphorylases.

A major contribution of genetic modification is the modification of various cereal starches to reduce amylose content and produce high amylopectin starch. These waxy starches are desirable for various characteristics. They are desirable in various noodles, for modification of amylose characteristics in extrudates, and to extend the shelf-life of baked goods (18).

Waxy starches are produced by modification of the enzyme involved in amylose synthesis, granule-bound starch synthase (GBSS). While naturally occurring mutations in various wheats have resulted in waxy wheat starch, biotechnology to modify the expression of the GBSS genes is used to produce waxy starches, including rice, maize and wheat. Modification by decreasing the levels of enzymes such as starch synthase and starch branching enzyme is employed to increase amylose levels.

Modification by decreasing levels of GBSS results in increased amylopectin levels.

Regular cereal starches (up to 27% amylose) typically form opaque pastes and firm gels. Genetic modification techniques are applied to either decrease or increase the amylose to amylopectin ratios. Low amylose cereal starches (waxy maize, waxy rice, waxy wheat) lack GBSS, and therefore contain less than 1% amylose. These therefore do not effectively form gels but instead clear pastes. Genetically modified high amylose starches form highly resistant and firmer gels (41). Increasing amylose content also increases early onset of gelation. High amylose maize starch — amylomaize — is modified to have high levels of amylose, 50–70%. The granules of amylomaize are more resistant to swelling and therefore form much firmer and more rigid gels (11,92).

Genetically modified potato starch has been shown to be suitable in processing and preparation of starch noodles, as these have greater transparency and higher flexibility (93). This may be due to higher amylose content. Modification of starch synthesis to increase overall yields of starch in food products is carried out by modifying levels of adenosine triphosphatase (ATPase) and starch branching enzymes (56).

Genetic modification of reactive groups such as phosphates is used to change the composition of starch by decrease of the starch branching enzyme (56).

B. RESISTANT STARCH PRODUCTION BY AUTOCLAVING

Autoclaving and steam processing are used in the production of resistant starch. Resistant starch produced by this technique is retrograded starch (RS$_3$), as it involves gelatinization and subsequent retrogradation of starch, rendering it resistant to digestive amylases. Autoclaving has been shown to modify resistant starch content in grain sorghum (94). High amylose starches which are most susceptible to retrogradation are therefore preferred for this process.

High pressure autoclaving has been standardized for the production of resistant starch (91,95). Starch with a high volume of water is gelatinized in a high pressure autoclave with stirring until a homogenous gel is obtained. The mixture is then cooled and frozen to facilitate retrogradation.

C. OTHER PROCEDURES

Other procedures employed in starch modification include microwave solubilization (96,97). Corn starch modified by microwave heating for a short period of time (32–90 seconds) at 900 W has decreased swelling ability (96). Microwave pre-solubilization of starch at 180 W for 10 minutes is employed in food analysis (97). In the presence of dilute hydrochloric acid, there is complete hydrolysis of starch in 5 minutes of microwave processing. This is attributable to the superheating produced by the presence of the ions. These procedures are proposed to substitute for the more expensive and time-consuming enzyme hydrolysis procedures commonly used.

REFERENCES

1. JN BeMiller, RL Whistler. Carbohydrates. In: OR Fennema. ed. Food Chemistry. 3rd ed. New York: Marcel Dekker, 1996, pp 158–221.
2. S Hizukuri. Starch: Analytical aspects. In: AC Eliasson. ed. Carbohydrates in Food. New York: Marcel Dekker, 1996, pp 347–430.
3. RI Ihekeronye, PO Ngoddy. Integrated Food Science and Technology for the Tropics. Hong Kong: Macmillan Publishers, 1985, 378 pp.
4. C Jarvis, JRL Walker. Simultaneous rapid spectrophotometric determination of total starch, amylose and amylopectin. J Sci Food Agric, 63(1):53–57, 1993.
5. JP Mua, DS Jackson. Retrogradation and gel textural attributes of corn starch amylose and amylopectin fractions. Journal of Cereal Science, 27:157–166.
6. Y Pomeranz. Functional Properties of Food Components. 2nd ed. New York: Academic Press, 1991, 569 pp.
7. W Praznik, A Huber, S Watzinger, RHF Beck. Molecular characteristics of high amylose starches. Starch, 46(3):88–94, 1994.
8. Z Czuchjowska, A Klamczynski, B Paszczynska, BK Baik. Structure and functionality of barley starches. Cereal Chem, 75(50):747–754, 1998.
9. J Yoon, S Lim. Molecular fractionation of starch by density-gradient ultracentrifugation. Carbohydr Res, 338(7): 611–617, 2003.
10. YL Jane, JF Chen. Effect of amylose molecule size and amylose branch chain length on paste properties of starch. Cereal Chem, 69:60–65, 1992.
11. CG Oates. Toward an understanding of starch granule structure and hydrolysis. Trends Food Sci Technol, 8: 375–382, 1997.
12. HS Su, W Lu, KC Chang. Microstructure and physicochemical characteristics of starches in six bean varieties and their bean paste products. Lebensm.-Wiss. U.-Technol, 31:265–273, 1997.
13. JMV Blanshard. Starch granule structure and function. In: T Gaillard. ed. Starch: Properties and Potential, Critical Reports on Applied Chemistry, Vol. 13, New York: John Wiley & Sons, 1987, pp 16–54.
14. TY Bogracheva, S Ring, V Morris, JR Lloyd, TL Wang, CL Hedley. The use of mutants to study the structural and functional properties of pea starch. In: PJ Frazier, P. Richmond, AM Donald. eds. Starch: Structure and Functionality. Proceedings of an International Conference Sponsored by the Food Chemistry Group of the Royal Society of Chemistry in Association with the Institute of Food Science and Technology Research Subject Group Held at the University of Cambridge, UK, 1996, pp 230–237.
15. D French. Organization of starch granules. In: RWhistler, JN BeMiller, EF Paschelli. eds. Starch Chemistry and Technology. New York: Academic Press, 1984, pp 183–247.
16. R Hoover, T Vasanthan. Effect of heat-moisture treatment on the structure and physicochemical properties of cereal, legume and tuber starches. Carbohydr Res, 252: 33–53, 1994.
17. LL Niba, MM Bokanga, FL Jackson, DS Schlimme, BW Li. Physicochemical properties and starch granular characteristics of flour from various *Manihot esculenta* (cassava) genotypes. J Food Sci, 67(5):1701–1705, 2002.
18. RA Graybosch. Waxy wheats: origin, properties, and prospects. Trends Food Sci Technol, 9:135–142, 1998.
19. JR Stark, A Lynn. Biochemistry of plant polysaccharides. Biochemical Soc Transactions, 20:7–12, 1992.
20. E Nebesny, J Rosicka, M Tkaczyk. Effect of enzymatic hydrolysis of wheat starch on amylose-lipid complexes stability. Starch, 54:603–608, 2002.
21. WR Morrison. Starch lipids: a reappraisal. Starch, 33: 408–410, 1981.
22. R Hanselmann, W Burchard, M Ehrat, HM Widmer. Structural properties of fractionated starch polymers

and their dependence on the dissolution process. Macromolecules, 29:3277–3282, 1996.

23. K Shibanuma, Y Takeda, S Hizukuri, S Shibata. Molecular structures of some wheat starches. Carbohydr Polym, 25:111–116, 1994.

24. KN Waliszeski, MA Aparicio, LA Bello, JA Monroy. Changes of banana starch by chemical and physical modification. Carbohydr Polym, 52:237–242, 2003.

25. E Bright-See, V Jazmaji. Estimation of the amount of dietary starch available to different populations. Can J Physiol Pharm, 69(1):56–59, 1991.

26. MJEC van der Maarel, B van der Veen, JCM Uitdehaag, H Leemhuis, L Dijkhuizen. Properties and applications of starch-converting enzymes of the α-amylase family. J Biotech, 94:137–155, 2002.

27. CY Lii, YH Chang. Study of starch in Taiwan. Food Rev Intl, 7(2):185–203, 1991.

28. DJ Gallant, B Bouchet, A Buleon, S Perez. Physical characteristics of starch granules and susceptibility to enzymic degradation. European J Clin Nutr, 46(Suppl): S3–S16, 1992.

29. A Garcia-Alonso, A Jimenez-Escrig, N Martin-Carron, L Bravo, F Sauro-Calixto. Assessment of some parameters involved in the gelatinization and retrogradation of starch. Food Chem, 66:181–187, 1999.

30. L Bravo, P Siddhuraju, F Saura-Calixto. Effect of various processing methods on the in vitro starch digestibility and resistant starch content of Indian pulses. J Agric Food Chem, 46:4667–4674, 1998.

31. D Dufour, JJ Hurtada, CC Wheatley. Characterization of starches from non-cereal crops cultivated in Tropical America: comparative analysis of starch behavior under different conditions. In: RH Howeler, GG Oates, GM O'Brien GM. eds. Cassava Starch and Starch Derivatives. Proceedings of the International Symposium Held in Guangxi, China, Nov 11–15, 1996, pp 42–56.

32. R Hoover. Composition, molecular structure and physicochemical properties of tuber and root starches: a review. Carbohydr Polym, 45:253–267, 2001.

33. S Abd-Aziz. Sago starch and its utilization. J Biosci Bioeng, 94(6):526–529, 2002.

34. M Hermann. Starch noodles from edible canna. In: J Janick. ed. Progress in New Crops. Arlington: ASHS Press, 1996, pp 507–508.

35. GH Ryu, PE Neumann, CE Walker. Pasting of wheat flour extrudates containing conventional baking ingredients. J Food Sci, 58(3):567–573, 1993.

36. C Lii, Y Shao, K Tseng. Gelation mechanism and rheological properties of rice starch. Cereal Chem, 72(4):393–399, 1995.

37. J Ju, GS Mittal. Physical properties of starch-based fat substitutes. J Food Proc Preserv, 19:361–383, 1995.

38. H Charley, C Weaver. Foods: A Scientific Approach. Engelwood Cliffs, NJ: Prentice Hall, 1997.

39. SE Case, T Capitani, JK Whaley, YC Shi, P Trzasko, R Jeffcoat, HB Goldfarb. Physical properties and gelation behavior of a low-amylopectin maize starch and other high-amylose maize starches. J Cereal Sci, 27: 301–314, 1998.

40. DL Shandera, DS Jackson. Effect of corn wet-milling conditions (sulfur dioxide, lactic acid, and steeping temperature) on starch functionality. Cereal Chem, 75(5): 632–637.

41. L Slade, H Levine. Recent advances in starch retrogradation. In: SS Stivala, V Crescenzie, ICN Dea. eds. Industrial Polysaccharides, New York: Gordon and Breach, 1987, pp 387–430.

42. L Slade, H Levine. Non-equilibrium melting of native granular starch: Part 1.Temperature location of the glass transition association with gelatinization of A-type cereal starches. Carbohydr Polym, 8:83–208, 1988.

43. AG Maaurf, YB Che Man, BA Asbi, AH Junainah, JF Kennedy. Gelatinization of sago starch in the presence of sucrose and sodium chloride as assessed by differential scanning calorimetry. Carbohydr Polym, 45: 335–345, 2001.

44. BJ Oosten. Tentative hypothesis to explain how electrolytes affect gelatinization temperature of starch in water. Starch, 34:233, 1982.

45. JL Jane. Mechanism of starch gelatinization in neutral salt solutions. Starch, 45:161–166, 1993.

46. M Wootton, A Bamunuarachchi. Application of differential scanning calorimetry to starch gelatinization. III. Effect of sucrose and sodium chloride. Starch, 32: 126–129, 1980.

47. LL Lai, AA Karim, MH Norziah, CC Seow. Effects of Na_2CO_3 and NaOH on DSC thermal profiles of selected native cereal starches. Food Chem, 78:355–362.

48. MH Gomez, CM McDonough, LW Rooney, RD Waniska. Changes in corn and sorghum during nixtamilization and tortilla baking. J Food Sci, 54: 330–336, 1989.

49. O Gaouar, C Amyard, N Zakhia, GM Rios. Enzymatic hydrolysis of cassava starch into maltose syrup on a continuous membrane reactor. J Chem Tech Biotech, 69(3):367–375, 1997.

50. R Anuradha, AK Suresh, KV Venkatesh. Simultaneous saccharification and fermentation of starch to lactic acid. Proc Biochem, 35:367–375, 1999.

51. LH Lim, DG Macdonald, GA Hill. Hydrolysis of starch particles using immobilized barley α-amylase. Biochem Eng Journal, 13:53–62, 2003.

52. JF Robyt, J Choe, JD Fox, RS Hahn, EB Fuchs. Acid modification of starch granules in alcohols: reactions in mixtures of two alcohols combined different ratios. Carbohydr Res, 283:141–150, 1996.

53. L Kunlan, X Lixin, L Jun, P Jun, C Guoying, X Zuwei. Salt-assisted acid hydrolysis of starch to D-glucose under microwave irradiation. Carbohydr Res, 331:9–12, 2001.

54. P Linko. Enzymes in the industrial utilization of cereals. In: JE Kruger, D Lineback, CE Stautter. eds. Enzymes and Their Role in Cereal Science and Technology. St. Paul, MN: American Association of Cereal Chemists Inc, 1987, pp 145–235.

55. RL Tomas, JC Oliveira, KL McCarthy. Influence of operating conditions on the extent of enzymatic conversion of rice starch in wet extrusion. Lebensm.-Wiss. U.-Technol, 30:50–55, 1997.

56. CJ Slattery, IH Kavakli, TW Okita. Engineering starch for increased quantity and quality. Trends Plant Sci, 5(7):291–298, 2000.

57. KA Schmidt, TJ Herald, KA Khatib. Modified wheat starches used as stabilizers in set-style yogurt. J Food Qual, 24:421–434, 2001.

58. PJ Lillford, A Morrison. Structure/Function Relationship of starches in food. In: PJ Frazier, P. Richmond, AM Donald. eds. Starch: Structure and Functionality. Proceedings of an international conference sponsored by the Food Chemistry Group of the Royal Society of Chemistry in association with the Institute of Food Science and Technology Research Subject Group Held at the University of Cambridge, UK, 1996, pp 1–8.

59. Y Wang, V Truong, L Wang. Structure and rheological properties of corn starch as affected by acid hydrolysis. Carbohydr Polym, 52:327–333, 2003.

60. RE Kim, SY Ahn. Gelling properties of acid-modified red bean starch gels. Agric Chem Biotech, 39:49–53, 1996.

61. W Xiaodong, G Xuan, SK Rakshit. Direct fermentative production of lactic acid on cassava and other starch substrates. Biotech Lett, 19(9):841–843, 1997.

62. S Chatel, A Voirin, A Luciani, J Artaud. Starch identification and determination in sweetened fruit preparations. J Agric Food Chem, 44:502–506, 1996.

63. V Fergason. High amylose and waxy corns. In: AR Hallauer. ed. Specialty Corns. Boca Raton: CRC Press, 1994, pp 55–77.

64. C Mestres, N Zakhia, D Dufour. Functional and physico-chemical properties of sour cassava starch. In: PJ Frazier, P Richmond, AM Donald. eds. Starch Structure and Functionality. Royal Society of Chemistry Information Services Special Publication No 205, Cambridge, 1997, pp 42–50.

65. N Badrie, WA Mellowes. Cassava starch or amylose effects on characteristics of cassava (*Manihot esculenta* Crantz) extrudate. J Food Sci, 57(1):103–107, 1992.

66. SN Subrahmanyam, RC Hoseney. Shear thinning properties of sorghum starch. Cereal Chem, 72(1):7–10, 1995.

67. J Giese. Developing low-fat meat products. Food Technol, 46(4):100–108, 1992.

68. KL Morris, MB Zemel. Glycemic index, cardiovascular disease and obesity. Nutr Rev, 57(9 Pt 1):273–276, 1999.

69. HN Englyst, GJ Hudson. Starch and health. In: PJ Frazier, P. Richmond, AM Donald. eds. Starch: Structure and Functionality. Proceedings of an international conference sponsored by the Food Chemistry Group of the Royal Society of Chemistry in association with the Institute of Food Science and Technology Research Subject Group held at the University of Cambridge, UK, 1996, pp 9–19.

70. S Holt, J Brand, C Soveny, JHansky. Relationship of satiety to postprandial glycemic insulin and cholecytokinin responses. Appetite, 18:129–141, 1992.

71. DE Thomas, JR Brotherhood, JC Brand. Carbohydrate feeding before exercise: effect of glycemic index. Int J Sports Med, 12:180–186, 1991.

72. PM Rosin, FM Lajolo, EW Menezes. Measurement and characterization of dietary starches. J Food Comp Anal, 15:367–377, 2002.

73. A Raben, I Macdonald, A. Astrup. Replacement of dietary fat by sucrose or starch: effects on 14 day ad libitum energy intake, energy expenditure and body weight in formerly obese and never-obese subjects. Int J Obes Relat Metab Disord, 21(10):846–859, 1997.

74. KM Behall, JC Howe. Effect of long term consumption of amylose vs amylopectin starch on metabolic variables in human subjects. Am J Clin Nutr, 61(2):334–340, 1995.

75. JC Howe, WV Rumpler, KM Behall. Dietary starch composition and level of energy intake alter nutrient oxidation in "carbohydrate-sensitive" men. J Nutr, 126(9):2120–2129, 1996.

76. G Seewi, G Gnauck, R Stute, E Chantelau. Effects on parameters of glucose homeostasis in healthy humans from ingestion of leguminous versus maize starches. Eur J Nutr, 38(4):183–189.

77. U Smith. Carbohydrates, fat and insulin action. Am J Clin Nutr, 59(3 Suppl):686S–689S, 1994.

78. NM Delzenne, MR Roberfroid. Physiological effects of non-digestible oligosaccharides. Lebensm-Wiss. U.-Technol, 27:1–6, 1994.

79. HN Englyst, SM Kingman, JH Cummings. Classification and measurement of nutritionally important starch fractions. Eur J Clin Nutr, 46(Suppl 2):S33–S50, 1992.

80. V Skrabanja, I Kreft. Resistant starch formation following autoclaving of buckwheat (*Fagopyrum esculentum* Moench) groats. An in vitro study. J Agric Food Chem, 46:2020–2023, 1998.

81. DL Topping, PM Clifton. Short-chain fatty acids and human colonic function: roles of resistant starch and nonstarch polysaccharides. Phys Revs, 81(3):1031–1064, 2001.

82. SG Haralampu. Resistant starch — a review of the physical properties and biological impact of RS3. Carbohydr Polym, 41:285–292, 2000.

83. SP Plaami. Content of dietary fiber in foods and its physiological effects. Food Rev Intl, 13(1):29–76, 1997.

84. ML Dreher, CJ Dreher, JW Berry. Starch digestibility: a nutritional perspective. Crit Rev Food Sci Nutr, 20(1):47–71, 1984.

85. I Bjork, Y Grandfelt, H. Liljeberg, J Tovar, NG Asp. Food properties affecting the digestion and absorption of carbohydrates. Am J Clin Nutr, 59(3 Suppl):699S–705S, 1994.

86. I Noah, F Guillon, B Bouchet, A Buleon, C Molis, M Gratas, M Champ. Digestion of carbohydrate from white beans (*Phaseolus vulgaris* L.) in healthy humans. J Nutr, 128:977–985, 1998.

87. B van der Merwe, C Erasmus, JRN Taylor. African maize porridge: a food with slow in vitro starch digestibility. Food Chem, 72:347–353, 2001.

88. HG Liljeberg, AK Akerberg, IM Bjorck. Effect of glycemic index and content of indigestible carbohydrates of cereal-based breakfast meals on glucose tolerance at lunch in healthy subjects. Am J Clin Nutr, 69(4):647–655, 1999.

89. R Ahmed, I Segal, H Hassan. Fermentation of dietary starch in humans. Am J Gastroenterol, 95(4):1017–1020, 2000.

90. A Govindji. Dietary advice for African-Caribbean people with diabetes. Nutr Food Sci, 3:33–36, 1994.

91. DB Thompson. Strategies for the manufacture of resistant starch. Trends Food Sci Tech, 11:245–253, 2000.

92. CO Moore, JV Tuschoff, CW Hastings, RV Schanefelt. Applications of starches in foods. In: R Whistler, JN BeMiller, EF Paschelli. eds. Starch Chemistry and Technology. New York: Academic Press, 1984, pp 575–591.

93. SY Kim, DP Wiesenborn. Starch noodle quality as related to potato genotypes. J Food Sci, 61(1):248–252, 1996.

94. LL Niba, J Hoffman. Resistant starch levels in grain sorghum (*Sorghum bicolor* M.) are influenced by soaking and autoclaving. Food Chem, 81:113–118, 2003.

95. A Escarpa, MC Gonzalez, E Manas, L Garcia-diz, F Saura-Calixto. Resistant starch formation: standardization of a high-pressure autoclave process. J Agric Food Chem, 44(3):924–928, 1996.

96. LA Bello-Perez, P Colonna, P Roger, O Paredes-Lopez. Structural properties of starches dissolved by microwave heating. Starch, 50(4):137–141, 1998.

97. A Caballo-Lopez, MD Luque de Castro. Fast microwave-assisted free sugars washing and hydrolysis pre-treatment for the flow injection determination of starch in food. Talanta, 59:837–843, 2003.

4 Functional Properties of Carbohydrates: Polysaccharide Gums

Steve W. Cui and Qi Wang
Food Research Program, Agriculture and Agri-Food Canada

CONTENTS

I. INTRODUCTION

Gums are long chain polysaccharides widely used in the food and many other industries as thickeners, stabilizers, and texture modifiers. Gums and related polysaccharides are produced in nature as storage materials, cell wall components, exudates, extracellular substances from plants or microorganisms, and in some cases from exoskeletons of shellfish such as lobsters, shrimps and crabs (e.g., chitosan). Some polysaccharides are simple in sugar composition, such as cellulose and β-D-glucans, which contain only one type of monosaccharide (e.g., β-D-glucose), while others are rather complex and may contain up to six types of monosaccharides plus one or two types of uronic acids. Common monosaccharides and uronic acids present in natural polysaccharides include D-glucose, D-galactose, D-mannose, D-xylose, L-arabinose, L-rhamnose, L-fucose, D-galacturonic acid, D-gulucuronic acid, D-mannuronic acid, and L-guluronic acid. The primary structure of a polysaccharide, i.e., monosaccharide composition, linkage patterns, and molecular weight, defines the solubility and conformation of the polymer chains in aqueous solutions, which in turn dictate the functional properties of the gums exhibited in food and other systems.

Polysaccharides can be linear or branched polymers. With the same molecular weight, linear polysaccharides generally have poorer solubility and higher viscosity than branched counterparts due to their extended conformation in solutions (if soluble or dispersible). Perfectly linear homoglycans such as cellulose are either difficult to dissolve or insoluble in aqueous medium due to excessive intra- and intermolecular interactions (mainly through hydrogen bonding), which make them less useful as hydrocolloidal gums. Irregularity introduced by substitution or branching to the linear chain increases solubility. Highly branched polysaccharides are usually very soluble but exhibit lower viscosity in solutions because of their smaller hydrodynamic volumes compared to liner molecules with the same molecular weight. The variations in monosaccharide composition, linkage patterns, molecular weight, and molecular weight distribution of gums contribute to the unique functional properties exhibited by each gum.

The goal of the present chapter is to provide information on the basic structural and functional properties and major applications of all commercial gums and some emerging gums in food and other industries. For detailed descriptions of chemical structure, molecular characterization, physicochemical properties, and applications of these gums, readers are referred to several comprehensive books and chapters (1–5).

II. FUNCTIONAL PROPERTIES OF POLYSACCHARIDE GUMS

A. VISCOSITY ENHANCING OR THICKENING PROPERTIES

When polysaccharide gums are dissolved into solution, one remarkable phenomenon is the considerable increase in solution viscosity; gums restrict the movement of water molecules and in extreme cases gels are formed. The ability of polysaccharide gums to increase viscosity or to thicken the aqueous system is the most important property of such polymers. The shape and conformation of polysaccharides are determined by their primary sequence structure. Once the structure is determined, the shape and/or conformation of a polysaccharide are more or less fixed, and the molecular weight (size) and number of polysaccharide molecules in a given volume (concentration) become important in determining their functional properties. In addition, environmental factors such as solution pH, temperature, presence of certain ions, and ionic strength of the system have significant influences on the conformation of polysaccharide chains, and hence their functional properties.

Solution viscosity of a gum almost always increases with concentration, but not necessarily in a linear manner. At low concentrations, dilute gum solutions normally exhibit Newtonian flow behavior (independent of shear rate) in which polymer molecules are free to move independently without intermolecular entanglements. For most random coil polysaccharides, the relationship between zero-shear specific viscosity (η_{sp}) and concentration (c) follows $\eta_{sp} \propto c^{1.1-1.3}$. When the polymer concentration is increased to a critical point (critical concentration C*), the viscosity of the solution increases sharply due to entanglement of polymer molecules. This is called the semi-dilute region within which polysaccharide gums usually exhibit shear thinning flow behavior where viscosity decreases with increase in shear rate.

The viscosity of most gum solutions decreases with increased temperature, although some gums are more resistant to temperature changes. For example, the viscosity of xanthan gum solution is relatively unchanged over a wide range of temperatures (−4°C to 93°C) (4). There are other extremes, such as methyl cellulose, where the viscosity increases as the temperature increases, and eventually gels are formed at higher temperature. Other factors influencing viscosity include pH, ionic strength, and presence of co-solutes with effects differing in individual gums.

B. GELLING PROPERTIES

All hydrocolloids have viscosity enhancing or thickening properties, but only a few are able to gel. Gelation of polysaccharides is caused by the cross-linking (covalently and/or non-covalently) of long polymer chains to form a continuous three-dimensional network which traps and immobilizes water and forms a firm and rigid structure resistant to flow under force. Gelation of polysaccharides usually involves three stages: 1) Polysaccharide gums have to be dissolved/dispersed at temperature above the melting point. At this stage, polymer chains exist in a coiled conformation. Upon cooling, polymer chains start to form ordered structures such as helices. 2) Formation of a gel network with further cooling. At this stage, helices begin to aggregate by forming cross-links or super-junctions, and a continuous network is eventually developed. 3) Aging stage where existing helices or aggregations are further enhanced and some new helices are formed. Contraction of gel networks may occur with the liberation of free water ("weeping" or syneresis). Most of the polysaccharide gels are thermally reversible below 100°C with defined setting and melting temperature ranges. There is a minimum concentration for each polysaccharide, below which gel cannot be obtained. Some gels exhibit thermal hysteresis where the melting temperature is significantly higher than the setting temperature, e.g., agarose gels (6). However, there are a few gelling gums which do not follow the above rules. Some gums form gels upon heating while others can form gels by changing ionic strengths and pH or introducing specific ions. A wide range of gels with different textures, such as soft, elastic, very firm, and brittle, can be prepared by selecting different types of polysaccharides and by varying gelation conditions.

C. SURFACE ACTIVITY AND EMULSIFYING PROPERTIES

Although polysaccharides are hydrophilic compounds not conventionally perceived to be surface active, many polysaccharide gums are used to stabilize emulsions that already contain an emulsifier (proteins or surfactants). The universal role of gums in emulsion systems is to thicken the continuous phase, thereby inhibiting or slowing droplet flocculation and/or creaming. There are a few exceptions of gums that actually exhibit surface activity; these gums play double roles in emulsion systems: as an emulsifier and a thickener. In most cases, surface activity of these gums is attributed to the protein component associated with the polysaccharides, while in other situations, the surface activity is due to the presence of hydrophobic functional groups, such as in the cases of methyl cellulose and propylene glycol alginate. Although it is still controversial regarding what is responsible for the surface activity, fenugreek gum does exhibit excellent emulsifying and emulsion stabilizing properties even at very low protein content (e.g., <0.5%) (7). Detailed applications of these gums as emulsifiers are described in the following sections.

III. CHEMISTRY, FUNCTIONAL PROPERTIES, AND APPLICATIONS OF POLYSACCHARIDE GUMS IN FOOD AND OTHER INDUSTRIES

A. GUMS FROM EXUDATES

The earliest gum known to humans is from plant exudates. Many plants exude a viscous, gummy liquid when wounded and the liquid will dry to form hard, glassy, tear-drop-like balls or other shapes of masses. The exudates are hand collected, sorted/graded, and further processed to meet the application needs. Gum arabic, tragacanth, karaya, and ghatti are exuded gums that are commercially significant.

1. Gum Arabic

a. Source and structure
Gum arabic, or acacia gum, is prepared from the exudate of *Acacia* trees, mostly from *senegal* species, and sometimes mixed with *seyal* species. Natural gum is in the form of spherical balls resembling tear drops, collected by hand and processed before use. Almost all commercial gum arabic is produced from the Sahelian regions of Africa.

Gum arabic consists of a mixture of a relatively low-molecular-weight polysaccharide (~0.25 × 10⁶ daltons, a major component) and a high-molecular-weight hydroxyproline-rich glycoprotein (~2.5 × 10⁶ daltons, a minor component) (8). It is a heavily branched polysaccharide; the main chain consists of (1→3)-linked β-D-galactopyranosyl residues. The side chains are two to five units in length made of (1→3)-linked β-D-galactopyranosyl units, joined to the main chain by (1→6)-linkage. Both main and side chains are substituted by α-L-arabinofuranosyl, α-L-rhamnopyranosyl, β-D-glucuronopyranosyl, and 4-O-methyl-β-D-glucuronopyranosyl units. The monosaccharide composition of gum arabic varies with gum sources, e.g., gum from *Acacia senegal* contains about 44% galactose, 27% arabinose, 13% rhamnose, and 16% glucuronic acid of which only 1.5% are 4-O-methylated. In contrast, gum arabic from *Acacia seyal* contains 38% galactose, 46% arabinose, 4% rhamnose, and 12% total glucuronic acid (of which 5.5% are 4-O-methylated) (8). These compositional and structural differences affect their functionalities, e.g., gum arabic from *Acacia senegal* is a much better emulsifier than gum from *Acacia seyal*.

b. Functional properties and applications
Gum arabic is readily dissolved in water to give clear solutions with light colors ranging from very pale yellow to orange brown. It is a typical low viscosity gum and the solutions exhibit Newtonian flow behavior even at concentrations as high as 40%. Higher concentration solutions can be

prepared up to 55%. A major functional property of gum arabic is its ability to stabilize oil-in-water emulsions. The protein-rich high-molecular-weight species are preferentially adsorbed onto the surface of oil droplets while the carbohydrate portion inhibits flocculation and coalescence by electrostatic repulsions and steric forces (8). The major application of gum arabic is in the confectionary and beverage industries for stabilizing emulsions and flavor encapsulation. In the confectionary industry, gum arabic is used to prevent sugar crystallization and to emulsify the fatty components. Examples of such products include pastilles, caramel, and toffee. Gum arabic has also been used in chewing gums, cough drops, and candy lozenges. Good stability under acidic conditions makes gum arabic useful in beverages, e.g., it is used as an emulsifier in the production of concentrated citrus juices and cola flavor oils of soft drinks (3). Gum arabic stabilized flavor oils can be spray-dried to form microencapsulated powders that can be easily incorporated into dry food products such as soup and dessert mixes.

2. Tragacanth Gum

a. Source and structure

Tragacanth gum is dried exudates from branches and trunks of *Astragalus gummifer* Labillardiere or other species of *Astragalus* grown in West Asia (mostly in Iran, some in Turkey). After hand collection, the exudates are graded, milled, and sifted to remove impurities. Tragacanth gum is composed of a water-soluble fraction and a water-insoluble fraction. The water-soluble fraction, accounting for 30–40% of total gum, is a highly branched neutral polysaccharide consisting of L-arabinose side chains attached to D-galactosyl backbones (9, 10). The D-galactosyl residues in the core chains are mostly 1→6-linked, sometimes 1→3-linked, whereas the branching L-arabinosyl residues are mutually joined by 1→2-, 1→3-, and/or 1→5-linkages. The water-insoluble fraction, the major fraction (60–70%), is an acidic polysaccharide consisting of D-galacturonic acid, D-galactose, L-fucose, D-xylose, L-arabinose, and L-rhamnose, and is called tragacanthic acid or bassorin. It has a (1→4)-linked α-D-galacturonopyranosyl backbone chain with randomly substituted xylosyl branches linked at the 3 position of the galacturonic acid residues. Some of the xylosyl residues are attached by an α-L-fucosyl or a β-D-galactosyl residue at the 2 positions (3, 11).

b. Functional properties and applications

Tragacanth gum swells rapidly in both cold and hot water to form a viscous colloidal suspension rather than a true solution. When added to water, the soluble tragacanthin fraction dissolves to form a viscous solution while the insoluble tragacanthic acid fraction swells to a gel-like state, which is soft and adhesive. When more water is added, the gum first forms a uniform mixture; after 1 or 2 days, the suspension will separate into two layers with dissolved tragacanthin in the upper layer and insoluble bassorin in the lower layer.

The viscosity of the suspension reaches a maximum after 24 hours at room temperature, and hydration can be accelerated by an increase in temperature. The suspension typically exhibits shear thinning behavior. The ability to swell in water, forming thick, viscous dispersions or pastes, makes it an important gum in the food, pharmaceutical, and other industries. It is the most viscous of the natural water-soluble gums and is an excellent emulsifying agent with good stability to heat, acidity, and aging.

Food applications of tragacanth gum include salad dressings, oil and flavor emulsions, ice creams, bakery fillings, icings, and confectionary. In the pharmaceutical and cosmetic industries, tragacanth gum is used as an emulsifier and stabilizer in medicinal emulsions, jellies, syrups, ointments, lotions, and creams. Gum tragacanth is also a good surface design thickener since it is a good medium for mixing with natural dyes and conveying controlled design onto fabric. It allows easy painting, stamping, and stenciling, and ensures a good control over color placement.

3. Gum Karaya

a. Source and structure

Gum karaya is from the exudates of *Sterculia urens*, trees of the Sterculiaceae family grown in India. It is a branched acidic polysaccharide with high molecular weight. Gum karaya contains 37% uronic acid and 8% acetyl groups. The backbone chain consists of (1→4)-linked α-D-galacturonic acid and (1→2)-linked α-L-rhamnosyl residues with side chains of (1→3)-linked β-D-glucuronic acid, or (1→2)-linked β-D-galactose on the galacturonic acid unit where one half of the rhamnose is substituted by (1→4)-linked β-D-galactose (12, 13). The quality of the gum varies significantly depending on the season of collection: summer usually gives high yields and high viscosity gum. During storage, the viscosity of gum karaya can be lost when exposed to high temperature and high humidity. The decrease in viscosity is more significant when the particle size is small. Preservatives may be added to prevent viscosity loss.

b. Functional properties and applications

Similar to gum tragacanth, gum karaya does not dissolve in water to give a clear solution but swells to many times its own weight to give a dispersion. The type of dispersion is influenced by the particle size of the product. For example, coarse granulated gum karaya produces a discontinuous, grainy dispersion whereas a fine powdered product gives a homogenous dispersion. Dispersion of gum karaya exhibits Newtonian flow behavior at low concentration ($<0.5\%$) and shear thinning behavior at semi-dilute concentrations ($0.5\% < c < 2\%$) (13). Further increase in gum concentration produces a paste resembling spreadable gels. An increase in temperature improves solubility in water, but excessive heat will cause degradation of the polysaccharides, resulting in non-recoverable loss of viscosity. At extreme pHs and in the presence of sodium, calcium, and aluminium salts, the viscosity of gum karaya dispersion decreases.

Gum karaya is used to stabilize packaged whipped cream products, spread cheeses and other dairy products, frozen desserts and salad dressings, and as acid-resistant stabilizers in acidified products. It is also used as a water binder in bread, processed meats, and low-calorie dough-based products such as pasta (11). Other applications of karaya gum include dental adhesives, bulk laxatives, and adhesives for ostomy rings. Gum karaya is also used in the manufacture of long-fibered, lightweight papers in the paper industry and as a thickening agent in the textile industry to help print the dye onto cotton fabrics.

4. Gum Ghatti

a. Source and structure

Gum ghatti is an amorphous translucent exudate of *Anogeissus latifolia,* a tree of the Combretaceae family grown in India. It contains L-arabinose, D-galactose, D-mannose, D-xylose, and D-glucuronic acid in the ratio of 10:6:2:1:2, plus traces of a 6-deoxyhexose. The detailed structure of gum ghatti has not been clearly established. Its main chain consists of β-D-galactopyranosyl residues connected by (1→6)-linkages and D-glucopyranosyluronic acid units connected by (1→4)-linkages (9).

b. Functional properties and applications

Similar to gum karaya and tragacanth, gum ghatti does not dissolve in water to give clear solutions, but can be dispersed to form a colloidal dispersion. The dispersion exhibits non-Newtonian flow behavior and its viscosity is between those of gum arabic and gum karaya dispersions at the same concentration. Gum ghatti is an excellent emulsifier and can be used to replace gum arabic in more complex systems (13). The pH of gum ghatti dispersions is 4.8, and the viscosity increases with increase in pH, reaching a maximum at pH 8 (3). The viscosity of gum ghatti dispersions increases with time regardless of solution pH; however, addition of sodium salts, such as sodium carbonate and sodium chloride, results in decrease in viscosity. Loss in viscosity also occurs when the gum dispersions are not protected by preservatives against bacterial attack. Gum ghatti is used as an emulsifier and stabilizer in beverages and butter-containing table syrups, and as a flavor fixative for specific applications. Gum ghatti is also used to prepare powdered, stable, oil-soluble vitamins, and as a binder in making long-fibered, lightweight papers.

B. Gums from Plants

Gums of plant origin other than exudates are also important for food use. These include storage polysaccharides from seeds and tubers, mucilages from seed coats, and cell wall materials from fruits and cereals.

1. Galactomannans (Locust Bean, Tara, Guar, and Fenugreek Gums)

a. Source and structure

Galactomannans are a group of storage polysaccharides from various plant seeds. There are four major sources of seed galactomannans: guar (*Cyamopsis tetragonoloba*), locust bean (*Ceratonia siliqua*), tara (*Caesalpinia spinosa* Kuntze) and fenugreek (*Trigonella foenum-graecum* L.). Among these, only guar and locust bean gums are of considerable industrial importance and the use of tara and fenugreek is limited due to availability and price. Most of the guar crop produced worldwide is grown in India and Pakistan. The plant has also been cultivated in tropical areas such as South and Central America, Africa, Brazil, Australia, and the semi-arid regions of the southwest United States. Locust bean is produced mostly in Spain, Italy, Cyprus, and other Mediterranean countries. Fenugreek is grown in northern Africa, the Mediterranean, western Asia, and northern India, and has been recently cultivated in Canada.

The production of commercial guar, locust bean, and tara gums is similar, involving separation of endosperms from the seed hull and germ, grinding and sifting of the endosperm to a flour of fine particle size and sometimes purifying by repeated alcohol washings. The final product is a white to cream-colored powder. The amount and molecular weight of galactomannans found in the endosperm extract can vary significantly depending on the source of seed and growing conditions. Most commercial gums contain >80% galactomannan. Low-molecular-weight grades are produced from acid, alkaline, or enzyme hydrolysis of native gums. Fenugreek gum is extracted from the endosperm or ground whole seed with water or dilute alkali, and yields vary from 13.6% to 38%, depending on the variety/cultivar and extraction methods (14). Commercial fenugreek gum products, such as Fenu-pure and Fenu-life, contain over 80% galactomannas with about 5% proteins. Laboratory-prepared material involves pronase treatment of the gum samples, which produces a product of much higher purity with less than 0.6% protein contaminates (15).

Seed galactomannans consist essentially of a linear (1→4)-β-D-mannopyranose backbone with side groups of single (1→6)-linked α-D-galactopyranosyl units. The molar ratio of galactose to mannose varies with origins, but are typically in the range 1.0:1.0~1.1, 1.0:1.6–1.8, 1.0:3.0, and 1.0:3.9~4.0 for fenugreek, guar, tara, and locust bean gums, respectively. The distribution of D-galactosyl residues along the backbone chain is considered irregular, where there are longer runs of unsubstituted mannosyl units and block condensation of galactosyl units (16, 17).

b. Functional properties and applications

The solubility of galactomannan gums increases with the degree of galactose substitution. Guar and fenugreek gums are readily dissolved in cold water whereas locust bean gum is only slightly soluble in cold water but can be dissolved in hot water. The hydration rate and solution viscosity depend on factors such as particle size, pH, temperature, etc. Guar gum solutions are reported to be stable over the pH range 4.0–10.5, and the highest hydration rate is reported at ~ pH 8.0 (18). Hydration rates are reduced in the presence of salts and other water-binding agents such as sucrose.

Like many polysaccharides found in nature, these galactomannans are polydisperse, high-molecular-weight polymers. Average molecular weight varies, typically from 1.0 to 2.5 million Daltons. The galactomannan molecules exist as an extended ribbon-like structure at solid state and adopt a flexible coil-like conformation in solution. All four types are highly efficient thickening agents. Given the same molecular weight and polymer concentration, the thickening powder decreases in the order of the increase of galactose contents, i.e., locust bean > tara > guar > fenugreek. The rheological properties of some galactomannan solutions show a considerable departure from classical random coil-like behavior (19). In particular, there is a lower coil overlap parameter $C^*[\eta]$ ~2.5 in comparison with $C^*[\eta]$ ~4 for most other disordered coils, and a stronger dependence of specific viscosity on concentration ($\eta_{sp} \propto c^{~4.5}$ in contrast to $\eta_{sp} \propto c^{~3.3}$). This is attributed to intermolecular associations at high concentrations.

Galactomannan gums are compatible with most hydrocolloids. There is a useful synergistic increase in viscosity and/or gel strength by blending galactomannan gums with certain linear polysaccharides including xanthan, κ-carrageenan, and agarose. The synergistic interactions are more pronounced with galactomannans of lower galactose contents.

Fenugreek and guar gums are non-gelling polysaccharides whereas locust bean and tara gum solutions may form weak gels upon freeze-thaw treatment, or by adding large amounts of ethylene glycol or sucrose. Gelation of galactomannans can also be induced by the addition of cross-linking agents such as borax and transition metal ions. The synergistic interactions of locust bean and tara gums with some gelling polysaccharides, such as κ-carrageenan and agarose, may enhance gelation, impart a desirable elastic character, and retard syneresis in these gels. These mixed gels have been used to form sheeted, fruit-flavored snack products and to produce hair gels.

Polysaccharides are generally considered non-surface active agents and the apparent surface activity is frequently attributed to the presence of small amounts of proteins. However, purified fenugreek gum (with less than 0.6% proteins and used in less than 1%) appears to be more efficient than guar and locust bean gums in lowering interfacial free energy. Fenugreek gum is also more concentration-efficient than gum arabic and xanthan gum in stabilizing oil/water emulsions.

Guar and locust bean gums are the most extensively used gums in the world. In the food industry they are widely used as thickening and stabilizing agents, usually in amounts of <1% of the food weight. They are used as stabilizers to improve shelf-life, to prevent creaming or settling in salad dressings, soft drinks, and fruit juices, to influence crystallization, and to improve freeze-thaw behavior of frozen products such as ice-cream and frozen desserts. They are also used as thickener or water-binding agents in pie fillings, icings, meat products, and pet foods. Addition of guar gum to baked products and pastry reduces the degree of starch retrogradation and improves texture and shelf-life. Guar gum is a potential dietary supplement in weight control and treatment of diabetes and hyperlipidemia. Guar and locust bean gums and their derivatives also have wide applications in other industries including pharmaceutical, mining, paper, textile, and construction (18).

2. Pectins

a. Source and structure

Pectin is a generic name for a group of polysaccharides extracted from cell walls of plant tissues. The main commercial pectins are produced from citrus peels and apple pomace, although other raw materials are also used including sugar beet pulp, sunflower seed head, peach pulp, and potato pulp. Pectin is mainly composed of an α-(1→4)-linked D-galacturonic acid backbone chain interrupted by α-(1→2)-linked L-rhamnose residues and the mole-percent of rhamnose varies with the source of pectin (20). The carboxyl groups of galacturonic acids are partly methylesterified and in certain pectins are partially acetylated. The degree of esterification higher than 50% is defined as high methoxyl (HM) pectin; the degree of esterification lower than 50% is defined as low methoxyl (LM) pectin. The molecules have "smooth regions" consisting of blocks of galacturonic acid residues and "hairy regions" with condensation of the side-chains. Often, arabinan, galactan, or arabinogalactan side chains are attached to the C-4 position of the rhamnose residues. Other sugars such as glucuronic acid, L-fucose, D-glucose, D-mannose, and D-xylose are sometimes found in the side-chains.

b. Functional properties and applications

In the solid state, pectin molecules exist as right-handed helices which are stabilized by intra- and intermolecular hydrogen bonding and/or intermolecular calcium ions forming an ordered and fairly stiff structure. It is generally accepted that the backbone adopts a worm-like conformation in solution. Several studies on the solution properties of pectins suggested that pectin molecules are further aggregated into either rods or segmented rods in solution and held together by non-covalent forces (21).

Pectins are highly heterogeneous with respect to their molecular weight. For isolated and purified pectins, the molecular weight is largely determined by the extraction modes and conditions. The average molecular weight from various fruit sources is typically the order of

$10^4 \sim 10^5$ daltons (22). Pectins are generally soluble in water and the solubility usually decreases with increasing ionic strength and molecular weight and decreasing degree of esterification. Aqueous pectin dispersions show rheological behavior similar to many other commercial polysaccharides, and the viscosity decreases with increasing temperature but increases with increasing concentration. The viscosity of aqueous pectin solutions also depends on molecular weight, degree of esterification, electrolyte concentration, type and concentration of co-solute, and pH. Addition of salts of monovalent cations, such as sodium chloride to pectin, dispersions reduces viscosity (23), whereas the addition of calcium or other polyvalent cations increases viscosity of pectin dispersions. In a calcium-free solution, viscosity decreases when pH is increased. Because of its low molecular weight, pectin is not an efficient thickener compared to other high-molecular-weight polysaccharides.

For both high methoxyl (HM) and low methoxyl (LM) pectins, gels can be prepared at concentration above $0.5 \sim 1\%$. Both high molecular weight and high concentration favor gel formation and enhance gel strength. Other intrinsic and extrinsic factors such as pH, amount and type of co-solutes, and the degree of esterification (DE) are also important with different effects on HM and LM pectins. HM pectins form thermally irreversible gels at sufficiently low pH (pH<~3.6) and in the presence of sugars or other co-solutes at a concentration of greater than ~50% by weight. The DE and overall distribution of hydrophilic and hydrophobic groups have major effects on gelation. Commercial HM pectin is classified as rapid-set, medium-set, and slow-set types. Sucrose and other co-solutes also affect gelation although to a lesser extent. The amount of co-solute required increases with increasing DE. LM pectins require calcium or other divalent cations for gelation, and the reactivity to calcium is governed by the proportion and distribution of carboxyl groups and DE. The relative amount of calcium affects the gelling properties of LM pectins considerably. Gelation is favored by increased soluble solids and decreased pH. LM pectin gels prepared at low pH are thermally reversible whereas those prepared at neutral pH are thermally irreversible.

The main uses of pectins are as gelling agents in various food applications including dairy, bakery, and fruit products. HM pectins have long been used in traditional jams and jellies, whereas LM pectins are used in low-calorie, low-sugar jams and jellies. Pectin gels can be used as an alternative to gelatine in fruit desserts and amidated LM pectins are used to prepare milk gels and desserts. Pectins are also used as a protein dispersion stabilizer in acidified dairy products such as yoghurt and milk-based fruit drinks and other protein drinks prepared from soya and whey. The enhanced emulsion stability is caused by interaction between pectin and protein particles (24).

3. Konjac Glucomannan

a. Source and structure
Konjac mannan, or glucomannan, is prepared from the tubers of the konjac plant (*Amorphophallus konjac*). Konjac is a perennial plant unique to Asia and is specially cultivated in Japan. In the production of konjac flour, two-year-old tubers are sliced into thin chips and subsequently dried and milled. Further purification of konjac flour is achieved by washing with ethanol aqueous solutions to remove proteins, lipids, and soluble salts. Purified konjac flour contains typically 88% carbohydrates, 1.7% ash, 0.9% lipids, and 0.5% protein (25). Konjac polysaccharide is a copolymer consisting of random blocks of β-D-glucose and β-D-mannose in the ratio of 2:3. All the monosaccharide units are joined together by $1 \rightarrow 4$ linkages with occasional substitutions of acetyl group (5–8%) attached at the 3 position of the mannose or both mannose and glucose residues (26, 27).

b. Functional properties and applications
In the solid state, konjac glucomannan has a crystalline structure. X-ray diffraction characterization revealed that it has extended two-fold helices (28). Konjac glucomannan yields a high viscosity solution, but extra efforts such as extensive stirring are needed to dissolve the gum. The solution is a typical non-Newtonian system showing shear thinning behavior. A thermo-irreversible gel is formed when konjac glucomannan solution is heated in alkali conditions. A possible gelling mechanism is that hydrolysis of the acetyl groups under alkali conditions promotes intra- and intermolecular hydrogen bonding leading to "cross-linking" of the glucomannan molecules. However, this hypothesis cannot explain why the gel is thermo-irreversible. Another interesting property of konjac glucomannan is its synergism with other hydrocolloids. Mixture of konjac glucomannan and xanthan gum form gels at a total concentration as low as 0.1%. Thermo-reversible gels can be prepared when konjac glucomannan is mixed with agarose or carrageenan solutions.

Alkali konjac gel is a popular traditional Japanese food (*Kon-nyaku*). Thermo-reversible gels formed from interactions between konjac glucomannan and other gums also have applications in products such as health jellies. Konjac flour is suitable for thickening, gelling, texturing, and water binding. It is a major ingredient for some vegetarian meat products and is also used in fat-free or low-fat meat products.

4. Soluble Soybean Polysaccharides

a. Source and structure
Water-soluble soybean polysaccharide (SSPS) is the cell wall material of the cotyledons of soybeans. Commercial SSPS is extracted with dilute acid from by-products produced from the manufacturing of soy proteins or tofu.

The extract is filtered and/or centrifuged, and dried to give a yield of ~45% (29).

SSPS is a highly branched pectic polysaccharide. The backbone consists of a galacturonan (GN) and a rhamnogalacturonan (RG). The RG structure consists of a diglycosyl repeating unit: $(1\rightarrow4)$-α-D-galacturonic acid-$(1\rightarrow2)$-α-L-rhamnopyranose units with β-D-galactan side-chains. The side-chains are substituted with L-fucosyl and L-arabinosyl residues, which are linked to the C-4 of the rhamnosyl residues. The degree of polymerization is estimated to be 43–47 which is longer than those of fruit pectins. SSPS is highly polydisperse in molecular weight. Three to four fractions with molecular weights ranging from 4,700 to 542,000 daltons were identified (30).

b. Functional properties and applications

Similar to gum arabic, SSPS is a low viscosity gum. It is soluble in cold water and exhibits Newtonian flow behavior at a concentration as high as 10%. When the concentration is increased to 20%, it exhibits shear thinning flow behavior. Unlike pectins, the viscosity of SSPS solution is not sensitive to salts, including NaCl, $CaCl_2$ and KCl; however, the viscosity increases with increase in sugar concentration (e.g., sucrose). The viscosity is also sensitive to pH and temperature, decreases with decrease in pH and increase in temperature, and the effect is reversible.

SSPS could be used in the food industry as a stabilizing and thickening agent. Addition of 10% SSPS has less effect than wheat bran on color and surface smoothness of Chinese steamed bread but has a stronger detrimental effect on volume and texture (29). Recent applications of SSPS include stabilizing milk proteins under acidic conditions (31).

5. Flaxseed Gum

a. Source and structure

Flaxseed gum is extracted from the seed or hull (seed coat) of the flax plant (*Linum usitatissimum*). Flaxseed gum is composed of a neutral arabinoxylan and acidic pectic polysaccharide. The neutral arabinoxylan has a $(1\rightarrow4)$-β-D-xylosyl backbone to which arabinose side-chains are attached to the 2 and/or 3 positions. The acidic polysaccharide has a backbone of $(1\rightarrow2)$-linked α-L-rhamnopyranosyl and $(1\rightarrow4)$-linked D-galactopyranosyluronic acid residues, with side-chains of L-fucose and D-galactose, with the former at the non-reducing end. The ratio of L-rhamnose, L-fucose, D-galactose, and D-galacturonic acid is 2.6:1:1.4:1.7 (5, 32).

b. Functional properties and applications

Flaxseed gum exhibits Newtonian flow behavior at low concentrations and shear thinning behavior at high concentrations. Flaxseed gum is a low to medium viscosity gum and the viscosity is influenced by pH, with higher viscosity at pH 6–8, and lower viscosity at pH 2–6. Viscosity of flaxseed gum solutions decreases with increase in temperature. Flaxseed gum demonstrates surface activity and the ability to stabilize oil/water emulsions.

In food applications, flaxseed gum has been used as an egg white substitute in bakery products and ice creams. It can be used in medicinal preparations, e.g., ointments and pastes containing flaxseed gum are effective in the treatment of furunculosis, carbunculosis, impetigo, and ecthyma (33). Flaxseed gum is used as a bulk laxative, a cough emollient agent, and a stabilizer in barium sulphate suspensions for X-ray diagnostic preparations (34). Flaxseed gum solution is also used as a saliva substitute because it possesses lubricating and moisture-retaining characteristics resembling those of natural saliva (35). The stringy and fast drying properties of flaxseed gum make it suitable for hairdressing preparations and hand cream formulations. At 2.5% concentration, flaxseed gum is a good base for eye ointments. Other applications of flaxseed gum include printing, textile, and cigar papers.

6. Yellow Mustard Gum

a. Source and structure

Yellow mustard gum is a mucilage deposit in the epidermal layer of yellow mustard seed (*Sinapis alba*). It is water-soluble and can be extracted from whole seed or seed coat (bran). Yellow mustard gum is a mixture of two polysaccharides, a linear 1,4-linked β-D-glucan with ethyl substitutes and a branched acidic rhamnogalacturonan composed of, disaccharide repeating unit: $(1\rightarrow2)$-α-L-Rhamp-$(1\rightarrow4)$-α-D-GalpA as backbone chains. The side-chains are composed of a terminal non-reducing end 4-O-Me-β-D-GlcpA, and/or $(1\rightarrow6)$-β-D-Galp which is attached at the 4 position of the rhamnose residues in the backbone chain. The ratio of the 4-substituted and unsubstituted rhamnose is 2:1 (5).

b. Functional properties and applications

Yellow mustard gum solution/dispersion is a non-Newtonian system exhibiting shear thinning flow behavior and weak gel structures resembling xanthan gum. It also demonstrates surface activity and emulsifying capacity. The gum solution has a high viscosity over a wide range of pH. Similar to xanthan gum, yellow mustard gum has synergistic interactions with galactomannans leading to considerable increase in solution viscosity or formation of thermo-reversible gels (e.g., with locust bean gum).

Yellow mustard gum is an ideal stabilizer for salad dressings and fruit juice concentrates. It is also used in cosmetics, e.g., a skin care moisturizing lotion prepared using this gum gives a favorable hand feeling (36).

7. Cereal β-Glucan

a. Source and structure

Mix linked $(1\rightarrow3)(1\rightarrow4)$-$\beta$-D-glucans are cell wall polysaccharides of cereal endosperm and aleurone cells. The content of β-D-glucans in cereals follows the order of barley (3–11%), oats (3.2–6.8%), rye (1–2%), and wheat (<1%). It is a linear, unbranched polysaccharide containing a single type of monosaccharide, β-D-glucose. β-D-Glucans from different cereals share a common structural feature: with consecutive blocks of (1→4)-linked β-D-glucose (mostly 2 or 3, and sometimes up to 14) interrupted by a single (1→3)-linked β-D-glucose. The β-(1→3)-linked cellotriosyl unit (trisaccharide) is the major building block (58–72%), followed by β-(1→3)-linked cellotetraosyl unit (tetrasaccharide, 20–34%). The ratio of cellotriose/cellotetraose is about 2.0–2.4 in oats, 3.0 in barley, and 3.5 in wheat (37).

b. Functional properties and applications

β-D-Glucan solution exhibits a wide range of rheological behavior, from viscoelastic fluid, weak gel to real gel, depending on molecular weight and concentration. Solutions of high-molecular-weight β-D-glucans are typically viscoelastic fluids of the "random coil" type. In contrast, low-molecular-weight β-glucans are able to form gels at reduced temperature or favored solvent properties. The gelling property depends on molecular weight and structural regularity (tri-/tetra ratio). The higher the tri-/tetra ratio, the more regular is the structure, and the easier in gel formation. Above the minimum molecular weight for gelation, lower molecular weight favors gel formation (5, 38).

Commercially, there are two β-D-glucan products: Oatrim and Glucagel. Oatrim is made by treating oat bran or flour with a thermo-stable α-amylase at high temperature. Its main component is dextrins, but its functionality appeared to be attributed to β-glucans and dextrins. Oatrim is used in bakery products, frozen desserts, processed meats, sauces, and beverages. Because it mimics the texture of fats, Oatrim is also used as a fat replacer in low-fat or no-fat products (39).

Glucagel is produced by partial hydrolysis of barley β-D-glucan and is a low-molecular-weight product (15,000 to 150,000 daltons) which can form gels at 2% concentration. Glucagel has gelling and fat mimetic properties and is used as a fat substitute in bakeries, dairy products, dressings, and edible films (40, 41).

Oat β-D-glucan is recognized as having important health benefits. It may lower cholesterol levels and reduces glycemic response, and is recommended as a good dietary fiber supplement. Oat β-D-glucan is also used in cosmetics as a moisturizer in lotions and hand creams.

8. Psyllium Gum

a. Source and structure

Psyllium gum is from the seed of *Plantago*, a plant comprising about 200 species of herbs or shrubs widely distributed in the temperate regions of the world. The gum is deposited in the seed coat (husk, hull), and has a long history of medicinal use.

Psyllium gum is a mixture of polysaccharides containing heteroxylans with a (1→3)- and (1→4)-linked β-D-xylopyranosyl backbone with short side-chains attached to position 2 of some of the 1,4-linked β-D-xylopyranosyl residues and to position 3 of other 1,4-linked β-D-xylopyranosyl residues (42). The side-chains consist of β-D-xylopyranosyl and α-L-arabinofuranosyl residues. 1→4-linked α-D-GalpA residues are also present in addition to small amounts of 1,2,4-linked Rhap and 1,3-, 1,6-, and 1,3,6-linked Galp. The latter monosaccharides may arise from a small portion of pectic polysaccharides.

b. Functional properties and applications

Psyllium gum does not dissolve completely in water but swells to a mucilagenous dispersion with the general appearance of wallpaper paste (33, 43). A 2.0% psyllium gum dispersion exhibits gel-like structure, similar to that of xanthan gum which generates a "weak-gel" network by entanglement of rigid, ordered molecular structures (44). Increasing the concentration of psyllium gum from 1% to 2% gives a significant increase in gel strength. However, freshly prepared solutions/dispersions of psyllium gum (1%) show flow properties similar to those of disordered coils, with a Newtonian plateau at low shear rate. Upon aging, psyllium gum solutions form cohesive gels and show obvious syneresis. The gels continue to contract on storage over long periods (to about 30% of their original volume after three months). This contraction process can be accelerated by freezing and thawing cycles. However, psyllium gum is stable in high-salt solutions (e.g., 2.5 M NaCl) which are formed by neutralization of the alkaline extract over a prolonged storage, with no evidence of gelation or precipitation.

Psyllium gum is used with other gums in bakeries to replace wheat gluten. Adding psyllium gum and hydroxypropylmethylcellulose (HPMC) at 2% and 1%, respectively, to rice flour gives a loaf volume close to that of hard wheat control (43). The effectiveness of the psyllium-HPMC system arises from the psyllium network stabilizing gas cells formed during proving, and preventing them from collapsing during initial stages of heating in the baking oven. When temperature is further increased, HPMC starts to gel and stabilizes the gas cells.

As a dietary fiber, psyllium gum lowered plasma LDL-cholesterol levels by 6–20% in mildly hypercholesterolemic individuals, although conflicting results were reported (45, 46). Psyllium gum has been used as a demulcent in dysentery, erosion of intestines, dry coughs, burns, excoriations, and inflammations of the eyes (33, 47). It is extensively used as a bulk laxative. When ingested with the proper amount of water, it swells and increases the size of the fecal mass, and has a lubricant effect equal to that of oil but without oil's disadvantages. The water-holding capacity and gelling property of psyllium gum can be used to delay and reduce allergic reactions by holding toxins and allergens in the gel structure.

9. Pentosans/Arabinoxylans

a. Source and structure

Arabinoxylans or pentosans are the primary construction material of the cell wall in some cereals, such as wheat and rye, and are also present in oats and barley. According to solubility, cereal arabinoxylans are classified as water-soluble and water-insoluble. The water-soluble wheat arabinoxylans are present mainly in the flour (endosperm cell walls), while the water-insolubles can be found in both the bran and flour fractions. Insoluble arabinoxylans are cross-linked with proteins through phenolic ester bonds which can be rendered water-soluble by treating with alkali or specific enzymes.

Arabinoxylans consist of a backbone of $(1\rightarrow4)$-linked β-D-xylopyranose residues to which α-L-arabinofuranose units are attached through O-3 and/or O-2,3 positions of the xylose residues. The distribution of the α-L-arabinosyl branches along the backbone chain are random with some regions heavily substituted and others unsubstituted (smooth domain) (48). The pattern and degree of substitution vary with cereal sources and tissue locations in the grain.

b. Functional properties and applications

Arabinoxylans are random coil polysaccharides in aqueous solutions, and exhibit Newtonian flow behavior at low concentrations and shear thinning behavior at higher concentrations. Because of the presence of ferulic acid, wheat flour arabinoxylans can form thermo-irreversible gels upon oxidation (48). In comparison, arabinoxylans from wheat bran can form thermo-reversible gels upon cooling (5). Wheat and rye arabinoxylans are important functional ingredients in baked products affecting water binding, dough rheology, and starch retrogradation. They also protect gas retention in dough due to viscous influence on the gluten-starch films (49).

C. GUMS FROM SEAWEEDS

Seaweed or algae is an important natural source for hydrocolloidal gums. Most seaweed extracts are gelling agents. However, their chemical compositions and structures vary significantly due to the sources of raw material and processing conditions, so do their gelling mechanism.

1. Agar

a. Source and structure

Agar, or agar agar, is extracted from red seaweeds (*Rhodophycae*). It is commercially obtained from *Gelidium* spp. and *Gracilariae* spp. The Japanese are pioneers in processing agar, called "*Kanten*" in Japanese, meaning "cold days" or "cold weather," reflecting the weather conditions used to remove water from agar gels through freeze-thaw cycles which are still being used in modern agar processing plants. The alternative procedure is a syneresis method, in which the absorbed water is eliminated by applying a proper force.

Agar contains a major component, agarose, and a minor component, agaropectin. Agarose is the gelling component which has a molecular weight about 120,000 daltons. It is a linear polymer consisting of a $(1\rightarrow3)$-β-D-galactopyranosyl and $(1\rightarrow4)$-3,6-anhydro-α-L-galactopyranosyl residues as building units. Agaropectin is a heterogeneous mixture of polysaccharides of lower molecular weights. Their structures are similar to agarose but slightly branched and sulfated, and they may also have methyl and pyruvic acid ketal substituents (6, 50).

b. Functionality and applications

Agar is referred to as the queen of the gelling agents. The gelling property is due to the three equatorial hydrogen atoms on the 3,6 anhydro-L-galactose residues of agarose to form hydrogen bonds. The gel network contains double helices formed from left-handed threefold helices. These double helices are stabilized by the presence of water molecules bound inside the double helical cavity. Exterior hydroxyl groups allow aggregation of these helices to form suprafibers. The gelling temperature is around 38°C and the melting temperature is about 85°C, which gives very high gelling hysteresis. With this enormous gelling power and hysteresis property, agar has found broad applications in food and other industries. It is used in the baking industry because of its heat-resistant gel properties, and is widely used as a stabilizer in pie fillings, icings, toppings, and glazes. The heat-resistant gelling properties help to prevent chipping, cracking or sweating of icings, toppings, and glazes in baked goods. Agar is particularly effective in forming a stiff gel at low concentrations and it is compatible with most other gums. At around 40°C and upon setting, agar gel forms an impervious moisture barrier between icing and wrapping and it has the unique property of not sticking to the wrapping. Agar is also widely used in the confectionary industry as a gelling agent, and in preparing canned meat, fish, and poultry products.

Addition of a small portion of locust bean gum to *Gelidium* agar (1:9) may enhance gel strength and improve gel texture; in particular, it increases the elasticity of the gel (6). This is due to the synergistic interaction between locust bean gum and agar which has practical applications in the food industry where less brittle texture is desired. However, this interaction is only limited to agar from species of *Gelidium* and *Pterocladia*. Due to its excellent gelling characteristics and high resistance to metabolization by microorganisms, agar is used in biotechnology applications such as in microbiological culture media where it forms clear, stable, and firm gels.

2. Algin (Alginates)

a. Source and structure

Alginates or algin are the salts and derivatives of alginic acid, an acidic polysaccharide extracted from the brown seaweeds (Phaeophyceae). The main species of commercial significance include *Laminaria hyperborea*, *L. digitata*, *L. japonica*, *Macrocystis pyrifera*, *Ascophyllum nodosum*, *Eclonia maxima*, *Lessonia nigrescens*, *Durvillea antarctica*, and *Sargassum* spp. Natural alginate is insoluble due to its salt derivatives obtained during growth in seawater, including calcium, magnesium, and barium salts. In order to extract the material, a pre-extraction treatment is necessary to convert the insoluble cations into protons by treating milled algae tissue with dilute mineral acids. The next step is to neutralize with sodium carbonate or sodium hydroxide, and alginic acid is converted into water-soluble sodium salt. Following the removal of algal particles by sifting, floatation, centrifugation, and filtration, sodium alginate is precipitated by alcohol, calcium chloride, or mineral acids. A derivative of alginate, propylene glycol alginate (PGA), is produced from alginate by an esterification reaction with propylene oxide.

Alginate is an unbranched polymer containing β-(1→4)-linked D-mannuronic acid (**M**) and α-(1→4)-linked L-guluronic acid (**G**) residues (3, 51). It is a copolymer composed of three types of blocks: two homopolymeric blocks consisting of the same residues of M or G, respectively, and a block with strictly alternating residues (i.e., GMGMGMGM). The lengths and sequences of the three blocks vary considerably with the source of algae, place and season of collection, as well as part of the algae from which the alginate is extracted. The differences in chemical structures account for their differences in functionalities and applications.

b. Functional properties and applications

In commercial alginate products, the following factors are important in determining functionality: type of cations, M/G ratio, molecular weight and residual calcium. Sodium salt is the most common form of alginates. Potassium, ammonium, and calcium salts and free alginic acid are also available (3).

The primary function of alginates is to form thermally stable cold-setting gels in the presence of calcium ions. Alginate gels can be heat treated without melting although they may eventually degrade. Gelling properties and gel strengths of alginate gels depend on the type and mode of ion binding ($Mg^{2+} \ll Ca^{2+} < Sr^{2+} < Ba^{2+}$) (52). Therefore, the control of cation addition is critical for the production of homogeneous gels. High **G** alginates produce strong brittle gels with good heat stability (except if present in low-molecular-weight molecules), but water weepage (syneresis) occurs on freeze-thaw whereas high **M** alginates produce weaker but more elastic gels with good freeze-thaw stability. Two basic methods have been used to control the introduction of cross-linking ions: diffusion and internal setting. The diffusion method lets the cross-linking ion (e.g., Ca^{2+}) diffuse from an outer reservoir into an alginate solution which is used for the restructuring of foods such as artificial berries, pimiento strips, and onion rings. Internal setting differs from the former in that the Ca^{2+} ions are released in a controlled fashion from an inert calcium source within the alginate solution. The controlled release of Ca^{2+} is usually achieved by a change of pH and/or by limited solubility of calcium salt. The internal setting gels found wide applications in food, pharmaceutical, and cosmetic applications, such as cold water dessert gel, instant imitation bakery jelly, and facial masque (52).

The molecular weights of commercial alginates are between 12,000 and 190,000 daltons. Higher-molecular-weight favors gel strength and viscosity enhancement. However, it is sometimes desirable to use a higher concentration of low-molecular-weight alginates to obtain strong gels and to avoid excessively high viscosity prior to gelation.

Chemically modified alginates, e.g., propylene glycol esters of alginic acid (PGAs), are very different from alginates in functionality. They are much more tolerant to calcium ions and acidic environments such as in milk-based products and salad dressings (51). PGAs also exhibit surface activities due to esterification, and can be used as an emulsifier and foam stabilizer.

3. Carrageenans

a. Source and structure

Carrageenans are popular seaweed gums extracted from red seaweed (Rhodophycae). The main species used are *Eucheuma cottonii*, *E. spinosum*. *E. cottonii*, and *E. spinosum* which are spiny bushy plants growing along the coasts of the Philippines, Indonesia, and other islands in the Far East. Other species of commercial significance include *Chrondrus crispus* from around the coasts of the North Atlantic and *Gigartina* sp. from the cold deep coastal waters of South America. Based on the origins and processing conditions, three types of carrageenan gums are on the market, namely kappa (κ), iota (ι), and lambda (λ) carrageenans. The process of producing carrageenan gums is rather complex, involving washing and cleaning of the seaweed, alkaline extraction, followed by coarse and fine filtrations, solvent precipitations and/or freeze-thaw cycles and finally, drying, grinding, and blending.

Carrageenan gums consist of alternating (1→3)-linked-β-D-galactopyranose and (1→4)-linked-α-D-galactopyranose sugar units. The three gums differ from one another in their content of 3,6-anhydro-D-galactose and number and position of ester sulfate groups (53).

κ-Carrageenan is composed of alternating (1→3)-β-D-galactopyranose-4-sulfate and (1→4)-3,6-anhydro-α-D-galactopyranose units. It is produced by alkaline elimination of μ-carrageenan isolated mostly from the tropical seaweed *Eucheuma cottonii* (also known as *Kappaphycus alvarezii*). Typical food grade κ-carrageenans contain 25% of ester sulfate and 35% of 3,6-anhydro-D-galactose, which is close to the theoretical maximum.

ι-Carrageenan is composed of alternating (1→3)-β-D-galactopyranose-4-sulfate and (1→4)-3,6-anhydro-α-D-galactopyranose-2-sulfate units. ι-Carrageenan is produced by alkaline elimination of μ-carrageenan isolated from the Philippines seaweed *Eucheuma denticulatum* (also called *Spinosum*). The major difference between κ- and ι-carrageenan amount of 2-sulfate on the 1,4-linked 3,6-anhydro-D-galactose. As the degree of sulfation increases from 25% in κ- to about 50% in ι-carrageenans, there is a noticeable weakening of gelling properties arising from decreased potassium sensitivity.

λ-Carrageenan is mainly composed of (1→3)-β-D-galactopyranose-2-sulfate-(1→4)-α-D-galactopyranose-2,6-disulfate repeating. It is isolated mainly from *Gigartina pistillata* or *Chondrus crispus* and can be converted into θ-carrageenan (theta-carrageenan) by alkaline elimination.

b. Functional properties and applications

All carrageenan gums are highly flexible molecules which, at higher concentrations, interact with each other to form double-helical zones (3). Food-grade carrageenans have molecular weights in the range of $2–4 \times 10^5$ daltons. Gel formation of κ- and ι-carrageenans requires gel-inducing and gel-strengthening cations, such as K^+ and/or Ca^{2+} and it involves helix formation upon cooling from a hot solution. Carrageenans are used mainly as gelling, thickening, and suspending agents. κ-Carrageenan gels are firm, clear, and brittle with poor freeze-thaw stability. These gels may be softened (and are generally regarded to be synergistically strengthened) by mixing with locust bean gum. Ionic binding of ι-carrageenan is less specific and increasing ionic strength promotes formation of junction zones leading to soft elastic gels with good freeze-thaw stability. λ-Carrageenan is non-gelling as it lacks 3,6-anhydro groups in the 1→4-linked α-D-galactopyranosyl residues which are necessary for forming the initial double helix. λ-Carrageenan can act as a cryoprotectant, and a combination of λ-carrageenan with locust bean gum improves the freeze-thaw behavior of frozen products (54).

κ-Carrageenan stabilizes dairy products due to its interactions with casein micelles (~200 nm diameter), preventing whey separation. It is used in ice creams as a second stabilizer to prevent LBG and β-casein from phase separation (55). Carrageenan is also used as a water binder in cooked meats and as a thickener in toothpaste and puddings.

D. Gums from Microbial Fermentation

Some microorganisms produce slimy materials such as extracellular polysaccharides, structural polysaccharides, or intracellular storage polysaccharides. The extracellular polysaccharides are water-soluble and exhibit unique functional properties, and are hence an important source of hydrocolloids. Since the fermentation process can be controlled and processed in large quantity, gums from microbial production are more consistent than naturally occurring gums.

1. Xanthan Gum

a. Source and structure

Xanthan gum is an extracellular polysaccharide produced commercially by aerobic submerged fermentation from *Xanthomonas campestris* (56). The primary structure of xanthan gum is a β-(1→4)-D-glucopyranosyl backbone with tri-sugar unit side-chains consisting of a β-D-glucuronic acid residue between two D-mannopyranosyl residues, which is attached to the backbone at the 3-position of alternative β-D-glucosyl residues. In the side-chains, the terminal β-D-mannosyl residue is glycosidically linked to the 4-position of the β-D-glucuronic acid, which in turn is linked to the 2-position of the α-D-mannose. About 40% of the terminal mannose residues are 4,6-pyruvated while almost all the inner mannose is 6-acetylated (57).

b. Functional properties and applications

Xanthan is considered a non-gelling gum and is best known for its unique shear thinning flow behavior and weak gel structures. It hydrates rapidly in cold water, but proper hydration depends on particle size, solvent quality, and rate of agitation. Since the viscosity of xanthan gum solutions/dispersions is relatively temperature independent and the polymer is resistant to acids, alkali, and enzymes, it is a popular thickener and stabilizer in the food industry. The most striking property of xanthan gum is the very high low-shear viscosity coupled with its strongly shear-thinning characteristics. The relatively low viscosity at high shear rate provides the advantages of easy to mix, pour, and swallow, and the high viscosity at low shear rate gives good suspension and coating properties to colloidal suspensions at rest. This makes xanthan gum a perfect stabilizer for salad dressings, sauces, gravies, syrups, and toppings. In dairy products, such as ice creams, sour cream, and sterile whipping cream, xanthan gum provides optimal viscosity, long-term stability, improved transfer characteristics during processing, heat shock protection, and ice crystal control. In baked goods, xanthan gum contributes to smoothness, air incorporation and retention, hence improved volume, texture, and moisture retention of refrigerated dough. Blending of xanthan gum with dry cake ingredients helps uniform hydration and batter mixing, which are important for the overall quality of finished cakes, particularly after storage (58).

Xanthan gum exhibits pronounced synergistic interactions with galactomannans and glucomannans (59, 60). These interactions result in increased viscosity, and in some cases formation of thermo-reversible, soft elastic gels. Experimentally, mixture of xanthan-locust bean gum forms thermo-reversible gels at polymer concentrations as low as 0.1%; in contrast, xanthan-guar gum mixtures only exhibit increased viscosity regardless of the concentration. It is necessary to heat the mixtures to about 90 to 95°C to achieve maximum synergism as this not only unfolds the xanthan structure but also helps to fully hydrate the locust bean gum. The extent of interaction between xanthan gum and galactomannans is reduced at low pH and high salt concentrations. The optimum ratio of interaction is 50:50 for xanthan–LBG mixture and 20:80 for xanthan–guar mixture (4).

2. Gellan Gum

a. Source and structure

Gellan gum is a bacterial exocellular polysaccharide, commercially produced by inoculating a fermentation medium with *Sphingomonas elodea* (ATCC 31461). Gellan gum is composed of a linear tetrasaccharide repeating unit: →3)-α-D-glcp- (1→4)-β-D-glcpA-(1→4)-β-D-Glcp-(1→4)-α-L-rhap-(1→ (61, 62). There are two acyl substitutions on the 3-linked glucose, a L-glyceryl at O(2) and an acetyl at O(6) positions. The average degree of substitution is one glycerate per repeat unit and one acetate every two repeats.

b. Functionality and applications

The functional property of gellan gum is dependent on the degree of acylation and presence of counter ions. High acyl (HA) gellan gum can form soft, elastic, transparent, and flexible gels by cooling the hot solutions when concentration is above 0.2%. The gels set and melt at 70–80°C with no thermal hysteresis and the gelling property is not affected by the presence of counter ions. In contrast, low acyl (LA) gellan gum forms hard, non-elastic brittle gels when binding with a wide variety of ions, such as Ca^{2+}, Mg^{2+}, Na^+, K^+, and H^+; the divalent ions are more efficient than the monovalent ions in promoting gelation. The gel strength of LA gellan gum increases with increasing ion concentration until a maximum is reached. Increase of ion concentration also results in increased gel setting and melting temperatures. Sugar has a negative influence on the gelation of LA gellan gum which is often described to have a 'snap set' since gelation occurs rapidly once the setting temperature is reached. In contrast to HA gellan gum, significant thermal hysteresis is observed for LA gellan gels. However, under most conditions, LA gellan gels are not thermo-reversible below 100°C. The minimum gelling concentration of LA gellan gum can be as low as 0.05% in the presence of cations (63).

Both LA and HA gellan gums are commonly used as gelling agents and can be used to prepare dessert jellies with a variety of textures. Gellan gum is used in dairy products and sugar confectionery. LA gellan gum is used to modify traditional gelatin dessert jellies. An interesting application of gellan gum is to prepare structured liquids by applying shear stress either during or after gelation. These structured liquids are extremely efficient suspending agents (61).

3. Curdlan Gum

a. Source and structure

Curdlan gum is an extracellular polysaccharide commercially produced by microbial fermentation of a mutant strain of *Alcaligenes faecalis* var. *myxogenes*. Curdlan is a linear, homopolymer composed entirely of (1→3)-β-D-glucosidic linkages. Native curdlan has a granular structure and is water-insoluble but can be dissolved in sodium hydroxide solutions (64), cadoxen aqueous solution, and dimethyl sufoxide (DMSO).

b. Functional properties and applications

Curdlan gum can form gels by heating the suspensions or reduce the pH of an alkali solution. Heat treatment of curdlan suspensions may produce two types of gels, depending on temperature. A thermo-reversible low-set gel is obtained by heating gum suspensions at 55°C followed by cooling. A thermo-irreversible high-set gel requires heating up to 80°C or higher. The gel strength increases with heating temperature (gelation starts at 55°C) but stays constant between 60–80°C. Further increase in temperature results in steady increase of gel strength (64, 65). At the same heating temperature, gel strength increases with increased concentration. The addition of co-solute also has significant effects on gel strength, e.g., adding borate to curdlan suspension significantly increases gel strength, and adding urea markedly reduces gel strength (65).

Curdlan is a tasteless, odorless, and colorless product with wide food applications. It is used in making tofu noodles and other processed cooked foods as texture modifier, binding, and moisture improvement agents. Curdlan is used in noodle dough to reduce leaching of soluble ingredients, giving a clear broth with improved texture and mouthfeel. Addition of curdlan in processed meats modifies texture and improves water-holding capacity. Other food applications include processed rice cake, ice creams, jellies, sausages, and hams. It is also a popular low-energy ingredient in dietetic foods.

4. Dextran

a. Source and structure

Dextran is a group of α-glucans produced by exocellular bacteria Lactobacillaceae, particularly the genera *Lactobacillus, Leuconstoc,* and *Streptococcus.* Commercially important dextran is produced by *Leuconstoc mesenteroides* B-512 (F) (66). Dextran is a homo-polysaccharide composed primarily of 1→6-linked α-D-glucopyranose units (~95%) with branches at C-3 and/or C-4, occasionally at C-2. About 80% of the branches are single D-glucose. The molecular weight of dextrans can be 40 to 600 million daltons, however, the molecular weight of commercial food-grade dextrans is below 100,000 daltons.

b. Functional properties and applications

Dextran is a fine, white powder, very soluble in both cold and hot water giving clear solutions with low viscosity. A solution can be made to contain up to 50% dextran. The viscosity of dextran solution (2%) is independent of shear rate and unaffected by co-solutes, salts, or changes in the pH (3–10). Dextran has good water-holding capacity and imparts good bodying attributes to liquid systems. It also exhibits effective emulsifying and stabilizing properties.

The most important use of dextran is as a blood plasma extender with strict control of molecular weight (75,000 ± 25,000 daltons). Other pharmaceutical applications include cryo-protective agent to protect cells from freezing damage, suspending agent for X-ray opaque compositions, binder for tablets, stabilizing agent for water-insoluble vitamin preparations and a stomach-irritant preventive, a pharmaceutical taste masking agent, and a drug encapsulating agent in combination with methycellulose.

Dextrans with molecular weight below 100,000 daltons are permitted by the U.S. Food and Drug Administration as Generally Regarded as Safe (GRAS) until their deletion in 1973 due to the lack of use (67). The apparent lack of interest in dextran in foods is probably due to its high solubility and low solution viscosity (66). Bread prepared from yeast-raised dough containing 1–2% dextran was soft with a greater volume and longer shelf-life (68). The addition of dextran (up to 0.5%) to ice cream conferred excellent stability and heat-shock resistance. Dextran can be used as a stabilizer for confectionery to prevent crystallization, improve moisture retention, increase viscosity, and maintain flavor. It can also be used in soft drinks, flavor extracts, milk beverages, and icing compositions. Other food applications include fish products, meats, vegetables, and cheeses.

E. Chemically Modified Gums

Cellulose is the most abundant polysaccharide in plants. Natural cellulose is completely insoluble in aqueous media due to extensive intra- and intermolecular hydrogen bonding. However, certain treatments and chemical modification can render cellulose water-soluble and the derived products exhibit unique functional properties, making them useful as hydrocolloids in many industrial applications. About a third of the purified cellulose is used as base material for water-soluble derivatives and a wide range of products with designed properties, depending on the groups involved and degree of derivatization.

1. Microcrystalline Cellulose (MCC)

a. Source and structure

Microcrystalline cellulose (MCC) is produced by treating purified cellulose with a strong mineral acid, such as hydrogen chloride (69). Acid hydrolysis removes the amorphous regions of cellulose and gives a product consisting primarily of crystallite aggregates. Powdered MCC is produced by drying the acid hydrolysates. Dispersible MCC can be prepared by further processing the hydrolysates by wet mechanical disintegration, which breaks up the aggregates to microcrystals, followed by co-processing with a hydrophilic barrier or other hydrocolloids, such as guar gum, xanthan gum, or carboxylmethylcellulose.

b. Functional properties and applications

Colloidal MCC exhibits thixotropic flow behavior in which viscosity decreases with increase in shear stress, and once the stress is removed, viscosity will recover gradually over time (70). MCC dispersions have good thermo-stability which is useful in the preparation of heat-stable products. MCC can also be used to modify textures, resulting in a cleaner mouthfeel and good flavor release, and making a useful fat replacer in emulsion products. In addition, MCC is a good suspending agent for particles and solids.

MCC has many applications in pharmaceutical, food, and paper industries. Examples include bar mixes to add creaminess and pulpiness. In batters and breadings, MCC improves cling and reduces drying time and fat absorption during frying. MCC also adds creaminess in chocolate drinks in addition to its ability to suspend solids and add opacity to the product (69).

2. Carboxymethylcellulose (CMC)

a. Source and structure

Carboxymethylcellulose (CMC) is produced by reacting alkali cellulose with monochloroacetic acid. The substitution is mostly at 2-O and 6-O, occasionally at 3-O positions. The degree of substitution (DS) is generally 0.6–0.95 per monomeric unit (maximum DS is 3) (62, 71).

b. Functional properties and applications

CMC is readily dissolved in cold water, with maximum viscosity and best stability at pH 7–9. The rheological properties of CMC are determined by the uniformity of substitution and degree of polymerization (DP). CMC solutions with medium to high DP are pseudoplastic, whereas solutions of low DP exhibit low viscosity and are less pseudoplastic. Medium and high viscosity gum solutions with 0.4–0.7 DS, especially those that are less uniformly substituted, are thixotropic. In contrast, evenly substituted, high DS, medium and high DP gums show no or less thixotropic behavior in solutions (71).

Gelation of CMC can be induced by adding trivalent metal ions (e.g., aluminum) or subjecting the solution to high shear. Gels ranging from soft to very firm can be prepared by selecting different grades of CMC and types of metal ions. The gel structure is also dependent on polymer concentration, DP, pH, and metal cation to carboxylate anion ratio.

Food grade CMC is widely used in the food industry as a thickener, stabilizer, and suspending agent. CMC can be used to improve the volume yield during baking by encouraging gas bubble formation; it is also used in frozen desserts and soft-serve ice creams to control ice crystal growth, and to improve mouthfeel, body, and texture. CMC is used in pet food to bind water, thicken gravy, aid extrusion, and bind fines. Because CMC is insoluble in acidic stomach fluids but soluble in alkaline intestinal fluids, it is a good coating for powders and tablets in the pharmaceutical industry. In the cosmetic industry, CMC is used as a stabilizer for hand lotions and vitamin-oil emulsions. CMC also found applications in textiles and detergents (62).

3. Methylcellulose

a. Source and structure
Methylcellulose (MC) is prepared by etherifying the available hydroxyl groups of cellulose chain by conversion of cellulose into alkali cellulose in sodium hydroxide, followed by reaction with methyl chloride (62). Many MC derivatives are available, but the most important one is hydroxypropylmethylcellulose (HPMC).

b. Functional properties and applications
MC solutions exhibit shear thinning flow behavior at 0.5% concentration and above. The pseudoplastic property is enhanced with increases in concentration and molecular weight. A unique functional property of MC and HPMC is their inverse temperature solubility and thermo-gelling property; they can form gels when the temperature reaches above a critical level due to hydrophobic interactions between high-substituted regions, which consequently stabilizes intermolecular hydrogen bonding. The gels break down upon cooling. Another unique property of MC and HPMC is their surface activity, making them useful emulsifiers for oil-in-water emulsions.

Due to the multifunctional properties, MC and HPMC are used as emulsifiers and stabilizers in French dressings and in low-oil or no-oil salad dressings (72). MC is often used in fried foods to reduce oil absorption through film formation and thermal gelation. In addition, batter adhesion and matrix food cohesion are improved by adding MC and/or HPMC. MC is used in baked goods including cakes, doughnuts, breads, cookies, fruit pie fillings, icings, and glazes. The thermal gelation property prevents boil-over of pastry fillings and aids gas retention during baking. MC retards water migration in frozen baked products during freeze-thaw cycles. MC is also used in non-dairy whipped toppings because of its surface active properties. In the pharmaceutical industry, MC is used in tablet film coating, controlled drug release and ointments. MC and its derivatives are also used as adhesives for wallpapers, controlled release agents for pesticides and fertilizers, and emulsifiers and stabilizers in shampoo and hair conditioners.

4. Hydroxypropylcellulose and Hydroxyethylcellulose

a. Source and structure
Hydroxypropylcellulose (HPC) and hydroxyethylcellulose (HEC) are prepared by reactions of alkali cellulose with propylene oxide and ethylene oxide, respectively, at elevated temperature and pressure (62, 73). The substitution patterns of HPC and HEC are random and lead to significant number of hydroxyl groups unsubstituted along the backbone chain. The molar substitution (MS) of commercial HPC is between 3–4; in comparison, commercial water-soluble grades HEC has a much wider MS value, from 1.8 to 3.8. The molecular weight of HPC and HEC ranges from 50k to 1,300k daltons.

b. Functional properties and applications
HPC is soluble in cold water, but becomes insoluble at temperature above 45°C. It has good film forming and surface active properties and can be used to stabilize toppings, especially at high ambient temperatures. HPC is soluble in ethanol, and has potential applications in alcoholic beverages. It is also used as a thickener in solvent-based adhesives, alcohol-based hair dressings, grooming aids, perfumes, inks, and paint removers. In the polymer industry, HPC is used as a secondary stabilizer in the suspension polymerization of vinyl chloride.

HEC with a DS greater than 1.6 is soluble in hot or cold water. The viscosity decreases with increase in temperature. HEC solutions exhibit Newtonian flow behavior at low shear rate and shear thinning behavior at high shear rate. It is useful as a thickener, viscosity control additive, protective colloid, binder, suspending agent, and film former in many industrial applications, including latex paints, emulsion polymerization, petroleum, paper, and pharmaceutical products. The largest use of water-soluble HEC is for thickening latex paints because of its solubility, low foaming characteristics, high thickening efficiency, and good compatibility with universal coloring systems.

5. Chitin and Chitosan

a. Source and structure

Chitin is the second most abundant natural biopolymer on Earth and is composed of α-(1→4)-linked 2-acetamido-2-deoxy-β-D-glucose (N-acetylglucosamine). Chitin is found in exoskeletons, peritrophic membranes, and cocoons of insects. Chitin is water-insoluble, but can be converted to water-soluble derivatives such as chitosan. Commercial chitin is prepared from shells of lobster, crab, or shrimp which are grounded and treated with 5% hydrochloric acid to remove minerals. The demineralized shell is further processed with pepsin or trypsin to remove proteins. Alkali deproteinization is also used and preferred if the final product is deacetylated chitin, i.e., chitosan. Chitosan is prepared by N-deacetylation of chitin under strong alkali conditions. The degree of acetylation of commercial chitosans is about 0.20 (74, 75).

b. Functional properties and applications

Chitosan is insoluble in organic solvents but soluble in aqueous acidic media. Following protonation of the amino groups, it forms a unique polycationic structure, while other polysaccharides usually give a neutral or anionic structure. Unlike most gelling polysaccharides, chitosan forms gels through chemical and enzymatic reactions. A thermo-irreversible gel can be prepared by treating chitosan in acetate salt solution with carbodiimide to restore acetamido groups. Gelation is probably attributed to hydrophobic interactions which are thermally favored. Chitosan gel can also be prepared by introducing large organic counter ions, such as 1-naphthol-4-sulphonic acid or 1-naphthylamine-4-sulphonic acid.

Chitosan is also chemically modified for specific applications, e.g., a stable and self-supporting gel can be obtained by enzyme treatment of tyrosine glucan, which is synthesized by reacting chitosan with 4-hydroxy-phenylpyruvic acid. The enzyme tyrosinase oxidizes phenol to quinine which forms cross-links with the free amino groups. Chitosan can also be cross-linked with glutaraldehyde in lactic acid to produce a colorless, rigid, and infusible gel up to 200°C (74).

Chitin, chitosan, and their derivatives have a wide range of applications in pharmaceutics, biomaterials, foods, water treatments, biotechnology, cosmetics, textiles, and membranes. Chitosan is a good film former and is recommended for textile finishing, paper sheet formation, glass fiber coating, dye application, shrink proofing of wool, photographic application, and cement setting retardation. Chitosan is also used as a dietary fiber for weight control.

IV. FUTURE PROSPECTS AND NEW DEVELOPMENT

There have been continuous efforts in the field of hydrocolloids to reduce production costs, improve functionality, explore novel applications of existing gums, and discover new gums from natural resources. Although the use of new hydrocolloid gums in foods is limited by extremely high costs required to pass legislative approval, there are gums that have long history of use in foods which could easily get approval for food uses. Currently, we have a good understanding of the basic structures and functional properties of most gums, but problems arise on a daily basis at the production level due to inconsistency of the gum supplies and lack of knowledge on how these gums interact with other food ingredients, such as starch, proteins, oils, etc. Therefore, the following areas are recommended for future research: 1) improve manufacturing practice to produce consistent gum products; 2) further understand the structure-function relationships of hydrocolloids and their interactions with other food ingredients; 3) develop new hydrocolloids from natural sources. Most hydrocolloids, particularly non-starch polysaccharides, are conceived as dietary fibers. Some natural polysaccharides or oligosaccharides are biologically active, such as tissue repairing, anti-carcinogenic, anti-inflammatory, and immuno-modulatory. These polysaccharides are potential ingredients for functional foods or neutraceuticals in addition to their role as thickeners and stabilizers. More research should be directed to these bioactive polysaccharides.

REFERENCES

1. GO Phillips, PA Williams. Handbook of Hydrocolloids. Boca Raton, FL: CRC Press, 2000.
2. RL Whistler, JN BeMiller. Industrial Gums. San Diego, CA: Academic Press, 1993.
3. M Glicksman. Food Hydrocolloids, Vol I. Boca Raton, FL: CRC Press, 1982.
4. M Glicksman. Food Hydrocolloids, Vol II. Boca Raton, FL: CRC Press, 1983.
5. W Cui. Polysaccharide gums from agriculture products: processing, structure and functional properties. Lancaster, PA: Technomic Publishing Company Inc, 2001.
6. R Armisén, F Galatas. Agar. In: GO Phillips, PA Williams. eds. Handbook of Hydrocolloids. Boca Raton, FL: CRC Press, 2000, pp 21–40.
7. N Garti, Z Madar, A Aserin, B Sternheim. Fenugreek galactomannans as food emulsifiers. Lebens Wissen Technol 30: 305–311, 1997.
8. PA Williams, GO Phillips. Gum arabic. In: GO Phillips, PA Williams. eds. Handbook of Hydrocolloids. Boca Raton, FL: CRC Press, 2000, pp 155–168.
9. GO Aspinall. Gums and mucialges. Adv Carbohydr Chem 24: 333–379, 1969.

10. DMW Anderson, MME Bridgeman. The composition of the proteinaceous polysaccharides exuded by *Astragalus microcephalus*, *A. gummifer* and *A. kurdicus*—the sources of turkish gum tragacanth. Phytochem 24: 2301–2304, 1985.

11. W Wang. Tragacanth and karaya. In: GO Phillips, PA Williams. eds. Handbook of Hydrocolloids. Boca Raton, FL: CRC Press, 2000, pp 231–246.

12. AM Stephen, SC Chums. Gums and mucialges. In: AM Stephen. ed. Food Polysaccharides and Their Applications. New York: Marcel Dekker, 1995, pp 377–425.

13. RL Whistler. Exudate gums. In: RL Whistler, JN BeMiller. eds. Industrial Gums. San Diego, CA: Academic Press, 1993, pp 309–339.

14. P Andrews, L Hough, KN Jones. Mannose-containing polysasaccharides. Part II. The galactomannan of fenugreek seed. J Amer Chem Soc 74, 2744–2750, 1952.

15. Y Brummer, W Cui, Q Wang. Extraction, purification and physicochemical characterization of fenugreek gum. Food Hydrocoll 17: 229–236, 2003.

16. J Hoffman, S Svensson. Studies of the distribution of the D-galactosyl side chain in guaran. Carbohydr Res 65: 65–71, 1978.

17. BV McCleary, AH Clark, ICM Dea, DA Rees. The fine-structures of carob and guar galactomannans. Carbohydr Res 139: 237–260, 1985.

18. PA Sandford, J Baird. Industrial utilisation of polysaccharides. In: GO Aspinall. ed. The Polysaccharides, Volume II. New York: Academic Press, 1983, pp 411–490.

19. FM Goycoolea, ER Morris, MJ Gidley. Viscosity of galactomannans at alkaline and neutral pH: evidence of 'hyperentanglement' in solution. Carbohydr Polym 27: 69–71, 1995.

20. P Ryden, RR Selvendran. Cell-wall polysaccharides and glycoproteins of parenchymatous tissues of runner bean (*Phaseolus coccineus*). Biochem J 269: 393–402, 1990.

21. ML Fishman, P Cooke, B Levaj, DT Gillespie, SM Sondey, R Scorza. Pectin microgels and their subunit structure. Arch Biochem Biophys 294: 253–260, 1992.

22. M Corredig, W Kerr, L Wicker. Molecular characterization of commercial pectins by separation with linear mix gel permeation columns in-line with multi-angle light scattering detection. Food Hydrocoll 14: 41–47, 2000.

23. F Michel, JL Doublier, JF Thibault. Investigations on high-methoxyl pectins by potentiometry and viscometry. Prog Food Nutr Sci 6: 367–372, 1982.

24. E Dickinson, L Eriksson. Particle flocculation by adsorbing polymers. Adv Colloid Interface Sci 34: 1–29, 1991.

25. S Takigami. Konjac mannan. In: GO Phillips, PA Williams. eds. Handbook of Hydrocolloids. Boca Raton, FL: CRC Press, 2000, pp 413–424.

26. K Katsuraya, K Okuyama, K Hatanaka, R Oshima, T Sato, K Matsuzaki. Constitution of konjac glucomannan: chemical analysis and ^{13}C NMR spectroscopy. Carbohydr Polym 53: 183–189, 2003.

27. K Nishinari, PA Williams, GO Phillips. Review of the physico-chemical characteristics and properties of konjac mannan. Food Hydrocoll 6: 199–222, 1992.

28. T Yui, K Ogawa, A Sarko. Molecular and crystal structure of konjac glucomannan in the mannan II polymorphic form. Carbohydr Res 229: 41–55, 1992.

29. H Maeda. Soluble soybean polysaccharide. In: GO Phillips, PA Williams. eds. Handbook of Hydrocolloids. Boca Raton, FL: CRC Press, 2000, pp 309–320.

30. A Nakamura, H Furuta, H Maeda, T Takao, Y Nagamatsu. Structural studies by stepwise enzymatic degradation of the main backbone of soybean soluble polysaccharides consisting of galacturonan and rhamnogalacturonan. Biosci Biotech Biochem 66: 1301–1313, 2002.

31. A Nakamura, H Furuta, M Kato, H Maeda, Y Nagamatsu. Effect of soybean soluble polysaccharides on the stability of milk protein under acidic conditions. Food Hydrocoll 17: 333–343, 2003.

32. G Muralikrishna, PV Salimath, RN Tharanathan. Structural features of an arabinoxylan and a rhamnogalacturonan derived from linseed mucilage. Carbohydr Res 161: 265–271, 1987.

33. JN BeMiller, RL Whistler, DG Barkalow. Aloe, chia, flaxseed, okara, phylliums seed, quince seed, and tamarind gums. In: RL Whistler, JN BeMiller. eds. Industrial Gums. San Diego, CA: Academic Press, 1993, pp 227–256.

34. N Tufegdzic, E Tufegdzic, A Georgijevic. Floculation and stabilization of barium sulfate suspensions by hydrophilic colloids. Chem Abstr 62: 8944f, 1965.

35. R Attstrom, PO Glantz, H Hakansson, K Larsson. Saliva substitute. US Patent 5,260,282, 1993.

36. W Cui, MNA Eskin, NF Han, ZZ Duan, X Zhang. Extraction process and use of yellow mustard gum. US Patent 6,194,016, 2001.

37. W Cui, PJ Wood. Relationships between structural features, molecular weight and rheological properties of cereal β-D-glucans. In: K Nishinari. ed. Hydrocolloids: Physical Chemistry and Industrial Applications of Gels, Polysaccharides and Proteins. London: Elsevier Science Publishers, 2000, pp 159–168.

38. N Bohm, W-M Kulicke. Rheological studies of barley $(1\rightarrow3)(1\rightarrow4)$-[β]-glucan in concentrated solution: mechanistic and kinetic investigation of the gel formation. Carbohydr Res 315: 302–311, 1999.

39. CJ Carriere, GE Inglett. Nonlinear viscoelastic solution properties of oat-based [β]-glucan/amylodextrin blends. Carbohydr Polym 40: 9–16, 1999.

40. KR Morgan, CJ Roberts, SJB Tendler, MC Davies, PM Williams. A 13C CP/MAS NMR spectroscopy and AFM study of the structure of Glucagel (TM), a gelling [β]-glucan from barley. Carbohydr Res 315: 169–179, 1999.

41. K Morgan. Cereal β-glucans. In: GO Phillips, PA Williams. eds. Handbook of Hydrocolloids. Boca Raton, FL: CRC Press, 2000, pp 287–307.

42. AB Samuelsen, E Hanne Cohen, B Smestad Paulsen, LP Brull, JE Thomas. Oates. Structural studies of a heteroxylan from Plantago major L. seeds by partial hydrolysis, HPAEC-PAD, methylation and GC-MS, ESMS and ESMS/MS. Carbohydr Res 315: 312–318, 1999.

43. A Haque, ER Morris, RK Richardson. Polysaccharide substitutes for gluten in non-wheat bread. Carbohydr Polym 25: 337–344, 1994.

44. A Haque, RK Richardson, ER Morris, ICM Dea. Xanthan-like 'weak gel' rheology from dispersions of ispaghula seed husk. Carbohydr Polym 22: 223–232, 1993.

45. SD Turley, JM Dietschy. Mechanisms of LDL-cholesterol lowering action of psyllium hydrophillic mucilloid in the hamster. Biochim Biophys Acta 1255: 177–184, 1995.

46. GMA Van Rosendaal, EA Shaffer, R Brant, RJ Bridges, AL Edwards. Failure of cholesterol-lowering by psyllium. Am J Gastroenterol 95: 2487, 2000.

47. JE Montague. Payllium seed: the latest laxative. New York: Montague Hospital for Intestinal Ailments, 1932.

48. MS Izydorczyk, CG Biliaderis. Cereal arabinoxylans: advances in structure and physicochemical properties. Carbohydr Polym 28: 33–48, 1995.

49. CG Biliaderis, MS Izydorczyk, O Rattan. Effect of arabinoxylans on bread-making quality of wheat flours. Food Chem 53: 165–171, 1995.

50. HH Selby, RL Whistler. Agar. In: RL Whistler, JN BeMiller. eds. Industrial Gums. San Diego, CA: Academic Press, 1993, pp 87–103.

51. K Clare. Algin. In: RL Whistler, JN BeMiller. eds. Industrial gums. San Diego, CA: Academic Press, 1993, pp 105–143.

52. KI Draget. Alginates. In: GO Phillips, PA Williams. eds. Handbook of Hydrocolloids. Boca Raton, FL: CRC Press, 2000, pp 379–395.

53. AP Imeson. Carrageenan. In: GO Phillips, PA Williams. eds. Handbook of Hydrocolloids. Boca Raton, FL: CRC Press, 2000, pp 87–102.

54. GH Therkelsen. Carageenan. In: RL Whistler, JN BeMiller. eds. Industrial Gums. San Diego, CA: Academic Press, 1993, pp 145–180.

55. S Thaiudom, HD Goff. Effect of [κ]-carrageenan on milk protein polysaccharide mixtures. Int Dairy J 13: 763–771, 2003.

56. G Sworn. Xanthan gum. In: GO Phillips, PA Williams. eds. Handbook of Hydrocolloids. Boca Raton, FL: CRC Press, 2000, pp 103–115.

57. P Jansson, L Kenne, B Lindberg. Structure of the extracellular polysaccharide from xanthomonas campestris. Carbohydr Res 45: 275–282, 1975.

58. DJ Pettit. Xanthan gum. In: M Glicksman. ed. Food Hydrocolloids, Vol I. Boca Raton, FL: CRC Press, 1982, pp 127–149.

59. TM Bresolin, M Milas, M Rinaudo, F Reicher, JL Ganter. Role of galactomannan composition on the binary gel formation with xanthan. Int J Biol Macromol 26: 225–231, 1999.

60. G Paradossi, E Chiessi, A Barbiroli, D Fessas. Xanthan and glucomannan mixtures: synergistic interactions and gelation. Biomacromolecules 3: 498–504, 2002.

61. KS Kang, DJ Pettitt. Xanthan, gellan, welan, and rhamsan. In: RL Whistler, JN BeMiller. eds. Industrial Gums. San Diego, CA: Academic Press, 1993, pp 341–397.

62. JCF Murray. Cellulosics. In: GO Phillips, PA Williams. eds. Handbook of Hydrocolloids. Boca Raton, FL: CRC Press, 2000, pp 219–230.

63. G Sworn. Gellan gum. In: GO Phillips, PA Williams. eds. Handbook of Hydrocolloids. Boca Raton, FL: CRC Press, 2000, pp 117–135.

64. T Harada, M Terasaki, A Harada. Curdlan. In: RL Whistler, JN BeMiller. eds. Industrial Gums. San Diego, CA: Academic Press, 1993, pp 427–445.

65. K Nishinari, H Zhang. Curdlan. In: GO Phillips, PA Williams. eds. Handbook of Hydrocolloids. Boca Raton, FL: CRC Press, 2000, pp 269–286.

66. AN de Belder. Dextran. In: RL Whistler, JN BeMiller. eds. Industrial Gums. San Diego, CA: Academic Press, 1993, pp 399–425.

67. A Jeanes. Extracellular microbial polysaccharides. Food Technol 5: 34–40, 1974.

68. RT Bohn. Addition of dextran to bread doughs. US Patent 2,983,613, 1961.

69. H Iijima, K Takeo. Microcrystalline cellulose: an overview. In: GO Phillips, PA Williams. eds. Handbook of Hydrocolloids. Boca Raton, FL: CRC Press, 2000, pp 331–346.

70. K Nishinari, E Mitoshi, T Takaya. Rheological properties of aqueous dispersions of microcrystalline cellulose. In: PA Williams, GO Phillips. eds. Gums and Stabilisers for the Food Industry, Vol. 9. Cambridge, UK: Royal Society of Chemistry, 1998, pp 16–25.

71. R Feddersen, SN Thorp. Sodium carboxymethylcellulose. In: RL Whistler, JN BeMiller. eds. Industrial Gums. San Diego, CA: Academic Press, 1993, pp 537–578.

72. JA Grover. Methylcellulose and its derivatives. In: RL Whistler, JN BeMiller. eds. Industrial Gums. San Diego, CA: Academic Press, 1993, pp 475–504.

73. AJ Desmarais, RF Wint. Hydroxyalkyl and ethyl ethers of cellulose. In: RL Whistler, JN BeMiller. eds. Industrial Gums. San Diego, CA: Academic Press, 1993, pp 505–535.

74. M Terbojevich, RAA Muzzarelli. Chitosan. In: GO Phillips, PA Williams. eds. Handbook of Hydrocolloids. Boca Raton, FL: CRC Press, 2000, pp 367–378.

75. RL Whistler. Chitin. In: RL Whistler, JN BeMiller. eds. Industrial Gums. San Diego, CA: Academic Press, 1993, pp 601–604.

5 Food Protein Analysis: Determination of Proteins in the Food and Agriculture System

Richard Owusu-Apenten
Department of Food Science, Pennsylvania State University

CONTENTS

I. INTRODUCTION

A. DEFINITIONS AND PERSPECTIVES

Protein analysis is the development of methods, instrumentation, and strategies for obtaining information about the quantity and composition of proteins within a sample; analysis also extends to the study of the kinetic and thermodynamic behavior of proteins. A food protein is any protein of interest, in food science and technology, in relation to enhancing the supply of food, which is wholesome, nutritious, affordable, and safe. Two broad areas of food protein analysis are readily recognizable: (i) quantitative analysis – determination of the total amount of protein, and (ii) qualitative analysis – fractionation, characterization, and identification of proteins. Of course, so-called qualitative methods also yield quantitative (i.e., numerical) data related to the concentrations of specific proteins in a mixture, molecular mass, isoelectric point, etc.

The major areas of application for food protein analysis are: (a) protein quantitation, (b) protein speciation – including the detection of cultivars, varieties, genetic polymorphism, and adulteration, (c) tests for physical functionality – defined as protein physicochemical properties of interest in food processing, (d) tests for nutritional quality, and (e) detection of bioactive agents including allergens, inhibitors, microbial toxins, as well as functional ingredients. Figure 5.1 summarizes some of the major techniques for food protein analysis

The aim of this chapter is to provide a brief outline of selected techniques for food protein analysis. The principles behind different techniques are well described in the general literature. Less well discussed are the many practical and scientific issues confronted by food protein analysts. In the remainder of Section I, we consider the scope for food protein analysis. Section II covers protein quantitation methods, Section III deals with protein fractionation analysis by

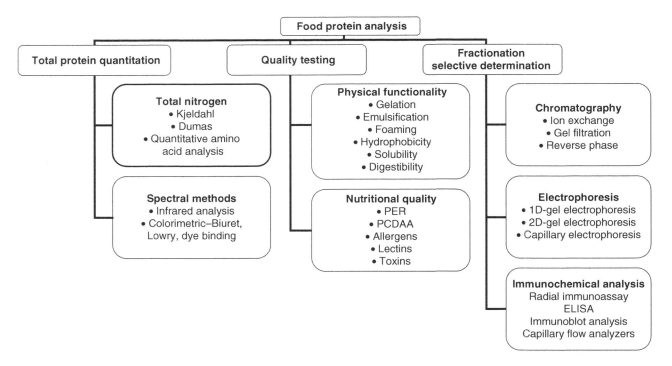

FIGURE 5.1 Some of the major areas of food protein analysis.

electrophoresis, chromatography and mass spectrometry. Section IV provides a brief overview of proteomics, which features high-throughput techniques for protein identification. Food protein analysis is a vast discipline. Only selected themes are introduced in this chapter. Some spectral methods, i.e., colorimetric (e.g., biuret, Lowry, Coomassie blue, bicinchoninic acid, etc.) or spectrophotometric (e.g., ultraviolet absorbance) methods of analysis, were reviewed recently (1) and are not covered here. The following monographs and reviews provide further reading (1–5).

B. FOOD PROTEINS

The major food protein groups are listed in Table 5.1. They are mostly industrial proteins produced from well-known food commodities, including milk, wheat, maize, soybean, peanut, canola, fish, egg, meat, some animal by-products. The manufacturing processes involve standard unit operations, e.g., particle size reduction, solubilization, membrane separation, ion exchange, and dehydration. Processing can lead to changes in protein structure, not all of which are "undesirable." Denaturation is effectively harnessed to create interesting high-protein foods (5).

A key requirement for food protein analysis is reproducibility. Consistent protein readings are necessary for fair decision-making about product quality, pricing, and compliance with food legislation. Other desirable assay characteristics include high speed, and low capital and running costs for analysis. Assay sensitivity is not a premium because food samples are readily available. On the contrary, large

TABLE 5.1
Schema for Food Protein Analysis-1

Some Major Protein Ingredients	Specific Proteins
Animal protein ingredients	Specific animal proteins
• Blood proteins	• Blood serum albumins
• Egg protein	• β-Lactoglobulin,
• Milk protein	α-lactalbumin, casein
• Muscle – fish, poultry and meat	• Ovalbumin
• Skin & feather – gelatin	• Myosin
• Carcass and by-products, bone meal	• Collagen
Plant protein ingredients	Specific plant proteins
• Cereals – vital gluten	• Albumins, globulins
• Legume – protein isolates	• Prolamins, glutelins
(soy, peas, sesame)	• Residue proteins[*]
• Tuber – potato protein	
• Leaf protein	
Microbial proteins or single	
cell protein (SCP)	

[*] Residue proteins refer to cereal storage proteins not extracted using conventional Osborne solvents.

sample sizes lead to concerns about representative sampling. Accuracy, the closeness of a measurement to a real value, is not of paramount concern because bias (deviation from the true reading) is readily determined by calibration.

Table 5.2 shows the movement of protein within the food system from agricultural production through to the consumer. Protein analysis is important at all levels of the food system. Farm gate prices for many commodities, e.g., grain and milk, are partly determined by their protein

TABLE 5.2

Schema for Food Protein Analysis-2

The Food System	IFT[a] Expert Areas in Food Science
Agricultural production	Food chemistry & analysis
↓	Food safety & microbiology
Processing & packaging	Food processing & engineering
↓	Nutrition
Transportation & distribution	Other - legislation
↓	
Wholesale & retail	
↓	
Consumption	

[a] IFT refers to the Institute of Food Technologists.

content. Pricing of farm inputs (e.g., animal feeds) is also affected by levels of protein nitrogen. Recent legislation requires that feed intended for ruminants is free from animal protein. Protein ingredient manufacturers and users require functionality testing, ingredient standardization, optimization, and quality control (Figure 5.1). High protein foods (cheese, milk, meat, fish) are potential targets for adulteration and undeclared substitution – leading to a need for methods to ensure product authenticity. Detection of protein allergens and toxins assumes considerable importance at the consumer end of the food system. Table 5.2 lists also the main food science expertise areas recognized by the Institute of Food Technologists (IFT). All the sub-disciplines in food science offer some opportunity for protein analysis. The schemes in Figure 5.1 and Tables 5.1 and 5.2 provide an indication of the wide scope for food protein analysis.

C. FOOD PROTEIN ANALYSIS-GENERAL CONSIDERATIONS

According to accepted guidelines (6), one should consider the scope and purpose of food protein analysis – type of method (empirical, definitive, screening) and their intended use (research, quality control, surveillance, enforcement). Assay selection should follow desktop research (literature review) and discussions with people having relevant experience. One should obtain some notion of the strengths and disadvantages of different assays (bias, equipment cost, running cost, limit of detection, precision, specificity, speed, etc.). The degree of training necessary is another factor. Initial method development should be followed by optimization. As a rule, most off-the-shelf protein assays are not optimized for specific food samples with regard to interferences (additives, contaminants, flavors) or food matrix effects. Consider whether to use a commercially available ready-made kit. Sample clean-up may be necessary for complex foods, whether raw or processed. Particle size reduction and adequate mixing are important before sampling. Accuracy can be confirmed by comparing the results of one assay with that of an established method.

Consider forms of sample storage and transport where protein tests are performed off-site.

II. QUANTITATION OF FOOD PROTEINS

A. KJELDAHL METHOD

Biological materials are transformed water, carbon dioxide, sulfur dioxide and ammonia when heated at 370–400°C in concentrated sulfuric acid. About 100–250 mg of food material requires 3–10 ml of concentrated sulfuric acid along with potassium sulfate, hydrogen peroxide, or metal oxide catalyst for digestion. There is sample charring followed by decomposition to form a clear-green liquid. Nitrogen (from urea, amino acids, peptides, proteins, nucleic acid, etc.) is converted to ammonium sulfate. Collection and quantitation of ammonia involves (a) neutralization with sodium hydroxide, (b) distillation and absorption by 4% standard boric acid, and (c) titrimetric analysis in the presence of a suitable titration indicator. Sample nitrogen, S_N (g-N per 100 g foodstuff), can be calculated from Eq. 5.1:

$$S_N = \frac{14.01 * V_{TITRANT} * N_{TITRANT} * 100}{Wt(g) * 1000} \quad (5.1)$$

where $V_{TITRANT}$ is the volume of titrant corrected for blank readings, N is the normality of titrant (0.1M) and Wt(g) is the weight of food sample (grams) digested. Finally, values for S_N are converted to crude protein (cP) by multiplying with K_F (the nitrogen-to-protein conversion factor). For animal proteins K_F has a default value of 6.25 assuming that such proteins contain 16% N.

$$cP (\%) = S_N \text{ (g-N per 100 g foodstuff)} * K_F \text{ (g-protein per g-N)} \quad (5.2)$$

The accuracy of Kjeldahl analysis is impaired when samples contain high levels of non-protein nitrogen (NPN). For plant foods a default K_F-value of 6.25 overestimates protein content (7). Yeoh & Wee (8) determined K_F for 90 plant species from first principles. Leaf protein content was determined by amino acid analysis (next section). Then S_N was determined via the Kjeldahl method. From Eq. 5.2, we see that $K_F = cP/S_N$. Three distinct K_F parameters were identified: (i) K_A – ratio of protein to amino acid-N excluding amide-N from glutamine and asparagine residues, (ii) K_A' – ratio of protein to amino acid-N and ammonia, or (iii) Kp – Kjeldahl factor; this is protein content (from amino acid analysis) divided by S_N including contributions from NPN. As a matter of interest, the value for K_A, K_A' or Kp was 6.16 ± 0.05, 5.72 ± 0.12 or 4.43 ± 0.4 (g-protein per g-N), respectively.

Plant leaves contained 0.9–12% free amino acid and ≤30% NPN. Ezeagu et al. (9) reported K_F for 13 tropical seeds with a mean protein content of 19.83 ± 6.43% for

10-leguminoseae. They found $K_A = 7.13 \pm 0.23$, $K_A' = 5.94 \pm 0.34$, and $K_p = 4.97 \pm 1.07$. Clearly the default K_p value is not 6.25 for legumes. Multiplying the average value for S_N (4.14%) by K_p gave accurate estimates for cP (20.5%).

Mushrooms and other fungi have high levels of NPN, mostly ammonia, urea, free amino acids, and chitin. Mattila et al. (10) found that K_p was 4.7 ± 0.21 for several mushroom species. Protein levels reported for brown or white *Agaricus bisporus* (27% dry weight) were comparable to values found by Weaver et al. (11), but significantly lower than the value of 7% DW reported by others (12).

Kjeldahl analysis remains one of the most reliable methods for protein quantitation. Further research is needed to address the relation between Kjeldahl and other methods of food protein analysis (13), accuracy issues for K_p (7–10), rapid (colorimetric) methods for ammonia determination (14), and collaborative testing for novel foods (15,16).

B. DUMAS METHOD — COMBUSTION NITROGEN ANALYZERS

The sample is heated in a combustion nitrogen analyzer (CNA) oven at 950–1000°C within a high (99+%) oxygen atmosphere. Most of the gases produced by combustion (carbon dioxide, sulfur dioxide, and water vapor) are removed using adsorbents. The remaining nitrogen oxide is reduced to elemental nitrogen and measured by a thermal conductivity detector. Instrument output (S_N) is converted to cP after multiplying by K_F (Eq. 5.2). Table 5.3 shows some examples of CNA applications for food analysis. The Dumas method is approved by the CGC (Canadian Grain Commission), AOAC (Association of Official Analytical Chemist), AOCS (American Oil Chemists' Society), ASBC (American Society of Brewing Chemists), AFI (American Feed Industry), BRF-International (Brewing Research Foundation-International), IOB (Institute of Brewing), and EBC (European Brewing Convention).

TABLE 5.3
Analysis of Food Proteins Using the Dumas or Combustion Method

Sample	Reference
Animal feeds	Sweeney (17)
Brewing grains	Buckee (18), Johnson & Johansson (19)
Cereal grains	Bicsak (20), Williams, Sobering & Antoniszyn (21)
Dairy products	Wiles, Gray & Kissling (22), Simonne et al. (23)
Fruit	Huang et al. (24)
Infant food	Bellemonte, Costantini & Giammorioli (25)
Meat products	King-Brink & Sebranek (26)
Oilseeds	Duan & DeClercq (27), Berner & Brown (28)
Potatoes	Young, Mackerron & Davies (29)

Source: Adapted from Ref. 1.

Williams (21) discussed sources of error during combustion analysis. Equipment error is possible from infrequent or sporadic instrument use, poor maintenance, and instrument malfunction. Common sources of sampling error include incorrect weighing and the presence of trapped air (nitrogen). EDTA (ethylenediaminetetraacetic acid) used for calibration should be highly pure and low in moisture.

C. QUANTITATIVE AMINO ACID ANALYSIS

Amino acid concentration (C_T; mole per g) is routinely determined during the nutritional evaluation of many foodstuffs. Multiplying C_T by the formula weight for each amino acid (F_i, g per-mole) gives the weight of that amino acid (AA_m) per gram of sample (Eq. 5.3a). Protein content is the sum of all amino acids within the sample (Eq. 5.3b).

$$AA_m = C_T * F_i \qquad (5.3a)$$

$$cP = \Sigma \, (AA_m) \qquad (5.3b)$$

Results from quantitative amino acid analysis (QAA) are normally corrected for proline and tryptophan. Such corrections are necessary because acid hydrolysis of proteins destroys tryptophan, and many colorimetric reagents for detection of amino acids fail to react with proline (1). Nowadays, QAA is used mainly to assess values for K_F, which are needed for both the Kjeldahl and Dumas protein assays (7–10). Examples of QAA include the determination of proteins in peanuts (30), vegetables from Japan (31), meat, seafoods, baked goods, and fruits (32).

D. NEAR INFRARED ANALYSIS

Protein determination by near infrared (NI) analysis began in the 1970s (33,34). Protein, moisture, fat, starch, and fiber levels can be determined simultaneously. Other advantages of NI analysis include high sensitivity, high sample throughput, and high precision. NI analysis is non-destructive and the instrumentation is rugged and well suited for on-site operation. The AACC has approved NI analysis for cereals and grains including barley, oats, rye, triticale, wheat of all classes, and soybean (35). More recent developments have led to NI analysis for on-line or real time monitoring. Several monographs (36,37) and reviews (38–40) provide further details about NI analysis. There are very few reviews dealing solely with NI analysis of food proteins.

During near infrared reflectance (NIR) measurements, radiation reflected from the sample is sensed using a lead sulfide detector and an integrating optical sphere (41). Log (1/R) is linearly related to protein concentration. In the NI transmission (NIT) mode, a double beam of radiation passes through the sample and reference cells. Protein concentration is directly proportional to log (1/transmittance). Commercial NIR instruments include the Grain Quality Analyzer (Neotech Corporation, Silver

Spring, MD), Grain Analyzer Computer (Dickey-John, Auburn, IL), Infratec 1225 (Tectator AB, Sweden), Inframatic 8100 & 8144 (PerCon Instruments), InfraAlyzer 300 & 400 (Technicon) and the NIRSystems Model 6500 instrument (NIRSystems,[1] Silver Spring, MD). The following instruments were used in an NIT mode: MilkoScan 104, 203B, 605, etc. (Foss Electric), Multipec M (Shields Instruments, UK) and the NIRSystems Model 6500 instrument (NIRSystems, Silver Spring, MD). Recent developments in NI instrumentation have been reviewed (36,37). Collaborative trials were reported for NI analysis for milk (42), barley (43), wheat (44–46), meat (47), and kernel wheat (48).

1. Near Infrared Analysis of Grain Proteins

A recent example of grain analysis by NIR is described by Corbellini & Canevara (49) using 100 bread wheat (*T. aestivum* L.) samples from Italy. Analysis was performed for ground wheat as well as kernel wheat. Over the range of 7.8–14.7% protein ($S_N \times 5.7$) content, the correlation coefficient (r) for NIR and Kjeldahl results was > 0.98. Other protein-related quality attributes are measurable by NIR (Table 5.4). It is possible to correlate NI instrument output with grain moisture content, kernel hardness, sedimentation value, water absorption, and loaf volume. In addition to multilinear regression analysis, sophisticated multicomponent analysis, such as principal component analysis or partial least squares calibration, enable grain quality assessment by NIR (50, 51).

2. Near Infrared Analysis of Meat and Milk Proteins

NIR results for ground lamb and beef were affected by sample homogeneity, particle size, and temperature (62). Results from NIR and Kjeldahl analysis showed only moderate correlation (r = 0.67–0.8). Higher correlation of $r \approx 0.99$ was reported in more recent studies for protein determination in fresh chicken (63), mutton (64), trout (65), and meat patties (66). The precision of NIR results appears to match or surpass those from Kjeldahl results. Furthermore, the NIR format leads to greater reproducibility as compared to NIT. However, the coefficient of variation for meat protein analysis (2.71–3.43%) was considered too high for NIR to be adopted for regulatory purposes (67). Sources of error for NIR and NIT measurements (21) include instrumental error, temperature variations, changes in relative humidity, and stray light. Operator error is often the result of inadequate training. NIR was applied for protein determination in milk powder and semi-solid dairy products including whey protein (68), nonfat dried milk (69), cheese (70,71), and fermented products (72,73).

III. FRACTIONATION ANALYSIS OF FOOD PROTEINS

A. ELECTROPHORESIS AND CHROMATOGRAPHY

Electrophoresis and chromatography are the foremost methods for food protein fractionation (74,75). High resolution polyacrylamide gel electrophoresis (PAGE) is available in a range of formats. Chromatography also offers a variety of separation chemistries (Table 5.5). The principles of electrophoresis and chromatography are described in References (76–78). During PAGE analysis, protein molecules migrate under the influence of an applied potential difference. The rate of migration is

TABLE 5.4

Characterization of Grain Quality Using Near Infrared Analysis[a]

Sample-Type of Analysis	References
Bread making quality — water absorption and protein content	Delwiche & Weaver (52), Delwiche et al. (53), Millar & Bar L'Helgouac'h (54)
Essential amino acids	Fontaine et al. (55)
Grain grading, hard red winter vs. spring wheat — protein content	Delwiche et al. (56)
Heat damage (wheat kernels)	Wang et al. (57)
Insect infestation — insect protein, chitin & moisture	Ridgway & Chambers (58)
Kernel hardness — γ-zein content	Eyherabide et al. (59)*
Vitreous vs. non-vitreous wheat	Dowell (60), Wang et al. (61)

[a] NIR unless otherwise indicated with (*) for NIT analysis.

TABLE 5.5

Methods for Food Protein Fractionation*

Electrophoresis	Chromatography
Gel electrophoresis	*HPLC or FPLC*
Native PAGE, acid-PAGE, urea-PAGE, SDS-PAGE, Isoelectric focusing (IEF)-PAGE, two-dimensional PAGE	Size exclusion, ion exchange, hydrophobic interaction, reverse phase, hydroxyapatite, affinity
Capillary electrophoresis	
CAE, CGE, CIEF, HICE	

* See accompanying text for explanation of abbreviations.

[1] A number of corporate takeovers have affected producers of NI instruments. Neotec Corporation (1966–1981) introduced the first commercial NI instrument in 1972 and microprocessor-controlled NI instruments in 1974. The company was bought by Pacific Scientific Corporation in 1981. In 1989, Perstorp Analytical (Sweden) purchased the NIR operations from Pacific Scientific and renamed it NIRSystems. Ownership passed to Foss-Electric (Denmark) in 1997. Foss-NIRSystems is based in Silver Spring, MD, the home of Neotech Corporation. Extract from http://www.foss.dk/c/p/default.asp?width = 1024.

dependent on protein charge-to-mass ratio. Protein bands separated by PAGE are visualized by staining (for example, with Coomassie blue dye or silver stain), destaining, and scanning with a densitometer. Native-PAGE is widely applied for identifying genetic polymorphism in milk and cereal proteins. A single amino acid difference for beta-lactoglobulin A and B leads to distinct protein bands during native-PAGE. Acid (acid-PAGE) or urea (urea-PAGE) can be added to gels in order to improve protein solubility. Acid-PAGE allows the identification or differentiation of cereal cultivars based on the analysis of their storage proteins (79,80). Fractionation of milk caseins frequently involves urea-PAGE (81,82).

Addition of ampholyte to native or urea-PAGE formats yields isoelectric focusing-PAGE (IEF-PAGE), which fractionates proteins on the basis of their isoelectric point (pI). IEF-PAGE requires high voltages and consequently the gels are thinner than those used for conventional PAGE to allow increased heat dissipation. Another PAGE format of interest involves sodium dodecylsulfate (SDS). Addition of this detergent encourages protein subunit dissociation, denaturation, and transformation into negatively charged polymers. During SDS-PAGE, proteins are separated on the basis of their molecular mass. Examples of food proteins analyzed by PAGE are provided in References 74, 75, and 83.

Proteins can be transferred from polyacrylamide gels by electroblotting and fixed to synthetic (nitrocellulose, polypropylene, or polyvinylinefluoride) membranes before staining. The membrane-bound protein can also be analyzed using highly specific antibodies as probes. Immunoblotting is an important screening method for food allergens (84,85). Finally, protein zones from PAGE can be excised for analysis using techniques such as mass spectrometry (see below).

Capillary electrophoresis is a relatively recent development in food protein analysis (86,87). Proteins are separated within a small diameter capillary. Various detectors are compatible with CE including fluorescence, refractive index, UV absorbance, and mass spectrometers. A range of protein separation methods is possible, such as capillary affinity electrophoresis (CAE), capillary gel electrophoresis (CGE), capillary isoelectric focusing (CIEF), and hydrophobic interaction capillary electrophoresis (HICE). The principles of CE are described in several reviews (77,86,88,89). Applications to dairy and cereal products are discussed in References 90 and 91, respectively.

B. MASS SPECTROMETRY OF FOOD PROTEINS

The principles of mass spectrometry (MS) are well known. Only a brief outline is provided here. A food sample is bombarded with high energy electrons in an evacuated chamber. Molecular ions produced by bombardment

TABLE 5.6
Mass Spectrometric Analysis of Food Proteins

Technique	Comments
FAB	• Protein + glycerol are bombarded by Xe or Cs ions at 8–40 keV. Sample is introduced into MS port.
ESI	• Protein solution disintegrates from the tip of capillary polarized at ±3000–5000 V. Electrospray is fed to MS port.
MALDI	• Protein + large excess of crystalline matrix is irradiated by a laser. The matrix absorbs energy, vaporizes, and ionizes protein.

Application areas*	
Aggregation	Molecular mass analysis
Cheese ripening and maturation	Polymorphism
Denaturation	Post-translational modification
Glycation	Process effects
Heat effects	Proteolysis
Irradiation	Purity
Meat postmortem	Sequence determination
	Sulfur/disulfide exchange

* Compiled from References 92–98.

are accelerated via an electric field, past a set of electromagnets, towards a detector. The detection time for molecular ions is proportional to their mass-to-charge ratio $(m_i/z_i)^{1/2}$. Techniques for generating protein ions for MS analysis were only developed in the mid-1980s. The best known of these desorption techniques are fast atom bombardment (FAB), matrix assisted laser desorption ionization (MALDI), and electrospray ionization (ESI). The theory, principles, and instrumentation for protein MS analysis have been reviewed (92). Table 5.6 summarizes each desorption method and types of information available from MS analysis of proteins. Process-induced changes in food proteins appear to be readily detectable. For example, ESI-MS analysis of beta-lactoglobulin from 109 cows showed it to be covalently modified by a 324 Da species, probably lactose (93). The mechanism of heme protein denaturation was also examined by ESI-MS (94). Proteolysis of caseins during cheese manufacture and ripening was readily followed by MALDI-MS (95). Virtually all the major food protein groups have been analyzed by MS including milk, egg, meat and cereal proteins as reviewed in References 96–98.

IV. PROTEOMICS

The term proteome was introduced by Wilkins et al. in 1995 to describe the "entire PROTEin complement expressed by a genOME, or by a cell or tissue type" (99). Proteomics is the wholesale identification of proteins comprising a proteome using large-scale, high-throughput technologies, primarily 2D gel electrophoresis and MS. In the so-called post-genomics era, interest has extended to the subsidiary topics of transcriptomics, proteomics, and metabolomics (Figure 5.2). The transcriptome and metabolome refer to the total profile of RNA and metabolites within a cell, respectively (100). Protein functions other than metabolism – the entirety of enzymatic reactions within a cell – are also of interest. Proteomics is considered a protein-based method for gene expression analysis.

The rationale for proteomics can be seen from the central dogma of molecular biology, postulated by Francis Crick in 1958. The direction of information flow within cells is DNA → RNA → protein → function (101). Transcription of DNA leads to time-dependent expression of cell function. However, the relation between genome and cell function is complicated due to the presence of regulatory mechanism, redundancy, or amplification processes during information transfer. The study of proteomics is clearly essential because (i) proteins are the machinery that perform day-to-day functions within a cell, (ii) there is a low correlation between the number of genes and the number of proteins within a cell, (iii) differential gene expression occurs at different times and in different parts of the organism, and (iv) single genes can encode for more than one protein due to post-translational modification.

There are five essential steps for proteomics research: (i) sample preparation – cells, tissues, or organelles are homogenized to produce a protein extract. Care is needed to avoid protein modification by endogenous proteases, chemical modification or denaturation; (ii) protein separation by 2D electrophoresis. Typically, IEF (1D) and SDS-PAGE (2D) analysis is followed by protein visualization and densitometry leading to a 2D digital representation of the separated proteins. With the new generation of densitometers it is possible to perform a comparative image analysis of hundreds of protein spots resolved by 2D electrophoresis. The key is to discover differences between specific protein (spots) for the control and treatment sample; (iii) protein identification – protein spots of interest

are excised from the 2D gel, digested with trypsin, then subjected to HPLC or CE analysis; (iv) peptide sequencing – the products of proteolysis are analyzed by MALDI-MS or ESI-MS as described in Section IIIB. Sophisticated MS instrumentation can now provide protein molecular mass as well as sequence information, (v) Bioinformatics – the application of computerized informatics tools to biological data. Peptide sequences are compared with the DNA- sequence database in order to identify the protein of interest. Digitized 2D gel patterns can also be compared directly with computerized library data for protein identification (99).

The impact of proteomics on food science and technology could be considerable (100,102). It may be possible to correlate changes in protein expression or post-translational modification with specific treatments, be they developmental, environmental, nutritional, or hormonal. Potential areas for proteomics research in food related areas include the study of protein structure function relations, functional ingredients, food-borne pathogens (103), allergens (104), food adulteration, novel ingredients, starter cultures (105), muscle or meat science (106), and the identification of protein markers for grain quality (107).

V. CONCLUSION

Aspects of food protein analysis are reviewed in this chapter. Food proteins were defined as those proteins which are of interest in food science. Food protein analysis is a vast topic but still emerging as an integrated discipline. Novel techniques for protein quantitation and characterization are being developed. The food system and food science expertise areas (Tables 5.1–5.2) were suggested as schema for defining the perspective of this rapidly evolving subject. The first part of the chapter emphasized "approved" methods for protein quantitation which are used within the food industry (Figure 5.1). Further research on Kjeldahl and Dumas analysis is needed to establish national and international protocols for a wide range of foods. Further developments in NIR analysis are needed in the areas of instrumentation and pattern recognition software. On-line NIR analysis for products on conveyor belts will probably increase (108). An example of a commercially available NIR on-line instrument is the MM170 analyzer from NDC Infrared Engineering (109). The trend towards diode array NIR instrumentation will lead to more rapid acquisition of spectra, increased portability, and more affordable instrumentation. Section III dealt with selected methods for protein fractionation, and the chapter culminated with a discussion of proteomics (Section IV). Though less than 10-years old, high-throughput protein analysis within a proteomics framework is now firmly on the food science agenda.

| • DNA→ | • mRNA→ | • Proteins→ | • Function |

(A)

Genome		Proteome	
	Transcriptoms		Metabolome
Genomics		Proteomics	Metabolomics
	Transcriptomics		

(B)

FIGURE 5.2 Information flow in cells is from DNA (genome) to mRNA (transcriptome) to proteins (proteome) to a variety of protein functions (phenome, physiome, and metabolome).

REFERENCES

1. R. Owusu-Apenten. Food Protein Analysis: Quantitative Effects on Processing. New York: Marcel Dekker, 2002, 485 pp.
2. PR Shewry, GL Lookhart (editors). Wheat Gluten Protein analysis. St. Paul, MN: American Association of Cereal Chemists, 2003, 198 pp.
3. RY Yada, RL Jackman, JL Smith, AG Marangoni. Analysis: Quantitation and physical characterization. In Food Proteins: Properties and Characterization. S Nakai, H W Modler (editors). New York: VCH Publishers Inc, 1996, pp. 333–403.
4. R Grappin, B Ribadeau-Dumas. Analytical methods for milk proteins. In Advanced Dairy Chemistry 1 — Protein. Fox, P. F. (Editor). New York: Elsevier Applied Science, 1992, pp. 1–62.
5. WY Aalbersberg, RJ Hamer, P Jsperse, HHJ de Jong, CG de Kruif, P Walstra, FA de Wol (editors). Industrial Proteins in Perspective (Progress in Biotechnology vol. 23). New York: Elsevier, 2003.
6. AOAC. Collaborative study guidelines. J Assoc Off Anal Chem 78(5):143A–157A, 1995; Guidelines for collaborative study procedure to validate characteristics of a method of analysis. J Assoc Off Anal Chem 72:694–704, 1989.
7. J Mosse. Nitrogen to protein conversion factor for ten cereals and size legumes or oilseeds. A reappraisal of its definition and determination. Variation according to species and to seed protein content. J Agric Food Chem 38:18–24, 1990.
8. H-C Yeoh, W-C Wee. Leaf protein contents and nitrogen-to-protein conversion factors for 90 plant species. Food Chem 49:245–250, 1994.
9. IE Ezeagu, JK Petzke, CC Metges, AO Akinsoyinu, AD Ologhobo. Seed protein contents and nitrogen-to-protein conversion factors for some uncultivated tropical plant seeds. Food Chem 78(1):105–109, 2002.
10. P Matila, P Salo-Vaanen, K Konko, H Aro., T Jalava. Basic composition and amino acid contents of mushrooms cultivated in Finland. J Agric Food Chem 50(22):6419–6422, 2002.
11. JC Weaver, M. Kroger, LR Kneebone. Comparative protein studies (Kjeldahl, dye binding and amino acid analysis) of nine strains of Agaricus bisporus (Lange) Imback mushrooms. J Food Sci 42:364–366, 1977.
12. A Braaksma, DJ Schaap. Protein analysis of the common mushroom Agaricus bisporus. Postharvest Biol Technol 7(1/2):119–127, 1996.
13. M Soral-Śmietana, R Amarowicz, A Świgoń, L Sijtsma. Comparison of solubility of pea protein hydrolysate by three analytical methods. Int J Food Science Nutri 50:407–411, 1999.
14. T Yasuhara, K Nokihara. High-throughput analysis of total nitrogen content that replaces the classic Kjeldahl method. J Agric Food Chem 49:4581–4583, 2001.
15. NJ Thiex, H Manson. Determination of crude protein in animal feed, forage, grain, and oilseeds by using block digestion with a copper catalyst and steam distillation into boric acid: Collaborative study. J AOAC Int 85(2):309–317, 2002.
16. JM Lynch, DM Barbano, JR Fleming. Determination of the total nitrogen content of hard, semi-hard and processed cheese by the Kjeldahl method: Collaborative study. J AOAC Int 85(2):445–455, 2002.
17. RA Sweeney. Generic combustion method for determination of crude protein in feeds: Collaborative study. J Assoc Off Anal Chem 72:770–774, 1989.
18. GK Buckee. Review of methods for the measurement of total nitrogen. Ferment 8:357–361, 1995.
19. BA Johnson, CG Johansson. Determination of total soluble nitrogen content of malt and beer by the Dumas combustion method: Collaborative trial. J Inst Brew 105:360–364, 1999.
20. RC Bicsak. Comparison of Kjeldahl method for determination of crude protein in cereal grains and oils seeds with generic combustion method: collaborative study. J Assoc Off Anal Chem 76:780–786, 1993.
21. P Williams, D Sobering, J Antoniszyn. Protein testing methods at the Canadian Grain Commission. Proceedings of the Wheat Protein Symposium. Saskatoon, Sask. March 9 and 10, 1998 [conference paper online]. World Wide Web citation. Available from:http://www.cgc.ca/Pubs/confpaper/Williams/ProteinOct98/protein1-e.htm.
22. PG Wiles, IK Gray, RC Kissling. Routine analysis of proteins by Kjeldahl and Dumas methods: review and inter-laboratory study using dairy products. J AOAC Int 81:620–632, 1998.
23. EH Simonne, AH Simonne, RR Eitenmeiller, HA Mills, CP Cresman III. Could the Dumas method replace the Kjeldahl digestion for nitrogen and crude protein determinations in foods? J Sci Food Agric 73:39–45, 1997.
24. CJ Huang, R. McDonald, RS Lyon, E Elkins. Comparison of Kjeldahl method for crude protein determination in fruit and vegetable products with combustion method. IFT Annual Meeting 1995, 198 pp.
25. G Bellemonte, A Costantini, S Giammorioli. Comparison of modified automatic Dumas method and the traditional Kjeldahl method for nitrogen determination in infant food. J Assoc Off Anal Chem 70:227–229, 1987.
26. M King-Brink, JG Sebranek. Combustion method for determination of crude protein in meat and meat products: Collaborative study. J Assoc Off Anal Chem 76:787–793, 1993.
27. JK Duan, DR DeClercq. Comparison of combustion and Kjeldahl methods for determination of nitrogen in oilseeds. J Am Oil Chem Soc 71:1069–1072, 1994.
28. DL Berner, J Brown. Protein nitrogen combustion method collaborative study. I. Comparison with Smalley total Kjeldahl nitrogen and combustion results. J Am Oil Chem. Soc 71:1291–1293, 1994.
29. MW Young, DKL Mackerron, HV Davies. Calibration of near infrared reflectance spectroscopy to estimate nitrogen concentration in potato tissues. Potato Res 40:215–220, 1997.
30. JB Misra. Variation in nitrogen-to-protein conversion factor for peanut. Peanut Sci 28(2):48–51, 2001.

31. S Fujihara, A Kasuga, Y Aoyagi. Nitrogen-to-protein conversion factors for common vegetables in Japan. J Food Sci 66(3):412–415, 2001.

32. PP Salo-Vaananen, PE Koivistoinen. Determination of protein in foods: comparison of net protein and crude protein (N × 6.25) values. Food Chem 57(1):27–31, 1996.

33. PC Williams. Application of near infrared reflectance spectroscopy to analysis of cereal grains and oil seeds. Cereal Chem 52(4):561–576, 1975.

34. BS Miller, Y Pomeranz, WO Thompson, TW Nolan, JW Hughes, G Davis, NG Jackson, DW Fulk. Inter-laboratory and intra-laboratory reproducibility of protein determination in hard red winter wheat by Kjeldahl and near infrared procedures. Cereal Food World 23(4):198–200, 1978.

35. AACC. American Association of Cereal Chemists Approved Methods. St. Paul, MN: AACC, 1996. AACC Method 39-01, 19010, 39-11, 39-20, 39-21, 39-35, 39-70A.

36. BG Osborne, T Fearn, PH Hindle. Practical NIR spectroscopy with application in food and beverage analysis. Harlow (UK): Longman Scientific & Technical, 1993, 227 pp.

37. P Williams, K Norris (editors). Near-Infrared Technology in the Agricultural and Food Industries. St. Paul, MN: American Association of Cereal Chemists, 2001, 296 pp.

38. DA Biggs, G Johnsson, LO Sjaunja. Analysis of fat, protein, lactose and total solids by infra-red absorption. Bull Int Dairy Fed 208:21–30, 1987.

39. F Siebert. Infrared-spectroscopy applied to biochemical and biological problems. Methods Enzymol 246: 501–526, 1995.

40. A O'Sullivan, B O'Connor, A Kelly, MJ McGrath. The use of chemical and infrared methods for analysis of milk and dairy products. Int J Dairy Tech 52(4):139–148, 1999.

41. P Rotolo. Near infrared reflectance instrumentation. Cereal Food World 24(3):94–98, 1979.

42. BS Lahner. Evaluation of Aegys MI 600 Fourier transform infrared milk analyzer for analysis of fat, protein, lactose, and solids nonfat: a compilation of eight independent studies. JAOAC 79(6):1388–1399, 1996.

43. M Munar, D Christopher, M Edney, D Habernicht, R Joy, M Joyce, G Laycock, R Seiben, W Swenson, G Casey. Protein and moisture in whole-grain barley by near-infrared spectroscopy. J Am Soc Brew Chem 56(4):189–194, 1998.

44. BS Miller, Y Pomeranz, WO Thompson, TW Nolan, JW Hughes, G Davies, NG Jackson, DW Fulk. Inter-laboratory and intra-laboratory reproducibility of protein determination in hard red winter wheat by Kjeldahl and near infrared procedures. Cereal Foods World 23(4):198–201, 1978.

45. BG Osborne, T Fearn. Collaborative evaluation of universal calibrations for the measurement of protein and moisture in flour by near infrared reflectance. J Food Technol 18(4):453–460, 1983.

46. G Downey, S Byrne. Protein determination of wheat in trade by near infrared reflectance spectroscopy. Calibration and instrument performance over a four year period. Sciences des Aliments 7(2):325–336, 1997.

47. OC Bjarno. Multicomponent analysis of meat products by infrared spectrophotometry: Collaborative study. JAOAC 65(3):696–700, 1982.

48. SR Delwiche, RO Pierce, OK Chung, BW Seabourn. Protein content of wheat by near-infrared spectroscopy of whole grain: Collaborative study. JAOAC 81(3):587–603, 1998.

49. M Corbellini, MG Canevara. Estimate of moisture and protein content in whole grains of bread wheat (T. aestivum L.) by near infrared reflectance spectroscopy. Italian J Food Sci 6(1):95–102, 1994.

50. H Martens, T Naes. Multivariate Calibration. New York, John Wiley & Sons, 1989, 418 pp.

51. MF Devau, D Bertrand, G Martin. Discrimination of bread-baking quality of wheats according to their variety by near-infrared reflectance spectroscopy. Cereal Chem 63(2):151–159, 1986.

52. SR Delwiche, G Weaver. Bread quality of wheat flour by near-infrared spectrophotometry: Feasibility of modeling. J Food Sci 59(2):410–415, 1994.

53. SR Delwiche, RA Graybosch, CJ Peterson. Predicting protein composition, biochemical properties, and dough-handling properties of hard red winter wheat flour by near-infrared reflectance. Cereal Chem 75(4): 412–416, 1998.

54. S Millar, C Bar-L'Helgouac'h. Rapid assessment of wheat and flour quality using near infrared (NIR) spectroscopy. New-Food 5(3):70–75, 2002.

55. J Fontaine, B Schirmer, J Horr. Near-infrared reflectance spectroscopy (NIRS) enables the fast and accurate prediction of essential amino acid contents. II. Results for wheat, barley, corn, triticale, wheat bran/middlings, rice bran, and sorghum. J Agric Food Chem 50(14):3902–3911, 2002.

56. SR Delwiche, Y-R Chen, WR Hruschka. Differentiation of hard red wheat by near-infrared analysis of bulk samples. Cereal Chem 72(3):243–247, 1995.

57. D Wang, FE Dowell, DS Chung. Assessment of heat-damaged wheat kernels using near-infrared spectroscopy. Cereal Chem 78(5):625–628, 2001.

58. C Ridgway, J Chambers. Detection of external and internal insect infestation in wheat by near-infrared reflectance spectroscopy. J Sci Food Agric 71(2):251–264, 1996.

59. GH Eyherabide, JL Robutti, FS Borras. Effect of near-infrared transmission-based selection on maize hardness and the composition of zeins. Cereal Chem 73(6):775–778, 1996.

60. FE Dowell. Differentiating vitreous and nonvitreous durum wheat kernels by using near-infrared spectroscopy. Cereal Chem 77(2):155–158, 2000.

61. D Wang, FE Dowell, R Dempster. Determining vitreous subclasses of hard red spring wheat using visible/near-infrared spectroscopy. Cereal Chem 79(3):418–422, 2002.

62. WG Kruggel, RA Field, ML Riley, HD Radloff, KM Horton. Near-infrared reflectance determination of fat,

protein, and moisture in fresh meat. J Assoc Off Anal Chem 64(3):692–696, 1981.

63. EV Valdes, JD Summers. Determination of crude protein and fat in carcass and breast muscle samples of poultry by near infrared reflectance spectroscopy. Poultry Sci 65(3):485–490, 1986.

64. DT Bartholomew, CI Osuala. Use of the InfraAlyzer in proximate analysis of mutton. J Food Sci 53(2):379–382, 1988.

65. EV Valdes, JL Atkinson, JW Hilton, S Leeson. Near infrared reflectance analysis of fat, protein and gross energy of chicken and rainbow trout carcasses. Can J Animal Sci 69(4):1087–1090, 1989.

66. EK Oh, D Grossklaus. Measurement of the components in meat patties by near infrared reflectance spectroscopy. Meat Science 41(2):157–162, 1995.

67. E Lanza. Determination of moisture, protein, fat, and calories in raw pork and beef by near infrared spectroscopy. J Food Sci 48(2):471–474, 1983.

68. RJ Baer, JF Frank, M Loewenstein, GS Birth. Compositional analysis of whey powders using near infrared diffuse reflectance spectroscopy. J Food Sci 48(3):959–961, 989, 1983.

69. S Barabassy. The application of near infrared spectroscopy (NIR) technique for non-destructive investigation of mixed milk powder products. Mljekarstvo 51(3): 263–272, 2001.

70. JF Frank, GS Birth. Application of near infrared reflectance spectroscopy to cheese analysis. J Dairy Sci 65(7):1110–1116, 1982.

71. JL Rodriguez-Otero, M Hermida, A Cepeda. Determination of fat, protein, and total solids in cheese by near-infrared reflectance spectroscopy. J AOAC International 78(3):802–806, 1995.

72. JL Rodriguez-Otero, M Hermida. Analysis of fermented milk products by near-infrared reflectance spectroscopy. JAOAC-International 79(3):817–821, 1999.

73. JL Rodriguez-Otero, JA Centeno, M Hermida. Application of near infrared transflectance spectroscopy to the analysis of fermented milks. Milchwissenschaft 52(4):96–200, 1997

74. E D Strange, EL Malin, DL van Hekken, JJ Basch. Chromatographic and electrophoretic methods for analysis of milk proteins. J Chromatography 624:81–102, 1992.

75. JA Bietz, DG Simpson. Electrophoresis and chromatography of wheat proteins: available methods, and procedures for statistical evaluation of the data. J Chromatography 624:53–80, 1992.

76. BD Hames, D Rickwood. Gel electrophoresis of proteins: a practical approach. London: IRL Press, Ltd. 1981.

77. H Sorensen, S Sorensen, C Bjergegaard, S Michaelsen. 1998. Chromatography and capillary electrophoresis in food analysis. London: Royal Society of Chemistry, 1998.

78. R Kellner, F Lottspeich, HE Meyer (Editors). Microcharacterization of Proteins. New York: VCH, 1994.

79. RJ Cooke, EM Cliff. Barley cultivar characterisation by electrophoresis. I. A method for acid polyacrylamide gel electrophoresis of hordein proteins. J Nat Inst Agric Botany 16(2):189–195, 1983.

80. RL Clements. A study of gliadins of soft wheats from the eastern United States using a modified polyacrylamide gel electrophoresis procedure. Cereal Chem 64(6):442–448, 1987.

81. DL van Hekken, MP Thompson. Application of PhastSystem® to the resolution of bovine milk proteins on urea-polyacrylamide gel electrophoresis. J Dairy Sci 75(5):1204–1210, 1992.

82. T Considine, A Healy, AL Kelly, PLH McSweeney. Proteolytic specificity of elastase on bovine alpha$_{s1}$-casein. Food Chemistry 69(1):19–26, 2000.

83. CW Wrigley, JC Autran, W Bushuk. Identification of cereal varieties by gel electrophoresis of the grain proteins. Adv Cereal Sci Technol 5:211–259, 1982.

84. J Matuz, R Poka, I Bodizar, E Szerdahelyi, G Hajos. Structure and potential allergenic character of cereal proteins. II. Potential allergens in cereal samples. Cereal Res Comm 28(4):433–442, 2000.

85. SS Tueber, SK Sathe, WR Peterson, KH Roux. Characterization of the soluble allergenic proteins of cashew nut (Anacardium occidentale L.). J Agric Food Chem 50(22):6543–6549, 2002.

86. CA Monnig, RT Kennedy. Capillary electrophoresis. Anal Chem 66(12):280R–314R, 1994.

87. D Yiyang. Capillary electrophoresis in food analysis. Trends Food Sci Technol Trends 10(3):87–93, 1999.

88. A Guttman. Capillary sodium dodecyl sulfate-gel electrophoresis of proteins. Electrophoresis 17(8):1333–1341, 1996.

89. T Wehr, R Rodriguez-Diaz, Cheng-Ming-Liu. Capillary electrophoresis of proteins. Adv Chromatography 37: 227–361, 1997.

90. I Recio, L Amigo, R Lopez-Fandino. Assessment of the quality of dairy products by capillary electrophoresis of milk proteins. J Chrom B 697(1/2):231–242, 1997.

91. SR Bean, JA Bietz, GL Lookhart. High-performance capillary electrophoresis of cereal proteins. J Chromatography A 814(1/2):25–41, 1998.

92. AL Burlingame, RK Boyd, SJ Gaskell. Mass spectrometry. Anal Chem 68(12):599R–651R, 1996.

93. R Burr, CH Moore, JP Hill. Evidence of multiple glycosylation of bovine beta-lactoglobulin by electrospray ionisation mass spectrometry. Milchwissenschaft 51(9):488–492, 1996.

94. BJ Adams, SJ Lock. Electrospray mass spectrometric study of haem changes during peroxidase denaturation. Food Chem 58(1/2):173–175, 1997.

95. AM Gouldsworthy, J Leaver, JM Banks. Application of a mass spectrometry sequencing technique for identifying peptides present in Cheddar cheese. Int Dairy J 6(8/9):781–790, 1996.

96. R Beavis. New methods in the mass spectrometry of proteins. Trends Food Sci 2(10):251–253, 1991.

97. J Leonil, V Gagnaire, D Molle, S Pezennec, S Bouhallab. Application of chromatography and mass spectrometry to the characterization of food proteins and derived peptides. J Chromatography A 881:1–21, 2000.

98. HF Alomirah, I Alli, Y Konishi. Applications of mass spectrometry to food proteins and peptides. J Chromatography A 893:1–21, 2000.

99. MR Wilkins, JC Sanchez, AA Gooley, RD Appel, I Humphery-Smith, DF Hochstrasser, KL Williams. Progress with proteome projects: Why all proteins expressed by a genome should be identified and how to do it. Biotech Genetic Eng Rev 13:19–50, 1995.

100. MJ van der Werf, FHJ Schuren, S Bijlsma, AC Tas, B Van Ommen. Nutrigenomics: Application of genomics technologies in nutritional science and food technology. J Food Sci 66(6):772–780, 2001.

101. F Crick. Central dogma of molecular biology. Nature 227:56–1563, 1970.

102. F Kvasnička. Proteomics: general strategies and applications to nutritionally relevant proteins. J Chromatography B 787:77–89, 2003.

103. B Weimer, D Mills. Enhancing foods with functional genomics. Food Technol 56(5):184, 186–189, 2002.

104. M Tichá, V Pacáková, K Štulík. Proteomics of allergens. J Chromatography B 771:343–353, 2002.

105. M-C Champomier-Vergés, E Maguin, M-Y Mistou, P Anglade, J-F Chich. Lactic acid bacteria and proteomics: current knowledge and perspectives. J Chromatography B 771:329–342, 2002.

106. R Lametsch, E Bendixen. Proteome analysis applied to meat science: Characterizing post mortem changes in porcine muscle. J Agric Food Chem 49:4531–4537, 2001.

107. GB Cornish, DJ Skylas, S Iriamornpun, F Bekes, OR Larroque, CW Wrigley, M Wootton. Grain proteins as markers of genetic traits in wheat. Aust J Agric Res 52(11/12):1161–1171, 2001.

108. T Isaksson, BN Nilsen, G Togersen, RP Hammond, Ki Hildrum. On-line, proximate analysis of ground beef directly at a meat grinder outlet. Meat Science 43(3–4):245–253, 1996.

109. NDC Infrared Engineering North America, http://www.ndc.com/home.html.

6 Protein: Denaturation

Srinivasan Damodaran
Department of Food Science, University of Wisconsin–Madison

CONTENTS

I. INTRODUCTION

Proteins perform various functions in processed foods. The functional properties of proteins, such as foaming, emulsifying, gelling, thickening, texturizing, dough forming, whipping, curdling, water binding, flavor binding, and fat binding properties, are important for imparting desirable sensory attributes in a variety of food products. These various functional properties of proteins emanate from two molecular attributes of proteins, namely hydrodynamic properties and physicochemical attributes of the protein's surface (1). While the hydrodynamic properties relate to the size and shape of the molecule, the properties of a protein's surface relate to its topology and to the pattern of distribution of polar and non-polar patches. Although these molecular attributes of proteins in their native state can be determined fairly precisely from their crystallographic structure, it has been difficult to predict their functionality in a complex food milieu. This is principally due to denaturation of proteins that inevitably occurs during food processing, which might alter both their hydrodynamic attributes (shape and size) and surface characteristics. In the denatured state, the intensity of intermolecular interactions between proteins, or between

proteins and other constituents in the food milieu, would dramatically alter the proteins' functionality.

The extent of denaturation of proteins in a food milieu depends on the susceptibility of intra-molecular interactions that hold the compact native protein structure to temperature, pressure (shear), pH, ionic strength, types of ions, and specific and non-specific interactions with other food components such as sugars, polysaccharides, lipids, and other additives. It should be recognized, however, that from a food application standpoint, protein denaturation during processing is not always undesirable. In fact, in some cases it is highly desirable. For instance, partial denaturation of proteins at the air-water and oil-water interfaces improve their foaming and emulsifying properties (2, 3), whereas excessive thermal denaturation of soy proteins diminishes their foaming and emulsifying properties (4). In protein beverages, where high solubility and dispersibility of proteins is a necessity, even partial denaturation of protein during processing may cause flocculation and precipitation during storage and thus may adversely affect the sensory attributes of the product. Thus, to develop appropriate processing strategies, a basic understanding of the environmental and other factors that affect structural stability of proteins in food systems is imperative.

II. PROTEIN STRUCTURE

Protein structure is a highly complex architecture. A polypeptide chain containing hundreds of main chain covalent bonds can theoretically assume numerous configurations in three-dimensional space. Yet, under physiological pH, temperature, and ionic strength conditions, proteins always assume a particular native folded conformation. This native conformation represents a thermodynamic equilibrium state in which the free energy of the molecule is usually at the lowest possible level and it is achieved through optimization of various intra-molecular interactions within the polypeptide chain as well as interactions of its constituent amino acid residues with the surrounding aqueous medium.

At the molecular level, protein structure can be defined in terms of four levels. The primary structure denotes the linear sequence of amino acid residues in the polypeptide chain. Intuitively, one would expect this linear structure to possess chain flexibility similar to that of random coil polymers. However, this is not the case. The amide linkage between amino acid residues, which constitute one-third of the covalent bonds in the backbone of a polypeptide chain, possesses a partial double bond character and this substantially restricts the flexibility of the chain. Furthermore, depending on the amino acid sequence, the bulky side chains of amino acid residues impose additional restrictions on local flexibility of polypeptide chains. As a result of such sequence-imposed local restrictions on flexibility, polypeptides do not behave like other natural polymers, such as polysaccharides or nucleic acids, and synthetic polymers in solution. These restrictions on local flexibility play the critical role of guiding the protein toward attaining a particular folded native conformation. Thus, the primary structure of a protein is believed to possess the coded information for its final three-dimensional structure.

The secondary structure refers to regular conformations in polypeptide chains. This regularity of conformation occurs when the dihedral angles of each amino acid residue in a segment of the polypeptide assume the same set of values. The α-helix and β-sheet are the two regular structures found in polypeptides. Segments of polypeptide chain where consecutive amino acid residues assume different sets of dihedral angles tend to be in a disordered state and those regions are termed a periodic structures. The secondary structures in proteins arise as a result of short-range non-covalent interactions that tend to minimize local free energy of the protein chain.

The tertiary structure refers to the overall three dimensional arrangement of the folded polypeptide chain. For most proteins, the folded tertiary structure is roughly spherical in shape with irregular topography. The crevices on the surface, which are inaccessible to solvent water, are non-polar in nature. In food proteins, these crevices act as binding sites for hydrophobic ligands, such as fat and flavor molecules. The tertiary structure of a protein is the net result of optimization of various short and long-range interactions within the polypeptide chain and represents a state that has the lowest possible free energy under physiological conditions. In a monomeric protein, i.e., a protein that contains only one polypeptide chain, the surface of the protein that contacts with surrounding solvent water is predominantly polar and hydrophilic. However, in some proteins, depending on amino acid composition and sequence, some surface regions of the tertiary fold may be non-polar. In such instances, the protein molecules aggregate via hydrophobic interaction; an aggregated structure of the protein, which contains more than one polypeptide chain, is referred to as the *quaternary* structure.

A. NON-COVALENT FORCES

Folding of a protein from a nascent unfolded state to a folded native conformation is driven by several non-covalent interactions within the molecule. These include van der Waals forces, steric strains, hydrogen bonding, electrostatic, and hydrophobic interactions. The van der Waals interactions are short range in nature and therefore involve interactions between neighboring atoms. Although most of the main chain and side-chain covalent bonds in proteins are single bonds, their rotational freedom is hindered because of steric constraints from side-chain groups. Thus, steric strains indirectly limit the number of configurations accessible to various segments of polypeptides.

Proteins contain several groups that can form hydrogen bonds. The greatest number of hydrogen bonds in proteins occurs between the NH and CO groups of main chain amide bonds. The maximum strength of hydrogen bonds formed between N-H and C=O groups in proteins is about 4.5 Kcal mol^{-1}. The majority of hydrogen bonds in proteins occur in α-helix and β-sheet structures. The stability of these secondary structures is partly attributable to these hydrogen bonds. The vectorial orientation of hydrogen bonds in α-helices renders it to behave like a macro dipole. When two such α-helices come close and orient themselves in anti-parallel directions and form a bundle, the macro dipole-dipole interactions between these helices can stabilize such conformations (5). However, because water itself can hydrogen bond with amide groups in proteins, formation of hydrogen bonds between amide groups in proteins is not thermodynamically stable in an aqueous environment. More importantly, they do not, and cannot, act as the driving force for protein folding. Thus, their existence in α-helix and β-sheet structures might be the result of other interactions that create a non-polar environment where the hydrogen bonding and other macro dipole-dipole interactions become stable. Based on these considerations, it is fair to say that hydrogen bonds in proteins are only pseudo-stable and their stability depends on maintenance of the non-polar environment.

Electrostatic interactions in proteins at neutral pH arise mainly between the positively charged ε-amino groups of lysine, arginine, and histidine residues and the side-chain carboxyl groups of glutamate and aspartate residues. Depending on the relative numbers of these groups, a protein assumes either a net positive or a net negative charge at neutral pH. The stability of electrostatic interactions is dependent on the dielectric constant of the local environment. They are stronger in a non-polar environment than in a polar environment. In aqueous solutions, because of the high dielectric screening effect of water on charged groups, attractive and repulsive electrostatic interactions between charged groups in proteins are very insignificant. Thus, charged groups located on the surface of the protein do not greatly influence the stability of protein structure. On the other hand, if a salt bridge occurs between two buried opposite charges in the interior of a protein, where the dielectric constant is about 2–4, it can contribute very significantly to the structural stability of the protein.

Hydrophobic interactions between non-polar side-chain groups are considered to be the major driving force for protein folding in aqueous solutions. These interactions arise as a result of thermodynamically unfavorable interaction between solvent water and non-polar groups in proteins. The unfavorable free energy change occurs neither because of phobia between hydrocarbon and water nor because of attraction between hydrocarbons. In fact, the negative free energy change for dipole-induced dipole interaction between water and hydrocarbons is greater than the induced dipole-induced dipole interactions between hydrocarbons. The origin of hydrophobic interactions is rooted in the fact that the affinity between water molecules is much greater than between water and hydrocarbon; that is, the negative free energy change for water-water interaction is greater than water-hydrocarbon interaction. Because of this thermodynamically driven preferential interaction, water tends to minimize the surface area of direct contact with hydrocarbon chains and maximize its interaction with other water molecules. Water accomplishes this by forcing the hydrocarbon chains to aggregate. In proteins, this hydrophobic aggregation/association process is the main driving force for the folding of the protein chain. As the non-polar residues are removed from the aqueous environment, the non-polar regions created within the molecule allow formation of hydrogen bonds in such water-deficient regions as the interior of α-helix and β-sheet structures.

From the above discussions, it can be summarized that the folding of a protein from a nascent unfolded state to a folded native state is driven by a simple but fundamental thermodynamic requirement that a majority of non-polar groups be buried in the interior of the protein, away from contact with the aqueous phase, and that a majority of hydrophilic polar and charged groups be located on the surface of the protein in contact with the surrounding aqueous phase in such a manner that the global free energy of the molecule is at the lowest possible level (1). In partial accordance with this dictum, almost all charged and hydrophilic groups are found on the surface of the protein and most, but not all, of the non-polar groups are buried in the interior. The inability to bury all non-polar groups is essentially related to steric constraints imposed by the polypeptide chain. In most globular proteins, about 40% of the protein's surface is non-polar.

The structural stability of the folded state under a given set of solution conditions depends on two opposing forces: the sum of the energetics of hydrophobic interactions and other non-covalent interactions, such as hydrogen bonds, attractive and repulsive electrostatic interaction, and van der Waals interactions which favor folding of the polypeptide chain, and the conformational entropy of the polypeptide chain which opposes folding of the chain. Thus, the net stability of a folded protein molecule is

$$\Delta G_{U \leftrightarrow N} = (\Delta G_{H\text{-bond}} + \Delta G_{ele} + \Delta G_{H\phi} + \Delta G_{vdW}) - T\,\Delta S \tag{6.1}$$

Here $\Delta G_{H\text{-bond}}$, ΔG_{ele}, $\Delta G_{H\phi}$, and ΔG_{vdW} are free energy changes for hydrogen bonding, electrostatic, hydrophobic, and van der Waals interactions, respectively and $T\Delta S$ is the free energy change arising from the decrease in configurational entropy of the polypeptide chain as a result of folding at temperature T. For most proteins the transformation from an unfolded state (U) to the folded state (N) is spontaneous, implying that $\Delta G_{U \leftrightarrow N}$ is negative. The net stability, $\Delta G_{U \leftrightarrow N}$, is in the range of -5 to -20 kcal mol^{-1} (Table 6.1). This marginal stability suggests that the favorable free energy change emanating from numerous non-covalent interactions is greatly offset by the unfavorable free energy change arising from the loss of configurational entropy of the chain.

TABLE 6.1

Free Energy Change for Unfolding of Proteins at 25°C

Protein	$\Delta G_{N \leftrightarrow U}$ (kcal mol^{-1})	Ref.
Actin	6.6	63
Bovine serum albumin	7.2	
Carbonic anhydrase	10.5	64
α-Chymotrypsin (bovine)	12.9	65
Cytochrome c	8.3	65
Lysozyme (chicken)	13.5	65
α-Lactalbumin	5.3	66
β-Lactoglobulin	6.6	67
Ovalbumin	5.9	68
Papain	20.7	69
Pepsin	10.8	70
Ribonuclease A	6.0	65
Alkaline phosphatase	20.0 (30°C)	71
Troponin	4.7 (37°C)	72

The spontaneous transformation of a protein from an unfolded state to a folded conformation in an aqueous medium often resembles that of a hetero-polymer chain collapsing on itself from an expanded state to a compact state driven by the non-covalent interactions (6). This is schematically shown in Figure 6.1. Note that because of the partial double bond character of the amide linkage and local steric restrictions caused by bulky side-chains, protein chains do not behave as a true random coil polymer even in a fully unfolded, denatured state.

III. DENATURATION

The low $\Delta G_{U \leftrightarrow N}$ values indicate that the tertiary structure of proteins is only marginally stable. Any change in the thermodynamic environment of the protein, such as pH, ionic strength, temperature, pressure, or presence of other solutes, can readily cause a shift in the equilibrium in favor of the denatured state. Two terminologies are often used to define alterations in protein structure. Subtle changes in the tertiary structure that do not greatly alter the topographical features of the protein are usually identified as conformational adaptation. This kind of change in structure occurs when a substrate, inhibitor, or a low-molecular-weight ligand binds to a protein. Breakdown of the tertiary fold along with unfolding of the secondary structures is often termed "denaturation."

While the native structure of a protein is a well-defined entity with structural coordinates for each and every atom in the molecule obtainable from its crystallographic structure, it is not the case for the denatured state. Denaturation is a phenomenon wherein a well-defined initial state of a protein formed under physiological conditions is transformed into an ill-defined final state under non-physiological conditions by the application of a denaturing agent. It does not involve any chemical changes in the protein. In the denatured state, because of a greater degree of rotational motions of dihedral angles of the polypeptide chain, the protein can assume several configuration states differing only marginally in free energy (Figure 6.1).

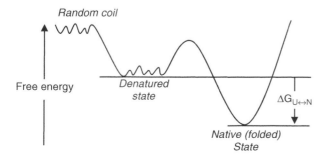

FIGURE 6.1 Schematic representation of the free energy of a protein as a function of its conformational state.

A. MEASUREMENT OF DENATURATION

Since conformation of a protein is not a quantifiable property, and the "denatured state" is not a precisely definable one, the thermodynamics of transformation of a protein from the native state to a denatured state is often determined by measuring changes in physical and chemical properties, such as viscosity, sedimentation coefficient, extinction coefficient, fluorescence, optical rotation, circular dichroism, enzyme activity, and reactivity of sulfhydryl groups of the protein. These intrinsic properties of proteins are conformation-dependent and they are modified significantly as the protein is progressively unfolded from the native state to a denatured state.

The majority of globular proteins so far studied exhibit a "two-state transition" denaturation model. The two-state model stipulates that a protein molecule can only exist either in the native or in the denatured state, but not in an intermediate state. The experimental evidence for this comes from the fact that when changes in a physical property y of a protein are monitored as a function of the concentration of a denaturant or temperature, the property y changes abruptly within a narrow range of denaturant concentration (or temperature), indicating that the transition from the native state to the denatured state is a highly cooperative process. That is, when certain critical intra-molecular interactions in the native state are destabilized by the denaturant, other interactions in the protein become highly unstable, and as a consequence the whole structure unravels within a small range of increment of denaturant concentration. An example of this phenomenon is shown in Figure 6.2 for urea and guanidine hydrochloride-induced denaturation of cytochrome c (7).

For a two-state transition model, the equilibrium between the native and the denatured state is given by

$$N \xleftarrow{\quad K_D \quad} D$$

$$K_D = \frac{[D]}{[N]} \tag{6.2}$$

Here K_D is the equilibrium constant. If $y_{(X)}$ is the value of the property y in the presence of a denaturant at concentration X, and $y_{N(X)}$ and $y_{D(X)}$ are the values of the native and denatured states, respectively, at denaturant concentration X, then the equilibrium constant for denaturation can be expressed as

$$K_{D(X)} = \frac{f_{D(X)}}{f_{N(X)}} = \frac{y_{(X)} - y_{N(X)}}{y_{D(X)} - y_{(X)}} \tag{6.3}$$

where $f_{D(X)}$ and $f_{N(X)}$ are the fraction of molecules in the denatured and native states, respectively, at denaturant concentration X. The free energy change $\Delta G_{D(X)}$ is determined from the equation

$$\Delta G_{D(X)} = -RT \ln K_{D(X)} \tag{6.4}$$

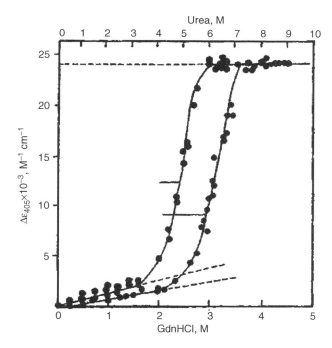

FIGURE 6.2 Guanidine hydrochloride (curve 1) and urea-(curve 2) induced unfolding of cytochrome c at pH 6 and 25°C (from Ref. 7). The ordinate represents change in molar extinction coefficient of the protein at 293 nm as a function of denaturant concentration.

where R is the gas constant and T is the temperature. The effect of the denaturant concentration on $\Delta G_{D(X)}$ generally follows the linear relation (7)

$$\Delta G_{D(X)} = \Delta G_{D(0)} - m_d \, [X] \qquad (6.5)$$

where $\Delta G_{D(0)}$ is the free energy change in the absence of the denaturant, obtained from the intercept, and m_d is the slope.

Although many proteins follow the two-state denaturation model, recent evidence suggests that certain proteins, such as α-lactalbumin, carbonic anhydrase B, and bovine growth hormone, show deviations from the two-state model (8–11). These proteins, under certain denaturation conditions, follow a three-state transition model

$$N \rightleftharpoons A \rightleftharpoons D \qquad (6.6)$$

where A is a stable intermediate state. The intermediate state is described as the "molten globule" state. The conformation of protein in the molten globule state is neither in the fully folded form nor in the fully unfolded form. The characteristic features of the molten globule state, which is sometimes referred to as the third thermodynamic state (11), are 1) its secondary structure content in terms of α-helix, β-sheet, and aperiodic structures, is very similar to that of the native conformation, 2) its overall shape and dimension is very close to that of the native state such that its intrinsic viscosity is almost the same as that of the

native state, 3) the environment of the side-chains, as measured by tryptophan fluorescence, is very similar to that of the native state, and 4) in spite of the presence of secondary structures, the enthalpy of the molten globule is almost the same as that of the denatured state (9).

Acid- or alkali-induced transitions in proteins typically produce an unfolded state characterized as the molten globule state. This phenomenon has been very well studied in the cases of α-lactalbumin, carbonic anhydrase B, and bovine growth hormone. The stability of this state depends on the ionic strength. At low ionic strength, the molten globule, also known as the A state, becomes fully unfolded because of electrostatic repulsion. In addition to acid and alkaline induced transitions, structural states similar to that of molten globule are also produced under other conditions. For instance, complete removal of bound calcium from α-lactalbumin produces a partially unfolded state that is identical to that produced in the acid transition (12, 13). Stable but partially denatured state produced by mild heating, which has a structure different from that of the A state, is also categorized as a molten globule (14, 15). The molten globule state is also formed by reduction of intra-molecular disulfide bonds in proteins (16). Thus, it appears that the molten globule can be defined as any partially unfolded but stable and roughly globular state of a protein formed under a variety of experimental conditions, but having an enthalpy content similar to that of the fully unfolded state.

IV. MECHANISM OF DENATURATION

A. TEMPERATURE-INDUCED DENATURATION

Many unit operations in food processing and preservation involve heating and cooling. These processes invariably cause protein denaturation. Typically, most proteins undergo thermal denaturation at elevated temperatures, but certain proteins, e.g., myoglobin, exhibit "cold denaturation" at sub-ambient temperatures as well. In such proteins, the $\Delta G_{N \leftrightarrow U}$ versus temperature profile exhibits a bell-shaped curve with an optimum temperature for maximum stability.

Proteins exhibit vast differences in their thermal stability. For instance, most enzymes are unstable even at 45°C, which is only a few degrees above the physiological temperature at which they function optimally, whereas other enzymes, such as alkaline phosphatase, are stable at higher temperatures. Non-enzyme proteins, especially food proteins such as whey proteins and legume proteins, are usually stable up to 70–80°C. In general, enzymes/proteins from thermophilic and thermotropic organisms are more heat stable than those from psychrophilic and mesophilic species.

The mechanism of temperature-induced denaturation of proteins primarily involves the effect of temperature on the stability of non-covalent interactions. In this respect, the hydrogen bonding and electrostatic interactions, which are exothermic in nature, are destabilized, and hydrophobic interactions, which are endothermic, are stabilized as the temperature is increased. In addition to non-covalent interactions, temperature dependence of conformational entropy, $T\Delta S_{conf}$, also plays a major role in the stability of proteins. The net stability of a protein at a given temperature is then the sum total of these interactions.

In globular proteins, the majority of charged groups exist on the surface of the protein molecule, fully exposed to the high dielectric aqueous medium. Because of the dielectric screening effect of water, attractive and repulsive electrostatic interactions between charged residues are greatly reduced. For instance, the strength of electrostatic interaction between two charged residues at a distance of 5 Å in water is only about ± 0.8 kcal mol^{-1}, which is comparable to thermal kinetic energy at 25°C. In contrast, in an environment having a dielectric constant of 4, which is comparable to that of protein interior, the strength of the same ion-pair interaction would be about ± 16 kcal mol^{-1}. In addition, at physiological ionic strength, screening of charged groups in proteins by counter ions further reduces electrostatic interactions in proteins. Because of these facts, the influence of temperature on electrostatic interactions in proteins would be negligible. Similarly, hydrogen bonds are unstable in an aqueous environment and therefore their stability in proteins is dependent on hydrophobic interactions that create local low dielectric environment. This implies that so long as a non-polar environment is maintained, the hydrogen bonds in proteins would remain intact when the temperature is increased. These facts suggest that although polar interactions are affected by temperature, they generally do not play a significant role in heat-induced denaturation of proteins. Based on these considerations, the stability of the native state of a protein can be simply regarded as the net free energy difference emanating from hydrophobic interactions that tend to minimize the nonpolar surface area of the protein molecule and the positive free energy change arising from the loss of conformational entropy of the chain ($T\Delta S$). That is,

$$\Delta G_{fold} = \Delta G_{H\phi} + \Delta G_{conf} \qquad (6.7)$$

The temperature dependence of the stability of the protein at constant pressure is then given by (17)

$$\frac{\partial \Delta G_{fold}}{\partial T} = \frac{\partial \Delta G_{H\phi}}{\partial T} + \frac{\partial \Delta G_{conf}}{\partial T} \qquad (6.8)$$

Hydrophobic interactions are strengthened at higher temperatures; therefore, $\partial \Delta G_{H\phi}/\partial T < 0$. Conformational entropy increases upon unfolding of the protein; therefore, $\partial \Delta G_{conf}/\partial T > 0$. As the temperature is increased, the interplay between these opposing forces reaches a point at which $\partial \Delta G_{fold}/\partial T > 0$. The temperature at which this occurs signifies the denaturation temperature of the protein.

In dilute solutions under certain heating conditions, thermal denaturation of globular proteins is completely reversible. At high concentration, e.g., >1%, protein-protein interaction between unfolded protein molecules hinders refolding of the protein. Prolonged heating of protein solutions at high temperatures, viz., >90°C, can cause irreversible denaturation of proteins regardless of the protein concentration. This is mainly due to chemical changes in proteins, such as destruction of cysteine and cystine residues and deamidation of asparagine and glutamine residues at high temperatures (18, 19).

In addition to denaturation at above ambient temperatures, several proteins have been shown to undergo denaturation at cold temperatures. For instance, myoglobin exhibits maximum stability at about 30°C and is destabilized at lower and higher temperatures (20). Several food proteins also undergo reversible dissociation and denaturation at cold temperatures. For example, glycinin undergoes reversible aggregation and precipitation when stored at 2°C (21). The cold temperature-induced denaturation of proteins is mainly due to a decrease in the stability of hydrophobic interactions at low temperatures.

The fact that the hydrophobic (solvophobic) force and the conformational entropy are the two important forces manifestly controlling thermodynamic stability of proteins tentatively suggests that the stability of proteins might be in some way depend on the amino acid composition. However, studies have shown that thermal denaturation temperature of proteins is not correlated with the mean hydrophobicity of amino acid residues in proteins (22). On the other hand, correlations between certain groups of amino acid residues and thermal stability have been found. For instance, statistical analysis of 15 proteins of known amino acid composition and thermal denaturation temperatures has revealed that the denaturation temperature of these proteins increased linearly with the number percentage of the sum of Asp, Cys, Glu, Lys, Leu, Arg, Trp, and Tyr residues, whereas it decreased linearly with the number percentage of the sum of Ala, Gly, Ser, Thr, Val, and Tyr residues (23). No other combinations of the 20 different amino acid residues in proteins showed a statistically significant correlation with the denaturation temperature. It is likely that attractive interactions between positively and negatively charged groups and the hydrophobic Leu, Trp, and Tyr residues in the first group might be responsible for imparting stability, whereas the highly flexible Gly, Ala, and Ser residues in the second group may tend to increase conformational entropy of proteins and thereby contribute to instability.

Thermal stability of proteins from thermophilic and hyperthermophilic organisms, which can withstand extremely high temperatures, is attributed to their unique amino acid composition (24). These proteins contain lower levels of Asn and Gln residues than those from mesophilic organisms. The implication here is that because Asn and Gln are susceptible to deamidation at high temperatures, higher levels of these residues in mesophilic proteins may partly contribute to instability. The Cys, Met, and Trp contents, which can be oxidized easily at high temperatures, are also very low in thermostable proteins. On the other hand, thermostable proteins have high levels of Ile and Pro (25, 26). It is believed that the high Ile content might help in better packing of the interior core of the protein (27), which reduces buried cavities or void spaces. Absence of void spaces can reduce mobility of the polypeptide chain at high temperatures and this will minimize the increase in its configurational entropy of the polypeptide chain at high temperatures. A high content of Pro, especially in the loop regions of the protein chain, is believed to provide rigidity to the structure (28, 29). However, comparison of packing volumes of hydrophobic residues in the interior core of homologous glutamate dehydrogenases from mesophilic and hyper-thermophilic organisms has shown no significant difference between them (30), implying that the Ile content and the packing volume may not be really critical for thermostability. On the other hand, examination of crystallographic structures of several proteins/enzymes from thermophilic organisms shows that these thermostable proteins contain a significantly higher number of ion-pairs in crevices on the surface and a substantially higher amount of buried water molecules engaged in hydrogen bonding bridge between segments than in their mesophilic counterparts (30, 31). In other words, it appears that polar interactions (both salt bridges and hydrogen bonding between segments) in the protein interior are responsible for thermostability of proteins from thermophilic and hyper-thermophilic organisms. As discussed earlier, it is conceivable that the presence of 3 to 4 salt bridges between oppositely charged groups in the protein interior could increase the stability of protein structure by about 64 kcal/mol. In spite of these findings, a real understanding of the molecular factors contributing to hyper-thermostability of proteins is still elusive. Apparently, a combination of salt bridges, a strong hydrophobic core, and reduced conformational flexibility seems to be involved in thermostability of proteins.

Water content of dry protein powders affects their thermal denaturation. As the water content is increased from zero to about 0.4 g/g, which incidentally corresponds to monolayer coverage for most proteins, the denaturation temperature of proteins decreases asymptotically and reaches a value that is similar to the denaturation temperature of the protein in a dilute solution (32). This is due to the plasticizing effect of water, which promotes segmental mobility in proteins.

Small-molecular-weight solutes, such as salts and sugars, affect the denaturation temperature of proteins. For instance, addition of 0.5 M NaCl to α-lactalbumin increases its denaturation temperature by about 5°C (33). Sucrose and glucose at 50 wt% level also elevates the denaturation temperature by about 5°C in α-lactalbumin (33). On the other hand, the denaturation temperature of soy glycinin is elevated by about 15°C and that of soy conglycinin by about 12°C in the presence of 0.5 M NaCl compared to the control (34). Interaction of vanillin with ovalbumin decreases both the temperature and the enthalpy of denaturation of ovalbumin (35). Addition of up to 40 wt% sucrose to whey protein isolate solution significantly increased both the denaturation temperature and the gelation temperature (36). The gels formed in the presence of sucrose were more rigid than the control. Addition of calcium at 1–10 mg/g of protein during isoelectric precipitation of soy protein significantly increased the denaturation temperature of soy proteins, especially the 11S fraction; the enthalpy of denaturation, however, was not affected (37). These observations suggest that the magnitude of impact of small-molecular-weight solutes on thermal stability of proteins is dependent on the intrinsic properties of proteins and their response to changes in the external environment.

B. Pressure-Induced Denaturation

Proteins are inherently highly flexible. This high flexibility is the underlying reason for their marginal stability under physiological conditions. This flexibility and marginal stability, which arise due to various competing and balancing forces, are necessary requirements for functioning of enzymes under physiological conditions, because a highly rigid protein cannot exhibit conformational adaptability required for binding of substrates and other ligands.

The flexibility of proteins arises because of void spaces or cavities in the interior of the protein. The void spaces in the interior are created by imperfect packing of the residues as the protein chain collapses on itself during folding. In aqueous solutions, the partial specific volume, $\bar{v}^0$, of a protein consists of

$$\bar{v}^0 = V_c + V_{cav} + \Delta V_{sol} \qquad (6.9)$$

Here V_c is the sum of constitutive volumes of atoms in the protein, V_{cav} is the volume of cavities in the protein, and ΔV_{sol} is the volume change due to hydration (38). Among these three parameters, V_c is constant for a given protein molecules since atomic volumes are incompressible. Thus, V_{cav} and ΔV_{sol} are the main parameters that affect partial specific volumes of proteins.

The pressure-induced denaturation is caused by compressibility of the cavities or void spaces in the interior of a protein. Differentiation of Equation 6.9 with pressure under iso-entropic (i.e., adiabatic) conditions results in

$$(\partial \bar{v}^0/\partial P) = (\partial V_{cav}/\partial P) + (\partial \Delta V_{sol}/\partial P) \qquad (6.10)$$

The adiabatic compressibility is defined as

$$\bar{\beta}_s = -\frac{1}{\bar{v}^0} \frac{\partial \bar{v}^0}{\partial P} \qquad (6.11)$$

Thus, Equation 6.10 can be expressed in terms of adiabatic compressibility as

$$\bar{\beta}_s = -\frac{1}{\bar{v}^0}\left[\frac{\partial V_{cav}}{\partial P} + \frac{\partial V_{sol}}{\partial P}\right] \qquad (6.12)$$

When hydrostatic pressure is applied, compression of the cavities results in a reduction in volume, i.e., $\partial V_{cav}/\partial P < 0$, but disruption of the hydration shells of charged and polar surfaces causes an increase in volume, i.e., $\partial V_{sol}/\partial P > 0$ (38). Because of these two opposing effects, the net compressibility or decrease in the volume is only marginal. However, if the compressibility arising from $\partial V_{cav}/\partial P$ alone is considered, the compressibility of proteins is an order of magnitude greater than water (38).

The adiabatic compressibility, $\bar{\beta}_s$, of some proteins is shown in Table 6.2. It should be noted that fibrous proteins, such as gelatin, F-actin, myosin, and tropomyosin, have negative compressibility, indicating that the increase in volume due to disruption of hydration shells, i.e., $\partial V_{sol}/\partial P > 0$, is more dominant than the volume decrease due to elimination of cavities. It is possible that these fibrous proteins might be devoid of cavities altogether and therefore $\partial V_{cav}/\partial P$ might be almost close to zero. The positive compressibility values of globular proteins suggest that the negative volume change due to compression of cavities is much greater than the positive volume change from hydration effects. It should be noted that although the partial specific volume of β-casein (0.744 ml g^{-1}) is greater than that of α_s-casein (0.739 ml g^{-1}) and κ-casein (0.739 ml g^{-1}), its adiabatic compressibility is significantly lower than those of α_s- and κ-caseins. This might be related to higher proline content of β-casein (17%) than α_s- and κ-caseins. Because

TABLE 6.2
Adiabatic Compressibility, $\bar{\beta}_s$, of Proteins[1]

Protein	$\bar{\beta}_s$ (cm^2 dyn^{-1} 10^{12})
Gelatin	−2.5
F-actin	−6.3
Myosin	−18.0
Tropomyosin	−41.0
α-Casein	7.74
α_s-Casein	5.68
β-Casein	3.80
κ-Casein	7.49
Whole casein	6.67
α-Lactalbumin	8.27
β-Lactoglobulin	8.45
Lysozyme	4.67
Myoglobin	8.98
Peroxidase	2.36
Ovalbumin	9.18
Ovomucoid	3.38
Bovine serum albumin	10.50
Cytochrome c	0.066

[1] Compiled from References 73 and 74.

of lack of rotational freedom of the dihedral angle φ of the N-C$_\alpha$ bond of proline residues, protein segments containing proline residues often behave like a stiff rod (39). It is conceivable that the uniform distribution of 35 proline residues along the backbone chain in β-casein may render the protein to behave as a stiff rod with only limited flexibility. Among the globular proteins listed in Table 6.2, cytochrome c has the lowest adiabatic compressibility.

Under very high hydrostatic pressure, the collapse of the cavities formed as a result of imperfect packing of amino acid residues causes unfolding of the protein. In the unfolded state, elimination of the cavities decreases the volume, and hydration of the exposed hydrophobic residues also leads to a reduction in the volume of the solvent. Thus, pressure-induced denaturation usually results in a net reduction in the volume of the system (protein+water).

The free energy change under pressure-induced denaturation of protein is related to its volume change according to the equation

$$\Delta V = d(\Delta G)/dP \qquad (6.13)$$

The pressure-induced denaturation of single-chain proteins has been measured by monitoring changes in fluorescence emission and UV absorption spectra of tryptophan residues, and changes in turbidity (40–42). A critical review of the data in the literature suggests the following. In single chain proteins, pressure-induced denaturation occurs only at very high pressures. For most proteins, the midpoint of pressure-induced structural transition is in the range of 4–8 kilobars (43). In oligomeric proteins, dissociation of subunits occurs at 1–2 kilobars, followed by unfolding of the subunits at higher pressures. The volume change in proteins upon pressure-induced unfolding is typically about 0.5% of the total volume of the protein molecule, which is considerably smaller than the theoretically predicted value of about 2%. This tentatively suggests that proteins may retain some residual folded structures even at pressures as high as 10 kilobars. This may partly explain complete reversibility of pressure-induced unfolding in most proteins, including oligomeric proteins. For most single chain proteins, the free energy change at the midpoint of transition at neutral pH and ambient temperature is in the range of 10–20 kcal mol^{-1}. This value is comparable to that obtained from heat-induced or urea and guanidine hydrochloride-induced denaturation. Taken together, the smaller than expected volume change in proteins might indicate that proteins may assume a molten globule state, instead of the completely unfolded state, under high pressure since the enthalpy content of the molten globule state and the fully unfolded state are almost the same.

In addition to causing protein denaturation, high hydrostatic pressure disrupts the integrity of macromolecular assemblies, such as biomembranes, ribosomes, and bacterial cell walls. Disruption of cell membrane is often irreversible, which results in inactivation of vegetative cells. For this reason, high-pressure treatment of food products is being examined for its effectiveness as a tool for food preservation (44–46). At sufficiently high protein concentration, pressure denaturation can cause non-thermal gelation of proteins (47, 48). Exposure of myosin to pressures up to 800 MPa for 20 min causes denaturation and polymerization of myosin; the polymerized structure contains both hydrogen bonds (as judged from differential scanning calorimetry (DSC)) and disulfide cross-links (49). Pressure-induced gels are softer in texture than the heat-induced gels. However, pressure-induced gels retain color, flavor, and vitamins and other nutrients that are destroyed to some extent in thermally processed foods and in heat-induced gels.

C. DENATURATION BY SMALL-MOLECULAR-WEIGHT ADDITIVES

Several small-molecular-weight solutes, such as urea, guanidine hydrochloride, detergents, sugars, and neutral salts, affect protein stability in aqueous solutions. While urea, guanidine hydrochloride, and detergents destabilize the native conformation of proteins, sugars tend to stabilize the native structure. In the case of neutral salts, while certain salts, such as sulfate and fluoride salts of sodium, termed as kosmotropes, stabilize protein structure, other salts, such as bromide, iodide, perchlorate, and thiocyanate, termed as chaotropes, destabilize protein structure.

The stabilizing or destabilizing effects of small-molecular-weight additives on proteins is believed to follow a general mechanism. This is related to their preferential interaction with the aqueous phase and the protein surface. Additives that stabilize protein structure bind very weakly to the protein surface but enhance preferential hydration of the protein surface (Figure 6.3). Such additives are generally excluded from the region surrounding the protein; that is, their concentration near the protein is lower than in the bulk solution. This concentration gradient presumably creates an osmotic pressure gradient surrounding the protein molecule, sufficient enough to elevate the thermal denaturation temperature. For instance, studies on protein stabilization by glycerol using the electrospray ionization mass spectrometry (ESI-MS) technique have shown that in glycerol solutions lysozyme assumes a slightly compressed state compared with its state in water (50). This might be due to creation of an exclusion zone around the protein surface for glycerol and development of an osmotic pressure gradient.

In the case of additives that destabilize protein structure, the opposite seems to be true. That is, those additives that decrease the stability of proteins preferentially bind to the protein surface and cause dehydration of the protein. In such cases, water molecules are excluded from the

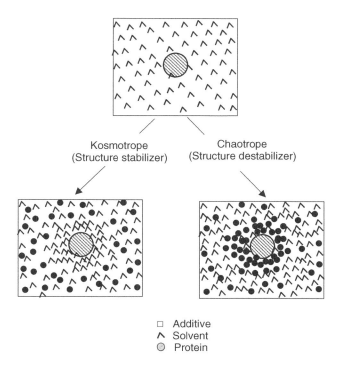

Kosmotrope (Structure stabilizer) Chaotrope (Structure destabilizer)

□ Additive
∧ Solvent
◎ Protein

FIGURE 6.3 Schematic representation of preferential binding of solute and solvent molecules with proteins in the cases of kosmotropes (structure stabilizers) and chaotropes (structure destabilizers).

region surrounding the protein and the concentration of the additive in this water-excluded region is higher than in the bulk solvent. Favorable interaction of such additives with protein surface, particularly the non-polar surface, promotes unfolding of the protein so that the buried non-polar surfaces are further exposed for favorable interaction with the additive.

When a protein is exposed to a mixture of stabilizing and destabilizing solutes, the net effect on protein stability generally follows an additivity rule. For example, sucrose and polyols are considered to be protein structure stabilizers, whereas guanidine hydrochloride is a structure destabilizer. When sucrose is mixed with guanidine hydrochloride, the concentration of guanidine hydrochloride required for unfolding proteins increased with increase of sucrose concentration (51). It was also observed that the structure of water was altered in the presence of guanidine hydrochloride and urea. However, addition of polyhydric compounds such as sucrose countered this urea and guanidine hydrochloride-induced change in water structure. Thus, the increase in guanidine hydrochloride and urea concentrations required for unfolding proteins in the presence of sucrose and other polyhydric compounds might be due to mutually opposing effects of these compounds on water structure (51). This also underscores that changes in water structure in the presence of additives are involved in some fundamental way in the transmission of the effects of additives on protein stability. The exact mechanism is still elusive, partly because "water structure" is not yet a well-defined concept.

Theoretical statistical thermodynamic analyses have shown that the excluded volume of additives has three distinct types of effects on protein stability (52): 1) Small-size solutes strongly denature proteins, 2) medium-size solutes stabilize proteins at low solute concentrations and destabilize them at high concentrations, and 3) large-size solutes stabilize the native state of proteins across the whole liquid region. In agreement with this theory, stabilizers tend to be large-size molecules such as sugars, polymers, polynols, nonionic, and anionic surfactants while denaturants tend to be small-size molecules such as alcohols, glycols, amides, formamides, ureas, and guanidium salts.

The mechanism of preferential binding to or exclusion from protein surface of additives in aqueous solutions is a complex one. Various molecular interactions between the additive and protein (both with the protein surface and protein interior) are involved. These interactions include electrostatic and van der Waals interactions (consisting of Debye-Keesom and London dispersion interactions) with proteins, as well as their interaction with solvent water. It has been pointed out (53, 54) rather convincingly that preferential binding or exclusion of ions from a protein surface in aqueous electrolyte solutions can be fully explained only by including, in addition to electrostatic interactions, dispersion interactions between ions and the protein.

1. Urea and Guanidine Hydrochloride

Both urea and guanidine hydrochloride denature proteins at very high concentrations. Guanidine hydrochloride is a more potent denaturant than urea. For globular proteins the midpoint of unfolding transition occurs at 4–6 M urea and at 3–4 M guanidine hydrochloride concentrations. Generally, globular proteins are completely denatured in 8 M urea and 6 M guanidine hydrochloride. The mechanism of denaturation of proteins by urea and guanidine hydrochloride is related to their solubilizing effect on both polar and non-polar amino acid residues. Solubility studies on non-polar amino acids have shown that the free energy change for transfer of non-polar groups from water to urea and guanidine hydrochloride solutions is favorable (55). This transfer free energy is proportional to the accessible surface area of the non-polar solute, which is about -7.1 cal mol^{-1} Å^{-2} for 8 M urea and -8.3 cal mol^{-1} Å^{-2} for 6 M guanidine hydrochloride (55). Because urea and guanidine hydrochloride interact more favorably with both polar and non-polar groups (via ion-dipole and dispersion interactions) on the protein surface than does water, they preferentially bind to proteins. This preferential interaction further leads to unfolding and solubilization of buried non-polar residues. This shift in equilibrium from native state to the unfolded state is driven by the thermodynamic

requirement to increase the area of contact between protein non-polar surfaces and the denaturant.

2. Neutral Salts

Neutral salts affect protein stability via two different mechanisms. At low concentrations (<0.5 M), non-specific electrostatic interactions with charged groups on protein surface results in neutralization of electrostatic (repulsive) interactions within a protein and this often leads to stabilization of protein structure. Salts also affect the pK$_a$ of ionizable groups in proteins, especially the acidic residues, which causes changes in thermal stability of proteins (56). At higher concentrations, neutral salts exert ion-specific effects on protein stability depending on their relative position in the Hofmeister Series (56). The effects of anions on protein stability are greater than the cations and follows the order $F^->SO_4^{2-}>Cl^->Br^->I^->ClO_4^->SCN^->Cl_3CCOO^-$. F^- and SO_4^{2-} actually increase the stability of protein structure (kosmotropes), whereas Br^-, I^-, ClO_4^-, SCN^-, and Cl_3CCOO^- ions destabilize protein structure (chaotropes). The stabilizing and destabilizing effects of these ions on protein structure are manifested in the form of elevation and depression of the denaturation temperature (T_d) of proteins. For instance, Figure 6.4 shows the effect of neutral salts on T_d of β-lactoglobulin (58). At high concentrations, Na$_2$SO$_4$ and NaCl significantly raise the denaturation temperature, whereas NaSCN and NaClO$_4$ lower the denaturation temperature of β-lactoglobulin.

Several theories have been proposed to explain the effects of neutral salts on protein structure and stability (57, 59). Experimental evidence indicates that the effects of salts on protein stability are related to their relative ability to bind to proteins and affect its hydration. Salts that stabilize protein structure weakly bind to the protein surface and enhance hydration of the protein, whereas salts that destabilize protein structure bind strongly to protein surface and cause dehydration of the protein (60). However, the fundamental reasons for differential binding of salts, for example monovalent salts, to proteins are not well understood. It appears that ion binding to proteins cannot be simply explained using classical electrostatic potential on the surface. It might also involve dispersion forces between the ion and the apolar interior of the protein (54). The dispersion potential, which relates to ion-dipole polarizability effects, is dependent on ionic radius and concentration and the dielectric susceptibility of the protein. On a more fundamental level, differences in interaction of salts with proteins must be related to free energy differences between interaction with solvent water and protein surface. In this case, ions might affect the thermodynamic state of water and alter its solvent properties. It has been shown that salts that stabilize protein structure also enhance hydrogen-bonded structure of water, and salts that destabilize protein structure also break down the hydrogen-bonded structure of water (59).

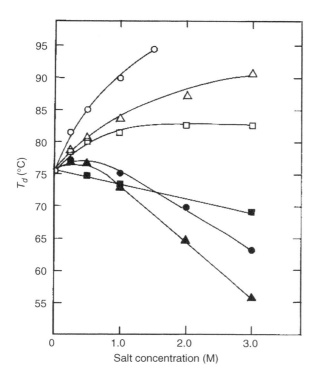

FIGURE 6.4 Effects of various sodium salts on thermal denaturation temperature of β-lactoglobulin. ○, Na_2SO_4; △, NaCl; □, NaBr; ●, $NaClO_4$; ▲, NaSCN; ■, urea (from Ref. 55).

3. Detergents

Detergents, especially anionic detergents such as sodium dodecyl sulfate (SDS), are potent denaturing agents. Unlike urea and guanidine hydrochloride, SDS can denature proteins at 3–8 mM concentration. The mechanism of denaturation involves strong binding of SDS to hydrophobic groups in the crevices of the protein molecule, which results in destabilization and solubilization of buried hydrophobic regions. Proteins bind up to about 1.4 g of SDS per gram of protein. Because of this high binding capacity, proteins in SDS solution become highly negatively charged and consequently electrostatic repulsion between segments also play a role in protein unfolding. Unlike in other denaturing environments, the denatured state of proteins in SDS solution is generally not in a random or aperiodic conformation; invariably they assume a helical rod-type shape. Because of strong binding via hydrophobic interactions, detergent-induced denaturation of proteins is mostly irreversible, whereas denaturation by urea and guanidine hydrochloride is generally reversible under appropriate conditions.

4. Organic Solvents

The mechanism of protein denaturation by organic solvents such as ethanol, propanol, and acetone is complex. This is because these water miscible organic solvents affect various molecular forces, such as electrostatic, hydrogen bonding, and hydrophobic interactions, in proteins differently. However, the effects are mediated mainly via a decrease in the dielectric constant of the solvent medium. First, when a water-miscible organic solvent is added to a protein solution, the decrease in the permittivity of the medium increases electrostatic repulsion between like charges and enhances attraction between unlike charges. The repulsive interactions tend to unfold the protein, whereas the attractive electrostatic interactions tend to stabilize the structure. The latter becomes crucial if the protein contains a salt bridge between a carboxyl and an amino group in a partially exposed crevice on the surface of the protein. Second, because apolar residues in proteins are more soluble in an organic solvent and in an aqueous-organic solvent mixture than in water, the hydrophobic interactions within the protein are weakened and consequently the buried non-polar groups tend to become exposed to the solvent, which results in unfolding of the tertiary structure of the protein. Third, although the tertiary (and quaternary) structure of the protein may unfold, the secondary structures, viz., α-helix and β-sheet, which are stabilized by hydrogen bonds, may not unfold. In the low dielectric environment of the aqueous-organic solvent mixture, strengthening of these dipole-dipole interactions may actually stabilize the secondary structure. In fact, a recent study has shown that in the entire range of aqueous-organic mixtures, that is, from pure water to pure organic solvent, the secondary structure of lysozyme and subtilsin remained essentially intact (61). It is noteworthy that several enzymes retain their activity in neat organic solvents and that is the basis for non-aqueous enzymology (61). Hexane extraction of oil from dry soybeans and other oilseeds at low temperature causes very little denaturation of soy proteins. However, when the moisture content of soybean is high (>10%), hexane extraction often leads to partial denaturation of soy proteins.

Exposure of proteins to polar organic solvents at elevated temperature usually causes extensive denaturation. In the case of food proteins, this results in poor aqueous solubility of the protein. For example, hot aqueous ethanol treatment (55% ethanol at 80°C) caused complete denaturation of pea protein isolate and a large reduction in its protein dispersibility index (62). A significant reduction in the trypsin inhibitory activity of pea protein isolate also was observed. However, treatment with higher ethanol concentration (65%) and lower treatment temperature (65°C) minimized protein insolubility and caused only a marginal reduction in trypsin inhibitory activity.

5. pH-Induced Denaturation

Proteins are either negatively or positively charged at neutral pH. Since this represents the physiological pH, the native structure of the protein represents an equilibrium structure with a global minimum free energy that has already taken into account the preexisting repulsive and attractive electrostatic interactions. However, at pH values away from the neutral pH, changes in the state of ionization of various charged residues in proteins alter the electrostatic free energy of the protein, resulting in conformational changes. Most proteins are very stable at their isoelectric pH, where the net charge of the protein is zero and electrostatic repulsive interactions are at a minimum. However, many proteins unfold at pH values below 5 and above 10. This unfolding is not simply because of changes in the ionization state of the charged residues on the surface of the protein, but is related to ionization of residues that are partially or fully buried in the protein. Specifically, in many proteins histidine ($pK_a = 6.0$) and tyrosine residues ($pK_a = 9.6$) are buried in the un-ionized form in proteins. When the pH of the solution is decreased below 5.0, ionization of the buried histidine residues can cause unfolding. Similarly when the pH of the solution is increased above 10, ionization of buried tyrosine residues can unravel the protein structure. The pH-dependent ionization of charged residues on the surface of the protein also may contribute to protein denaturation. Protonation of carboxyl groups ($pK_a = 4.6$) at acidic pH eliminates negative charge and the protein becomes highly positively charged. On the other hand, deprotonation of lysine residues ($pK_a = 10.2$) at pH above 10.5 decreases the positive charge and the protein becomes highly negatively charged. In both situations, increased electrostatic repulsion between surface charges may also contribute to unfolding of the protein. If salt bridges between positively and negatively charged residues in partially buried surface crevices of proteins are involved in the stability of native structure of proteins, then protonation (of the carboxyl group) and/or deprotonation (of the amino group) of one of the groups of the salt bridge can significantly perturb protein structure. In many cases, the pH-induced denaturation of proteins is reversible, but prolonged exposure to extreme pH values can cause hydrolysis of certain peptide bonds, deamidation of asparagine and glutamine residues, and destruction of cysteine residues via β-elimination reaction. Such chemical alterations in proteins would result in irreversible denaturation.

V. SUMMARY

Despite the presence of numerous intra-molecular interactions, proteins exist in a metastable state. Thermodynamically, the net stability of the native structure of proteins is only about 5–20 kcal mol^{-1}. Because of this, destabilization of a few critical interactions in a protein by temperature, salts, pH, and other small-molecular-weight denaturants can cause cooperative unraveling of the native structure. In the case of food proteins, the majority of which are oligomeric proteins, the denaturation phenomenon is more complex than that in monomeric proteins. In oligomeric proteins, the

denaturation process may follow a three-state model, the first being the dissociation of the oligomer into monomers and the second being unfolding of the monomers. In some proteins these two processes may occur in a de-coupled manner and in other proteins these may be coupled together. Such complex structural transitions in proteins may affect their functional properties as food protein ingredients. They also affect the nutritional properties of proteins, e.g., digestibility. Proteins that are resistant to thermal denaturation also are less digestible, e.g., soy proteins. Thus, a fundamental understanding of the structural stability of food proteins and their denaturation behavior under various environmental conditions as encountered in a food milieu is essential for understanding their structure-function relationships in food systems.

REFERENCES

1. S Damodaran. Structure-function relationship of proteins. In: NS Hettiarachchy, GR Ziegler. eds. Protein Functionality in Food Systems. New York: Marcel Dekker, 1994, pp. 1–38.
2. Z Haiming, S Damodaran. Heat-induced conformational changes in whey protein isolate and its relation to foaming properties. J Agric Food Chem 42:846–855, 1994.
3. LP Voustinas, E Cheung, S Nakai. Relationship of hydrophobicity to emulsifying properties of heat denatured proteins. J Food Sci 48:26–32, 1983.
4. N Matsudomi, H Mori, A Kato, K Kobayashi. Emulsifying and foaming properties of heat denatured soybean 11S globulin in relation to their surface hydrophobicity. Agric Biol Chem 49:915–919, 1985.
5. CN Pace. The stability of globular proteins. CRC Crit Rev Biochem 3:1–43, 1975.
6. KA Dill, D Stigter. Modeling protein stability as heteropolymer collapse. Advan Protein Chem 46:59–104, 1995.
7. R Gupta, F Ahmad. Protein stability: Functional dependence of denaturational Gibbs energy on urea coancentration. Biochemistry 38:2471–2479, 1999.
8. OB Ptitsyn. Protein folding: Hypotheses and experiments. J Protein Chem 6:272–293, 1987.
9. K Kuwajima. The molten globule state as a clue for understanding the folding and cooperativity of globular protein structure. Proteins: Structure Function Genetics 6:87–103, 1989.
10. JJ Ewbank, TE Creighton. The "molten globule" protein conformation probed by disulfide bonds. Nature 350:518–520, 1991.
11. W Pfeil. Is the molten globule a third thermodynamic state of protein? The example of α-lactalbumin. Proteins: Structure Function Genetics 30:43–48, 1998.
12. DA Dolgikh, RI Gilmanshin, EV Brazhnikov, VE Bychkova, GV Semisotnov, S Venyaminov, OB Ptitsyn. α-Lactalbumin compact state with fluctuating tertiary structure? FEBS Lett 136:311–315, 1981.
13. K Kuwajima, Y Harushima, S Sugai. Influence of Ca^{2+} binding on the structure and stability of bovine

α-lactalbumin studied by circular dichroism and nuclear magnetic resonance spectra. Int J Peptide Protein Res 27:18–27, 1986.

14. PP de Laureto, E Frare, R Gottardo, A Fontana. Molten globule of bovine alpha-lactalbumin at neutral pH induced by heat, trifluoroethanol, and oleic acid: A comparative analysis by circular dichroism spectroscopy and limited proteolysis Proteins: Structure Function Genetics 49:385–397,2002.

15. K Gast, D Zirwer, H Welfle, VE Bychkova, OB Ptitsyn. Quasielastic light scattering from human a-lactalbumin: Comparison of molecular dimensions in native and 'molten globule' states. Int J Biol Macromol 8:231–236, 1986.

16. SW Cai, BR Singh. Role of the disulfide cleavage induced molten globule state of type A botulinum neurotoxin in its endopeptidase activity. Biochemistry 40:15327–15333, 2001.

17. KA Dill, DOV Alonso, K Hutchinson. Thermal stabilities of globular proteins. Biochemistry 28:5439–5449, 1989.

18. CH Wang, S Damodaran. Thermal destruction of cysteine and cystine residues of soy protein under conditions of gelation. J Food Sci 55:1077–1080, 1990.

19. TJ Ahren, AM Klibanov. The mechanism of irreversible enzyme inactivation at 100°C. Science 228:1280–1284, 1985.

20. PL Privalov. Cold denaturation of proteins. CRC Crit Rev Biochem 25:281–305, 1990.

21. WJ Wolf, DA Sly. Cryoprecipitation of soybean 11S protein. Cereal Chem 44:653–657, 1967.

22. HB Bull, K Breese. Thermal stability of proteins. Arch Biochem Biophys 158:681–686, 1973.

23. PK Ponnuswamy, R Muthusamy, P Manavalan. Amino acid composition and thermal stability of proteins. Int J Biol Macromol 4:186–190, 1982.

24. RJM Russell, GL Taylor. Engineering thermostability: Lessons from thermophilic proteins. Curr Opin Biotechnol 6:370–374, 1995.

25. D Shortle, WE Stites, AK Meeker. Contributions of the large hydrophobic amino acids to the stability of Staphylococcal nuclease. Biochemistry 29:8033–8041, 1990.

26. K Watanabe, K Chishiro, K Kitamura, Y Suzuki. Proline residues responsible for thermostability occur with high frequency in the loop regions of an extremely thermostable oligo-1,6-glucosidase from Bacillus thermoglucosidasius KP1006. J Biol Chem 266:24287–24294.

27. RJM Russell, DW Hough, MJ Danson, GL Taylor. The crystal structure of citrate synthase from the thermophilic archaeon, Thermoplasma acidophilium. Structure 2:1157–1167, 1994.

28. S Nakamura, T Tanaka, RY Yada, S Nakai. Improving the thermostability of Bacillus stearothermophilus neutral protease by introducing proline into the active site helix. Protein Engineering 10:1263–1269, 1997.

29. Y Li, PJ Reilly, C Ford. Effect of introducing proline residues on the stability of Aspergillus awamori. Protein Engineering 10:1199–1204, 1997.

30. KSP Yip, TJ Stillman, K Britton, PJ Artymium, PJ Baker, SE Sedelnikova, PC Engel, A Pasquo, R Chiaraluce, V Consalvi, R Scandurra, DW Rice. The structure of Pyrococcus furiosus glutamate dehydrogenase reveals a key role for ion-pair networks in maintaining enzyme stability at extreme temperatures. Structure 3:1147–1158, 1995.

31. CF Aguilar, L Sanderson, M Moracci, M Ciaramella, R Nucci, M Rossi, L Pearl. Crystal structure of the β-glycosidase from the hyperthermophilic archeon Sulfolobus solfataricus. J Mol Biol 271:789–802, 1997.

32. Y Fujita, Y Noda. The effect of hydration on the thermal stability of ovalbumin as measured by means of differential scanning calorimetry. Bull Chem Soc Jpn 54:3233–3234, 1981.

33. JI Boye, I Alli, AA Ismail. Use of differential scanning calorimetry and infrared spectroscopy in the study of thermal and structural stability of α-lactalbumin. J Agric Food Chem 45:1116–1125, 1997.

34. S Damodaran. Refolding of thermally unfolded soy proteins during the cooling regime of the gelation process: Effect on gelation. J Agric Food Chem 36:262–269, 1988.

35. VY Grinberg, NV Grinberg, AY Mashkevich, TV Burova, VB Tolstoguzov. Calorimetric study of interaction of ovalbumin with vanillin. Food Hydrocolloids 16:333–343, 2002.

36. A Kulmyrzaev, C Bryant, DJ McClements. Influence of sucrose on thermal denaturation, gelation and emulsion stabilization of whey proteins. J Agric Food Chem 48:1593–1597, 2000.

37. AA Scilingo, MC Anon. Calorimetric study of soybean protein isolates – Effects of calcium and thermal treatments. J Agric Food Chem 44:3751–3756, 1996.

38. K Gekko. Flexibility of globular proteins in water as revealed by compressibility. In: H Levine, L Slade, Eds. Water Relationships in Food. New York: Plenum Press, 1991, pp. 753–771.

39. C Branden, J Tooze. In: Introduction to Protein Structure. New York: John Wiley & Sons, 1980, p. 628.

40. RS Garcia, JA Amaral Jr, P Abrahamsohn, S Verjovski-Almeida. Dissociation of F-actin induced by hydrostatic pressure. Eur J Biochem 209:1005–1011, 1992.

41. PTT Wong, IS Girons, Y Guillou, GN Cohen, O Barzu, HH Mantsch. Pressure-induced changes in the secondary structure of the Escherichia coli methionine repressor protein. Biochim Biophys Acta 996:260–262, 1989.

42. SJ Tumminia, JF Koretz, JV Landau. Hydrostatic pressure studies of native and synthetic thick filaments: in vitro myosin aggregates at pH 7.0 with and without C-protein. Biochim Biophys Acta 999:300–312, 1989.

43. G Weber, HG Drickamer. The effect of high pressure upon proteins and other biomolecules. Quarterly Rev Biophys 16:89–112, 1983.

44. DG Hoover, C Metrick, AM Papineau, DF Farkas, D. Knorr. Biological effects of high hydrostatic pressure on food microorganisms. Food Technol (Chicago), pp. 99–107, 1989.

45. DE Johnston, BA Austin, RJ Murphy. Effects of high hydrostatic pressure on milk. Milchwissenschaft 47:760–763.

46. T Ohshima, H Ushio, C Koizumi. High pressure processing of fish and fish products. Trends Food Sci Technol 4:370–375, 1993.

47. DE Johnston, BA Austin, RJ Murphy. Properties of acid-set gels prepared from high pressure treated skim milk. Milchwissenschaft 48:206–209, 1993.

48. K Yamamoto, T Miura, T Yasui. Gelation of myosin filament under high hydrostatic pressure. Food Structure 9:269–277, 1990.

49. K Angsupanich, M Edde, DA Ledward. Effect of high pressure on myofibrillar proteins of cod and turkey. J Agric Food Chem 47:92–99, 1999.

50. R Grandori, I Matecko, P Mayr, N Muller. Probing protein stabilization by glycerol using electrospray mass spectrometry. J Mass Spectrometry 36:918–922, 2001.

51. LS Taylor, AC Williams, HGM Edwards, V Mehta, GS Jackson, IG Badcoe, AR Clark. Sucrose reduces the efficiency of protein denaturation by a chaotropic agent. Biochim Biophys Acta 1253:39–46, 1995.

52. YQ Zhou, CK Hall. Solute excluded-volume effects on the stability of globular proteins: A statistical thermodynamic theory. Biopolymers 38:273–284, 1996.

53. J Mahanty, BW Ninham. Dispersion Forces. London: Academic Press, 1976.

54. BW Ninham, V Yaminsky. Ion binding and ion specificity: The Hofmeister effect and Onsager and Lifshitz theories. Langmuir 13:2097–2108, 1997.

55. TE Creighton. Electrophoretic analysis of the unfolding of proteins by urea. J Mol Biol 129:235–264, 1979.

56. Y Abe, T, Ueda, H Iwashita, Y Hashimoto, H Motoshima, Y Tanaka, T Imoto. Effect of salt concentration on pKa of acidic residues in lysozyme. J Biochem 118:946–952, 1995.

57. KD Collins, MW Washabaugh. The Hofmeister effect and the behavior of water at interfaces. Q Rev Biophys 18:323–422, 1985.

58. S Damodaran. Influence of protein conformation on its adaptability under chaotropic conditions. Int J Biol Macromolec 11:2–8, 1988.

59. PH von Hippel, T Schleich. The effects of neutral salts on the structure and conformational stability of macromolecules in solution. In: SN Timasheff, GD Fasman, Eds. Structure and Stability of Biological Macromolecules. New York: Marcel Dekker, 1969, pp. 417–574.

60. T Arakawa, SN Timasheff. Mechanism of protein salting-in and salting-out by divalent cation salts: Balance between hydration and salt binding. Biochemistry 23:5912–5923, 1984.

61. K Griebenow, AM Klibanov. On protein denaturation in aqueous-organic mixtures but not in pure organic solvents. J Am Chem Soc 118:11695–11700, 1996.

62. GH Tolman. Effect of hot aqueous ethanol treatment on antinutritional factors, protein denaturation and functional properties in raw pea and pea protein isolate. Animal Feed Sci Technol 56:159–168, 1995.

63. CC Contaxis, CC Bigelow, CG Zarkadas. The thermal denaturation of bovine cardiac G-actin. Can J Biochem 55:325–331, 1977.

64. P Cupo, W El-Deiry, PL Whitney, WM Awad. Stabilization of proteins by guanidination. J Biol Chem 255:10828–10833, 1980.

65. GI Makhatadze, PL Privalov. Thermodynamic properties of proteins. In: JE Mark, ed. Physical Properties of Polymers Handbook. New York: AIP Press, 1996, p. 91.

66. TM Hendrix, Y Griko, P Privalov. Energetics of structural domains in alpha-lactalbumin. Protein Sci 5:923–931, 1996.

67. M Hollecker, TE Crieghton. Effect on protein stability of reversing the charge on amino groups. Biochim Biophys Acta 701:395–404, 1982.

68. F Ahmad, A Salahuddin. Reversible unfolding of the major fraction of ovalbumin by guanidine hydrochloride. Biochemistry 15:5168–5175, 1976.

69. W Pfeil. Unfolding of proteins. In: HJ Hinz, Ed. Thermodynamic Data for Biochemistry and Biotechnology. Berlin-New York: Springer-Verlag, 1986, p. 349.

70. PL Privalov, PL Mateo, NN Khechinashvili, VM Stepanov, LP Revina. Comparative thermodynamic study of pepsinogen and pepsin structure. J Mol Biol 152:445–464, 1981.

71. K Wuthrich, G Wagner, R Richarz, W Braun. Correlations between internal mobility and stability of globular proteins. Biophys J 32:549–560, 1980.

72. AL Jacobson, G Devin, H Braun. Thermal denaturation of beef cardiac troponin and its subunits with and without calcium ion. Biochemistry 20:1694–1701, 1981.

73. K Gekko, Y Hasegawa. Compressibility-structure relationship of globular proteins. Biochemistry 25:6563–6569, 1986.

74. K Gekko, Y Hasegawa. Effect of temperature on the compressibility of native globular proteins. J Phys Chem 93:426–433, 1989.

7 Food Protein Functionality

Jeff D. Culbertson
Department of Food Science and Toxicology, University of Idaho

CONTENTS

I. INTRODUCTION

Functionality has been described as the non-nutritive roles that food constituents play in a food system. More formally, functional properties are the physical and chemical properties that affect the behavior of molecular constituents in food systems. Functionality of ingredients is important in the preparation, processing, storage, quality, and sensory attributes of foods (1). Proteins in foods are multifunctional and may be the principal structural component in many food systems, including products from meat and poultry, eggs, dairy, cereals, and legumes. Proteins contribute significantly to the sensory attributes and overall quality of products of which they are a component. Knowledge of protein functionality is critical for the development of new products and the improvement of existing ones. An example is the use of less expensive protein sources as replacements in traditional food products. Use of less expensive proteins not only allows for cost reduction, but also can increase the utilization of food materials that previously might have been considered waste products. As our society increases in complexity,

TABLE 7.1
Important Functional Properties of Proteins in Several Food Systems

Functional Property	Food System(s)
Solubility	Infant formulas, protein beverages, beer, yogurt drinks
Water-holding ability (capacity)	Tumbled hams, deli meats, frankfurters, poultry products, yogurt
Gelation	Frankfurters, custards, gelatin, comminuted meat and poultry products
Emulsification	Ice cream, liquid coffee creamers, salad dressings, milk, mayonnaise, gravies
Foaming	Angel and sponge cakes, meringues, soufflés, marshmallows, whipped cream and toppings

the demand for new food products requires us to understand protein functionality so that we can modify or control their behavior in new food systems.

Functional properties commonly associated with proteins include solubility, gelation, emulsification, foaming, and water-holding capacity. Table 7.1 lists these functional properties and gives examples of foods which commonly exhibit them. Smith (2) classified functional properties into three broad categories: 1) hydration properties such as solubility or water retention, 2) protein-protein interactions such as gelation, and 3) surface properties such as emulsification and foaming.

In many foods systems, proteins are multifunctional in that they might play a number of different functional roles in a given food. Additionally, a given food might require several different proteins so that all of the functional needs of the food are met. Excellent examples of this are highly ground or comminuted muscle foods systems such as frankfurters or bologna. Those products require proteins that exhibit good solubility, gelation, water-holding capacity, and emulsification. Because the naturally occurring proteins in muscle might not perform all of these roles well, it is necessary to add functional proteins to these formulations in the form of food protein ingredients. Protein additives available for use in

formulated foods come from many sources and are in high demand by the food industry. As seen in Table 7.2, protein ingredients are extracted and purified (or partially purified) from both plant and animal sources. Besides native source, the major functional protein in each is also listed. Typically, protein ingredients are called concentrates if they contain between 50–80% protein and isolates if their concentration is greater than 90% (2).

The major factors that influence the functional properties of a protein are its biochemical nature and how it was affected by extraction and purification into a food ingredient. Perhaps of paramount importance is the primary structure, or amino acid sequence, of the protein. This sequence dictates how the protein might fold in regular patterns (secondary structure) and how it might appear in three dimensions (tertiary structure). Whether or not a protein is a single unit or contains multiple subunits (quaternary structure) is also a function of primary structure. The tertiary and quaternary structures of proteins are very important to the overall functionality of the proteins. These structures dictate the physicochemical properties of the protein including surface charge, hydrophobicity, stability to heat and chemicals, molecular flexibility, and dissociation behavior. The physicochemical properties of proteins are what determine how it functions in a food system. Thus, if we can understand the physical and chemical properties of a protein we can begin to predict how it might behave in a food. Understanding these principles also allows us to manipulate the physical and chemical characteristics of a protein during food preparation and subsequent processing. We can also use this knowledge to perhaps alter the properties of a protein ingredient to change how it functions in a food.

Figure 7.1 illustrates how the physicochemical properties of a protein might be altered. Food proteins can be altered by processing operations, environmental conditions, or interactions with other ingredients in the food system. Processing conditions that might alter functional properties include heating, drying, freezing, mixing or shearing, and pressurizing. Environmental conditions that influence protein functionality are ionic strength, pH, types of salts present, and oxidation-reduction potential. Environmental conditions tend to overlap with ingredient interactions, since many ingredients have a strong

TABLE 7.2
Major Functional Proteins: Their Sources and Food Use Examples

Major Functional Protein	Source	Use
Gluten: glutenin, gliadin	Wheat	Bakery, pasta, bread
Legumin: 11S and 7S globulins	Legumes	Soy protein isolates, texturized vegetable protein, infant formulas
Casein	Milk	Whipped toppings
Alpha lactalbumin Beta lactoglobulin	Whey	Whey protein isolates, ice cream, infant formula
Myosin	Muscle (beef, poultry)	Frankfurters, deli meats, massaged and tumbled hams, lunchmeats, surimi
Gelatin	Rendering of beef, fish (collagen)	Gelatin desserts, yogurt
Ovalbumin, ovomucin	Egg white	Angel and sponge cakes, soufflés, meringues

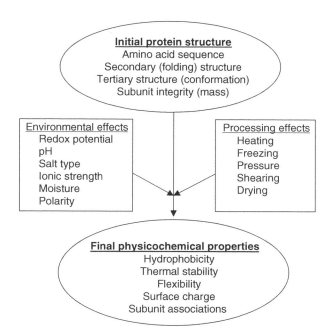

FIGURE 7.1 Effects of environment and processing on the structure and physicochemical properties of proteins.

influence on the environment in which a protein exists. An example is the presence and type of ions and salts that might be added in the form of an ingredient. The presence and types of lipids or fats have a powerful influence on the physicochemical properties of proteins. An example is the inclusion of a small amount of egg yolk in a mixture of egg white proteins that are meant to be foamed. The lipids present in the egg yolk will interact with the egg white proteins and markedly reduce their ability to foam in terms of overall volume and foam stability.

Small changes in formulation (and thus environment) or processing can greatly alter the functionality of food proteins. A classic example is the effect of salt on the functional properties of muscle proteins in processed meats such as frankfurters and lunchmeat (3). The addition of 1.5–2.5% salt solubilizes the meat proteins and allows them to bind water and form an elastic, rubbery gel. This results in the typical texture and sensory quality that we expect in a hot dog or frankfurter. If the salt is not present, the hot dog has poor water binding and gelation, which results in a brittle, tough product.

Storage of food ingredients or finished foods will also influence the functionality of food proteins. Proteins may partially unfold or denature during storage, leading to aggregation and loss of solubility. If a food system contains oxidizing lipid, proteins may react with lipid breakdown products to form unstable aggregates, brown polymers, and otherwise dramatically change in terms of function in the food. When frozen for extended periods, proteins may lose their ability to bind and hold water, thus creating excessive drip in the thawed product.

Because food systems are so complex, protein functionality has been traditionally studied in model systems where many of the interactions with ingredients or processing can be controlled or removed. These studies involve the use of very controlled conditions which are carefully defined so that reproducible results might be obtained. A number of model systems have been developed for each functional property. Functional property tests should be based on a fundamental physical property of a protein. An error that some researchers have repeated is the development of tests that are based solely on equipment available in the researchers' laboratory. In the next section we will examine some of the individual functional properties of proteins that determine their use and application in various foods.

II. FUNCTIONAL PROPERTIES OF FOOD PROTEINS

A. PROTEIN SOLUBILITY

The solubility of a protein many times determines its use in foods. Solubility may be the most important aspect of functionality for a protein. In beverages, foams, and emulsions, a protein must be soluble to have functionality. Foaming, gelation, and water binding are also influenced by solubility. In some cases, e.g., water binding, less soluble proteins may function more efficiently. Using classical biochemical terminology, albumins are water-soluble proteins; globulins are salt soluble; glutelins are soluble at high pH values; and prolamines are most soluble in alcohols. The solubility of a protein is determined by its primary structure—the sequence of amino acids in the protein chain. If a protein has a polar surface due to the presence of polar amino acids, it will have good solubility in a polar solvent such as water. Since the pH of a solution will influence the overall charges on a protein, the use of a protein in a given food is many times dictated by the pH of the food system. Proteins with higher contents of hydrophobic amino acids, fewer charges on their surface, or those which contain many subunits tend to have limited water solubility.

As we will see, heat-treated proteins unfold and tend to form less soluble aggregates. Thus, solubility may be used as an index of denaturation of the protein due to exposure to heat, processing or storage. Solubility is markedly affected by pH, polarity of the solvent, temperature, and concentration of dissolved salts.

1. Effect of pH

Surfaces of proteins have net charges due to their amino acid content and the pH of their environment. Amino acid residues such as argenine or lysine can provide positive charges for protein surfaces, while aspartic or glutamic acids can yield negative charges. The charges present depend on the pH of the food system. When a protein has equal numbers of positive and negative charges on its surface it has minimal solubility. This is called the pI or isoelectric point of the protein. At this point the protein has a net charge of zero. There is minimal solubility because intermolecular repulsion is at a minimum and proteins will tend to aggregate. At pH values above the pI of a protein it has a net negative charge. At pH values below the pI, it will have a net positive charge. In both cases the presence of pronounced surface charges will result in intermolecular repulsion and enhanced solubility.

2. Effect of Salt Concentration

Solubility is also affected by the type and concentration of salts in a food system. As salts increase in concentration proteins become more soluble. This is called "salting in" of a protein and is attributed to the ability of salt ions to enhance the surface charges on proteins. In foods, sodium chloride is commonly used for this purpose. Salt concentrations may be adjusted in a product to enhance the functional properties of the food system. At high salt concentrations, usually above 1 molar, protein solubility decreases. This is thought to be due to salt competing with the proteins for available water for solvation. This effect is called "salting out" and is rarely seen in foods as the concentration of salt required is so high that the food would be inedible.

3. Protein Denaturation

In their natural state, proteins tend to have highly folded structures. Many are "globular" or roughly spherical in shape. This is called their "native" structure. These native structures tend to be very sensitive to conditions which would cause them to change their shape or conformation in a food setting. If a protein unfolds or unravels due to large changes in its surface charges and conformation, it is said to be denatured. For most proteins, denaturation is an irreversible process. Proteins can be denatured by very low or high pH values, organic solvents, high salt concentrations, mechanical shear, and elevated temperatures. Single strands of denatured protein are unstable, leading them to form aggregates which can form gels, foams, or precipitates. The temperature at which proteins denature varies widely due to differences in amino acid sequence and other environmental conditions, such as pH or salt concentration. As denaturation proceeds, protein molecules change in regard to surface charges, shape, size, and hydrophobicity. Most thoroughly denatured proteins are insoluble. When foods are cooked or otherwise thermally processed, the majority of proteins in them become denatured. Denatured protein functions differently from native proteins. Since the solubility of a protein is many times dependent on native structure, denaturation can be simply measured by looking at how soluble a known protein is under certain conditions.

Since denaturation results in loss of solubility, it is undesirable in many food systems where solubility is important. An example is the preparation of protein products for use in foods that rely on protein functionality. Egg whites are pasteurized to destroy pathogenic bacteria; however, the process to do so must be sufficiently gentle so that the finished product can be used in the baking industry to make products such as angel food cake. If the whites were harshly heated, the desired proteins would denature and the ingredient would not function in the finished food. On the other hand, denaturation may cause desirable changes in some food systems, such as in the manufacture of gelatin from collagen or the gelling of egg whites during the cooking of an egg. Some ingredients, such as whey protein concentrates, are available in a variety of degrees of denaturation for application in different products (4, 5). Whey products used for foaming applications have less denaturation than those sold for use as water-binding agents.

4. Measurements of Solubility

One must always remember that any test used to measure a functional property is empirical and thus the results will vary with the test conditions selected. Many solubility tests are based on suspending and stirring a known amount of protein in a buffered solution, followed by centrifugation to remove insoluble components with subsequent protein analysis (colorimetric or Kjeldahl) of the supernatant. The results depend greatly on the protein concentration used, pH, buffer ionic strength, and centrifugal force. Over 70 methods have been published to measure the water-holding capacity and solubility of dairy proteins (6). To obtain results that can be compared to other data and laboratories, it is always best to use a standard method if available. Two commonly used standard methods are published by the American Oil Chemists Society (AOCS) (7) and the American Association of Cereal Chemists (AACC) (8).

B. GELATION

A protein gel is a three-dimensional cross-linked network of protein molecules imbedded in an aqueous solvent (9). Many processed foods are gels such as custards, yogurts, cheeses, frankfurters, and gelatin-based desserts. Most gels are very high in water content (up to 95–98%), yet still have characteristics of solid or rigid food materials. Gelation is based on the denaturation of proteins, followed by their intermolecular association to form matrices which trap water, fat, and other food ingredients. The formation of gels is influenced by heat, pH, pressure or shearing, and the presence of various solvents. The majority of edible food gels based on protein are formed due to heating.

Food gels fall into two categories: thermally reversible and thermally irreversible. Thermally irreversible gels are also called "thermoset" gels and represent the largest group of edible gels. Included in the group are gels based on the muscle protein myosin and ovalbumin, an egg protein. Thermoset gels form chemical bonds that will not break during reheating of the gel and thus remain rigid if reheated. An example would be reheating a cooked egg white. Thermoplastic gels are thermoreversible and will "melt" when reheated due to the reversible nature of the bonds which hold the strands of the gel together. The collagen breakdown product gelatin is the most common example of a thermally reversible gel. Some types of protein, such as alpha-lactalbumin from whey, will form either type of gel depending on the environmental conditions in the food system during heating (5).

1. Properties of Thermoset (Irreversible) Gels

Most thermoset gels are the result of protein unfolding and denaturation followed by aggregation of the molecules into a cross-linked network. During this process, heated proteins partially unfold and form clumps or aggregates. As the "gel-point" temperature is reached, these aggregates unfold further and rapidly cross-link to form a gel (4). This network is generally formed via non-covalent bonds such as hydrophobic interactions and hydrogen bonds. Occasionally, disulfide bonds may be involved. In order for a stable gel to set, there must be a balance between the charges on the denatured protein surfaces and the water molecules in the system. If the protein-protein attraction is too weak, the proteins will remain in solution and a viscous fluid will result. If the attractive forces are too strong, the proteins will aggregate and precipitate. The proper amount of denaturation will result in proteins that interact sufficiently to form a matrix that will also hold a large amount of water.

2. Factors Affecting Thermoset Gel Properties

As one might predict, environmental conditions such as pH and salt concentration, as well as heating rate and final temperature greatly affect the properties of a thermoset gel. Thermoset gels can be opaque and turbid or transparent and clear. Turbid gels are formed when repulsive forces between the protein molecules are low (such as pH values close to the isoelectric point). When heated, the proteins tend to form grape-like aggregate clusters which then are cross-linked together upon further heating (10). Transparent gels are more likely to form when protein molecules are highly charged and repulse each other until denaturation occurs. In transparent gels the protein molecules tend to form structures which resemble "strings of pearls" where individual molecules form chains which occasionally cross-link with other strands. Various researchers have examined the differing properties of gels formed from a single type of protein when conditions of pH, ionic strength, and heating are varied (11). Manipulation of environmental factors can produce turbid, transparent, or hybrid gels from the same protein.

3. Thermoplastic Gels (Thermoreversible)

The most extensively studied protein which forms thermoplastic gels is gelatin, a product of refined collagen. Collagen is a triple-stranded helical protein used in a variety of structural roles in many species. When heated it dissociates into single proteins strands called gelatin that assume random coil configurations. When gelatin is dissolved in hot water, it attempts to reform its original triple helix structure. If the mixture is cooled, gelatin strands will randomly reform sections of the helical structure resulting in the formation of a cross-linked matrix. The sections where intermolecular bonding occurs are called "junction zones." The bonds used to form the matrix are hydrogen bonds, which are thermally reversible. Heating a gelatin gel will cause the hydrogen bonds in a junction zone to dissociate and the matrix/gel will melt. Upon cooling, the gel will reform.

4. Measurements of Gel Properties

As with solubility, a range of functional tests for protein gels exists. Although it might seem appropriate to use a model system where only the protein and water are studied, the impact of other food system components, such as fat or ground particulate matter (such as spices), can be very great and cannot always be ignored. In general, the more simple a model system is, the less likely it will mimic what occurs in a real food, such as a frankfurter (2).

Quality control operations in the food industry have developed a number of empirical tests to relate the properties of gelled products to their acceptability by consumers. An example would be measuring the amount of force required to shear through a cross-section of a frankfurter. Samples of finished product can be gathered off the processing line and sheared as a means of ensuring proper product formulation and processing. However, these types of tests are only valuable for measuring specific products which that particular company produces.

A common test used to test gel strengths is the "torsion test" (12). A gel of appropriate size and shape is twisted in a rheometer until the gel breaks or ruptures. The force required to rupture the cross-sectional area of the gel can be calculated and compared to other properties, such as sensory evaluation results. Several gel strength tests have been widely accepted for use in this manner (13, 14).

C. WATER BINDING

Water binding is an important functional property for several reasons: 1) most foods contain high amounts of water and if their chemistry changes in a manner that would cause the formation of free water or drip loss, consumers would be displeased, 2) increasing the amount of water a product can hold effectively can increase the profitability of a given product, and 3) both product yield and sensory quality are highly dependent on the proper moisture content of a finished food. Water-binding capacity is the amount of water that is bound or retained by a protein under highly defined conditions.

Water is usually be bound to the surface of a protein by hydrogen bonding, which is sometimes called dipole bonding. Hydrogen bonding results from water's interaction with the R group of amino acids which are dipoles, such as serine and threonine, or ionic, such as lysine or aspartic acid. Water bound to the surface of proteins in this manner is called "monolayer" water and is very tightly associated with the protein. Other water associated with the protein or protein matrices can be trapped in capillary structures and pores. In food systems, water can also be held in cells and other structural networks. Water that is not associated with the monolayer on the protein surface is called free water and moves unhindered throughout the food system. Depending on the food or model system, water-binding capacity tests measure a mixture of the free and bound water present.

1. Factors Influencing Water Binding

For a given food system, the protein concentration, temperature, salt type and concentration, and degree of denaturation impact on the water binding exhibited. In addition, small polar molecules, such as sugars or sugar alcohols, will enhance water binding by proteins in general. As the protein concentration increases, so does the water binding observed. Generally, water binding increases as temperature increases. In some cases the proteins will form gels, which will enhance the binding of water by the system. Many types of whey protein and soy protein isolates will form gels when heated above 80°C. Enhanced binding in gels is due to water being bound by both hydrogen bonds and by being trapped in pores.

Ions also influence water binding. Sodium chloride binds to charged groups on protein surfaces and weakens intermolecular bonds. This is a positive effect in systems which utilize muscle fibers as part of the structural elements of the food. Salt allows the muscle proteins to distance themselves from others within the muscle fiber and thus increase the number of sites for water to bind. In various muscle types, water binding may be increased 2–3 fold by the presence of salt (15).

The pH of a system markedly influences its ability to bind water. This is due to changes in the surface charges on a protein as the pH is altered. Water binding is lowest at the isoelectric point (pI) of a protein. As the pH is adjusted away from the isoelectric point the ionic charges

on the protein increase dramatically and water binding is enhanced. As the pH is lowered from the isoelectric point the protein assumes a net positive charge. Conversely, as the pH is increased, a net negative charge is seen.

2. Methods of Measurement

Water-binding model systems must be carefully defined if reproducible results are expected. Most of the methods are empirical and are usually designed for a specific product or application. At least 15 different methods have been developed to measure the water binding of various muscle/meat proteins (16). In general, two main types of tests exist. One is based on sorption—the adsorptions of water by a dry powder of protein. The other is sometimes called "expressible moisture" where a product is subjected to a force and the amount of moisture expelled is measured. The force is usually pressure or centrifugation. These types of tests must be carefully designed so that the actual internal structure of the gel or food is not destroyed when the pressure is applied. This would lead to an underestimation of the water binding for the system since water that normally would have been trapped in the matrix would be expressed (17).

D. EMULSIFICATION

An emulsion is a mixture of two immiscible liquids in which one is dispersed in the other in the form of droplets (18). It is common practice to call the liquid in the droplets the dispersed, internal, or discontinuous phase. The surrounding phase is called the external or continuous phase. Emulsions in which the dispersed phase is a lipid are called "oil in water" emulsions (o/w). Water in oil emulsions contain droplets of water dispersed in a lipid continuous phase. Egg yolk and milk are examples of natural emulsions. Many manufactured foods are intentional emulsions including ice cream, salad dressings, chocolate, mayonnaise, cakes, frosting, butter, and spreads. Food emulsions are far more complex than a droplet of one phase suspended in another. Foods contain many other materials such as air, particulates or other dispersed solids, partially crystallized fat, and gels.

1. Principles of Emulsification

When a liquid is exposed to air, the surface between them is in a state of tension. This so-called "surface tension" is due to the attractive forces between molecules in the liquid that are enhanced by exposure to air. In lay terms, the molecules "bunch" together to decrease their exposure to the air surface. When two immiscible liquids, such as water and oil are in contact, the region of contact is called the interface, with the development of "interfacial tension." As the interfacial area increases, the stability of the mixture decreases. An example would be the creation of temporary emulsion of oil in water by forming millions of small droplets of oil suspended in the water phase. One can imagine creating this mixture by blending several milliliters of oil into a cup of water in a high speed mixer. This type of mixture is called a "temporary emulsion," for although there would initially be millions of oil droplets, they would rapidly coalesce into a separate oil layer which would form on top of the aqueous phase. Coalesced droplets have less surface area exposed to the water, and thus are more stable. Vinegar and oil salad dressing is a classic example of temporary emulsions.

To stabilize emulsions it is necessary to add molecules which decrease the interfacial tension between mixtures of lipids and water. Surfactants are molecules that contain both hydrophobic (non-polar) and hydrophylic (polar) regions in their structure. When added to a system that contains both lipids and water, surfactants rapidly migrate to the interfaces between the two phases. At the interface, the surfactants orient their polar region towards the aqueous phase and their non-polar region towards the lipid phase. Since proteins contain amino acid residues that can be polar and non-polar they can be excellent surfactants in food systems. Figure 7.2 illustrates the coating of an oil or fat droplet with a protein molecule. Once the droplet or air bubble is coated, the interfacial tension between the two

phases is markedly lowered and the tendency to coalesce is greatly reduced. The simplistic illustration in Figure 7.2 shows a single molecule of protein unfolding on the oil surface. In a real emulsion, there are thousands of molecules involved on the surface of a single droplet. If a sufficient reduction in interfacial tension is achieved, the emulsion can be stable for long periods of time.

2. Factors Affecting Protein-Based Emulsions

Food emulsions are complex systems which are normally created by using large amounts of energy to form very small particles of one phase which become suspended in another. Higher energy inputs normally result in smaller droplets and enhanced activity of any surfactants that are present. To work well as a surfactant, a protein must be able to migrate to the interface, orient polar and non-polar side chains into the proper phases, and form a stable film around the droplet. In many cases proteins may partially unfold or denature during these activities. After unfolding and orientation towards the proper phase, proteins form multiple layers on the droplet surface due to intermolecular ionic, hydrogen, and hydrophobic bonding between unfolded protein strands. The formation of superior emulsions by proteins relates to their ability to form viscous yet flexible films around the surface of droplets (19).

Most food emulsions are oil in water. In forming o/w emulsions, the initial water solubility of the protein is very important. Therefore, factors such as protein concentration, pH, salts, ionic strength, and temperature strongly affect the emulsification ability of proteins. Other factors that influence their ability to emulsify are related to the physicochemical properties of the protein, such as surface charge, surface hydrophobicity, molecular flexibility, ease of denaturation, and dissociation behavior of subunits. Table 7.3 lists the factors which can be important to the formation and stability of protein-based emulsions.

Since proteins vary in physicochemical properties, it is not unexpected that researchers have seen varying results when studying the effects of pH, salts, and temperature on the emulsification ability of proteins. Because proteins have unique primary, secondary, and quaternary structures, environmental effects such as pH must be determined for each individual protein. In general, proteins near their isoelectric point (pI) are poor emulsifiers, presumably due to poor solubility. As the pH is adjusted away from the pI, improvement in emulsification is generally seen and is probably due to enhanced solubility. Very low or high pH may lead to poor emulsification even though the proteins might be very soluble. In this case, the proteins are so highly charged they do not interact to form films on the surface of the dispersed phase. If proteins are coated with an excess of charges they will not form cohesive, flexible films (19). Proteins with multiple subunits, such as the soybean storage protein legumin, may exhibit

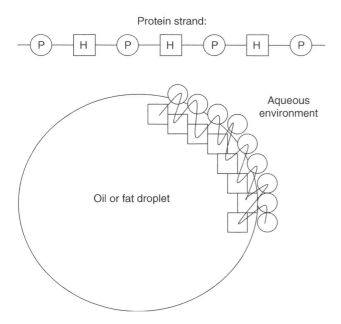

Protein strand:

FIGURE 7.2 Formation of a protein stabilized emulsion. The protein is represented by the connected circles and squares, which are defined as follows:
Squares are hydrophobic (H) amino acid residues which orient towards the oil or fat phase.
Circles are hydrophylic (P) amino acid residues which orient towards the aqueous phase.
The continuous line represents the peptide bonds connecting the amino acids.

TABLE 7.3
Factors Affecting Formation and Stability of Protein-Based Emulsions

Environmental factors	Temperature, pH, salt concentration, salt type, ionic strength, other ions, other food components
Protein characteristics	Solubility, ease of denaturation, surface hydrophobicity, surface charge, isoelectric point, flexibility, elasticity of protein film
Processing parameters	Amount and rate of energy input (shear), oil or fat type, oxidative state of lipid, temperature
Aqueous phase	Viscosity

improved emulsification activity at pH values where the subunits are encouraged to dissociate (20).

Several researchers have shown that surface hydrophobicity can be highly related to the ability of proteins to act as emulsifiers (21). In general, proteins that are water soluble but which have large numbers of hydrophobic groups on their surface tend to be superior emulsifiers. With increased surface hydrophobicity, a larger portion of the protein strand might be able to interact with the oil or fat droplet and form stronger protein films (22). Results have shown that proteins with high surface hydrophobicities, such as casein or bovine serum albumin (BSA), are superior emulsifiers compared to proteins with low surface hydrophobicities, such as collagen or gelatin (21).

3. Methods of Measurement

As with other model systems tests, the results of protein emulsification evaluations are often highly empirical. Comparison of results between laboratories is only possible when strict testing conditions are maintained. Although the absolute numbers obtained in these tests may vary from lab to lab, the ranking of different proteins in terms of ability to emulsify or emulsion stability are often similar. The results seen in rapid tests may not give the same results seen in a true food system. Many food companies, however, cannot wait a year for results when they are evaluating proteins for use in products under development and subject to an accelerated development time table.

Emulsions are commonly tested for two parameters: stability and capacity. Emulsification capacity is normally measured as the maximum amount of oil a protein may emulsify. A classic test of emulsification capacity is that of Wang and Kinsella (23), where the maximum amount of oil that a protein can emulsify is determined by a titration method. Oil is added to a protein solution in a blender or mixer until the emulsion fails, which is determined by a rapid decrease in viscosity. Advantages are that the procedure is quick and simple. Disadvantages are that the results are highly dependent on the equipment used to generate the emulsions and the protein:lipid ratios encountered in the test are not commonly encountered in food systems (24). Another widely used technique is the Emulsification Activity Index (EAI) developed by Pearse and Kinsella (25). In this assay, the interfacial area created

in an emulsion is measured by a spectrophotometric assay. As the ability of a protein to emulsify increases, smaller and smaller emulsion droplets are formed, which can be measured by light scattering principles. Advantages of this method are that it is a rapid technique that does not rely on the use of an external force to break the emulsion. Disadvantages are: 1) emulsions must be prepared under very standardized conditions (e.g., sample container volume, homogenizer or mixer manufacturer, speed or power settings) and 2) several studies have found poor correlations between EAI and emulsion stability (24).

Emulsion stability can be measured by a variety of methods. Choice of method depends on the type of instability or emulsion breakdown observed in the actual food system where the protein may be used. Separation and clustering of fat or oil droplets on the top of an emulsion is called "creaming" and is a marked sign of emulsion breakdown. A standard test for creaming (26) involves the placement of an emulsion in a graduated cylinder which is held in an environmental chamber. The height of the boundary between the top of the creaming layer and the residual emulsion is measured as it decreases with time. Advantages of the test are that it can be set up rapidly and it can be easily used to determine how pH, ionic strength, and protein concentration impact emulsion stability. Disadvantages are that lengthy storage times under highly controlled conditions are required (24). A more rapid test is the Emulsion Volume Index where centrifugation in microhematocrit tubes is used to accelerate the forces which cause emulsion breakdown (27). Advantages are that analysis times are much shorter and other researchers have found correlations between EVI and longer term stability testing of actual products (24). If time is not essential, it is possible to use a long-term storage test to evaluate emulsion stability by measuring droplet size distribution and concentration in a hermetically sealed container (28). Although the test can duplicate actual storage conditions of products, it may take over a year to complete (24).

E. FOAMING

Emulsions and foams are similar types of food systems in that they contain two distinct phases. In foams, the liquid or solid continuous phase surrounds a dispersed gaseous phase which is usually air. Many times a protein which emulsifies well will also foam well. The first step in the formation of a foam is the migration of proteins to the interface between air bubbles and the aqueous phase. At the interface the protein will unfold and orient their non-polar regions toward the air phase. As proteins adsorb on the bubble surface, they begin to form layers of partially denatured proteins which encapsulate the air bubble and prevent the foam from collapsing (29). Foams may be produced by mechanical agitation (whipping) or sparging, which is the injection of gas through very small orifices to produce bubbles. Most food foams are produced by whipping and include meringues, soufflés, whipped cream, non-dairy whipped toppings, angel food or sponge cakes, and ice cream. Yeast leavened breads are foams that are produced by the trapping of carbon dioxide bubbles by the gluten protein matrix.

1. Factors Affecting Foaming

As with other functional properties, solubility plays a critical role in foaming. Good foaming proteins also exhibit one or more of the following molecular properties: 1) high rates of diffusion and adsorption at the interface, 2) ability to unfold and denature at the interface, and 3) ability to form intermolecular associations with other molecules that result in the formation of cohesive films around the air bubble (1). The surface hydrophobicity of proteins correlates with its ability to form foams (21). Since it is important for a protein to unfold on the interface, the foaming ability of some proteins can be improved by a mild heat treatment or chemical modification which loosens the protein structure and allows it to unfold more rapidly. Enhanced film formation through increased intermolecular bonding is also generally seen. Excessive denaturation will decrease foam formation and stability by decreasing initial protein solubility and causing protein films to form at the interface that are inflexible and stiff. This is a result of excessive intermolecular interaction between protein strands.

In regard to foaming ability, egg whites (albumen) form some of the highest quality foams due to the properties of the constituent proteins, ovalbumin, globulins, and ovomucoid. During the foaming of egg whites, acids such as cream of tartar (potassium acid tartrate) are added after an initial whipping period. The acid lowers the pH and reduces the net charge on the protein which allows the protein strands to interact more strongly. It also facilitates the denaturation of proteins to increase the elasticity of protein films around the air bubbles. Overall, a more stable film results. Addition of the tartrate before the initial foaming causes the proteins to unfold prematurely and interact before they reach the air bubble surface, which results in decreased foam volumes and stabilities (1).

In most cases, the foaming ability of proteins in inhibited by the presence of lipids. Contamination of egg white

with as little as 0.03% egg yolk completely inhibits foaming (30). It is theorized that lipid is absorbed at the air/water interface within the foam and causes the protein film to rupture. Conversely, high concentrations of saturated fat can stabilize foams. An example is whipped dairy cream in which cold coalesced fat droplets can surround protein-encapsulated air bubbles, resulting in a very stable foam.

The amount of energy used during foam formation impacts on foam stability. Energy inputs must be sufficient to create very small air bubbles and assist in the denaturation of proteins due to shear forces. Over-whipping, however, may cause the foam to dehydrate and collapse, leading to decreased foam volume and stability. Energy input must not cause the proteins to denature prior to encountering air bubbles. Denatured protein may fail to reach the air bubble surface and precipitate by interacting with other protein molecules in solution. The denatured protein may also form more brittle films on the air bubble surface.

2. Methods of Measurement

As previously mentioned, the results of functional tests many times are empirical and depend on the methods used and the laboratory in which they are performed. Several methods have been published for foaming proteins, including shaking, sparging (gas injection), and whipping (31). Most food foams are prepared by whipping. Results from a model system test that is based on whipping might be better correlated to actual foods since the method of preparation more closely resembles actual food preparation. Both foam volume and foam stability are important in the manufacture of foods, so it would be valuable to gather data in a model system on those two parameters. Wilde and Clark (29) have published foamability and stability methods that have been widely accepted. The methods use inexpensive equipment but care should be taken to use identical procedures between different laboratories. Another widely used test determines the percent overrun of a foam and involves the removal of samples at various times to determine foam density (32). Stability tests for foams commonly use a "half-life" determination where the time for half of the foam to break down or half the original liquid volume to return to the liquid state is measured.

III. APPLICATION OF FUNCTIONAL PROPERTIES

A. INTENTIONAL MODIFICATION OF PROTEIN FUNCTIONAL PROPERTIES

The manufacture of many modern food products relies on the use of proteins for their functionality. The proteins may be a natural constituent of the food, such as in muscle, or the proteins may be added as an ingredient due to their ability to solubilize, bind water, gel, emulsify, or foam. As we have discussed, the functional properties of proteins are interrelated and associated with the structures of the protein molecule. Although we can obtain protein from a multitude of sources, not all proteins are highly functional due to their primary, secondary, tertiary, or quaternary structures. For example, several yeast proteins and many plant proteins have limited functionality when used in their native conformation. Solubility may be a problem for some types of proteins and require the addition of salts to enhance their functionality. An example is in the manufacture of frankfurters where 0.5–1.5% salt is commonly used to enhance the functionality of myosin in gel formation. Protein modification has the potential to enhance the use of many less functional and less expensive proteins to perhaps make foods more economical and perhaps more desirable in a nutritional sense.

Modification is the intentional alteration of the physicochemical properties of a protein by chemical, physical, or enzymatic means to improve functional properties (33). Many of the alterations simply increase solubility, since it is paramount to most functional properties. For proteins with substantial quaternary structures, such as the legume storage proteins, improvement is related to the disruption of the bonding between individual subunits. In other cases it might be the alteration of amino acids on the protein surface to make them more polar or the disruption of hydrophobic cores of proteins to decrease their molecular density.

As we have learned, a protein's ability to emulsify or foam is related to its ability to migrate to an interface and denature or unfold. Some types of modification will "loosen" up the native structure of a protein through chemical, physical (e.g., heating), or enzymatic means to allow the protein to migrate, unfold, and interact more substantially on the interface in either emulsions or foams. These types of treatments can also enhance the ability of water to bind within a protein or the ability of protein strands to interact to form gels; thus both water-binding and gelation behavior of proteins can be enhanced by modification.

1. Chemical Modification

A variety of chemical modifications have been used to enhance the functionality of proteins from plants, animals, and microorganisms. These generally involve the use of a chemical agent to modify the protein by reacting to covalently alter the amino acid residues on its surface. Acylation reactions that involve the direct addition of chemical groups through the R groups (side chains) of amino acids have the most potential to modify proteins. Researchers have examined modification of surface charge via the creation of esters with acetic, succinic, phosphoric, and a number of fatty acids. Sugars and other oligosaccharides have also been attached to the surfaces of proteins (33).

The common sites for acylation are the epsilon and alpha amino groups of proteins. Lysine is a particularly reactive amino acid, followed by tyrosine and cysteine. Alteration of surface charge and surface hydrophobicity through these modifications is the likely mechanism for functionality improvement.

For chemically altered proteins to be acceptable for human foods they must be nontoxic and digestible (34). Typically, modified proteins can be tested using protocols outlined by the Food and Drug Administration (FDA). A number of different tests can be used to determine the impact on nutritive value (33). Because lysine is an essential amino acid for many species and is also a major site for modification, decreases in nutritive value are seen in chemically modified proteins. Protein Efficiency Ratios (PER) for modified proteins typically range from 40–100% of the values for their unmodified counterparts (33). Since physical and enzymatic methods do not alter amino acid composition dramatically, they are preferred methods for modifying proteins.

2. Enzymatic Modification

Enzymatic modification of proteins includes partial hydrolysis, covalent attachment of functional groups, and the incorporation of cross-links between protein molecules (35).

Protein hydrolysis is the most widely used of these techniques. Proteolysis is easy to control, very rapid, and occurs under ambient conditions. There is very low risk for the formation of toxic residues. Proteolysis is considered by many to be the most cost-effective way to enhance protein functionality (35). Because proteolysis produces peptides that are smaller in size and which contain less secondary structure than the original proteins, their solubility is increased. Enhanced solubility is directly related to the degree of hydrolysis and related to increases in functional properties such as foaming and emulsification. Partial hydrolysis has been used to improve the functionality of a wide variety of proteins from beef, chicken, dairy, fish, yeast, corn, wheat, and peas. Proteolysis is commercially used to prepare functional protein products for use as food ingredients. Depending on the source of protein, optimal peptide size for one functionality, such as foaming, does not always equate to optimal functionality for another, such as emulsification. Proteolysis is quite interesting in that it is possible to fine tune the process to obtain protein ingredients that are optimized for a given functionality.

Enhanced functionality due to cross-linking or covalent attachment of a hydrophylic or hydrophobic residue is also an area of intense research. Several very functional natural proteins, such as ovomucin, the superior foaming protein from egg white, have surfaces that are highly polar due the presence of glycosyl groups. Researchers have been able to produce protein products with excellent foaming abilities from soy and casein using enzymes which attach very polar groups to their surface (36). Another enzyme, peptidoglutaminase, has also been examined as a means of improving functionality (37). The enzyme increases the negative charges on a protein by converting glutamine and aparagine to their negatively charged counterparts, glutamic and aspartic acids. This technology appears to have potential for widespread use since many insoluble proteins from soy, peas, beans, dairy, and wheat have substantial numbers of glutamine and aparagine residues on their surface.

3. Physical Modification

Heat is the major way in which physical modifications are carried out with proteins. For example, the industry is replete with many soy protein products that have been modified by heating to improve foaming, emulsification, water-binding, and gelation properties (38). Heat causes proteins to partially denature through changes in secondary and primary structure. In theory, this should increase the functionality of the protein by improving its ability to unfold at interfaces and form films around air bubbles or lipid droplets. In particular, the gelling ability of several proteins, such as those from dairy whey, has been substantially improved through heat treatment (4). Many of the procedures used to manufacture heated protein ingredients for use in formulated foods are proprietary. It is known, however, that the procedures used to maximize the functionality of a protein source for one application are usually not the same for another. In other words, heating techniques used to enhance foaming or gelling are not the same as for emulsification (4).

A specific type of modification of plant proteins using heat has widespread application. Texturized Vegetable Protein (TVP) is commonly used in the processed food and food service industry to bind water and fat. Most TVP products are made from soy and are manufactured under very specific environmental conditions of temperature, pH, ionic strength, and pressure. TVP is produced using extrusion techniques where the proteins are subjected to heat, pressure, and shear forces simultaneously. The proteins are extensively denatured and insoublized; however, the resulting matrix is almost sponge-like in its ability to bind other liquids, such as excess fat and moisture, in food systems.

One interesting application of physical alteration of proteins is the manufacture of several fat substitutes through the manipulation of their physical characteristics. Using a process generically called "microparticulation,"

proteins from milk and/or eggs are denatured and refolded into smaller, denser particles that can act as lubricants during the chewing and swallowing of foods. These materials have the mouthfeel of lipids, but are actually a blend of proteins and water. Simplesse (registered trade name by the NutraSweet Company) is an example. Since these ingredients are proteins, they cannot be used in products that will see extremes of environment, such as heat or pH, since they would most likely denature under such conditions. Their use is probably limited to products that will only see low temperature heating processes, such as pasteurization.

IV. SUMMARY

The functional properties of proteins are defined as their physical or chemical properties that affect foods during their preparation, processing, storage, and consumption. They contribute greatly to the quality and acceptability of a wide range of natural and processed/prepared foods in the food supply. Proteins are considered by many experts to be the most multifunctional components of foods in that they can play many different roles in foods. Natural products made from meat, poultry, dairy, eggs, cereal grains, and legumes, as well as the majority of formulated foods developed and marketed through the food industry, all rely on the functionality of proteins for their acceptability and quality.

The functional properties include solubility, water-holding ability or capacity, gelation, emulsification, and foaming. Solubility is paramount for the successful use of proteins in most food systems. To function in a food the protein must be able to migrate throughout the aqueous phase to seek interfaces (foaming and emulsification), hold water, or form extensive three-dimensional networks (gelation). The solubility of a protein is determined by its amino acid sequence and is greatly influenced by environmental factors such as solvent polarity, pH, temperature, and concentration of dissolved salts.

Food gels are diverse structures primarily composed of immobilized water held within a cross-linked protein matrix. Both thermally reversible (gelatin) and thermally irreversible (frankfurters) gels are important food products. The ability of a protein to gel is primarily evaluated by measuring the texture or strength of the gel using a torsion test.

Water binding by proteins is influenced by temperature, concentration of protein, concentration of salt, degree of protein denaturation, and the presence of other compounds, such as sugars or alcohols. Two main methods, water absorption and expressible moisture, are commonly used to measure the water binding of proteins.

Emulsification and foaming are cousins in the protein functionality family. They both rely on similar properties of the protein in the food system, such as solubility and ease of denaturation. Proteins must be able to migrate to the interface formed with the second phase of oil in emulsions and air in foams. Proteins must be able to form cohesive, multilayered, flexible films around droplets of lipid or air. The main model tests involve measuring the overall ability of a protein to emulsify or foam, as well as the stability of the emulsion or foam created.

The functional properties of proteins are often measured using model systems that can vary widely from researcher to researcher. To make the results of our research valuable, we must strive to use protocols that are widely accepted and used by our colleagues. In many cases, model systems do not mimic the conditions seen in real food systems. We tend to measure, and correctly so, the fundamental properties that are related to the desired functional property seen in the food.

The modification of proteins by chemical, physical, and enzymatic methods has increased the utilization of less conventional protein sources and decreased the costs of manufacture for a number of food products. Most methods attempt to increase the solubility of proteins. Although chemical methods are effective, there are questions regarding safety and nutritional losses. Enzymatic and physical methods have been adapted for use in the protein ingredients industry. Heating remains the most widely used modification technique and has been very successful in increasing the functionality of a wide range of proteins, particularly those from soybeans and whey. Texturization produces very useful protein ingredients which have the ability to adsorb excess moisture and fat in foods. Lastly, the ability of proteins to be compressed allows them to be used as fat substitutes in foods.

REFERENCES

1. Smith, D.M. and Culbertson, J.D. 2000. Proteins: Functional Properties, Ch. 9. In *Food Chemistry: Principles and Applications*, G.L. Christen and J.S. Smith (Eds.). pp. 131–148. STS. West Sacramento, CA.

2. Smith, D.M. 2003. Measurement of Functional Properties: Overview of Protein Functionality Testing. Unit B5.1.1–B5.1.9. In *Current Protocols in Food Analytical Chemistry, Vol. 1*, E.W. Harkins (Ed.). pp. Unit B5.1.1. John Wiley & Sons, Inc., New York.

3. Schwenke, K. D. 1997. Enzyme and chemical modification of proteins. Ch 13. In *Food Proteins and Their Applications*, S. Damodaran and A. Paraf (Eds.). pp. 393–423. Marcel Dekker, Inc., New York.

4. Beuschel, B.C., Culbertson, J.D., Partridge, J.A. and Smith, D.M. 1992. Gelation and emulsification properties of partially insolubilized whey protein concentrates. J. Food Sci. 57:605–609.

5. Hung, T.Y. and Smith, D.M. 1993. Dynamic rheological properties and microstructure of partially insolubilized whey protein concentrate and chicken breast salt soluble protein gels. J. Agric. Food Chem. 41:1372–1378.

6. Kneifel, W. Paquin, P, Albert, T. and Richard, J.P. 1991. Water-holding capacity of proteins with special regard to milk proteins and methodological aspects—A review. J. Dairy Sci. 74:2027–2041.

7. AOCS. 1999. Official Methods and Recommended Practices, 5th ed. American Oil Chemists Society, Champaign, Ill.

8. AACC. 2000. Approved Methods, 10th ed. American Association of Cereal Chemists, St. Paul, MN.

9. Clark, A. H. 1992. Gels and Gelling. Ch. 5. In *Protein Functionality in Foods*, H.G. Schwartzberg and R.W. Hartel (Eds.). pp. 263–305. Marcel Dekker, Inc., New York.

10. Doi, E. 1993. Gels and gelling of globular proteins. Trends Food Sci. Technol. 4:1–5.

11. Foegeding, E.A. and Hamann, D.D. 1992. Physico-chemical aspects of muscle tissue behavior. Ch 8, in *Physical Chemistry of Foods*. H.G. Schwartzberg and R.W. Hartel (Eds.). pp. 423–441. Marcel Dekker, Inc., New York.

12. Gel Consultants, Inc. 1991. Torsion Gelometer Manual, Gel Consultants, Inc., Raleigh, NC.

13. Vittayanont, M., Steffe, J.F., Flegler, S.L. and Smith, D.M. 2003. Gelation of chicken pectoralis major myosin and heat-denatured beta-lactoglobulin. J. Agric. Food Chem. 51:760–765.

14. Lee, C.M., Filipi, I.Y., Xiong, Y., Smith, D.M., Regenstein, J., Damodaran, S., Ma, C.Y. and Haque, Z.U. 1997. Standardized failure compression test of protein gels from a collaborative study. J. Food Sci. 62:1163–1166.

15. Richardson, R.I. and Jones, J.M. 1987. The effects of salt concentration and pH upon water binding, water-holding and protein extractability of turkey meat. Int. J. Food Sci. Technol. 22:683–692.

16. Honikel, K.O. 1987. How to measure the water binding capacity of meat: Recommendation of standardized methods. In *Evaluation and Control of Meat Quality in Pigs*, P.V. Tarrant, G. Eikelenboom and G. Monin (Eds.). pp. 129–142. Martinus Nijhoff. Dordrecht, the Netherlands.

17. Krocher, P.N. and Foegeding, E.A. 1993. Microcentifuge-based method for measuring water-holding of protein gels. J. Food Sci. 58:1040–1046.

18. Cameron, D.R., Weber, M.E., Idziak, E.S., Neufeld, R.J. and Cooper, D.G. 1991. Determination of interfacial areas in emulsions using turbidimetric and droplet size data; Correction of the formula for emulsifying activity index. J. Agric. Food Chem. 39:655–659.

19. Dickinson, E. 1994. Protein stabilized emulsions. J. Food Engineering 8:59–74.

20. Halling, P.J. 1981. Protein stabilized foams and emulsions. Crit. Rev. Food Sci. Nutr. 15:155–203.

21. Nakai, S., Li-Chan, E. and Arteaga, G.E. 1996. Measurement of surface hydrophobicity. In *Methods of Testing Protein Functionality*, G.M. Hall (Ed.). pp. 226–259. Blackie Academic and Professional. New York.

22. Damordaran, S. 1997. Protein-stabilized foams and emulsions. Ch. 3. In *Food Proteins and Their Applications*, S. Damodaran and A. Paraf (Eds.). pp. 57–110. Marcel Dekker Inc., New York.

23. Wang, J.C. and Kinsella, J.E. 1976. Functional properties of novel proteins: Alfalfa leaf protein. J. Food Sci. 41:286–292.

24. Smith, D.M. 2003. Measurement of Functional Properties: Overview of Protein Functionality Testing. Unit B5.1.1–B5.1.9. In *Current Protocols in Food Analytical Chemistry, Vol. 1*, E.W. Harkins (Ed.). pp. B5.1.6. John Wiley & Sons, Inc., New York.

25. Pearce, K.N. and Kinsella, J.E. 1978. Emulsifying properties of proteins: Evaluation of a turbidimetric technique. J. Agric. Food Chem. 26:716–723.

26. Weiss, Jochen. 2002. Emulsion Stability Determination. Unit D3.4.1–D3.4.17. In *Current Protocols in Food Analytical Chemistry*, Vol. 1, E.W. Harkins (Ed.). pp. D3.4.4. John Wiley & Sons, Inc., New York.

27. Fligner, K.L., Fligner, M.A. and Mangino, M.E. 1991. Accelerated tests for predicting long-term creaming stability of infant formula emulsion systems. Food Hydrocolloids 5:269–280.

28. McClements, D.J. 1999. *Food Emulsions: Principles, Practice and Techniques.* CRC Press, Boca Raton, FL.

29. Wilde, P.J. and Clark, D. C. 1996. Foam formation and stability. Ch. 5. In *Methods of Testing Protein Functionality*, G.M. Hall (Ed.). pp. 110–152. Blackie Academic and Professional, New York.

30. Dickenson, E. 1994. Protein stabilized emulsions. J. Food Engineering. pp. 59–74.

31. Phillips, L.G., German, J.G., O'Neil, T.E., Foegeding, E.A., Harwalker, V.R., Kilara, A., Lewis, B.A., Mangino, M.E., Morr, C.V., Regenstein, J.M., Smith, D.M. and Kinsella, J.E. 1990. Standardized procedure for measuring foaming properties of three proteins: A collaborative study. J. Food Sci. 55:1441–1444.

32. Phillips, L.G., Haque, Z. and Kinsella, J.E. 1987. A method for the measurement of foam formation and stability. J. Food Sci. 52:1074–1077.

33. Schwenke, K.D. 1997. Enzyme and chemical modification of proteins. Ch. 13, In *Food Proteins and Their Applications*, S. Damoraran and A. Paraf (Eds.). pp. 393–423. Marcel Dekker, Inc., New York.

34. Singh, H. 1991. Modification of food proteins by covalent cross-linking. Trends in Food Sci. Tech. 2:196–200.

35. Vojdani, F. and Whitaker, J.R. 1994. Chemical and enzymatic modification of proteins for improved functionality. Ch. 9. In *Protein Functionality in Food Systems*, N.V. Hettiarachchy and G.R. Ziegler (Eds.). pp. 261–309. Marcel Dekker, Inc., New York.

36. Kato, A., Wada, T., Kobayashi, K., Seguro, K. and Motoki, M. 1991. Ovomucin-food protein conjugates prepared through the transglutaminase reaction. Agric. Biol. Chem. 55:1027–1031.

37. Hamada, J.S. 1992. Effects of heat and proteolysis on deamidation of food proteins using peptidoglutaminase. J. Agric. Food Chem. 40:719–823.

38. Hill, S.E. 1996. Emulsions. Ch. 6. In *Methods of Testing Protein Functionality*, G.M. Hall (Ed.). pp. 153–185. Blackie Academic and Professional, New York.

8 Lipid Chemistry and Biochemistry

Mark P. Richards
Muscle Biology & Meat Science Laboratory, University of Wisconsin–Madison

CONTENTS

I. INTRODUCTION

Although the intake of excess fat may result in significant health problems, it is important to note that fats are a critical part of a proper diet. The human body can produce most fatty acids but certain "essential" fatty acids (e.g., linoleic and linolenic acid) are typically derived from lipid-containing foods since the body cannot produce them. In addition, fats in foods are sources of vitamins A, D, E, and K. There is considerable evidence that therapeutic components that can improve human health are endogenous to food fats. Fats also contribute unique flavors and physical properties to the foods that consumers find desirable.

The two major classes of fats in foods are phospholipids (PL) and triacylglycerols (TAG). Phospholipids are constituents of cell membranes while TAG are fatty globules that exist primarily as coalesced droplets in biological tissues. Other types of fats include sterols, waxes, and carotenoids. Lipid is a term used to encompass all types of compounds that are soluble in organic solvents and therefore classified as fats. Olive oil contains only triacylglycerols while muscle foods contain both PL and triacylglycerols. Food emulsions can contain only TAG (e.g., margarine) or TAG and PL (e.g., mayonnaise). The egg portion of mayonnaise supplies PL, which cause the water phase and the oil phase to be continuous. In other words, yolk phospholipids act as emulsifiers. Phospholipids and TAG are each susceptible to oxidation during storage that results in the formation of off-odors and off-flavors, which effectively end shelf life. Loss of nutritional value can also occur due to oxidation of the lipid and co-oxidation of proteins and vitamins (1). Triacylglycerols and phospholipids can be modified so that desirable functional properties are made available. These functional properties include physical attributes, flavor stability, caloric value, therapeutic effects, and nutrient content. This chapter will primarily focus on 1) factors that promote or inhibit lipid oxidation processes, and 2) chemical modification of lipids that improve their functional and nutraceutical properties. Further, the chemistry involved in food processes such as oil refining, frying, and food irradiation will be addressed.

II. NOMENCLATURE

The core portion of any lipid comprises repeating units of the hydrocarbon group $(-CH_2)_n$. Saturated hydrocarbons are typically named with a numerical prefix and the termination "ane" (e.g., octane is an 8-carbon saturated hydrocarbon). The suffix "ene" indicates the presence of double bonds also expressed as "unsaturation" in the hydrocarbon. Fatty acids contain an acid group (-COOH) bound to the hydrocarbon tail (Figure 8.1). At pH values above the pKa for each fatty acid, the fatty acid will exist mainly in its conjugated base form (COO^-). The charge on the fatty acid will control its reactivity.

The shorthand for c-9 octadecenoic acid (oleic acid) is 18:1ω9. This indicates there are 18 carbons and one double bond. The ω9 indicates that the double bond is nine carbons in from the end of the hydrocarbon portion. c-11 octadecenoic acid (asclepic acid, 18:1ω7) also exists in nature but is less prevalent than oleic acid. This molecule is identical to oleic acid except that the double bond is seven carbons in from the hydrocarbon tail. The omega symbol (ω) is assigned because nutritional and health impact of different fatty acids are related to the locations of the dou-

ble bonds. Omega-3, ω-3, and n-3 are often used interchangeably. Linolenic acid (18:3ω6 or 18:3 cis-6, cis-9, cis-12) indicates that there are three double bonds. The 6, 9, 12 are the positions where the double bonds begin counting the carboxylic acid group as the first carbon (Figure 8.1). The *cis* conformation is indicative that both alkyl groups adjacent to the double bond are aligned in the same direction. *Trans* fatty acids have the alkyl groups pointing in opposite directions. Most polyunsaturated fatty acids have 1,4-pentadiene structures as illustrated in Figure 8.1. Conjugated fatty acids will have one of the double bonds shifted one carbon closer to the adjoining double bond. Desaturases and elongases cause smaller and more saturated fatty acids (e.g., linoleic acid 18:2ω6) to be converted to longer and less saturated fatty acids (e.g., arachidonic acid 20:4 ω6).

Each membrane phospholipid contains two fatty acids and a single polar head group esterified to glycerol 3-phosphate (Figure 8.2). Typical head groups bound to the phosphate portion include ethanolamine, choline, and serine. These head groups are polar and orient themselves toward the aqueous phase while the fatty acids assemble away from the water phase to form a lamellar membrane bilayer (Figure 8.3). Sterols, proteins, and glycolipids imbedded in the membrane are not illustrated. Other molecular arrangements of phospholipids are possible including inverted micelles (2). Triacylglycerols contain a glycerol backbone on which three fatty acids are esterified. Locations of the fatty acids are designated as sn-1, sn-2, and sn-3. A more extensive review of nomenclature of lipids including different sphingolipids, waxes, sterols, and carotenoids is available (3).

III. LIPID OXIDATION

Lipid oxidation needs to be controlled during storage in order to prevent the formation of off-odors and off-flavors in foods. Desired color and nutritional attributes are also compromised when oxidation of lipids is unimpeded

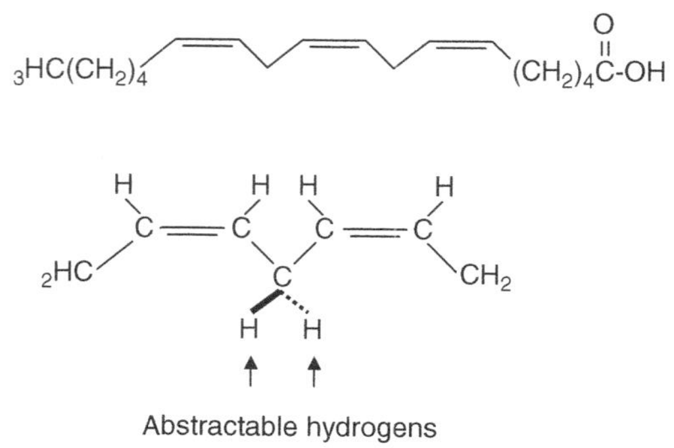

FIGURE 8.1 (Top) Structure of cis-6, cis-9, cis-12 linolenic acid (18:3ω6). (Bottom) The 1,4-pentadiene unit within most polyunsaturated fatty acids.

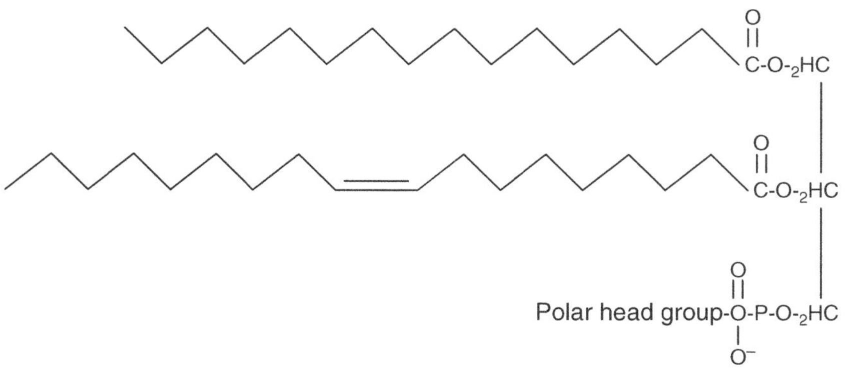

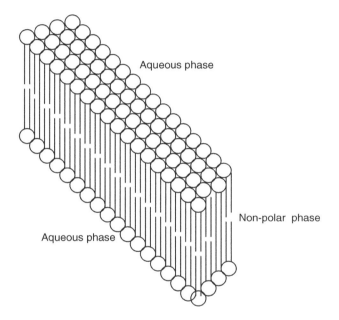

FIGURE 8.2 Basic structure of a glycerophospholipid.

Aqueous phase

Non-polar phase

Aqueous phase

FIGURE 8.3 A simplified representation of a membrane bilayer.

$$LH \longrightarrow L^\bullet + H^\bullet \quad \text{[Initiation]}$$

$$L^\bullet + O_2 \longrightarrow LOO^\bullet$$

$$LOO^\bullet + LH \longrightarrow LOOH + L^\bullet \quad \text{[Propagation]}$$

$$L^\bullet + L^\bullet \longrightarrow L\text{-}L \quad \text{[Termination]}$$

FIGURE 8.4 Initiation, propagation and termination of lipid peroxidation.

This causes the formation of a lipid alkyl radical ($L^\bullet$) that reacts with oxygen to form a peroxyl radical ($LOO^\bullet$). The peroxyl radical can then abstract a hydrogen atom from a different polyunsaturated fatty acid to form a lipid hydroperoxide (LOOH) and another alkyl radical (propagation). It should be kept in mind that small amounts of pre-formed lipid hydroperoxides exist in freshly processed oils, muscle foods and even biological tissues *in vivo* (6, 7). This may decrease the importance of controlling true 'initiators' of lipid oxidation and switch the emphasis to a better understanding of food constituents that break down lipid hydroperoxides. The breakdown of lipid hydroperoxides by metals, heme, heme proteins, and hydroperoxide lyases causes the formation of key volatiles (e.g., aldehydes and ketones) that are responsible for the undesirable odors and flavors associated with lipid oxidation.

Oleic acid (18:1) is generally more susceptible to lipid oxidation than any saturated fatty acids. This is because the lower bond energy of hydrogen atoms adjacent to a double bond allows for more easy abstraction compared to hydrogen atoms in fatty acids lacking double bonds. Most fatty acids with two or more double bonds possess the 1,4-pentadiene structure (Figure 8.1). Hydrogen atoms in the center of the 1,4-pentadiene are around 20 times more abstractable than the abstractable hydrogen of oleic acid (8). Increasing the number of double bonds increases the number of 1,4-pentadiene units and thus increases susceptibility to lipid oxidation. The relative rates of lipid oxidation of oleate (1 double bond): linoleate (2 double bonds): linolenate (3 double bonds) was reported to be 1:12:25 (9).

during storage. The mechanism and rate of lipid oxidation will vary depending on the system under investigation. Interfacial properties, processing temperature, particle size, fatty acid unsaturation, and non-lipid constituents will differ among different systems (e.g., a bulk oil, salad dressing emulsion, raw muscle, cooked meat). Therefore the optimal strategies used to inhibit lipid oxidation processes will change from system to system. This should be kept in mind as general principles of lipid oxidation reactions are discussed. Attention to lipid oxidation has rapidly expanded in recent years due to the growing accumulation of evidence that the onset of various disease states may be related to intake of oxidized food lipids and ingesting critical amounts of antioxidants may improve human health (4, 5).

The classical description of lipid oxidation processes begins with the initiation step where a hydrogen atom is abstracted from a polyunsaturated fatty acid (Figure 8.4).

This was the case in pure lipid systems. In different liposome preparations, oxidative stability decreased as the degree of fatty acid unsaturation increased (10). However, the order of oxidative stability was found to increase with increasing degree of unsaturation when different fatty acids were dispersed in 1% Tween 20 and exposed to iron salts and ascorbate (11). Although atypical, this indicates that under certain conditions highly unsaturated fatty acids are more resistant to lipid oxidation than more saturated ones. In oil-in-water emulsions, fatty acid composition, the physical states of the lipids, content of tocopherols, and activity of transition metals were implicated as factors controlling rates of lipid oxidation (12).

In muscle foods the situation is even more complex. A multitude of components are present that can either accelerate or slow down lipid oxidation processes. Water-washing of muscle fibers from various animal species was used to obtain a wide range of fatty acid unsaturation (13). Washing the muscle removes aqueous antioxidants and pro-oxidants while insoluble myofibrillar proteins and membrane phospholipids remain after washing. Metmyoglobin or iron was added to the washed fibers to stimulate lipid oxidation. The general trend was that lipid oxidation occurred more rapidly in washed muscle containing elevated levels of polyunsaturated fatty acids (fish > chicken > beef). It has also been shown that the ability of fish, poultry, and beef hemoglobins to promote lipid oxidation in a washed muscle system occurred in the following order (fish > chicken > beef) (14). Therefore, the reactivity of different hemoglobins in various muscle foods should be considered as a causative factor in addition to fatty acid unsaturation and endogenous antioxidant capacity.

Compartmentation of cellular and extracellular reactants should be critical in controlling rates of lipid oxidation. Takama et al. (15) suggested that minced flesh of trout was susceptible to rancidity due to the dispersed blood pigments in the flesh caused by the mechanical destruction of the tissue. Crushing plant tissue brings formerly segregated reactants together to stimulate various reactions including oxidation of lipid (16). Critical cellular components and additional factors that control rates of lipid oxidation are discussed below. In any discussion pertaining to lipid oxidation, it is important to realize that any component that accelerates lipid oxidation under one set of conditions can be inhibitory under different conditions.

A. METALS

Low-molecular-weight metals are potent catalysts of lipid oxidation. Copper and iron are two of the more potent metal catalysts in biological systems. Only ferrous ions and oxygen are needed to produce hydrogen peroxide (H_2O_2) as seen in reactions 1 and 2:

$$Fe^{2+} + O_2 \rightarrow Fe^{3+} + {}^{-\bullet}O_2 \quad \text{[reaction 1]}$$

$$ {}^{-\bullet}O_2 + 2H^+ \rightarrow H_2O_2 \quad \text{[reaction 2]}$$

Ferrous iron (Fe^{2+}) can then react with H_2O_2 or preformed lipid hydroperoxides to produce hydroxyl or alkoxyl and hydroxyl radicals, respectively (reactions 3 and 4). Hydroxyl and alkoxyl radicals are capable of abstracting a hydrogen atom from a polyunsaturated fatty acid and hence initiate/propagate lipid oxidation (17).

$$Fe^{2+} + H_2O_2 \rightarrow Fe^{3+} + {}^{-}OH + {}^{-\bullet}OH \quad \text{[reaction 3]}$$

$$Fe^{2+} + LOOH \rightarrow Fe^{3+} + {}^{-\bullet}OH + LO^{-\bullet} \quad \text{[reaction 4]}$$

Reaction 3 is termed the Fenton reaction. Hydroxyl radical can also be produced via the Haber-Weiss reaction (reaction 5). A "ferryl ion" is produced from Fenton reagents and relevant as an initiator of lipid oxidation (reaction 6); even in the absence of H_2O_2, ferryl ion can be produced from the reaction of Fe^{2+} and the "perferryl ion" complex ($Fe^{2+}O_2$) (18).

$$ {}^{-\bullet}O_2 + H_2O_2 \rightarrow O_2 + OH^- + {}^{\bullet}OH \quad \text{[reaction 5]}$$

$$Fe^{2+} + H_2O_2 \rightarrow Fe^{2+}O + H_2O \quad \text{[reaction 6]}$$
$$\text{Ferryl ion}$$

Chelators such as ethylenediaminetetraacetic acid (EDTA) and adenosine diphospate (ADP) are widely used to enhance the ability of iron to promote lipid peroxidation (19). Ascorbate increased the ability of iron to stimulate lipid oxidation by reducing ferric iron (Fe^{3+}) to ferrous iron (Fe^{2+}) (20). Antioxidant properties of ascorbate and metal chelators are discussed later (Section V.F and V.G). Ferric iron can also be reduced enzymatically (e.g., membrane bound reductase, ADP and NADH). Although Fe^{2+} did eventually stimulate lipid oxidation in sarcoplasmic reticulum, increasing concentrations of Fe^{2+} increased the lag phase prior to lipid oxidation; this suggested that Fe^{2+} initially was an antioxidant by reducing membrane antioxidant radicals to their active form (21). Fe^{2+} could then stimulate lipid oxidation after the antioxidant capacity was exhausted. Lipolysis, cooking temperatures, ascorbate, peroxides and extended storage times have the ability to increase iron concentrations in biological systems by stimulating the release of iron from proteins including ferritin, transferrin, hemoglobin, and myoglobin (22–26).

B. HEME PROTEINS

Hemoglobin and myoglobin are the predominant heme proteins (HP) in muscle foods. The blood protein hemoglobin is a tetrameric protein while myoglobin from the interior of muscle cells is a monomer (single polypeptide chain). Hemoglobin tetramers dissociate into monomers and dimers upon dilution and with decreasing pH (27, 28).

Certain aquatic and land animals possess multiple hemoglobins with different chromatography characteristics (29, 30). These factors can cause erroneous determination of hemoglobin and myoglobin content in tissue extracts. Heme proteins consist of a globin chain(s) and a heme ring(s), the latter containing an iron atom. The iron is primarily in the ferrous state ($HP\text{-}Fe^{2+}$) *in vivo*. Met heme protein ($HP\text{-}Fe^{3+}$) accumulates post mortem via a proton or deoxygenated HP mechanism (reactions 7 and 8) (31). A general term for the formation of metHP from ferrousHP is heme protein autoxidation.

$$\text{oxy}(+2)HP + H^+ \rightarrow \text{met}(+3)HP + {}^\bullet OOH \qquad [\text{reaction 7}]$$

$$\text{deoxy}(+2)HP + O_2 \rightarrow \text{met}(+3)HP + {}^{-\bullet}O_2 \qquad [\text{reaction 8}]$$

Met heme protein formation is likely critical to the onset of lipid oxidation since metHP reacts with either H_2O_2 or lipid hydroperoxides to form the ferryl HP radical that is capable of initiating lipid oxidation (reactions 9 and 10) (32). MetHP is much more likely to unfold and release its heme group compared to ferrous HP (33, 34). Released or displaced heme can react with lipid peroxides to form various lipid radical species that have the ability to propagate lipid oxidation processes (reaction 11) (35–37). Bohr effects occur in certain fish hemoglobins (38). This decreases oxygen affinity of the heme protein at post mortem pH values and hence increases met heme protein formation (reaction 8). It is still unclear if ferrous forms of heme proteins can react with lipid hydroperoxides to stimulate lipid oxidation processes although some potential pathways have been suggested involving oxyHP and deoxyHP (39, 40).

$$\text{met}(+3)HP + H_2O_2 \rightarrow HP^{+\bullet}\text{ferryl}(+4) = O + H_2O$$
$$[\text{reaction 9}]$$

$$\text{met}(+3)HP + LOOH \rightarrow HP^{+\bullet}\text{ferryl}(+4) = O + LOH$$
$$[\text{reaction 10}]$$

$$\text{heme}(+3) + LOOH \rightarrow \text{Heme}(+3)\text{-}O^\bullet + LO^\bullet \quad [\text{reaction 11}]$$

C. PEROXIDES

There are numerous sources of hydrogen peroxide in biological systems. Equations 1 and 2 describe an iron, oxygen, and proton-mediated mechanism of formation. NADPH-cytochrome P450 reductase produces ${}^{-\bullet}O_2$ that dismutates to H_2O_2 (19). Production of H_2O_2 in mitochondrial and peroxisomal fractions has been described (41). H_2O_2 production in erythrocytes was mainly attributed to hemoglobin autoxidation (42). H_2O_2 was produced at a rate of 14 nmol/g of fresh weight/30 min in turkey muscle at $37°C$ (43). High concentrations of H_2O_2 will cause release of iron from the heme ring of heme proteins (25).

Like H_2O_2, lipid hydroperoxides (LHP) react with metals or heme proteins to produce free radical species that propagate lipid oxidation. Further, the collection of volatiles that produce rancid odor result from LHP breakdown. Trace amounts of LHP are required for lipoxygenase activity, converting iron in the active site from the ferrous to ferric form (44). Reduction of lipid hydroperoxides to alcohols with compounds such as ebselen and triphenylphosphine often abolishes any lipid oxidation that was observed prior to reduction (45, 46). Tocopherol-mediated lipid peroxidation was found to require Cu^{2+} and low levels of lipid hydroperoxides (47). Fe^{2+} reacts with lipid hydroperoxides around 20 times faster than with hydrogen peroxide (48). Protein hydroperoxides may also exacerbate lipid oxidation processes (49). Non-lipid surfactant hydroperoxides increased rates of lipid oxidation in oil-in-water emulsions (50).

D. ROLE OF OXYGEN

Oxygen not only peroxidizes alkyl radicals to propagate lipid oxidation (Figure 8.4) but also is a source of activated oxygen species (Figure 8.5). Unlike ${}^{-\bullet}O_2$, ${}^\bullet OOH$ can cross membranes, which may increase its pro-oxidative character (51). The oxygen concentration in marine oils is fairly constant between $20°C$ and $60°C$ but rapidly decreases between $60°C$ and $80°C$ (52). The O_2 concentrations in these oils at $20°C$ (0.44 to 1.25 mM) exceed the O_2 concentration found in water at the same temperature (around 0.30 mM). In 80% oxygen and 20% carbon dioxide packaging, oxygen penetrated 1.7 to 11 mm into different muscle foods (beef > pork > lamb) (53). At high ratios of $[O_2]/[H_2O_2]$, the ferryl ion initiation (reaction 6) is believed to dominate while Fenton reagents (reaction 3) are more prevalent at lower ratios (18). In CCl_4-induced lipid peroxidation of hepatocytes, a distinct maximum was obtained at 7 mm Hg oxygen while iron-mediated lipid oxidation in microsomes differed in oxygen dependence depending on whether initiation or propagation phases were considered (54). Metmyoglobin formation in beef occurred most rapidly at around 11 mm Hg oxygen (55). Non-destructive oxygen sensors are available to measure the oxygen content in headspace of different packaging systems (56). Carotenoids are believed to be more effective antioxidants at low oxygen concentrations compared to higher oxygen concentrations (57).

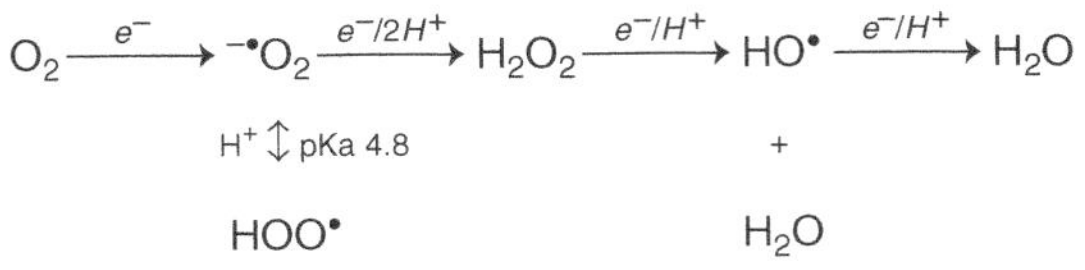

$$O_2 \xrightarrow{e^-} {}^{-\bullet}O_2 \xrightarrow{e^-/2H^+} H_2O_2 \xrightarrow{e^-/H^+} HO^\bullet \xrightarrow{e^-/H^+} H_2O$$

$$H^+ \updownarrow pKa\ 4.8 \qquad\qquad +$$

$$HOO^\bullet \qquad\qquad H_2O$$

FIGURE 8.5 One-electron reductions of oxygen.

E. LIPOXYGENASES AND MYELOPEROXIDASES

Lipoxygenases are responsible for flavor deterioration in beans during frozen storage (58). Lipoxygenases "initiate" lipid oxidation processes by hydrogen abstraction from a polyunsaturated fatty acid. The off-flavor is due to the volatiles that are produced from breakdown of the lipoxygenase-derived lipid hydroperoxides. Fresh fish aromas are believed to result in part from lipoxygenases that enzymically peroxidize fatty acid substrates (59). These enzymes may also be responsible for formation of rancid odors by providing critical amounts of lipid hydroperoxides that can be broken down by metals or heme proteins to produce rancid odor. Some of the confusion surrounding the presence or absence of lipoxygenases in animal tissues may be due to the quasi- lipoxygenase activities of myoglobin and hemoglobin (60, 61). Esculetin has been utilized as a specific lipoxygenase inhibitor; however, esculetin is a phenolic compound that has general free radical scavenging ability and should not be considered a specific inhibitor of lipoxygenase.

Myeloperoxidases are found in white blood cell neutrophils. Myeloperoxidase catalyzes the reaction of chloride and hydrogen peroxide that produces hypochlorous acid which in turn reacts with $^{\bullet-}O_2$ and yields hydroxyl radical (62). This reaction was found to be six orders of magnitude faster than the Haber-Weiss reaction (reaction 5) and does not require iron.

F. LIPOLYSIS

Lipolysis results in the formation of free fatty acids. Lipolysis occurs due to enzyme action or heat and moisture. Free fatty acids are responsible for both undesirable and desirable flavors (e.g., milk rancidity or positive flavors in cheese, bread, and yogurt). Cabbage phospholipase D decreased the formation of lipid oxidation products in beef homogenates and egg yolk phosphatidylcholine liposomes (63). Adding free fatty acids to fresh salmon flesh, at levels of free fatty acids that accumulated during 6 months at $-10°C$ storage, increased taste deterioration in fresh minced salmon (64). The amount of taste deterioration from each fatty acid was 22:6n-3 > 16:1n-7 > 18:2n-6 > 20:5n-3). This suggested that hydrolysis of triacylglycerols negatively impacted sensory quality. A review on lipolysis effects in fish muscle indicated that triacylglycerol hydrolysis results in increased lipid oxidation while phospholipid hydrolysis was inhibitory (65).

G. PHOTOACTIVATED SENSITIZERS (SINGLET OXYGEN)

Oxygen can exist in the triplet ($^3O_2$) or singlet state ($^1O_2$). Triplet oxygen is the normal state of oxygen while singlet oxygen is generated via photosensitization by natural pigments in food (e.g., riboflavin or chlorophyll). The two electrons in the antibonding 2p orbitals of $^3O_2$ have the same spin and are in different orbitals. This creates a small repulsive electronic state. In $^1O_2$, the two electrons are in a single antibonding orbital and have opposite spins; therefore, electrostatic repulsion will be great. $^1O_2$ is thus at a higher energy state than $^3O_2$, and $^1O_2$ is more electrophillic than $^3O_2$. This causes $^1O_2$ to react readily with moieties of high electron density such as double bonds in unsaturated fatty acids (8). This direct addition of $^1O_2$ to unsaturated fatty acids initiates lipid oxidation without the need for hydrogen abstraction as is the case with free radical-mediated initiation. Nine or more conjugated double bonds (e.g., carotenoids) are required for physical quenching of singlet oxygen (66). Other compounds such as tocopherols and amines can quench singlet oxygen by a charge transfer mechanism (67).

H. FAT CONTENT

Release of c-9 aldehydes into headspace decreased with increasing oil content in oil-in-water emulsions (68). This suggested that the impact of certain odor compounds is decreased by elevated levels of fat via solubilization of the component into the oil phase. A study was conducted that examined the effect of added triacylglycerols on rates of hemoglobin-catalyzed oxidation of washed cod muscle lipids. No difference in rate or extent of lipid oxidation catalyzed by hemoglobin was obtained when washed cod muscle (around 0.7% phospholipids) was compared to the washed cod muscle containing up to 15% added triacylglycerols (69). This indicated that triacylglycerols did not accelerate rates of lipid oxidation during storage. Similar non-effects of added triacylglycerols were obtained in cooked lipid-extracted muscle fibers (70). Increasing fat contents did not increase oxidized oil odor in frozen stored catfish (71).

I. EFFECT OF COOKING

Consumers are finding less time to prepare meals. The food industry is responding to this by increasing the availability of pre-cooked meats. A major problem with pre-cooked meats is the development of an objectionable warmed-over flavor via lipid oxidation (72). This warmed-over flavor occurs more rapidly during refrigerated compared to frozen storage temperatures. It has been suggested that released iron from heme proteins promotes warmed-over flavor in pre-cooked beef (23). The evidence for this was that the low-molecular-weight fraction in an aqueous extract of beef muscle stimulated lipid oxidation of washed muscle fibers much better than the high-molecular-weight fraction (73). On the other hand, in pre-cooked fish, heme proteins were believed to be the active catalysts due to higher pro-oxidative activity in the high-molecular-weight fraction of the fish muscle (74).

Polyphosphates inhibited lipid oxidation in pre-cooked beef, which may be due to iron chelating properties of the phosphates (73). Inhibitors of warmed-over flavor were produced in meat during retorting but could not be extracted from raw beef. This suggests that the high temperature processing caused formation of products that inhibit lipid oxidation (75). Browning reactions that involve carbohydrates and amino acids were believed to impart this antioxidant effect.

Lipid oxidation is much less of a problem in pre-cooked meats that are cured. Cured meats contain nitrite in the formulation. The primary way that nitrite is believed to exert its antioxidant effect is by conversion of nitrite to nitric oxide (NO) that binds to the iron atom in the heme ring of heme proteins. The NO-ligand may be antioxidative by preventing release of heme or iron during cooking and storage or by decreasing heme protein reactivity. Nitrite can also act as an antioxidant by chelating metals and scavenging free radicals. Nitrite may be toxic at elevated levels and therefore it is critical to control the residual nitrite content in the product.

IV. MEASURING RATES OF LIPID OXIDATION IN FOOD SYSTEMS

Lipid hydroperoxides are primary lipid oxidation products that are precursors to rancidity. Lipid hydroperoxides need to be broken down to form the low-molecular-weight volatile compounds (secondary products) that impart rancidity. It is imperative to measure primary and secondary lipid oxidation products. To accentuate this point, tocopherol enriched lipoproteins had higher levels of conjugated dienes (primary product) than lipoproteins containing little tocopherol (76). Standing alone, this errantly suggests that tocopherol was a pro-oxidant. Fortunately, these researchers also measured thiobarbituric reactive substances (TBARS) which indicated less formation of the secondary products in the tocopherol enriched samples. Apparently, tocopherol stabilized the hydroperoxides. Thus, a more complete picture is realized when measuring both primary and secondary lipid oxidation products.

Sensory analysis should be done whenever possible since human subjects can determine the point at which the product becomes undesirable which ultimately determines shelf life. Degree of rancidity or quality perception is harder to pinpoint using chemical indicators of lipid oxidation. Single time point measurements are also discouraged. Primary and secondary lipid oxidation products commonly increase, reach a maximum, and then decrease substantially. This can create a situation where one sample is perceived to be minimally oxidized but in fact had undergone extensive oxidation well before the measurement. Thus, measuring lipid oxidation products at multiple time points during storage is suggested so that a kinetic curve can be obtained which demonstrates a lag phase, exponential phase and plateau, or decrease phase.

Common lipid oxidation indicators that are measured during storage of lipid-containing foods include lipid peroxides, conjugated dienes, headspace volatiles, thiobarbituric acid reactive substances (TBARS), anisidine value, oxygen consumption, and carotene bleaching. A description of these and other methods including those used in fried products is available (8). Very good correlations between TBARS and headspace volatiles (e.g., hexanal, pentenal) were determined in cooked turkey during 4°C storage (77). TBARS are unlikely to provide useful results if the starting material has already undergone considerable oxidation. Rancidity can develop before any detectable change in fatty acid composition occurs. For example, no difference in fatty acid composition was found when fresh mackerel muscle was compared to extensively rancid mackerel muscle (78). This should not be a surprise considering that extremely small amounts of fatty acid precursors are required to produce the amount of volatiles needed for sensory impact (79).

Numerous pitfalls exist when measuring rates of lipid oxidation. Thermogravimetric methods entail weighing the sample until a rapid increase in weight occurs due to oxygen adding to the lipid. This can be done under isothermal conditions or programming from ambient to elevated temperatures. The drawback is that by the time a spike in weight occurs, detection of rancidity had previously occurred. Bulk oils are sometimes heated to 90°C to shorten the storage period needed to produce quantifiable levels of lipid oxidation. The amount of oxygen that is soluble in oil decreases substantially at elevated temperatures. This causes the mechanism of oxidation to be different from that which would occur at lower temperatures. Both the AOM and Rancimat method have been considered unreliable due to the high temperatures that are used (80). More reasonable methods to accelerate the rate of lipid oxidation in oils and emulsions are to store samples at 50°C and add metals or hemin to the system. It is interesting to note that fish held at −10°C was more susceptible to lipid oxidation than muscle stored at around 0°C. The temperature deceleration effect was apparently less substantial than the effect of freeze concentration of reactants (81). The mechanism of lipid oxidation at −20°C (commercial storage) may also be different than −10°C considering that less tissue damage should occur at the lower temperature due to faster freezing rate and smaller sized ice crystals.

V. ANTIOXIDANTS

Food antioxidants are used to inhibit lipid oxidation reactions that cause quality deterioration (e.g., flavor, color, texture, nutrient content). It is important to note that any compound that is antioxidative under one set of conditions can become pro-oxidative under different conditions. As an example of this point, ascorbate has been found to both inhibit and accelerate lipid oxidation depending on the concentration of linoleate hydroperoxides in the system (82). The main antioxidant mechanisms are free radical scavenging, chelation of metals, removal of peroxides or reactive oxygen species, and quenching of secondary lipid oxidation products that produce rancid odors (83).

A. FREE RADICAL SCAVENGERS

Some typical free radicals that can initiate/propagate lipid oxidation and hence be scavenged by antioxidants include hydroxyl ($^\bullet$OH), alkoxyl (LO$^\bullet$), peroxyl radicals (LOO$^\bullet$), and ferryl heme protein radicals (HP$^{+\bullet}$ferryl(+4)=O) (84). $^\bullet$OH is one of the strongest biological oxidants (Table 8.1) and therefore will react with nearly any molecule that it encounters. This might limit the amount of $^\bullet$OH that will react with fatty acids. Peroxyl radicals are likely prevalent since the reaction of oxygen with alkyl radicals that forms after hydrogen abstraction from a fatty acid is highly favored both thermodynamically and kinetically. Alkoxyl radicals will form due to breakdown of lipid hydroperoxides by heme or reduced metal complexes. Alkoxyl radicals can undergo β-scission reactions that produces a short chain alkyl radical (RCH$_2$$^\bullet$) that reacts readily with O$_2$ to form peroxyl radicals (17).

There are numerous free radical scavengers (FRS) that are either endogenous to the food or incorporated during processing. The antioxidant effectiveness will depend on hydrogen bond energies (85). The donation of hydrogen from a generic phenolic antioxidant to an alkoxyl radical is depicted in Figure 8.6. The ability of a particular FRS to donate hydrogen to a free radical can be predicted from standard one-electron reduction potentials (17). Any compound that has a reduction potential lower than that of a free radical is capable of donating hydrogen to that free radical (Table 8.1). For example, catechol has a lesser reduction potentials than alkoxyl radical. Thus, catechol can donate hydrogen to the alkoxyl radical. This donating

TABLE 8.1
Standard One-Electron Reduction Potentials of Components Involved in Free Radical Reactions

[Oxidized / Reduced] Couple	E° ′ (mV)
HO$^\bullet$, H$^+$ / H$_2$O	2310
LO$^\bullet$, H$^+$/ LOH	1600
LOO$^\bullet$, H$^+$ / LOOH	1000
PUFA$^\bullet$, H$^+$ / PUFA-H	600
Catechol$^\bullet$, H$^+$ / catechol	530
α-Tocopheroxyl$^\bullet$, H$^+$ / α-tocopherol	500
Ascorbate$^{\bullet-}$, H$^+$ / ascorbate$^-$	282

Adapted from Ref. 17.

ability of catechol competes with the undesirable reaction of alkoxyl radicals with polyunsaturated fatty acids (PUFA-H) (Table 8.1) and hence inhibits lipid oxidation processes. It should be kept in mind that the reduction potential of a compound changes as a function of pH, temperature, and concentration of the compound(s) of interest.

A potential drawback is that the FRS becomes a free radical itself after donating hydrogen to the alkoxyl radical (Figure 8.6) (Table 8.1). The most efficient FRS exist as low energy radicals after scavenging. The benefit of existing as a low energy radical is that the radical is unlikely to abstract hydrogen from polyunsaturated fatty acids. Low energy radicals result from resonance delocalization (Figure 8.6). The conjugated ring structure of the phenolic allows the phenolic radical to reside at multiple sites on the molecule. As the radical migrates from site to site, a low energy radical results that possesses low reactivity. Evidence of low reactivity can be gleaned from the one-electron reduction potentials. Any radical with reduction potential less than a polyunsaturated fatty acid (e.g., catechol radical) cannot abstract hydrogen from the fatty acid; hence the antioxidant radical cannot initiate/propagate lipid oxidation processes (Table 8.1).

Efficient FRS in their radical form should also not react with oxygen. If reaction with oxygen occurs, a free radical peroxide forms (FR-OOH). The free radical peroxide cannot be regenerated by reducing equivalents as can occur when the FRS is in a resonance delocalized form (FR$^\bullet$). The net effect is depletion of the antioxidant upon reaction with oxygen. Further free radical peroxides can decompose to species capable of furthering oxidation. Note that ascorbate has a one-electron reduction potential that is less than tocopherol (Table 8.1) and thus ascorbate can regenerate tocopherol from tocopheroxyl radicals.

Thus, phenolic compounds are efficient FRS due to their hydrogen donating properties and resonance delocalization of the phenoxyl radical. There is a multitude of phenolic free radical scavengers available to food scientists. The synthetic phenolics butylated hydroxy toluene (BHT), butylated hydroxy anisole (BHA), tertiary butyl hydroquinone (TBHQ), and propyl gallate (PG) (Figure 8.7) are commonly used in the food industry due to their low cost of production although consumers prefer natural FRS such as tocopherols and plant phenolics.

B. SYNTHETIC PHENOLICS

Propyl gallate (PG) is poorly soluble in oils and sensitive to heat degradation (e.g., frying temperatures). Substitution of the propyl group with octyl or dodecyl groups provides more heat stability and lipid solubility. Gallates have been used to stabilize meat products, baked goods, fried products, confectionaries, nuts, and milk products (86). Butylated hydroxyanisole (BHA) volatilizes upon frying,

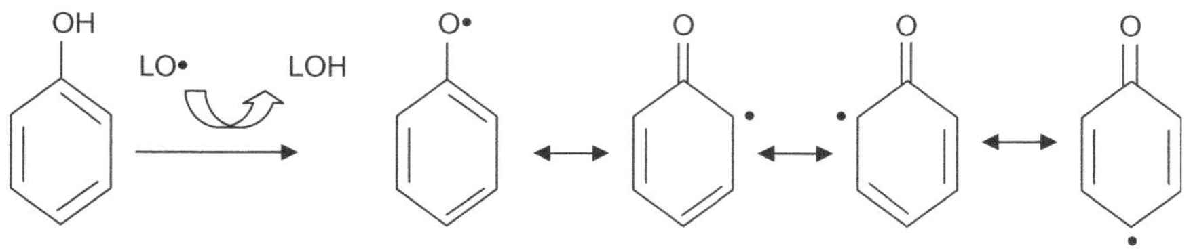

FIGURE 8.6 Free radical scavenging by a phenolic compound and resonance stabilization of the resulting phenoxyl radical. Adapted from Ref. 85.

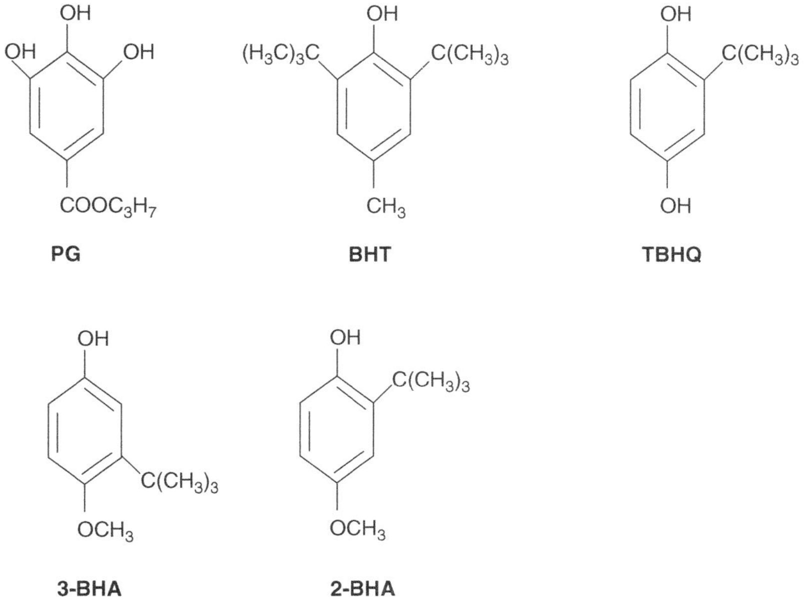

FIGURE 8.7 Structures of various synthetic antioxidants.

but residual BHA does protect fried foods. BHA is a mixture of two isomers (Figure 8.7). The $-C(CH_3)_3$ group on the conjugated ring increases oil solubility and enhances resonance stabilization of the phenoxy radical. This alkyl group on the conjugated ring also enhances hydrogen-donating properties. Butylated hydroxytoluene is highly soluble in oil due to its two $-C(CH_3)_3$ groups and single methyl group (Figure 8.7). TBHQ has two hydroxy groups and significant solubilities in a wide range of fats, oils, and solvents. The order of antioxidant efficacy in fish oil stored at 60°C was TBHQ> PG=BHA>BHT (87).

C. TOCOPHEROLS AND TOCOTRIENOLS

Tocopherols are of plant origin and exist in four forms (α, β, γ, δ). The structures of the isomers are illustrated in Figure 8.8. Tocopherols are soluble in oils and ethanol. When tocopherol reacts with a peroxyl radical, at least five resonance structures of the tocopherol radical can form (83). BHA, BHT, and PG are considerably more stable to heat treatment than α-tocopherol (86). α-, β-, γ-, and δ-tocopherol inhibited formation of

cholesterol oxidation products to different degrees in metal-induced oxidation of unilamellar phospholipid-choleseterol liposomes (88). In beef muscle, tocopherolquinone and 2,3-epoxy-tocopherolquinone were the dominant tocopherol oxidation products and lower amounts of 5,6-epoxy-tocopherolquinone and tocopherolhydroquinone were detected (89). This was consistent with mainly a peroxyl radical scavenging function of tocopherol but also some scavenging of other free radicals. Predominant amounts of the 2,3- and 5,6-epoxy-tocopherolquinone products would suggest a nearly exclusive mechanism of peroxyl-radical scavenging. When examining Atlantic mackerel, a substantial amount of tocopherol was present in stored muscle that was highly rancid (90). This suggested that tocopherol was not an effective antioxidant in the mackerel muscle. Tocotrienols are similar in structure to tocopherols but contain three unsaturated units in the isoprenoid chain. γ- and δ-tocotrienols extended shelf life of coconut fat better or in a manner similar to their corresponding tocopherols during 60°C storage and exposure to frying temperatures (91).

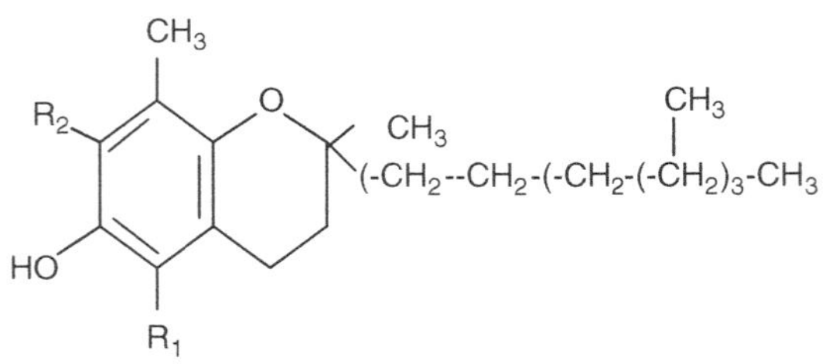

Type	R1	R2
Alpha	-CH₃	-CH₃
Beta	-CH₃	-H
Gamma	-H	-CH₃
Delta	-H	-H

FIGURE 8.8 Structures of tocopherols.

D. PLANT PHENOLICS

Simple plant phenolics contain a single conjugated ring with various substitutions. These compounds are usually water soluble and examples are gallic acid and hydroxycinnamic acid. Anthocyanidins are 3-ringed structures that exist as protonated cations at acidic pH values, are colorless open-ringed structures at intermediate pH values, and are anions at higher pH values. Glycosylated anthocyaninidins are termed anthocyanins and are the common red pigments in fruits. Flavan 3-ols are colorless compounds that are common in tea. Epicatechin is an example of a flavan-3-ol (Figure 8.9). Quercetin is a flavonol and is one of the most abundant flavonoids (Figure 8.9). Flavonoids is a general term that includes anthocyanins, flavonols, flavones, isoflavones, and chalcones. A quercetin metabolite was found to have antioxidant properties in a liposomal membrane (92). Linked flavan-3-ol repeated molecules are high molecular weight, generally poorly soluble in water, and referred to as proanthocyanidins, procyanidins, tannins, or heteropolyflavans (93). Extensive structural diversity exists

in different plant phenolics. In rosemary leaf extract, carnosol, carnosic acid, rosmarinic acid, and rosmaridiphenol have antioxidant potency (86).

The rate of peroxyl radical scavenging by quercetin and epicatechin was greater in non-polar solvents compared to hydrogen bonding solvents (94). In a liposomal model system that generate free radicals during metal-induced peroxidation, 1) antioxidant activity increased with increasing hydroxy substitutions present on the B ring for anthocyanidins but the opposite was observed for the flavan-3-ol, catechin, 2) substitution by methoxyl groups decreased antioxidant activity of anthocyanidins, and 3) substitution of a galloyl group at position 3 of the flavonoid moiety decreased antioxidant activity of the catechin (95).

Many phenolic antioxidants have been characterized in grapes, berries, teas and spices. Beet root pigments were found to have free radical scavenging properties (96). Betanidin 5-O-beta-glucoside in beet was found to inhibit lipid oxidation at low concentrations (97). In pineapple juice, phenolic compounds containing cysteine, glutamyl, and glutathione linkages were identified (98). Proteins (casein or albumin) decreased antioxidant efficacy of tea flavanols (99). Freezing and storage had negligible effects on antioxidant capacity of raspberry phenolics (100). Ferryl myoglobin, a possible pro-oxidant in muscle tissue, was reduced by epigallocatechin gallate from green tea (101). The antioxidant effects of tea catechins in raw chicken muscle were attributed to free radical scavenging ability and iron chelating effects (102).

E. CAROTENOIDS

Carotenoids are fat-soluble pigments. Canthaxanthin and astaxanthin possess oxo groups at the 4 and 4'-positions in the β-ionone ring (Figure 8.10). β-carotene and zeaxanthin do not contain oxo groups and were found to be less inhibitory to methyl linoleate peroxidation than canthaxanthin or astaxanthin (103). β-carotene, however, can scavenge free radicals. Peroxyl radicals either add directly to the hydrocarbon portion of the molecule displacing an unsaturation site or add to the β-ionine ring forming a β-carotene cation radical; these oxidation products, however, are

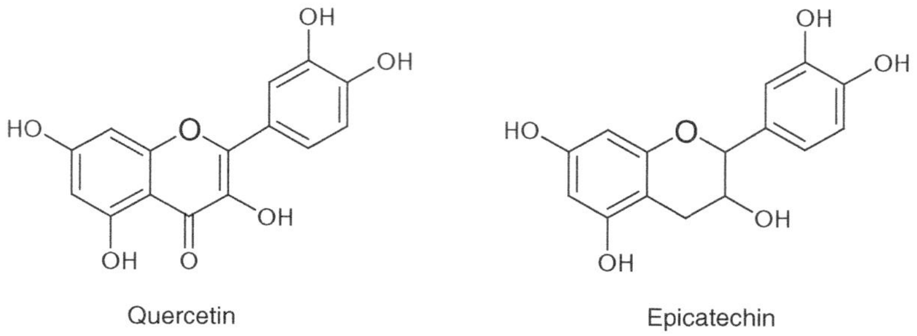

Quercetin   Epicatechin

FIGURE 8.9 Structures of the flavonoids quercetin and epicatechin.

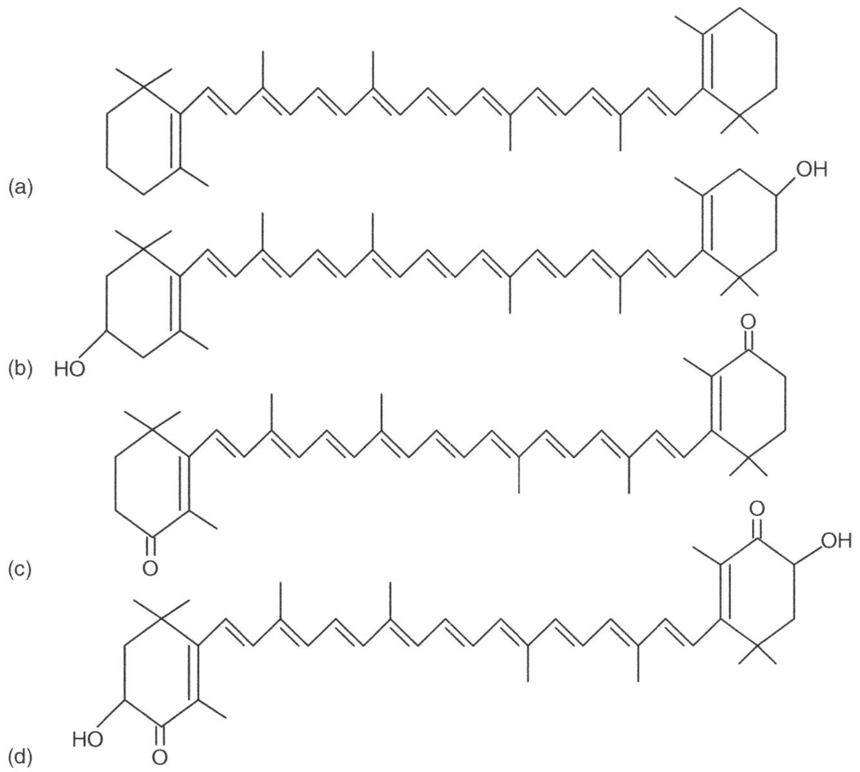

FIGURE 8.10 Structures of various carotenoids. (a) β-carotene, (b) zeaxanthin, (c) canthaxanthin, (d) astaxanthin.

susceptible to breakdown that results in formation of alkoxyl radicals (83). There is evidence that carotenoids are effective antioxidants at low oxygen concentrations but not higher oxygen concentrations (57). Carotenoids including lycopene can inactivate singlet oxygen by physical quenching of the activated oxygen specie (104).

F. Other Free Radical Scavengers and Reductants

Uric acid is present in plasma and can inhibit lipid oxidation by scavenging free radicals or singlet oxygen (105). Ascorbate is believed to scavenge tocopheroxyl free radicals thereby regenerating tocophopherol (17). Ascorbate can also scavenge various free radicals such as $\cdot^- O_2$, $\cdot OOH$, and $\cdot OH$ (48). Like flavonoids, ascorbate reduces hypervalent forms of heme proteins to potentially inhibit lipid oxidation in muscle foods (106). Heme oxygenase converts heme into bilirubin. Bilirubin is believed to scavenge free radicals, which results in formation of biliverdin that is reduced back to bilirubin by NADH and biliverdin reductase. This redox cycle was used to explain the high antioxidant power of bilirubin *in vivo* (107). It is not known how effective bilirubin inhibits lipid oxidation in food systems. Ubiquinol is a phenolic compound that is conjugated to an isoprenoid chain and is associated with mitochondrial membranes. Oxidation of ubiquinol results in formation of semiubiquinone radical. Dietary ubiquinone increased ubiquinol levels in lipoproteins and decreased lipid oxidation rates (108). Ubiquinol is considered a weak free radical scavenger due to internal hydrogen bonding that interferes with abstraction of its phenolic hydrogen by free radicals (109).

A potent natural antioxidant from shrimp was tentatively identified as a water-soluble, polyhydroxylated derivative of an aromatic amino acid (110).

G. Metal Inactivators

Ethylenediamine tetraacetic acid (EDTA) can inhibit lipid oxidation by forming an inactive complex with metals. EDTA can either promote or inhibit lipid oxidation depending on the iron/EDTA ratio, which modulates the effective charge in the system (111). EDTA is approved for use in foods at low concentrations. It is poorly soluble in fats and oils but only small amounts are needed for maximum activity. EDTA protected lard better than a combination of BHT and citric acid (86). It should be noted that EDTA indirectly acts as a free radical scavenger. Jimenez and Speisky (112) showed that glutathione scavenged free radicals less effectively in the presence of copper than when EDTA was mixed with copper prior to addition of gluathione. The ability of EDTA to tie up copper or form a chelate with glutathione apparently increased the free radical scavenging ability of glutathione. The carboxylic acid groups of EDTA are protonated at low pH values (i.e., when pH is below the pKa for the acid groups of EDTA). This interferes with the ability of EDTA to complex metals or other cellular components.

Desferrioxamine is often used as a "metal chelator" in research studies, but this can lead to errant results since desferrioxamine can also act as a free radical scavenger (113). EDTA, tartaric acid and citric acid are other commonly used metal chelators in the food industry. Citrate esters improve oil solubility but at least two free carboxyl groups are needed for effective metal inactivation. Propylene glycol increases solubility of citric acid in oils and fats (86). Sodium tripolyphosphate can act as an antioxidant via metal chelation (114). A disadvantage of using metal chelators in general is that iron bioavailability during digestion may be compromised.

Ceruloplasmin inhibits metal-catalyzed oxidation via its ferroxidase activity. The ferroxidase converts Fe^{2+} to Fe^{3+}, a less catalytic form of iron (115). Transferrin (plasma protein) and ferritin (muscle cell protein) can inactivate metals by chelation of iron but also can release iron causing a pro-oxidant effect; lipolysis and ascorbate, respectively are capable of triggering the iron release (22, 116). Carnosine is a B-alanylhistidine dipeptide found in skeletal muscle at high concentrations. It is capable of chelating copper, scavenging peroxyl radicals, and forming adducts with aldehydes (117). Histidine was found to inhibit non-enzymatic iron mediated lipid oxidation apparently due to formation of an inactive chelate but histidine was also found to activate enzymic pathways of lipid oxidation (118).

H.   ENZYMES THAT INACTIVATE OXIDATION INTERMEDIATES

Superoxide anion ($^-$•O_2) can be produced by heme protein autoxidation or by any process that causes addition of an electron to oxygen (119). Superoxide can reduce Fe^{3+} to Fe^{2+}, the more pro-oxidative form of iron. In addition, the pKa of $^-$•O_2 is around 4.5. Thus at pH values below 4.5, the conjugate acid •OOH is the predominant form which can directly initiate lipid oxidation (84). Superoxide dismutase is present in cells and extracellular fluids to remove $^-$•O_2 resulting in formation of oxygen and hydrogen peroxide.

Hydrogen peroxide (H_2O_2) can react with either low-molecular-weight iron or heme proteins to form free radicals that initiate/propagate lipid oxidation processes. Biological systems are equipped with antioxidants to deal with this stress. Catalase, a heme-containing enzyme reacts with H_2O_2 to form water and oxygen (120). In plants and algae, ascorbate peroxidase removes H_2O_2 and forms monodehydroascorbate and water. Glutathione peroxidase removes H_2O_2 and forms water and oxidized glutathione. The reaction of glutathione peroxidase with lipid hydroperoxides results in formation of an alcohol, water, and oxidized glutathione. Compounds such as methionine and thiodipropionic acid can also decompose peroxides but at much slower rates than the enzymes.

I.   SCAVENGING OF LIPID OXIDATION BREAKDOWN PRODUCTS

Lipid oxidation breakdown products (e.g., aldehydes, ketones, hydrocarbons) form a mixture of volatiles that causes objectionable flavors and odors. Carnosine, anserine, histidine, lysine, albumin, and sulfur or amine containing compounds have the ability to bind aldehydes and therefore decrease rancidity in foods (83). These "scavengers" should be examined in relation to browning of beef considering that lipid oxidation derived aldehydes accelerated the conversion of oxyMb to metMb and hence have the capacity to accelerate browning in beef (121).

J.   OTHER MECHANISMS OF ANTIOXIDANT ACTION

Spermine was found to inhibit lipid oxidation in hepatocytes of CCL_4-treated rats; a possible mechanism was formation of polyamine-phospholipid complexes (122). Conjugated linoleic acid (CLA) has been shown to decrease rates of lipid oxidation in muscle tissue (123). The mechanism may be related to the ability of dietary CLA to decrease polyenoic fatty acid concentrations in the muscle (124). Organosulfur compounds such as diallyl sulfide and N-acetyl cysteine may exert their antioxidant protection by modulating antioxidant enzymes such as catalase and glutathione-s-transferase (125).

K.   INTERFACIAL, CHARGE, AND LOCATION EFFECTS

Deciding which antioxidant(s) to utilize in a particular food system is a formidable task. Having water and lipid soluble antioxidants was found to maximize extension in shelf life of mayonnaise prepared from fish oil (126). However, cost limitation is a factor that limits amounts of antioxidant addition. Most foods have a water phase, lipid phase and water-lipid interface. Location of different antioxidants should affect antioxidant potency. Membrane phospholipids are believed to be more prone to lipid oxidation than triacylglycerols in muscle foods so protecting membrane lipids is desired (127). δ-Tocopherol could be preferentially incorporated into isolated membranes compared to triacylglycerols by proper selection of antioxidant solvent (ethanol instead of corn oil) (128). In minced chicken muscle containing added triacylglycerols, δ-tocopherol could be preferentially incorporated into the membrane fraction if the antioxidant was added to the lean muscle before addition of TAG lipids (129). Hydrophilic antioxidants (trolox and ascorbic acid) were generally more effective than more hydrophobic compounds (tocopherol and ascorbyl palmitate) in bulk oils while the hydrophobic compounds were more effective in oil-in-water emulsions (130, 131). However, when comparing carnosic acid to the more hydrophobic methyl carnosate, the latter was a more effective antioxidant in both bulk oils and emulsions (132). Benzoic acid, a water-soluble phenolic, partitioned into the oil phase of a whey-protein stabilized emulsion more than could be explained by oil/water partitioning alone (133). This suggested that benzoic acid bound to protein adsorbed at the interface. In oil-in-water emulsions, excess surfactant solubilized phenolic antioxidants into the aqueous phase but the removal of antioxidants from the oil or oil interface phases did not accelerate lipid oxidation (134). The ability of excess surfactant to cause lipid hydroperoxides and iron to partition into the aqueous phase (away from oil droplets) may explain the ability of excess surfactant to inhibit lipid oxidation in oil-in-water emulsions (50, 135). Positively charged protein emulsifiers inhibited lipid oxidation more effectively than negatively charged emulsifiers in oil-in-water emulsions (136). This was attributed to the ability of the positive charge of the protein interface to repel iron away from the oil phase. The ability of Trolox to inhibit lipid oxidation in liposomes was least when the membrane bilayer and trolox molecule were negatively charged and removing the repulsive forces by altering membrane type or pH increased antioxidant efficacy (137). More studies are needed to evaluate the distribution of antioxidants in different phases in conjunction with lipid oxidation kinetics during storage.

VI. PRODUCTION OF FATS AND OILS

Production of fats and oils from plant, animal, fish, and dairy lipids can be broken into four classifications: recovery, refining, conversion, and stabilization. Pressing or solvent extraction are common processes to liberate oil from plant seeds. Care should be taken during transportation of seeds to prevent cell rupture prior to oil extraction. Lipases and lipoxygenases in the cytosol that mix with TAG prematurely due to decompartmentation will be detrimental to oil quality (i.e., formation of free fatty acids and peroxidized lipids prior to extraction will reduce TAG purity and hence yields). Heating during or prior to the pressing step (115°C for 60 min) inactivates lipases and lipoxygenases. Other benefits of heating are rupturing of cell wells, decrease in oil viscosity, and coagulation of proteins. Elevated moisture levels are discouraged due to the ability of excess water to facilitate hydrolysis of esterified lipids. Recovery of animal fat and marine oil is also a high temperature process called rendering. Trimmings, cannery waste, bones, offal, tallow and lard can be subjected to rendering to produce valued added oils and fats.

Refining is the removal of non-TAG components including free fatty acids, phospholipids, pigments, protein, and wax. The degumming step is a water wash that removes phosphatides (e.g., lecithin, phospholipids). Hydration in the presence of heat makes phosphatides insoluble in the oil allowing removal by centrifugation. Heating of oil contaminated with phosphatides can result in foaming and even fire due to the surfactant properties of the phospholipids. The next step in refining is neutralization. Free fatty acids and phosphatides react with sodium

hydroxide to form a soap (e.g., saponified material). Subsequent bleaching removes undesirable pigments typically by use of neutral clays. Waxes are then removed by cooling the oil to around 7°C for 4 hours and filtering at 18°C. The final step in refining is deodorizing, which removes hexane, pesticides, and peroxide decomposition products that can potentially impart off-odors and off-flavors. Deodorization is accomplished by steam distillation at high temperatures (180°C to 270°C) under vacuum. Freshly deodorized oils should have a peroxide value of zero and a free fatty acid content of less than 0.03% (138). Ideally fat-soluble antioxidants such as tocopherols are retained in the purified oil. Unfortunately, refining strips antioxidants from the TAG which often requires post-processing addition of antioxidants to pure oil.

The conversion processes winterization and fractional crystallization are physical processes that alter the lipids and thus are out side the scope of this chapter. Various chemical processes of conversion (e.g., interesterification) and stabilization (e.g., hydrogenation) are described later in this chapter. Stabilization techniques for fats and oils are also discussed in the preceding section on antioxidants.

VII. MODIFICATION OF LIPIDS AND PRODUCTION OF SPECIALTY FATS

This section describes the numerous chemical processes that are available to modify the functional properties of food lipids. Functional properties include 1) oxidative stability, 2) plastic range, 3) flavor properties, 4) nutrient content, 5) health promoting effects, and 6) caloric value. Increasing fatty acid saturation or redistributing fatty acids on the glycerol backbone to improve functionality can be accomplished in bulk oils by treatment with low-molecular-weight catalysts. In other cases, more specific alteration of lipids is accomplished through the use of enzymes to improve functionality. Endogenous enzymes in yeasts, molds, and bacteria utilize nonlipid or lipid containing carbon sources to produce a wide array of different specialty lipids (e.g., cocoa-butter substitutes, triacylglycerols rich in omega-3 fatty acids, biosurfactants, polyunsaturated fatty acids, wax esters, and hydroxy fatty acids). A thorough description of the emerging fields of "lipid biotechnology" and "structured lipids" is available (139, 140). Some specific examples that utilize lipases to produce specialty lipids are cited in Section VII.C of this chapter. The opportunity to modify lipids "pre-harvest" is addressed in Section VII.D.

A. HYDROGENATION

Hydrogenation is done for two important reasons: 1) provides a semi-solid fat at room temperature from an oil source and, 2) increase oxidative stability during storage. Hydrogenation involves mixing oil with a catalyst such as nickel at elevated temperatures (140°C to 225°C).

Hydrogen gas is then introduced with agitation. Once the desired saturation is obtained, the material is cooled and the catalyst is removed by filtration. Typical products that result include shortenings and margarine. A disadvantage of this process is the formation of trans fatty acids that are considered unhealthy.

B. NON-ENZYMATIC INTERESTERIFICATION

Factors that contribute to textural properties of fats include not only degree of fatty acid unsaturation and the chain length but also the location of fatty acids on the glycerol backbone. Chemical interesterification "randomizes" the location of the different fatty acids, thereby improving the utility of the fat. Spreadability, melting point, and solid-fat content temperature profile are modified by the randomization. This process typically involves the use of sodium methoxide (0.1%) as a catalyst. The catalyst should function at low temperatures (around 50°C) to avoid polymerization and decomposition of lipids during interesterification. Moisture inactivates the catalyst. Therefore, the water content must be below 0.01%. Free fatty acids and lipid peroxides must be below 0.1% and 1%, respectively. The catalyst must be soluble in the lipid.

The mechanism of interesterification using alkaline bases involves nucleophillic attack by the catalyst towards the slightly positive carbonyl carbon. This attack liberates a fatty acid methyl ester and a resulting glycerate anion (Figure 8.11). The glycerate anion is the nucleophile for subsequent carbonyl attacks. This process continues until all the available fatty acids have exchanged positions. Sodium methoxide also removes an acidic hydrogen from the carbon alpha to the carbonyl carbon. The carbanion produced is a powerful nucleophile.

On occasion randomness is not desirable. If the fat is maintained below its melting point, interesterification proceeds with the formation of more saturated triacylglycerols. This "directed interesterification" produces a product with a higher solids content at higher temperatures, which extends its plastic range.

A practical application of interesterification involves the modification of lard. In its native form, lard has negative attributes including grainy texture, poor appearance, poor creaming capacity, and limited plastic range (141). The graininess is due to a preponderance of palmitic acid at the sn-2 position. Randomization decreases the amount of palmitic acid and the sn-2 position and hence decreases graininess. Directed interesterification resolves the plastic range problem. Improvement in plasticity and stability is due to alterations in the polymorphic behavior. The interesterified lard crystallizes into a β'-2 form that promotes the improved functionality (8).

Fish oils are liquid at room temperature due to their high content of polyunsaturated fatty acids including

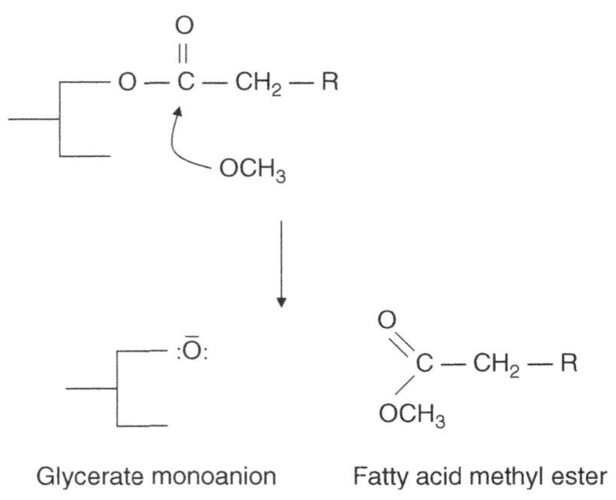

FIGURE 8.11 Proposed mechanism of chemical interesterification. Adapted from Ref. 141.

omega-3 fatty acids (e.g., 22:6 and 20:5). Ingestion of omega-3 fatty acids are noted for their ability to decrease incidences of various diseases but are also highly susceptible to lipid oxidation in foods, which causes off-flavors and off-odors. A possible route to increased consumption of these fatty acids with less quality loss during storage is chemical interesterification. Interesterification of a hydrogenated vegetable oil and the fish oil will produce a mixture of fatty acids on the glycerol backbone ranging from highly saturated to highly unsaturated. The saturated TAGs can be removed by low temperature fractional crystallization and centrifugation. The fraction obtained with intermediate unsaturation (moderately higher temperature crystallization) comprises TAGs containing both saturated fatty acids and the highly coveted omega-3 fatty acids. Compared to the starting fish oil, this results in triacylglycerols 1) with a greater plastic temperature range increasing product applications, 2) more resistance to lipid oxidation due to the incorporation of the saturated fatty acids, and 3) a relatively more stable source of omega-3 fatty acids for incorporation into foods. An area of concern would be the stability of the omega-3 fatty acids at the temperatures used during chemical interesterification. An alternative process that requires lower reaction temperatures is enzymatic interesterification.

C. ENZYMATIC MODIFICATION OF LIPIDS

Enzymatic interestification is accomplished using lipases from bacterial, yeast, and fungal sources. The regio- and stereospecificity obtained through the use of lipases is a marked advantage over chemical interesterification. Enzymatic interesterification requires less severe reaction conditions, products are more easily purified, and produces less waste than chemical interesterification. Enzymatic interesterification is more expensive at the present time although advances are expected to lower costs. In any event, certain processes can be accomplished with lipases that are not achievable via chemical inter-esterification. For example, it is optimal to incorporate stearic acid (18:0) at the sn-1 or sn-3 position because stearic acid is least absorbed at these positions compared to the sn-2 position (142). This is advantageous since caloric value is decreased while maintaining a long chain saturated fatty acid that expands the plastic range. An sn-1,3 lipase facilitates the regioselectivity desired whereas chemical interesterification cannot. Since fatty acids at the sn-2 position are more efficiently absorbed than those at the sn-1,3 positions, the ideal location for essential fatty acids is at the sn-2 position. Fatty acids at sn-2 will be shuffled to other positions on the triacylglyc-erol in chemical interesterification, which is undesirable. The sn-1,3 lipases, however, allow those endogenous fatty acids to remain at the sn-2 site.

The major triacylglycerols in cocoa butter all contain oleic acid at the sn-2 position (1-palmitoyl-2-oleoyl-3-stearoyl-glycerol, 1,3-dipalmitoyl-2-oleoyl-glycerol, and 1,3-distearoyl-2-oleoyl-glycerol). Palm oil is rich in palmitic and oleic acid but lacks appreciable amounts of steric acid. Thus, palm oil has been reacted with stearic acid and an sn-1,3 specific lipase; replacement of palmitic acid with stearic acid at the sn-1 or sn-3 position produced an effective cocoa butter substitute. Chemical interesterification will randomize the location of all the fatty acids and produce a less effective substitute. Cocoa butter is an expensive material due to its limited quantities and unique melting properties (hard and brittle at room temperature but melts as it is warmed in the mouth).

The reaction of fatty acids with esters such as those found in triacylglycerols is termed acidolysis. Another acidolysis reaction involves incorporating capric acid (10:0) and caproic acid (6:0) into an oil stock. This is ben-eficial since these fatty acids are readily oxidized in the liver and therefore are excellent sources of energy as opposed to normal storage fat for individuals having defi-ciencies in fat absorption.

Transesterification is the exchange of acyl groups between two esters, specifically between two tricacyl-glycerols. Mixtures of hydrogenated cotton oil (rich in stearic and palmitic acid) and olive oil (rich in oleic) can be reacted in the presence of the proper lipase and mini-mal water to create a cocoa butter substitute. To separate the desired TAG from the undesired TAG, trisaturated TAG can be removed by crystallization in acetone or tem-perature differentials that crystallize out the more satu-rated triacylglycerols. This process can also be performed using sodium methoxide catalyst instead of lipases but again the randomization of oleic acid from the sn-2 posi-tion in the chemical interesterification should produce a less effective substitute than a sn-1,3 lipase-driven inter-esterification that regiospecifically alters the starting oil stocks, thereby maintaining oleic acid at the sn-2 position.

Alcoholysis is the esterification reaction between an alcohol and an ester. The most common alcoholysis is the production of mono- and diacylglycerol surfactants (e.g., emulsifiers) by reacting glycerol with triacylglycerols. Specifically, this reaction is termed glycerolysis and is usually performed using nonspecific lipases. The newly formed mono- and diacylglycerols are isolated by temper-ature-induced crystallization. In glycerolysis, Tc is defined as the critical temperature below which mono-acylglycerols crystallize out of the reaction mixture (143). This pushes the equilibrium of the reaction to produce more monoacylglycerols. Vegetable oils have low melting points and hence low Tc due to the abundance of polyun-saturated fatty acids compared to animal fats. By reducing the temperature below the Tc for vegetable oils (Tc = 5°C to 10°C), yields of monoacylglycerols can be increased.

D. MODIFICATION OF LIPIDS PRIOR TO HARVEST

Genetic manipulation of lipid biosynthesis is a possible route to improve functionality of TAG and phospholipids (144). For example, the overexpression of cis-9 desaturase in transgenic tomato results in increases in 16:1(cis 9), 16:2(cis 9,12), and 18:2(cis 9,12) fatty acids, which enhance positive flavor attributes in the fruit mediated by a lipoxygenase/hydroperoxidelyase/isomerase/reductase enzyme system (145, 146). Apparently the enhanced fatty acids are precursors for the desirable flavor compounds in tomato. In cell membranes, phosphatidyl glycerol contain-ing two saturated fatty acids is correlated with decreased chilling injury in plants. Incorporating plastidic sn-glyc-erol-3-phosphate acyltransferase (GPAT) from a chilling-insensitive species (spinach) into a moderately chilling sensitive species (tobacco) increased disaturated phos-phatidyl glycerol and was successful at decreasing chilling injury in the tobacco (147). Oxidative stability of trans-genic canola oil was improved by decreasing the activity of a cis 15-endogenous desaturase using antisense tech-nology (148). This lowered the 18:3 (cis 9,12,15) content from 6.9% to 1.4% in the oil. Although lipid stability was improved by this technique, 18:3 is an essential fatty acid so functionality is improved at the expense of nutritional quality. A thorough review of genetic engineering of crops that produce modified vegetable oils is available (149).

E. FAT REPLACERS

Fat replacers can be primarily carbohydrate, protein, or lipid based. Protein or carbohydrates replacers are called *mimetics* and tend to absorb water readily but cannot carry lipid-soluble flavor compounds. The other category of fat replacers, called *substitutes*, will typically contain fatty acids esterified to a carbohydrate. The fatty acids provide desirable physical properties of fats but are not readily cleaved by lipases during digestion. In other words, the lipids are not metabolized and therefore caloric intake is reduced per gram or fat ingested. An example of a fat substitute is raffinose polyester. Raffinose is made up of galactose-glucose-fructose units. The eleven available hydroxy groups can potentially be esterified with fatty acids. As the degree of substitution increases the susceptibility to hydrolysis and absorption will decrease (150). Sucrose fatty acid esters act as emulsifiers, texturizers, and protective coatings in various foods products.

Benefat™ consists of short chain fatty acids (e.g., 2:0, 3:0, 4:0) and a long chain saturated fatty acid (stearic acid, 18:0). Short chain fatty acids have low caloric value because they are easily hydrolyzed by digestive lipases and readily converted to carbon dioxide (151). Stearic acid is only partially absorbed, especially if located at the sn-1 or sn-3 position. Benefat is around 5 kcal/g while typical fats are 9 kcal/gram. Currently, Benefat is produced by base-catalyzed interesterification of hydrogenated vegetable oils with TAGs of acetic, propionic, and/or butyric acids (152). The ratios of the short chain fatty acids and the long chain saturated fatty acid can be varied not only providing a low caloric intake but also the physical properties required for specific food applications. Benefat can be used in cookies, baked goods, dairy products, dressings, dips, and sauces (150).

VIII. CHEMISTRY OF FRYING

Frying of oils results in distinctive fried flavors and undesirable off-flavors if the oil is overly deteriorated. Off-flavors are manifested via 1) hydrolysis, 2) oxidation, and 3) polymerization reactions. The interaction of steam, water, and oil will hydrolyze TAG into mono-acylglycerols, di-acylglycerols, and free fatty acids. With increased time even glycerol will be produced due to complete hydrolysis of an individual triacylglycerol. Little glycerol can be detected in frying oils since glycerol volatilizes around 150°C and frying temperatures are typically higher. Factors that control hydrolysis are oil temperature, interface area between oil and aqueous phases, water level, and steam level (153). Metals that contaminate the oil interact with lipid hydroperoxides to form free radical species that initiate and propagate oxidation reactions in the presence of oxygen. Frying temperatures will greatly increase the rate of these fundamental lipid oxidation processes and stimulate reactions that may not occur at lower temperatures resulting in an array of oxidation products including aldehydes, ketones, alcohols, esters, hydrocarbons, and lactones. These low-molecular-weight compounds that form due to degradation of the frying oil are considered "volatile," contributing desirable and undesirable flavors. Polymerization is common in frying where molecules cross-link often as a free radical-free radical reaction. As polymerization increases so too does viscosity of the oil. Most polymerized products are nonvolatile (e.g., dimeric fatty acids, TAG-trimers) and hence

do not produce flavor. However, with further heating these non-volatile compounds can be degraded to off-flavor and toxic products. Degradation products negatively affect not only flavor and safety but also color and texture of the fried products.

Antioxidants and antifoam are added to frying oil to extend frying life. Other measures of delaying degradation of oil quality include utilizing fresh oil, using an oil low in polyunsaturated fatty acids and contaminating metals, filtration of oil with adsorbents, turnover of oil, and decreasing exposure of oil to oxygen. Antifoam will aid in reducing exposure of oil to oxygen. Continuous heating is better than discontinuous heating in extending frying life of the oil (153). Not all oxidation that occurs with frying is negative. For instance, 2-4-decadienal is considered a positive flavor compound. Often a preliminary batch of fried foods is prepared and discarded so that the subsequent batches have a desired flavor profile. More unsaturated oils oxidize faster than less saturated oils which decreases the amount of time needed to obtain a proper frying flavor in the food.

Free fatty acid content is an unreliable measure of frying oil quality. There still is not a fully appropriate single test to assess frying oil quality. The FoodOil sensor (FOS) (Northern Instruments Corp., Lino Lakes, MN) measures dielectric constant of frying oil compared to fresh oil and has had some success. The dielectric constant increases with increasing polarity so that once a certain value is reached the oil needs change.

IX. FOOD IRRADIATION

The purpose of food irradiation is to destroy microorganisms and hence extend shelf life. Lipids can be adversely affected. Typical dosages range from 1 to 10 kGy. Sterilization is achieved at doses of 10–50 kGy. When ionization radiation is absorbed by matter, ions, and excited molecules are produced. These ions, and excited molecules can dissociate to form free radicals. Reactions induced by irradiation prefer to react near the oxygen portion of TAG (154). Reaction occurs preferentially near the oxygen due to the high localization of electron deficiency on the oxygen atom. This explains the preponderance of aldehydes with the same chain length as the most abundant parent fatty acid (cleavage at location b) (Figure 8.12). Cleavage at locations c and d results in hydrocarbons that have one and two carbons less, respectively, than the parent fatty acid, which also is more common than a random assortment of hydrocarbons. Alternatively, free radicals can combine. For instance, two alkyl radicals react to form a dimeric hydrocarbon; acyl and alkyl radicals result in a ketone; acyloxy and alkyl radicals produce an ester; alkyl radicals can react with various glyceryl residue radicals to form alkyl glyceryl diesters and glyceryl ether diesters.

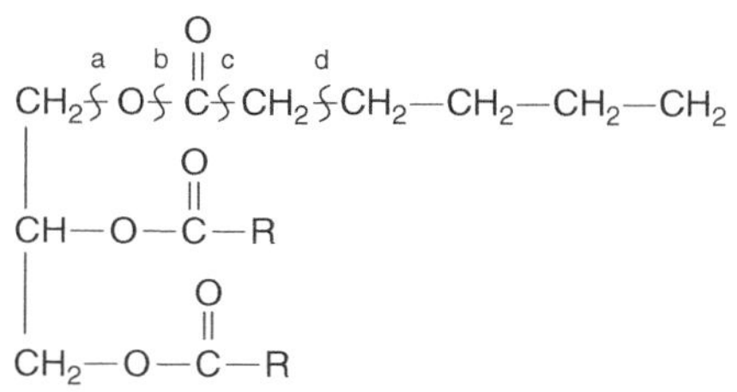

FIGURE 8.12 Cleavage sites on a triacylglycerol due to radiolysis. Adapted from Ref. 8.

Irradiation was found to accelerate lipid oxidation in raw pork patties and raw turkey breast that was aerobically packed (155, 156). Lipid oxidation was accelerated by irradiation (3 kGy) in aerobically packed, pre-cooked chicken (157). Irradiation caused formation of a brown pigment in raw beef and pork, but not turkey (158). Carbon monoxide was implicated as the cause of pinking in irradiated raw turkey breast muscle (159).

REFERENCES

1. J Kanner. Oxidative processes in meat and meat products: quality implications. Meat Sci 36: 169–189, 1994.
2. DW Stanley. Biological membrane deterioration and associated quality losses in food tissues. Crit Rev Food Sci Nutr 30: 487–553, 1991.
3. SF O'Keefe. Nomenclature and classification of lipids. In: CC Akoh and DB Min. Food Lipids. New York: Marcel Dekker, 1998, 1–36.
4. D Kritchevsky. Fats and oils in human health. In: CC Akoh and DB Min. Food Lipids. New York: Marcel Dekker, 1998, 449–461.
5. J Kanner, T Lapidot. The stomach as a bioreactor: dietary lipid peroxidation in the gastric fluid and the effects of plant-derived antioxidants. Free Rad Biol Med 31: 1388–1395, 2001.
6. JP Thomas, B Kalyanaraman, AW Girotti. Involvement of preexisting lipid hydroperoxides in Cu^{2+}-stimulated oxidation of low-density lipoproteins. Arch Biochem Biophys 315: 244–254, 1994.
7. T Miyazawa, T Suzuki, K Fujimoto, M Kinoshita. Age-related change of phosphatidylcholine hydroperoxide and phosphotidylethanolamine hydroperoxide levels in normal human red blood cells. Mech Ageing Dev 86: 145–150, 1996.
8. WW Nawar. Lipids. In: OR Fennema. Food Chemistry. New York: Marcell Dekker 1996, 225–319.
9. DB Min. Lipid oxidation in edible oils. In: CC Akoh and DB Min. Food Lipids. New York: Marcel Dekker, 1998, 283–296.
10. M-C Yin, C Faustman. Influence of temperature, pH, and phospholipid composition upon the stability of myoglobin and phospholipid: a liposomal model. J Agric Food Chem 41: 853–857, 1993.
11. K Miyashita, E Nara, T Ota. Oxidative stability of polyunsaturated fatty acids in an aqueous solution. Biosci Biotech Biochem 57: 1638–1640, 1993.
12. EN Frankel, T Satue Gracia, AS Meyer, JB German. Oxidative stability of fish and algae oils containing long-chain polyunsaturated fatty acids in bulk and in oil-in-water emulsions. J Agric Food Chem 50: 2094–2099, 2002.
13. JZ Tichivangana, PA Morrissey. Metmyoglobin and inorganic metals as pro-oxidants in raw and cooked muscle systems. Meat Sci 15: 107–116, 1985.
14. MP Richards, AM Modra, R Li. Role of deoxyhemoglobin in lipid oxidation of washed cod muscle mediated by trout, poultry and beef hemoglobins. Meat Sci 62: 157–163, 2002.
15. K Takama. Changes in the flesh lipids of fish during frozen storage. V. Accelerative substances of lipid oxidation in the muscle of rainbow trout. Bull Faculty Fisheries 25: 256–263, 1974.
16. AI Virtanen. On enzymic and chemical reactions in crushed plants. IV Enzymes. Arch Biochem Biophys Supp 1: 200–208, 1962.
17. GR Buettner. The pecking order of free radicals and antioxidants: Lipid peroxidation, alpha-tocopherol, and ascorbate. Arch Biochem Biophys 300: 535–543, 1993.
18. SY Qian, GR Buettner. Iron and dioxygen chemistry is an important route to initiation of biological free radical oxidations: an electron paramagnetic resonance spin trapping study. Free Rad Biol Med 26: 1447–1456, 1999.
19. BA Svingen, JA Buege, FO O'Neal, SD Aust. The mechanism of NADPH-dependent lipid peroxidation. J Biol Chem 254: 5892–5899, 1979.
20. K Yamamoto, M Takahashi, E Niki. Role of iron and ascorbic acid in the oxidation of methyl linoleate micelles. Chem Lett 6: 1149–1152, 1987.
21. C-H Huang, HO Hultin, S Jafar. Some aspects of Fe^{2+}-catalyzed oxidation of fish sarcoplasmic reticular lipid. J Agric Food Chem 41: 1886–1892, 1993.
22. C Balagopalakrishna, L Paka, S Pillarisetti, IJ Goldberg. Lipolysis-induced iron release from diferric transferrin: Possible role of lipoprotein lipase in LDL oxidation. J Lipid Res 40: 1347–1356, 1999.
23. JO Igene, JA King, AM Pearson, JI Gray. Influence of heme pigments, nitrite, and non-heme iron on development of warmed-over flavor (WOF) in cooked meats. J Agric Food Chem 27: 838–842, 1979.
24. EA Decker, B Welch. Role of ferritin as a lipid oxidation catalyst in muscle foods. J Agric Food Chem 38: 674–677, 1990.
25. S Harel, MA Salan, J Kanner. Iron release from metmyoglobin, methemoglobin and cytochrome c by a system generating hydrogen peroxide. Free Rad Res Comms 5: 11–19, 1988.
26. EA Decker, HO Hultin. Factors influencing catalysis of lipid oxidation by the soluble fractions of mackerel muscle. J Food Sci 55: 947–950, 953, 1990.
27. RW Kranen, TH van Kuppevelt, HA Goedhart, CH Veerkamp, E Lambooy, JH Veerkamp. Hemoglobin and myoglobin content in muscle of broiler chickens. Poultry Sci 78: 467–476, 1999.
28. A Dumoulin, LR Manning, WT Jenkins, RM Winslow, JM Manning. Exchange of subunit interfaces between

recombinant adult and fetal hemoglobins. J Biol Chem 272: 31326–31332, 1997.

29. G Zolese, R Gabbianelli, GC Caulini, E Bertoli, G Falconi. Steady-state fluorescence and circular dichroism of trout hemoglobins I and IV interacting with tributyltin. Protein-Struct Funct Genet 34: 443–452, 1999.

30. JE Knapp, MA Oliveira, Q Xie, SR Ernst, AF Riggs, ML Hackert. The structural and functional analysis of the hemoglobin D component from chicken. J Biol Chem 274: 6411–6420, 1999.

31. RE Brantley, SJ Smerdon, AJ Wilkinson, EW Singleton, JS Olson. The mechanism of autooxidation of myoglobin. J Biol Chem 268: 6995–7010, 1993.

32. J Kanner, S Harel. Initiation of membranal lipid peroxidation by activated metmyoglobin and methemoglobin. Arch Biochem Biophys 237: 314–321, 1985.

33. MS Hargrove, AJ Wilkinson, JS Olson. Structural factors governing hemin dissociation from metmyoglobin. Biochemistry 35: 11300–11309, 1996.

34. Q Tang, WA Kalsbeck, JS Olson, DF Bocian. Disruption of the heme iron-proximal histidine bond requires unfolding of deoxymyoglobin. Biochemistry 37: 7047–7056, 1998.

35. AL Tappel. Unsaturated lipide oxidation catalyzed by hematin compounds. J Biol Chem 217: 721–733, 1955.

36. SW Ryter, RM Tyrrell. The heme synthesis and degradation pathways: role in oxidant sensitivity. Free Rad Biol Med 28: 289–309, 2000.

37. CP Baron, LH Skibsted, HJ Andersen. Concentration effects in myoglobin-catalyzed peroxidation of linoleate. J Agric Food Chem 50: 883–888, 2002.

38. A Riggs. Properties of hemoglobins. In: WS Hoar and DJ Randall. Fish Physiology The Nervous System, Circulation, and Respiration, Vol IV. New York: Academic Press, 1970, 209–252.

39. PJ Thornalley, RJ Trotta, A Stern. Free radical involvement in the oxidative phenomena induced by tert-butyl hydroperoxide in erythrocytes. Biochim Biophys Acta 759: 16–22, 1983.

40. BJ Reeder, MT Wilson. Mechanism of reaction of myoglobin with the lipid hydroperoxide hydroperoxyoctadecadienoic acid. Biochem J 330 (Pt 3): 1317–1323, 1998.

41. A Boveris, N Oshino, B Chance. The cellular production of hydrogen peroxide. Biochem J 128: 617–630, 1972.

42. C Giulivi, P Hochstein, KJ Davies. Hydrogen peroxide production by red blood cells. Free Rad Biol Med 16: 123–129, 1994.

43. S Harel, J Kanner. Hydrogen peroxide generation in ground muscle tissues. J Agric Food Chem 33: 1186–1188, 1985.

44. S Yamamoto. Mammalian lipoxygenases: molecular structures and functions. Biochim Biophys Acta 1128: 117–131, 1992.

45. B Tadolini, G Hakim. The mechanism of iron (III) stimulation of lipid peroxidation. Free Rad Res 25: 221–227, 1996.

46. N Hogg, C Rice-Evans, V Darley-Usmar, MT Wilson, G Paganga, L Bourne. The role of lipid hydroperoxides in the myoglobin-dependent oxidation of LDL. Arch Biochem Biophys 314: 39–44, 1994.

47. M Iwatsuki, E Niki, D Stone, VM Darley-Usmar. alpha-tocopherol mediated peroxidation in the copper (II) and met myoglobin induced oxidation of human low density lipoprotein: the influence of lipid hydroperoxides. FEBS Lett 360: 271–276, 1995.

48. B Halliwell, JMC Gutteridge. Free Radicals in Biology and Medicine. 3rd ed. New York: Oxford University Press, 1999, 297.

49. JM Gebicki. Protein hydroperoxides as new reactive oxygen species. Redox Report 3: 1–12, 1997.

50. CD Nuchi, DJ McClements, EA Decker. Impact of tween 20 hydroperoxides and iron on the oxidation of methyl linoleate and salmon oil dispersions. J Agric food Chem 49: 4912–4916, 2001.

51. B Halliwell, JMC Gutteridge. Free Radicals in Biology and Medicine. 3rd ed. New York: Oxford University Press, 1999, 292.

52. PJ Ke, RG Ackman. Bunsen coefficient for oxygen in marine oils at various temperatures determined by an exponential dilution method with a polarographic oxygen electrode. J Amer Oil Chem Soc 50: 429–435, 1973.

53. B Kilic, RG Cassens. Penetration of substances into muscle foods. J Muscle Foods 9: 91–100, 1998.

54. H de Groot, T Noll. The role of physiological oxygen partial pressures in lipid peroxidation. Theoretical considerations and experimental evidence. Chem Phys Lipids 44: 209–226, 1987.

55. DA Ledward. Metmyoglobin formation in beef stored in carbon dioxide enriched and oxygen depleted atmospheres. J Food Sci 35: 33–37, 1970.

56. M Smiddy, M Fitzgerald, JP Kerry, DB Papkovsky, CK O'Sullivan, GG Guilbault. Use of oxygen sensor to non-destructively measure the oxygen content in modified atmosphere and vacuum packed beef: impact of oxygen content on lipid oxidation. Meat Sci 66: 105–110, 2002.

57. GW Burton, KU Ingold. β-carotene: an unusual type of lipid antioxidant. Science 224: 569–573, 1984.

58. JI Reyes De Corcuera, RP Cavalieri. Improved amperometric method for the rapid and quantitative measurement of lipoxygenase activity in vegetable tissue crude homogenates. J Agric Food Chem 50: 997–1001, 2002.

59. DB Josephson, RC Lindsay, DA Stuiber. Enzymic hydroperoxide initiated effects in fresh fish. J Food Sci 52: 596–600, 1987.

60. SI Rao, A Wilks, M Hamberg, PR Ortiz de Montellano. The lipoxygenase activity of myoglobin. J Biol Chem 269: 7210–7216, 1994.

61. H Kühn, R Götze, T Schewe, SM Rapoport. Quasi-lipoxygenase activity of haemoglobin. Eur J Biochem 120: 161–168, 1981.

62. LK Folkes, LP Candeias, P Wardman. Kinetics and mechanisms of hypochlorous acid reactions. Arch Biochem Biophys 323: 120–126, 1995.

63. CD Dacaranhe, J Terao. Effect of cabbage phospholipase D treatment on the oxidative stability of beef homogenate and egg yolk phosphatidylcholine liposomes. J Food Sci 67: 2619–2624, 2002.

64. HHF Refsgaard, PMB Brockhoff, B Jensen. Free polyunsaturated fatty acids cause taste deterioration of salmon during frozen storage. J Agric Food Chem 48: 3280–3285, 2000.

65. RL Shewfelt. Fish muscle lipolysis—a review. J Food Biochem 5: 79–100, 1981.

66. P Di Mascio, TP Devasagayam, S Kaiser, H Sies. Carotenoids, tocopherols and thiols as biological singlet molecular oxygen quenchers. Biochem Soc Trans 18: 1054–1056, 1990.

67. DG Bradley, DB Min. Singlet oxygen oxidation of foods. Crit Rev Food Sci Nutr 31: 211–236, 1992.

68. AM Haahr, WLP Bredie, LH Stahnke, B Jensen, HHF Refsgaard. Flavour release of aldehydes and diacetyl in oil/water systems. Food Chem 71: 355–362, 2000.

69. I Undeland, HO Hultin, MP Richards. Added triacylglycerols do not hasten hemoglobin-mediated lipid oxidation in washed minced cod muscle. J Agric Food Chem 50: 6847–6853, 2002.

70. JO Igene, AM Pearson. Role of phospholipids and triglycerides in warmed-over flavor development in meat model systems. J Food Sci 44: 1285–1290, 1979.

71. RG Brannan, MC Erickson. Sensory assessment of frozen stored channel catfish in relation to lipid oxidation. J Aquat Food Prod Tech 5: 67–80, 1996.

72. CYW Ang, BG Lyon. Evaluations of warmed-over flavor during chilled storage of cooked broiler breast, thigh and skin by chemical, instrumental, and sensory methods. J Food Sci 55: 644–648, 1990.

73. K Sato, GR Hegarty. Warmed-over flavor in cooked meats. J Food Sci 36: 1098–1102, 1971.

74. C Koizumi, S Wada, T Ohshima. Factors affecting development of rancid odor in cooked fish meats during storage at 5°C. Nippon Suisan Gakkaishi 53: 2003–2009, 1987.

75. K Sato, GR Hegarty, HK Herring. The inhibition of warmed-over flavor in cooked meats. J Food Sci 38: 398–403, 1973.

76. C Laureaux, P Therond, D Bonnefont-Rousselot, SE Troupel, A Legrand, J Delatrre. Alpha-tocopherol enrichment of high-density lipoproteins: stabilization of hydroperoxides produced during copper oxidation. Free Rad Biol Med 22: 185–194, 1997.

77. NP Brunton, DA Cronin, FJ Monahan, R Durcan. A comparison of solid-phase microextraction (SPME) fibres for measurement of hexanal and pentanal in cooked turkey. Food Chem 68: 339–345, 2000.

78. Y Xing, Y Yoo, SD Kelleher, WW Nawar, HO Hultin. Lack of changes in fatty acid composition of mackerel and cod during iced and frozen storage. J Food Lipids 1: 1–14, 1993.

79. C Milo, W Grosch. Changes in the odorants of boiled trout (Salmo Fario) as affected by the storage of the raw material. J Agric Food Chem 41: 2076–2081, 1993.

80. EN Frankel. Stability methods. In: Lipid Oxidation. Dundee: The Oily Press, 1998, 99–114.

81. IP Ashton. Understanding lipid oxidation in fish muscle. In: HA Bremmer. Safety and Quality Issues in Fish Processing. Boca Raton, FL: CRC Press, 2002, 254–285.

82. J Kanner, H Mendel. Prooxidant and antioxidant effect of ascorbic acid and metal salts in beta carotene-linoleate model system. J Food Sci 42: 60–64, 1977.

83. EA Decker. Antioxidant mechanisms. In: CC Akoh and DB Min. Food Lipids. New York: Marcel Dekker, 1998, 397–421.

84. J Kanner, JB German, JE Kinsella. Initiation of lipid peroxidation in biological systems. CRC Crit Rev Food Sci Nutr 25: 317–364, 1987.

85. F Shahidi, PK Janitha, PD Wanasundara. Phenolic antioxidants. Crit Rev Food Sci Nutr 32: 67–103, 1992.

86. DL Madhavi, RS Singhal, PR Kulkarni. Technological aspects of food antioxidants. In: DL Madhavi, SS Deshpande and DK Salunkhe. Food Antioxidants: Technological, Toxicological, and Health Perspectives. New York: Marcel Dekker, 1996, 267–359.

87. JK Kaitaranta. Control of lipid oxidation in fish oil with various antioxidative compounds. J Am Oil Chem Soc 69: 810–813, 1992.

88. A Valenzuela, H Sanhueza, S Nieto. Differential inhibitory effect of alpha-, beta-, gamma-, and delta-tocopherols on the metal-induced oxidation of cholesterol in unilamellar phospholipid-cholesterol liposomes. J Food Sci 67: 2051–2055, 2002.

89. C Faustman, DC Liebler, JA Burr. Alpha-tocopherol oxidation in beef and in bovine muscle microsomes. J Agric Food Chem 47: 1396–1399, 1999.

90. D Petillo, HO Hultin, J Kryznowek, WR Autio. Kinetics of antioxidant loss in mackerel light and dark muscle. J Agric Food Chem 46: 4128–4137, 1998.

91. K-H Wagner, F Wotruba, I Elmadfa. Antioxidative potential of tocotrienols and tocopherols in coconut fat at different oxidation temperatures. Eur J Lipid Sci Technol 103: 746–751, 2001.

92. M Shirai, JH Moon, T Tsushida, J Terao. Inhibitory effect of a quercetin metabolite, quercetin 3-O-beta-D-glucuronide, on lipid peroxidation in liposomal membranes. J Agric Food Chem 49: 5602–5608, 2001.

93. CG Krueger, MM Vestling, JD Reed. Matrix-assisted laser desorption/ionization time-of-flight mass spectrometry of heteropolyflavan-3-ols and glucosylated heteropolyflavans in Sorghum [Sorghum bicolor (L.) Moench]. J Agric Food Chem 51: 538–543, 2003.

94. P Pedrielli, GF Pedulli, LH Skibsted. Antioxidant mechanism of flavonoids. Solvent effect on rate constant for chain-breaking reaction of quercetin and epicatechin in autoxidation of methyl linoleate. J Agric Food Chem 49: 3034–3040, 2001.

95. NP Seeram, MG Nair. Inhibition of lipid peroxidation and structure-activity-related studies of the dietary constituents anthocyanins, anthocyanidins, and catechins. J Agric Food Chem 50: 5308–5312, 2002.

96. M Wettasinghe, B Bolling, L Plhak, H Xiao, K Parkin. Phase II enzyme-inducing and antioxidant activities of beetroot (Beta vulgaris L.) extracts from phenotypes of different pigmentation. J Agric Food Chem 50: 6704–6709, 2002.

97. J Kanner, S Harel, R Granit. Betalains—a new class of dietary cationized antioxidants. J Agric Food Chem 49: 5178–5185, 2001.

98. L Wen, RE Wrolstad, VL Hsu. Characterization of sinapyl derivatives in pineapple (Ananas comosus [L.] Merill) juice. J Agric Food Chem 47: 850–853, 1999.

99. MJ Arts, GR Haenen, LC Wilms, SA Beetstra, CG Heijnen, HP Voss, A Bast. Interactions between flavonoids and proteins: effect on the total antioxidant capacity. J Agric Food Chem 50: 1184–1187, 2002.

100. W Mullen, AJ Stewart, ME Lean, P Gardner, GG Duthie, A Crozier. Effect of freezing and storage on the phenolics, ellagitannins, flavonoids, and antioxidant capacity of red raspberries. J Agric Food Chem 50: 5197–5201, 2002.

101. M Hu, LH Skibsted. Kinetics of reduction of ferrylmyoglobin by (-)-epigallocatechin gallate and green tea extract. J Agric Food Chem 50: 2998–3003, 2002.

102. SZ Tang, JP Kerry, D Sheehan, DJ Buckley. Antioxidative mechanisms of tea catechins in chicken meat systems. Food Chem 76: 45–51, 2002.

103. J Terao. Antioxidant activity of beta-carotene-related carotenoids in solution. Lipids 24: 659–661, 1989.

104. P Palozza, NI Krinsky. Antioxidant effects of carotenoids in vivo and in vitro: an overview. Methods Enzymol 213: 403–420, 1992.

105. BN Ames, R Cathcart, E Schwiers, P Hochstein. Uric acid provides an antioxidant defense in humans against oxidant- and radical-caused aging and cancer: a hypothesis. Proc Natl Acad Sci USA 78: 6558–6862, 1981.

106. M Kroger-Ohlsen, LH Skibsted. Kinetics and mechanism of reduction of ferrylmyoglobin by ascorbate and D-isoascorbate. J Agric Food Chem 45: 668–676, 1997.

107. DE Baranano, M Rao, CD Ferris, SH Snyder. Biliverdin reductase: a major physiologic cytoprotectant. Proc Natl Acad Sci USA 99: 16093–16098, 2002.

108. D Mohr, VW Bowry, R Stocker. Dietary supplementation with coenzyme Q10 results in increased levels of ubiquinol-10 within circulating lipoproteins and increased resistance of human low-density lipoprotein to the initiation of lipid peroxidation. Biochim Biophys Acta 1126: 247–254, 1992.

109. KU Ingold, VW Bowry, R Stocker, C Walling. Autoxidation of lipids and antioxidation by alpha-tocopherol and ubiquinol in homogeneous solution and in aqueous dispersions of lipids: unrecognized consequences of lipid particle size as exemplified by oxidation of human low density lipoprotein. Proc Natl Acad Sci USA 90: 45–49, 1993.

110. LJdR Pasquel, JK Babbitt. Isolation and partial characterization of a natural antioxidant from shrimp (Pandalus jordani). J Food Sci 56: 143–145, 1991.

111. Y Tampo, S Onodera, M Yonaha. Mechanism of the biphasic effect of ethylenediaminetetraacetate on lipid peroxidation in iron-supported and reconstituted enzymatic system. Free Rad Biol Med 17: 27–34, 1994.

112. I Jimenez, H Speisky. Effects of copper ions on the free radical-scavenging properties of reduced gluthathione: implications of a complex formation. J Trace Elem Med Biol 14: 161–167, 2000.

113. J Kanner, S Harel. Desferrioxamine as an electron donor. Inhibition of membranal lipid peroxidation initiated by H_2O_2-activated metmyoglobin and other peroxidizing systems. Free Rad Res Comms 3: 1–5, 1987.

114. A Mikkelsen, G Bertelsen, LH Skibsted. Polyphosphates as antioxidants in frozen beef patties. Z Lebensm Unters Forsch 192: 309–318, 1991.

115. B Halliwell, JM Gutteridge. The antioxidants of human extracellular fluids. Arch Biochem Biophys 280: 1–8, 1990.

116. J Kanner, L Doll. Ferritin in turkey muscle tissue: a source of catalytic iron ions for lipid peroxidation. J Agric Food Chem 39: 247–249, 1991.

117. EA Decker, SA Livisay, S Zhou. A re-evaluation of the antioxidant activity of purified carnosine. Biochemistry (Mosc) 65: 766–770, 2000.

118. MC Erickson, HO Hultin. Influence of histidine on lipid peroxidation in sarcoplasmic reticulum. Arch Biochem Biophys 292: 427–432, 1992.

119. HP Misra, I Fridovich. The generation of superoxide during autoxidation of hemoglobin. J Biol Chem 247: 6960–6962, 1972.

120. L Goth. Heat and pH dependence of catalase. A comparative study. Acta Biol Hung 38: 279–285, 1987.

121. MP Lynch, C Faustman, LK Silbart, D Rood, HC Furr. Detection of lipid-derived aldehydes and aldehyde:protein adducts in vitro and in beef. J Food Sci 66: 1093–1099, 2001.

122. S Ohmori, T Misaizu, M Kitada, H Kitagawa, K Igarashi, S Hirose, Y Kanakubo. Polyamine lowered the hepatic lipid peroxide level in rats. Res Commun Chem Pathol Pharmacol 62: 235–249, 1988.

123. M Du, DU Ahn, KC Nam, JL Sell. Influences of dietary conjugated linoleic acid on volatile profiles, color and lipid oxidation of irradiated raw chicken meat. Meat Sci 56: 387–395, 2000.

124. SA Livisay, S Zhou, C Ip, EA Decker. Impact of dietary conjugated linoleic acid on the oxidative stability of rat liver microsomes and skeletal muscle homogenates. J Agric Food Chem 48: 4162–4167, 2000.

125. MC Yin, SW Hwang, KC Chan. Nonenzymatic antioxidant activity of four organosulfur compounds derived from garlic. J Agric Food Chem 50: 6143–6147, 2002.

126. SS Jafar, HO Hultin, AP Bimbo, JB Crowther, SM Barlow. Stabilization by antioxidants of mayonnaise made from fish oil. J Food Lipids 1: 295–311, 1994.

127. G Gandemer, A Meynier. The importance of phospholipids in the development of flavour and off-flavour in meat products. In: K Lundstrom, I Hansson and E Wiklund. Composition of Meat in Relation to Processing, Nutritional and Sensory Quality: From Farm to Fork. Utrecht: ECCEAMST, 1995, 119–128.

128. H Sigfusson, HO Hultin. Partitioning of delta-tocopherol in aqueous mixtures of TAG and isolated muscle membranes. J Am Oil Chem Soc 79: 691–697, 2002.

129. H Sigfusson, HO Hultin. Partitioning of exogenous delta-tocopherol between the triacylglycerol and membrane lipid fractions of chicken muscle. J Agric Food Chem 50: 7120–7126, 2002.

130. EN Frankel, SW Huang, J Kanner, JB German. Interfacial phenomena in the evaluation of antioxidants: bulk oils vs emulsions. J Agric Food Chem 42: 1054–1059, 1994.

131. SW Huang, A Hopia, K Schwarz, EN Frankel, JB German. Antioxidant activity of α-Tocopherol and Trolox in different lipid substrates: bulk oils vs oil-in-water emulsions. J Agric Food Chem 44: 444–452, 1996.

132. SW Huang, EN Frankel, K Schwarz, R Aeschbach, JB German. Antioxidant activity of carnosic acid and

methyl carnosate in bulk oils and oil-in-water emulsions. J Agric Food Chem 44: 2951–2956, 1996.

133. BL Wedzicha, S Ahmed. Distribution of benzoic acid in an emulsion. Food Chem 50: 9–11, 1994.

134. MP Richards, W Chaiyasit, DJ McClements, EA Decker. Ability of surfactant micelles to alter the partitioning of phenolic antioxidants in oil-in-water emulsions. J Agric Food Chem 50: 1254–1259, 2002.

135. YJ Cho, DJ McClements, EA Decker. Ability of surfactant micelles to alter the physical location and reactivity of iron in oil-in-water emulsion. J Agric Food Chem 50: 5704–5710, 2002.

136. JR Mancuso, DJ McClements, EA Decker. Ability of iron to promote surfactant peroxide decomposition and oxidize alpha-tocopherol. J Agric Food Chem 47: 4146–4149, 1999.

137. LR Barclay, MR Vinqvist. Membrane peroxidation: inhibiting effects of water-soluble antioxidants on phospholipids of different charge types. Free Rad Biol Med 16: 779–788, 1994.

138. LA Johnson. recovery, refining, converting, and stabilizing edible fats and oils. In: CC Akoh and DB Min. Food Lipids. New York: Marcel Dekker, 1998, 181–228.

139. KD Mukherjee. Lipid biotechnology. In: CC Akoh and DB Min. Food Lipids. New York: Marcel Dekker, 1998, 589–640.

140. CC Akoh. Structured lipids. In: CC Akoh and DB Min. Food Lipids. New York: Marcel Dekker, 1998, 699–728.

141. D Rousseau, AG Marangoni. Chemical interesterification of food lipids: theory and practice. In: CC Akoh and DB Min. Food Lipids. New York: Marcel Dekker, 1998, 251–281.

142. S Ray, DK Bhattacharyya. Comparative nutritional study of enzymatically and chemically interesterified palm oil products. J Am Oil Chem Soc 72: 327–330, 1995.

143. WM Willis, AG Marangoni. Enzymatic interesterification. In: CC Akoh and DB Min. Food Lipids. New York: Marcel Dekker, 1998, 397–421.

144. KL Parkin. Biosynthesis of fatty acids and storage lipids in oil-bearing seed and fruit tissues of plants. In: CC Akoh and DB Min. Food Lipids. New York: Marcel Dekker, 1998, 729–778.

145. GJ Budziszewski, KP Croft, DF Hildebrand. Uses of biotechnology in modifying plant lipids. Lipids 31: 557–569, 1996.

146. C Wang, C-K Chin, C-T Ho, C-F Hwang, JJ Polashock, CE Martin. Changes of fatty acids and fatty acid-derived flavor compounds by expressing the yeast-9 desaturase gene in tomato. J Agric Food Chem 44: 3399–3402, 1996.

147. N Murata, O Ishizaki Nishizawa, S Higashi, H Hayashi, Y Tasaka, I Nishida. Genetically engineered alteration in the chilling sensitivity of plants. Nature 356: 710–713, 1995.

148. GM Fader, AJ Kinney, WD Hitz. Using biotechnology to reduce unwanted traits. INFORM 6: 167–169, 1995.

149. VC Knauf, AJ Del Vecchio. Lipid biotechnology. In: CC Akoh and DB Min. Food Lipids. New York: Marcel Dekker, 1998, 779–805.

150. CC Akoh. Lipid-based synthetic fat substitutes. In: CC Akoh and DB Min. Food Lipids. New York: Marcel Dekker, 1998, 559–588.

151. JR Hayes, JW Finley, GA Leveille. In vivo metabolism of SALATRIM fats in the rat. J Agric Food Chem 42: 500–514, 1994.

152. RE Smith, JW Finley, GA Leveille. Overview of SALATRIM, a family of low-calorie fats. J Agric Food Chem 42: 432–434, 1994.

153. K Warner. Chemistry of frying fats. In: CC Akoh and DB Min. Food Lipids. New York: Marcel Dekker, 1998, 167–180.

154. WW Nawar. Lipids. In: OR Fennema. Food Chemistry. New York: Marcel Dekker, 1985, 139–244.

155. X Chen, C Jo, JI Lee, DU Ahn. Lipid oxidation, volatiles and color changes of irradiated pork patties as affected by antioxidants. J Food Sci 64: 16–19, 1999.

156. KC Nam, SJ Hur, H Ismail, DU Ahn. Lipid oxidation, volatiles, and color changes in irradiated raw turkey breast during frozen storage. J Food Sci 67: 2061–2066, 2002.

157. M Du, DU Ahn, KC Nam, JL Sell. Volatile profiles and lipid oxidation of irradiated cooked chicken meat from laying hens fed diets containing conjugated linoleic acid. Poultry Sci 80: 235–241, 2001.

158. KE Nanke, JG Sebranek, DG Olson. Color characteristics of irradiated aerobically packaged pork, beef, and turkey. J Food Sci 64: 272–278, 1999.

159. KC Nam, DU Ahn. Carbon-monoxide-heme pigment is responsible for the pink color in irradiated raw turkey breast meat. Meat Sci 60: 25–33, 2002.

9 Fats: Physical Properties

Francisco J. Hidalgo and Rosario Zamora
Instituto de la Grasa

CONTENTS

I. INTRODUCTION

The physical properties of fats and oils are of great practical importance so it is necessary to understand the makeup of these materials and how they should be used (1–9). Thus, many technical applications of fatty materials, including their uses in edible products, depend on the oiliness, surface activity, solubility, melting behavior, or other physical properties peculiar to long-chain compounds (10). Because fats and oils are mainly composed of mixtures of triacylglycerols, the physical properties of these molecules are going to determine the physical characteristics of the oil or fat. Thus, these characteristics are dependent on such factors as seed or plant source, degree of unsaturation, length of carbon chains, isomeric forms of the constituent fatty acids, molecular structure of the triacylglycerols, and processing. This chapter will review the most important physical properties of triacylglycerol molecules as well as of the most common edible fats and oils.

II. CRYSTALLIZATION AND POLYMORPHISM

Crystallization from solution is usually a slow process that first requires supercooling and then leads to nucleation and crystal growth. A high degree of supercooling will be conductive to nucleation, and very small crystals will be formed. At temperatures closer to the crystallization point, crystal growth will be favored and large crystals will be formed (2). Once formed, crystals, which may be stable or metastable, are able either to modify their habit or undergo phase transitions, respectively. Both processes result in polymorphic behavior, a behavior common to fats and other lipids (11–22).

A. CRYSTALLINE STRUCTURE OF TRIACYLGLYCEROLS

In the solid state, molecules adopt the ideal conformation and arrangement in relation to their neighbors in order to optimize intra- as well as intermolecular interactions and achieve close-packing. The smallest building unit of a crystal, the repeating unit of the whole structure, is called the unit cell (Figure 9.1). The crystal structure is obtained by repetition of this unit in the three axial directions (5). Only seven different cells are necessary to include all possible point lattices. These correspond to the seven crystal systems into which all crystals can be classified (Table 9.1).

Of these seven crystal systems, it is now accepted that three predominate in crystalline triacylglycerols (23). Usually, the most stable form of triacylglycerols has a triclinic subcell with parallel hydrocarbon–chain planes ($T_\parallel$). A second common subcell is orthorhombic with perpendicular chain phases ($O_\perp$). The third common subcell type is hexagonal (H) with no specific chain plane conformation (24). This hexagonal form exhibits the lowest stability.

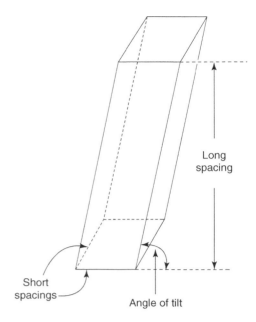

FIGURE 9.1 The triclinic unit cell for long-chain compounds.

TABLE 9.1
The Seven Crystal Systems

System	Angles and Axial Lengths
Cubic	All axes equal and all at right angles
	$a = b = c$ and $\alpha = \beta = \gamma$ and $= 90°$
Tetragonal	Two of three axes equal and all at right angles
	$a = b \neq c$ and $\alpha = \beta = \gamma$ and $= 90°$
Rhombohedral	All axes equal and none at right angles
	$a = b = c$ and $\alpha = \beta = \gamma$ and $\neq 90°$
Hexagonal	Two axes = 120° and the third at 90° relative to them
	$a = b \neq c$ and $\alpha = \beta = 90°$ and $\gamma = 120°$
Orthorhombic	All axes unequal and all at right angles
	$a \neq b \neq c$ and $\alpha = \beta = \gamma$ and $= 90°$
Monoclinic	Three unequal axes having one pair not equal to 90°
	$a \neq b \neq c$ and $\alpha = \gamma = 90° \neq \beta$
Triclinic	All axes unequal and none at right angles
	$a \neq b \neq c$ and $\alpha \neq \beta \neq \gamma$ and $\neq 90°$

Source: Ref. 11.

Interpretation of X-ray crystallography data from trilaurin and tricaprin resulted in representation of triacylglycerols in a tuning fork conformation when crystalline (Figure 9.2). The fatty acids esterified at the sn-1 and sn-2 positions of glycerol are extended and almost straight. The sn-3 ester projects 90° from sn-1 and sn-2, folds over at the carboxyl carbon, and aligns parallel to the sn-1 acyl ester. Molecules are packed in pairs, in a single layer arrangement, with the methyl groups and glycerol backbones in separate regions. The main cell is triclinic centered and contains two molecules; the subcell is also triclinic.

In addition to these bilayer structures, triacylglycerols may also be arranged in trilayers (Figure 9.2) (25–27).

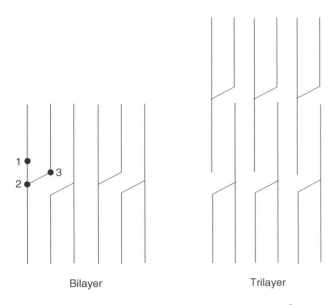

FIGURE 9.2 Double and triple chair arrangements of β form.

TABLE 9.2

Characteristics of the Polymorphic Forms of Monoacid Triacylglycerols

Characteristic	α Form	β′ Form	β Form
Chain packing	H	$O_\perp$	$T_\parallel$
Short spacing (Å)	4.15	4.2, 3.8	4.6, 3.9, 3.7
IR bands (cm-1)	720	727, 719	717
Density	Least dense	Intermediate	Most dense
Melting point	Lowest	Medium	Highest
Morphology	Amorphous-like	Rectangular	Needle shaped

Source: Refs. 10, 12, 15.

Thus, a trilayer structure occurs when the *sn*-2 position of the triacylglycerol contains a fatty acid that is either *cis*-unsaturated or of a chain length different by four or more carbons from those on the *sn*-1 and *sn*-2 positions (28). Also, a trilayer structure has been predicted to arise if the *sn*-2 position contained a saturated acyl ester with unsaturated moieties occupying the *sn*-1 and *sn*-3 positions (29). When unsaturation results in a *trans* configuration around the carbon–carbon double bond, the crystal structure exhibits the normal bilayer appearance (12).

B. POLYMORPHISM AND PHASE BEHAVIOR OF NATURAL FATS

Polymorphism is the ability of fat crystals to exist in more than one crystal form or modification. In the case of natural fats, these crystal forms are α, β′, and β, in order of increasing stability (Table 9.2). The changes among these phases are monotropic, and, therefore, proceeds in the solid phase from lower to higher stability. The forms differ in crystalline structure and in melting points, and correspond to the crystal structures described for natural fats in Section II.A. Thus, the most stable and with highest melting point $T_\parallel$ is the β polyform. Another polyform, with variable stability and a melting point lower than β, is β′, which has orthorhombic subcell packing ($O_\perp$). Finally, phases with the hexagonal subcell have the lowest melting point and represent the α polymorph.

In addition to these three basic polymorphs, other polymorphs showing subtle differences may be observed. Within groups having the same subcell, lower melting polymorphs are designated with a progressively higher subscript. In addition, the bilayer or trilayer structure of the triacylglycerol is designated with 2 or 3 following the polymorph description. Thus, β′₂-2 designates a bilayer of a β′ polymorph with the second highest melting point.

The fatty acid makeup and position in the glycerides of the fat solids and temperature history are the two main factors in determining polymorphic behavior (1). Other factors include kind and quantity of impurities, nature of possible solvent, and degree of supercooling. A high level of fatty acids of identical chain length results in a slow conversion rate of β′ to β and a coarsening of crystal structure. The more heterogeneous of fatty acid makeup, the more likely it will be β′ and fine-grained or needlelike crystals. Thus, mixed fatty acid triacylglycerols, such as those in lauric fats, tend to be β′-stable.

If a fat is cooled rapidly, the tendency is to form the small, α-crystals. These generally do not last long and convert rapidly to the β′ needlelike crystals. These β′ crystals are considered highly stiffening and, hence, are the form of choice for plastic shortenings (1). Depending on the glyceride composition and the temperature history, the β′-form may convert to the most stable β-form. This form has large, coarse, platelike crystals. These are not stiffening; hence, those hydrogenated fats exhibiting this behavior are the choice for the solids in fluid shortenings (1). Generally speaking, β′-forms melt about 5–10°C higher than the α-forms, and the β-forms also melt about 5–10°C higher than the β′-forms. Fats that tend to crystallize in β-forms include soybean, corn, olive, sunflower, and safflower oils, as well as cocoa butter and lard. On the other hand, cottonseed, palm, and rapeseed oils, milk fat, tallow, and modified lard tend to produce β′ crystals that tend to persist for long periods.

1. Milk Fat

As with many natural fats, the temperature at which crystallization occurs influences milk fat firmness, crystalline conformation, and percentage of solid fat. Hardness variability in milk results from different thermal treatments and may be better understood considering the presence of three milk fat fractions, which are observed by using differential scanning calorimetry. These fractions are defined as high-, middle-, and low-melting fractions (HMF, MMF, and LMF, respectively). LMF is liquid at ambient temperature. Stable polymorphs of MMF and HMF were found to be a mixture of β'-2 + β'-3, and β-2, respectively (30,31).

2. Palm Oil

Palm oil is expressed from the pulp of the oil palm (*Elaeis guineensis*) fruit and is unique among vegetable oils because of the large percentage (10–15%) of saturated acyl esters at the *sn*-2 position of the triacylglycerols. In addition, it has almost 5 % of free fatty acids that play a role in the hardness. At room temperature, the oil appears as a slurry of crystals in oil. Three polymorphs have been determined: β'_2, α-2, and the stable β'_1 form (32). The β' stability has resulted in the addition of palm oil to oils destined for shortening or margarine, since β-tending fats can result in gritty textures.

3. Lauric Fats

Lauric fats are those fats rich in laury acyl esters in the triacylglycerol molecule, mainly coconut oil and palm kernel oil. Two polymorphs have been identified in these fats: α and β'-2. The α form is fleeting and can be recognized only after rapid cooling, as it quickly transforms into the β'-2 polymorph (33–35). The melting point of these fats is sharp at 22°C for coconut and 25°C for palm kernel oil (36).

4. Liquid Oils

Evaluations of polymorphism in fats that are liquid at room temperature are limited. Cottonseed and peanut oils crystallize in a β'_2 form that is transformed into a stable β'_1-2 form. Four other oils (corn, safflower, sunflower, and soybean) show polymorphism similar to that of peanut and cottonseed, but these four fats developed a stable β-2 form (12).

5. Hydrogenated Fats

Complete hydrogenation eliminates the asymmetry, often leading to β stable polymorphs. Thus, soybean, peanut, sunflower, corn, and sesame oils, are converted to hydrogenated fats having stearoyl esters and consequently show the stable β-2 form. For oils rich in palmitic, hydrogenation leads to fats containing a high proportion of 1,3-dipalmitoyl-2-stearoyl-*sn*-glycerol (PStP). Because the rearrangement of PStP into a stable β form is hindered by misalignment of the methyl end plane of the β' unit cell (23), a fat rich in this triacylglycerol will stay in the β' form. On the other hand, a hydrogenated fat rich in StPSt can transform into a stable β form. The high PStSt fats have equally stable β' and β forms, and any transformation to the β form occurs over a long period of time (12).

6. Cocoa Butter

Cocoa butter occupies a special place among natural fats because of its unusual and highly value physical properties. Products containing cocoa butter, such as chocolate, are solid at room temperature; have a desirable "snap"; and melt smoothly and rapidly in the mouth, giving a cooling effect with no greasy impression on the palate. The main characteristic of cocoa butter is the presence of a high content of symmetrical monounsaturated triacylglycerols (1-palmitoyl-2-oleyl-3-stearoyl-*sn*-glycerol (POSt), 1,3-distearoyl-2-oleyl-*sn*-glycerol (StOSt), and 1,3-dipalmitoyl-2-oleyl-*sn*-glycerol (POP) account for about 80% of the total). The polymorphic behavior of cocoa butter is more complex than that of its component glycerides, and a specific system for cocoa butter is often used. This was introduced by Wille and Lutton (37) and recognizes six different polymorphs –I, for the lowest melting form, through VI, for the highest melting form (Table 9.3). Another system in use recognizes only five polymorphs, designated γ, α, β', β_2, and β_1, in order of increasing stability and melting point (42–45).

The desirable physical properties of cocoa butter and chocolate – snap, gloss, melting in the mouth, and flavor release – depend on the formation of polymorph V or β_2, which has to be obtained under controlled temperature conditions (41,46). After a long storage or unfavorable storage conditions such as extreme temperatures, chocolate may show "bloom." This is a grayish covering of the surface caused by crystals of the most stable β phase (phase VI) (41). Eventually the change progresses to the interior of the chocolate and the resulting change in crystal structure and melting point makes the product unsuitable for consumption.

7. Confectionery Fats

Cocoa butter is the primary fat used in chocolate. Its expense has led to the development of other fats, used alone or in combination, to replace some or all cocoa butter in cocoa-containing confections. These confectionery

TABLE 9.3

Nomenclature and Melting Point (°C) of Cocoa Butter Polymorphs

Form	Melting Point[a]	Form	Melting Point[a]
I	17.3–17.9	γ	16–18
II	23.3–24.4	α	21–24
III	25.5–27.7		
IV	27.3–28.4	β'	27–29
V	33.0–33.8	β_2	34–35
VI	34.6–36.3	β_1	36–37

[a] Values correspond to the range of the different values described in the literature.

Source: Refs. 12, 37–45.

or specialty fats can be classified into cocoa butter equivalents (CBE) and cocoa butter substitutes (CBS) (47). Essentially, a CBE is a mixed fat that provides a fatty acid and triacylglycerol composition similar to those of cocoa butter. A CBS is a fat that provides some of the desired physical characteristics to a confection independent of its dissimilar chemical composition to that of cocoa butter.

Miscibility is an important characteristic of confectionery fats. When fats of different composition are mixed, the melting point or the solid fat content of the blend may be lower than that of the individual components (eutectic effects). This happens when cocoa butter is mixed with a CBS that may lead to unacceptable softening. Mixing of cocoa butter and CBE gives no eutectic effect, and this type of fat can be used in any proportion with cocoa butter, analogously to milk fat (33). However, it has been reported that minor components of milk fats exert a significant influence on the crystallization behavior when milk fat is mixed with cocoa butter and other confectionery fats, having, for instance, a softening effect and antibloom properties (8,48,49). CBEs are generally based on three raw materials – shea oil, illipe butter, and palm – oil and processed by fractionation. CBEs also require the same tempering procedures as cocoa butter, since they will exhibit polymorphism similar to that of cocoa butter. It is also possible to tailor make CBEs to higher solid content and melting point than some of the softer types of cocoa butter. These fats are described as cocoa butter improvers (CBIs).

CBSs are available in two types, lauric and nonlauric. Lauric CBSs are based on palm kernel oil or coconut oil and are not compatible with cocoa butter. They do not need tempering, and the crystals formed are stable. Nonlauric CBSs are produced by hydrogenation of liquid oils, frequently followed by fractionation and/or blending. These products, especially those made from palm olein, are very stable in the β′ form. Nonfractionated CBSs are used in compound-coating fats for cookies. The fractionated, hydrogenated CBSs have better eating quality and can tolerate up to 25% cocoa butter when used in coatings.

C. TECHNIQUES TO DETERMINE CRYSTALLIZATION AND POLYMORPHISM

The techniques used to elucidate crystal structures are either spectroscopic or microscopic. Spectroscopic techniques include X-ray diffraction and Raman and infrared spectroscopy. Microscopic techniques include polarized light and electron microscopy (50).

1. Infrared and Raman Spectroscopy

The region of major interest in an IR spectrum for the study of fat polymorphism is the methylene rocking vibration mode which appears between 670 and 770 cm^{-1}. The spectra vary according to the polymorphic form. The nomenclature for polymorphs is as follows: a doublet at 728 and 718 cm^{-1} indicates the presence of the β′ form, a singlet at 720 cm^{-1} the α form, and a singlet a 717 cm^{-1} the β modification (51). In addition, vibrational (infrared and Raman) spectra have given fruitful information on molecular conformations of aliphatic chains and olefinic groups, and methyl end packings (52–54).

Raman spectroscopy is also used to identify the different states of order of lipids (55). Two regions are of interest: the C-C stretching vibration region at about 1100 cm^{-1}, and the C-H stretching vibration region at about 2850 cm^{-1}. Lipids with crystalline chains show two sharp peaks near 1065 and 1130 cm^{-1}, whereas these peaks are shifted towards a broad band near 1090 cm^{-1} when the chain melts. The ratio 1080/1130 can be taken as a measure of the degree of a liquid-type order (56). In addition, a peak at 2850 cm^{-1} corresponds to symmetric vibrations of methylene groups characteristic for the liquid state, whereas a peak at 2890 cm^{-1} is caused by antisymmetric vibrations of methylene groups and dominates when hydrocarbon chains are crystalline (57).

2. X-Ray Diffraction

The principle of X-ray diffraction is to excite an anticathode which will emit X-rays being diffracted by the crystal structure at a specific angle. The angle depends on the distance between two crystal planes, d, and d is different for each crystal structure. The chain packing of the triacylglycerol molecules determines the spacing between adjoining molecules. The cross-sectional structures determine the short spacings (Figure 9.1). Each of the chain-packing subcells is characterized by an unique set of X-ray diffraction lines in the wide-angle region between 3.5 and 5.5 Å. The nomenclature used to identify lipid crystal forms was proposed by Larsson (40) and is based on the following criteria: a form that gives only one strong short-spacing line near 4.15 Å is termed α; a form that gives two strong short-spacing lines near 3.80 and 4.20 Å and also shows a doublet in the 720 cm^{-1} region of the infrared absorption spectra is termed β′; a form that does not satisfy criterion two is termed β (Table 9.2).

X-ray diffraction is a powerful analytical technique to identify polymorphic phases unambiguously in both pure triacylglycerol systems and edible fats (43,58–60). In addition, recent developments in high-energy accelerators and X-ray detectors have reduced the exposure times of the sample to the order of milliseconds. Thus, with synchrotron radiation X-ray diffraction, the kinetics of rapid triacylglycerol polymorphic transformations has been elucidated under both isothermal and nonisothermal conditions in pure and mixed triacylglycerol systems (18,61–63).

The complex structure of the crystal network is determined by the fractal dimension, D, which describes the relation between the number of crystals in a crystal aggregate and its radius, R (64,65). In general, the higher the D value, the more compact the crystal dispersion and, in the case of triacylglycerols, its value changes with ageing of the system after crystallization. In turn, the magnitude of D affects the value of the elastic modulus and, therefore, the texture of the crystal dispersion at a given temperature (e.g., mouthfeel, spreadability). Although the rheology of fat crystal dispersions determines important properties in vegetable oil system (i.e., texture, sedimentation), still more research is needed to understand the structure-property relationship (65).

3. Microscopic Techniques

Polarized light spectroscopy allows under certain circumstances to differentiate the α (platelets), β' (small needles), and β (larger and growing in clump) forms. This technique makes it possible to view crystals in the range of 0.5–100 μm (66).

In contrast to polarized light microscopy, electron microscopy resolves details in areas of 0.1 μm. However, since fine structures of fats are temperature sensitive, special techniques such as freeze-fracture or freeze-etching are required (66). Structures of liquid and crystallized fat in systems such as butter and margarine can be characterized in micrographs due to the amorphous appearance of the originally liquid fat (67).

III. THERMAL AND RHEOLOGICAL PROPERTIES, AND OTHER PHYSICAL CONSTANTS

A. MELTING

1. Melting Points

The melting point is the temperature at which a solid fat becomes a liquid oil. Thus, an individual fatty acid or triacylglycerol has a specific complete melting point for each polymorphic form (Table 9.4 collects the melting points of common triacylglycerols in their three polymorphic forms). Complications arise in fats and oils because they are essentially mixtures of mixed triacylglycerols which crystallize in several crystal forms (Table 9.5 collects triacylglycerol composition of some common fats and oils). These molecules, although of the same chemical structure, differ in chain length, unsaturation, and isomerism. Each component in these products has its own melting point. Fats, therefore, do not have sharp melting points, but a melting range. What is commonly known as the melting point of a fat is in reality the end of the melting range. Table 9.6 collects melting and solidification points of some common fats and oils. In addition, softening points (74) and congeal points (75) are sometimes reported.

TABLE 9.4
Melting Points (°C) of Common Triacylglycerols

TAG[a]	Form		
	α	β′	β
LaLaLa	15.0	34.5	46.5
MMM	33.0	46.0	58.0
PPP	45.0	56.6	66.1
StStSt	54.9	64.1	73.4
AAA	62.0	69.0	78.0
PStP	47.0	68.9	65.5
PPSt	47.4	59.9	62.9
PStSt	50.6	60.8	65.0
StPSt	51.8	64.0	68.5
POP	18.1	30.5	35.3
PPO	18.5	35.4	40.4
POSt	18.2	33.2	38.2
StPO	25.3	38.7	40.5
PStO	25.5	37.4	–
StOSt	23.5	36.6	41.2
StStO	30.4	42.2	42.1
StESt	46.0	58.0	61.0
StRSt	25.8	48.0	–
PLP	–	18.6	–
OPO	–	–	18.7
POO	−4.0	2.5	19.2
StOO	−1.5	8.6	23.0
OOO	−32.0	−11.8	5.1
EEE	15.5	37.0	42.0
LLL	−33.7	−21.0	−10.0
LnLnLn	−44.6	–	−24.2

[a] Abbreviations: TAG, triacylglycerol. Fatty acids in TAG: A, arachidic; E, elaidic; L, linoleic; La, lauric; Ln, linolenic; M, miristic; P, palmitic; R, ricinoleic; and St, stearic.
Source: Refs. 7, 8, 41, 68.

The more complex and diversified the mixture of triacylglycerols in the fat, the greater the melting range. If the melting range is less than 5°C, the fat is considered to be non-plastic (cocoa butter, for example). If the melting range is significant (in certain cases it may exceed 40°C) the fat is called plastic. This happens for the majority of natural and processed fats.

The temperature at which a fat or oil is completely melted depends on various factors (12), including the average chain length of the fatty acids (in general, the longer the average chain length, the higher the melting point); the positioning of the fatty acids on the glycerol molecule (as an example, safflower oil, which has a long average chain length, will melt like a medium chain length triacylglycerol); the relative proportion of saturated to unsaturated fatty acids (the higher the proportion of unsaturated fatty acids, the lower the melting point); and the processing techniques employed, for example the degree and selectivity of hydrogenation and winterization.

TABLE 9.5
Triacylglycerol Composition of Common Fats and Oils

Fat or Oil	TAG																					
	PPSt	PStSt	PPO	PStO	StStO	PPL	StStL	PStL	POO	StOO	OOO	POL	StOL	OOL	PLL	PLLn	StLL	OLL	OLLn	LLL	LLLn	Others
Cocoa butter			16.0 [b]	36.0	25.0		< 2	3.0	4.5	5.5	< 2	< 3	< 1	< 0.2	< 3							
Corn			< 1			2.1			4.8 [d]		2.6	12.3 [c]	[d]	9.9	16.8		[c]	22.9		26.5	< 2	0.2
Cottonseed			3.4			9.0		< 2	2.5		< 1	17.1	< 2	5.7	24.5		2.1	13.1		13.5		5.1
Grapeseed												15.9 [c]		10.3	17.0		[c]	21.0		35.7		0.1
Hazelnut			< 0.3	< 0.1					9.0	4.0	52.0	3.0		20.5	< 1			5.5		< 2		
Lard	2.3	6.1	7.7	18.8	< 2			4.8	24.5	5.6 [e]	5.8	9.2		3.5	< 1							8.7
Olive [f]	< 1		2.9	< 1		<1			23.1	3.6	43.1	4.5		10.4	< 1			< 1				
Olive [g]	< 1		5.3	< 2		2.1			20.0	3.7	21.8	12.3		18.2	2.8			5.8		< 1		
Peanut			2.3	2.2		2.9			6.7	< 2	11.8	12.9	3.0	19.4	5.1		< 2	18.3		2.0		10.5
Soybean			< 2	< 1		< 2			< 2		< 2	7.8	3.0	7.6	13.1	2.8	4.2	20.4	5.0	19.3	7.5	2.9
Sunflower			< 1			< 1			< 1		< 1	4.0	2.1	6.5	11.3		7.5	29.1		36.3		1.0
Tallow	5.2	11.1	11.2	13.8	4.1				22.8	11.2 [e]	6.9 [d]	2.1	[d]	< 2								9.7

[a] Abbreviations: TAG, triacylglycerol. Fatty acids in TAG: A, arachidic; E, elaidic; L, linoleic; La, lauric; Ln, linolenic; M, miristic; P, palmitic; R, ricinoleic; and St, stearic.
[b] Also includes MStO. [c] Also includes StLL. [d] Also includes StOL. [e] Also includes PPP. [f] From Spain. [g] From Tunisia.

Source: Refs. 8, 41, 68, 69.

TABLE 9.6
Melting Points (°C) of Common Fats and Oils

Fat or Oil	Melting Point (°C)	Solidification Point (°C)
Butter	36	
Castor		−12 to −18
Cocoa butter	31–35	28–29
Coconut	24–26	14–23
Corn	−10 to −20	−10 to −18
Cottonseed	10–15.5	−6 to 4
Grapeseed		−11 to −17
Hazelnut		−18 to −20
Lard	32–38	27–32
Linseed		−18 to −27
Olive	−9 to 0	−9 to −2
Palm	30–37	20–40
Palm kernel	23–30	20–24
Peanut	8–13	0–3
Rapeseed		−8 to −18
Safflower (high linoleic)		−15
Sesame		−3 to −6
Soybean	−15	−10 to −16
Sunflower	−15	−16 to −18
Tallow	40–50	27–38

Source: Refs. 68–73.

2. Specific Heat and Heat of Fusion

Specific heat, c_p, is defined as the amount of heat required to increase the temperature of 1 g of material by 1°C. It is believed to be largely independent of the molecular weight for oils, but it does increase with unsaturation (10). In addition, the specific heats of the solid and liquid states of fatty compounds are different. Fats at temperatures just above their melting points have specific heats of ~0.5 cal/g. Their solid forms have lower values. The specific heat of oils has often been observed to increase linearly with temperature (76). Other workers, however, have observed nonlinear increases at higher temperatures (77,78), although these increases may be due to autoxidation reactions (79). Specific heat data for some simple triacylglycerols are given in Table 9.7. Specific heat data of common fats and oils are given in Table 9.8.

The transformation of solid to liquid releases the latent heat of crystallization. Transformation of a lower to a higher polymorphic form also is an exothermic reaction. The heat of fusion (Hf) of a fatty material includes the amount of energy required to melt a gram of material and the heat of crystal transition. Heat (with negative sign) is released when a fat crystal is transformed from a less stable form to a more stable form. Heat of fusion data for several monoacid triacylglycerols are given in Table 9.9 and they increase with chain length. The corresponding values for common fats and oils are collected in Table 9.10.

TABLE 9.7
Specific Heat (c_p) of Triacylglycerols

TAG[a]	c_p (cal/g · °C) [b]	
	Liquid	Solid
LaLaLa	0.510 (66)	−
	0.530 (97.1)	
MMM	0.518 (65.3)	−
	0.534 (91.9)	
PPP	0.519 (65.7)	−
	0.539 (96.0)	
StStSt	0.530 (79.0)	0.259 (−77.1, β)
	0.542 (98.5)	0.310 (−30.3, β)
		0.273 (−81.0, α)
		0.346 (−36.5, α)

[a] Abbreviations: TAG, triacylglycerol. Fatty acids in TAG: La, lauric; M, miristic; P, palmitic; and St, stearic.
[b] Numbers in parentheses indicate the temperature in °C.
Source: Ref. 80.

TABLE 9.8
Specific Heat (c_p) of Common Fats and Oils

Fat or Oil	Temperature (°C)	c_p (cal/g · °C)
Castor	20	0.435
Coconut	20–30	0.511
Corn	20–30	0.415
Cottonseed	19.3	0.475
Grapeseed	20–30	0.395
Lard	20–30	0.483
Linseed	40	0.48
Olive	20–30	0.475
Palm	20–30	0.5
Peanut	20–30	0.490
Rapeseed	20–30	0.469
Sesame	20–30	0.478
Soybean	19.7	0.458
Sunflower	20–30	0.430
Tallow	30–38	0.55

Source: Refs. 70, 73, 76–78, 81.

B. PLASTICITY

Plasticity is defined as the capability of fats of being molded by largely maintaining the deformation due to a stress after removal of the stress. This is a consequence of the semisolid state of fats at room temperature. Their solid character is the result of the presence of a certain proportion of crystallized triacylglycerols. As the temperature drops, more of the triacylglycerols solidify and the fat becomes progressively firmer. On the other hand, as the temperature rises, most solid triacylglycerols melt and the fat becomes progressively softer until it has practically no "body" or plasticity at all, and eventually it becomes completely melted (82).

TABLE 9.9

Heat of Fusion (ΔH_f) and Transition of Triacylglycerols

TAG[a]	Transition	Temperature (°C)	ΔH_f (cal/g)
LaLaLa	β→Liq	46.3	46.2
MMM	β→Liq	57.0	50.3
	α→Liq	32.3	34.6
	α→β	32.2	−12.6
PPP	β→Liq	65.7	53.1
	α→Liq	44.7	37.4
	α→β	44.7	−13.3
StStSt	β→Liq	72.5	54.5
	α→Liq	54.0	38.9
	α→β	54.0	−13.7

[a] Abbreviations: TAG, triacylglycerol. Fatty acids in TAG: La, lauric; M, miristic; P, palmitic; and St, stearic.

Source: Ref. 80.

TABLE 9.10

Heat of Fusion (ΔH_f) of Common Fats and Oils

Fat or Oil	ΔH_f (cal/g)
Butter	24.5
Cocoa butter	35.0
Coconut	30.6
Cottonseed	16.8
Lard	29.2
Linseed	18.2
Olive	20.3
Palm	22.6
Palm kernel	32.0
Peanut	21.7
Rapeseed	19.8
Sesame	16.3
Soybean	17.9
Sunflower, crude	19.0
Tallow	27.3

Source: Refs. 69, 70, 76.

If a fat or a shortening that is workable over a wide temperature range is desired, then it should be made up of a combination of triacylglycerols ranging widely in melting points. By the same reason, when a fat or shortening with a narrow temperature range of workability is needed, it is made up of a greater amount of triacylglycerols of similar melting points.

One of the most important properties of fats is the solid fat content (41). It is dependent on temperature and temperature history, and it is related to different physical properties of the fats, including hardness, heat resistance, waxiness, coolness, and flavor release (83). Fats may retain their solid character with solid fat contents as low as 12 to 15%. Below this level, fats become pourable and lose their plastic character. The relationship between hardness and solid fat content indicates that there is only a range of solids that results in a product being neither too hard nor

too soft. This is called the plastic range of fats. Shortening is an example of a product that requires an extended plastic range. The solid fat content (SFC) as a function of temperature of some natural fats is collected in Table 9.11.

Plastic fats combine the physical properties of both solids and liquids. This is caused by the presence of a three-dimensional network of crystals in which a considerable amount of liquid oil is immobilized. A plastic fat is usually workable at room temperature when the solid fat content lies between 20 and 40%. Under the influence of weak attractive forces between crystals, mostly due to van der Waals forces, a three-dimensional structure is formed that lends the product a good deal of resistance to deformation. As a result of the presence of this fat crystal network, plastic fats exhibit a yield value. Thus, the product behaves like a rigid solid until the deforming stress exceeds the yield value and the fat start flowing like a viscous liquid. The application of a shear stress to such product is accompanied by structural breakdown and a decrease in strength. This is also known as work softening. The consistency of plastic fats is determined by a number of factors, including solid fat content, crystal size and shape, and polymorphic form.

The earliest developed technique for solid fat content determination was dilatometry. It remains a recommended method of the American Oil Chemists' Society (84) but it has been largely replaced by various nuclear magnetic resonance methods (85,86). Lipid crystallization and, therefore, changes in solid fat content, can also be measured by differential scanning calorimetry (87) or by using ultrasounds (88).

TABLE 9.11

Solid Fat Content (SFC) of Common Fats and Oils

Fat or Oil	SFC[a]				
	10	30	50	70	90
Butter	28.0°C	16.0°C	10.5°C	2.0°C	−12.0°C
Cocoa butter	32.5°C	30.5°C	29.0°C	25.5°C	8.0°C
Coconut	23.0°C	20.5°C	16.0°C	10.0°C	−1.0°C
Cottonseed	3.5°C	−6.0°C	−11.0°C	−23.0°C	−28.5°C
Lard	40.0°C	29.5°C	17.5°C	2.5°C	−7.5°C
Linseed, crude	−8.5°C	−13.5°C	−15.5°C	−17.0°C	−23.0°C
Olive	6.0°C	−2.0°C	−5.5°C	−8.0°C	−11.0°C
Palm, crude	31.5°C	16.5°C	12.0°C	7.5°C	−6.0°C
Palm kernel	26.0°C	23.0°C	18.5°C	8.5°C	−6.5°C
Peanut, crude	−3.0°C	−7.5°C	−12.5°C	−15.5°C	−19.5°C
Rapeseed	3.0°C	2.0°C	1.0°C	−1.0°C	−4.5°C
Sesame	−4.0°C	−10.0°C	−15.5°C	−19.5°C	−22.5°C
Soybean	−5.5°C	−11.5°C	−13.0°C	−14.0°C	−20.0°C
Sunflower, crude	−10.0°C	−13.0°C	−14.5°C	−15.5°C	−18.0°C
Tallow	46.5°C	41.0°C	31.0°C	15.5°C	5.0°C

[a] Data indicate the temperature at which the SFC shown at the top of the column is achieved.

Source: Ref. 70.

C. Viscosity

Viscosity is a measure of internal friction of a liquid to resist flow. It is usually denoted by η, and defined as the ratio between the shear stress (in force per unit area) and the shear rate (the velocity gradient between the moving and stationary phases). The viscosity, η, carries a dimension of poise (P) or dyne/(cm² · s). Water has a value of 1 centipoise (cP) at 20°C. The viscosities of triacylglycerols or oils (Tables 9.12 and 9.13, respectively) are much higher than that of water, which can be attributed primarily to the intermolecular attractions of the long-chain fatty acids of their triacylglycerols. This is one of the reasons why the oils exhibit their unique oily characteristics

TABLE 9.12
Viscosities of Triacylglycerols

TAG[a]	Viscosities (cP)				
	60°C	70°C	75°C	80°C	85°C
LaLaLa	13.59	10.30	9.11	8.09	7.22
MMM	17.71	13.42	11.70	10.35	9.20
PPP		16.79	14.67	12.92	11.44
StStSt			18.50	16.21	14.31

[a] Abbreviations: TAG, triacylglycerol. Fatty acids in TAG: La, lauric; M, miristic; P, palmitic; and St, stearic.
Source: Refs. 89, 90.

TABLE 9.13
Viscosities of Common Fats and Oils

Fat or Oil	Viscosity (cP)				
	20°C	30°C	40°C	50°C	60°C
Castor	950–1100	453	232	128	
Cocoa butter			42		
Coconut		34	24	17–20	13
Corn	56–66		31		18
Cottonseed	65–69		33		
Grapeseed	53–58				
Hazelnut	66–76				
Lard			35	25	17–20
Linseed	42–47	33	24	18	
Olive	75–79		42		
Palm			40	25–31	
Palm kernel		36	25	17–20	
Peanut	68–82	49	33	24	
Rapeseed	86–97	56	38	27	
Safflower[a]	52–54				
Safflower[b]	70–75				
Sesame	64–67	42	29	21	
Soybean	53–58	43	32	23	
Sunflower	51–57	40	28	20	
Tallow			42	30	19–20

[a] High linoleic.
[b] High oleic.
Source: Refs. 10, 69, 70, 76, 91–93.

and have the ability to form oily or lubricating films. This lubricating action is very important in the preparation of some foods, such as grilled foods (1).

Vegetable oils follow Newtonian flow behavior, i.e., at a given temperature a constant value of viscosity is obtained independent of the force applied to the oil. As a result, oil viscosity (η) is defined as the slope of the shear stress-shear rate curve, also known as the flow curve (65).

In general, the viscosity of oils decreases slightly with an increase in unsaturation, and, therefore, hydrogenated oils are slightly more viscous than original oils (94). In addition, for an equivalent degree of unsaturation, oils and fats containing a greater proportion of fatty acids of relatively low molecular weight are slightly less viscous than those containing a higher proportion of high-molecular-weight acids. Most common oils range in viscosity from 20 to 50 cP at ambient temperature. An exception is castor oil, which has a viscosity exceptionally high because of its high content of ricinoleic acid.

The viscosity of highly polymerized oils is much greater than that of normal oils. For this reason, viscosity is occasionally referred to in determining the conditions of fats used in deep frying. During use in the frying kettle, the viscosity of a frying fat or oil will tend to increase as oxidation and polymerization increase (95). This can be related to polymer development and tendency toward foaming.

Viscosity is also an important parameter in the process of melt crystallization. The dry fractionation of oils to produce a solid and a liquid fraction is greatly influenced by the viscosity of the oil at the fractionation temperature. Toro-Vazquez and Gallegos-Infante (96) have described the relationship between viscosity and crystallization in a system containing saturated triacylglycerols and liquid oil.

D. Vapor Pressure

The vapor pressure, defined as the pressure associated with the vapor in equilibrium with a condensed phase, is very low in triacylglycerols of long-chain fatty acids. Therefore, they can only be satisfactorily distilled by molecular or short-path distillation. These values decrease as chain length increases (Table 9.14). Analogous values and behavior are also observed in fats and oils (Table 9.15).

E. Smoke, Flash, and Fire Points

The smoke, flash, and fire points are important properties when oils or fats are heated in contact with air, as in frying operations. These indices are often used as a quick quality control means for a critical process step such as deodorization. In this case, lower than normal smoke, flash, or fire points indicate the presence of an excess of residual nontriacylglycerol impurities, such as free fatty acids, monoacylglycerols, and other volatiles, which should be largely removed during steam deodorization.

TABLE 9.14
Vapor Pressure of Triacylglycerols

TAG[a]	Temperature (°C)	
	0.05 mm Hg	0.001 mm Hg
LaLaLa	244	188
MMM	275	216
PPP	298	239
StStSt	313	253
StOSt	315	254
MPSt	297	237
PLaSt	290	232
MLaSt	282	223

[a] Abbreviations: TAG, triacylglycerol. Fatty acids in TAG: La, lauric; M, miristic; P, palmitic; and St, stearic.
Source: Ref. 97.

TABLE 9.15
Vapor Pressure of Fats and Oils

Oil	Temperature (°C)	
	0.05 mm Hg	0.001 mm Hg
Cottonseed	250[a]	
Olive	308	253
Peanut	250[a]	
Soybean	308	254

[a] Values at 0.04 mm Hg.
Source: Refs. 68, 91.

The smoke point is the temperature at which smoking is first detected in a laboratory apparatus protected from drafts and provided with special illumination (98). The flash point is the temperature at which volatile products are evolved at such rate that they are capable of being ignited but do not support combustion. The fire point is the temperature at which the volatile products will support continuous combustion. Smoke, flash, and fire points of common fats and oils are shown in Table 9.16.

The smoke and flash points of fats and oils are greatly dependent on content of free fatty acids and to a lesser degree on partial glycerols. The influence of degree of unsaturation is minimal, but chain length has an important effect. Oils containing short-chain fatty acids (e.g., the lauric acids) have lower smoke and flash points than oils with predominantly longer fatty acids. According to Formo (10), the smoke points of corn, cottonseed, and peanut oils vary from about 232°C at a free fatty acid content of 0.01% to about 94°C at 100% free fatty acid content. The flash points correspondingly decrease from about 329 to 193°C and the fire points from 362 to 221°C.

F.   HEAT OF COMBUSTION

The heat of combustion is defined as the amount of heat released when a definite quantity of a substance is

TABLE 9.16
Smoke, Flash, and Fire Points of Common Fats and Oils

Fat or Oil	Free Fatty Acids (%)[a]	Smoke Point (°C)	Flash Point (°C)	Fire Point (°C)
Castor	n. s.	200	298	335
Coconut	0.2	194	288	329
Corn	n. s.	227	326	359
Cottonseed	0.04	223	322	342
	0.18	185	318	357
Lard	2.30		282	352
Linseed	n. s.	160	309	360
Olive (virgin)	n. s.	199	321	361
Palm	0.06	223	314	341
Peanut	n. s.	229		
	0.09	207	315	342
	0.11	198	333	363
Rapeseed	0.08	218	317	344
Safflower, crude	1.7	159	317	362
Sesame	n. s.	165	319	
Soybean	n. s.	234	328	363
	0.04	213	317	342
Sunflower	n. s.	253		
	0.1	209	316	341
Tallow	2.5		263	332
	0.5		324	357

[a] Abbreviation: n. s., not specified.
Source: Refs. 70–73, 99.

completely oxidized at constant pressure or constant volume. All fats and oils have very similar heat of combustion values and they are about 9.4 kcal/g. These values are collected in Table 9.17.

G.   THERMAL CONDUCTIVITY

Thermal conductivity describes the ease with which heat passes through a material. Specifically, it quantifies the

TABLE 9.17
Heat of Combustion of Common Fats and Oils

Fat or Oil	Heat of Combustion (Kcal/g)
Castor	8.880
Coconut	9.020
Corn	9.413
Cottonseed	9.447
Lard	9.449
Linseed	9.364
Olive	9.456
Peanut	9.410
Rapeseed	9.680
Sesame	9.394
Soybean	9.478
Sunflower	9.499
Tallow	9.485

Source: Refs. 10, 69, 70, 73.

rate of flow of thermal energy through a material in the presence of a temperature gradient, given by the amount of heat transfer across a unit area in a unit amount of time, divided by the negative of the space rate of change in temperature in the direction perpendicular to the unit area. Fats are relatively poor conductors of heat (10) and the thermal conductivity decreases with the temperature (100). Thermal conductivity data for common fats and oils are given in Table 9.18.

H. THERMAL DIFFUSIVITY

Thermal diffusivity is the thermal conductivity divided by the product of specific heat capacity and density. It is more generally applicable than thermal conductivity in most heat transfer problems. Thermal diffusivity values for some fats and oils are given in Table 9.19.

TABLE 9.18
Thermal Conductivity (cal/cm · s) of Common Fats and Oils

Fat or Oil	Temperature				
	20°C	40°C	60°C	80°C	100°C
Butter	$4.02 \cdot 10^{-4}$ [a]				
Castor	$4.00 \cdot 10^{-4}$			$3.85 \cdot 10^{-4}$ [c]	
Corn	$4.14 \cdot 10^{-4}$	$4.06 \cdot 10^{-4}$	$4.00 \cdot 10^{-4}$	$3.83 \cdot 10^{-4}$	$3.72 \cdot 10^{-4}$
Cottonseed	$4.00 \cdot 10^{-4}$	$3.92 \cdot 10^{-4}$	$3.89 \cdot 10^{-4}$	$3.81 \cdot 10^{-4}$	$3.72 \cdot 10^{-4}$
Grapeseed	$4.03 \cdot 10^{-4}$	$3.89 \cdot 10^{-4}$	$3.81 \cdot 10^{-4}$	$3.69 \cdot 10^{-4}$	$3.57 \cdot 10^{-4}$
Lard	$5.55 \cdot 10^{-4}$				
Olive	$4.00 \cdot 10^{-4}$			$3.85 \cdot 10^{-4}$ [c]	
Peanut	$4.02 \cdot 10^{-4}$ [b]				
Rapeseed	$3.79 \cdot 10^{-4}$				
Sesame	$4.31 \cdot 10^{-4}$	$4.19 \cdot 10^{-4}$	$4.08 \cdot 10^{-4}$	$3.97 \cdot 10^{-4}$	$3.83 \cdot 10^{-4}$
Soybean	$4.21 \cdot 10^{-4}$	$4.11 \cdot 10^{-4}$	$3.97 \cdot 10^{-4}$	$3.88 \cdot 10^{-4}$	$3.76 \cdot 10^{-4}$
Sunflower	$4.00 \cdot 10^{-4}$	$3.92 \cdot 10^{-4}$	$3.89 \cdot 10^{-4}$	$3.81 \cdot 10^{-4}$	$3.72 \cdot 10^{-4}$
Tallow	$8.33 \cdot 10^{-4}$		$4.17 \cdot 10^{-4}$		

[a] Data at 10°C.
[b] Data at 4°C.
[c] Data at 71°C.
Source: Refs. 70, 100, 101.

TABLE 9.19
Thermal Diffusivity (m²/h) of Common Fats and Oils

Fat or Oil	Temperature				
	20°C	40°C	60°C	80°C	100°C
Corn	0.391	0.385	0.366	0.351	0.338
Cottonseed	0.403	0.388	0.372	0.359	0.345
Grapeseed	0.401	0.382	0.367	0.356	0.342
Sesame	0.364	0.349	0.334	0.319	0.304
Soybean	0.380	0.363	0.350	0.334	0.320
Sunflower	0.340	0.322	0.310	0.295	0.281

Source: Ref. 70.

I. THERMAL EXPANSION

The thermal expansion is defined as the increase in the size of a substance when the temperature of the substance is increased. The thermal expansion coefficients are the proportionally constants that related these increases. Fat and oils have thermal expansion coefficient values in the range $6.6 \cdot 10^{-4} - 7.8 \cdot 10^{-4}$ mL/g · °C (Table 9.20). These values increase approximately linearly with temperature for liquid oils (79).

J. DIELECTRIC CONSTANT

The dielectric constant is the property of a material that determines how much electrostatic energy can be stored per unit volume of the material when unit voltage is applied. It is quantified as the ratio of electric flux density produced in a material to the value in free space produced by the same electric field strength. In fats and oils, most values are in the range of about 3.0–3.2, and, therefore, dielectric constants are not a particularly distinguishing characteristic. Castor and oiticica oils, however, which contain oxygenated fatty acids (ricinoleic and licanic acids, respectively), have higher dielectric constants (around 4.0). Oxidation increases the dielectric constant of oils by the introduction of polar groups (104). On the other hand, thermal polymerization without considerable oxidation has relatively little effect (10). Dielectric constants for some common fats and oils are given in Table 9.21.

K. DENSITY

The density of a material is a measure of the mass per unit volume. Liquid oils have a density between 0.91 and

TABLE 9.20
Thermal Expansion of Common Fats and Oils

Fat or Oil	Thermal Expansion Coefficient (mL/g · °C)
Butter	$6.64 \cdot 10^{-4}$
Castor	$6.90 \cdot 10^{-4}$
Cocoa butter	$7.72 \cdot 10^{-4}$
Coconut	$6.77 \cdot 10^{-4}$
Corn	$7.22 \cdot 10^{-4}$
Cottonseed	$6.75 - 7.30 \cdot 10^{-4}$
Linseed	$6.90 \cdot 10^{-4}$
Olive	$7.19 - 7.27 \cdot 10^{-4}$
Palm	$7.24 \cdot 10^{-4}$
Palm kernel	$7.02 \cdot 10^{-4}$
Peanut	$6.52 - 6.75 \cdot 10^{-4}$
Rapeseed	$6.71 \cdot 10^{-4}$
Sesame	$6.87 \cdot 10^{-4}$
Soybean	$6.70 - 7.24 \cdot 10^{-4}$
Sunflower	$6.61 - 7.46 \cdot 10^{-4}$
Tallow	$7.26 \cdot 10^{-4}$

Source: Refs. 70, 79, 102, 103.

TABLE 9.21
Dielectric Constants (λ) of Common Fats and Oils

Fat or Oil	Temperature (°C)[a]	λ
Castor	11	4.62
Cocoa butter	40	2.99
Coconut	n. s.	3.44
Cottonseed	20	3.15
Linseed	20	3.19
Olive	21	3.11
Peanut	11	3.03
	20	3.05
Sesame	13	3.02
Sunflower	20	3.11

[a] Abbreviation: n. s., not specified.
Source: Ref. 70.

TABLE 9.23
Density of Solid Triacylglycerols

TAG or Fat[a]	Polymorphic Form	Temperature (°C)	Density (g/mL)
LaLaLa	β	−38.6	1.057
MMM	β	−38.4	1.050
PPP	β	−38.2	1.047
StStSt	β	−38.6	1.043
	β'	−38.0	1.017
	α	−38.0	1.014
OOO	Highest m. p.	−38.7	1.012
Lard	Highest m. p.	−38.6	1.005

[a] Abbreviations: m. p., melting point; TAG, triacylglycerol. Fatty acids in TAG: La, lauric; M, miristic; P, palmitic; and St, stearic.
Source: Ref. 108.

0.92 g/mL at 25°C, and this value decreases as the temperature increases (Table 9.22). Oil density generally increases with lower molecular weight fatty acids and by hydrogenation (76,94,107). The densities of solid fats are generally higher than those of their liquid states. In addition, the various types of crystal forms, α, β', and β, melting at progressively higher temperatures, also show increasing densities (Table 9.23).

TABLE 9-22
Density of Common Fats and Oils

Fat or Oil	Density (g/mL)		
	20°C	40°C	60°C
Canola	0.914–0.917		
Castor	0.955–0.968	0.942–0.952	
Cocoa butter		0.906–0.909	
Coconut	0.926	0.908–0.920	
Corn	0.917–0.925	0.905–0.911	
Cottonseed	0.917–0.925	0.905–0.908	
Grapeseed	0.923–0.926	0.896–0.920	
Hazelnut	0.912–0.915	0.899–0.904	
Lard	0.916	0.896–0.906	
Linseed	0.928–0.933	0.914–0.922	
Olive	0.910–0.916	0.899–0.905	
Palm	0.922	0.895–0.900	
Palm kernel	0.930	0.899–0.913	
Peanut	0.914–0.920	0.906–0.912	
Rapeseed	0.910–0.916	0.897	
Safflower[a]	0.922–0.927		
Safflower[b]	0.910–0.916		
Sesame	0.915–0.923	0.910–0.913	
Soybean	0.921–0.924	0.906–0.912	
Sunflower	0.920–0.925	0.906–0.910	
Tallow	0.936–0.952[c]	0.893–0.904	0.885–0.887

[a] High linoleic.
[b] High oleic.
[c] Data at 15°C.
Source: Refs. 10, 69, 70, 72, 73, 102, 105, 106.

L. SOLUBILITY

Fats and oils are almost completely insoluble in water. When they are held together in systems such as cake batters or butterfat in milk, these systems require the use of food emulsifiers and/or mechanical means such as homogenizers. These same fats, oils, and fatty acids are completely miscible with most organic solvents, such as hydrocarbons, ethers, esters, and so on, at temperatures above their melting points. The solubility of fats in organic solvents increases with temperature, decreases with increasing mean molecular weight, and increases with increasing unsaturation. This last is the basis for fractional crystallization of fats into a number of fractions based on molecular weight and unsaturation. Alcohols from methanol to octanol have the property of being miscible with the liquid portion of plastic fats but not the solid. This has been used as a method for the separation of solid fat (109). The Crismer value is sometimes used to measure the solubility of an oil in a standard solvent mixture, composed of t-amyl alcohol, ethyl alcohol, and water in volume proportion 5:5:0.27. This value is characteristic within a narrow limit for each kind of oil (110). Examples of such values are 68.5–71.5 for olive oil, 67–70 for canola (low erucic rapeseed oil) and 76–82 for high erucic rapeseed oil (111,112). The miscibility of an oil is related to the solubility of glycerides and is affected mainly by the unsaturation and chain length of the constituent fatty acids.

Water is slightly soluble in oil at 0°C, with solubility amounting to about 0.07 and 0.14% at 32°C (2).

Some selected solubility data of nitrogen, oxygen, hydrogen, and carbon dioxide are shown in Table 9.24. With the exception of carbon dioxide, the solubilities of these gases in oil usually increase with temperature.

M. SURFACE TENSION, INTERFACIAL TENSION, AND EMULSIFICATION

Surface tension is the force acting on molecules at the surface of the oil that tends to pull them into the bulk of the

TABLE 9.24
Solubility of Gases in Oils

Fat or Oil	I. V.[a]	Temperature (°C)	Solubility (mL gas/100 mL Oil)			
			Nitrogen	Hydrogen	Oxygen	Carbon Dioxide
Butter	n. s.	40	10.1[b]	5.4	14.2	109.5
	n. s.	60	9.6[b]	6.8	12.7	91.0
Cottonseed	n. s.	40	8.7[b]	4.7	12.7	87.6
	104.3	30.5	7.1	4.6		
	104.3	49.6	7.8	5.4		
	104.3	147.8	11.8	10.2		
Lard	n. s.	40	8.8[b]	5.0	11.5	100.3
	70.1	41.5	7.7	5.2		
	70.1	147.3	12.1	10.4		
	1[c]	64.3		6.1		92.0
	1[c]	67.0	8.4		14.5	
	1[c]	84.7			15.4	
	1[c]	88.0				79.1
	1[c]	139.4	11.7	9.8		61.9
Soybean	n. s.[d]	22.5			3.2	
	n. s.[e]	22.5			1.3	
Sunflower	n. s.[d]	22.5			2.9	
	n. s.[e]	22.5			1.9	

[a] Abbreviations: I. V., iodine value; n. s., not specified.
[b] Data correspond to the solubility of air.
[c] Hydrogenated lard.
[d] Data correspond to the crude oil.
[e] Data correspond to the refined oil.
Source: Refs. 10, 68, 70, 113.

liquid. The interfacial tension is the surface tension at the surface separating two non-miscible liquids. Surface and interfacial tensions against water for different oils are given in Tables 9.25 and 9.26, respectively, and are similar among them (114).

Interfacial tensions may be decreased by the use of emulsifiers (115). Thus, the presence of monoacylglycerols and lecithin decreases the interfacial tension between oil and water from 30 to <10 dyne/cm. This reduction of interfacial tension lowers the energy required to homogenize the oil/water mixture, thus making possible the fine oil-in-water or water-in-oil dispersions.

Acylglycerols with three fatty acids attached to a glycerol molecule have minimal emulsification properties. However, fats and oils are important constituents of emulsions (116–124). An emulsion consists of a three-phase system composed of a continuous phase (the phase or medium in which the disperse phase is suspended), a disperse phase (the phase which is disrupted or finely divided within the emulsion), and an emulsifier (16). The emulsifier is present at the interface between the dispersed phase and the continuous phase, and keeps them apart; it reduces the interfacial tension between the two liquids, enabling one liquid to spread more easily around the other; and it forms a stable, coherent, viscoelastic film that prevents or delays coalescence of the dispersed emulsion droplets.

TABLE 9.25
Surface Tension of Oils

Fat or Oil	Surface Tension (dyne/cm)				
	17°C	20°C	50°C	80°C	130°C
Castor	34.9	34.0	32.2	30.0	
Coconut		21.4[a,b]		28.4	24.0
		33.6[b]			
Corn		34.8[b]			
Cottonseed		33.2[a]		31.4	27.5
		35.5			
Linseed		34.6[a]			
		36.4			
Olive	36.0–36.8	32.6	30.5	29.1	
Palm kernel		32.4[a]			
		33.5			
Peanut	44.4	31.6[a]			
		34.6			
Sesame	36.3				
Soybean		34.1[a]			
		35.8			
Rapeseed	35.3	34.5[a]	29.6	28.1	
		32–34			

[a] Data correspond to crude oil.
[b] Data at 25°C.
Source: Refs. 2, 68, 70, 71, 93.

TABLE 9.26
Interfacial Tension of Oils

Oil	Interfacial Tension (dyne/cm) at 70°C
Cottonseed	29.8
Peanut	29.9
Soybean	30.6

Source: Ref. 68.

These properties of the emulsifiers are a consequence of their structure: the molecules contain two distinct sections, one having polar or hydrophilic character, the other having nonpolar or hydrophobic properties. The relative sizes of the hydrophilic and hydrophobic sections of an emulsifier mostly determines its behavior in emulsification. To make the selection of the proper emulsifier for a given application and to predict the type of emulsion that will be formed, the so-called hydrophile-lipophile balance (HLB) system has been developed. It is a numerical expression for the relative simultaneous attraction of an emulsifier for water and for oil. Emulsifiers with HLB in the range 2–6 tend to form water-in-oil (W/O) emulsions, those with HLB in the range 7–9 are good wetting agents, and those with HLB in the range 10–18 tend to form oil-in-water (O/W) emulsions (115). HLB values of some commercial nonionic emulsifiers are given in Table 9.27. These values can be estimated from experimental measurements of its cloud point or can be calculated from a knowledge of the number and type of hydrophilic and lipophilic groups that it contains, according to the equation:

HLB = 7 + Σ (hydrophilic group numbers) − Σ (lipophilic group numbers)

Hydrophilic and lipophilic group numbers have been tabulated (115,116,125).

Foods contain many natural emulsifiers, of which phospholipids and proteins are the most common (126,127). Mono- and diacylglycerols are examples of emulsifiers that are added to products in order to provide ease of mixing. They absorb at the interface, reducing interfacial tension, and increasing the spreadability of the continuous phase, or the wettability of the dispersed phase.

Many natural and processed foods exist either partly or wholly as emulsions, or have been in an emulsified state at some time during their existence (117,128–132). Milk is the most common example of a naturally occurring food emulsion (133). Mayonnaise, salad dressing, cream, ice cream, butter, and margarine are all examples of manufactured food emulsions. Powdered coffee whiteners, sauces, and many desserts are examples of foods that were emulsions at one stage during their production but subsequently were converted into another form (116).

TABLE 9.27
HLB Values of some Commercial Nonionic Emulsifiers

Emulsifier	HLB
Sorbitan trioleate	1.8
Sorbitan tristearate	2.1
Mono- and di-acilglycerols	3.2–3.5
Glycerol monostearate	3.8
Sorbitan monooleate	4.3
Sorbitan monostearate	4.7
Sorbitan monopalmitate	6.7
Sorbitan monolaurate	8.6
Polyoxyethylene sorbitan monostearate	9.6
Polyoxyethylene sorbitan monooleate	10.0
Polyoxyethylene sorbitan trioleate	11.0
Glycerol monostearate	11.0
Polyoxyethylene monostearate	11.1–16.0
Polyoxyethylene monolaurate	12.8
Sodium oleate	18
Sucrose monoester	20
Potassium oleate	20
Sodium stearoyl lactylate	22
Sodium lauryl sulfate	40

Source: Refs. 41, 115.

N. ULTRASONIC PROPERTIES

Ultrasonic velocity in triacylglycerols or oils is a measure of the speed of sound in these food components. It is related to its fatty acid composition and the supramolecular lipid structure. This is one of the most important variables in predicting the velocity of sound in an emulsion. The speed of sound in oils decreases monotically with temperature (134), is similar for oils and water at 20°C (79), and is lower in solid fats than oils. Ultrasonic velocities for some triacylglycerols as well as for some common oils are given in Tables 9.28 and 9.29, respectively.

The ultrasonic attenuation coefficient is a measure of how much ultrasound is dissipated in an oil per unit distance. This coefficient has little direct value beyond predicting the ultrasonic properties of an emulsion. However, in this application, a precise value is essential. The attenuation coefficient increases with frequency at a single temperature (79). Attenuation and its frequency dependence tend to decrease with increased temperature. Ultrasonic attenuation coefficients for some common oils are given in Table 9.29.

IV. OPTICAL AND SPECTROSCOPIC PROPERTIES

A. COLOR

Fatty acids and triacylglycerols, are colorless and essentially transparent to visible light. Natural fats and oils, however, often contain pigments that partially absorb transmitted light. Most of these pigments are removed from fats and oils by the refining and bleaching process,

TABLE 9.28
Ultrasonic Properties of Triacylglycerols

TAG [a]	Ultrasonic Velocity (m/s)		
	20°C	40°C	70°C
LaLaLa		1357	
PPP			1290
PSP			1292
SSS			1301
POP		1389	1293
PPO		1390	1295
POS		1392	1297
PSO		1393	
SPO		1394	
SOS			1302
OOO	1463	1397	1304
LLL	1474	1407	

[a] Abbreviations: TAG, triacylglycerol. Fatty acids in TAG: La, lauric; M, miristic; P, palmitic; and St, stearic.
Source: Refs. 108, 135, 136.

TABLE 9.29
Ultrasonic Properties of Fats and Oils

Fat or Oil	Ultrasonic Velocity (m/s)			Ultrasonic Attenuation Coefficient (at 20°C)	
	20°C	40°C	70°C	2 MHz	5 MHz
Butter		1359			
Castor	1494	1457			11.0
Coconut		1362			
Corn	1470	1403	1308		
Cottonseed		1405			
Grapeseed			1309		
Linseed		1414			
Olive	1466	1401	1302	6.5	1.94
Palm	1459	1399	1298		
Palm kernel		1368			
Peanut	1466	1405	1308	3.6	1.0
Rapeseed	1468	1411	1308	3.6	1.0
Safflower	1472	1408	1310	4.0	1.18
Sesame		1403			
Soybean	1470	1405	1309	4.9	
Sunflower	1472	1407	1311		

Source: Refs. 79, 135–139.

but some of them remain and most oils have their specific color, which is a consequence of the type and amount of natural pigments present. Therefore, some oils are naturally darker than others (68).

Carotene is the predominant red/yellow color pigment in soybean, safflower, and sunflower oils, among others. Carotene becomes colorless when subjected to the temperatures encountered in the edible oil processing steps. The oxidation products and other pigments found in these refined oils can be removed by adsorption on diatomaceous earth in the edible oil processing step referred to as bleaching. Most

of the red color found in cottonseed oil, on the other hand, comes from a minimal residual level of gossypol and gossypol derivatives, especially a complex gossypurpurin. While some of the pigments that contribute to oil colors can be removed by adsorption on bleaching earths and any carotene is rendered colorless by heating, the gossypol can only be removed by alkali refining. The level of color removal that can be achieved is, to a great extent, dependent on the handling and storage of the seed and crude oil prior to refining.

In addition, poor grade of crude oil or improper processing and handling may produce oils and fats which are darker than usual. Thus, insufficient refining may leave residual phospholipids that will darken the oil during deodorization. Vegetable oils and shortening will also darken after being stored for a long time or at elevated temperatures due to the oxidation of tocopherol to tocoquinones. During frying, oil darkening is further complicated by the polymerization of oil and interaction between the oil and other components of the food being fried (95).

Color may be determined by a number of procedures. The Lovibond method determines color by matching the color of the light transmitted through a specific depth of liquid fat or oil to the color of the light originating from the same source, transmitted through glass color standards (140). Results are given in red and yellow units describing the combination that matches the sample color. By using this methodology, the maximum accepted values for edible oils are collected in Table 9.30. Other methods that also determine color by comparison with permanent color standards or glasses of known color characteristics have also been described (142,143).

Color can also be determined spectrophotometrically. In this case the oil or fat is dissolved in the required solvent and the transmittance or the extinction of the solution is then determined at the specified wavelengths with reference to pure solvent (144). These absorptions may be expressed as specific extinctions (the extinction of 1% solution of the oil in the specified solvent, in a thickness of 1 cm), conventionally indicated by K (145). K values are usually employed to define olive oil quality (146).

TABLE 9.30
Lovibond Colors of Edible Oils[a]

Fat or Oil	Red	Yellow
Coconut	1.0	10
Cottonseed	2.5	
Palm	3.0	
Palm kernel	1.5	
Peanut	2.0	25
Safflower	1.5	15
Soybean	1.0	
Sunflower	2.0	20

[a] Maximum accepted values are indicated.
Source: Refs. 71, 73, 99, 105, 106, 141.

B. REFRACTIVE INDEX

The refractive index of a fat is a measure of the relative velocities of light in air and in the material to be tested. It is defined as the ratio of the sine of the incident angle of light from air and the sine of the refractive angle in the medium. This index, which can be easily measured, is influenced by wavelength, temperature, density, and constitution, and it is employed to examine the purity and concentration of a liquid sample, and to control the progress of some reactions such as hydrogenation and isomerization. For lipids, the refractive index normally increases with the hydrocarbon chain length and with the number of double bonds and conjugation, and decreases with an increase in the temperature (the refractive index for an oil drops by 0.00035 per °C). The refractive indices of some triacylglycerols and common fats and oils are given in Tables 9.31 and 9.32, respectively.

TABLE 9.31
Refractive Indices of Triacylglycerols

TAG[a]	Temperature 60°C
LaLaLa	1.440
MMM	1.443
PPP	1.445
StStSt	1.447
StLaLa	1.444
LaStLa	1.444
StPP	1.447
PStSt	1.447
LaStSt	1.445
StLaSt	1.446
PStSt	1.446
StPSt	1.448
StMP	1.444
StLaP	1.443
StPM	1.444
StPLa	1.443
StMLa	1.442
LaLaO	1.446
LaOLa	1.446
PPO	1.448
POP	1.448
StStO	1.449
StOSt	1.449
LaOO	1.450
MOO	1.451
POO	1.451
StOO	1.452
OOO	1.455
LLL	1.465
LnLnLn	1.474

[a] Abbreviations: TAG, triacylglycerol. Fatty acids in TAG: La, lauric; M, miristic; P, palmitic; St, stearic; O, oleic; L, linoleic; and Ln, linolenic.
Source: Refs. 89, 147.

TABLE 9.32
Refractive Indices of Common Fats and Oils

Fat or Oil	Temperature		
	20°C	40°C	60°C
Butter		1.455	1.447
Canola	1.465–1.467		
Castor	1.476–1.481	1.466–1.473	
Cocoa butter		1.456–1.458	
Coconut	1.454 [c]	1.448–1.450	1.441
Corn	1.474–1.477	1.465–1.466	> 1.447
Cottonseed	1.470–1.473	1.464–1.468	
Grapeseed	1.473–1.476	1.464–1.471	
Hazelnut	1.470–1.471	1.462–1.463	
Lard		1.457–1.461	1.451–1.453
Linseed	1.479–1.484	1.472–1.475	
Olive	1.468–1.471	1.461–1.462	
Palm		1.453–1.458	
Palm kernel	1.457 [c]	1.450–1.452	1.443
Peanut	1.470–1.474	1.461–1.463	
Rapeseed	1.472–1.473	1.464–1.466	
Safflower [a]	1.474–1.478		
Safflower [b]	1.470–1.474		
Sesame	1.474–1.477	1.465–1.468	
Soybean	1.473–1.477	1.465–1.469	> 1.447
Sunflower	1.474–1.476	1.466–1.468	
Tallow		1.448–1.460	1.450–1.454

[a] High linoleic.
[b] High oleic.
[c] Data at 25°C.
Source: Refs. 69–73, 93, 99, 105, 106.

C. ULTRAVIOLET SPECTROSCOPY

Monoene and methylene-interrupted polyene acids and their triacylglycerols absorb ultraviolet light at wavelengths too low for convenient study. Therefore, the use of ultraviolet spectroscopy in the study of fats and oils is confined to systems containing or generating conjugated unsaturation. Thus, ultraviolet spectroscopy is a valuable tool and it is broadly employed for detecting fatty acids and their corresponding triacylglycerols with conjugated double bonds. Conjugated dienes show a single absorption peak at 230–235 nm, whereas conjugated trienes show three peaks at ~260, 270, and 280 nm. Methylene-interrupted polyenes undergo double bond migration to produce compounds with conjugated unsaturation in reactions such as oxidation or hydrogenation and the appearance of absorption at appropriate wavelength has been employed in the study of such processes. Thus, the edible oil industry estimates spectrophotometrically at 233 nm the amounts of conjugated dienes in the finished fats and oils (148), and the K234 and K270 are indexes of olive oil quality (146,149).

D. INFRARED (IR) SPECTROSCOPY

The infrared spectra has been applied to solid lipids to provide useful information about polymorphism, crystal structure, conformation and chain length of fats and oils, and it is also frequently employed for identification and quantitative analysis of fats and oils. Most oils containing the usual mixture of saturated and unsaturated acids have similar infrared spectra. Superimposed on this there may be additional absorption bands associated with less common functional groups. A selection of the bands of interest in the study of fats and oils is collected in Table 9.33.

The most frequent use of infrared spectroscopy is in the recognition of *trans* isomers. The *trans*-double bond

TABLE 9.33

Infrared Absorption Bands of Interest in the Study of Fats and Oils

Functional Group	Absorption (cm⁻¹)	Functional Group	Absorption (cm⁻¹)
O–H stretching		**C=C stretching**	
Free O–H	3640–3600	–CH=CH₂	1645
Bonded O–H (single-bridged dimer)	3600–3500	–CH=CH– (cis)	1660
		–CH=CH– (trans)	1675 weak
Bonded O–H (double-bridged polymer)	3400–3200	–CH=CH–CH=CH–	1650, 1600
Hydroperoxide (O–O–H)	3560–3530	**C–H bending**	
Acid (O–H)	3000–2500	–CH₃	1460 (δ_{as})
			1380 (δ_s)
C–H stretching		–COOCH₃	1440–1435
=CH₂	3080 (ν_{as})		1365–1356
	2975 (ν_s)	–CH₂–	1470
=CH–	3020	–CH=C₂	1420
–CH₃	2960 (ν_{as})	–CH=CH–	1415
	2870 (ν_s)		
–CH₂–	2925 (ν_{as})	**C–O stretching and C–O bending**	
	2850 (ν_s)	Ester	
–CHO	2820, 2720	–CO–O– two bands at	1300–1050
		R–CO–O–R	1190
C=O stretching		R–CO–O–CH₃	1165
Ester		–C=C–CO–O–	1300–1250
–CO–O–	1735		1200–1050
–C=C–CO–O–	1720		
–CO–O–C=C–	1760	Acid	
νC=C	1690–1650	–COOH	1420
			1300–1200
Acid			
Saturated		Carboxylate	
monomer	1760	–COO⁻	1400
dimer	1710		
α,β-unsaturated		Alcohol	
monomer	1720	Free OH	1250 (δ)
dimer	1690	Associated OH	1500–1300 (δ)
		Primary OH	1050
Carboxylate		Secondary OH	1100
ν_{as}CO	1610–1550	Tertiary OH	1150
ν_sCO	1400		
		C–H bending (out of plane)	
Aldehyde		–CH=CH– *(cis)*	730–675
–CHO	1725	–CH=CH– *(trans)*	968
α,β-unsaturated	1685		
α,β-γ,δ-unsaturated	1675	**Skeletal and "breathing"**	
		Epoxide	
Ketone		*trans*	916–880
–CO–	1715	*cis*	838–829
α,β-unsaturated	1675		
νC=C	1650–1600		
α,β-γ,δ-unsaturated	1665		

produces a characteristic absorption at 968 cm^{-1} that does not change for additional double bonds unless these are conjugated, when there are small changes from this value. Therefore, this absorption can be employed to estimate the percentage of *trans* of the total amount of double bonds (146,150,151). There is not a similar diagnostic infrared absorption band for *cis* unsaturation, but Raman spectra show strong absorption bands at 1665 ± 1 cm^{-1} (*cis*-olefin) and 1670 ± 1 cm^{-1} (*trans*-olefin).

Carbonyl compounds have a strong absorption band in the region 1650–1750 cm^{-1}. The wavelength varies slightly with the nature of the carbonyl compounds (Table 9.33) and this may be of diagnostic value. Thus, this band has been suggested for free acidity determination in oils (152) and it is usually employed for measurement of fat content in automatic analyzers (153). Other applications of infrared spectra are the determination of iodine value, saponification value, free acid, oxidative stability, and carotene content, among others (3,154–156). By using Fourier transform infrared spectrometers (FTIR), these parameters can be measured by simple menu-driven procedures in a few minutes. The results are not only obtained more quickly, but without recourse to solvents or laborious titrimetric methods.

Near infrared spectroscopy, covering the region 800–2500 nm, is also being employed in fat and oil analysis. Thus, methods to determine fatty acid composition, peroxide value, oil content of individual seeds, recognition of individual vegetable oils, oil oxidation and in-line measurement of tempered cocoa butter and chocolate, among others, have been developed (3,157–160).

E. RAMAN SPECTROSCOPY

As commented above, Raman spectroscopy may be appropriate to use for the simultaneous analysis of the *cis* and *trans* content of oils, since *cis* and *trans* carbon-carbon double bond stretching bands can be observed simultaneously. By using this technique, the *cis/trans* isomer ratios were determined with a precision of 1% (161). The carbon-carbon double bond stretch and the methylene scissor intensity ratios have also been used to determine iodine values. In addition, the total unsaturation in oils and margarines can also be determined (162).

F. NUCLEAR MAGNETIC RESONANCE (NMR) SPECTROSCOPY

NMR spectroscopy is used in two ways in the study of fats and oils. With low-resolution instruments, it is possible to determine the proportion of solid and liquid in a fat and the content of oil in a seed. High-resolution spectrometers, on the other hand, are used to mainly examine solutions and give information about the solute.

1. Low-Resolution NMR

Differently to high-resolution NMR, broad band NMR does not distinguish among hydrogen nuclei in different atomic environments. Two techniques can be employed, namely wide-line NMR or pulsed NMR, and both distinguish between hydrogen atoms in liquid and solid environments. Nowadays, the most widely used technique is pulsed NMR. By using this technique, a measurement related to the total number of hydrogen nuclei is followed by a second measurement after 70 μs to determine only those hydrogen nuclei in a liquid environment. This determination depends on the fact that the signal for hydrogen nuclei in solid triacylglycerols decays much more quickly (less than 1% remains after 70 μs) than that of hydrogen nuclei in a liquid environment (which requires about 10000 s).

These measurements require only about 6 seconds and are used routinely for the study of margarine and other confectionery fats and of cocoa butter and similar substances. However, though the measurement is so quick, it may have

TABLE 9.34

Chemical Shift Assignments of Main ^{1}H NMR Signals of Fats and Oils[a]

Chemical Shift (ppm)	Assignment
Glycerol and Unsaturated Protons	
5.40–5.26	O9/O10/L9/L10/L12/L13/Ln9/Ln10/Ln12/Ln13/Ln15/Ln16
5.26–5.20	β-Glycerol
4.32–4.10	α-Glycerol
Saturated Protons	
2.75	Ln11/Ln14
2.72	L11
2.34	L2/Ln2
2.23	O2
2.22	S2
2.03	Ln17
2.00	L8/L14
1.99	Ln8
1.95	O8/O11
1.57	L3/Ln3
1.56	O3
1.55	S3
1.28	L chain/Ln chain
1.23	O chain
1.19	S chain
0.93	Ln18
0.84	L18
0.82	O18/P16/St18

[a] Assignments are abbreviated by fatty acid and carbon number. 1(3)- and 2-Positions of glycerol are designated by the Greek symbols α and β, respectively. Labeling of acyl chains: S, saturated; P, palmityl; St, stearyl; O, oleyl; L, linoleyl; Ln, linolenyl chain. Depending on the oil composition and experimental conditions, a lower number of signals is usually observed.

TABLE 9.35
Chemical Shift Assignments of Main ^{13}C NMR Signals of Fats and Oils[a]

Chemical Shift (ppm)	Assignment	Chemical Shift (ppm)	Assignment	Chemical Shift (ppm)	Assignment
Carbonyl Carbons		**Aliphatic Carbons**		29.22	L5β
176–174	Fatty acids	34.25	P2β/St2β	29.21	O5α/Ln5β
173.29	P1α	34.23	O2β	29.19	L5α/Ln5α
173.26	O1α	34.20	L2β/Ln2β	29.17	O6β/St4α
173.25	St1α	34.09	P2α/St2α	29.16	P4α
173.22	L1α/Ln1α	34.06	O2α	29.15	O6α/L6β
172.88	P1β	34.04	L2α/Ln2α	29.14	L6α/Ln6β
172.85	O1β/St1β	31.98	St16αβ	29.13	O4α/St4β/Ln6α
172.82	Ln1β	31.96	P14αβ	29.12	P4β
172.81	L1β	31.94	O16αβ	29.11	L4α
Olefinic Carbons		31.55	L16αβ	29.10	Ln4α
131.96	Ln16αβ	29.80	O12αβ	29.09	O4β
130.23	Ln9α	29.76	O7β/St11αβ/St12αβ/St13αβ/St14αβ	29.07	L4β
130.22	L13β	29.74	O7α/P11αβ/P12αβ/St10αβ	29.06	Ln4β
130.21	L13α/Ln9β	29.73	P10αβ	27.26	O11αβ
130.06	O10β	29.72	St9αβ/St8αβ	27.23	L14αβ/Ln8αβ
130.04	O10α	29.70	P8αβ/P9αβ/St7β	27.21	O8αβ/L8αβ
130.01	L9α	29.68	P7β/St7α	25.66	L11αβ
129.98	L9β	29.66	P7α	25.65	Ln11αβ
129.74	O9α	29.65	L7β	25.56	Ln14αβ
129.71	O9β	29.63	L7α	24.95	P3β/St3β
128.32	Ln12β	29.62	Ln7β	24.92	O3β
128.31	Ln12α	29.61	Ln7α	24.91	St3α
128.26	Ln13α	29.56	O14αβ/St5β	24.90	L3β/P3α/Ln3β
128.25	Ln13β	29.54	P5β	24.88	O3α
128.12	L10β	29.53	St5α	24.86	L3α/Ln3α
128.10	L10α	29.52	P5α	22.73	St17αβ
127.93	L12α	29.42	St15αβ	22.72	P15αβ
127.92	L12β	29.40	P13αβ	22.71	O17αβ
127.80	Ln10β	29.37	L15αβ	22.59	L17αβ
127.79	Ln10α	29.36	O13αβ/O15αβ	22.57	Ln17αβ
127.15	Ln15α	29.35	St6β	14.29	Ln18αβ
127.14	Ln15β	29.33	P6β	14.13	P16αβ/St18αβ
Glycerol Carbons		29.32	St6α	14.12	O18αβ
68.93	β-Glycerol	29.31	P6α	14.08	L18αβ
62.13	α-Glycerol	29.24	O5β		

[a] Assignments are abbreviated by fatty acid and carbon number. 1(3)- and 2-Positions of glycerol are designated by the Greek symbols α and β, respectively. Labeling of acyl chains: S, saturated; P, palmityl; St, stearyl; O, oleyl; L, linoleyl; Ln, linolenyl chain. Depending on the oil composition and experimental conditions, a lower number of signals is usually observed.

to be preceded by a lengthy tempering routine. Without controlling tempering the results would not be reproduced from day to day or between laboratories. The tempering regime varies with the kind of fat but a typical procedure for cocoa butter involves melting at 100°C then holding at 60°C (1 h), 0°C (1.5 h), 26°C (40 h), 0°C (1.5 h), and finally at the measuring temperature for 1 h. For many fats the long tempering at 26°C can be omitted (3).

For oilseed breeders, the NMR method is often used to estimate the oil content of oilseeds in a nondestructive manner. This information is of commercial value and can assist seed breeders and agronomists in their studies to develop improved varieties. Pulsed NMR is also employed in lipid crystallization studies (163).

2. High-Resolution ^{1}H NMR

The use of ^{1}H NMR in the study of oils, fats and food lipids has increased particularly because of the great amount of information that high field instruments can provide in a very short period of time (164). The NMR spectrum consists of a series of sharp signals whose frequencies and multiplicities can be related to the chemical nature of the different hydrogen atoms (methyl, methylene, olefin, etc.) and whose intensities are directly related to the number of hydrogens producing the signal (165,166). In this spectrum, all hydrogen atoms having the same chemical surroundings produce signals at the same frequency. The position of a resonance signal in the spectrum is called the chemical shift (δ). In the ¹H NMR spectra of fats and oils the resonances appear between δ 4.10 and 5.40 ppm for glycerol and unsaturated protons, and saturated protons signals appear between δ 0.80 and 2.80 ppm. Table 9.34 collects the assignation of most common signals.

By using the information contained in the spectra, ¹H NMR has been employed, among others, to determine the iodine value, number of double bonds, average molecular weight, proportion of acyl groups in the triacylglycerol molecule, *n*-3 polyunsaturated fatty acid proportion, and docoxahexahenoic acid content (167–176). Some attempts to apply ¹H NMR spectroscopy to oil authenticity have also been carried out (177).

¹H NMR spectroscopy may also be employed to determine minor oil components, but the signals of these components should not overlap with those of the main components, their concentration be high enough to be detected, and high field equipment be employed. Thus, the determination of saturated and unsaturated aldehydes in virgin olive oils as well as diacylglycerols have been described (170,177,178).

3. High-Resolution ¹³C NMR

High-resolution ¹³C NMR spectra are more complex than ¹H spectra and they do not provide quantitative information so easily. Nevertheless, they contain much more structural information (chemical shifts and intensities) if this can be teased out of the data provided with each spectrum. ¹³C NMR resonances of fats and oils can be grouped into four well-defined spectral regions: carbonyl carbons ranging from 173.3 to 172.8 ppm; unsaturated carbons ranging from 132.0 to 127.1 ppm; glycerol carbons ranging from 69.1 to 61.6 ppm; and aliphatic carbons ranging from 34.3 to 14.0 ppm. The assignation of the different signals has been the objective of many studies and it is nowadays clearly resolved (179–181). The main resonances observed in the ¹³C NMR spectra of fats and oils are collected in Table 9.35.

Information contained in these spectra has been employed for edible oil authenticity determination and quality controls, including the analysis of fatty acid composition and distribution of fatty acids in the triacylglycerol molecule, the free fatty acid, iodine value, and diacylglycerol determination, the analysis of minor components, the oil stability prediction, the determination of polar components and oil colors, etc. (182–198). All these data suggest that with only one analysis, NMR allows the determination of a large number of components with very little or without any manipulation of the oil samples that nowadays need many different analyses. In addition, the application of multivariate statistics to NMR spectral data increases considerably the potential of the technique. However, and because minor components of the oils are

playing an essential role in defining oil authenticity and quality, concentration of these compounds (either by using a chromatographic procedure or by the use of unsaponifiables) or their observation during routine analysis by using special probes seem to be a necessary requisite to achieve a routine application of NMR to most aspects of oil analysis.

REFERENCES

1. H Lawson. Food Oils and Fats. Technology, Utilization and Nutrition. New York: Chapman and Hall, 1994, pp 28–38.
2. JM deMan. Chemical and physical properties of fatty acids. In: CK Chow, ed. Fatty Acids in Foods and Their Health Implications, 2nd ed. New York: Marcel Dekker, 2000, pp 17–46.
3. FD Gunstone. Fatty Acid and Lipid Chemistry. London: Blackie, 1996, pp 129–165.
4. N Widlak, ed. Physical Properties of Fats, Oils, and Emulsifiers. Champaign, Illinois: AOCS Press, 1999.
5. K Larsson. Lipids – Molecular Organization, Physical Functions and Technical Applications. Dundee, Scotland: The Oily Press, 1994, pp 7–45.
6. AG Marangoni, SS Narine, eds. Physical Properties of Lipids. New York: Marcel Dekker, 2002.
7. M Ollivon, R Perron. Physical properties of fats. In: A Karleskind, ed. Oils and Fats Manual. A Comprehensive Treatise, vol 1. Paris, France: Lavoisier Publishing, 1996, pp 445–544.
8. T Koyano, K Sato. Physical properties of fats in food. In: KK Rajah, ed. Fats in Food Technology. Sheffield, UK: Sheffield, 2002, pp 1–29.
9. K Larsson. Tailoring lipid functionality in foods. Trends Food Sci Technol 5:311–315, 1994.
10. MW Formo. Physical properties of fats and fatty acids. In D Swern, ed. Bailey's Industrial Oil and Fat Products, 4th ed, vol. 1. New York: John Wiley & Sons, 1979, pp 177–232.
11. R Boistelle. Fundamentals of nucleation and crystal growth. In: N Garti, K Sato, eds. Crystallization and Polymorphism of Fats and Fatty Acids. New York: Marcel Dekker, 1988, pp 189–226.
12. PJ Lawler, PS Dimick. Crystallization and polymorphism of fats. In: CC Akoh, DB Min, eds. Food Lipids. Chemistry, Nutrition, and Biotechnology, 2nd ed. New York: Marcel Dekker, 2002, pp 275–300.
13. N Widlak, R Hartel, S Narine, eds. Crystallization and Solidification Properties of Lipids. Champaign, Illinois: AOCS Press, 2001.
14. N Garti, K Sato, eds. Crystallization Processes in Fats and Lipid Systems. New York: Marcel Dekker, 2001.
15. WW Nawar. Lipids. In: OR Fennema, ed. Food Chemistry, 2nd ed. New York: Marcel Dekker, 1996, pp 225–319.
16. VA Vaclavik. Essentials of Food Science. New York: Chapman and Hall, 1998, pp 215–248.

17. K Sato. Uncovering the structures of β′ fat crystals: what do the molecules tell us? Lipid Technol 13:36–40, 2001.

18. K Sato. Solidification and phase transformation behavior of food fats. Fett/Lipid 101:467–474, 1999.

19. L Hernqvist. Crystal structures of fats and fatty acids. In: N Garti, K Sato, eds. Crystallization and Polymorphism of Fats and Fatty Acids. New York: Marcel Dekker, 1988, 97–137.

20. M Goto, DR Kodali, DM Small, K Honda, K Kozawa, T Uchida. Single crystal structure of a mixed-chain triacylglycerol:1,2-Dipalmitoyl-3-acetyl-sn-glycerol. Proc Nat Acad Sci USA 89:8083–8086, 1992.

21. E Dickinson, DJ McClements. Fat crystallisation in oil-in-water emulsions. In: E Dickinson, DJ McClements, eds. Advances in Food Colloids. Glasgow, UK: Chapman & Hall, 1995, pp 211–246.

22. AG Marangoni, RH Hartel. Visualisation and structural analysis of fat crystal networks. Food Technol 52:46–51, 1998.

23. JW Hagemann. Thermal behavior and polymorphism of acylglycerides. In: N Garti, K. Sato, eds. Crystallization and Polymorphism of Fats and Fatty Acids. New York: Marcel Dekker, 1988, pp 97–137.

24. CW Hoerr, FR Paulika. The role of x-ray diffraction in studies of the crystallography of monoacid saturated triglycerides. J Am Oil Chem Soc 45:793–797, 1968.

25. K Larsson. The crystal structure of the β-form of triglycerides. Proc Chem Soc 87–88, 1963.

26. ES Lutton. Triple chain-length structures of saturated triglycerides. J Am Oil Chem Soc 70:248–254, 1948.

27. K Larsson. Molecular arrangement of triglycerides. Fette Seifen Anstrichm 4:136–142, 1972.

28. S de Jong, TC van Soest, MA van Schaick. Crystal structures and melting points of unsaturated triacylglycerols in the β-phase. J Am Oil Chem Soc 68:371–378, 1991.

29. DM Small, ed. The Physical Chemistry of Lipids. New York: Plenum Press, 1986.

30. RE Timms. The phase behavior of mixtures of cocoa butter and milk fat. Lebensm Wiss Technol 13:61–65, 1980.

31. RE Timms. The phase behavior and polymorphism of milk fat, milk fat fractions and fully hardened milk fat. Aust J Dairy Tech 35:47–53, 1980.

32. U Persmark, KA Melin, PO Stahl. Palm oil, its polymorphism and solidification properties. Riv Ital Sost Gras 53:301–306, 1976.

33. GM Chapman, EE Akehurst, WB Wright. Cocoa butter and confectionery fats. Studies using programmed temperature X-ray diffraction and differential scanning calorimetry. J Am Oil Chem Soc 48:824–830, 1971.

34. A Hvolby. Expansion of solidifying saturated fats. J Am Oil Chem Soc 51:50–54, 1974.

35. U Riiner. Polymorphism of fats and oils investigated by temperature programmed X-ray diffraction. Lebensm Wiss Technol 3:101–106, 1970.

36. NOV Sonntag. Composition and characteristics of individual fats and oils. In: D Swern, ed. Bailey's Industrial Oil and Fat Products, 4th ed, vol 1. New York: Wiley, 1979, pp 289–477.

37. RL Wille, ES Lutton. Polymorphism of cocoa butter. J Am Oil Chem Soc 43:491–496, 1966.

38. TR Thomas, PS Dimick. Isolation and thermal characterization of high-melting seed crystals formed during cocoa butter solidification. J Am Oil Chem Soc 66:1488–1493, 1989.

39. L Hernqvist. Chocolate temper. In: ST Beckett, ed. Industrial Chocolate Manufacture and Use. London: Blackie & Sons, 1988, p. 159.

40. K Larsson. Classification of glyceride crystal forms. Acta Chem Scand 20: 2255–2260, 1966.

41. JM deMan. Principles of Food Chemistry, 3rd ed. Gaithersburg, Maryland: Aspen Publishers, 1999, pp 33–110.

42. C Loisel, G Keller, G Lecq, C Bourgaux, M Ollivon. Phase transitions and polymorphism of cocoa butter. J Am Oil Chem Soc 75:425–439, 1998.

43. K van Malssen, R Peschar, H Schenk. Real-time X-ray powder diffraction investigations on cocoa butter. I. Temperature-dependent crystallization behaviour. J Am Oil Chem Soc 73:1209–1215, 1996.

44. K van Malssen, R Peschar, H Schenk. Real-time X-ray powder diffraction investigations on cocoa butter. II. The relationship between melting behaviour and composition of β-cocoa butter. J Am Oil Chem Soc 73:1217–1223, 1996.

45. K van Malssen, R Peschar, C Brito, H Schenk. Real-time X-ray powder diffraction investigations on cocoa butter. III. Direct β-crystallization of cocoa butter: Occurrence of a memory effect. J Am Oil Chem Soc 73:1225–1230, 1996.

46. KW Smith. Cocoa butter and cocoa butter equivalents. In: FD Gunstone, ed. Structured and Modified Lipids. New York: Marcel Dekker, 2001, pp 401–422.

47. GG Jewell. Vegetable fats. In: ST Beckett, ed. Industrial Chocolate Manufacture and Use. Glasgow, UK: Blackie, 1988, pp 227–235.

48. RA Tietz, RW Hartel. Effects of minor lipids on crystallization of milk fat–cocoa butter blends and bloom formation in chocolate. J Am Oil Chem Soc 77:763–771, 2000.

49. KL Ransom-Painter, SD Williams, RW Hartel. Incorporation of milk fat and milk fat fractions into compound coatings made from palm kernel oil. J Dairy Sci 80:2237–2248, 1997.

50. JB German, C Simoneau. Phase transitions of edible fats and triglycerides: Theory and Applications. In: MA Rao, RW Hartel, eds. Phase/State Transitions in Foods. Chemical, Structural, and Rheological Changes. New York: Marcel Dekker, 1998, pp 187–216.

51. IL Woodrow, JM deMan. Polymorphism in milk fat shown by X-ray diffraction and infrared spectroscopy. J Dairy Sci 51:996–1000, 1968.

52. J Yano, S Ueno, K Sato, F Kaneko, DR Kodali, DM Small. Acyl conformation of polymorphic forms in SOS and OSO. In: N Widlak, ed. Physical Properties of Fats, Oils, and Emulsifiers. Champaign, Illinois: AOCS Press, 1999, pp 49–63.

53. J Yano, S Ueno, K Sato, T Arishima, N Sagi, F Kaneko, M Kobayashi. FT-IR study of polymorphic transformations

in SOS, POP, and POS. J Phys Chem 97:12967–12973, 1993.

54. A Minato, J Yano, S Ueno, K Smith, K Sato. FT-IR study on microscopic structures and conformations of POP-PPO and POP-OPO molecular compounds. Chem Phys Lipids 88:63–71, 1997.

55. K Larsson. Conformation-dependent features in the Raman spectra of simple foods. Chem Phys Lipids 10:165–176, 1973.

56. L Hernqvist. Structure of triglycerides in the liquid state and fat crystallization. Fette Seifen Anstrichm 86:297–300, 1984.

57. K Larsson. Significance of crystalline hydrocarbon chains in aqueous dispersions and emulsions of lipids. Chem Phys Lipids 14:233–235, 1975.

58. IT Norton, CD Lee-Tuffnell, S Ablett, SM Bociek. A calorimetric, NMR and X-ray diffraction study of the melting behavior of tripalmitin and tristearin and their mixing behavior with triolein. J Am Oil Chem Soc 62:1237–1244, 1985.

59. M Ollivon, C Loisel, C Lopez, P Lesieur, F Artzner, G Keller. Simultaneous examination of structural and thermal behaviors of fats by coupled X-ray diffraction and differential scanning calorimetry techniques: Application to cocoa butter polymorphism. In: N Widlak, R Hartel, S Narine, eds. Crystallization and Solidification Properties of Lipids. Champaign, Illinois: AOCS Press, 2001, pp 34–41.

60. A Blaurock. A new meaning to "high energy foods." INFORM 4:254–259, 1993.

61. M Kellens, W Meeussen, C Riekel, H Reynaers. Time resolved X-ray diffraction studies of the polymorphic behavior of tripalmitin using synchroton radiation. Chem Phys Lipids 52:79–98, 1990.

62. M Kellens, W Meeussen, A Hammersley, H Reynaers. Synchroton radiation investigations of the polymorphic transitions in saturated monoacid triglycerides. Part 2: Polymorphism study of a 50:50 mixture of tripalmitin and tristearin during crystallization and melting. Chem Phys Lipids 58:145–158, 1991.

63. S Ueno, J Yano, H Seto, Y Amemiya, K Sato. Synchrotron radiation X-ray diffraction study of polymorphic crystallization in triacylglycerols. In: N Widlak, ed. Physical Properties of Fats, Oils, and Emulsifiers. Champaign, Illinois: AOCS Press, 1999, pp 64–78.

64. AG Marangoni. The nature of fractality in fat crystal networks. Trends Food Sci Technol 13:37–47, 2002.

65. JF Toro-Vazquez, M Charó-Alonso. Physicochemical aspects of triacylglycerides and their association to functional properties of vegetable oils. In: JR Whitaker, F Shahidi, A Lopez-Munguia, RY Rickey, G Fuller, eds. Functional Properties of Proteins and Lipids. Washington, D.C.: American Chemical Society, 1998, pp 230–253.

66. JM deMan. Microscopy in the study of fats and emulsions. Food Microstruct 1:209–222, 1982.

67. W Buchheim. Aspects of sample preparation for freeze-fracture/freeze-etch studies of proteins and lipids in food systems. Food Microstruct 1:189–208, 1982.

68. PJ Wan. Properties of fats and oils. In: RD O'Brien, WE Farr, PJ Wan. Champaign, Illinois: AOCS Press, 2000, pp 20–48.

69. A Karleskind, ed. Oils and Fats Manual. A Comprehensive Treatise. Paris, France: Lavoisier Publishing, 1996, pp 445–544.

70. F Joly. Constantes Physiques et Thermophysiques des Corps Gras, 3rd ed. Paris, France: Institut des Corps Gras, ITERG, 1982.

71. CT Young. Peanut oil. In: YH Hui, ed. Bailey's Industrial Oil and Fat Products, 5th ed, vol 2. New York: John Wiley & Sons, 1996, pp 377–392.

72. SS Deshpande, US Deshpande, DK Salunkhe. Sesame oil. In: YH Hui, ed. Bailey's Industrial Oil and Fat Products, 5th ed, vol 2. New York: John Wiley & Sons, 1996, pp 457–495.

73. EF Sipos, BF Szuhaj. Soybean oil. In: YH Hui. Bailey's Industrial Oil and Fat Products, 5th ed, vol 2. New York: John Wiley & Sons, 1996, pp 497–601.

74. American Oil Chemists' Society (AOCS). Method Cc3-25. In: D Firestone, ed. Official Methods and Recommended Practices, 5th ed. Champaign, Illinois: American Oil Chemists' Society, 1999.

75. American Oil Chemists' Society (AOCS). Method Cc14-59. In: Firestone, ed. Official Methods and Recommended Practices, 5th ed. Champaign, Illinois: American Oil Chemists' Society, 1999.

76. RE Timms. Physical properties of oils and mixtures of oils. J Am Oil Chem Soc 62:241–248, 1985.

77. B Kowalski. Determination of specific heats of some edible oils and fats by differential scanning calorimetry. J Therm Anal 34:1321–1326, 1988.

78. T Kasprzycka-Guttman, D Odzeniak. Specific heats of some oils and a fat. Thermochim Acta 191:41–45, 1991.

79. JN Coupland, DJ McClements. Physical properties of liquid edible oils. J Am Oil Chem Soc 74:1559–1564, 1997.

80. GH Charbonnet, WS Singleton. Thermal properties of fats and oils. VI. Heat capacity, heats of fusion and transition, and entropy of trilaurin, trimyristin, tripalmitin, and tristearin. J Am Oil Chem Soc 24:140–142, 1947.

81. PE Clark, CR Waldeland, RP Cross. Specific heats of vegetable oils from 0 to 280°C. Ind Eng Chem 38:350–353, 1946.

82. JM deMan, L deMan. Texture of fats. In: AG Marangoni, SS Narine, eds. Physical Properties of Lipids. New York: Marcel Dekker, 2002, pp 191–217.

83. U Bracco. Effect of triglycerides structure on fat absorption. Am J Clin Nutr 60:1002S–1009S, 1994.

84. American Oil Chemists' Society (AOCS). Method Cd10-57. In: D Firestone, ed. Official Methods and Recommended Practices, 5th ed. Champaign, Illinois: American Oil Chemists' Society, 1999.

85. American Oil Chemists' Society (AOCS). Method Cd16-81. In: D Firestone, ed. Official Methods and Recommended Practices, 5th ed. Champaign, Illinois: American Oil Chemists' Society, 1999.

86. American Oil Chemists' Society (AOCS). Method Cd16b-93. In: D Firestone, ed. Official Methods and Recommended Practices, 5th ed. Champaign, Illinois: American Oil Chemists' Society, 1999.

87. B Wunderlich. Thermal Analysis. San Diego: Academic Press, 1990.

88. JN Coupland. Ultrasonic characterization of lipid crystallization. In: N Widlak, R Hartel, S Narine, eds. Crystallization and Solidification Properties of Lipids. Champaign, Illinois: AOCS Press, 2001, pp 132–145.

89. RB Joglekar, HE Watson. Physical properties of pure triglycerides. J Soc Chem Ind 47:365T–368T, 1928.

90. D Valeri, AJA Meirelles. Viscosities of fatty acids, triglycerides and their binary mixtures. J Am Oil Chem Soc 74:1221–1226, 1997.

91. LA Jones, CC King. Cottonseed oil. In: YH Hui, ed. Bailey's Industrial Oil and Fat Products, 5th ed, vol 2. New York: John Wiley & Sons, 1996, pp 159–240.

92. H Noureddini, BC Teoh, LD Clements. Viscosities of vegetable oils and fatty acids. J Am Oil Chem Soc 69:1189–1191, 1992.

93. LR Strecker, MA Bieber, A Maza, T Grossberger, WJ Doskoczynski. Corn oil. In: YH Hui, ed. Bailey's Industrial Oil and Fat Products, 5th ed, vol 2. New York: John Wiley & Sons, 1996, pp 125–158.

94. H Topallar, Y Bayrak, M Iscan. Effect of hydrogenation on density and viscosity of sunflowerseed oil. J Am Oil Chem Soc 72:1519–1522, 1995.

95. K Warner. Chemistry of frying oils. In: CC Akoh, DB Min, eds. Food Lipids. Chemistry, Nutrition, and Biotechnology, 2nd ed. New York: Marcel Dekker, 2002, pp 205–221.

96. JF Toro-Vazquez, A Gallegos-Infante. Viscosity and its relationship to crystallization in a binary system of saturated triacylglycerides and sesame oil. J Am Oil Chem Soc 73:1237–1246, 1996.

97. ES Perry, WH Weber, BF Daubert. Vapor pressures of phlegmatic liquids. I. Simple and mixed triglycerides. J Am Chem Soc 71:3720–3726, 1949.

98. American Oil Chemists' Society (AOCS). Method Cc9a-48. In: D Firestone, ed. Official Methods and Recommended Practices, 5th ed. Champaign, Illinois: American Oil Chemists' Society, 1999.

99. HF Davidson, EJ Campbell, RJ Bell, RA Pritchard. Sunflower oil. In: YH Hui, ed. Bailey's Industrial Oil and Fat Products, 5th ed, vol 2. New York: John Wiley & Sons, 1996, pp 603–689.

100. GWC Kaye, WF Higgins. The thermal conductivities of certain liquids. Proc Royal Soc London A117:459–470, 1928.

101. MS Qashou, RI Vachon, YS Touloukian. Thermal conductivity of foods. ASHRAE Trans 78:165–183, 1972.

102. H Noureddini, BC Teoh, LD Clements. Densities of vegetable oils and fatty acids. J Am Oil Chem Soc 69:1184–1189, 1992.

103. MSR Subrahmanyam, HS Vedanayagam, P Venkatacharyulu. Estimation of the Sharma constant and thermoacoustic properties of vegetable oils. J Am Oil Chem Soc 71:901–905, 1994.

104. BP Caldwell, HF Payne. Dielectric constant and effective dipole moment of drying oils. Ind Eng Chem 33:954–960, 1941.

105. Y Basiron. Palm oil. In: YH Hui, ed. Bailey's Industrial Oil and Fat Products, 5th ed, vol 2. New York: John Wiley & Sons, 1996, pp 271–375.

106. J Smith. Safflower oil. In: YH Hui, ed. Bailey's Industrial Oil and Fat Products, 5th ed, vol 2. New York: John Wiley & Sons, 1996, pp 411–455.

107. JD Halvorsen, WC Mammel Jr, LD Clements. Density estimation for fatty acids and vegetable oils based on fatty acid composition. J Am Oil Chem Soc 70:875–880, 1993.

108. AE Bailey, WS Singleton. Dilatometric investigations of fats. III. Density, expansibility, and melting dilation of some simple triglycerides and other fats. Oil Soap 22:265–271, 1945.

109. P Chawla, JM deMan. Measurement of the size distribution of fat crystals using a laser particle counter. J Am Oil Chem Soc 67:329–332, 1990.

110. American Oil Chemists' Society (AOCS). Method Cb4-35. In: D Firestone, ed. Official Methods and Recommended Practices, 5th ed. Champaign, Illinois: American Oil Chemists' Society, 1999.

111. MR Sahasrabudhe. Crismer values and erucic contents of rapeseed oils. J Am Oil Chem Soc 54:323–324, 1977.

112. NAM Eskin, BE McDonald, R Przybylski, LJ Malcolmson, R Scarth, T Mag, K Ward, D Adolph. Canola oil. In: YH Hui, ed. Bailey's Industrial Oil and Fat Products. 5th ed, vol 2. New York: John Wiley & Sons, 1996, pp 1–95.

113. L Aho, O Wahlroos. A comparison between determinations of the solubility of oxygen in oils by exponential dilution and chemical methods. J Am Oil Chem Soc 44:65–66, 1967.

114. RO Feuge. Interfacial tension of oil-water systems containing technical mono- and diglycerides. J Am Oil Chem Soc 24:49–52, 1947.

115. CE Stauffer. Emulsifiers and stabilizers. In: KK Rajah, ed. Fats in Food Technology. Sheffield, UK: Sheffield Academic Press, 2002, pp 228–274.

116. DJ McClements. Lipid-based emulsions and emulsifiers. In: CC Akoh, DB Min, eds. Food Lipids: Chemistry, Nutrition, and Biotechnology, 2nd ed. New York: Marcel Dekker, 2002, pp 63–101.

117. DJ McClements. Food Emulsions: Principles, Practice and Techniques. Boca Raton, Florida: CRC Press, 1999.

118. BK Paul, SP Moulik. Microemulsions: An overview. J Disper Sci Technol 18:301–367, 1997.

119. SE Hill. Emulsions and foams. In: SE Hill, DA Ledward, JR Mitchell, eds. Functional Properties of Food Macromolecules. Gaithersburg, Maryland: Aspen, 1998, pp 302–334.

120. M Abe. Macro- and microemulsions. J Jpn Oil Chem Soc 47:819–843, 1998.

121. FD Gunstone. Food applications of lipids. In: CC Akoh, DB Min, eds. Food Lipids. Chemistry, Nutrition, and Biotechnology, 2nd ed. New York: Marcel Dekker, 2002, pp 729–750.

122. I Johansson, M Svensson. Surfactants based on fatty acids and other natural hydrophobes. Curr Opin Colloid Interf Sci 6:178–188, 2001.

123. CD Nuchi, P Hernandez, DJ McClements, EA Decker. Ability of lipid hydroperoxides to partition into surfactant micelles and alter lipid oxidation rates in emulsions. J Agric Food Chem 50:5445–5449, 2002.

124. DJ McClements, R Chanamai. Physicochemical properties of monodisperse oil-in-water emulsions. J Dispers Sci Technol 23:125–134, 2002.

125. HT Davis. Factors determining emulsion type: Hydrophile-lipophile balance and beyond. Colloids Surfaces A 91:9–24, 1994.

126. MC Erickson. Chemistry and function of phospholipids. In: CC Akoh, DB Min, eds. Food Lipids. Chemistry, Nutrition, and Biotechnology, 2nd ed. New York: Marcel Dekker, 2002, pp 41–62.

127. L Lethuaut, F Metro, C Genot. Effect of droplet size on lipid oxidation rates of oil-in-water emulsions stabilized by protein. J Am Oil Chem Soc 79:425–430, 2002.

128. S Friberg, K Larsson. Food Emulsions, 3rd ed. New York: Marcel Dekker, 1997.

129. E Dickinson, G Stainsby. Colloids in Foods. London: Applied Science, 1982.

130. E Dickinson. Introduction to Food Colloids. Oxford: Oxford University Press, 1992.

131. DG Dalgleish. Food emulsions. In: J Sjoblom, ed. Emulsions and Emulsion Stability. New York: Marcel Dekker, 1996, pp 287–325.

132. P Walstra. Disperse systems: Basic considerations. In: OR Fennema, ed. Food Chemistry, 3rd ed. New York: Marcel Dekker, 1996, p 85.

133. HE Swaisgood. Characteristics of milk. In: OR Fennema, ed. Food Chemistry, 3rd ed. New York: Marcel Dekker, 1996, p 841.

134. CA Miles, GAJ Fursey, RCD Jones. Ultrasonic estimation of solid/liquid ratios in fats, oils and adipose tissue. J Sci Food Agric 36:215–228, 1985.

135. DJ McClements, MJW Povey. Ultrasonic velocity measurements in some liquid triglycerides and vegetable oils. J Am Oil Chem Soc 65:1787–1790, 1988.

136. TH Gouw, JC Vlugter. Physical properties of triglycerides III: Ultrasonic sound velocity. Fette Seifen Anstrich 69:159–164, 1967.

137. N Gladwell, C Javanaud, KE Peers, RR Rahalkar. Ultrasonic behavior of edible oils: correlation with rheology. J Am Oil Chem Soc 62:1231–1236, 1985.

138. HL Kou. Variation of ultrasonic velocity and absorption with temperature and frequency in high viscosity vegetable oils. Jpn J Appl Phys 10:167–170, 1971.

139. C Javanaud, RR Rahalkar. Velocity of sound in vegetable oils. Fat Sci Technol 90:73–75, 1988.

140. American Oil Chemists' Society (AOCS). Method Cc13e-92. In: D Firestone, ed. Official Methods and Recommended Practices, 5th ed. Champaign, Illinois: American Oil Chemists' Society, 1999.

141. EC Canapi, YTV Agustin, EA Moro, E Pedrosa Jr, MLJ Bendaño. Coconut oil. In: YH Hui, ed. Bailey's Industrial Oil and Fat Products, 5th ed, vol 2. New York: John Wiley & Sons, 1996, pp 97–124.

142. American Oil Chemists' Society (AOCS). Method Cc13a-43. In: D Firestone, ed. Official Methods and Recommended Practices, 5th ed. Champaign, Illinois: American Oil Chemists' Society, 1999.

143. American Oil Chemists' Society (AOCS). Method Cc13b-45. In: D Firestone, ed. Official Methods and Recommended Practices, 5th ed. Champaign, Illinois: American Oil Chemists' Society, 1999.

144. American Oil Chemists' Society (AOCS). Method Cc13c-50. In: D Firestone, ed. Official Methods and Recommended Practices, 5th ed. Champaign, Illinois: American Oil Chemists' Society, 1999.

145. American Oil Chemists' Society (AOCS). Method Ch5-91. In: D Firestone, ed. Official Methods and Recommended Practices, 5th ed. Champaign, Illinois: American Oil Chemists' Society, 1999.

146. D Firestone, E Fedeli, EW Emmons. Olive oil. In: YH Hui, ed. Bailey's Industrial Oil and Fat Products, 5th ed, vol 2. New York: John Wiley & Sons, 1996, pp 241–269.

147. DH Wheeler, RW Riemenschneider, CE Sando. Preparation, properties and thiocyanogen absorption of triolein and trilinolein. J Biol Chem 132:687–699, 1940.

148. American Oil Chemists' Society (AOCS). Method Ti1a-64. In: D Firestone, ed. Official Methods and Recommended Practices, 5th ed. Champaign, Illinois: American Oil Chemists' Society, 1999.

149. American Oil Chemists' Society (AOCS). Method Cd16-61. In: D Firestone, ed. Official Methods and Recommended Practices, 5th ed. Champaign, Illinois: American Oil Chemists' Society, 1999.

150. M Adam, MM Mossoba, T Lee. Rapid determination of total *trans* fat content by attenuated total reflection infrared spectroscopy: An international collaborative study. J Am Oil Chem Soc 77:457–462, 2000.

151. American Oil Chemists' Society (AOCS). Method Cd14d-99. In: D Firestone, ed. Official Methods and Recommended Practices, 5th ed. Champaign, Illinois: American Oil Chemists' Society, 1999.

152. AA Ismail, FR van de Voort, G Emo, J Sedman. Rapid quantitative determination of free fatty acids in fats and oils by Fourier transform infrared spectroscopy. J Am Oil Chem Soc 70:335–341, 1993.

153. FR van de Voort, AA Ismail. Proximate analysis of foods by mid-FTIR spectroscopy. Trends Food Sci Technol 2:13–17, 1991.

154. L Sedman, FR van de Voort, AA Ismail, P Maes. Industrial validation of Fourier transform infrared trans and iodine value analyses of fats and oils. J Am Oil Chem Soc 75:33–39, 1998.

155. E Bertran, M Blanco, J Coello, H Iturriaga, S Maspoch, I Montoliu. Determination of olive oil free fatty acid by Fourier transform infrared spectroscopy. J Am Oil Chem Soc 76:611–616, 1999.

156. MH Moh, YB Che Man, BS Badlishah, S Jinap, MS Saad, WJW Abdullah. Quantitative analysis of palm carotene using Fourier transform infrared and near infrared spectroscopy. J Am Oil Chem Soc 76:249–254, 1999.

157. YB Che Man, MH Moh. Determination of free fatty acids in palm oil by near infrared reflectance spectroscopy. J Am Oil Chem Soc 75:557–562, 1998.

158. S Bolliger, Y Zeng, EJ Windhab. In-line measurement of tempered cocoa butter and chocolate by means of near-infrared spectroscopy. J Am Oil Chem Soc 76:659–667, 1999.

159. H Li, FR van de Voort, AA Ismail, R Cox. Determination of peroxide value by Fourier transform near-infrared spectroscopy. J Am Oil Chem Soc 77:137–142, 2000.

160. G Yildiz, RL Wehling, SL Cuppett. Method for determining oxidation of vegetable oils by near-infrared spectroscopy. J Am Oil Chem Soc 78:495–502, 2001.

161. GF Bailey, RJ Horvat. Raman spectroscopic analysis of the *cis/trans* isomer composition of edible vegetable oils. J Am Oil Chem Soc 49:494–498, 1972.

162. H Sadeghi-Jorabchi, PJ Hendra, RH Wilson, PS Belton. Determination of the total unsaturation in oils and margarines by Fourier-transform Raman spectroscopy. J Am Oil Chem Soc 67:483–486, 1990.

163. AJ Wright, SS Narine, AG Marangoni. Comparison of experimental techniques used in lipid crystallization studies. In: N Widlak, R Hartel, S Narine, eds. Crystallization and Solidification Properties of Lipids. Champaign, Illinois: AOCS Press, 2001, pp 120–131.

164. MD Guillen, A Ruiz. High resolution ^{1}H nuclear magnetic resonance in the study of edible oils and fats. Trend Food Sci Technol 12:328–338, 2001.

165. A Crookell. NMR oilseed analysis in the plant and lab. INFORM 8:515–520, 1997.

166. TM Eads, WR Croasmun. ^{1}H NMR applications to fats and oils. J Am Oil Chem Soc 65:78–83, 1988.

167. LF Johnson, JN Schoolery. Determination of unsaturation and average molecular weight of natural fats by nuclear magnetic resonance. Anal Chem 34:1136–1139, 1962.

168. LV Nielsen. Studies on the relationship between unsaturation and iodine value of butterfat by high resolution nuclear magnetic resonance (NMR). Milchwissenschaft 31:598–602, 1976.

169. Y Miyake, K Yokomizo, N Matsuzaki. Rapid determination of iodine value by ^{1}H nuclear magnetic resonance spectroscopy. J Am Oil Chem Soc 75:15–19, 1998.

170. R Sacchi, M Patumi, G Fontanazza, P Barone, P Fiodiponti, L Mannina, E Rossi, AL Segre. A high-field ^{1}H nuclear magnetic resonance study of the minor components in virgin olive oils. J Am Oil Chem Soc 73:747–758, 1996.

171. R Sacchi, F Addeo, L Paolillo. ^{1}H and ^{13}C NMR of virgin olive oil. An overview. Magn Reson Chem 35:S133–S145.

172. KK Ketshajwang, J Holmback, SO Yeboah. Quality and compositional studies of some edible leguminosae seed oils in Botswana. J Am Oil Chem Soc 75:741–743, 1998.

173. Y Miyake, K Yokomizo, N Matsuzaki. Rapid determination of iodine value by ^{1}H nuclear magnetic resonance spectroscopy. J Am Oil Chem Soc 75:15–19, 1998.

174. R Sacchi, I Medina, SP Aubourg, F Addeo, L Paolillo. Proton nuclear magnetic resonance rapid and structure-specific determination of ω-3 polyunsaturated fatty acids in fish lipids. J Am Oil Chem Soc 70:225–228, 1993.

175. M Aursand, JR Rainuzzo, H Grasladen. Quantitative high-resolution ^{13}C and ^{1}H nuclear magnetic resonance of ω-3 fatty acids from white muscle of atlantic salmon (Salmo salar). J Am Oil Chem Soc 70:971–981, 1993.

176. T Igarashi, M Aursand, Y Hirata, IS Gribbestad, S Wada, M Nonaka. Nondestructive quantitative acids and n-3 fatty acids in fish oils by high-resolution ^{1}H nuclear magnetic resonance spectroscopy. J Am Oil Chem Soc 77:737–748, 2000.

177. L Mannina, M Patumi, P Fiordiponti, MC Emanuele, AL Segre. Olive and hazelnut oils: a study by high-field ^{1}H NMR and gas chromatography. Ital J Food Sci 2:139–149, 1999.

178. AL Segre, L Mannina. ^{1}H NMR study of edible oils. Recent Res Develop Oil Chem 1:297–308, 1997.

179. FD Gunstone. High resolution ^{13}C NMR spectroscopy of lipids. In: WW Christie, ed. Advances in Lipid Methodology–Two. Dundee, Scotland: The Oily Press, 1993, pp 1–68.

180. L Mannina, C Luchinat, MC Emanuele, A Segre. Acyl positional distribution of glycerol tri-esters in vegetable oils: a ^{13}C NMR study. Chem Phys Lipids 103:47–55, 1999.

181. G Vlahov, AD Shaw, DB Kell. Use of ^{13}C nuclear magnetic resonance distortionless enhancement by polatization transfer pulse sequence and multivariate analysis to discriminate olive oil cultivars. J Am Oil Chem Soc 76:1223–1231, 1999.

182. FD Gunstone. ^{13}C-NMR studies of mono-, di- and tri-acylglycerols leading to qualitative and semiquantitative information about mixtures of these glycerol esters. Chem Phys Lipids 58:219–224, 1991.

183. FJ Hidalgo, G Gómez, JL Navarro, R Zamora. Oil stability prediction by high-resolution ^{13}C nuclear magnetic resonance spectroscopy. J Agric Food Chem, 20:5825–5831, 2002.

184. S Ng. Analysis of positional distribution of fatty acids in palm oil by ^{13}C NMR spectroscopy. Lipids 20:778–782, 1985.

185. S Ng. Quantitative analysis of partial acylglycerols and free fatty acids in palm oil by ^{13}C nuclear magnetic resonance spectroscopy. J Am Oil Chem Soc 77:749–755, 2000.

186. S Ng, PT Gee. Determination of iodine value of palm and palmkernel oil by carbon-13 nuclear magnetic resonance spectroscopy. Eur J Lipid Sci Technol 103:223–227, 2001.

187. PE Pfeffer, J Sampugna, DP Schwartz, JN Shoolery. Analytical ^{13}C NMR: detection, quantitation, and positional analysis of butyrate in butter oil. Lipids 12:869–871, 1977.

188. R. Sacchi. High resolution NMR of virgin olive oil. In: GA Webb, PS Belton, AM Gil, I Delgadillo, eds. Magnetic Resonance in Food Science. A View to the Future. Cambridge, U.K.: The Royal Society of Chemistry, 2001, pp 213–226.

189. AD Shaw, A di Camillo, G Vlahov, A Jones, G Bianchi, J Rowland, DB Kell. Discrimination of the variety and region of origin of extra virgin olive oils using ^{13}C NMR and multivariate calibration with variable reduction. Anal Chim Acta 348:357–374, 1977.

190. G Vlahov. Improved quantitative ^{13}C nuclear magnetic resonance criteria for determination of grades of virgin

olive oils. The normal ranges for diglycerides in olive oil. J Am Oil Chem Soc 73:1201–1203, 1996.

191. G Vlahov. Application of NMR to the study of olive oils. Progr Nuclear Magn Reson Spec 35:341–357, 1999.

192. KF Wollenberg. Quantitative high resolution ^{13}C nuclear magnetic resonance of the olefinic and carbonyl carbons of edible vegetable oils. J Am Oil Chem Soc 67:487–494, 1990.

193. R Zamora, V Alba, FJ Hidalgo. Use of high-resolution ^{13}C nuclear magnetic resonance spectroscopy for the screening of virgin olive oils. J Am Oil Chem Soc 78:89–94, 2001.

194. R Zamora, G Gómez, MC Dobarganes, FJ Hidalgo. Oil fractionation as a preliminary step in the characterization of vegetable oils by high-resolution ^{13}C NMR spectroscopy. J Am Oil Chem Soc 79:261–266, 2002.

195. R Zamora, G Gómez, FJ Hidalgo. Classification of vegetable oils by high-resolution ^{13}C NMR spectroscopy using chromatographically obtained oil fractions. J Am Oil Chem Soc: 79:267–272, 2002.

196. R Zamora, G Gómez, FJ Hidalgo. Quality control of vegetable oils by ^{13}C NMR spectroscopy. In PS Belton, AM Gil, GA Webb, DN Rutledge, eds. Magnetic Resonance in Food Science: Latest Developments. Cambridge UK: The Royal Society of Chemistry, 2003, pp 231–232.

197. R Zamora, FJ Hidalgo. Analysis of unsaponifiable matters from edible oils by high-resolution ^{13}C nuclear magnetic resonance. INFORM 5:495, 1994.

198. R Zamora, JL Navarro, FJ Hidalgo. Identification and classification of olive oils by high-resolution ^{13}C nuclear magnetic resonance. J Am Oil Chem Soc 71:361–364, 1994.

10 The Water-Soluble Vitamins

Francene Steinberg and Robert B. Rucker
Department of Agricultural and Environmental
Science and Nutrition, University of California

CONTENTS

I. INTRODUCTION

The water-soluble vitamins consist of a mixed group of chemical compounds. Their classification into specific chemical groups depends on both chemical characteristics and functions. The letter designations (vitamins B_1, B_2, B_3, etc., C) represent in part remnants from the past as the discovery of given dietary growth or curative factors were given letter designations.

Vitamins are novel in their roles as "external" or dietary regulatory agents. They have largely evolved to serve: 1) specific cofactor and/or co-substrate functions, 2) as regulatory agents, or 3) as antioxidants. All of the vitamins undergo specific and metabolically controlled modifications before activation or conversion into their functional forms. The most limiting events that control function are often a specific step(s) in cofactor formation, e.g., a phosphorylation reaction or ATP addition.

The use of broad functional categories as headings to organize this chapter was chosen. For example, niacin, riboflavin, and ascorbic acid serve primarily as redox cofactors. The roles of thiamin, pyridoxine (vitamin B-6) and pantothenic acid (as a component of coenzyme A) are distinguished because of their importance to carbohydrate, protein and amino acid, and acyl and acetyl transport, respectively. Folic acid, vitamin B-12 (cobalamin), and biotin will be discussed in relationship to their roles in single-carbon or CO_2 transfer reactions.

II. VITAMINS IMPORTANT IN REDOX REACTIONS

A. ASCORBIC ACID (VITAMIN C)

Ascorbic acid functions primarily as a cofactor for microsomal mono-and dioxygenases (hydroxylases) and oxidases. In most animals, ascorbic acid is synthesized from glucose in the liver. In birds and reptiles, ascorbic acid synthesis takes place primarily in the kidney. In animals that require ascorbic acid, e.g., humans, it is a deficiency of gulonolactone oxidase, the last step in ascorbic acid synthesis, which results in the need for a dietary source (Figure 10.1; 12).

1. Chemistry

Ascorbic acid (2,3-enedial-glulonic acid) is a powerful cellular reducing agent and is of general importance as an antioxidant because of its high reducing potential. Both of the hydrogens of the enediol group dissociate, which result in the acidity of ascorbic acid ($pK_1 = 4.2$). When ascorbic acid plays a role in reductions, the reaction usually occurs in a stepwise fashion with monodehydroascorbic acid, as a semiquinone intermediate. This intermediate then disproportionates to ascorbic acid, and dehydroascorbic acid (Figure 10.1).

2. Absorption, Tissue Distribution, and Metabolic Functions

Dietary ascorbic acid is absorbed from the duodenum and proximal jejunum. Measurable, albeit small, amounts of ascorbic acid also cross the membranes of the mouth and gastric mucosa. Although some controversy exists regarding the relationship between dietary intake and the intestinal absorption of ascorbic acid, studies indicate that within the physiological ranges of intake (40–200 milligrams per day for humans or ~5–25 mg/kJ of diet); 80–90% of the vitamin is absorbed. Uptake at apical membranes involves a specialized Na^+-dependent, carrier-mediated system. Exit of ascorbic acid from enterocytes utilizes a Na^+-dependent carrier system. To date, two Na^+-dependent L-ascorbic acid transporters have been cloned and partially characterized. The preference for these transporters is for L-ascorbic acid. Dehydroascorbic acid uptake is facilitated by hexose transporters (3, 12).

In tissues, the highest concentration of ascorbic acid is found in the adrenal and pituitary glands followed by the liver, thymus, brain, and pancreas. In diabetic animals, the ascorbic acid content of tissue is often depressed, which may be due to competition for uptake between dehydro forms of ascorbic acid and glucose (3).

Ascorbic acid is maintained in cells by several mechanisms. Ascorbic acid reductases maintain L-ascorbic acid in the reduced form, which is less susceptible to easy diffusion. Within most cells, measurable amounts of ascorbic acid are also maintained as the 2-sulfate derivative. The ability to maintain ascorbic acid in the reduced state and as ascorbic acid-2-sulfate appear important in maintaining cellular ascorbic acid levels (12).

In the neonate, glutathione is also very important to ascorbic acid recycling. In this regard, an argument can be made for a dietary need for ascorbic acid in the neonates of some animal species in which the adult does not have a dietary requirement. For example, the levels of glutathione are relatively low in neonate rat and mouse tissues. As ascorbic acid is oxidized to dehydroascorbic acid, there is the need for conservation, because dehydroascorbic acid is easily degraded. Glutathione in its

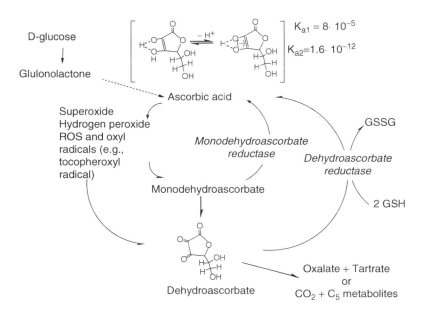

FIGURE 10.1 Ascorbic acid. In most animals ascorbic acid is derived from glucose. Gulonolactone is produced from glucose and its oxidation to ascorbic acid is catalyzed by gulonolactone oxidase (dashed line). The K_as for the two dissociable protons in ascorbic acid are indicated. At pH 7, dehydroascorbic acid can be reduced to ascorbic acid with a $Eo' = 0.08$, e.g., dehydroascorbate $+ 2e^- + 2H^+ \leftrightarrow$ ascorbate. In a biological system, reduction of the monodehydroascorbic acid to ascorbic acid occurs by the NADH-requiring enzyme, monodehydroascorbic acid reductase. Reduction of dehydroascorbic acid utilizes reduced glutathione and is catalyzed dehydroascorbic acid reductase, also known as glutaredoxin.

reduced form serves as the reducing substrate for glutaredoxin, an enzyme that can maintain ascorbic acid in a reduced state (3, 12).

As a cellular reducing agent, ascorbic acid plays a number of very important roles. It serves as a cofactor for mixed-function oxidations that result in the incorporation of molecular oxygen into various substrates. Examples include the hydroxylation of proline in collagen, elastin, C1q complement, and acetylcholine esterase. Some of the P-450-dependent hydroxylases that carry out the hydroxylation of steroids, drugs, and other xenobiotics also have a need for ascorbic acid (12).

Ascorbic acid-dependent hydroxylation steps also occur in the biosynthesis of carnitine and the hydroxylation of tyrosine in the formation of catecholamines. Most of the enzymes involved in these processes are metal-requiring enzymes, in which the role of ascorbic acid is to maintain the metal (usually Cu or Fe) in a reduced state.

3. Requirement, Deficiency, and Toxicity

Most animals with the exception of primates, guinea pigs, some snakes, fruit-eating bats, birds such as passerines, and salmonid fish synthesize ascorbate (Figure 10.1). Impaired collagen synthesis is a principle feature of ascorbic acid deficiency, which is evidenced in capillary fragility, bleeding gums, delayed wound healing, and impaired bone formation. Connective tissue lesions are primarily a result of under-hydroxylated collagen

(at specific prolyl and lysyl residues). This can result in abnormal collagen degradation and, as a consequence, decreased collagen production. In addition, the inability to deal with metabolic stress requiring normal adrenal gland function and abnormal fatty acid metabolism (carnitine synthesis) can be signs of scurvy.

The current requirement for humans is 75 mg per day (U.S. RDA for the healthy adults) or 30–60 mg per 1000 kcal or 4 MJ of diet (4; Table 10.1). Because of the mechanisms in place to homeostatically regulate ascorbic acid, evidence of toxicity, other than gastric upset, is seldom reported (e.g., diarrhea, gastric irritation). Evidence of toxicity, however, may be manifest, when ascorbic acid is consumed in gram quantities per day. Of interest, ascorbic acid intake in this range can result in decreased histamine production and facilitate reduction of nitrosamines and other putative cancer promoting agents with similar chemical characteristics. The interaction with nitrosamines occurs primarily in the stomach, and is chemical in nature owing to ascorbic acid's potential to function as an excellent reducing agent. The anti-histamine effects from pharmacologic exposure of ascorbic acid are in part the basis for its use as an analgesic in the treatment of "common colds."

When fed in excess of metabolic need, tissue levels of ascorbic acid are homeostatically maintained. Homeostasis occurs by the induction of ascorbic acid decarboxylases, which initiates enhanced degradation of ascorbate to CO_2 and C-4 or C-5 fragments (12).

TABLE 10.1
The Daily Reference Intakes for the Water-Soluble Vitamins (Part 1)[a]

Vitamin	Age Condition	EAR[b]	RDA[c]	AI[d]	UL[e]	Vitamin	Age Condition	EAR	RDA	AI	UL
Ascorbic Acid	Years	mg/day	mg/day	mg/day	mg/day	Niacin	Years	mg/day	mg/day	mg/day	mg/day
	0–0.5	–	–	40	–		0–0.5	–	–	2.	–
	0.5–1	–	–	50	–		0.5–1	–	–	4.	–
	1–3	13	15	–	400		1–3	5	6	–	10
	4–8	22	25	–	650		4–8	6	8	–	15
	9–13	39	45	–	1200		9–13	9	12	–	20
	14–18	63	75	–	1800		14–18	12	14 (M), 16 (F)	–	30
	19–>70	75	90	–	2000		19–>70	11	14 (M), 16 (F)	–	35
	19–30 Pregnancy	70	85	–	2000		19–30 Pregnancy	13	17	–	35
	19–30 Lactation	100	120	–	2000		19–30 Lactation	13	17	–	35
Riboflavin	Years	mg/day	mg/day	mg/day	mg/day	Thiamin	Years	mg/day	mg/day	mg/day	mg/day
	0–0.5	–	–	0.3	–		0–0.5	–	–	0.2	
	0.5–1	–	–	0.4	–		0.5–1	–	–	0.3	
	1–3	0.4	0.5	–	–		1–3	0.4	0.5	–	
	4–8	0.5	0.6	–	–		4–8	0.5	0.6	–	
	9–13	0.8	0.9	–	–		9–13	0.7	0.9	–	
	14–>70	0.9 (M), 1.1 (F)	1.1 (M), 1.3 (F)	–	–		14–>70	0.9 (M), 1.0 (F)	1.1 (M), 1.2 (F)	–	
	19–30 Pregnancy	1.2	1.4	–	–		19–30 Pregnancy	1.2	1.4	–	
	19–30 Lactation	1.3	1.6	–	–		19–30 Lactation	1.2	1.5	–	
Pantothenic Acid	Years	mg/day	mg/day	mg/day	mg/day	Vitamin B-6	Years	mg/day	mg/day	mg/day	mg/day
	0–0.5	–	–	1.7	–		0–0.5	0–0.5	–	–	0.1
	0.5–1	–	–	1.8	–		0.5–1	0.5–1	–	–	0.3
	1–3	–	–	2	–		1–3	0.4	0.5	–	30
	4–8	–	–	3	–		4–8	0.5	0.6	–	40
	9–13	–	–	4	–		9–13	0.8	1.0	–	60
	14–>70	–	–	5	–		14–>70	1.1	1.3	–	80
	19–30 Pregnancy	–	–	6	–		19–30 Pregnancy	1.1	1.3	–	100
	19–30 Lactation	–	–	7	–		19–30 Lactation	1.1	1.3	–	100

The Daily Reference Intakes for the Water-Soluble Vitamins (Part 2)[a]

Vitamin	Age Condition					Vitamin	Age Condition				
Biotin	Years	μg/day	μg/day	μg/day	μg/day	Folic Acid	Years	μg/day	μg/day	μg/day	μg/day
	0–0.5	–	–	5.0	–		0–0.5	–	–	65	–
	0.5–1	–	–	6.0	–		0.5–1	–	–	80	–
	1–3	–	–	8.0	–		1–3	120	150	–	300
	4–8	–	–	12	–		4–8	160	200	–	400
	9–13	–	–	20	–		9–13	320	400	–	1000
	14–>70	–	–	25	–		14–>70	320	400	–	1000
	19–30 Pregnancy	–	–	30	–		19–30 Pregnancy	520	600	–	1000
	19–30 Lactation	–	30	–			19–30 Lactation	520	600	–	1000

(*Continued*)

TABLE 10.1 *(Continued)*

Vitamin	Age Condition	EAR[b]	RDA[c]	AI[d]	UL[e]
Vitamin	Years	µg/day	µg/day	µg/day	µg/day
B-12	0–0.5	–	–	0.4	–
	0.5–1	–	–	0.5	–
	1–3	0.7	0.9		–
	4–8	1	1.2	–	–
	9–13	1.5	1.8	–	–
	14–>70	2	2.4	–	–
	19–30 Pregnancy	2.2	2.6		–
	19–30 Lactation	2.2	2.6	-	–

[a] Dietary Reference Intakes (DRI) — Reference values that are quantitative estimates of nutrient intakes to be used for planning and assessing diets for apparently healthy people. There are 4 reference values: the EARs, RDAs, AIs, and UIs.

[b] Estimated Average Requirement (EAR) — The nutrient intake value that is estimated to meet the requirement of half of the healthy individuals in a group. The EAR is used to assess the adequacy of dietary intakes within a population and it is used to develop the RDAs.

[c] Recommended Dietary Allowances (RDA) — The average daily dietary intake level that is sufficient to meet the nutrient requirements of nearly all (97–98%) healthy individuals in a designated group.

[d] Adequate Intake (AI) — AI is used when the RDA for a nutrient is not available. It is a recommended daily intake that is based on observed or experimentally determined approximations of nutrient intake by a group of healthy people. An AI is developed when there is no EAR or research to help develop the RDA for a nutrient.

[e] Tolerable Upper Intake Level (UL) — Highest level of daily nutrient intake that is likely to pose no risks of adverse health effects to almost all individuals in the general population.

4. Food Sources and Stability

Ascorbic acid is widely distributed in fruits and vegetables, with foods such as citrus fruits, berries, kiwi, peppers, Brussels sprouts, and broccoli being particularly high in this vitamin. Ascorbic acid is relatively unstable and easily destroyed during processing and storage of foods. It is labile to neutral and alkaline conditions, heat, light, and exposure to oxygen. The rate of decomposition is accelerated by the presence of metals, especially iron and copper, and by enzymes such as peroxidases. Food preservation techniques that act to limit losses of ascorbic acid are blanching of vegetables, pasteurization, and deaeration of juices to limit oxygen and inactivate the enzymes. Additionally, packaging in containers that limit exposure to light and oxygen will maintain ascorbate concentrations. Erythorbic acid, a biologically inactive analog of ascorbic acid, is often added to foods as an antioxidant to preserve freshness. A summary of chemical characteristics for ascorbic acid and other B-vitamins is given in Table 10.2 (4, 13).

III. THE B VITAMINS

A. NIACIN

Throughout the 18th and 19th centuries, the disease pellagra was prevalent in Western Europe and the southern region of the United States. This disease would eventually became associated with the vitamin, niacin, and the consumption of corn (maize), as a principle source of dietary energy. The nutritional availability of niacin in corn is relatively low bioavailability. Corn also has a low content of tryptophan. As shown in Figure 10.2, niacin can be generated upon tryptophan degradation.

Normally, niacin is derived from foods, such as corn, by hydrolysis of NAD (nicotinamide adenosyl dinucleotide) and NADP (nicotinamide adenosyl phosphodinucleotide) by the action of pancreatic or intestinal nucleosides and phosphatases. As most human diets now contain adequate tryptophan, and available NAD and NADP, niacin deficiency is seldom observed (6).

1. Chemistry

NAD and its phosphorylated form, NADP, are two coenzymes derived from niacin. Both contain an unsubstituted pyridine 3-carboxamide that is essential to function in redox reactions with a chemical potential near −0.32 V. Virtually all cells are capable of converting niacin to NAD. Most enzymes that require NAD are oxidoreductases (dehydrogenases).

NAD catalyzes a diverse array of reactions, such as the conversion of alcohols and polyols to aldehydes or ketones. The most common mechanisms involve the sterospecific abstraction of a hydride ion [H: (-)] from the substrate with its subsequent transfer. It is of interest that cells generally delegate NAD to enzymes in catabolic

TABLE 10.2
Stability of Water-Soluble Vitamins

Vitamin	Effect of pH			Oxygen	UV Light	Heat
	Acid	Neutral	Alkaline			
Ascorbic Acid	S	U	U	U	U	U
Biotin	S	S	U	S	S	S
Cobalamin (B-12)	S	S	S	U	U	S
Folic acid	S	U	U	U	U	U
Niacin	S	S	S	S	S	S
Pantothenic acid	U	S	U	S	S	U
Pyridoxine (B-6)	S	S	S	S	U	U
Riboflavin (B-2)	S	S	U	S	U	S
Thiamin (B-1)	S	S	U	U	S	U

S=Stable, U=Unstable.

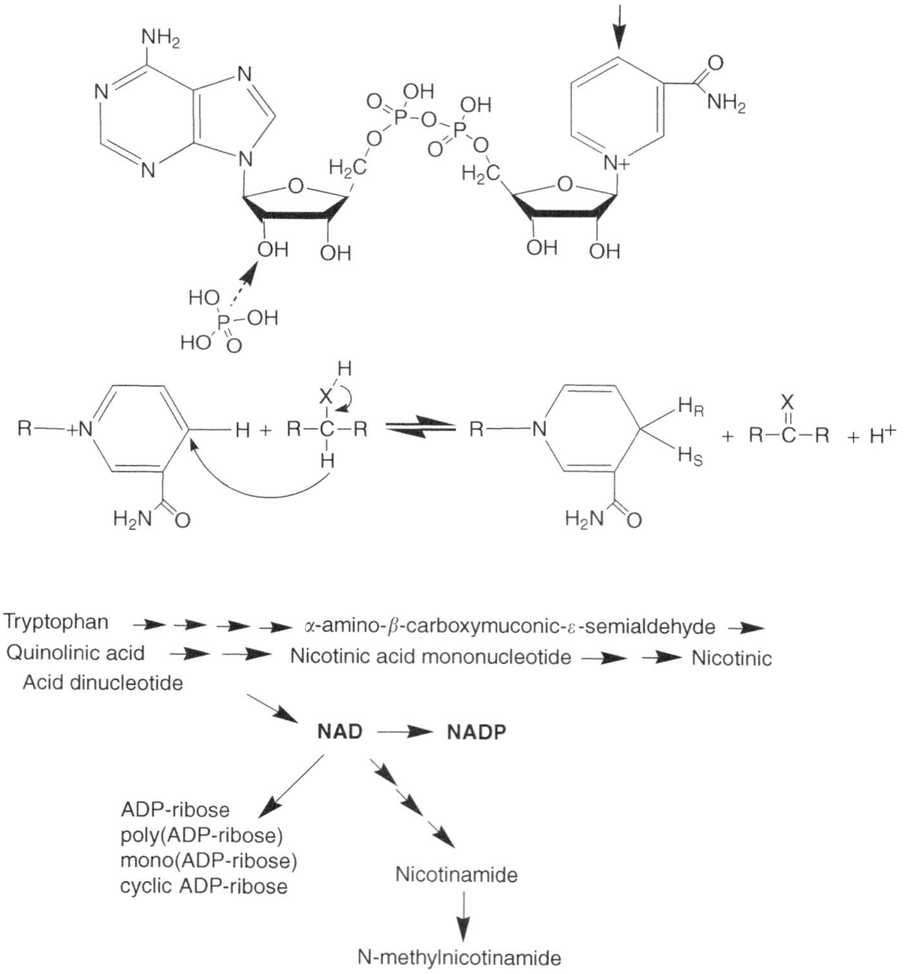

FIGURE 10.2   NAD and NADP. The structures for NAD and NADP (via ATP-derived phosphate addition to NAD, cf. dashed arrow) and their site of hydrogen transfer (solid arrow) are indicated along with a mechanism of hydrogen transfer. The HR and HS designations are shown to indicate that the transfer occurs with stereospecificity. NAD and NADP are products of tryptophan degradation through the quinolate portion of the tryptophan degradation pathway. In addition to acting as a reductant, NAD is precursor to ribosylations and cyclic ribosylated products that are important to cellular regulation.

pathways, whereas NADP is utilized in synthetic pathways. An additional and equally important function of NAD is its role as a substrate in poly- and monoribosylation reactions. Mono and polyribosylation post-translational chemical modifications are important in many cellular regulatory functions (see next section).

2. Absorption, Tissue Distribution, and Metabolism

Transporters for niacin uptake have been identified, but are not as well characterized as some of the other vitamin transporters. As noted, NAD may be derived from tryptophan through the so-called quinolinate pathway (Figure 10.1). About half the niacin as NAD or NADP is associated with enzymes; the remainder is available as a substrate for mono- and polyribosylation reactions that are important in the regulation of a broad range of enzymes. In the nuclei of cells, polyribosylation of specific histones precedes the normal process of DNA repair. When niacin is in excess, most mammals convert it to N-methylnicotinamide, which has a low renal threshold and is excreted (6).

3. Requirements, Toxicity, and Pharmacology

Niacin is needed in amounts corresponding to 14 to 16 mg per day or 4–6 mg per 1000 kcal or 4 MJ of diet (4; Table 10.1). Niacin requirements are often expressed as equivalents, where one equivalent corresponds to 1 mg of niacin. The conversion of tryptophan to niacin produces about 1 mg or equivalent of niacin for every 60 mg of tryptophan degraded (Figure 10.2).

There are a number of therapeutic uses for pharmacologic doses of niacin-derived compounds, when increased blood flow is desirable. Nicotinic acid can cause vasodilatation when consumed in amounts of 100 mg or more. Niacin in gram quantities is an effective lipid-lowering agent (increases HDL). However, in some individuals, flushing, gastric irritation, and other similar side effects caused by pharmacologic doses of nicotinic acid or niacin may preclude use (6).

4. Food Sources and Stability

Niacin is found in high levels in animal tissues (chicken, fish, beef – especially liver), and peanuts, and in moderate amounts in whole grains such as wheat and barley, enriched cereal products, mushrooms, and some vegetables such as corn and peas. Niacin is very stable in a variety of conditions. Indeed some treatments such as moderate heat and alkali treatment of corn can result in greater niacin availability (Table 10.2). An excess of water used in cooking and processing of foods can result in leaching of the vitamin, as is similar for all water-soluble vitamins (4).

B. RIBOFLAVIN

Riboflavin was one of the first of the B vitamins identified (10). Originally, it was thought to be the heat stable factor responsible for the prevention of pellagra. Riboflavin is present in tissue and cells as FAD (flavin adenine dinucleotide) and FMN (flavin adenine mononucleotide). FAD and FMN are cofactors in aerobic processes, usually as cofactors for oxidases, although FAD can also function in anaerobic environments as a dehydrogenase cofactor.

1. Chemistry

Flavins, such as riboflavin derivatives (Figure 10.3), are ideally suited to catalyze one electron, one-proton transfer reactions. Oxygen is often utilized as a co-substrate in the redox reactions catalyzed by FAD- and FMN-containing enzymes. Carbon-carbon double bond formation and redox of sulfur-containing compounds, e.g., lipoic acid, are catalyzed also by flavoproteins. NADP(H) + H$^+$ commonly serves as a reductant in processes to regenerate FAD and FMN. Riboflavin has a number of designations, some of which are still in use (vitamin B-2, vitamin G, ovoflavin, uroflavin, lactoflavin, heptoflavin).

Riboflavin was separated and identified from other B vitamins, because it is heat stable, but light instable and fluorescent. The chemical name for riboflavin is 6,7-dimethyl-9-(d-1'-ribityl) isoalloxazine. Deviations in structure can markedly affect activity (10). For example, the polyol side-chain must be in the D-form and substitution in other positions causes loss of activity or gives rise to compounds that have inhibitory activity, e.g., 5,6-dimethyl (isoriboflavin).

2. Absorption, Tissue Distribution, and Metabolism

Like most water-soluble vitamins, riboflavin is absorbed in the proximal part of the small intestine by a carrier-mediated process. Riboflavin is not particularly soluble. There are upper limits to riboflavin's availability, which are dictated in part by solubility. In this regard, an important chemical characteristic that is attributed to the ribose moiety is improved water solubility. Isoalloxazines are not particularly water-soluble.

Intestinal riboflavin uptake is adaptively regulated by dietary levels, and by specific intracellular protein kinase-mediated regulatory pathways. Over-supplementation with pharmacological amounts of riboflavin can lead to a significant and specific down-regulation in riboflavin uptake; riboflavin deficiency causes a significant and specific up-regulation in intestinal riboflavin uptake. Factors that have been shown to interfere with the normal intestinal riboflavin uptake process include alcohol and certain tricyclic drugs (e.g., chlorpromazine).

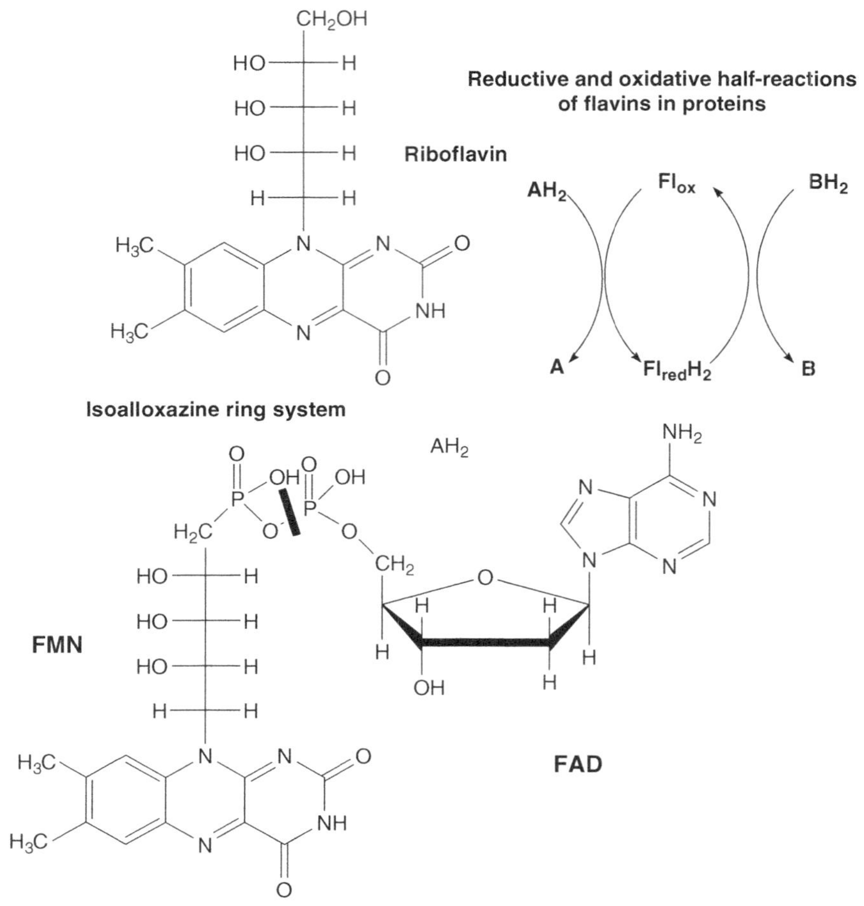

FIGURE 10.3 Riboflavin, FMN, and FAD. When associated with flavoproteins, the reductive and oxidative half-reactions for FMN and FAD occur wherein the nitrogens at positions 1 and 5 are involved. Redox of the isoalloxazine ring involves the following transition: $-N^1H\text{-}C\text{=}C\text{-}N^5H\text{-} \leftrightarrow -N^1\text{=}C\text{-}C\text{=}N^5\text{-}$.

Transport to tissues can be perturbed by boric acid and certain drugs, e.g., theophylline and penicillin, which displace riboflavin (or FMN) from known binding proteins (e.g., albumin > globulins > fibrinogen).

Once in cells, riboflavin is phosphorylated to FMN. In most cells about 20% of the riboflavin is present as FMN and of the remainder, over 70% is present as FAD with 1 or 2% as free riboflavin. Urine is the major route of excretion for riboflavin, although some FMN is excreted in bile (10 and refs. cited therein).

3. Metabolism and Requirements

The requirements for riboflavin, 1.1 to 1.3 mg/day, are lower than those for niacin or ascorbic acid because riboflavin is tightly associated with the enzymes that serve as a cofactor, and accordingly turns over much slower than niacin or ascorbic acid (Table 10.1; 4). In some cases, FMN is covalently bound (e.g., as in succinic dehydrogenase). Riboflavin is not toxic, primarily because of its regulated uptake at the intestinal level, and its relatively low solubility compared to other B-vitamins.

In humans, signs of riboflavin deficiency include lesions of the oral cavity, the lips, and the angle of the mouth (cheilosis), inflammation of the tongue (glossitis) and accompanying seborrhic dermatitis. Like other severe B-vitamin deficiencies, the filiform papillae of the tongue may also be lost with changes in color from pink to magenta. Anemia and increased vascularization of the eye are present in some animals with riboflavin deficiency.

4. Food Sources and Stability

The best sources of riboflavin are milk and dairy products. Other good sources are meats, especially liver, eggs, dark green leafy vegetables, and fortified breakfast cereals (4). Today, milk and breakfast cereals make the greatest contributions to riboflavin intake in the U.S. and the U.K. Riboflavin is stable to acid pH, heat, and oxygen, but is very susceptible to destruction by light, resulting in the inactive compounds lumiflavin and lumichrome (Table 10.2; 13). These compounds and other oxidative products can contribute to off-flavors due to oxidative damage to milk lipids. Milk exposed to visible spectrum light will lose 50% of its riboflavin content after two hours, thus the importance of packaging milk in opaque containers.

IV. B-VITAMINS IMPORTANT TO SPECIFIC FEATURES OF CARBOHYDRATE, PROTEIN, OR LIPID METABOLISM

A. THIAMIN

Studies on thiamin played an important role in the development of early concepts on the function and importance of vitamins. For example, the demonstration by the Dutch medical officer, Christian Eijkman, that polyneuritis could be produced in an experiment animal by dietary manipulation was conceptually very important. Eijkman and his colleagues fed a diet of polished rice, presumably low in thiamin, to chickens (one of the first uses of an animal model to study disease) and observed characteristic features of beriberi, such as head retraction, a common neurological sign in animals. The focus on rice and the observation that there appeared to be a curative principle in rice bran led to the eventual isolation of thiamin. This sequence of events and experimental protocols provided the underpinnings that led to the discovery of vitamins as precursors to cofactors (19).

1. Chemistry

The five-member (thiazole) ring of thiamin contains an arrangement of atoms (-N=CH-S-) called an *ylid*. The central carbon has carbanion character that acts as an electron-rich center for reactions that are commonly characterized as decarboxylations and transketolations (Figure 10.4). Thiamin is not stable to heat or alkali.

2. Absorption, Tissue Distribution, and Metabolism

Thiamin occurs in the human body as free thiamin and its mono-, di-, and triphosphorylated forms: thiamin monophosphate, thiamin pyrophosphate (TPP), which is designated as thiamin diphosphate, and thiamin triphosphate (TTP), which is found mostly in neural tissue. TPP and TTP are the cofactor forms of thiamine.

Thiamin is essential to the utilization of carbohydrates as energy sources, because of roles in TCA cycle regulation, and perturbations in the pentose phosphate – related carbohydrates pathways. In the TCA cycle, the principle enzymes are pyruvate dehydrogenase and α-ketoglutarate dehydrogenase. These enzymes catalyze the decarboxylations of pyruvate and α-ketoglutarate. TPP is also a cofactor for transketolase reactions. Transketolation is a central activity in the metabolic sequence known as the pentose phosphate pathway. One of the most important intermediates of this pathway is ribose-5-phosphate, a phosphorylated 5-carbon sugar, required for the synthesis of the high-energy ribonucleotides, ATP, GTP, the nucleic acids, DNA and RNA, and the niacin-containing coenzyme NADPH, which is essential for a number of biosynthetic reactions. A deficiency of thiamin can lead to decreased production of NADPH, which impacts synthetic processes, such as fatty acid biosynthesis. In addition, it is evident from the neurological disorders caused by thiamine deficiency that thiamin plays a vital role in nerve function. In the brain, TTP is proposed to function in ion transport. The concentration of thiamin in the brain is resistant to changes in dietary concentration. Stimulation of nerves results in the release of thiamine monophosphate and free thiamine with accompanying decrease of cellular thiamine pyrophosphate and thiamine triphosphate and changes in Na^+ and K^+ gradients (19).

Human thiamin deficiency, beriberi, is termed dry, wet, or cerebral, depending on the systems that involved. The main feature of dry (paralytic or nervous) beriberi is peripheral neuropathy, including abnormal (exaggerated) reflexes, diminished sensation, and weakness in the legs and arms. Muscle pain and tenderness are also features. When cardiovascular manifestations occur, the term wet beriberi is used. Signs include a rapid heart rate, cardiac enlargement, and edema. Ultimately, congestive heart failure may be the cause of death. Cerebral beriberi can lead to Wernicke's encephalopathy and Korsakoff's psychosis. Signs include abnormal eye movements, stance and gait abnormalities, and abnormalities in mental function, e.g., confusion (19).

3. Requirements, Pharmacology, and Toxicity

The requirement for thiamin is 1.1 to 1.2 mg per day or 0.5 mg per 1000 kcal or 4 MJ of diet (4; Table 10.1). Factors that influence requirements are inadequate intake, strenuous physical exertion, fever, pregnancy, breastfeeding, and adolescent growth, or exposure to antagonists, such as tannins, alcohol (sufficient to cause inflammatory bowel conditions), and thiaminases, enzymes in many foods, particular mollusks, and the muscle of fish. Individuals who habitually eat raw freshwater fish, raw shellfish, and ferns are at higher risk of thiamin deficiency because these foods contain a thiaminase. For example, an acute neurological syndrome (seasonal ataxia) in Nigeria has even been associated with thiamin deficiency precipitated by a thiaminase in African silkworms, a traditional high-protein food for some Nigerians.

Antagonists include pyrithiamine and oxythiamine, which act to inhibit the phosphorylation of thiamin. Amprolium (coccidiostat) inhibits thiamin absorption.

4. Food Sources and Stability

Thiamin is present in most animal and plant foods, but is especially prominent in whole grains, organ meats, pork,

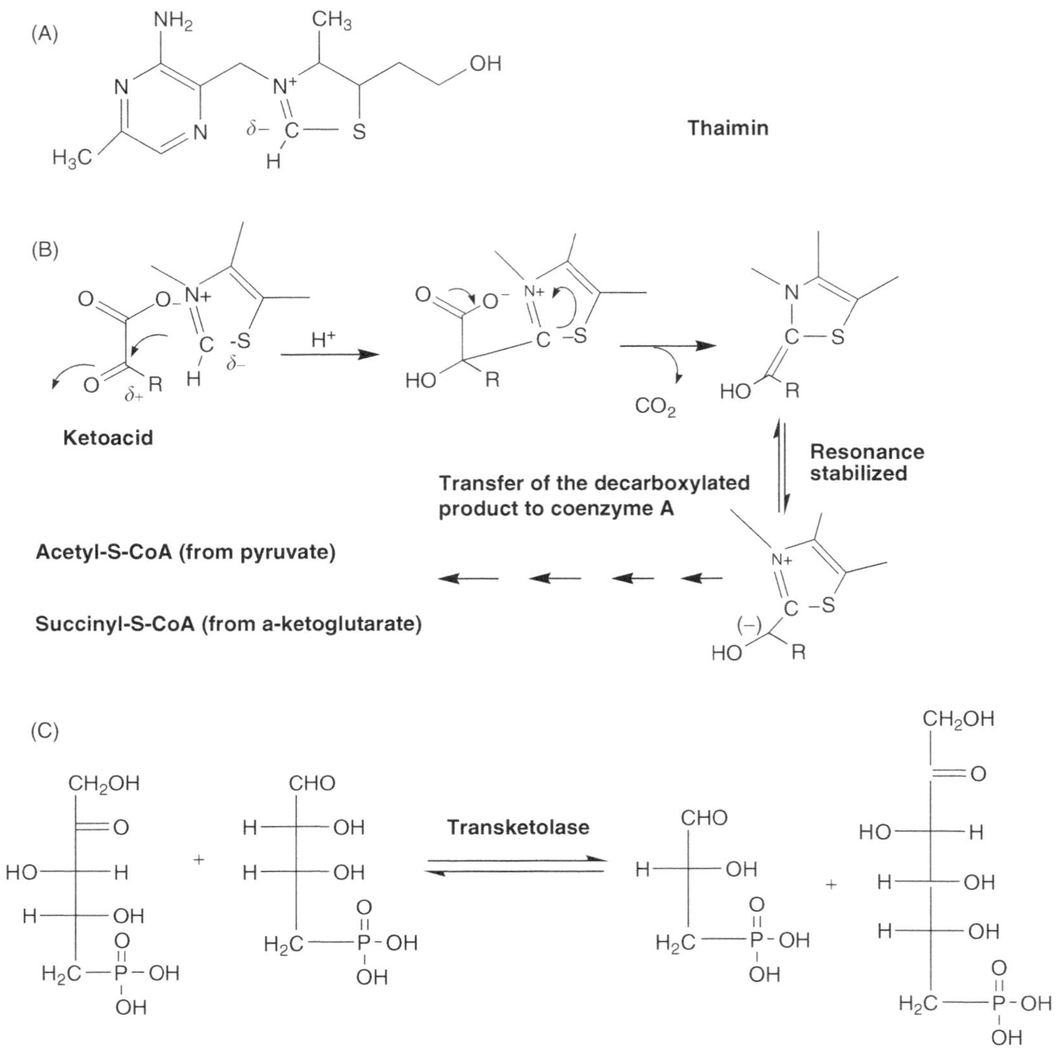

FIGURE 10.4   Thiamin. The carbanion character of thiamin [A] facilitates the non-oxidative and oxidative decarboxylation of α-ketoacids [B] and transketolase reactions [C].

eggs, nuts, and legumes. Many food cooking and processing conditions will negatively affect thiamin content, as it is unstable in neutral and alkaline conditions, and with heat, oxygen, and sulfur exposure (Table 10.2). Milling of whole grains will remove the bran where thiamin and other B vitamins are in greatest concentrations; however, the current practice of fortification has restored thiamin levels in flours and grain-based products (13).

B.   PANTOTHENIC ACID

Roger William discovered pantothenic acid in 1933, and observed that it was an essential growth factor for yeast and lactic acid bacteria. Over the next 15 years, pantothenic acid was shown to be essential in animals. Pantothenic acid serves as a component of coenzyme A (Figure 10.5) and as a part of phosphopantotheine, e.g., at the acyl carrier site in acyl carrier protein (ACP) (18). Recently, pantothenic acid has been shown to be present

in a number of other enzymes where thioesters facilitated transfer reactions are essential (5).

1.   Absorption, Tissue Distribution, and Metabolism

Both Coenzyme A (CoASH) and ACP are present in foods. Consequently, absorbed pantothenic acid must first be released from CoASH and ACP, steps that involve the actions of peptidases and nucleosidases. The mechanism of absorption of pantothenic acid in the small intestine involves the same carrier-mediated Na^+-dependent system that transports biotin (15). Similarly, colonic absorption of pantothenic acid was found to involve the biotin-Na^+-dependent, carrier-mediated system. The interaction between biotin and pantothenic acid transport has also been described in other tissues such as the blood brain barrier, the heart, and the placenta, but the importance of this interaction is not understood.

2. Metabolic Functions and Requirements

CoASH is the principle moiety for the vectoral transport of acyl and acetyl groups in synthetic and catabolic reactions. A deficiency is characterized by impaired acetyl and acyl metabolism. The ability to utilize fatty acids as fuels is clearly compromised in experimental pantothenic acid deficiency. There is also an increased production of short chain fatty acids and ketone bodies, which can lead to severe metabolic acidosis. Dermal lesions occur because of impaired fatty acid metabolism. Selected aspects of pantothenic acid utilization and CoASH regulation are given in Figure 10.5.

The requirement for pantothenic acid is about 5 mg per day or 2 mg per 1000 kcal (~4 MJ) of diet. Even at gram intakes, pantothenic acid does not appear to be toxic (4).

3. Food Sources and Stability

Good dietary sources of pantothenic acid are meats, organ meats, eggs, nuts and legumes, cereals and some vegetables such as broccoli. The vitamin is stable in neutral pH, but unstable outside of this range, and also susceptible to degradation by heat treatment.

C. PYRIDOXINE

Pyridoxine or vitamin B-6 is a collective term for pyridoxine, pyridoxal, and pyridoxyl amine. Pyridoxine is most abundant in plants; pyridoxal and pyridoxyl amine are most abundant in animal tissues. The active form of vitamin B-6 is phosphorylated at the 5 position, e.g., pyridoxal-5-phosphate (7).

1. Chemistry

The most common of the reactions catalyzed by vitamin B-6 containing enzymes is the transaminase reaction. Transaminations are essential to the interconverson of amino acids to corresponding α-keto acids. The mechanism is also useful for reactions important to producing racemic amino acid mixtures (e.g., the conversion of L-alanine to D-alanine) and α, β–addition or elimination reactions. An example of an α, β–elimination reaction is the conversion of serine to pyruvic acid or the conversion of homocysteine plus serine to cystathionine. The basic feature of the transamination mechanism is electron withdrawal from the α-carbon resulting in a proton liberation, which sets the stage for subsequent substitution and additional reactions (Figure 10.6; 7).

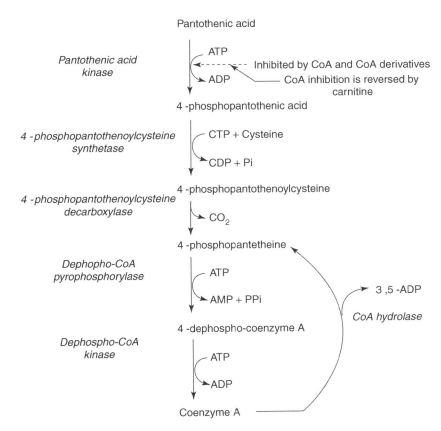

FIGURE 10.5 Synthesis of Coenzyme A (CoASH) from pantothenic acid. The synthesis of CoASH from pantothenic acid is regulated in part by feedback inhibition, e.g., by CoA derivatives at the step catalyzed by pantothenic acid kinase. Carnitine also plays a role in regulation.

The second most common reaction involves electron withdrawal from the α-carbon and carboxylic acid group carbon, which results in decarboxylation (Figure 10.6). Decarboxylation reactions include the conversions of tyrosine to tyramine, 5-hydroxytryptophan to serotonin, histidine to histamine, and glutamate to γ–aminobutyric acid (GABA). Signs of convulsions associated with vitamin B-6 deficiency are attributed to insufficient activity of pyridoxal-5″-phosphate-dependent, L-glutamate decarboxylase.

A third type of reaction involves electron withdrawal from the β,γ-carbons of amino acids (Figure 10.6). This sets the stage for hydride condensations or aldol reactions. A good example of an aldol reaction is the conversion of serine to glycine with the transfer of the β-carbon (as formaldehyde) to another vitamin cofactor, tetrahydrofolic acid in single carbon reactions (see the next section). Another example of a hydride condensation is the formation of α-aminolevulinic acid, the first step in heme biosynthesis.

Another important function of vitamin B-6 (as pyridoxal-5′-phosphate), independent of amino acid metabolism, is its role in glycogen phosphorylase. Glycogen phosphorylase catalyzes the hydrolysis of ether (α-1 to 4 C-O-C) bonds in glycogen to form glucose-6-phosphate. Ether bonds are best catalyzed through acid-mediated mechanisms. The acid proton in this instance is derived from the phosphate group of pyridoxal-5′-phosphate. This important mechanism was only elucidated recently. Previously, it was speculated that the association of vitamin B-6 with glycogen phosphorylase was primarily some type of storage mechanism for B-6.

2. Absorption, Tissue Distribution, and Metabolism

Vitamin B-6 is absorbed in the upper gut by energy-dependent pathways. Muscle, kidney, and liver are rich in pyridoxal enzymes, e.g., glycogen phosphorylase (in

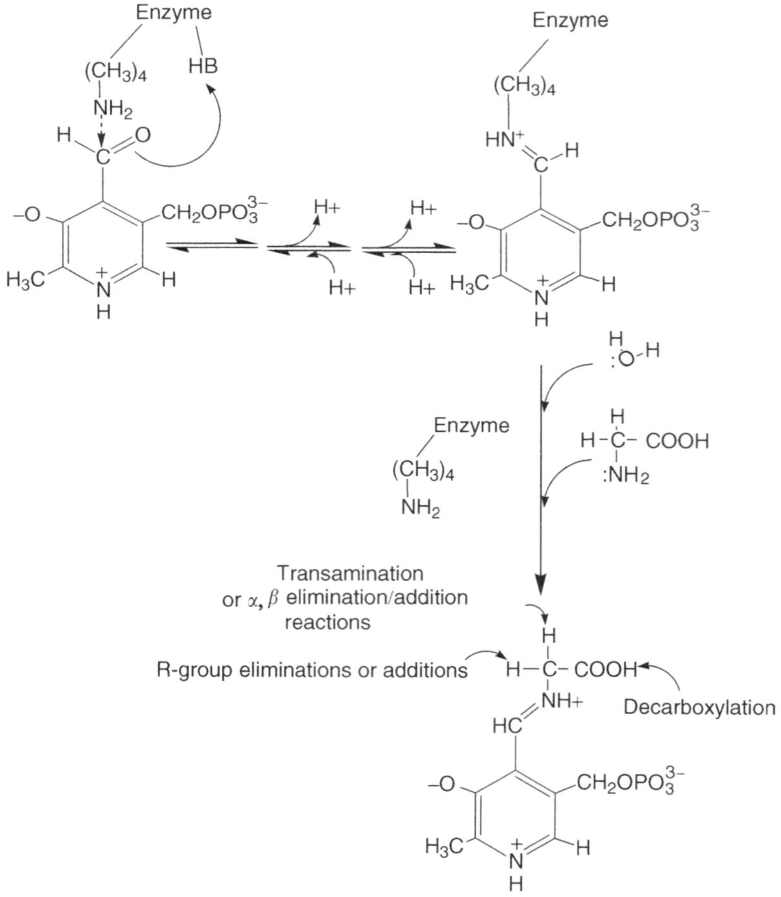

FIGURE 10.6 Pyridoxal-5′-phosphate. Vitamin B-6, as pyridoxal-5′-phosphate, is linked to pyridoxal-5′-phosphate containing enzymes by an dissociable imine linkage with a lysyl residue at the enzyme's active site. By a process of transamination given amino acids are transferred to pyridoxal-5′-phosphate. Depending on the enzyme and nature of the enzymatic process, transamination reactions, α,β-elimination/addition, R-group elimination/addition, or decarboxylation reactions can occur.

muscle) and amino acid catabolizing enzymes and transaminases (in liver and kidney).

The major form of vitamin B-6 in cells is pyridoxal −5′-phosphate. The conversion of the pyridoxal form of the vitamin to pyridoxic acid signals elimination from the body (7 and refs. cited).

3. Requirements, Pharmacology, and Toxicity

Vitamin B-6 deficiency is rarely seen as most diets provide adequate amounts. Normally, the vitamin B-6 is met at 1.3 or more mg per day or about 0.3 mg per 1000 kcal (4MJ) of diet (Table 10.1; 4). Drug-induced vitamin B-6 deficiency can occur following administration of the tuberculostatic drug, isoniazid (isonicotinic acid hydrazide). This drug forms hydrazone derivatives with pyridoxal or pyridoxal phosphate, which can then act to inhibit pyridoxal-containing enzymes. Patients receiving long-term isoniazid therapy respond to the administration of supplemental vitamin B-6. Penicillamine (β-dimethylcysteine) used in the treatment of Wilson's disease also can interfere with normal B-6 metabolism due to the formation of thiazole derivatives. A naturally occurring antagonist to vitamin B-6, linatine (1-amino-D-proline) is present in flax seed, which forms a stable product with pyridoxal phosphate (7).

The most important signs of B-6 deficiency relate to defects in amino acid metabolism. Neurologic signs occur because of reduced synthesis of important biogenic amines from amino acid precursors (7), and anemia is a consequence of decreased heme synthesis. Adverse effects have only been documented from vitamin B-6 supplements and never from food sources. Chronically high doses of pyridoxine can result in painful neurological symptoms known as sensory neuropathy. Symptoms include pain and numbness of the extremities, and in severe cases difficulty walking. Sensory neuropathy typically develops at doses of pyridoxine in excess of 1,000 mg per day. At intakes below 200 mg/day, sensory neuropathy is not observed.

4. Food Sources and Stability

The richest sources of vitamin B-6 are meats and whole grains. Heat and light are the two primary treatments that negatively affect the stability of the vitamin (Table 10.2). Similar to other B vitamins, milling of whole grains and removal of the bran will result in significant losses of pyridoxine. Fortification of cereal products will restore B vitamin levels (4).

V. B-VITAMINS INVOLVED IN SINGLE CARBON AND CO_2 TRANSFER REACTIONS

A. BIOTIN

Biotin was discovered following a long search for factors important to the understanding of the condition, egg white poisoning, which was associated with poor growth, alopecia, and dermatitis in animals exposed to raw eggs and egg whites as a primary source of dietary protein. It was eventually found that biotin-binding factors in eggs could reduce biotin availability (see below).

1. Chemistry

Biotin functions in enzymatic carboxylation reactions as a cofactor for CO_2 − fixing enzymes. Examples include: acetyl CoA carboxylase, which is essential for fatty acid synthesis; propionyl CoA carboxylase, which participates in odd chain fatty acid metabolism; pyruvate carboxylase, which is involved in the formation of oxaloacetate, an important obligatory step in reverse glycolysis and gluconeogenesis; and β-methylcrotonyl CoA, important in leucine metabolism (9).

Biotin is covalently bound in carboxylases and trans-carboxylases by peptidyl linkage between the carboxylic acid moiety of biotin and the ε-amine function of peptidyl lysine (extends from the side chain associated with the sulfur-containing ring of biotin, which is only partially depicted in Figure 10.7). The biotin-lysine adduct is called biocytin. Biocytin can be cleaved by the enzyme biocytinase to generate free biotin.

2. Metabolism and Requirements

Biotin is found in highest concentrations in the liver. In plant foods, biotin is present in relative high concentrations in most cereals. Dietary biotin exists in free and protein bound forms. The latter form is digested first by gastrointestinal proteases and peptidases to generate biocytin (N-biotinyl-L-lysine) and eventually free biotin plus lysine. Like the other water-soluble vitamins, biotin is taken up by specialized Na^+-dependent carrier-mediated mechanisms. At the basolateral membrane, biotin exits cells via a Na^+-dependent carrier system. In adult humans, biotin uptake is significantly higher in the duodenum and jejunum compared to ileum. As noted previously, biotin shares the transporter with pantothenic acid (15, 18).

When biotin-containing carboxylases are degraded in cells, biotin is also released as biocytin. Cellular biocytinases catalyze its cleavage to release free biotin for reutilization. In the absence of this enzyme, biotin reutilization is compromised. Re-biotinylation requires ATP to catalyze the formation of a peptide bond between biotin and a lysyl group at the active center of targeted carboxylases (9).

The nutrition need for biotin is expressed as an "Adequate Intake" and amounts to ~25 micrograms per day (Table 10.1; 4). Reasons for the relatively lower requirements are: biotin is covalently attached to a limited number of enzymes that it serves as a cofactor; biotin is extensively reutilized; significant amounts of biotin are produced by the gut microflora.

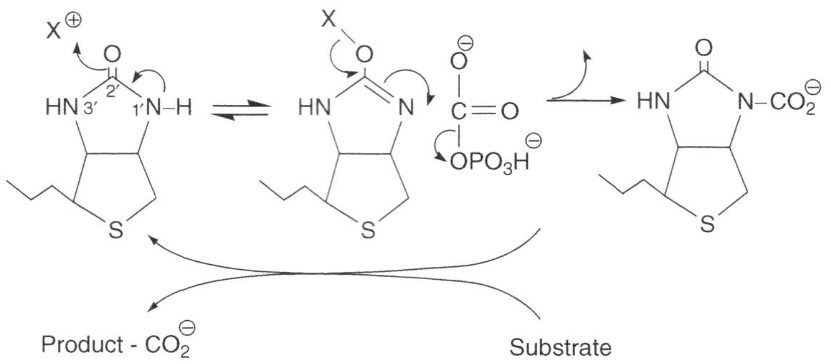

FIGURE 10.7   Biotin.

Nevertheless, nutritional problems associated with biotin status can occur. Biotin and biocytin have a high affinity for certain proteins, particularly avidin in egg white. The consumption of raw egg albumin can induce biotin deficiency, due to the strong association of biotin with avidin rendering dietary biotin unavailable. Ingestion of significant quantities of raw egg white by fur-bearing animals and pigs has led to the condition initially described as "egg white injury."

Biotin deficiency leads to impairment of gluconeogenesis and fat metabolism. Biotin deficiencies can also induce severe metabolic acidosis. The inability to carry out fat metabolism, also markedly affects the dermis. Alopecia and dermatitis are characteristics of biotin deficiency in most animals (9).

3.   Food Sources and Stability

Biotin in animal foods is found in highest concentrations in the liver, but also in meats, milk, and egg yolk. In plant food, biotin is present in relative high concentrations in most cereal grains, as well as nuts, mushrooms, and some green vegetables. It is relatively stable to most treatments, with the exception of heat and alkaline conditions, which result in minor losses.

B.   Folic Acid and Vitamin B-12

Vitamin B-12 and folic acid will be discussed together, because their functions and metabolism are uniquely linked (Figure 10.8). Knowledge regarding folic acid and B-12 evolved from efforts to better understand macrocytic anemias and certain degenerative neurologic disorders (8). The Scottish physician, Combe, recognized in the early 1800s that certain forms of macrocytic anemia appeared related to a disorder of the digestive organs. In classic studies by Minot, Murphy, Castle, and others, it became clearer that the disorder was associated with gastric secretions and in some cases could be reversed by consuming raw or lightly cooked liver.

In parallel studies, folic acid was also associated with macrocytic anemia. Large-scale efforts throughout the 1940s and 1950s and careful clinical and basic studies eventually led to the isolation of folic acid and vitamin B-12.

1.   Chemistry Folic Acid

The folates are a group of heterocyclic compounds composed of 4-(pteridin-6-ylmethyl)-aminobenzoic acid conjugated with one or more L-glutamate units. Folate and folic acid are the preferred synonyms for pteroylglutamate and pteroylglutamic acid, respectively, and designate any members of the family of pteroylglutamates having various levels of reduction of the pteridine ring, one-carbon substitutions, and differing numbers of glutamate residues (Figure 10.8; 2).

The reactions that involve folic acid include the generation and utilization of formaldehyde, formimino, and methyl groups. For these conversions to occur, folic acid must be reduced in the form of tetrahydrofolic acid (THFA). Reduction brings the nitrogen at positions 5 and 10 closer together and changes their electrochemical properties, which facilitates the formation of the various THFA single carbon derivatives.

The formyl, methanyl, and methylene forms of THFA are utilized for purine synthesis and in thymidylate (i.e., DNA-related) synthesis. These reactions are essential to cell division and proliferation. Folate also participates in reactions involved in the interconversion and catabolism of amino acids. Much of the folate in the body is also in the form of methyl-THFA for eventual methyl transfer reactions. Removal of the methyl group from methyl-THFA and its eventual irreversible transfer to methionine by the vitamin B-12 requiring enzyme, methionine synthetase, represents an important interaction between folic acid and vitamin B-12 (1, 2).

2.   Chemistry: Vitamin B-12

Vitamin B-12 consists of a porphyrin-like structure of tetrapyrrole rings with a monovalent cobalt metal at the center (Figure 10.9; 1). A 5′,6′-dimethylbenzimidazolyl nucleotide is also linked to the tetrapyrrole rings via a phosphate sugar linkage. Vitamin B-12 catalyzes the

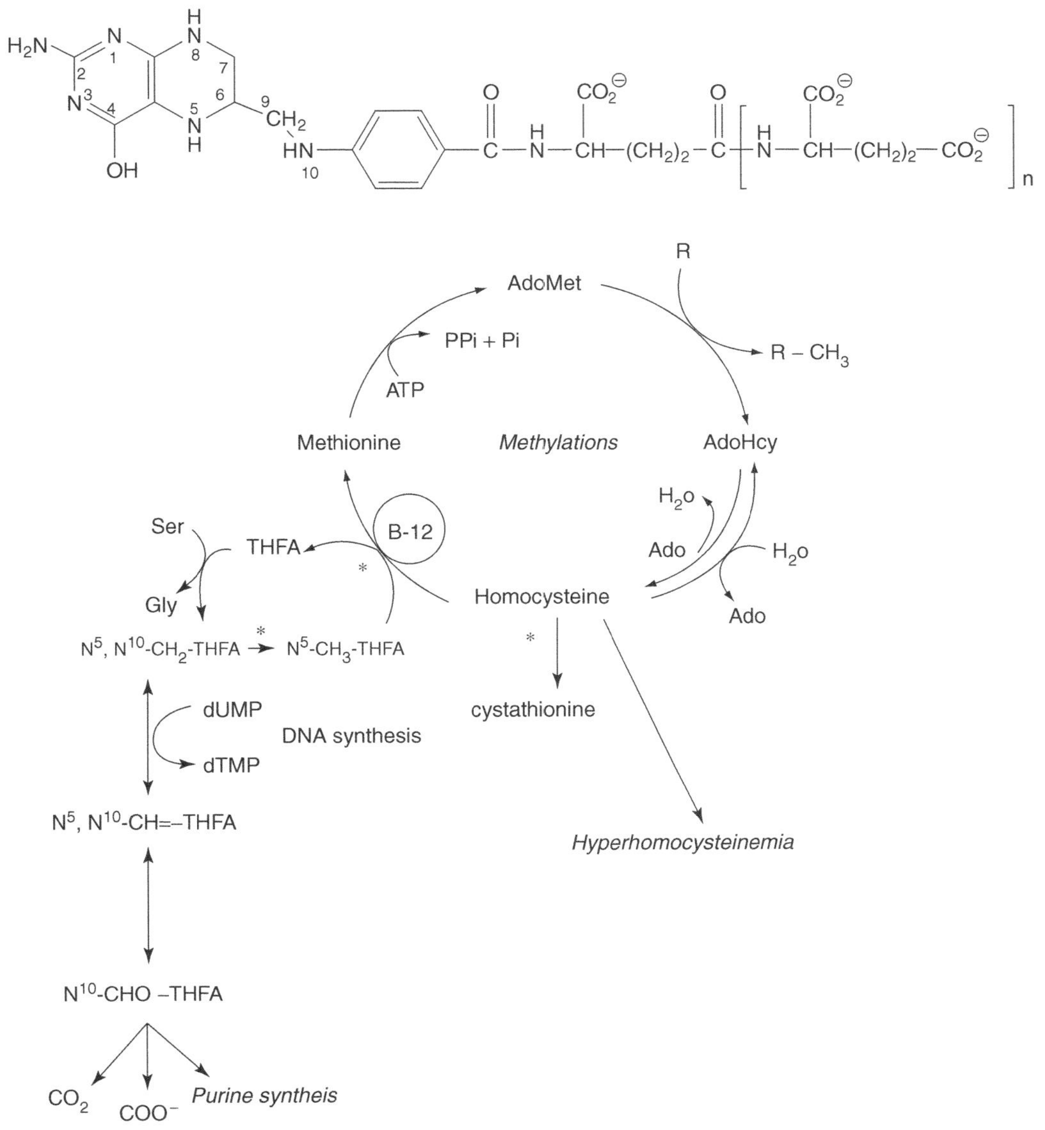

FIGURE 10.8 Folic acid. Basic features of the folic acid structure are shown. Folate is essential to: 1) methylation reactions (via the vitamin B-12-dependent methionine synthetase step), 2) DNA synthesis (via single carbon transfer from N^5, N^{10}-methylene-THFA in the conversion deoxyuridylate to deoxythymidylate), 3) purine synthesis (via transfer of a single carbon from N^{10}-formyl-THFA into the purine pathway). Not shown are reduction steps that result in the regeneration of THFA (at positions 5 and 8) from oxidized folic acid.

conversion of homocysteine to methionine via transfer of a methyl moiety derived from methyl-THFA. Vitamin B-12 in the form of the adenosyl derivative can also catalyze the conversion of methylmalonyl CoA to succinyl CoA. Deficiency of vitamin B-12 leads to intracellular accumulation of metabolites of these two reactions, homocysteine and methylmalonic acid (1, 2, 8, 13, 16).

3. Digestion, Metabolism, and Tissue Distribution

Folate absorption requires processing of food-derived folates from poly- to monoglutamyl forms. The proximal part of the small intestine is the main site of absorption of dietary folate. A specialized carrier-mediated system is involved in folate uptake across the apical membrane of the absorptive cells, as well as other cells. The factors that negatively affect intestinal folate absorption are alcohol consumption and the use of certain pharmacological agents like sulfasalazine and phenytoin (Dilantin). An important step in the digestive process is the conversion of polyglutamyl folate to monoglutamyl folate by intestinal polyglutamyl hydrolase.

There are a number of substances in unprocessed foods (e.g., uncooked beans) that act as folate hydrolase inhibitors. In plasma, there are specific carrier proteins, which take folic acid to targeted cells. In this regard,

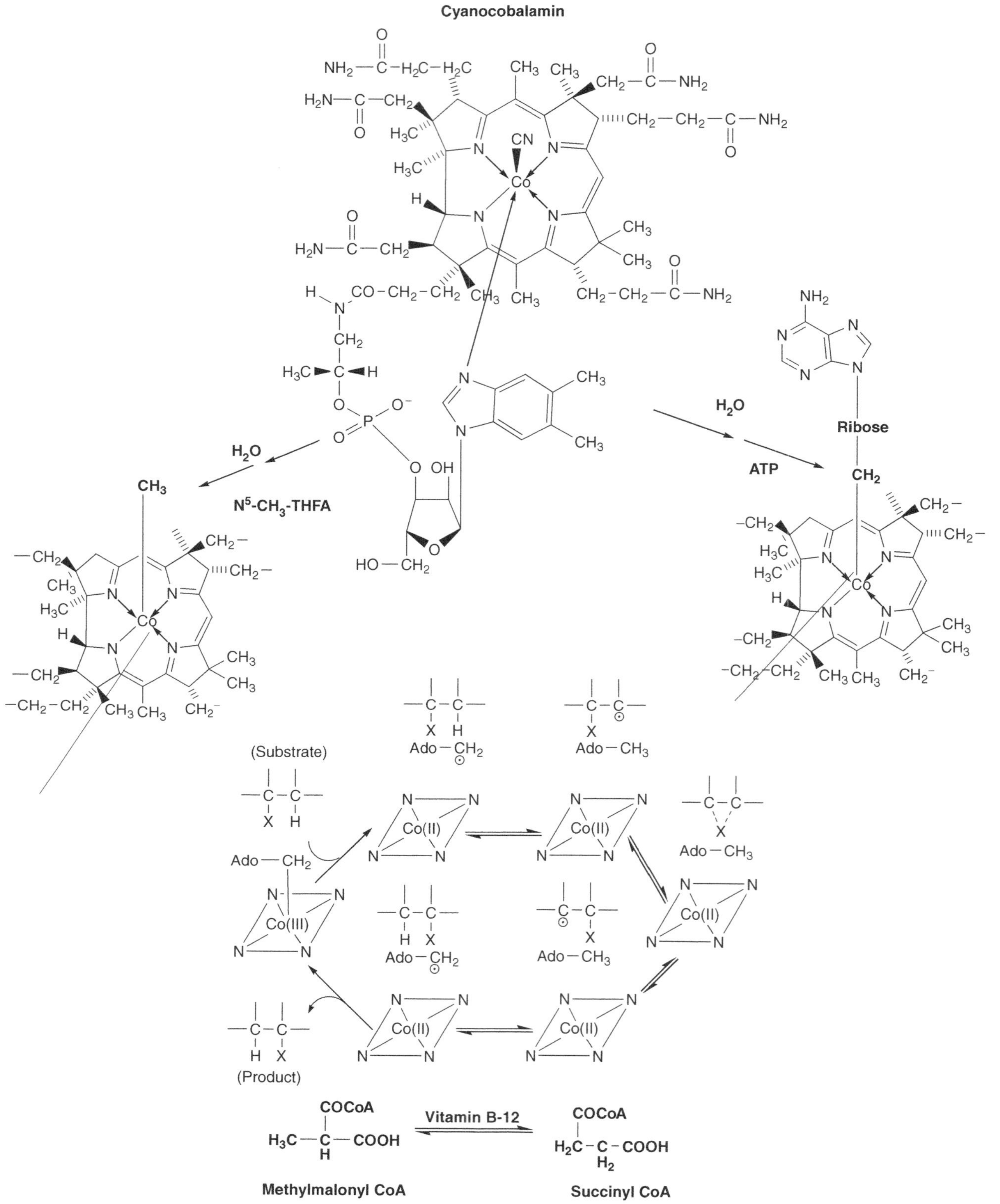

FIGURE 10.9 Cyanocobalamin. Commercial preparations of vitamin B-12 usually have a cyano group coordinated with the cobalt (associated with the corrin ring of vitamin B-12). In an aqueous environment the cyano group can be displaced by water for the eventual transfer of a methyl group (donated by N5-methyl-THFA) or an adenosyl moiety (from ATP). Methylated vitamin B-12 serves as a cofactor for methionine synthetase (see Figure 10.7). Adenosylated vitamin B-12 serves as a cofactor for unusual isomerase reactions, such as the conversion of methylmalonyl CoA to succinyl CoA. A mechanism for this process is shown, which involves the redox of cobalt in the corrin ring of cobalamin (Co+3«Co+2).

ethanol can also markedly decrease folate biliary secretion, thereby reducing availability to body tissues from liver. In tissues, the distribution of folates is largely dependent on the concentration of folate dependent enzymes. Methyl-THFA mono glutamate is rapidly transported (bound to carrier proteins) to liver. Uptake proceeds through a receptor-mediated endocytotic process and is then quickly converted to folate in various polyglutamyl forms (2).

Steps important to processing of vitamin B-12 involve first release from foods under acidic conditions. Vitamin B-12 then binds to proteins produced by cells of the gastric fundus, pancreas, and salivary gland. Two proteins have been identified, which are designated as R protein and intrinsic factor. Vitamin B-12 first binds to R protein and is released in the intestinal lumen by the action of pancreatic and intestinal proteinases and peptidases, to allow vitamin B-12 to bind to intrinsic factor. Intrinsic factor is a small-molecular-weight glycoprotein, which is made in stomach parietal cells (1). The vitamin B-12 – intrinsic factor complex then interacts with receptors on the intestinal brush border localized in the midgut (i.e., ileum). Interference with R protein or intrinsic factor production, or inflammatory disease affecting the ileum, or overproduction of intestinal microflora can adversely affect the availability of vitamin B-12 (1).

After vitamin B-12 is taken up by luminal cells, it is transported into the lysosomes where the vitamin B-12 – intrinsic factor complex is degraded and the vitamin B-12 is released and vectorally directed for release into plasma. Vitamin B-12 is transported in plasma by one of three specific transport proteins, transcobalmin I, II, or III. Transcobalmin I carries vitamin B-12 to the liver. Transcobalmin II carries vitamin B-12 from the liver to peripheral tissues. Note that the processing of folate and vitamin B-12 in and out of tissues differs from that for other water-soluble vitamins. The process is receptor mediated and endocytotic, in contrast to involvement of an active sodium-dependent transporter (1).

4. Requirements, Pharmacology, and Toxicity

Decreased production of methanyl and methylene forms of folate can result in decreased purine synthesis and thymidylate formation from uridylate. The latter can cause replicating cells to arrest in the S-phase of the cell cycle. Epithelial cells are often most affected by folate deficiency (2, 8). The consequences range from megaloblastic anemia to growth retardation. Accordingly, aggressive supplementation of folic acid has been associated with a decrease in the appearance of certain developmental defects, e.g., abnormal neutral tube closure (2, 11, 13, 16).

As noted, the most important link between folate and vitamin B-12 occurs at the methionine synthetase step, where 5-methyl THFA serves as a substrate with homocysteine to form methionine. In this regard, recent studies have suggested that low folate levels may play a role in the etiology of coronary artery disease because of the association of elevated homocysteine as a risk factor in vascular disease (8).

The movement of single carbon units from folate through methionine synthetase in the formation of methionine is also important for S-adenosylmethionine (SAM) formation. SAM is essential to methylation of phospholipids, and production of methylated forms of various amino acids and carbohydrates. SAM also serves as the methyl source in DNA methylation.

Deficiencies of both vitamin B-12 and folic acid produce clinical signs of macrocytic anemia and disynchronies in growth and development owing to the importance of folic acid to purine and DNA synthesis. Chronic deficiencies of either folic acid or B-12 can also promote fatty liver disease and indirectly influence extracellular matrix maturation stability by causing abnormal elevations in homocysteine (1, 2, 8, 11, 13, 16). Such signs and symptoms are attributable to both THFA and B-12 deficiencies, because of the integral relationship of vitamin B-12 to THFA regeneration. Dietary intakes of folic acid, sufficient to maintain functional THFA levels, can mask the initial signs of vitamin B-12 deficiency (e.g., macrocytic and megaloblastic anemia). Prolonged vitamin B-12 deficiency in humans results in serious neurologic disorders due to degeneration of the myelin sheath (1).

The requirement for folic acid is 400 μg per day (Table 10.1; 4). However, there are some conditions in which the folic acid requirements are conditionally high, e.g., when either natural or pharmacological folic acid agonists are present in the diet. A range of genetic polymorphisms in proteins important to folate metabolism can also influence the folic acid requirement. Alterations in folate hydrolase, folate reductase, or methionine synthetase that cause changes in the affinity for folate binding are all known to impact folate requirements (2).

The requirement for vitamin B-12 is 2.4 μg per day or 1 μg per 1000 kcal (~4 MJ) of diet (Table 10.1; 4). Although vitamin B-12 deficiency is rare, disease of the stomach, proximal duodenum, or ileum and pancreatic insufficiency can affect folic acid and vitamin B-12 absorption, respectively.

5. Food Sources and Stability

Folic acid: Foods that are particularly high in folate are oranges, green leafy vegetables, and whole grains. Fortification with folic acid to all enriched cereal grain foods was begun in the U.S. in 1998 by mandate of the Food and Drug Administration (11). The primary objective of this program was to provide increased folic acid to women of childbearing age in order to decrease the occurrence of neural tube defects (NTD). The fortification program has successfully decreased NTDs by 19%, but any longer term health benefits on other diseases is unknown at this time. Folic acid is stable in acid pH, but is rapidly destroyed in neutral or alkaline conditions and is unstable to prolonged heat, oxygen, and light exposure.

Dietary sources of B-12 are meats with liver being the highest followed by dairy products and some seafoods (1, 2, 4). B-12 is also present in yeast and fortified cereals. The reliance on primarily animal products for vitamin B-12 means that strict vegetarians are potentially at risk for B-12 deficiency. B-12 is relatively stable and destroyed only by extended heat treatments and exposure to light and oxygen (Table 10.2).

VI. CONCLUDING COMMENTS

Additional compounds, mostly derived from carbohydrate and amino acid metabolites, are listed with the vitamins, because of conditional dietary needs or functions in metabolic regulation. Many of these compounds typically perform specialized transport function, particularly in relation to fatty acids. Examples include choline (a major source of methyl groups in the diet), inositol (important in signal transduction), and carnitine (required for the transportation of fatty acids from the cytosol into the mitochondria). Taurine, queuine, the ubiquinones (coenzyme Q), the tetrahydrobiopterins, pyrroloquinoline quinone (17), and lipoic acid could also be added to the list, because of their novel roles in metabolism.

Regarding the need for vitamins, acute deficiencies for most water-soluble vitamins can be induced under experimental conditions. Frank deficiency diseases are rarely seen in most populations unless specific food sources are severely limited due to food distribution problems, environmental problems such as drought, or severe economic constraints that limit access to food. However, marginal deficiencies can be observed when individuals consume a monotonous diet in which relatively few foods constitute a source of calories. Genetic polymorphisms in proteins involved in vitamin metabolism may also affect vitamin nutriture and result in increased needs. When a defect is associated with a vitamin deficiency, what often defines why the defect occurs is the K_m for the association or binding of the vitamin with proteins associated with the defect (e.g., a specific enzyme). In such cases, the K_m or related constants is usually high. In addition, disturbances of absorption (e.g., pancreatic insufficiency, biliary obstructions, alcohol, enteropathies), antagonists (e.g., antibiotics, tannins, caffeic acid, alcohol), or metabolic conditions (e.g., pregnancy, diabetes) may contribute to the increased need for given vitamins (14).

REFERENCES

1. Beck WS, Cobalamin (Vitamin B12) In: Handbook of Vitamins, 3rd Edition, Eds: Rucker, RB, Suttie, JW, McCormick, D, & Machlin, LJ, Dekker Inc., New York, pp. 463–512, 2001.

2. Brody T & Shane B, Folic Acid In: Handbook of Vitamins, 3rd Edition, Eds: Rucker, RB, Suttie, JW, McCormick, D, & Machlin, LJ, Dekker Inc., New York, pp. 427–462, 2001.

3. Carr AC & Frei B, Toward a new recommended dietary allowance for vitamin C based on antioxidant & health effects in humans. Am J Clin Nutr 69:1086–1107, 1999.

4. Food & Nutrition Board, Institute of Medicine. Dietary reference intakes. Washington, DC: National Academy Press, Washington, D.C., 1998.

5. Joshi AK, Zhang L, Rangan VS, & Smith S, Cloning, expression, and characterization of a human 4'-phosphopantetheinyl transferase with broad substrate specificity. J Biol Chem 278:33142, 2003.

6. Kirk, JB & Rawling JM. Niacin, In: Handbook of Vitamins, 3rd Edition, Eds: Rucker, RB, Suttie, JW, McCormick, D, & Machlin, LJ, Dekker Inc., New York, pp. 213–254, 2001.

7. Leklem JE, Vitamin B-6 In: Handbook of Vitamins, 3rd Edition, Eds: Rucker, RB, Suttie, JW, McCormick, D, & Machlin, LJ, Dekker Inc., New York, pp. 339–396, 2001.

8. Mason JB, Biomarkers of nutrient exposure & status in one-carbon (methyl) metabolism. J Nutr 133:941S–947S, 2003.

9. Mock DM, Biotin In: Handbook of Vitamins, 3rd Edition, Eds: Rucker, RB, Suttie, JW, McCormick, D, & Machlin, LJ, Dekker Inc., New York, pp. 397–426, 2001.

10. Powers HJ, Riboflavin (vitamin B-2) and health, Am J Clin Nutr 77:1352–1360, 2003.

11. Quinlivan EP & Gregory JF, Effect of food fortification on folic acid intake in the United States. Am J Clin Nutr 77:221–225, 2003.

12. Johnston CS, Steinberg FM, & Rucker RB, Ascorbic acid, In: Handbook of Vitamins, 3rd Edition, Eds: Rucker, RB, Suttie, JW, McCormick, D, & Machlin, LJ, Dekker Inc., New York, pp. 529–554, 2001.

13. Reddy MB & Love M, The impact of food processing on the nutritional quality of vitamins and minerals. Adv Exp Med Biol 459:99–106, 1999.

14. Rucker RB & Steinberg FM, Vitamin requirements. Relationship to basal metabolic need & functions. Biochem Mol Biol Educ 30:86–89, 2002.

15. Said, HM, Cellular uptake of biotin: mechanisms and regulation. J Nutr 129:490S–493S, 1999.

16. Selhub J Folate, vitamin B12 & vitamin B6 & one carbon metabolism. J Nutr Health Aging 6:39–42, 2002.

17. Steinberg F, Stites TE, Anderson P, Storms S, Chan I, Eghbali S, & Rucker RB, Pyrroloquinoline quinone improves growth and reproductive performance in mice fed chemically defined diets. Exp Biol Med 228:160–166, 2003.

18. Tahiliani AG & Beinlich CJ, Pantothenic acid in health & disease. Vitam Horm 46:165–228, 1991.

19. Tanphaichitr V, Thiamine In: Handbook of Vitamins, 3rd Edition, Eds: Rucker, RB, Suttie, JW, McCormick, D, & Machlin, LJ, Dekker Inc., New York, pp. 275–316, 2001.

11 Fat-Soluble Vitamins

Lin Ye and Ronald R. Eitenmiller
Department of Food Science and Technology, University of Georgia

CONTENTS

I. INTRODUCTION

The fat-soluble vitamins include vitamin A, vitamin D, vitamin E, and vitamin K. Knowledge of their roles in metabolism and maintenance of health has greatly expanded over the recent past decades. Consumer interest has been energized by many diet-health relationships that, in some cases, have been well documented. Such interest and the expanding knowledge base has led to rapid growth of the use of fat-soluble vitamins in supplements and functional food products, increased fortification of food, the need to improve global food composition data banks, technology improvements in synthesis and food technological aspects, and increased need for accurate analytical methods both for scientific and regulatory use. Recent publication of the Dietary Reference Intakes (1–3) has added new perspectives on human requirements and diet planning. This chapter provides an overview of chemistry and nutrition of the fat-soluble vitamins.

II. VITAMIN A AND CAROTENOIDS

Night blindness resulting from vitamin A deficiency represents one of the earliest recognized dietary deficiency diseases (4). Scientific studies began in the early 20th century, and McCollum and Davis reported (1913) the presence of a lipid-like substance in butter and egg yolk required for the growth of young rats. The factor was named fat-soluble A in 1916, and the name vitamin A was first used in 1920 to emphasize the discovery of the first fat-soluble vitamin, differentiating it from the water-soluble vitamins. The structure of vitamin A was determined in 1931. The vitamin A activity of β-carotene was identified in 1929, and the term "provitamin A" was then used to differentiate carotenoid precursors of vitamin A from carotenoids without potential to form vitamin A. Plant carotenoids are, therefore, the precursors of all vitamin A found in the animal kingdom. Dietary vitamin A, by convention, is called preformed vitamin A when all-trans-retinol or its esters are consumed as a dietary constituent of animal products or through use of supplements (5). Identification of roles for vitamin A in gene expression, embryonic development, and immunological function (1) has greatly expanded interest in the nutritional significance of vitamin A to human well-being. Likewise, identification of functions other than as a precursor for vitamin A for both provitamin A carotenoids and other carotenoids such as lutein and lycopene have confirmed their significance as health-promoting components of a well-balanced diet (6).

A. CHEMISTRY

1. Vitamin A

Vitamin A refers to all isoprenoid compounds from animal products with the biological activity of all-trans-retinol (Figure 11.1). All-trans-retinol is the parent structure to most retinoids and contains a substituted β-ionone ring (4-{2,6,6-trimethyl-2-cyclo-hexen-1-yl}-3-buten-2-one) (5) with a side chain of three isoprenoid units linked at the 6-position of the β-ionone ring. The conjugated double-bond system includes the 5,6-β-ionone ring carbons and the isoprenoid side chain. Retinoids include all substances with vitamin A activity and many structurally similar synthetic compounds without vitamin A activity (7). Various retinoids are identified as significant for cell differentiation, immunity, and embryonic development. All-trans-retinoic acid, retinol esters, and various cis-isomers are significant metabolites (Figure 11.1). 13-cis-Retinol is frequently found in food extracts as a result of isomerization of all-trans-retinol during the extraction process (8). Acetate and palmitate esters of all-trans-retinol are the primary commercial forms of vitamin A used by the pharmaceutical and food industry in supplements and fortified foods. Esterification stabilizes the vitamin toward oxidation. Availability of the esters in beadlet or encapsulated products adds further stability during processing and marketing of supplements and fortified foods. The USP standard is retinyl acetate. Physical properties of all-trans-retinol, retinyl esters, and closely related retinoids are provided in Table 11.1.

2. Carotenoids

Carotenoids comprise an extensive family of plant pigments, and as many as 1000 occur naturally in the plant kingdom (6, 9). In the plant, carotenoids function in photosynthesis as light harvesting pigments that supplement the ability of chlorophyll to capture light energy (10, 11). They protect the photosynthetic apparatus by quenching reactive oxygen species ($^1O_2$, $^3O_2$, O_2^{2-}) and acting as free radical interceptors, thus preventing oxidative events which can irreversibly damage cell membranes and DNA (11).

Carotenoids are formed by the head-to-tail linkages of eight isoprene units to provide a C_{40} skeleton. Nomenclature for the carotenoids specified by the International Union of Pure and Applied Chemistry (IUPAC) and the International Union of Biochemistry (IUB) was reviewed by Weedon and Moss (12). Structures of common provitamin A carotenoids and other significant carotenoids to the human are given in Figure 11.2. Lycopene, which shows the acyclic hydrocarbon backbone chain, is considered the parent compound (12). Modifications of lycopene produce the diverse family of the carotenoids found throughout the plant kingdom. β-carotene (Figure 11.2) is characterized by the presence of β-ionone rings on both ends of the hydrocarbon chain. Oxygenation produces the xanthophylls. Oxygen functions include hydroxylation at the 3- or 4-position to produce lutein and β-cryptoxanthin, respectively, and ketolation to yield canthaxanthin. Other structural variants include aldehydes, epoxy, carboxy, methoxy, and

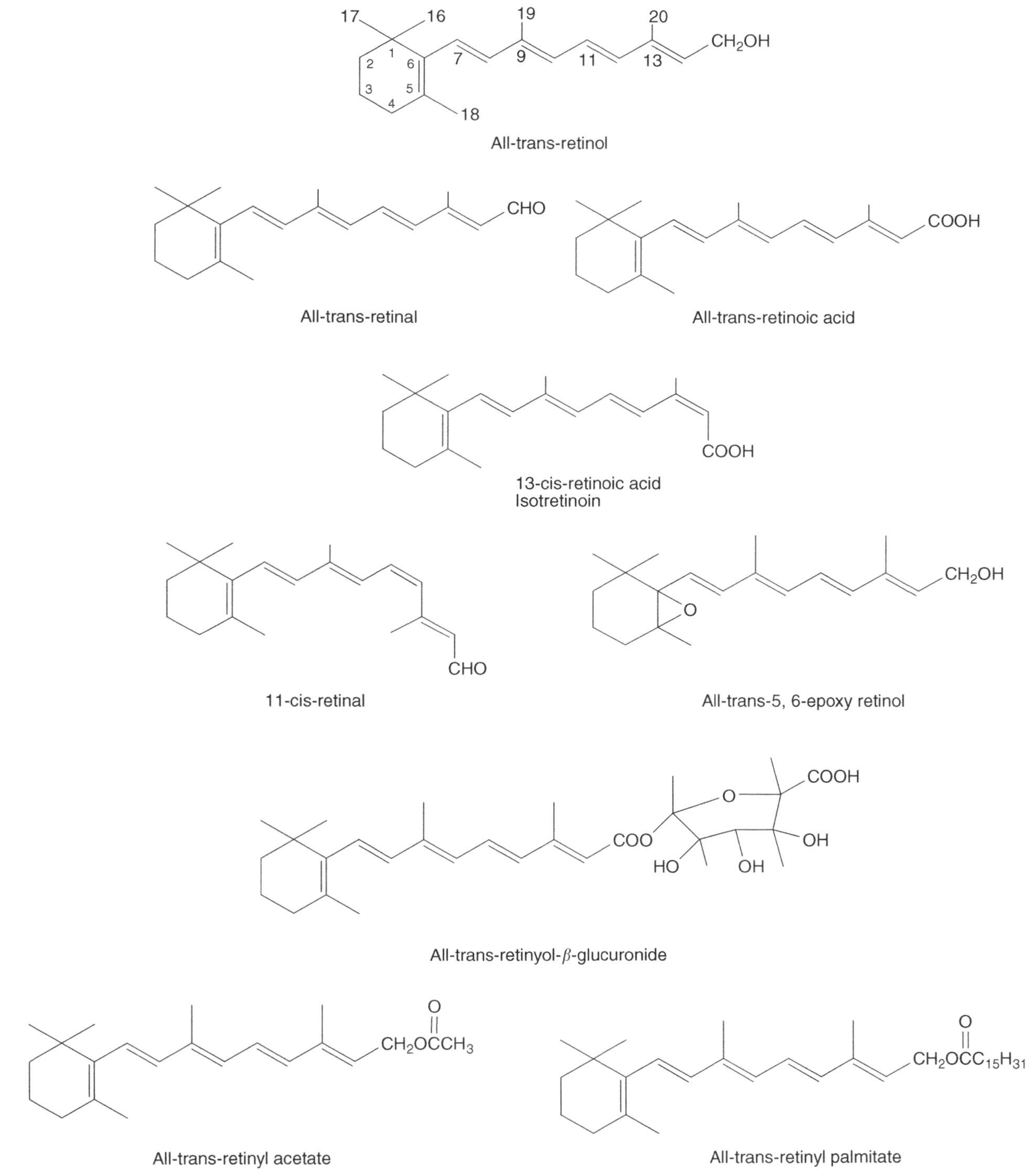

FIGURE 11.1 Structures of vitamin A, its metabolites and esters.

various other oxygenated forms. Some of the most frequently occurring carotenoids include the hydrocarbons lycopene, phytoene, and phytofluene, carotenal esters, and carotenol fatty acid esters (5).

The most commonly occurring provitamin A carotenoids in plant foods are β-carotene, α-carotene, γ-carotene,

and β-cryptoxanthin. cis-Isomers are biologically not as active compared to the all-trans naturally occurring carotenoids. Vitamin A activity depends on the presence of one, non-hydroxylated β-ionone ring in the provitamin A structure. Presence of the β-ionone ring allows conversion to all-trans-retinol (6). Acyclic hydrocarbons (lycopene,

TABLE 11.1
Physical Properties of Retinol, Other Retinoids, and Selected Carotenoids

Substance[a]	Molar Mass	Formula	Solubility	Melting Point, °C	Crystal Form	UV Absorption[b]				Fluorescence[d]	
						λ max nm	E$^{1\%}_{1cm}$	ε × 10³	Sol[c]	Ex nm	Em nm
All-trans-retinol CAS No. 68-26-8 10073	286.45	$C_{20}H_{30}O$	Soluble in abs alcohol, methanol, ether, chloroform, fats, oils; practically insoluble in water or glycerol	62–64	Yellow prisms	325	1845	[52.8]	EtOH	325	470
						325	**1810**	**[51.8]**	H		
13-cis-retinol CAS No. 2052-63-3 6495	286.45	$C_{20}H_{30}O$		58–60	Pale yellow needles	328	1689	[48.4]	EtOH		
11-cis-retinol	286.45	$C_{20}H_{30}O$				319	1220	[34.9]	EtOH		
						318	**1200**	**[34.4]**	H		
All-trans-retinyl acetate CAS No. 127-47-9 10073	328.5	$C_{22}H_{32}O_2$		57–58	Pale yellow prismatic	325	1560	[51.2]	EtOH	325	470
						325	**1590**	**[52.2]**	H		
All-trans-retinyl palmitate CAS No. 79-81-2 10073	524.86	$C_{36}H_{60}O_2$		28–29	Amorphous or crystalline	325	940	[49.3]	EtOH	325	470
All-trans-retinal CAS No. 116-31-4 8249	284.43	$C_{20}H_{28}O$	Soluble in ethanol, chloroform, cyclo-hexane, petr ether, oils; practically insoluble in water	61–64 (trans)	Orange crystals	383	1510	[42.9]	EtOH		
13-cis-retinal	284.44	$C_{20}H_{28}O$				**368**	**1690**	**[48.1]**	H		
						375	1250	[35.6]	EtOH		
						363	**1365**	**[38.8]**	H		
11-cis-retinal 8249	284.44	$C_{20}H_{28}O$		63.5–64.4	Orange prisms	380	878	[25.0]	EtOH		
						365	**928**	**[26.4]**	H		
All-trans-retinoic acid CAS No. 302-79-4 244	300.43	$C_{20}H_{28}O_2$	Soluble in DMSO; practically insoluble in water, mineral oil, glycerin	180–182	Crystals	350	[1508]	45.3	EtOH		
13-cis-retinoic acid CAS No. 4759-48-2 5249	300.44	$C_{20}H_{28}O_2$		174–175	Reddish-orange plates	354	[1325]	39.8	EtOH		
9-cis-retinoic acid CAS No. 5300-03-8 244	300.43	$C_{20}H_{28}O_2$		190–191	Yellow fine needles	345	[1228]	36.9	EtOH		
Provitamin A Carotenoids											
β-carotene CAS No. 7235-40-7 1866	536.87	$C_{40}H_{56}$	Soluble in CS$_2$, hexane, chloroform	183	Red rhombic square leaflets	425	–	–	LP		
						453	2592	139			
						479	–	–			
α-carotene CAS No. 7488-99-5 1865	536.87	$C_{40}H_{56}$	Freely soluble in CS$_2$, chloroform; soluble in ether, hexane	187.5	Deep purple prisms	422	2505	134	LP		
						444	2800	150			
						474	–	–			

Name	CAS No. / Merck	Formula	MW	Solubility	M.P. (°C)	Description	λ max (nm)	ε or E(1%)	[ref]	Solvent
β-cryptoxanthin	CAS No. 472-70-8 **2636**	$C_{40}H_{56}O$	552.87	Freely soluble in chloroform, CS₂, benzene, pyridine	158–159 (racemic) 169 (natural)	Red plates with metallic luster	452, 480	2380, 2080	[132], [115]	EM
γ-carotene	CAS No. 472-93-5 **1867**	$C_{40}H_{56}$	536.87	Somewhat less soluble than β-carotene	152–153.5 (synthetic) 177.5 (natural)	Red plates (synthetic) Deep-red prisms (natural)	437, 462, 494 / 508.5, 475, 446	2055, 3100, 2720	[110], [166], [146]	PE / C
β-Apo-8′-carotenal	CAS No. 1107-26-2	$C_{30}H_{40}O$	416.65	Freely soluble in chloroform; sparingly soluble in acetone	136–142 (decomp)	Powder with dark metallic sheen	457	2640	110	LP
Other Carotenoids										
Phytoene			544.95				275, 285, 296 / 286	1250 / 915	68 / 50	LP / H
Phytofluene	CAS No. 540-05-6 **7473**	$C_{40}H_{68}$	548.97	Freely soluble in petr ether, ether, benzene; practically insoluble in water, methanol, ethanol	B.P. 140–185	Pale orange viscous oil	331, 348, 367	1350	73	LP
Lycopene	CAS No. 502-65-8 **5640**	$C_{40}H_{56}$	536.87	Soluble in chloroform, hexane; almost insoluble in methanol, ethanol	172–173	Long, deep red needles	446, 472, 505	2250, 3450, 3150	185	PE
Lutein	CAS No. 127-40-2 **10120**	$C_{40}H_{56}O_2$	568.87	Soluble in fats and fat solvents; insoluble in water	183	Yellow prisms with metallic luster	421, 445, 475	2550	145	EtOH
Zeaxanthin	CAS No. 144-68-3 **10171**	$C_{40}H_{56}O_2$	568.87	Slightly soluble in petr ether, ether, methanol; soluble in CS₂, hexane, chloroform, pyridine, ethyl acetate	207 (Zechmeister) 215.5 (Kuhn)	Yellow rhombic plates with steel-blue metallic luster	426, 452, 479 / 450, 450	–, 2348 / 2540, 2480, 2480	133 / 144, 141	LP / EtOH
Canthaxanthin	CAS No. 514-78-3 **1758**	$C_{40}H_{52}O_2$	564.84	Soluble in chloroform, oil; very slightly soluble in acetone	217 (decomp)	Violet crystal	466, 470	2200, 2250	124, 127	LP, Cy
Violaxanthin	CAS No. 126-29-4 **10059**	$C_{40}H_{56}O_4$	600.87	Soluble in alcohol, methanol, ether; almost insoluble in petr ether	200	Orange prisms	420, 443, 470	–, 2550, –	153	EtOH
Neoxanthin		$C_{40}H_{56}O_4$	600.87				416, 439, 467	–, 2243, –	135	EtOH
Astaxanthin	CAS No. 472-61-7 **860**	$C_{40}H_{52}O_4$	596.84		182–183	Needles	438, 503, 472, 470, 485	2470, 2135, 2100	148, 124, 125	CS₂, EtOH, H, C

[a] Common or generic name, CAS No. – Chemical Abstract Service number, bold print designates the Merck Index monograph number.

[b] Values in brackets are calculated from corresponding ε or $E^{1\%}_{1cm}$ values.

[c] Solvent: EtOH=ethanol, H=hexane, LP=light petroleum, PE=Petroleum ether, Cy=Cyclohexane, C=Chloroform, CS₂=Carbon disulphide.

[d] In isopropanol.

Source: Refs. 16–19, 22, 29.

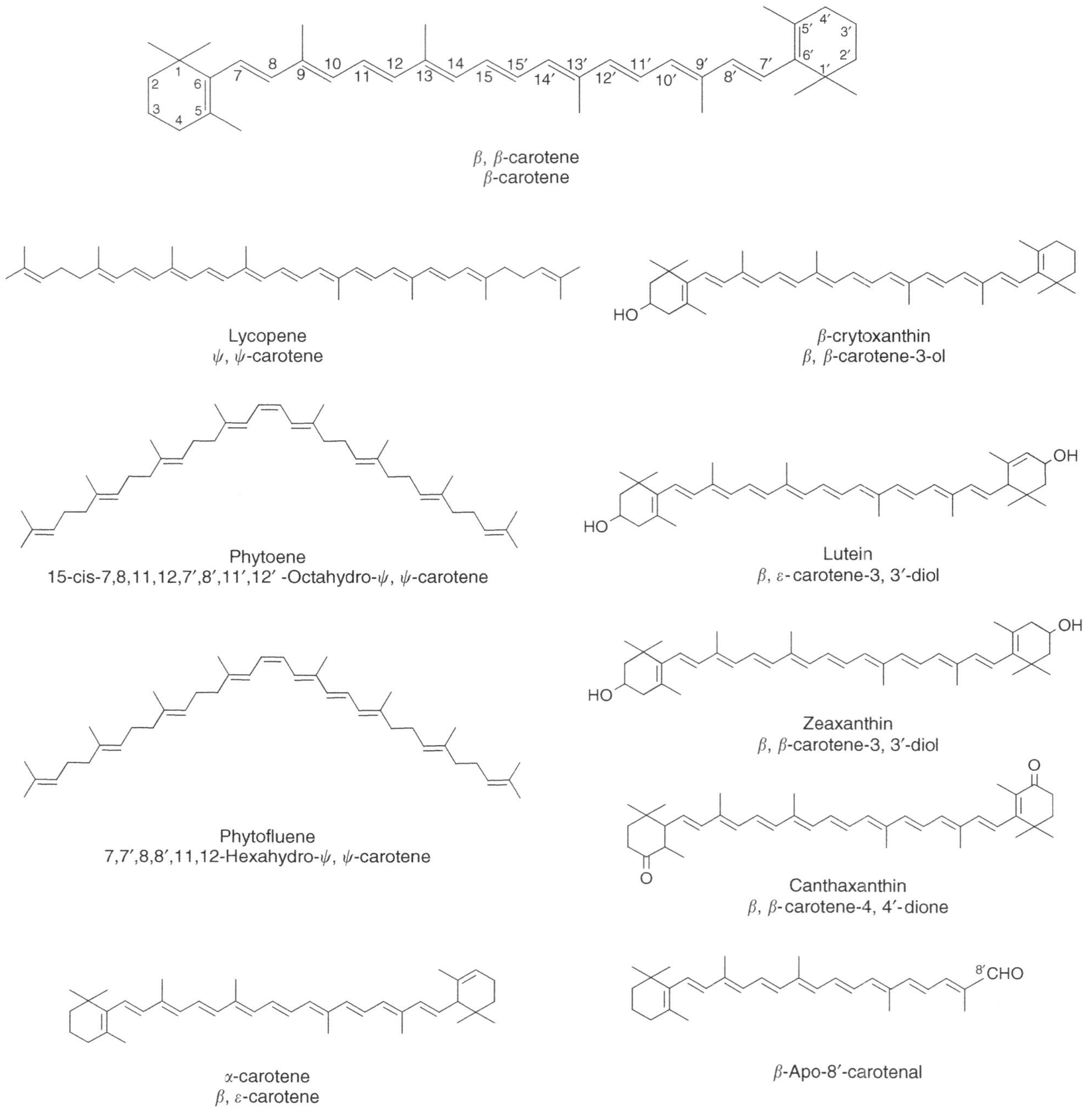

FIGURE 11.2 Structures of commonly occurring carotenoids.

phytoene, phytofluene), therefore, are not provitamin A carotenoids. Carotenoids with one hydroxylated ring or other oxygen function on one ring usually possess less than 50% of the biological activity of β-carotene (β-cryptoxanthin). Hydroxylation of both β-ionone rings (lutein) leads to a complete absence of vitamin A activity. Conversion of the provitamin A carotenoids to all-trans-retinol can occur by central oxidative cleavage at the 15,15′ double bond to yield two moles of vitamin A per mole of β-carotene or by

random oxidative cleavage that yields only one or two moles of vitamin A per mole of β-carotene, depending on the point of cleavage (13–15). Central cleavage is accomplished by β-carotene-15,15′-dioxygenase within the intestinal absorptive cells (1).

Physical properties of various carotenoids are provided in Table 11.1. β-Carotene and β-apo-8′-carotenal are added to margarines, salad dressings, and other foods to enhance color as well as to fortify the products. In the poultry industry, xanthophyll concentrates derived from the marigold are added to rations to enhance yellow to red pigmentation in the skin and in egg yolks. The xanthophylls deposited in the skin and yolks do not add to the vitamin A activity of the products, since xanthophylls lack vitamin A activity.

3. Spectral Properties

The conjugated double bond system of the retinoids gives the compounds strong UV absorption properties. UV absorption maxima (Table 11.1) vary with structural modification of the all-trans-retinol. Effects on UV absorption by structural variations of the retinoids indicate that maximal absorption ranges from 318 to above 360 nm. Absorption maxima vary with solvent and the presence of cis-isomers (Z-). Isomerization to the cis-form decreases the absorption maxima and $E^{1\%}_{1cm}$ values relative to all-trans-retinol (Table 11.1) (17, 20).

All-trans-retinol and retinyl esters fluoresce strongly at λ_{ex} from 325 to 490 nm. Fluorescence intensity is greater in non-polar solvents; therefore, fluorescence is an ideal detection mode for normal-phase liquid chromatography-based analytical systems compared to UV detection (5, 21). Most other retinoids other than retinol and its esters do not fluoresce and oxidation of the alcohol results in lower fluorescence (20).

Carotenoids contain eleven π electron conjugated double bonds and, thus, possess strong primary absorption in the visible region due to the long conjugated double bond system. The bright and varied pigmentation of the carotenoids characterize the strong, visible region absorption. Published absorbance maxima are given in Table 11.1. Spectra commonly show two to three absorption maxima between 400 and 500 nm. A characteristic UV absorption peak occurs in cis-isomers approximately 142 nm below the longest-wavelength absorption maxima of the all-trans carotenoid (22). cis-Isomers show UV maxima between 330 to 340 nm and a downward shift of the entire spectrum (20, 22). Absorption intensity is affected by solvent or mobile phase composition (23, 24). Detection at 450 nm is commonly used as a detection mode for β-carotene after LC resolution.

4. Stability

Eitenmiller and Landen (5) summarized studies that exist in the literature on the stability of all-trans-retinol and β-carotene in foods during processing and storage. Little information exists on the stability of other retinoids or carotenoids such as lycopene and lutein. However, due to similarities in chemical properties, stability characteristics would be somewhat similar. Ball (25) provided an excellent review of the stability of all-trans-retinol and β-carotene with many specific literature citations.

Significant facts regarding the stability of all-trans-retinol and carotenoids presented by Eitenmiller and Landen (5) include the following:

1. Conversion of all-trans to cis-isomers is easily induced by light, acids, metals, lipoxygenase action, and heat processing, acting independently or synergistically.

2. All-trans-retinol and the carotenoids are oxidatively unstable. Autoxidation of lipids can induce rapid loss of vitamin A activity. Some carotenoids are active singlet oxygen quenchers. This ability is directly related to the number of double bonds in the conjugated double bond system. β-Carotene, lutein, and other carotenoids preferentially react with singlet oxygen, converting it to the triplet state (26). The excited triplet state carotenoids can thermally disperse excess excited state energy through chemical reactions that destroy the carotenoids (27). Degradation products include various cleavage products.

3. Carotenoids scavenge free radicals at low oxygen pressures (<155 mm Hg) and act as primary chain-breaking antioxidants. Carotenoids, like β-carotene, trap peroxyl radicals through the addition of the radical at the 5,6-double bond of the carotenoid with conversion to peroxides (27).

4. All-trans-retinol and the carotenoids become more unstable as the food matrix is disrupted or the compounds are removed from the matrix by extraction prior to analysis. Destruction of the food matrix can liberate lipoxygenases that catalyze isomerization.

5. Blanching of plant products prior to freezing inactivates lipoxygenase and removes oxygen from the tissue. Thus, carotenoids are protected from lipoxygenase-initiated oxidative degradation during freezer storage.

6. Air drying or freeze drying can produce large losses in all-trans-retinol or the carotenoids. Storage of freeze-dried foods, because of the open, porous nature of the product, requires removal of oxygen with inert gas or vacuum to stabilize the vitamin A activity. Losses can be considerable during the drying process.

7. All-trans-retinol and the carotenoids are relatively stable at alkaline pH. Therefore, saponification can be used for sample extraction if the reaction vessel is evacuated and protected from light. Saponification at ambient temperature can be used to slow isomerization reactions that are more predominant at elevated temperatures.

8. All-trans-retinyl palmitate and all-trans-retinyl acetate are the commonly available commercial

forms of vitamin A used for food fortification and by the pharmaceutical industry. The ester forms are more stable to oxidation. However, conversion of all-trans to cis-isomers can readily occur. Most LC procedures will resolve the all-trans from the cis-isomers, which is essential to accurately assess biological activity. Encapsulation of concentrates in a matrix of gelatin, microcrystalline cellulose, or modified starch inhibits oxidation and isomerization. Antioxidants including tocopherols and other free radical interceptors are usually added to vitamin A preparations to inhibit oxidation.

Due to the lability of all-trans retinol and the carotenoids to oxidation and isomerization, precautions must be taken during analysis of foods and other biological samples to avoid conditions adverse to the analytes. Precautions to minimize destruction during extraction and determinative chromatography include the following (5, 28):

1. During all phases of sample handling, exclude oxygen. Air should be replaced by vacuum or inert gas.
2. Addition of antioxidants such as butylated hydroxytoluene (BHT), pyrogallol, ascorbic acid, or combinations is necessary prior to saponification. Low levels of antioxidants in extracting solutions and mobile phases are often added to protect the retinoids and carotenoids from oxidation.
3. Trans- to cis-isomerization (E → Z) is promoted at elevated temperatures. Therefore, use of the lowest practical temperature is recommended. Use of solvents with low boiling points is preferred. For rotary evaporation, 40°C should not be exceeded. Solutions should be stored at −20°C, preferably lower.
4. All sunlight should be avoided. Analytical steps and extractions should be completed in dim light, diffused sunlight, or under gold fluorescent light. Solutions of sample analytes and standards should be stored in low actinic glassware whenever possible. Isomerization rapidly occurs through light activation and is a common source of cis-isomer formation in biological sample extracts.
5. Acid must be avoided. All solvents must be acid free. Addition of Triethylamine (TEA) at 0.001% is useful to neutralize low acid levels in some solvents.
6. Alkaline conditions can lead to base-catalyzed isomerization, especially if exposure to light occurs.

B. NUTRITION AND BIOCHEMISTRY OF VITAMIN A

1. Functions of Vitamin A

Functional roles of vitamin A continue to be identified as the scientific basis of its relationship to cell growth and differentiation and immunological function becomes better understood. Specifically, vitamin A is required for normal vision, gene expression, reproduction, embryonic development, growth and immunological function.

The role of vitamin A in maintenance of eye health and the visual cycle is quite well understood. Retinoic acid is required for normal differentiation of the cornea, conjunctival membranes, and photoreceptor rod and cone cells of the retina (1, 7). In the visual cycle, all-trans-retinol is isomerized to 11-cis-retinol which is oxidized to 11-cis-retinal (29). In the rod cells, 11-cis-retinal is bound to opsin to form the visual pigment, rhodopsin. Absorption of light by rhodopsin isomerizes 11-cis-retinal to all-trans-retinal which triggers signaling to neuronal cells in the visual cortex of the brain (1). All-trans-retinal is released from the protein, converted back to all-trans-retinol, and stored as all-trans-retinyl esters, completing the cycle (1, 7, 29).

Identification of two families of nuclear receptors, retinoic acid receptors (RAR) and retinoid receptors (RAX), has helped explain the role of vitamin A in cell differentiation. In the nucleus, all-trans- and 9-cis-retinoic bind with RAR and 9-cis retinoic acid binds with RAX. The activated receptors regulate gene expression significant to embryonic development and integrity of epithelial cells (1, 7, 29).

The relationship of vitamin A deficiency to decreased disease resistance and increased child mortality in areas of the world lacking proper food supplies has been recognized for decades. Vitamin A influences immune response through maintenance of circulating natural killer cells with anti-viral and anti-tumor activity, by increasing phagocytic activity, and by increasing production of cytokines which regulate production of T and B lymphocytes (1). Fortunately, in vitamin A deficient individuals, immune function can be improved through supplementation of the diet with vitamin A.

2. Vitamin A Deficiency

Vitamin A deficiency is characterized by changes in the eye that can cause irreversible blindness. Clinical symptoms are referred to as xerophthalmia. The initial stage of development of xerophthamia is night blindness or the inability to adapt to dim light due to decreased ability to regenerate rhodopsin. At this stage, addition of supplementary vitamin A will reverse the disease. Progression of the disease leads to corneal and conjunctival xerosis (dryness) due to a decreased amount of globlet cells and to the appearance of Bitot's spots on the conjunctiva. Final stages are referred to as keratomalacia or ulceration and scarring of the cornea that leads to loss of vision. Other symptoms include skin lesions, loss of appetite, epithelial keratinization of epithelial tissue, impaired embryonic development, lack of growth and increased susceptibility to infections (1, 30–32).

While vitamin A deficiency in developed countries is not prevalent and is limited to individuals with fat absorption abnormalities, chronic liver disease, and alcoholics (32), it continues to be the leading cause of blindness world-wide and greatly contributes to infant and child mortality. Recent estimates indicate that 250,000 to 500,000 children go blind annually due to lack of vitamin A (1, 33, 34). Although fortification programs can be successful in improving vitamin A status at low cost, large segments of the world's population can still benefit from fortification of staple foods or through provision of supplements. The role of the food industry and public health organizations in this regard can still dramatically improve human well-being.

3. Hypervitaminosis A

Vitamin A toxicity can occur from high intake of foods high in vitamin A or high potency supplements. Toxicity to retinoids has been classified as acute, chronic, and teratogenic (1, 29). Acute toxicity results from a single dose or a limited number of large doses over a short time period. A single dose greater than 200 mg (>200,000 RAE (retinol activity equivalent), >660,000 IU or 0.7 mmol) or all-trans-retinol can result in acute toxicity in adults. For children, 50% of the adult dose can cause acute toxicity (29). Symptoms include nausea, vomiting, headache, increased cerebrospinal fluid pressure, vertigo, blurred vision, muscle incoordination, and bulging fonanel in infants (1). Chronic toxicity results from ingestion of large doses at or above 30 mg (30,000 RAE) per day for months or years (1). Symptoms of chronic toxicity include alopecia, ataxia, liver abnormalities, membrane dryness, bone and skin changes, visual impairment, and nervous system effects (1, 29). Most symptoms are reversible when vitamin A intake is decreased (29). Teratogenic effects can result from single, large doses (30–90 mg) or long-term intakes that result in chronic toxicity (29). Common teratogenic defects include physical malformations, heart, kidney, and thymic disorders, and central nervous system disorders (29).

4. Dietary Reference Intakes

Based on newer information on absorption of dietary carotenoids, the Institute of Medicine (1) established the retinol activity equivalent (RAE) to replace the retinol equivalent (RE) as a measure of the vitamin A activity of dietary provitamin A carotenoids. One RAE is defined as 1 µg of all-trans-retinol, 12 µg of all-trans-β-carotene and 24 µg of other provitamin A carotenoids (usually limited to α-carotene and β-cryptoxanthin). International units (IU)

are used for labeling pharmaceuticals, supplements, and foods. One microgram of all-trans-retinol equals 3.33 IU of vitamin A activity. The Reference Daily Intake (RDI) set by the Nutritional Labeling and Education Act of 1990 (NLEA) is 5000 IU.

Establishment of the RAE was based on the accepted carotene: retinol equivalency ratio (µg) of a low dose of purified β-carotene in oil of 2:1, indicating that 2 µg of β-carotene in oil yields 1 µg of retinol (1). Differences between RE conversion factors and RAE factors stem from absorption studies that show that 6 µg of dietary β-carotene is equivalent to 1 µg of purified β-carotene in oil (1). Since previous data indicated 3 µg of dietary β-carotene was equal to 1 µg of β-carotene in oil (6 × 2:1 = 12:1), the RAE calculation doubles the amounts of dietary provitamin A carotenoids required to provide 1 µg of retinol or 1 RAE as compared to calculation of RE values. The Institute of Medicine report (1) emphasizes that vitamin A intake from provitamin A carotenoids has been overestimated by previous assumptions made on carotenoid absorption from mixed meals including fruits and vegetables. Implications to the presentation of food composition databank information are significant in that reliable data on carotenoid composition of fruit and vegetables are still somewhat limited.

The ability of the scientific community to reliably quantify carotenoids from fruits and vegetables has greatly improved with the introduction of a C_{30} stationary phase designed to provide high absolute retention, enhanced shape recognition of carotenoid isomers, and to moderate silanol activity of the support (35). This LC support has gained wide acceptance, with utilization for multi-analyte analyses including the tocopherols (36, 37). With a LC reversed-phase method based on the C_{30} support, Darnoko et al. (37) quantified tocopherols and 13 carotenoids in red palm oil. The C_{30} support adds a new dimension to LC assay of fat-soluble vitamins from foods and supplements and expands the capability to use reversed-phase systems, in general, for fat-soluble vitamin assay.

Dietary Reference Intake (DRI) values for vitamin A range from an Adequate Intake (AI) of 400 µg RAE/day (RAE, retinol activity equivalents) for the 0- to 6-month infant to Recommended Dietary Allowance (RDA) values of 700 µg RAE/day for adult women and 900 µg RAE/day for adult men. The RDA increases to 1300 µg RAE/day for lactating women (19–50 years) (1). The Tolerable Upper Intake Level (UL) is 3000 µg RAE/day for adults (Table 11.2).

5. Food Sources and Dietary Intake

Significant dietary sources of preformed vitamin A include organ meats (liver), fish oils, butter, eggs, whole milk, and fortified reduced fat and skim milk, other dairy products, and high fat species of fish including tuna and sardines (8). Fortification of foods with retinyl palmitate and/or

TABLE 11.2
Dietary Reference Intake Values for the Fat-Soluble Vitamins

Life Stage Group	EAR[a] Male	EAR[a] Female	RDA[b] Male	RDA[b] Female	AI[c] Male	AI[c] Female	UL[d]
			Vitamin A (µg RAE/d)				Preformed Vitamin A (µg/d)
0 through 6 mo					400	400	600
7 through 12 mo					500	500	600
1 through 3 y	210	210	300	300			600
4 through 8 y	275	275	400	400			900
9 through 13 y	445	420	600	600			1,700
14 through 18 y	630	485	900	700			2,800
>19 y	625	500	900	700			3,000
Pregnancy							
14 through 18 y		530		750			2,800
19 through 50 y		550		770			3,000
Lactation							
14 through 18 y		885		1,200			2,800
19 through 50 y		900		1,300			3,000
			Vitamin D (µg/d)				(µg/d)
0 through 12 mo					5	5	25
1 through 50 y					5	5	50
51 through 70 y					10	10	50
>70 y					15	15	50
Pregnancy							
14 through 50 y						5	50
Lactation							
14 through 50 y						5	50
			Vitamin E (mg α-T/d)				Any Form of Supplementary α-T (mg/d)
0 through 6 mo					4	4	
7 through 12 mo					5	5	
1 through 3 y	5	5	6	6			200
4 through 8 y	6	6	7	7			300
9 through 13 y	9	9	11	11			600
14 through 18 y	12	12	15	15			800
19 through 70 y	12	12	15	15			
> 70 y	12	12	15	15			
Pregnancy							
14 through 18 y		12		15			800
19 through 50 y		12		15			1,000
Lactation							800
14 through 18 y		16		19			1,000
19 through 50 y		16		19			
			Vitamin K (µg/d)				
0 through 6 mo					2	2	
7 through 12 mo					2.5	2.5	
1 through 3 y					30	30	
4 through 8 y					55	55	
9 through 13 y					60	60	
14 through 18 y					75	75	
19 through 70 y					120	90	
>70 y					120	90	

(continued)

TABLE 11.2 *(Continued)*

Life Stage Group	EAR[a]		RDA[b]		AI[c]		UL[d]
	Male	Female	Male	Female	Male	Female	
Vitamin K (µg/d)							
Pregnancy							
14 through 18						75	
19 through 50						90	
Lactation							
14 through 18						75	
19 through 50						90	

[a]EAR=Estimated Average Requirement. The intake that meets the estimated nutrient needs of half of the individual in a group.

[b]RDA=Recommended Dietary Allowance. The intake that meets the nutrient need of almost all (97–98%) of individuals in a group.

[c]AI=Adequate Intake. The observed average or experimentally determined intake by a defined population or sub-group that appears to sustain a defined nutritional status, such a growth rate, normal circulating nutrient values, or other functional indicators of health. The AI is needed if sufficient scientific evidence is not available to derive an EAR. The AI is not equivalent to an RDA.

[d]UL=Tolerable Upper Intake Level.

Source: Refs. 1–3.

β-carotene helps to prevent vitamin A deficiency in countries that require fortification. Commonly used food vehicles for delivery of vitamin A include fluid milk, dry milk, margarine, and some edible oils. Choice of the proper food for delivery of vitamin A depends on which foods are consumed by the target population. In the United States, milk is fortified with not less than 2,000 IU of vitamin A (retinyl palmitate), and margarine is fortified with no less than 15,000 IU per pound (by a combination of retinyl palmitate and β-carotene) (38).

Provitamin A carotenoids are widely distributed throughout the plant kingdom. However, reliable quantitative data only exist for β-carotene, α-carotene, and β-cryptoxanthin in some fruit and vegetables. Minor carotenoids with provitamin A activity provide only small amounts to the total vitamin A in human diets because of lower natural levels compared to the primary provitamin A carotenoids. Color or color intensity cannot be used to predict the vitamin A activity of a food due to the complexity of carotenoid profiles and the fact that most carotenoids such as lycopene have zero vitamin A activity. The red color of ripe tomatoes is primarily due to lycopene and most tomato cultivars are quite low in vitamin A activity (5). An excellent database exists that was formulated through efforts of the United States Department of Agriculture and the National Cancer Institute. The database contains compositional information on 2400 fruits and vegetables for β-carotene, α-carotene, β-cryptoxanthin, lutein plus zeaxanthin, and lycopene (39–41). The database provides the most easily applied tool to estimate dietary intake (42). Estimation of dietary intake of non-provitamin A carotenoids has become more significant to public health as new, functional roles are identified for carotenoids such as lutein and lycopene. Although

β-carotene and several other carotenoids are clinically associated with lower risk of several chronic diseases, the DRI Panel on Antioxidants and Related Compounds (3) supported increased consumption of fruits and vegetables but did not set DRIs for β-carotene or other carotenoids. The Panel did not recommend use of supplemental β-carotene other than as a source of provitamin A for the control of vitamin A deficiency.

The Institute of Medicine report on DRIs for vitamin A (1) gives quite good, documentable data on vitamin A intake in the U.S. based upon the Third National Health and Nutrition Examination Survey (NHANES) (43). The following facts pertaining to vitamin A intake were delineated:

1. The median dietary intake of vitamin A is 744 to 811 µg RAE for men and 530 to 716 µg RAE for women.
2. For adults, 25 to 50% had vitamin A intakes less than the estimated average requirement (EAR) of 500 µg RAE/day for women and 625 µg RAE/day for men.
3. The data suggest that many adults in the U.S. have lower liver stores of vitamin A than is considered optimal. However, intake is sufficient to avoid clinically measurable deficiency.
4. Conversion factors based upon the RAE factors give dietary intake levels that are lower compared to older estimates calculated using retinol equivalent (RE) factors. Therefore, greater amounts of provitamin A carotenoids are needed to meet vitamin A requirements.
5. Carrots provide 25% of the β-carotene in the U.S. diet.

6. Cantaloupe, broccoli, squash, peas, and spinach are major contributors of β-carotene.
7. Carrots contribute 51% of the α-carotene in the U.S. diet.
8. Fruits are the only sources of β-cryptoxanthin.
9. All provitamin A carotenoids contribute 26 and 34% of vitamin A consumed by men and women, respectively. Previous estimates indicated that approximately 75% of the vitamin A in the U.S. diet originated as preformed vitamin A from animal products.

III. VITAMIN D

Rickets was initially identified in 1919 as a deficiency of a fat-soluble factor in dogs fed fat-free diets and kept indoors in the absence of sunlight (44). The deficiency state was cured by feeding cod liver oil. The fat-soluble, antirachitic factor was named vitamin D in 1925 by McCollum's research group and proven to be produced in the skin by ultraviolet irradiation. Vitamin D was isolated as ergocalciferol or vitamin D_2 from irradiated ergosterol from yeast in 1931. The structure was identified in 1932. Cholecalciferol or vitamin D_3 was later characterized and shown to be the antirachitic factor in cod liver oil. Better understanding of the intermediary metabolism of vitamin D occurred in the 1970s with the identification of the hydroxylated metabolites, 25-hydroxyvitamin D_3 (25(OH)D_3) and 1 α, 25 dihydroxy D_3 (1 α, 25(OH)$_2D_3$). Biologically, 1 α, 25(OH)$_2D_3$ is the primary metabolically active form known as calcitriol. Vitamin D, as a general term, is referred to as calciferol (2).

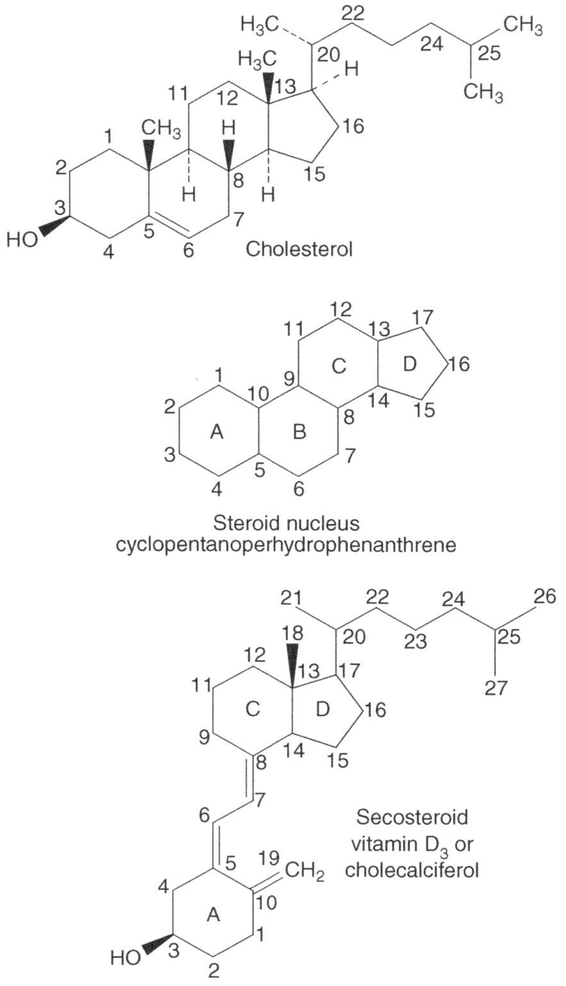

A. CHEMISTRY

Vitamin D refers to steroids that are antirachitic. Structures of vitamin D_3 (cholecalciferol) and the steroid nucleus are given in Figure 11.3. The International Union of Pure and Applied Chemists – International Union of Biochemistry (IUPAC-IUB) nomenclature rules for steroid structure are used to characterize the ring system (45, 46). The rings (A, B, C, D) are derived from the cyclopentanoperhydrophenanthrene steroid structure. Cholesterol serves as the parent compound (Figure 11.3) (46). In nature, 7-dehydrocholesterol and ergosterol are the provitamin forms for cholecaliferol (D_3) or ergocalciferol (D_2). Previtamin D_2 requires opening of the D ring at the 9,10 bond. The open-ring vitamin D forms are secosteroids. Accepted IUPAC-IUB systematic names are 9,10-seco(5Z,7E)-5,7,10(19) cholestatriene-3β-ol for vitamin D_3 and 9,10-seco(5Z,7E)-5,7,10(19),22 ergostatetraene-3β-ol for vitamin D_2. Conversions of the provitamins to previtamins D_2 and D_3 by irradiation to vitamin D_2 and vitamin D_3 are shown in Figure 11.4 along with the structures of the hydroxylated vitamin forms (25(OH)D_3 and 1 α, 25(OH)$_2D_3$). Vitamin D_2 and vitamin D_3 structurally vary by a double bond at C-22 and a methyl group at C-24

FIGURE 11.3 Structures of vitamin D_3, cholesterol, steroid, nucleus.

in vitamin D_2. Since the structures are quite similar, chemical and physical properties are similar (Table 11.3).

1. Spectral Properties

Vitamin D has a characteristic broad UV spectrum with maximum absorption near 264 nm and a minimum near 228 nm (47). The vitamin does not fluoresce. Because vitamin D is present, even in fortified foods, at quite low concentrations, most methods of quantification by LC rely on extract clean-up and concentration prior to determinative chromatography (5). With proper sample treatment, UV detection at 264–265 nm is sensitive and specific enough to provide reliable data. UV detection is generally not sensitive enough to quantify hydroxylated metabolites in serum or biological tissues.

2. Stability

Stability of vitamin D is excellent in the absence of water, light, acidity, and at low temperatures (47). The

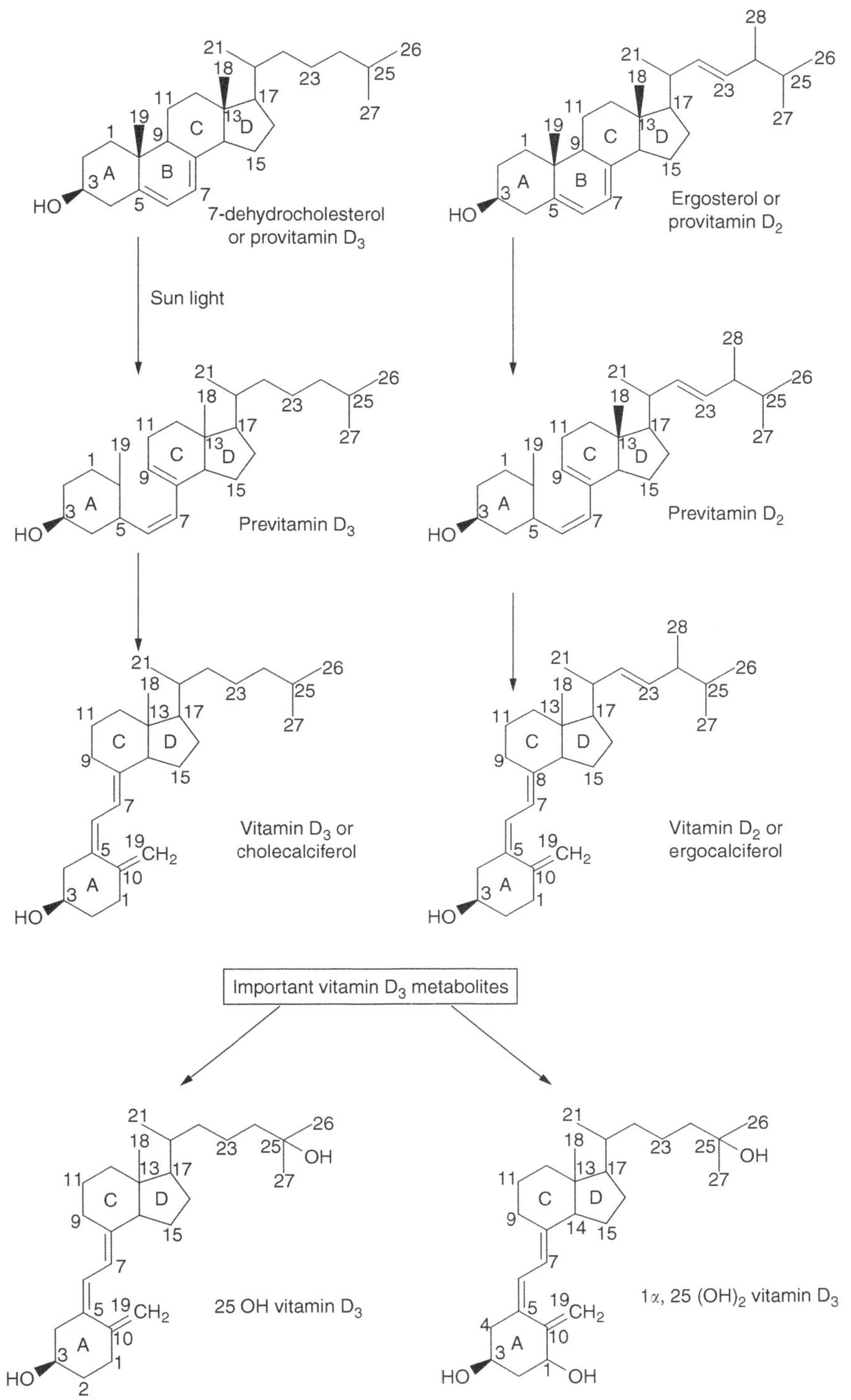

FIGURE 11.4 Structures of vitamin D, its precursors and metabolites (from Ref. 8).

5,6-trans-isomer and isotachysterol can form when exposed to acid or light (48). For food samples, saponification provides a convenient first step in extraction of vitamin D, since the stability under alkaline conditions is quite good. Precautions discussed in the vitamin A-carotenoid section of this chapter must be adhered to for extraction of vitamin D even though vitamin D is considered to be much more stable to oxidation compared to vitamin A. Oxidation can be a predominate route for decomposition at the conjugated double bond system at the 5,6 and 7,8 positions of the sec-osteroid structure. However, vitamin D is less susceptible to oxidative losses than vitamin A, carotenoids or vitamin E (47). Since various environmental conditions can lead to isomerization of vitamin D_2 and vitamin D_3 to the previtamin

TABLE 11.3
Physical Properties of Vitamin D, Hydroxylated Forms, Vitamin E and Vitamin K

Substance[a]	Molar Mass	Formula	Solubility	Melting Point EC	Crystal Form	λ max nm	$E^{1\%}_{1cm}$	ε×10⁻³	Fluorescence[c] λEx	λEm
Vitamin D₃ CAS No. 67-97-0 **10079**	384.64	$C_{27}H_{44}O$	Soluble in most organic solvents; insoluble in water	84–85	Fine needles	264	485	18.3		
Vitamin D₂ CAS No. 50-14-6 **10078**	396.65	$C_{28}H_{44}O$	Soluble in most organic solvents; insoluble in water	115–118	Prisms yellow to white	264	462	19.4		
25(OH) vitamin D₃ CAS No. 19356-17-3 **1638**	400.64	$C_{27}H_{44}O_2$	Soluble in most organic solvents; insoluble in water	82–83		265	[454]	18.2		
1α,25(OH)₂ vitamin D₃ CAS No. 32222-06-3 **1643**	416.63	$C_{27}H_{44}O_{33}$	Slightly soluble in methanol, ethanol, and ethyl acetates; insoluble in water	111–115	White crystalline powder	264	[418]	19		
α–T CAS No. 59-02-9 **9571**	430.7	$C_{29}H_{50}O_2$	Freely soluble in oils, fats, acetone, alcohol, chloroform, ether	2.5 ~ 3.3		292	75.8	[3265]	295	320
β–T CAS No. 16698-35-4 **9572**	416.68	$C_{28}H_{48}O_2$	Freely soluble in oils, fats, acetone, alcohol, chloroform, ether	296		296	89.4	[3725]	297	322
γ–T CAS No. 54-28-4 **9573**	416.68	$C_{28}H_{48}O_2$	Freely soluble in oils, fats, acetone, alcohol, chloroform, ether	−2 ~ −3		298	91.4	[3808]	297	322
δ–T CAS No. 119-13-1 **9574**	402.65	$C_{27}H_{46}O_2$				298	87.3	[3515]	297	322
α–T3 CAS No. 58864-81-6 **9576**	424.66	$C_{29}H_{44}O_2$				292	91.0	[3864]	290	323
β–T3 CAS No. 490-23-3 **9577**	410.63	$C_{28}H_{42}O_2$				294	87.3	[3585]	290	323
γ–T3 CAS No. 59-02-9	410.64	$C_{28}H_{42}O_2$				296	90.5	[3716]	290	324
δ–T3 CAS No. 59-02-9	396.61	$C_{27}H_{40}O_2$				297	88.1	[3494]	292	324
α-tocoperyl acetate CAS No. 58-95-7 (l) 52225-20-4 (dl) **9571**	472.74	$C_{31}H_{52}O_3$	Freely soluble in acetone, chloroform, ether	26.5~ 27.5 −27.5		286	40-44	[1891– 2080]	285	310
α-tocopheryl succinate CAS No. 4345-03-3 **9571**	530.79	$C_{33}H_{54}O_5$	Practically insoluble in water	76 ~ 77		286	38.5	[2044]	–	–
Phylloquinone Vitamin K₁ CAS No. 84-80-0 **7465**	450.69	$C_{31}H_{46}O_2$	Sparingly soluble in methanol; soluble in ethanol, acetone, benzene, petr ether, hexane, dioxin, chloroform, ether	–	None yellow viscous oil	242 248 260 269 325	396 419 383 387 68	[17.8] [18.9] [17.3] [17.4] [3.1]		

(continued)

TABLE 11.3 (*Continued*)

Substance[a]	Molar Mass	Formula	Solubility	Melting Point EC	Crystal Form	Spectral Properties[b]			Fluorescence	
						λ max nm	$E^{1\%}_{1cm}$	$\varepsilon \times 10^{-3}$	λ_{Ex}	λ_{Em}
Menaquinone-4 Vitamin $K_{2(20)}$ CAS No. 863-61-6 MK-4 **5855**	444.65	$C_{31}H_{40}O_2$		35	Yellow crystals	248	439	[19.5]		
Menaquinone-6	580.88	$C_{41}H_{56}O_2$		50	Yellow crystals	243	304	[17.7]		
Vitamin $K_{2(30)}$						248	320	[18.6]		
CAS No. 84-81-1						261	290	[16.8]		
MK-6						270	292	[16.9]		
5855						325–328	53	[3.1]		
Menaquinone-7	649	$C_{46}H_{64}O_2$		54	Light	243	278	[18.0]		
Vitamin $K_{2(35)}$					yellow	248	195	[19.1]		
CAS No. 2124-57-4					micro-	261	266	[17.3]		
MK-7					crystalline	270	267	[17.3]		
5855					plates	325-328	48	[3.1]		
Menadione Vitamin K_3 CAS No. 58-27-5 **5853**	172.18	$C_{11}H_8O_2$	Insoluble in water; moderately soluble in chloroform, carbon tetrachloride	105–107	Bright yellow crystals					

[a]Common or generic name; CAS No. – Chemical Abstract Service number, bold print designates the Merck Index monograph number, l = Natural form, dl = Synthetic form.
[b]In ethanol (in petroleum ether for vitamin K), values in brackets are calculated from corresponding $E^{1\%}_{1cm}$ or ε value.
[c]In hexane.
Source: Refs. 16, 25, 86–88, 131–133.

forms, analytical methods must be capable of measuring all biologically active forms, including the previtamins, to accurately assess vitamin D activity. Thermal interconversion is difficult to completely avoid during sample preparation prior to quantification.

Vitamin D is quite stable to food processes used for fluid milk or in the production of nonfat dry milk. Research has shown that light and air exposure of fluid milk in the marketing channel results in only small losses of vitamin D (48). Documentation of degradation during the production of spray-dried, fortified whole milk showed that vitamin D was stable to the preheating by direct steam injection to 95°C, five-stage evaporation and spray-drying. No significant losses were noted (49).

B. Nutrition and Biochemistry of Vitamin D

1. Functions of Vitamin D

Vitamin D functions as a steroid hormone. In this respect, vitamin D_2 and D_3 undergo conversion through hydroxylation to the biologically active 1 α, 25(OH)$_2$D form.

25(OH)D is initially formed in the liver by the action of vitamin D 25-hydroxylase. The 25(OH)D constitutes the primary circulating form of vitamin D, and circulating levels can be used as an indication of overall vitamin D status. In the kidney, 25(OH)D is hydroxylated by 25-hydroxyvitamin D-1 α-hydroxylase to 1 α, 25(OH)$_2$D (50, 51). The dihydroxy form is then transported to target tissues where receptor binding occurs. Hydroxylation in the kidney also forms 24R, 25(OH)$_2$D, although actions for this dihydroxy form of vitamin D are not clearly established (51). Overall, the actions of 1 α, 25(OH)$_2$D include maintenance of serum calcium and phosphorous concentrations and mobilization of monocytic stem cells in the bone marrow to become mature osteoclasts (2). In this regard, 1 α, 25(OH)$_2$D regulates mineral homeostasis by stimulation of the intestinal lumen-to-plasma flux of calcium and phosphorous, stimulation of renal resorption of calcium and phosphorous, and stimulation of bone resorption to increase calcium and phosphorous levels in the serum (51). Osteoblast formation is controlled at the bone cell differentiation level. In the kidney, regulation of the overall vitamin D endocrine system occurs through control of activity of the 25(OH)$_2$D-1 α-hydroxylase. Other accepted roles for 1 α, 25(OH)$_2$D include general effects on cell regulation and differentiation, regulation of protein synthesis, essentiality for insulin secretion, neural function and brain metabolism, immunological function, estrogen synthesis (52), and antiproliferative effects on various cancers (53–60). Detailed discussion on the complex vitamin D endocrine system has been presented by Norman and colleagues (44, 51).

2. Vitamin D Deficiency

Inadequate intake of vitamin D, lack of exposure to sunlight or metabolic failure to convert vitamin D to 1 α, 25(OH)$_2$D, or a combination of the factors leads to deficiency (2). Deficiency states are characterized by inadequate mineralization or demineralization of the skeleton. These states are referred to as rickets in children and osteomalacia in adults. Deficiency due to inadequate intake or exposure to sunlight responds to supplementation of the diet but vitamin D-resistant rickets does not. Vitamin D-resistant rickets arises through genetic disorders and includes loss of the renal resorption system for phosphate, absence of the 25-hydroxy-vitamin D-1 α-hydroxylase in the kidney and through disruption of the vitamin D receptor gene (61). Rickets in children produces widening at the end of long bones, rachitic rosary, deformations in the skeleton (bowed legs, knocked knees, curvature of the spine, and others) (2). Osteomalacia in adults results in loss of calcium from the bone with bone pain, muscular weakness, and development of a porous bone structure (2, 44). Absence of sufficient 1 α, 25(OH)$_2$D leads to decreased circulating calcium levels and an increased production of parathyroid hormone (PTH). PTH stimulates calcium mobilization from the bone, conserves calcium excretion and increased excretion of phosphorous with the effect of bone demineralization and osteoporosis (62–64).

3. Hypervitaminosis D

Hypervitaminosis D can occur through improper use of supplements, excessive intake of foods fortified with vitamin D or rarely through manufacturing errors of supplements or food resulting in improperly labeled products with excessively high vitamin D levels. Current Upper Tolerable Intake Levels (UL) range from 25 to 50 µg/day (Table 11.2); however, severe effects have been noted at intakes of 250–1,250 µg/day or higher (2). Symptoms include increased intestinal absorption of calcium and increased resorption of calcium from bone resulting in hypercalcemia. Hypercalcemia can lead to loss of renal function. Other symptoms include anorexia, nausea, vomiting, thirst, polyuria, muscular weakness, joint pain, and general disorientation with eventual death (44).

4. Dietary Reference Intakes

Dietary Reference Intakes (DRIs) for vitamin D are limited to Adequate Intakes (AI) and Tolerable Upper Intake Levels (UL) (2). AIs range from 5 µg/day for infants through 50 year adults and 15 µg/day (600 IU/day) for older adults (>70 year). The AI recommendations assume that no vitamin D is available from synthesis in the skin by exposure to sunlight (2). UL values range from 25 µg/day for infants (0–6 months) to 50 µg/day for all other age groups (Table 11.2). Regarding development of hypervitaminosis D, only a small degree of safety exists between the AIs and the levels that can produce symptoms of hypervitaminosis D. For infants (AI-5 µg/day) 45 µg of vitamin D per day has been established as the NOAEL (highest level at which no adverse effects have been observed) (2). This level represents an intake only 9 times higher than the AI. The UL for infants is set at 25 µg/day (5 times the AI). For adults, the UL is 50 µg/day or 10 times the AI.

5. Vitamin D Sources for the Human

a. Synthesis in the Skin

The availability of vitamin D from unfortified foods is limited, and the major source to the human is synthesis in the skin upon exposure to sunlight. Synthesis is completely dependent upon exposure to the sun and varies with season, climate, and environmental conditions that can limit exposure to the sun (65). 7-Dehydrocholesterol from cholesterol is photoconverted to previtamin D$_3$ by exposure to UV irradiation between 290 and 315 nm (Figure 11.4). The previtamin D$_3$ is then isomerized to vitamin D$_3$. Likewise, ergosterol can be converted to previtamin D$_2$ by photoconversion. However, plant foods are generally devoid of vitamin D activity. Variability of sunlight exposure, particularly during winter months, makes dietary supply of vitamin D essential to avoid deficiency.

b. Food Sources and Dietary Intake

Vitamin D content of food and supplements is reported on an international unit (IU) or microgram basis (2). One IU of vitamin D is defined as the activity of 0.025 µg of cholecalciferol (vitamin D$_3$) measured by the rat or chick bioassay. The United States Pharmacoepial (USP) standard is either vitamin D$_2$ or vitamin D$_3$ since biological activity for the human is equal. Applications are developing for the use of 25(OH)D in supplements and for food fortification (66). The activity of 25(OH)D is 5 times that of vitamin D$_3$ (1 IU=0.005 µg) (2).

Fortified foods represent the only concentrated dietary sources of vitamin D other than some fatty fish (salmon), liver of some aquatic mammals, some fish oils and eggs from hens that have been fed rations containing high levels of vitamin D (2). The lack of many naturally occurring significant vitamin D sources, and the fact that consumption of higher vitamin D-containing foods requires large intake levels to meet the vitamin D requirement places a significant emphasis on the role of food fortification in ensuring an adequate dietary supply of vitamin D. In the United States, the primary vehicle for food fortification is fluid milk. Although fortification of fluid milk is optional (38), most fluid dairy products are fortified with 400 IU/quart (10 µg/quart or 9.6 µg/L). Margarine fortification in the United States is optional, and most commercial margarines are only fortified with retinyl palmitate and β-carotene (8). Vitamin D_2 and vitamin D_3 can be used interchangeably for food fortification; however, for fluid milk products, most are fortified with vitamin D_3. Synthetic vitamin D_2 or D_3 is readily available to the food and supplement industries.

Since food fortification with vitamin D requires the addition of µg levels to the food on a per serving basis, problems have occurred with both over- and underfortification of fluid milk and infant formulas which must contain 40 IU/100 kcal. Surveys have noted wide variability in vitamin D content of milk and infant formula products arising from processing errors (67–69).

Dietary intake in the United States was estimated at a median level of 2.9 µg/day for young women from the second National Health and Nutrition Examination Survey (NHANES II) (2). However, it is recognized that reliable intake data do not exist (2). Lack of reliable data results from analytical difficulties, variable composition of fortified foods, and because food intake surveys have not emphasized vitamin D (2). Recommendations pertaining to the dietary reference intakes (DRI) were limited to average intake values (AI) due to the lack of reliable data required to set estimated average requirements (EARs) and recommended dietary allowances (RDAs). Average intake values range from 5 µg/day for infants to 15 µg/day for adults 70 years or older with the assumption that no vitamin D is available from sunlight exposure. Further, it is recognized that older individuals are more susceptible to conditions leading to vitamin D deficiency (2).

IV. VITAMIN E – TOCOPHEROLS AND TOCOTRIENOLS

Evans and Bishop discovered and characterized a fat-soluble nutritional factor necessary for reproduction and fetal death in rats (70). Published in 1922, the factor was designated "Factor X" and the antisterility factor. The name, vitamin E, was given since its discovery closely followed the discovery of vitamin D. A vitamin E active compound was isolated from wheat germ oil by the Evans' research group and named α-tocopherol (α-T) from the Greek words *tocos* (birth) and *ferein* (bringing) to denote the essentiality of the vitamin to reproduction in rats (71). The "ol" ending denoted that the compound was an alcohol (72). Other significant early historical events of vitamin E research include

the isolation of β- and γ-tocopherol (β-, γ-T) from vegetable oil in 1934 (73), determination of the structure of α-T in 1937 (74, 75), synthesis of α-T in 1938 (76), recognition of the antioxidant activity of the tocopherols (77), recognition that α-T was the most effective tocopherol in prevention of vitamin E deficiency (73), isolation of δ-tocopherol (δ-T) from soybean oil in 1947 (78), and identification of the four naturally occurring tocotrienols (α-T3, β-T3, γ-T3, δ-T3) (79, 80). Quantification of the vitamin E content of the diet was initiated in the late 1940s. Publication of the paper "Vitamin E Content of Foods" in 1950 (81) represents one of the earliest documentations of dietary levels.

A. CHEMISTRY OF VITAMIN E

Vitamin E is the collective term for fat-soluble 6-hydroxychroman compounds that exhibit the biological activity of α-T measured by the rat resorption-gestation assay. Tocol (Figure 11.5) (2-methyl-2-(4',8',12'-trimethyltridecyl)-chroman-6-ol) is generally considered the parent compound of the tocopherols. Accepted nomenclature has been set by the IUPAC-IUB Joint Commission on Nomenclature (82–84). Naturally occurring vitamin E consists of α-, β-, γ-, and δ-T and the corresponding α-, β-, γ-, and δ-T3 (tocotrienol), (Figure 11.5). The tocopherols are characterized by the 6-chromanol ring structure methylated to varying degrees at the 5-, 7-, and 8-positions. At position 2, there is a C16 saturated side chain. The tocotrienols are unsaturated at the 3', 7', and 11' positions of the side chain. The specific tocopherols and tocotrienols, therefore, differ by the number and positions of the methyl groups on the 6-chromanol ring. α-Tocopherol and α-T3 are trimethylated; β-T, β-T3, γ-T, and γ-T3 are dimethylated; and δ-T and δ-T3 are monomethylated (Figure 11.5). Trivial and chemical names are given in Figure 11.5.

The tocopherols possess three asymmetric carbons (chiral centers) at position 2 of the chromanol ring and at positions 4' and 8' of the phytyl side chain. Synthetic α-T (all-rac-α-T) is a racemic mixture of equal parts of each stereoisomer. Therefore, each tocopherol has eight (3) possible optical isomers. Only RRR-tocopherols are found in nature. The eight isomers of all-rac-α-T (RRR-, RSR-, RRS-, RSS-, SRR-, SSR-, SRS-, and SSS-) are depicted in Figure 11.6. Only the 2R-stereoisomeric forms (RRR-, RSR-, RRS-, and RSS) of α-T are considered active forms of vitamin E for the human (3). The tocotrienols arising from 2-methyl-2-(4',8',12'-trimethyl-trideca-3',7',11'-trienyl) chroman-6-ol (non-methylated ring structure) have only one chiral center at position 2. Consequently, only 2R and 2S stereoisomers are possible. Unsaturation at position 3' and 7' of the phytyl side chain permits four cis/trans geometric isomers. The eight potential tocotrienol isomers are given in Table 11.4. Only the 2R, 3' trans, 7' trans isomer exists in nature. Isolation and elucidation of the structural properties of the tocotrienols

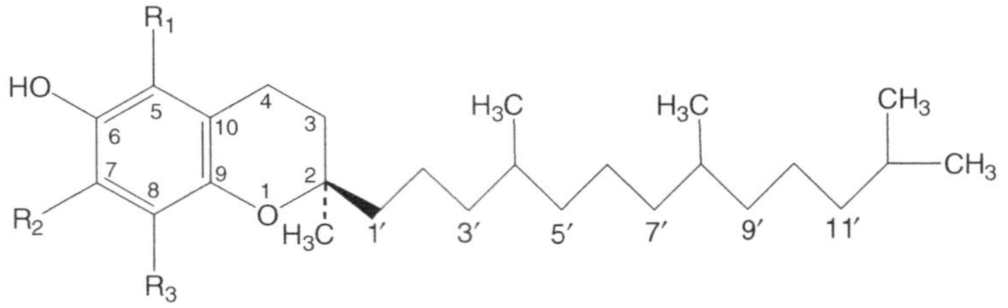

Tocopherols

Trivial name	Chemical name	Abbreviation	Ring position		
			R^1	R^2	R^3
Tocol	a	-	H	H	H
α-tocopherol	5,7,8-trimethyltocol	α-T	CH_3	CH_3	CH_3
β-tocopherol	5,8-dimethyltocol	β-T	CH_3	H	CH_3
γ-tocopherol	7,8-dimethyltocol	γ-T	H	CH_3	CH_3
δ-tocopherol	8-methyltocol	δ-T	H	H	CH_3

a = 2-methyl-2-(4′,8′,12′-trimethyltridecyl) chroman-6-ol

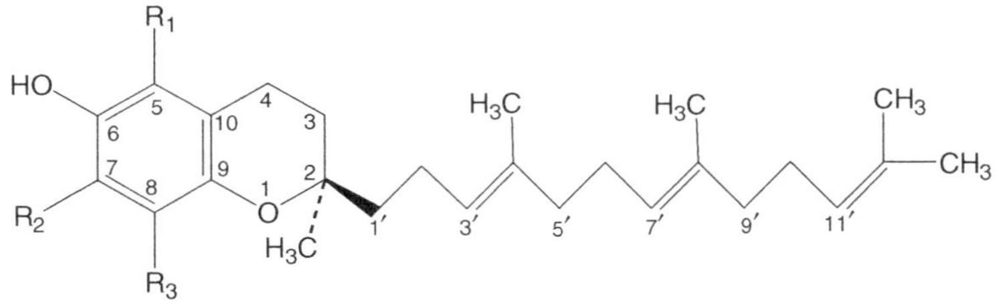

Tocotrienols

Trivial name	Chemical name	Abbreviation	Ring position		
			R^1	R^2	R^3
Tocol	b	-	H	H	H
α-tocotrienol	5,7,8-trimethyltocotrienol	α-T3	CH_3	CH_3	CH_3
β-tocotrienol	5,8-dimethyltocotrienol	β-T3	CH_3	H	CH_3
γ-tocotrienol	7,8-dimethyltocotrienol	γ-T3	H	CH_3	CH_3
δ-tocotrienol	8-methyltocotrienol	δ-T3	H	H	CH_3

b = 2-methyl-2-(4′,8′,12′-trimethyltrideca-3′,7′,11′-trienyl) chroman-6-ol

FIGURE 11.5   Structural interrelationship of tocopherols and tocotrienols.

was accomplished in the 1960s (80, 85). Physical properties of various vitamin E forms are given in Table 11.3.

1. Spectral Properties

UV and fluorescence properties of vitamin E compounds are given in Table 11.3. Maximal UV absorption for tocopherols, tocotrienols and their esters occurs between 292 and 298 nm. Minimum absorption is between 250 and 260 nm (25, 89–92). Esterification at the C-6 hydroxyl shifts the absorption to shorter wavelengths. For example, all-rac-α-tocopheryl acetate has maximal absorption at 286 nm (88, 91, 92). Intensity of absorption decreases with esterification. Reported $E^{1\%}_{1cm}$ values for all-rac-α-tocopheryl acetate range from 40 to 44 compared to 75.8 to 91.8 for the tocopherols and tocotrienols (88).

Vitamin E alcohols possess strong native fluorescence that provides an ideal and very specific mode of detection for LC-based methods. Excitation of the chroman ring near or at maximal absorption produces maximal emission at 320 nm or slightly higher wavelengths. Many quantitative methods are based on excitation at 292 nm and emission at 320 nm (88). Vitamin E esters show only weak fluorescence compared to the alcohols. Older literature (prior to 1985) often states that α-tocopheryl acetate does not fluoresce. However, the ester shows weak fluorescence sufficient to quantify the ester that is easily detected by currently available fluorescent detectors. By measuring the α-tocopheryl acetate as the ester and avoiding saponification of the sample, accurate measure of the biological activity is possible. Biological activity of all-rac-α-tocopheryl acetate is lower than that of RRR-α-T.

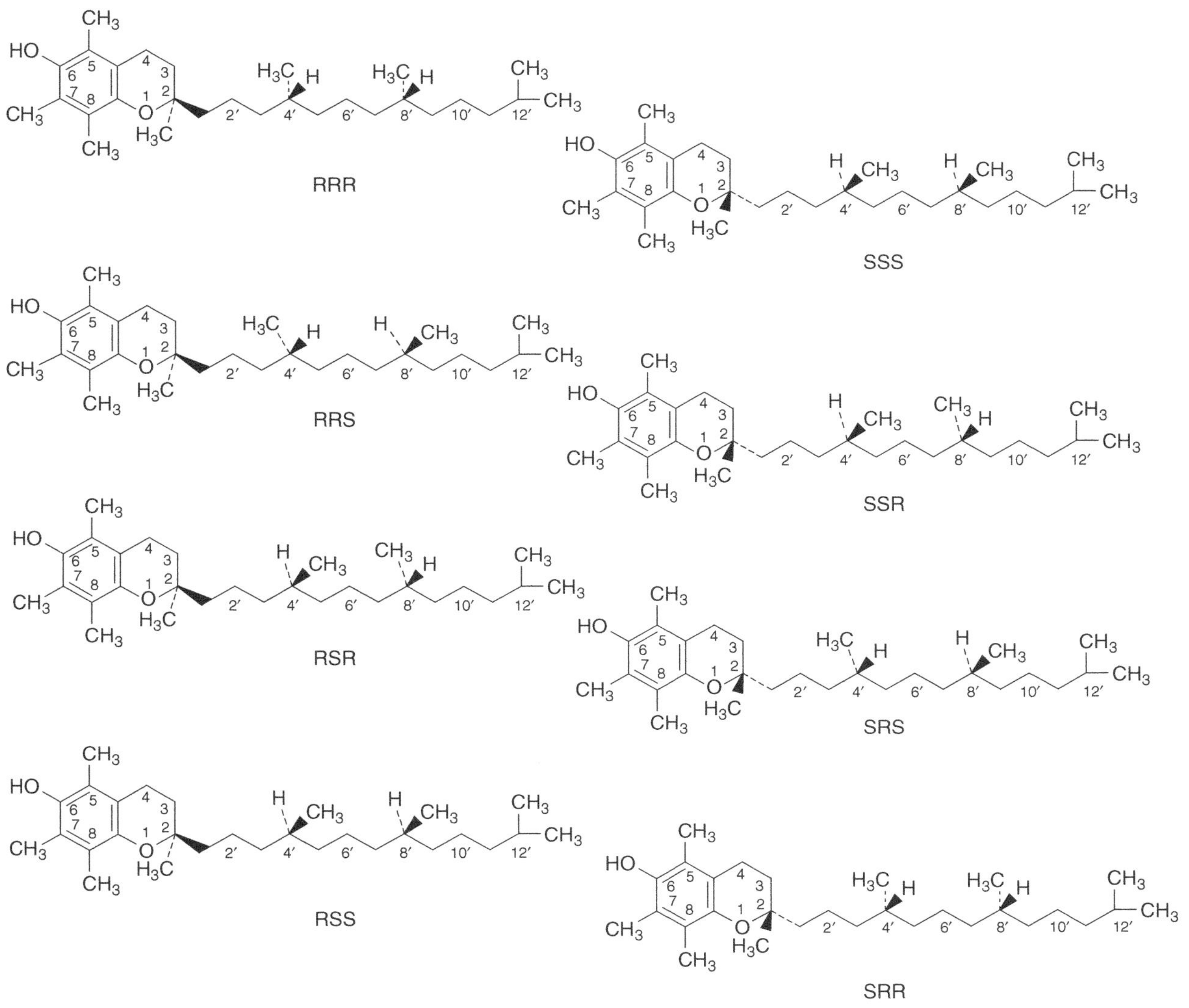

FIGURE 11.6 Stereoisomers of α-tocopherol (from Ref. 8).

TABLE 11.4
The Eight Possible RS, Cis/Trans Isomers of the Tocotrienols

R Configuration Position 2	S Configuration Position 2
2R, 3′cis, 7′cis	2S, 3′cis, 7′cis
2R, 3′cis, 7′trans	2S, 3′cis, 7′trans
2R, 3′trans, 7′cis	2S, 3′trans, 7′cis
2R, 3′trans, 7′trans	2S, 3′trans, 7′trans

2. Stability

Vitamin E is a natural antioxidant, acting as a chain-breaking, primary antioxidant to intercept peroxyl free radicals in biological systems. As an antioxidant, α-T, or other vitamin E alcohols, is, thus, converted into the α-tocopheryl radical and to termination products consisting of dimers and trimers and various oxygenated forms.

Since it is active in any fat system undergoing oxidation, oxidative losses can become substantial quite rapidly. Losses are accelerated by light, heat, irradiation, alkali pH, lipoxidase activity, metals, and by the presence of other proxidants in the fat system, including pre-formed free radicals (88). Tocopherols and tocotrienols are stable to heat and alkaline conditions necessary for saponification of lipids. Therefore, saponification is routinely used for extraction of vitamin E prior to analysis by LC.

Frying of foods normally results in loss of the native vitamin E components in the edible oil. Heat combined with incorporation of air with the food, the polyunsaturated nature of the oil and introduction of proxidants into the oil provides an ideal environment for oxidation. Vitamin E through its antioxidant action, combined with some loss through volatilization, leads to rapid loss of vitamin E from the frying oil. Refining of edible oil produces some loss of native vitamin E, primarily at the deodorization stage. However, loss is not enough to desta-bilize the oil to oxidation. Deodorizer sludge, once a by-product of edible oil refining with little value, now rep-resents the raw material source for isolation of natural vitamin E. Natural vitamin E is in demand world-wide for use in supplements, feeds, and cosmetics (72).

B. NUTRITION AND BIOCHEMISTRY OF VITAMIN E

1. Functions of Vitamin E

Vitamin E is the primary, lipid-soluble, chain-breaking antioxidant that combines actions with other lipid and water-soluble antioxidants to provide cells an efficient defense against free radical damage. Free radicals are chemical species capable of independent existence that contain one or more unpaired electron (93). Free radical generation occurs when organic molecules undergo homolytic cleavage of covalent bonds and each fragment retains one electron of the original bonding electron pair. Two free radicals are produced from the parent molecule with net negative charges. The free radicals have the abil-ity to react with an electron of opposite spin from another molecule. Free radical generation also occurs when a non-radical molecule captures an electron from an electron donor. During normal metabolism, many reactive oxygen species (ROS) and reactive nitrogen species (RNS) are produced (94). ROS and RNS include both radicals and oxidants capable of generation of free radicals (95, 96). Common ROS and RNS are given in Table 11.5.

Oxidants and oxygen radicals formed from triplet oxygen by reaction with other radicals or by photoexcita-tion, metabolism, irradiation, metal catalysis, or heat are the major inducers of oxidative stress in living systems. They also initiate antioxidative events in raw and processed foods. RNS, particularly nitric oxide (NO$^{\cdot}$)

TABLE 11.5
Reactive Oxygen and Nitrogen Species

Radicals	Nonradicals
ROS	
Superoxide, $O_2^{\cdot -}$	Fe-oxygen complex
Hydroxy, OH$^{\cdot}$	Hydrogen peroxide, H_2O_2
Alkoxy, LO$^{\cdot}$	Singlet oxygen, $^1O_2$
Hydroperoxyl, $HO_2^{\cdot}$	Ozone, O_3
Peroxy, $LO_2^{\cdot}$	Hypochlorous acid, HOCl
RNS	
Nitric oxide, NO$^{\cdot}$	Nitrous acid, HNO_2
Nitrogen dioxide, $NO_2^{\cdot}$	Dinitrogen tetroxide, N_2O_4
	Dinitrogen trioxide, N_2O_3
	Peroxynitrate, $ONOO^-$
	Peroxynitrous acid, ONOOH
	Nitronium cation, NO_2^+
	Alkyl peroxynitrates, ROONO

contributes to oxidative stress along with ROS. Nitric oxide acts as a biological messenger with regulatory func-tions in the central nervous, cardiovascular, and immune systems (97). It is synthesized through the oxidation of arginine to NO$^{\cdot}$ by nitric oxide synthetase (NOS:EL 1.14.13.39). Nitric oxide synthetase is highly active in macrophages and neutrophilis where NO$^{\cdot}$ and superoxide anion ($O_2^{\cdot -}$) are produced during the oxidative burst trig-gered by inflammation (98).

α-Tocopherol is located in the cell membranes and protects lipoproteins. It scavenges peroxy free radicals, protecting unsaturated fatty acids. Lipid-generated free radicals have greater affinity for reaction with α-T than with unsaturated fatty acids located within the cell mem-brane. It is an efficient chain-breaking antioxidant since it can rapidly transfer the phenolic H$^+$ at C-6 to lipid peroxy radicals. The α-T becomes the α-tocopheroxyl radical, which is stabilized by resonance.

Potency of α-T as an antioxidant depends upon its molecular properties and orientation within the cell mem-brane. In the membrane, the phytyl side chain is embed-ded within the bilayer (Figure 11.7) with the chromanol ring and the 6-hydroxyl positioned toward the surface of the membrane. Hydrogen bonding and hydrophobic inter-actions between the chromanol ring, the phytyl tail, and fatty acids stabilize the membrane and position the chro-manol ring to facilitate hydrogen atom donation to lipid peroxy radicals. The α-tocopheroxyl radical migrates from the lipid bilayer to the surface of the membrane, facilitating regeneration of α-T by ascorbic acid and other water-soluble reducing agents that act as hydrogen donors to the α-tocopheroxyl radical.

Non-autoxidative roles for α-T have been recently delineated which cannot be fulfilled by other tocopherols or tocotrienols. These functions at the molecular level appear to be highly significant to understanding the onset of many chronic diseases. Several critical reviews exist that indicate that the molecular control aspects of vitamin E are just beginning to be understood (98–103). α-Tocopherol acts as a cell signaling molecule at the posttranscriptional level or at the gene expression level. Many of these cell signaling functions of α-T are operative through inhibition of protein kinase C (PKC). PKC enzymes are phospholipid-dependent serine/threonine kinases that participate in regu-lation of cell growth, death, and stress responsiveness (104). α-Tocopherol acts at the posttranscriptional level by activating protein phosphatase PP$_2$A which dephophory-lates PKC (105, 106). Some specific physiological responses regulated by PKC include cell proliferation, platelet adhesion and aggregation, immune response, free radical production and gene expression. Now regulation of gene expression at the transcriptional stage is accepted as a primary regulatory function of α-T.

Specific non-antioxidant functions for α-T3 have been identified that are not fulfilled by α-T. Hendrich et al. (107)

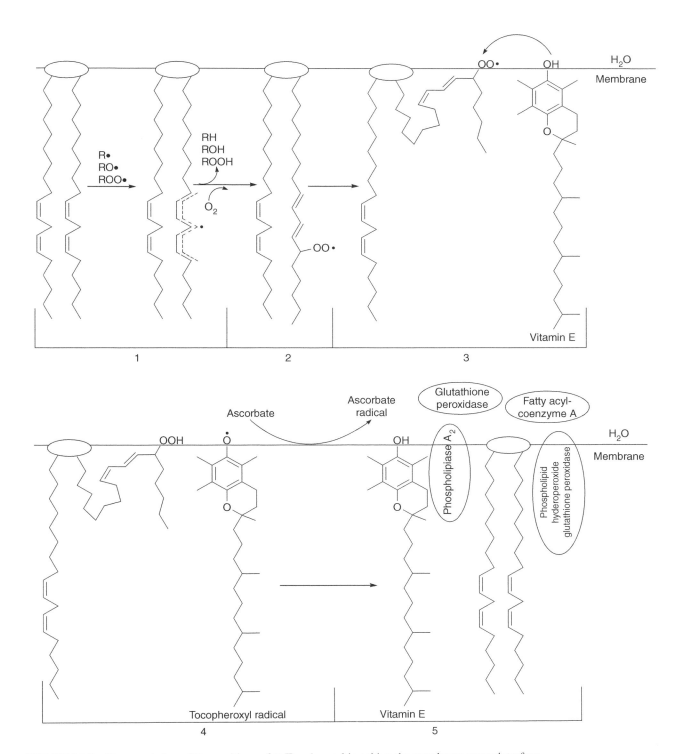

FIGURE 11.7 Representation of the positions of α-T and ascorbic acid at the membrane-water interface.

suggested that tocotrienols should be considered as a specific group of food components independent of the tocopherols due to specific differences in action that differ from actions of α-T. Such specific actions include posttranscriptional suppression of 3-hydroxy-3-methylglutaryl Co A reductase (HMG-Co A reductase) through a cell signaling event (108, 109). The ability of tocotrienol supplements to lower human total serum cholesterol levels is currently controversial (110).

2. Vitamin E Deficiency

Vitamin E deficiency in humans is almost always due to factors other than dietary insufficiency. Deficiency results from genetic abnormalities in production of the α-tocopherol transfer protein (α-TTP), fat malabsorption syndromes, and protein-energy malnutrition (3). Fat-malabsorption can be related to pancreatic and liver abnormalities that lower fat absorption, abnormalities of the intestinal cells, length of the intestine and defects in the synthesis or assembly of the chylomicrons (61). Genetic abnormalities in lipoprotein metabolism can produce low levels of cylomicrons, very low density lipoproteins (VLDL) and low density lipoprotein (LDL) that affects absorption and transport of vitamin E (111). Abetalipoproteinemia is an autosome recessive genetic disorder leading to mutations in the microsomal triglyceride transfer protein (112). The disease is associated with ataxia and impaired intestinal absorption of lipids and vitamin E, since the triglyceride transfer protein participates in the transport of lipids and other fat-soluble substances. Defects in the gene that codes for α-TTP leads to an inherited autosomal recessive disease referred to as familial isolated vitamin E deficiency or ataxia with vitamin E deficiency (AVED) (112–114). Changes in α-TTP result in inefficient transfer of RRR-α-T from the liver and recycling of plasma RRR-α-T.

Clinical symptoms include many neurological problems stemming from peripheral neuropathy with degeneration of the large-caliber axons in the sensory neurons (3). Common symptoms are ataxia, muscle weakness and hypertrophy, neurological abnormalities, reproductive disorders, abnormalities of the liver, bone marrow, and brain (61). At the cellular level, increased oxidation can occur due to increased oxidative stress.

3. Dietary Reference Intakes

When establishing the dietary reference intakes (DRIs) for vitamin E, the Institute of Medicine, Panel on Dietary Antioxidants and Related Compounds decided that human requirements should only be based on the 2-R isomers of α-T (RRR-, RSR-, RRS-, RSS-) (3). This decision stems from the accumulated evidence of the strong selectivity of α-TTP for the 2-R isomers in the liver which leads to preferential secretion of the 2-R isomers into nascent VLDL. Other forms of vitamin E (2-S isomers of α-T, β-T, γ-T, δ-T, tocotrienols) are primarily secreted into the bile and excreted. The selection process is not 100% effective; however, only small amounts of other dietary and supplemental vitamin E forms are delivered to the cells.

For adults, EAR and RDA are 12 and 15 mg of α-T per day, respectively (Table 11.2). The UL value includes all forms of α-T from supplemental intake of all-rac-α-T. The UL is 1000 mg/day.

Since the DRI values refer only to 2R-α-T forms, discussion is necessary on the units used to report vitamin E concentrations in foods and pharmaceuticals. Currently used units include the following:

1. International Units (IU) and USP Units

$$Molar\ Conversion\ Factor\ (\mu mol/IU) = \frac{USP\ Conversion\ Factor\ (mg/IU) \times 1000\ (\mu mol/mol)}{Molecular\ Weight\ (mg/mol)}$$

Calculation for RRR-α-tocopheryl acetate:

$$Molar\ Conversion\ Factor\ (\mu mol/IU) = \frac{USP\ Conversion\ Factor\ (mg/IU) \times 1000\ (\mu mol/mol)}{Molecular\ Weight\ (mg/mol)}$$

$$= \frac{0.735\ (mg/IU) \times 1000\ (\mu mol/mol)}{472\ (mg/mol)} = 1.56\ (\mu mol\ /\ IU)$$

$$\alpha\text{-}T\ Conversion\ Factor\ (mg/IU) = \frac{Molar\ Conversion\ Factor\ (\mu mol/IU) \times 430\ (mg/mol)}{1000\ (\mu mol/mol) \times R}$$

Where R=2 for synthetic vitamin E and esters, R=1 for natural vitamin E and esters. So, the α-T conversion factor for RRR-α-tocopheryl acetate is determined as follows:

$$\alpha\text{-}T\ Conversion\ Factor\ (mg/IU) = \frac{Molar\ Conversion\ Factor\ (\mu mol/IU) \times 430\ (mg/mol)}{1000\ (\mu mol/mol) \times R}$$

$$= \frac{1.56\ (\mu mol/IU) \times 430\ (mg/mol)}{1000\ (\mu mol/mol) \times 1} = 0.067\ (mg/IU)$$

The United States Pharmacopeia (USP) (115) defined the IU of vitamin E as 1 mg of all-rac-α-tocopheryl acetate based on biological activity measured by the rat fetal absorption test. Biological activities of various vitamin E forms in relation to the activity of all-rac-α-tocopheryl acetate are given in Table 11.6. After 1980, the USP discontinued use of the IU and replaced it with USP units based on the same basis of biological activity as the IU (3). One USP unit is defined as the activity of 1 mg of all-rac-α-tocopheryl acetate. Therefore, USP units and IUs are equivalent (116).

The Institute of Medicine, Panel on Dietary Antioxidants and Related Compounds (3) recommended that USP units be redefined by USP to take into account the fact that all-rac-α-T has only 50% of the activity of RRR-α-T present in nature or with other 2R stereoisomers found in all-rac-α-T preparations that are used for food fortification and in supplements (3). Factors to convert USP units (IUs) to RRR-α-T or other 2R-isomers of α-T are given in Table 11.7.

Derivation of the conversion factors given in Table 11.7 follows the general formula:

2. α-Tocopherol Equivalents

TABLE 11.6
Biological Activity of Natural and Synthetic Vitamin E Forms[a]

Vitamin E Forms	Biological Activity	
	USP Units (IU)/mg	Compared to RRR-α-T (%)
Natural Vitamin E (RRR-)		
α-Tocopherol	1.49	100
β-Tocopherol	0.75	50
γ-Tocopherol	0.15	10
δ-Tocopherol	0.05	3
α-Tocotrienol	0.75	50
β-Tocotrienol	0.08	5
γ-Tocotrienol	Not known	Not known
δ-Tocotrienol	Not known	Not known
Synthetic		
2R4′R8′R α-tocopherol	1.49	100
2S4′R8′R α-tocopherol	0.46	31
Allrac-α-tocopherol	1.10	74
2R4′R8′S α-tocopherol	1.34	90
2S4′R8′S α-tocopherol	0.55	37
2R4′S8′S α-tocopherol	1.09	73
2S4′S8′R α-tocopherol	0.31	21
2R4′S8′R α-tocopherol	0.85	57
2S4′S8′S α-tocopherol	1.10	60
RRR-α-tocopheryl acetate	1.36	91
RRR-α-tocopheryl acid succinate	1.21	81
Allrac-α-tocopheryl acetate	1.00	67
Allrac-α-tocopheryl acid succinate	0.89	60

[a]*Source*: Ref. 8.

α-Tocopherol Equivalents (α-TEs) were defined for recommending dietary intakes of vitamin E based on biological activity of tocopherols and tocotrienols determined by the rat fetal absorption test (Table 11.6) (117). One mg of α-TE is the activity of 1 mg of RRR-α-T. Total α-TEs (mg) of mixed diets containing only RRR-isomers is determined by multiplying the amount (mg) of α-T by 1.0, β-T by 0.5, γ-T by 0.1, α-T3 by 0.3, and γ-T3 by 0.05. In fortified foods, the conversion factors for all-rac-α-T and all-rac-α-tocopheryl acetate are 0.74 and 0.67, respectively. Use of the α-TE unit has been the accepted way of reporting vitamin E concentration in foods for approximately the past two decades. The Panel on Antioxidants and Related Compounds (3) determined from USDA food intake survey data that 80% of the α-TE from foods arises from RRR-α-T. Therefore, to convert α-TE mg to RRR-α-T, the conversion factor is 0.8.

The following conversions are fully explained in the Dietary References Intake report (3):

a. mg of α-T in a meal = mg of α-TE × 0.8
b. mg of α-T in a food, fortified food, or multivitamin = IU (USP unit) of RRR-α-T × 0.67 or IU (USP Unit) of all-rac-α-T × 0.45

Anytime both natural and synthetic forms of α-T are present, analytical procedures must be capable of resolution of the specific compounds in order to apply the above formulas. Almost always in a fortified food, both RRR-α-T and all-rac-α-tocopheryl acetate will exist together.

4. Food Sources and Dietary Intake

The second National Health and Nutrition Examination Survey (NHANES II) has been extensively evaluated to show dietary sources of vitamin E in the United States. Major food groups contribute the following percentages of total vitamin E: fats and oils, 20.2; vegetables, 15.1; meat, poultry, and fish, 12.6; desserts, 9.9; breakfast cereals, 9.3; fruit, 5.3; dairy products, 4.5; mixed main dishes, 4.0; nuts and seeds, 3.8; soups, sauces, and gravies, 1.7 (3, 117). Data collected from the Continuing Survey of Food Intakes by Individuals (CSFII, 1994) are given in Table 11.8 (D. Haytowitz, personal communication, 2003). The tabulation shows that high oil content foods are major sources but cereals fortified with α-tocopheryl acetate are also significant sources. Raw tomatoes and tomato products, due to high consumption, are significant sources of vitamin E in the U.S. diet.

Using the CSFII and NHANES data as well as other studies, the DRI committee estimated the median intake of α-T from food and supplements at 9.8 mg for men and 6.8 mg for women (3). It was emphasized that data on vitamin E intake from food intake surveys might be low due to potential for underreporting of energy and fat intake, problems with assessment of fats and oils added during food preparation, uncertainty about the types of fats added, and the variability of food composition tables.

TABLE 11.7

Conversion Factors to Calculate α-Tocopherol from International Units or USP Units to Meet Dietary Reference Intakes for Vitamin E[a]

	USP Units (IU)/mg	mg/USP Units (IU)	μmol/USP Unit (IU)	α-Tocopherol mg/USP Unit (IU)
Natural Vitamin E				
RRR-α-tocopherol	1.49	0.67	1.56	0.67
RRR-α-tocopheryl acetate	1.36	0.74	1.56	0.67
RRR-α-tocopheryl acid succinate	1.21	0.83	1.56	0.67
Synthetic Vitamin E				
All-*rac*-α-tocopherol	1.1	0.91	2.12	0.45
All-*rac*-α-tocopheryl acetate	1	1	2.12	0.45
All-*rac*-α-tocopheryl acid succinate	0.89	1.12	2.12	0.45

[a] *Source*: Ref. 8.

TABLE 11.8

Significant Sources of Vitamin E in the Diet in the United States[a]

		% Vitamin E in U.S. Diet[b]
1	Margarine, regular stick, 80% fat	5.5
2	Salad dressing, mayonnaise, soybean oil, with salt	4.3
3	Oil, soybean, salad or cooking	3.1
4	Cereals, ready-to-eat, Total	2.8
5	Oil, corn, salad or cooking	2.7
6	Shortening, composite, household	2.5
7	Salad dressing, Italian, commercial, regular, with salt	2.4
8	Peanut butter, smooth, with salt	2.3
9	Snacks, potato chips, plain, salted	2.3
10	Eggs, whole, raw, fresh, frozen	2
11	Sauce, pasta, spaghetti/marinara, ready-to-serve	1.6
12	Oil, canola	1.4
13	Tomato products, canned, sauce	1.2
14	Shortening, composite, institutional	1.1
15	Rolls, hamburger or hot dog, plain	1
16	Margarine-like spread, tub, composite, 60% fat, with salt	1
17	Milk, cow, whole, fluid, 3.3% fat	1
18	Oil, cottonseed, salt or cooking	0.9
19	Tomato products, canned, puree, without salt	0.9
20	Fast foods, chicken, breaded, fried, boneless, plain	0.9
21	Broccoli, cooked, boiled, drained	0.9
22	Tomatoes, red, ripe, raw	0.7

[a]*Source*: D. Haytowitz, 2003.
[b]Calculated on the basis of mg α-tocopherol equivalents (mg α–TE).

Although the estimated median intakes for men and women are below the RDA of 15 mg of α-T per day (Table 11.2) and many clinical studies exist that indicate beneficial responses to supplemental vitamin E, the panel believed that clinical evidence was too limited to recommend use of vitamin E supplements for the general population.

V. VITAMIN K

Vitamin K was characterized through the efforts of several research groups in the 1930s. Observations by Dam in Denmark showed that chicks developed blood with poor clotting properties and fatal hemorrhages when fed diets extracted with ether (118). Addition of the ether extract back to the diet alleviated the deficiency. The fat-soluble factor was named vitamin K by Dam in 1935 based on the word "koagulation." In 1939, the vitamin K form (2-methyl-3-phytyl-1,4-naphthoquinone) was isolated by research groups led by Dam and Doisy (119, 120). The vitamin K_1 designation was given along with the generic name of phylloquinone. Vitamin K_2, the menaquinone-n (MK-n) form, was isolated from fermented fish meal by Doisy's group in 1939. Vitamin K_1 was synthesized by Doisy's group in 1939. In 1943, both Dam and Doisy were awarded Nobel Prizes for their work on isolation and synthesis of vitamin K.

A. CHEMISTRY

Vitamin K compounds consist of 2-methyl-1,4-naphthoquinone and all derivatives providing antihemorrhagic activity of vitamin K_1 (phylloquinone). 2-Methyl-1,4-naphthoquinone (Figure 11.8) is the parent compound of the family but does not occur in nature (120). It is commonly used in animal rations and is commercially referred to as menadione (vitamin K_3, MK-0) and, formerly, as menaquinone. Naturally occurring vitamin K forms include vitamin K_1 and the vitamin K_2 series. Vitamin K_1 is phylloquinone (2-methyl-3-phytyl-1,4-naphthoquinone) (Figure 11.8). Vitamin K_1 is synthesized in the plant kingdom and constitutes the primary food source of vitamin K activity (120). Alkylation at carbon-3 of the 2-methyl-1,4-napthoquinone ring with five-carbon isoprenoid units produces the vitamin K series. Vitamin $K_{1(20)}$, the most common phylloquinone, contains four isoprenoid units of which three are reduced. The reduced side chain or phytyl side chain at carbon-3

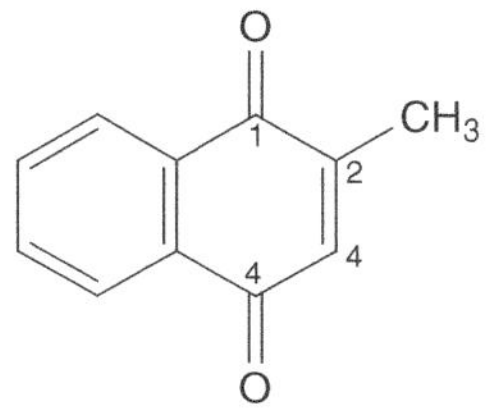

FIGURE 11.8 Structures of vitamin K and water-soluble menadione forms.

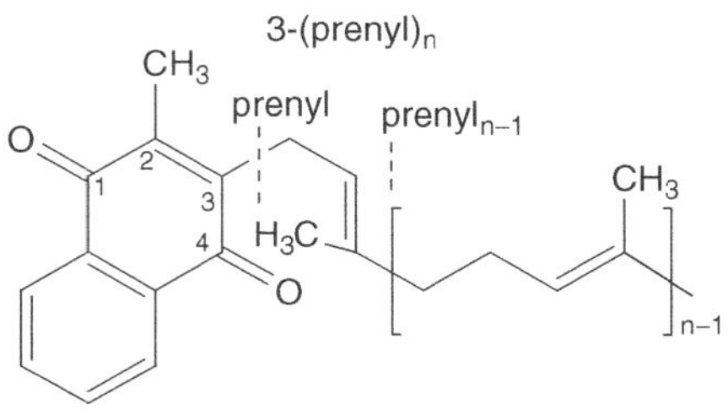

of the 2-methyl-1,4-naphthoquinone ring with one double bond characterizes the phylloquinones. The United States Pharmacopeia (USP) designates vitamin K_1 as phytonadione. USP phytonadione is a mixture of E and Z isomers with not more than 21% Z isomer content (115). Natural phylloquinone is 2′-E, 7′R, 11′R (118).

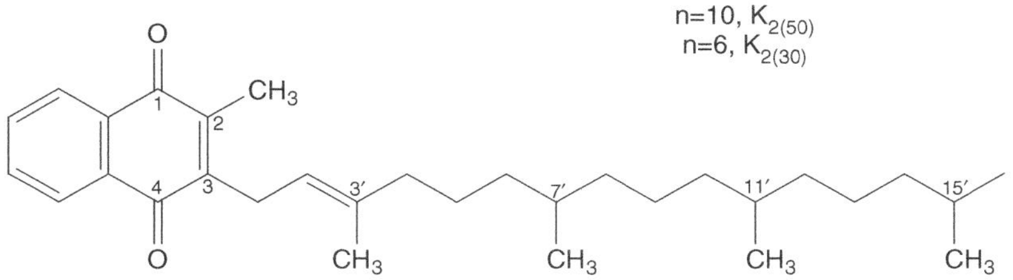

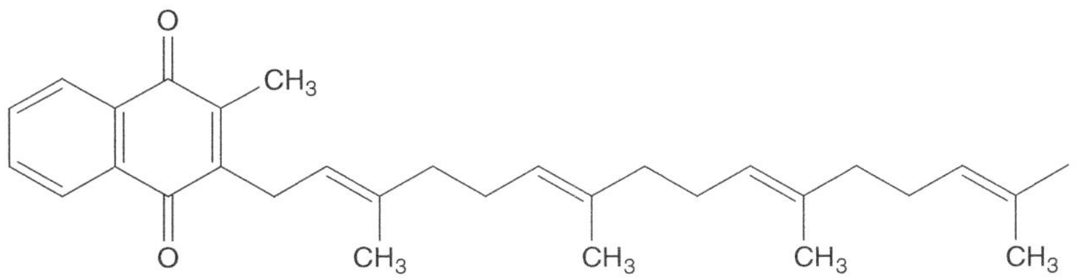

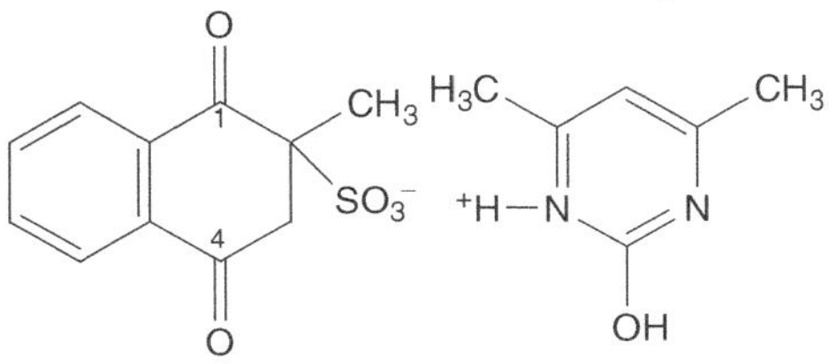

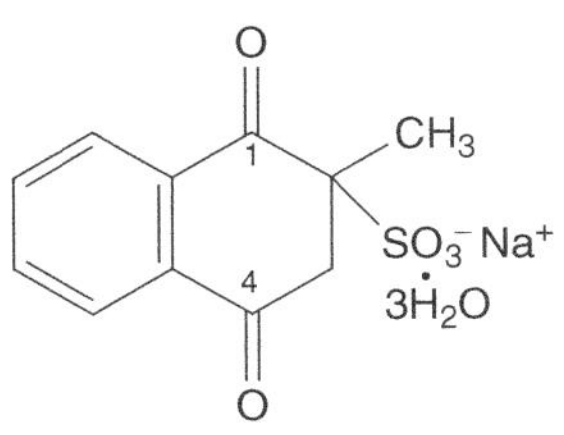

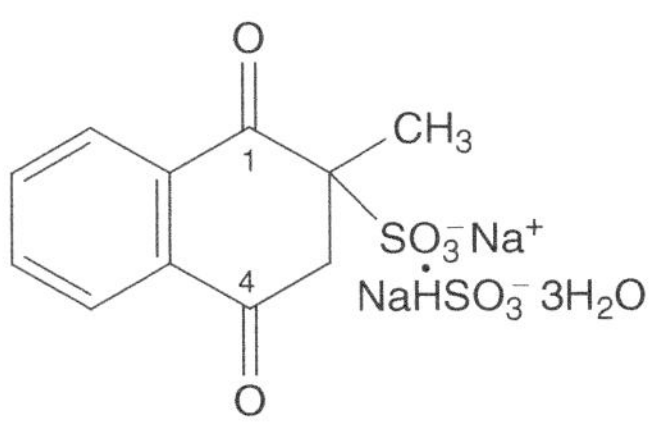

Vitamin K_2 (menaquinone-n series, MK-n) (Figure 11.8) have polyisoprenoid side chains at carbon-3 of the

2-methyl-1,4 naphthoquinone ring. Vitamin K_2 compounds are synthesized by bacteria except MK-4 is synthesized by birds and animals from menadione (119). Side chains are unsaturated and usually contain 4–13 isoprenoid units. The MK-n designation gives the number of prenyl groups in the side chain. One or more of the isoprenoid units may be reduced. Reduction usually occurs at the second isoprenoid units from the naphthoquinone ring (118). Physical properties of vitamin K compounds are given in Table 11.3.

Vitamin K compounds other than menadiones that are modified to increase water solubility are lipid-soluble and soluble in non-polar solvents. Vitamin K_1 (20) is synthesized and used by the food and supplement industries and for use in olestra-containing products (121). Menadione is toxic and not used for human supplements. It is an important nutritional additive to poultry and animal rations. Vitamin K_1 is not used in animal feeds due to cost (25). In poultry rations, chemotherapeutic agents inhibit intestinal synthesis of vitamin K and, therefore, increase dietary requirements (25). Stabilized forms of menadione with increased water solubility are available to the feed industry. These include menadione sodium bisulfate (MSB), menadione sodium bisulfite complex (MSBC), and menadione dimethyl-pyrimidol bisulfite (MPB) (Figure 11.8). The menadione salts are absorbed more efficiently than menadione and show greater stability due to their water solubility.

1. Spectral Properties

Both phylloquinones and menaquinones show UV spectra characteristic of the naphthoquinone ring. Phylloquinone shows absorption maxima at 242, 248, 260, 269, and 325 nm in hexane. The UV spectrum of menadione in hexane has an absorption maximum at 252 nm (25). Vitamin K compounds do not fluoresce. Conversion of the quinone to the hydroquinone induces strong fluorescence. Postcolumn reduction to the hydroquinone forms the basis of excellent quantitative procedures currently used for assay of vitamin K in foods, supplements, and other biological samples (122). The hydroquinone shows maximal fluorescence at $\lambda_{ex} = 244, \lambda_{em} = 418$.

2. Stability

Vitamin K is quite stable to oxidation and food processing and preparation conditions (122). It is unstable to light and alkalinity. Instability to alkalinity eliminates the use of saponification for extraction from foods; so, it is difficult to include extraction of vitamin K with multi-analyte procedures that rely on saponification as the initial step of the assay. Reducing agents destroy the biological activity of vitamin K_1. Isomerization of trans- to cis-isomers leads to loss of biological activity. Presence of variable quantities

of the cis-isomer in vitamin K concentrates requires that quantitative methods be capable of resolving cis- and trans-forms to accurately estimate biological activity (122).

B. NUTRITION AND BIOCHEMISTRY OF VITAMIN K

1. Functions of Vitamin K

Vitamin K is a cofactor for vitamin K-dependent carboxylase required for the posttranslational conversion of glutamic acid to gamma-carboxy-glutamyl residues (Gla) (120, 123). Numerous Gla-containing proteins are known. These include the blood coagulation proteins consisting of prothrombin (factor II, factors VII, IX, and X, and proteins C, S, and Z) (120). Three Gla proteins including osteocalcin, matrix Gla protein, and protein S (120, 123) are bone matrix components. Various other Gla proteins have been identified, but the functions for such vitamin K-dependent proteins are not clearly understood (120).

2. Vitamin K Deficiency

Deficiency of vitamin K in the adult is rare. It is defined as vitamin K-responsive hypoprothrombinemia characterized by an increase in prothrombin time (PT) (1). It usually results from fat malabsorption syndromes, liver disease, and antibiotic treatments that inhibit synthesis of vitamin K_2 by the gut microflora. Anticoagulant treatment with coumarin produces a secondary deficiency by disruption of vitamin K function and inhibition of synthesis of vitamin K-dependent clotting proteins.

In human infants, deficiency of vitamin K commonly occurs and is named hemorrhagic disease. The deficiency occurs through poor placental transfer of vitamin K from the mother to the fetus and lack of bacterial synthesis in the gut of the newborn baby. Other factors include the low concentration of vitamin K in breast milk and low concentrations of blood clotting factors at birth (120). Hemorrhages occurs in the skin, subcutaneous tissue, GI tract, umbilical cord, and intracranially. Central nervous system disorders can occur if untreated. Hemorrhagic disease is prevented by intramuscular injection of vitamin K_1 (0.5–1 mg) or oral dosage (2.0 mg) within 6 hours of birth (120). Breast-fed infants develop hemorrhagic disease more frequently than formula-fed infants because human milk is low in vitamin K. Infant formula is fortified at a minimum of 4 μg per 100 kcal as specified by the Infant Formula Act of 1980 (124).

3. Dietary Reference Intakes

The panel on DRIs for vitamin K was unable to establish average requirements for vitamin K because of lack of data; therefore, only Adequate Intake (AI) values were set (1). The AI levels are 120 and 90 μg/day for adult men and women, respectively (Table 11.2). Tolerable Upper Intake Levels (ULs) were not established, since no adverse effects have been reported at high intake levels (1).

4. Food Sources and Dietary Intake

Leafy green vegetables, certain legumes, and vegetable oils are considered good sources of vitamin K. Vitamin K_1 is the primary food source, and green leafy vegetables provide 40 to 50% of the total intake (125). Milk and dairy products, meats, eggs, cereals, fruits and vegetables, are low but consistent sources of vitamin K to the U.S. diet (122). Reliable data did not exist for the vitamin K content of the diet until excellent LC procedures were developed during the 1990s by Sadowski and colleagues (126–129). Establishment of methodology and collection of reliable data led to the development of a reliable database to estimate intake of vitamin K_1 (130). The database was based on vitamin K_1 intake in women's diets collected from the 1990 Food and Drug Administration Total Diet Study (130). Major food sources were spinach, collards, broccoli, iceberg lettuce, and coleslaw with salad dressing. Addition of fats and oils to mixed dishes is a significant source of vitamin K_1 (125). The panel on DRIs for vitamin K estimated the median intakes of vitamin K_1 for men and women to be 89 to 117 µg and 79 to 88 µg per day, respectively (1). Data from the Third National Health and Nutrition Examination Survey (NHANES III) (43) were used to estimate the intakes.

REFERENCES

1. Institute of Medicine. Food and Nutrition Board. Dietary Reference Intakes for Vitamin A, Vitamin K, Arsenic, Boron, Chromium, Copper, Iodine, Iron, Manganese, Molybdenum, Nickel, Silicon, Vanadium, and Zinc. Washington, D.C.: National Academy Press, 2002, pp 82–196.
2. Institute of Medicine. Food and Nutrition Board. Dietary Reference Intakes for Calcium, Phosphorous, Magnesium, Vitamin D, and Fluoride. Washington, D.C.: National Academy Press, 1999, pp 250–287.
3. Institute of Medicine. Food and Nutrition Board. Dietary Reference Intakes for Vitamin C, Vitamin E, Selenium, and Carotenoids. Washington, D.C.: National Academy Press, 2000, pp 186–283.
4. W Friedrich. Vitamin A and Its Provitamins. In: Vitamins. Berlin: Walter de Gruyter, 1988, pp 65–142.
5. RR Eitenmiller, WO Landen, Jr. Vitamin A and carotenoids. In: Vitamin Analyses for the Health and Food Sciences. Boca Raton: CRC Press, 1998, pp 3–75.
6. GJ Handelman. The evolving role of carotenoids in human biochemistry. Nutrition 17:818–822, 2001.
7. AC Ross. Vitamin A and carotenoids. In: ME Shils, JA Olson, M Shike, AC Ross, eds. Modern Nutrition in Health and Disease, 9th ed. Philadelphia: Lippincott Williams and Wilkins, 1998, pp 305–327.
8. L. Ye, RR Eitenmiller. Analysis of fat-soluble vitamins in food. In: L Nollet ed. Handbook of Food Analysis. New York: Marcel Dekker, Inc., 2004, pp 431–485.
9. ST Mayne. Beta-carotene, carotenoids, and disease prevention in humans. FASEB J 10:690–701, 1996.
10. HA Frank, JS Jasuea, JA Bautista, I Van der Hoef, FJ Jansen, J Lugtenburg, G Wiederrecht, RL Christensen. Spectroscopic and photochemical properties of open-chain carotenoids. J Phys Chem 106:2083–2092, 2002.
11. H-D Martin, C Jäger, C Ruck, M Schmidt. Anti- and prooxidant properties of carotenoids. J Prakt Chem 341:302–308, 1999.
12. BCL Weedon, GP Moss. Structure and nomenclature. In: G Britton, S Liaaen-Jensen, H Pfaner, eds. Carotenoids, Vol. 1A, Isolation and Analysis. Basel: Birkhäusen Verlag, 1995, pp 27–70.
13. JW Erdman, Jr., TL Bierer, ET Gugger. Absorption and transport of carotenoids. Ann NY Acad Sci 691:76–85, 1993.
14. RS Parker. Bioavailability of carotenoids. Eur J Clin Nutr 51:S86–S90, 1997.
15. NI Krinsky, X-D Wang, G Tang, RM Russel. Mechanism of carotenoid cleavage to retinoids. Ann NY Acad Sci 691:167–176, 1993.
16. S Budavari. The Merck Index. 13th ed., Whitehouse Station: Merck and Co., Inc., 2001.
17. AB Barua, JA Olson, HC Furr, RB van Breemen. Vitamin A and carotenoids. In: AP De Leenheer, WE Lambert, JF Van Bocxlaer, eds. Modern Chromatographic Analysis of Vitamins, 3rd ed., New York: Marcel Dekker, 2000, pp 1–74.
18. HC Furr, AB Barua, JA Olson. Analytical methods. In: MB Sporn, AB Roberts, DS Goodman, eds. The Retinoids, Biology, Chemistry and Medicine, 2nd ed., New York: Raven Press, 1994, pp 179–209.
19. JA Olson. Vitamin A. In: LJ Machlen, ed. 2nd ed., Handbook of Vitamins, New York: Marcel Dekker, 1991, pp 1–57.
20. AP De Leenheer, WE Lambert, E Meyer. Chromatography of retinoids. In: MA Livnea, L Packer, eds. Retinoids, Progress in Research and Clinical Applications. New York: Marcel Dekker, 1993, pp 551–568.
21. E Brinkmann, L Dehne, HB Oei, R Tiebach, W Baltes. Separation of geometrical retinol isomers in food samples by using narrow-bone high performance liquid chromatography. J Chromatogr A 693:271–279, 1995.
22. G Britton. UV/Visible spectroscopy. In: B Britton, S Liaaen-Jensen, H Pfaner, eds. Carotenoids, Vol. 1B, Spectroscopy. Basel: Birkhäusen Verlag, 1995, pp 13–62.
23. H Nyambaka, J Ryley. An isocratic reversed-phase HPLC separation of the stereoisomers of the provitamin A carotenoids (α- and β-carotene) in dark green vegetables. Food Chem 55:63–72, 1996.
24. C Emenhiser, LC Sander, SJ Schwartz. Capability of a polymeric C_{30} stationary phase to resolve cis-trans carotenoid isomers in reversed-phase liquid chromatography. J Chromatogr 707:205–216, 1995.
25. GFM Ball. Chemical and biological nature of the fat-soluble vitamins, Chapter 2. Fat Soluble Vitamin Assays,

Food Analysis – A Comprehensive Review. London: Elsevier Applied Science Publishers, 1988, pp 7–56.

26. DW Reische, DA Lillard, RR Eitenmiller. Antioxidants. In: C Akoh, D Min, eds. New York: Marcel Dekker, 2002, pp 489–516.

27. DC Liebler. Antioxidant reactions of carotenoids. Ann NY Acad Sci 691:20–31, 1993.

28. K Schiedt, S Liaaen-Jensen. Isolation and analysis. In: G. Britton, S Liaaen-Jensen, H Pfaner, Eds. Carotenoids, Vol. 1A, Isolation and Analysis, Basel: Birkhäusen Verlag, 1995, pp 81–108.

29. JA Olson. Vitamin A. In: RB Rucker, JW Suttie, DB McCormick, LJ Machlin, eds. Handbook of Vitamins, 3rd ed., New York: Marcel Dekker, 2001, pp 1–50.

30. H van der Berg. Vitamin A intake and status. Eur J Clin Nutr 50:S7–S12, 1996.

31. NW Solomons. Vitamin A and carotenoids. In: BA Bowman, RM Russell, eds. Present Knowledge in Nutrition, 8th ed., Washington, D.C.: ILSI Press, 2001, pp 127–145.

32. Food Standards Agency, UK. Safe Upper Levels for Vitamins and Minerals, May 2003. http://www.food-standards.gov.uk/multimedia/pdfs/vitmin2003.pdf.

33. World Health Organization. Global prevalence of vitamin A deficiency. Micronutrient Deficiency Information System Working Paper, No. 2. Geneva: WHO, 1995.

34. A Sommer, KP West, Jr. Vitamin A Deficiency, Health, Survival and Vision. New York: Oxford University Press, 1996.

35. LC Sander, KE Sharpless, NE Craft, SA Wise. Development of engineered stationary phases for the separation of carotenoids isomers. Anal Chem 66:1667–1674, 1994.

36. A Schieber, M Marx, C Carle. Simultaneous determination of carotenes and tocopherols in ATBC drinks by high-performance liquid chromatography. Food Chem 76:357–362, 2002.

37. D Darnoko, E Cheryan, J Moros, EG Perkins. Simultaneous HPLC analysis of palm carotenoids and tocopherols using a C-30 column and photodiode array detector. J Liq Chrom & Rel Technol 23:1873–1885, 2000.

38. 21 CFR, 131, Milk and Cream; 166, Margarine.

39. AR Mangels, JM Holden, GR Beecher, MR Forman, E Lanza. Carotenoid content of fruits and vegetables: an evaluation of analytic data. J Am Diet Assoc 93:284–296, 1993.

40. JK Chug-Ahuja, JM Holden, MR Forman, AR Mangels, GR Beecher, E Lanza. The development and application of a carotenoid database for fruits, vegetables, and selected multicomponent foods. J Am Diet Assoc 93:318–323, 1993.

41. USDA, NCI, Carotenoid Food Composition Database Version I, 1993.

42. LC Yong, MR Forman, GR Beecher, BI Graubard, WS Campbell, ME Reichmann, PR Taylor, E Lanza, JM Holden, JT Judd. Relationship between dietary intake and plasma concentrations of carotenoids in pre-menopausal women: application of the USDA-NCl

Carotenoid food-composition database. J Am Clin Nutr 60:223–230, 1994.

43. National Center for Health Sciences. Third National Health and Nutrition Examination Survey, 1988–94: Reference Manual and Reports (CD-ROM). Hyattsville, MD: Centers for Disease Control and Prevention, 1996.

44. AW Norman. Vitamin D. In BA Bowman, RM Russell, eds., Present Knowledge in Nutrition, 8th ed., Washington, D.C.: ILSI Press, 2001, pp 146–155.

45. Commission on the Nomenclature of Biological Chemistry. Definative rules for the nomenclature of amino acids, steroids, vitamins and carotenoids. J Am Chem Soc 82:5575–5586, 1960.

46. IUPAC-IUB. Nomenclature of vitamin D, recommendations 1981. Eur J Biochem 124:223–227, 1982.

47. RR Eitenmiller, WO Landen, Jr. Vitamin D, In: Vitamin Analysis for the Health and Food Sciences. Boca Raton: CRC Press, 1998, pp 77–107.

48. SA Renken, JJ Warthesen. Vitamin stability in milk. J Food Sci 58:552–556, 1993.

49. H Indyk, V Littlejohn, DC Woollard. Stability of vitamin D_3 during spray-drying of milk. Food Chem 57:283–286, 1996.

50. HL Henry, AW Norman. Studies on calciferol metabolism. IX. Renal 25-hydroxy-vitamin D_3-1-hydroxylase. Involvement of cytochrome P-450 and other properties. J Biol Chem 249:7529–7535, 1974.

51. ED Cullins, AW Norman. Vitamin D. In: RB Rucker, JW Suttie, DB McCormick, LJ Machlin, eds. Handbook of Vitamins, 3rd ed., New York: Marcel Dekker, 2001, pp 51–113.

52. K Kinuta, H Tanaka, T Mariuake, K Aya, S Kato, Y Seino. Vitamin D is an important factor in estrogen biosynthesis of both female and male gonads. Endocrinology 141:1317–1324, 2000.

53. H Lal, R Pandey, SK Aggarwal. Vitamin D: Non-skeletal actions and effects on growth. Nutr Res 19:1683–1718, 1999.

54. D Krill, J Stoner, BR Konety, MJ Becich, RH Getzenberg. Differential effects of vitamin D on normal human prostate epithelial and stromal cells in primary culture. Urology 54:171–177, 1999.

55. M Lipkin, HL Newmark. Vitamin D, Calcium and prevention of breast cancer: A review. J Am Coll Nutr 18:392S–397S, 1999.

56. D Feldman, XY Zhao, AV Krishnan. Editorial/Mini-Review: Vitamin D and prostate cancer. Endocrinology 141:5–9, 2000.

57. GJCM van den Bemd, HAP Pols, JPTM van Leeuwen. Anti-tumor effects of 1,25-dihydroxyvitamin D_3 and vitamin D analogs. Curr Pharm Design 6:717–732, 2000.

58. BR Konety, E Leman, B Veitmeier, J Arlotti, R Dhir, RH Getzenberg. In vitro and in vivo effects of vitamin D (calcitriol) administration on the normal neonatal and prepubertal prostate. J Urology 164:1812–1818, 2000.

59. CM Hansen, D Hansen, PK Hom, L Binderup. Vitamin D compounds exert anti-apoptotic effects in human osteosarcoma cells in vitro. J Steroid Biochem & Mole Biol 77:1–11, 2001.

60. BR Konety, JP Lavelle, B Pirskalaishvili, R Dhir, SA Meyers, TST Nguyen, P Hershberger, MR Shuring, CS Johnson, DL Trump, ML Zeidel, RH Getzenberg. Effects of vitamin D (calcitriol) on transitional cell carcinoma of the bladder in vitro and in vivo. J Urology 165:253–258, 2001.

61. RE Olsen, PL Munson. Fat-soluble vitamins. In: PL Munson, RA Mueller, GR Breese, Eds. Principles of Pharmacology. New York: Chapman and Hall, 1994, pp 927–947.

62. O Sahota. Osteoporosis and the role of vitamin D and calcium-vitamin D deficiency, vitamin D insufficiency and vitamin D sufficiency. Age Ageing 29:301–304, 2000.

63. EF Eriksen, H Glerup. Vitamin D deficiency and aging: implications for general heath and osteoporosis. Biogerontology 3:73–77, 2002.

64. HCJP Janssen, MM Samson, HJJ Verhaar. Vitamin D deficiency, muscle function, and falls in elderly people. Am J Clin Nutr 75:611–615, 2002.

65. LM Gartner, FR Greer. Prevention of rickets and vitamin D deficiency: New guidelines for vitamin D intake. Pediatrics 111:908–910, 2003.

66. T Peregrin. Expanding vitamin D fortification: A balance between deficiency and toxicity. J Am Diet Assoc 102:1214–1216, 2002.

67. JT Tanner, J Smith, P Defibaugh, G Angyal, M Villalobos, MP Bueno, ET McGarrahan, HM Wehr, JF Muniz, BW Hollis, Y Koh, P Reich, KI Simpson. Survey of vitamin content of fortified milk. J Assoc Off Anal Chem 71:607–610, 1988.

68. MF Holick, Q Shao, WW Liu, TC Chen. The vitamin D content of fortified milk and infant formula. New Engl J Med 326:1178–1181, 1992.

69. TC Chen, Q Shao, H Heath, MF Holick. An update on the vitamin-D content of fortified milk from the United States and Canada. New Engl J Med 329:1507–1507, 1993.

70. HM Evans, KS Bishop. On the existence of a hitherto unrecognized dietary factor essential for reproduction. Science 56:650–651, 1922.

71. HM Evans, OH Emerson, GA Emerson. The isolation from wheat germ oil of an alcohol alpha-tocopherol, having the properties of vitamin E. J Biol Chem 113:319–332, 1936.

72. A Papas. The Vitamin E Factor. New York: Harper Collins Publishers, Inc., 1999.

73. OH Emerson, GA Emerson, A Mahammad, HM Evans. The chemistry of vitamin E. Tocopherols from various sources. J Biol Chem 122:99–107, 1937.

74. E Fernholz. The thermal decompostion of α-tocopherol. J Am Chem Soc 59:1154–1155, 1937.

75. E Fernholz. On the constitution of alpha-tocopherol. J Am Chem Soc 60:700–705, 1938.

76. P Karrer, H Frizsche, BH Ringier, A Solomon. Synthese des alpha-tocopherol. Helv Chim Acta 21:820–825, 1938.

77. HS Olcott, OH Emerson. Antioxidants and the autoxidation of fats. IX. The antioxidant properties of tocopherols. J Am Chem Soc 59:1008–1009, 1937.

78. MG Stern, CD Robeson, L Weisler, JG Baxter. δ-Tocopherol I. Isolation from soybean oil and properties. J Am Chem Soc 69:869–874, 1947.

79. JF Pennock, FW Hemming, JD Kerr. Reassessment of tocopherol chemistry. Biochim Biophys Res Commun 17:542–548, 1964.

80. KJ Whittle, PJ Durphy, JF Pennock. The isolation and properties of δ-tocotrienol. Biochem J 100:138–145, 1966.

81. PL Harris, ML Quaife, WJ Swanson. Vitamin E content of foods. J Nutr 40:367–381, 1950.

82. IUPAC-IUB Commission on Biochemical Nomenclature. Nomenclature of tocopherols and related compounds. Recommendations 1973. Eur J Biochem 46:217–219, 1974.

83. IUPAC-IUB Joint Commission on Biochemical Nomenclature (JCBN). Nomenclature of tocopherols and related compounds. Recommendations 1981. Eur J Biochem 123:473–475, 1982.

84. AIN Committee on Nomenclature. Nomenclature policy: Generic descriptors and trivial names for vitamins and related compounds. J Nutr 120:12–19, 1990.

85. H Mayer, J Metzger, O Isler. Die Stereochemic von natürlichem γ-Tocotrienol (Plastochromanol-3), und Plastochromanol-8. Helv Chim Acta 50:1376–1393, 1967.

86. S Kijima. Chemistry of Vitamin E. In: M Mino, H Nakamura, AT Diplock, HJ Kayden, eds. Vitamin E. Tokyo: Japan Scientific Societies Press, 1993, pp 3–12.

87. LJ Machlin, ed. Handbook of Vitamins, 2nd ed., New York: Marcel Dekker, 1991, p 105.

88. RR Eitenmiller, WO Landen, Jr. Vitamin E. Vitamin Analysis for the Health and Food Sciences. Boca Raton: CRC Press, 1998, pp 109–148.

89. W Friedrich, Vitamin E. In: Vitamins. Berlin: Walter de Gruyter, 1988, pp 217–283.

90. S Kasparek. Chemistry of tocopherols and tocotrienols. In: LJ Machlin, ed. Vitamin E: A Comprehensive Treatise, New York: Marcel Dekker, 1980, pp 7–65.

91. IM Kofler, PL Sommer, HR Bollinger, B Schmidili, M Vecchi. Physiochemical properties and assay of the tocopherols. In: RS Harris, IG Wool, GF Marrian, KV Thimann, eds. Vitamin and Hormones, Vol. 20. New York: Academic Press, 1962, pp 407–439.

92. P Schudel, H Mayer, O Isler. Tocopherols II. Chemistry. In: WH Sebrell, Jr., RS Harris, eds. The Vitamins, Vol. V. New York: Academic Press, 1972, pp 168–218.

93. RB McCoy, MM King. Vitamin E: Its role as a biological free radical scavenger and its relationship to the microsomal mixed-function oxidase system. In: LJ Machlin, ed. Vitamin E. A Comprehensive Treatise. New York: Marcel Dekker, Inc, 1980, pp 289–317.

94. GW Burton. Vitamin E: molecular and biological function. Proc Nutr Soc 53:251–262, 1994.

95. M Namki. Antioxidants/antimutagens in food. Crit Rev Food Sci Nutr 29:273–300, 1990.

96. B Halliwell, Antioxidants in human health and disease. Annu Rev Nutr 16:33–60, 1996.

97. L del Rio, FJ Corpas, LM Sandalio, JM Palma, M Gomez, JB Barroso. Reactive oxygen species, antioxidant systems and nitric oxide in peroxisomes. J Exp Botany 53:1255–1272, 2002.

98. JA Thomas. Oxidative stress and oxidant defense. In: ME Shills, JA Olson, M Shike, AC Ross, eds. Modern

Nutrition in Health and Disease, 9th ed. Baltimore: Williams and Wilkens, 1999, pp 751–760.

99. L Packer, SU Weber, G Rimback. Molecular aspects of α-tocotrienol antioxidant action and cell signaling. J Nutr 131:3695–3735, 2001.

100. R Ricciarelli, J-M Zingg, A Azzi. Vitamin E 80th anniversary: A double life, not only fighting radicals. IUBMB Life 52:71–76, 2001.

101. R Ricciarilli, J-M Zingg, A Azzi. Vitamin E: protective role of a Janus molecule. FASEB J 15:2314–2325, 2001.

102. The 80th anniversity of vitamin E: Beyond its antioxidant properties. Biol Chem 383:457–465, 2002.

103. G Rimback, AM Minihane, J Majewicz, A Fischer, J Pallauf, F Virgli, PD Weinberg. Regulation of cell signaling by vitamin E. Proc Nutr Soc 61:415–425, 2002.

104. R Brigelius-Flohé, FJ Kelly, JT Salonen, J Nenzil, J-M Zingg, A Azzi. The European perspective on vitamin E: current knowledge and future research. Am J Clin Nutr 76:703–716, 2002.

105. R Gopalakrishna, U Gundimeda. Antioxidant regulation of protein kinase C in cancer prevention. J Nutr 132:38195–38235, 2002.

106. R Ricciarelli, A Tasinate, S Clement, NK Ozer, D Boscoboinik, A Azzi. Alpha-tocopherol specifically inactivates cellular protein kinase C alpha by changing its phosphorylation state. Biochem J 334:243–249, 1998.

107. S Hendrich, KW Lee, X Xu, HJ Wang and PA Murphy. Defining food components as new nutrients. J Nutr 124:S1789–S1792, 1994.

108. AA Qureshi, WB Burger, DM Peterson, CE Elson. The structure of an inhibitor of cholesterol biosynthesis isolated from barley. J Biol Chem 261:10544–10550, 1986.

109. RA Parker, BC Pearce, RW Clark, DA Gordon, JJ Wright. Tocotrienols regulate cholesterol production in mammalian cells by post transcriptional suppression of 3-hydroxy-3-methylglutaryl-coenzyme A reductase. J Biol Chem 268:11230–11238, 1993.

110. D Kerckhoffs, F Brouns, G Hornstra, RP Mensink. Effects on the human serum profile of β-glucan, soy-protein and isoflavones, plant sterols and stanols, garlic and tocotrienols. J Nutr 132:2494–2505, 2002.

111. DJ Rader, HB Brewer. Abetalipoproteinemia – new insights into lipoprotein assembly and vitamin E metabolism from a rare genetic disease. JAMA 270:865–869, 1993.

112. N Gordon. Hereditary vitamin E deficiency. Dev Med Child Neurol 43:133–135, 2001.

113. K Ouahchi, M Arita, H Kayden, F Hentati, M Ben Hamida, R Sukol, H Arai, K Inoue, JL Mandel, M Koening. Ataxia with isolated vitamin E deficiency is caused by mutations in the α-tocopherol transfer protein. Nat Genet 8:141–145, 1995.

114. L Cavalier, K Ouahchi, HJ Kaydeb, S DiDonato, Z Reutennauer, JL Mandel, M Koenig. Ataxia with isolated vitamin E deficiency: heterogeneity of mutations and phenotypic variability in large number of families. Am J Human Genet 62:301–310, 1998.

115. United States Pharmacopeial Convention. U.S. Pharmacopeia National Formulary. USP 25/NF20. Nutritional Supplements, Official Monographs, United States Pharmacopeial Convention, Rockville, MD, 2002.

116. National Research Council. Recommended Dietary Allowances. 10th ed., Washington, D.C.: National Academy Press, 1989, p 100.

117. SP Murphy, AF Subar, G Block. Vitamin E intakes and sources in the United States. Am J Clin Nutr 52:361–367, 1990.

118. W Friedrich. Vitamin K. In: Vitamins. Berlin: Walter de Gruyter. 1988, pp 288–338.

119. RE Olson. Vitamin K. In: ME Shels, JA Olson, M Shike, AC Ross, eds., Modern Nutrition in Health and Disease, 9th ed., Philadelphia: Lippincott Williams and Wilkens, 1998, pp 363–380.

120. G Ferland. Vitamin K. In: BA Bowman, RM Russell, eds., Present Knowledge in Nutrition, 9th ed., Washington, D.C.: ILSI Press, 2001, pp 164–172.

121. 21 CFR172.867, Olestra.

122. RR Eitenmiller, WO Landen, Jr. Vitamin K. In: Vitamin Analyses for the Health and Food Sciences. Boca Raton: CRC Press, 1998, pp 149–184.

123. A Zitterman. Effects of vitamin K on calcium and bone metabolism. Cur Opin Clin Nutr Metabol Care 4:483–487, 2001.

124. The Infant Formula Act of 1980 (Public Law 96-359, 94 Stat. 1190–1195). Section 412, 21 United States Code 350a, 21CFR107.100.

125. SL Booth, JW Suttie. Dietary Intake and Adequacy of Vitamin K_1. J Nutr 128:785–788, 1998.

126. G Ferland, JA Sadowski. Vitamin K_1 (phylloquinone) content of edible oils: effects of heating and light exposure. J Agric Food Chem 40:1869–1873, 1992.

127. G Ferland, JA Sadowski. Vitamin K_1 (phylloquinone) content of green leafy vegetables: effects of plant maturation and geographical growth location. J Agric Food Chem 40:1874–1877, 1992.

128. SL Booth, JA Sadowski, JL Weihrauch, G Ferland. Vitamin K_1 (phylloquinone) content of foods: a provisional table. J Food Comp Anal 6:109–120, 1993.

129. SL Booth, KW Davidson, JA Sadowski. Evaluation of a HPLC method for the determination of phylloquinone (vitamin K_1) in various food matrices. J Agric Food Chem 42:295–300, 1994.

130. SL Booth, JAT Pennington, JA Sadowski. Food sources and dietary intakes of vitamin K_1 (phylloquinone) in the American diet: data from the FDA Total Diet Study. J Am Diet Assoc 96:149–154, 1996.

131. W Friedrich, Vitamin D. In: Vitamins. Berlin: Walter de Gruyter, 1988, pp 141–216.

132. HF DeLuca. Vitamin D. In: The Fat-Soluble Vitamins. New York: Plenum Press, 1978, pp 69–132.

133. TS Shin, JS Godber. Isolation of four tocopherols and four tocotrienols from a variety of natural sources by semi-preparative high performance liquid chromatography. J Chromatogr A 678:49–58, 1994.

12 Fundamental Characteristics of Water

Chung Chieh
Department of Chemistry, University of Waterloo

CONTENTS

I. INTRODUCTION

Water, a natural occurring and abundant substance that exists in solid, liquid, and gas forms on the planet Earth, has attracted the attention of artists, engineers, poets, writers, philosophers, environmentalists, scientists, and politicians. Every aspect of life involves water as food, as a medium in which to live, or as the essential ingredient of life. The food science aspects of water range from agriculture, aquaculture, biology, biochemistry, cookery, microbiology, nutrition, photosynthesis, power generation, to zoology. Even in the narrow sense of food technology, water is intimately involved in the production,

washing, preparation, manufacture, cooling, drying, and hydration of food. Water is eaten, absorbed, transported, and utilized by cells. Facts and data about water are abundant and diverse. This chapter can only selectively present some fundamental characteristics of water molecules and their collective properties for readers when they ponder food science at the molecular level.

The physics and chemistry of water are the backbone of engineering and sciences. The basic data for the properties of pure water, which are found in the CRC Handbook of Chemistry and Physics (1), are useful for food scientists. However, water is a universal solvent, and natural waters contain dissolved substances present in the environment. All solutes in the dilute solutions modify the water properties. Lang's Handbook of Chemistry (2) gives solubility of various gases and salts in water. Water usage in the food processing industry is briefly described in the Nalco Water Handbook (3). For water supplies and treatments, the Civil Engineering Handbook (4) provides practical guides. The Handbook of Drinking Water Quality (5) sets guidelines for waters used in food services and technologies. Wastewater from the food industry needs treatment, and the technology is usually dealt with in industrial chemistry (6). Most fresh food contains large amounts of water. Modifying the water content of foodstuffs to extend storage life and enhance quality is an important and widely used process (7).

A very broad view and deep insight on water can be found in "Water – A Matrix of Life" (8). Research leading to our present-day understanding of water has been reviewed in the series "Water – A Comprehensive Treatise" (9). The interaction of water with proteins (10, 11) is a topic in life science and food science. Water is the elixir of life and H_2O is a biomolecule.

II. WATER AND FOOD TECHNOLOGY

Water is an essential component of food (12). Philosophical conjectures abound as to how Earth evolved to provide the mantle, crust, atmosphere, hydrosphere, and life. Debates continue, but some scientists believe that primitive forms of life began to form in water (13). Complicated life forms developed, and their numbers grew. Evolution produced anaerobic, aerobic, and photosynthetic organisms. The existence of abundant life forms enabled parasites to appear and utilize plants and other organisms. From water all life began (14). Homo sapiens are integral parts of the environment, and constant exchange of water unites our internal space with the environment.

The proper amount of water is also the key to sustaining and maintaining a healthy life. Water transports nutrients and metabolic products throughout the body to balance cell contents and requirements. Water maintains biological activities of proteins, nucleotides, and carbohydrates, and participates in hydrolyses, condensations, and chemical reactions that are vital for life (15). On average, an adult consumes 2 to 3 L of water: 1–2 L as fluid, 1 L ingested with food, and 0.3 L from metabolism. Water is excreted via the kidney, skin, lung, and anus (16). The amount of water passing through us in our lifetimes is staggering.

Aside from minute amounts of minerals, food consists of plant and animal parts. Water is required for cultivating, processing, manufacturing, washing, cooking, and digesting food. During or after eating, a drink, which consists of mostly water, is a must to hydrate or digest the food. Furthermore, water is required in the metabolic process.

Cells and living organisms require, contain, and maintain a balance of water. An imbalance of water due to freezing, dehydration, exercise, overheating, etc. leads to the death of cells and eventually the whole body. Dehydration kills far more quickly than starvation. In the human body, water provides a medium for the transportation, digestion, and metabolism of food in addition to many other physiological functions such as body temperature regulation (17).

Two thirds of the body mass is water, and in most soft tissues, the contents can be as high as 99% (16). Water molecules interact with biomolecules intimately (9); they are part of us. Functions of water and biomolecules collectively manifest life. Water is also required for running households, making industrial goods, and generating electric power.

Water has shaped the landscape of Earth for trillions of years, and it covers 70% of the Earth's surface. Yet, for food production and technology it is a precious commodity. Problems with water supply can lead to disaster (5). Few brave souls accept the challenge to stay in areas with little rainfall. Yet, rainfall can be a blessing or a curse depending on the timing and amount. Praying for timely and bountiful rainfall used to be performed by emperors and politicians, but water for food challenges scientists and engineers today.

III. WATER MOLECULES AND THEIR MICROSCOPIC PROPERTIES

Plato hypothesized four *primal substances*: water, fire, earth, and air. His doctrine suggested that a combination and permutation of various amounts of these four *primal substances* produced all the materials of the world. Scholars followed this doctrine for 2000 years, until it could not explain experimental results. The search of fundamental substances led to the discovery of hydrogen, oxygen, nitrogen, etc., as chemical elements. Water is made up of hydrogen (H) and oxygen (O). Chemists use H_2O as the universal symbol for water. The molecular formula, H_2O, implies that a water molecule consists of two H atoms and one O atom. However, many people are confused by its other chemical names such as hydrogen oxide, dihydrogen oxide, dihydrogen monoxide, etc.

A. ISOTOPIC COMPOSITION OF WATER

The discoveries of electrons, radioactivity, protons, and neutrons implied the existence of isotopes. Natural isotopes for all elements have been identified. Three isotopes of hydrogen are protium (^1H), deuterium (D, ^2D or ^2H), and radioactive tritium (T, ^3T or ^3H), and the three stable oxygen isotopes are ^{16}O, ^{17}O, and ^{18}O. The masses and abundances of these isotopes are given in Table 12.1. For radioactive isotopes, the half-lives are given.

Random combination of these isotopes gives rise to the various isotopic water molecules, the most abundant

TABLE 12.1

Isotopes of Hydrogen and Oxygen, and Isotopic Water Molecules Molar Mass (amu), Relative Abundance (%) or Half Life

Isotopes of Hydrogen			Stable Isotopes of Oxygen		
^1H	^2D	^3T	^{16}O	^{17}O	^{18}O
1.007825	2.00141018	3.0160493	15.9949146	16.9991315	17.9991604
99.985%	0.015%	12.33 years	99.762%	0.038%	0.200%
Isotopic water molecules **molar mass (amu) and relative abundance (%, ppm or trace)**					
$H_2{}^{16}O$	$H_2{}^{18}O$	$H_2{}^{17}O$	$HD^{16}O$	$D_2{}^{16}O$	$HT^{16}O$
18.010564	20.014810	19.014781	19.00415	19.997737	20.018789
99.78%	0.20%	0.03%	0.0149%	0.022 ppm	trace

one being $^1H_2{}^{16}O$ (99.78%, its mass is 18.010564 atomic mass units (amu)). Water molecules with molecular masses about 19 and 20 are present at some fractions of a percent. Although $HD^{16}O$ (0.0149%) is much more abundant than $D_2{}^{16}O$ (heavy water, 0.022 part per million), D_2O can be concentrated and extracted from water. In the extraction process, HDO molecules are converted to D_2O due to isotopic exchange. Rather pure heavy water (D_2O) is produced on an industrial scale especially for its application in nuclear technology, which provides energy for the food industry.

A typical mass spectrum for water shows only mass-over-charge ratios of 18 and 17, respectively, for H_2O^+ and OH^+ ions in the gas phase. Other species are too weak for detection, partly due to condensation of water in mass spectrometers.

The isotopic composition of water depends on its source and age. Its study is linked to other sciences (18). For the isotopic analysis of hydrogen in water, the hydrogen is reduced to a hydrogen gas and then the mass spectrum of the gas is analyzed. For isotopes of oxygen, usually the oxygen in H_2O is allowed to exchange with CO_2, and then the isotopes of the CO_2 are analyzed. These analyses are performed on archeological food remains and unusual food samples in order to learn their origin, age, and history.

B. STRUCTURE AND BONDING OF WATER MOLECULES

Chemical bonding is a force that binds atoms into a molecule. Thus, chemists use H-O-H or HOH to represent the bonding in water. Furthermore, spectroscopic studies revealed the H–O–H bond angle to be 104.5° and the H–O bond length to be 96 picometers (pm = 10^{-12} m) for gas H_2O molecules (19). For solid and liquid, the values depend on the temperature and states of water. The bond length and bond angles are fundamental properties of a molecule. However, due to the vibration and rotational motions of the molecule, the measured values are average or equilibrium bond lengths and angles.

The mean van der Waals diameter of water has been reported as nearly identical with that of isoelectronic neon (282 pm). Some imaginary models of the water molecule are shown in Figure 12.1.

An isolated water molecule is hardly static. It constantly undergoes a vibration motion that can be a combination of any or all of the three principal modes: symmetric stretching, asymmetric stretching, and bending (or deformation). These vibration modes are indicated in Figure 12.2.

Absorption of light (photons) excites water molecules to higher energy levels. Absorption of photons in the

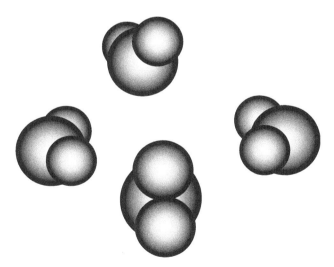

FIGURE 12.1 Some imaginative models of water molecules.

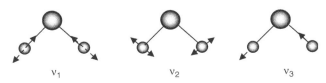

ν_1 ν_2 ν_3

FIGURE 12.2 The three principal vibration modes of the water molecule, H_2O: ν_1, symmetric stretching; ν_2, bending; and ν_3, asymmetric stretching.

infrared (IR) region excites the vibration motion. Photons exciting the symmetric stretching, bending, and asymmetric stretching to the next higher energy levels have wave numbers 3656, 1594, and 3756 cm^{-1}, respectively, for H_2O (20). These values and those for other water molecules involving only ^{16}O are given in Table 12.2.

The spectrum of water depends on temperature and density of the gaseous H_2O. A typical IR spectrum for the excitation of only the fundamental vibration modes consists of three peaks around 1594, 3656, and 3756 cm^{-1}. Additional peaks due to excitation to mixed modes appear at higher wave numbers.

Rotating the H_2O molecule around the line bisecting the HOH angle by 180° (360°/2) results in the same figure. Thus, the molecules have a 2-fold rotation axis. There are two mirror planes of symmetry as well. The 2-fold rotation and mirror planes give the water molecules the symmetry point group C_{2v}.

Rutherford's alpha scattering experiment in 1909 showed that almost all atomic mass is in a very small atomic nucleus. In a neutral atom the number of protons in the nucleus is the same as the number of electrons around the nucleus. A proton and an electron have the same amount, but different kinds of charge. Electrons occupy nearly all of the atomic volume, because the radius of an atom is 100,000 times that of the nucleus.

Electrons, in quantum mechanical view, are waves confined in atoms, and they exist in several energy states called orbitals. Electrons in atoms and molecules do not have fixed locations or orbits. Electron states in an element are called electronic configurations, and their designation for H and O are $1s^1$, and $1s^2 2s^2 2p^4$, respectively. The superscripts indicate the number of electrons in the orbitals $1s$, $2s$, or $2p$. The electronic configuration for the inert helium (He) is $1s^2$, and $1s^2$ is a stable core of electrons. Bonding or valence electrons are $1s^1$ and $2s^2 2p^4$ for H and O, respectively.

The valence bond approach blends one $2s$ and three $2p$ orbitals into four bonding orbitals, two of which accommodate two electron pairs. The other two orbitals have only one electron each, and they accommodate electrons of the H atoms bonded to O, thus forming the two H–O bonds. An electron pair around each H atom and four electron pairs

around the O atom contribute stable electronic configurations for H and O, respectively. The Lewis dot-structure, Figure 12.3, represents this simple view. The two bonding and two lone pairs are asymmetrically distributed with major portions pointing to the vertices of a slightly distorted tetrahedron in 3-dimensional space. The two lone pairs mark slightly negative sites and the two H atoms are slightly positive. This charge distribution around a water molecule is very important in terms of its microscopic, macroscopic, chemical, and physical properties described later. Of course, the study of water continues and so does the evolution of bonding theories. Moreover, the distribution of electrons in a single water molecule is different from those of dimers, clusters, and bulk water.

The asymmetric distribution of H atoms and electrons around the O atom results in positive and negative sites in the water molecule. Thus, water consists of polar molecules.

The **dipole moment, μ,** is a measure of polarity and a useful concept. A pair of opposite charge, q, separated by a distance, d, has a dipole moment of $μ = d\,q$ with the direction pointing towards the positive charge as shown in Figure 12.4.

The dipole moment of individual water molecules is 6.187×10^{-30} C m (or 1.855 D) (21). This quantity is the vector resultant of two dipole moments due to the O–H bonds. The bond angle H–O–H of water is 104.5°. Thus, the dipole moment of an O–H bond is 5.053×10^{-30} cm. The bond length between H and O is 0.10 nm, and the

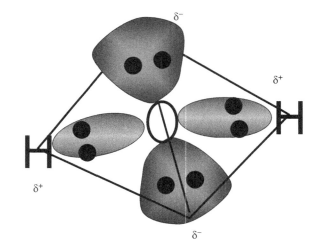

FIGURE 12.3 A tetrahedral arrangement of the Lewis dot-structure and charge distribution of the H_2O molecule.

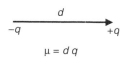

FIGURE 12.4 Separation of a positive and a negative charge q at a distance d results in a dipole, $μ = d\,q$.

TABLE 12.2
Absorption Frequencies of D_2O, H_2O, and HDO Molecules for the Excitation of Fundamental Modes to a Higher Energy Level

Vibration Mode	Absorption Energies in Wave Numbers (cm^{-1})		
	H_2O	HDO	D_2O
Symmetric stretching	3656	2726	2671
Bending	1594	1420	1178
Asymmetric stretching	3756	3703	2788

partial charge at the O and the H is therefore $q = 5.053 \times 10^{-20}$ C, 32% of the charge of an electron (1.6022×10^{-19} C). Of course, the dipole moment may also be considered as separation of the electron and positive charge by a distance 0.031 nm.

It should be pointed out that the dipole moments of liquid and solid water appear to be higher due to the influence of neighboring molecules. For the liquid and solid, macroscopic properties need be considered.

C. HYDROGEN BONDS

Attraction among water molecules is more than polar-polar in nature. The O atoms are small and very electronegative. As a result, the positive H atoms (protons) are very attractive to the negative O atoms of neighboring molecules. This O- - -H – O strong attraction is called a **hydrogen bond**, a concept popularized by L. Pauling (22). Furthermore, hydrogen atoms bonded to atoms of N and F, neighboring elements of O in the periodic table, are positive, and they form hydrogen bonds with atoms of N, O, or F. The strength of hydrogen bonds depends on the X–H - - - Y (X or Y are N, O, or F atoms) distances and angles; the shorter the distances, the stronger are the hydrogen bonds.

When two isolated water molecules approach each other, a dimer is formed due to hydrogen bonding. The dimer may have one or two hydrogen bonds (Figure 12.5). Dimers exist in gaseous and liquid water. When more water molecules are in close proximity, they form trimmers, tetramers and clusters. Hydrogen bonds are not static, they exchange protons and partners constantly. Hydrogen bonding is a prominent feature in the structures of various solid phases of water usually called ice as we shall see later.

Water molecules not only form hydrogen bonds among themselves, they form hydrogen bonds with any molecule that contains N–H, O–H, and F–H bonds. Foodstuffs such as starch, cellulose, sugars, proteins, DNA, and alkaloids contain N–H and O–H groups, and these are both H-donors and H-acceptors of hydrogen bonds of the type N- - H–O, O- -H–N, N- -H–N, etc. A dimer depicting the hydrogen bond and the van der Waals sphere of two molecules is shown in Figure 12.6 (23).

Carbohydrates (starch, cellulose and sugars) contain H–C–O–H groups. The O–H groups are similar to those of water molecules, and they are H-acceptors and H-donors for hydrogen bonds. Proteins contain O–H, R–NH_2 or $R_2 >$ NH groups, and the O–H and N–H groups are both H-donors and H-acceptors for the formation of hydrogen

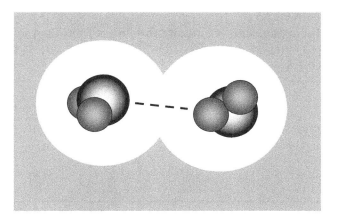

FIGURE 12.6   Hydrogen bond and the van der Waals sphere of two water molecules, after M.F. Martin (23).

bonds. Thus, water molecules have intimate interactions with carbohydrates and proteins.

IV. MACROSCOPIC PROPERTIES OF WATER

Collectively, water molecules exist as gas, liquid, or solid depending on the temperature and pressure. These **phases** of water exhibit collective or macroscopic properties such as phase transitions, crystal structures, liquid structures, vapor pressures, and volume-pressure relationships of vapor. In addition, energies or enthalpies for melting, vaporization, and heating are also important for applications in food technology.

Thermodynamic constants for phase transitions given in Table 12.3 are those of pure water. Natural waters, of course, contain dissolved air, carbon dioxide, organic substances, microorganisms, and minerals. Water in food or used during food processing usually contains various organic and inorganic substances. These solutes modify the properties of water and caution should be taken to ensure proper values are applied in food technology.

The triple point of water defines the temperature of 273.16 K in the SI unit system. The division of 1/2 73.16 in thermodynamic temperature scale is approximately 1°C.

Water has many unusual properties due to its ability to form hydrogen bonds and its large dipole moment. As a result, the melting, boiling, and critical points for water are very high compared to substances of similar molar masses. In general, the higher the molar masses, the higher are the melting and boiling points of the material. Associated with these properties are its very large heat of melting, heat capacity, heat of vaporization, and heat of sublimation. Moreover, its surface tension and viscosity are also very large. Thermodynamic energies and volume changes for phase transitions of H_2O are summarized in Table 12.3. These data are mostly taken from the Encyclopedia of Chemical Technology, Vol. 25 (1991) (24).

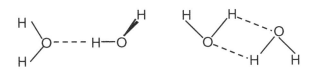

FIGURE 12.5   Two possible structures of the water dimer, $(H_2O)_2$.

TABLE 12.3
Thermodynamic Constants for Phase Transitions of H_2O (molar mass, 18.015268 g mol^{-1}) at 101.314 kPa Pressure

	Fusion (Melting)	Vaporization	
		Boiling	Sublimation
Temperature K	273.15	373	273.16
ΔH kJ mol^{-1}	6.01	40.66	51.06
ΔS J mol^{-1} K^{-1}	22.00	108.95	186.92
ΔE kJ mol^{-1}	6.01	37.61	48.97
ΔV L mol^{-1}	−1.621	30.10	−

Energy change of phase transition: ΔH, enthalpy; ΔS, entropy; ΔE, internal energy. ΔV: volume change of phase transition.

A. CRYSTAL STRUCTURES AND PROPERTIES OF ICE

Hydrogen bonding is prominent in the crystal structures of various solid phases of H_2O. The triple point of water is at 273.16 K and 4.58 torr (611 Pa). The melting point at 1.00 atm (760 torr or 101.325 kPa) is 273.15 K in the Kelvin scale. When water freezes at these temperatures and atmospheric pressure or lower, the solids are hexagonal ice crystals usually designated as I_h. Properties of I_h are given in Table 12.4. Snowflakes have many shapes because their growth habit depends on temperature and vapor pressure, but they all exhibit hexagonal symmetry, due to the hexagonal structure of ice (25).

However, from a geometric point of view, the same bonding may also be arranged to have cubic symmetry. The existence of cubic ice has been confirmed. When water vapor deposits onto a very cold, 130–150 K surface or when small droplets are cold under low pressure at high altitude, the ice has a cubic symmetry usually designated as I_c. At still higher pressures, different crystal forms

TABLE 12.4
Properties of Ice at 273.15 K

Heat of formation ΔH_f	292.72 kJ mol^{-1}
Density	0.9168 g cm^{-3}
Heat capacity	2.06 J g^{-1} K^{-1}
ΔH_{fusion}	6.01 kJ mol^{-1}
Dielectric constant at 3 kHz	79
Thermal expansion coefficient	
Volumetric	120 × 10^{-6} cm^3 g^{-1} K^{-1}
Linear	52.7 × 10^{-6} cm g^{-1} K^{-1}

designated as ice II, III, IV, ... etc., up to 13 phases of cubic, hexagonal, tetragonal, monoclinic, and orthorhombic symmetries have been identified (26). The polymorphism of solid water is very complicated. Some of these ice forms are made under very high pressures, and water crystallizes into solid at temperatures above the normal melting or even boiling temperatures. Ice VII is formed above 10 G Pa (gigapascal) at 700 K (26).

When liquid water is frozen rapidly, the molecules have little chance of arranging into crystalline ice. The frozen liquid is called **amorphous ice** or **glassy ice**.

The basic relationships between nearest neighboring water molecules are the same in both I_h and I_c. All O atoms are bonded to four other O atoms by hydrogen bonds, which extend from an oxygen atom towards the vertices of a tetrahedron. A sketch of the crystal structure of hexagonal I_h is shown in Figure 12.7 (27). In I_h, hydrogen positions are somewhat random due to thermal motion, disorder, and exchanges. For example, the hydrogen may shift between locations to form H_3O^+ and OH^- ions dynamically throughout the structure. In this structure, bond angles or hydrogen-bond angles around oxygen atoms are those of the idealized tetrahedral arrangement of 109.5° rather than 104.5° observed for isolated molecules. Formation of the

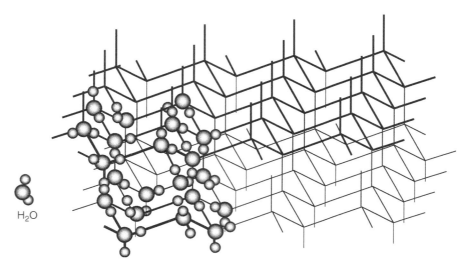

H_2O

FIGURE 12.7 Ordered crystal structure of ice, bond distance: O–H, 100 pm; H- - -O, 175 pm; and O–H- - -O, 275 pm.

hydrogen bond in ice lengthens the O–H bond distance, 100 pm compared to 96 pm in a single water molecule. The diagram illustrates a crystal structure that is completely hydrogen bonded, except for the molecules at the surface.

Each O atom of hexagonal ice I_h is surrounded by four almost linear O–H - - O hydrogen bonds of length 275 pm, in a tetrahedral fashion. Each C atom of cubic diamond is also surrounded by four C–C covalent bonds of length 154 pm. Thus, the tetrahedral coordination can either be cubic or hexagonal, from a geometrical viewpoint. Indeed, the uncommon cubic ice and hexagonal diamond have been observed, giving a close relationship in terms of spatial arrangement of atoms between ice and diamond (26). Strong hydrogen bonds make ice hard, but brittle. The structure is related to its physical properties, which vary with temperature.

The pressure of H_2O vapor in equilibrium with ice is called the **vapor pressure of ice**, which decreases as the temperature decreases. At the triple point or 0°C, the pressure is 611.15 Pa. When ice is slightly overheated to 0.01°C, the pressure increases to 611.657 Pa. However, at this temperature, the vapor pressure of liquid water is lower. The vapor pressures of ice between 0°C and – 40°C are listed in Table 12.5 at 1°C interval. Various models can be used to estimate the vapor pressure at other temperatures. One method uses the Clausius-Clapeyron differential equation

$$\frac{\mathrm{d}p}{\mathrm{d}T} = \frac{H}{T\,\Delta V}$$

where p is the pressure, T is the temperature (K), H is the latent heat or **enthalpy** of phase transition, and ΔV is the difference in volume of the phases. The enthalpy of sublimation for ice depends on the temperature. At the freezing point, the enthalpy of sublimation for ice is 51 (51.06 in Table 12.3) kJ mol^{-1}, estimated from the vapor pressure at 0 and –1°C. The enthalpy of sublimation is required to overcome hydrogen bonding, dipole, and intermolecular attractions. The energy required in freeze-drying processes varies, depending on temperature and other conditions. Water in solutions and in food freezes below 0°C.

The number of hydrogen bonds is twice the number of water molecules, when surface water molecules are ignored. The energy required to separate water molecules from the solid is the enthalpy of sublimation (55.71 J mol^{-1}). Half of this value, 26 kJ mol^{-1}, is the energy to separate the H- -O linkages, and it translates into 0.26 eV, per H- -O bond. These values are close to those obtained by other means (25, 26, 28–30). Several factors contribute to this linkage, and the hydrogen-bond energy is less than 0.26 eV.

B. PROPERTIES OF LIQUID WATER

The macroscopic physical properties of this common but eccentric fluid at 298 K (25°C) are given in Table 12.6. Water has unusually high melting and boiling points for a substance of molar mass of only 18 daltons. Strong hydrogen bonds and high polarity account for this.

The heat of formation is the energy released when a mole of hydrogen and half a mole of oxygen at 298 K and 1.00 atm react to give one mole of water at 298 K. This value differs from that for ice in Table 12.4 due to both temperature and phase differences. As temperature increases, the average kinetic energy of molecules increases, and this affects water's physical properties. For example, surface tension of water decreases, whereas the thermal conductance increases as the temperature increases. Heat capacity at constant pressure (C_p), vapor pressure, viscosity, thermal conductance, dielectric constant, and surface tension in the temperature range 273–373 K (0–100°C) are given in Table 12.7.

Liquid water has the largest heat capacity per unit mass of all substances. Large quantities of energy are absorbed or released when its temperature changes. The large heat capacity makes water an excellent reservoir and transporter of energy. A large body of water moderates climate. The heat capacity C_p of water varies between 4.1 to

TABLE 12.5
Aqueous Vapor Pressure (Pa) in Equilibrium with Ice between 0 and – 40°C (at 0.01°C, p is 611.657 Pa)

t (°C)	– 0 ■	– 1 ■	–2 ■	–3 ■	– 4 ■
– ■ 0	611.15	259.90	103.26	38.01	12.84
– ■ 1	562.67	237.74	93.77	34.24	
– ■ 2	517.72	217.32	85.10	30.82	
– ■ 3	476.06	198.52	77.16	27.71	
– ■ 4	437.47	181.22	69.91	24.90	
– ■ 5	401.76	165.30	63.29	22.35	7.20
– ■ 6	368.73	150.68	57.25	20.04	
– ■ 7	338.19	137.25	51.74	17.96	
– ■ 8	309.98	124.92	46.73	16.07	
– ■ 9	283.94	113.62	42.16	14.37	

Missing digits of t, ■, in the row are found in the column, and vice versa. These values are taken from the CRC Handbook of Chemistry and Physics (1).

TABLE 12.6
Properties of Liquid Water at 298 K

Heat of formation ΔH_f	285.89 kJ mol^{-1}
Density at 3.98°C	1.000 g cm^{-3}
Density at 25°C	0.9970480 g cm^{-3}
Heat capacity	4.17856 Jg^{-1} K^{-1}
$\Delta H_{vaporization}$	55.71 kJ mol^{-1}
Dielectric constant	80
Dipole moment	6.24×10^{-30} C m
Viscosity	0.8949 mP? s^{-1}
Velocity of sound	1496.3 m s^{-1}
Volumetric thermal expansion coefficient	0.0035 cm^3 g^{-1} K^{-1}

TABLE 12.7

Properties of Liquid Water in the Range 273–373 K (0–100°C)

Temp.t (°C)	Heat Capacity Cp ($J g^{-1} K^{-1}$)	Viscosity (mPa s)	Thermal Conductance ($W K^{-1} m^{-1}$)	Dielectric Constant	Surface Tension ($mN m^{-1}$)
0	4.2176	1.793	561.0	87.90	75.64
10	4.1921	1.307	580.0	83.96	74.23
20	4.1818	1.002	598.4	80.20	72.75
30	4.1784	0.797	615.4	76.60	71.20
40	4.1785	0.653	630.5	73.17	69.60
50	4.1806	0.547	643.5	69.88	67.94
60	4.1843	0.466	654.3	66.73	66.24
70	4.1895	0.404	663.1	63.73	64.47
80	4.1963	0.354	670.0	60.86	62.67
90	4.2050	0.315	675.3	58.12	60.82
100	4.2159	0.282	679.1	55.51	58.91

More detailed data can be found in the CRC Handbook of Chemistry and Physics (1).

4.2 J g^{-1} K^{-1} (74 to 76 J mol^{-1} K^{-1}) even at temperature above 100°C and high pressure. The enthalpy of vaporization for water is also very large (55.71 kJ mol^{-1} at 298 K). Thus, energy consumption is high for food processing when water is involved.

Water and aqueous solutions containing only low molar-mass solutes are typical Newtonian fluids for which the **shear stress** is proportional to **shear strain rate**. Viscosity is the ratio of shear stress to shear strain rate. On the other hand, viscosity of solutions containing high molar-mass substances depends on shear strain rate. For pure water, the viscosity decreases from 1.793 to 0.282 mPa s (millipascal seconds; identical to centipoise (cp)) as temperature increases from 0 to 100°C. Thus, the flow rate through pipes increases as water or solution temperature increases.

The dielectric constant of water is very large, and this enables water to separate ions of electrolytes, because it reduces the electrostatic attraction between positive and negative ions. Many salts dissolve in water. When an electric field is applied to water, its dipole molecules orient themselves to decrease the field strength. Thus, its dielectric constant is very large. The dielectric constant decreases as temperature increases, because the percentage of molecules involved in hydrogen bonding and the degree of order decrease (28, 29). The measured dielectric constant also depends on the frequency of the applied electric field used in the measurement, but the variation is small when the frequency of the electric field is less than 100 MHz. The dielectric behavior of water allows water vapor pressure to be sensed by capacitance changes when moisture is absorbed by a substance that lies between the plates of a capacitor. These sensors have been developed for water activity measurement (31).

The light absorption coefficients are high in the infrared and ultraviolet regions, but very low in the visible region. Thus, water is transparent to human vision.

The variation of vapor pressure as a function of temperature is the bases for defining **water activities** of food. Liquid water exists between the triple-point and the critical-point temperatures (0–373.98°C) at pressures above the vapor pressures in this range.

As with ice, the vapor pressure of liquid water increases as the temperature increases. Vapor pressures of water (in kPa instead of Pa for ice in Table 12.5) between the triple and critical points, at 10°C interval, are given in Table 12.8. When the vapor pressure is 1.00 atm (101.32 kPa) the temperature is the boiling point (100°C). At slightly below 221°C, the vapor pressure is 2.00 atm. The critical pressure at the critical temperature, 373.98°C, is 217.67 atm (22,055 kPa). Above this temperature, water cannot be liquefied, and the phase is called **supercritical water**.

The partial pressure of H_2O in the air at any temperature is the **absolute humidity**. When the air is saturated with water vapor, the **relative humidity** is 100%. The unsaturated vapor pressure divided by the vapor pressure of water as given in Table 12.8 at the temperature of the air is the **relative humidity**. The temperature at which the vapor pressure in the air becomes saturated is the **dew point**, at which dew begins to form. However, when the dew point is below 273 K or 0°C, ice crystals (frost) begin to form. Thus, the relative humidity can be measured by finding the dew point. Dividing the vapor pressure at the dew point by the vapor pressure of water at the temperature of the air gives the relative humidity. The transformations between solid, liquid, and gaseous water play important roles in hydrology and in the transformation of the environment on Earth. Phase transitions of water combined with the energy from the sun make the weather.

TABLE 12.8

Vapor Pressure (kPa) of Liquid H_2O between Triple and Critical Points at Every 10°C

t°C	0■ ■	1■ ■	2■ ■	3■ ■
■00	0.6113	101.32	1553.6	8583.8
■10	1.2281	143.24	1906.2	9860.5
■20	2.3388	198.48	2317.8	11279
■30	4.2455	270.02	2795.1	12852
■40	7.3814	361.19	3344.7	14594
■50	12.344	475.72	3973.6	16521
■60	19.932	617.66	4689.4	18665
■70	31.176	791.47	5499.9	21030
■80	47.375	1001.9	6413.2	22055*
■90	70.117	1254.2	7438.0	

* Critical pressure at 373.98°C.

Missing digits of t, ■, in the row are found in the column, and vice versa. Values from the CRC Handbook of Physics and Chemistry (2003) (1), which lists vapor pressure at 1° interval.

TABLE 12.9

The Density of Water (g/mL) as a Function of Temperature between 0 and 39°C (31)

t°C	0 ■	1 ■	2 ■	3 ■
■ 0	0.9998426	0.9997021	0.9982063	0.9956511
■ 1	0.9999015	0.9996074	0.9979948	0.9953450
■ 2	0.9999429	0.9994996	0.9977730	0.9950302
■ 3	0.9999627	0.9993792	0.9975412	0.9947971
■ 4	0.9999750*	0.9992464	0.9972994	0.9943756
■ 5	0.9999668	0.9991016	0.9970480	0.9940359
■ 6	0.9999430	0.9989450	0.9967870	0.9936883
■ 7	0.9999043	0.9987769	0.9975166	0.9933328
■ 8	0.9998509	0.9985976	0.9962370	0.9929695
■ 9	0.9997834	0.9984073	0.9956511	0.9925987

Missing digits of t, ■, in the row are found in the column, and vice versa.

Density is a collective property, and it varies with temperature, isotopic composition, purity, etc. The International Union of Pure and Applied Chemistry (IUPAC) has adopted the density of pure water from the ocean as the density standard. The isotopic composition of ordinary water is constant, and the density of pure water between 0 and 39°C extracted from (32) is given in Table 12.9.

The density of cage-like ice I_h, due to 100% of its molecules involved in hydrogen-bonded is only 9% lower than that of water. This indicates that water has a high percentage of molecules involved in the transient and dynamic hydrogen bonding. The percentage of hydrogen-bonded water molecules in water decreases as temperature increases, causing water density to increase. As temperature increases, the thermal expansion causes its density to decreases. The two effects cause water density to increase from 0 to 3.98°C, reaching its maximum of 1.0000 g mL^{-1} and then decrease as temperature increases.

Incidentally, at 8°C, the density of water is about the same as that at 0°C. At 25°C, the density decreases 0.3% with respect to its maximum density, whereas at 100°C, it decreases by 4%. Dense water sinks, and convection takes place when temperature fluctuates at the surface of lakes and ponds, bringing dissolved air and nutrients to various depths of waters for the organism living in them. On the other hand, the pattern of density dependence on temperature of water makes temperatures at the bottoms of lakes and oceans vary little if the water is undisturbed. When water freezes, ice begins to form at the surface, leaving the water at some depth undisturbed. Water at the bottom remains at 4°C, preserving various creatures living in water.

When hydrogen bonded to tissues and cells or in food, water has a unique order and structure, and the vapor pressure and density differ from those of pure water. Yet, the collective behavior of water molecules sheds some light regarding their properties in food, cells, tissues, and solutions.

V. CHEMICAL PROPERTIES OF WATER

Water is a chemical as is any substance, despite the confusion and distrust of the public regarding the term "chemical." Thus, water has lots of interesting chemical properties. It interacts intimately with components of food particularly as a solvent, due to its dipole moment and its tendency to form a hydrogen bond. These interactions affect the chemical properties of nutrients, including their tendency to undergo oxidation or reduction, to act as acids or bases, and to ionize.

A. WATER AS A UNIVERSAL SOLVENT

Water is dubbed a universal solvent because it dissolves many substances due to strong interactions between water molecules and those of other substances. Entropy is another driving force for a liquid to dissolve or mix with other substances. Mixing increases disorder or entropy.

1. Hydrophobic Effect and Hydrophilic Effect

Because of its large dielectric constant, high dipole moment and ability to donate and accept protons for hydrogen bonding, water is an excellent solvent for polar substances and electrolytes, which consist of ions. Molecules strongly interact with water-loving molecules are **hydrophilic**, due to hydrogen bonding, polar-ionic or polar-polar attractions. Nonpolar molecules that do not mix with water are **hydrophobic** or **lipophilic**, because they tend to dissolve in oil. Large molecules such as proteins and fatty acids that have hydrophilic and hydrophobic portions are **amphipathic** or **amphiphilic**. Water molecules strongly intermingle with hydrophilic portions by means of dipole-dipole interaction or hydrogen bonding.

The lack of strong interactions between water molecules and lipophilic molecules or the nonpolar portions of amphipathic molecules is called the **hydrophobic effect**, a term coined by Charles Tanford (33). Instead of a direct interaction with such solutes, water molecules tend to form hydrogen-bonded cages around small nonpolar molecules when the latter are dispersed into water. Hydrogen-bonded water molecules form cages, called **hydrates** or **clathrates**. For example, the clathrate of methane forms stable crystals at low temperatures (34).

Nonpolar chains in proteins prefer to stay together as they avoid contact with water molecules. Hydrophilic and hydrophobic effects play important roles in the stability and state of large molecules such as enzymes, proteins, and lipids. Hydrophobic portions of these molecules stay together, forming pockets in globular proteins. Hydrophilic and hydrophobic effects cause nonpolar portions of phospholipids, proteins, and cholesterol to assemble into bilayers or biological membranes (34).

2.   Hydration of Ions

Due to its high dielectric constant, water reduces the attractions among positive and negative ions of electrolytes and dissolves them. The polar water molecules coordinate around ions forming hydrated ions such as $Na(H_2O)_6^+$, $Ca(H_2O)_8^{2+}$, $Al(H_2O)_6^{3+}$, etc. Six to eight water molecules form the first sphere of hydration around these ions. Figure 12.8 is a sketch of the interactions of water molecules with ions. The water molecules point the negative ends of their dipoles towards positive ions, and their positive ends towards negative ions. Molecules in the hydration sphere constantly and dynamically exchange with those around them. The number of hydrated-water molecules and their lifetimes have been studied by various methods. These studies reveal that the hydration sphere is one-layer deep, and the lifetimes of these hydrated-water molecules are in the order of picoseconds (10^{-12} s). The larger negative ions also interact with the polar water molecules, not as strong as those of cations. The presence of ions in the solution changes the ordering of molecules even if they are not in the first hydration sphere (9).

The hydration of ions releases energy, but breaking up ions from a solid requires energy. The amount of energy depends on the substance, and for this reason, some are more soluble than others. Natural waters in the ocean, streams, rivers and lakes are in contact with minerals and salts. The concentrations of various ions depend on the solubility of salts (35) and the contact time.

Drinking water includes all waters used in growth, processing, and manufacturing of food. J. De Zuane divides ions in natural water into four types in The Handbook on Drinking Water Quality (5).

Type A includes arsenic, barium, cadmium, chromium, copper, fluoride, mercury, nitrate, nitrite, and selenium ions. They are highly toxic, yet abundant.

Type B includes aluminum, nickel, sodium, cyanide, silver, zinc, molybdenum, and sulfate ions. Their concentrations are also high, but they are not very toxic.

Type C consists of calcium, carbonate, chloride, iron, lithium, magnesium, manganese, oxygen, phosphate, potassium, silica, bromine, chlorine, iodine, and ozone. They are usually present at reasonable levels.

Type D ions are present usually at low levels: antimony, beryllium, cobalt, tin, thorium, vanadium, and thallium.

Most metals are usually present in water as cations, with a few as anions. However, some chemical analyses may not distinguish their state in water. The most common anions are chloride, sulfate, carbonate, bicarbonate, phosphate, bromide, iodide, etc. Toxicity is a concern for ions in water, but some of these ions are essential for humans.

Pure water has a very low electric conductivity, but ions in solutions move in an electric field making electrolyte solutions highly conductive. The conductivity is related to total dissolved solids (TDS), salts of carbonate, bicarbonate, chloride, sulfate, and nitrate. Sodium, potassium, calcium, and magnesium ions are often present in natural waters because their soluble salts are common minerals in the environment. The solubilities of clay (alumina), silicates, and most common minerals in the Earth's crust, are low.

3.   Hard Waters and Their Treatments

Waters containing plenty of dissolved CO_2 (H_2CO_3) are acidic and they dissolve $CaCO_3$ and $MgCO_3$. Waters with dissolved Ca^{2+}, Mg^{2+}, HCO_3^-, and CO_3^{2-} are called **temporary hard waters** as the hardness can be removed by boiling, which reduces the solubility of CO_2. When CO_2 is driven off, the solution becomes less acidic due to

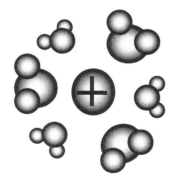
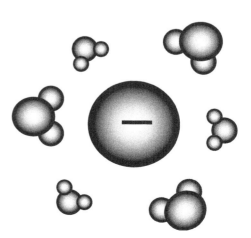

FIGURE 12.8   The first hydration sphere of most cations $M(H_2O)_6^+$, and anions $X(H_2O)_6^{-1}$. Small water molecules are below the plane containing the ions, and large water molecules are above the plane.

the following equilibria (the double arrows, $\leftrightarrows$, indicate reversible reactions):

$$H^+ \text{ (aq)} + HCO_3^- \text{ (aq)} \leftrightarrows H_2CO_3 \text{ (aq)} \leftrightarrows H_2O + CO_2 \text{ (g)}$$

$$HCO_3^- \text{ (aq)} \leftrightarrows H^+ \text{ (aq)} + CO_3^{2-} \text{ (aq)}$$

Reducing the acidity increases the concentration of CO_3^{2-} and solids $CaCO_3$ and $MgCO_3$ precipitate:

$$Ca^{2+} \text{ (aq)} + CO_3^{2-} \text{ (aq)} \leftrightarrows CaCO_3 \text{ (s)}$$

$$Mg^{2+} \text{ (aq)} + CO_3^{2-} \text{ (aq)} \leftrightarrows MgCO_3 \text{ (s)}$$

Water containing less than 50 mg L^{-1} of these substances is considered soft; 50–150 mg L^{-1} moderately hard; 150–300 mg L^{-1} hard; and more than 300 mg L^{-1} very hard.

For the **lime treatment**, we determine the amount of dissolved Ca^{2+} and Mg^{2+} first and then add an equal number of moles of lime, $Ca(OH)_2$, to remove them by these reactions:

$$Mg^{2+} + Ca(OH)_2(s) \rightarrow Mg(OH)_2(s) + Ca^{2+}$$

$$Ca^{2+} + 2\,HCO_3^- + Ca(OH)_2(s) \rightarrow 2\,CaCO_3(s) + 2\,H_2O$$

Permanent hard waters contain sulfate (SO_4^{2-}) ions with Ca^{2+} and Mg^{2+}. Calcium ions, Ca^{2+}, of the sulfate solution can be removed by adding sodium carbonate:

$$Ca^{2+} + Na_2CO_3 \rightarrow CaCO_3 \text{ (s)} + 2\,Na^+$$

Hard waters cause scales or deposits to build up in boilers and pipes, and they are usually softened by ion exchange with resins or zeolites. In these processes, the calcium and magnesium ions are taken up by the zeolite or resin that releases sodium or hydrogen ions into the water. Reverse osmosis has also been used to soften hard water.

However, water softening replaces desirable calcium and other ions by sodium ions. Thus, soft waters are not suitable drinking waters. Incidentally, bakers use hard water because the calcium ions strengthen the gluten proteins in dough mixing. Some calcium salts are added to dough to enhance bread quality.

4. Properties of Aqueous Solutions

Waters containing dissolved substances are aqueous solutions; their physical properties differ from those of pure water. For example, at the same temperature, the H_2O vapor pressures of solutions are lower than those of pure water, resulting in **boiling point elevation** (higher), **freezing point depression** (lower), and osmotic pressure.

Concentrations can be expressed in several ways: part per million (ppm), percent, moles per liter, mole fraction, etc. The mole fraction of water is the fraction of water

molecules among all molecules and ions in the system. The vapor pressure of an ideal solution, $P_{solution}$, is the vapor pressure of water (at a given temperature), P°_{water}, modified by the mole fraction X_{water}.

$$P_{solution} = X_{water}\, P^\circ_{water} \quad (X_{water} < 1)$$

If the solute has a significant vapor pressure, P_{solute} is also modified by its mole fraction,

$$P_{solute} = X_{solute}\, P^\circ_{solute}$$

For non-ideal solutions, in which water and solute strongly interact, the formulas require modifications. A practical method is to use an **effective mole fraction** X defined by:

$$P_{solution}\,/\,P^\circ_{water} = X$$

In any case, the vapor pressures of solutions containing nonvolatile electrolytes are lower than those of pure water at their corresponding temperature.

Phase transitions take place when the vapor pressures of the two phases are the same. Because vapor pressures of solutions are lower, their melting points are lower but their boiling points are higher. The difference in temperature, ΔT, is proportional to the concentrations of all solutes, $m_{all\text{-}solute}$ (molality),

$$\Delta T = K\, m_{all\text{-}solute}$$

where K is either the molar boiling point elevation constant, K_b, or the molar freezing point depression constant K_f. For water, $K_f = 1.86$ K L kg^{-1}, and $K_b = 0.52$ K L kg^{-1}. Due to ionization of electrolytes, positive and negative ions should be treated as separate species and all species should be included in $m_{all\text{-}solute}$.

The tendency of water molecules from a dilute solution to diffuse into a more concentrated solution, through semipermeable membranes, has a measurable quantity called **osmotic pressure**, π, which is proportional to the concentration (mol per kg of water) of all dissolved species, $m_{all\text{-}solute}$ in mol kg^{-1} and temperature T in K,

$$\pi = -\,m_{all\text{-}solute}\, R\, T$$

where R is the gas constant 8.3145 J mol^{-1} K^{-1}. Water molecules diffuse from pure water ($\pi = 0$) into the solution, and the osmotic pressure is therefore given as a negative value here. Theoretically, a solution with $m_{all\text{-}solute} = 1.0$ mol kg^{-1} of water, $\pi = -2477$ J kg or -2.477 kJ kg at 298 K. Note $m_{all\text{-}solute} = \Sigma m_i$ (m_i being the concentration of ion or molecule i) in the van't Hoff equation, which is often used in other literature.

Solutions having the identical osmotic pressure are isotonic. Applying more pressure to a solution to compensate for the osmotic pressure causes water molecules to diffuse through membranes, generating pure or fresh waters. This process is called **reverse osmosis**, and it has been used to soften water or desalinate seawater, converting it to fresh water.

The lowering of vapor pressure and the osmotic pressure of solutions play important roles in hydration and dehydration of food and in living cells. Solutions containing proper concentrations of nutrients and electrolyte have been used to medically treat dehydrated patients. J.R. Cade and his coworkers applied these principles to formulate drinks for athletes; he and his coworkers were credited as the inventors of the sports drink Gaterade (36). The concept of a balanced solution for hydration became a great business decade after its invention.

B. ACIDITY AND ALKALINITY OF WATER

Acidity and alkalinity are also important characteristics of water due to its dynamic self-ionization equilibrium

$$H_2O \ (l) \leftrightarrows H^+ + OH^-,$$

$$K_w = [H^+][OH^-] = 1 \times 10^{-14} \text{ at 298 K and 1 atm}$$

where $[H^+]$ and $[OH^-]$ represent the molar concentrations of H^+ (or H_3O^+) and OH^- ions, respectively, and K_w is called the **ion product of water** (see tables in Refs. 1 and 36). Values of K_w under various conditions have been evaluated theoretically (37, 38). Solutions in which $[H^+] = [OH^-]$ are said to be neutral. At 298 K, for a neutral solution,

$$pH = -\log [H^+] = pOH = -\log [OH^-] = 7 \text{ (at 298 K)}$$

The H^+ ions or protons dynamically exchange with protons in other water molecules. The self-ionization and equilibrium are present in all aqueous solutions, including acid and base solutions, as well as in pure water. Water is both an acid and a base.

Strong acids such as $HClO_4$, $HClO_3$, HCl, HNO_3, and H_2SO_4 ionize completely in their solutions to give H^+ (H_3O^+) ions and anions: ClO_4^-, ClO_3^-, Cl^-, NO_3^-, and HSO_4^-, respectively. Strong bases such as $NaOH$, KOH, and $Ca(OH)_2$ also ionize completely giving OH^- ions and Na^+, K^+, and Ca^{2+} ions, respectively. In an acidic solution, $[H^+]$ is greater than $[OH^-]$. In a 1.0 mol L^{-1} HCl solution, $[H^+] = 1.0$ mol L^{-1}, pH = 0.

Weak acids such as formic acid HCOOH, acetic acid (CH_3COOH), ascorbic acid ($C_6H_8O_6$), oxalic acid ($H_2C_2O_4$), carbonic acid (H_2CO_3), benzoic acid (C_6H_5-COOH), malic acid ($C_4H_6O_5$), lactic acid H_3CCH-(OH)COOH, and phosphoric acid (H_3PO_4) also ionize in their aqueous solutions, but not completely. The ionization of acetic acid is represented by the equilibrium

$$CH_3COOH \ (aq) \leftrightarrows H^+ \ (aq) + CH_3COO^- \ (aq),$$

$$K_a = 1.75 \times 10^{-5} \text{ at 298 K}$$

where K_a is the **acid dissociation constant**.

The solubility of CO_2 in water increases with its (CO_2 partial) pressure, according to Henry's law, and the chemical equilibria for the dissolution are

$$H_2O + CO_2 \ (g) \leftrightarrows H_2CO_3 \ (aq)$$

Of course, H_2CO_3 dynamically exchanges H^+ and H_2O with other water molecules, and this weak diprotic acid ionizes in two stages with their acid constants, K_{a1} and K_{a2}.

$$H_2O + CO_2 \ (aq) \leftrightarrows H^+ \ (aq) + HCO_3^- \ (aq),$$

$$K_{a1} = 4.30 \times 10^{-7} \qquad \text{(at 298 K)}$$

$$HCO_3^- \ (aq) \leftrightarrows H^+ \ (aq) + CO_3^{2-} \ (aq),$$

$$K_{a2} = 5.61 \times 10^{-11}$$

Constants K_{a1} and K_{a2} increase with temperature. At 298 K, the pH of a solution containing 0.1 mol L^{-1} H_2CO_3 is 3.7. Acidophilic organisms may grow, but most pathogenic organisms are neutrophiles and they cease growing. Soft drinks contain other acids – citric, malic, phosphoric, ascorbic acids, etc. – which lower the pH further.

Ammonia and many nitrogen-containing compounds are weak bases. The ionization equilibrium of NH_3 in water and the **base dissociation constant** K_b are

$$NH_3 + H_2O \leftrightarrows NH_4^+ \ (aq) + OH^-$$

$$K_b = 1.70 \times 10^{-5} \quad \text{at 298 K.}$$

Other weak bases react with H_2O similarly.

The ionization or dissociation constants of inorganic and organic acids and bases are extensive, and they have been tabulated in various books (39–41).

Amino acids and proteins contain acidic and basic groups. At some specific pH called the **isoelectric point**, they carry no charge, but exist as zwitterions. For example, the isoelectric point for glycine is pH = 6.00 and it exists as the zwitterion $H_2C(NH_3^+)COO^-$.

C. OXIDATION-REDUCTION REACTIONS IN WATER

Oxidation of hydrogen by oxygen not only produces water, but also releases energy. At the standard conditions, the electrochemical half reaction equations are:

$$H_2 = 2 H^+ + 2 e^- \qquad E° = 0.000 \text{ V (defined)}$$

$$O_2 + 4 H^+ + 4 e^- = 2 H_2O \qquad E° = 1.229 \text{ V}$$

The cell reaction and the cell potential at the standard condition for it are:

$$2 H_2 + O_2 = 2 H_2O \qquad \Delta E° = 1.229 \text{ V}$$

Proper setups for harvesting this energy are the goals of hydrogen-fuel-cell technology. The cell potential ΔE for non-standard conditions depends on pH and temperature. Its value is related to the energy released in the reaction. A plot of ΔE versus pH yields a Pourbaix diagram, which is useful to evaluate the stability of various species in water. Water can be a reducing or oxidizing reagent, because it offers protons or electrons. Applying a voltage to pass electrons through a chemical cell decomposes water by electrolysis.

Waters containing dissolved oxygen cause additional reactions, for example:

$2 H_2O + 2 e^- = H_2 + 2 OH^-$ $\qquad E° = -0.828$ V

$O_2 + 2 H^+ + 2 e^- = H_2O_2$ $\qquad E° = 0.682$ V

$O_2 + H_2O + 2 e^- = HO_2^- + OH^-$ $\qquad E° = 0.076$ V

$O_2 + 2 H_2O + 2 e^- = 4 OH^-$ $\qquad E° = 0.401$ V

At the proper conditions, a suitable chemical reaction driven by the potential takes place.

Oxidation-reduction reactions involving water usually are due to proton or electron transfer. These oxidation-reduction reactions occur for the growth, production, manufacture, digestion, and metabolism of food.

Water participates in oxidation-reduction reactions in many steps of photosynthesis, resulting in the fixation of CO_2 into biomolecules, releasing oxygen atoms of water as O_2. Engineering a new generation of plants with greater photosynthetic capacity facing lack of waters challenges geneticists (42) and botanists. We now understand photosynthesis in great detail from the studies by many scientists. Photosynthetic reactions are related to food production, but they are so complex that we can only mention them here (43).

The oxidation-reduction reactions of water cause corrosion on metal surfaces. Not only is deterioration of facilities very costly for the food industry, corrosion of pipes results in having toxic metal ions Cu^{2+} and Pb^{2+} in drinking water. The concern about lead ions in drinking water led the Environmental Protection Agency to ban the use of high-lead solders for water pipes. These reactions are electrochemical processes. Galvanic effects, high acidity, high flow rate, high water temperature, and the presence of suspended solids accelerate corrosion, as do lack of Ca^{2+} and Mg^{2+} ions in purified waters. The formation of scales protects the metal surface. However, balancing the clogging against surface protection of pipes is a complicated problem, requiring scientific testing and engineering techniques for a satisfactory solution.

D. THE HYDROGEN BOND AND CHEMICAL REACTIONS

Enzymes are mostly large protein molecules, and they are selective and specific catalysts responsible for most reactions in biological bodies. Folding of the long protein provides specific 3-dimensional selective pockets for their substrates. The pockets not only fix the substrates in position, they also weaken certain bonds to facilitate specific reactions. This is the mechanism by which enzymes select their substrates and facilitate their specific reactions.

Hydrogen bond strength is stronger in nonaqueous media than in aqueous solutions as the charge densities on the donor and acceptor atoms increase (44). Hydrogen bonds between the enzyme and its substrate can be stronger than those in an aqueous environment, thus speeding up the reaction rate even further.

The hydrolysis of peptide linkage is the reaction of a protein with water:

$R\text{-}C(=O)\text{-}NH\text{-}R' + H_2O \rightarrow R\text{-}C(=O)OH + H_2N\text{-}R'$

This type of reaction can be catalyzed by acids, bases, and enzymes.

VI. WATER ACTIVITY

Water is a nutrient and a component in food groups: grains, meat, dairy, fruits and vegetables. Furthermore, major nutrients such as carbohydrates, proteins, water-soluble vitamins, and minerals are hydrophilic. Even parts of fat or lipid molecules are hydrophilic, but the alkyl chains of fats and proteins experience the hydrophobic effect in an aqueous environment (45).

Foodstuffs interact with water by means of polar, hydrogen-bonding, and hydrophobic interactions. The results of these interactions change the chemical potential (properties) of water. Foodstuffs dissolve in or absorb water. Thus, water within food may be divided into bound water, affected water, and free water in the order of their interaction strength. The bound water molecules are similar to those in the first hydration sphere of ions, and those close to the first sphere are affected water molecules. Further away from the interface are free water molecules. The structure and properties of the first two types change. Interaction of water with dietary fiber is an example (46). Thus, properties of water in food are different from those of pure water.

Water molecules in both liquid and vapor phases can participate in hydration reactions. At equilibrium in a system with two or more phases, their vapor pressure or chemical potential, μ, must be equal. The chemical potential, μ, of a solution or water-containing foodstuff must be equal at a given temperature T, and

$$\mu = \mu_w + R T \ln (p/p_w),$$

where R is the gas constant (8.3145 J mol^{-1} K^{-1}), p is the vapor pressure of the solution or of water in foodstuff, and p_w is the vapor pressure of pure water at the same temperature. The ratio p/p_w is called the **water activity**

a_w (= p/p_w), which is related to the water chemical potential of water in solutions or in the foodstuff. For ideal solutions and for most moist foods, a_w is less than unity, $a_w < 1.0$ (31).

Both water activity and relative humidity are fractions of the vapor pressure of pure water. Methods for their measurements are the same. We have mentioned the measurement by changes in capacitance earlier. Water contents have a sigmoidal relationship with water activities, $a_w = 1.0$ for infinitely dilute solutions, $a_w > 0.7$ for dilute solutions and moist foods, and $a_w < 0.6$ for dry foods. Of course, the precise relationship depends on the material in question. In general, if the water vapor of the atmosphere surrounding the food is greater than the activity of the food, water is absorbed. Otherwise, dehydration takes place. The water activity reflects the combined effects of water-solute, water-surface, capillary, hydrophilic, and hydrophobic interactions. The water activity of a foodstuff is a vital parameter, because it affects its texture, taste, safety, shelf life, and appearance.

Furthermore, controlling water activity rather than water content is important. When $a_w < 0.9$, most molds are inhibited. Growth of yeasts and bacteria also depends on a_w. Microorganisms cease growing if $a_w < 0.6$.

VII. WATER POTENTIAL

Similar to water activity in food, **water potential** is a term used in plant, soil, and crop sciences. Water potential, represented by Ψ (psi) or Ψw, is a measure of the free energy of water in a system: soil, material, seeds, plants, roots, leaves, or an organism. Water potential is the difference between the chemical potential of pure water and water in the system at the same temperature. Pure water has the highest free energy: $\Psi = 0$ for pure water by convention, and $\Psi < 0$ for solutions. Water diffuses from high potential to low potential. Physiological processes decrease as the water potential decreases.

In general, water potential, Ψw, is a combined effect of osmotic (Ψs), matrix (interface and water binding Ψm), turgor (Ψt) pressures, and gravity (Ψg).

$$\Psi w = \Psi s + \Psi m + \Psi t + \Psi g$$

Osmotic pressure, Ψs, is always present due to solutes in the fluids. The metric pressure, Ψm, is related to bound-, affected-, and free-waters in the system. The outwardly directed pressure extended by the swelling protoplast against the wall is called **turgor pressure**, Ψt. Usually, this term is insignificant until the cell is full, and at such point, Ψt increases rapidly and stops when $\Psi w = \Psi t$. Otherwise, the cell ruptures. The mechanical rigidity of succulent plant parts, the opening of stomata and the blossom are usually the results of turgor pressure. In systems such as tall plants and soil science, pressure due to the gravitational pull of water, Ψg, is also included in the water potential.

For example, the water potential of potato tissues can be measured by incubating them in a series of solutions of known osmotic pressures. The potato will neither lose nor gain water if the osmotic pressure of the solution equals the water potential of potato tissues. The osmotic pressure ($\pi = -mRT$) may be evaluated from a known concentration m, using the equation given earlier. Instead of energy units, water potential is often expressed in units of pressure (megapascal, MPa), which is derived by dividing the energy by the molar volume (0.018 L mol^{-1} for H_2O) of water (47).

There are many other methods for water potential measurements depending on the system: soil, leaf, stem, organism, etc. The soil water potential is related to the water available for the plants growing on the soil. Water potential of a plant or leaf indicates its health or state with respect to water. Thus, water potential is a better indicator for plant, agriculture, irrigation, and environmental management than water content. Water moves through plants because

$$\Psi_{water} = 0 > \Psi_{soil} > \Psi_{root} > \Psi_{stem} > \Psi_{leaf}$$

Thus, the concept of water potential and water activity are very useful in growth, manufacture, handling, storage, and management of food.

VIII. LIVING ORGANISMS IN WATER

The closer we look, the more we see. Living organisms on Earth are so complicated that their classification and phylogeny are still being studied and revised. New relationships are proposed to modify the five kingdoms proposed by Robert Whittaker in 1969. Nevertheless, most of the earliest unicellular living organisms in the Monera and Protista kingdoms are still living in water. Both the numbers of species and individuals are staggering. For example, photosynthesis by algae in oceans consumes more CO_2 than that by all plants on land. Algae were probably present on Earth before other organisms. Many phyla (divisions) of fungi, plantae, and animalia kingdoms also make water their home. Both numbers and species of organisms living in water are probably more than those on land. The subject of living organisms in water is fascinating, but we can only mention some fundamentals about their relationships to water here. Certainly, every aspect of living organisms in water is related to food, because Homo sapiens is part of the food chain, if not at the top of it.

All life requires energy or food. Some living organisms receive their energy from the sun whereas others get their energy from chemical reactions in the aquatic media. Chemical reactions are vital during their lives. For example, some bacteria derive energy by catalyzing the oxidation of iron sulfide, FeS_2, to produce iron ions $Fe(H_2O)_6^{2+}$ and elemental sulfur. Water is the oxidant, which in turn reduces oxygen (48). Chemical reactions provide energy for bacteria to sustain their lives and to reproduce. Factors affecting life in water are minerals, solubility of the mineral, electrochemical potentials of the material, acidity (pH), sunlight, dissolved oxygen level, presence of ions, chemical equilibria, etc. Properties of water influence life in general, and in the aquatic system in particular. As the population grows, aquaculture probably will be seen as a more efficient way of supplying protein for the ever-increasing population.

Regarding drinking water, we are concerned with aquatic organisms invisible to the naked eye. Pathogenic organisms present in drinking water cause intestinal infections, dysentery, hepatitis, typhoid fever, cholera, and other illnesses. Pathogens are usually present in waters contaminated with human and animal wastes that enter the water system via discharge, run offs, flood, and accidents at sewage treatment facilities. Insects, rodents, and animals can also bring bacteria to the water system (49, 50). Testing for all pathogenic organisms is impossible, but some organisms share common living conditions with some pathogenic bacteria. Thus, water testing can use these harmless bacteria as indicators for drinking water safety.

IX. WATER RESOURCE, SUPPLY, TREATMENT, AND USAGE

About 70% of the Earth's surface is covered with water, but only about 2% is covered by fresh water. Ocean waters are salty; only a small percentage is fresh water resources (lakes, rivers, and underground). Fresh water is needed for drinking, food, farming, washing, and manufacturing.

When salty water freezes, the ice so formed contains very little salt, if any. Thus, nearly all ice, including the massive ice at the polar cap, is fresh water. In fact, the ice cap in the Antarctic contains a lot of fresh water ice, but that cannot be considered a water resource.

Hydrologists, environmentalists, and scientists, engineers, sociologists, economists, and politicians are all concerned with problems associated with water resources. Solutions to these problems require experts and social consensus.

X. SUBCRITICAL AND SUPERCRITICAL WATERS

Waters at temperatures between the normal boiling and critical points (0 to 373.98°C) are called **subcritical waters**, whereas the phase above the critical point is **supercritical water**. In the 17th century, Denis Papin (a physicist) generated high-pressure steam using a closed boiler, and thereafter pressure canners were used to preserve food. Pressure cookers were popular during the 20th century. Analytical chemists have used subcritical waters to extract chemicals from solids for analysis since 1994 (51).

Water vapor pressures up to its critical point are given in Table 12.8, but data on polarity, dielectric constant, surface tension, density, and viscosity above 100°C are scarce. In general, these properties decrease as the temperature increases. In fact, some drop dramatically for supercritical water. On the other hand, some of them increase with pressure. Thus, properties of sub- and supercritical waters can be manipulated by adjusting temperature and pressure to attain desirable properties.

As the polarity and dielectric constant decrease, water becomes an excellent solvent for non-polar substances such as those for flavor and fragrance. However, foodstuffs may degrade at high temperatures. Applications of sub- and super-critical water are relatively recent events, but applications of supercritical CO_2 (critical temperature 32°C) for chemical analyses started in the 1980s, and investigations of supercritical water followed. However, research and development have been intensified in recent years (52). Scientists and engineers explore the usage of supercritical water for waste treatment, polymer degradation, pharmaceutical manufacturing, chromatographic analysis, nuclear reactor cooling, etc. Significant advances have also been made in material processing, ranging from fine particle manufacture to the creation of porous materials.

Water has been called a green solvent compared to the polluting organic solvents. Sub- and super-critical waters have been explored replacements of organic solvents in many applications including the food industry (53). However, supercritical water is very reactive, and it is corrosive for stainless steels that are inert to ordinary water. Nevertheless the application of sub- and super-critical waters remains a wide-open field.

XI. POSTSCRIPT

Water, ice, and vapor are collections of H_2O molecules, whose characteristics determine the properties of all phases of water. Together and in concert, water molecules shape the landscape, nurture lives, fascinate poets, and captivate scientists. Human efforts to understand water have accumulated a wealth of science applicable in almost all disciplines, while some people take it for granted.

Water molecules are everywhere, including outer space. They not only intertwine with our history and lives, they are parts of us. How blessed we are to be able to associate and correlate the phenomena we see or experience to the science of water.

An article has a beginning and an end, but in the science of water, no one has the last word, as research and exploration on water continue, including its presence in outer space (54). Writing this chapter provoked my fascination on this subject, and for this reason, I am grateful to Professors Wai-kit Nip, Lewis Brubacher, and Peter F. Bernath for their helpful discussions and encouragement.

REFERENCES

1. D.R. Lide, ed. CRC Handbook of Chemistry and Physics, 83rd ed. Boca Raton, CRC Press (2002–2003).
2. J.A. Dean, ed. Lange's Handbook of Chemistry, 15th ed. New York, McGraw-Hill (1999).
3. (No contributor or authorship for this section) Uses of water — food processing industry, in The Nalco Water Handbook, F.N. Kemmer, ed., 2nd ed. New York, McGraw-Hill (1988), pp. 28.1–28.14.
4. The following are from The Civil Engineering Handbook, 2nd, ed., W.F. Chen and J.Y.R. Liew, eds., Boca Raton, CRC Press (2003). (a) R.M. Sykes and E.E. Whitlatch, Water and wastewater planning, pp. 8.1–8.58. (b) R.M. Sykes and H.W. Walker, Physical water and wastewater treatment processes, pp. 9.1–9.151. (c) R.M. Sykes, H.W. Walker, and L.S. Weavers, Chemical water and wastewater treatment processes, pp. 10.1–10.56. (d) R.M. Sykes, Biological wastewater treatment process, pp. 11.1–11.132.
5. J. De Zuane, Handbook of Drinking Water Quality, 2nd ed., New York, Van Nostrand Reinhold (1997).
6. W.J. Lacy, Industrial Wastewater and Hazardous Material Treatment Technology, in Riegel's Handbook of Industrial Chemistry, 9th ed., J.A. Kent, ed. (1992), pp. 31–82.
7. S. Sokhansanj and D.S. Jayasm, Drying of Foodstuffs, in Handbook of Industrial Drying, 2nd ed. A.S. Mujumdar, ed. New York, Marcel Dekker (1995), pp. 589–625.
8. F. Franks, Water — a matrix of life, 2nd ed., London, Royal Society of Chemistry (2000).
9. F. Franks, ed. Water — a comprehensive treatise, Vols. 1–6. New York, Plenum Press (1972).
10. F. Franks, Protein Biotechnology: isolation, characterization, and stabilization, in Characterization of Proteins, F. Flanks ed. Totowa, NJ, Humana Press (1993).
11. F. Franks, Biophysics and Biochemistry at Low Temperatures, London, Cambridge University Press (1985).
12. A.H. Eusmiuger, M.E. Eusmiuger, J.E. Konlache, J.R.K. Robson, Foods & Nutrition Encyclopedia, Vol. 2. Boca Raton, CRC Press (1993), pp. 2279–2293.
13. S.W. Fox, The Emergence of Life: Darwinian Evolution from the Inside. New York, Basic Books Inc. (1988).
14. J. Buettner-Janusch, Origin of Man, Physical Anthropology, New York, John Wiley & Sons (1966).
15. M.J. Taylor, Physico-chemical principles in low temperature biology, in The Effects of Low Temperature on Biological Systems, B.W.W. Grout and G.J. Morris, eds., London, Edward Arnold (1987).
16. R.M. Chew, Water metabolism of mammals, in Physiological Mammalogy, W.V. Mayer and R.G. Van Gelder, eds., Vol. 2, New York, Academic Press (1965), pp. 44–178.
17. J.D. Hem, Water — Sources and Quality Issues, in Encyclopedia of Chemical Technology, J.I. Kroschwitz and M. Howe-Grant, eds., Vol. 25, New York, John Wiley & Sons (1991), pp. 361–382.
18. J.R. Dojlido and G.A. Best, Chemistry of Water and Water Pollution, New York, Ellis Horwood (1993).
19. A.D. Buckingham, The structure and properties of a water molecule, in Water and Aqueous Solutions, G.W. Neilson, eds., Bristol, Adam Kilger (1985), pp. 1–10.
20. D. Eisenberg and W. Kauzmann, The Sructure and Properties of Water, Oxford, Oxford University Press (1969).
21. S.L. Shostak, W.L. Ebenstein, and J.S. Muenter, The dipole moment of water. I. Dipole moments and hyperfine properties of H_2O and HDO, in the ground and excited vibrational states, J. Chem. Phys. 94, pp. 5875–5882 (1991).
22. L. Pauling, The Nature of the Chemical Bond, 3rd ed. Itaca, Cornell University Press (1960).
23. M.F. Martin, The Water Molecule, sbu.ac.uk/water/molecule.html (accessed May, 2003).
24. J.J. Morgan and W. Stumin, (Water) Properties, in Encyclopedia of Chemical Technology, J.I. Kroschwitz and M. Howe-Grant ed., Vol. 25, New York, John Wiley & Sons (1991), pp. 382–405.
25. B. Kamb, Structure of the ice, in Water and Aqueous Solutions Structure, Thermodynamics and Transport processes, New York, Wiley-Interscience (1972), pp. 9–25.
26. V.F. Petrenko and R.W. Whitworth, Physics of Ice, New York, Oxford University Press (1999).
27. J. McNamara, Introduction to Ice Structure and Surfaces, mch3w.ch.man.ac.uk/theory/staff/student/mbdtsma/www/poster/ice.htm (accessed July, 2003).
28. S.J. Suresh and V.M. Naik, Hydrogen bond thermodynamic properties of water from dielectric constant data, J. Chem. Phys. 113, pp. 9727–9732 (2000).
29. E. Espinosa, E. Molins, C. Lecomte, Hydrogen bond strengths revealed by topological analyses of experimentally observed electron densities, Chem. Phys. Lett. 285, pp. 170–173 (1998).
30. J.S. Rolinson, The lattice energy of ice and the second virial coefficient of water vapor, Trans Faraday Soc 47, pp. 120–129.
31. R. Marsili, Water Activity, foodproductdesign.com/archive/1993/1293QA.html (accessed July, 2003).
32. K.N. Marsh, ed., Recommended Reference Materials for the Realization of Physicochemical Properties, Oxford, Blackwell Scientific Publications (1987).
33. C. Tanford, The Hydrophobic Effect: Formation of Micelles and Biological Membranes, 2nd ed., New York, John Wiley & Sons (1980).
34. D.E. Sloan, Clathrate Hydrates of Natural Gases, New York, Marcel Dekker (1998).
35. T. Moeller and R. O'Connor, Ions in Aqueous Systems: an Introduction to Chemical Equilibrium and Solution Chemistry, New York, McGraw-Hill (1972).
36. M. Hermes, Gaterade, chemcases.com/gaterade/index2.htm (accessed Aug., 2003).
37. W.L. Marshall and E.U. Franck, Ion Product of Water Substance, 0–1000°C, 1–10,000 bars, New international formulation and its background, J. Phys. Chem. Ref. Data 10, pp. 295–306 (1981).
38. G.J. Tawa and L.R. Pratt, Theoretical calculation of the water ion product K_W, J. Am. Chem. Soc. 117, pp. 1625–1628 (1995).

39. D.D. Perrin, Ionisation Constants of Inorganic Acids and Bases in Aqueous Solution, Toronto, Pergamon Press (1982).

40. D.D. Perrin, Dissociation Constants of Organic Bases in Aqueous Solution, London, Butterworths (1965).

41. G. Kortüm, W. Vogel, and K. Andrussow, Dissociation Constants of organic acids in aqueous solution, London, Butterworths (1961).

42. G.A. Berkowitz, Water and salt stress, in Photosynthesis – A Comprehensive Treatise, A.S. Raghavendra, ed., New York, Cambridge University Press (1998), pp. 226–237.

43. R.P.F. Gregory, Photosynthesis, New York, Chapman and Hall (1989).

44. S. Shan and D. Herschlag, The change in hydrogen bond strength accompanying charge rearrangement: implications for enzymatic catalysis, Proc. Natl. Acad. Sci. USA Vol. 93 (Biochemistry), pp. 14474–14479 (1996).

45. H.A. Guthurie and M.F. Picciano, Human Nutrition, New York, Bosby (1995).

46. M.F. Chaplin, Fibre and water binding, in Proceedings of the Nutrition Society, 62, 223–227 (2003).

47. W. Larcher, Physiological Plant Ecology: Ecophysiology and Stress Physiology of Functional Groups, New York, Springer-Verlag (1995)

48. J. Barret, M.N. Hughes, G.I. Karavaiko, and P.A. Spencer, Metal Extraction by Bacterial Oxidation of Minerals, New York, Ellis Horwood (1993).

49. R.A. Coler, Water Pollution Biology: A Laboratory/Field Handbook, Lancaster, PA, Technomic Publishing Co. (1989).

50. S.L. Percival, J.T. Walker, and P.R. Hunter, Microbiological aspects of biofilms and drinking water, Boca Raton, CRC Press (2000).

51. S.B. Hawthorne and A. Kubatova, Hot (subcritical) water extraction, in A Comprehensive Analytical Chemistry XXXVII, Sampling and Sample Preparation for Field and Laboratory, J. Pawliszyn, ed., New York, Elsevier (2002), pp. 587–608.

52. J. Pawliszyn and N. Alexandrou, Indirect supercritical fluid extraction of organics from water matrix samples, Water Pollution Research Journal of Canada, 24(2), 207–214 (1989).

53. J.W. King, Sub- and supercritical fluid processing of agrimaterials: Extraction, fractionation and reaction modes, in Supercritical Fluids – Fundamentals and Applications. E. Kiran, P.G. Debeneditti and C.J. Peters eds. NATO Science Series, Series E: Applied Sciences, (2000), Vol. 366, Ch. 19, pp. 451–488.

54. P.F. Bernath, The spectroscopy of water vapour: Experiment, theory, and applications, Phys. Chem. Chem. Phys., 4, pp. 1501–1509 (2002).

13 Bioactive Amines

Maria Beatriz Abreu Glória
Departamento de Alimentos, Universidade Federal de Minas Gerais

CONTENTS

I. DEFINITION, CLASSIFICATION, AND PHYSICO-CHEMICAL CHARACTERISTICS

It has long been known that certain amines fulfill a number of important metabolic and physiologic functions in living organisms. They are formed during normal metabolic processes and are, therefore, present in foods.

Bioactive or biologically active amines (Figure 13.1) are aliphatic, cyclic, and heterocyclic organic bases of low molecular weight (74, 102, 165). They are derivatives of ammonia in which the hydrogen atoms are replaced by one, two, or three alkyl moieties to give, respectively, primary, secondary, or tertiary amines. Many different structures of varying complexity are found (166).

Most of the amines have been named after their precursor amino acids, e.g., histamine originates from histidine, tyramine from tyrosine, tryptamine from tryptophan, and so on. However, the names cadaverine and putrescine are associated with decomposition and putrefaction, and spermine and spermidine with seminal fluids where they were found for the first time (59, 102).

Bioactive amines can be classified on the basis of the number of amine groups, chemical structure, biosynthesis, or physiological functions (9, 160, 165). According to the number of amine groups, they can be monoamines (tyramine, phenylethylamine), diamines (histamine, serotonin, tryptamine, putrescine, cadaverine), or polyamines (spermine, spermidine, agmatine). Based on the chemical structure, amines can be aliphatic (putrescine, cadaverine, spermine, spermidine, agmatine), aromatic (tyramine, phenylethylamine), or heterocyclic (histamine, tryptamine, serotonin). They can also be classified as indolamines (serotonin) and imidazolamines (histamine). According to the biosynthetic pathway, amines can be natural or biogenic. Natural amines – spermine, spermidine, putrescine and histamine – are formed during *de novo* biosynthesis, e.g., *in situ* as required from their precursors (9, 74). Biogenic amines are formed by bacterial decarboxylation of free amino acids. Histamine can be either natural (stored in mast cells or basophils) or biogenic. Based on the physiological functions, amines are classified as polyamines and biogenic amines. Polyamines play an important role in growth while biogenic amines are neuro- or vasoactive (9). This is the most widely used classification and will be the one considered throughout this chapter.

The common and chemical names, the molecular formulas and weights, and the physico-chemical characteristics of some bioactive amines are summarized in Table 13.1. The molecular weights are usually low, varying from 88.15 (putrescine) to 202.34 (spermine). The amines behave as

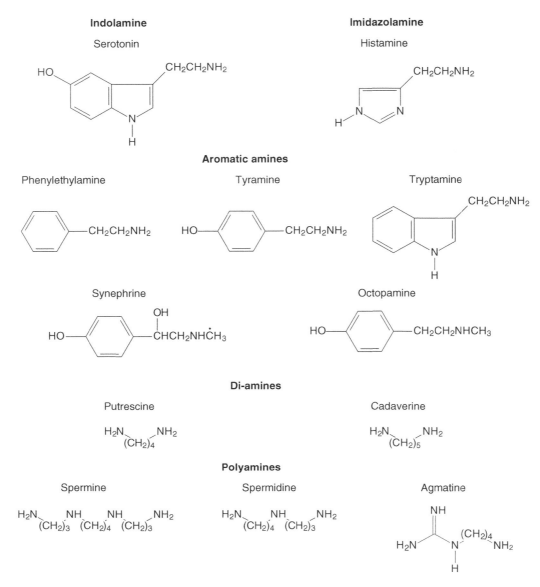

FIGURE 13.1 Classification and chemical structures of some bioactive amines.

cations, being protonated at physiological pH values (123). The pK_a for amines lies between 6 and 11 (41, 101, 166).

At room temperature, the free amines are either liquid, syrupy liquid, crystal, or needle. The boiling points vary from 128 to 210 °C, and the melting points from 9 to 231 °C. The solubility varies widely depending on the amine and on its form – salt or free base (101, 213). At high pH values, dissociation of amine salts into free amines may occur. The refractive index has been reported by Lide (101) for putrescine (1.4969), cadaverine (1.463), and phenylethylamine (1.5290). Density of cadaverine is 0.873 g/mL. Maximum UV absorptions for tryptamine are 222, 282, and 290 nm in ethanol; 224 and 278 nm in acetonitrile:water, 20:80; and 225 and 278 nm in methanol:water, 15:85. Maximum UV absorptions for tyramine and histamine are, respectively, 226 and 275 nm and 225 nm in

acetonitrile:water, 20:80; and 228 and 275 nm and 228 nm in methanol:water, 15:85 (34). For synephrine and octopamine, maximum UV absorption values are 231 and 272 nm, and for tyramine 231 and 275 in acetate buffer (pH 4,9):acetonitrile, 9:91 (200, 213). The stability varies with the amines. Some amines can absorb CO_2. Synephrine is stable to light and air. Serotonin hydrochloride is sensitive to light and aqueous solutions are stable at pH 2.0 to 6.4. Decomposition of octopamine hydrochloride can occur at 170 °C (213).

Few sensory data on amines are available. This represents an area that deserves further attention. However, a few amine-based compounds can be used by the flavor compounder. For example, phenylethylamine, is recognized by the Flavor Extract Manufacturers' Association as FEMA # 3220, and has a fishy odor (108).

TABLE 13.1
Common and Chemical Names, Molecular Formulas and Weights, and Physico-Chemical Characteristics of some Bioactive Amines

Amine	Chemical Name	Molecular Formula	MW[1]	Melting Point °C	Boiling Point °C	pK_a	Solubility[2]
AGMATINE	4-(aminobutyl) guanidine; 1-amino-4-guanidobutane	$C_5H_{14}N_4$	130.19	231 ($C_5H_{14}N_4 \cdot H_2SO_4$)	—	—	1 – ethanol ($C_5H_{14}N_4 \cdot H_2SO_4$); 2 – H_2O ($C_5H_{14}N_4 \cdot H_2SO_4$)
PUTRESCINE	1,4-butane-diamine; tetramethylenediamine	$C_4H_{12}N_2$	88.15	23–24; 280	158–160	$pK_{a1} = 9.35$; $pK_{a2} = 10.80$ (20 °C)	1 – benzene; diethyl ether; 3 – H_2O; 4 – H_2O ($C_4H_{12}N_2 \cdot 2HCl$ & $C_4H_{12}N_2 \cdot 2HCl$); ethanol
SPERMIDINE	N-(3-aminopro-pyl)-1,4-butane-diamine; N-(γ-amino-propyl)	$C_7H_{19}N_3$	145.24	256–258 ($C_7H_{19}N_3 \cdot 3HCl$)	128–130	$pK_{a1} = 8.15$; $pK_{a2} = 9.74$; $pK_{a3} = 10.24$	3 – H_2O; ethanol; diethyl ether
SPERMINE (gerontine, musculamine, neuridine)	N,N'-bis(3-aminopropyl)-1,4-butane-diamine; N,N'-bis(3-aminopropyl) tetramethylenediamine	$C_{10}H_{19}N_3$	202.34	55–60	141–142	$pK_{a1} = 7.91$; $pK_{a2} = 8.68$; $pK_{a3} = 10.21$; $pK_{a4} = 10.56$	1 – benzene; petroleum ether; diethyl ether; 3 – H_2O; lower alcohols; chloroform
CADAVERINE (animal conine)	1,5-pentanediamine; pentamethylenediamine	$C_5H_{14}N_2$	102.18	9; 225–230 ($C_5H_{14}N_2 \cdot 2HCl$)	178–180	$pK_{a1} = 10.05$; $pK_{a2} = 10.93$ (25 °C)	1 – absolute alcohol ($C_5H_{14}N_2 \cdot 2HCl$); 2 – diethyl ether; 3 – H_2O; etanol; H_2O ($C_5H_{14}N_2 \cdot 2HCl$)
PHENYLETHYL-AMINE	benzene ethanoamine	$C_8H_{11}N$	121.18	—	197.5	$pK_{a1} = 9.84$ (25 °C)	3 – H_2O; CCl4; 4 – diethyl ether
HISTAMINE	1H-imidazole-4-ethanamine; 2-(4-imidazolyl)-ethylamine	$C_5H_9N_3$	111.15	83–84; 244–246 ($C_5H_9N_3 \cdot 2HCl$)	209–210	$pK_{a1} = 6.04$; $pK_{a2} = 9.75$ (25 °C)	2 – diethyl ether; 3 – H_2O; ethanol; chloroform; 4 – H_2O ($C_5H_9N_3 \cdot 2HCl$) methanol
OCTOPAMINE (norsympatol, norsynephrine)	α-(aminomethyl)-4-hydroxy-benzene-methanol; α-(aminomethyl)-p-hydroxybenzyl alcohol	$C_8H_{11}NO_2$	153.18	160	—	—	4 – H_2O ($C_8H_{11}NO_2 \cdot HCl$)
SEROTONIN	5-hydroxy-tryptamine; 5-hydroxi-3-(β-amino-ethyl) indol	$C_{10}H_{12}N_2O$	176.21	167–168 ($C_{10}H_{12}N_2O \cdot HCl$)	—	$pK_{a1} = 9.8$; $pK_{a2} = 11.1$ (25 °C)	1 – 100% ethanol; acetone; pyridine; chloroform; ethyl acetate; diethyl ether; benzene; 2 – metanol; 95% ethanol; 3 – H_2O ($C_{10}H_{12}N_2O \cdot HCl$)
SYNEPHRINE (analeptin, ethaphene, oxedrine, p-sympatol, simpalon)	4-hydroxy-α[(methylamino)methyl]-benzene-methanol; 1-(4-hydroxiphenyl)-2-methylamino-ethanol	$C_9H_{13}NO_2$	167.2	184–185; 151–152 ($C_9H_{13}NO_2 \cdot HCl$)	—	—	3 – ethanol; 4 – H_2O ($C_9H_{13}NO_2 \cdot HCl$ & $C_9H_{13}NO_2 \cdot$ tartrate)
TRYPTAMINE	1H-indole-3-ethanamine; 3-(2-aminoethyl) indole	$C_{10}H_{12}N_2$	160.21	118 ($C_{10}H_{12}N_2 \cdot HCl$)	205–207	$pK_{a1} = 10.2$ (25 °C)	1 – H_2O; diethyl ether; benzene; chloroform; 3 – etanol, acetone
TYRAMINE	4-(2-aminoethyl)phenol; 2-p-hydroxy phenyl-ethyl amine	$C_8H_{11}NO$	137.18	164–165; 269 ($C_8H_{11}NO \cdot HCl$)	205–207	$pK_{a1} = 9.74$; $pK_{a2} = 10.52$ (25 °C)	1 – H_2O; 2 – H_2O: benzene; xylene; 3 – boiling ethanol

[1] MW = Molecular weight.
[2] Solubility: 1=insoluble, 2=fairly soluble, 3=good, 4=very good.
Source: Refs. 41, 101, and 213.

Wang et al. (206) investigated the odor threshold of polyamines. They reported that free polyamines have an unpleasant, almost putrid, ammoniacal odor. In food, because of their basic groups, polyamines normally bind with the acidic groups of other food components, notably those in nucleic acids or lipids. However, at high pH, free polyamines could result. The determination of odor thresholds for putrescine, spermidine, and spermine by an informal panel of nine people provided odor descriptions which varied widely from sodium hypochlorite bleach, dusty, and musty, to putrid, amine, and ammoniacal. Using a formal panel of 15 members, the odor threshold of the polyamines, e.g., polyamine concentration at which 50% of the panelists gave a positive response, was determined. Spermine and putrescine had odor thresholds in water of the same magnitude (2.4 and 2.2 mg/100 g, respectively), while those of cadaverine (19.0 mg/100 g) and spermidine (12.9 mg/100 g) were approximately six to nine times higher. However, when 2% soybean flour was added, odor thresholds increased significantly, from five to ten times greater than those in water, reaching values of 10.9 g for putrescine and 102.5 mg/100 g for spermidine.

II. PHYSIOLOGICAL IMPORTANCE

Bioactive amines participate in important metabolic and physiological functions in living organisms. Biogenic amines are generally either psychoactive, neuroactive, or vasoactive. Psychoactive amines, such as histamine and serotonin, affect the nervous system by acting on neural transmitters in the central nervous system. Vasoactive amines act directly or indirectly on the vascular system. Pressor amines – tyramine, tryptamine, and phenylethylamine – cause a rise in blood pressure by constricting the vascular system and increasing the heart rate and force of contraction of the heart. However, tyramine does it indirectly by causing the release of noradrenaline from the sympathetic nervous system (158, 165). Serotonin and histamine are also strongly vasoactive (139).

Histamine is a powerful biologically active chemical that can exert many responses within the body. Although mast cells and blood basophiles contain large amounts of histamine stored in special granules, the effect of histamine does not appear unless special reactions (i.e., an allergic reaction) release it into the bloodstream. Histamine exerts its effects by binding to receptors on cellular membranes which are found in the cardiovascular system and in various secretory glands (87). Histamine is a strong capillary dilator and can produce hypotensive effects. It can directly stimulate the heart, cause contraction or relaxation of extravascular smooth muscle (excite the smooth muscle of the uterus, intestine and respiratory tract), stimulate both sensory and motor neurons, and control gastric acid secretion. It also mediates primary and immediate symptoms in allergic responses (139, 158, 165, 173, 177).

Serotonin is a vaso- and bronco-constrictor, reduces the volume and acidity of the gastric juice, has anti-diuretic effect, stimulates smooth muscle, and affects carbohydrate metabolism (63). When introduced into the afferent circulation, serotonin causes a release of prostaglandin and other vasoactive substances. Serotonin is a neurotransmitter, particularly in the central nervous system. It is involved in the regulation of a number of important functions, including sleep, thirst, hunger, mood, and sexual activity (42).

Tyramine is taken up into adrenergic nerves and causes a massive release of noradrenaline. It has a marked effect on the release of the putative neurotransmitter amines dopamine, noradrenaline, and serotonin from nerve terminals (42).

Phenylethylamine and tryptamine are endogenous constituents of many tissues, including brain. Both can cross the blood-brain barrier with ease. It is conceivable that large amounts of phenylethylamine and tryptamine from foodstuffs may enter the central nervous system and lead to side-effects of psychiatric nature. It has been reported that phenylethylamine and tryptamine can inhibit uptake and stimulate release of catecholamines and serotonin from a variety of preparations of brain and heart tissues. It has also been demonstrated that phenylethylamine can affect binding of serotonin to its receptor sites in the human and rat brain. Introduction of tryptamine into the afferent circulation can cause a release of prostaglandin and other vasoactive substances into the systemic circulation (42).

There is evidence, particularly with respect to the invertebrate nervous system, suggesting that octopamine may be a neurotransmitter. Less is known about synephrine, although it has been shown to be a constituent of various tissues and body fluids. Synephrine is used pharmacologically as a stimulant, decongestant, and in the treatment of hypotension in oral form (42, 165).

Polyamines are indispensable components of all living cells, where they play essential roles in cell metabolism, growth, and differentiation (11). During normal and adaptive growth, polyamines are involved in a variety of growth-related processes which reflect their multifunctional character. Polyamines have various electrostatic interactions with macromolecules especially DNA, RNA, and protein and are involved in the regulation and stimulation of their synthesis (104).

Diverse effects of the polyamines on cell replication have been identified, such as the control and initiation of translation and regulation of its fidelity, stimulation of ribosome subunit association, enhancement of RNA and DNA synthesis, and reduction in the rate of RNA degradation. Polyamines stabilize the structure of tRNA and help condense DNA and covalently modify proteins (9, 10). Polyamines stimulate the rate of transcription, the amino acid activation, and the rate of translation during the course of protein synthesis (148). Polyamines also stimulate cell differentiation and interact and module various intracellular messenger systems (104). The most important function of polyamines, one in which they cannot be replaced by any other positively charged molecule, is to act as second messengers, thereby mediating the action of all known hormones and growth factors (9).

Polyamines interact with different components of the cell membrane thus modulating its functions. They are, therefore, important in the permeability and stability of cellular membranes (9, 48, 104, 160). During the period that follows birth, antigenic macromolecules can penetrate the small intestinal mucosal membranes in quantities that may be of immunologic importance. Polyamines reduce mucosal permeability to macromolecules and prevent food allergies by decreasing mucosal permeability to allergenic proteins (27, 147).

According to Drolet et al. (48) and to Bardocz (9), spermine and spermidine, as well as the diamines putrescine and cadaverine, are efficient free radical scavengers in a number of chemical and *in vitro* enzyme systems. They could inhibit lipid peroxidation and prevent senescence. Levels of superoxide radical formed either enzymatically with xanthine oxidase or chemically from riboflavin or pyrogallol were significantly inhibited. The more reactive hydroxyl radical generated by the Fenton reaction was also effectively scavenged by spermine and spermidine. The efficacy of polyamine scavenging appears to be correlated with the number of amino groups (48, 168).

Polyamines are essential for the maintenance of the high metabolic activity of the normally functioning and healthy gut. They are involved in the repair of gut damage caused by the deleterious components of the food and/or bacteria (11, 104). The development of gastrointestinal tract in ruminants and non-ruminants is dependent upon the increases in ornithine decarboxylase (ODC) activity and in polyamines content in the mucosa (123). Studies performed with rats indicated that during the third postnatal week, rapid intestinal maturation occurs and this period is characterized by an increase in epithelial cell proliferation and differentiation, resulting in histological and enzymatic maturation of the small bowel epithelium, marked increase in mucosal thickness, and increase in mature mucosal enzyme activities. Prior to this process of epithelial maturation, a ten- to twenty-fold increase in mucosal ODC activity and a concomitant increase in S-adenosyl-L-methionine decarboxylase (SAMDC) activity as well as putrescine, spermidine, and spermine content were found (104, 123). Simultaneous administration of α-difluoromethyl ornithine (DFMO), a potent irreversible ODC inhibitor, to the nursing mother or directly to the newborn rat pups, resulted in a marked attenuation of the increase in mucosal ODC and polyamine content which was followed by a significant delay in biochemical and histological maturation of the intestinal epithelium (123).

According to Löser (104), polyamines in milk exert various direct and indirect throphic effects on the immature intestine and play an important role as luminal growth factors for intestinal maturation and growth. The protective effect of milk against a newborn's allergies could be explained by its high levels of polyamines. They bring about a decrease in protein permeability, diminishing the amount of allergens reaching the intestinal submucosa, and thus allow a better maturation of the immune system in susceptible newborn (106, 147).

Because of the diversity of the roles of polyamines in cellular metabolism and growth, they are important in health and disease. The requirement for polyamines is particularly high in rapidly growing tissues, e.g., in the young during periods of intense growth and in the mucosa of the gastrointestinal tract. Similarly, during periods of wound healing, post-surgery recovery, liver regeneration, and compensatory growth of the lung, requirements are also high. In healthy adults, however, requirements should not be as high because polyamines are only needed to replace cells and mediate the action of hormones and growth factors (9, 123). Studies are needed to determine the daily requirements.

Three sources of polyamines have been identified: biosynthesis *in situ* from amino acids, direct ingestion from the diet and synthesis, and release by the bacterial flora resident in the gastrointestinal tract of the individual. It is now clear that the diet is an important source of polyamines and it is likely to supply at least a part of the polyamines required to sustain normal metabolism (9).

III. SYNTHESIS

The synthesis of the biogenic amines histamine, tyramine, tryptamine, phenylethylamine, and cadaverine occur through decarboxylation of the precursor amino acids histidine, tyrosine, tryptophan, phenylalanine, and lysine, respectively. In the synthesis of serotonin, tryptophan is transformed by tryptophan hydrolase in 5-hydroxitryptophan, which is decarboxylated by aromatic amino acid decarboxylase in 5-hydroxytryptamine or serotonin. Tyrosine is the precursor of the phenolic amines octopamine and synephrine in citrus (165).

The generalized reaction for amino acid decarboxylation is indicated in Figure 13.2. Aldehyde amination can be another route of synthesis, carried out by aldehyde transaminases (166).

Prerequisites for the formation of amines in foods are the availability of free amino acids, high processing temperatures, or the presence of decarboxylase-positive microorganisms and favorable conditions for microbial growth and decarboxylase activity. Free amino acids occur as such in foods, but may also be released from proteins as a result of proteolytic activity or thermal degradation. The formation of amines by high processing temperatures has been demonstrated by Cirilo et al. (38) during coffee roasting. Longer roasting time (12 compared to 6 minutes) at

$$\begin{array}{c} \text{COOH} \\ | \\ R - CH - NH_2 \end{array} \longrightarrow R - CH_2 - NH_2 + CO_2 \qquad (1)$$

$$\begin{array}{c} \text{COOH} \\ | \\ R - CHO + R' - CH - NH_2 \end{array} \longrightarrow R - CH_2 - NH_2 + \begin{array}{c} \text{COOH} \\ | \\ R' - C = O \end{array} \qquad (2)$$

FIGURE 13.2 Formation of amines by amino acid decarboxylation (1) and by aldehyde amination (2).

300 °C in a Probat roaster caused significant increase in spermidine and serotonin levels and formation of agmatine. Decarboxylase-positive microorganisms may constitute part of the associated population of the food or may be introduced by contamination before, during, and after processing (74, 108).

Two mechanisms of action for amino acid decarboxylation have been identified: a pyridoxal phosphate dependent and a non-pyridoxal phosphate dependent reaction. Pyridoxal phosphate joined in a Schiff base linkage to the amino group of a lysil residue forms the active site of the enzymes. The carbonyl group of pyridoxal phosphate reacts readily with the amino acid to form Schiff base intermediates, which are then decarboxylated with the elimination of water to yield the corresponding amines and the original pyridoxal phosphate moiety. Non-pyridoxal phosphate-catalyzed decarboxylation involves a pyruvoyl residue instead. The pyruvoyl group is covalently bound to the amino group of a phenylalanine residue of the enzyme and is derived from a serine residue. The pyruvoyl residue acts in a manner similar to pyridoxal phosphate in the decarboxylation reaction (158)

Regarding the formation of amines by microorganism decarboxylase activity, several studies have been performed to investigate the production of amines by species isolated from fish, cheese, meat products, vegetables, and alcoholic beverages. These studies indicated that many species of *Escherichia*, *Enterobacter*, *Salmonella*, *Shigella*, and *Proteus* are active biogenic amines formers. Certain species of *Achromobacter*, *Lactobacillus*, *Leuconostoc*, *Pseudomonas*, *Pediococcus*, *Streptococcus*, *Micrococcus*, and *Propionibacterium* are also capable of amine production (16, 23, 51, 82, 149, 195).

In fermented foods, the applied starter cultures may also affect amine production. Straub et al. (174) investigated the production of putrescine, cadaverine, histamine, tyramine, and phenylethylamine by 523 strains of 35 species of food fermentation microorganisms. These authors observed that some strains of carnobacteria, *Lactobacillus buchneri*, *L. curvatus*, *L. reuteri*, and *Staphylococcus carnosus* were proficuous amine producers. However, some strains of *L. alimentarius*, *L. brevis*, *L. bavaricus*, *L. delbrueckii* ssp. *Lactis* and *Micrococcus* spp. were capable of producing amines at smaller quantities. The importance of selecting

starter cultures based on their potential for amine production is emphasized.

The amino acid decarboxylating activity of some food microorganisms is indicated in Table 13.2. The production of amines by bacteria is affected by pH, temperature, oxygen tension, presence of vitamins and cofactors, and availability of free amino acids and of fermentable sugars. In pH values of 2.5 to 6.5, the production of amines by the bacteria is stimulated as a protection against the acidic environment (201). The activity of decarboxylases is dependent on the microorganism's growth phase, being higher at the stationary phase. With regard to the temperature, decarboxylases are more active at temperatures lower than 30 °C and without action at temperatures above 40 °C. However, at temperatures between 0 and 10 °C, the activity will depend on the microorganisms present (7, 74).

Polyamine synthesis is a more complex process, although the first few steps also include decarboxylation reactions. There are several proven biosynthetic pathways responsible for polyamine production (Figure 13.3). Putrescine is an obligate intermediate in polyamine synthesis. In animals the first step is decarboxylation of ornithine by ODC (EC 4.1.1.17). In plants and some microorganisms, an alternative pathway exists to produce putrescine from arginine via agmatine by arginine decarboxylase (ADC; EC 4.1.1.19). An additional path for the formation of putrescine is via citrulline (9, 59, 168, 202).

Both ODC and ADC are dependent on pyridoxal phosphate. Agmatinase is the enzyme that converts agmatine to putrescine. Agmatine is metabolized to putrescine in a two-step conversion. Agmatine iminohydrolase (AIH) catalyzes the formation of N-carbamoylputrescine, which is converted to putrescine by N-carbamoylputrescine amido hydrolase (NCPAH). N-carbamoylputrescine can also be formed from citrulline by citrulline decarboxylase (CDC). The arginine pool can be increased through protein degradation. Ornithine and urea formation from arginine allows recovery of nitrogen and carbon (59).

Spermidine and spermine are formed by the subsequent addition of an aminopropyl moiety to putrescine and spermidine, respectively. These reactions are catalyzed by the aminopropyltransferase enzymes spermidine synthase (SpdS, EC 2.5.1.16) and spermine synthase (SpmS, EC 2.5.1.22). The aminopropyl group is derived from methionine via *S*-adenosyl-L-methionine (SAM) in a reation

TABLE 13.2
Amino Acid Decarboxylating Activity of Food Microorganisms

Amine	Microorganism	Ref.
HISTAMINE	*Achromobacter histaminum*	7
(Histidine decarboxylase)	*Acinetobacter calcoaceticusvar, A. lwofii, A. nitratum*	33
	Aeromonas spp. *A. hydrophila*	36
	Alteromonas putrefaciens	49
	Betabacterium spp.	51
	Citrobacter diversus, C. freundii	72
	Clostridium perfringens, C. bifermentans, C. fallax, C. novyi	117
	Edwardsiella spp.	122
	Enterobacter aerogenes, E. agglomerans, E. cloacae, E. intermedium	139
	Escherichia coli, E. freundii	140
	Hafnia alvei	142
	Klebsiella oxytoca, K. pneumoniae	144
	Lactobacillus 30a; L. acidophilus, L. alimentarius, L. arabinose, L. bavaricus, L. buchneri, L. bulgaricus, L. casei, L. delbrueckii, L. fermentum, L. helveticus, L. plantarum, L. reuteri, L. sanfrancisco	145
	Morganella morganii (Proteus morganii)	146
	Oenococcus oeni (Leuconostoc oenos)	159
	Pediococcus cereviseae	160
	Photobacterium histaminum, P. phosphoreum	173
	Proteus mirabilis, P. reptilivora, P. rettgeri, P. stuartii, P. vulgaris	174
	Providencia alcalifaciens, P. stuartii	178
	Pseudomonas aeruginosa, P. fluorescens, P. putida, P. putrefaciens, P. reptilvora	182
	Ristella spp.	
	Salmonella enteriditis, S. paratyphi, S. schottmuelleri, S. typhi	
	Serratia liquefaciens, S. odorifera	
	Shigella spp.	
	Staphylococcus xylosus	
	Streptococcus faecalis, S. faecium, S. lactis, S. mitis	
	Vibrio alginolyticus	
TYRAMINE	*Betabacterium* spp.	33
(Tyrosine decarboxylase)	*Carnobacterium divergens, C. Galinarum, C. maltaromicus, C. piscicola*	51
	Clostridium aerofoetidum, C. sporogenes	53
	Enterococcus faecalis, E. faecium	58
	Escherichia coli	71
	Lactobacillus brevis, L. buchneri, L. bulgaricus, L. curvatus, L. delbrueckii ssp. *lactis, L. hilgardii, L. paracasei, L. pentoaceticus* Rudensis, *L. pentosus, L. plantarum, L. rhamnosus*	114
	Lactococcus lactis	121
	Leuconostoc mesenteroids, L. paramesenteroids	122
	Micrococcus varians	132
	Oenococcus oeni (Leuconostoc oenos)	139
	Proteus mirabilis	140
	Pseudomonas fluorescens, P. reptilivora	159
	Serratia liquefaciens	160
	Staphylococcus carnosus, S. piscifermentans, S. saprophyticus	173
	Streptococcus faecalis, S. faecium, S. durans (group D)	174
CADAVERINE	*Edwardsiella cloacae, E. hoshinae, E. ictaluri, E. tarda*	72
(Lysine decarboxylase)	*Enterobacter aerogenes, E. gergoviae*	112
	Escherichia coli, E. blattae	142
	Fusobacterium varium	145
	Hafnia alvei	159
	Klebsiella planticola, K. pneumoniae, K. oxytoca, K. terrigena	174
	Kluyvera ascorbata	183
	Lactobacillus acidophilus, L. bavaricus, L. brevis, L. casei, L. curvatus, L. hilgardii	
	Micrococcus spp.	

(continued)

TABLE 13.2   (*Continued*)

Amine	Microorganism	Ref.
	Obesumbacterium aeruginosa, O. proteus	
	Pseudomona aeruginosa, P. fluorescens	
	Salmonella choleraesuis, S. gallinarum, S. pullorum, S. typhi	
	Serratia fonticola, S. liquefaciens, S. marcescens, S. odorifera	
	Staphylococcus carnosus	
	Vibrio alginolyticus, V. campbelli, V. cholerae, V. harveyi, V. parahaemolyticus, V. vulniticus	
	Yersinia ruckeri	
PUTRESCINE	*Cedecea davisae*	6
(Ornithine decarboxylase)	*Citrobacter amalonaticus, C. diversus, C. freundii,*	50
	Edwardsiella hoshinae, E. tarda	72
	Enterobacter cloacae, E. aerogenes, E. gergoviae, E. intermedium, E. sakazakii	112
	Escherichia coli, E. blattae	142
	Hafnia alvei	159
	Klebsiella pneumoniae	174
	Kluyvera ascorbata, K. cryocrescens	183
	Lactobacillus bavaricus, L. brevis, L. buchneri, L. casei, L. curvatus, L. plantarum, L. hilgardii	
	Micrococcus kristinae, M. varians	
	Morganella morganii	
	Obesumbacterium proteus	
	Proteus mirabilis	
	Pseudomonas aeruginosa, P. aureofaciens, P. fluorescens, P. putida	
	Salmonella choleraesuis, S. paratyphi, S. pullorum	
	Serratia fonticola, S. liquefaciens, S. marcescens	
	Shigella sonnei	
	Staphylococcus carnosus, S. epidermidis	
	Vibrio alginolyticus, V. cholerae, V. harveyi, V. parahaemolyticus, V. vulnificus	
	Yersinia enterocolitica , Y. frederiksenii, Y. intermedia, Y. kristensenii, Y. ruckeri	
PHENYLETHYLAMINE	*Enterococcus* spp.	71
(Phenylalanine decarboxylase)	*Lactobacillus curvatus, L. delbrueckii* ssp. *lactis, L. farciminis, L. hilgardii, L. brevis*	121
	Leuconostoc mesenteroids, L. paramesenteroids	122
	Micrococcus spp.	174
	Staphylococcus carnosus, S. epidermidis, S. piscifermentans	
AGMATINE	*Lactobacillus hilgardii*	6
(Arginine decarboxylase)		
TRYPTAMINE	*Lactobacillus bulgaricus*	33
(Tryptophane decarboxylase)		

catalyzed by the enzyme SAMDC (AdoMetDC; EC 4.1.1.50). The 5′-methyltioadenosine, resulting from the liberation of the aminopropyl group by SAM is converted in methyltioribose and in methionine, recycling the –SCH$_3$ group which warrants the synthesis of polyamines (59, 168, 202).

The rate-limiting enzymes for polyamines synthesis are ODC and SAMDC. DFMO is an irreversible inhibitor of ODC (26). A similar difluoromethyl analog of arginine (DFMA) can also inhibit putrescine formation from arginine. Both inhibitors are highly specific and in most cases DFMA can also be partially metabolized to urea and DFMO, thereby indirectly inhibiting ODC. Methylglyoxal bis-guanylhydrazone (MGBG) is the most common inhibitor of SAMDC, which catalyzes the step committing SAM to the synthesis of polyamines (59).

The regulation of polyamine biosynthesis is complex and precise control prevents overproduction and deficiency of polyamines in animals (130). Several regulatory mechanisms contribute to the regulation of intracellular polyamine homeostasis. Intracellular polyamine concentrations are primarily regulated by intracellular polyamine *de novo* synthesis, conversion and degradation as well as uptake of extracellular polyamines. Preliminary regulatory mechanisms are intracellular *de novo* synthesis via ODC, reconversion of polyamines via interconversion pathway (spermine/spermidine N-1-acetyltransferase and polyamine oxidase) and oxidative degradation of polyamines (46, 104).

Uptake of extracellular polyamines from the gut lumen was found to be a further important regulatory mechanism of polyamine metabolism. It is well established that the

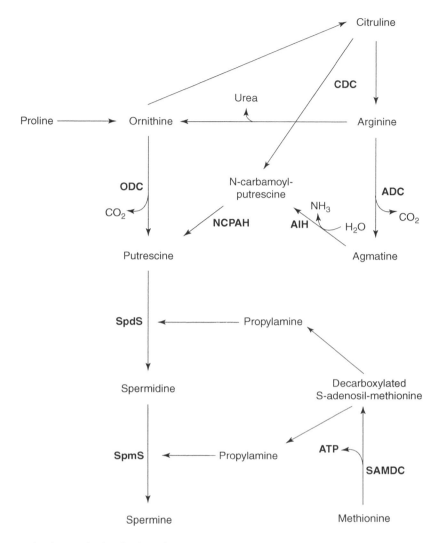

FIGURE 13.3 Pathways for the synthesis of polyamines.

alimentary tract is an important source of polyamines and that dietary as well as to some extent gut bacterial-derived polyamines significantly contribute to the total polyamine body pool. These findings stress the importance of a rapid uptake of dietary, luminal (brush-border membrane) polyamines by the intestinal mucosa upon demand with a consecutive passage through the blood stream (basolateral membrane) to the body (104).

IV. CATABOLISM OF BIOACTIVE AMINES

Healthy individuals can metabolize amines present in foods by acetylation and oxidation (9, 165). Biogenic amines are oxidized by monoaminoxidases (MAO; EC 1.4.3.4) and diaminoxidases (DAO; EC 1.4.3.6). Polyamines are usually acetylated first, then oxidized by polyaminoxidases (PAO; EC 1.5.3.11).

The general equation for the oxidation of amines by amine oxidases (166) is shown in Figure 13.4 and results

$$RCH_2NH_2 + O_2 + H_2O \rightarrow H_2O_2 + RCHO + NH_3 \qquad (1)$$

$$\overset{+}{R\text{-}CH_2NRR'R''} + \tfrac{1}{2}O_2 \rightarrow RCHO + \overset{+}{NH_2R'R''} \qquad (2)$$

FIGURE 13.4 Equations for the oxidation of amines by amine oxidases in the (1) absence and (2) presence of catalase.

in aldehydes, ammonia, and hydrogen peroxide (H_2O_2). According to Marley and Blackwell (113), it is the ionized form of the amine, i.e., the form that is not readily absorbed from the gut, that reacts with the enzyme. Amines that are not ionized to any extent are not oxidized. The overall reaction in the presence of catalase is also shown in Figure 13.4. The aldehyde formed may be oxidized further to the corresponding carboxylic acid.

Amine oxidases belong to a large class of deaminating oxidases (amine:oxygen oxidoreductases) widely distributed among all living organisms. This class of enzymes is

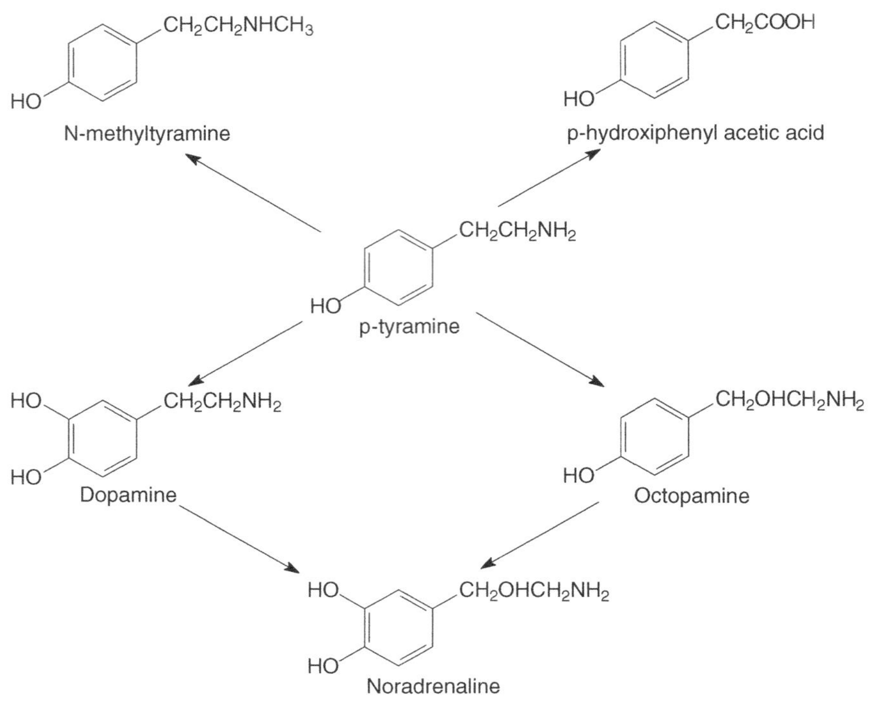

FIGURE 13.5 Tyramine metabolism in man.

divided into two subclasses: copper- and FAD-containing amino oxidases. The copper containing are active on primary amino groups and the FAD-dependent cleave secondary amino groups (134). The amine oxidases contain copper and are sensitive to carbonyl groups. Enzyme activity is usually inhibited by carbonyl reagents and metal chelators (166). Many aliphatic amines of the series $CH_3(CH_2)_nNH_2$ are substrates for the enzyme. The rate of oxidation and affinity vary with the number of carbon atoms in the carbon chain. With increasing length of chain, the rate of oxidation increases, a maximum being reached with 5 or 6 carbon atoms (113). Any substrate of amine oxidase, because it has affinity for the enzyme, may interfere with the oxidation of another substrate.

Tyramine may undergo one of several different catabolic reactions (Figure 13.5). According to Bieck & Karl-Heinz (17), tyramine is extensively metabolized in the gastrointestinal mucosa and liver. The major route is the oxidative deamination to p-hydroxyphenylacetic acid. It is catalyzed by MAO. Other pathways are oxidation to octopamine by dopamine-β-hydroxylase and methylation to N-methyltyramine by N-methyltransferase. Conjugation with either sulphate or acetate groups is also possible. Sulfate conjugation to the o-sulfate accounts for 10–15% of the total dose in urine after oral tyramine administration (17, 60, 87, 115, 139).

Serotonin is oxidized by MAO in man to 5-hydroxyindolacetic acid (5-HIAA). Deamination of tryptamine

by monoamine oxidase has also been demonstrated. These amines compete with tyramine as substrate for the enzyme. Such substrate competition could be relevant with a food that contains a number of amines deaminated by amine oxidase (113).

Histamine can also be catabolized by several different catabolic reactions (Figure 13.6). The two main routes are oxidation to imidazole-acetaldehyde and methylation to 1,4-methylhistamine. Indeed, in mammals, 60 to 80% of the metabolites of histamine are derived from oxidative deamination. Amine oxidases are involved in both routes. They convert 1,4-methylhistamine to the corresponding aldehyde and play a minor role in the conversion of histamine to imidazole-acetaldehyde. Inhibitors of monoamine oxidase could therefore interfere with either of these stages, although the metabolism of 1,4-methylhistamine is the one most likely to be affected since diamine oxidase is primarily involved in the conversion of histamine to imidazole-acetaldehyde (113). Percentage recovery of histamine and its metabolites in the urine 12 hours after intradermal ^{14}C-histamine administration in human males indicated that the majority of the radioactivity was recovered as N-methylimidazole acetic acid (42–47%), followed by imidazole acetic acid conjugated with ribose (16–23%), as imidazole acetic acid (9–11%), as N-methylhistamine (4–8%), and as histamine (2–3%) (211).

DAO is a non-selective enzyme and also oxidizes putrescine and cadaverine. In fact, histamine is not the

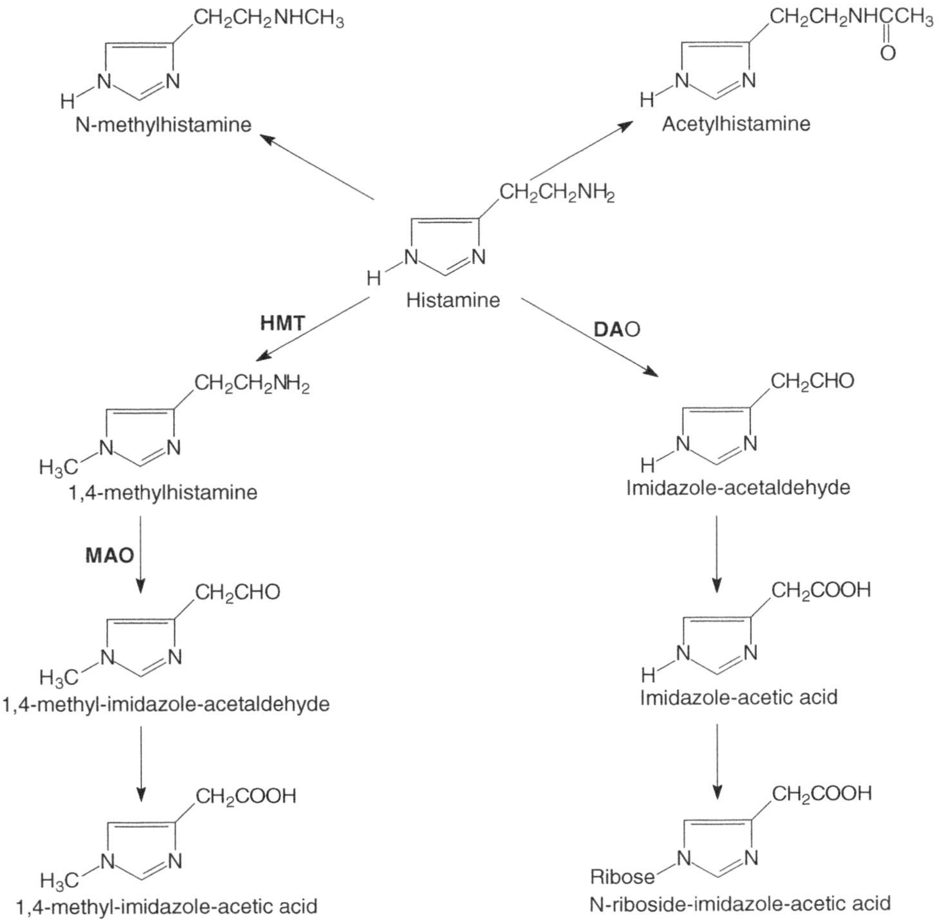

FIGURE 13.6   Histamine metabolism in man.

favored substrate of DAO, being deaminated at about one-third the rate of putrescine and cadaverine. Histamine N-methyl transferase (HMT) is very selective for histamine and requires S-adenosylmethionine as a methyl donor (183).

Several studies were undertaken to assess the potential inhibitory effect of various chemicals on histamine metabolizing enzymes. Taylor and Lieber (181) investigated 37 chemicals and observed that seven strongly inhibited rat jejunal mucosa HMT, while eight inhibited DAO. The most potent inhibitors of HMT activity were tyramine (99%), phenylethylamine (99%), tryptamine (98%), octopamine (94%), agmatine (87%), aminoguanidine (81%), and nicotine (78%), whereas cadaverine, indole, tartrazine, theophylline, thiamin, and trimethylamine gave intermediate levels of inhibition. The most potent inhibitors of DAO activity were aminoguanidine (100%), anserine (100%), carnosine (100%), histamine (99%), agmatine (97%), thiamin (92%), cadaverine (87%), and tyramine (77%). Caffeine, hypoxanthin, indole, 1-methylhistidine, phenylethylamine, piperazine, spermidine, spermine,

synephrine, theobromine, theophylline, tryptamine, and xanthine gave intermediate levels of DAO inhibition.

Acidic but not basic drugs are rapidly absorbed from the stomach. This is because the gastric mucosa is selectively permeable to undissociated forms of drugs. Consequently, basic substances such as histamine, serotonin, or tyramine present in foods would be ionized at the acid pH of the stomach and therefore not absorbed whereas in the duodenum and distal gut the alkaline pH would convert them to the un-ionized form which is lipid soluble and more easily absorbed. Once the amines have crossed the intestinal wall, they are carried in the portal blood to the liver and then to the lungs before having access to the systemic circuit (113).

Putrescine and cadaverine are oxidatively deaminated by the reaction of DAO (EC 1.4.3.6). DAO converts putrescine yielding 4-aminobutyraldehyde after cyclization to form Δ^1-pyrroline, with the release of ammonia and hydrogen peroxide (Figure 13.7). Cadaverine is converted via oxidation and cyclization to the 6-membered piperidine ring of anabasine and other alkaloids (62).

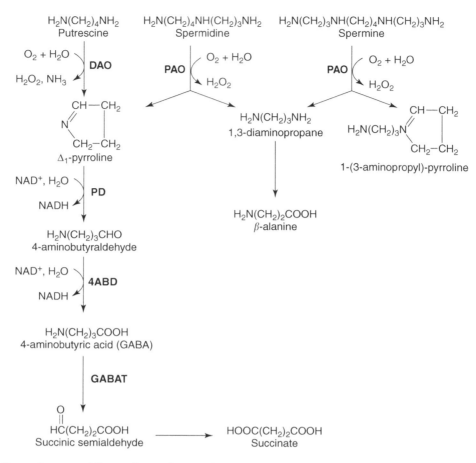

FIGURE 13.7   Putrescine, spermidine, and spermine metabolism in man.

The polyamine oxidases (PAO) are specific for polyamines, and they have FAD as a cofactor (59). Polyamine oxidases degrade spermidine and spermine via the oxidative cleavage at the secondary amino group (153). Degradation of spermidine by PAO yields Δ^1-pyrroline, 1,3-diaminopropane, and hydrogen peroxide, while spermine oxidation yields 1,3-aminopropylpyrroline along with diaminopropane and hydrogen peroxide. Diaminopropane can originate β-alanine (62, 168, 202).

The 4-aminobutyraldehyde formed by the oxidation of putrescine and spermidine can be further oxidized to 4-aminobutyric acid (GABA) by a NAD-dependent pyrroline dehydrogenase (4-aminobutyraldehyde dehydrogenase, 4ABD). This enzyme has been found where DAO or PAO activity is present. The product of this reaction, GABA, can be transaminated and the resulting succinic acid incorporated into the Krebs cycle (Figure 13.7). This metabolic sequence can account for the complete recycling of the carbon and nitrogen from di/polyamines. It may also explain the fact that, in at least some cases, di- and polyamines can be used as organic nitrogen sources by some cells (59, 202).

It has been demonstrated that there is a conversion of spermine and spermidine back into putrescine. The enzymatic reaction of such a reversal pathway has been established; it involves two enzymes acting sequentially, spermidine/spermine N-1-acetyltransferase (SAT; EC 2.3.1.57) and polyamine oxidase (PAO, EC 1.5.3.11) (57).

The amounts of polyamines reaching the body are different for individual polyamines. One hour after rats were intubated with ^{14}C-labeled putrescine, only 29–39% of the label was found as polyamines, with 11–15% remaining as putrescine. Spermidine and spermine were better conserved: 79% of spermidine and 72–74% of spermine were recovered in the original form. If conversion to the other two natural polyamines is also taken into account, 87–96% of the radioactive spermidine and 79–82% of spermine was conserved in polyamine form (10). Since spermidine and spermine are better preserved for further utilization in the body, they are considered the right polyamines to be absorbed from foods.

Catabolism of histamine or tyramine can also be achieved by bacteria. Tyramine oxidase from *Sarcina lutea* was observed to oxidatively deaminate tyramine in the presence of oxygen and to form p-hydroxyphenyl-acetaldehyde, ammonia, and hydrogen peroxide. *Aspergillus niger* and *Trichosporon* sp. possess amine oxidases that oxidize a wide range of primary amines. Numerous bacteria possess diamine oxidase and are able to degrade histamine, including *Pseudomonas aeruginosa*,

E. coli, Proteus vulgaris, Serratia flava, and *Clostridium feseri.* In the intestine of man, *E. coli* and *E. aerogenes* are capable of acetylating histamine (124, 139).

V. TOXICOLOGICAL ASPECTS

Amines in foods do not usually represent any health hazard to individuals unless excessive amounts are ingested or the natural mechanism for their catabolism is genetically deficient or impaired by diseases or pharmacological agents (45, 139). Individuals with respiratory and coronary problems, hypertension, or vitamin B_{12} deficiency are at risk because they are sensitive to lower amounts of amines. Men with gastrointestinal problems (gastritis, irritable bowel syndrome, Crohn's disease, stomach, and colonic ulcers) are also at risk since the activity of oxidases in their intestines is usually lower than that in healthy individuals. Patients taking medication that are inhibitors of MAO, DAO, and PAO activity can also be affected, as such drugs prevent amine catabolism. These MAO and DAO inhibitors are used for the treatment of stress, depression, Alzheimer's and Parkinson's diseases, pulmonary tuberculosis, malaria, panic syndrome, and social phobia (60, 61).

Bioactive amines have been implicated as the causative agents in a number of food poisoning episodes (Table 13.3), particularly histamine and tyramine toxicity (158, 177). Tryptamine and phenylethylamine are associated with migraine (87). Furthermore, the importance of polyamines in tumor growth is widely recognized (9, 137).

The most frequent food-borne intoxication caused by amines involves histamine. Histamine intoxication is also referred to as "scombroid poisoning" due to its association with the consumption of scombroid fish; however, non-scombroid fish, cheese, and other foods have also been implicated in some cases (173). The disease manifests several minutes to a few hours after ingestion of the histamine containing food (79). At first, a flushing of the face and neck is usually observed, accompanied by a feeling of heat and general discomfort. Often it is followed by an intense throbbing headache. Other symptoms may be cardiac palpitations, dizziness, faintness, thirst, swelling of the lips, urticaria, rapid and weak pulse, and gastrointestinal complaints (abdominal cramps, nausea, diarrhea). However, the most common symptoms are rash, diarrhea, sweating, and headache. In severe cases, bronchospasms, suffocation and severe respiratory distress are reported. Recovery is usually complete within 8 h (12, 139, 158, 165).

TABLE 13.3
Toxic Effects of Bioactive Amines

Toxic Effects	Amines Involved	Food Associated	Symptoms
Histamine intoxication or scombroid poisoning	Histamine (toxic effect is potentiated by putrescine, cadaverine, spermine, tryptamine, tyramine, phenylethylamine, ethanol)	Scombroid fish: tuna, bonito, mackerel, skipjack, herring Other fish: sardines, anchovy, mahi-mahi Cheese: Swiss, Gouda, Cheddar, Gruyere, Cheshire; Sauerkraut; sausage; wine	**Gastrointestinal:** nausea, vomiting, diarrhea, abdominal cramps **Neurological:** throbbing headache, palpitation, flushing, burning throat, itching, rapid and weak pulse, dizziness, faintness, tingling **Hemodynamic:** hypotension, capillary dillatation **Cutaneous:** rash, urticaria, edema, localized inflamation **Severe cases:** bronchospasms, suffocation, severe respiratory distress
Tyramine intoxication	Tyramine	Cheese Beer Wine	Headache, fever, increased blood pressure, vomiting, perspiration, pupils and palpebral tissue dilatation, salivation, lacrimation, increased respiration, palpitation, dyspnea
Cheese reaction[1] or hypertensive crisis (associated with patients under MAOI drugs)	Tyramine 2-phenylethylamine	Cheese: Gouda, Swiss, Gruyere, Cheddar Beer, wine, yeast extract, Chocolate, pickled herring, Dry sausage, broad beans	Hypertensive crisis, severe headache, cerebral hemorrhage, neuronal sequel, cardiac failure, pulmonary edema, visual alterations, palpitation, nausea, sweat, vomit, muscle contractions, excitation, mental confusion, high blood pressure, fever, perspiration
Migraine	Tyramine 2-phenylethylamine tryptamine serotonin	Cheese Chocolate Beer Wine	Throbbing headache, migraine attack
Increased growth hyperplasia	Spermine spermidine	Meat	Increased growth of tumors

[1] MAOI-monoaminoxidase inhibitors.

Source: Refs. 9, 139, and 177.

TABLE 13.4
Histamine Poisoning Episodes in Different Countries

Country	Years	No. of Outbreaks	No. of Cases*	Implicated Foods*
Canada	1975–1981	6		Fish (tuna, mahi-mahi, mackerel)
				Cheese (cheddar)
Denmark	1976–1982	33	–	Tuna, mackerel
	1993–1998	13	–	–
Finland	1993–1998	9	> 772	–
France	1980–1983	10	> 500	Fish (albacore, tuna, sardines, herring)
				Cheese (Gruyere)
				Meat (ham)
	1993–1997	38	–	–
Germany	1971–1982			Fish (mackerel, sardine, tuna)
				Sauerkraut
Japan	1950–1954	14	1215	Dried saury, canned mackerel, Iwashi
				sakuraboshi, frigate tuna
	1970–1980	42	4122	Fish (tuna, mackerel, sardine, dorado,
				marlin, kamaboko, anchovy)
				Chicken
The Netherlands	1967			Gouda cheese
New Zealand	1973–1975			Skipjack tuna, mackerel, kahawai, kingfish, trumpeter fish
Sweden	1993–1998	4	12	–
United Kingdom	1976–1982	136	439	Mackerel, bonito, sprats, pilchard, sardine, tuna, anchovy, kipper, gefilte fish
	1987–1996	105	405	Tuna, mackerel, salmon
United States of America	1968–1981	110	888	Fish (tuna, mahi-mahi, mackerel, bonito, albacore, jack, blue fish, snapper, kumu, skipjack, yellow tail, anchovy)
				Cheese (Swiss)
	1973–1987	202	1216	Finfish
	1988–1998	5	31	Tuna, mahi-mahi, yellow fin tuna, yellow tail

* Information not available.

Source: Refs. 15, 31, 152, 177, and 212.

Cases of histamine intoxication have been reported in the United States, Japan and United Kingdom. A few incidents have also been reported in several other countries as indicated in Table 13.4. However, outbreaks and cases of histamine poisoning are often not reported since it is relatively mild, has short duration and many patients do not seek medical attention. Furthermore, many physicians remain unaware of histamine poisoning and do not consider it as a possible diagnosis. Even when medical attention is sought and a correct diagnosis is made, only a few countries keep official records of incidents (177). Therefore, it would be safe to assume that the true incidence of histamine poisoning is unknown.

Fish incriminated in outbreaks of histamine poisoning included scombroid (tuna, bonito, mackerel, skipjack, albacore, bluefin tuna, herring and saury) and non-scombroid fish (mahi-mahi, sardines, pilchards, herring, bluefish, jack mackerel, anchovies, kahawai, black and striped marlin), which contained high histamine levels (12, 139). Misidentification of the fish involved in outbreaks may occur on occasion due to different common names used in different places. The type of fish consumed, the method of harvesting, and the consumption patterns are important factors in determining the likelihood of histamine poisoning (177).

Cases of cheese-related histamine poisoning were also reported. The first case was reported in the Netherlands in 1967 and was associated with Gouda cheese. Since then, several cases have been reported after consumption of Gouda, Swiss, Gruyere, Cheddar, and Cheshire cheeses (158, 173, 177, 180). Other foods have also been implicated in incidents of histamine poisoning, among them chicken, sauerkraut, and ham. Fermented foods and proteinaceous foods subject to spoilage are particularly likely to contain large amounts of histamine. Sauerkraut, yeast extract, wine, and fermented, dry sausages can, on occasion, have sufficient histamine levels to cause a toxic response if enough quantities are consumed (66, 139, 177).

Outbreaks of histamine poisoning have also been observed in patients on antituberculosis therapy. Such outbreaks were associated with interaction of fish or cheese containing high histamine levels with isoniazid and other nicotinamide derivatives (154, 179).

Marley and Blackwell (113) reported that following intravenous injection of 0.1 mg of histamine phosphate, facial flushing, pulse quickening, fall in the blood pressure and rise in cerebrospinal fluid pressure occurs within 20 seconds and the onset of histamine headache occurs 1 min after injection. They also reported that less than 225 mg of histamine taken orally usually does not produce symptoms, although susceptible subjects (allergy, asthma, or peptic ulcers) might be adversely affected by smaller quantities. According to Taylor (177), some mild effects of histamine poisoning were observed in humans by orally administrating 100 to 180 mg of histamine in combination with good quality tuna. The paradox between the lack of toxicity of pure histamine and the apparent toxicity of smaller doses in fish or cheese could explain the existence of potentiators of histamine toxicity. These compounds would act to decrease the threshold dose of histamine needed to provoke an adverse reaction. They would enable absorption of amounts of histamine larger than could be achieved in their absence.

Two hypotheses have been used to justify the effect of potentiators on histamine poisoning: barrier disruption and inhibition of histamine metabolizing enzymes (179). In the first hypothesis, potentiators would interfere with the protective actions of intestinal mucin, which binds to histamine and prevents its passage across the intestinal wall. According to Chu and Bjeldanes (37) and Shalaby (158), such compounds are spermine, spermidine, cadaverine, and putrescine.

In the case of inhibition of histamine metabolizing enzymes, potentiators would inhibit DAO or HMT. DAO is not selective towards histamine but also oxidizes other diamines. Inhibitors of DAO include agmatine, cadaverine, tyramine, putrescine, phenylethylamine, anserine, carnosine, thiamin, semicarbazide, carbonyl reagents, imidazole derivatives, and the pharmacological agents: aminoguanidine and isoniazid (79, 139, 154, 183). Many antihistaminic drugs are DAO inhibitors. Some inhibitors of MAO are also somewhat effective as DAO inhibitors (177). The inhibitors of HMT include agmatine, tyramine, cadaverine, putrescine, tryptamine, and phenylethylamine (183). This enzyme is also inhibited by antimalarial drugs, among them, quinacrine, chloroquin, and amodiaquin (79, 173, 177). According to Hui and Taylor (79), amines were less potent inhibitors of DAO and HMT, compared to pharmacological compounds.

The toxic effect of histamine can also be potentiated by the presence of ethanol, which potentiates the effect of amines by directly or indirectly inhibiting amine oxidase (69, 138).

The threshold toxic dose for histamine in foods is not precisely known since the existence of potentiators could dramatically influence it. Based on experience acquired in the investigation of hundreds of histamine poisoning incidents, the U.S. Food and Drug Administration established 10 mg/100 g as the hazard action level for histamine in tuna (56).

Tyramine is the second type of amine involved in intoxication. When foods containing high tyramine levels are ingested, large amounts of non-metabolized tyramine can reach the blood stream. This causes release of noradrenaline from the sympathetic nervous system, leading to a variety of physiological reactions (Table 13.3). There is an increase in blood pressure by peripheral vasoconstriction and by increasing the cardiac output (87, 158). Tyramine can also dilate the pupils and the palpebral tissue, cause lacrimation, salivation, fever, vomit, and headache, and increase respiration and blood sugar (51, 60, 87, 113, 115). When consuming foods rich in tyramine, about 30% of individuals with classical migraine can have headaches. These tyramine-sensitive patients appear to suffer from a deficiency of the enzyme responsible for the formation of the sulfate conjugate of tyramine (42).

Ingestion of foods rich in tyramine by individuals under MAOI treatment results in a dangerous illness known as "cheese reaction." Such a name was given since most of the cases involved cheese. However, it is not the only type of food incriminated, since cases have also been reported with yeast extracts (marmite), pickled herring, dry sausage, alcoholic beverages, broad beans, chicken liver, beer, among others (60, 68, 87, 113). Cheese reaction consists in a hypertensive crisis, usually accompanied by severe headache. The attacks last from 10 minutes to 6 hours, during which hypertension and headache fluctuate. There can be visual alterations, nausea, vomit, muscle contraction, mental confusion, or excitation. Neck stiffness and photophobia can occur. Chest pain simulating angina pectoria, acute heart failure, pulmonary edema, neuronal sequel, and cerebral hemorrhage have also been described. Fatal incidents have been reported in the literature (60, 61, 87, 113, 158).

MAOI drugs have been widely used due to their efficacy in the treatment of malaria, tuberculosis, depression, atypical depression, social phobia, panic and anxiety syndromes, bulimia, Parkinson's and Alzheimer's (60, 94, 139). They include antidepressants, antihypertensive, antimicrobial, and antineoplastic drugs, among them isoniazid, tranylcypromine, isocarboxazid, pargyline, phenelzine, procarbazine, furazolidone, moclobemide, and ipronazide (87, 113, 115, 165). In order to prevent hypertensive attacks when prescribing these drugs, it is necessary to warn patients to avoid foods containing tyramine (42, 60, 139, 165). Foods that require absolute restriction on an MAOI regimen include aged cheese, smoked or pickled fish, cured or spoiled meat, yeast extract, marmite, sauerkraut, and broad beans. Foods that should be avoided unless tyramine contents are known are red wine, meat extracts, soy sauce, dry sausage, and draft beer (60, 64, 115).

In man, 20–80 mg of tyramine injected intravenously or subcutaneously causes a marked elevation of blood pressure. In individuals on MAOI, as little as 6 mg taken orally within a 4 h period can be deleterious (139, 176).

Tryptamine has pharmacological action similar to tyramine. High levels of tryptamine can exert direct effect on smooth muscles, cause headache, and increase blood pressure by constriction of the vascular system (87, 139, 165).

Phenylethylamine, like tyramine, causes an increase in blood pressure by liberating noradrenaline from tissue stores. Phenylethylamine may be the precipitant of migraine headache (87, 139, 165). Levels of 3 mg of phenylethylamine cause migraine headaches in susceptible individuals. Migraine has been observed about 12 h after ingestion of chocolate which contained phenylethylamine. Chocolate has also been implicated in a well-documented hypertensive attack in a patient taking the MAOI pargyline (139).

Even though putrescine and cadaverine have less pharmacological activity than the aromatic amines, after ingestion of very large amounts of these compounds, toxic effects can be observed. Intoxication symptoms reported are hypotension, bradycardia, dyspnea, lockjaw, and paresis of the extremities. However, the most important consequence of these compounds in food is probably the potentiation effect of the toxicity of other amines (66, 87).

Serotonin has been widely discussed as a possible cause of migraine headache, but the evidence is not clear. High levels in foods have been responsible for intestinal discomfort and fibrosis of the myocardium. Serotonin is a powerful vasoconstrictor and vasopressor when 1 mg is injected, but an oral dose of 20 mg has no effect. Although there are no definite reports of intoxication due to serotonin, elevated levels of its metabolites are biochemical signals of pheochromocytoma and malignant carcinoid. Therefore, plant products rich in serotonin like banana, pineapple, fig, walnut, and tomato should be excluded from the diet before attempting to diagnose carcinoid tumor (139, 165).

High spermine levels can cause kidney toxicity, and can affect blood coagulation and pressure, heart beat, and respiration (108).

Due to the diversity of the roles of polyamines in cellular metabolism and growth, rapidly growing tissues require very large amounts of polyamines. Accordingly, the importance of putrescine, spermine, and spermidine in tumor growth is widely recognized, and the inhibition of polyamine biosynthesis in tumor-bearing individuals is a major target of cancer therapy research (9, 11, 137). The capacity of tumor cells to synthesize polyamines by the decarboxylation of ornithine is higher than that of non-transformed tissues (10). Polyamines also have an effect on the non-specific immune system specialized in tumor killing, on the plasma concentration of interleukin-1 and -6, and on the tumor necrosis factor concentration (54). Polyamines absorbed from exogenous sources, mainly

food, and the gastrointestinal tract, also play an important role in tumor growth (10).

In order to stop the formation of polyamines, the enzyme ODC can be inhibited. Although DFMO is an efficient and irreversible blocker of ODC, it does not completely stop growth as polyamines are also formed by alternative routes. A polyamine deprivation regimen in combination with polyamine oxidase and antibiotics suitable for the partial decontamination of the gastrointestinal tract, have been shown to reduce growth of tumor and to enhance the efficacy of chemotherapy (10, 54, 137).

Some amines can be nitrosated, or act as precursors for compounds capable of forming nitrosamines, some of which are carcinogenic to several species of animals. Putrescine and cadaverine, upon heating, can be converted to pyrrolidine and piperidine, respectively, from which N-nitrosopyrrolidine and N-nitrosopiperidine are formed upon heating and reaction with nitrite or nitric oxide (158). Spermidine, spermine, and agmatine can also react with nitrite to form nitrosamines in foods or *in vivo* in the gastrointestinal tract over a wide range of biological and environmental conditions (68, 74). A reaction product of tyramine and nitrite, 3-diazotyramine, induced oral cavity cancer in rats (47).

The determination of the exact toxicity threshold of amines is extremely difficult. The toxic dose is dependent on the efficiency of the detoxification mechanism of different individuals. Upper limits of 10 mg of histamine, 10 mg of tyramine, and 3 mg of 2-phenylethylamine in 100 g of foods have been suggested (74). In the case of alcoholic beverages the proposed limits are 2 to 8 mg of histamine and 8 mg tyramine per liter. However, ingestion of foods containing 6 mg of tyramine can cause migraine and 10 to 25 mg can cause hypertensive crisis in individuals taking MAOI drugs (35, 60).

Til et al. (186) investigated the acute and subacute toxicity of five amines in Wistar rats. The approximate LD_{50} values observed were as follows. Tyramine and cadaverine showed the lowest acute toxicity of more than 2000 mg/kg body weight. The approximate LD_{50} of putrescine was 2000 mg/kg, while spermidine and spermine showed the highest acute toxicity, namely 600 mg/kg body weight. The no-observed-adverse-effect level (NOAEL) was 2000 ppm (180 mg/kg body weight/day) for tyramine, cadaverine, and putrescine, 1000 ppm (83 mg/kg body weight/day) for spermidine, and 200 ppm (19 mg/kg body weight/day) for spermine.

VI. OCCURRENCE OF AMINES IN FOODS

Bioactive amines are inherent to living organisms and, therefore, are present in plants, meat, and dairy products. The amount and type of amines in foods depend on the nature and origin of the commodity. However, they can change during production, processing, fermentation, and storage. It can also be affected by hygienic conditions.

Amines are resistant to heat treatment employed in food processing. Based on these findings, amines have been considered good indicators of the freshness, spoilage, and of the degree of quality of fresh and processed food products, reflecting the quality of the raw material used and of hygienic conditions prevalent during processing.

It is evident that all types of food, whether originated from plants or animals, contain putrescine, spermine, and spermidine. In addition to these most common compounds, other amines may also occur naturally. During fermentation or spoilage, spermine content can decrease, because it can be used as a nitrogen source by some microorganisms. There is also formation and accumulation of different types of biogenic amines.

Much still remains unknown about the concentration of amines in food products. Most data available relate to specific amines, mainly histamine and tyramine in fish, cheese, meat, and alcoholic beverages. Comprehensive studies on the levels of all amines are useful from the toxicological, sensorial, and technological points of view. Recent work has focused on the role of polyamines in plant physiology and also on animal health and growth. However, bioactive amines is obviously an area deserving further detailed investigation.

A.   FRUITS AND VEGETABLES

The polyamines spermidine and spermine occur ubiquitously in the plant kingdom, together with their diamine precursor putrescine. Polyamines are required for normal development and can be used as organic nitrogen sources. Work on higher plants suggests that polyamines play a critical role in several processes, among them, root growth, somatic embryogenesis, control of intracellular pH, flower and fruit development, and response to abiotic stress, such as potassium deficiency, osmotic shock, drought, and pathogen infection. They are also important in the synthesis of secondary metabolites of biological interest, for example, nicotine and alkaloids (59, 129, 168, 202).

A relation has been found between the synthesis of polyamines and the inhibition of ethylene biosynthesis. This has been interpreted as a result of metabolic competition by the same precursor, i.e., S-adenosylmethionine. Furthermore, polyamines can scavenge free radicals involved in the conversion of 1-aminocyclopropane-1-carboxylic acid to ethylene. Therefore, exogenous application of polyamines to delay fruit ripening has been proposed and used with promising results (55, 95).

Polyamines are associated with cell walls and cell membranes. They modulate pectinesterase and bind to pectin, delaying fruit softening and senescence (93, 99). The firming effect of the polyamines is similar to that of calcium chloride, and may be due to its ability to bind to cell walls and membranes, stabilizing them, or by making cell walls less accessible to wall-softening enzymes

(93, 135). Another hypothesis is that polyamines inhibit the action of enzymes involved in softening or wall degradation. For instance, Kramer et al. (93) found polyamines to have inhibitory effect on polygalacturonase extracted from apples that had been inoculated with fungus. Exogenous application of polyamines to microsomal membranes resulted in a reduction in fluidity at the membrane surface through association of the polyamines with membrane lipid. Polyamines can also delay membrane deterioration by interaction with anionic components of the membrane and stabilizing the bilayer surface. The radical scavenging properties of polyamines have also been suggested to be involved in protecting membranes from lipid peroxidation and other oxidative stresses (70).

In higher plants, polyamines occur in the free form, electrostatically bound to negatively charged molecules or conjugated to small molecules, such as cinnamic acids, e.g., p-coumaric, ferulic, and caffeic acids, resulting in hydroxycinnamic acid amides (HACCs). These compounds have been implicated in a variety of plant growth and developmental processes. More recently, HACCs have begun to attract renewed attention with several studies suggesting an important role in plant responses to pathogens (202).

Besides the polyamines spermidine, spermine, and putrescine, other amines are also naturally present in fruits and vegetables, among them phenylethylamine, serotonin, tryptamine, histamine, cadaverine, agmatine, adrenaline, noradrenaline, octopamine, synephrine, agmatine, and aliphatic amines. Some amines may have a protective role in deterring predators. Serotonin is one of the active principles that occurs in the stinging hairs of *Mucuna pruriens*, *Girardinia heterophylla*, and *Urtica* spp. (167). Histamine occurs in stings of *Jatropha urens* and *Urtica dioica* (166). Some amine conjugates are important as antifungal and antiviral agents. Some aliphatic amines simulate the smell of rotting meat, thereby attracting pollinating insects (165, 167). Some amines are quite important as precursors of compounds of biological significance. For instance, the plant hormones indol-3-yl-acetic acid (IAA) and phenylacetic acid are derived from tryptamine and phenylethylamine, respectively. The tryptamines are also precursors of the tricyclic beta-carboline alkaloids formed by condensation with one or two carbon moiety (42, 167).

Aliphatic volatile amines are widespread in food plants. In the late 1960s and early 1970s several studies were conducted to identify these compounds. Dimethylamine, ethylamine, propylamine, isopropylamine, and butylamine were found in most of the products analyzed, among them apple, banana, potato, cocoa, coffee, oat, soybean, and tea. Other amines detected included hexylamine in apple, isoamylamine in banana and cocoa, ethylmethylamine in coffee, trimethylamine in cocoa and tea, and triethylamine in cocoa (108, 165).

The occurrence of bioactive amines in different fruits and vegetables is indicated in Table 13.5. Tyramine has been

TABLE 13.5
Occurrence of Amines in Fruits and Vegetables

Common Name	Amine Present	Reference
Almond	PHM	165
Apple	DM, E, P, B, HX, IP, PUT, SPD	11, 165
Apricot	SRT	42
Avocado	TYM, DOP, SRT	40, 139, 165, 188
Banana	DM, E, IB, IA, PR, TYM, DOP, NADR, SRT, OCT, TRM, HIM, PHM, SRT, PUT, SPD	2, 40, 42, 159, 165, 188, 210
Barley	DM, E, IB, IA, TYM, HOR, TRM, SRT, GRA	165, 167
Bean (sprout)	SPD, SPN, PUT, CAD, HIM	172
Bean (red, kidney)	PUT, SPD, SPN	11
Beet (leaf)	DOP, HIM, PHM	125, 165
Bell pepper	OCT	210
Broccoli	SPD, SPN, AGM, PUT	172
Cabbage	PHM, PUT, SPD, SPN	11, 125
Cabbage, Chinese	SPD, SPN, PUT, HIM, TYM	163
Cabbage, red	PHM	125
Calamondin	SYN	165
Capers	SPD, AGM, PUT	172
Carrots	PHM, PUT, SPD, SPN	11, 125
Cassava	SPD, PUT	172
Cauliflower	SPD, SPN, AGM, PUT, PHM	11, 125, 172
Cherry	SRT	42
Citrange	TYM, SYN	165
Cocoa	DM, TM, E, TE, B, IB, IA, TYM, TRM, SRT, PHM	42, 86, 165
Coffee	DM, EM, E, P, IB, SRT	38, 165
Collard greens	SPD, SPN, AGM, PUT	199
Cucumber	PUT, SPD, SPN	11
Date	SRT	165
Eggplant	TYM, TRM, SRT, SPD, SPN, PUT, HIM	42, 141, 159, 188
Elderberry	TYM	210
Endive	SPD, SPN, PUT, TYM	163
Fig	SRT	165
Grapefruit	PUT	11
Green beans	PUT, SPD, SPN	11
Green gram (seed)	TYM	165
Green onion	SPD, SPN, AGM, PUT, TYM	172
Hearts of palm	SPD, SPN, PUT	172
Hop	HIM, GRA, HOR	165
"Jilo"	SPD, SPN, AGM, PUT, HIM, TYM	172
Kale	PHM	125
Lemon	TYM, SYN, OCT	42, 165
Lettuce	PUT, SPD	11
Lettuce, American	SPD, PUT, AGM	39
Lettuce, iceberg	SPD, SPN, PUT, TYM	163
Maize	TYM, HIM, PHM	165
Mandarin	OCT, SYN	42
Millet (seed)	TYM, HOR	165
Oat	DM, E, P, IP, B, IB, A	165
Onion	PUT, SPD, SPN	11
Orange	TYM, OCT, SYN, NADR, TRM, OCT, PUT, SPD	11, 40, 42
Parsley	SPD, SPN, PUT, TYM	172
Passion fruit	SRT	165
Papaya	SRT	165
Peach	SRT	42
Pears	PUT, SPD, SPN	11
Peas	PUT, SPD, SPN	11
Pineapple	TYM, SRT	42, 165

(continued)

TABLE 13.5 (*Continued*)

Common Name	Amine Present	Reference
Potato	TYM, TRM, DOP, NADR, DE, P, IB, PUT, SPD, SPN	11, 42, 165, 188
Plantain	SRT	113
Plum	TYM, NADR, TRM, SRT	40, 42, 165, 188
Purslane	DOP, NADR	165
Radicchio	SPD, SPN, PUT, TYM	163
Radish	PHM, PUT, SPD, SPN	11, 125
Raspberry	TYM	40, 165
Rhubarb	PHM	125
Rice	PUT, SPD, SPN	10
Soybean	DM, EM, E, P, IB, PUT, SPD, SPN	11, 165
Spinach	SPD, PHM, AGM, PUT, HIM, TYM, DOP	125, 159, 165, 172, 188
Swede	PHM	125
Tangerine	TYM, HOR, OCT, SYN	42, 165, 210
Taro	TYM	165
Tea	PHM, DM, TM, E, P, IB, IA	165
Temple	TYM, OCT, SYN	165
Tomato	TYM, TRM, SRT, HIM, SPD, PUT, HIM	11, 42, 159, 165, 167, 172, 188
Walnut	SRT, TYM	165, 210
Watermelon	TRM	165

A=amylamine, ADR=adrenaline, AGM=agmatine, B=butylamine, CAD=cadaverine, DE=diethylamine, DM=dimethylamine, DOP=dopamine, E=ethylamine, EM=ethylmethylamine, GRA=gramine, HIM=histamine, HOR=hordenine, HX=hexilamine, IA=isoamylamine, IB=isobutylamine, IP=isopropylamine, NADR=noradrenaline, OCT=octopamine, P=propylamine, PHM=phenylethylamine, PR=propanolamine, PUT=putrescine, SPD=spermidine, SPN=spermine, SRT=serotonin, SYN=synephrine, TE=triethylamine, TM=trimethylamine, TRM=triptamine, TYM=tyramine.

detected in cabbage, lettuce, chicory, radish, tomato, potato, green onion, spinach, eggplant, elderberry, avocado, banana, plum, grapes, raspberry, pineapple, orange, lemon, and tangerine (40, 115, 188). Other phenolic amines such as octopamine and synephrine occur in citrus. Octopamine was also found in banana (165). Histamine has been found in cabbage, eggplant, tomato, beet, and spinach. Tryptamine was reported in tomato, eggplant, barley, orange, plum, and watermelon (59, 164, 188). Cadaverine is naturally found only in plants of the *Leguminosae* family (168, 172). Phenylethylamine was detected in beet, cabbage, cauliflower, rhubarb, carrots, radish, maize, and banana (165). Serotonin has been most frequently reported in banana, plantain, pineapple, plum, peach, avocado, tomato, apricot, eggplant, coffee, and walnut (40, 59, 188, 197). Due to the specific occurrence of bioactive amines in the plant kingdom, they have been used as a tool for taxonomic studies. However, some of them can also be formed by decarboxylases from contaminant microorganisms (59, 168, 172).

Most of the studies on polyamines in fruits and vegetables were performed recently, in the last decade. It is well known that spermidine is the prevalent amine followed by putrescine. Most fruits and vegetables contain only small amounts of polyamines; however soybean and chicory were found to contain the largest amounts (130).

As indicated in Table 13.6, very few studies investigated several amines simultaneously in fruits and vegetables. Therefore, information is still lacking on the levels of amines and on the influence of many factors including

plant species and variety, type of tissue, conditions of growth, stage of development, degree of ripening, processing, and storage conditions (164, 188).

The tyramine content of fruits is generally low. Raspberries contain the highest reported levels, averaging 4.8 mg/100 g. Similar levels have been found in ripe banana pulp. Red plum, orange, and avocado contain between 0.6 and 2.3 mg/100 g, but most fruits contain 0.1 mg/100 g or less (42). With a few exceptions, fruits and vegetables contain very low levels of histamine. Histamine concentration in fresh tomatoes and maize is less than 0.4 mg/100 g, while levels in spinach and eggplant vary from 3 to 6 mg/100 g. Baking reduced histamine content in spinach and eggplant. Fresh fruits and vegetables generally contain less than 1 mg of phenylethylamine per 100 g. The highest level (4 mg/100 g) was found in swede. It was also reported in grapes (42, 125). The tryptamine content of plants has been reported to be less than 0.5 mg/100 g in several fruits and vegetables (42). Synephrine is most prevalent in citrus fruits. The juices of tangerines and Cleopatra mandarins contain 13 and 28 mg/100 mL, respectively, while orange and lemon juice contain 1.9 mg/100 g (42, 210). Generally, low quantities of octopamine have been detected in orange, lemon, tangerine (0.1 mg/100 g), mandarin (0.2 mg/100 g), and banana, with similar levels reported in their juices. Octopamine has been reported in bell pepper at levels of 23.4 mg/100 g (210). Serotonin has been detected in some fruits at levels of 0.1 to 0.2 mg/100 g in papaya, 0.1 to 0.4 mg/100 g in

TABLE 13.6
Types and Levels of Bioactive Amines in Fruits and Vegetables

Product	SPD	SPN	AGM	PUT	CAD	HIM	TYM	TRM	PHM	SRT	Source
APPLE	0.14–0.28	nd	0.04–0.17	—	—	—	—	—	—	—	11, 130
BANANA											3
Green	1.04	nd	nd	0.75	nd	nd	nd	nd	nd	1.73	
Ripe	1.07	nd	nd	0.83	nd	nd	nd	nd	nd	1.22	
Overripe	0.95	nd	nd	0.33	nd	nd	nd	nd	nd	0.71	
BEAN, broad											157
Fresh	1.67	1.79	—	0.72	0.87	0.85	0.62	2.43	0.43	—	
Germinated	0.62	1.43	—	5.56	3.26	1.72	1.36	13.6	1.03	—	
BEAN, green	0.77–0.88	0.46–0.55	—	0.43–0.54	—	—	—	—	—	—	11
BEAN, kidney	1.90–2.00	2.28–2.57	—	0.04	—	—	—	—	—	—	11
BEAN, sprout	1.37–2.83	0.12–0.43	nd	1.84–5.90	0.58–12.0	0.49–8.75	nd	nd	nd	nd	172
BROCCOLI	1.98–15.2	nd–1.60	0.72	0.34–3.17	nd–0.12	nd	nd	nd	nd	nd	54, 129, 172
CABBAGE	0.32–0.36	0.32–0.36	—	0.04–0.16	—	—	—	—	—	—	11
CAPERS	0.19–0.57	nd	nd–0.20	0.13–0.24	nd	nd	—	—	—	—	172
CARROT	0.36–1.19	nd–0.38	—	0.07–0.35	nd	—	—	—	—	—	11, 54, 130
CASSAVA, cooked	0.16–0.27	nd	nd	0.08–0.61	nd	nd	nd	nd	nd	nd	172
CAULIFLOWER	0.47–3.93	nd–1.29	nd–1.89	0.13–0.89	nd–0.10	nd	nd	nd	nd	nd	11, 54, 172
CHICKPEA											157
Fresh	30.7	1.82	—	0.79	1.05	0.58	0.37	3.02	0.19	—	
Germinated	1.84	1.7	—	6.28	3.95	1.78	1.21	29.9	0.48	—	
CHICORY	39.2–75.4	nd	—	15.0–120	—	—	—	—	—	—	95
COFFEE											38
Green	0.6	0.44	nd	1.03	nd	nd	nd	nd	nd	1.13	
Roasted, 6 min	0.12	nd	nd	nd	nd	nd	nd	nd	nd	0.16	
Roasted, 12 min	0.2	nd	0.12	nd	nd	nd	nd	nd	nd	0.29	
COLLARD GREENS	2.28	0.38	0.24	0.67	nd	nd	nd	nd	nd	nd	199
CORN	4.85	nd	—	8.62	—	—	—	—	—	—	130
CUCUMBER	0.15–1.03	nd–0.28	—	0.32–0.87	nd–0.06	—	—	—	—	—	11, 54
EGGPLANT											172
Whole	0.66–1.15	0.12–0.90	nd	1.22–4.04	nd	3.69–12.5	0.12–0.47	nd	nd	nd	
Peel	1.15b	0.51	0.33	3.4	nd	10.1a	14.1	nd	nd	nd	
Pulp	0.87b	0.19	nd	4.42	nd	0.29b	nd	nd	nd	nd	
Seed	2.11a	0.23	0.18	5.1	nd	8.20a	nd	nd	nd	nd	

Amine Levels (mg/100 g)[1]

											Ref.
HEARTS OF PALM, canned	0.52–0.94	0.17–0.55	0.07–0.18	nd	nd	nd	nd	nd–0.78	nd	nd	nd	172
JILO	0.37–0.91	nd–0.25	nd–0.25	0.27–2.70	nd	0.18–1.20	0.14–0.50	nd	nd	nd	172
LENTIL, sprout	6.44	1.59	6.04	2.19	15.4	—	—	—	—	—		162
LETTUCE	0.42–1.03	nd–0.18	0.03	0.12–0.73	0.07	nd	nd	nd	nd	nd		39
LUPINE												157
Fresh	3.67	4.06	—	0.82	0.52	0.86	0.78	1.17	0.12	—		
Germinated	0.53	0.63	—	8.46	2.69	1.64	1.22	56.7	0.64	—		
MUNG BEAN, sprout	3.39	0.42	5.26	nd	1.56	nd	0.23–0.63	nd	nd	nd		162
ONION GREENS	0.26–1.23	nd–0.09	nd–0.48	nd–0.14	nd	—	—	—	—	—		172
ONION	0.55–0.81	0.08–0.12		0.55–0.72	—							11
ORANGE	0.04–1.16	nd–0.12		9.51–15.3	nd							11, 54, 130
ORANGE, mandarin	nd–0.45	nd–0.30		6.73–20.0	nd–2.16							54
PARSLEY	0.79–3.77	nd–0.71	nd	0.30–0.87	nd	nd	nd	nd	nd	nd		172
PEAR	3.02–7.60	0.81–4.93		2.36–2.42	—	—	—	—	—	—		54
PEAS												11, 90
Cooked	6.21–6.82	3.35–7.17		0.54–0.59	—	—	—	—	—	—		
Frozen	0.29–8.84	0.16–0.85		1.17–10.7	0.19–0.42	0.23–0.38	0.41–1.65	0.13–2.44	—	—		
POTATO	0.83–1.88	nd–0.40		0.58–1.76		nd–0.13						11
RADISH												11, 162
Fresh	0.04–0.06	0.12–0.16		0.02–0.03	—	—	—	—	—	—		
Sprout	12.5	1.76	1.29	4.92	—	0.91	—	—	—	—		
RASPBERRY	—	—			—	—	1.28–9.25	—	—	—		40
RICE, polish	0.55	0.29		0.09	—	—	—	—	—	—		130
SOYBEAN	3.32–28.9	2.97–4.93		0.16–4.14	—	—	—	—	—	—		130
SPINACH												90, 130, 172
Fresh	0.75–2.42	0.06–0.19	0.35–1.22	0.11–0.80	nd	nd	0.06–0.11	0.33–0.77	nd	nd		
Puree	0.13–1.54	0.14–0.38		0.25–11.9		0.19–0.77	0.21–0.98	0.35–3.18	0.14–1.43	—		
STRAWBERRY	0.38–0.67	0.03–0.13	0.11–0.33		—	—	—	—	—	—		135
TOMATO												11, 54, 90, 130, 172
Fresh	0.16–0.70	nd–0.14	nd	0.19–12.2	nd–0.05	nd–0.31	nd–0.09	nd–0.03	nd–0.01	nd–0.12		
Paste	0.27–1.58	0.21–0.29		0.79–4.11	0.14–1.76	0.20–10.1	0.30–3.11	0.26–1.98	—	—		
Ketchup	0.11–3.34	0.14–1.21		0.24–16.5	0.14–13.1	0.20–1.80	0.45–14.9	0.13–7.25	—	—		
WHEAT, flour	1.33	0.38		0.15			—	—	—	—		130

[1] nd=not detectable; —=not determined. **SPN=spermine**, SPD=spermidine, AGM=agmatine, PUT=putrescine, CAD=cadaverine, HIM=histamine, TYM=tyramine, TRM=tryptamine, PHM=phenylethylamine, SRT=serotonin.

passion fruit, 1.0–1.2 mg/100 g in avocado and fig, 1.2 to 7.8 mg/100 g in pineapple and banana. The serotonin content in plantain is substantially higher. Banana peel contains higher serotonin levels than the pulp (3, 165, 188). Serotonin has also been detected in green and roasted coffee. Green beans of *Coffea arabica* L. cv red catuaí contained 0.94 mg/100 g of serotonin, while American (300 °C/6 min) and French (300 °C/12 min) roasted beans contained 0.16 and 0.29 mg/100 g, respectively (38).

Spermidine levels are high in tissues undergoing growth and in seeds, which are responsible for the preservation of the specie (59, 168, 172). Studies by Starling (172) corroborated this distribution pattern of spermidine in vegetables of the *Solanaceae* family. Moreover, this investigator detected higher histamine levels in the peel of these vegetables, which reinforces their role as plants protectors.

Studies on the influence of polyamines during development of fruits such as avocado, mandarin, apple, tomato, pear, pepper, litchi, and olive, revealed peak levels of putrescine and spermidine and rapid cell proliferation during early stages of growth and, then, decreasing values as the fruits grow and become ripe (129, 141, 155, 187). However, different results were observed during eggplant development and ripening (141). The serotonin content in bananas is affected by the degree of ripening. As the fruit ripens, serotonin in the peel increases steadily while in the pulp it increases and then decreases (188, 197). However, the levels of serotonin and putrescine decreased as the fruit changed from ripe to over-ripe (3).

Changes in bioactive amine levels and profiles at pre-harvest stage have been reported in response to various kinds of stress, including those from water (39, 204), mineral deficiency (13, 168), acid, herbicide, ozone-caused damages (41), osmotic shock, temperature or altitude variation (165), and chilling injury (129, 203). These reports have demonstrated that most of the stress conditions resulted in an increase of polyamine levels, particularly putrescine.

In a variety of fruits and vegetables, chilling injury is manifested by significant increases in polyamine levels. Putrescine accumulated in different products exposed to chilling temperature, among them lemon (116, 190), broccoli (129), grapefruit, pepper (116), and zucchini squash (92, 156, 203). Chilling injury caused a decrease of spermidine and spermine levels in zucchini squash (92, 156), but an increase of spermidine in peaches (191). Pretreatment of zucchini squash with CO_2 alleviated chilling injury and caused a smaller increase in putrescine (156). Infiltration of zucchini squash with spermidine prior to storage at 2.5 °C was efficient in reducing chilling injury (92). Acording to Serrano et al. (156) polyamines can prevent chilling injury by protecting membrane lipids from peroxidation.

Many researchers studied the relationship between food freshness and amine levels. In this respect, bioactive amines may be indicators of the freshness and quality of fruits and vegetables. During storage at 5 °C for 6 days, total amine content increased in Chinese cabbage from 2.0 to 3.4 mg/100 g, in chicory from 1.5 to 2.1 mg/100 g, in iceberg lettuce from 1.4 to 2.4 mg/100 g, and in radishes from 1.9 to 2.6 mg/100 g fresh weight. Among the amines detected, only putrescine concentration markedly and continuously increased during storage. Putrescine levels increased 3- to 8-fold depending on the type of vegetable. Spermidine and tyramine contents varied randomly and probably resulted from endogenous plant cell metabolism. The total bacterial numbers reached a maximum of 4×10^7 CFU/g at the end of storage, with *Enterobacteriaceae* representing ca 90 to 99% of the total microbial population. A relationship was established between *Enterobacteriaceae* population and putrescine concentration (164). Storage temperature affected markedly putrescine and spermidine contents of broccoli buds packed in polyethylene pouches. Spermidine levels decreased with storage time; however, at 2 °C the rate was slower compared to 23 °C. At 2 °C there was a significant increase in putrescine levels, whereas at 23 °C the levels decreased (129).

There is evidence that direct application of polyamines can have beneficial effects on the shelf life of fruits. During controlled atmosphere storage of apples, reduced rates of softening correlated with increased levels of endogenous polyamines (93). Pressure infiltration of polyamines caused an immediate increase in apple firmness and a decrease in softening rate at 0 °C. In addition, vacuum infiltration of polyamines in tomatoes resulted in firmer fruits than water-infiltrated ones (135).

The exogenous application of putrescine was shown to increase fruit firmness and to retard softening during storage (135, 205). However, vacuum-infiltrated spermine and spermidine (10 mM or 100 mM) significantly increased firmness of strawberry slices, whereas putrescine was not as effective. The greater ability of spermidine and spermine to bind isolated polysaccharides may explain why putrescine was less effective at increasing firmness of strawberry slices than spermidine and spermine at the same concentrations (93, 135).

Processed vegetables usually contain higher biogenic amine levels compared to the fresh product (90). During processing, the incorporation of ingredients can alter amine profile and levels. Furthermore, microorganisms with amino acid decarboxylase activity can be introduced either by addition of starter cultures or by contamination (74). Cocoa beans contain relatively low quantities of phenylethylamine and tyramine. During fermentation there was an increase in the levels of these amines, while roasting increased phenylethylamine levels substantially (42, 86). During coffee roasting there was a significant change in amine profile with total loss of putrescine and spermine, and decrease of spermidine and serotonin levels (38).

During germination of legume grains, protein is synthesized rapidly and increased levels of polyamines are expected. Furthermore, there is development of biogenic amines due to physiological changes in the tissues during sprouting and/or the activity of bacterial decarboxylase enzymes. The warm and moist environment is conducive to the rapid proliferation of microorganisms including *Enterobacteriaceae* and *Pseudomonas* spp., known to produce amino acid decarboxylases. During germination of *Phaseolus mungo*, putrescine content sharply increased, spermine levels decreased, and spermidine fluctuated, resulting in an overall increase in polyamines. The increase of putrescine levels was also observed in the germination of pea and maize, in bean and soybean seedlings, and in lentil sprouts (157, 162).

B. Fermented Beverages

Bioactive amines are among the major factors determining the quality of fermented beverages such as wine and beer (151). High amine levels can make the product unfit for consumption due to toxicological aspects. Furthermore, amines can also be significant in terms of aroma and flavor. In general, a weakening of the flavor impression is attributed to amines, whereby an unpleasant, bitter aftertaste has been noted and described as off-taste in wine and mousy in beer (45). Although tyramine and histamine are the major amines investigated in fermented products, several different amines have been detected. The types and concentrations of amines in fermented beverages vary widely (Table 13.7).

The origin of bioactive amines in wines is still a matter of controversy. Some amines are normal constituents of grapes with amounts varying with variety, soil type and composition, fertilization and climatic conditions during growth, and degree of maturation. Putrescine and spermidine are usually abundant in grapes, whereas agmatine, cadaverine, spermine, histamine, tyramine, and phenylethylamine have been found in small amounts (69, 73, 131, 151, 198). Lower amine levels in grapes were observed to be formed in cooler and rainier seasons (151). The degree of maturity of grapes is important since nitrogen content in the pulp is two to five times higher in ripened grapes (216).

Several amines can be formed and accumulate during wine making, among them putrescine, tyramine, histamine, and phenylethylamine, while spermidine levels decrease (73, 151). Reports are contradictory on the origin of biogenic amine during wine making. According to Vidal-Carou et al. (198), there was a slight formation of tyramine and no histamine formation during alcoholic fermentation of Spanish wines. On the contrary, Buteau et al. (25) found histamine production during alcoholic fermentation. However, in these studies there was no control of the microbial population present in the must; therefore, the formation of amines could not be attributed solely to the yeast.

Most researchers attribute the formation of biogenic amines, especially tyramine and histamine, to the action of bacteria involved in malolactic fermentation (25, 170, 198).

The rates of formation and the levels of amines accumulated vary widely according to the type of microorganisms and vinification practices. One evidence of amine formation during malolactic fermentation was reported by Soufleros et al. (170). During malolactic fermentation carried out by indigenous lactic acid bacteria, amino acid concentrations decreased significantly while biogenic amines increased. Another evidence was the negative correlation with malic and citric acids content (146). Delfini (44) compared the ability of several strains of *Leuconostoc* spp., *Lactobacillus* spp., and *Pediococcus* spp. to produce histamine, and observed that *Pediococcus damnosus* (*P. cerevisiae*) could produce significant amounts of histamine while *Leuconostoc oenos* (*O. oeni*) strains were poor producers of biogenic amines. Lafon-Lafoucade (96) suggested that histamine build-up occurred mainly as a result of bacteria growth in poor media. Lonvaud-Funel & Joyeux (105) showed that histamine production by *O. oeni* was stimulated in media without glucose or malic acid and depended particularly on the histidine concentration. Under those conditions, histidine decarboxylation contributed an additional energy source for the bacteria as already demonstrated for other microorganisms (120). Moreno-Arribas et al. (122) isolated *Lactobacillus brevis* and *L. hilgardii* capable of tyramine and phenylethylamine formation from wines containing high amine levels. They observed that the factors affecting tyramine formation were tyrosine levels in the must and also the presence of sugars, mainly glucose. However, malolatic fermentation does not necessarily result in the formation of biogenic amines (198).

Biogenic amines can also be formed in wine by the action of contaminant microorganisms, e.g., enteric bacteria. In this case, formation of amines has been related to the lack of hygiene during wine making. Based on this assumption, histamine alone or together with other amines can be an indicator of the quality of raw materials employed or unsanitary conditions prevailing during wine production (25, 170, 198).

Other factors during the vinification process can affect amine formation, among them must treatment, length of fermentation in the presence of pulp and skin, alcohol content, sulfur dioxide concentration, added nutrients, pH, temperature, use of proteolytic enzymes, length of maturation or aging step, and quantity and type of finings and clarification agents (6, 25, 69, 73, 98, 102, 151, 169, 171, 194, 198, 216).

According to Battaglia and Frolich (14), concentrations of 5 mg/L of histamine may provoke headache after the consumption of 0.5 L of wine. Therefore, the content of bioactive amines in wines may be regulated in the future following the implemented regulations by FDA for fish (56). Moreover, some countries have established limits for histamine in wines. Switzerland recommends 10 mg/L as maximum level, Germany 2 mg/L, Belgium 5 mg/L, and France 8 mg/L (97).

TABLE 13.7
Types and Levels of Bioactive Amine in Wines and Beers

Beverage (number of samples)	Range of Amine Levels (mg/L)[1]								
	SPD	SPN	AGM	PUT	CAD	HIM	TYM	TRM	PHM
WINE									
Pinot noir (36)	nd–2.35	nd–2.38	nd–8.37	2.43–203	nd–2.07	nd–23.98	nd–8.31	nd–5.51	nd–0.89
Cabernet Sauvignon (53)	nd–4.03	nd–1.17	nd–1.61	3.15–23.6	nd–1.51	nd–10.10	nd–7.53	nd	nd–1.37
Cabernet Franc (30)	0.07–0.30	nd	nd	0.77–1.43	nd	nd–1.37	0.30–0.83	nd	0.17–0.50
Merlot (30)	0.03–0.23	nd	nd	0.97–1.10	nd	0.07–1.67	0.33–0.50	nd	0.20–1.13
Bordeaux (25)	—	—	—	4.03	0.88	4.91	7.31	—	—
Canadian									
Red wines (26)	—	—	—	2.19	0.32	3.66	4.27	—	—
White wines (12)	—	—	—	1.25	nd	1.86	nd	—	—
Porto wines (17)	—	—	—	3.33	0.23	3.48	2.17	—	—
BEER									
Lager (46)	nd–6.00	nd–1.41	2.10–46.8	0.85–9.80	0.15–2.60	nd–0.90	0.30–3.10	nd–0.80	nd–0.70
Ale (18)	—	—	1.10–15.7	2.60–9.70	nd–4.20	0.50–2.00	1.90–17.4	—	—
Stout (10)	0.31–1.38	nd–2.05	2.80–16.8	1.99–5.84	0.30–1.37	nd–0.85	0.48–36.8	nd–10.1	nd–0.69
Ice (5)	0.60–0.80	nd–0.30	3.20–4.00	3.90–4.50	0.10–0.20	nd	0.70–1.40	nd	nd
Bock (23)	0.25–2.10	nd–1.73	4.80–35.1	1.55–6.30	0.15–1.72	nd–1.46	0.81–5.05	nd–3.50	nd–1.72
Non-alcoholic (7)	1.35–2.30	nd–1.20	6.35–8.59	2.30–4.95	nd–0.50	nd–0.62	0.60–3.30	nd–1.41	nd–0.32
Kriek (9)	—	—	1.10–3.40	3.50–5.10	1.90–15.2	1.60–14.0	6.70–36.4	—	—
Spontaneous fermentation (12)	—	—	1.00–18.8	2.80–15.2	0.40–39.9	nd–21.6	0.8–67.6	—	—

[1] nd=not detected; —=not determined. SPD=spermidine, SPN=spermine, AGM=agmatine, PUT=putrescine, CAD=cadaverine, HIM=histamine, TYM=tyramine, TRM=tryptamine, PHM=phenylethylamine.

Source: Refs. 68, 69, 83, 171, and 216.

The types and levels of amines detected in beers are indicated in Table 13.7. Agmatine and putrescine were often detected in beer, being the prevalent amines. Spermidine, spermine, cadaverine, histamine, tryptamine, and phenylethylamine occurred sporadically (68, 83). Kriek and spontaneous fermentation beers showed the highest histamine and tyramine levels (83). Amine levels in beers varied widely, being affected mainly by raw materials, brewing techniques, and microbial contamination during brewing (45, 85, 215).

Some amines at low levels are normal constituents of the raw materials for beer production, such as putrescine, agmatine, and spermidine. Malt can contribute significantly to amine contents in wort and beer. High levels of putrescine, agmatine, spermine, and spermidine and low levels of histamine, phenylethylamine, tryptamine, and cadaverine are usually found in malt. Tyramine, putrescine, spermine, spermidine, and agmatine have been detected in barley. Relatively high levels of tyramine, phenylethylamine, putrescine, spermine, spermidine, and agmatine have been detected in hops; however, its contribution to amine levels in the beer is not significant since the amount used is very small. The use of judicious choice of adjuncts (corn syrup, corn, wheat, barley, or rice) could result in lower amine levels. Rice was observed to be useful in reducing biogenic amines levels in worts and beers (68, 84, 89, 166, 215).

During beer production and storage several amines can be formed and accumulate. The formation of amines during brewing occurs principally during main fermentation (89). High amine production has also been observed during malting (84). During mashing and wort boiling, some amines such as tyramine and agmatine can accumulate. Their formation is attributed to thermal amino acid decarboxylation and possibly to enzymatic activity in the malt (45, 84). Acidified compared to original wort showed increased amine levels (45). During fermentation, *Saccharomyces uvarum*, a top or ale yeast, and *Saccharomyces cereviase* var. *uvarum*, a bottom or lager yeast, did not produce histamine or tyramine (85, 215). *Saccharomyces cereviase* var. *uvarum* recycling with phosphoric acid treatment did not influence biogenic amine formation (82).

During fermentation, wort contamination by amino acid decarboxylase bacteria such as lactic acid bacteria, might occur, leading to the formation of biogenic amines, mainly histamine, tyramine, tryptamine, phenylethylamine, and cadaverine (45, 83, 215). Therefore, biogenic amines could be associated with hygienic conditions during brewing (32, 45, 68, 82, 215). *Lactobacillus brevis* was responsible for tyramine and putrescine production in wort fermented with a top-fermenting yeast (215). *Pediococcus* spp. produced tyramine during beer fermentation and the amount produced depended on the contaminants counts (84). Experiments with beer spoilage microorganisms showed that *Lactobacillus frigidus*, *L. brevissimilis*, *L. brevis*, and *L. casei* produced higher amine levels compared to *L. plantarum*, *L. lindneri*, and *Pediococcus damnosus*. Moreover, commercial samples with *lactobacillus* contamination, had higher levels and different amine profiles (45). Wort contamination with *Enterobacter agglomerans*, *E. cloacae*, *E. intermedium*, and *Serratia marcescens* produced increased levels of putrescine and cadaverine. Wort contaminated with *Serratia marcescens* incubated at 27 °C produced higher amine levels compared to 6 °C (65). Therefore, biogenic amines could be used as indicators of microbial contamination.

C. MILK AND DAIRY PRODUCTS

The types and levels of bioactive amines found in milk and dairy products are indicated in Table 13.8. In general, amine content in milk and dairy products is quite low,

except for cheeses which can contain very high levels. Polyamines are naturally present in cow's milk. Spermine is the prevalent amine (34%), followed by putrescine (17%), spermidine (15%), and agmatine (3%) (11, 150). Serotonin and phenylethylamine were also detected in fresh milk corresponding to 16 and 15% of total amine levels, respectively (150). In reconstituted powdered milk (149), UHT milk (4), and yogurt (128) the amine profile changed, keeping similar total levels. There was loss of spermine and putrescine. Cadaverine, which is not inherent to milk, was also detected. Its presence could be correlated with *Enterobacteriaceae* counts, suggesting contamination of the product during processing (112).

A variety of amines has been found in different types of cheese (Table 13.8). In general, spermine and spermidine are present at low levels. The levels of other types of amines vary widely, depending on the cheese, ripening time or aging, and type of microorganisms present. However, high histamine and tyramine levels have been reported in several types of cheese (81, 173, 189).

Cheeses represent an ideal environment for biogenic amine production. Whether or not amines accumulate and

TABLE 13.8
Types and Levels of Bioactive Amines in Milk and Dairy Products

Product	Range of Amine Levels (mg/100 g)[1]									
	SPD	SPN	AGM	PUT	CAD	HIM	TYM	TRM	PHM	SRT
MILK[2]										
Fresh	0.01–0.16	0.13–0.26	nd–0.03	nd–0.21	nd	nd	nd	nd	0.04–0.17	nd–0.28
Powdered	0.21–0.29	0.07–0.10	0.59–0.64	nd	0.03–0.04	nd	nd	nd	nd	nd
UHT	0.05–0.13	0.07–0.15	nd	0.04–0.08	0.02–0.08	nd	nd	nd	nd	nd–0.39
YOGURT[2]	nd–0.04	nd–0.02	nd–0.04	nd	nd–0.03	nd	nd	nd	nd	—
CHEESE										
Blue cheese	—	—	—	9.6–23.7	42.3–227	nd–409	2.2–166	nd–110	—	—
Camembert	—	—	—	nd–60.5	nd–118	nd–48.0	2.30–200	nd–6.00	nd	—
Cheddar	—	—	—	nd–99.6	nd–40.8	nd–154	nd–153	nd–30	—	—
Feta	—	—	—	0.16–19.3	0.03–8.28	nd–8.46	nd–24.6	0.22–0.57	0.08–0.70	—
Gorgonzola	0.13–3.23	0.07–0.55	nd–1.79	1.2–124	5.8–428	1 .7–191	8.9–255	2.4–43	0.07–1.03	nd–1.81
Gouda	nd–1.35	nd–1.13	nd–1.34	nd–107	nd–99.5	nd–30.5	nd–67	nd–88	nd–1.92	nd–3.04
Grated	nd–1.23	0.07–0.80	nd–1.41	nd–6.30	0.07–13.4	nd–8.80	nd–21.3	nd–0.34	nd–1.98	nd–1.27
Minas	nd–2.10	0.07–2.58	nd–0.04	nd–2.64	nd–0.30	nd–2.50	nd	nd–0.72	nd–0.64	nd–0.31
Mozzarella	nd–1.06	nd–1.31	nd–0.13	nd–1.37	nd–2.34	nd–11.3	nd–1.56	nd–0.35	nd–0.26	nd–0.47
Parmesan	nd–0.15	0.07–0.09	nd	nd–1.36	nd–0.25	nd–27.2	nd–29	nd–1.70	nd–0.04	nd–0.23
Processed	nd	nd–10.0	—	nd–6.00	nd–12.0	nd	nd–16.0	nd	nd–40.0	—
Provolone	nd–2.38	0.07–0.97	nd–0.18	nd–8.17	nd–111	nd–6.04	nd–0.44	nd–1.08	nd–1.40	nd–1.40
Swiss	—	—	—	—	—	nd–250	nd–180	nd–1.60	—	—
Montasio										
60 days	—	—	—	0.06–1.01	0.02–0.40	0.55–1.82	0.21–3.51	0.01–0.36	0.07–0.44	—
90 days	—	—	—	0.06–3.84	0.07–1.00	1.63–6.43	1.32–8.63	0.02–0.23	0.04–1.97	—
150 days	—	—	—	12.9–110	0.50–3.02	10.1–37.8	12.8–37.4	0.18–0.81	0.77–2.00	—

[1] nd=not detectable; —=not determined. SPD=spermidine, SPN=spermine, AGM=agmatine, PUT=putrescine, CAD=cadaverine, HIM=histamine, TYM=tyramine, TRM=tryptamine, PHM=phenylethylamine, SRT=serotonin.

[2] Unit=mg/L.

Source: Refs. 4, 11, 81, 128, 149, 150, 173, 189, and 192.

persist in cheese depends on a number of factors. Biogenic amine formation can be affected by the availability of free amino acids and the presence of microorganisms, both added or contaminant, capable of amino acids decarboxylation. Conditions favorable for microbial growth and decarboxylase activity are also important, e.g., pH, salt concentration, temperature, water activity, ripening temperature and time, storage temperature, presence of suitable cofactors, and amine catabolism by means of mono- and diaminoxidase (51, 58, 72, 143, 173, 189).

Cheese is a protein-rich food, and amino acid is mainly brought about by the action of proteolytic enzymes from the starter and the rennet which contribute to the breakdown of casein (87). Amino acid decarboxylating enzymes show optimum activity at acid pH as a mechanism of environment neutralization against an excessive pH decrease which is incompatible with the bacteria's growth. The pH of cheese, 5.0–6.5, is the optimum range for most decarboxylase activity (5, 51, 143). The production of histamine and other biogenic amines is accelerated by high temperatures during production and manufacture of cheese (51, 87, 173). The increase in the concentration of salt can decrease amine formation, but salt-tolerant, amine-producing bacteria need to be controlled (51, 87, 143, 173, 175). The cofactor piridoxal phosphate, necessary for decarboxylase activity mainly over tyrosine, lysine, and ornithine, is present in milk and cheese at levels of 42 to 215 μg/100 g, which is sufficient to saturate the decarboxylases required for amine production (51, 143). However, there can be a decrease in biogenic amine levels due to catabolic activity of some microorganisms. Bacteria capable of metabolizing histamine (*Pseudomonas aeruginosa*, *Escherichia coli*, *Proteus vulgaris*, *Serratia flava*, *Clostridium feseri*) and tyramine (*Sarcina lutea*, *Aspergillus niger*, *Trichosporum* spp.) have been reported in the literature (139, 143).

Numerous bacteria, both intentional (starter cultures) and adventitious, have been reported as being capable of amine production at levels depending on bacterial densities and synergistic effects between microorganisms (81). The decarboxylase-positive microorganisms can be part of the natural population of the milk, or can be introduced as starter culture or by contamination, before and during cheese making and after processing. According to Joosten and Northold (88), it is necessary to have densities of 10^7 to 10^9 CFU/g in order to produce high concentrations of amines.

The hygienic quality of milk is very important in the formation of biogenic amines in cheese (143, 173). Cheese made with milk of poor microbial quality contains higher amine levels than cheese made with high quality milk (5, 87, 133). Among contaminating microorganisms, *Enterococcus* ssp. are notorious tyramine formers. *Enterococcus faecalis* was associated with considerable production of biogenic amines including phenylethylamine

(126). *Enterobacteriaceae* species, even at low densities, have been observed to produce and accumulate histamine, tyramine, putrescine, cadaverine, and phenylethylamine (51, 88, 112, 126, 173). *Clostridium* can produce histamine, tryptamine, and tyramine (51). Gram-negative microorganisms can increase the concentrations of putrescine and cadaverine in cheese (87, 112, 133).

According to Fernández-García et al. (58) and Greif et al. (72), lactic starter cultures used in the production of cheese can be an important critical point in the production of biogenic amines. The production of acid is the first manifestation of their growth. A second major change is the alteration of proteins. Starter cultures hydrolyze proteins and increase free amino acids levels which can be used for their growth (143). Several starter cultures have been observed to possess amino acid decarboxylase activity (87, 173). According to Straub et al. (174), several fermentation organisms failed to produce amines in phosphate buffer. However, in milk, *Lactobacillus* ssp. play a major role in histamine, tyramine, and putrescine accumulation. Various species of *Lactobacillus* produce histamine, e.g., *L. bulgaricus*, *L. casei*, *L. acidophilus* (51, 133, 173). *Lactococcus lactis* was observed to produce histamine, tyramine, and tryptamine (33). Wild lactococcal and leuconostoc strains were capable of tyramine formation (71). According to González de Llano et al. (71), Halász et al. (74), and Straub et al. (174), the amine forming ability should be taken into account when selecting starter cultures.

The influence of temperature, rennet, and NaCl on bioactive amines formation in milk by a commercial starter culture containing *Lactococcus lactis* ssp. *cremoris* and *L. lactis* ssp. *lactis* was investigated by Santos et al. (149). Sterilized reconstituted dry milk was inoculated with 1% culture in the presence or not of rennet and NaCl and incubated at 20 and 32 °C/24 h. There was a change in the levels of amines natural to milk. Histamine, serotonin, phenylethylamine, and tryptamine were also formed. Tyramine was only formed at 32 °C. Addition of rennet favored the formation of putrescine, tyramine, and tryptamine. Incorporation of NaCl in the milk for cheese manufacture decreased agmatine, spermidine, putrescine, histamine, and tyramine levels. By decreasing incubation temperature and adding NaCl, it was possible to minimize bioactive amine formation.

Pasteurization of milk can affect amine formation in cheese. In cheeses made from pasteurized milk, decarboxylase-positive bacteria usually remain at low levels, with reduced risk of biogenic amine formation even if the substrate is enriched in free amino acids by proteolytic enzymes. However, in cheeses made from raw milk, where a considerable population of decarboxylase-positive lactic acid bacteria is more likely to occur, formation of biogenic amines was enhanced by the higher levels of free amino acids (58). Pasteurization can be alternatively achieved by high pressure treatment of milk. Besides destroying pathogenic flora of milk, cheese made with high-pressure-treated milk ripens faster as it promotes higher proteolysis, without increasing levels of biogenic amines (128).

Another factor that may affect amine formation during cheese manufacture is the aging process. Tyramine concentration increased in Gouda cheese from milk with added tyrosine or with proteolysis faster than normal (87). Indeed, incorporation of proteinases to accelerate the ripening process of raw milk Hispanico cheese resulted in higher tyramine concentration, which increased with cheese age. However, it did not affect histamine formation (58). The longer the aging process, the higher the content of some biogenic amines as indicated for Montasio cheese (Table 13.8).

Although it is very difficult to elaborate cheese free of biogenic amines, efforts should be made to elucidate amine formation in cheese in order to optimize technology and secure low amine levels, mainly of the most dangerous ones (143). Use of raw material of good hygienic quality, pasteurization of cheese milk, use of hygienic practices during manufacture, prevention of temperature abuse throughout production, and selection of starters with low decarboxylase activity are measures to avoid the accumulation of these undesirable compounds (126, 127, 189).

D. FISH

Small amounts of bioactive amines occur naturally in fish (Table 13.9). Under normal physiological conditions, fish muscle contains high levels of spermine and spermidine and low levels of histamine and putrescine (9, 68, 118).

Several factors have been observed to affect amine levels in fish. Fish-to-fish and seasonal variations are observed due to genetics, environment, sex, physiological stage, and tissue sampled (1, 43, 53, 117, 195). Scombroid fish, such as tuna, bonito, mackerel, yellowfin, and bluefin, are particularly susceptible to histamine formation as they contain large amounts of free histidine (7, 31, 177). However, fish from other families (Scomberesocidae, Pomatomidae, Coryhaenidae, Carangidae, Clupeidae, and Engraulidae) are also susceptible. Data are contradictory with respect to both histidine and histamine levels in light and dark muscles (7, 68, 208). However, no significant difference in biogenic amines levels was found between samples from different parts along the light muscle of *Thunnus thynnus* and upper and lower loin light muscles of *T. alalunga*, respectively (68, 195).

The microbial flora of the fish also plays an important role in the formation of amines. However, it may be transient, varying with the environment, diet and hygienic conditions during capture, handling, processing, and storage (29). Several species, either natural or contaminant, are capable of producing histamine, such as *Morganella morganii, Klebsiella pneumonia, K. oxytoca, Hafnia*

alvei, Clostridium perfringens, Lactobacillus delbrueckii, Escherichia coli, Citrobacter freundii, Enterobacter cloacae, E. aerogenes, E. agglomerans, Proteus mirabilis, P. vulgaris, Serratia liquefaciens, Acinetobacter lwoffi, Pseudomonas putrefaciens, P. putida, P. fluorescens, Vibrio alginolyticus, and *Aeromonas hydrophyla* (1, 7, 23, 103, 117, 142, 195, 214). However, *Morganella morganii, Hafnia alvei,* and *Klebsiella pneumoniae* are the main histamine-producing bacteria which have been isolated from fish implicated in histamine poisoning outbreaks (177).

Other factors that influence the levels of amines in fish include place of capture, air, water and fish temperature, post-capture handling practices, chilling and freezing systems and rates, and storage conditions (7, 56, 68, 136). Several handling techniques have been used in commercial fishery. According to Dawood et al. (43) and Hardy and Smith (75), eviscerated fish contained lower concentrations of amines than whole samples. However, Price et al. (136) did not find significant differences in the quality and histamine levels of round, bled, or dressed albacore. Several investigations have demonstrated that storage temperature is a critical factor influencing histamine and other amine formation in fish muscle (49, 67, 182, 195). According to Ababouch et al. (1), freshly caught sardines contained high levels of bacteria located on the skin and the gills. These bacteria invaded and grew rapidly in sardine muscle, reaching 5×10^8 and 6×10^8 cfu/g, respectively, after 24 h at room temperature and 8 days in ice. Histamine, cadaverine, and putrescine accumulated to levels of 235, 105, and 30 mg/100 g, respectively, after 24 h storage at room temperature and after 8 days storage in ice. The requirement for rapid and uninterrupted refrigeration after catch can never be over-emphasized. The United States Food and Drug Administration (FDA) established a guidance level for histamine in fish at the dock or before processing of 5 mg/100g. The FDA also states that rapid chilling of fish immediately after catch is the most important strategy to limit histamine formation. The internal temperature of the fish should be brought to 10 °C or below within 6 hours of death. Chilling from 10 to 4.4 °C or less should not take longer than 18 hours. Any time above 4 °C significantly reduces the expected safe shelf life (56).

Studies have indicated that the levels of spermine and spermidine decrease and those of putrescine and histamine increase during storage and deterioration of fish such as tuna, rainbow trout, salmon, sardine and some fresh water fish, e.g., snapper, carp, catfish, "tambaqui," "lambari," and "tilápia" (23, 43, 67, 118). There is also formation and accumulation of cadaverine, tyramine, tryptamine, and phenylethylamine. The rates of change, however, are affected by storage temperature, pH, oxygen, nutrients presents, incorporation of additives, and packaging system (1, 23, 117, 118, 142, 195, 207). Studies on the influence of temperature on histamine formation by *Morganella morganii* and *Hafnia alvei*, prolific histamine

TABLE 13.9
Mean Levels of Bioactive Amines in Different Tissues of Tuna, in Tuna of Different Quality and in Tuna Affected by Storage Temperature and Canning

Fish	Mean Amine Level (mg/100 g)[1]						
	SPD	SPN	PUT	CAD	HIM	TYM	PHM
ALBACORE TUNA							
light muscle							
upper loin	0.26b	0.68	0.22	0.13	nd	nd	nd
lower loin	0.25b	1.21	0.14	0.11	nd	nd	nd
dark muscle	0.79a	2.5	0.06	0.07	nd	nd	nd
TUNA FISH							
good	0.44	0.95	0.12	0.15	0.38	—	—
borderline	0.36	0.67	0.23	1.03	2.36	—	—
decomposed	0.07	0.12	0.25	1.93	25.3	—	—
TUNA							
fresh	—	—	0.04	0.02	nd	nd	nd
0 °C/21 days	—	—	0.52	2.44	10.8	1.38	nd
8 °C/9 days	—	—	1.11	5.62	368	3.25	0.69
20 °C/3 days	—	—	0.45	10.84	687	1.71	0.81
ALBACORE TUNA							
before canning	0.43	0.73a	0.20a	0.06	0.07b	0.04a	0.01b
after caning	0.49	0.35b	0.09b	0.04	0.11a	0.00b	0.24a

[1] nd–not detectable, —=not determined. Mean values with different letter in the same group differ statistically (p < 0.05, Tukey test). SPD=spermidine, SPN=spermine, PUT=putrescine, CAD=cadaverine, HIM=histamine, TYM=tyramine, PHM=phenylethylamine.

Source: Refs. 68, 118, and 195.

formers, indicated that at 1 °C, no histamine was formed, whereas at 19 and 30 °C, the highest levels were found (7). Veciana-Nogués et al. (195) investigated the influence of temperature on bioactive amine formation in tuna and observed similar evolution profile at the three temperatures, although the highest amounts were achieved in samples stored at the higher temperature. There was a great increase in histamine followed by cadaverine. Formation of histamine, tyramine, and cadaverine were related to mesophilic microorganisms, *Enterobacteriaceae*, and coliforms. According to Du et al. (49), as histamine levels exceeded 5 mg/100 g in tuna fillets stored at 4, 10, and 22 °C, the total bacterial counts reached 10^7 cfu/g and the histamine producers reached 10^2 to 10^3 cfu/g. Histamine production by *Klebsiella pneumonia* was reduced as the concentration of NaCl increased, with marked inhibition occurring at 5.5% NaCl (184). Use of antimicrobial agents may provide an additional impediment to bacterial histamine production. Potassium sorbate at a concentration of 0.5% inhibited growth and histamine production by selected strains of *Morganella morganii* and *K. pneumonia* (182). Sodium chloride at 1% stimulated amine formation; however, levels above 3% or 2% combined with 0.5% clove completely inhibited growth and amine

production by *Enterobacter aerogenes* in mackerel broth (209). Vacuum packaging did not show any beneficial effect in controlling bacterial growth and histamine production on tuna samples (207). Canning of fish does not affect significantly histamine levels. However, significant losses are observed for spermine, putrescine, and tyramine and accumulation for phenylethylamine (68, 80).

Based on the changes observed in bioactive amines, Mietz and Karmas (118) proposed a chemical index to evaluate the quality of tuna. It is calculated by the sum of the levels of putrescine, histamine, and cadaverine divided by the sum of spermine and spermidine added by 1. Nominal cutoff values were 0 to 1 for good quality, 1 to 10 for borderline, and higher than 10 for decomposed tuna fish. This index compared favorably to sensory and authentic pack value scores. It was considered adequate to evaluate the quality or freshness of tuna and other types of fish and seafood, among them salmon, rockfish, snapper, lobster, and shrimp (119). In some species of fish, the presence of tyramine can also be detected during storage and deterioration. Based on these findings, Veciana-Nogués et al. (195) proposed for the quality assessment of tuna the use of an index calculated from the sum of the contents of histamine, tyramine, cadaverine, and putrescine. According to these authors, it showed good correlation with both storage time and organoleptic assessment and the level of 5 mg/100 g could be a guiding limit value for tuna and anchovy acceptance.

A maximum average histamine content of 10 mg/100 g has been established by several countries and communities (European Community and Mercosur) for acceptance of canned tuna and other fish belonging to the Scombridae and Scomberesocidae families (56). Because of the potentiating effect of other amines on the toxic effect of histamine, European regulation recommends the use of HPLC technique for the determination of the amines (107).

E. MEAT AND MEAT PRODUCTS

Spermine, spermidine, and putrescine occur naturally in meat. Meat is very susceptible to chemical and physical changes during storage of fresh meat or during processing of meat products. It is also susceptible to proteolysis by microorganisms and endogenous or microbial enzymes, which can liberate amino acids. The biogenic amines histamine, putrescine, tyramine, tryptamine, 2-phenylethylamine, and cadaverine can, then, be formed (76, 102, 196). Since biogenic amines are metabolites of microbial activity and are resistant to heat treatment (67, 102), they have been considered to be a useful index of quality of fresh and processed meat, reflecting the quality of the raw material used and the hygienic conditions prevalent during its processing. Amine levels in different types of fresh and stored meat are indicated in Table 13.10.

Immediately after slaughter, high levels of spermine and spermidine and traces of putrescine and cadaverine have been detected in red and white chicken meat. Spermine is the prevalent amine contributing with 70% of total amine levels. Low levels of histamine are also detected in thighs. During storage at 4 ± 1 °C, there was a decrease in spermine, spermidine levels remained constant, and putrescine, cadaverine, histamine, and tyramine were formed. At 15 days, higher levels of amines were found in breast compared to thigh. An index based on the ratio of the polyamines spermidine/spermine levels was considered appropriate for the evaluation of chicken meat quality (161).

Amine types and levels detected in chicken-based products, mortadella, frankfurters, sausage, meatballs, hamburger, and nuggets varied widely, indicating that ingredients added and processing affected amine profiles. Nuggets were the only products with an amine profile similar to that of fresh chicken meat. There was prevalence of spermidine over spermine for most of the products, suggesting the incorporation of significant amounts of vegetable protein in the formulations. Significantly higher biogenic amine levels were observed in sausages, which could indicate the use of low quality raw material or of contamination during processing and storage (161).

In fresh pork meat, spermine was the prevalent amine followed by low levels of spermidine and agmatine. No significant difference was observed between loin and leg tissues. During storage of pork loin at 5 ± 1 °C, mean spermine and spermidine levels remained constant, and putrescine, cadaverine, and histamine were formed. Cadaverine was detected on the 4th day of storage when mesophilic and psychrotrophic counts reached 4.9×10^5 and 7.9×10^5 cfu/g, respectively. Putrescine and histamine were detected only on the 12th day, with counts of 1.3×10^6 and 1.9×10^8 cfu/g for mesophilic and psychrotrophic microorganisms, respectively (193). Small changes in spermine and spermidine levels and formation and accumulation of putrescine, cadaverine, histamine, and tyramine were also observed by Hernández-Jover et al. (78). They suggested that the sum of these four biogenic amines could be a useful index to evaluate meat freshness, with values below 5 mg/kg indicating high hygienic quality meat.

Spermine was also the prevalent amine in fresh beef, followed by spermidine. Low levels of histamine were also detected in some samples (30, 76). At 4 °C, vacuum-packed beef had three times the shelf life of the unpacked product and lower levels of histamine, putrescine, and cadaverine (91).

Cooked meat products such as ham and mortadella showed prevalence of spermine over spermidine as observed for fresh meat; however, levels were lower compared to fresh products due to dilution of meat with fat and other ingredients used in the manufacturing process. The levels of biogenic amines varied widely (76, 78).

Much higher amounts of biogenic amines have been reported in dry fermented sausages. Tyramine was the prevalent amine, followed by putrescine, but their contents fluctuated widely. The presence of tryptamine and phenylethylamine was found to be common in the majority of the ripened products, although at low levels (28, 52, 76). Although the contents reported for certain amines are occasionally higher than those reported for fish products, there is still a lack of information on the incidence of histamine and tyramine intoxication with these products. However, sausages have been incriminated in migraine headaches and in hypertensive crisis episodes (60, 76).

Production of dry sausages offers favorable conditions for the formation of biogenic amines. There is growth of microorganisms for several days, and a certain degree of proteolysis takes place giving rise to the presence of free amino acids, which favors amino acid decarboxylase activity. Furthermore, raw material quality, thawing conditions, ripening temperature, and addition of a properly selected starter culture can affect formation and accumulation of biogenic amines. Therefore, these are important critical control points in amine formation (18, 111).

Good quality raw material only contributes with spermine and spermidine to the sausage. However, high

TABLE 13.10
Types and Levels of Bioactive Amines in Different Fresh, Stored, and Deteriorated Meat and Meat Products

Product	Amine Levels (mg/100 g)[1]									
	SPD	SPN	AGM	PUT	CAD	HIM	TYM	TRM	PHM	SRT
CHICKEN										
Fresh breast	0.73	1.79	nd	nd	nd	nd	nd	nd	nd	nd
Fresh thigh	0.72	1.62	nd	nd	nd	0.07	nd	nd	nd	nd
Breast storage/4 °C										
4 days	0.77a	1.72a	nd	nd	nd	nd	nd	nd	nd	nd
10 days	0.60a	1.25b	nd	nd	nd	nd	nd	nd	nd	nd
15 days	0.87a	1.12b	nd	2.04	0.43	1.03	1.74	nd	nd	nd
Products										
Hot dog	1.19–2.66	0.06–1.71	nd	nd–0.14	nd–0.15	nd–0.12	nd–0.14	nd	nd	nd–0.09
Mortadella	0.49–2.43	0.64–1.59	nd	nd–1.92	nd–0.54	nd–0.72	nd–0.14	nd	nd	nd–0.08
Sausage	0.34–1.11	0.60–1.46	nd	0.08–8.20	nd–6.68	nd–4.66	nd–3.36	nd–2.08	nd	nd–0.67
Meatball	0.35–1.86	0.51–1.10	nd	nd–0.16	nd–0.10	nd	nd–0.14	nd	nd	nd–0.13
Hamburger	0.42–2.44	0.45–1.56	nd	nd–0.19	nd–0.41	nd–0.08	nd–0.27	nd	nd	nd–0.22
Nugget	0.29–0.81	0.54–1.28	nd	nd	nd	nd	nd	nd	nd	nd
PORK										
Fresh loin	0.22	3.03	0.09	nd	nd	nd	nd	nd	nd	nd
Fresh leg	0.22	3.37	0.11	nd	nd	nd	nd	nd	nd	nd
Loin storage/5°C										
4 days	0.41	1.67	nd	nd	0.13b	nd	nd	nd	nd	nd
8 days	0.1	1.94	nd	nd	0.24b	nd	nd	nd	nd	nd
12 days	0.89	2.65	nd	0.14b	0.33b	0.36	nd	nd	nd	nd
16 days	0.63	3.36	nd	0.47a	2.02a	0.67	nd	nd	nd	nd
BEEF										
Fresh	0.19–0.42	1.80–4.46	—	nd	nd	nd–0.20	—	nd	—	—
Unpacked 12 days	—	—	—	1.04a	0.52	nd	—	—	—	—
Vacuum 12 days	—	—	—	0.11b	0.31	nd	—	—	—	—
COOKED										
Ham (20)	0.14–0.35	0.64–3.57	—	nd–1.24	nd–2.88	nd–0.09	nd–7.81	—	—	—
Mortadella (20)	0.10–0.89	0.76–3.22	—	nd–0.57	nd–4.00	nd–0.48	nd–6.70	nd–0.50	nd–0.50	—
DRY SAUSAGE										
Italiano (21)	0.06–1.29	1.67–5.93	0.05–1.01	5.33–11.8	0.68–12.8	0.09–12.1	12.6–23.0	0.02–1.16	0.61–3.10	nd–0.94
Milano (15)	0.04–0.29	0.61–3.01	0.05–0.16	3.42–6.23	0.08–9.50	nd–0.28	5.87–14.3	0.07–1.67	0.02–0.84	nd
Hamburguês (9)	0.12–1.40	2.55–3.33	0.04–1.57	3.72–6.73	1.98–5.38	nd–1.61	11.9–15.5	0.07–0.77	0.18–0.43	nd–0.01
Salaminho (9)	0.07–0.17	0.55–1.39	0.12–0.19	3.99–4.46	0.73–2.73	0.01–0.33	5.84–10.6	0.02–0.26	0.04–0.42	nd
Chorizo (20)	0.19–1.00	1.38–4.35	—	0.26–41.6	nd–65.8	nd–31.4	2.92–62.7	nd–8.78	nd–5.15	—
Salchichón (22)	0.07–1.38	0.69–4.25	—	0.55–40.0	nd–34.2	nd–15.1	5.33–51.3	nd–6.51	nd–3.47	—
Fuet (11)	0.09–1.10	0.94–3.01	—	0.22–22.2	0.54–5.13	nd–35.8	3.18–74.3	nd–6.78	nd–3.37	—
Sobrasada (7)	0.24–0.70	1.03–1.78	—	0.18–50.1	0.30–4.16	0.28–14.3	5.76–50.1	nd–6.48	0.02–3.85	—

[1] nd=not detectable; —=not determined. SPD=spermidine, SPN=spermine, AGM=agmatine, PUT=putrescine, CAD=cadaverine, HIM=histamine, TYM=tyramine, TRM=tryptamine, PHM=phenylethylamine, SRT=serotonin.

Source: Refs. 28, 30, 76, 91, 161, and 193.

amounts of biogenic amines in sausages can be related to the use of low hygienic quality meat (76, 77, 132). The choice of good quality raw materials helps minimize the number of amine-producing bacteria. Furthermore, biogenic amine formation may be affected by the thawing time and storage temperature of raw material (110). Fresh lean meat stored for 5 days at -20 °C maintained hygienic quality and low tyramine, cadaverine, and putrescine content. However, when stored for 5 days at 4 °C, sausages formed amines earlier and accumulated up to 50-fold higher amounts. Storage temperatures of 15 °C, compared to 4 °C, favored proteolytic and decarboxylase reactions, resulting in increased amine concentration (20). Isolates obtained from raw sausages showed histamine-forming activity, most of them belonging to the *Enterobacteriaceae* family, *Klebsiella oxytoca*, *Enterobacter aerogenes*, and *E. cloacae* (144).

Intense proteolysis takes place during the dry curing process, mainly due to muscle proteinases (76). Proteolysis during fermentation is favored by the denaturation of proteins as a consequence of acidity, dehydration, and action of sodium chloride. The activity of endogenous but also microbial proteases modifies the composition of the non-protein nitrogen fraction, including the production of free amino acids (18).

Dry sausages can be spontaneously fermented by wild microbial flora. However, tyramine and putrescine are usually produced and accumulated. The use and selection of starter cultures can reduce the production of these and other amines (77, 110). Starter culture shortens the fermentation process and also reduces the growth of deleterious microorganisms (76). They usually consist of one or several strains of lactic acid bacteria and the group of catalase-positive cocci, including micrococci and staphylococci, or a combination of both (18). Lactic acid production by lactic acid bacteria has a preservative effect, and facilitates the drying process, the development of the typical curing color, and the cohesion of the sausages. However, the production of biogenic amines in meat and meat products has often been related to lactic acid bacteria, *Enterobacteriaceae* and *Pseudomonas*. Micrococci and staphylococci also contribute to sausage ripening by enhancing the development of the characteristic flavor and color. Catalase production protects against color changes and rancidity, while nitrate and nitrite reductase aid reddening and reduce residual nitrite content (21).

Several reports on the effect of different combinations of starter cultures on biogenic amines formation and accumulation *in vitro* and in sausage are available. *Staphylococcus carnosus* and *S. xylosus* were considered safe starter cultures according to their tyramine production *in vitro* (114). However, *S. carnosus* was observed to have a remarkable potential to form biogenic amines, but not *S. xylosus* (174). Indeed, *S. carnosus* did not prevent

the formation of tyramine and phenylethylamine by contaminant lactic acid bacteria during sausage ripening (110). Sausages made with *S. carnosus* and *S. xylosus* showed strong proteolysis but had lower amounts of tyramine compared to naturally fermented sausages (18).

The use of *Lactobacillus sake*, *Pediococcus pentosaceus*, *Staphylococcus carnosus*, and *S. xylosus* inhibited formation of putrescine but not tyramine during ripening of Turkish "soudjoucks" (8). *L. sakei* and *Staphylococcus* spp. drastically reduced tyramine, cadaverine, and putrescine accumulation (21, 22). *L. curvatus* only attenuated tyramine content compared to *L. sakei*; however, both were able to limit production of putrescine and cadaverine and to prevent tryptamine and phenylethylamine formation by the wild flora (22). Mixtures of *Pediococcus cereviseae* and *L. plantarum* were unable to produce significant levels of histamine and tyramine (140). Histamine production was lower in sausage fermented by mixed starter cultures of *Lactobacillus plantarum*, *Pediococcus acidolactici*, and *Micrococcus roseus* compared to those fermented by natural microflora (16). Some strains of *Enterococcus*, *L. curvatus*, or *S. carnosus* produced tyramine and phenylethylamine (121).

The technological conditions used to produce sausages can also affect amine formation since they affect the growth and activity of the microorganisms present. The largest diameter contained higher amines levels than thinner sausages. Histamine levels in "sobrasada" and tyramine, histamine, putrescine, and cadaverine levels in sausages were higher in the central part compared to the edges (19, 196). The choice of optimal processing temperature for the amine-negative starter culture is an important critical control point in the formation and levels of biogenic amines (111). Addition of glucono-delta-lactone (GLD) to sausage causes a faster decrease in pH, stabilizes the color, simplifies production, and suppresses microorganisms which cause spoilage (streptococci, coliforms, and total plate counts), thereby decreasing significantly the levels of histamine and putrescine (109). However, sausages produced with 0.3% GLD contained higher histamine and tyramine levels and less acceptable organoleptic evaluation (24). Moreover, tyramine degradation by microorganisms with tyramine oxidase activity, such as *Micrococci* during ripening, can be used (100).

A recommended upper limit of 10 to 20 mg/100 g for histamine in meat products has been proposed by the Netherlands Institute of Dairy Research and by the Czech Republic (121, 185). A recommendation should be extended for tyramine in meat products. Furthermore, the addition of selected starter culture, the use of proper technological conditions favoring starter development, and the utilization of raw materials with good hygienic quality make it possible to produce fermented sausages nearly free of biogenic amines (21).

REFERENCES

1. L Ababouch, ME Afilal, H Benabdeljelil, FF Busta. Quantitative changes in bacteria, amino acids and biogenic amines in sardine (*Sardina pilchardus*) stored at ambient temperature (25–28°C) and in ice. Int J Food Sci Technol 26:297–306, 1991.

2. RC Adão. Influência da radiação gama no amadurecimento e nos teores de aminas biogênicas em banana prata (*Musa acuminata* × *Musa balbisiana*). MS dissertation, Universidade Federal de Minas Gerais, Belo Horizonte, MG, Brazil, 1998.

3. RC Adão, MBA Glória. Bioactive amines and carbohydrates changes during ripening of banana cv 'Prata' *Musa acuminata* × *Musa balbisiana*. Food Chem 90:705–711, 2005.

4. AAP Almeida, TML Silveira, MBA Glória. Aminas bioativas em leite integral UHT comercializado na região de Belo Horizonte, MG. Rev ILCT 58(333):235–238, 2003.

5. P Antila, V Antila, J Mattila, H Hakkarainen. Biogenic amines in cheese. II. Factors influencing the formation of biogenic amines, with particular reference to the quality of the milk used in cheese making. Milchwissenschaft 39(7):400–404, 1984.

6. ME Arena, MC Manca de Nadra. Biogenic amine production by *Lactobacillus*. J Appl Microbiol 90:158–162, 2001.

7. SH Arnold, WD Brown. Histamine (?) toxicity from fish products. Adv Food Res 24:114–154, 1978.

8. K Ayhan, N Kolsarici, GA Ozkan. The effects of a starter culture on the formation of biogenic amines in Turkish soudjoucks. Meat Sci 53:183–188, 1999.

9. S Bardocz. Polyamines in food and their consequences for food quality and human health. Trends Food Sci Technol 6:341–346, 1995.

10. S Bardocz. The role of dietary polyamines. Eur J Clin Nutr 47:683–690, 1993.

11. S Bardocz, G Grant, DS Brown, A Ralph, A Pusztai. Polyamines in food — implications for growth and health. J Nutr Biochem 4:66–70, 1993.

12. BA Bartolomew, PR Berry, JC Rodhouse, RJ Gilbert. Scombrotoxic fish poisoning in Britain: features of over 250 suspected incidents from 1976–1986. Epidemiol Infect 99:775–782, 1987.

13. LC Basso, TA Smith. Effect of mineral deficiency on amine formation in higher plants. Phytochemistry 13:875–883, 1974.

14. R Battaglia, D Frolich. HPLC determination of histamine in wine. J High Resolut Chromatogr Commun 2:100–101, 1978.

15. NH Bean, PM Griffin. Foodborne disease outbreaks in the United States, 1973–1987: pathogens, vehicles and trends. J Food Prot 53(9):804–817, 1990.

16. JS Berwal, R Kumar. Effect of starter cultures on production of histamine and levels of nitrite in fermented sausages. J Food Sci Technol 35(2):187–190, 1998.

17. PR Bieck, A Karl–Heinz. Tyramine potentiation during treatment with MAOIs. In: SH Kennedy. ed. Clinical Advances in Monoamine Oxidase Inhibitor Therapies.

American Psychiatric Publishing, Arlington, VA, 83–109, 1994.

18. S Bover-Cid, M Izquierdo-Pulido, MC Vidal-Carou. Effect of proteolytic starter cultures of *Staphylococcus* spp. on biogenic amine formation during ripening of dry fermented sausages. Int J Food Microbiol 46:95–104, 1999a.

19. S Bover-Cid, S Schoppen, M Izquierdo-Pulido, MC Vidal-Carou. Relationship between biogenic amine contents and the size of dry fermented sausages. Meat Sci 51:305–311, 1999b.

20. S Bover-Cid, M Izquierdo-Pulido, MC Vidal-Carou. Influence of hygienic quality of raw materials on biogenic amine production during ripening and storage of dry fermented sausages. J Food Prot 63(11):1544–1550, 2000.

21. S Bover-Cid, M Izquierdo-Pulido, MC Vidal-Carou. Mixed starter cultures to control biogenic amine production in dry fermented sausages. J Food Prot 63(11): 1556–1562, 2000.

22. S Bover-Cid, M Hugas, M Izquierdo-Pulido, MC Vidal-Carou. Reduction of biogenic amine formation using a negative amino acid decarboxylase starter culture for fermentation of Fuet sausages. J Food Prot 63(2):237–243, 2000.

23. ALG Brandão. Potencial de formação de aminas biogênicas em peixes de piscicultura. MS dissertation, Universidade Federal de Minas Gerais, Belo Horizonte, MG, Brazil, 1996.

24. S Buncic, LJ Paunovic, V Teodorovic, D Radisie, G Vojinovic, D Smiljanic, M Baltic. Effects of glucono-delata-lactone and *Lactobacillus plantarum* on the production of histamine and tyramine in fermented sausages. Int J Food Microbiol 17:303–309, 1993.

25. C Buteau, CL Duitschaever, GC Ashton. High-performance liquid chromatographic detection and quantitation of amines in must and wine. J Chromatogr 284:201–210, 1984.

26. JP Buts. Bioactive factors in milk. Arch Pediatr 5(3):298–306, 1998.

27. JP Buts, N De Keyser, L De Raedemaeker, E Collette, EM Sokal. Polyamine profiles in human milk, infant artificial formulas and semi-elemental diets. J Pediatr Gastroenterol Nutr 21(1):44–49, 1995.

28. J Caccioppoli. Características físico-químicas e aminas bioativas em salames. MS dissertation, Universidade Federal de Minas Gerais, Belo Horizonte, MG, Brazil, 2002.

29. MM Cahill. Bacterial flora of fishes: a review. Microb Ecol 19:1–41, 1990.

30. C Cantoni. Ammine biogene di prodotti carnei nazionali. Ind Alimentari 34:9–12, 1995.

31. CDC. Epidemiological notes and reports on scombroid fish poisoning. Centers for Disease Control and Prevention. www.cdc.gov/mmwr.htm. Accessed September, 2003.

32. G Cerutti, C Finoli, S Peluzzi, Avecchio. Non-volatile amines in beer: origin and occurrence. Monatsschr Brauwiss 38:296–299, 1985.

33. H Chander, VK Batish, S Babu, R Singh. Factors affecting amine production by a selected strain of *Lactobacillus bulgaricus*. J Food Sci 54(4):940–942, 1989.

34. SF Chang, JW Ayres, WE Sandine. Analysis of cheese for histamine, tyramine, tryptamine, histidine, tyrosine and tryptophane. J Dairy Sci 68:2840–2846, 1985.

35. JP Chaytor, B Crathorne, MJ Saxby. The identification, estimation and significance of 2-phenylethylamine in foods. J Sci Food Agric 26:593–598, 1975.

36. CM Chen, CI Wei, JA Koburger, MR Marshall. Comparison of four agar media for detection of histamine-producing in tuna. J Food Prot 52:808–813, 1989.

37. CH Chu, LF Bjeldanes. Effect of diamines, polyamines and tuna fish extracts on the binding of histamine to mucin *in vitro*. J Food Sci 47:79–80, 88, 1981.

38. MPG Cirilo, AFS Coelho, CM Araújo, FRB Gonçalves, FD Nogueira, MBA Glória. Profile and levels of bioactive amines in green and roasted coffee. Food Chem 82:397–402, 2003.

39. AFS Coelho. Qualidade de alface Americana (*Lactuca sativa* L.) minimamente processada. MSc Dissertation, Universidade Federal de Minas Gerais, Belo Horizonte, MG, Brazil, 2001.

40. DE Coffin. Tyramine content of raspberries and other fruit. J Assoc Offic Anal Chem 53:1071–1073, 1970.

41. R Conca, MC Bruzzoniti, E Mentasti, C Sarzanini, P Hajos. Ion chromatographic separation of polyamines: putrescine, spermidine and spermine. Anal Chim Acta, 439:107–114, 2001.

42. RT Coutts, GB Baker, FM Pasutto. Foodstuffs as sources of psychoactive amines and their precursors: content, significance and identification. Adv Drug Res 15:169–232, 1986.

43. AA Dawood, RN Karkalas, RN Roy, CS Williams. The occurrence of non-volatile amines in chilled-stored rainbow trout (*Salmo irideus*). Food Chem 27:33–45, 1988.

44. C Delfini. Ability of wine malolactic bacteria to produce histamine. Sci Aliments 9:413–416, 1989.

45. S Donhauser, D Wagner, E Geiger. Biogenic amines: significance, occurrence and assessment. Brauwelt Int 2:100–107, 1993.

46. B Dorhout, CM van Beusekom, M Huisman, AW Kingma, E de Hoog, ER Boersma, FAJ Muskiet. Estimation of 24-hour polyamine intake from mature human milk. J Pediatr Gastroenterol Nutr 23:298–302, 1996.

47. ME Doyle, CE Steinhart, BA Cochrana. Food Safety. Marcel Dekker, New York, pp. 254–259, 1993.

48. G Drolet, EB Dumbroff, RL Legge, JE Thompson. Radical scavenging properties of polyamines. Phytochemistry 25(2):367–371, 1986.

49. WX Du, CM Lin, AT Phu, JA Cornell, MR Marshall, CI Wei. Development of biogenic amines in yellowfin tuna (*Thunnus albacores*): effect of storage and correlation with decarboxylase-positive bacterial flora. Food Microb Saf 67(1):292–301, 2002.

50. F Durlu-Ozkaya, K Ayhan, N Vural. Biogenic amines produced by Enterobacteriaceae isolated from meat products. Meat Sci 58:163–166, 2001.

51. ST Edwards, WE Sandine. Public health significance of amines in cheese. J Dairy Sci 64:2431–2438, 1981.

52. HS Eerola, AX Roig-Sagués, TK Hirvi. Biogenic amines in Finnish dry sausages. J Food Saf 18:127–138, 1998.

53. RR Eitenmiller, JW Wallis, JH Orr, RD Phillips. Production of histidine decarboxylase and histamine by *Proteus morganii*. J Food Prot 44(11):815–820, 1981.

54. KA Eliassen, R Reistad, U Risoen, HF Ronning. Dietary polyamines. Food Chem 78:273–280, 2002.

55. M Esti, G Volpe, L Massignan, D Compagnone, E La Notte, G Palleschi. Determination of amines in fresh and modified atmosphere packaged fruits using electrochemical biosensors. J Agric Food Chem 46:4233–4237, 1998.

56. FDA. Fish & Fisheries Products Hazards & Controls Guide. 244 pp. FDA, Office of Seafood, Washington, D.C., 1996.

57. ME Ferioli, L Pirona, O Pinotti. Prolactin and polyamine catabolism: specific effect on polyamine oxidase activity in rat thymus. Mol Cel Endocrinol 165:51–56, 2000.

58. E Fernández-García, J Tomillo, M Nuñez. Formation of biogenic amines in raw milk hispánico cheese manufactured with proteinases and different levels of starter culture. J Food Prot 63(11):1551–1555, 2000.

59. HE Flores, CM Protacio, MW Signs. Primary and secondary metabolism of polyamines in plants. Phytochemistry 23:329–393, 1989.

60. CS Fuzikawa, C Hara, MBA Glória, FL Rocha. Monoamine oxidase inhibitors and diet – Update and practical recommendations for clinical use. J Bras Psiq 48(10):453–460, 1999.

61. MA Gagne, A Wollin, H Navert, G. Pinard. Prog Neuro-Psychopharmacol Bio Psychiat 6:483–486, 1982.

62. AW Galston, R Kaur-Sawhney. Polyamines as endogenous growth regulators. In PJ Davies. Plant Hormones and Their Role in Plant Growth and Development. Kluwer Academic, London, 280–295, 1990.

63. C Garcia, A Mariné. Contenido de serotonina em alimentos frescos y elaborados. Rev Agroquim Tecnol Aliment 23:60–70, 1983.

64. DM Gardner, KI Shulman, SE Walker, SAN Tailor. The making of a user friendly MAOI diet. J Clin Psychiatry 57(3):99–104, 1996.

65. E Geiger, D Wagner, F Briem, S Englet. Biogenic amines in malt and beer preparation. Brauwelt Int IV, 328–330, 1996.

66. MBA Glória. Amines. In B Caballero, L Trugo, P Finglas. Encyclopedia of Food Science and Nutrition. Academic Press, London, 173–181, 2003.

67. MBA Glória, MA Daeschel, C Craven, KS Hilderbrand Jr. Histamine and other biogenic amines in albacore tuna. J Aquatic Food Products Technol 8(4):55–69, 1999.

68. MBA Glória, M Izquierdo-Pulido. Levels and significance of biogenic amines in Brazilian beers. J Food Comp Anal 12:129–136, 1999.

69. MBA Glória, BT Watson, L Simon-Sarkadi, MA Daeschel. A survey of biogenic amines in Oregon Pinot noir and Cabernet Sauvignon wines. Am J Enol Vitic 49(3):279–282, 1998.

70. GA Gonzalez-Aguilar, L Zacarias, MT Lafuente. Ripening affects high-temperature-induced polyamines and their changes during cold storage of hybrid fortune mandarins. J Agric Food Chem 46:3503–3508, 1998.

71. G González de Llano, P Cuesta, A Rodríguez. Biogenic amine production by wild lactococcal and leuconostoc strains. Lett Appl Microbiol 26(4):270–274, 1998.

72. G Greif, M Drdak, M Greifova. Determination of biogenic amines produced by some strains of bacteria. VIII Proceed Eurofood Chem, Vienna, Austria, 355–360, 1995.

73. G Hajós, A Sass-Kiss, E Szerdahelyi, S Bardocz. Changes in biogenic amine content of Tokaj grapes, wines, and Aszu-wines. J Food Sci 65(7):1142–1144, 2000.

74. A Halász, A Baráth, L Simon-Sarkadi, W Holzapfel. Biogenic amines and their production by microorganisms in food. Trends Food Sci Technol 5:42–49, 1994.

75. R Hardy, JGM Smith. The storage of mackerel (*Scomber scombrus*). Development of histamine and rancidity. J Sci Food Agric 27:595–599, 1976.

76. T Hernández-Jover, M Izquierdo-Pulido, MT Veciana-Nogués, A Mariné-Font, MC Vidal-Carou. Biogenic amine and polyamine contents in meat and meat products. J Agric Food Chem 45(6):2098–2102, 1997a.

77. T Hernández-Jover, M Izquierdo-Pulido, MT Veciana-Nogués, A Mariné-Font, MC Vidal-Carou. Effect of starter cultures on biogenic amine formation during fermented sausage production. J Food Prot 60(7):825–830, 1997b.

78. T Hérnandez-Jover, M Izquierdo-Pulido, MT Veciana-Nogués, MC Vidal-Carou. Biogenic amine sources in cooked cured shoulder pork. J Agric Food Chem 44(10):3097–3101, 1996.

79. JY Hui, SL Taylor. Inhibition of in vivo metabolism in rats by foodborne and pharmacologic inhibitors of diamine oxidase, histamine N-methyltransferase and monoaminoxidase. Toxicol Appl Pharmacol 81:241–249, 1985.

80. C Ienistea. Significance and detection of histamine in food. In: BC Hobbs, JHB Christian, eds. The microbiological safety of food. Academic Press, London, 327–343, 1973.

81. N Innocente, P D'Agostin. Formation of biogenic amines in a typical semi hard Italian cheese. J Food Prot 65(9):1498–1501, 2002.

82. M Izquierdo-Pulido, J Font-Fábregas, MC Vidal-Carou. Influence of *Saccharomyces cerevisiae* var. *uvarum* on histamine and tyramine formation during beer fermentation. Food Chem 54:51–54, 1995.

83. M Izquierdo-Pulido, T Hernández-Jover, A Mariné-Font, MC Vidal-Carou. Biogenic amines in European beers. J Agric Food Chem 44:3159–3163, 1996.

84. M Izquierdo-Pulido, A Mariné-Font, MC Vidal-Carou. Biogenic amines formation during malting and brewing. J Food Sci 59:1104–1107, 1994.

85. M Izquierdo-Pulido, MC Vidal-Carou, A Mariné-Font. Determination of biogenic amines in beers and their raw materials by ion-pair liquid chromatography with post-column derivatization. J AOAC Int 76:1027–1032, 1993.

86. M Jalon, C Santos-Buelga, JC Rivas-Gonzalo, A Mariné-Font. Tyramine in cocoa and derivatives. J Food Sci 48:545–547, 1983.

87. HMLJ Joosten. The biogenic amine contents of Dutch cheese and their toxicological significance. Neth Milk Dairy J 42:25–42, 1988.

88. HMLJ Joosten, MD Northold. Conditions allowing formation of biogenic amines in cheese. 2. Decarboxylative properties of some non-starter bacteria. Neth Milk Dairy J 41:259–280, 1987.

89. P Kalac, V Hlavatá, M Krízek. Concentrations of five biogenic amines in Czech beers and factors affecting their formation. Food Chem 57:209–214, 1996.

90. P Kalac, S Svecová, T Pelikánová. Levels of biogenic amines in typical vegetable products. Food Chem 77:349–351, 2002.

91. I Kaniou, G Samouris, T Mouratidou, A Eleftheriadou, N Zantopoulos. Determination of biogenic amines in fresh unpacked and vacuum-packed beef during storage at 4°C. Food Chem 74:515–519, 2001.

92. GF Kramer, CY Wang. Correlation of reduced chilling injury with increased spermine and spermidine levels in zucchini squash. Physiol Plant 76:479–484, 1989.

93. GF Kramer, CY Wang, WS Conway. Inhibition of softening by polyamine application in Golden Delicious and McIntosh apples. J Amer Soc Hort Sci 116:813–817, 1991.

94. R Kraus. Hypertensive episodes with tranylcypromine treatment. J Clin Psychopharmacol 9:232–233, 1989.

95. EO Krebsky, JMC Geuns, M De Proft. Polyamines and sterols in Cichorium heads. Phytochemistry 50:549–553, 1999.

96. S Lafon-Lafoucade. L'histamine des vins. Cannaiss Vigne Vin 2:103–115, 1975.

97. P Lehtonen. Determination of amines and amino acids in wine: a review. Am J Enol Vitic 47:127–133, 1996.

98. MC Leitão, HC Teixeira, MT Barreto Crespo, MV San Romão. Biogenic amines occurrence in wine. Amino acid decarboxylation and proteolytic activities expression by *Oenococcus oeni*. J Agric Food Chem 48:2780–2784, 2000.

99. VA Leiting, L Wicker. Inorganic cations and polyamines moderate pesctinesterase activity. J Food Sci 62(2):253–255, 1997.

100. RGK Leuschner, WP Hammes. Tyramine degradation by micrococci during ripening of fermented sausage. Meat Sci 49(3):289–296, 1998.

101. DR Lide. ed. CRC Handbook of Chemistry and Physics: A Ready-Reference Book of Chemical and Physical Data. Boca Raton: CRC Press, 1995.

102. AS Lima, MBA Glória. Aminas bioativas em alimentos. Bol SBCTA 33(1):70–79, 1999.

103. EI Lopez-Sabater, JJ Rodríguez-Jerez, AR Roig-Sagués, MAT Mora-Ventura. Bacteriological quality of tuna fish (*Thunnus thynnus*) destined for canning: effect of tuna handling on presence of histidine decarboxylase bacteria and histamine level. J Food Prot 57(4):318–323, 1994.

104. C Löser. Polyamines in human and animal milk. Brit J Nutr 84(1):S55–S58, 2000.

105. A Lounvaud-Funel, A Joyeux. Histamine production by wine lactic acid bacteria: isolation of a histamine-producing strain of *Leuconostoc oenos*. J Appl Bacteriol 77:401–407, 1994.

106. DW Lundgren. Alterations in polyamine levels in rat blood during pregnancy and lactation. Biochem J 130:71–76, 1972.

107. JB Luten, W Bouquet, LA Seuren, MM Burggraaf, G Riekwel-Booy, P Durand, M Etienne, JP Gouyou, A Landrein, A Ritchie, M Leclerq, R Guinet. Biogenic amines in fishery products: standardization methods within EC. In: HH Huss, ed. Quality assurance in the fish industry. Elsevier, London, 427–439, 1992.

108. A Maga. Amines in foods. CRC Crit Rev Food Sci Nutr 10:373–399, 1978.

109. RL Maijala, SH Eerola, MA Aho, JA Hirn. The effect of GDL-induced pH decrease on the formation of biogenic amines in meta. J Food Prot 56(2):125–129, 1993.

110. RL Maijala, S Eerola, S Lievonen, P Hill, T Hirvi. Formation of biogenic amines during ripening of dry sausages as affected by starter culture and thawing time of raw materials. J Food Sci 60(6):1187–1190, 1995.

111. RL Maijala, E Nurmi, A Fischer. Influence of processing temperature on the formation of biogenic amines in dry sausages. Meat Sci 39(1):9–22, 1995.

112. M Marino, M Manfreni, S Moret, G Rondinini. The capacity of *Enterobacteriaceae* species to produce biogenic amines in cheese. Lett Appl Microbiol 31:169–173, 2000.

113. E Marley, B Blackwell. Interactions of monoamine oxidase inhibitors, amines and foodstuffs. Adv Pharmacol Chemother 8:185–239, 1970.

114. F Masson, G Johansson, MC Montel. Tyramine production by a strain of *Carnobacterium divergens* inoculated in meat–fat mixture. Meat Sci 52:65–69, 1999.

115. BJ McCabe. Dietary tyramine and other pressor amines in MAOI regimens: a review. J Am Diet Assoc 86:1059–1064, 1986.

116. RE McDonald, MM Kushad. Accumulation of putrescine during chilling injury of fruits. Plant Physiol 82:324–326, 1986.

117. BL Middlebrooks, PM Toom, WL Douglas, RE Harrison, S McDowell. Effects of storage time and temperature on the microflora and amine development in Spanish mackerel. J Food Sci 53:1024–1029, 1988.

118. JL Mietz, E Karmas. Chemical quality index of canned tuna as determined by HPLC. J Food Sci 42:155–158, 1977.

119. JL Mietz, E Karmas. Polyamine and histamine content of rockfish, salmon, lobster and shrimp as an indicator of decomposition. J AOAC 61(1):139–145, 1978.

120. D Molenaar, JS Bosscher, B Ten Brink, AJM Drissen. WN Konings. Generation of a proton motive force by histidine decarboxylation and electrogenic histidine/histamine antiport in *Lactobacillus buchneri*. J Bacteriol 175:2864–2879, 1993.

121. MC Montel, F Masson, R Talon. Comparison of biogenic amine content in traditional and industrial French dry sausages. Sci Alim 19:247–254, 1999.

122. V Moreno-Arribas, S Torlois, A Joyeux, A Bertrand, A Lonvaud-Funel. Isolation, properties and behaviour of tyramine-producing lactic acid bacteria from wine. J Appl Microbiol 88:584–593, 2000.

123. T Motyl, T Ploszaj, A Wojtasik, W Kukulska, M Podgurniak. Polyamines in cow's and sow's milk. Comp Biochem Physiol 111B(3):427–433, 1995.

124. T Nagatsu. Application of high performance liquid chromatography to the study of biogenic amine-related enzymes. J Chromatogr 566(2):287–307, 1991.

125. GB Neurath, M Dunger, FG Pein, D Ambrosius, O Schreiber. Primary and secondary amines in the human environment. Food Cosmet Toxicol 15:275–282, 1977.

126. MJR Nout. Fermented foods and food safety. Food Res Int 27:291–298, 1994.

127. S Novella-Rodríguez, MT Veciana-Nogués, AJ Trujillo-Mesa, MC Vidal-Carou. Profile of biogenic amines in goat cheese made from pasteurized and pressurized milks. J Food Sci 67(8):2940–2944, 2002.

128. S Novella-Rodríguez, MT Veciana-Nogués, MC Vidal-Carou. Biogenic amines and polyamines in milks and cheeses by ion-pair high performance liquid chromatography. J Agric Food Chem 48(11):5117–5123, 2000.

129. H Ohta, K-I Yoza, Y Takeda, Y Nogata. Influence of storage temperature on the polyamine levels and ethylene production in broccoli (*Brassica oleracea*, Itálica group). Biosci Biotech Biochem 57(5):831–832, 1993.

130. A Okamoto, E Sugi, Y Koizumi, F Yanagida, S Udaka. Polyamine content of ordinary foodstuffs and various fermented foods. Biosci Biotech Biochem 61(9):1582–1584, 1997.

131. CS Ough. Measurement of histamine in California wines. J Agric Food Chem 19(2):241–244, 1971.

132. P Paulsen, F Bauer. Biogenic amines in fermented sausages. 2. Factors influencing the formation of biogenic amines in fermented sausages. Fleisch Int (4):32–34, 1997.

133. KD Petridis, H Steinhart. Biogenic amines in hard cheese production. I. Factors influencing the biogenic amine content in end-product by way of Swiss cheese. Deuts Lebensm-Rundsch 92:114–120, 1996.

134. P Pietrangeli, B Mondovi. Amine oxidases and tumours. NeuroToxicol 25(1–2):317–324, 2004.

135. T Ponappa, JC Scheerens, AR Miller. Vacuum infiltration of polyamines increases firmness of strawberry slices under various storage conditions. J Food Sci 58:361–364, 1993.

136. RJ Price, EF Melvin, JW Bell. Post mortem changes in chilled round, bled, and dressed albacore. J Food Sci 56:318–321, 1991.

137. V Quemener, Y Blanchard, L Chamaillard, R Havouis, B Cipolla, JP Moulinoux. Polyamine deprivation: a new tool in cancer treatment. Anticancer Res 14:443–448, 1994.

138. F Radler, KP Fath. Histamine and other biogenic amines in wines. In JM Rantz. Proceed Int Symp Nitrogen Grape Wine. Am Soc Enol Vitic. Davis, California 185–195, 1991.

139. SL Rice, RR Eitenmiller, PE Koehler. Biologically active amines in food: a review. J Milk Food Technol 39:353–358, 1976.

140. SL Rice, PE Koehler. Tyrosine and histidine decarboxylase activities of *Pediococcus cerevisiae* and *Lactobacillus* species and the production of tyramine in

fermented sausage. J Milk Food Technol 39(3):166–169, 1976.

141. SDC Rodríguez, B López, AR Chaves. Changes in polyamines and ethylene during the development and ripening of eggplant fruits (*Solanum melongena*). J Agric Food Chem 47:1431–1434, 1999.

142. JJ Rodríguez-Jerez, EI Lopez-Sabater, MM Hernández-Herrero, MT Mora-Ventura. Histamine, putrescine and cadaverine formation in Spanish semipreserved anchovies as affected by time/temperature. J Food Sci 59(5):993–997, 1994.

143. AX Roig-Sagués, MM Hernández-Herrero, JJ Rodríguez-Jerez, EJ Quinto-Fernández, MT Mora-Ventura. Aminas biogenas en queso: riesgo toxicologico y factores que influyen en su formacion. Alimentaria 98(294):59–66, 1998.

144. AX Roig-Sagués, MM Hernández-Herrero, EI Lopez-Sabater, JJ Rodríguez-Jerez, MT Mora-Ventura. Histidine decarboxylase activity of bacteria isolated from raw and ripened salsichón, a Spanish cured sausage. J Food Prot 59(5):516–520, 1996.

145. AX Roig-Sagués, MM Hernández-Herrero, JJ Rodríguez-Jerez, EI Lopez-Sabater, MT Mora-Ventura. Histidine decarboxylase activity of *Enterobacter cloacae* S15/19 during production of ripened sausages and its influence on the formation of cadaverine. J Food Prot 60(4):430–432, 1997.

146. GC Rollan, E Coton, A Lounvaud-Funel. Histidine decarboxylase activity of *Leuconostoc oenos* 9204. Food Microbiol 12:455–461, 1995.

147. N Romain, G Dandrifosse, F Jeusette, P Forget. Polyamine concentration in rat milk and food, human milk and infant formulas. Pediat Res 32(1):58–63, 1992.

148. J Sanguansermsri, P Gyorgy, F Zilliken. Polyamines in human and cow's milk. Am J Clin Nutr 27:859–865, 1974.

149. WC Santos, MR Souza, MMOP Cerqueira, MBA Glória. Bioactive amines formation in milk by *Lactococcus* in the presence or not of rennet and NaCl at 20 and 32°C. Food Chem 81:595–606, 2003.

150. PL Saraiva. Proteólise e aminas bioativas em leite resfriado inoculado com *Pseudomonas fluorescens*. MSc dissertation, Universidade Federal de Minas Gerais, Belo Horizonte, MG, Brazil, 2003.

151. A Sass-Kiss, E Szerdahelyi, G Hajós. Study of biologically active amines in grape and wines by HPLC. Chromatographia Suppl 51:S316–S320, 2000.

152. A Scoging. Scombrotoxic (histamine) fish poisoning in the United Kingdom: 1987–1996. Commun Dis Pub Health 1(3):204–205, 1998.

153. M Sebela, Z Lamplot, M Petrivalsky, D Kopecny, K Lemr, I Frébort, P Pec. Recent news related to substrates and inhibitors of plant amine oxidases. Biochim Biophys Acta 1647:355–360, 2003.

154. N Senanayake, S Vyravanathan. Histamine reactions due to ingestion of tuna fish (*Thunnus argentivittatus*) in patients on anti-tuberculosis therapy. Toxicon 19:184–185, 1981.

155. M Serrano, MC Martínez-Madrid, F Riquelme, F Romojaro. Endogenous levels of polyamines and abscisic acid in pepper fruits during growth and ripening. Physiol Plant 95:73–76, 1995.

156. M Serrano, MT Pretel, MC Martínez-Madrid, F Romojaro, F Riquelme. CO_2 treatment of zucchini squash reduces chilling-induced physiological changes. J Agric Food Chem 46:2465–2468, 1998.

157. AR Shalaby. Changes in biogenic amines in mature and germinating legume seeds and their behavior during cooking. Nahrung 44:23–27, 2000.

158. AR Shalaby. Significance of biogenic amines to food safety and human health. Food Res Int 29(7):675–690, 1996.

159. MH Silla-Santos. Amino acid decarboxylase capability of microorganisms isolated in Spanish fermented meat products. Int J Food Microbiol 39:227–230, 1998.

160. MH Silla-Santos. Biogenic amines: their importance in foods. Int J Food Microbiol 29:213–231, 1996.

161. CMG Silva, MBA Glória. Bioactive amines in chicken breast and thigh after slaughter and during storage at $4 \pm 1°C$ and in chicken-based meat products. Food Chem 78:241–248, 2002.

162. L Simon-Sarkadi, WH Holzapfel. Biogenic amines and microbial quality of sprouts. Z Lebensm Unters Forsch 200:261–265, 1995.

163. L Simon-Sarkadi, WH Holzapfel. Determination of biogenic amines in leafy vegetables by amino acid analyzer. Z Lebensm Unters Forsch 198:230–233, 1994.

164. L Simon-Sarkadi, WH Holzapfel, A Halasz. Biogenic amine content and microbial contamination of leafy vegetable during storage at 5°C. J Food Biochem 17:407–418, 1994.

165. TA Smith. Amines in food. Food Chem 6:169–200, 1980–1981.

166. TA Smith. Amines. In: PK Stumpf, EE Conn. eds. The Biochemistry of Plants. New York: Academic Press, pp. 249–268, 1981.

167. TA Smith. Phenethylamine and related compounds in plants. Phytochemistry 16:9–18, 1977.

168. TA Smith. Polyamines. Ann Rev Plant Physiol 36:117–143, 1985.

169. C Somavilla, F Bravo, B Inigro, P Burdaspal. Histaminogénesis. IV. Acumulación de histamina en medios naturales y seme-sintéticos. Alimentaria 2:37–42, 1986

170. E Soufleros, ML Barrios, A Bertrand. Correlation between the content of biogenic amines and other wine compounds. Am J Enol Vitic 49(3):266–278, 1998.

171. SC Souza, KH Theodoro, ÉR Souza, S Motta, MBA Glória. Bioactive amines in Brazilian wines: Types, levels and correlation with physico-chemical parameters. Braz Arch Biol Technol 48:53–62, 2005.

172. MFV Starling. Perfil e teores de aminas biogênicas em hortaliças. MSc Dissertation, Universidade Federal de Minas Gerais, Belo Horizonte, MG, Brazil, 1998.

173. JE Stratton, RW Hutkins, SL Taylor. Biogenic amines in cheese and other fermented foods: a review. J Food Prot 54:460–470, 1991.

174. BW Straub, M Kicherer, SM Schilcher, WP Hammes. The formation of biogenic amines by fermentation organisms. Z Lebensm Unters Forsch 201(1):79–82, 1995.

175. SS Sumner, F Roche, SL Taylor. Factors controlling histamine production in Swiss cheese inoculated with *Lactobacillus buchneri*. J Dairy Sci 73:3050–3058, 1990.

176. SAN Tailor, KI Shulman, SE Walker, J Moss, D Gardner. Hypertensive episode associated with phenelzine and tap beer – a reanalysis of the role of pressor amines in beer. J Clin Psychopharmacol 14:5–14, 1994.

177. SL Taylor. Histamine food poisoning: toxicology and clinical aspects. CRC Crit Rev Toxicol 17:91–121, 1986.

178. SL Taylor, LS Guthertz, M Leatherwood, F Tillman, ER Lieber. Histamine production by food-borne bacterial species. J Food Saf 1:173–187, 1978.

179. SL Taylor, JY Hui, DE Lyons. Toxicology of scombroid poisoning. In EP Ragelis. ed. Seafood Toxins. American Chemical Society, Washington, D.C., 417–429, 1984.

180. SL Taylor, TJ Keefe, ES Windham, JF Howell. Outbreak of histamine poisoning associated with the consumption of Swiss cheese. J Food Prot 45(5):455–457, 1982.

181. SL Taylor, ER Lieber. In vitro inhibition of rat intestinal histamine-metabolizing enzymes. Food Cosmet Toxicol 17:237–240, 1979.

182. SL Taylor, MW Speckhard. Inhibition of bacterial histamine production by sorbate and other antimicrobial agents. J Food Prot 47(7):508–511, 1984.

183. SL Taylor, SS Sumner. Determination of histamine, putrescine and cadaverine. In: DE Kramers, eds. J Liston. Seafood quality determination. Elsevier, Amsterdam, 235–245, 1986.

184. SL Taylor, NA Woychik. Simple medium for assessing quantitative production of histamine by *Enterobacteriaceae*. J Food Prot 45(8):747–751, 1982.

185. B Ten Brink, C Damink, HM Joosten, JHJ Huis Int Veld. Occurrence and formation of biologically active amines in foods. Int Food Microbiol 11:73–84, 1990.

186. HP Til, HE Falke, MK Prinsen, MI Willems. Acute and subacute toxicity of tyramine, spermidine, spermine, putrescine and cadaverine in rats. Food Chem Toxicol 35:337–348, 1997.

187. A Toumadje, DG Richardson. Endogenous polyamine concentrations during development, storage and ripening of pear fruits. Phytochemistry 27(2):335–338, 1988.

188. S Udenfriend, W Lovenberg, A Sjoerdsma. Physiologically active amines in common fruits and vegetables. Arch Biochem Biophys 85:487–490, 1959.

189. S Vale, MBA Glória. Biogenic amines in Brazilian cheeses. Food Chem 63(3):343–348, 1998.

190. D Valero, D Martínez-Romero, M Serrano, F Riquelme. Postharvest gibberellin and heat treatment effects on polyamines, abscisic acid and firmness in lemons. J Food Sci 63(4):611–615, 1998.

191. D Valero, M Serrano, D Martínez-Romero, F Riquelme. Polyamines, ethylene and physicochemical changes in low-temperature-stored peach (*Prunus persica* L. Cv May-crest). J Agric Food Chem 45:3406–3410, 1997.

192. K Valsamaki, A Michaelidou, A Polychroniadou. Biogenic amine production in Feta cheese. Food Chem 71:259–266, 2000.

193. MC Vasconcelos-Neto. Características físico-químicas, microbiológicas e aminas bioativas na carne suína. MSc

194. M.B Vazquez-Lasa, M Iniguez-Crespo, M González-Larraina, A González-Guerrero. Biogenic amines in Rioja wines. Am J Enol Vitic 49(3):229, 1998.

195. MT Veciana-Nogués, A Mariné-Font, MC Vidal-Carou. Biogenic amines as hygienic quality indicators of tuna. Relationships with microbial counts, ATP-related compounds, volatile amines and organoleptic changes. J Agric Food Chem 45:2036–2041, 1997.

196. MT Veciana-Nogués, MC Vidal-Carou, A Mariné-Font. Histamine and tyramine during storage and spoilage of anchovies, *Engraulis encrasicholus*: relationships with other fish spoilage indicators. J Food Sci 55(4):1192–1193, 1195, 1990.

197. G Vetorazzi. 5-Hydroxytryptamine content of bananas and banana products. Food Cosmet Toxicol 12:107–113, 1974.

198. MC Vidal-Carou, ML Izquierdo-Pulido, A Mariné-Font. Histamine and tyramine in Spanish wines: their formation during the wine making process. Am J Enol Vitic 41:160–167, 1990.

199. VS Vieira. Aminas bioativas, atividade enzimática e influência de 1–metilciclopropeno e benziladenina em couve minimamente processada. MSc Dissertation. Universidade Federal de Minas Gerais, Belo Horizonte, MG, Brazil, 2003.

200. SM Vieira, J Tavares-Neto, FB Custodio, MBA Glória. Aminas bioativas em sucos e refrigerantes de laranja – estudos preliminares. XVIII Congresso Brasileiro de Ciência e Tecnologia de Alimentos 1277–1280, 2002.

201. MN Voigt, RR Eitenmiller. Production of tyrosine and histidine decarboxylase by dairy-related bacteria. J Food Prot 40(4):241–245, 1977.

202. DR Walters. Polyamines and plant disease. Phytochemistry 64(1):97–107, 2003.

203. CY Wang, ZL Ji. Effect of low oxygen storage on chilling injury and polyamines in zucchini squash. Sci Hort 39:1–7, 1989.

204. SY Wang, L Steffens. Effect of paclobutrazol on water stress-induced ethylene biosynthesis and polyamine accumulation in apple seedling leaves. Phytochemistry 24(10):2185–2190, 1985.

205. CY Wang, WS Conway, JA Abbott, GF Kramer, CE Sams. Postharvest infiltration of polyamines and calcium influences ethylene production and texture changes in Golden Delicious apples. J Am Soc Hort Sci 118:801–806, 1993.

206. LC Wang, BW Thomas, K Warner, WJ Wolf, WF Kwolek. Apparent odor thresholds of polyamines in water and 2% soybean flour dispersions. J Food Sci 40:274, 1975.

207. CI Wei, CM Chen, JA Koburger, WS Otwell, MR Marshall. Bacterial growth and histamine production on vacuum packaged tuna. J Food Sci 55(1):59–63, 1990.

208. CN Wendakoon, M Murata, M Sakaguchi. Comparison of non-volatile amine formation between the dark and white muscles of mackerel during storage. Nippon Suisan Gakkaishi 56(5):809–818, 1990.

209. CN Wendakoon, M Sakaguchi. Combined effect of sodium chloride and clove on growth and biogenic

dissertation, Universidade Federal de Minas Gerais, Belo Horizonte, MG, Brazil, 2003.

amine formation of *Enterobacter aerogenes* in mackerel muscle extract. J Food Sci 56(5):410–413, 1993.

210. TA Wheaton, I Stewart. The distribution of tyramine, N-methyltyramine, hordenine octopamine and synephrine in higher plants. Lloydia 33(2):244–254, 1970.

211. MV White. The role of histamine in allergic diseases. J Allergy Clin Immunol 86:599–605, 1990.

212. WHO. WHO Surveillance Programme for Control of Foodborne Infections and Intoxications in Europe. 7th Report. Country Reports. www.bgvv.de/internet/ 7threport-fr.htm (accessed in September, 2003).

213. M Windholz. ed. The Merck Index: An Encyclopedia of Chemicals, Drugs, and Biologicals, 12a ed. Rahway, NJ: Merck, 1996, 2066 pp.

214. DH Yoshinaga, HA Frank. Histamine-producing bacteria in decomposing skipjack tuna (*Katsuwonus pelamis*). Appl Environm Microbiol 44(2):447–452, 1982.

215. JA Zee, RE Simard, M Desmarais. Biogenic amines in Canadian, American and European beers. Can Inst Food Sci Technol J 14:119–122, 1981.

216. JA Zee, RE Simard, L Heureux. Biogenic amines in wines. Am J Enol Vitic 34:6–9, 1983.

14 Pigments in Plant Foods

JaeHwan Lee
Department of Food Science and Technology, Seoul National University of Technology

Steven J. Schwartz
Department of Food Science and Technology, The Ohio State University

CONTENTS

I. INTRODUCTION

The appearance of foods, especially color, is one of the major contributors to consumers' food choices. Color level also influences the sweetness and flavor of foods (1–3). Pigments in plants are responsible for the coloration of fruits and vegetables. Naturally occurring pigments from plants are generally considered safe due to their presence in edible plant materials and are exempt from the toxicological testing that synthetic dyes must undergo. Consumers' preferences are shifting from synthetic food dyes to natural food colorants due to a perceived health concern and potential health benefit of some pigments: β-carotene is a nutrient precursor of vitamin A, chlorophyll derivatives are potential chemo preventatives, lycopene is associated with decreasing the risk of several types of cancer, and phenolic anthocyanins in wines have been implicated in reducing heart disease (4, 5).

Color perception of food is the result of the pigments' ability to reflect or emit the electromagnetic spectrum of light energy and stimulate the retina in eye. The majority four pigments from plant foods can be classified into four groups depending on their structures: chlorophylls (tetrapyrroles), carotenoids (tetraterpenoids), anthocyanins (*O*-heterocyclic), and betalains (*N*-heterocyclic) (4, 6). Generally, chlorophylls and carotenoids are lipid-soluble pigments and flavonoids and betalains are water-soluble pigments (2). Chlorophylls are green pigments ubiquitously found in photosynthetic tissues of higher plants. Carotenoids are a large group of compounds that provide yellow to red coloration in plants. Flavonoids, especially anthocyanins, provide red, blue, and violet colors of many fruits and vegetables. Betalains are responsible for the red and yellow colors in beef root and amaranth (4, 7).

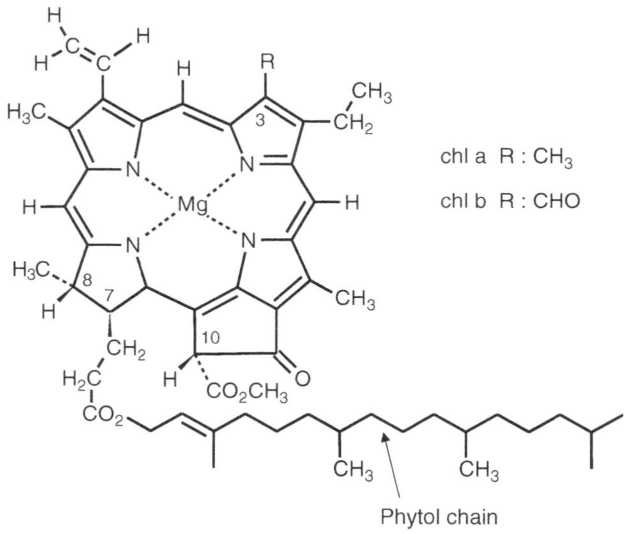

II. CHLOROPHYLL

Chlorophylls are present in green plants capable of photosynthesis. Chlorophylls are the most abundant pigments among biologically produced pigments (8, 9). In foods, chlorophylls are widely distributed in green leafy edible plants and vegetables.

A. STRUCTURES OF PIGMENT AND ITS DERIVATIVES

Chlorophylls are derived from porphyrin complexed with magnesium. The porphyrin ring is a fully unsaturated and conjugated macrocyclic structure with tetrapyrrole units in which the pyrrole rings are joined by methylene bridges. Several chlorophylls are found in plants. Chlorophyll *a* (blue-green) and *b* (yellow-green) are present in green plants in the ratio of 3:1 (Figure 14.1). The magnesium in chlorophylls can be removed easily by acids and chlorophyll *a* and *b* form pheophytins *a* and *b* (olive-brown color), respectively. Hydrolysis of the phytol side chain forms the water-soluble chlorophyllide derivative. Both the removal of phytol group and magnesium can generate pheophorbide, which is also water soluble (Figure 14.2) (4, 7, 10). The C10 carbomethoxy groups (CO_2CH_3) of pheophytins and pheophorbide can be removed by thermal processing and pyropheophytin and pyropheophorbide are formed, respectively (Figure 14.2).

B. CHEMICAL PROPERTIES

1. Thermal Processing

Thermal processing can isomerize the C10 carbomethoxy groups (CO_2CH_3) of chlorophyll *a* and *b*, and produce chlorophyll *a'* and *b'*, respectively (11). The colors of epimers are the same as that of parent chlorophylls due to their identical spectral properties. Thermal processing enhances removal of Mg in the tetrapyrrole center in weakly acidic conditions forming the olive-brown colored pheophytins. Chlorophyll *b* is more stable to thermal processing than chlorophyll *a* due to the electron withdrawing effects of its C3 formyl group. Thermal degradation of chlorophylls in vegetable tissue is affected by pH. In alkaline condition (pH 9.0), chlorophyll is stable to

FIGURE 14.1 The structure of chlorophyll *a* and *b*.

chl a   R : CH₃

chl b   R : CHO

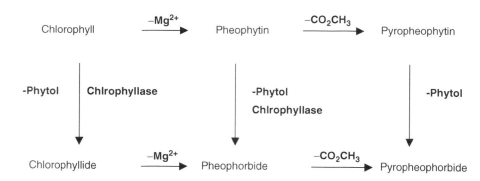

FIGURE 14.2 Reaction of chlorophylls and derivatives.

heat treatment while it is unstable in acidic condition (pH 3.0). Thermal processing for chlorophylls is sequential: Chlorophyll changes to pheophytin by first removing Mg and finally to pyropheophytin by loss of the C10 carbomethoxy groups (12). Canned products of vegetables contain mainly pheophytin and pyropheophytin, which are responsible for the olive-brown color in many canned vegetables (11, 12).

2. Allomerization

Chlorophylls in alcohol or other solvents exposed to oxygen can be oxidized and produce blue-green color compounds, which is called allomerization. The major allomerization products are 10-hydroxychlorophyll and 10-methoxylactones. The main allomerization product of chlorophyll *b* is 10-methoxylactones (8, 13).

3. Photodegradation

Chlorophylls in plant tissue are protected from degradation during photosynthesis when located within the plant matrix. However, when exposed to light chlorophylls in solution are light sensitive and degrade into colorless chlorophyll derivatives. It is believed that photodegradation of chlorophylls is due to the opening of tetrapyrrole rings and fragmentations of chlorophylls into small molecules (14). Chlorophylls are well-known photosensitizers, which can be excited by light absorption and generate many reactive oxygen species, including hydroxyl radicals and singlet oxygen. Singlet oxygen and hydroxyl radicals can react with the tetrapyrrole ring of chlorophylls and produce peroxides and more free radicals, which eventually degrade chlorophylls into colorless photodegradation products (7, 15).

4. Enzymatic Decomposition

Chlorophyllase is an esterase and can catalyze the removal of the phytol group from chlorophylls and pheophytins to form chlorophyllides and pheophorbies, respectively (Figure 14.2). Chlorophyllase can be active only on porphyrins with a C10 carbomethoxy group (CO_2CH_3) and hydrogens at the C7 and C8 positions (16). The activity of chlorophyllase is optimum at the temperature between 40°C and 82°C (7, 17) and some mild heat treatment can activate the chlorophyllase enzyme (18). Chlorophyllase in vegetable tissue loses its activity when vegetables are heated over 100°C.

C. Physical Properties

Chlorophyll is located in chloroplasts of green plants. Approximate chlorophyll contents of selected green vegetables are shown in Table 14.1. Due to the biological variability and differences among varieties, chlorophyll content in Table 14.1 should be used as a general guide (18). Chlorophylls can absorb visible light between 600 and 700 nm (red region) and between 400 and 500 nm (blue region). Depending on the presence of the metal atom in the tetrapyrrole center, the color of chlorophylls can change. Replacement of magnesium with Sn^{2+} and Fe^{3+} give a grayish-brown color while copper and zinc ions retain a green color (10). The stability of chlorophylls can be increased by substituting magnesium with copper. Copper chlorophyll complexes have better stability to oxygen, light, and alkaline conditions. Chlorophylls in leaves are broken down during senescence. Chlorophylls in fruits are often present in an unripe state such as in tomatoes and gradually disappear during ripening (19). In

TABLE 14.1
Approximate Chlorophyll Content in Selected Vegetables

| Vegetables | | Chlorophyll Content (µg/g plant tissue) | | |
		a	*b*	Total
Spinach	Fresh tissue	1380	440	1576
	Dry tissue	6980	2490	
	Canned-dry tissue	830 (Phe *a*) 4000 (Pyro *a*)		
Peas	Fresh tissue	106	12	
	Dry tissue	34 (Phe *a*) 33 (Pyro *a*)	13 (Phe *b*) 12 (Pyro *b*)	
Lettuce	Fresh tissue	334	62	
Kale	Fresh tissue	1370	464	1870
Celery	Leaves-fresh tissue	1143	225	
	Stalk—fresh tissue	29	7	
Asparagus	Fresh tissue	139	74	180–300
	Dry tissue	180 (Phe *a*) 110 (Pyro *a*)	51 (Phe *b*) 30 (Pyro *b*)	
Beans	Fresh tissue	54	17	
	Dry tissue		230–870	
	Canned-Dry tissue	340 (Phe *a*) 260 (Pyro *a*)	180 (Phe *b*) 95 (Pyro *b*)	

Chl = Chlorophyll, Phe = Pheophytin, Pyro = Pyropheophytin.
Adapted from Ferruzzi and Schwartz (18).

Europe, copper chlorophyll derivatives have been used as colorants in sugar confectionary, ice cream, dessert mixes, and cheeses with a combination of other colorants while in the U.S. the use of the derivatives is limited toothpaste and tooth powder (9).

III. CAROTENOIDS

Carotenoids are the most widely distributed pigments in nature with over 700 carotenoids identified. Carotenoids are located in the chloroplasts of plants and often masked by more dominant chlorophyll pigments. In humans, some carotenoids can act as precursors of vitamin A and have been associated with biological activities to inhibit specific chronic diseases (7, 20).

A. STRUCTURES OF PIGMENT AND ITS DERIVATIVES

Carotenoids are a group of tetraterpenoids. The basic carotenoid structural backbone consists of isoprenoid units formed either by head-to-tail or by tail-to-tail biosynthesis. There are primarily two classes of carotenoids: carotenes and xanthophylls. Carotenes are hydrocarbon carotenoids and xanthophylls contain oxygen in the form of hydroxyl, methoxyl, carboxyl, keto, or epoxy groups. Lutein in green leaves and zeaxanthin in corn are typical xanthophylls. The structures of carotenoids are acyclic, monocyclic, or bicyclic. For example, lycopene is acyclic, γ-carotene is monocyclic, and α- and β-carotenes are bicyclic carotenoids (4). Double bonds in carotenoids are conjugated forms and usually the all *trans* forms of carotenoids are found in plant tissues (Figure 14.3).

Carotenoids are distributed in a wide range of fruits and vegetables containing chlorophyll pigments. The most common carotenoid in plant tissue is β-carotene, which exhibits a yellow color. Tomatoes (lycopene), carrots (α- and β-carotenes), pumpkin (β-carotenes), corn (lutein and zeaxanthin), and sweet potatoes (β-carotenes) are other typical examples. Annatto, which is the seed of the tropical bush *Bixa orellana*, is in the class of carotenoids and has a yellow to orange color. The major coloring annatto pigment is *cis*-bixin used in dairy products such as cheese (7) (Figure 14.3).

B. CHEMICAL PROPERTIES

1. Thermal Processing

Carotenoids are relatively stable during typical thermal processing. However, severe heat treatment can induce isomerization of carotenoids and even fragmentation of carotenoids into volatile compounds. Isomerization of carotenoids can be induced by heat, acid, or light.

2. Oxidation

Carotenoids are easily oxidized due to the presence of conjugated double bonds in molecules. In the case of β-carotene, epoxides and carbonyl compounds are first formed. Further oxidation results in the formation of short-chain mono- and deoxygenated compounds including epoxy-β-ionone. Extensive oxidation causes the loss of color in carotenoids (4, 7).

3. Enzyme Effects

Lipoxygenase indirectly accelerates the oxidation of carotenoids and loss of pigments. Lipoxygenase first catalyzes the formation of peroxides of unsaturated double bonds in fatty acids and the generated peroxides of fatty acids react with carotenoids. The coupled reactions are efficient enough to be used for measuring the activity of lipoxygenase in plant tissue (21).

C. PHYSICAL PROPERTIES

Red, yellow, and orange fruits, root crops, and vegetables are rich in carotenoids. The color of carotenoids ranges from yellow to red depending on the number of conjugated double bonds. Carotenoids show three distinct maxima in the visible spectrum (Table 14.2) (10). The absorption of light of carotenoids is between 430 and 480 nm. A minimum of 7 conjugated double bonds is needed to produce the characteristic yellow color. Currently β-carotene, β-apo-8′-carotenal, and canthaxanthin have been synthesized and used in food industry. Carotenoids from plant extracts and/or individual compounds have been used to impart a color to foods products, including margarine, ice cream, cheese products, beverages, and bakery products (22).

D. NUTRITIONAL AND FUNCTIONAL PROPERTIES

1. Nutritional Effects

Carotenoids can serve as precursors of provitamin A. Provitamin A activity requires that the carotenoids possess a retinoid structure (β-ionone ring). β-Carotene possesses the highest provitamin A activity due to the two β-ionone rings in the structures (Figure 14.4). *Cis* forms of carotenoids have been reported to decrease provitamin A activity (23).

2. Antioxidant Effects

Carotenoids are known to serve as efficient singlet oxygen quenchers and free radical scavengers due to the many double bonds in the molecule. As the number of double bonds increases in carotenoids, the singlet oxygen quenching ability increases (20, 24). However, some carotenoids, such as β-carotene, may act as either an antioxidant or prooxidant depending on the conditions, especially oxygen concentration (20).

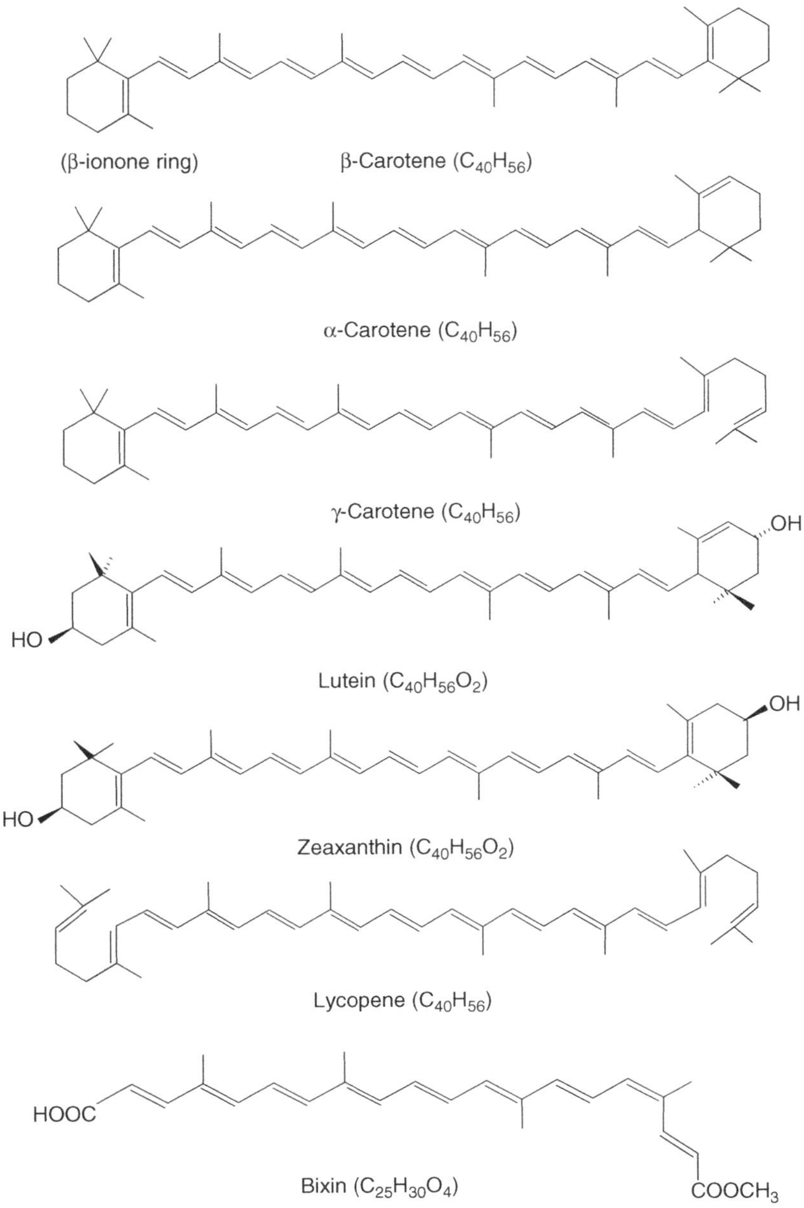

FIGURE 14.3 Structures of carotenoids.

TABLE 14.2
Absorption Wavelength Maxima for some Carotenoids

Compounds	Conjugated Double Bonds	Wavelength, nm (in petroleum ether)		
A. Effects of the number of conjugated double bonds				
Phytoene	3	275	285	296
Phytofluence	5	331	348	367
ξ-Carotene	7	378	400	425
Neurosporene	9	416	440	470
Lycopene	11	446	472	505
B. Effects of the ring structure				
γ-Carotene	11	431	462	495
β-Carotene	11	425	451	483

IV. FLAVONOIDS

The red and blue colors in flowers and fruits are due to the presence of flavonoid pigments especially anthocyanins. Other groups of flavonoids are responsible for the yellow or white color of flowers. Some brown or black colors in nature arise from either oxidation of flavonoids or chelation with metals (25). Flavonoids are polyphenolic compounds. Approximately 5,000 flavonoid compounds are reported in the literature (26).

A. ANTHOCYANINS

Anthocyanins are generally located in petal epidermal cells in the plant vacuoles (27). Anthocyanins give a wide

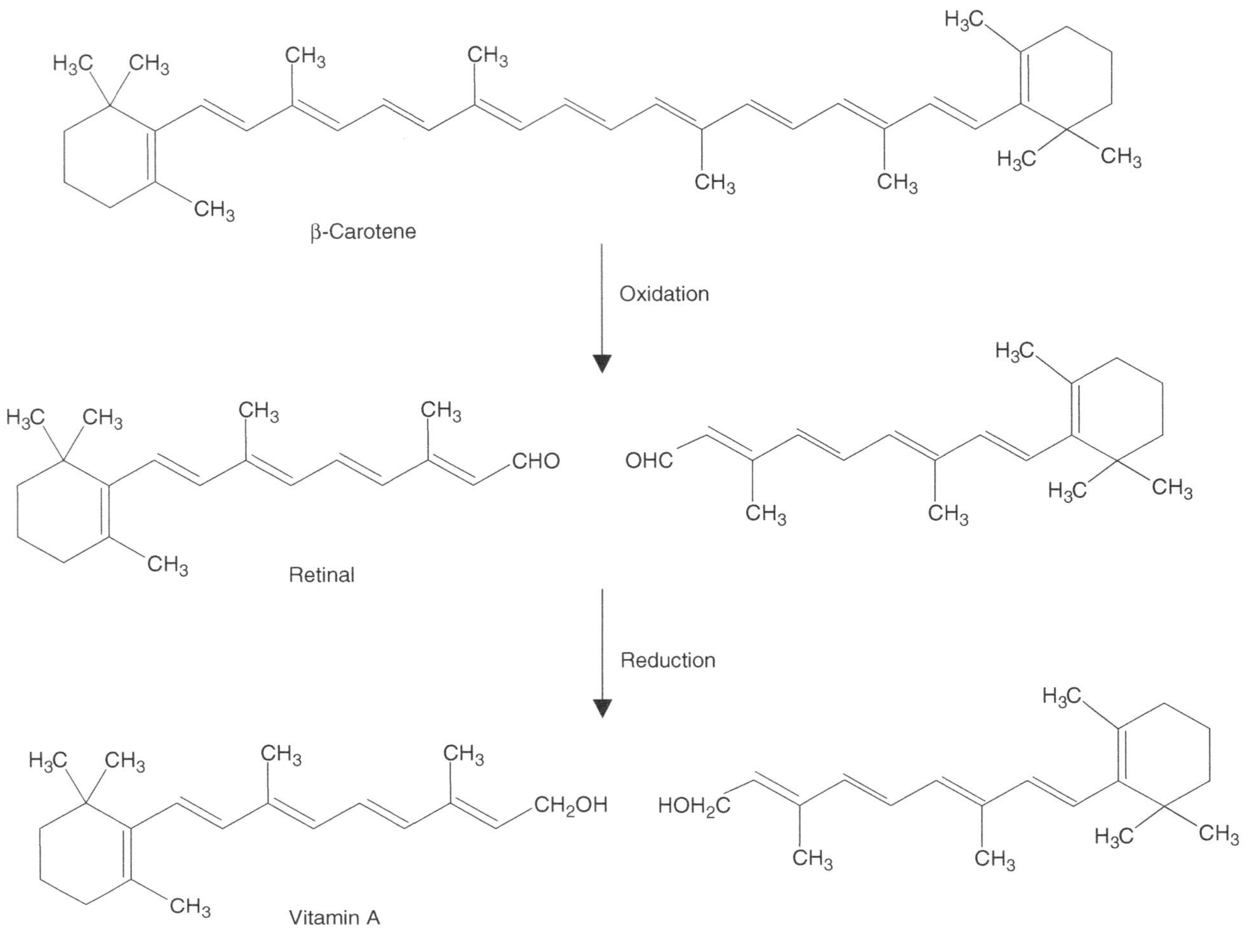

FIGURE 14.4　Formation of retinal and vitamin A from β-carotene.

range of colors with red, blue, purple, violet, magenta, and orange in many fruits and vegetables. The word anthocyanin comes from two Greek words: *anthos*, flower, and *kyanos*, blue. More than 300 anthocyanin pigments have been identified in nature (7, 26, 28).

1.　Structures of Pigment and Its Derivatives

The chemical structures of anthocyanins and flavonoids are *O*-heterocyclic compounds (Figure 14.5). The basic carbon skeleton structure of anthocyanins is $C_6C_3C_6$. Anthocyanins are present in polyhydroxy and/or polymethoxy derivatives of salts. The types of anthocyanins differ depending on the number of hydroxy or methoxy groups, the type, number, and sites of bound glycosidic sugars, and the type and number of aliphatic or aromatic acids attached to the sugars (Figure 14.6). Some anthocyanins exist complexed with metals, such as Fe, Al, and Mg (28, 29).

Anthocyanins always exist as glycosides in nature. The aglycone of anthocyanin, a sugar free form, is known as anthocyanidins. Anthocyanidins are very unstable. Glycosidic substitution of anthocyanins increases the stability and water solubility of these pigments. Common glycosidic sugars in anthocyanins are one or two molecules of

glucose, galactose, arabinose, xylose, and rhamnose. The sugar moiety is usually attached to the C3-position of the hydroxyl group. Increasing the number of sugar residues within the anthocyanin molecule tends to increase the stability. Acylation of the sugar residues in anthocyanins can also increase the stability of these pigments (26, 30). Acylated anthocyanins are highly colored above pH 4.0, while conventional anthocyanins are colorless above pH 4.0 (26). Acids found in acylated anthocyanins are cinnamic (*p*-coumaric, caffeic, ferulic) and aliphatic (malic, succinic, and acetic) acids. Only 6 anthocyanins are commonly found in foods out of known 22 aglycones, including pelargonidin, cyanidin, delphinidin, peonidin, petunidin, and malvidin (Figure 14.6) (26). As the number of hydroxyl groups of anthocyanins increases, the blue color of anthocyanins increases (pelargonidin → cyanidin → delphinidin). As the number of methoxyl group or glycoside linkages within anthocyanins increases, the red color of anthocyanins increases (cyaniding → peonidin; pelargonidin → pelargonidin-3-glucoside) (10).

2.　Chemical Properties

Anthocyanin pigments are relatively unstable and influenced mainly by pH and temperature. Other factors

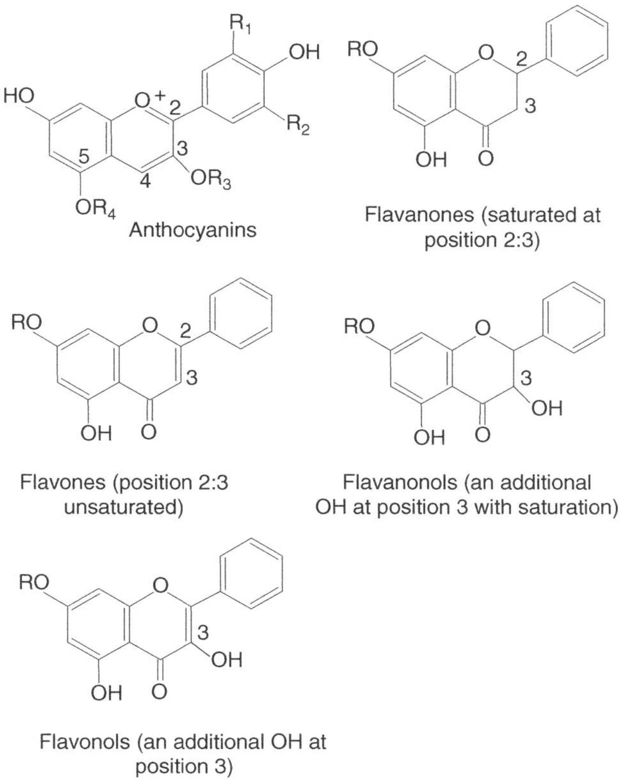

FIGURE 14.5 The chemical structures of flavonoids and anthocyanins. R_1 and $R_2 = -H$, -OH, or $-OCH_3$, $R_3 = -$ glycosyl, $R_4 = -$ glycosyl or –H.

influencing the stability of anthocyanin pigments are enzymes, oxygen concentration, ascorbic acid, sulfur dioxide, metal ions, and sugars.

The color stability of anthocyanins also depends on the substituents. Increased hydroxylation decreases stability, while methylation tends to increase pigment stability, which is due to the blocking of reactive hydroxyl groups.

a. pH effects

Color and structures of anthocyanin pigments in an aqueous medium changes depending on pH: the blue quinonoidal base, the red flavylium cation (R^+), the colorless carbinol base, and the colorless chalcone (Figure 14.7). Two compounds, red flavylium cation and colorless carbinol base, are important during pH changes from 1 to 6. At low pH, red flavylium cation dominates while at pH 4–6, the colorless carbinol base prevails. As the pH increases, the carbinol base increases and the color becomes weaker. The loss of color is due to a pH-dependent hydration at the C2 position of red flavylium cation.

$$R^+ + H_2O \leftrightarrows ROH + H^+$$

In alkali solutions (pH 8–10), highly colored ionized anhydro bases are formed. At pH 12, the fully ionized chalcones are the predominant pigments of anthocyanins. The major limitation of anthocyanin pigments as food colorants is the

reduction of color intensity, changes in hue, and instability at upper pH (31, 32). However, anthocyanins in plants have vivid color and are quite stable within the plant matrix. The color of anthocyanins in plants may be stabilized through the self association of cationic forms, copigmentation with other flavonoids, formation of metal complexes with Fe, Al or Mg, and/or intramolecular interactions between acyl groups and phenolic groups (31).

b. Thermal processing

Thermal processing may easily degrade anthocyanin pigments. Thermal processing can change the equilibrium of the four types of anthocyanins toward a colorless chalcone derivative because all the reactions are heat sensitive (31).

$$\text{Quinonoid} \leftrightarrows \text{Flavylium} \leftrightarrows \text{Carbinol base} \leftrightarrows \text{Chalcone}$$

c. Enzyme effects

Glycosidases and polyphenol oxidases can cause the loss of color from anthocyanin pigments. Glycosidases hydrolyze glycosidic linkages and produce sugars and aglycone. Anthocyanidins are less water soluble than their corresponding anthocyanins and can transform to colorless products. Polyphenol oxidase oxidizes anthocyanins in the presence of oxygen and *o*-diphenols. The enzyme first oxidizes *o*-diphenols into *o*-benzoquinone, which reacts with anthocyanins to form oxidized anthocyanins and degradation products (7, 29).

d. Other factors affecting stability of anthocyanin

Oxygen can react with double bonds of anthocyanin pigments resulting in loss of color. The color stability of anthocyanins in many fruit products, such as grape and cranberry juices, can be increased by removing oxygen using vacuum processing or adding nitrogen headspace (7, 32). It has been known that ascorbic acid and anthocyanin pigments disappear simultaneously in fruit juice. Oxidation of ascorbic acid produces hydrogen peroxide, which cleaves the pyrylium ring and produces colorless esters and coumarin derivatives (29).

Generally, light accelerates the decomposition of anthocyanin pigments especially in fruit juices and red wines. Anthocyanins with C5 hydroxyl groups are more susceptible to photodegradation than without C5 hydroxyl groups. In red wine, acylated and methylted diglycosides are more stable than nonacylated diglycosides, which are more stable than monoglycosides (26, 33, 34).

High concentrations of sugar can stabilize the anthocyanin pigments, which may be due to the lowering of water activity in the system. Water can react with flavylium cation at the C2 position and form colorless carbinol base. At low concentration of sugars, not only water but sugar itself can accelerate the degradation of anthocyanins. Brown pigments in fruit juices can be formed from anthocyanins and furfural or hydroxylmethylfurfural, which are Maillard browning reaction products (29).

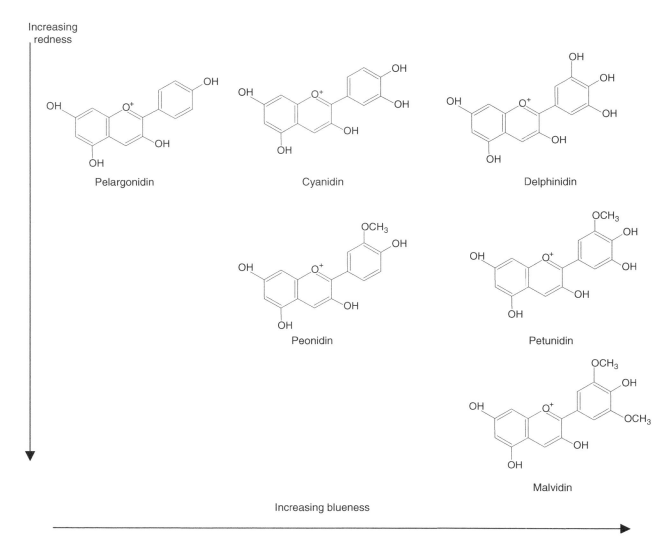

Increasing redness

Increasing blueness

FIGURE 14.6 The most common anthocyanins in foods.

Metal complexes of anthocyanins are common and stabilize the color of anthocyanin-containing foods. Metals, including Ca, Fe, Al, and Sn, have protective effects on the anthocyanin stability in cranberry juices (29). However, a fruit discoloration, or "pinking" in pears and peaches, is believed to come from a metal anthocyanin complex.

Sulfur dioxide (SO_2), an antimicrobial agent in some fruit products, can react with anthocyanins at the C4 position and produce colorless pigments. This bleaching process can be reversible by desulfuring using thorough washing procedures before further processing.

The more concentrated anthocyanins show higher stability than less concentrated pigments (26). Copigmentation of anthocyanins with other polyphenolic compounds and metal ions can improve the stability and intensity of the color (29, 35).

3. Physical Properties

The color of anthocyanins and anthocyanidins arises from the excitation of many double bonds through absorbing light energy. Anthocyanidins have two absorption maxima: one in the visible light spectrum at 500–550 nm and a second in the ultraviolet spectrum at 280 nm. Anthocyanins in selected fruits, vegetables, and food products are shown in Table 14.3.

Currently, grapes and red cabbage are commercially available major anthocyanin sources (26). Fruit juices, vegetable juices, jellies, jams, ice cream, yogurts, canned candies, and bakery fillings are the main food products where anthocyanin pigments are applied. Europe, Asia, and South America use anthocyanin pigments to a less limited extent compared to the U.S. (28).

B. OTHER FLAVONOIDS

Flavonoids include flavones, flavonols, flavanones, flavanonols, and anthocyanins, which are all based on a common structure (Figure 14.5). The flavones have a double bond between C2–C3, while flavanones are saturated at C2–C3. Flavonols possess an additional hydroxyl group at the C3 position and flavanonols are

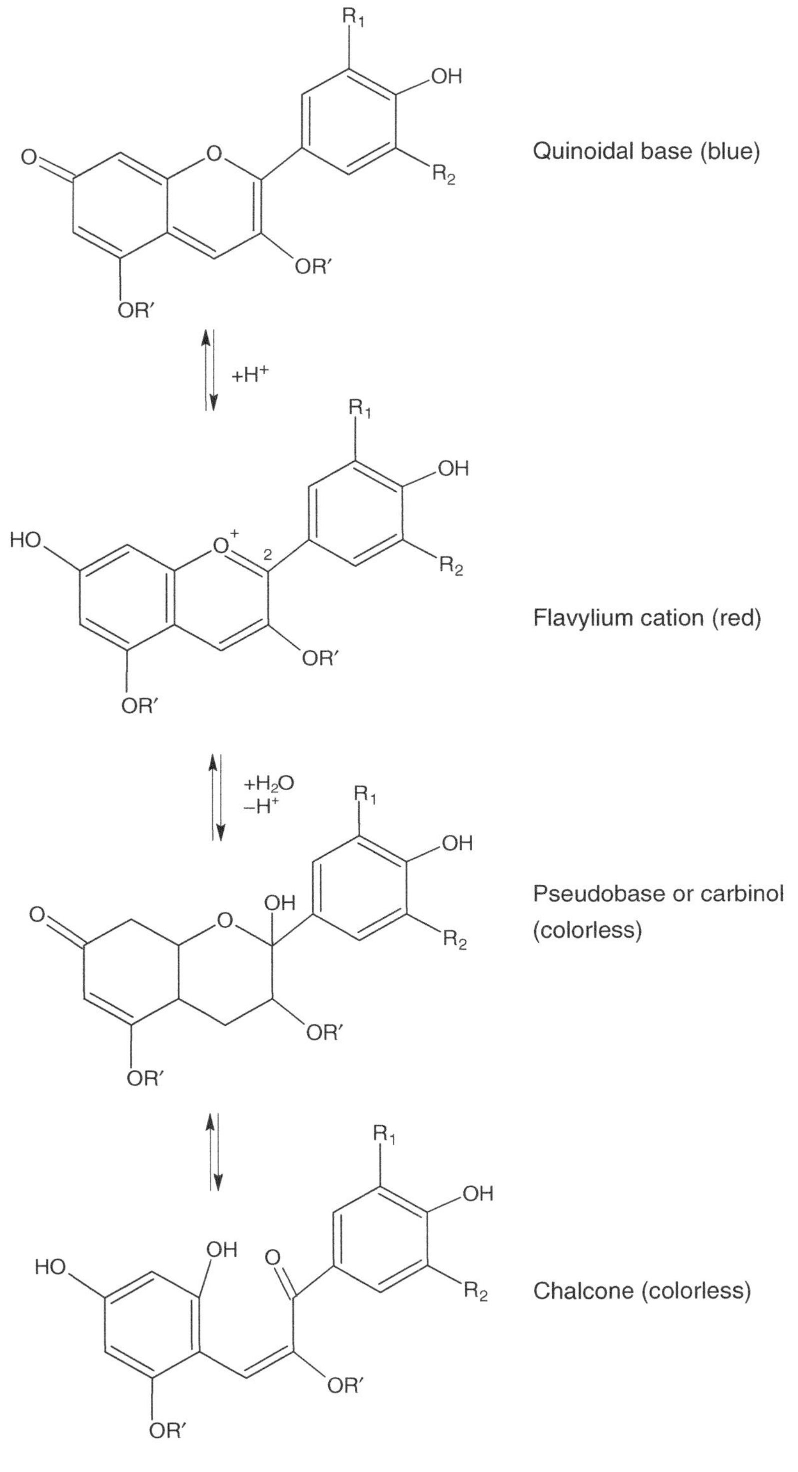

FIGURE 14.7 Structure changes of anthocyanins at 25°C with pH. R = sugar moiety.

saturated between C2 and C3 with hydroxyl group at the C3 position. Each flavonoid group is different depending on the number of hydroxyl, methoxyl, and other substituents on the two benzene rings. The most ubiquitous flavonoid is quercetin, 3, 5, 7, 3′, 4′-pentahydroxy flavone (4).

The spectral absorption of flavonoids occurs between 280 and 390 nm depending on the substituents and chelation

with metals. Metals such as iron and aluminum increase the yellow color of flavonoids. Flavonoids play important roles in the formation of color in processed foods through metal chelation and copigmentation with other pigments (35).

Tannins are water-soluble polyphenolic compounds that can react with protein and other polymers such as polysaccharides. The color of tannins ranges from

TABLE 14.3
Anthocyanins in Selected Fruits, Vegetables, and Food Products

Fruit or Vegetable	Anthocyanins
Apple	Cy-3-gal, Cy-3-ara, Cy-7-ara
Pear	Cy-3-gal
Peach	Cy-3-glc
Plum/prune	Cy-3-gal, Cy-3-rut, Peo-3-glu, Peo-3-rut
Cherry	Cy-3-sop, Cy-3-gal, Cy-3-rut, Cy-3-glc, Cy-3-glc-rut
Raspberry	Cy-3-glc, Cy-3-glc-rut, Cy-3-rut, Cy-3-sop, Cy-3-glc-sop
Strawberry	Pg-3-glc, Pg-3-gal, Cy-3-glc
Grapes	Cy-3-glc, Del-3-glc, Peo-3-glc, Pet-3-glc, Mv-3-glc, Mv-3,5-diglc
Orange	Cy-3-glc, Del-3-glc
Cabbage(red)	Cy-3-glc
Banana	Pet-3-gly
Fig	Cy-3-gly
Wines	Cy-, Del-, Peo-, Pet-, and Mv-3-glc, and 3,5-diglc
	Cy-, Del-, Peo-, and Mv acyl derivatives
Potato	Pg-, Peo-, Pet-, and MV-3-rut-5-glc-coumaric esters and Pg, Cy-, Del- and Pet-3-rut

Cy=Cyanidin, Del=Delphinidin, Mv=Malvidin, Peo=Peonidin, Pet=Petunidin, Pg=Pelargonidin, ara=arabi-
noside, gal=galactoside, glc=glucoside, gly=glycoside, rut=rutinoside, sop=sophoroside.

yellowish-white to light brown, and tannin contributes to the astringency in foods. Proanthocyanidins, condensed tannins, are colorless compounds and can convert to colored compounds during food processing. Proanthocyanidins are present in cocoa beans, apples, pears, and other fruits (36).

V. BETALAINS

Betalains are found in beetroot and amaranth, and provide red and yellow colors to these plants. The red betalains are known as betacyanins and the yellow betalains are betaxanthins. Betalains are water-soluble and located in the vacuoles of plant cells (37, 38).

A. STRUCTURES OF PIGMENT AND ITS DERIVATIVES

General structures of betalains, *N*-heterocyclic compounds, are the condensation of a primary or secondary amine with betalamic acid (Figure 14.8). Betacyanin pigments contain 1, 2, 4, 7, 7 pentasubstituted 1, 7-diazaheptamethin system and exhibit a light absorption maximum at 540 nm. Betaxanthins do not have 1, 2, 4, 7, 7 pentasubstituted 1, 7-diazaheptamethin system and the light absorption maximum is approximately 480 nm. Depending on the substituents, various betacyanins can be present such as betanidin, betanin, amaranthin, isobetanidin, isobetanin, and isoamaranthin. Isobetanidin, isobetanin, and isoamaranthin are the epimers of betanidin, betanin, amaranthin, respectively, at C15 positions (Figure 14.8). Betanin from red beet and amaranthin from amaranth are major sources of betalain pigments. Betaxanthins possess an amino acid substituents rather than the indole nucleus found in betacyanins (Figure 14.8). Indicaxanthin, vulgaxanthin-I, and vulgaxanthin-II

are betaxanthins with proline, glutamine, and glutamic acid, respectively, as the amino acid substituent. Betacyanins can be converted into betaxanthins in the presence of excessive amino acids, which indicates that betacyanins and betaxanthins are structurally related.

B. CHEMICAL PROPERTIES

1. Thermal Processing

Betanin, the major pigment found in beetroot, degrades to betalamic acid and cyclopa-5-*O*-glucoside either under mild alkaline condition, heating of alkaline solutions, or during thermal processing (Figure 14.9). This reaction requires water, indicating that water activity affects the stability of betanin in food products. Low water activity helps to retain their pigments. This reaction is reversible during thermal processing and betanin can be regenerated through Schiff-base condensation between the aldehyde group of betalamic acid and amine of cyclopa-5-*O*-glucoside. Heat treatment increases the isomerization of betanin into isobetanin (38).

2. Other Factors Affecting Betalain Stability

Betalain can be oxidized in the presence of oxygen and degrades the color of its pigments. Light exposure also accelerates the oxidation of betalain. The presence of antioxidants, such as ascorbic acid and isoascorbic acid, can improve stability (38).

C. PHYSICAL PROPERTIES

Betalain solutions show a maximum light absorbance at 537–538 nm between pH 3.5 and 7.0. Below pH 3.5,

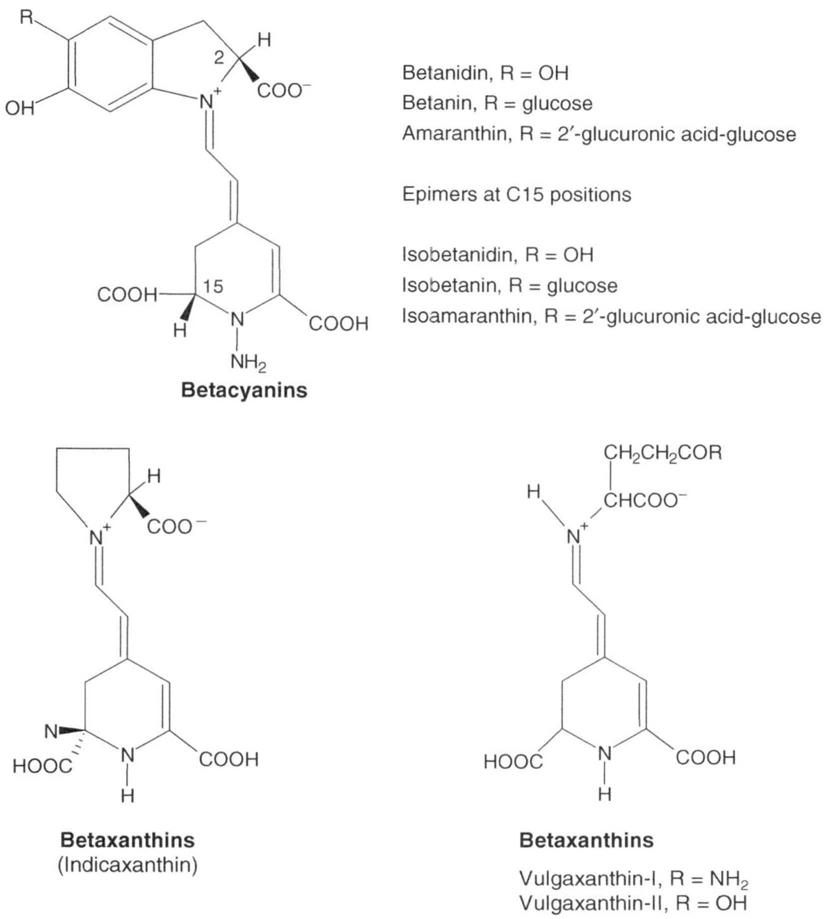

Betanidin, R = OH
Betanin, R = glucose
Amaranthin, R = 2′-glucuronic acid-glucose

Epimers at C15 positions

Isobetanidin, R = OH
Isobetanin, R = glucose
Isoamaranthin, R = 2′-glucuronic acid-glucose

Betacyanins

Betaxanthins
(Indicaxanthin)

Betaxanthins

Vulgaxanthin-I, R = NH$_2$
Vulgaxanthin-II, R = OH

FIGURE 14.8 General structures of betalaines (betacyanins and betaxanthins).

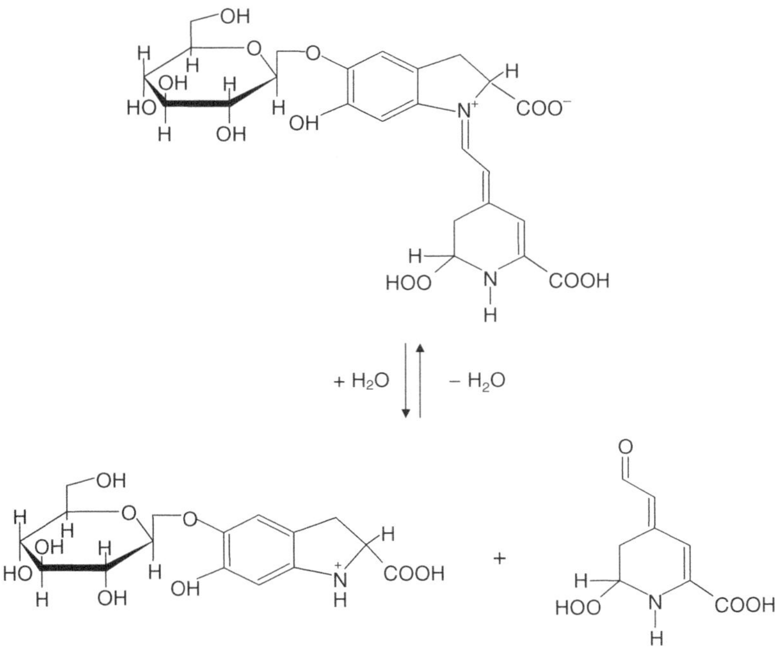

FIGURE 14.9 Betalain degradation mechanism.

maximum absorption of betalain shifts towards shorter wavelengths (535 nm at pH 2.0), while above 7.0, the maximum absorption shifts to longer wavelengths (544 nm at pH 9.0). The antioxidant effects of betalain on lipid peroxidation have been reported (39). Extracts of beetroot containing these pigments are used in foods, particularly confectionary products (29, 38).

REFERENCES

1. FJ Francis. Quality as influenced by color. Food Quality Preference 6:149–155, 1995.

2. SJ Schwartz. Pigment analysis. In: SS Nielsen. ed. Food Analysis: Introduction to Chemical Analysis of Foods. 2nd ed. Gaithersburg, MD: Aspen Publishers, 1998, pp. 261–271.

3. C Calvo, A Salvador, SM Fiszman. Influence of colour intensity on the perception of colour and sweetness in various fruit-flavoured yoghurts. Eur Food Res Tech 213:99–103, 2001.

4. JM deMan. Principles of Food Chemistry. 3rd ed. Gaithersburg, MD: Aspen Publishers, 1999, pp. 239–262.

5. ML Nguyen, SJ Schwartz. Lycopene. In: GJ Lauro, FJ Francis. eds. Natural Food Colorants. New York: Marcel Dekker, 2000, pp. 153–192.

6. GAF Hendry. Natural food colours. In: GAF Hendry, JD Houghton. eds. Natural Food Colorants. New York: AVI, 1992, pp. 1–38.

7. JV von Elbe, SJ Schwartz. Colorants. In: OR Fennema. ed. Food Chemistry. 3rd ed. New York: Marcel Dekker, 1996, pp. 651–722.

8. AH Jackson. Structure, properties and distribution of chlorophylls. In: TW Goodwin. ed. Chemistry and Biochemistry of Plant Pigments. Vol. 1. New York: Academic Press, 1976, pp. 1–63.

9. GAF Hendry. Chlorophylls. In: GJ Lauro, FJ Francis. eds. Natural Food Colorants. New York: Marcel Dekker, 2000, pp. 228–236.

10. B Grosch. Food Chemistry. Heidelberg, Germany: Springer-Verlag, 1986, pp. 569–570, 596–602.

11. SJ Schwartz, SL Woo, JH Von Elbe. High-performance liquid chromatography of chlorophylls and their derivatives in fresh and processed spinach. J Agric Food Chem 29:533–535, 1981.

12. SJ Schwartz, TV Lorenzo. Chlorophyll stability during continuous processing and storage. J Food Sci 56:1056–1062, 1991.

13. PH Hynninen. Mechanism of the allomerization of chlorophyll: inhibition of the allomerization by carotenoid pigments. Zeitschrift für Naturforschung, Teil B: Anorganische Chemie, Organische Chemie 36B, 1010–1016, 1981.

14. A Struck, E Cmiel, S Schneider, H Scheer. Photochemical ring-opening in meso-chlorinated chlorophylls. Photochemistry and Photobiology 51: 217–222, 1990.

15. CS Foote. Photosensitized oxidation and singlet oxygen: consequences in biological systems. In: WA Pryor. ed. Free Radicals in Biology. Vol. 2. New York: Academic Press, 1976, pp. 85–133.

16. RF McFeeters. Substrate specificity of chlorophyllase. Plant Physiol 158:377–381, 1975.

17. GA Martinez, PM Civello, AR Chaves, A Raquel, MC Anon. Partial characterization of chlorophyllase from strawberry fruit (Fragaria ananassa, Duch.). J Food Biochem 213–226, 1995.

18. MG Ferruzzi, SJ Schwartz. Overview of chlorophylls in foods. In: SJ Schwartz. ed. Current Protocols in Food Analytical Chemistry. New York: John Wiley & Sons, Inc, 2001, pp. F4.1.1–F4.1.9.

19. JW Heaton, AG Marangoni. Chlorophyll degradation in processed foods and senescent plant tissues. Trends in Food Sci Tech 7:8–15, 1996.

20. J Oliver, A Palou. Review: Chromatographic determination of carotenoids in foods. J Chrom A 881:543–555, 2000.

21. PM Swamy, P Suguna. Influence of calcium chloride and benzyladenine on lipoxygenase of Vigna unguiculata leaf discs during senescence. Physilogia plantarum 84:467–471, 1992.

22. G Britton. Carotenoids. In: GAF Hendry, JD Houghton. eds. Natural Food Colorants. New York: AVI, 1992, pp. 141–182.

23. T Van Vliet, F Van Schaik, WHP Schreurs, H Van den Berg. In vitro measurement of β-carotene cleavage activity: methodological considerations of the effects of other carotenoids on β-carotene cleavage. Int J Vit Nut Res 66:77–85, 1996.

24. AV Rao, S Agarwal. Role of lycopene as antioxidant carotenoid in the prevention of chronic disease: a review. Nutr Res 19:305–323, 1999.

25. T Swain. Nature and Properties of Flavonoids. In: TW Goodwin. ed. Chemistry and Biochemistry of Plant Pigments. Vol. 1. New York: Academic Press, 1976, pp. 425–463.

26. FJ Francis. Anthocyanins and betalains: composition and application. Cereal Foods World 45:208–213, 2000.

27. JB Harborne, CA Williams. Anthocyanins and other flavonoids. Plant Sci Lab 18:310–333, 2001.

28. RE Wrolstad. Anthocyanins. In: GJ Lauro, FJ Francis. eds. Natural Food Colorants. New York: Marcel Dekker, 2000, pp. 237–252.

29. RL Jackman, JL Smith. Anthocyanins and betalains. In: GAF Hendry, JD Houghton. eds. Natural Food Colorants. New York: AVI, 1992, pp. 184–241.

30. DK Dougall, DC Baker, E Gakh, M Redus. Biosynthesis and stability of monoacylated anthocyanins. Food Tech 51:69–71, 1997.

31. CF Timberlake, P Bridle. Anthocyanins. In: J Walford. ed. Developments in Food Colours—1. London: Applied Science Publishers LTD, 1980, pp. 115–149.

32. MS Starr, FJ Francis. Oxygen and ascorbic acid effect on the relative stability of four anthocyanin pigments in cranberry juice. Food Technol 22:1293–1295, 1968.

33. G Mazza. Anthocyanins in grapes and grape products. Crit Rev Food Sci Nutr 35:314–371, 1995.

34. P Bridle, CF Timberlake. Anthocyanins as natural food colours—selected aspects. Food Chem 58:103–109, 1997.

35. AJ Davis, G Mazza. Copigmentation of simple and acylated anthocyanins with colorless phenolic compounds. J Agric Food Chem 41:716–720, 1993.

36. C Santos-Buelga, A Scalbert. Proanthocyanidins and tannin-like compounds—nature, occurrence, dietary intake and effects on nutrition and health. J Sci Food Agric 80:1094–1117, 2000.

37. D Strack, T Vogt, V Schliemann. Recent advances in betalain research. Phytochemistry 62:247–269, 2003.

38. JH von Elbe, IL Goldman. The betalains. In: GJ Lauro, FJ Francis. eds. Natural Food Colorants. New York: Marcel Dekker, 2000, pp. 11–30.

39. J Kanner, S Harel, R Granit. Betalains—a new class of dietary catioized antioxidants. J Agric Food Chem 49:5178–5185, 2001.

Part B

Food Categories

15 Carbonated Beverages

Daniel W. Bena
PepsiCo International

CONTENTS

I. BACKGROUND INFORMATION

A. HISTORY OF SOFT DRINKS

The first carbonated beverage, of sorts, was provided by nature, and dates back to antiquity, when the first carbonated natural mineral waters were discovered—although they weren't usually used for drinking. Instead, they were used for bathing by the ancient Greeks and Romans, owing to their purported therapeutic properties. It wasn't until thousands of years later, in 1767, that the British chemist, Joseph Priestley, was credited with noticing that the carbon dioxide he introduced into water gave a "pleasant and acidulated taste to the water in which it was dissolved" (1). The history of carbonated soft drinks (CSDs) is somewhat sparse during its early evolution, but most agree that development of CSDs is due, in large part, to pharmacists.

Today, carbonated beverages are primarily recognized for their refreshing and thirst-quenching properties. In the early to middle 1800s, however, it was these pharmacists who experimented with adding "gas carbonium," or carbon dioxide, to water, and supplementing its palatability with everything from birch bark to dandelions in the hopes of enhancing the curative properties of these

carbonated beverages (2). "Soft drinks," a more colloquial yet very common name for carbonated beverages, distinguish themselves from "hard drinks," since they do not contain alcohol in their ingredient listing (3). This is in clear contrast to other beverages, such as distilled spirits, beer, or wine. These non-alcoholic, carbonated beverages are also called "pop" in some areas of the world, due to the characteristic noise made when the gaseous pressure within the bottle is released upon opening of the package (4). Figure 15.1 provides a brief illustration of the major milestones in the history of American soft drinks.

CSDs, "pop," soda—whatever the moniker given to these beverages, one thing is clear: they have been an important part of our popular culture for decades, and will continue to be for many years to come.

B. SOFT DRINK FACTS AND FIGURES

Few people consciously consider how something as ostensibly simple as "soda pop" can markedly affect the economy on several fronts. The National Soft Drink Association (NSDA), founded in 1919 as the American Bottlers of Carbonated Beverages (ABCB), today represents hundreds of beverage manufacturers, distributors, franchise

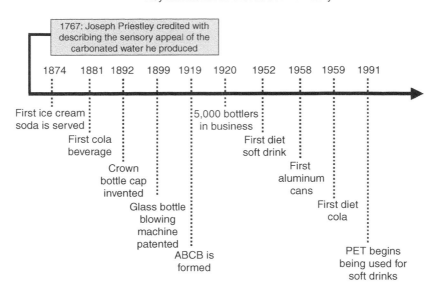

FIGURE 15.1 Key milestones in the U.S. beverage industry.

companies and support industries in the United States. According to the NSDA, Americans consumed nearly 53 gallons of carbonated soft drinks per person in 2002, and this translated into retail sales in excess of $61 billion. Nearly 500 bottlers operate across the United States, and provide more than 450 different soft drink varieties, at a production speed of up to 2,000 cans per minute on each operating line! Figure 15.2 summarizes the apportionment of total soft drink production in the year 2000.

Finally, as an industry, soft drink companies employ more than 183,000 people nationwide, pay more than $18 billion in state and local taxes annually, and contribute more than $230 million to charities each year. Few could argue that the soft drink industry has earned its place in the history of the American (and global) economy!

C. CARBONATION SCIENCE

Before discussing the process of manufacturing carbonated soft drinks, it is important to establish some fundamental chemical/physical concepts with regard to the carbonation process itself. Simply put, in the beverage industry, "carbonation" is the introduction of carbon dioxide gas into water, as depicted in Figure 15.3.

The favorable results of this simple combination are many: (1) the carbonation provides the characteristic "refreshing" quality for which carbonated beverages are most popular; (2) the dissolved carbon dioxide acts as both a bacteristat and a bactericide; and (3) the carbon dioxide dissociates in aqueous medium to form carbonic acid, which depresses the pH of the solution, thereby making the product even more protected from microbial

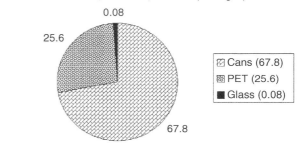

FIGURE 15.2 Distribution of cans, PET, and glass CSD packages.

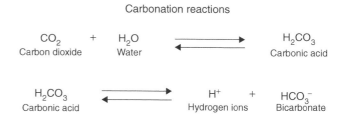

FIGURE 15.3 Carbonation reactions.

harm (5). All in all, from a microbiologic perspective, carbonated soft drinks are innately very safe beverages.

Once the carbon dioxide is introduced into the water, which will ultimately join with flavors and sweeteners to form the complete beverage, the beverage technologist must understand how to measure and express the level of carbonation. The accepted convention in the beverage industry is *not* to measure carbon dioxide as a true concentration, expressed in parts per million, or milligrams per liter. Instead, carbonation is expressed in units called "volumes." The concept is ultimately based on the physical gas laws of Henry, Boyle, and Charles, wherein pressure, temperature, and volume are closely interdependent. The colder the liquid, the more gas can be dissolved within it. Even within the industry, however, there is some confusion over what the exact definition of a "volume" is (6), usually arising from the temperature included in the definition. For our purposes, we will define one "volume" based on the Bunsen coefficient, described by Loomis as, "The volume of gas (reduced to 0°C and 760 mm) which, at the temperature of the experiment, is dissolved in one volume of the solvent when the partial pressure of the gas is 760 mm" (7). More informally, and to put this concept in perspective, consider a 10-ounce bottle of carbonated beverage, representing roughly 300 ml of liquid. If this carbonated beverage is prepared at one "gas volume," the package would contain approximately 300 cc of carbon dioxide. We would consider this very low carbonation from a sensory perspective, and would have a barely noticeable "fizz" upon removal of the closure. Imagine, however, for the same 300 ml of liquid, we carbonate to four gas volumes (a level typical of many products on the market today). This means that roughly 1200 cc of carbon dioxide has been introduced into the same 300 ml volume of liquid. More gas, into the same amount of liquid, and the same vessel size—imagine the increase in pressure contained within the bottle. This example explains why the characteristic "pop" of soda pop is heard when a bottle is uncapped, or a can is opened!

For the purposes of this text, the discussion of carbonation has been somewhat oversimplified, in order to make the concept more easily understood. As with any industry, the more one investigates any given topic, the more complicated and scientifically intense the subject usually becomes. Carbonation, for example, can be affected by a variety of factors, including other solids present in the liquid being carbonated, temperatures of the gas and the liquid, atmospheric pressure/altitude, and how far carbon dioxide varies from ideal gas behavior (8). These are cited merely for consideration, but are outside the scope of this chapter.

D. PROCESS OVERVIEW

The process of manufacturing carbonated beverages has remained fundamentally the same for the last several decades. Certainly, new equipment has allowed faster filling speeds, more accurate and consistent fill heights, more efficient gas transfer during carbonation, and other improvements, but the process remains one of cooling water, carbonating it, adding flavor and sweeteners, and packaging it in a sealed container. Figure 15.4 illustrates the overall process in somewhat more detail, as we continue to build upon the basic foundation we will be discussing throughout this chapter. As we proceed, the figures depicted will become more complete, as each critical process to carbonated beverage manufacture is explained.

Carbonated beverage production begins with careful measurement of the formula quantities of each component into the syrup blending tank. Critical components include the concentrate, which contains the bulk of the flavor system; the sweetener, which typically includes the nutritive sweeteners high-fructose syrup or sucrose (in the case of

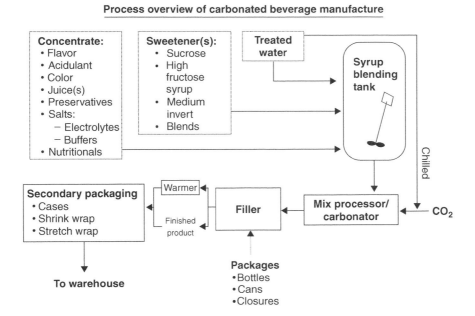

Process overview of carbonated beverage manufacture

FIGURE 15.4 Process overview of carbonated beverage manufacture.

diet beverages, these are replaced with one of the high-potency sweeteners available); and water, which generally begins as municipal drinking water, and is further purified within the beverage plant. These are then blended to ensure homogeneity of the batch according to carefully prescribed standard operating procedures.

Once blending in the syrup tank is complete, the "finished syrup" is tested for correct assembly, then pumped to the mix processor, where the syrup is diluted to finished beverage level with chilled, carbonated, treated water (often a 1:6 dilution of syrup:treated water, although this varies by product). After this, the now carbonated beverage-level solution proceeds to the filler, where it is fed (usually volumetrically, by gravity) into bottles or cans, then sealed (capped in the case of bottles, seamed in the case of cans). Then, the finished product is either passed through a warmer, in order to avoid excessive condensation from forming (depending on the type of secondary packaging used), or sent directly to secondary packaging. This can include plastic or cardboard cases, shrink wrap, stretch wrap, or even more innovative devices. After packaging, the product is palletized, and stored in the warehouse until it is ready for distribution.

II. RAW MATERIALS PREPARATION

A. CONCENTRATE

In the carbonated soft drink industry, "concentrate" is the name given to a mixture of many different categories of ingredients, illustrated in Figure 15.5.

The most notable of these, and, indeed, the topic of many urban legends surrounding its utter secrecy, is the flavor component. This is where the proprietary formulations of essential oils are found, which combine to form the characteristic flavor of the trademark beverage. Flavor components can include a single, "primary" component, or be distributed in various ways among multiple components—for example, a high-potency sweetener supplied as a dry salt as part of a secondary flavor component. In general, the majority of flavor systems include primary flavor

components, and these fall into three broad categories: (1) simple mixtures, (2) extracts, or (3) emulsions.

Simple mixtures. These are perhaps the simplest of the flavor categories to understand, but they also represent the minority of those in existence. Here, a combination of miscible liquids, or easily soluble solids, are blended together to form a homogenous aqueous mixture. Because so many essential flavor oils are not readily water soluble, the beverage technologist must abandon the idea of the simple mixture for one of the other, more flexible categories of flavors.

Extracts. As the name implies, this category of flavors involves extracting the desired flavor constituents from essential oils. Simply put, the extraction solvent—usually ethanol (although sometimes propylene glycol is used)—is used to partition those flavor constituents which are soluble in the solvent, but not freely soluble in the water directly. In this way, these flavor compounds become fully dissolved in the ethanol first. Then, this ethanolic "extract" (which is, in effect, an ethanolic solution of the flavor compounds) is added to water. Since ethanol is freely miscible with water, it acts as a carrier vehicle to help dissolve or disperse the otherwise water-insoluble flavor constituents (9). Today, equipment for both batch and continuous liquid extraction of flavor oils is available, and more novel approaches have also been developed (for example, gas extraction, super-critical fluid extraction, and other patented processes).

Emulsions. This third category is likely the largest, encompassing the bulk of the flavor systems available today. In the carbonated beverage industry, oil-in-water (or o/w) emulsions are the standard. This model involves an oil (lipophilic) internal phase, and an aqueous (hydrophilic) external phase, being made "compatible" by the use of a surfactant, or emulsifier. Surfactants are compounds that are amphiphilic; that is, there are both hydrophilic and lipophilic portions of the same molecule! This facilitates a decrease in the surface tension when oil and water are mixed together, and also allows the lipophilic portion to align with the oil, and the hydrophilic portion to align with the water (10). In so doing, the emulsifier forms a bridge, of sorts, between the two phases, and allows them to be dispersed, without gross separation, for the desired length of time (generally at least as long as the technical shelf life of the beverage).

Since carbonated beverages are of low pH, owing in part to the carbonic acid from the dissolved carbon dioxide, but also from the acid components of the formulae, acid hydrolysis is one of the major concerns to the beverage flavor developer. By positioning itself between the oil and water phases, the emulsifier protects the sensitive flavor oils from chemical degradation in this acidic environment. In addition, the emulsifier protects the flavors oils from oxidation from the naturally dissolved oxygen in the water which constitutes the aqueous phase. So, a well-designed

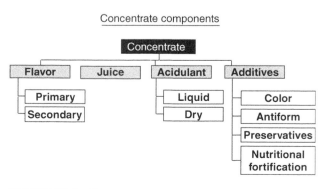

FIGURE 15.5 Concentrate components.

and prepared emulsion can dramatically extend the sensory shelf-life of the flavor system, and the overall physical stability of the beverage.

In addition to the flavors, Figure 15.5 also depicts a variety of other components which may be part of the concentrate. These include juices, which must be handled and stored carefully in order to preserve their quality, acidulants (both liquid and dry), and a host of other additives, depending on their desired function (for example, antifoam, preservative, nutrients, etc.).

B. WATER

Water is the major component in carbonated beverages, and represents anywhere from 85 to near 100% of the finished product. Interestingly, it is unlike any other ingredient, since we rarely have the number of options for water supply that we have with other raw materials! Obviously, then, particular diligence must be employed when selecting a water supply. Beverage plants use water from ground supplies, surface supplies, or both. Ground supplies include springs, deep and shallow wells, and artesian aquifers. Surface supplies include rivers, lakes, streams, and reservoirs. Within these sources, there is wide variation in type and content of inorganic (for example, metals, minerals, sulfate, chloride, nitrate), organic (for example, volatile organics, natural organic matter), microbiologic (bacteria, viruses, protozoa), and radiologics (radionuclides, alpha- and beta-activity). Table 15.1 provides a relative comparison of some characteristics of ground and surface supplies (11).

One critical point of which to be aware is that municipal treatment plants should not normally be depended upon to consistently supply water suitable for the needs of most carbonated beverage manufacturers. While the municipality treats the water so that it is safe to drink, and aesthetically pleasing to the consumer (potable and palatable), they cannot afford to consider the needs of all industrial end users, so they may not consistently supply a water of the high quality needed for producing our finished product and ensuring the beverage a long shelf life. There is also the possibility of contamination of the city water as it passes through the distribution system from the municipal treating plant to the beverage plant. This is particularly true with respect to organic matter and metal content, such as iron. The quality of the water used for carbonated soft drinks must be considered from several perspectives:

(1) *Regulatory Compliance*: The water used must be in compliance with all presiding local and national laws and guidelines. This jurisdiction is generally clear in the United States, between the Environmental Protection Agency and the Food and Drug Administration. However, as you consider the international beverage locations, the regulatory picture sometimes becomes more cloudy.

(2) *Beverage Stability*: Intuitively, as the major ingredient in carbonated soft drinks, the constituents in water can have a profound impact on the overall quality and shelf life of our beverage products. For example, if alkalinity is not

TABLE 15.1
Comparison of Ground and Surface Water Supplies

Parameter	Ground Water	Surface Water
Total dissolved solids	Higher	Lower
Suspended solids	Lower	Higher
Turbidity and color	Lower	Higher
Alkalinity	Higher	Lower
Total organic carbon	Lower	Higher
Microbiology		
Protection from bacteria and viruses	Highly protected	Highly susceptible
Protection from protozoa	Almost completely protected	Highly susceptible
Presence of iron and/or manganese bacteria	Common	Rare
Hydrogen sulfide gas	Common	Uncommon
Aeration/dissolved oxygen	Lower	Higher
Temperature	More consistent	More variable
Flow rate	Very slow (1 m/day)	Very fast (1 m/sec)
Flow pattern	Laminar	Turbulent
Susceptibility to pollution through surface run-off	Low	High
Time for a contaminant plume to resolve	Very long—often decades, potentially centuries	Usually short—days/months; sometimes years

Source: Bena, D. 2003. Water Use in the Beverage Industry, in Food Plant Sanitation (YH Hui, ed.). Marcel Dekker, New York.

controlled, the acidic profile of the beverage formulae will be compromised, making the beverage more susceptible to microbial growth and spoilage.

(3) *Sensory*: Many contaminants, even at levels within drinking water standards, may adversely affect the finished beverage. For example, some algae produce compounds (geosmin and methyl isoborneol) which are sensory active at levels as low as nanograms per liter (12). These can result in "dirty, musty" flavor and aroma in finished products.

(4) *Plant Operations*: Water for non-product (auxiliary) uses must also meet the performance standards of the carbonated soft drink producer. These standards and guidelines are usually enacted to prevent corrosion (for example, from high chloride content in heat exchangers) and scaling (for example, from hardness salts in boilers), which may result in premature equipment failure and/or loss of operational efficiency.

Whether the beverage plant has its own well, or the water supply comes from a modern municipal treatment plant, each individual water supply presents its own particular problems. In most, if not all cases, the incoming raw water which supplies a beverage plant already meets the applicable standards for potability of drinking water. The beverage producer then further purifies the water to meet the quality necessary for its products. This treatment can take many forms, but the three largest categories of in-plant beverage water treatment are (1) conventional lime treatment systems (CLTS), (2) membrane systems (including reverse osmosis, nanofiltration, and ultrafiltration), and (3) ion-exchange. Volumes have been written about each treatment modality, and a detailed discussion is beyond the focus of this chapter. However, a brief summary of each treatment category is provided below (13).

(1) Conventional lime treatment systems (CLTS). This treatment chain represents the majority of most beverage treatment armadas worldwide, although the balance is quickly shifting in favor of membrane technologies. CLTS involves the addition of a coagulant (as an iron or aluminum salt), hydrated lime (for pH control), and chlorine (for oxidation and disinfection) to a reaction tank. The agitation is gently controlled over the course of a two-hour retention time, during which a floc begins to form, grow, and settle, bringing contaminants with it to the bottom of the tank, where they await discharge. Figure 15.6 illustrates what happens in this reaction vessel.

Historically, and as little as twenty-five years ago, conventional lime treatment was regarded as the "ideal" treatment for raw water of virtually any quality. Indeed, this system, coupled with the required support technology—fine sand filtration, granular activated carbon, polishing filtration, and ultraviolet irradiation—does address a broad range of water contaminants. The advantages and

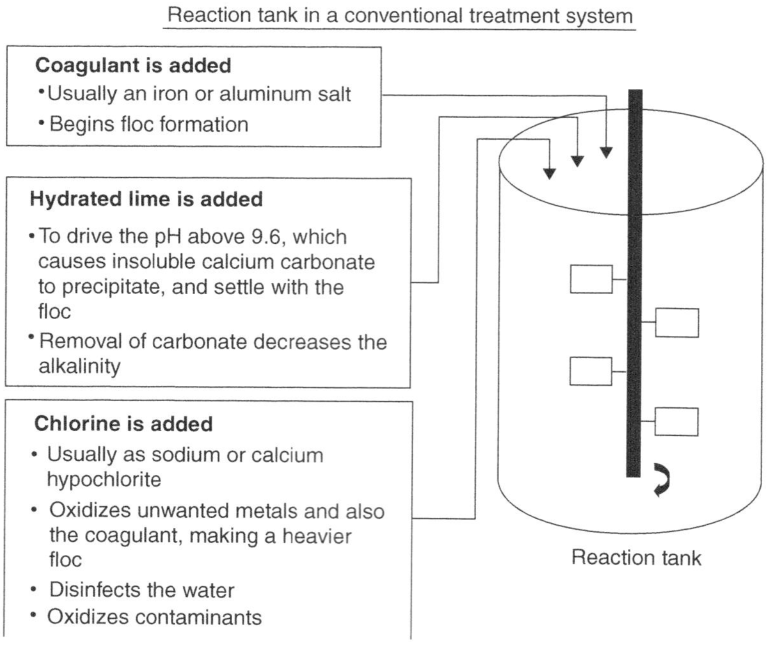

Reaction tank in a conventional treatment system

Coagulant is added
• Usually an iron or aluminum salt
• Begins floc formation

Hydrated lime is added
• To drive the pH above 9.6, which causes insoluble calcium carbonate to precipitate, and settle with the floc
• Removal of carbonate decreases the alkalinity

Chlorine is added
• Usually as sodium or calcium hypochlorite
• Oxidizes unwanted metals and also the coagulant, making a heavier floc
• Disinfects the water
• Oxidizes contaminants

Reaction tank

FIGURE 15.6 Reaction tank in a conventional lime treatment system.

disadvantages of conventional lime treatment are summarized in Table 15.2.

(2) Membrane technology. Clearly, this has seen the most growth in recent years with the advent of more resistant membrane materials of construction and more flexible rejection characteristics. Included in this category is the prototype of the cross-flow, polymeric membrane filtration systems—reverse osmosis, along with nanofiltration and ultrafiltration (both polymeric and ceramic). By carefully controlling the membrane pore size during manufacture, and the applied pressure during operation, reverse osmosis membranes can effectively remove in excess of 99% of many dissolved species—down to the ionic level (for example, dissolved calcium or sulfate). Table 15.3 illustrates the relative capabilities of the three major membrane processes with regard to a variety of constituents possible in the incoming water (14).

Since reverse osmosis is often the cited "membrane standard" against which the performance of others are judged, the advantages and disadvantages of reverse osmosis are listed in Table 15.4.

Also worth mentioning, though not discussed, among this group are the "hybrid" technologies, which include novel membrane and ion-exchange utilization. Examples are electrodialysis technology for removal of ionic species in water, and continuous electrodeionization.

(3) Ion-exchange. This technology is routinely utilized for partial or complete demineralization of the water supply, softening, or dealkalization, or it can be customized for selective removal of a specific contaminant (for example, denitratization). In simplest terms, ion-exchange involves using a selective resin to exchange a less desirable ion with a more desirable ion. Of course, a great deal of chemical research goes into the development of these selective resin materials, but the functional outcome remains

TABLE 15.2
Advantages and Disadvantages of CLTS

Advantages	Disadvantages
Removes alkalinity and hardness	Does not effectively reduce nitrate, sulfate, or chloride concentration
Removes organic debris, particulates, and natural organic matter (NOM)	Sludge formation and disposal requirements
Reduces metal concentrations (iron, manganese, arsenic, others) and some radionuclides	May promote the formation of disinfection by-products (trihalomethanes) under certain conditions
Reduces some color compounds (tannins), off-tastes, and off-odors	Often difficult to operate consistently in waters with very low dissolved solids
Reduces bacteria, virus, and protozoan populations	Relatively large space requirements on plant floor ("footprint")

Source: Bena, D. 2003. Water Use in the Beverage Industry, in Food Plant Sanitation (YH Hui, ed.). Marcel Dekker, New York.

TABLE 15.3
Relative Comparison of Reverse Osmosis, Nanofiltration, and Ultrafiltration

Component	Reverse Osmosis	Nano-Filtration	Ultrafiltration
Alkalinity	95 to 98%	50 to 70%	None
TDS	95 to 98%	50 to 70%	None
Particulates	Nearly 100%	Nearly 100%	Nearly 100%
Organic matter	Most > 100 MW	Most > 200 MW	Some > 2000 MW
THM precursors	90 + %	90 + %	30 to 60%
Sodium	90 to 99%	35 to 75%	None
Chloride	90 to 99%	35 to 60%	None
Hardness	90 to 99%	50 to 95 + %	None
Sulfate	90 to 99%	70 to 95 + %	None
Nitrate	90 to 95%	20 to 35%	None
Protozoa	Near 100%	Near 100%	Near 100%
Bacteria	Near 100%	Near 100%	Near 100%
Viruses	Near 100%	Near 100%	Near 100%
Operating pressure	200 to 450 psi	100 to 200 psi	80 to 150 psi

Approximate removal percentages. Actual performance is system-specific.
Source: Adapted from Brittan, PJ. Integrating Conventional and Membrane Water Treating Systems. International Society of Beverage Technologists Short Course for Beverage Production, Florida, 1997.

TABLE 15.4

Advantages and Disadvantages of Reverse Osmosis

Advantages	Disadvantages
Removes nearly all suspended material, and greater than 99% of dissolved salts in full-flow operation	Pretreatment must be carefully considered, and typically involves operating costs for chemicals (acid, antiscalant, chlorine removal)
Significantly reduces microbial load (viruses, bacteria, and protozoans)	Does not produce a commercially sterile water
Removes nearly all natural organic matter (NOM)	Membranes still represent a substantial portion of the capital cost, and may typically last 3–5 years
May be designed as a fully automated system with little maintenance	Low solids water may be aggressive toward piping and equipment, so this must be considered for downstream operations
Relatively small space requirements on the plant floor ("footprint")	High pressure inlet pump is required

Source: Bena, D. 2003. Water Use in the Beverage Industry, in Food Plant Sanitation (YH Hui, ed.). Marcel Dekker, New York.

straightforward. For example, softening resins are often employed to remove hardness (calcium and magnesium) from the water entering boilers and heat exchangers. In this application, the hardness ions are not wanted. The softening resin (for example, a sodium zeolite clay) is charged with active and replaceable sodium ions. When the "hard" water passes across the softening bed, the resin has a selectivity for calcium and magnesium, so it replaces them for sodium. The result is that the water exiting the softener is virtually free of calcium and magnesium (since they were replaced by sodium), and is safe to use in boilers and other equipment, since it will no longer have the tendency to form scale.

To supplement the major treatment systems mentioned above, the carbonated beverage producer often utilizes a host of other "support technologies," including activated carbon filtration (to remove organic contaminants and chlorine), sand filtration (to remove particulates), and primary and secondary disinfection (using chlorine, ozone, ultraviolet, heat, or a combination). By the time the treated water is finished, it is microbially and chemically safe, clear, colorless, and ready to be used for syrup and beverage production.

C. SWEETENERS

The two major categories of sweetener types are nutritive (that is, they provide some caloric value) and "high potency" (that is, the type used in diet beverages, since they are many times sweeter than sucrose, and generally non-caloric). There are several high potency sweeteners available to the worldwide beverage developer (aspartame, acesulfame potassium, and others), and they are almost exclusively, if not always, included as part of the "concentrate" flavor system as a dry substance package. As such, their quality can be more easily controlled by the vendor, as with any of the other concentrate ingredients, and minimal intervention is needed at the carbonated soft drink manufacturing facility. These high potency sweeteners, therefore, will not be addressed in this chapter. A concise treatise on the topic, however, is provided by the International Society of Beverage Technologists (15).

Next to water, however, the nutritive sweeteners represent the second most prevalent ingredient in the finished beverage. The most common nutritive sweeteners used in the carbonated soft drink industry are sucrose and high fructose syrups, with sucrose (from cane or beet) being the most common internationally. Within the United States, nearly all of the nutritive sweetener used in carbonated beverages is high fructose corn syrup (HFCS, either 42 or 55%). In 1996, the U.S. corn refining industry produced over 21 billion pounds of high fructose corn syrups, representing only about 12% of the total corn crop (16).

Although high fructose syrups may be obtained from other starting materials, like wheat or tapioca starch, corn remains the most prevalent starting material. A starch slurry is first digested by the addition of alpha-amylase enzyme, which results in gelatinization and ultimate dextrinization of the starting starch. Then, glucoamylase enzyme is added to result in an enriched glucose syrup (95% glucose). After this the glucose syrup is purified via particle filtration, activated carbon adsorption, and both cation and anion exchange. Then, evaporation brings the solids content within range for effective passage through the isomerization column containing the glucose isomerase enzyme. This enzyme converts much of the 95% glucose syrup to fructose, which is again purified as before and evaporated. The result is HFCS-55 of high quality. In some formulae and/or markets, HFCS-42 is used, which is simply a blend of the HFCS-55 with the 95% glucose stream to result in a product which is 42% fructose. The generic process by which corn starch is transformed to high fructose corn syrup is illustrated in Figure 15.7 (17).

In general, HFCS-55 (55% fructose) is a highly pure ingredient, due, in large part, to the activated carbon, cation, and anion exchange steps required of the process. However, the most recent research highlights the occurrence of potent sensory-active compounds which could form via chemical or microbial pathways in HFCS,

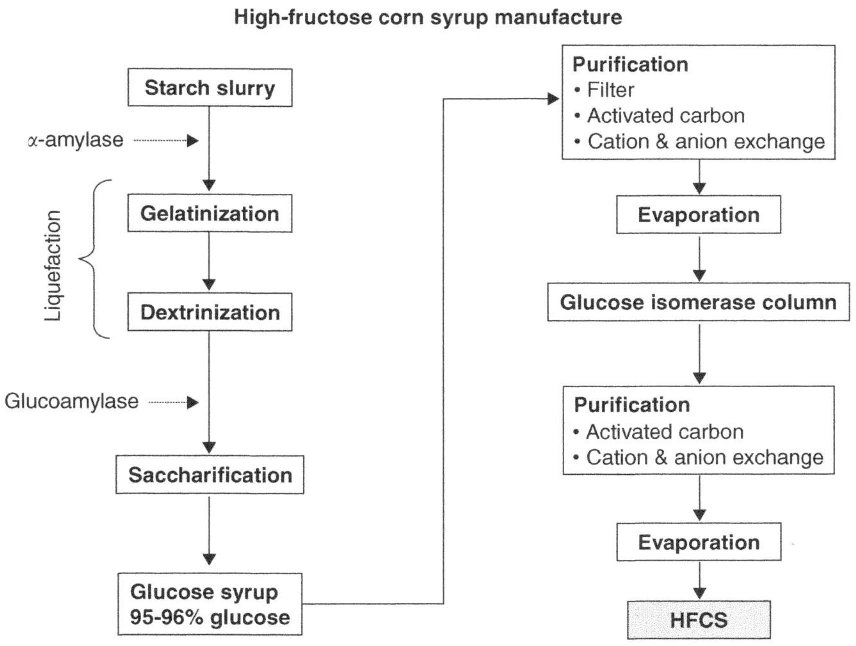

High-fructose corn syrup manufacture

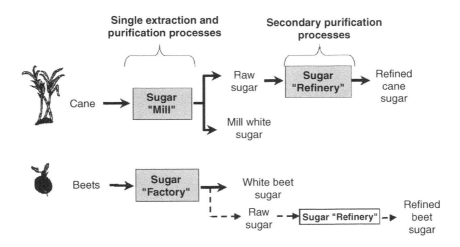

FIGURE 15.7   High fructose corn syrup manufacture.

Comparison of sugar beet and sugar cane processing

FIGURE 15.8   Cane vs. beet sugar process flow.

including isovaleraldehyde, 2-amino acetophenone, and maltol (18). When properly produced and stored, no additional treatment is necessary at the beverage plant.

Sucrose, though the clear exception in the North American beverage industry, continues to be the mainstay for international beverage markets. It may be obtained from sugar cane or sugar beet, following two distinct separation and purification schemes, as depicted in Figure 15.8 (19).

The three indicators of sucrose quality generally recognized by the sugar industry are color, ash, and turbidity. Internationally, depending on the quality of the available

sucrose, it is not uncommon to subject the incoming granular or liquid sucrose to additional treatment at the beverage plant. Ash, or residual inorganic minerals, remains difficult to adequately treat at the carbonated soft drink plant, so great effort is made to source sucrose with an acceptable ash content (as defined by the individual company specifications). Turbidity is easily remedied at the beverage plant via an in-line filtration step, often incorporating diatomaceous earth as a filter aid. Color, considered by some as the primary indicator of sucrose quality, is also able to be treated at the beverage plant, but typically requires hot treatment through activated carbon. This removes color and many sensory-active compounds, and also serves to render the sucrose free of most viable microorganisms. Figure 15.9 (19) briefly summarizes the handling and treatment of sucrose at the carbonated soft drink facility.

Liquid sucrose, usually commercially available at 67 Brix concentration (67 Brix is equivalent to 67% sucrose, by weight), is sometimes used for the production of carbonated soft drinks. Two distinct disadvantages of using liquid sucrose instead of granulated sucrose include the following: (1) the end user ultimately pays for shipping 33% water, since the ingredient is only 67% sucrose solids, as compared to granulated sucrose, which is 100% sucrose solids, and (2) this water also means that the liquid has a higher water activity than granulated sucrose, making it much more susceptible to microbial spoilage. With liquid sucrose operations, absolutely diligent transport and handling procedures are imperative.

The last, less common type of nutritive sweetener used in this industry is medium invert sugar. Chemically, this product has similarities to both sucrose and high fructose corn syrup. With medium invert sugar, or MIS, the starting material is liquid sucrose, which is then treated with one of three processes: (1) heat and acid, (2) ion-exchange, or (3) invertase enzyme. The end result of any of these processes is that roughly 50% of the starting sucrose is transformed into "invert sugar," an equimolar mixture of glucose and fructose. At this point, the inversion process is stopped,

and the final commercial product contains 50% sucrose, 25% glucose, and 25% fructose. This gained favor over liquid sucrose in the beverage industry for two main reasons: (1) the finished material is 76 Brix, vs. 67 Brix for liquid sucrose, so less water is shipped, and (2) MIS has a much lower water activity, and is, therefore, much more microbiologically stable.

In summary, the producers of carbonated soft drinks have several options at their disposal for providing the sweetness to the consumer, which is so characteristic of these products. Internationally, sucrose is the major sweetener used, while in the United States, high fructose corn syrup is preferred. Irrespective of the type of sweetener, the beverage industry has treatment methods at its disposal to ensure that this ingredient consistently meets the high standards of chemical and microbial quality necessary to be used in the production of syrup and beverage.

D. CARBON DIOXIDE

At normal temperatures and pressures, carbon dioxide is a colorless gas, with a slightly pungent odor at high concentrations. When compressed and cooled to the proper temperature, the gas turns into a liquid. The liquid in turn can be converted into solid dry ice. The dry ice, on absorbing heat, returns to its natural gaseous state.

We learned a little of the history of carbonation earlier in this chapter, since the concept is so critical to the production of carbonated soft drinks. Just as critical is the

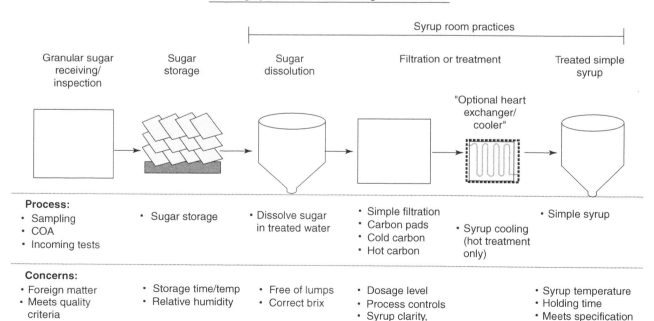

FIGURE 15.9 Sucrose handling and treatment at the beverage plant.

quality of the carbon dioxide used in this application. For many years, the quality of carbon dioxide was minimized, largely because there were no uniformly available methods with which to test the gas, as an ingredient. Those procedures that were available required special expertise to properly sample and handle this cryogenic gas. The standards of quality of the carbon dioxide used in beverages were traditionally relegated to the U.S. Compressed Gas Association (CGA), whose "quality verification levels" were incorporated into the beverage company's specification system. Then, in 1999, the International Society of Beverage Technologists (ISBT) developed the Quality Guidelines and Analytical Procedure Bibliography for Bottlers' Carbon Dioxide (20). This was a cross-corporate effort by carbon dioxide suppliers, end-users, testing labs, and allied businesses to completely update the obsolescent guidelines which had been recognized for decades. The guidelines are only available for purchase through ISBT (www.bevtech. org); they include parameters related to health/safety, sensory, and good manufacturing practices at the supplier.

Carbon dioxide may be obtained and purified from a number of different "feed gas" sources, the majority of which are listed in Table 15.5.

There are other more "exotic" sources which are often the result of carbon dioxide being generated as a by-product during an organic chemical synthesis. In addition to commercial supplies, some carbonated beverage plants produce and purify their own carbon dioxide. The most common feed gas sources for these applications are combustion (where the flue gas is recovered, concentrated, then purified) and breweries (where the CO_2 generated from microbial metabolism is recovered and purified). Whether supplied commercially or in-house, the carbon dioxide used in carbonated soft drinks is of high quality (greater than 99.9% CO_2); in most cases, it even exceeds that of medical grade gas.

The liquid carbon dioxide which is delivered to beverage plants is generally stored in large "bulk receivers," which are vertically or horizontally oriented steel tanks with urethane foam or vacuum insulation. In the most common arrangement, carbon dioxide is withdrawn from

the liquid phase at the bottom of the tank, and vaporized by one of several methods. Due to this withdrawal, the equilibrium between vapor and liquid in the tank remains dynamic. The air gases (oxygen, nitrogen) partition into the vapor phase of the vessel, and are routinely purged to maintain the purity of the carbon dioxide within the bulk receiver. Similarly, some components preferentially partition, in trace amounts, into the liquid phase of the carbon dioxide (liquid CO_2 is an excellent solvent). Many beverage plants choose to subject the freshly vaporized carbon dioxide to one final step of purification just prior to the point of use. This is usually a simple filtration through activated carbon alone, or through a mixed adsorbent bed of carbon (to remove organic contaminants); a silica-based desiccant (to remove moisture); and a molecular sieve (to remove sulfur compounds and some oxygenates).

In addition to the quality considerations already discussed, carbon dioxide safety is a key consideration for beverage industry technologists. Carbon dioxide is not usually considered to be a toxic gas in the generally accepted sense of the term (that is, poisonous) and is normally present in the atmosphere at a concentration of approximately 0.03% (300 ppm). Under normal circumstances, carbon dioxide acts upon vital functions in a number of ways, including respiratory stimulation, regulation of blood circulation, and acidity of body fluids. The concentration of carbon dioxide in the air affects all of these. High concentrations are dangerous upon extended exposure, due to increased breathing and heart rates and a change in the body acidity. OSHA (Occupational Safety and Health Administration) establishes regulations governing the maximum concentration of CO_2 and the time-weighted average for exposure to CO_2. These regulations should be reviewed before installation of any CO_2 equipment, and the requirements fully met during operation and maintenance.

Since carbon dioxide is heavier than air, it may accumulate in low or confined areas. Adequate ventilation must be provided when carbon dioxide is discharged into the air. At lower levels where carbon dioxide may be concentrated, self-contained breathing apparatus or supplied-air respirators must be used. Filter type masks should not be used. Appropriate warning signs should be affixed outside those areas where high concentrations of carbon dioxide gas may accumulate, and lock-out/tag-out procedures should be followed, as appropriate (21).

III. SYRUP PREPARATION

Most carbonated beverage formulae begin with a "simple syrup," which is usually a simple combination of the nutritive sweetener (sucrose, HFCS, MIS) and treated water. In some cases, it may also contain some of the salts outlined in the specific beverage document, depending on the order of addition which is required. Once the sweetener is completely dissolved, and the simple syrup is a

TABLE 15.5
Feed Gas Sources for Carbon Dioxide

✓ Combustion
✓ Wells/Geothermal (Natural CO_2 Wells)
✓ Fermentation (Breweries, ethanol plants, etc.)
✓ Hydrogen or Ammonia Plants
✓ Phosphate Rock
✓ Coal Gasification
✓ Ethylene Oxide Production
✓ Acid Neutralization

Adapted from CGA-6.2. 2000. Commodity Specification for Carbon Dioxide. U.S. Compressed Gas Association, Table 3, Page 5.

homogenous batch, then the flavor and remaining components are added to form the "finished syrup." All simple syrup should be filtered before being pumped to the finished syrup blending/storage tanks.

Using Granulated Sucrose. Accurate weighing of granulated sugar is important. Granulated sugar is normally received in bulk form or in bags. Internationally, receipt in 50- or 100-pound jute or paper bags is not uncommon. It is extremely important that the sugar received by either means should be dry and free of lumps. Moist sugar creates two immediate and serious problems: (1) moist sugar can have high microbial counts, much of which will be yeast. Yeast is a serious problem for carbonated beverages, since it can lead to fermentation and eventual spoilage of the finished product. (2) Moist sugar makes accurate measuring difficult, since the moisture content is being weighed, in addition to the sucrose solids. This makes final control of the batch difficult and inconsistent.

Sugar in lumps will create difficulties in making simple syrup and will take longer to dissolve. Lump sugar is usually an indication that the sugar was not fully dried during refinery production or was stored improperly (22). Never use bulk sugar systems when faced with wet or even slightly moist sugar. It will cause "bridging" (flow restriction) in silo storage and make effective handling impossible. It is critical that any bulk sugar supply is consistently dry and that the storage environment can be controlled to ensure constant low humidity. Even the most modern silo can "bridge" when faced with a moisture problem.

Granulated sugar should always be added slowly into the treated water already measured into the tank. While sugar is being added, the tank agitator should be in constant operation. The agitation should continue until the sugar is completely dissolved. After the sugar has been completely dissolved, and the simple syrup has been filtered into the blending/storage tank, the syrup is checked for sugar content (Brix). Table 15.6 outlines intuitive, but useful, reasons for off-target Brix readings.

Using Liquid Sugars. There are three main types of liquid sugars that are used for syrup production, as discussed earlier: liquid sucrose, medium invert sugar, and high fructose syrups. Making simple syrup from liquid sucrose is similar to the procedure employed when using granulated sugar. The first step is to check the Brix of the liquid sucrose to find out how much water must be added to the batch to bring the Brix of the simple syrup to the level required by the formula. Most companies beverage documents include a table that specifies how much of the liquid sucrose and additional treated water should be added to the batch based on Brix. When liquid sucrose supplies are received at the plant, they should be accompanied by an analysis sheet comparing the tank load against the company standards.

Medium Invert Sugar is resistant to microbial spoilage when being transported from supplier to plant, and while in storage. However, good sanitation procedures are still required, as well as special precautions to prohibit secondary infection. When liquid invert shipments are received at the plant, they should be accompanied by an analysis sheet comparing the tank load against standards. The formula document should include a table that specifies how much of the sweetener and additional treated water should be added to the batch based on Brix and the percent inversion. When testing for Brix in MIS samples, a correction factor must be used on refractometer readings to compensate for the non-sucrose solids as a result of inversion.

Using High Fructose Syrups. For liquid sugars, in general, a sample should be taken before the sugar is accepted, and the analysis should confirm that the material is within standards. The installation, including receiving station, pumps, air blower/ultraviolet lamp, tanks and piping/fittings, should be of approved materials (stainless steel) and in accordance with the individual beverage company's design guidelines. High fructose syrup is subject to crystallization, so storage temperatures should be controlled (generally maintained between 75°F/24°C and 85°F/29°C), by the use of indirect heating. The receiving station is a critical point and should be fully cleaned and hot sanitized before every delivery. As with MIS, when testing for Brix in HFS samples, a correction factor must be used on refractometer readings to correct to true Brix and compensate for the non-sucrose solids.

No matter what type of nutritive sweetener is used, once the simple syrup has been correctly prepared in the mixing tank, it should be pumped through the syrup filter into the storage tank so that the other concentrate components may be added. Most simple syrups will be in Brix range between 60–65, which makes them extremely susceptible to microbial spoilage, again, with yeast the most likely culprit. Be sure to recognize and respect any time constraints included in the syrup preparation instructions. For example, a general "rule of thumb" is that simple syrup should not be kept longer than four hours before converting it to finished syrup. If hot sugar processing is used, remember to atemperate the simple syrup to

TABLE 15.6
Possible Brix Errors during Simple Syrup Production

High Brix	Low Brix
Weighing error - excess sugar	Weighing error - short sugar
Faulty scale	Faulty scale
Instrument error	Not weighing sugar bags
Too little water	Too much water
	Instrument error
	Moist sugar

Source: Delonge, H. 1994. Pepsi-Cola Production Manual, Volume 2, Sugar and Sugar Handling.

ambient temperature prior to the addition of concentrate. This will help minimize thermal degradation of the flavor oils. Also, it is very important to add the individual components in the specific order detailed in the syrup preparation instructions. Incorrect order of addition can lead to a variety of problems, including changes in viscosity, flavor degradation, nutrient breakdown, and precipitation of insoluble materials in the syrup tank.

IV. CARBONATION

Earlier in this chapter, we discussed the history, theory, and principle of introducing carbon dioxide gas into water to produce a carbonated beverage. We also addressed the importance of the quality of this carbon dioxide, as well as of the treated water used to dissolve it. In this section, we will discuss the practical aspects of carbonation control.

"Mix processing" refers to the process of combining the finished syrup, treated water, and carbon dioxide in the correct proportions to meet beverage specifications. In addition to the proportioning function, mix processing will usually incorporate deaeration, mixing, carbonating, and cooling, depending on the manufacturer's design and the type of products being handled. The design of mix processing systems will vary from one manufacturer to another, incorporating the features that the manufacturer feels are advantageous to controlling production.

The primary function of the carbonating unit or the carbonator is to add carbon dioxide to the product. It must be carbonated to the level that, after filling and closing, results in a product within the standards for beverage carbonation. Some carbonating units incorporate cooling in the same tank or unit. The product can be slightly pre-carbonated with CO_2 injection and then exposed to a CO_2 atmosphere directly where cooling is in progress. Other systems separate the carbonating and cooling steps. The three most common forms of carbonating technology incorporate one or a combination of the following: (1) conventional (atmospheric exposure) introduction, (2) CO_2 injection, or (3) CO_2 eduction.

The ability of water, or beverage, to absorb carbon dioxide gas, is largely dependent on the efficiency of the carbonating unit (23). Other factors that influence CO_2 absorption include (1) product type, (2) product temperature, (3) CO_2 pressure, (4) time and contact surface area, and (5) air content. If the water temperature rises, the gas pressure must be increased if the same absorption of CO_2 is to be maintained. Conversely, if the temperature of the water or beverage entering the carbonating unit drops, the CO_2 becomes more soluble, and the pressure must be decreased to keep the volumes of carbonation within standards. Automatic CO_2 controls compensate for fluctuations in temperature, pressure, and flow. This allows the carbonating unit to produce a constant CO_2 gas absorption. Such controls are standard in modern processing

units, which are available as basic units, or with computer interfaces to track the variation in product temperature, pressure, flow, and final CO_2 gas volumes absorbed during operating hours.

In many ways, this is a gross oversimplification of a process which, to this day, sometimes eludes strict control. Certainly, equipment has dramatically improved over the years, but loss of carbon dioxide remains a significant issue in terms of overall plant productivity. New membrane carbonation systems hold great promise for continuing this evolution, by helping to carbonate, at least in theory, more precisely and accurately than ever before. It is yet to be seen if these systems will endure the economic challenges, industry acceptance, and rigors of time.

V. FILLING, SEALING, AND PACKING

In the most fundamental terms, this section will address the introduction of the now freshly prepared and carbonated finished beverage into the package, and sealing it in a manner so as to preserve its integrity: simple in theory, sometimes challenging in application. The bottle filling unit includes bottle handling/transfer components, a filling machine, and a capper/crowner.

The purpose of the filler is to fill returnable and nonreturnable bottles to a predetermined level. It should do this efficiently while minimizing foaming and deliver the bottle to a crowner or closure machine to be sealed, or, in the case of cans, to the lid seamer. A discussion of the design and engineering of filling machines is beyond the scope of this chapter, and is normally relegated to the specific operating manuals supplied by the respective equipment vendor.

Carbonated beverage fillers, to prevent the loss of carbon dioxide from the freshly carbonated beverage, must be counter-pressured. The advantage in using CO_2 gas for counterpressure purposes at the filler bowl is to reduce product air content. With can fillers, this is possible because the counterpressure gas is normally purged from the can to the atmosphere as part of the filling process. Most bottle fillers presently in use vacate the counterpressure gas back into the filler bowl as the bottle is being filled. The empty bottle moving into the sealing position (at the filling valve) already contains air. Even if the counterpressure gas is CO_2, vacating this mixture (air and CO_2) back into the filler bowl assures that the bowl will contain (predominantly) air. This can negate the advantage of CO_2 as a counterpressure gas, and actually be wasting CO_2 to the point of an economic disadvantage. In place of carbon dioxide, air or nitrogen is sometimes used as the counterpressure gases.

Imagine what happens when a carbonated beverage is agitated, and then quickly uncapped. Sometimes, this same type of foaming that results can occur during filling. Foaming at the filler, even in small amounts, can cause a number of problems. Some of these deal with product

TABLE 15.7
Problems Resulting from Foaming at the Filler

Quality	Economics/Operations
✓ Underfilled package	✓ Impact on filling speed
✓ Product residue on bottle	✓ Loss of CO_2 and product
✓ Incorrect CO_2 level	✓ Increased BOD (biochemical oxygen demand) to the drain (sewer surcharge)
	✓ Increased cost of clean-up

Source: Delonge, H. 1994. Pepsi-Cola Production Manual, Volume 2. Carbonation.

quality, others with economics or plant operation, and are summarized in Table 15.7 (24).

The cause(s) of foaming in a filling operation can range from a simple problem, that can be corrected quickly, to one requiring extensive trial and error testing. Many times, the troubleshooting exercise requires a combination of technical skill, creativity, and experience. Some causes of foaming at the filler are summarized in Figure 15.10.

When the problem is a single valve, or occurs for a short period of time, it is usually easy to troubleshoot and correct. On-going foaming problems can be extremely difficult to correct. Manuals supplied by the manufacturer of the filler/mix processor usually address troubleshooting foaming problems in detail, and should be consulted. If the problem persists, contact the filler manufacturer.

One of the problems which can result from excessive foaming at the filler, aside from the poor aesthetics of "sticky" packages, is the formation of mold colonies on the external walls of the package. This might also be evident in the thread areas of bottles when the cap is removed. Proper sealing of the newly filled package is a critical step in the processing of carbonated soft drinks. The closure can be a variety of different types, including crimp-on metal crowns on glass bottles, screw-on metal or plastic caps on plastic bottles, or a seamed lid onto a can body. Each of these applications requires different equipment, but the over-riding objectives are the same: (1) withstand the pressure from the carbon dioxide in this closed system, (2) provide the consumer with a safely sealed product, and one with tamper evidence, (3) prevent leakage of product out of the package, and (4) help contribute to the visual appeal of the overall package.

After proper application of the closure or lid, some beverage manufacturing plants pass the bottles and cans through a warmer, which is a tunnel of water sprays of carefully controlled temperature. The purpose is to bring the temperature of the filled packages (still cold from the

Some causes of foaming at the filler

✓ Syrup over-agitation
✓ Dirty bottles
✓ Dirty filler bowl
✓ Excessively carbonated product
✓ Warm product (inadequate refrigeration)
✓ Line leaks (air introduction)
✓ Valve failure
✓ Vent tube spreading rubber wrong position or missing
✓ Vent tube scored, missing, loose, incorrect size
✓ Inadequate drainage after washing or rinsing
✓ Particulates in water
✓ Improper carbo-cooler operation
✓ Inadequate carbo-cooler capacity, or operating beyond capacity
✓ Incorrect centering cup insert
✓ Product characteristics (more common in diets)
✓ Incorrect setting of valve operating/snift cams
✓ Bent valve operating levers

✓ Glass quality and configuration
✓ Excess air or dissolved oxygen in water
✓ High syrup temperatures; warm bottles
✓ Too high a liquid level in bowl
✓ Frequent start/stop operation of filler (over-agitation of product)
✓ Carbo-cooler outlet valve not opening fully
✓ Incorrect bowl pressure setting
✓ Hot or contaminated CO_2
✓ Damaged snift ferrule
✓ Rough transfer on A-frame
✓ Silicate or carbonate scale/deposits from water
✓ Worn valve liquid seal (skirt)
✓ Dirty valve screens
✓ Poor/leaking counterpressure seal
✓ Worn pump seals on water, syrup, or beverage transfer pumps (air eduction)

FIGURE 15.10 Some causes of foaming at the filler. Source: Bena (25).

chilled carbonated water introduced at the mix processor) up to close to ambient. The main reason for this is to prevent excessive condensation, which can lead to problems, depending on the secondary and tertiary packaging that are used.

For example, in the U.S. and in many countries internationally, it is common to place bottles of carbonated beverage into rigid plastic crates for transport to a retail outlet. In these instances, warming is not usually needed, since the plastic crates are essentially inert, and allow for adequate air flow and ventilation of the product. Some products, however, perhaps because of a particular marketing promotion, will shrink wrap multiple bottles together, then place them in a cardboard case box, and then stack them on a pallet which is stretch-wrapped for structural stacking integrity. In the second example, if the bottles were not warmed after filling, there is a high probability that the excess condensation would be trapped (by the shrink wrap), absorbed by the cardboard (presenting a mold risk), and then subjected to a "green house effect" from the poor ventilation of the stretch wrap. It becomes quickly evident that a beverage producer's job is not complete simply because the product makes it safely to a sealed container!

VI. QUALITY CONTROL AND ASSURANCE

In this section, we will distinguish quality "control" from quality "assurance" by having control refer to testing typically performed by the beverage plant, either immediately on-site or at a local contract lab. "Assurance" will refer to the subject of a broader, usually centrally managed program (for example, frequent testing of the product from the trade by a central corporate laboratory). Typically, the bulk of testing performed in a carbonated beverage facility falls under the category of quality control. Each company prescribes its own specific testing protocol, including the parameters to test, analytic test methods to apply, and frequency. In addition, a rigorous quality program would clearly outline the actions to be taken (and by whom) in the event that this testing demonstrates an out-of-specification situation.

Since there is no single protocol for all plants to follow, Figure 15.11 summarizes the major categories of testing to consider when evaluating a beverage plant's quality monitoring scheme. This list is by no means exhaustive, but it does provide an idea of how rigorous the monitoring and control in a beverage plant should be.

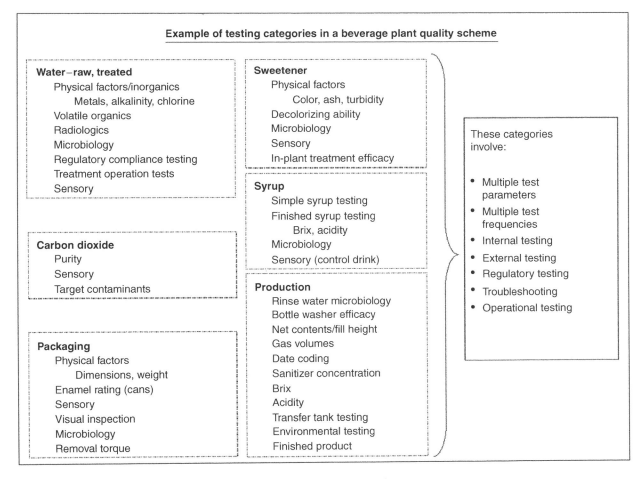

Example of testing categories in a beverage plant quality scheme

Water−raw, treated
- Physical factors/inorganics
  - Metals, alkalinity, chlorine
- Volatile organics
- Radiologics
- Microbiology
- Regulatory compliance testing
- Treatment operation tests
- Sensory

Carbon dioxide
- Purity
- Sensory
- Target contaminants

Packaging
- Physical factors
  - Dimensions, weight
- Enamel rating (cans)
- Sensory
- Visual inspection
- Microbiology
- Removal torque

Sweetener
- Physical factors
  - Color, ash, turbidity
- Decolorizing ability
- Microbiology
- Sensory
- In-plant treatment efficacy

Syrup
- Simple syrup testing
- Finished syrup testing
  - Brix, acidity
- Microbiology
- Sensory (control drink)

Production
- Rinse water microbiology
- Bottle washer efficacy
- Net contents/fill height
- Gas volumes
- Date coding
- Sanitizer concentration
- Brix
- Acidity
- Transfer tank testing
- Environmental testing
- Finished product

These categories involve:
- Multiple test parameters
- Multiple test frequencies
- Internal testing
- External testing
- Regulatory testing
- Troubleshooting
- Operational testing

FIGURE 15.11 Example of testing categories in a beverage plant quality scheme.

In addition to this quality control scheme, most larger beverage companies have developed formalized quality assurance schemes, which are usually under a centralized corporate management. The programs generally include some auditing function to visit the production plants for compliance to standards and guidelines, and sampling of finished products from the trade. These programs vary in terms of their focus and rigor, but trade sampling provides perhaps the best representation of what the consumers in a particular market are receiving. From this perspective, the data obtained are of extreme value, and must be reviewed in concert with in-plant and external data, in order to provide the best overall picture of quality performance.

VII. FINISHED PRODUCT

Low pH, high acidity, carbonation, and often ingredients that provide some natural antimicrobial activity (for example, d-limonene in citrus oils) all combine to make carbonated soft drinks a robust category of beverages. Of course, "robust" is a relative term, so as not to imply that carbonated beverages are completely immune to problems in finished product. The formulae, however, go a long way in providing a margin of "designed" product safety.

In fact, for non-fruit-juice-containing carbonated beverages, the types of problems which are typically encountered in the trade are relatively few, and rarely, if ever, present a health or safety threat to the consumer. Microbiologically, we have already mentioned the possibility of having mold form where the overall moisture in the environment is not controlled. For example, remember the scenario of freshly filled bottles, moist with condensation, then shrink wrapped, palletized, and stretch wrapped. The resulting "green house" effect could easily provide the necessary conditions in which mold could grow. In finished product, however, these beverages might contain a variety of organisms, but they will not remain viable under the conditions of the beverage. Only aciduric organisms can multiply, and these include some molds, yeasts, lactic acid bacteria, and acetic acid bacteria (26). Of these, the clear majority of microbial problems are caused by spoilage yeast. This "spoilage" normally refers to any condition which affects the design appearance, flavor, or aroma of the product, and is usually a problem of aesthetics where carbonated soft drinks are concerned.

In addition, as with any packaged products, the packaging materials can be the source of finished product problems. For example, misapplication of closures may occur, where removal torque is so high that consumers have difficulty opening the bottles. In areas of the world where returnable bottles are used, depending on their handling, they can become badly scuffed, presenting an unappealing look to the consumer.

Many problems with finished product can be—and are—averted before the product ever leaves the beverage facility. This is due, in large part, to the diligent monitoring of the soft drink manufacturing process from beginning to end. We have already learned that the raw materials are held to high standards of quality upon receipt, and some—like water, sucrose, and carbon dioxide—are often further purified within the beverage plant itself. Then, these raw materials are combined into a finished syrup, and it is checked against standards of assembly and quality. This finished syrup is then diluted and carbonated, filled, then sealed to form the final beverage. The final product is tested chemically, microbially, and sensorially, to ensure that it meets the highest standards of its trademarked brand.

This said, the summary above represents only a small portion of the quality systems that overarch most finished products, and which are clearly beyond the scope of this chapter. Suffice to say that many beverage companies begin to control quality as far back in the supply chain as possible, so far, that some companies own their own citrus groves in order to strictly control the quality of the orange juice used in their orange-juice containing beverages! In addition, as the principles of HACCP (Hazard Analysis and Critical Control Points) become more commonplace in the beverage industry, many bottlers and canners are voluntarily formulating their own HACCP plans to formalize the monitoring and control of their processes. All of this is done with a single, predominant end-goal in mind, to provide the consumer with consistently high-quality, great tasting, refreshing beverages.

REFERENCES

1. Jacobs, M.B. 1951. Chemistry and Technology of Food and Food Products, 2nd ed. New York, Interscience Publishers.
2. National Soft Drink Association (NSDA). 2003. The History of America and Soft Drinks Go Hand in Hand. NSDA, Washington, D.C.
3. National Soft Drink Association (NSDA). 1999. Frequently Asked Questions About Soft Drinks, NSDA, Washington, D.C.
4. Riley J.J. 1972. A History of the American Soft Drink Industry: Bottled Carbonated Beverages, 1807–1957. New York, Arno Press.
5. Granata, A.J. 1946. Carbonic Gas and Carbonation in Bottled Carbonated Beverage Manufacture, Beverage Production and Plant Operation. NSDA, Washington, D.C.
6. Medina, A.S. 1993. Carbonation Volumes in Aqueous Solution. Proc ISBT, Homosassa, FL, p. 237.
7. Loomis, A.G. 1928. Int. Crit. Tables, Volume 3, No. 260.
8. Glidden, J. 2001. White Paper: Net Contents Determination by Weight. Pepsi-Cola internal document.
9. Woodruff, J.G. 1974. Beverage Acids, Flavors, and Acidulants. Beverages: Carbonated and Non-Carbonated, AVI Publishing, Westport, CT.

10. Banker, G. 1996. Disperse Systems. Modern Pharmaceutics, Third Edition. Marcel Dekker, New York.

11. Bena, D. 2003. Water Use in the Beverage Industry, in Food Plant Sanitation (YH Hui, ed.). Marcel Dekker, New York.

12. Suffet, I.H. (ed.). 1995. Advances in Taste and Odor Treatment and Control. Cooperative Research Report of the American Water Works Association Research Foundation and the Lyonnaise des Eaux, AWWA-RF, Denver, CO.

13. Bena, D. 2003. Water Use in the Beverage Industry, in Food Plant Sanitation (Y.H. Hui, ed.). Marcel Dekker, New York.

14. Brittan, P.J. 1997. Integrating Conventional and Membrane Water Treating Systems. International Society of Beverage Technologists Short Course for Beverage Production, Homosassa, FL, 1997.

15. Koch, R. 2000. Worldwide High Intensity Sweetener Marketplace. Proceedings of the International Society of Beverage Technologists, Homosassa, FL.

16. Hobbs, L. 1997. Sweeteners and Sweetener Handling Systems. International Society of Beverage Technologists Short Course for Beverage Production, Florida International University, Miami, 1997.

17. Boyce, C. (Ed.). 1986. Novo's Handbook of Practical Biotechnology. Novo Industri, Denmark.

18. Finnerty, M. 2002. Sensory Testing of High Fructose Corn Syrup. Proceedings of the International Society of Beverage Technologists, Homosassa, FL.

19. Galluzzo, S. 2000. Sugar Quality Tool. PepsiCo Beverages International, Purchase, NY.

20. McLeod, E. (Exec. Dir.). 2001. The Quality Guidelines and Analytical Procedure Bibliography for Bottler's Carbon Dioxide. ISBT, Homosassa, FL.

21. Selz, P. 1999. Carbon Dioxide Product Literature. Toromont Process Systems, Inc., Calgary, Alberta, Canada.

22. Delonge, H. 1994. Pepsi-Cola Production Manual, Volume 2, Sugar and Sugar Handling.

23. Jacobs, M. 1959. Manufacture and Analysis of Carbonated Beverages. Chemical Publishing Company, New York.

24. Delonge, H. 1994. Pepsi-Cola Production Manual, Volume 2. Carbonation, Pepsi-Cola, Purchase, NY.

25. Bena, D. 2001. Management and Control of Thread Mold. Pepsi-Cola Technical Bulletin, Purchase, NY.

26. Ray, B. 2001. Fundamental Food Microbiology, second edition. CRC Press, Boca Raton, FL.

16 Muffins

Nanna Cross
Consultant, Chicago, IL

CONTENTS

I. BACKGROUND INFORMATION

A. HISTORY OF MUFFINS

English muffins originating in London were made from yeast dough in contrast to quick-bread muffins served in early America. Muffins are described as a quick bread since "quick-acting" chemical leavening agents are used instead of yeast, a "longer-acting" biological leavening agent. Muffins have become increasingly popular as a hot bread served with meals or eaten as a snack. Freshly baked muffins are served in restaurants and bakeries and consumers can buy packaged ready-to-eat muffins from grocery stores and vending machines. It is possible for restaurants and small bakeries to serve a muffin of a consistent high quality with the availability of dry mixes, frozen muffin batter, and pre-deposited frozen muffins available on the wholesale market.

B. HEALTH CONCERNS

The economic burden of chronic disease is a worldwide problem. Chronic diseases contributed to 60% of the deaths worldwide in 2001 (55). The increasing rate of obesity and the ageing of the population are expected to impact the burden of chronic disease. Those with obesity are at greater risk and have an earlier onset of the chronic diseases of diabetes, cardiovascular diseases, cancer, and stroke. Ageing increases the risk for all chronic diseases. Nearly one-quarter of the population in developed countries is made up of those above 60 years of age, with expectations for the numbers to increase to one-third of the population by 2025 (55).

The problems of overweight and obesity are growing rapidly around the world and co-exist with malnutrition in developing countries (55). Surveys of U.S. adults done in 1999–2000 showed that 64% of adults were overweight and 30% were obese (21). The percentage of children and adolescents in the U.S. who are overweight has tripled in the past 30 years with 15% of 6–19 year olds being overweight in 1999–2000 (41).

Obesity rates have increased threefold or more in some parts of North America, Eastern Europe, the Middle East, the Pacific Islands, Australasia, and China since 1980 (54). The prevalence rates of overweight and obesity are growing rapidly in children and adults in such countries as Brazil and Mexico where malnutrition and obesity co-exist in the same household (9). Countries with the highest percentage (5% to 10%) of overweight preschool children are from the Middle East (Qatar), North Africa (Algeria, Eqypt, and Morocco), and Latin America, and the Caribbean (Argentina, Chile, Bolivia, Peru, Uruguay, Costa Rica, and Jamaica) (10).

Globalization of food and the availability of energy-dense snack and "fast foods" have had a significant impact on dietary patterns and the incidence of chronic disease in both developing and developed countries (27). For example, Coca-cola and Pepsi soft drinks and McDonald's, Pizza Hut, and Kentucky Fried Chicken fast foods are now available worldwide (27). Changes in dietary patterns combined with a sedentary lifestyle have increased the rates of obesity and chronic disease. Dietary factors related to chronic disease are excessive intakes of calories, fat—especially saturated fat—and sodium, and low intakes of fruits and vegetables and whole-grain breads and cereals (52).

National dietary guidelines recommend limiting intakes of total fat, saturated fat, trans fat, cholesterol, free sugars, and sodium, and promote dietary fiber from whole grain breads and cereals and fruits and vegetables (56). In 2002, consumers in the U.S. reported making food choices in an effort to avoid fat, sugar, calories, and sodium, and to increase fiber intake (39). Consumers chose fat free foods or foods low in fat 74% to 80% of the time and selected low calorie foods and low sodium foods 76% and 67% of the time, respectively. High fiber foods were chosen 75% of the time and 40% reported using organic foods (39).

The food industry has responded to concerns of consumers and public health officials by developing "healthy" food products, lower in saturated fat, trans fat, cholesterol, sodium, sugar, and calories. New ingredients have been developed by food scientists in government and industry to use as fat replacers and sugar replacers to use in preparing baked products that are lower in calories and saturated and trans fat (Table 16.1, Table 16.2). The newest category of ingredients is concentrated bioactive compounds with specific health benefits (Table 16.3) (43). These ingredients are added to formulations during food processing to enhance the health benefits of specific food products or to develop "functional foods." Individual foods, such as apples, blueberries, oats, tomatoes, and soybeans, are being marketed as functional foods because of the health benefits of components of these foods. For example, diets that include oat fiber and soy protein lower serum cholesterol, and lycopene in tomatoes reduces the risk of prostrate cancer. Apples and blueberries contain unique antioxidants shown to reduce the risk for cancer (42). Examples of bioactive ingredients available to the baking industry are OatVantage™ (Nature Inc., Devon, PA) a concentrated source of soluble fiber, and FenuPure™ (Schouter USA, Minneapolis, MN), a concentrated source of antioxidants from fruits and vegetables.

C. FOOD LABELING AND HEALTH CLAIMS

The Nutrition Labeling and Education Act (NLEA) issued by the Food and Drug Administration (FDA) in the U.S. in 1990 required food labels to include nutrition content on all packaged foods to be effective in 1994 (11). Information required on the Nutrition Facts portion of the food label are the serving size and the amount per serving

TABLE 16.1
Ingredients Used as Fat Replacers in Baked Products

Brand Name	Composition	Supplier
Carbohydrate Based		
Beta-Trim™	Beta-glucan and oat amylodextrin	Rhodia USA, Cranbury, NJ
Fruitrim®	Dried plum and apple puree	Advanced Ingredients Capitola, CA
Just Like Shorten™	Prune and apple puree	PlumLife division of TreeTop, Selah, WA
Lighter Bake™	Fruit juice, dextrins	Sunsweet, Yuma City, CA
Oatrim®	Oat maltodextrin	Quaker Oats, Chicago, IL
Paselli FP	Potato maltodextrin	AVEBE America, Inc., Princeton, NJ
Z-Trim	Multiple grain fibers	U.S. Department of Agriculture
Low and Noncaloric Lipid Based		
Enova™	Diglycerides	Archer Daniels Midland/Kao LLC, Decatur, IL
Benefat®	Triglycerides modified by substituting	Danisco Culter, New Century, KS
Salatrim/Caprenin	short or medium chain fatty acids	Proctor & Gamble, Cincinnati, OH
Olestra/Olean®	Sucrose polyester	Proctor & Gamble, Cincinnati, OH

TABLE 16.2
Ingredients Used as Sugar Replacements in Baked Products

Sweetener	Brand Name	Sweetness Compared to Sucrose	Supplier
Acesulfame-K	Sunett®	200% sweeter	Nutrnova, Somerset, NJ
Sucralose	Splenda®	600% sweeter	Splenda, Inc., Fort. Washington, PA

TABLE 16.3
Ingredients Marketed for Specific Health Benefits

Brand Name	Composition	Health Benefit	Supplier
Caromax™ Carob Fiber	Carob fruit fiber; soluble fiber, tannins, polyphenols, lignan	Lower serum cholesterol	National Starch & Chemical, Bridgewater, NJ
FenuPure™	Fenugreek seed concentrate; galactomannan	Regulate blood glucose; lower serum cholesterol	Schouten USA, Inc., Minneapolis, MN
Fibrex®	Sugar beet fiber; soluble fiber, lignan	Lower serum cholesterol; regulate blood glucose	Danisco Sugar Malmo, Sweden
MultOil	Diglycerides + phytosterols	Lower serum cholesterol	Enzymotec Migdal HaEmeq, Israel
Nextra™	Decholesterolized tallow and corn oil; free of trans fat	Reduce the risk for coronary heart disease	Source Food Technology, Durham, NC
Novelose 240	Corn fiber; high amylose, resistant fiber	Reduce risk for colon cancer	National Starch & Chemical, Bridgewater, NJ
Nutrifood®	Fruit and vegetable liquid concentrates; source of antioxidants–carotenoids, anthocyanins, polyphenols	Reduce risk for chronic diseases–cancer, diabetes, and cardiovascular disease	GNT USA, Inc., Tarrytown; NYGNT Germany, Aachen, Germany
OatVantage™	Beta-glucans, a soluble fiber	Lower serum cholesterol	Nurture, Inc., Devon, PA

of calories, protein, fat, saturated fat, cholesterol, carbohydrates, fiber, sodium, calcium, vitamins A and C, and iron. A 1993 amendment to the NLEA authorized food manufacturers to add health claims related to specific food components (11) (Table 16.4). However, many "functional foods" lack the scientific evidence to meet FDA criteria to make health claims (50). A 2003 amendment to NLEA requires that trans fatty acids be listed under saturated fat on the Food Facts label by January 1, 2006 (11).

The Codex Alimentarius Commission of the Food and Agriculture Organization of the United Nations World Health Organization (FAO/WHO) Codex Guidelines on Nutrition Labeling adopted in 1985 are similar to the

TABLE 16.4
Health Claims Approved for Food Labeling in the U.S.[1]

Food Component	Health Claim
Calcium	Osteoporosis
Dietary fat	Cancer
Dietary saturated fat and cholesterol	Coronary heart disease
Fiber-containing grain products, fruits and vegetables	Cancer
Sodium	Hypertension
Folate	Neural tube defects
Dietary sugar alcohol	Dental caries
Fruits, vegetables and grain products that contain fiber, particularly soluble fiber	Coronary heart disease
Soy protein	Coronary heart disease
Whole-grain foods	Heart disease and certain cancers
Plant sterols/stanol esters	Coronary heart disease
Potassium	High blood pressure and stroke

[1] FDA/CFSAN. 2002b. Food labeling and nutrition. Information for industry. A food labeling guide. Appendix C. Health claims. http://www.cfsan.fda.gov/~dma/flg-6C.html. Accessed on July 3, 2003.

NLEA implemented by the FDA in 1994 (13). The Codex Alimentarius Commission adopted the Codex Guidelines for the use of Nutrition Claims on food labels in 1997 (14). Codex standards are voluntary and each country within the United Nations is free to adopt food-labeling standards. The European Union that includes 15 member states in Europe also sets guidelines for nutrition labeling and nutrition claims, subject to requirements of individual member states.

The Food Standards Agency of the United Kingdom (U.K.) was established in 2000 as the regulatory agency to set policy for food labeling in Great Britain and Northern Ireland (23). The Food Standards Australia New Zealand (22) specifies the requirements for food labeling in these countries (22). Health Canada published new food labeling regulations January 1, 2003, making nutrition labeling mandatory for most foods and allowing diet-related health claims on food labels for the first time (26).

D. FOOD LABELING STANDARDS FOR ORGANICALLY GROWN FOODS

The Organic Foods Production Act of 1990 passed by the U.S. Congress required the U.S. Department of Agriculture to develop certification standards for organically produced agricultural products (2). Producers who meet the standards may specify the percentage of the product that is organic on the food label if 70% or more of the ingredients in the product are organically grown (2). The

Codex Alimentarius Commission has also published standards for labeling organically grown foods (15). Organic fruits and vegetables are produced without using conventional pesticides, petroleum-based fertilizers, or sewage sludge-based fertilizers. Animal products identified as organic come from animals given organic feed without antibiotics or growth hormones. Food products that have been developed through genetic modification cannot be labeled as organically grown foods (2,15).

E. INGREDIENT LABELING FOR POSSIBLE ALLERGENS

The Codex Alimentarius Commission of FAO/WHO and FDA/CFSAN require that food labels list all ingredients known to cause adverse responses in those with food allergies or sensitivities (11,20). The FDA requires listing ingredients from eight foods that account for ~90% of all food allergies. These foods are peanuts, soybeans, milk, eggs, fish, shellfish, tree nuts, and wheat (20). Codex standards require listing ingredients from these same eight foods plus all cereals that contain gluten—rye, barley, oats, and spelt—lactose, and sulphite in concentrations of 10 mg/kg or more (11). Gluten, lactose, and sulphite are listed on food labels because these substances cause distress for some, even though these substances are not considered allergens. Individuals with celiac disease or gluten intolerance eliminate all sources of gluten from the diet. A small percentage of individuals lack lactase, the enzyme needed to digest lactose, and avoid dairy products and all other foods with lactose additives.

Food processing plants are required to follow Good Manufacturing Practices (GMP) to avoid possible cross-contamination with trace amounts of allergens during processing. An example of possible cross-contamination is using the same plant equipment to prepare "nut free" muffins after the equipment was used to prepare muffins with nuts (49). An example of GMP is dedicating food-processing plants to the production of allergenic free foods (49).

Small bakeries, defined by the number of employees or annual gross sales, and restaurants are exempt from the FDA food labeling requirements. Food labeling to identify foods that have been genetically modified through bioengineering (GM) is voluntary (16). However, because of consumer concerns about GM foods, managers of bakeries may choose to include a statement on the ingredient label such as "we do not use ingredients produced by biotechnology" (16,17). Consumers with food allergies have learned to read the list of ingredients on the food label to identify any possible sources of allergens. Managers of small bakeries that use nuts or soy flour in their operation, but unable to follow GMP because of the added cost, may choose to alert consumers with a statement on the ingredient label, such as "this product was made on equipment that also makes products containing tree nuts." Making a decision to sell bakery products made with organic ingredients requires assessing the market for these products, the availability of organic ingredients, and the expected income from the operation.

II. RAW MATERIALS PREPARATION

A. SELECTION AND SCALING OF INGREDIENTS

Muffins made by large commercial bakeries are cake type muffins while those made in the home or small institutions are bread muffins. The differences between cake and bread muffins are that cake muffins are higher in fat and sugar and use soft wheat flours. A common problem encountered in bread type muffins is tunnel formation resulting from overdevelopment of gluten. However, this problem is avoided in cake muffins since sugar, fat, and soft wheat flours interfere with gluten development and prevent tunnel formation. Bread muffins contain 12% of both fat and sugar compared to 18% to 40% fat and 50% to 70% sugar in cake muffins (5).

Formulas for a standard cake muffin and bran muffin are shown in Table 16.5. Ingredient formulas used by commercial bakeries are based on the weight of flour at 100% (25). The amounts of other ingredients are a percentage of flour weight (Baker's percent). For example,

$$\frac{\text{total weight of muffin ingredient}}{\text{total weight of flour}} \times 100\% =$$
$$\% \text{ of the ingredient}$$

If the weight of another ingredient is the same weight as flour, the percent for that ingredient is also 100%. The advantage of using Baker's percent is that batch sizes can be easily increased or decreased by multiplying the percent for each ingredient by the same factor. Weighing all ingredients, including liquids, is faster and more accurate than using measurements, especially in large commercial bakeries.

1. Flour

Flour is the primary ingredient in baked products. Flour represents 30% to 40% of the total batter weight in most cake muffins (5). Most muffin formulas contain a blend of cake or pastry flour and a high protein flour such as bread flour, or all bread flour (51). The protein in flour is needed to provide structure in quick breads made with limited amounts of sugar. Flour contains starch and the proteins, glutenin, and gliadin, which hold other ingredients together to provide structure to the final baked product. Hydration and heat promote gelatinization of starch, a process that breaks hydrogen bonds, resulting in swelling of the starch granule, which gives the batter a more rigid structure (27).

Substituting whole-wheat flour, wheat germ, rolled oats, or bran for part of the flour is an excellent way to increase fiber. Other flours used in muffins include cornmeal, soy, oat, potato, and peanut. An acceptable product is possible when cowpea or peanut flours are substituted for 25% or when whole-wheat flour or corn meal is substituted for 50% of all-purpose flour (29). Acceptable muffins have been prepared when soy protein flour was substituted for 10% to 20% (47) or 100% of all-purpose flour (6). None of these flours contains glutenin or gliadin except whole wheat, and large pieces of bran in whole-wheat flour cut and weaken gluten strands. Thus, there is minimal gluten development when these flours are used; however, the muffins tend to be crumbly and compact unless other modifications are made in the formula.

2. Sugar

Amounts of sugar in muffins range from 50% to 70% based on flour at 100% (5). Sugar contributes tenderness, crust color, and moisture retention in addition to a sweet taste. Sucrose promotes tenderness by inhibiting hydration of flour proteins and starch gelatinization. Sugar is hygroscopic (attracts water) and maintains freshness. Corn syrup, molasses, maple sugar, fruit juice concentrates, and honey are used as sweeteners for flavor variety. Honey or molasses is often used as a sweetener in whole wheat or bran muffins to cover the bitter flavor of the bran (51). The quantity of liquid will need to be decreased if these sweeteners are used instead of sucrose because of the high water content in these syrups.

Chemical changes in sugars during baking contribute characteristic flavors and browning. Carmelization of sugar is responsible for the brown crust of muffins. Carmelization involves dehydration and polymerization (condensation) of sucrose (35). Reducing sugars such as dextrose, corn syrup, or high fructose corn syrup are often added to muffins at levels of 1% to 3% to increase crust color (51). Reducing sugars react with amino acids in flour, milk, and eggs to form a complex responsible for the flavor and brown crust of muffins.

The reaction between the aldehyde or ketone group in reducing sugars and the amino acids in protein is described as the Maillard reaction (37). This Maillard reaction together with carmelization contributes to the characteristic flavor and color of the crust of a baked muffin. Crust temperatures reach 100°C and above, which lower water activity. Both the high temperature and low water activity are necessary for the Maillard reaction to occur (38).

Sugar replacers such as acesulfame-K and sucralose (Table 16.2) can be substituted for all or part of the sugar. Sugar replacers, however, do not contribute to tenderness, browning, or moisture retention, thus other formula modifications are necessary for an acceptable product. For example, adding a small amount of molasses or cocoa for

TABLE 16.5
Muffin Formulas Listed by Baker's Percent and Weight[1,2]

Ingredient	Basic Cake Muffin Baker's %	Weight gm	Bran Muffin Baker's %	Weight gm
Flour	100.00	990	–	–
Bread flour	–	–	50.0	4545
Cake flour	–	–	18.75	1704
Bran	–	–	31.25	2842
Sugar	60.00	5455	31.25	2842
Baking powder	5.00	455	1.50	136
Baking soda	–	–	2.20	220
Salt	1.25	114	1.50	136
Milk powder	7.50	682	12.50	1136
Molasses	–	–	37.50	3409
Shortening	40.00	3636	18.75	1704
Whole eggs (liquid)	30.00	2727	12.50	1136
Honey	–	–	19.00	1727
Water	60.00	5455	100.00	990
Raisins	–	–	25.00	2273
Total	303.75	27616	316.70	32790

Mixer: Hobart N-50 with 5 quart bowl and paddle agitator.
Directions for basic cake muffin formula:
Blend dry ingredients together by mixing for 1 minute at low speed.
    Add shortening and eggs and mix for 1 minute at low speed.
    Add water and mix for 1 minute at low speed.
Scaling Weight: 2.5 ounces batter.
Yield: 2–1/2 dozen muffins.
Bake: at 205°C for 19–21 minutes in a gas-fired reel oven.
Directions for bran muffin formula:
    Blend dry ingredients and mix for 1 minute at low speed.
    Add shortening, eggs, honey, molasses, and 50% (4.5 kg) of the water and mix for 1 minute at medium low speed.
    Add the remaining water and mix for 1 minute at low speed.
    Add raisins and mix at low speed for 3 minutes or until raisins are dispersed.
Scaling Weight: 3 ounces batter.
Yield: 3 dozen muffins.
Bake: at 193°C for 20–25 minutes in a gas-fired reel oven.

[1] Benson RC. 1988. Technical Bulletin. Muffins. Manhattan, KS: American Institute of Baking 19(6):1–4.
[2] Doerry W. 1995. Chapter six: Cake muffins. In: Breadmaking. Vol 2: Controlled Baking. Manhattan, KS: The American Institute of Baking. pp. 208–213.

color to substitute for color from carmelization of sucrose. The shelf life of muffins prepared without sugar would be very limited.

3. Fat

Muffins contain 18% to 40% fat based on flour at 100% (5). Fat contributes to the eating qualities of tenderness, flavor, texture, and a characteristic mouthfeel. Fat keeps the crumb and crust soft and helps retain moisture, and thus contributes to keeping qualities or shelf life (36). Fat enhances the flavor of baked products since flavor components dissolve in fat. Both shortening and vegetable oils are used in muffins.

To meet the demands of the consumer, muffin formulas are being modified to reduce total, saturated fat, trans fat, and calories, and to increase the amount of monounsaturated and polyunsaturated fat. Canola oil and flaxseed meal are being added to muffins to increase the proportion of monounsaturated fat. Muffins made with reduced fat and polyunsaturated fatty acids (13% safflower oil) were comparable in sensory and physical characteristics to the standard muffin made with shortening at 20% (8). Low fat and fat free muffins are available ready to eat and as frozen batters or dry mixes for bakeoff.

Various fat replacers have been classified by their macronutrient base (Table 16.1). Carbohydrate- and lipid-based fat replacers can be used to prepare muffins acceptable to the consumer. Lipid-based fat replacers that have the same chemical and physical characteristics of triglycerides are described as fat substitutes (1). These products provide the same characteristics as fat but with fewer calories. Monoglycerides, diglycerides, and modified triglycerides are examples of fat substitutes that replicate the mouthfeel and sensory qualities of baked products made with shortening.

Enova™ (Archer Daniels Midland KAO LLC, Decatur, IL) is an example of a diglyceride that is lower in calories than other oils and being marketed as beneficial in weight management (45). Benefat® (Danisco Culter, New Century, KS) and Caprenin (Proctor & Gamble, Cincinnati, OH) are examples of triglycerides modified by substituting shorter chain fatty acids (1). Sucrose polyesters of six to eight fatty acids are marketed as Olean® (Procter & Gamble, Cincinnati, OH), a fat substitute with the same physical qualities as shortening without the calories since sucrose polyesters are not digested or absorbed in the human intestinal tract.

A commercial shortening product (Nextra™) (Source Food Technology, Durham, NC) made from decholesterolized tallow and corn oil is being marketed to the baking industry as a trans-free fat to replace shortening (44). Other methods used by the food industry to decrease the amount of trans fat are 1) blending hydrogenated fat high in stearic acid with unhydrogenated oils, and 2) interesterifying (rearranging) unhydrogenated oils with saturated-fat-based oils (30).

Carbohydrate-based fat replacers are described as fat mimetics. These include cellulose, corn syrup, dextrins, fiber, gum, maltodextrins, polydextrose, starches, and fruit based purees. Z-trim, developed by a U.S. Department of Agriculture scientist, is a mixture of plant fibers (31). Fat mimetics replicate the mouthfeel and texture of fat in baked products and extend the shelf life by binding water and trapping air (3). Acceptable low fat cake muffins (5% fat) used 2% pregelatinized dull waxy starch and corn syrup (3.6%) to replace fat (28).

Fruit purees or pastes of one or more fruits—apples, dates, figs, grapes, plums, prunes, and raisins—are being promoted as fat replacers. Just Like Shorten™ is a mixture of dried prunes and apples. The fruit purees have humectant properties, promote tenderness and moistness, increase shelf life, and can replace some of the sugar and/or fat in muffins and cakes.

Formulas will need to be developed based on adjustments in ingredients when fat replacers are substituted for all or part of the fat in the formula. New formulas need to be prepared and the muffins evaluated using the muffin scorecard (Table 16.6) as well as evaluating the shelf life. Several formula adjustments may be necessary before an acceptable muffin is developed.

4. Leavening Agents

The amount of baking powder used in muffins varies between 2% and 6% based on flour at 100% with lower amounts in muffins with ingredients that increase acid (5). Gases released by a leavening agent influence volume and cell structure. During baking, heat increases gas volume and pressure to expand cell size until proteins are coagulated (35). Stretching of the cell walls during baking improves texture and promotes tenderness (35).

The quantity of leavening used in a baked product depends on the choice of leavening agent as well as other ingredients. Formulation of baking powders considers the amount of leavening acids needed to neutralize baking soda or sodium bicarbonate, an alkaline salt. Double-acting baking powder (most commonly used in muffins) contains both slow- and fast-acting acids (37). Fast-acting acids are readily soluble at room temperature while slow-acting acids are less soluble and require heat over extended time to release carbon dioxide. Formulations of slow- and fast-acting acid leavening agents control the reaction time and optimize volume (7). An example of a formulation to neutralize sodium bicarbonate is a mixture of slow- and fast-acting acids—monocalcium phosphate monohydrate (a fast-acting acid) combined with sodium aluminum sulfate (a slow-acting acid). Development of baking powder requires consideration of the unique neutralizing value (NV) and the rate of reaction (ROR) or the percent of carbon dioxide released during the reaction of sodium bicarbonate with a leavening acid during the first eight minutes of baking (4,7).

Baking soda is used in addition to double-acting baking powder when muffins contain acidic ingredients such as sour cream, yogurt, buttermilk, light sour cream, molasses, and some fruits and fruit juices (37). Baking soda in the amount of 2% to 3% in addition to baking powder is added to acidic batters (5).

Sodium carbonate is a product of an incomplete reaction in formulas with excess sodium bicarbonate. Excess sodium carbonate results in a muffin with a soapy, bitter flavor, and a yellow color because of the effect of an alkaline medium on the anthoxanthin pigments of flour (38). Also, formulas with too much baking powder or soda results in a muffin with a coarse texture and low volume because of an overexpansion of gas, which causes the cell structure to weaken and collapse during baking. Inadequate amounts of baking powder will result in a compact muffin with low volume. Figures 16.1 and 16.2 show different chemical reactions for fast-acting and slow-acting baking powders (37).

5. Whole Eggs

Liquid eggs contribute 10% to 30% of muffin batter based on flour at 100% and dried eggs contribute 5% to 10% (5). Eggs provide flavor, color, and a source of liquid. Upon baking, the protein in egg white coagulates to provide structure. Adding egg whites to muffin batter provides structure to the finished product and a muffin that is

TABLE 16.6
Scorecard for Muffins[1]

Evaluator	Product	Date
External Qualities		
1a. Volume	Score	

Specific Volume: $\pi r^2 \times$ height = weight in grams (cm) 1=low volume, compact cells;
   5=light with moderate cells; 7=large volume, large cells and/or tunnels

1b. Contour of the surface
1=absolutely flat; 3=somewhat rounded; 5=pleasingly rounded;
   7=somewhat pointed; 9=very pointed

1c. Crust color
1=much too pale; 3=somewhat pale; 5=pleasingly golden brown;
   7=somewhat too brown; 9=much too brown

Internal Qualities

1d. Interior color
1=much too white; 3=somewhat white; 5=pleasingly creamy;
   7=somewhat too yellow; 9=much too yellow

1e. Cell uniformity and size
1=much too small; 3=somewhat thick; 5=moderate;
   7=somewhat too large; 9=numerous large tunnels

1f. Thickness of cell walls
1=extremely thick; 3=somewhat thick; 5=normal thickness;
   7=somewhat too thin; 9=much too thin

1g. Texture
1=extremely crumbly; 3=somewhat crumbly; 5=easily broken,
   7=slightly crumbly; 9=tough, little tendency to crumble

1h. Flavor
1=absolutely not sweet enough; 3=not nearly sweet enough;
   5=pleasingly sweet; 7=somewhat too sweet; 9=much too sweet

1i. Aftertaste
1=extremely distinct; 3=somewhat distinct; 5=none

1j. Aroma
1=lack of aroma; 5=sweet and fresh aroma; 9=sharp,
   bitter, or foreign aroma

1k. Mouthfeel
1=gummy, cohesive; 3=somewhat gummy; 5=tender,
   light and moist; 7=somewhat dry and tough; 9=tough and hard to chew

Overall Acceptability
1=very unacceptable; 3=somewhat acceptable;
   5=very acceptable

[1] Modified from McWilliams M. 2001. Chapter 3: Sensory evaluation. In: Foods: Experimental Perspectives. 4th ed. Upper Saddle River, NJ: Prentice Hall. pp. 33–57.

easily broken without excessive crumbling (48). Substituting egg whites for whole eggs, however, will result in a dry, tough muffin unless the formula is adjusted to increase the amount of fat (48). Fat in the yolk acts as an emulsifier and contributes to mouthfeel and keeping qualities.

6. Nonfat Dry Milk Powder

Milk powder represents 5% to 12% of the muffin batter based on flour at 100% (5). Milk powder is added to dry ingredients and water or fruit juice is used for liquid in muffin formulas. Milk powder binds flour protein to provide strength, body, and resilience—qualities helpful in reducing damage during packing and shipping (51). In addition, milk powder adds flavor and retains moisture. The aldehyde group from lactose in milk combines with the amino group from protein upon heating, contributing to Maillard browning.

7. Sodium Chloride

The amount of salt in muffins is 1.5% to 2% based on flour at 100% (5). The function of sodium chloride is to enhance the flavor of other ingredients. Sodium chloride may be omitted from the formula without compromising flavor, if other ingredients such as dried fruit or spices are added for flavor.

$$3CaH_4(PO_4)_2 \quad + \quad 8NaHCO_3 \quad \rightarrow \quad Ca_3(PO_4)_2$$

Monocalcium   Sodium   Tricalcium
Phosphate   Bicarbonate   Phosphate

$$+ \; 4Na_2HPO_4 \; + \; 8CO_2 \; + \; 8H_2O$$

Disodium   Carbon   Water
Phosphate   Dioxide

FIGURE 16.1 Formation of bicarbonate of soda from a fast-acting acid salt.

Step 1.

$$Na_2(Al)_2(SO_4)_4 + 6H_2O \rightarrow 2Al(OH)_3 + Na_2SO_4 + 3H_2SO_4$$

Sodium   Water   Aluminum   Sodium   Sulfuric
Aluminum   Hydroxide   Sulfate   Acid
Sulfate

Step 2.

$$3H_2SO_4 \; + \; 6NaHCO_3 \; \rightarrow \; 3Na_2SO_4 \; + \; 6H_2CO_3 \; \rightarrow$$

Sulfuric   Sodium   Sodium   Carbonic
Acid   Bicarbonate   Sulfate   Acid

$$6CO_2 \; + \; 6H_2O$$

Carbon   Water
Dioxide

FIGURE 16.2 Formation of bicarbonate of soda and carbon dioxide from from a slow-acting acid salt.

8. Liquids

Liquids perform several functions in baked products (5). These include dissolving dry ingredients and gelatinization of starch and providing moistness in the final baked product. Insufficient liquid results in incomplete gelatinization of the starch and a muffin with insufficient structure to support expansion of air volume. The muffins will have non-uniform cell structure, overly crumbly texture, low volume, and a dip in the top.

9. Additional Ingredients

Other ingredients are often added to muffins for variety in flavor, texture, and color, and to increase the specific nutrients or health components such as fiber, vitamins and minerals, or antioxidants from fruit and vegetable extracts. Part of the flour may be replaced with cornmeal, bran, whole-wheat, oat, or other flours to increase the fiber content. Adjustments in the amount of water in the formula are necessary when whole-wheat flour, bran, or other concentrated sources of fiber are added because fiber absorbs a great deal of water (51). An example of a concentrated source of fiber is Caromax™ (National Starch & Chemical, Bridgewater, NJ)(42). Nutrifood® (GNT USA, Tarrytown, NY), a liquid concentrate marketed as a blend of the antioxidants carotenoids, anthocyanins, and polyphenols is an example of a bioactive ingredient (43).

Other ingredients can be substituted for part of the liquid. For example, applesauce, bananas, shredded carrots, or zucchini. Variations in texture are achieved by adding fresh fruit such as apples or blueberries or dried fruit such as dates, raisins, or apricots. Nuts and poppy seeds complement the flavor of sweet muffins while grated cheese, whole-kernel corn, green peppers, chopped ham, and bacon add interest to corn muffins. Added flavorings include cinnamon, nutmeg, allspice, cloves, and orange or lemon zest. Topping mixtures such as chopped nuts, cinnamon, and sugar are added to the batter after depositing.

III. PROCESSING STAGE 1

A. MIXING

There are two primary methods for mixing muffins—the cake method and the muffin method. The cake method involves creaming sugar and shortening together, followed by adding liquid ingredients with the final addition of dry ingredients. The muffin method of mixing involves two to three steps. First, dry ingredients are mixed together; second, shortening or oil and other liquids are mixed together; and third, the liquids are added to the dry ingredients and mixed until the dry ingredients are moistened. Additional ingredients are added at the end of the mixing cycle or after depositing the muffin batter. Institutional or commercial bakeries use a mixer on slow speed for three to five minutes. Inadequate mixing results in a muffin with a low volume, since some of the baking powder will be too dry to react completely.

IV. PROCESSING STAGE 2

A. DEPOSITING

The traditional size of muffins is two ounces although today muffins are marketed in a wide range of sizes from one-half ounce mini-muffins to muffins five ounces or larger in size (51). For institutions or bakeries, small batter depositors are available that will deposit four muffins at a time. Also available are large piston type depositors that maintain accurate flow of the batter (5).

V. PROCESSING STAGE 3

A. BAKING

Many physical and chemical changes occur in the presence of heat to transform a liquid batter into a final baked muffin. Solubilization and activation of the leavening agent generates carbon dioxide that expands to increase the volume of the muffin. Gelatinization of starch and coagulation of proteins provide permanent cell structure and crumb development. Carmelization of sugars and Maillard Browning of proteins and reducing sugars promote browning of the crust. Reduced water activity facilitates Maillard Browning as well as crust hardening (38).

The choice of oven, baking pans, and baking temperature influence the final baked product (5). A good flow of heat onto the bottom of the pan is necessary to produce a good product. Muffin tins are usually placed directly on the shelf or baking surface. The appropriate oven temperature is related to scaling and the type of oven. Standard two-ounce muffins are baked at 204°C or slightly higher in a deck oven. Deck ovens may be stacked and are often used in small retail bakeries since these are less expensive and easier to maintain than reel or rotary ovens. Reel ovens consist of an insulated cubic compartment six or seven feet high. A Ferris wheel type mechanism inside the chamber moves four to eight shelves in a circle, allowing each shelf to be brought to the door for adding or removing muffin tins from the shelves (32). Retail bakers often prefer the reel oven since several hundred to several thousand pounds of batter can be baked each day. Rack ovens may be stationary or the racks may be rotated during baking.

VI.   PROCESSING STAGE 4

A.   COOLING

Products should be cooled prior to wrapping. This allows the structure to "set" and reduces the formation of moisture condensation within the package. Condensed moisture creates an undesirable medium that promotes yeast, mold, bacterial growth, and spoilage.

VII.   PROCESSING STAGE 5

A.   PACKAGING

Muffins may be wrapped individually, in the tray in which they are baked, or transferred into plastic form trays for merchandizing (5). The shelf life of muffins is three to five days for wrapped muffins, and four to seven days for those packaged wrapped in foil or plastic wrap. The storage life of muffins is significantly influenced by exposure to oxygen and moisture (46). Cake muffins have a longer shelf life than bread muffins because of the high sugar content and lower water activity (51). Added ingredients such as cheese, ham, and dried fruits, high in sodium or sugar content, reduce water activity and increase the shelf life.

VIII.   FINISHED PRODUCT

A muffin fresh out of the oven will vary in appearance based on the formula, whether the formula is for a cake or bread muffin; the size of the muffin, mini-muffin or

mega-muffin; and the desired shape from flat or mushroom shaped tops to the traditional bell-shaped muffin (51). In general, a desirable muffin product has a symmetrical shape, a rounded top golden brown in color, cells that are uniform and moderate in size, a sweet flavor and pleasant aroma, is tender and moist, is easily broken apart, and is easy to chew with a pleasant aftertaste.

A.   MUFFIN EVALUATION

Bakers can use the Table 16.6 Scorecard for Muffins to evaluate muffins in the process of developing or modifying muffin formulas. Large commercial bakeries may use more sophisticated methods to evaluate bakery products, such as gas chromatography to evaluate flavor components.

1.   Volume

Compact muffins with small cells or large muffins with peaked tops and tunnels are undesirable in all types of muffins. Diameter is a more important criterion than volume for evaluating mushroom and flat topped muffins. For bell shaped muffins, volume can be evaluated objectively by measuring the height and width of the muffin ($\pi r^2 \times$ height). The volume can be determined indirectly by measuring the circumference of a cross section of the muffin in cubic centimeters and dividing by the weight in grams. This can be done by measuring the height of the muffin at the highest point, then slicing off the top of the muffin and measuring the diameter of the muffin.

2.   Contour of the Surface

The muffin should be rounded with a pebbled surface.

3.   Color of Crust

Crust color should be a pleasing golden brown, not pale or burnt.

4.   Interior Color

Crumb color should be a pleasant creamy color, not white and not too yellow. Crumb color will be darker with whole grain flour or added ingredients such as nuts or dried fruits, or spices.

5.   Cell Uniformity and Size

Cell structure can be evaluated by making a vertical cut in the muffin to form two equal halves and then making an ink print or photocopy (34). A desirable muffin should have a uniform cell structure without tunnels.

6.   Thickness of Cell Walls

Uniform thick-walled cells are desirable. Coarseness, thin-cell walls, uneven cell size, and tunnels indicate poor grain.

7. Texture

Texture depends on the physical condition of the crumb and is influenced by the grain. A desirable muffin should be easily broken, and slightly crumbly. Extreme crumbling, or toughness with lack of crumbling, are undesirable characteristics.

8. Flavor

An acceptable muffin should have a pleasingly sweet flavor. Flat, foreign, salty, soda, sour, or bitter tastes are undesirable.

9. Aftertaste

An acceptable muffin should have a pleasant, sweet aftertaste, not bitter or foreign.

10. Aroma

Aroma is recognized by the sense of smell. The aroma may be sweet, rich, musty, or flat. The ideal aroma should be pleasant, fresh, sweet, and natural. Sharp, bitter, or foreign aromas are undesirable.

11. Mouthfeel

Mouthfeel refers to the textural qualities perceived in the mouth. Characteristics can be described as gritty, hard, tough, tender, light, and moist. A desirable muffin is tender, light, and moist, and requires minimal chewing.

ACKNOWLEDGMENTS

The information in this chapter has been derived from a chapter in *Food Chemistry Workbook*, edited by J.S. Smith & G.L. Christen, Science Technology System, West Sacramento, California, 2002. Used with permission.

The author acknowledges Ron Wirtz, Ph.D., former Library Director, AIB, and currently Head, Education & Information Services, Greenblatt Library, Medical College of Georgia.

REFERENCES

1. Akoh CC. 1998. Scientific status summary. Fat replacers. Food Technol 52(3):47–53.
2. AMS/USDA. 2003. The National Organic Program. Background information. http://www.ams.usda.gov/nop/FactSheets/Backgrounder.html. Accessed on July 8, 2003.
3. American Dietetic Association. 1998. Position of the American Dietetic Association: Fat replacers. J Am Diet Assoc 98(4):463–468.
4. Anonymous. 2003. I. Leavening acids. http://www.gallard.com/baking.htm. Accessed on June 1, 2003.
5. Benson RC. 1988. Technical Bulletin. Muffins. American Institute of Baking 10(6):1–4.
6. Bordi PL, Lambert CU, Smith J, Hollender R, Borja ME. 2001. Acceptability of soy protein in oatmeal muffins. Foodserv Res Int 13(2):101–110.
7. Borowski R. 2000. Leavening basics. Baking & Snack. November 1. http://bakingbusiness.com/archives/archive_article.asp?ArticleID=36622. Accessed on June 19, 2003.
8. Berglund PT, Hertsgaard DM. 1986. Use of vegetable oils at reduced levels in cake, piecrust, cookies, and muffins. J. Food Sci 51(3):640–644.
9. Chopra M. 2002. Globalization and food: Implications for the promotion of "healthy" diets. In: World Health Organization. Globalization, Diets and Noncommunicable Diseases, Geneva, pp. 1–16.
10. de Onis M, Blossner M. 2000. Prevalence and trends of overweight among preschool children in developing countries. Am J Clin Nutr. 72(4):1031–1039.
11. DHHS/FDA. 2003. Food labeling: Trans fatty acids in nutrition labeling: Consumer research to consider nutrient content, and health claims. Federal Register. 68(133):41434–41438.
12. Doerry WT. 1995. Chapter six: Cake muffins. In: Breadmaking. Vol 2: Controlled Baking. Manhattan, KS: The American Institute of Baking, pp. 208–213.
13. FAO/WHO. 2001. Codex general standards for the labeling of prepackaged foods. Codex Alimentarious – Food Labelling – Complete Texts – Revised 2001. Rome: Joint FAO/WHO Food Standards Programme CODEX ALIMENTARIUS COMMISSION. http://www.fao.org/DOCREP/005/Y2770E. Accessed on July 3, 2003.
14. FAO/WHO. 2001. Codex guidelines on nutrition labeling. Codex Alimentarious – Food Labelling – Complete Texts – Revised 2001. Rome: Joint FAO/WHO Food Standards Programme CODEX ALIMENTARIUS COMMISSION. 2001. http://www.fao.org/DOCREP/005/ Y2770E. Accessed on July 3, 2003.
15. FAO/WHO. 2001. Section 2. Description and definitions. Codex Alimentarious – Organically Produced Foods. Rome: Joint FAO/WHO Food Standards Programme Codex Alimentarious Commission. http://www.fao.org/DOCREP/005/Y2772E/Y2772E00.htm. Accessed on July 8, 2003.
16. FDA/CFSAN. 2001. Guidance for industry. Voluntary labeling indicating whether foods have or have not been developed using bioengineering. http://www.cfsan.fda.gov/~dms/bio/abgu.html. Accessed on July 7, 2003.
17. FDA/CFSAN. 2002. Food labeling and nutrition. Information for industry. http://www.cfsan.fda.gov/~dms/lab-ind.htm. Accessed on July 3, 2003.
18. FDA/CFSAN. 2002. Food labeling and nutrition. Information for industry. A food labeling guide. Appendix C. Health Claims. http://www.cfsan.fda.gov/~dms/flg-6C.html Accessed on July 3, 2003.
19. FDA/CFSAN. 2002. Food labeling and nutrition. Small business food labeling exemption. http://www.cfsan.fda.gov/~dms/lab-ind.htm. Accessed on July 3, 2003.
20. FDA/ORA. 2001. Compliance Policy Guide: Compliance Policy Guidance for FDA Staff. Sec.

555.250. Statement of policy for labeling and preventing cross-contact of common food allergens. Apr 19. http://www.fda.gov/ora/compliance_ref/cpg/cpgfod/cpg555-250.htm. Accessed on July 5, 2003.

21. Flegal KM, Carroll MD, Ogden CL, Johnson CL. 2002. Prevalence and trends in obesity among US adults, 1999–2000. JAMA. 288(14):1723–1727.

22. Food Standards Australia New Zealand. 2003. Food labelling. http://www.foodstandards.gov/au/whatsinfood/foodlabelling.cfm. Accessed on June 25, 2003.

23. Food Standards of UK. 2003. About us. http://www.food.gov.uk/aboutus. Accessed on July 11, 2003.

24. Food Standards of UK. 2003. Claims on labels. http://www.food.gov.uk/foodlabelling/claimsonlabels. Accessed on July 11, 2003.

25. Gisslen W. 2000. Chapter 1. Basic principles. In: Gisslen W. Professional baking. 3rd ed. New York: John Wiley & Sons, Inc. pp. 3–16.

26. Health Canada. 2003. Nutrition Labelling website. http://www.hc-sc.gc.ca/hpfb-dgpsa/onpp-bppn/labelling-etiquetage/index-e.html. Accessed on June 25, 2003.

27. Hawkes C. 2002. Marketing activities of global soft drink and fast food companies in emerging markets: a review. In: World Health Organization. Globalization, diets and noncommunicable diseases, Geneva, pp. 1–78.

28. Hippleheuser AL, Landberg LA, Turnak FL, 1995. A system approach to formulating a low-fat muffin. Food Technol 49(3):91–95.

29. Holt SD, McWatters KH, Resurreccion AVA. 1992. Validation of predicted baking performance of muffins containing mixtures of wheat, cowpea, peanut, sorghum, and cassava flours. J Food Sci 57(2):470–474.

30. Hunter JE. 2002. *Trans* fatty acids: Effects and alternatives. Food Technol 56(12):140.

31. Inglett GE. 1997. Development of a dietary fiber gel for calorie-reduced foods. Cereal Foods World 42(3):81–83, 85.

32. Matz SA. 1988. Chapter nine: Oven and baking. In: Equipment for Bakers. McAllen, TX: Pan Tech International, pp. 319–362.

33. McWilliams M. 2001. Chapter 3: Sensory evaluation. In: Foods: Experimental Perspectives. 4th ed. Upper Saddle River, NJ: Prentice Hall, pp. 33–57.

34. McWilliams M. 2001. Chapter 4: Objective evaluation. In: Foods: Experimental Perspectives. 4th ed. Upper Saddle River, NJ: Prentice Hall, pp. 59–81.

35. McWilliams M. 2001. Chapter 6: Physical aspects of food preparation. In: Foods: Experimental Perspectives. 4th ed. Upper Saddle River, NJ: Prentice Hall. pp. 97–119.

36. McWilliams M. 2001. Chapter 12: Fats and oils in food products. In: Foods: Experimental Perspectives. 4th ed. Upper Saddle River, NJ: Prentice Hall, pp. 245–265.

37. McWilliams M. 2001. Chapter 17: Dimensions in baking. In: Foods: Experimental Perspectives. 4th ed. Upper Saddle River, NJ: Prentice Hall, pp. 381–413.

38. McWilliams M. 2001. Chapter 18: Baking applications. In: Foods: Experimental Perspectives. 4th ed. Upper Saddle River, NJ: Prentice Hall, pp. 415–449.

39. NMI. 2003. Health and Wellness Trends Report 2003. Harleyville, PA: Natl Marketing Institute.

40. O'Brien Nabors, L. 2002. Sweet choices: Sugar replacements for foods and beverages. Food Technol 56(7):28–30, 34, 45.

41. Ogden CL, Flegal KM, Carroll MD, Johnson CL. 2002. Prevalence and trends in overweight among US children and adolescents, 1999–2000. JAMA 288(14):1728–1732.

42. Pszczola DE. 2001. Antioxidants: From preserving food quality to quality of life. Food Technol 55(6):51–59.

43. Pszczola DE. 2002. Evolving ingredient components offer specific health value. Food Technol 56(12):50–71.

44. Pszczola DE. 2002. Bakery ingredients: Past, present, and future directions. Food Technol 56(1):56–72.

45. Pszczola DE. 2003. Putting weight-management ingredients on the scale. Food Technol 57(3):41–57.

46. Rice J. 2002. Packed for life. Bakery & Snack. February 1. http://www.bakingbusiness.com/archives_article.asp?ArticleID=48958. Accessed on June 6, 2003.

47. Sim J, Tam N. 2001. Eating qualities of muffins prepared with 10% and 20% soy flour. J Nutr Recipe Menu Dev 3(2):25–34.

48. Stauffer CE. 2002. Eggs: Extra Benefits. Baking & Snack. February 1. http://www.bakingbusiness.com/tech/channel.asp?ArticleID=48984. Accessed on January 20, 2003.

49. Taylor SL, Hefle SL. 2001. Scientific status summary. Food allergies and other food sensitivities. Food Technol 44(9):68–93.

50. Wahlqvist ML, Wattanapenpaiboon N. 2002. Can functional foods make a difference to disease prevention and control? In: Globalization, Diets and Noncommunicable diseases, Geneva, World Health Organization, pp. 1–18.

51. Willyard M. 2000. Muffin technology (update). Manhattan, KS: American Institute of Baking, 22(10):1–6.

52. WHO. 2001. Nutrition and NCD Prevention. Department of Noncommunicable Disease Prevention and Health Promotion, Geneva, http://www.who.int/hpr/nutrition/index.shtml. Accessed on June 5, 2003.

53. WHO. 2002. 1. Global ageing: A triumph and a challenge. In: Active Ageing. A Policy Framework. Geneva, pp. 6–18.

54. WHO. 2002. Overview. In: Reducing Risks, Promoting Healthy Life. The World Health Report 2002, Geneva, pp. 7–14.

55. WHO. 2003. 2. Background. In: Diet, Nutrition and the Prevention of Chronic Disease: Report of a Joint WHO/FAO Expert Consultation. WHO Technical Report Series 916, Geneva, pp. 4–12.

56. WHO. 2003. 5. Population nutrient intake goals for preventing diet-related chronic diseases. In: Diet, Nutrition and the Prevention of Chronic Disease: Report of a Joint WHO/FAO Expert Consultation. WHO Technical Report Series 916, Geneva, pp. 54–70.

17 Cereals–Biology, Pre- and Post-Harvest Management

Yizhong Cai and Harold Corke
Cereal Science Laboratory, Department of Botany, The University of Hong Kong

CONTENTS

I. INTRODUCTION

Cereals are the most important crops in the world. They dominate world agricultural production since they directly or indirectly provide a large proportion of the human sustenance. About half of the plowed land in the world is used for growing the principal cereals. Cereal grains commonly contain 60–70% starch and 7–14% protein. They are the most important source of carbohydrates for humans and domestic animals, and also provide a substantial proportion of protein. Cereals are the staple foods for many people everywhere on the globe, particularly in the developing countries, because they are a relatively cheap source of calories and protein compared to meat.

Grain is a collective term applied to cereals. The main cereal grains include wheat, rice, maize, barley, sorghum, rye, oats, and millets. The majority of the world population subsists mostly on wheat, rice, and maize. These three cereals account for more than 80% of total cereal grain yield in the world. Other cereals belong to minor cereal crops called coarse grains. Most cereals can be used as staple grains for humans, but maize, barley, oats, and grain sorghum can also be used as feed grains for livestock, particularly in developed countries.

Cereals are members of the grass family Gramineae, being monocotyledonous angiosperms. They show great genetic diversity and are ubiquitous, ranging in adaptation from the semi-arid and humid tropics to both wet and dry temperate zones, and even to very cold climates (e.g., rye and oats). Typical characteristics include fibrous root systems, an upright stalk with nodes and internodal spacing and a pithy stalk, and narrow long blade leaves with parallel veins. Cereal grains are single-seed fruits called caryopses. The seed consists of seed coat, embryo (germ) and endosperm. Cereal grains contain starch, protein, lipid, fiber, vitamins, and minerals.

Cereals are comparatively easy to grow and harvest, to store, and to process into versatile and popular foods. The chemical, physical, and biological properties of cereal grains determine their suitability for a specific market. Grain yield and quality are genetically controlled and climatically influenced, and also are dependent on field, pre- and post-harvest management during the growing, harvesting, drying and storage periods. Cereal grain losses occur throughout production, harvesting, threshing, drying, storage, marketing, and distribution. These losses are estimated to be nearly 20–30% of grain yield. Therefore, it is important for proper field, pre- and post-harvest managements to reduce or eliminate losses of cereal grains and provide high quality product to market.

II. BIOLOGICAL CHARACTERISTICS

Cereals are usually referred to their common names, such as durum wheat and common wheat. In botanical classification, cereals are monocotyledonous plants belonging to

TABLE 17.1
Scientific and Common Names of Major Cereals in the Grass Family (Gramineae)

Common Name	Scientific Name (genus and species name)
Common wheat	*Triticum aestivum*
Durum wheat	*Triticum durum*
Rice	*Oryza sativa*
Maize (corn)	*Zea mays*
Barley	*Hordeum vulgare*
Grain sorghum	*Sorghum vulgare*
Common oats	*Avena sativa*
Rye	*Secale cereale*
Foxtail millet	*Setaria italica*
Pearl millet	*Pennisetum glaucum*

the Gramineae family. Each cereal has a genus, and the genus contains more than one species or subspecies. Each species of cereals has different varieties. Table 17.1 shows the genus, species, and common names of major cereal crops. Figure 17.1 shows the morphology of major cereal plants (1). General biological traits of different parts in cereal plants are described in the following sections.

A. ROOTS

Cereal plants have seminal or primary roots and coronal roots. Seminal roots produce when the seed germinates. Wheat, barley, rye, and maize commonly develop 3, 5, or 7 seminal roots, whereas rice and sorghum produce only a single branched seminal root. Seminal roots may function until the plant matures. After the young cereal plant unfolds a few leaves, coronal roots arise from stem nodes underground and develop into an elaborate root system. Coronal roots normally grow below soil surface, but sometimes arise from the nodes above soil surface as aerial roots (e.g., maize and sorghum). The root systems are responsible for absorption of water, fertilizers and mineral nutrients, and also for anchor and support of the plants.

B. STEMS

Stems of cereals are divided into nodes and internodes, being cylindrical, or nearly so. The length of internodes varies with position and by species. The basal internodes generally remain short. In addition to main stem, branches called tillers may grow from subterranean nodes in most cereals. A number of tillers can be produced from the primary stem, and they in turn develop others. The number of tillers varies significantly among different species and varieties of cereals. Generally 5–40 tillers may arise from a single seed under favorable planting conditions. Most cereals (e.g., wheat, rice, barley, oats, rye, and finger millet) are thin-stemmed grassy plants, but maize, sorghum, and pearl millet have thick stems more similar to sugar cane than grass.

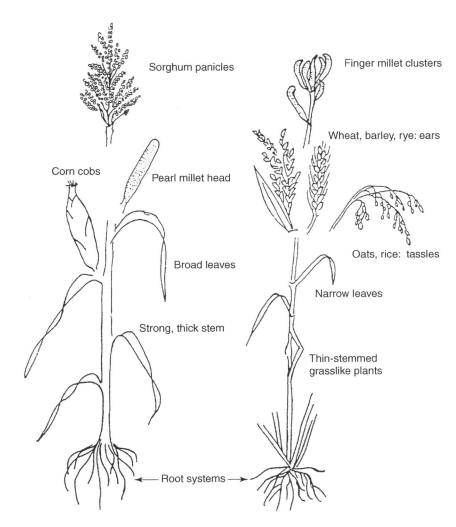

FIGURE 17.1 Morphology of major cereal plants. (Adapted from Ref. 1.)

The functions of stems are to support the plants and be responsible for transportation of water, fertilizers, and mineral nutrients. Resistance to lodging, the capacity of stems to withstand the adverse effects of rain, wind, and even diseases and pests, is an important characteristic of cereals because plant lodging usually results in serious loss of yield. Short, thick, heavy stems with thick walls are considered to be the best insurance against lodging. Excessive soil nitrogen may accelerate plant growth, which easily leads to increased lodging. A suitable balance of nitrogen, phosphorus, and potassium in the soil reduces lodging to a minimum (2).

C. LEAVES

Leaves of cereals consist of sheath and blade (lamina), arising from buds that are lateral appendages of the stems. Cereal leaves are characterized by long, narrow, flat blades that taper to a point. The leaves of maize, sorghum, and pearl millet are broader and larger than those of other cereals. The leaf veins usually run parallel. At the junction

of the sheath and blade is a thin membranous outgrowth called ligule that often is of taxonomic value. Lateral outgrowths called auricles occur above the ligule. Rice and barley have long clasping smooth auricles, while wheat has shorter hairy auricles, and rye has very short auricles. Oat sheath has no auricles. The sheaths of rye and oats and the leaf margins of oats have hairs (2). Furthermore, the shapes of the shieldlike ligule at the base of each leaf blade are also different. These leaf traits are very helpful to distinguish between cereal plants at the earlier developmental stages.

Leaves are mainly responsible for photosynthesis and transpiration. In photosynthesis, carbon dioxide and water react in the presence of light and chlorophyll in leaves and produce food and oxygen. In order for photosynthesis to take place, the stomata must be open, exposing the mesophyll tissues to carbon dioxide in the air. With the stomata open, the tissues are also exposed to the drying influence of air, resulting in evaporation. Evaporation of water through open stomata of leaves is called transpiration.

D. INFLORESCENCES

Flowers of cereals are grouped on an axis of the inflorescence. The inflorescence of wheat, barley, and rye is a spike in which the sessile spikelets are attached along a rachis. Inflorescence of rice, oats, sorghum, and most of the millets is a branched panicle bearing spikelets on pedicels. A spikelet contains one or more florets subtended or enclosed by two bracts (lemma and palea) known as glumes. In the floret are the stamens, pistil, and lodicules. There are three stamens in each floret, except for rice which has six. Most cereals have perfect or bisexual flowers which contain both stamens and pistils. Maize and wild rice have separate staminate and pistillate flowers borne on the same plant. The staminate and pistillate flowers of maize are borne in separate inflorescences on the same plant. The staminate flowers are borne in the tassel at the top of the stalk, while the pistillate flowers are located in spikes which terminate lateral branches arising in the axils of lower leaves.

Cereals may be naturally self-pollinated (wheat, rice, barley, and oats), cross-pollinated (sorghum and proso millets), or naturally cross-pollinated (maize, rye, and pearl millet) (2, 3). Reproduction of cereal crops is by means of inflorescences which develop grains or seeds through pollination and fertilization.

E. GRAINS

The structure, chemical composition, and physical properties of cereal grains determine their suitability for a specific market. Knowledge of grain structure, composition, and physical properties is essential to drying, storage, milling, and even food processing of cereal grains.

1. Grain Structure

Cereal crops, like other members of the grass family, produce one-seeded fruit which is a caryopsis, but generally called a grain or kernel. Botanically, caryopsis contains a seed and a fruit coat (pericarp) which surrounds the seed and adheres tightly to a seed coat. The seed consists of a seed coat, an embryo (germ), and an endosperm. All cereal grains have these parts in approximately the same relationship to

each other. The caryopsis of all cereals develops within floral envelopes which are actually modified leaves. These are called chaffy parts (glumes), and constitute the hulls or husks of cereal grains. In the threshing process, hulls are separated from the naked caryopsis, such as wheat, maize, sorghum, millets, rye, and naked barley, but not from rice, oats, and most cultivars of barley because their floral envelopes cover the caryopsis so closely and completely that they remain attached to the caryopsis after threshing. In addition, the kernels of wheat, rye, barley, and oats usually have a longitudinal crease (ventral furrow).

Cereal grains include pericarp, seed coat, endosperm, and embryo. The pericarp is composed of several layers and surrounds the entire seed. The starch-rich endosperm contains simple or compound starch granules, and it is the principal portion of the grains serving as food reserve for the embryo. The outermost layer of endosperm is called the aleurone layer, consisting of a single layer or more layers. Peripheral to the aleurone is a series of highly compressed remnant cell layers comprising the nucellus, seed coat, and pericarp. These, in combination with the aleurone layer, are usually referred to as the bran.

Grain size and proportions of the major parts of mature kernels from eight cereals are shown in Table 17.2 (4–6). Table 17.3 compares the major structural characteristics of

TABLE 17.2

Grain Size and Proportions of the Major Parts of Mature Cereal Kernels

Cereal	Germ (%)	Pericarp (%)	Aleurone (%)	Endosperm (%)
Wheat	2–3	12–15	—81–86—	
Rice	3.5	1.5	4–6	89–92
Maize	8.4–10	5.5–8		82–84
Barley	3.4	18.3	—79—	
Sorghum	7.8–12.1	—7.3–9.3—		80–85
Oats	3.7	—28.7–41.4—		54.9–67.6
Rye	3.5	12	—85—	
Pearl millet	17.4	—7.5—		75

Source: Adapted from Refs. 4–6.

TABLE 17.3

Structural Characteristics of Cereal Grains from Commerce

Cereals	Caryopsis Type	Ventral Furrow	Aleurone Thickness	Starch Granules
Wheat	Naked	Prominent	Single cell	Simple
Rice	Covered	Absent	Multiple	Compound
Maize	Naked	Absent	Single	Simple
Barley	Covered	Present, not prominent	Multiple	Simple
Sorghum	Naked	Absent	Single	Simple
Oats	Covered	Present, not prominent	Multiple	Compound
Rye	Naked	Prominent	Single cell	Simple
Pearl millet	Naked	Absent	Single	Simple

Source: Adapted from Refs. 4 and 7.

the cereal grains of commerce (4, 7). Longitudinal cross sections of the kernels from the three major cereals (wheat, rice, and maize) are shown in Figures 17.2, 17.3, and 17.4 (4, 5, 8, 9).

a. Wheat

Wheat kernels are 5–8 mm in length, 2.5–4.5 mm in width, and 30–45 mg in weight. The kernel size and shape of the wheat vary significantly depending on cultivars and kernel position in the spike. Also, there is wide variation in endosperm texture (hardness) and color of the wheat kernels. Wheat pericarp comprises about 12–15% of the kernel weight, removed in the milling process along with the aleurone layer of endosperm. Wheat endosperm constitutes 81–86% of the kernel weight, being the major end product of a wheat flour mill, whereas germ accounts for only about 2–3%.

Wheat pericarp surrounds the whole seed and includes outer and inner layers. The seed coat has three layers, a thick outer cuticle, a thin inner cuticle, and a pigment layer (only for colored wheat). The aleurone layer is the outermost layer of endosperm, containing thick-walled cells. Wheat germ is composed of two major parts, embryonic axis (rudimentary root and shoot) and scutellum (cotyledon). The starchy endosperm of wheat contains starch granules embedded in or surrounded by an amorphous protein matrix. Three types of cells (peripheral, prismatic, and central) make up most of the wheat endosperm. Wheat endosperm usually varies in hardness (texture) and appearance (vitreousness) among different cultivars. Generally, high-protein hard wheat varieties

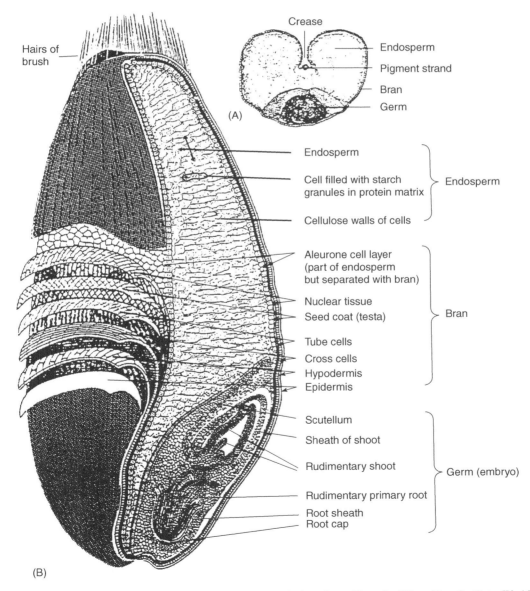

FIGURE 17.2 Diagram of a wheat kernel in (A) cross and (B) longitudinal sections. (From the Wheat Flour Institute, Washington, D.C.)

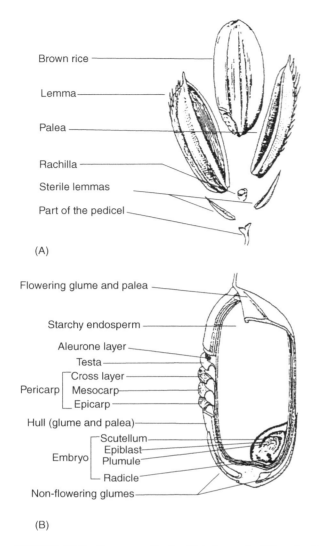

FIGURE 17.3 Structure of a (paddy) rice grain (A) and mid-longitudinal section (B). (Adapted from Ref. 9.)

tend to be vitreous, whereas low-protein soft wheat varieties tend to be opaque.

b. Rice

Rice grains are also called paddy or rough rice because of attached husks. Based on the length-to-width ratio, rice grains are divided into three grain types, long-grain, medium-grain, and short-grain. The grain is about 5–10 mm in length, 1.5–5.0 mm in width, and 20–35 mg in weight. A paddy rice grain consists of the husk (lemma and palea) (~20% in weight) and the brown rice kernel. Brown rice (rice after removing husk) contains pericarp (about 2%), seed coat and aleurone layer (about 5%), germ (3–4%), and endosperm (89–92%). After removing the pericarp during milling, brown rice produces white rice (milled rice). Rice endosperm is both hard and vitreous. Some rice cultivars have opaque areas called white belly, resulting from air spaces in the endosperm. The thin-walled endosperm cells are tightly packed, with polygonal compound starch

granules and protein bodies. Protein bodies are more numerous in the cells just inside the aleurone layer than in cells near the center of endosperm. In addition to oats, rice is the only cereal with compound starch granules.

c. Maize

Compared to other cereal grains, maize has a unique shape and low specific gravity. Maize kernels are the largest cereal grains, weighing 250–300 mg each (wider variation 150–600 mg), 8–17 mm in length, and 5–15 mm in width. They are flat because of pressure during growth from adjacent kernels on the cob, have a blunt crown and a pointed conical tip cap. Maize kernel is composed of four parts, tip cap, pericarp, germ, and endosperm. The tip cap is often separated from the kernels along with the shelling process. Pericarp makes up about 5–7% of the kernel weight and germ constitutes about 8–11%. The endosperm comprises 82–84% of the kernel weight, being the major end product of maize flour mill.

There are seven major types of maize kernels, including dent, flint, flour, sweet, pop, waxy, and pod maizes (10). Their major differences are based on quality, quantity, and pattern of endosperm composition. Dent maize is characterized by the presence of corneous, horny endosperm at the sides and back of the kernels, whereas the central core is soft and floury. The indented crown is peculiar to dent types and is the basis for the term "dent corn." Flint maize has a thick, hard, vitreous endosperm layer surrounding a small, soft, granular center. The kernels are smooth and rounded. Popcorn is the most primitive race of maize, characterized by a very hard, corneous endosperm, essentially a small-kernelled flint. Flour corn is one of the oldest maizes, characterized by soft endosperm throughout the kernel. The endosperm of flour corn is almost floury, with little or no corneous endosperm. Sweet corn is believed to have originated from a mutation of a Peruvian race. The sugary gene of sweet corn retards normal conversion of sugar to starch, and the kernel accumulates a water-soluble polysaccharide, making up about 12% of the dry weight of sweet corn (but only 2–3% in other types). The kernel starch of waxy maize is almost amylopectin, a branched-chain α-D glucose polymer. Waxy maize is used to manufacture starch. Pod corn is an ornamental type with long glumes enclosing each kernel except husks covering the ear, but not grown commercially.

2. Grain Composition

High level of starch (starchy seeds) is the most important characteristic of all cereal grains. The starch contents of cereals usually account for 55~75% of total grain weight. Protein is another important component in cereal grains, consisting of 6~14%. Most cereal grains contain a low level of lipids, normally below 2~3%. Of all cereal grains, maize contains the highest level of oils; oil content of some varieties reaches about 6%. Additionally, moisture contents of cereal grains commonly range from 12 to 15%. Cereal fiber is an important source of human dietary fiber. Typical composition of three major cereals (wheat, rice, and maize)

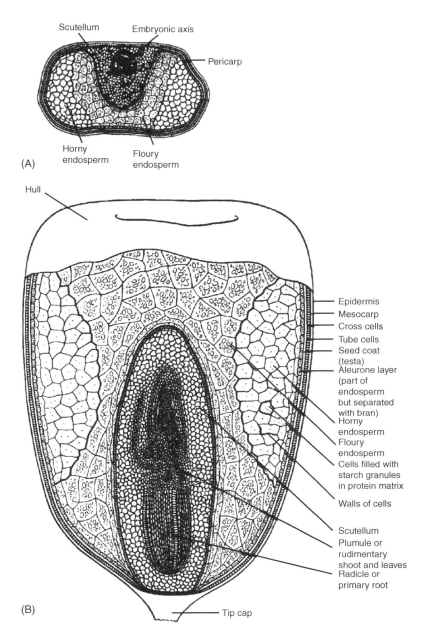

FIGURE 17.4 Diagram of a corn kernel in (A) cross and (B) longitudinal sections. (From the Corn Refiners Association.)

TABLE 17.4
Typical Composition of Three Major Cereal Grains[a]

Cereals	Starch (%)	Protein (%)	Fat (%)	Fiber (%)
Wheat	69.7	10.6	1.9	1.0
Rice (brown)	64.3	7.3	2.2	0.8
Maize	63.6	9.8	2.0	4.9

Source: Data from Refs. 5 and 11.

[a] At 14% moisture content.

is shown in Table 17.4 (5, 11). Other nutritional constituents of cereals have also been extensively investigated, including minerals and vitamins (10, 12, 13).

The chemical composition of the different parts in cereal grains varies widely, depending on position within the grain and also between grains of different species and varieties. Table 17.5 shows the composition distribution of endosperm, germ, and bran in wheat grain (14). Starch is mostly distributed in the endosperm. Protein and lipids normally occur in germ. Bran and germ contain more pentosans (cellulose) and minerals (14).

3. Physical Properties of Grains

Physical properties of cereal grains commonly include 1000-kernel weight, bulk density or test weight, repose angle,

TABLE 17.5
Composition Distribution of Endosperm, Germ, and Bran in Wheat Grain (%, dw)

Grain Parts	Total Weight (%)	Starch (%)	Protein (%)	Fat (%)	Pentosans (%)	Mineral (%)
Endosperm	82–85	70–85	8–13	1–1.6	0.5–3.0	0.3–0.8
Bran	15	0	7–8	1–5	30–40	3–10
Germ	3	20	35–40	15	20	5–6
Total Grain	100	60–70	10–14	1.5–2.5	5–8	1.6–2.0

Source: Adapted from Ref. 14.

porosity, thermal conductivity, grain hardness, etc. (4, 5). These properties are important in the design of handling equipment, drying and storage facilities, and influence drying and storage of cereal grains. Principal physical properties of the three major cereals are shown in Table 17.6 (5, 15).

The weight of grain is ordinarily given as the 1000-kernel weight. The 1000-kernel weight of maize is significantly higher than that of wheat and rice, which can translate to a lower drying rate for maize kernels. The weight of a given volume of grain including the voids is the bulk density, a widely used property which usually determines the bin volume required to store a certain mass of grain, and also affects the grain velocity in a continuous-flow grain dryer at a certain capacity. Wheat has the highest bulk density, while rice has the lowest. The void space in a mass of grain is expressed as a percentage of the total volume of the grain, and is called the porosity. The porosity of the three grains varies between 40% and 48%, typical of cereal grains. Resistance of bulk grain to airflow is, in part, a function of the porosity and the grain size.

When poured on a level surface, grain forms a pile whose outer edge makes an angle to that surface. The value of the angle is specific to the grain and is called the angle of repose which determines the maximum angle of a pile of the grain with the horizontal plane. It is important in the filling of a flat storage facility when grain is not piled at a uniform bed depth but rather is peaked. The slope of a pile of grain may be less than the angle of repose but not greater.

The specific heat expresses the energy required by a unit mass of grain to increase in temperature by 1°C. Of the three cereal grains, maize requires the most energy to reach

TABLE 17.6
Major Physical Properties of Wheat, Rice, and Maize (Typical Grains) at 12–16% Moisture Content (wb)

Physical Properties	Wheat	Rice	Corn
1000-kernel weight (g)	32	27	325
Bulk density (kg/m³)	805	590	745
Test weight (kg/L)	77	58	72
Porosity (%)	41	48	40
Repose angle (°)	31	36	35
Specific heat (J/kg · °C)	1.67	1.51	2.01
Conductivity (W/m · °C)	0.137	0.106	0.159
Specific surface area (m²/m³)	1181	1132	784

Source: Adapted from Refs. 5 and 15.

the desired temperature at which the optimal evaporation rate of water occurs. Thermal conductivity is a determination of the resistance to the conduction of thermal energy within individual cereal grains. In grain with high conductivity, the thermal gradients in the kernels disappear faster during drying than in equal sized kernels of another grain with lower conductivity. The specific surface area refers to the kernel area per unit volume of cereals which exchanges energy and moisture with air during the drying process. For same volumes, there is more heat and mass transfer area for wheat and rice than for maize.

III. GROWTH PROCESSES AND PRODUCTION

A. GROWTH CYCLES AND HABITS

In general terms, the completed life cycle of plants refers to the stages that occur from the time a seed is planted until a new seed is produced, including seed sowing, germination, vegetative growth, reproductive growth, production of seeds, and death. Cereal plants pass through a typical vegetative growth and reproductive growth cycle (16). They grow primarily in a vegetative stage and then go into a reproductive stage. Stalks and leaves grow first and then start flowering and producing grains. Vegetative growth still continues during the reproductive stage, but at a much slower rate than prior to the start of reproduction.

Higher plants can be classified as annuals, winter annuals, biennials, or perennials (3). All cereals are normally annuals; that is, they complete the life cycle in one season. However, certain rice and sorghum species (e.g., wild rice) are able to live as perennials for several years in mild climates. Except in very cold climates, some cereals behave as winter annuals; that is, they live through the winter as small plants in the vegetative stage, and send up stalks and flower in the spring. There are spring and winter types of wheat, barley, oats, and rye. Winter varieties are planted in the fall, vernalized (require freezing temperature) during the fall and winter, and produce seeds and are harvested in the next summer. Spring varieties usually live in cold on mild climates, and are sown in the spring and harvested in the late summer and fall.

The length of the vegetative and reproductive period of any cereals or cereal varieties is greatly determined by temperature, photoperiod, plant nutrition, and growth hormones, and also by genetic factors that affect reactions to these conditions. Each cereal species has an approximate minimum, optimum, and maximum temperature at which growth occurs, although varieties of a species may differ somewhat in their temperature reaction. When the mean temperature is 10°C below the optimum, the time required to grow a crop to maturity is about doubled. All cereal varieties with a winter growth habit, as well as some spring small-grain varieties, require cold for initiation of the flower primordia. Warmer temperatures favor rapid growth and flowering after the initial floral structure is formed.

Photoperiod is also an important factor affecting growth habits. When nights (daily dark periods) are short and days (photoperiods) are long, long-day cereals (wheat, barley, oats, and rye) can flower normally, otherwise their growth period will delay. Some can flower even under continuous light. However, when nights are long and days are short, short-day cereals (rice, maize, sorghum, oats, and millets) can flower normally, otherwise their growth period will postpone. They need a daily dark period for 3–5 weeks to initiate flowering. Additionally, soil rich in nitrogen will keep down the carbon-nitrogen ratio and delay flowering in wheat, barley, oats, and rye, known as nitronegative cereals, but favor early flowering in maize, sorghum, rice, and millets, called nitropositive cereals, unless the nitrogen supply is excessive. Therefore, wheat, barley, oats, and rye are cool-season, long-day, nitronegative, winter or spring habit plants, whereas rice, maize, sorghum, and millets are warm-season, short-day, nitropositive, spring habit plants.

B. DISTRIBUTION AND PRODUCTION

Cereals grown in temperate climates are wheat, maize, barley, rye, grain sorghum, oats, and some millets. Important cereals grown in hot climates are rice, sorghum, pearl millet, and finger millet. Winter rye, wheat, barley, and oats can be suitable for cold climates. The world production of major cereals is shown in Table 17.7 (1). Wheat, rice, and maize are the three most important cereal crops, accounting for 70–80% of total area and total yield in the world. Major cereals are grown and distributed in about 170 countries and regions. The principal areas of cereal production are located in North America, China, Europe, India, Argentina, Australia, and Northern Africa (2, 17).

Wheat, the most important cereal crop in the world, is grown widely in the northern hemisphere in Europe and North America, but large quantities are also planted in China (the largest production of any country), Australia, India, Russia, and South America (Table 17.8) (14). About 95% of rice in the world is produced in Monsoon Asia, an area that extends across the southeastern part of Asia from India to Japan and includes most of the adjacent tropical and subtropical island countries. Maize is the highest yield cereal crop, distributing mainly in the United States, Canada, China, Brazil, Europe, and Africa.

TABLE 17.7
World Production of Major Cereals (1996)[a]

Cereals	Area		Yield			Countries	
	M Ha	%	M T	%	T/Ha	Number	%
Wheat	230	32.3	584	28.5	2.54	120	71
Rice	151	21.3	562	27.4	3.73	112	66
Maize	140	19.7	577	28.1	4.12	149	88
Barley	67	9.4	155	7.6	2.33	98	58
Sorghum	47	6.6	69	3.4	1.46	93	55
Oats	17	2.4	31	1.5	1.79	71	42
Rye	11	1.5	23	1.1	2.05	52	31
Millets	37	5.2	30	1.5	0.81	68	40
Total	710	100	2050	100	2.89	170	100

Source: Data from Ref. 1.

[a]M Ha, million hectare; M T, million tonnes; T/Ha, tonnes per hectare.

TABLE 17.8
Major Wheat-Producing Countries and Regions of the World (1997–1998)

Country/Regions	Yield (million tonnes)	Percentage (% total)
China	121.0	20.1
EU	95.8	15.9
USA	68.6	11.4
India	68.7	11.4
Russia	44.0	7.3
Europe	34.6	5.7
Canada	23.5	3.9
Australia	17.5	2.9
Pakistan	17.0	2.8
Turkey	16.0	2.6
Argentina	12.7	2.1

Source: Data from Ref. 14.

C. FACTORS AFFECTING GRAIN PRODUCTION AND QUALITY BEFORE HARVEST

In addition to climate (days of sunshine, temperature, and precipitation), many other factors influence grain production and quality of cereal crops, including varieties, cropping systems (e.g., rotation), soils, fertilizers, water, weeds, diseases, insect pests, and so on. Grain yield and quality are formed and determined during the growing season. Thus, varietal selection, suitable rotation arrangement, and favorable field management are essential to cereal production.

The great contribution of good varieties to profitability of cereal production and quality is well recognized. Good varietal selection and utilization is the most important strategy to increase yield and improve quality. Numerous breeders and farmers are devoting to the breeding and improvement of new cereal varieties. Many excellent varieties with high yield, good quality, and resistance to diseases and pests, have been selected and bred for extensive production in many countries including some developing countries. Modern biotechnology will play a more important role in these aspects.

Principal field managements include seed sowing, cultivation, fertilizers and water management, weed control, and disease and insect control. In addition to varieties, the yield and quality of all cereal crops are strongly dependent on the availability of an adequate supply of soil mineral nutrients and water throughout the growing season. The higher the yield potential, the higher the nutrient demand is. Nitrogen (N), phosphorus (P), and potassium (K) are three major nutritional elements required by cereal crop growth, largely affecting both grain yield and quality. Crop nutrition demand is normally met through the application of inorganic fertilizers (N, P, and K), although in organic cereal systems additional nutrients can only be supplied from manures and other organic sources. During major fertilizer application, an adequate ratio of N, P, and K should be controlled, normally around 3:1:1 (various ratio for different crop species/varieties); otherwise it will cause abnormal growth and affect grain quality. Other essential trace elements include sulfur, calcium, magnesium, iron, zinc, boron, and so on, normally being supplied by the fertile soil (17).

Water is also essential to the life processes of cereal plants. Water shortage occurs at the vegetative growth stages, which frequently makes shorter plants and earlier maturity. Water shortage at flowering and maturity periods usually causes serious decrease of grain yield and produces many bad grains. For different cereals, irrigation and drainage in the field should be conducted at the adequate growth stages. For instance, rice needs more water during tillering stage and flowering period, and irrigation should be done. At late tillering stage it is required to drain water for controlling tillers, and at late maturity drainage should be done again for full maturity and drying field for harvest.

Additionally, the presence of weeds, diseases, and insect pests during growth obviously reduces cereal grain yield, and influences grain quality. Control of weeds, diseases, and pests is also an important field management measure to maintain and protect grain quantity and quality during the growing season. In addition to using varieties with strong resistance to diseases and pests, pesticides/fungicides and bio-insecticides are usually used. Herbicides are widely applied to kill or control weeds in the field. Appropriate cultivations and rotations not only reduce the loss and damage from diseases and pests, but also control weed growth and decrease weed competition on cereals.

IV. HARVESTING AND THRESHING

Harvesting, threshing, drying, and storage are the important steps of pre- and post-harvest management between producing cereal grains and becoming various cereal food products. Successful, suitable, and efficient harvesting and threshing of cereal crops is one of the key steps to keep grain quality and quantity. It is desirable to know when to harvest, to understand harvesting and threshing machines and their operation, and to minimize losses during harvesting and threshing.

A. HARVESTING TIME

Cereal grains normally stop growing and gaining in dry weight when they approximately reach the hard-dough stage, or when the moisture content drops below 20~40%. Further ripening is only a desiccated process of the kernels, not accompanied by transport of nutrients into the grains. Ripening is not entirely uniform among different heads or different grains within a head. Most cereals at the hard-dough stage have a moisture content of 25~35%, the heads are usually light yellow, and the kernels are too firm to be cut easily with the thumbnail. Grain quality normally starts to deteriorate in the field prior to harvest. Rainfall prior to and during the harvest period may induce ear diseases and premature sprouting, and high grain moisture contents may necessitate increased drying costs. Cereal grains should be harvested as near maturity as possible to avoid losses of prematurity and overmaturity (3, 18).

Premature harvest reduces yield and quality of cereal grains. Underdeveloped grains are low in test weight, starch content, and market value. Cereal crops are usually harvested 7 days or more before they are ripe and allowed to dry under cool humid conditions, or 3 to 4 days early under warm dry conditions, without appreciable loss in yield and quality (3). Wheat grain sometimes draws material from the straw after it is cut when nearly ripe. Considerably more growth has occurred when immature barley grains were left to dry in the head than when they were threshed immediately.

Delayed harvest also influences grain yield and quality. Losses from the delayed harvest are caused by shattering, crinkling, lodging, and leaching. For instance, delay in rice harvesting leads to lower yield because of lodging and shattering, and overmaturity may induce the formation of longitudinal and multiple transverse cracks in rice grains. Formation of such cracks leads to milling losses. Delaying wheat harvest may result in grains with high α-amylase content, lower specific weight and protein content, which seriously reduce grain quality for breadmaking. Cereal stems may crinkle down or break over soon after maturity, especially in damp weather. Oats are more susceptible than barley to crinkling, while barley is more susceptible than wheat or rye. Most tall-stalked grain sorghum varieties go down soon after maturity or after a frost. Weathered or sun-bleached grains are unattractive and often bring a lower grade and price on the market. Overmature grains exposed to wet and dry weathering for long periods in the field are

TABLE 17.9
Moisture Contents for Wheat, Rice, and Maize at Harvest and for Safe Storage (%, wb)

Cereals	Maximum Harvest Moisture	Optimum Harvest Moisture	Moisture for Safe Storage	
			6–12 months	Over 1 year
Wheat	20	18	14	13
Rice (paddy)	38	22	14	13
Corn	25	23	14.5	13

Source: Data from Ref. 5.

lowered in test weight because the grains swell when damp and do not shrink to their original volume after drying (3).

Moisture contents of wheat, rice and maize at harvest are shown in Table 17.9 (5). Grain moisture content at harvest is an important consideration, and usually varies with seasons and geographic regions. In wheat, grain moisture at harvest should be about 10~20%. Rice is harvested at a moisture content of 20~30%. Maize is harvested at considerably higher moisture levels than wheat, especially at higher latitudes. Maize is often harvested at 30~35% moisture in the northern Corn Belt of the United States, and at 35~45% in Eastern Europe (5). In Britain, cereal grain is often harvested at moisture contents of about 16~20%, whilst in exceptionally late seasons in northern regions grain may be harvested at around 25% (18).

Barley is commonly harvested at about 15% moisture, but sometimes producers started harvesting at 30~40% moisture, resulting in a higher yield because of reduced losses at harvest. The fresh barley grain is either artificially dried for food use or stored in silage-type bins for livestock feed. Oats should be at around 13~14% moisture for harvest; however, since oats shatter easily, it is common practice to cut and windrow them when the grain contains about 20% moisture. When it dries to a moisture content of 13~14%, the grain is combined. Sorghum should be harvested at 18~20% moisture if it is to be dried, but at around 13% moisture if it is to go directly to storage (19).

B. METHODS AND MACHINES OF HARVESTING AND THRESHING

Nowadays, all cereal crops can be harvested by modern machines that replace traditional harvesting tools, such as hand sickle, scythe, and cradle. Because of high working efficiency, machine harvesting and threshing saves time and labor, reduces cost, and is extensively used in developed countries (17). However, manual harvesting and threshing is still widely used in most developing countries. For example, rice harvesting is mostly done manually in Asia and Africa. The rice plants are cut near the ground with a sickle, allowed to dry in the field, collected, stacked, and threshed. In Asia and Africa, paddy rice is traditionally threshed by manually beating the straws against a slat or stone, or by trampling under feet of animals, bullock draw carts, tractor wheels, or tractor-drawn roller. However, the drum thresher is also widely used nowadays for rice threshing in Japan, China, India, and others.

There are many types of machines for crop harvesting and threshing, such as harvester-threshers, mowers, windrowers, strippers, pickers, choppers, balers, rakes, cubers, stackers, and conditioners (3, 17). The word combine is used to describe machines that combine several harvesting and threshing operations into one. Grain combine is usually adapted to each cereal crop by making small changes in the cutter bar, the reel, or the thresher (cylinder or similar mechanism). For example, for maize, the cutter bar-reel combination used for wheat is replaced by a header which strips the ear of maize off the stalk.

The most common combine is the harvester-thresher combination used to harvest most cereal crops. Bishop et al. (19) summarized the basic operation of the combine, including the following procedures: 1) the grain is cut and conveyed to a thresher; 2) the thresher removes the grain from the head, or stalk, or cob; 3) the grain is separated from the hulls, straw, cob, pods, leaves, or similar plant materials; 4) the grain is cleaned by removing the rest of the chaff, dirt, and remaining trash; and 5) the grain is transferred to a bin. Additionally, in operating a combine, the various parts must be properly adjusted. The reel and cutter bar should be adjusted to the correct height, and the correct cylinder speed in the thresher should be employed for different grains.

The harvest-thresher or combine is most extensively and the earliest used to harvest wheat and barley. Maize is commonly harvested with a combination picker-sheller or a combine with a special header. These two machines can remove ears of maize from the stalk. The ears are then shelled by the machine, the grain is sent to the bin, and the rest of the plant material is discarded back onto the field. Combine harvesters are also used for rice harvesting in some developed countries. Sorghum may be harvested with a simple combine. Sorghum grain is relatively soft, and speed of the cylinder that threshes the grain has to be reduced to prevent grain damage.

Conditions of cereal crops at harvest have a significant influence on combine performance, e.g., severely lodged cereals not only produce inferior quality grains, but also reduce combine speed and efficiency. The presence of weeds also interferes with harvesting and often leads to higher grain moisture contents and contamination with weed seeds which increase cleaning costs.

C. HARVESTING AND THRESHING LOSSES

Losses in yield can be due to improper harvesting techniques or harvesting too early or too late. If harvest begins too early, plants have not reached full maturity, causing shrinkage of the grain. If harvested too late, plants can lodge or stalks can break, grain can shatter or ears can drop, and quality will deteriorate.

Factors affecting harvester efficiency and yield losses include combine adjustments, field speed, kernel moisture levels, and lodging. Suitable adjustment and operation of harvest equipment helps minimize harvest losses, and losses should not exceed 3% from a properly adjusted and operated combine.

Threshing losses are caused by incomplete threshing, physical damage by beaters in the machine, or even by hand spillage and cleaning losses in the winnowing and screening processes, which immediately follow threshing. Incomplete stripping is common in areas of high labor cost, causing paddy losses up to 12%. When harvesting takes place in the rainy season, the paddy is wet and can easily choke cleaners on mechanical threshers and cause losses. Maize shelling losses are also caused by incomplete stripping of grain from cob, kernel breakage in the machine, and kernel scratching. Small-toothed shellers give low damage with 3% loss, and threshing machines and combine harvesters can give more than 5% broken grains (20).

V. DRYING AND STORAGE

Drying and storage are important post-harvest managements for achieving high quality grain to meet market requirements. After harvesting, it is necessary to clean, dry, and store cereal grains and protect their quality and quantity properly until cereals are processed into food products. To protect cereal grains appropriately after harvesting, producers need to know how to clean, dry, and store grains, to regulate storage conditions (temperature and moisture), and to control insects, microorganisms, and rodents.

A. GRAIN CLEANING

For drying and good storage, chaff, dust, straw particles and broken grains should be removed from harvested grains. Weeds and other impurities (e.g., mud, stone, and sand) must be also separated from grains. For good quality to market, the grain must be as near 100% as possible of one variety free from broken, discolored grains and shriveled, undersized grains of the same variety. A typical grain cleaner often consists of two parts, a shaking screen and a fan driven from the same motor. Straw and other large objects are removed by screening, and dust and other lightweight materials are blown out by aspiration. Machines used to remove unwanted grains include three types: slotted cylindrical grader, indented cylinder, and optical sorter (20). Bailey (21) also introduced grain cleaning methods and equipment. Three common cleaning and separating methods are used in elevators, those using air streams, perforated screens, and indents.

B. PRINCIPLES OF DRYING AND STORAGE

Moisture is one of the major factors contributing to the deterioration of cereal grain quality during storage. Moisture content of grains is defined as the amount of water that can be removed without alterations in chemical structure, which varies depending on the types of grains (e.g., covered husk, naked, or pearled kernels), moisture at harvest, harvesting method, chemical composition, relative humidity of atmosphere, and seasonal fluctuations. Safe storage moisture content of grains is commonly defined as the amount of water at which the rate of respiration is low enough to prevent generation of heat and consequent deterioration (22, 23). For safe storage, wheat, rice, and maize grains have to be dried to 14% moisture or lower (Table 17.9) (5). For long-term storage (over 1 year), lower moisture contents are recommended to prevent microbial growth and insect reproduction. For short-term storage (1–3 months), moisture can be slightly higher (above 15%).

Equilibrium moisture content (EMC) is also important to grain drying and storage. EMC is defined as the moisture content of material after exposed to a particular environment for an infinite period of time, usually depending on humidity and temperature of the environment (5). Moisture content of cereal grains tends to equilibrate with the moisture of surrounding air. Wet grains lose moisture to dry air, and dry grains absorb moisture from wet air. Also, the amount of water held by a volume of air depends on temperature. When drying with air of a specified temperature and humidity, grain can dry to no lower than the EMC. Once the grain has reached the EMC, no further moisture transfer will occur. Dry grain will absorb moisture when exposed to air leading to an EMC higher than current moisture content of the grain (23). As shown in Table 17.10, EMC values increase with increase of relative humidity and decrease slightly with increase of storage temperature (5, 23). Furthermore, EMC values usually vary with differences in grain structures and maturity of various cereal grain species/varieties.

Infestation of insects and microorganisms is affected by interaction of grain moisture, relative humidity, and storage temperature (21, 22). Insects attack grains at moisture content above 8% at all ranges of relative humidity, if the storage temperature is above 19°C. Molds harm grains at above 60~65% relative humidity and above 12% moisture, irrespective of temperature at 20–40°C. To control both insects and molds, grains should be stored at or below 19°C and 60~65% relative humidity. This basically coincides with 12~14% EMC in the grains. However, it may not be economically feasible to maintain storage temperature at or below 19°C. Thus, safe storage moisture of grains is usually based on EMC at 27°C and 70% relative humidity, particularly in developing countries (Table 17.11) (22–24). Drying cereal grains to safe moisture levels and storing in moisture-proof structures sufficiently

TABLE 17.10

Equilibrium Moisture Contents (EMC) of Cereal Grains (%, db)

Cereals	Temp (°C)	\multicolumn{10}{c}{Relative Humidity (%)}									
		10	20	30	40	50	60	70	80	90	100
Barley	10	4.7	6.8	8.6	10	12	13	15	18	21	30.6
	20	4.6	6.6	8.4	10	11	13	15	17	21	29.9
Maize (yellow)	10	5.0	7.5	9.7	11	13	16	18	21	26	38.3
	20	4.6	6.9	8.9	10	12	14	17	20	24	35.2
	27[a]	4.2	6.4	7.9	9.2	10.3	11.5	12.9	14.8	17.5	–
	50[a]	3.6	5.7	7.0	8.1	9.3	10.5	11.9	13.8	16.3	–
Rice (rough)	10	6.3	8.6	10.4	12	13	15	17	19	22	29.5
	20	5.9	8.0	9.7	11	12	14	16	18	20	27.7
Sorghum	10	6.4	8.7	10.5	12	13	15	17	19	22	29.5
	20	6.2	8.4	10.2	11	13	14	16	18	21	28.6
Wheat (durum)	10	5.9	8.3	10.3	12	13	15	17	20	23	32.7
	20	5.6	7.9	9.7	11	13	14	16	19	22	31.0
Wheat (soft)	10	6.4	8.6	10.3	11	13	14	16	18	21	28.1
	20	6.1	8.2	9.8	11	12	14	15	17	20	26.7
Oats[a]	25	4.5	6.6	8.2	9.4	10.3	11.4	12.8	15.0	18.2	23.9
Rye[a]	25	5.3	7.4	8.8	9.8	10.8	12.2	13.9	16.3	19.6	25.7

Source: Adapted from Refs. 5 and 23.

[a] EMC (%, wb).

TABLE 17.11

Recommended Storage Moisture Content of Cereals Grains (%, wb)

Cereals	\multicolumn{3}{c}{Duration of Storage in Midwest United States}			Storage at 27°C and 70% Relative Humidity[a]
	Through Winter	Through Summer	More Than 1 Year	
Barley	14	13	13	
Maize	15	14	13	13.0
Oats	14	13	13	
Rye	14	13	13	
Sorghum	15	14	13	13.5
Wheat	14	13	13	13.5
Wheat flour				12.0
Paddy rice				14.0
Milled rice				12.0
Millets				15.0

Source: Adapted from Refs. 22–24.

[a] This storage condition is particularly suitable for the developing countries.

resistant to insects, molds, and rodents would greatly reduce storage losses.

C. DRYING METHODS AND FACILITIES

1. Sun Drying or Natural Air Drying

In ancient times, harvested grains were usually sun-dried or air-dried. This traditional drying method is still widely used by farmers in developing countries and some developed countries. The bulk of the grain is still dried by spreading the wet grain in thin layer on the ground in open air to be dried by the sun. Sun drying is a very simple and cheap method of drying cereal grains harvested in the warm part of the year, but is not suitable for large quantities of grains, and not under wet weather conditions.

2. Mechanical Drying

Since industrialized times, mechanical drying has gradually replaced traditional drying methods. Mechanical drying essentially involves forcing or sucking ambient or heated air through the mass of grains. The major features of mechanical drying methods are: 1) drying rate can be controlled by regulating air temperature ventilating through the grains; 2) grains can be dried irrespective of weather, and does not depend on natural resources like solar energy; 3) losses due to insects, birds, rodents, or rains are eliminated; 4) it requires little space for drying; 5) turnover is high; and 6) drying cost is much higher than sun drying (22).

a. Drying systems

Mechanical drying systems can be divided into on-farm drying and off-farm drying (5). On-farm driers have three categories: bin, non-bin, and combination driers. Bin driers are normally low-capacity and low-temperature systems, able to produce excellent quality grain. Non-bin driers, the most popular drier type in the United States, are high-capacity and high-temperature systems that frequently overheat and overdry the grain, thus easily causing grain quality deterioration. Combination drying uses the non-bin high-temperature drier to dry the grain from harvest moisture content to 16–20% and completes the drying process with in-bin drying. Combination drying has the advantages of both systems (i.e., high capacity and good quality), but requires additional investment and is more complicated.

Off-farm or elevator grain driers also have three categories: crossflow, concurrent flow, and mixed flow, which are high-capacity and high-temperature units. Crossflow models dry grain nonuniformly, causing considerable stress cracking of the kernels. Mixed-flow driers dry the grain more uniformly; the dried grain is normally of higher quality than that dried in crossflow models. Concurrent-flow driers have counterflow coolers and produce the highest quality grain; their disadvantages are relatively high capital cost and complexity of the technology. A significant improvement in grain quality can be obtained with off-farm driers by optimizing the operating parameters and by installing automatic drier controllers.

Salunkhe et al. (22) summarized the two major types of mechanical drying systems advocated for either batch or bulk drying process in developing countries, i.e., low-temperature drying and medium-temperature drying systems. In low-temperature drying, there is an increase in airflow through the grains by means of a fan. The grains gradually reach a moisture level in equilibrium with the relative humidity of ambient air which must be below 70% for such drying. Various drying-cum-storage structures employed for such process are on-the-floor drying, in-bin drying, or tunnel drying. Medium-temperature drying is needed when air humidity is above 70%, initial grain moisture is too high, or ambient temperature is too low to effect drying before deterioration begins. Warm air is blown through a bed of grain of controlled depths, and the drying process ceases before EMC is reached. This can be applied for both batch and bulk drying. Medium-temperature driers have several types, such as tray drier, radial-flow drier, sack drier, and multi-duct ventilated flow drier.

Brook (23) comprehensively described the mechanical grain drying systems commonly used in the United States, including 1) Fans: two typical fans, axial-flow fan and centrifugal-flow fan, are used for forcing drying air through a mass of grain. 2) Low-temperature bin driers: drying with natural air or air with temperature increased by up to 5°C. Drying and storage occur in the same bin, called an in-bin drier which consists of high-capacity fans, grain unloading equipment, perforated drying floor, heater, spreader, and grain stirrer (Figure 17.5) (23). These are low initial investment and low-drying-capacity systems best for grains with low moisture levels at harvest and for drier geographical areas with low humidity. 3) High-temperature bin-batch driers: can dry batches of grains with heated air and remove moisture in a shorter time, with drying temperatures of 35–60°C. In these systems, drying and storage occur in separate bins. They require moderate initial investment and medium energy use, and often cost less per unit drying capacity but require more labor because of transfer of each batch to storage. Two typical high-temperature bin-batch

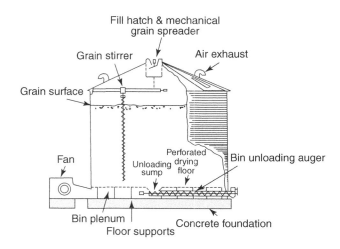

FIGURE 17.5   Low-temperature bin drier. (From Ref. 23.)

driers include on-floor bin-batch driers and roof bin-batch driers. 4) High-temperature column driers: characterized by multiple vertical columns that hold grains while the air is forced horizontally through grains, with airflows of 80–100 m³/min·t and with drying temperatures up to 100°C. These are advanced driers which require moderate to high initial investment and high energy use. Three common types of high-temperature column driers are manual batch column driers, automatic batch driers, and continuous-crossflow column driers. 5) Continuous-flow bin driers: have a bin with a perforated drying floor, fan, heater, grain spreader, grain-unloading equipment, and an auger to transfer grain to storage. They unload hot and dried grains semicontinuously from the bottom of the drying bin to storage bins for cooling. Grain flow is automatically controlled to limit overdrying, with typical airflows of 10–25 m³/min·t and with drying temperatures of less than 80°C. 6) Others: concurrent-flow driers, fluidized-bed driers, spouted bed driers, rotary drum driers, and so on. These belong to high-investment and high-drying-capacity drying systems. New drying technologies, such as differential grain-speed crossflow drying, multistage concurrent-flow drying, multistage mixed-flow drying, and cascading-rotary drying, have the potential to decrease energy consumption and grain deterioration by about 50%.

b. Cooling equipment

Cooling equipment is one part of the drying systems. Grains dried through any heated air driers should be cooled in time, otherwise causing quality deterioration. Delayed-cooling methods are usually used to decrease energy consumption during high-temperature drying, increase drier throughput, and reduce stress cracks and breakage susceptibility.

The three most commonly used delayed-cooling methods are in-bin cooling, dryeration, and combination high- and low-temperature drying (23). The in-bin/in-storage cooling is the simplest delayed-cooling method suitable for any type of high-temperature driers. Dryeration is an energy-efficient method of delayed-cooling and drying completion, and can cut 15–30% off energy consumption of high-temperature drying while increasing drying capacity, although dryeration requires more management. With dryeration, hot grains are transferred to the cooling bin immediately after drying. Cooling is delayed at least 4 hours for steeping or tempering. After grains are cooled in the dryeration bin, they should be moved to storage. Combination high- and low-temperature drying is most suitable for crops harvested too wet for safe low-temperature bin drying, particularly wet maize (>22% moisture content). A combination system normally costs more than a single drying method, but can give high drying capacity, flexibility of high-temperature drying, and energy savings and superior grain quality of low-temperature drying.

3. Drying Losses

Drying losses are caused by underdrying or overdrying, from pre-harvest to post-storage. Two kinds of losses often occur. The first is actual removal of moisture from the grain system, and the second is damage to the grain during drying, leading to subsequent loss during milling (15).

Modern drying systems normally cause lower losses to most cereal grains. However, drying of rice or maize by mechanical driers requires more care to avoid losses in processing properties. In developing countries, threshed grains or harvested ears are usually spread on a hard surface in the farmyards for sun drying, which easily causes higher grain losses. Part of the grains may be eaten by birds and other animals, or may be blown away. If grains are rewetted in the drying yard by a sudden storm, they will be damaged.

D. Storage Methods and Facilities

Since ancient times, peasants have used traditional methods and containers to store cereal grains, such as small buildings, earthenware pots, small wooden containers, underground pits, outdoor piles, woven bags and baskets. Most traditional methods and containers are still employed in many developing countries. In recent centuries, advanced storage technologies and facilities have been developed to provide safe storage environments of grains and to maintain grain quality and quantity more efficiently.

Various types of storage facilities have been introduced (15, 21, 22), including piles of unprotected grain on the ground, underground pits or containers, piles of bagged grain, storage bins of many sizes, shapes, and types of construction. Major classifications are farm storage, bin sites, country elevators, and terminal elevators. Storage structures and facilities should meet the following major requirements: 1) provide maximum protection from moisture, insects, molds, and rodents; 2) have aeration design for regulation of storage temperature and relative humidity; 3) allow smooth in-and-out movement of grains; 4) be sufficiently airtight for fumigation; and 5) have capacity to protect grains from fire.

1. Farm Storage Facilities

Harvested cereal grains are often or temporarily stored at the farm in developing countries. Farm storage structures are constructed from locally available materials which are simple and cheap, and are based on the principle of hermetic storage with aeration facilities. Major structure types of farm storage in India include circular steel bin, plastic bin, pre-fabricated steel bin with hopper bottom, aluminum bin, reinforced cement concrete bin, cement masonry bin, welded wire-mesh bin, ferro-cement bin, and so on (22). In China, simple storage structures are built with local cheap materials, e.g., sticks, mud, stalk or straw, timber.

Modern farm silo is basically a large cylinder of corrugated galvanized steel, with means of access for cleaning, input, and extraction of grain and, sometimes, a built-in drier consisting of a fan with air heater and a means of distributing the warm air through the grain so that moisture can be removed (15). Since modern silo is with good storage conditions, and is durable and secure from attack by predators and even thieves, it has replaced other storage facilities for farm storage in developed countries.

2. Commercial Storage Facilities

Commercial storage systems involve storage of large quantities of cereal grains, with better storage structures and functions. In China, storage facilities of town-level and county-level, normally constructed of concrete, are the important commercial storage systems, with moisture- and rodent-proof structures, and with an arrangement for controlled aeration as well as fumigation.

Elevators are the most common, advanced commercial storage facilities in developed countries. In addition to storage, elevators have other functions such as sorting, cleaning, sizing, drying, and fumigation. They serve the marketing system by equating supply with demand, by providing convenient means for transferring title by endorsement of warehouse receipts, and by transferring grain from one transportation facility to another such as trucks to cars, cars to barges, and barges to ocean vessels.

Country elevators receive grains directly from producers. These storage facilities are usually constructed of wood, concrete, or steel. Their main function is to accumulate grains from nearby farms, to reload them into transportation facilities such as trucks, railroad cars, or barges, and to send them to market. Country elevators were originally intended to serve an area limited by horse and wagon delivery, and their storage capacity was very small. Truck transport from farms has broadened access areas, and elevator sizes have increased accordingly. The largest elevators approach the size of terminal elevators and are often referred to as subterminals.

Terminal elevators are ordinarily constructed in transportation terminals and larger markets. Their storage capacity is very large, normally ranging in total storage space from 5,000 to 500,000 tons or more (200,000 to 20 million bushels). They receive grains from country elevators by truck or railroad and transfer them to storage or into other transportation equipment such as barges or other vessels. Terminal elevators also equip with high-capacity facilities for cleaning, drying, and conditioning of grains.

Flat bins are auxiliary bins of large capacity in connection with terminal elevators. The pressure of grain surpluses requiring safe storage for long periods leads to the construction of flat bins. These bins are built wider and lower than common silo storage bins to reduce costs and side-pressures, thus can provide ample storage space at the lowest possible cost. Floors are directly on the ground, handling equipment is kept at a minimum, and the roof tends to follow the slope of the pile of grains. Large bins may be directly attached to the elevator or may be built adjacent to it.

Additionally, the slip-form storage bins (silo-type bins) for construction of round concrete bins were developed in about 1900 and are still in commercial use. The slip-form consists of a concentric, double-ring form into which concrete is poured. Often two or more rows of round bins are built side by side to form a block of bins. The areas between the circles also become bins, and are called interstitial or star bins. Concrete silos may be as high as 40 m. Although other shapes such as oval or hexagonal have been tried with concrete, the round form gives the greatest strength with the least material.

In developed countries, grain is almost completely handled and stored in bulk, but in developing countries bag storage is still practical and common, since farms are often scattered and labor for filling and loading bags costs is low. Bag is made of plant fiber or woven polymer threads. Air can pass through this barrier, and moisture can migrate from or into the grain, but grain in bags can normally be accepted for storage at 1–2% higher moisture content than for bulk storage. Bags with grains are usually stored in a well-sealed and secure warehouse with regulating openings for controlled ventilation and complete building fumigation. Openings can be used for both natural air and fan-controlled aeration. Bags should be carefully stacked so that alternate layers are placed that can be covered with a tarpaulin for fumigation. A one-meter corridor is left between stacks for the operatives to pass when examining the storage state.

E. AERATION AND STORED GRAIN MANAGEMENT

Dried grains should be aerated as soon as possible after they are put into storage. Frequent aeration during storage is necessary to control grain temperature, to avoid formation of hot spots due to insect and mold activity, to reduce the risk of grain damage or spoilage, and to maintain grain quality (22, 25).

1. Effects of Aeration

Aeration is the process of moving air at ambient temperature through stored grains in order to decrease or increase grain temperature to desired level (5). The major effect of aeration is to control and maintain a uniform temperature in stored grains and to keep that temperature as low as is practical. Also, aeration can equalize grain moisture and remove odors from stored grains. Use of fumigants with aeration systems can permit their distribution through the grain in deep bins and silos.

2. Aeration Systems

An aeration system mainly consists of fan and duct systems. The major considerations in the design of aeration systems are airflow rate, fan selection, and air distribution (25). The airflow rate recommended depends on purpose of aeration, type of stored grains, storage structures, and climate conditions. Fan selection is based on airflow rate and type and depth of stored grains. There are two common kinds of fans used for aeration, axial-flow fans which are suitable for horizontal storage structures, and centrifugal fans suitable for vertical storage structures. Other fans, such as radial-bladed fans, are suitable for vertical low-capacity bins. Occasionally, aeration fans are mounted on top of storage bins or silos. Some aeration systems are equipped with two fans, a pressure fan on the bottom and a suction fan on top. Airflow is usually downward in a suction system and upward in a pressure aeration system.

Duct systems are used for air distribution. Most aeration systems use perforated ducts to distribute the air and provide for air movement whether out of the duct into the grain in a pressure aeration system or into the duct from the grain in a suction system. Many farm bins are equipped with full-perforated false floors or partial perforated floors. In flat storages, large bins, and tanks, more than one ventilating duct is required, and the layout of the duct system is also important.

3. Operation and Management of Aeration Systems for Stored Grains

Foster and Tuite (25) described how to operate aeration systems, including seasonal aeration operating schedules, daily fan operation, and airflow direction regulation. Aeration practices depend on local climate, e.g., the mean temperature difference between the warmest month and coldest month is 28°C in the Corn Belt of the United States. The mean daily humidity of the air is usually below that in equilibrium with grain at safe storage moisture content, except in winter. Under mean climatic conditions, grain can be aerated continuously without undesirable moisture increase.

Once grains are put into storage, they should be aerated immediately to remove harvest or dryer heat. The temperature should be uniformly reduced to 15–20°C for summer-harvested grains and to 10–15°C for fall-harvested grains. Grains are aerated in late fall and winter to cool them to below 5°C. Weather in late November and early December is usually suitable for cooling grains to near mean winter temperatures. Once this is completed, no further aeration is recommended until spring. In March or April, grains may be aerated to warm them to above 10°C. After spring aeration is started, it should continue until grains are uniformly warmed to near mean outdoor temperature. As the warming front moves through, moisture condenses on the cold grains, providing ideal conditions for rapid mold growth. Continued aeration keeps the condensation area moving and helps avoid serious spoilage.

Most seasonal aeration schedules described above are based on daily 24-hour fan operation. In much of the United States, mean humidity in the fall cooling and spring warming periods permits continuous fan operation without increasing moisture of cereal grains above the safe level (13–15%). However, in rainy seasons or regions with higher humidity, fan operation should be limited or even prohibited in high-humidity weather. For instance, in Central, Eastern, and Southern China, aeration is limited or prohibited in rainy weather of late spring and summer.

4. Losses during Storage

Insects, microorganisms, and rodents or birds cause major losses and deterioration of cereal grains during storage, especially in developing countries. Losses during storage may increase if condition of the received grains is unsatisfactory, if the storage sites and facilities are unsuitable for safe storage, or if there is poor management during storage or deterioration in storage environment. Transportation is temporary storage and may also cause losses under unsuitable environments, such as dirty and already infested railcar, or improper supervision (20).

Deterioration caused by insects, microorganisms, and rodents during storage is usually affected by the storage structures and environments. Higher storage temperature and grain moisture content may lead to multiplication and growth of insects and microorganisms. Poor storage management and unsuitable storage structures easily cause serious damage from rodents and birds. Additionally, cracked, broken, damp, and dirty grains with foreign materials (e.g., straw and trash) are more easily infested by insects and molds. Drying and cleaning of cereal grains before storage and appropriate storage management are important for reducing storage losses.

F. CONTROL OF INSECTS, MICROORGANISMS, AND RODENTS DURING STORAGE

Principal measures for decreasing storage losses are to prevent and control insects, microorganisms, and rodents. When grain storage starts, destruction from insects, microorganisms, and rodents may begin, with the rate of grain losses depending on storage conditions. The growth rate of microorganisms usually depends on grain moisture content and storage temperature, and that of insects mainly on storage temperature.

1. Insects

Insects are the major cause of losses of stored grains. Beetles, moths, and certain mites are serious pests of stored grains. Table 17.12 lists the major insects of stored cereal grains and their optimum growth temperatures (15, 22, 26). There are two major groups of storage insect, external and internal infesters. Almost all are either beetles (*Coleoptera*) or moths (*Lepidoptera*) (15). The nature of insect damage is classified into three types: 1) grains are bored inside, leaving the outer coat practically intact; 2) only the germ of grains is damaged; 3) a part of the grains, including the outer coat, is eaten (22). Rice weevil, maize weevil, granary weevil, lesser grain borer, and Angoumois grain moth develop and feed inside kernels. Infestation remains hidden until the adults emerge from the kernels. Other beetles feed primarily on broken and whole kernels. Grain-infesting insects are very sensitive to temperature, but insensitive to moisture. Generally, they grow slowly or not at all below 16°C, and cannot survive in temperatures of 42°C or above, and appear to thrive best at about 29°C. Storage pests are well adapted to live in a very dry environment.

Insects not only consume large quantities of grains but also decrease the quality by the presence of insect fragments, feces, and unnatural odors. Insects consume nutritious components, encourage moisture uptake by the infested grains, and promote growth of microorganisms. When insect population reaches a certain level, temperature of stored grains will increase rapidly. If insects are at over-growth, temperature may increase up to 45°C. When microorganisms are associated, temperature may rise even up to 75°C, causing massive spoilage of grains. Thus over-growth of insects usually results in serious losses of grain quality and quantity.

2. Microorganisms

Molds are also important damaging agents of stored grains. Under favorable moisture, temperature, and relative humidity, many molds can grow on grain surface. Common molds founds in grains belong to the genera *Aspergillus*, *Fusarium*, *Penicillium*, *Alternaria*, *Cladosporium*, and *Helminthosporium* (22).

TABLE 17.12
Insects of Stored Cereal Grains and Their Optimum Growth Temperature

Common Name	Scientific Name	Optimum Temp. (°C)	Minimum Temp. (°C)
Rice weevil	*Sitophilus oryzae* L.	27–31	17
Maize weevil	*Sitophilus zeamais* Motsch.	28	17
Grain weevil	*Sitophilus granaries* L.	26–30	15
Angoumois grain moth	*Sitotroga cerealella* Ol.	26–30	16
India meal moth	*Plodia interpunctella* Hub.	28–30	–
Almond moth	*Ephestia cautella* Walk	25	10
Rice moth	*Corcyra cephalonica* Staint	28–30	10
Lesser grain borer	*Rhizopertha dominica* F.	32–35	23
Larger grain borer	*Prostephanus truncatus*	–	–
Rust red grain beetle	*Tribolium castaneum* Herbst	32–35	22
Confused flour beetle	*Tribolium confusum* J. du Val.	30–33	21
Drug store beetle	*Stegobium paniceum* L.	–	–
Saw-toothed grain beetle	*Oryzaephilus surinamensis* L.	31–34	21
Khapra beetle	*Trogoderma granarium* Everts	33–37	24
Flat grain beetle	*Laemophiloeus pusillus* Schonherr.	–	–
Long headed flour beetle	*Latheticus oryzae*	35	–
Australia spider beetle	*Ptinus tectus*	25–35	10
Cadelle beetle	*Tenebroides mauritanicus* L.	–	–
Cigarette beetle	*Lasioderma serricorne* F.	–	–
Flour or grain mite	*Acarus siro* L.	21–27	7
Warehouse moths	*Ephestia* spp.	–	–

Source: Adapted from Refs. 15, 22, and 26.

The most dangerous and important fungi are from three genera: *Aspergillus*, *Fusarium*, and *Penicillium* (15). Most storage fungi cannot survive at grain moisture content below 17%. They can survive at 50°C and above 65% relative humidity, but are most destructive below 25°C and above 80–85% humidity. Fungal damage to stored grains includes losses of seed viability, nutritional and apparent quality, processing properties, and production of mycotoxins (e.g., aflatoxins and ochratoxin), heating, mustiness, and decay. *Aspergillus flavus*, *Furarium graminearum*, and *Penicillium verrucosum* produce alflatoxins, zearalenones, and citrinin/ochratoxins, respectively. These toxins are important from the point of health hazards. Aflatoxins are carcinogenic agents and ochratoxin can cause liver and kidney damage. Although mycotoxins-induced diseases are rare in developed countries, they commonly occur among rural populations in developing countries.

Bacteria are also found in stored grains, mainly belonging to the families Bacillaceae, Pseudomonadaceae, and Micrococcaceae. Activities of bacteria are normally affected by temperature and moisture content of the grains during storage. Bacteria require higher moisture content (>20%) and higher humidity (>90–95%) for their growth than fungi. Thermophilic bacteria can proliferate at 55°C and raise the temperature of infected grains to as high as 70–75°C. Bacterial damage to stored grains is similar to that of fungi, but occurs more rarely.

3. Rodents

Vertebrates (rodents and birds) cause extensive damage to grain in both field and store. Damage from rodents is a serious problem at farmer's and trader's level. Commensal rats and mice are the most destructive vertebrates on Earth. There are 21 common species of rodents that attack stored grains in different sites throughout the world (22). In addition to house mice, Norwegian rats and mice are conventional rodents.

Not only do rodents eat large quantities of grains, they also contaminate grains with urine, hairs, and excreta. Rodents are energetic creatures and eat about 10% of their body weight of food per diem. One rat will consume around 10 kg of grain each year and excrete 2–5 kg of droppings (15). Apart from consuming and contaminating grains, certain rodents can damage containers (e.g., bags and wooden, bamboo or mud bins, and make burrows in walls, warehouse floor, and cables) and spread diseases.

4. Control Methods and Measures

a. Control of storage temperature and moisture
An important measure of controlling insects and microorganisms is to keep a safe storage environment with cool temperature and low moisture. The recommended safe storage moisture contents of most cereal grains range from 13 to 15% (Table 17.11) (22–24). Lower temperatures increase shelf life of grains by decreasing respiratory

rate and inhibiting activities of insects and microorganisms. When grains are cooled below 15°C, most insects and fungi cannot grow. In developing countries, control of such low temperature will greatly increase storage costs. Generally, maintenance of temperature at about 27°C and relative humidity below 70% during storage are important. Frequent aeration during storage is necessary to avoid formation of hot spots due to activities of insects and microorganisms and to control uniform temperature throughout storage environments.

b. Cleanliness

Cleanliness is considered the most common means of reducing or eliminating pest infestation. It is important to thoroughly clean storage facilities before new grains are stored. Old infested grains, empty bags or sacks, chaff, webs, and other junk that may harbor insects must be cleaned out. The floor, walls, and roof structure should be brushed and sprayed with insecticide before storage. Cleaning of harvesting equipment and transportation tools is also required. Also, clean conditions around storage area and facilities can help keep rodent numbers down.

c. Use of fumigants and insecticides

Fumigants are quick-acting respiratory poisons which can be applied to static grains. Commonly used fumigants are methyl bromide, carbon disulfide, carbon tetrachloride, ethylene dichloride, ethylene dibromide, chloropicrin, hydrogen cyanide, and phosphine (3, 15). The effectiveness of each fumigant is dependent on species of insects, stage of development, temperature, humidity, application method, fumigant concentration, storage facilities, etc. Some recommendations for fumigation of stored grains are shown in Table 17.13 (15). Because chemical fumigants are also highly poisonous to man, precautions given on the labels of the chemical containers must be strictly followed. Great care is required in their application, and staff must be trained well. Gas masks should be worn during the use of fumigants. Storage bins and buildings that have been fumigated must be opened for ventilation for several hours or days before people can enter.

Insecticides that kill insects of stored grains belong to the contact type which can penetrate the insect cuticle and enter body tissue. Common contact insecticides include pyrethrum (pyrethrins), chlorinated hydrocarbon insecticides, organophosphorus insecticides, etc. (22). For example, pyrethrins can be used to kill insects on walls and floor of storage bins during cleaning, and can also be used as protecting agent by spraying on the grains.

d. Control measures of rodents

Rodents cause serious storage losses of cereal grains, particularly in developing countries. Relevant control measures include sanitation, removal of foods easily accessible to rodents, proofing, trapping, use of ultrasonic devices, biological control, single- or multi-dose poisons, tracking poisons, fumigations, and the use of chemosterilants, attractants, and repellants (22). The most common control measures are sanitation, use of anticoagulants, and fumigation of live burrows. Fumigation of live burrows with aluminum phosphide is a cheap and effective method with usually 100% killing after second fumigation. Anticoagulants were tested and also found to be effective in controlling rats.

e. Other control methods

Other promising control methods have been investigated, including modified atmosphere, irradiation, use of insect sex attractants, insect growth regulators, insect pathogens, parasites and predators, etc. (15, 22). As an alternative to fumigation, grain storage atmosphere can be made lethal or inhibitory to insects and microorganisms by reducing oxygen concentration, increasing carbon dioxide or nitrogen concentrations, or creating a partial vacuum (tight-air packaging). Radiation treatments usually cause mutation, sterilization, or death of insects and microorganisms, and are considered a control method for stored grains. The use of sex attractants produced by insects has been investigated to control stored-grain insects. Insect growth regulators can interfere with either morphogenesis or molting of insects. These compounds have intense biological activity, specificity, and little or no vertebrate toxicity. Because of economic factors or chemical toxicity, these promising control methods have, however, not yet been commonly used for stored grains.

TABLE 17.13
Some Recommended Fumigants and Used Dosages of Stored Cereal Grains[a]

Storage Structure or Situation	Application	Fumigants	Dosage (g/tonne)	Treatment Time (days)
Silos, deep bins	Admixture during filling	Phosphine	3–4	5
Flat bulk storage	Admixture by probe	Phosphine	3–4	5
Flat bulk storage	Surface application	Methyl bromide	34	1
Rail cars in transit	Gas jets at top of stack	Methyl bromide	58	1
Stacks under tarpaulins[b]	Gas jets at top of stack	Methyl bromide	28–54	1

Source: Adapted from Ref. 15.

[a] Fumigating is conducted at 20–25°C.

[b] Different cereals require various dosage: wheat, 34 g/tonne; rice, 28 g/tonne; maize, 36 g/tonne; and sorghum and millets, 54 g/tonne.

REFERENCES

1. DAV Dendy, BE Brockway. Introduction to cereals. In: DAV Dendy, BJ Dobraszczyk. eds. Cereals and Cereal Products: Chemistry and Technology. Gaithersburg, MD: Aspen Publishers, 2001, pp 1–22.

2. WH Leonard, JH Martin. Cereal Crops. New York: Macmillan Publishing Co., 1970.

3. JH Martin, WH Leonard, DL Stamp. Principles of Field Crop Production. New York: Macmillan Publishing Co., 1976, pp 3–322.

4. RC Hoseney, JM Faubion. Physical properties of cereal grains. In: DB Sauer. ed. Storage of Cereal Grains and Their Products, 4th ed. St. Paul, MN: Am Assoc Cereal Chem, 1992, pp 1–38.

5. DB Brooker, Bakker-Arkema, CW Hall. Drying and Storage of Grains and Oilseeds. New York: AVI (Van Norstrand Reinhold), 1992.

6. DH Simmonds. Structure, composition and biochemistry of cereal grains. In: Y Pomeranz. ed. Cereals '78: Better Nutrition for the World's Millions. St. Paul, MN: Am Assoc Cereal Chem, 1978, pp 105–137.

7. LW Rooney, JM Faubion, CE Earp. Scanning electron microscopy of cereal grains. In: DB Bechtel. ed. New Frontiers in Food Microstructure. St. Paul, MN: Am Assoc Cereal Chem, 1983, pp 201–239.

8. RC Hoseney. Structure of cereals. In: RC Hoseney, ed. Principles of Cereal Science and Technology, 2nd ed. St. Paul, MN: Am Assoc Cereal Chem, 1994, pp 1–28.

9. AB Blakeney. Rice. In: RJ Henry, PS Kettlewell, eds. Cereal Grain Quality, London: Chapman & Hall, 1996, pp 55–76.

10. LA Johnson. Corn: the major cereal of the Americas. In: K Kulp, JG Ponte, Jr. eds. Handbook of Cereal Science and Technology, 2nd ed. New York: Marcel Dekker, 2000, pp 31–80.

11. BO Juliano. Rice: Chemistry and Technology. St. Paul, MN: Am Assoc Cereal Chem, 1985.

12. NS Hettiarachchy, ZY Ju, T Siebenmorgen, RN Sharp. Rice: production, processing, and utilization. In: K Kulp, JG Ponte, Jr. eds. Handbook of Cereal Science and Technology, 2nd ed. New York: Marcel Dekker, 2000, pp 203–222.

13. ES Posner. Wheat. In: K Kulp, JG Ponte, Jr. eds. Handbook of Cereal Science and Technology, 2nd ed. New York: Marcel Dekker, 2000, pp 1–30.

14. BJ Dobraszczyk. Wheat and flour. In: DAV Dendy, BJ Dobraszczyk. eds. Cereals and Cereal Products: Chemistry and Technology. Gaithersburg, MD: Aspen Publishers, 2001, pp 100–139.

15. DAV Dendy. The storage and transportation of grains and their products. In: DAV Dendy, BJ Dobraszczyk. eds. Cereals and Cereal Products: Chemistry and Technology. Gaithersburg, MD: Aspen Publishers, 2001, pp 23–56.

16. HD Hughes, DS Metcalfe. Crop Production, 3rd ed. New York: Macmillan Publishing Co., 1972.

17. LC Pearson. Principles of Agronomy. New York: Reinhold Publishing Corp., 1967.

18. EJ Evans. Cereal production methods. In: G Owens. ed. Cereal Processing Technology. Cambridge, England: Woodhead Publishing Ltd, 2001, pp 7–26.

19. DD Bishop, LP Carter, SR Chapman, WF Bennett. Crop Science and Food Production. New York: McGraw Hill, Inc., 1983.

20. DAV Dendy. Postharvest losses. In: DAV Dendy, BJ Dobraszczyk. eds. Cereals and Cereal Products: Chemistry and Technology. Gaithersburg, MD: Aspen Publishers, 2001, pp 57–67.

21. JE Bailey. Whole grain storage. In: DB Sauer. ed. Storage of Cereal Grains and Their Products, 4th ed. St. Paul, MN: Am Assoc Cereal Chem, 1992, pp 157–182.

22. DK Salunkhe, JK Chavan, SS Kadam. Postharvest Biotechnology of Cereals. Boca Raton, FL: CRC Press, Inc., 1985.

23. RC Brook. Drying cereal grains. In: DB Sauer. ed. Storage of Cereal Grains and Their Products, 4th ed. St. Paul, MN: Am Assoc Cereal Chem, 1992, pp 183–218.

24. MWPS. Grain Drying, Handling and Storage Handbook, MWPS-13. Ames, IA: Iowa State University, 1988.

25. GH Foster, J Tuite. Aeration and stored grain management. In: DB Sauer. ed. Storage of Cereal Grains and Their Products, 4th ed. St. Paul, MN: Am Assoc Cereal Chem, 1992, pp 21–248.

26. LA Bulla, KJ Kramer, RD Speirs. Insects and microorganisms in stored grain and their control. In: Y Pomeronz. ed. Advances in Cereal Science and Technology, Vol. II. St. Paul, MN: Am Assoc Cereal Chem, 1978, pp 91–101.

18 Legumes: Horticulture, Properties, and Processing

Frank W. Sosulski and Krystyna Sosulski
GrainTech Consulting Inc.

CONTENTS

I. INTRODUCTION

In terms of agricultural production, cereals are the most important source of human food and animal feeds but the legume family, Leguminosae, encompasses an extremely diverse group of herbs, vines, shrubs and trees (1). The subfamily Papilionoideae has 600 genera and 13,000 species of plants which have fruits enclosed in a specific pattern in elongated pods and whose roots form symbiotic relationships with nitrogen-fixing bacteria in nodules. Over 80 legume species are consumed world-wide and represent the second most important food source. About 20 legume species are cultivated on an appreciable hectareage. These legume crops are primarily herbaceous annuals that can be consumed directly as mature dry seeds, as immature green seeds, or as whole green pods.

The most important food legumes are listed in Table 18.1 with their botanical names, global distribution, and approximate annual production. Soybean and peanut are grown widely for extraction of refined vegetable oils and high protein meals, but also have important whole seed uses. About one-half of the world production of peanut is crushed for production of edible oil and meal for animal feeds; much of the large U.S. crop is processed into peanut butter or roasted for direct consumption. On the other hand, over 80% of the world soybean production is pressed for the edible oil and valuable soybean meal, and only about 15% is processed directly into food products.

The low alkaloid sweet lupin (*L.angustifolius*) is a protein supplement in ruminant feeds and, after removal of 25% hull, in pig and poultry rations in Australia (Table 18.1). *Lupinus albus*, with 12% lipid, is grown in other

TABLE 18.1
Scientific and Common Names and Annual Production of Important Food Legumes

Name	Scientific Name	Common Names	Distribution	Production (mt)
Proteinaceous Oilseeds				
Peanut	*Arachis hypogaea* L.	Groundnut, goober	India, China, USA	23
Soybean	*Glycine max* (L) Merr.	Soyabean, Japan pea	USA, Brazil, China	175
Lupin	*Lupinus albus, luteus* and *angustifolius* L.	Sweet lupin, tarwi	Australia, Russia, Mediterranean	1
Starchy Pulses				
Common bean	*Phaseolus vulgaris* L.	Haricot, dry bean	Brazil, India, China	20
Dry pea	*Pisum sativum* L.	Field pea, garden pea	Russia, China, France	10
Chickpea	*Cicer arietinum* L.	Bengal gram, chana	India, Turkey, Pakistan	8.5
Fababean	*Vicia faba* L.	Broad bean, horse bean	China, Ethiopia, Egypt	3.5
Lentil	*Lens culinaris* Medik.	Masur, red dhal	India, Turkey, North America	3
Pigeon pea	*Cajanus cajan* (L) Millsp.	Red gram, Congo pea	Asia, Africa, South America	3
Cowpea	*Vigna unguiculata* (L) Walp.	Black-eyed pea, kaffir bean	Africa, Asia, Nigeria	1
Mung bean	*Vigna aureus, mungo,* and *radiata* (L.) Wilczek	Green, black, and golden gram	India, China, Thailand	1
Lima bean	*Phaseolus lunatus* L.	Butter bean, sieva bean	USA, Central and South America	<1

parts of the world. In efforts to breed an oilseed crop, lines with 16% oil have been reported.

Pulses have limited industrial applications and are mainly consumed directly as whole or dehulled split seeds. Common beans and dry peas constitute about one-half of global pulse production of about 58 mt, and production is widely distributed among countries in the Americas, Indian sub-continent, Asia, and Europe (Table 18.1). However, about 90% of global pulse utilization is concentrated in developing countries. In these low-income food-deficit areas, pulses contribute about 10% of the daily protein and 5% of the energy intake of human diets.

Driven by increasing demand from West Asia, North Africa, Central and South America, and India, production and export of the principal pulses has expanded in North America, Australia, China, Turkey, and Argentina. With respect to world trade, common beans and dry peas are the major imported pulses while lentils, chickpeas, and broad beans are also purchased by low-income countries.

II. MORPHOLOGY AND MICROSTRUCTURES OF SEEDS

Compared to cereal grains, legume seeds are medium to large in size (0.3–2.5 cm diameter), rounded in shape, with relatively hard texture. Seeds vary from white to colored or mottled in appearance and surfaces can be smooth, textured, or wrinkled (1). The proportions of the three major seed components are 8–18% seedcoat, 80–90% cotyledons (Figure 18.1), and 1–2% embryonic axis (not shown) (2). The seedcoat or testa protects the embryonic structures from water absorption, microbial and insect invasion. In lentils, the seedcoat exhibits a pattern of conical papillae

on the surface, about 3 µm at the base (Figure 18.2C). The outermost layer of the seedcoat is a thin waxy cuticle that serves as a hydrophobic barrier (Figures 18.1 and 18.2C). The major structure of the seedcoat is a single layer of vertical, elongated palisade cells. The thick walls of the palisade cells provide strength and rigidity to the seedcoat; the wall thickness and depth determine the proportions of 'hull' that is characteristic of each species. The thin layer of hourglass cells (5–6 µm thick) occurs, with interconnecting air spaces, below the palisade layer.

Between the hourglass cells and the cotyledon is a separate layer of flattened parenchyma cells (Figure 18.2C) that constitute the residue of the once prominent endosperm in the fertilized ovule (See Section IV.F, Dietary Fibre). When seeds are decorticated during processing, the endosperm layer separates with the seedcoat. The seed embryo consists of the embryonic axis and two cotyledons or seed leaves. The embryonic axis has a small plumule (foliage leaves) with shoot-tip, an embryonic stem (hypocotyl), and a radicle or root that are attached to, and enclosed by, the cotyledons.

There are two openings in the legume seedcoat (2). The small micropyle is the site where the pollen tube entered the valve, and is closed in some species. The large oval hilum is the scar where the seed was attached to the pod and is large enough to be a major factor in regulation of seed drying or rehydration (Figure 18.2A, B). Along the hilum length, but behind the opening, is the tracheid bar with numerous ducts that interconnect the pod and seed vascular systems. Although not an opening, there is a linear ridge on one end of the hilum, called the raphe, that arose from the fusion of the pod to the seedcoat during seed development (Figure 18.2A).

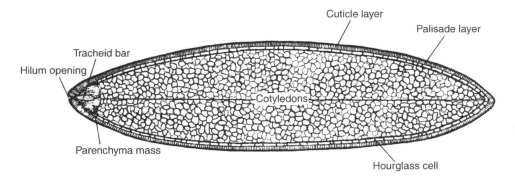

FIGURE 18.1 Schematic diagram of the structure of a cross section through a lentil seed. (From Ref. 2.)

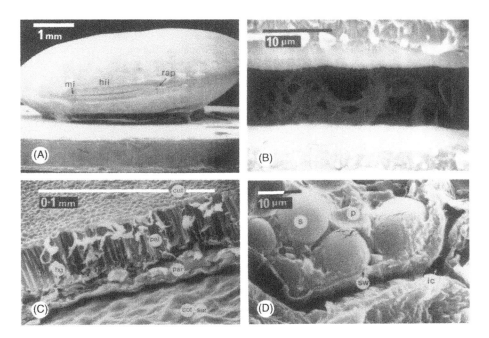

FIGURE 18.2 SEM micrographs of: (A) a gold-coated lentil seed illustrating the micropyle (mi), hilum (hil), and raphe (rap); (B) the hilum opening exposing the tracheid bar; (C) the lentil seedcoat showing the cuticle (cut) layer on the surface of the palisade (pal) cells, traces of hourglass (hg) cells in open spaces, parenchyma (par) layer, and the cotyledon surface (cot sur); (D) an exposed portion of the cotyledon with the storage cell wall (sw) enclosing several starch (s) granules in the protein matrix (p), and the intercellular spaces (ic). (From Ref. 2.)

The two large cotyledons contain nutrient reserves to support early shoot and root growth during germination (Figure 18.1) (2). Their large parenchyma cells (100–130 µm diameter) have thin tough cell walls (1–2 µm thick) that are cemented together by a layer of pectic substances called the middle lamella (Figure 18.2D). There are intercellular spaces between the cells, primarily at the junctures of three or more adjacent cells that facilitate water uptake and hydration. Each cotyledonary cell is packed with round or oval starch granules (10–30 µm dia) that have smooth surfaces, unlike the tightly packed angular granules in cereal endosperms. The legume starch granules are embedded in a thick protein matrix which also contains small protein granules.

III. THE HARD-TO-COOK PROBLEM

Most pulses are consumed directly as cooked whole or split (dehulled) seeds, and long cooking times are characteristically required to achieve the desired degree of softness, digestibility, and inactivation of heat-labile antinutrients. Slow water uptake by seeds has been associated with long cooking times, but dehulling and presoaking of seeds overnight can reduce cooking time, often by as much as 75%. Soybean and dry pea have only 5–8% hulls that are easily removed; other pulses contain 10–18% hulls that are removed by abrasive dehullers, or after soaking or boiling.

Tang et al. (3) found that the initial moisture contents of lentils markedly affected the route of moisture migration, rate of water absorption, imbibition time, and proportion of hardshell lentils. At moisture contents of 16–24%, moisture diffused mainly through the large surface of the seedcoat. The permeability of lentil seedcoats decreased with decreasing moisture content because of reduced pore and fissure sizes in the cuticle and palisade layers. When lentil moisture content was at 12%, the hilum opening became the dominant route for moisture to enter the seed. The width of lentil hilum openings also decreased with moisture content, and some hila were closed at 12% moisture content. Impermeable seedcoat and concurrent closing of the hilum opening resulted in hardshell lentils. The complexity of the hardshell and hard-to-cook phenomena in other legumes has been reviewed by Swanson et al. (4) and Stanley (5).

IV. CHEMICAL AND NUTRITIONAL COMPOSITION

A. ENERGY

The metabolizable energy contents of legume oilseeds are proportional to their oil or lipid contents (Table 18.2). With over 50% lipid, peanuts average 2255 kJ/100 g while soybean, lupin, and chickpea have 1695, 1565, and 1530 kJ/100 g, respectively. The starchy pulses contain about 1440 kJ/100 g of metabolizable energy which is similar to those of whole grain cereals but 5–7% less than in milled cereal flours. The metabolizable energy in pulses arises from their high compositions of starch and protein, but is subject to the slow rates of digestion described below.

B. LIPIDS

Most pulses are low in lipid, only 1–2% (Table 18.2), of which one half are neutral lipids (mono-, di-, and triacylglycerides) and the remainder are metabolic polar lipids (phospholipids, glycolipids, sterols, sterol esters, and lipoproteins) (6). On the other hand, the proteinaceous oilseeds like peanut and soybean are rich in neutral lipids and are commercial sources of edible oils. These neutral lipids are stored in the cotyledons as oil bodies or spherosomes and contain primarily unsaturated and polyunsaturated fatty acids in the triacylglycerols which have important functional and nutritional attributes. Many legumes contain linolenic acid as a component in the lipids, as well as the bound enzyme lipoxygenase, so that oxidative rancidity and off-flavor development are a problem once seed contents are mixed by grinding.

C. STARCH

While the oilseeds are nearly devoid of starch, it is the main component in pulses (Table 18.2). The large starch granules in the cotyledon cells are composed of a combination of two glucose polymers (7). Inside cell organelles these polymers are synthesized into interwoven strands to form the semicrystalline granules. Amylopectin, the larger polymer, is an α-1,4-linked glucose chain with α-1,6 branches, with molecular weights in the millions. Amylose is a smaller linear polymer composed of α-1,4-linked glucose units, and few branches. The number of glucose units in the amylose chain range from 1300 to 1900 among pulse species and the average molecular weight is 177,000. In pulses, the proportion of amylose to

TABLE 18.2
Energy and Chemical Constituents in Food Legumes

Common Name	Energy kJ/100 g	Protein*	Lipid	Starch	Sugars	Ash	Total Dietary Fiber
				% Dry Weight Basis			
Proteinaceous Oilseeds							
Peanut	2255	28	53	1	5	2	8
Soybean	1695	39	20	2	8	5	22
Lupin	1565	38	10	2	10	4	33
Starchy Pulses							
Common bean	1468	24	2	42	5	4	21
Dry pea	1418	20	1	52	5	3	17
Chickpea	1520	19	6	50	7	3	18
Fababean	1430	28	2	45	4	3	17
Lentil	1442	24	1	52	6	2	13
Pigeon pea	1443	21	2	46	6	4	19
Cowpea	1442	24	1	47	7	4	15
Mung bean	1445	25	1	47	4	4	23
Lima bean	1420	21	1	43	5	5	23

* N × 5.7.

amylopectin by weight is about 33:67, but amylose contents can vary from 20–65%. Tuber starches contain up to 20% amylose. Genotypes of the major cereals vary from 0–85% amylose, but 25% is normal for corn and wheat starch. As a class, pulse starches are considered to be high in amylose content.

The shape and size of starch granules are also characteristic of the plant source, those of legumes being oval, round, spherical, or kidney shaped with smooth surfaces and no apparent fissures (7). The starch granules in pulses vary widely in width (10–55 μm) and length (8–70 μm). Most of the pulse starches are simple granules, the exception being wrinkled pea starch, which appears to be a mixture of simple and compound granules, the latter being composed of 3–10 subunits joined together.

D. PROTEINS

The proteinaceous oilseeds are rich sources of protein, and the defatted meals are major protein supplements for cereal-based animal feeds (Table 18.2). Similarly, the pulses at 18–30% protein are major sources of protein for human nutrition in low-income countries.

There are enzymatic, structural, and globular storage proteins in pulses. Storage proteins account for 70–80% of seed nitrogen and occur within the cell as matrix or discrete protein bodies (1). The major storage proteins are classified as either legumin or vicilin, their subunit compositions and molecular weights being characteristic of the species. These are reported elsewhere under the appropriate section, for the legume species. (see Chapters 5–7, 19.)

While pulses are considered to be good sources of protein for human nutrition, their utilization may be quite inefficient. The digestibilities of pulse proteins can vary between 65 and 88%, depending on the structure and composition of storage proteins (8). Most pulse proteins are rich in essential amino acids, especially lysine and threonine. However, they are deficient in sulphur-containing amino acids, methionine, and cystine. The biological value of legume proteins, as measured by protein efficiency ratio (PER), may vary from 0.2 to 2.0 where a balanced protein like casein has a PER = 2.5. By blending a low PER pulse with a source of cereal protein rich in sulphur amino acids, PER values in the range of 1.8–2.0 can be obtained.

The Kjeldahl method for determination of total organic nitrogen (N) is a widely accepted procedure. However, the selection of the appropriate nitrogen-to-protein conversion factor (N:P factor) for calculating total protein content has been a point of controversy, and practices are not consistent among laboratories. Based on amino acid composition, the true N:P factors for common bean and dry pea were found to be 5.4, and the mean N:P factor for 23 diverse food products was 5.7 ± 0.3 (9). The latter factor was recommended for all mixed or blended food diets instead of the common factor of 6.25 which exaggerates the true protein content.

E. TOXINS AND ANTINUTRITIVE FACTORS

Food legume seeds may contain a wide range of constituents which have adverse effects on digestive enzyme activity, digestibility, nutrition, and health (10). Most commercial cultivars have been selected for reduced levels of these factors and heat processing inactivates the proteinaceous factors. Protease inhibitors in soybean, lima bean, common bean, and chickpea retard proteolytic enzyme activity (11). Lectins are polymeric proteins in soybean and common bean that bind to monosaccharides in glycoproteins of the cell membranes, causing lesions in the intestinal mucosa and reduced nutrient absorption. The presence of saponins in some cultivars of common bean and cowpea can reduce feed intake and cause growth depression, but the concentrations are usually too low for significant effects. Goitrogenic substances in soybean and peanut cause enlargement of the thyroid gland, an effect that is counteracted by administrating iodine. Certain cultivars of lima bean grown in some tropical countries contain a cyanogenic glycoside that is enzyme-hydrolyzed to release hydrogen cyanide during processing, causing outbreaks of cyanide poisoning. Lupin cultivars have been bred to eliminate alkaloids which are particularly poisonous but can be detected by their bitter taste. Vicine and convicine in fababean can cause a haemolytic anemia called favism in genetically susceptible individuals. Fortunately, the broad bean/fababean cultivars are consumed primarily as whole seeds and so can be readily avoided if one is susceptible.

F. DIETARY FIBER

Recent definitions of dietary fiber include all components of plant material that are resistant to the digestive secretions of the human upper gastrointestinal tract. These components are predominantly non-starch polysaccharides and lignin associated with the structure of cell walls. In legumes the main dietary fiber constituents are cellulose, xyloglucans, galactomannans, pectic polyuronides, and glycoproteins. While peanut is relatively low in total dietary fiber, other legumes contain 13–23% (Table 18.2), and are viewed favorably in control of many diseases associated with Western diets.

The cell walls in legume cotyledons are relatively thick (2) and resist physical disruption during processing and cooking, and subsequently during their passage through the alimentary tract (12). The cell walls constitute a barrier to digestive enzymes and delay the rate of starch and protein digestion. Thus legumes are an important component of low calorie diets. A slow rate of glucose absorption has been recorded for beans and other pulses, a favorable result for diabetics where high blood sugar levels are a problem. Beans and lentils in Western diets give relatively flat postprandial blood-glucose curves, often expressed numerically as the "glycaemic index." The slow digestion of legume starch has been attributed to the survival of intact cell walls after cooking, but evidence is presented in a later section on slow digestibility of starch granules as well (Section V.C).

Cell wall polysaccharides are also implicated in binding of essential minerals such as iron, zinc, and calcium when diets contain a high proportion of legumes (12). This adverse effect on mineral absorption in humans is exacerbated by the mineral binding effects of phytate (myo-inositol hexaphosphate) that is associated with legume cell walls. Mineral bioavailabilty can be greatly improved by commercial dephytinization procedures in the preparation of special dietary foods that are rich in fiber.

Most pulses are not rich sources of soluble fiber such as gums, pectins, and β-glucans which have an important role in controlling gastrointestinal and metabolic diseases. Legumes with fully developed endosperms as the storage organ, and reduced cotyledons in the seeds, have galactomannans as the reserve carbohydrates. Guar and locust bean contain water soluble gums with unique thickening properties that have many uses in ice cream, cheese, sauces, salad dressings and, industrially, in paper making, drilling muds, etc.

G. Sugars

Food legumes in general contain significant concentrations of free sugars (4–12%) (Table 18.2), which are composed of about 40% disaccharides (sucrose mainly) and 60% α-galactosides (raffinose, stachyose, and verbascose) (13). The latter group represents a problem for consumers since the human digestive system lacks the enzyme α-galactosidase. Thus this raffinose family of oligosaccharides passes into the large intestine where sugars are fermented anaerobically to produce gas.

H. Ash and Minerals

The ash content of pulses varies from 2–5% (Table 18.2). Quantitatively, pulses contain significant amounts of potassium, phosphorus, magnesium, and calcium (10). The high potassium-low sodium ratios of pulses are desired for people with hypertension. Pulses could be good dietary sources of calcium and phosphorus but the ratio is 1:2 while the desired balance is 2:1. Also, a high proportion of phosphorus in pulses is present in phytic acid bodies in the cotyledons which, during digestion, bind calcium as an insoluble salt that is not absorbed in the digestive tract (12). Pulses can provide a high proportion of daily requirements of iron, magnesium, manganese, and copper, but soluble minerals can leach into the cooking water and be lost during drainage.

I. Vitamins

Pulses are excellent sources of the water-soluble B vitamins, particularly thiamin, folic acid, and pantothenic acid, and contain significant quantities of nicotinic acid, riboflavin, and vitamin B6 (1,10). Differences between pulse species and environmental effects are large, and losses during domestic and commercial processing are significant. Pulse seeds are low in vitamin C and fat-soluble vitamins, although green seeds and pods can be good sources of carotenes, vitamin C and E.

J. Tannins and Polyphenols

The hulls of pulses contain about 50% cellulose, 20% hemicellulose, 20% pectin-like and water-soluble carbohydrates, and 2–12% lignin, condensed tannins, and procyanidin. The hydroxyl groups of the latter compounds form cross-links with proteins to cause seed hardening during storage and decreased protein digestibility during cooking (5).

The combination of slow or incomplete cooking, digestive enzyme inhibitors, low protein digestibility, and oligosaccharides are limiting factors in pulse utilization and contribute to the flatulence problem. Techniques for reducing the content of flatulence-producing constituents include breeding of low-oligosaccharides cultivars, germination before cooking, and use of hydrolytic enzymes.

V. PULSE PROCESSING AND UTILIZATION

A. Harvest and Storage

Some pulse species have an indeterminate growth habit; new flowers and pods are produced continuously until plant growth ceases due to heat, drought, or nutrient stress (14). Early harvested seeds at high moisture content are difficult to thresh, while low-moisture seeds from delayed harvest are susceptible to shattering and mechanical breakage. The optimum moisture content for threshing pulses is between 14% and 19%, wet basis. Variable topography in a field can result in seed moisture contents ranging from 18–55% (15). For some pulses, it is a general practice to swathe or chemically dessicate the crop so that seeds are dried uniformly in the field prior to threshing. Dessication results in more rapid seed drying, but longer cooking times have been reported.

Moisture content of seed has a marked influence on the storage stability of pulses. Thus, it is desirable to adjust the freshly harvested seeds from 19–20% to <14% moisture (14, 15). Artificial drying at maximum temperatures of <50°C will minimize seed breakage during subsequent handling, while heat treatments above 75°C will decrease seed germination.

Moisture content of the seeds continues to be an important factor influencing the quality of pulses during storage. Aeration of seeds during storage will reduce heat pockets and mold development. In tropical countries where seeds are stored at high temperature ($> 30°C$) and relative humidity ($> 80\%$), pulses develop a hard-to-cook (HTC) condition where seeds imbibe water slowly and fail to soften upon cooking. Investigators now distinguish between "hardshell" seeds that fail to absorb water and soften during soaking and those which take up water readily but fail to soften during cooking (HTC). Seedcoat and hilum characteristics determine the development of the hardshell condition while the properties of the cotyledon cell walls affect cooking properties. Postharvest losses due to pests, molds, cooking quality, and nutrition are substantial in tropical countries, often up to 50% of the stored pulse crop.

B. TRADITIONAL PROCESSING

Pulses have the advantage over many crops in their simplicity of preparation and in the variety of edible forms (1, 10). In many low-income countries, most pulses are consumed in the home by soaking the dry seeds and cooking in boiling water until soft. The cooking time should be sufficient to gelatinize the starch granules in the cotyledons, denature the proteins, and inactivate antinutritional factors.

Traditionally, pulses are soaked in cold water overnight (8–24 h) (10). Hydration can be enhanced by heating but microbial growth is also favored at elevated temperatures. As well, leaching or diffusion of low-molecular-weight constituents from the seed is accelerated by heat. Pulses with thick, tough seedcoats are abraded and cracked mechanically before soaking to promote moisture uptake. If seedcoats are unpalatable or contain undesirable constituents like tannins, the soaked seeds are hand-rubbed to remove the seedcoat and provide faster cooking and more digestible cotyledons.

In many African and Asian countries, pulses are commonly dehulled (dehusked) by cracking or milling the seeds, splitting the cotyledons, and even polishing the abraded surfaces (10). Both dry and wet decortication methods are practiced to produce dhal. Unfortunately, the yields of split dhal at the rural level may be as low as 65%. Industrial dehulling equipment to produce split peas, pigeon peas, lentils and chickpeas is available commercially. These units are generally expensive because the technical requirements include high yield of splits with minimal abrasion on the cotyledon surfaces. Polishing with organic solutions is necessary for commercial trade.

Dhals have a short cooking time and so are suitable for cooking with vegetables, condiments, and spices (10). Commonly, the dhals are cooked to a soft texture, mashed, and then boiled again with added water and other ingredients. Other home and industrial processing methods involve roasting, puffing, or parching the pulse seeds or dhal by applying dry heat at temperatures of 100–200°C

for 1–5 min. There are efficient roasters designed to apply direct heat with hot sand or ceramic beads. Roasted whole seeds or dhal have an appealing nutty flavor along with improved protein quality.

In Asian countries, food legumes are soaked and held at ambient temperatures for several days to facilitate germination (10). Enzymes activated during germination partially hydrolyze (digest) proteins, starch, and oligosaccharides, inactivate antinutrients, release minerals, and synthesize many vitamins. The sprouted grains may be consumed directly, or dehulled, roasted, and ground for use in blends with other foods.

The Japanese make extensive use of fermented soybean and soy flours for preparing a variety of nutritious food products. There is a similar range of Indonesian and Indian dishes prepared from germinated or fermented soybean, peanut, mung bean, and chickpea.

Canning greatly increases the convenience of using pulses in urban areas but the cost of industrial processing may be too high for low-income consumers. The dry peas, beans, lentils, chickpeas, and cowpeas may be soaked in brine or hot-water hydrated to inactivate enzymes, partially cooked, blended with sauce combinations, canned, sealed, and autoclaved, depending on the final product (10). Pork and beans are popular in North America while refried beans are a staple in Mexico.

C. RECENT ADVANCES IN STARCH FUNCTIONALITY

Pulses are occasionally ground into a flour for use in soups, gruels, infant foods, porridges, and blended food products. Unfortunately, the pulse flours hydrate poorly and form viscous, lumpy slurries that do not cook uniformly. For this reason, pulses are frequently cooked as whole seed or dhal before grinding to a paste and consuming after further steaming, frying, deep-fat frying, or boiling to give a product of uniform consistency. Also, when raw pulses are ground into flour and stored, they soon develop undesirable beany odors and flavors. Grinding releases lipoxygenases that catalyze the formation of peroxides from unsaturated fatty acids, especially linolenic acid, that degrade the fatty acid to low-molecular-weight reactive and volatile compounds. Applying dry heat to seeds for 6–8 min at 105°C will inactivate this enzyme, obviating the need for blanching or steaming that require immediate drying to control microbial contamination.

Refined pulse starches have few industrial or food applications, such as in mung bean noodles or in carbonless paper, because the large granules, often 20–40 µm in length, have a highly ordered crystalline structure with amylose molecules being uniformly distributed throughout the granule (16). In cereals and tubers, amylose occurs in micelles that permit entry of water into the central cavity of the granule and rapid water uptake, granule swelling, and elution of starch molecules. But the pulse starches exhibit restricted swelling power and solubility and are resistant to α-amylase attack. The high stability of pulse starches to thermal processing results in long cooking times for pulse flours as well as refined starches.

Cooking properties of starches can be evaluated experimentally in a recording viscoamylograph. Dilute slurries of refined native starch granules (6–12%) are stirred and heated at 1.5°C/min from 20–95°C and held at 95°C for 30 min before cooling. Cereal and root starches take up water rapidly, swell to high slurry viscosities, but the open granule structure progressively releases the amylose and amylopectin molecules into solution. Then viscosities drop rapidly as a free molecular slurry of starch is formed. The exposed hydroxy groups on the starch molecules are then free to interact and bond in various food and industrial applications.

The typical lack of strong functional properties in pulse starch products is illustrated in Figure 18.3 (17). The scanning electron micrographs of samples taken from the amylograph slurry of dry pea starch show slow granule swelling and water uptake during heating from 30–95°C. Only at near boiling are the granules expanded enough for amylose molecules to diffuse out. After 30 min at 95°C the slurry is still a mixture of partially disintegrated granules and free molecular starch. On cooling, this mixture forms a firm gel due to intermolecular bonding, but water is not held firmly and syneresis occurs during storage or in food preparations. Therefore, flours or refined starches from corn, waxy corn, wheat, and potato are preferred over legume starches for most food and industrial applications.

Considerable variability in amylograph viscosity curves among pulses has been noted by several investigators. For example, comparisons of the pasting viscosities for navy, northern, kidney, pinto, and black bean (*Phaseolus vulgaris*) identified black bean starch as being similar to cereal starches (16). The somewhat smaller granules of black bean exhibited a substantial increase in granule size and viscosity in the initial sampling at 30°C (Figure 18.4). Between 60°C and 75°C, the elution of molecules, and granule degradation, was substantial. At

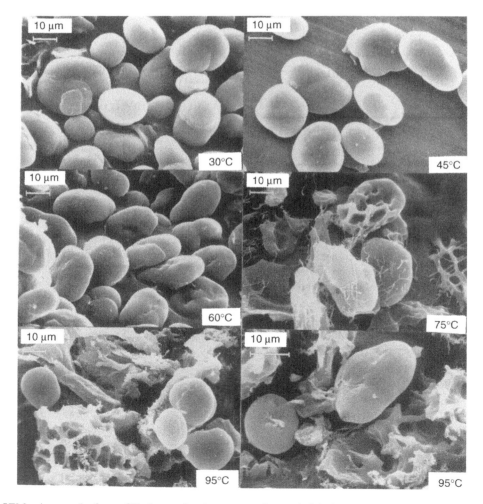

FIGURE 18.3 SEM-micrographs for an 8% slurry of native pea starch sampled during recording of the amylograph at 30°C, 45°C, 60°C, 75°C, 95°C, and after 30 min at 95°C. (From Ref. 17.)

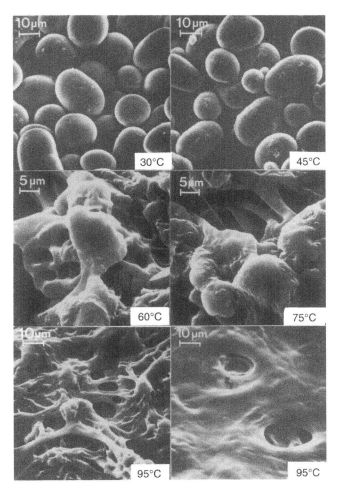

FIGURE 18.4 SEM-micrograph for a 9.5% (w/v) slurry of native black bean starch taken from the amylograph at 30°C, 45°C, 60°C, 75°C, 95°C, and after 30 min at 95°C. (From Ref. 16.)

95°C, there were only remnants of granules remaining, and after 30 min at 95°C, a slurry of free amylose and amylopectin was achieved. Further evaluations of pulse biotypes and cultivars are needed to find genotypes that exhibit better cooking properties in order to open the potential for starch extraction and utilization.

To expand the range in functional properties available for modern food and industrial applications, cereal and tuber starches are modified chemically by substituting low concentrations of reactive groups onto starch chains within the intact starch granule. Among the potential substitution groups used to modify corn starch (Figure 18.5), acetylation and hydroxypropylation improved the cooking properties of pulse starches but cross-linking with phosphorus oxychloride decreased water uptake and granule dissociation (7). The most effective agent for improving the cooking properties of native pulse starches is 3-chloro-2-hydroxypropyltrimethylammonium chloride (17). The formation of the cationic starch ether in a pulse starch results in rapid granule dispersion at near 50°C, yielding

a complete molecular dispersion on heating to 95°C (Figure 18.6). On cooling, the gel structure was firm and syneresis was eliminated after storage of the gels at 4°C and −15°C. Cationic starches are widely used as wet-end additives in paper making to improve sheet strength, give better retention of fines and as fillers. Cationization opens the way for pulse starches to compete functionally with modified corn, waxy corn, wheat and potato starches in a variety of industrial applications. However, the markets for these expensive modified starches are limited and highly competitive.

D.   RECENT ADVANCES IN PROTEIN FUNCTIONALITY

Characteristically, legume seeds are rich in protein and contain intermediate to high levels of lysine and threonine which are important in balancing deficiencies of these essential amino acids in cereal diets (Table 18.3) (18). Certain legume proteins, such as soybean, also exhibit strong functional properties, especially water solubility, water and fat binding, and emulsification. Thus soybean flours, protein concentrates, and isolates have been used widely as nutritional supplements and functional ingredients in processed and blended foods.

Due to the structural features of the cell walls and starch granules, starchy legume flours have weaker functional properties than defatted soybean or peanut flours. To overcome the adverse effects of the starch component, wet and dry milling processes have been developed to separate the protein and starch fractions in pulses to better assess the properties and potential uses of the protein.

The impact milling and air classification system (19) is a dry method involving mechanical dehulling on a resinoid disc, abrasive dehuller, followed by fine grinding on an impact mill that reduces the particle size to less than 325 mesh (Figure 18.7). Then the impact-milled flour is fractionated into light (protein) and dense (starch) particles by a single pass through an air classifier at a cut point of 15 micron (800 mesh) diameter between the two fractions. Usually the separated starch granules have considerable protein matrix adhering to their surfaces, in which case the starch fraction can be remilled and classified. The two protein fractions differ in composition, but are usually combined. The second milling will increase starch damage and may not be advisable in certain applications for this major component.

The wet milling process for pulses is adapted from corn and soybean technology (Figure 18.8). The coarsely ground flour is dispersed in dilute alkali, hydrated, screened to remove fiber, and then passed through a wet mill (20). Centrifugation of the slurry separates the starch granules, and the solubilized protein can be precipitated at its isoelectric pH to yield a protein curd. Washing the starch and protein isolates adds to the whey and wash losses.

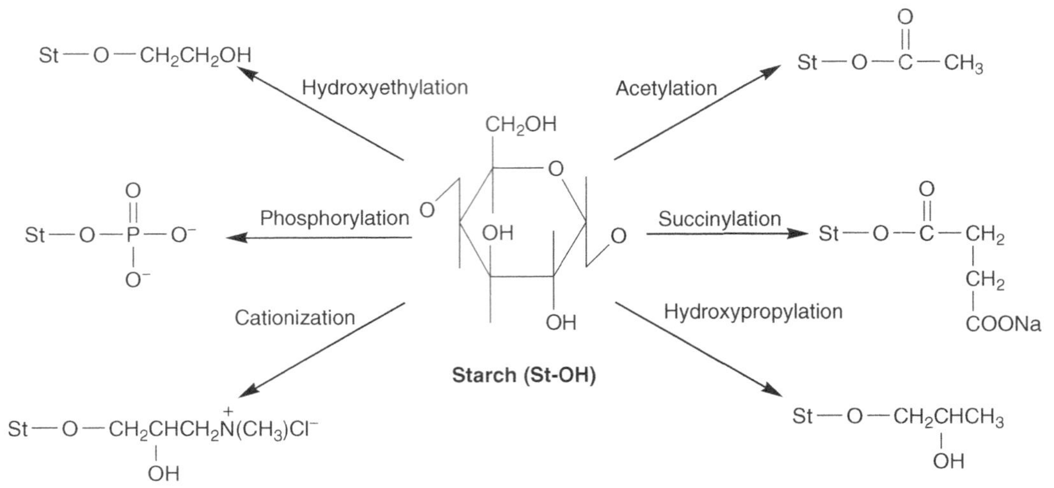

FIGURE 18.5 Chemical modifications of starch with substitution and cross-linking agents that alter the functional properties of starch for food and industrial applications.

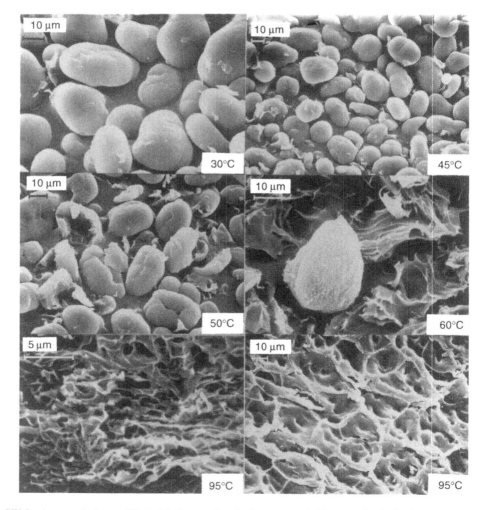

FIGURE 18.6 SEM-micrograph for an 8% (w/v) slurry of cationic pea starch (degree of substitution = 0.042) sampled from the amylograph at 30°C, 45°C, 50°C, 60°C, 95°C, and after 30 min at 95°C. (From Ref. 17.)

TABLE 18.3

Functional Properties of Flours, Protein Fractions, and Protein Isolates from Soybean and Dry Peas, Dry Basis

Legume and Product	Protein[a] %	Lysine	Methionine	Threonine	Nitrogen Solubility Index %	Water Holding Capacity g/g sample	Oil Absorption Capacity g/g sample	Oil Emulsification Capacity ml/g sample	Foam Volume at 60 min ml	Dry Product Color[b] Units
			g amino acid/100 g protein							
Soybean										
Flour	48	6.8	1.6	4.3	21	1.8	0.6	372	280	86
Isolate	82	6.3	1.5	4.1	31	3.2	1.1	451	95	85
Dry Pea										
Flour	25	7.7	1.3	3.8	80	0.9	0.4	346	180	91
Protein fraction	47	7.5	1.2	3.7	65	1.4	0.7	372	280	88
Isolate	80	7.2	0.9	3.3	38	2.7	1.0	366	210	80

[a] N × 5.7.
[b] 100 = white, 0 = black.
Source: Ref. 18.

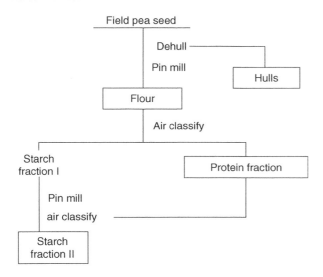

FIGURE 18.7 Flow diagram for pin milling and air classification of pulses into protein and starch fractions. (From Ref. 20.)

In a comparative study of dry and wet milling (20), pea flour containing 22% protein and 55% starch yielded an air-classified fine fraction containing 53% protein and a coarse fraction with 83% starch, dry basis (Figure 18.9). The fines also contained some broken starch granules plus most of the lipid, ash, sugars, flavour and colour compounds in the flour. The recovery of starch in the coarse fraction was very high (93%) but the starch content of 83% was not comparable to commercial corn starch at 95–99%.

The protein isolate from wet milling contained 88% protein, like soy protein isolate, and a refined starch containing <1.0% protein, as in corn starch (Figure 18.9). The refined fiber was light colored and relatively free of other constituents. The principal drawback of the wet milling system was the substantial losses of protein and starch in the whey and washes, and expensive effluent recovery procedures would need to be implemented.

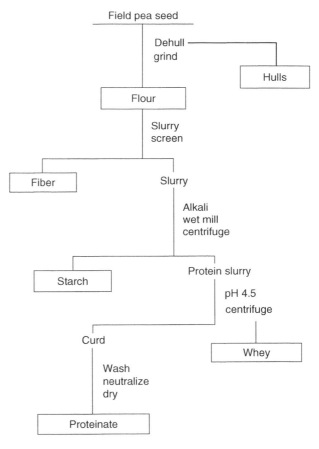

FIGURE 18.8 Flow diagram for preparation of refined fiber, refined starch and proteinate from pulses by wet milling techniques. (From Ref. 20.)

Direct comparisons of functionality in dry pea and soybean proteins have been made (18, 20). The protein fraction from air classification of pea flour was similar in protein content to soybean flour and was very similar to soybean in all functional properties (Table 18.3). The soybean isolate

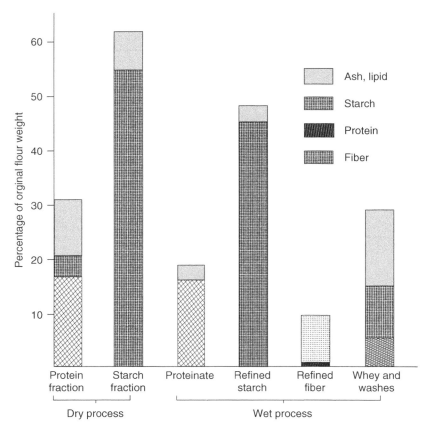

FIGURE 18.9   Yields of products from dry and wet milling of dehulled dry peas. (From Ref. 20.)

was superior to pea isolate in oil emulsification but inferior in foaming properties. The dominant color in all legume products was creamy-yellow and only the pea isolate was slightly darker than the other products.

Natural pea flour exhibited an exceptionally high nitrogen solubility (NSI) at the pH 6.6 used in this test while that of defatted soybean flour was particularly low (Table 18.3). Also the protein isolation procedure decreased the solubility of pea protein quite severely. To assess the effect of impact milling and the alkaline extraction/isoelectric precipitation treatments on nitrogen solubilities of these legumes, the pH dispersibility curves were determined from pH 2–11 (Figure 18.10). The soybean flour and isolate gave almost complete recovery of the product nitrogen as insoluble curd at pH 4–5, indicating the near absence of nonprotein nitrogen material. In dry pea flour and protein (concentrate) fraction, 10–15% of the total nitrogen was soluble protein and nonprotein compounds. During protein isolation, this soluble nitrogen appeared in the whey (Figure 18.9).

At pH levels above and below the isoelectric range, the soybean proteins in both flour and isolate showed only gradual increases in solubility (Figure 18.10). However, the native proteins in pea flour and protein fraction gave high nitrogen solubility values on both sides of the isoelectric

pH 4–5. The restricted protein solubility of both isolates between pH 6–9 might be due to the alkaline extraction treatment, acid denaturation, binding with phytin and, in the case of soybean, solvent extraction and desolventizing. For the pea, the alkaline and acid denaturation effect could be minimized by extracting protein at pH 7–8, an advantage over soybean.

In conclusion, the starch in pea flour had an adverse effect on functionality. By removing the starch component, the protein fraction exhibited comparable or superior functional properties to those of soybean flour, and should have potential applications in meat emulsions, bakery and beverage products. Pea protein isolate would also compete favorably with soybean isolate if pea starch has high value uses.

E.   POTENTIAL FOR AIR CLASSIFICATION

Air classification offers several advantages over wet milling. Only hulls, protein, and starch fractions are manufactured. No water or chemicals are added, so there is no effluent for disposal and microbial problems would be minimal. Electricity is the only essential utility for the two pieces of equipment, and the requirement for engineering skills among operators would be minimal. A seed cleaner

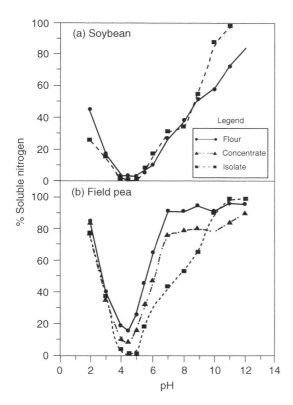

FIGURE 18.10 Nitrogen solubility curves for flours, air classified protein fraction and isolates of a) soybean and b) field pea. (From Ref. 18.)

countries. Therefore a legume starch fraction, manufactured locally, should find markets where a 95% pure starch at <1.0% protein is not essential.

Numerous studies have shown that nearly all pulses which contain starch can be air classified into fine and coarse fractions. Soybean and lupine yield no coarse fraction (21). Also, the lipids in chickpea interfered with fractionation efficiency and cause plugging of ducts during product transfer. Common bean is the main legume grown in low-income regions and has been evaluated extensively by air classification. As shown in Table 18.4, the intermediate protein level in beans still gives a high yield of fines (40%) with intermediate protein content (53%). The low starch content of the bean results in a low yield of starch fraction, which may be desirable if markets are limited. The starch granules in dry peas and lentils separate fully into high yields of starch fraction with high starch contents and less protein contamination. The dry pea and lentil fines are high in protein content although the yields are low. Fababean is a high protein pulse that gives consistently superior results in protein content of fines. Unfortunately, the vicine and convicine in the flour (about 0.7%) separated into 1.4% in the fines and 0.3% in the coarse fraction. When utilized as a supplement and functional ingredient in foods, susceptible individuals would not easily avoid the bean.

Among more tropical pulses, mung bean gave high yields and composition of protein and starch fraction while cowpea and lima bean were intermediate to the other legumes in air classification efficiency.

F. APPLICATIONS FOR AIR-CLASSIFIED FRACTIONS

Characteristically pulses have beany, bitter flavors which are usually removed effectively by aqueous extraction during soaking and cooking or wet milling. Unfortunately, the adverse flavors are concentrated into the protein fractions during air classification. Therefore, any potential applications would need to include appropriate wet heat

and grain dryer would be useful optional equipment as well as baggers and loaders.

Since most of the pulses are grown and utilized in low-income tropical and semi-tropical countries, the air classification of pulses should be particularly applicable in these areas. There is great market potential for the high lysine protein fraction in formulated nutritional foods, especially for infants. Also the wet milling of corn into refined corn starch is not done commonly in tropical

TABLE 18.4
Yield and Chemical Composition of Fine and Coarse Fractions from Air Classification of Impact-Milled Pulse Flours, % Dry Basis

Legume	Flour		Fine Protein Fraction			Coarse Starch Fraction		
	Protein[a] %	Starch %	Yield %	Protein %	Starch %	Yield %	Protein %	Starch %
Common bean	25	46	40	53	1	60	7	76
Dry pea	22	55	34	55	3	66	6	84
Fababean	31	52	37	70	2	63	8	81
Lentil	23	55	37	53	5	63	5	85
Cowpea	25	48	39	49	3	61	9	77
Mung bean	27	53	40	60	5	60	5	84
Lima bean	23	50	39	48	1	61	8	80

[a] N × 5.7.
Source: Ref. 21.

treatments to remove steam-volatile constituents. For example, blends of pea and fababean protein fractions with wheat flour at the 15% substitution level were mixed into dough, proofed, and baked by normal bread-making procedures (22). Despite the high levels of dilution with wheat flour, beany and grassy flavors did develop during dough fermentation, but these were driven off during baking. Loaf volumes and crumb textures were adversely affected by the supplements, but the addition of 2% vital gluten and 1% of dough conditioner per 100 g flour gave satisfactory bread volume and structure. Glycolipids like sucrose monolaurate and polyoxyethylene-8-stearate were the most effective conditioners.

Numerous attempts to prepare high-protein snack foods and breakfast cereals by extrusion cooking have not had commercial success. The protein fractions gave limited expansion, and the heat treatments in the barrel failed to fully debitter the product. With a lower flavor profile, extrusion of the starch fraction appeared feasible. Recently, Wang et al. (23) used a twin-screw co-rotating extruder to develop a pasta-like product from the pea starch fraction. Screw configurations were designed to gelatinize the starch, denature residual proteins, vent off adverse flavors, and texturize the extrudate. The product exhibited superior integrity, flavor, and texture after cooking than wheat semolina pasta, although cooking losses were higher. This product made entirely from the pea starch fraction by twin-screw extrusion would be a nutritional and functional alternative to wheat-based products for consumers who cannot tolerate wheat gluten.

REFERENCES

1. R Macrae, RK Robinson, MJ Sadler. Encyclopedia of Food Science, Food Technology and Nutrition. London: Academic Press, 1993, pp 2718–2730, 3841–3845.
2. J Tang, S Sokhansanj. Moisture diffusivity in Laird lentil seed components. Trans ASAE 36: 1791–1798, 1993.
3. J Tang, S Sokhansanj, FW Sosulski. Moisture-absorption characteristics of Laird lentils and hardshell seeds. Cereal Chem 71: 423–428, 1994.
4. BG Swanson, SJ Hughes, HP Rasmussen. Seed microstructure: Review of water imbibition in legumes. Food Microstruct 4: 115–124, 1985.
5. DW Stanley. A possible role for condensed tannins in bean hardening. Food Res Int 25: 187–192, 1992.
6. FW Sosulski, HM Gadan. Variations in lipid composition among chickpea cultivars. J Amer Oil Chem Soc 65: 369–372, 1988.
7. R Hoover, FW Sosulski. Composition, structure, functionality and chemical modification of legume starches: A review. Can J Physiol Pharmacol 69: 79–92, 1990.
8. G Sarwar, FW Sosulski, JM Bell. Nutritive value of field pea and fababean proteins in rat diets. Can Inst Food Sci Technol J 8: 109–112, 1975.
9. FW Sosulski, GI Imafidon. Amino acid composition and nitrogen-to-protein conversion factors for animal and plant foods. J Agr Food Chem 38: 1351–1356, 1990.
10. DK Salunkhe, SS Kadam, JK Chavan, Postharvest Biotechnology of Food Legumes. Boca Raton, FL: CRC Press, 1985, 160 pp.
11. K Elkowicz, FW Sosulski. Antinutritive factors in eleven legumes and their air-classified protein and starch fractions. J Food Sci 47: 1301–1304, 1982.
12. OL Kimer, PA Seib, RC Hoseney. Effect of minerals and apparent phytase activity in the development of the hard-to-cook state of beans. Cereal Chem 71: 476–482, 1994.
13. FW Sosulski, K Elkowicz, RD Reichert. Oligosaccharides in eleven legumes and their air-classified protein and starch fractions. J Food Sci 47: 498–502, 1982.
14. J Tang, S Sokhansanj, AE Slinkard, F Sosulski. Quality of artificially dried lentil. J Food Proc Engin 13: 228–238, 1990.
15. J Tang, S Sokhansanj, FW Sosulski, AE Slinkard. Effect of harvest methods on moisture content and quality of lentil seeds. Can J Plant Sci 72: 451–456, 1992.
16. R Hoover, F Sosulski. Studies on the functional characteristics and digestibility of starches from *Phaseolus vulgaris* biotypes. Starch/Starke 37: 181–191, 1985.
17. C Yook, F Sosulski, PR Bhirud. Effects of cationization on functional properties of pea and corn starches. Starch/Starke 46: 393–399, 1994.
18. FW Sosulski, AR McCurdy. Functionality of flours, protein fractions and isolates from field pea and faba bean. J Food Sci 52: 1010–1014, 1987.
19. JR Vose, MJ Basterrechea, PAG Gorin, AJ Finlayson, CG Youngs. Air classification of field peas and horsebean flours: Chemical studies of starch and protein fractions. Cereal Chem 53: 928–936, 1976.
20. FW Sosulski, K Sosulski. Composition and functionality of protein, starch and fiber from wet and dry processing of grain legumes. In: RL Ory, ed. Plant Proteins: Applications, Biological Effects, and Chemistry. Washington, D.C.: American Chemical Society, 1986, pp 176–189.
21. RT Tyler, CG Youngs, FW Sosulski. Air classification of legumes. 1. Separation efficiency, yield, and composition of the starch and protein fractions. Cereal Chem 58: 144–148, 1981.
22. SE Fleming, FW Sosulski. Breadmaking properties of four concentrated plant proteins. Cereal Chem 54: 1124–1140, 1977.
23. N Wang, PR Bhirud, FW Sosulski, RT Tyler. Pasta-like product from pea flour by twin-screw extrusion. J Food Sci 64: 671–678, 1999.

19 Asian Fermented Soybean Products

Li Lite
Department of Food Science and Nutritional Engineering, China Agricultural University

CONTENTS

I. INTRODUCTION

It is well known that soybean is originated in China, and has been cultivated there for over 5,000 years. Soybean is considered one of the five basic grains, along with rice, wheat, barley, and millet, which are essential to the Chinese diet and civilization. During the Qin Dynasty (about 200 A.D.), soybean was introduced to Korea from Northern China, and then to Japan and Southeast Asia. Soybean did not appear in Europe and North America until the 18th and 19th centuries, respectively. It is now cultivated all over the world (1).

Fermented soybean foods use either whole soybeans or soybean products as substrates, sometimes along with other cereals. Fermented soyfoods are produced by specific microorganisms or by several microorganisms acting in a sequential manner. The ultimate aim of fermentation is to develop food products having certain desirable characteristics such as flavor, aroma, texture, and keeping quality. During fermentation, protein and carbohydrate fractions are hydrolyzed into smaller constituents, which increase digestibility. Vitamins are also accumulated in the fermented products (2).

Despite the widespread cultivation of soybean, traditional fermented foods based on soybean are limited to the Orient. Most traditional soyfoods are known to have originated in China, and were then introduced to other Asian countries. After centuries of preparation, considerable modification and adaptation in processes had been made to suit specific environmental conditions and cultural practices. These traditional foods are increasingly popular in many Asian countries, and have been extensively developed and consumed in China, Korea, and Japan, and to a lesser extent in Indonesia, India, Malaysia, and Thailand. Table 19.1 lists some common indigenous fermented soyfood products consumed in various parts of Asia (2, 3).

Since fermented soyfoods are nutritious and highly digestible, they have played an important nutritional role in the Oriental population in the past, and will continue to do so in the future. Today, the preparation of many traditional fermented soybean products remains a household art, and only a few (such as soy sauce and *natto*) have evolved with modern biotechnological development and

are manufactured on a large scale. In this chapter, various fermented soybean products are discussed with respect to their preparation methods and utilization. Only products that have an important influence and are produced in large quantities are described.

II. SOY SAUCE (*JIANGYOU*)

Soy sauce is a dark brown liquid extracted from a fermented mixture of soybean and wheat or soybean only, with aroma and flavor similar to that of *miso*. First produced in the Zhou Dynasty (684–705 A.D.) in China, soy sauce is now widely consumed in China, Japan, Korea, and other Oriental countries, and is also used in North America and Europe as a condiment and coloring agent (4). Soy sauce is known as *jiangyou* (Mandarin) or *chiangyu* (Cantonese) in China, *shoyu* in Japan, *kanjang* in Korea, *Tao-yu* or *kecap* in Indonesia, and *tayo* in the Philippines (5).

A. QU (KOJI), KOJI STARTER, AND INOCULUM

Before describing the methods of preparing soy sauce, it is necessary to introduce some terms commonly used in fermented soybean products.

1. Qu (Koji)

Qu is the Chinese word for *koji*, and is an intermediate product for making soy sauce, soy paste, *douchi* (soy nuggets), *kecap*, and other similar products. *Qu*, which contains a large variety of enzymes, is made by growing molds on rice, barley, wheat, soybean, or a combination.

2. Koji Starter

Koji starter, also known as seed *koji*, *koji* seeds, or *tanekoji*, provides spores of microorganisms to make *koji*. Traditionally, wild spores of different molds were used as the starter for soy sauce, soy paste, and soy nuggets. However, in modern manufacturing, the making of *koji* starter begins with the growth of a selected mold strain, such as *Asperigillus oryzae* or *A. sojae*, in pure culture.

TABLE 19.1
Traditional Fermented Soybean Foods in Asia

Product	Region	Substrates	Microorganism(s)	Nature of Product	Product Use
Douchi (*Hamanatto*, *tao-si*, *tao-tjo*)	China, Japan, Philippines, East India	Whole soybean, wheat flour, salt, seasoning	*Mucor* spp., *Aspergillus oryzae*, *Bacillus subtilis*, *Pediococcus* spp., *Streptococcus* spp.	Solid beans, retain individual form, soft, raisin-like	Seasoning, snack
Kecap	Indonesia and vicinity	Soybean, wheat	*Aspergillus oryzae*, *Hansenula* spp., *Lactobacillus* spp., *Saccharomyces* spp.	Liquid	Condiment, seasoning
Kinema	Eastern Nepal, India (Sikkim, Darjeeling)	Soybean	*Bacillus subtilis*	Solid	Fried curry, side dish
Meitauza	China, Taiwan	Soybean	*Actinomucor elegans*	Solid	Fried in oil or cooked with vegetables
Meju	Korea	Soybean	*Asperigillus oryzae*, *Rhizopus* spp.	Paste	Seasoning
Fermented soybean paste (*Doujiang*, *miso*, *chiang*)	China, Japan other cereals, salt	Soybean and rice or *Lactobacillus* spp.	*Aspergillus oryzae*, *Torulopsis etchellsii*,	Paste	Soup base, seasoning
Natto	Japan	Whole soybean	*Bacillus natto*	Solid beans	Snack
Fermented soybean milk	China, Japan	Soybean	Lactic acid bacteria	Liquid	Drink
Soy sauce (*Jiangyou*, *shoyu*, *kecap*)	China, Japan, the Philippines, other parts of the Orient	Soybean and wheat, salt	*Aspergillus oryzae* or *A. soyae*, *Lactobacillus* spp., *Zygosaccharomyces rouxii*	Liquid	Seasoning for meat, fish, cereals, vegetables
Sufu (*Doufuru*, *furu*, *taokaoan*, *tao-hu-yi*)	China	Soybean curd, salt, seasoning, pigment	*Actinomucor elegans*, *Mucor hiemalis*, *M. silvaticus*, *M. subtilissimus*	Solid	Soybean cheese, condiment
Tauco	West Java (Indonesia)	Soybean, cereals	*Rhizopus oligosporus*, *Aspergillus oryzae*	Liquid	Drink
Tempeh	Indonesia and vicinity, Surinam	Soybean	*Rhizopus* spp., principally *R. oligosporus*	Solid	Fried, roasted, used as meat substitute in soup.

Different raw materials are used and sterile conditions are needed to avoid contamination.

3. Inoculum

Traditionally, in the making of soy sauce, soy paste, and soy nuggets, fermenting product from a previous batch was used as an inoculum to be mixed with salted *koji* and cooked soybeans. In recent years, pure cultures of *Zygosaccharomyces rouxii*, *Torulopsis* sp., and certain lactic acid bacteria such as *Pediococcus halophilus* and *Streptococcus faecalis* were used as inoculum, which speeds up fermentation and reduces contamination by weed yeasts and bacteria.

B. CLASSIFICATION OF SOY SAUCE

Differences among soy sauce samples are due to many factors, such as raw ingredients, microorganisms used in fermentation, processing conditions, and additives such as sweeteners and preservatives (6). According to the preparation principles, soy sauce can be divided into three groups: fermented soy sauce, chemical soy sauce, and semi-chemical soy sauce. It can be further divided based on differences in raw ingredients, methods of preparation, or duration of aging. There are two major kinds of fermented soy sauce in China according to fermentation procedures: 1) high-salt-high-water fermented soy sauce, in which soybeans or defatted soybean flakes and wheat flour are used as raw materials; and 2) low-salt-semidried-state fermented soy sauce, in which defatted soybean flakes and wheat bran are used as fermentation substrates. Chemical soy sauce is made by acid hydrolysis and will not be described in this chapter. To improve quality, chemical soy sauce is often blended with fermented soy sauce to semi-chemical products before being sold.

Five types of *shoyu* are available in Japan: *koikuchi*, *usukuchi*, *tamari*, *shiro*, and *saishikomi*. Of all the *shoyu* consumed in Japan, 85% is of the *koikuchi* type (7). *Koikuchi* is made from a mixture of soybean and wheat kernels in almost equal amount and is characterized by a

TABLE 19.2
Sugar Contents in Soy Sauce

Sugar	Content (% w/w)
Glucose	2.05
Galactose	0.17
Mannose	0.06
Xylose	0.06
Arabinose	0.08
Unidentified sugars	0.23
Disaccharides	0.65
Polysaccharides	1.15
Total	4.45

Source: Adapted from Ref. 28.

deep reddish brown color and a strong, pleasant aroma (7). *Usukuchi*, the second most popular type of *shoyu*, is commonly used to preserve the original flavor and color of foods. The remaining three types of *shoyu* are produced and consumed only in isolated localities for special uses. *Tamari shoyu* is similar to traditional Chinese soy sauce, with a soybean:wheat ratio of about 9:1 to 8:2. In contrast, *shiro shoyu* is made with a soybean:wheat ratio of 1:9 to 2:8, and fermentation is controlled to prevent color development. *Saishikomi shoyu* is produced similar to *koikuchi*, but the *koji* is mixed with raw soy sauce instead of a brine solution.

Traditional Indonesian *kecap* is a Chinese style soy sauce. However, industrial Indonesian *kecap* is a Japanese-type product (8).

C. PREPARATION OF SOY SAUCE

1. Chinese *Jiangyou*

Traditionally, Chinese soy sauce is produced from soybean only, but for industrial preparation, wheat flour or bran is added.

a. Traditional household method
The following is a typical method used in Northern China. The raw materials for *jiangyou* making are soybean, salt, and water. Soybean is selected and washed, and then boiled until the beans are soft enough to mash. The mashed soy mud is shaped into bean loaves of about 1–4 kg. The loaves are often made around the Chinese Spring Festival, acting as *qu*. They are placed in a warm room for spontaneous fermentation until the beginning of summer. The fermented loaves are crushed into lumps and mixed with water and salt in earthen vats. The vats are placed outdoors and exposed to sunlight to increase the temperature. The later stage fermentation lasts for at least 30 days, and the mixture is stirred thoroughly daily. The *moromi* becomes thick and dark after fermentation, and has a pleasant fermentative aroma and taste. The liquid is separated and transferred to another jar, and exposed to sunlight for several weeks. A premium grade soy sauce can then be made. Fresh brine can be added to the mash two or more times to extract the second and third grades soy sauce. This is also followed by several weeks of exposure to the sun.

b. Modern methods
Defatted soy meal and wheat bran are mixed at a ratio of 8:2 to 6:4, and the mixture is soaked in water and steamed. After cooling, the mixture is inoculated with a small amount of seed spores of *Aspergillus sojae* and/or *A. oryzae* to make *qu* in about 22–30 hours at 35°C.

For low-salt-semidried-state fermented soy sauce, the *koji* is mixed with 12–13°C Bé brine to make a *moromi*, with a water content of about 50% and a salt content lower than 10%. The *moromi* is fermented at a higher temperature (40–45°C) for half a month, and mixed with additional brine solution to increase the salt content to at least 15%. The *moromi* is in a semi-liquid state. Lactic acid bacteria and yeasts are added to the brine solution, and fermentation is allowed to continue for half a month or longer at 30–35°C.

For high-salt-high-water fermented soy sauce, the *koji* is mixed with 18°C Bé brine, and fermentation is carried out at 30°C or at room temperature for 3–6 months. This method is adopted by most manufacturers.

A combination of the above two methods has also been used. The low-salt-semidried-state *moromi* is first fermented at 40–42°C for 2 weeks, and then mixed with brine to form a high-salt-high-water *moromi*, fermented at 35–37°C for 15–20 days, followed by fermentation at 28–30°C for 30–100 days. In order to save rice and wheat grains, liquid hydrolysates of broken rice or wheat flour, produced by α-amylase and β-amylase from wheat bran, are used by some producers. The fermented mash is heated to more than 80°C and the liquid product is separated by gravity. The soy sauce may be pasteurized or mixed with benzoic acid before being clarified, bottled, and shipped to the market.

2. Japanese *Shoyu*

Although there are some variations in making different types of Japanese soy sauce, the basic steps are the same, including the treatment of raw materials, *koji* making, brine fermentation, pressing, and refining (Figure 19.1).

a. *Treatment of raw materials*

Soybeans or defatted soybean flakes are soaked in water to increase the moisture content to about 60% and then cooked with steam at 0.8–1.0 kg/cm^2 gauge pressure for 40–45 minutes, or by a high temperature short time (HTST) process (6–7 kg/cm^2, 20–30 seconds). The wheat kernels are heated with hot air at 150°C for 30–45 seconds at atmospheric pressure, and the roasted kernels are cracked into 4 to 5 pieces. When wheat flour and wheat bran are used, they are steamed after being moisturized (5), then the cooked soybeans are mixed with the roasted wheat (9).

b. *Preparation of koji*

The treated raw materials are inoculated with 0.1–0.2% seed spores of *Aspergillus sojae* and/or *A. oryzae*. After 2 to 3 days of solid culture at 25–28°C, the mixture becomes a greenish yellow mass as a result of mold growth and sporulation, and is called *koji*.

c. *Brine fermentation*

Matured *koji* is mixed with an equal amount of brine to make *moromi*. In general, the salt content is kept at around 17% (10). At the initial stage, *Penicillum halophilus* is added to the mash to produce lactic acid which lowers the pH, and to prepare the appropriate conditions for yeast fermentation to produce ethanol. The

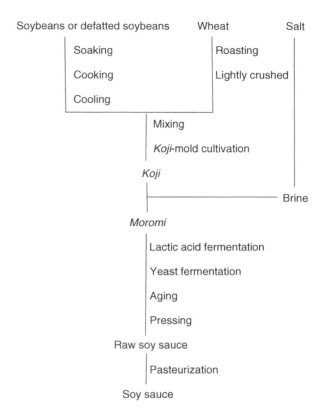

FIGURE 19.1 Flow chart of soy sauce manufacturing.

microorganism also plays an important role in the quality control of the mash, and has an influence on *shoyu* flavor and taste. To control growth rate, it is necessary to keep the fermenting mixture at 15°C in the first month, allowing the pH of the mash to decrease slowly from 6.5 to 5.0. Then *Zygosacchararomyces rouxii* and *Candida* species are added as starters. The temperature of the *moromi* is allowed to rise slowly from 15°C to nearly 28°C for vigorous alcoholic fermentation, and this temperature is kept for 4 months. After the completion of alcoholic fermentation, the temperature is kept at 15°C for 1 month (9, 10).

Lactic acid bacteria and yeast cells interact in a mash, and this affects the production of both lactic acid and ethanol (11). Immobilization of lactic acid bacteria and yeast cells in separate fermentors has been found to be effective for speeding up the production of *shuyo* (12, 13).

d. *Pressing and refining*

The next step in *shoyu* processing is pressing and refining, involving filtration, pasteurization, and packaging. The aged *moromi* is pressed to separate the soy sauce from the residue. The residue can be extracted with additional 20% brine to increase the yield. After pressing, the filtered raw soy sauce is pasteurized at 70–80°C for a few minutes to inactivate residual enzymes and undesirable microorganisms. It may be necessary to clarify the soy sauce further by centrifugation or sedimentation. The product is treated with caramel as a coloring agent and then packaged (9).

3. Indonesian *Kecap*

Kecap is a liquid seasoning widely used in Malaysia and Indonesia. In Indonesia, *kecap* is usually made by small-scale producers in a traditional manner. Black soybeans are used as the raw material (14). Commercial soy sauce factories have been established in Indonesia, and they apply modern Japanese technology for *kecap* production. Defatted soybean flakes and wheat are used instead of black soybeans (15).

In *kecap* processing, the cooked soybeans are made into *koji* by mixing with mold inoculum consisting of various species of *Aspergillus*. The *koji* is incubated for 48 hours in a room with controlled temperature and relative humidity. At the end of the solid-state fermentation, the *koji* is transferred to a fermentation tank containing brine at a concentration of 20–25%. This process, *moromi* fermentation, lasts at least 2 months, and the pleasant aroma of *kecap* is formed. *Pediococcus halophilus* is the dominant microorganism during the brining stage in *kecap* fermentation (16). *Kecap* liquid is withdrawn at the end of *moromi* fermentation and transferred to a sedimentation tank to precipitate the dispersed particles of raw *kecap*. Based on the formulation, liquid *kecap* can be blended with other ingredients to produce condensed *kecap*. The product is pasteurized for 15 minutes to destroy spoilage microbes. Finally, bottling and labeling of the end product are carried out.

D. CHEMICAL AND BIOCHEMICAL CHANGES DURING SOY SAUCE PROCESSING

Soy sauce is made by a two-step fermentation process with a mixture of molds, yeasts, and bacteria using soybean and wheat flour as raw materials. The first step involves fermentation with *Aspergillus sojae* and/or *A. oryzae* to make *koji* (9). During this period, enzymes from *koji*, such as proteinases, peptidases, and amylases, hydrolyze most of the proteins to peptides and amino acids, and almost all of the starches to simple sugars. These become the nutrients for the yeasts and lactic acid bacteria in the subsequent step of brine fermentation.

The second stage of fermentation involves *Pediococcus halophilus*, *Zygosaccharomyces rouxii*, *Candida versatilis*, and *Candida ethellsii*. All the microorganisms can tolerate a salt concentration of 18–20%. However, the brine effectively prevents the growth of undesirable microorganisms. Sugars are fermented by the salt-tolerant microorganisms into lactic acid, ethanol, and various aroma components (10). *Z. rouxii* produces ethanol and 4-hydroxy-2 (or 5)-ethyl-5 (or 2)-methyl-3 (2H)-furanone (HEMF). The latter is considered one of the important compounds for soy sauce flavor (12), reaching a maximum concentration at 16% NaCl when fermented by *shoyu* yeasts (13). Ethanol (2–3%) and many aromatic components are produced by *Z. rouxii*. The *Candida* yeasts produce phenolic compounds

such as 4-ethylguaiacol and 4-ethylphenol, which add characteristic aroma to soy sauce (10).

The yeasts and *koji* culture have strong esterase activities which could be responsible for the decomposition of the flavor esters during soy sauce brewing, lowering ester flavor in the product. Glutamic acid and aspartic acid are the major amino acids present in soy sauce, and the levels of arginine, tryptophan, and cystine are decreased during fermentation. The total acid content in soy sauce is about 0.95%, dominated by lactic and acetic acids (9). The glucose content in Japanese soy sauce is about 2.05%, different from the Chinese traditional soy sauce which has little fermentable sugars left for yeast growth after the growth of *Tetragenococcus halophilia* cells (18).

III. FERMENTED SOYBEAN PASTE (*DOUJIANG* AND *MISO*)

Fermented soybean paste is a popular traditional seasoning in Asia, especially in East Asia. It is commonly known as *jiang* or *doujiang* in China, *miso* or *misho* in Japan, *jang* in Korea, *tacho* in Indonesia, and *taosi* in the Philippines. Chinese *jiang* is believed to be the oldest form of fermented soy paste. According to the ancient Chinese book, *Analects of Confucius*, it has a history of more than 3,000 years (19). *Miso* and *jang* are considered to be derived from *doujiang*.

Fermented soybean paste is a light yellow to dark brown thick paste. It has a very salty taste due to high salt content (normally 12–15%, and ranges from 5% to 20%), and has a special flavor of fermented soybean. It is usually served with other foods as a seasoning or used as a condiment in food preparation.

The process of *doujiang* making is very similar to that of soy sauce preparation. The main steps include the preparation of starter, *qu or koji*, mixing the starter with salt and water, and fermentation. Figure 19.3 shows the flow chart of *doujiang* making using pure culture starter.

A. PREPARATION OF *DOUJIANG*

1. Traditional Household Method

The traditional method of making *doujiang* is almost the same as making *jiangyou*, but the liquid is not separated from the paste. Another household method of *doujiang* making differs from the former one mainly in the preparation of *qu*. Boiled soybean is mixed with a small amount of wheat flour. The mixture is then spread onto a bamboo tray and kept in an incubation room for a week to make *qu*.

2. Pure Culture Method

a. Preparation of starter
A mixture of soybean and wheat flour (in 2:3 to 3:2 ratios) is used for making *qu*. The wheat flour is usually cooked

by baking or steaming, which is labor and energy intensive. Many producers therefore use raw flour directly. The washed, soaked, steam-cooked, and cooled soybean is mixed with the flour, and inoculated with 0.15–0.3% seed spores. The process of *qu* making is the same as that in soy sauce processing (Figure 19.2).

b. Fermentation

Figure 19.3 shows the fermentation steps involved in *doujiang* making. Matured *qu* is poured onto a fermentation container and pressed slightly. The temperature will soon increase spontaneously to 40°C, and brine (14.5°C Bé) at 60–65°C is added. After the brine penetrates evenly into the *qu*, small amount of fine salt is dusted on the surface. The temperature of the *qu* will reach 45°C, and fermentation is carried out at this temperature for 10 days. Brine (24.0°C Bé) and fine salt are added, and the mixture is thoroughly stirred with a mechanical mixer or by compressed air. After fermentation for another 4–5 days, the *doujiang* can be bottled and marketed.

B. PREPARATION OF *MISO*

The basic steps of *miso* manufacturing are similar to those of *doujiang* making, including treatment of raw materials, preparation of *koji*, mixing of ingredients, and fermentation. However, *miso* is quite different from *doujiang* in terms of raw materials, sensory characteristics, and usage (20). The raw materials for *miso* making can be soybean alone or soybean with rice or barley. The taste of *miso* is sweeter than *doujiang*. *Miso* is often used to prepare various types of soup, whereas *doujiang* is usually used as a seasoning.

There are three kinds of *miso*, based on the use of raw materials: soybean *miso*, rice *miso*, and barley *miso*. Rice *miso* is used to illustrate the processing steps involved in *miso* making (Figure 19.4). Unlike Chinese *qu*, rice is used as the raw material for *koji* making. The washed and soaked rice is steam-cooked and cooled. The cooked rice is inoculated with *tane-koji* (*Aspergillus oryzae*). The soybeans are washed, soaked, steam-cooked (or boiled), mashed, and cooled. The matured rice *koji* is mixed with the cooked soybean paste, together with salt and other species of microorganisms in the fermentation containers. The mixture is fermented for more than 6 months, and the rice *miso* is ready to be packed.

Since excessive salt intake is regarded as one of the causes of hypertension, there has been increasing interest in developing low-salt fermentated soy pastes. A salt-free *miso* can be prepared by supplementing the *koji* with ethanol (21), or ethanol with sugars and polyols (22). Supplementation of ethanol in *miso* not only enables low-salt fermentation but also enhances flavor formation (23).

C. CHEMICAL AND BIOCHEMICAL CHANGES DURING *MISO* PROCESSING

Due to enzymatic hydrolysis of macromolecules such as polysaccharides and proteins, fermented soy paste contains digestible, small-molecular-weight components. Unpasteurized *miso* has been found to have a vitamin B_{12} content ranging from 0.15–0.25 µg/100 g (24). During fermentation, complex metabolites are formed and contribute to the aroma and taste of the product. One of these metabolites is HEMF, formed by *Zygosaccharomyces rouxii*, with a strong cake-like aroma and a threshold value of less than 0.04 ppb, and is regarded as the most effective component in enhancing the aroma of *miso* (25).

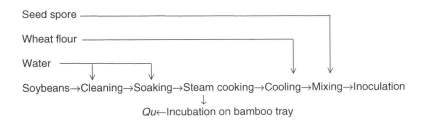

FIGURE 19.2 Pure culture method to make *qu*.

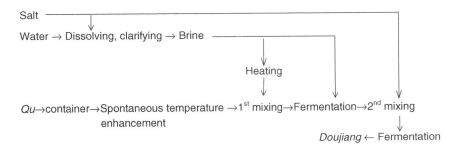

FIGURE 19.3 Pure culture method for *doujiang* making.

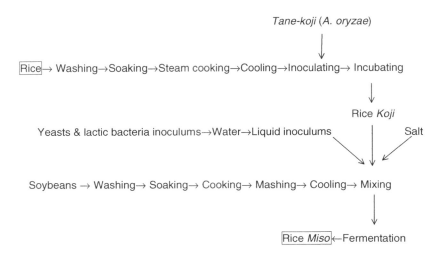

FIGURE 19.4   Flow chart of rice *miso* manufacturing.

Free amino acids are also very important components contributing to the taste of fermented soy paste.

IV.   SUFU (DOUFURU)

Sufu is a soft cheese type product made from soymilk curd (*tofu*) by the action of microorganisms (26). It has a long history and written records date back to the Wei Dynasty (220–265 A.D.) in China (27). *Sufu* has been widely consumed by Chinese in a way similar to cheese by Westerners, mainly as an appetizer or a side dish, e.g., with breakfast rice or steamed bread (26).

Because of the numerous dialects in China and difficulties of phonetic translation from Chinese to English, *sufu* has appeared in the literature under many different names, such as *tosufu, fu-su, fu-ru, toe-fu-ru, tou-fu-ru, dou-fu-ru, teou-fu-ru, fu-ju, fu-yu, jiang-dou-fu,* and *foo-yue* (27). Officially, *sufu* should be named *doufuru* or *furu* in Chinese.

There are many types of *sufu* prepared by various processes in different parts of China. Three main types of *sufu* can be identified according to processing methods and fermentation microorganisms: mold-fermented *sufu*, bacteria-fermented *sufu*, and enzymatically ripened *sufu*. *Sufu* can also be classified based on color and flavor, due to different dressing mixtures used in the ripening stage. According to the color and flavor of the products, *sufu* can be classified as red *sufu*, white *sufu*, grey *sufu*, sauce *sufu*, and colored *sufu* (28). Figure 19.5 shows the different types of commercial *sufu* products.

A.   MANUFACTURING PROCESSS OF SUFU

1.   Mold-Type Sufu

Four steps are involved in the manufacturing of mold-type *sufu*: preparation of soybean curd (*tofu*), preparation of

FIGURE 19.5   Commercial *sufu* products.

pehtze with a pure mold culture (fermentation), salting, and ripening. Figure 19.6 shows the flow chart of *sufu* manufacturing.

a.   Preparation of tofu

Soybeans are washed, soaked in water overnight or at 25°C for 5–6 hours, and ground. After removing the residue by filtering, soybmilk is collected. In order to inactivate the growth inhibitors and to remove some of the beany flavor, the soymilk is heated to a boil. The curdling process is initiated by the addition of salts, such as calcium sulfate and magnesium chloride when the milk has

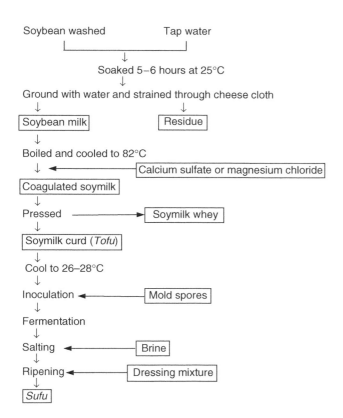

```
Soybean washed          Tap water
    └───────────┬──────────┘
                ↓
        Soaked 5–6 hours at 25°C
                ↓
Ground with water and strained through cheese cloth
    ↓                           ↓
[Soybean milk]              [Residue]
    ↓
Boiled and cooled to 82°C
    ↓  ◄──────[Calcium sulfate or magnesium chloride]
[Coagulated soymilk]
    ↓
Pressed ─────────►[Soymilk whey]
    ↓
[Soymilk curd (Tofu)]
    ↓
Cool to 26–28°C
    ↓
Inoculation ◄──────[Mold spores]
    ↓
Fermentation
    ↓
Salting ◄──────[Brine]
    ↓
Ripening ◄──────[Dressing mixture]
    ↓
[Sufu]
```

FIGURE 19.6 Flow chart of *sufu* manufacturing.

FIGURE 19.7 *Pehtze.*

been cooled to about 82°C. Generally, 20% more coagulant is used to produce *tofu* for *sufu* than for regular *tofu* production. Coagulant is added at a concentration of 2.5–3.5% (coagulant/dry soybean, w/w). The mixture is agitated vigorously to obtain a homogenous coagulum, and then set aside for 15 minutes to complete the coagulation. The coagulum is pressed to remove excess whey, and the resulting *tofu* is cut into cubes of desired sizes.

b. Preparation of pehtze (pizi)

The *tofu* cubes (2.5 × 3 × 3 cm) are placed in a tray with pinholes at the top and bottom to aid air circulation. They should be separated from one another since the mold mycelia must develop on all sides of the cubes. When the cubes are cooled to 35–40°C, they are inoculated by spraying on their surfaces with a pure culture of an appropriate fungus. The inoculated cubes, *pehtze* (or *pizi*) are usually incubated at 20–24°C for 3 to 7 days, with temperature and time dependent on the fungal starin used. For *Actinomucor taiwanensis* and some *Mucor* strains, the best fermentation temperature is above 30°C (29, 30). During incubation, the *pehtze* cubes are covered with white mycelia (Figure 19.7).

c. Salting

After the *pehtze* cubes are separated from each other and the mycelia on the surface are rubbed down, they are piled up in a jar with salt spread between layers. During the

salting period, the *pehtze* absorbs salt (not over 15%) and loses water, resulting in shrinkage and increase in hardness. Normally, the salting period lasts for 7–12 days, and the salted *pehtze* is washed with salty water. After being air-dried, it is transferred to another jar for further processing. The added salt not only retards mold growth, but most importantly, the salt solution releases mycelia-bound proteases which are not extracellular and can be easily eluted by salt or other ionic solutions, but not by water (31).

d. Ripening

Ripening involves a series of biochemical reactions catalyzed by microbial enzymes. The differences among various types of *sufu* are mainly due to the use of different dressing mixtures during ripening. The basic and most common brine contains 12% NaCl and rice wine with about 10% ethyl alcohol. Other ingredients include yellow wine, red kojic rice, soy mash, pimiento, fennel, garlic, shallot, ginger, etc. The ripening time varies for different *sufu* types with different dressing mixtures. Normally it is allowed to age for 2 to 6 months. The product is then bottled with brine and marketed.

2. Bacterial-Type *Sufu*

The preparation of *tofu* is the same as in the mold-type *sufu*. The *tofu* cubes are steamed at 1 kg/cm² for 20 minutes. After cooling to 20–30°C, the cubes are salted for 24 hours and washed with water, put into fermented trays, and incubated at 28–30°C for 5 to 6 days after inoculation. When the *pehtze* is covered with bacteria and secretes a yellow liquid, it is dried at 50–60°C for 8 to 10 hours. The dried *pehtze* is placed into jars with a dressing mixture of salt, red kojic rice, rice wine containing 50% ethyl alcohol and other seasonings. The jars are sealed and incubated at 35°C for 20 days. More dressing mixture is then added and a further 50 days of fermentation is carried out, resulting in the production of a red *sufu* (32).

B. Microorganisms for Fermentation

Usually, the microorganisms for mold-type *sufu* are *Mucor* spp. (33), and for bacteria-type *sufu Bacillus* spp. or *Micrococcus* spp. (34). The organisms must develop enzyme systems having high proteolytic and lipolytic activities, and also have white or light yellowish mycelium to ensure that the final product has an attractive appearance. The texture of the mycelial mat should also be dense and thick to prevent any distortion in the shape of the fermented cubes. Of course, the mold growth should not develop any disagreeable odors, astringent tastes, or mycotoxin. *Actinomucor elegans* (35), *Mucor hiemalis*, *M. silvaticus*, *M. prainii* (36), *M. sufu* (35), and *M. subtilisimus* all possess these characteristics. Among them, *Actinomucor elegans* and *A. taiwanensis* seems to be the best organisms and are used commercially in Beijing and Taiwan, respectively.

In addition to *Mucor* spp., *Rhizophus* spp., *Aspergillus oryzae* and *Monascus* spp. which are found in red *sufu*, many other species of microorganisms have been isolated, such as *Penicilium*, *Cladosporium*, *Alternaria*, *Bacillus*, *Staphylococcus*, *Micrococcus*, and *Corynebacterium*. Some researchers suggested that yeasts and bacteria play a role in the flavor and texture of *sufu*, and the predominant halophile is identified as *Tetragenococcus halophila*. Microorganisms isolated from *sufu* made in different regions of China are listed in Table 19.3.

Han found that *Bacillus cereus* in a few *sufu* samples was over 10^5 CFU/g, and *Staphylococcus aureus* enterotoxin A was detected in some of the white and grey *sufu* samples, indicating a potential hazard to consumers (37).

C. Chemical and Biochemical Changes during *Sufu* Processing

During *sufu* manufacturing, glycerol esters are hydrolyzed to fatty acids and glycerol, and glycerol is transformed into organic acids by bacteria. Glutamic acid and leucine are notably present in the water-soluble fraction. Alcohol is produced during the brining and ripening process, and esters are then chemically or enzymatically synthesized from alcohol and fatty acids. Nucleic acids, such as guanidine nucleotide, are the degradation products after the thalli have autolyzed, providing the delicious taste and aroma of *sufu* along with the free fatty acids, organic acids, esters, and seasonings in the dressing mixture such as pimiento, pepper, curry, and sesame oil. The complex flavor has been reported to contain 22 esters, 18 alcohols, 7 ketones, 3 aldehydes, 2 pyrazines, 2 phenols, and other volatile compounds (38). The sugar content of ripen *sufu* is about 5%, so it has a somewhat sweet taste. The added salt imparts a salty taste to the products.

In spite of the differences in color and flavor, most types of *sufu* have a similar proximate composition. As shown in Table 19.4, *sufu* is a nutritious food. The vitamin B_2 content in red *sufu* is 0.42–0.78 mg/100 g, and in grey *sufu*, it is up to 9.8–18.8 mg/100 g, lower only than that in animal livers. Moreover, *sufu* contains vitamin B_1 at 0.04–0.09 mg/100 g and nicotinic acid at 0.5–1.10 mg/100 g. Minerals are abundant in *sufu*, especially calcium, iron, and zinc (39).

V. SOY NUGGETS (*DOUCHI*)

Soy nuggets (*douchi* in Chinese) are made by fermenting soaked and boiled whole yellow soybeans or black

TABLE 19.3
Major Microorganisms Isolated from *Sufu* Made in Different Regions of China

Microorganism	Regions Where *Sufu* is Made
Mucor sufu	Shaoxing, Suzhou, Zhengjiang
Mucor rouvanus	Jiangsu
Mucor Wutongqiao	Wutongqiao in Sichuan
Mucor feavus	Wutongqiao in Sichuan
Mucor racemosus	Taiwan, Niuhuasi in Sichuan
Mucor hiemalis	Taipei
Mucor spp.	Taiwan, Guangdong, Guilin, Hangzhou
Avtinomucor elegans	Beijing, Taipei, HongKong
Rhizopus liquefiems	Jiangsu
Aspergillus oryzae	Jiangsu, Wutongqiao in Sichuan
Penicillium spp.	Jiangsu
Alternaria spp.	Jiangsu
Cladosporium spp.	Jiangsu
Bacillus spp.	Wuhan
Micrococcus luteus	Kedong in Helongjiang
Saccharomyces	Jiangsu, Wutongqiao in Sichuan

Source: Adapted from Ref. 33.

TABLE 19.4
Nutrient Composition of *Sufu*

Component	Content (per 100 g)
Water	56.3 g
Protein	15.6 g
Fat	10.1 g
Carbohydrate	7.1 g
Crude fiber	0.1 g
Ash	1.12 g
Cholesterol	Not detected
Caloric	703.4 KJ
Calcium	231.6 mg
Phosphorus	301.0 mg
Iron	7.5 mg
Zinc	6.89 mg
Vitamin B_1	0.04 mg
Vitamin B_2	0.13 mg
Nicotinic acid	0.5 mg
Vitamin B_{12}	1.77 mg

Source: Adapted from Ref. 43.

soybeans with microorganisms, and are consumed as seasonings (40). *Douchi* production involves two distinct steps of fermentation. The first, which occurs during *koji* making, is by fungi or bacteria (similar to *natto* making), leading to enzyme production. The second is by yeast and lactic acid bacteria, with added salt and seasonings such as shallot, ginger, or garlic, and results in the production of a delicious flavor.

Douchi is the first traditional fermented soyfood to be described in written records. It originated in China before the Han Dynasty (206 B.C.). The first record of *douchi* was in *Si Ji*, which was written by Si Maqian (about 104 B.C.). In *Ben Cao Gang Mu* (Chinese Materia Medica), written by Li Shizhen in the Ming Dynasty (1368–1644 A.D.), some health-enhancing functions of *douchi* were recorded, such as the enhancement of appetite, promotion of digestion, inducement of sweat and recovery from fatigue, soothing of the mood, and prevention of asthma, etc. Products similar to *douchi* are also produced in other Asian countries, for example, *hamanatto* in Japan, *tao-si* in the Philippines, and *tao-tjo* in Eastern India (5).

A. DOUCHI VARIETIES

There are various types of *douchi* produced in China (see Figures 19.8 and 19.9). According to the water content, *douchi* can be classified into dry *douchi* and water *douchi*. Dry *douchi* is fermented loose whole soybeans, produced mainly in Southern China. Water *douchi* is fermented soybeans with additional water, and the final products are sticky, somewhat like *natto*. It is made in Northern China and the family-made products (Figure 19.9) belong to this type (40). According to the selection of fermentation microorganisms, *douchi* can be classified into three varieties: *Aspergillus*-type, *Mucor*-type, and bacteria-type. Among them, the *Aspergillus*-type is the earliest and most common type.

B. PREPARATION OF DOUCHI

Douchi has been produced in China for a long time. Because of the diversity of climate, some famous brands are produced in various regions of China using different processing methods. Figure 19.10 shows the flow chart for the preparation of *Aspergillus*-type *douchi*.

1. Pre treatment of Raw Materials

Soybeans are cleaned to remove foreign matter and damaged or decomposed beans. They are soaked in water for 2–7 hours at a temperature below 40°C, until the water content reaches 45% (41). Boiling of soybeans is necessary to destroy contaminating bacteria that could interfere with fermentation, and to release nutrients required for mold growth. Traditionally, soybeans are boiled at 100° for 5 hours. For industrial preparation, soybeans are steamed at 0.1 MPa for 45 minutes to 1 hour. For bacterial-type *douchi*, soybeans are boiled at 100°C for 30–40 minutes.

The water content of soybeans should be controlled after boiling, so that the microorganisms can multiply and the beans remain intact. The best water content differs for different *douchi* varieties, about 50% for *Aspergillus*-type *douchi* and 45% for *Mucor*-type *douchi* (41).

2. Making of Qu

a. Aspergillus qu
Boiled soybeans are cooled to 35°C and inoculated with 0.3% *Aspergillus oryzae* or other *Aspergillus* spores, then incubated at about 25°C. If the temperature of soybeans is increased to 35°C, they should be cooled down by turning them over. When the soybeans are covered with yellow-greenish mycelium, usually the fermentation time is about 72 hours, and the *qu* is matured.

FIGURE 19.8 Commerical *douchi* products.

FIGURE 19.9 Homemade *douchi.*

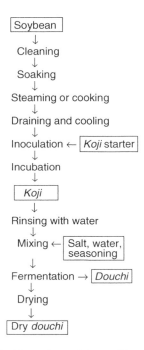

FIGURE 19.10 Flow chart of *Aspergillus*-type *douchi* manufacturing.

b. *Mucor* qu
Boiled soybeans are cooled to 30°C and inoculated with 0.5% *Mucor* strain spores, then incubated at 2–7°C, keeping the internal temperature of the beans below 18°C by ventilation. After 10–12 days, when the mycelium color changes to grey with a few black spores, the product is ready for harvest (41).

c. *Bacteria* qu
After boiling and draining, the soybeans are sealed and incubated at a high temperature (over 25°C) for 3–4 days. When the soybeans are covered with mucilage with a special flavor, the *qu* is matured.

3. Fermentation
Washing with water is a special processing step for the preparation of *Aspergillus*-type *douchi*. The *koji* is washed with water to remove the spores, mycelia, and part of the enzymes. Spores will impart a bitter and astringent flavor to the final product. Too much enzymes on the surface tend to hydrolyze the macromolecules excessively, causing soluble materials to increase, and the surface texture becomes coarse. Ordinarily, the washing time is about 10 minutes and the water content of the washed beans is 33–35%. After washing, the soybeans are stacked in containers without cover, and water is sprinkled occasionally to adjust the water content to about 50%.

Salt (18% w/w, soybean weight basis), a small amount of sugar, and a selected flavoring such as capsicum paste are mixed with the *koji* in order to obtain the desirable flavor (42). The mixture is put into jars, and one layer of soybean is loaded on top of another up to about 80% by volume. The jars are then sealed with plastic film.

The *Aspergillus*-type *douchi* is fermented in the jars at 30–35°C for 4–6 months, traditionally under sunlight. After fermentation, *douchi* are dried to 30% water content.

For *Mucor*-type *douchi*, the soybeans are not washed with water, but mixed with salt and flavoring directly. Fermentation is carried out at about 20°C for 10–12 months.

Salt is added to the soybeans to prevent metamorphose and to improve flavor, but the enzyme activities are inhibited, with an increase in fermentation time. Non-salt fermentation, carried out at a higher temperature (55–60°C), can shorten the fermentation time to 3–4 days.

C. CHEMICAL AND BIOCHEMICAL CHANGES DURING *DOUCHI* PROCESSING

The protein, fat, carbohydrate, and vitamin contents in *douchi* (Table 19.5) indicate that it is a nutritive food (43). During fermentation, the levels of free amino acids increase gradually (43). Glutamic acid is the predominant amino acid, contributing to the delicious flavor of *douchi*. Other types of flavor components are organic acids. In *douchi*, lactic acid content is high, followed by acetic and L-pyroglutamic acids (Table 19.5) (43).

VI. *NATTO* AND *KINEMA*

Natto is a whole or fractional, slimy, fermented soybean product (Figure 19.11) which has a characteristic aroma. It is made with soaked and steamed soybeans fermented by *Bacillus* species. *Natto* was originated from China in the Tang Dynasty, and was introduced to Japan along with Buddhism (44). In Northeastern Japan, it has been produced for about 1000 years. It is now widespread in Japan, and is also prepared in Korea, Thailand (*thua-nao*), and India (*kinema*) (45). *Natto* is served for breakfast and dinner along with rice, and is sometimes consumed with

TABLE 19.5
Nutrient Composition of *Douchi*

Components	Content (per 100 g)
Water	35–50 g
Protein	20 g
Fat	7.1 g
Carbohydrate	21.4 g
Total acid	1.5 g
Formal nitrogen	0.7–1.0 g
Calcium	184 mg
Phosphorus	198 mg
Iron	5.5 mg
Vitamin B_1	0.13 mg
Vitamin B_2	0.23 mg
Nicotinic acid	3.2 mg

Source: Adapted from Ref. 43.

FIGURE 19.11 *Natto.*

shoyu and mustard. It can also be used as an ingredient for sauce production or as a flavoring agent.

A. PREPARATION OF *NATTO*

Natto preparation is relatively simple when compared to other fermented soybean products which employ a series of microorganisms, such as *sufu* and soy sauce. Only one organism, *Bacilli subtilis,* an aerobic Gram-positive rod bacterium, is involved in the fermentation of *natto*. *Bacillus natto*, classified as a related strain of *B. subtilis*, is the most commonly used strain. Many new strains have been bred and are used to make *natto*, such as strains with high γ-glutamyltranspeptidase (GTP) activity (46), high thrombolytic activity (47), and high elastase activity (48), or strains that produce highly viscous products.

The traditional and industrial manufacturing processes for *natto* are shown in Figure 19.12. Round and small

soybeans with high content of soluble sugars are the ideal raw materials to produce *natto*. Since these soybeans have a small diameter, the steaming time can be shortened. Meanwhile, soluble sugars provide a carbon source for microbial growth, as well as a sweet taste to the final product. Soybeans are cleaned and soaked overnight in water, then cooked at 1.5 kg/cm^2 pressure for 30–40 minutes. Traditionally, the cooked soybeans are wrapped with rice straw, and kept in a warm place for 1–2 days. The rice straw provides *B. subtilis* and absorbs the unpleasant ammonia odor. In the industrial process, soybeans are inoculated with 1–3% pure culture suspension of *B. natto* and then packed in trays. After fermentation at 40°C for 18–24 hours, the beans are covered with a white sticky coating, and the products are ready for harvesting. In addition to refrigeration, drying at a low temperature is another effective method for prolonging the shelf life of *natto*.

B. CHEMICAL AND BIOCHEMICAL CHANGES DURING *NATTO* PROCESSING

One characteristics of *B. subtilis* is that it can secrete many extracellular enzymes such as proteases, amylases, GTP (49), levansucrase, and phytase (50). During fermentation, the quantity of soluble and dialyzable matters increases from 22% and 6% to 65% and 40%, respectively (51). Some chemical reactions are catalyzed by these enzymes, with the formation of flavors and sticky materials, including 2, 3-butanediol, acetic acid, propionic acid, iso-butyric acid, and γ-polyglutamic acid (52). A 60-fold increase in free amino acids was observed during fermentation, which accounted for about 26% of the total amino acid content (53). Since there is no lipase, the fat and fiber content of soybeans are kept almost constant (54). The content of soluble sugars, the carbohydrate source for *B. natto*, is very low. The levels of oligosaccharides such as sucrose, raffinose, and stachyose decreased during soaking, boiling, and fermentation (55).

C. *KINEMA*

Kinema is an indispensable dietary component in Nepal and the hilly regions of the Eastern states of the Indian subcontinent, where it has long been used as a meat substitute. *Kinema* is fried in oil, then cooked in water with vegetables and spices to prepare a thick curry, and eaten as a side dish with rice (56).

1. Preparation

To make traditional *kinema*, soybeans are washed, soaked overnight in water until soft and crushed lightly to dehull, boiled for about 90 minutes, crushed to grits, wrapped in fern leaves and sackcloth, and left to ferment for 1–3 days in a warm place (25–30°C) until the beans have a typical alkaline, *kinema* flavor and a desirable sticky consistency (57).

TABLE 19.6
Organic Acid Content in Different *Douchi* Products

Douchi Type	Product	Acetic Acid	L-Pyroglutamic Acid	Lactic Acid
Aspergillus type	Tianmashan *koji*	8.70	3.61	9.41
	Tianmashan *douchi*	38.94	7.98	88.89
	Yipinxing *koji*	5.87	1.10	2.94
	Yipinxing *douchi*	19.24	5.10	80.82
Mucor type	Yongchuan	3.40	5.10	12.89
	Black soybean	1.51	4.22	1.80

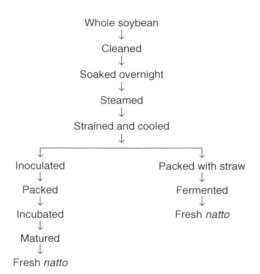

FIGURE 19.12 Traditional and industrial processes of *natto* making.

2. Microorganisms

Bacillus subtilis is the dominant microorganism and the sole fermentation organism found in *kinema*. *Enterococcus faecium*, *Candida parapsilosis*, and *Geotrichum cadidum* are the accompanying flora in *kinema* samples (58, 59). Among all starter cultures isolated from *kinema*, *Bacillus subtilis* KK2:B10 and GK-2:B10 are the best strains for improved *kinema* production (60). Organoleptically, the monoculture fermentation of soybean by *B. subtilis* produced the best quality *kinema* (61).

3. Microbiological Safety

Although *Staphylococcus aureus* has not been detected in any of the tested *kinema* samples, *Bacillus cereus* and *Escherichia coli* were present in several market samples, and some of them have the ability to produce diarrhoeal enterotoxin. *Enterobacteriaceae* and *Coliform* bacteria exceeded 10^5 CFU/g in most samples. It has been concluded that the traditional way of making *kinema* and its culinary use in curries is safe. However, for novel applications of *kinema*, safety precautions are advisable (58).

VII. *TEMPEH*

Tempeh is a fermented soyfood consisting of dehulled and tender-cooked soybeans bound together by a dense cottony mycelium of fragrant white *Rhizopus* mold into compact cakes or patties (62). It is a popular traditional Indonesian food produced by solid state fermentation (SSF). The technology was introduced by immigrants from Southeast China, and the product is similar to the Chinese *douchi*. *Tempeh* was then introduced to Malaysia, the Netherlands, and North America by Indonesian immigrants. It has now become quite popular in the United States and attracts attention in Japan and many European countries, particularly in the vegetarian market as a substitute for meat (63).

A. TYPES OF *TEMPEH*

Depending on the raw materials, several types of *tempeh* are produced in Indonesia, including the soybean *tempeh*, okara *tempeh*, velvet *tempeh*, and coconut or peanut presscake *tempeh*, or mixtures of these. In other countries, *tempeh* is made with other raw materials, such as common bean, lupin, horsebean, chickpea, and wheat.

Sold fresh, refrigerated, or frozen, *tempeh* is usually sliced and fried until its surface is crisp and golden brown, and it has a nice flavor and texture, which can be compared to those of fried chicken or fish sticks. Hence, *tempeh* is often consumed as a main dish or as a meat substitute, and has become a key source of protein in vegetarian diets. Most of all, the high vitamin B_{12} content led to its popularity among vegetarians in the Western world since plants do not contain this type of vitamin (64).

Tempeh can be served with grains and eggs for breakfast, or after frying, in salads, sandwiches, burgers, sauces, and soups for lunch or dinner.

B. MANUFACTURING PROCESS OF *TEMPEH*

Tempeh can be homemade or produced in factories. There are two dehulling methods, namely wet dehulling and dry dehulling. Figure 19.13 shows the flow chart of *tempeh* production in temperate climate regions (62).

1. Pretreatment of Raw Materials

Soybeans are cleaned and dehulled. Cleaning will remove damaged beans and foreign matter. Since the fermentating microorganism *Rhizopus oligosporus* cannot grow on whole soybeans, dehulling is essential. Wet dehulling is performed by hands or foots after precooking and the hulls are separated by skimming (65). Dry dehulling is performed by cracking the seeds with a stone or burr mill, followed by separation of the hulls with an air stream or by gravity separation (66).

2. Acidification and Cooking

Acidification lowers the pH, normally to 4.8–5.0, favoring mold growth and restricting the growth of potential spoilage bacteria (67, 68). Traditionally, soybeans are soaked in hot (initially at 100°C) or room temperature water for 8–22 hours, and bacterial fermentation results in acidification. Nowadays, acidification of soybeans is done by the addition of an acidulant such as vinegar, lactic acid, or acetic acid to the cooking water (66).

A basic boiling period, typically 40–60 minutes, is required to soften the beans and to kill spoilage bacteria and their spores. The cooked soybeans are drained, cooled to about 38°C, and dried till the moisture content reaches 45–55% (66, 69).

3. Inoculation and Incubation

After cooling, the cooked soybeans are inoculated. Usually 10^6 viable spores of *Rhizopus oligosporus* per 100 g of cooked soybeans gave optimal mold growth (70). Then the soybeans are packed and placed in a warm place for fermentation. Traditionally, banana leaves or other large leaves are used as *tempeh* containers. Nowadays, perforated polyethylene bags, *tofu* tubs, aluminum trays, or slatted wooden trays covered with perforated polyethylene sheets are used (71).

Temperature, time, and relative humidity are the three crucial factors in *temeph* fermentation. The best relative humidity is between 70 and 85%. Fermentation can be carried out at a temperature ranging from 25 to 37°C. The standard procedure in Indonesia is fermentation at 25°C for 44–52 hours, but moderate temperature fermentation (31°C) and high temperature fermentation (37°C) are recommended as well (69, 71). High temperature fermentation favors growth of *R. oligosporus* and *Klebsiella pneumoniae*, and the products contain more vitamin B_{12} than those with moderate temperature fermentation, but the shelf life is shortened and temperature control is more difficult (62).

4. Harvesting, Storage, and Preservation

When soybeans are covered with and bound together by white mycelia, fermentation is completed. Fresh *tempeh* can last for several days at room temperature without obvious changes, and its shelf life can be prolonged by freezing, drying, frying, dehydration, canning, or other preservation methods. In addition, blanching or steaming is also an effective means to extend shelf life.

C. Microorganisms for *Tempeh* Making

Wet dehulling *tempeh* production involves two distinct stages of fermentation. The first stage, which occurs during soaking, is bacterial, resulting in acidification and the growth of *Bacillus cereus* is prevented. The second stage

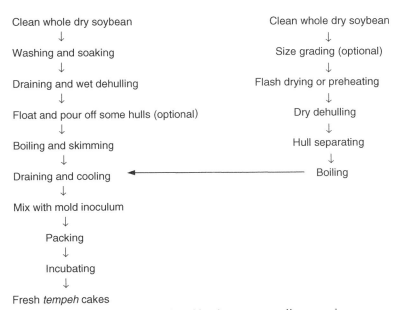

FIGURE 19.13 Wet and dry dehulling methods of *tempeh* making in temperate climate regions

is fungal, resulting in the growth of white mycelium on the bean cotyledons (68).

1. Microorganisms for Acidification

Lactic casei, Enterococcus faecium, Streptococcus dysgalactiae, and *Staphylococcus epidermidis* are the predominant species responsible for acidification (72), and *Citrobacter diversus, Enterobacter agglomerans, E. cloacae, Klebsiella pneumoniae,* and *K. oacenae* are present during soaking (73). *Lactic* and *Streptococci* spp. dominate the flora in both the unacidified and the acidified soaking water, while yeasts and coliforms are found only in unacidified water (74).

2. Microorganisms for Solid State Fermentation

There are three basic types of starters for *tempeh* fermentation: 1) pure culture mold starters typically containing only *Rhizopus oligosporus* spores, 2) mixed pure culture starters such as *R. oligosporus* and *Klebsiella pneumoniae,* and 3) mixed culture starters for traditional *tempeh,* containing a mixture of molds, bacteria, and/or yeasts. Because of its strong protease and lipase activity, *R. oligosporus* is the principal mold species used to make *tempeh,* and *R. oligosporus* NRRL 2710 is the recommended commercial strain (72). Other *Rhizopus* species such as *R. oryzae, R. chinensis, R. arrhizus,* and *R. stolonifer* are also considered suitable for *tempeh* making (75, 76).

The *Rhizopus* strains form riboflavin, nicotinic acid, nicotinamide, ergosterol, and vitamin B_6, but do not produce physiologically active vitamin B_{12} (75, 76). Vitamin B_{12} is synthesized by bacterial strains of *Propionibacterium, Pseudomonas, Clostridium,* and *Streptomyces* (77), and include *Klebsiella pneumoniae, K. terigena, K. planticola,* and *Enterobacter cloacae* (72). *K. pneumoniae* and *Citrobacter freundii* show the best vitamin B_{12} formation capability. In order to increase vitamin B_{12} content, the mold and bacterium mixed pure culture starters have been used (69).

3. Microbiological Safety

Rhizopus oligosporus inhibited the growth, sporulation, and aflatoxin production of *Asperigullius flavus,* and no

botulinal toxins were produced during the normal fermentation time of 24 hours or less (67). In early commercial *tempeh* production, *Enterobacteriaceae* and lactic acid bacteria were found in a majority of the samples, and *Staphylococcus aureus, Bacillus cereus,* and *Escherichia coli* were found in some samples at a level of 10^5 CFU/g. *Yersinia enterocolitica* was found in several samples, whereas *Salmonella* was not observed (63). Regardless, traditional *tempeh* is regarded as a safe food (69).

D. CHEMICAL AND BIOCHEMICAL CHANGES DURING *TEMPEH* PROCESSING

The composition of soybean is significantly altered by the physical and chemical treatments and the action of enzymes during fermentation in the making of *tempeh* (Table 19.7). *Rhizopus* spp. produces a variety of enzymes, including carbohydrases, lipases, proteases, endocellulase, xylanase, arabinase, α-D-galactosidases, etc. (72). Solid and nitrogen losses occur mainly during dehulling, soaking, and cooking, with little loss during fermentation. The initial pH increases to a high level after fermentation, hence biological acidification does not resulted in a sour tasting product (68). *Tempeh* is a nutritive food, as shown by its nutrient composition (Table 19.7). There is no marked difference in protein content between *tempeh* and unfermented soybeans, but an increase in free amino acid content can be observed during fermentation.

Tempeh is virtually non-flatulent since raffinose, stachyose, and other flatulence-causing carbohydrates found in soybeans are reduced. *Tempeh* is easily digested and can be tolerated by patients suffering from dysentery and nutritional edema (78).

R. oligosporus and *R. oryzae* have strong lipase activities and can break down soybean lipids into stearic, oleic, linolenic, linoleic, and palmitic acids, with linoleic acid predominating (79). The concentrations of calcium, phosphorus, iron, copper, zinc, magnesium, and manganese tend to be increased during fermentation, but potassium concentration decreases to a large extent (80). The bioavailability of zinc, calcium, iron, and magnesium increases due to their strong chelating properties, leading to a decrease in phytic acid content.

TABLE 19.7
Chemical Compositions of *Tempeh* Products

Tempeh	Moisture (%)	Protein (%)	Fat (%)	Carbohydrate (%)	Fiber (%)	Ash (%)
Fresh	60.4	19.5	7.5	9.9	1.4	1.3
Deep-fried	50.0	23.0	18.0	8.0	2.0	1.0
Freeze-dried	1.9	46.2	23.4	25.8	2.7	2.7
Fermented with *Rhizopus* sp. T-3	8.3	40.8	19.7	19.4	5.4	6.4
Cooked soybean	63.5	16.0	9.0	7.6	2.1	1.8

Source: Adapted from Refs. 2 and 73.

Riboflavin, pyridoxine, and nicotinic acid concentrations increase significantly over the 72-hour fermentation period as a result of their synthesis by different strains of *Rhizopus*, but the thiamine concentration decreases slightly (81). The highest reported value of vitamin B_{12} content in *tempeh* was 6.2 µg/1370 g. During fermentation, the total amount of vitamin E remains constant but the content of free tocopherols decreases (81).

VIII. HEALTH BENEFITS OF FERMENTED SOYBEAN PRODUCTS

Fermented soyfoods have some beneficial effects on human health, arising mainly from certain metabolically transformed components. Some examples of the health benefits of fermented soyfoods are illustrated below.

Angiotension inhibitory enzyme (ACE) activity has been detected in soy sauce, leading to reduced blood pressure in hypertensive rats after oral administration (82). Peptides with ACE activities were also found in water soluble fractions of *sufu* (83), water extracts of *douchi* (43), and *natto* extracts (84).

Isoflavones exist as aglycon in fermented soybean products. Isoflavones, genistein in particular, inhibit the activity of protein tyrosine kinases, thus reducing the risk of cancer (85). 8-Hydroxydaidzein, 8-hydroxygenistein, and syringic acid isolated from *miso* had high DPPH (1, 1-diphenyl-2-picrylhydrazyl) radical-scavenging activities (86). 6, 7, 4′-Trihydroxyisoflavone, and glycitein (87), 6, 7, 4′-trihydroxyisoflavone, daidzein, and genistein may be responsible for the antioxidant activity of *tempeh* (88). *Natto* also has antioxidation activity on unsaturated fatty acids, and shows protective effects on the free radical-mediated cellular damage induced by cumene hydroperoxide (89). Certain components such as saturated hydrocarbons (C30–C32, especially hentriacontane) are present in *natto* and they have possible antitumor-promoting activity (90). Lactic bacteria from *miso* could bind hereroccyclic amines, which are mutagenic and exist in cooked foods, especially fried and toasted foods rich in protein (91).

The insoluble peptides in *sufu* can lower cholesterol level in blood serum (85). Moreover, peptides with the capacity of binding cholic acid were found in water-insoluble fractions of *sufu*. A water-solube extract of *douchi* was found to exert a strong inhibitory activity against rat intestinal α-glucosidase (92). It was found that *douchi* has an anti-hyperglycemic effect and may have potential uses in the management of type-2 diabetic patients (93).

A strong fibrinolytic enzyme, nattokinase, and at least three pro-urokinase activators (PUA) which are different from nattokinase, have been purified from *natto* (94, 95). An enzyme with a strong fibrinolytic activity was purified from *douchi* (96). *Natto* is the only food known that naturally contains vitamin K2 (97), which may contribute to the relatively lower fracture risk in Japanese women (98).

Bacillus natto is effective in restraining the growth of *Salmonella* spp., *Escherichia coli* O157:H7, and microorganisms that can induce typhoid fever and diarrhea. Staphylococcal enterotoxin A (SEA) was fragmented into small peptides by subtilisin, an extracellular proteinase produced by *Bacillus natto* (99).

REFERENCES

1. YG Shi, L Ren. The manufacturing process of soybean products. Beijing, China: China Light Industry Press, 1993, pp 242–247.
2. HE Snyder, TW Kwon. Soybean Utilization. New York: Van Nostrand Reinhold, 1987.
3. MAK Ismail. The role of microorganisms in food fermentation with special reference to Malaysian fermented foods. Proceedings of the Second Asian Workshop on Solid Substrate Fermentation, Asian Subcommittee on Protein, Kuala Lumper, Malaysia, 1980.
4. D Fukushima. Fermented vegetable protein and related foods of Japan and China. Food Rev Int 1: 149–209, 1985.
5. KS Liu. Oriental soyfoods. In: CYW Ang, KS Liu, Y-W Huang. eds. Asian Foods: Science and Technology. Lancaster, PA: Technomic Publishing Company, Inc. 1999, pp 139–199.
6. I Keiko, A Tetsuo. Soy sauce classification by geographic region based on NIR spectra and chemomitrics pattern recognition. J Food Sci 62: 101–104, 1997.
7. S Masaoki. Influence of sodium chloride on the levels of flavor compounds produced by shoyu yeast. J Agric Food Chem 44: 3273–3275, 1996.
8. FMR Wilfred, WVV Henk. Characterization of *Tetragenococcus* halophila populations in Indonesian soy mash (*kecap*) fermentation. Appl Environ Microbiol 62: 1203–1207, 1996.
9. BS Luh. Industrial production of soy sauce. J Ind Microbiol 14: 467–471, 1995.
10. T Hamada, M Sugishita, Y Fukushima, T Fudase, H Motai. Continuous production of soy sauce by a bioreactor system. Process Biochem 26: 39–45, 1991.
11. K Iwasaki. Rapid continuous lactic acid fermentation by immobilized lactic acid bacteria for soy sauce production. Proc Biochem 28: 39–45, 1993.
12. K Iwasaki, M Nakajima, H Sasahara, A Watanabe. Rapid ethanol fermentation for soy sauce production by immobilized yeast cells. Agric Biol Chem 55: 2201–2207, 1991.
13. K Iwasaki, M Nakajima, H Sasahara. Porous alumina beads for immobilization of lactic acid bacteria and its application for repeated-batch fermentation in soy sauce production. J Ferment Bioeng 73: 375–379, 1992.
14. FMR Wilfred, KH Timotius, AH Prasetyo, AH Stouthamer, HWV Verseveld. Changes in microflora and biochemical composition during the baceman stage of traditional Indonesian *kecap* (soy sauce) production. J Ferment Bioeng 77: 62–70, 1994.
15. FMR Wilfred, A Anton, HWV Verseveld. Comparison between traditional and industrial soy sauce (*kecap*)

fermentation in Indonesia. J Ferment Bioeng 81: 275–278, 1996.

16. FMR Wilfred, KH Timotius, AH Prasetyo, AH Stouthamer, HWV Verseveld. Physiological aspects of the growth of the lactic acid bacterium *Tetragenococcus halophila* during Indonesian soy sauce (*kecap*) production. J Appl Microbiol 86: 348–352, 1999.

17. N Nunomura, M Sasaki, Y Asao, T Yokotsuka. Isolation and identification of 4-hydroxy-2(or 5)-ethyl-5(or 2)-methyl-3(2H)-furanone as a flavor component in *shoyu* (soy sauce). Agric Biol Chem 40: 491–495, 1976.

18. FMR Wilfred, KH Timotius, AB Prasetyo, AH Stouthamer, WVV Henk. Changes in microflora and biochemical composition during the baceman stage of traditional Indonesian *kecap* (soy sauce) production. J Ferment Bioeng 77: 62–70, 1994.

19. Y Tamotsu. Fermented protein foods in the Orient, with emphasis on *shoyu* and *miso* in Japan. In: BJB Wood. ed. Microbiology of Fermented Food. Vol. 1. New York: Elsevier Applied Science Publishers, 1985.

20. KY Liu. Soybeans: Chemistry, Technology and Utilization. New York: Chapman & Hall, 1997.

21. Y-Y Chiou. Proteolysis during the fermentation of ethanol-supplemented *miso*. J Food Sci 66: 1080–1083, 2001.

22. Y-Y Chiou. Salt-free *miso* fermentation using ethanol, sugars, and polyols. J Food Sci 64: 918–920, 1999.

23. K-L Ku, T-P Chen, Y-Y Chiou. Apparatus used for small-scale volatile extraction from ethanol-supplemented low-salt *miso* and GC-MS characterization of the extracted flavors. J Agric Food Chem 48: 3507–3511, 2000.

24. DD Truesdell, NR Green, PB Acosta. Vitamin B_{12} activity in *miso* and *tempeh*. J Food Sci 52: 493–494, 1987.

25. E Sugawara, Y Sakurai. Effect of media constituents on the formation by halophilic yeast of the 2 (or 5)-ethyl-5 (or 2)-methyl-4-hydroxy-3 (2H)-furanone aroma component specific to *miso*. Biosci Biotech Biochem 63: 749–752, 1999.

26. D Fukushima. Fermented vegetable (soybean) protein and related foods of Japan and China. J Am Oil Chem Soc 56: 357–362, 1979.

27. B-Z Han, FM Rombouts, MJR Nout. Chinese fermented soybean food. Int J Food Microbiol 65: 1–10, 2001.

28. YG Shi, L Ren. The Manufacturing Process of Soybean Products. Beijing, China: China Light Industry Press, 1993, pp 242–247.

29. D Fangxi, H Jianliang, L Hesong. Studies on screening for high temperature resistant *Mucor* strain of bean curd milk and conditions of proteinase production. J Hunan Agric Univ 22: 186–200, 1996 (in Chinese).

30. C-C Chou, F-M Ho, C-S Tsai. Effects of temperature and relative humidity on the growth of an enzyme produced by *Actinomucor taiwanensis* during *sufu pehtze* preparation. Appl Environ Microbiol 54: 688–692, 1988.

31. HL Wang. Release of proteinase from mycelium of *Mucor hiemalis*. J Bacteriol 93: 1794–1799, 1967.

32. J Liu. Technology of bacteria-type *fuyu* production. Chinese Condiment 3: 25–26, 2001 (in Chinese).

33. Y Zhou, H Li, X Zheng. Breeding of *sufu* producing strains. J Wuxi Inst Light Ind 13: 310–322, 1994 (in Chinese).

34. H Bai, D Liu, Y Zhang. Studies on the microorganism of Kedong *sufu*. J Beijing Union Univ 8: 20–23, 1994 (in Chinese).

35. Y-J Li. Study on the characteristics of *Mucor*, quest for a new processing for *sufu* preparation. Chinese Condiment 10: 5–9, 1999 (in Chinese).

36. S Bao. Identification and physiological properties of *Mucor prainii*, a strain for *fuyu* preparation. Chinese Condiment 9: 7–11, 1994 (in Chinese).

37. B-Z Han, RR Beumer, FM Rombouts, MJR Nout. Microbiological safety and quality of commercial *sufu*—a Chinese fermented soybean food. Food Control 12: 541–547, 2001.

38. C-H Hwan, C-C Chou. Volatile components of the Chinese fermented soya bean curd as affected by the addition of ethanol in ageing solution. J Sci Food Agric 79: 243–248, 1999.

39. M Yasuda, T Matsumoto, M Sakaguchi, S Kinjyo. Changes in protein and nitrogen compounds of *tofuyo* prepared by *Aspergillus oryzae* during fermentation. Nippon Shokuhin Kagaku Kaishi 41: 184–190, 1994 (in Japanese).

40. S Zhang, Y Liu. Preparation Technology of Seasoning. Guangzhou, China: South China University of Technology Press, 2000, pp 85–95.

41. M Kang. Handbook of Technology for Chinese and Foreign Famous Fermented Foods. Beijing, China: Chemical Industrial Press, 2001, pp 99–111.

42. X Li. Studies on the bacteria-type *douchi* preparation. Chinese Condiment 10: 14–17, 1999.

43. J Zhang. Studies on the fermentation mechanism and health functions of Aspergillus-type *douchi*. Ph.D. Dissertation, China Agricultural University, Beijing, China, 2003.

44. M Shinobu, *Natto*. Tokyo: Shogakukan Inc., 1997, pp 212–213.

45. JP Tamang. Role of microorganisms in traditional fermented foods. Indian Food Ind 17: 162–167, 1998.

46. N Toshirou, K Kumiko, I Yoshifumi. Chemical analysis of poly-γ-glutamic acid produced by plasmid-free *Bacillus subtilis* (*natto*): Evidence that plasmids are not involved in poly-γ-glutamic acid production. J Gen Appl Microbiol 43: 139–143, 1997.

47. C-T Chang, M-H Fan, F-C Kuo, H-Y Sung. Potent fibrinolytic enzyme from a mutant of *Bacillus subtilis* IMR-NK1. J Agric Food Chem 48: 3210–3216, 2000.

48. K Muramatsu, N Yamawake, K Kiuchi. Production of elastase by *Bacillus subtilis* (*natto*) KFP419. Nippon Shokuhin Kagaku Kaishi 45: 494–498, 1998 (in Japanese).

49. Y Ogawa, H Hosoyama, M Hamano, H Motai. Purification and properties of γ-glutamyltranspeptidase from *Bacillus subtilis* (*natto*). Agric Biol Chem 55: 2971–2977, 1991.

50. M Shimizu. Purification and characterization of phytase from *Bacillus subtilis* (*natto*) N-77. Biosci Biotech Biochem 56: 1266–1269, 1992.

51. JL Kiers, AEA Van Laeken, FM Rombouts, MJR Nout. *In vitro* digestibility of *Bacillus fermented* soya bean. Int J Food Microbiol 60: 163–169, 2000.

52. T Hara, S Ueda. Regulation of polyglutamate production in *Bacillus subtilis* (*natto*): transformation of high PGA productivity. Agric Biol Chem 46: 2275–2281, 1982.

53. PK Sarkar, LJ Jones, GS Craven, SM Somerset, C Palmer. Amino acid profiles of *kinema*, a soybean-fermented food. Food Chem 59: 69–75, 1997.

54. K Kiuchi, T Ohta, H Itoh, T Takaayahsi, H Ebine. Studies on lipids of *natto*. J Agric Food Chem 24: 404–407, 1976.

55. PK Sarkar, LJ Jones, GS Craven, SM Somerset, C Palmer. Oligosaccharide profiles of soybeans during *kinema* production. Lett Appl Microbiol 24: 337–339, 1997.

56. JP Tamang, PK Sarkar, CW Hesseltine. Traditional fermented foods and beverages of Darjeeling and Sikkim—a review. J Sci Food Agric 44: 375–385, 1988.

57. MJR Nout, D Bakshi, PK Sarkar. Microbiological safety of *kinema,* a fermented soya bean food. Food Control 9: 357–362, 1998.

58. PK Sarkar, B Hasenack, MJR Nout. Diversity and functionality of *Bacillus* and related genera isolated from spontaneously fermented soybeans (Indian *kinema*) and locust beans (African *soumbala*). Int J Food Microbiol 77: 175–186, 2002.

59. PK Sarkar, JP Tamang. The influence of process variables and inoculum composition on the sensory quality of *kinema*. Food Microbiol 11: 317–325, 1994.

60. JP Tamang, S Nikkuni. Selection of starter cultures for the production of *kinema*, a fermented soybean food of the Himalaya. World J Microbiol Biotech 12: 629–635, 1996.

61. JP Tamang. Development of pulverized starter for *kinema* production. J Food Sci Technol 36: 475–478, 1999.

62. W Shurtleff, A Aoyagi. *Tempeh* production. The Book of *Tempeh*. Vol. II. A Craft and Technical Manual. New York: New Age Foods, 1979.

63. RA Samson, JA Van Kooij, EDE Boer. Microbiological quality of commercial *tempeh* in the Netherlands. J Food Prot 50: 92–94, 1987.

64. V Herber. Vitamin B_{12}: plant sources, requirements and assay. Am J Clin Nutr 48: 852–858, 1988.

65. FG Winarno, NR Reddy. *Tempeh*. In: NR Reddy, MD Pierson, DK Salunkhe. eds. Legume-Based Fermented Foods. Boca Ration, FL: CRC Press, 1986, pp 95–117.

66. KH Steinkraus, JP Van Buren, LR Hackler, DB Hand. A pilot plant process for the production of dehydrated tempeh. Food Technol 19: 63–68, 1965.

67. N Tanake, SK Kovats, JA Guggisberg, L M Meske, MP Doyle. Evaluation of the microbiological safety of *tempeh* made from unacidified soybeans. J Food Prot 48: 438–441, 1985.

68. MJR Nout, FM Rombouts. Recent developments in *tempeh* research. J Appl Bacteriol 69: 609–633, 1990.

69. S Keuth, B Bisping. Formation of vitamins by pure cultures of *tempeh* moulds and bacteria during the *tempeh* solid substrate fermentation. J Appl Bacteriol 75:427–434, 1993.

70. HL Wang, EW Swain, LL Wallen, CW Hesseltine. Free fatty acids identified as antitryptic factor in soybeans fermented by *Rhizopus oligosporus*. J Nutr 105: 1351–1355, 1975.

71. KH Steinkraus. Indonesian *tempeh* and related fermentations. In: KH Steinkraus. ed. Handbook of Indigenous Fermented Foods, Vol. 9, New York: Marcel Dekker, 1983, pp 1–94.

72. AK Hachmeister, DYC Fung. *Tempeh*: a mold-modified indigenous fermented food made from soybeans and/or cereal grains. Crit Rev Microbiol 19: 137–188, 1993.

73. RK Mulyowodarso, GH Fleet, KA Buckle. The microbial ecology of soybean soaking for *tempeh* production. Int J Food Microbiol 8: 35–46, 1989.

74. M Ashenafi, M Busse. The microflora of soak water during *tempeh* production from various beans. J Appl Bacteriol 70: 334–338, 1991.

75. I Wiesel, HJ Rehm, B Bisping. Improvement of *tempeh* fermentations by application of mixed cultures consisting of *Rhizopus* sp. and bacterial strains. Appl Microbiol Biotech 47: 218–225, 1997.

76. S Keuth, B Bisping. Formation of vitamins by pure cultures of *tempeh* moulds and bacteria during the tempeh solid substrate fermentation. J Appl Bacteriol 75: 427–434, 1993.

77. W Shurtleff, A Aoyagi. The Book of *Tempeh*. New York: Harper and Row, 1979.

78. SD Ko, CW Hesseltine. *Tempeh* and related foods. In: AH Rose, ed. Economic Microbiology. Vol. 4. Microbial Biomass. London: Academic Press, 1979, pp 115–140.

79. S Sudarmadji, P Markakis. Lipid and other changes occurring during the fermentation and frying of *tempeh*. Food Chem 3: 165–170, 1978.

80. WB Van der Riet, AW Wight, JJL Cilliers, JM Datel. Food chemical analysis of *tempeh* prepared from South African-grown soybeans. Food Chem 25: 197–206, 1987.

81. J Denter, H-J Rehm, B Bisping. Changes in the contents of fat-soluble vitamins and provitamins during *tempeh* fermentation. Int J Food Microbiol 45: 129–134, 1998.

82. E Kinoshita, J Yamakoshi, M Kikuchi. Purification and identification of an angiotensin I-converting enzyme inhibitor from soy sauce. Biosci Biotech Biochem 57: 1107–1110, 1993.

83. IK Sakakibara, F Ibuki. Involvement of post-digestion hydropholic peptides in plasma cholesterol-lowing effect of dietary plant proteins. Agric Biol Chem 50: 1217–1222, 1986.

84. A Okamoto, H Hanagata, Y Kawamura, F Yanagida. Anti-hypertensive substances in fermented soybean, *natto*. Plant Foods Human Nutr 47: 39–47, 1995.

85. C Booth, DF Hargreaves, JA Hadfield, AT Mcgown, CS Potten. Isoflavones inhibit intestinal epithelial cell proliferation and induce apoptosis *in vitro*. Br J Cancer 80: 1550–1557, 1999.

86. A Hirota, S Taki, S Kawaii, M Yano, N Abe. 1, 1-Diphenyl-2-picrylhydrazyl radical-scavenging compounds from soybean *miso* and antiproliferative activity of isoflavone from soybean *miso* toward the cancer cell lines. Biosci Biotech Biochem 64: 1038–1040, 2000.

87. K Klus, G Brger-Papendorf, W Barz. Formation of 6, 7, 4′-trihydroxyisoflavone (factor 2) from soybean seed

isoflavones by bacteria isolated from *tempeh*. Biochem 34: 979–981, 1993.

88. H Murahimi, T Asakawa, J Terao, S Matsushita. Isoflavones in *tempeh*. Agric Biol Chem 48: 2971–2975, 1984.

89. T Hattori, H Ohishi, T Yokota, H Ohoami, K Watanabe. Antioxidative effect of crude antioxidant preparation from soybean fermented by *Bacillus natto*. Leben Wiss Technol 28: 135–138, 1995.

90. C Takahashi, N Kikuchi, N Katou, T Miki, F Yanagida, M Umeda. Possible anti-tumor-promoting activity of components in Japanese soybean fermented food, *natto*: Effect on gap junctional intercellular communication. Carcinogenesis 16: 471–476, 1995.

91. R Rajendran, Y Ohta. Binding of heterocyclic amines by lactic acid bacteria from *miso*, a fermented Japanese food. Can J Microbiol 44: 109–115, 1998.

92. F Hiroyuki, T Yamagami, K Ohshima. Fermented soybean-derived water soluble *touchi* extract inhibits α-glucosidase and is antiglycemic in rats and humans after single oral treatments. J Nutr 131: 1211–1213, 2001.

93. H Fujita, T Yamagami, K Ohshima. Long-term ingestion of a fermented soybean-derived *touchi* extract with α-glucosidase inhibitory activity is safe and effective in humans with borderline and mild type-2 diabetes. J Nutr 131: 2105–2108, 2001.

94. M Fujita, K Hong, Y Ito, R Fujh, K Kariya, S Nishimuto. Thrombolytic effect of nattokinase on a chemically induced thrombosis model in rat. Biol Pharm Bull 18: 1387–1391, 1995.

95. M Fujita, K Nomura, K Hong, Y Ito, A Asada, S Nishimuro. Purification and characterization of a strong fibrinolytic enzyme (nattokinase) in the vegetable cheese *natto*, a popular soybean fermented food in Japan. Biochem Biophys Res Comm 197: 1340–1347, 1993.

96. Y Peng, Q Huang, R-H Zhang, Y-Z Zhang. Purification and characterization of a fibrinolytic enzyme produced by *Bacillus amyloliquefaciens* DC-4 screened from *douchi*, a traditional Chinese soybean food. Comp Biochem Physiol Part B 134: 45–52, 2003.

97. Y Tsukamoto, H Ichise. Intake of fermented soybean (*natto*) increases circulating vitamin K2 (menaquinone-7) and γ-carboxylated osteocalcin concentration in normal individuals. J Bone Mineral Metabolism 18: 216–22, 2000.

98. M Kaneki, SJ Hedges, T Hosoi, S Fujiwara. Japanese fermented soybean food as the major determinant of the large geographic difference in circulating levels of vitamin K2: possible implications for hip-fracture risk. Nutrition 17: 315–321, 2001.

99. O Osawa, K Matsumoto. Digestion of staphylococcal enterotoxin by *Bacillus natto*. Antonie-van-Leeuwenhoek 71: 307–311, 1997.

20 Vegetables: Types and Biology

Jocelyn Shing-Jy Tsao
Department of Horticulture, National Taiwan University

Hsiao-Feng Lo
Department of Horticulture, Chinese Culture University

CONTENTS

I. DEFINITION OF VEGETABLES

A vegetable is defined as "an edible, usually succulent plant or a portion of it eaten with staples as main course or as supplementary food in cooked or raw form" (1).

II. IMPORTANCE OF VEGETABLES

More than 10,000 plant species are eaten as vegetables worldwide. Among these species, only 50 or so are commercially important (2). Vegetables contribute to humans essential minerals, vitamins, dietary fibers, proteins, fats, starches, and energy. Vegetables are a major source of vitamin C. The amounts of carotenes in pumpkins, capsicum peppers, and tomato are useful to mankind. Dietary fibers in vegetables include cellulose, hemicellulose, pectic substances, and lignin that are important in preventing several human diseases. Vegetables also neutralize the acid substances produced by other high-energy food (3). While organic acids and volatile compounds are responsible for flavor and aroma, chlorophyll, carotene, and anthocyanin make up the colors. Vegetables not only form an essential part of a well-balanced diet, but the flavor, aroma, and color also make them important in human diet and appetite (4).

III. DOMESTICATION OF VEGETABLES

All modern crops had their earliest beginnings as wild plants. These wild plants with specific characteristics attracted humans to harvest them for medicinal (5), herbal, or food purposes. Then the seeds and other plant parts were dispersed. It was the beginning step during plant domestication. Vegetables were brought into cultivation 10,000 years ago, so humans produced sufficient vegetables of their own. The following artificial selection creates gene recombination of higher yield and better quality (6). Evolution of consumption, production techniques, socio-economic interest, general political climate, production policy, international competition, and trade agreements made the structure of today's vegetable exploitation heterogeneous (7).

IV. CLASSIFICATION OF VEGETABLES

Vegetables are commonly grouped according to botany, edible parts, life cycle, sensitivity to temperature, family grouping, or accepted use (2). Other classification schemes include sensitivity to soil pH and chilling damage, tolerance to nutrient levels and salt, and depth of rooting (2–4, 8–10).

A. BOTANICAL CLASSIFICATION

Botanical classification is based on morphology, anatomy, embryology, physiology, biochemistry, etc. The successive groupings of plants are kingdom, division, subdivision, phylum, subphylum, class, subclass, order, family, genus, and species (2, 8), Predominant vegetables belong to the class Angiospermae that is grouped into subclasses Monocotyledoneae and Dicotyledoneae. Most vegetables belong to the Dicotyledoneae. There are fewer monocot vegetables, i.e., sweet corn, asparagus, yam, onion, etc. The genus and species make up the scientific name that is accepted worldwide. The climate requirements, the use for economic purposes, the disease and insect controls of a particular family or genus are often similar. Well-known families of vegetables are Solanaceae, Brassicaceae, Fabaceae, Alliaceae, and Apiaceae (10).

B. CLASSIFICATION BASED ON EDIBLE PART

Classification of vegetables by edible part informs a grower or handler about specific cultural or handling techniques. Common groupings includes root, stem, leaf, immature flower bud, fruit, and sprout. Root crops include carrot, radish, beet, turnip, and sweet potato. Stem vegetables are asparagus and potato. The yield and quality of root and stem vegetables are affected by soil texture, fertility, and irrigation. Leafy crops include lettuce, cabbage, celery, spinach, kale, and mustard that are very perishable. Edible parts of cauliflower, broccoli, and artichoke are immature flower buds. Immature fruits are harvested from pea, snap bean, lima bean, summer squash, cucumber, okra, sweet corn, and eggplant, but actually we eat the immature seeds of lima bean and sweet corn. Edible parts of cucurbits (pumpkin, white gourd, squash, muskmelon, and watermelon), tomato, and pepper are mature fruits (1–3, 8–10).

C. CLASSIFICATION BASED ON TEMPERATURE

Vegetables are separated into warm-season and cool-season vegetables based on temperature requirements for optimum growth and development. Warm-season crops are adapted to 18~29°C, intolerant to frost and mostly grown for edible fruits. Exceptions are sweet potato for storage root and New Zealand spinach for leaves. Cool-season vegetables have optimum growth at cooler temperature and are shallower rooted and smaller sized. Cool-season crops are grown for edible stems, leaves, roots, and immature flower parts. Asparagus, Brussel sprouts, broccoli, cabbage, celery, garlic, onion, pea, radish, artichoke, and spinach are cool-season vegetables. Harvested parts are usually stored near 0°C except potato (2, 8–10).

The sub-groupings of cool-season crops into hardy and half-hardy vegetables, and warm-season crops into tender and very tender vegetables, are based on the ability of young plants to withstand frost, and the ability of seeds to germinate at low temperatures. Hardy vegetables generally tolerate moderate frost without injury. Tender vegetables are susceptible to damage during cold weather. The very tender vegetables are easily damaged by light frost (10).

D. CLASSIFICATION BASED ON LIFE CYCLE

Vegetables are also classified based on their life span. Most vegetables are annuals that complete life cycles within one growing season. Biennial vegetables require two seasons for completing their life cycle. Many cole crops such as broccoli, cauliflower, cabbage, and root crops such as carrot are biennials but grown as annuals. Perennial vegetables complete their life cycle in more than two years. Rhubarb, globe artichoke, and asparagus are grown commercially as true perennials. Tomato, pepper, eggplant, potato, and sweet potato are perennials in their native environments but are grown as annuals for production in temperate regions (2, 3, 8–10).

V. TYPES OF VEGETABLE GROWING

There are several types of vegetable growing such as home gardening, commercial production, and processing production. Commercial vegetable production, includes at least three categories: fresh market, processing, and controlled environment production (5, 11).

A. HOME GARDENING

People grow vegetables in their own gardens to save money, for outdoor leisure, for fresher tasting and better quality vegetables, and for better nutrition and improved health (2).

B. COMMERCIAL PRODUCTION

The goal of commercial production of vegetables, either for fresh use or processing is only for economic profit.

Fresh Market. The harvested vegetables are sold for fresh use (2, 5, 11).

 a. **Market Garden.** Market gardens are located near but on the outskirts of population centers. A wide variety but small scales of high-profit crops are grown intensively and year-round. The harvested vegetables are for local consumption (2, 5, 11).

 b. **Truck Farm.** Truck farms are often located in inexpensive rural areas and near transportation systems. One or two crops are grown on a large acreage for distant markets. Transport over large distances permits specialization and the de-localization of production (2, 11).

 c. **Controlled Environment Production.** Vegetables are grown in the modified environment for optimal plant growth. Light, temperature, humidity, nutrients, and even composition of atmosphere may be controlled. Investment and production costs including heating and cooling are expensive (5).

C. PROCESSING PRODUCTION

Vegetables are highly perishable. Post-harvest decay is estimated to be more than 20~50% in the tropics and subtropics. Processing is one of the various feasible technological measures to reduce high post-harvest losses of vegetables (3). Now in processing production, vegetables are grown in the field as raw materials for processing, usually on large acreage, harvested by machines and through contracts. The contract specifies some production techniques, price at a given quality, and standards for acceptance of harvest. Growers usually have a low margin of profit (11).

VI. CONSUMPTION OF VEGETABLES

The per capita consumption of vegetables varies among countries and regions, according to people's eating habits and the supply. The average world consumption of vegetables is around 85 kg per person per year, with around 120 kg per capita in industrialized countries (12), and around 30 kg per capita in developing countries such as in sub-Saharan Africa and 150 per capita in China (7).

VII. COMMERCIALLY IMPORTANT VEGETABLE CROPS

A. ROOT CROPS

Several root crops are grown especially for their edible storage roots. They belong to different botanical families. Only one enlarged (fleshy) underground root is produced per plant for carrot (Apiaceae), table beet (Chenopodiaceae), radish, turnip, and rutabaga (Brassicaceae). Several fleshy roots are produced from one plant for sweet potato (Convolvulaceae). They are consumed either fresh or in processed forms. Most root crops have long storage life and extend the market supply over a long period. There are other minor root crops produced more on a regional basis, such as salsify (*Tragopogon porrifolius*) and black salsify (*Scorzonera hispanica*) of Compositae, parsnip (*Pastinaca sativa*) and celeriac (*A. graveolens* var.

rapaceurm) of Apiaceae, yam bean (*Pachyrrhizus erosus*) of Fabaceae, and horseradish (*Armoracia rusticana*) of Brassicaceae (13, 14).

The carrots, table beet, radish, turnip, and rutabaga are all direct-seeded to well-prepared seedbeds. After emergence, plants are thinned to desired population density. The crops are established more easily under cool-moist conditions (14).

1. Carrots [*Daucus carota* L. ssp. *sativus* (Htoffm.) Arcang]

Cultivated carrots, originating in Afghanistan and central Asia, became popular in Europe around the 13th century. European settlers brought carrots to the U.S. in the 17th century (15, 16). Carrots are now mainly grown in Asia and Europe. The Eastern/Asiatic carrots have reddish purple (anthocyanin-containing) or yellow roots, pubescent leaves, and a tendency for early flowering. Western carrots have orange, yellow, red, or white roots, less pubescent leaves and also a tendency to bolt. The western orange type developed as selections from yellow carrots for high carotenoid content were developed into modern cultivars. In the U.S. carrots are mainly grown for the fresh market with California being the leading state of acreage. For processing, Washington State leads the production (14).

Carrot is a cool-season crop with optimal mean growing temperatures ranging between 16 and 21°C. At these temperatures, root color and shape are also optimized. At a mean temperature of 12~13°C, roots tend to grow relatively long and slender, whereas at a constant 24°C, roots are shorter and thicker. Alternating low night and moderate day temperature also tends to produce long and slender roots. Temperature greater than 30°C, particularly in later stages of development, induces undesirable strong flavor and coarseness in the roots (16).

Carrot cultivars are classified by root shape and date of maturity (14):

   a. Danvers: roots medium to long with broad shoulders, tapering toward the tip (tapered tips).

   b. Imperator: roots slender, slightly longer and smoothly tapered, late maturing, good for storing, grown for winter market consumption.

   c. Nantes: roots nearly cylindrical shaped, medium to long, early maturing, eaten fresh in summer.

   d. Chatenay: medium to short and tapered with blunt end, maturing by mid-summer.

Carrots are usually mechanically harvested in 90~120 days of planting. Large-scale carrots are eaten raw, cooked, or processed into juice. The harvest stage is judged by suitability, before carrots achieve their full potential size or weight. Fresh carrots are marketed either topped or bunched with attached tops. Fresh cut-and-peel baby carrots are also available; they may also be cut into short pieces from mature carrots. Carrots are a good plant source of provitamin A, containing about 5~8 mg/100 g of β-carotene (14).

2. Radish (*Raphanus sativus* L.)

Radish is unknown in the wild state. Its origin may be in the eastern Mediterranean or in China, with a long history of cultivation. Now radishes are grown worldwide but consumed in great quantities by the Chinese, Korean and Japanese. Large variations exist in the shape, size, and color of the roots. Radishes were among the first European crops introduced into America by the Spaniards and grown by the early colonists (14, 16).

Radish is a cool-season vegetable crop with optimum growing temperature ranging between 15 and 20°C. At higher temperature, the enlargement of roots is retarded and results in coarseness and pungency (14).

Radishes are commonly grouped into four types (16):

   a. Western or small radishes, usually consumed raw as relishes.

   b. Oriental radishes, with mild-flavored large roots, usually cooked or pickled in the East.

   c. Leaf radishes, consumed as greens by the Chinese, also cultivated for fodder.

   d. Rat-tailed radishes, cultivated in Asia with young pods consumed raw, cooked, or pickled.

In the U.S. garden radishes are very popular in home gardens because of short growth cycle and easiness to grow. The white, long-rooted types are also popular in many regions.

3. Table Beets (*Beta vulgaris* L. Crassa Group)

Originating in Europe and Western Asia, the garden beet or table beet is one of the various forms of *Beta vulgaris* of the Chenopodiaceae family (17). It is closely related to Swiss chard, sugar beet, and fodder beet. The leaf beets were developed before the root beets, but the red root beets were cultivated by the Romans. The root beet is grown throughout Europe and America. The red pigment, betanin (a nitrogen-containing anthocyanin), can be used for food coloring. The table beet, introduced in 1800, is one of the most popular home garden crops in the U.S.

Table beets prefer a cool climate with sunny days. Temperatures for optimum growth range between 16 and 19°C. During hot weather, the roots may become tough. Beets are very sensitive to soil acidity, and require a pH of 6.2 to 6.8 (17).

Beet roots may vary in color and shape. The oblate to globe-shaped, red-rooted types are most popular. Most of the commercial production is for processing (14).

4. Turnip [*Brassica rapa* L. var. *rapa* (DC.) Metzz.] and Rutabaga [*B. napus* L. var. *napobrassica* (L.) Reichb.]

Both turnip and rutabaga are members of the Brassicaceae family. They are similar in plant size and general characteristics. Turnip is an ancient crop with its exact origin unknown while rutabaga is a crop of European origin known as Swede in Europe (13, 14). The turnip roots have little or no neck and a distinct taproot, while rutabagas have a thick neck bearing a number of leaf-base scars, and roots containing the taproot and those originating from the underside of the edible root.

Turnips and rutabagas are both cool-season crops, requiring 15~18°C for best root growth. Turnips are easy to grow and require a 2-month growth period. Rutabagas grow less rapidly and require an additional 4 weeks of growth.

Both turnip and rutabaga have swollen roots of different colors or shapes. However, most turnip cultivars are round and white-fleshed, and rutabaga cultivars are globe-shaped with yellow flesh. There are also turnip cultivars grown for green foliage (14).

5. Sweet Potato [*Ipomoea batatas* (L.) Lam]

Sweet potato, a member of the Convolvulaceae family, was originated from tropical America. It was grown for its storage roots in the New World long before Columbus arrived. Storage root of sweet potato is a major carbohydrate source in developing nations. It contains about 27% carbohydrate, provitamin A, vitamin C, calcium, and iron. Tender leaves and shoot tips are also used as vegetables in Southeast Asia. Other than food, sweet potato has industrial applications: as a source of starch, glucose, syrup, and alcohol. It is also used as livestock feed. Older vines are fodder for cattle, swine, and fish. Some vining cultivars can be used as ground cover or for ornamental purposes (18).

Sweet potato is a tender, warm-season crop. The best growing temperatures are 29°C days and 21°C nights, with an optimum mean of 24°C (14, 18). It is a perennial but commonly grown as an annual. Adventitious buds arise from fleshy storage roots, and develop into branching vines quickly covering the ground (18).

Sweet potato is vegetatively propagated by slips or vine cuttings. Thin skin of storage roots is easily broken. Four to seven days of 26.6~29.4°C and 85~90% RH curing promotes the formation of cork layers on wounded surfaces that prevent decay (18).

Storage roots of sweet potato as food have two types: soft-fleshed and firm-fleshed (18):

a. Soft-fleshed (wet): sweeter, softer, medium to deep orange flesh, commonly used for baking.

b. Firm-fleshed (dry): yellow skin with white, yellow, or light orange flesh, mostly used for boiling and frying.

B. STEM AND TUBER CROPS

Stem vegetables are those grown for their succulent tender shoots (asparagus, bamboo shoots), fleshy stems (kohlrabi, celtuce, strumous mustard), starchy underground tubers (potato), corms (taro), and succulent rhizomes (ginger). Among them, kohlrabi, celtuce, strumous mustard, and asparagus are seed propagated, and others are asexually propagated. The latter have low multiplication rate and need reliable sources for healthy growing materials. In the United States, asparagus and potatoes are of more commercial importance.

1. Potato (*Solanum tuberosum* L.)

The potato, native to the Andean regions of Peru and Bolivia, has been cultivated since early civilization (19). It is one of the most important food crops in the world. The Spaniards introduced it to Europe and Irish immigrants brought potatoes to New England in 1718. The potato is referred to as the "Irish potato" because of its association with the potato famine in Ireland in 1845–1846. Idaho and Washington State are the largest producers of potatoes in the United States (20).

Potatoes are grown for their tubers, the enlarged underground storage stems. In addition to their starch content, the tubers serve as a good source of vitamin C. The potato is also a source of moderate levels of protein and minerals. The protein of potato is richer in lysine than that of cereal, and its biological value is high. Potatoes can be cooked in a great variety of ways. They can also be processed into chips, French fries, flakes, and dehydrated products. French fries and potato chips are popular food items worldwide (19).

Potatoes are asexually propagated by healthy tubers, which are obtained from certified disease-free stocks grown in favorable cool areas. The young shoots develop from the buds or "eyes" of the seed tubers. It is a cool-season crop. The interaction of photoperiod and temperature are the most important factors affecting plant and tuber development. Long days delay the start of tuberization, and temperatures above 30°C prevent tuber initiation. Tubers are usually initiated about 45 days after planting. Following tuberization, tuber enlargement is ideal at mean temperatures of 17°C (19).

Based on skin color and texture, potato cultivars are classified as white, red, or russet. Russet tubers tend to be oblong and relatively dark colored and thick skinned at maturity. There are early, midseason, and late cultivars according to maturity time. Based on starch content or specific gravity, potatoes are grouped into baking, boiling, and processing types. Russet Burbank, the leading cultivar grown in the U.S., is excellent for frying and baking. Kennebec is an excellent all-purpose potato (20).

2. Asparagus (Asparagus officinalis L.)

Asparagus, a dioecious perennial monocot, is a member of the Liliaceae family (21). The region between the eastern Mediterranean and eastward to the Caucasus Mountains is the center of origin of asparagus (22). It has been cultivated for medicinal and food use for more than 2,000 years. In the 1600s it was introduced to America. Commercial production is centered in California, Washington State, and Michigan (23).

Priced as a gourmet item, asparagus produces tender spears, unexpanded shoots each year. Nutritionally, asparagus is a source of vitamins A and C (22). The plant is composed of ferns, a crown, and a root system. The fern is a photosynthetically active modified stem called a cladophyll. The crown is a series of rhizomes (underground root-like stems) attached to the plant base. Upper portions of the horizontal rhizome contain the buds from which spears arise. Fleshy and fibrous roots develop from the lower portion of the rhizome. The fleshy roots act as storage organs. The carbohydrates stored in crown and roots support spear growth in the spring.

Asparagus grows best under conditions of high light intensity, warm days, cool nights, low relative humidity, and adequate soil moisture. Optimum productivity occurs at 25~29°C during the day and 13~19°C at night (22).

Female plants generally produce larger spears than males, but the males produce more smaller-diameter spears. All male lines are developed for superior productivity with reduced seed production (23).

C. BULB CROPS

Bulb crops are all herbaceous monocot species of Allium and are members of Alliaceae family. The genus Allium contains about 500 species, mostly wild. The few species cultivated as vegetables are grown for their fleshy leaf bases and/or tender leaves. Only onions and garlic have prominent bulbs; all others have "pseudostems." All bulb crops contain the thio-allyl compound alliin which breaks down to give a number of volatile sulfur-containing compounds and give the characteristic odor and pungency of the crop. The chemical substances in onion and garlic especially are believed to be associated with reduced risks of cardiovascular diseases and certain cancers (21, 24).

The bulb crops are propagated by seeds (onion, Welsh onion, and Chinese chives), cloves (garlic), or division (Welsh onion and Chinese chive).

1. Onion (Allium cepa L. Cepa Group)

Originating in Central Asia, the common onion has been cultivated for more than 4,000 years (24, 25). As an important flavoring, onion is a very popular crop worldwide. Asia is the largest producer, with Japan and China taking a share of 27%. Columbus introduced the onion to America and it soon spread to all parts of the Americas. Onions have many culinary uses. They can also be processed into dry products such as rings, flakes, and powder for the food processing industry. Quercetin, a flavonoid in onions, provides the protective effect against cancer. Onions can be planted using sets (small bulbs produced in previous season), transplants, and seeds.

Onions are cool-season crops with optimum growth temperature ranging between 13 and 24°C. Onion bulbing is usually favored by long days. However, the length of day required for specific cultivars is different. Under favorable day length, temperatures of 21~27°C are favorable for bulb development. Low relative humidity extending into the harvest and curing periods are desirable (24, 25).

Onions are usually grouped by their day length requirement for bulbing. Within the group, there are early and late maturing cultivars. Onions can also be grouped into mild or pungent (26):

a. Short-day type (European onion): bulbing in response to 10~11 h of day length, mild, soft-fleshed bulbs for fresh use.
b. Intermediate-day type: bulbing in response to 12~13 h of day length, pungent, soft-fleshed for fresh use.
c. Long-day type (Spanish onion): bulbing in response to 14 or more hours of day length, pungent, hard, good for storage.

Bulbs vary in skin color, shape, and size. There are more yellow or brown onion cultivars than red or white cultivars.

2. Garlic (Allium sativum L.)

Originating in Central Asia, garlic has been cultivated from at least 2000 B.C. Widely grown in Asia, garlic is eaten not only for the bulbs, but also for its foliage and flower stalks. Each plant develops the bulb underground, and 8~20 cloves together form a cluster covered by white or purplish papery sheath. Garlic has long been believed to have medical advantages in addition to its flavoring use. It is dehydrated to produce garlic powder and garlic oil capsules made of garlic extracts as a diet supplement. In the U.S. most garlic is produced in California for the bulbs. The planting is carried out in late summer and fall from clean and healthy cloves. The plants overwinter in the field and resume rapid top growth after spring. Large cloves produce greater yields than small cloves.

Garlic is a cool-season crop with cloves germinating best in temperatures of 20~25°C. The optimum temperatures for plant growth and bulb development are 18~20°C and 20~25°C, respectively. Bulbing is initiated as temperatures and day length increase (24, 25).

Garlic cultivars can be grouped by their day length requirement for bulbing (26). Into "Late" and "Early" types. They can also be grouped into hardneck and softneck types. In the Orient, the softneck type is preferred for foliage production (27).

D. COLE AND RELATED CROPS

Cole crops originated along the East Mediterranean and Asia Minor. They are all members of the species *Brassica oleracea* of the family Brassicaceae. During domestication, many cultivated types with distinct edible parts have formed, including cabbage and Brussel sprouts (head), kohlrabi (thickened stem), cauliflower and broccoli (inflorescence), and kale and Chinese kale (foliage) (28–31).

1. Cabbage (*Brassica oleracea* L. *Capitata* Group)

Cabbage has been used as food for more than 3,000 years. The ancient Greeks held cabbage in high esteem. Cabbage was probably introduced by the Romans or Celts from the coastal regions of the Mediterranean Sea to the chalky coasts of England and northwestern France. Present-day cultivars most likely originated from wild non-heading types. Now cabbage is very popular worldwide and is grown extensively in Eastern Europe and the Far East (30).

Cabbage is a herbaceous biennial but grown as an annual. During vegetative development, the plant produces a succession of out-spreading leaves on a stem with very short internodes. About 20 new leaves incurve, overlap, and form a compact head. Leaves are broad, thick, fleshy, heavily veined, and covered with wax. Cabbage is durable for storing and shipping. It ranks higher than tomato but lower than spinach in mineral content (30).

Cabbages are grown for three types of markets: fresh market, late or stored market, and the sauerkraut market. There are several types of cabbage head (31):

a. Wakefield: pointed, small, pointed head, early maturing.
b. Copenhagen market: round, medium-large head, early maturing.
c. Flat Dutch: large, flat, very solid head.
d. Danish Ballhead: round-oval, medium-sized head, relatively late maturing, storable.
e. Savoy: medium-large, flat-globe-shaped head, crinkly leaves, good quality for fresh market.
f. Red: round, medium-sized heads, reddish-purple leaf.

2. Cauliflower (*Brassica oleracea* L. var. *botrytis* L.)

Both cauliflower and broccoli are of the cabbage family with cauliflower being more exact in environment and cultural requirement. Cauliflower is grown for the curd (head), which is the shortened shoot with bracts and undifferentiated flower parts at the terminal end of the plant axis. The curd may be white, creamy, yellowish green, purple or orange. However, pure white curds are preferred. Cauliflower was first mentioned in the U.S. in 1806. California leads in commercial production (30).

Optimum temperatures for growth are 15~20°C with an average maximum of 25°C and minimum of 8°C. Many tropical cultivars are early matured and require higher temperature and long days for good vegetative growth before forming curd. After the white head has developed to 5~7.5 cm, it is protected from sunburn and turning green by tying the outer leaves together over the head center or just bending a few outer leaves to cover. In Asia, blanching is achieved by covering the developing head with a piece of spun-bonded material which can be reused (28, 29).

Cauliflowers are generally grouped into three major types by maturity (30):

a. Super Snowball (early): dwarf with medium sized leaves and somewhat flattened, and maturing in 50~55 days after transplanting.
b. Snowball (mid-season): larger and later, large rounded and very dense curd, maturing 70~80 days after transplanting.
c. Winter (later): grown where winters are mild, maturing 150 or more days after transplanting.

The later the maturity is, the larger the curd. In California cauliflowers may also be grouped by curd size and density.

3. Broccoli (*Brassica oleracea* L. var. *italica* Plenck)

Broccoli evolved from wild cabbage earlier than cauliflower and was cultivated by the ancient Romans (28). However, it was relatively unknown in England until the 18th century. It was grown in the U.S. in the early 1800s (28–30), but its popularity came much later.

Broccoli is similar to cauliflower in the structure of its flower head. Unlike cauliflower, the edible plant portion is the inflorescence consisting of fully differentiated immature flower buds and the tender portion of the upper stem. These flower buds form a compact head. If the terminal inflorescence is removed, secondary inflorescences may develop in the axils of lower leaves.

Broccoli is the most nutritious of the cole crops in vitamin content, calcium, and iron. Its anticancer properties have been often reported. Per capita consumption continues to increase. California is the largest producer in the U.S. (30).

Broccoli is adapted to a range of soil types and can tolerate heat to a greater degree than cauliflower. The optimum temperatures for plant growth are 20~22°C and 18°C for head development. It is sensitive to boron deficiency (28, 29).

There is no major subgroup for broccoli. Cultivars of Calabrease, Green Comet, Green Duke, and Premium Crop are popular (30).

E. OTHER LEAFY VEGETABLES

Greens are grown for leafy portions both for cooking and salads. They are high in mineral and vitamin contents. All greens are more of specialty crops except spinach, which is produced on a large commercial scale. All greens in North America are cool-season crops except New Zealand spinach which is a warm-season crop (32).

Lettuce, endive-escarole, and chicory are leafy salad vegetables. Their tender leaf blades with a little petiole and stem are used fresh or raw in salads. They are excellent dietary sources of bulk and fiber. Only lettuce is grown on a large scale (34).

1. Chinese Cabbage, Pe-tsai (*Brassica rapa* L. Pekinensis Group)

Chinese cabbage is native to China and eastern Asia (32). Its recent popularity has resulted in a considerable increase in production in Europe and the U.S. It produces an elongated head. Moderate day and cool night temperatures are essential for productivity and quality. Temperatures ranging between 13~21°C are suitable for its growth (28).

High temperature during head formation causes a loose head and increased incidence of tipburn. There are several types of head: elongated, shorter, tall, and short and compact (28, 32).

2. Spinach (*Spinacia oleracea* L.)

Spinach is thought to be native to Central Asia. It ranks second only to broccoli in total nutrient concentration. Spinach is used fresh and for canning, freezing, and pureed baby food. Due to a short growth period of 30~50 days, annual spinach is cultivated between planting of other vegetable crops (33).

Spinach is usually dioecious, rarely monoecious. Dioecious types produce extreme male and vegetative male. The extreme male plant is small. While vegetative male and female plants produce more foliage and flower later, they are the preferred types for commercial production (33).

Spinach is a hardy, cool-season vegetable. It prefers 15~20°C for growth, 15°C for seed germination. Spinach is direct-seeded. Sized seed and specialized belt seeders are used to reduce seeding rate (33).

Cultivars of spinach are classified into three types (33):

a. Savoy type: large, fresh market use, suitable for long distance shipment for less anaerobic respiration.
b. Smooth-leaved: mostly for processing, preferred for easy washing of leaves.
c. Semi-savoyed type: for both fresh market and processing into frozen packs.

3. Lettuce (Lactuca sativa L. var. capitata)

Lettuce is native to the Mediterranean and inner Asia Minor. Until the 18th century, lettuce was widely used in the Americas. Now the U.S. leads in the production and consumption of lettuce in the world. Lettuce cannot be processed. It is a leafy salad vegetable (34).

Lettuce prefers 24°C for seed germination, and 18~23/7~11°C of day/night temperatures for growth. Lettuce is direct-seeded or transplanted. Coated or pelleted seeds are direct-seeded by seeders. Osmo-conditioning of seeds and fluid drilling are also used (34).

There are four distinct types of lettuce (34):

a. Crisphead type (Iceberg): large and solid head, usually over 0.9 kg and 15.2 cm in diameter, brittle and crisp leaves with prominent veins and midribs, very large outer leaves in medium to dark green, inner leaves tightly folded in light color, most durable for shipping and handling.
b. Butter-head type (Boston, Bibb, or semi-heading): smooth, soft, pliable leaves forming a loose head, better table quality and more delicate flavor than crisp-head type, leaves easily torn and bruised, mainly for local markets, often for greenhouse production.
c. Cos type (Romaine): long and narrow leaves, upright plant, long and somewhat loose heads, more tolerant to stress, best for local markets.
d. Loose-leaf type (bunching): not heading, early, easy to grow, popular in home garden, not suitable for long distance shipment because of its short market life, produced primarily in greenhouses in winter.

Stem lettuce or celtuce (*L. sativa* var. *asparagina* Bailey) is grown for its thick, succulent stem. It is usually cooked in stews and other dishes, or pickled. Stem lettuce is popular in the Far East, but not widely grown in the U.S.

4. Celery (Apium graveolens L. var. dulce)

Celery originated in Sweden. It was initially used for medicinal purposes. Now the long, fleshy, but low nutritive content petiole is harvested for its flavor and texture, mostly for the fresh market. It is used mainly as a salad crop, in soups, and a small portion is dehydrated. The seeds are also used as a condiment for flavor (35).

Celery is a biennial but grown as an annual. Outer ribs along the petiole's abaxial length are composed mainly of thick-walled collenchyma cells responsible for mechanical strength and stringiness. Celery demands a particular climate. It prefers 15.6~18°C for growth. The production costs per acre are the highest among all vegetable crops (35).

Celery cultivars are classified into two types (2).

a. Golden (yellow or self-blanching) type: golden foliages, earlier, less vigorous, thinner petioles, more sharply ribbed, stringy, more inferior in eating and keeping quality, primarily for specialty markets.
b. Green type: green foliages.
  (i) Utah type: predominate, many attractive and well-overlapped petioles, a well-developed heart.
  (ii) Summer Pascal type: excellent eating quality, generally lacking compactness, few petioles, poor heart development, less affected by cold, less likely to bolt in early planting.
  (iii) Slow Bolting type: less affected by cold, less likely to bolt in early planting.

Celeriac or knob root celery (*Apium graveolens* var. *rapaceum*) is grown for its enlarged roots. Smallage (*A. graveolens* var. *secalinum*), grown long before celery, is most popular in Asian and Mediterranean regions. It produces rosettes of long, thin petioled leaves (16, 36).

F. FRUIT VEGETABLES

Fruit vegetables are grown for their fruits for consumption. They are mainly grouped into cucurbits, legumes, and Solanum fruits. Within the same botanical family, different crop species have similar cultural requirements and pest problems. Other fruit vegetables include okra and sweet corn.

1. Cucurbitaceae

The Cucurbitaceae, a very important food crop family, has been consumed and utilized by human beings for more than 10,000 years. The gourd family consists of 118 genera, only 9 of which are used as vegetables. Among them, three genera, i.e., *Cucumis*, *Citrullus*, and *Cucurbita*, are of more commercial importance in the world; however, the others are of greater importance in Asia or other regions. These include the genera *Benincasa*, *Lagenaria*, *Luffa*, *Momordica*, *Sechium*, and *Trichosanthes*. The genera *Cucurbita* (pumpkin and squash) and *Sechium* (chayote) were domesticated in the Americas while the others were

of old World origin (originating in Asia and Africa). All are warm season crops and very susceptible to cold injury. However, some types adapt to cool and dry climates. They are herbaceous annuals except chayote which can be grown as perennial. These cultivated species of the Cucurbitaceae family have similar plant habits and cultural methods. They are also known as cucurbits or vine crops. The plant is either a climbing or trailing vine or a bush type. The bush type is of determinate growth and usually bears earlier than vine type. The root system consists of a deep taproot and highly branched short laterals with horizontal distribution similar to the range of plant canopy. They are grown mainly for their fruits. Other parts of the plant may also be consumed for food such as the seeds of watermelon and squash, the flowers of squash and luffa, and the shoots of chayote. Indeterminate vines continue to grow until the plant dies. Side shoots emerge from the leaf axils. Large leaves are borne singly and alternate (38–41).

Most cucurbits are monoecious, producing female and male flowers at separate nodes in the same plant. Usually female flowers are borne singly and male flowers either singly or in cluster in the leaf axils. Melons have andromonoecious type, producing perfect flowers and male flowers in the same plant. The gynoecious types, producing only female flowers, are also available in cucumber. The sex expression, a genetic trait, can be modified by environmental factors and growth regulators. High temperature and long days favor male blooms, while low temperature and short days favor female flowers. The use of ethephon induces female flowering while gibberellic acid and silver nitrate promote male flowers. The plants can be manipulated for the purpose of seed production (38–41).

Most cucurbits can be grown from direct seeding or by transplanting; however, special care is required for the latter practice (43). The seedlings are grown in individual containers to 3~4 true leaf stage to be transplanted. Most crops are direct-seeded in the field in the U.S. The plant spacing varies according to the plant types, with closer in-row spacing for small vined and bush types than for large vined ones. The plastic mulch can be used in the field to raise the temperature for early plantings. A critical period for water occurs during blooming and early fruit set. For sufficient pollination of the plants, the beehives may be brought into the field after female flowers bloom. Cultivation, weed control, irrigation, and pest control are managed similarly to all vine crops (39, 42).

a. Bitter melon (Momordica charantica L.)
Bitter melon, indeginous to the tropics of India or Southeast Asia, is very popular in tropical areas. It is distinct from other vegetable cucurbits by its delicate foliage, slender stems, and simple tendrils. The fruit surface is studded with protuberance. The bitterness of the fruit is due to momordicosides, glycosides of tetracyclic triterpenoids. Immature fruits are less bitter and can be

eaten raw or cooked. They may also be picked or dried for later use. At maturity the fruits turn orange and split open at the blossom end, to expose the bright red fleshy arils surrounding the seeds. The sweet arils can be eaten. Young shoots, leaves, and flowers are eaten as potherbs in India and southeast Asia. All parts of the whole plant are employed as folk medicine. The fruit of bitter melon is a good source of vitamin C, and has been also investigated as an agent inhibiting growth of the HIV virus.

Bitter melon requires warm, sunny areas with fertile, high water-retaining soils of pH 5.5~6.5. The optimum temperatures for seed germination are 30~35°C, for vine growth and fruiting, 25°C. Commercial crops are produced either on ground or on support in arch shape or in triangle shape. The fruits are usually protected from light and fruit flies with paper bags or crude fibers (42, 44).

The cultivated forms of bitter melon are grouped by fruit color into white, light green, and green; by fruit shape into spindle, pear-shaped, or elongated; by fruit size shape into regular (up to 30 cm long and 10 cm in diameter) and wild (up to 8 cm long and 4 cm in diameter); and by the shape of protuberence.

b. Pumpkins and squashes (Cucurbita spp.)

Pumpkins and squashes consist of four of the five cultivated species of the genus *Cucurbita*. They originated in tropical and subtropical America and have been cultivated for thousands of years. However, different types of pumpkins and squashes are not easily distinguished by botanical names or by morphological characteristics. The inter-crossability among different types and among species makes clear classification difficult. The classification is largely based on culinary use and stage of maturity. *C. moschata* is believed to have originated in Central America or northern South America, *C. maxima* in the Andes Mountains of South America, and both *C. pepo* and *C. argyrosperma* in northern Mexico and the southwestern U.S. After pumpkins were introduced to China and Japan, they became important vegetable crops there and many Oriental types were derived. This gives much diversity in fruit shape color and size to the crop (42, 44).

The crop requires a warm season with temperatures between 18 to 30°C for optimum growth. Optimum temperatures for seed germination are 25~30°C, and for fruit development, 25~27°C. Growth period from planting to harvest ranges from 40~60 days for summer squash to 80~140 days for pumpkins and winter squash. For early production, a light loamy soil is desired. Sunny, dry weather is important for successful pollination by honeybees and good fruit development (39, 42, 43).

C. maxima, in general, has better fruit quality in flavor and texture than *C. moschata*. But *C. moschata* has disease resistance and with stands high temperature better than *C. maxima*.

In the U.S. *Cucurbita* species with round and orange fruits are called pumpkins, while those that have fruits of other colors and shapes are called squashes (39, 43):

(i)   Summer squash: Commonly *C. pepo*, grown for their immature fruits with soft skin, including yellow crook neck and straight neck, scallop squash, cocozelle, and zucchini.

(ii) Winter squash: including all four *Cucurbita* species, grown for mature fruits usually with hard rind, such as acorn, hubbard, butternut, banana, and orange marrow.

(iii) Pumpkins: mostly *C. pepo* and *C. moschata*, grown for their ripe fruits used as an ingredient in pies.

The naked-seeded pumpkins are grown for their seeds to be roasted for snacks. *C. maxima* can grow to jumbo size (22~45 kg) for exhibition purposes.

c. Cucumber (Cucumis sativa L.)

Both cucumber and melon are members of genus *Cucumis*; each belongs to a different subgenus. Cucumber is indigenous to India and has been cultivated for more than 3,000 years. It also has a long history in China where it is considered a secondary center of genetic diversification. Early travelers brought cucumber to Mediterranean countries (42). In the early 14th century, cucumber was cultivated in the U.K. It was introduced to the U.S. by 1539. Now cucumber is widely used as fresh and processed products. The leading U.S. States for fresh market cucumbers are Georgia and Florida, while Michigan, North Carolina, and Texas lead in processing type production (43).

Cucumber requires temperature of 30°C during the day, 20°C at night for optimum plant growth. The seeds germinate best in 25~30°C, and in this range, fruits develop rapidly. The crop growth rate increases steadily as the temperature increases to 32°C (42, 43). Glasshouse cultivation is also common for the cucumber in Northern Europe, Asia, and the Middle East.

Cucumbers are divided by use into slicing type and pickling type, by culture into outdoor type and greenhouse type (39, 43):

(i)   Pickling cucumber: fruits cylindrical in shape with blocky ends and a medium green color.

(ii) Slicing cucumber: smooth, symmetrical, and white-spine fruits longer than pickling type, with glossy, dark-green skin.

(iii) Greenhouse cucumber: mostly parthenocarpic (set fruit without pollination).

d. Wax gourd (Benincasa hispida (Thunb.) Cogn)

Wax gourd is the only species of the genus *Benincasa*, which is named for Italian botanist Count Benincasa. The species name refers to the pubescence on the foliage and immature fruit. Of Indo-Malayan origin, wax gourd is an important vegetable in India, China, the Philippines, and elsewhere in Asia. Both mature and immature fruits are consumed, either cooked or picked. The mature fruits harvested in summer can be stored at 13~15°C and 70~75% RH for over 6 months. The name winter melon refers to its long storage life. The fruits are especially valued for their high water content, bland taste, and cooling properties. The sliced pulp is dried for later use, and sometimes candied in sugar syrup. The candied fruits are boiled to make the popular summer drink, wax gourd tea, served as a seasonal and festival specialty. The Chinese steam the entire mature fruit as a soup tureen with various stuffed ingredients. In addition to the food value, wax gourd is also important in traditional medical practices. The rinds and seeds are part of various medications throughout Southern Asia. The fruit wax is sometimes collected to make candles. Mo-kwa (*B. hispida* var. *Chieh-qua* How.), a botanical form of wax gourd, is usually grown for its immature fruit which is about 0.4~0.7 kg and 18~25 cm long. It is high yielding and more heat tolerant.

Wax gourd grows best in sunny, moderately dry areas. It requires fertile, well-drained soils of pH 5.5~6.4. The optimum temperatures for seed germination are 30~32°C and for plant growth and fruiting 24~27°C (42, 44). The cultivated forms of wax gourd can be divided by fruit shape into long cyclindrical and short cylindrical; by fruit size into small (1.5~5 kg) and large (7~20 kg); and by skin color and the presence of waxy white bloom on fruits into dark green, light green, and waxy.

e. Other Cucurbits

As many Asian immigrants moved to the U.S. other cucurbits of Asian or African origin become common in areas with large Oriental populations. These crops include immature fruits of smooth luffah (*Luffa aegyptaca* Miller), angled loofah [*L. acutangula* (L.) Roxb.], bitter melon (*Momordica charantia* L.), bottle gourd [*Lagenaria siceraria* (Mol.) Standl.], wax gourd or Mo-kwa, the immature fruits of *Benincasa hispida*. Among these, bitter melon also has medical use (42, 44).

2. Legumes

Vegetable legumes, all dicotyledonous annuals, are members of the Leguminosae (Fabaceae) family. The immature fruits are important vegetables and the dry seeds are an important staple food. In some, the leaves, tender shoots, or the roots are harvested and used as vegetables (47). Legumes may be classified according to the position of the cotyledons in the germinated seedlings. Epigeal is the type where cotyledons are above the ground; hypogeal is the type where cotyledons remain underground. Many legumes can assimilate their own source of nitrogen as a result of a symbiotic relationship with bacteria of *Rhizobium* in their root nodules. However, before successful symbiotic relationship is established, the crop still needs adequate supply of nitrogen in the soil for growth (46, 47).

Peas and broad beans are cool season crops while beans are warm season crops, intolerant of frost. Each legume species has strains or varieties adapted to a particular range of conditions. All vegetable legumes are direct-seeded to the field. The pole type or the tall cultivars are usually supported or trained to poles. Generally bush types require less time for flowering than the pole cultivars (48).

a. Common bean, Snap bean (Phaseolus vulgaris L.)

Common bean is the most widely cultivated bean in the genus *Phaseolus*. Over 7,000 years ago, on common bean originated in Central and South America. It was introduced to Europe in the 16th century and soon spread to other parts of the Old World (47). Beans are marketed fresh, canned, or frozen. Wisconsin is the largest bean-producing state for processing and Florida leads in fresh market production (48, 49).

The optimum soil temperature range for germination is 25~30°C. The optimum temperature range for growth is 16~30°C. Temperature above 30°C at flowering can cause flowers to abort. Vine types are adapted to cooler temperatures than bush types. The desirable maturity characteristics are undersized seed development and low sidewall fibers (47–49).

Common beans are divided into bush and vining types according to growth habits, and fresh market and processing cultivars according to uses. Based on pod color, common beans are either green-podded or yellow-podded, sometimes even purple-podded. Beans may also be classified by shape of the pod or color of the seeds (48).

b. Lima bean (Phaseolus lunatus L.)

There are two types of lima beans, the large-seeded and small-seeded types. They originated in both Central and South America before 5000 B.C. (47). The Native Americans spread the crop and it became an important vegetable crop in the U.S. It can be consumed fresh, frozen, or canned. The lima bean growth habit is similar to the common bean. California is the only state to harvest dry lima beans, both baby lima beans and large-seeded ones (48, 49).

Lima beans require a slightly warmer climate than common beans (47). They germinate at 15~30°C with an optimum soil temperature of 25°C. Mean monthly temperatures of 15~24°C are necessary to grow the crop. The small seeded type, being less restrictive, can tolerate hotter and drier conditions than the large-seeded one (47).

The U.S. cultivars have seed coats of white, creamy, buff, or light green. The large-seeded type is narrowly adapted, but is of better quality. The small-seeded type is grown widely (48):

(i) Bush type: productive with small seeds, ex. Henderson, Early Thorogreen.

(ii) Pole type: largely for home gardens (Pierce), producing small seeds.

c. Peas (Pisum sativum L. ssp. sativum)

As one of the most ancient crops, peas originated in the eastern Mediterranean region and Near East. Peas can be dated to 7,000~9,000 years ago (47, 48). Dry peas were utilized as food in Europe from very early days and green peas were not used until the 16th century (46). The edible podded types evolved in more recent times. In the Orient, the tender shoots of peas are used as greens (50). The term English pea reflects many cultivars of peas developed and grown in England. Columbus brought the pea to North America where it quickly spread to all parts. Commercial production in the U.S. is primarily for processing, including canning and freezing. Seeds are either smooth or wrinkled; the former is starchy and the latter is sweeter (48, 49).

Peas thrive in cool and moist weather. The crops grow best at mean temperatures of 13~18°C. Long days and cool temperature accelerate flowering. The smooth-seed types are more adapted to cool weather conditions than the wrinkle-seeded types. The edible podded types are more adapted to warm conditions than the green pea types. Heat units are commonly used to predict harvest dates for the processing industry (47).

There are several types of peas, including shelled peas, edible podded peas, and dry peas. Pea cultivars are classified by seed color, growth habit, seed quality, and pod appearance (48, 49):

(i) Dry peas: light green seed color, starchy.
(ii) Canning peas: most determinate, light green and sugary seeds.
(iii) Freeze peas: most determinate, dark green and sugary seeds.
(iv) Edible podded peas: pods lacking the stiff, papery inner parchment, the whole pods consumed.
  (a) Snow peas: sugary seeds slightly enlarged.
  (b) Snap peas: sugary seeds more developed and pod wall thickened.

d. Southern pea [Vigna unguiculata (L.) Walp. ssp. unguiculata (L.) Walp.]

The origin of Southern pea is rather obscure. It is possibly of tropical African origin (47) or from India (47, 48). There are three distinct cultivar groups in *Vigna unguiculata*, characterized by growth habit and pod character (48). The immature pods of all three are used as vegetables. The yard-long bean is more popular to the Southeast Asians with pods ranging from 30 to 75 cm in length. Catjang cowpea has erect small pods 7~12 cm long with small and cylindrical seeds. It is more common in India. Southern peas, also known as black-eye peas, are mostly confined to the southern U.S. They are grown primarily for the green shelled seeds, a large amount of which are processed and canned or frozen (48).

Southern pea grows best in hot, dry climates. Optimum temperatures for growth are 27~30°C during the day and 17~22°C at night. It tolerates heat better than common beans or lima beans. Fresh market peas may be harvested 16~17 days after bloom (47).

Cultivars of southern pea differ in maturity, in pod color, crowding of seeds in the pods. Black-eye peas refer to those having a dark outline or eye around the hilum. Other major types include purple hulled and creamy yellow. The large cultivars are well suited for pick-your-own and local sale (49).

3. Solanum Fruits

Solanum fruit crops, all of tropical origin, are members of the Solanaceae family. They include tomato, peppers (both bell pepper and chili), and eggplant, all grown as annuals for commercial production. Tremendous phenotype variations are available in fruit shape, size, and color. They are warm season crops with eggplant being more heat tolerant than pepper and tomato. Chili pepper can grow in higher temperature than bell pepper. The potato, in the same genus as the eggplant, is discussed under stem and tuber crops (20, 52).

These crops share similar disease problems. In some countries, grafting culture of tomato and eggplant on resistant stocks is used to combat soil-borne diseases. Early production can be forced by planting transplants to fields mulched by plastics. Direct seeding can be successfully used for later, especially processing, production. Transplants are usually greenhouse grown in plugs. Tomato and bell pepper are grown in glasshouses or other protective structures in some regions where climate limits field production (20).

a. Tomato [Lycopersicon esculentum (L.) Mill]

The tomato originated in the Andes of South America and evolved from the cherry tomato (*L. esculentum* var. *cerasiforme*). However it was introduced from Mexico to Europe early in the 16th century (37, 52). Early use of tomato was hampered by the belief that it was poisonous, because many of the Solanum species contain alkaloids. The tomato was introduced to the U.S. in 1710, and was produced in New Orleans in 1779 (51, 52).

On a worldwide basis, tomato is one of the most important vegetables or salad plants (37). The acid sweet taste and unique flavor account for its popularity and diverse usage. Although not among the most valuable crops in nutrient contents, tomato is an important source of vitamins A and C because of the substantial per capita consumption. The U.S. leads in total tomato production and processing. California and Florida lead the nation in fresh market and processing tomato, respectively (20).

Tomato requires temperatures of 25~30°C for optimum germination. Day temperatures of 25~30°C with night temperatures of 16~20°C are optimal for growth and flowering (20, 51, 52). Fruit set is best between 18~24°C with night temperatures more critical than day temperatures. Cultural practices of pruning, staking, and caging are used to increase light interception and aeration for production enhancement.

Tomatoes are classified as determinate and indeterminate in growth. Higher planting densities are given to the former type to compensate for their lower yield potential. Tomatoes are grouped into fresh market, processing, and home garden types according to use. Processing cultivars are usually determinate and ready for harvest in 75 days after field setting. The greenhouse tomatoes are indeterminate and the home garden types may be either determinate or indeterminate. Variation in shapes (globe to pear), fruit color (yellow, pink, and red), and size (cherry, beef) exist in different cultivars (20).

b. Pepper (Capsicum annuum L.)

With a long history of cultivation of more than 7,000 years, peppers are native to tropical and subtropical America (52). Among the five domesticated species in the genus *Capsicum*, *C. annuum* is the most widely cultivated and economically important species and includes both bell pepper and chili pepper. *C. frutescens* has small fruits. Tabasco is the best known cultivar and is grown commercially for making Tabasco sauce (20, 54).

Columbus introduced peppers to Europe, and subsequently to Africa and to Asia. Peppers were soon integrated into people's cuisine due to the characteristic flavor and pungency. In addition to use as food or spices, peppers are also used in pharmaceutical products such as pepper plaster. The pepper is an indispensable food in many countries. Asia is the largest producer with China leading in world production (53). In the U.S. New Mexico leads in chili pepper production while California leads in bell pepper production (55). Peppers are good sources of vitamins C and A.

The pepper is a warm-season crop. The optimum temperature for pepper growth and development is higher than that for tomato. The seeds germinate rapidly in 25~30°C. The base growing-degree-days temperature is 18°C. The average temperature for optimum growth is 21~30°C, for fruit set 20~25°C, and for color development 18~24°C. The plants are not photoperiod sensitive for flowering. The small fruit cultivars are more tolerant to high temperature extremes (51–53).

Peppers are classified into two main types, the sweet-fleshed fruit and the pungent fleshed fruit. They can also be grouped by fruit appearance and use. Classified by pod type, there are bell, pimiento, cheese, ancho, cayenne, Cuban, jalapeno, serrano, wax, and cherry, among others. Important commercial types are listed as follows (20, 54):

(i) Bell type: large blocky fruit with three to four lobes and thick flesh, mature green fruits harvested for fresh market, mature colored fruits in red, orange, or gold also in commercial markets.

(ii) Cherry peppers: round or slightly flattened fruits, orange to deep red when harvested, sweet or hot, small or large.

(iii) Chili type: pungent and thin flesh fruit, from cherry size to slender fruit up to 20 cm long.

(iv) Pimento peppers: fruit sweet with thick wall, conical or heart-shaped, turning red at maturity.

(v) Tabasco peppers: fruits 2.5~7.5 cm long, slim, tapered, and highly pungent.

Peppers can be fresh, canned, brined/pickled, frozen, fermented, dehydrated, and extracted for oleoresin (53).

c. Eggplant (Solanum melongena L.)

Native to India, eggplant is not as popular as tomato or pepper as a vegetable. However, it is widely used in China, India, Japan, and many Mediterranean countries. The name eggplant is believed to reflect the early forms with small, white fruits resembling eggs. There are in general three forms of eggplants: round egg-shape fruits, long slender fruits, and dwarf plant form (20, 51, 52). Fruit tissues contain high levels of phenolics; upon cutting they are quickly oxidized by enzymes, resulting a brown discoloration of the flesh (51).

Introduced to American gardens in 1806, the eggplant was primarily an ornamental curiosity until the 20th century. Commercial eggplant acreage is primarily located in Florida and New Jersey (20).

Eggplant is very sensitive to low temperatures and it requires a relatively long, warm growing season. Optimum temperatures for seed germination are 24~32°C, for growth and development, day temperatures of 22~30°C and night temperatures of 18~24°C. The elongated fruit type tends to be more resistant to high temperature than the round fruit type. To have high yield, plants require high light intensity (51, 52).

There are two basic types of eggplants based on fruit shape (52):

(i) Standard oval shaped type: large, smooth, glossy purplish-black fruit.

(ii) Oriental type: long slender purple-black fruit.

There are also types with white, yellow, or apple-green-colored fruits.

4. Sweet Corn (*Zea mays* L.)

Sweet corn is a monocot of the Poaceae (Gramineae) family. An ancient crop dating from about 5,000 B.C., corn originated in the highlands of central and southern America. Sweet corn originated from a mutation of grain corn (56). Corn was not popular initially because it was difficult to store. Commercial sweet corn production began about 200 years ago in the U.S. The U.S. leads the world in sweet corn production. In addition to fresh use, a considerable volume is processed by canning and freezing of kernels after removal from the cob (57).

Corn plants are monoecious with male flowers borne as the terminal inflorescence on the main stem and female flowers borne as lateral ear shoots. The basal nodes of an ear shoot are concentrated with little internode space. They form a tight husk around the developing ear. Each individual kernel is a single-seeded fruit composed of a small embryo and a large endosperm. Sweet corn kernels contain less starch, and more sugar and water-soluble polysaccharides which are responsible for the creamy texture (56).

The optimum temperature range for corn growth is 24~30°C. In general, the warmer the air temperatures, the faster the corn will grow to maturity (57). However, moderate temperatures are optimum for carbohydrate accumulation. Cool nights are particularly important at harvest time. Plants flower sooner when days are short. The crop is sensitive to soil acidity, requiring a soil pH of 6.0~6.8. It requires high water, but not waterlogging and high fertilization.

Sweet corn cultivars are classified by kernel color (yellow, white, and bicolor), maturity date (early and late), and use (market, freezing, canning, or shipping) Classified by kernel sweetness, there are the following (57):

(a) Standard sweet corn: containing the recessive *su 1*, traditional sweet corn flavor and texture.
(b) Modified sugary sweet corn: containing the sugary enhancer gene *se*, high sugar, thin pericarp.
(c) Supersweet corn: containing recessive *sh 2* gene, higher in sugar, lower in starch, tougher skinned.

G. BEAN SPROUTS

Bean sprouts are produced mostly from germinated seeds of mungbean [*Vigna radiata* (L.) Wilcz] and soybean [*Glycine max* (L.) Merr]. The use of bean sprouts has long history in China. The seeds are soaked for 24 h, sprouted, and allowed to grow in the dark for several days before harvest for consumption. The etiolated hypocotyls and young cotyledonary leaves are eaten with other vegetable dishes (58). The sprouts are a good source of vitamins B_1 and B_2 and dietary fiber. More than 20 kinds of sprouts have been developed. Among them, pea sprouts and alfalfa sprouts are popular vegetable sprouts grown from legume seeds. Light exposure a few days before harvest produces pea sprouts green in color. Sprouts are grown under light to harvest green sprouts. Daily watering is necessary. The growth of sprouts does not require supplemental nutrients but depends on the storage reserve of the seeds. Given optimum temperature for seed germination, water for sprouts to grow, and proper aeration, bean sprouts can be produced year round in controlled environments (58).

ACKNOWLEDGMENT

The information in this chapter from "Vegetables: types and biology," by J.S.J. Tsao and H.F. Lo, in *Handbook of Vegetable Preservation and Processing*, edited by: Y.H. Hui et al., Marcel Dekker, New York 2004.

REFERENCES

1. Asian Vegetable Research and Development Center. Introduction to vegetables and vegetable production systems. In: Vegetable Production Training Manual. Taiwan: Asian Vegetable Research and Development Center, 1992, pp. 1–24.
2. DR Decoteau. Classifying vegetable crops. In: Vegetable Crops. Upper Saddle River, NJ: Prentice Hall, 2000, pp. 32–38.
3. DK Salunkhe, SS Kadam. Introduction. In: Handbook of Vegetable Science and Technology. New York: Marcel Dekker, 1998, pp. 1–10.
4. JG Vaugban, CA Geissler. Introduction. In: The New Oxford Book of Food Plants. 2nd ed. New York: Oxford, 1999, pp. xiv–xx.
5. JM Swiader, GW Ware, JP McCollum. The vegetable industry. In: Producing Vegetable Crops. Engelwood Cliffs, NJ: Interstate Publishers, 1992, pp. 1–28.
6. DR Decoteau. History of vegetable crops. In: Vegetable Crops. Upper Saddle River, NJ: Prentice Hall, 2000, pp. 3–11.
7. A Segre. Global horticultural impact: fruits and vegetables in developing countries. Proceedings of the World Conference on Horticultural Research, Rome, 1998, Acta Horticulturae 495:69–100, 1999.
8. VE Rubatzky, M Yamaguchi. Vegetable classification. In: World Vegetables: Principles, Production, and Nutritive Values. 2nd ed. New York: Chapman & Hall, 1997, pp. 29–33.
9. LC Peirce. Classification of vegetables. In: Vegetables: Characteristics, Production, and Marketing. New York: John Wiley & Sons, 1987, pp. 163–172.
10. JM Swiader, GW Ware, JP McCollum. Classifying vegetables. In: Producing Vegetable Crops. Upper Saddle River, NJ: Interstate Publishers, 1992, pp. 29–53.
11. DR Decoteau. Understanding the vegetable industry. In: Vegetable Crops. Upper Saddle River, NJ: Prentice Hall, 2000, pp. 12–31.
12. U Avermaete. Global horticultural impact: fruits and vegetables in developed countries. Proceedings of the World Conference on Horticultural Research, Rome, 1998, Acta Horticulturae 495:39–67, 1999.

13. JG Vaugban, CA Geissler. Root vegetables. In: The New Oxford Book of Food Plants. 2nd ed. New York: Oxford, 1999, pp. 180–185.

14. DR Decoteau. Root crops. In: Vegetable Crops. Upper Saddle River, NJ: Prentice Hall, 2000, pp. 290–323.

15. VE Rubatzky, CF Quiros, PW Simmon. Introduction. In: Carrots and Related Vegetable Umbelliferae. Wallingford, U.K.: CABI Publishing, 1999, pp. 1–21.

16. VE Rubatzky, M Yamaguchi. Carrots, celery and other vegetable umbels. In: World Vegetables: Principles, Production, and Nutritive Values. 2nd ed. New York: Chapman & Hall, 1997, pp. 418–456.

17. VE Rubatzky, M Yamaguchi. Spinach, table beets, and other vegetable chenopods. In: World Vegetables: Principles, Production, and Nutritive Values. 2nd ed. New York: Chapman & Hall, 1997, pp. 457–473.

18. JM Swiader, GW Ware, JP McCollum. Sweet potatoes. In: Producing Vegetable Crops. Upper Saddle River, NJ: Interstate Publishers, 1992, pp. 495–512.

19. VE Rubatzky, M Yamaguchi. White or Irish potato. In: World Vegetables: Principles, Production, and Nutritive Values. 2nd ed. New York: Chapman & Hall, 1997, pp. 105–129.

20. DR Decoteau. Solanum crops. In: Vegetable Crops. Upper Saddle River, NJ: Prentice Hall, 2000, pp. 380–415.

21. JG Vaugban, CA Geissler. Stem, inflorescence and bulb vegetables. In: The New Oxford Book of Food Plants. 2nd ed. New York: Oxford, 1999, pp. 172–179.

22. VE Rubatzky, M Yamaguchi. Other succulent vegetables. In: World Vegetables: Principles, Production, and Nutritive Values. 2nd ed. New York: Chapman & Hall, 1997, pp. 640–703.

23. DR Decoteau. Perennial crops. In: Vegetable Crops. Upper Saddle River, NJ: Prentice Hall, 2000, pp. 266–289.

24. VE Rubatzky, M Yamaguchi. Alliums. In: World Vegetables Principles, Production, and Nutritive Values. 2nd ed. New York: Chapman & Hall, 1997, pp. 279–332.

25. LC Peirce. Alliums. In: Vegetables: Characteristics, Production, and Marketing. New York: John Wiley & Sons, 1987, pp. 271–285.

26. DR Decoteau. Bulb crops. In: Vegetable Crops. Upper Saddle River, NJ: Prentice Hall, 2000, pp. 324–342.

27. GH Lin. Garlic. In: BF Hung. ed. Taiwan Agriculture Encyclopedia (Crop edition—2). Taiwan: Harvest Farm Magazine, 1995, pp. 291–296.

28. VE Rubatzky, M Yamaguchi. Cole crops, other *Brassica* and other crucifer vegetables. In: World Vegetables: Principles, Production, and Nutritive Values. 2nd ed. New York: Chapman & Hall, 1997, pp. 371–417.

29. LC Peirce. Cole crops. In: Vegetables: Characteristics, Production, and Marketing. New York: John Wiley & Sons, 1987, pp. 207–228.

30. DR Decoteau. Cole crops. In: Vegetable Crops. Upper Saddle River, NJ: Prentice Hall, 2000, pp. 189–220.

31. JM Swiader, GW Ware, JP McCollum. Cole crops—cabbage, broccoli, cauliflower, and related crops. In: Producing Vegetable Crops. Upper Saddle River, NJ: Interstate Publishers, 1992, pp. 255–278.

32. FH Liao. Chinese cabbage. In: BF Hung. ed. Taiwan Farm Encyclopedia. Taiwan: Harvest Farm Magazine, 1995, pp. 323–326.

33. JM Swiader, GW Ware, JP McCollum. Spinach and other leafy vegetable greens. In: Producing Vegetable Crops. Engelwood Cliffs, NJ: Interstate Publishers, 1992, pp. 459–476.

34. JM Swiader, GW Ware, JP McCollum. Lettuce and other leafy salad vegetables. In: Producing Vegetable Crops. Engelwood Cliffs, NJ: Interstate Publishers, 1992, pp. 341–360.

35. JM Swiader, GW Ware, JP McCollum. Celery. In: Producing Vegetable Crops. Engelwood Cliffs, NJ: Interstate Publishers, 1992, pp. 309–322.

36. H Hwang. Celery. In: BF Hung. ed. Taiwan Agriculture Encyclopedia (Crop edition—2). Taiwan: Harvest Farm Magazine, 1995, pp. 355–360.

37. JG Vaugban, CA Geissler. Vegetable fruits. In: The New Oxford Book of Food Plants. 2nd ed. New York: Oxford, 1999, pp. 124–139.

38. RW Robinson, DS Decker-Walters. What are cucurbits. In: Cucurbits. UK: CAB International, 1997, pp. 1–22.

39. LC Peirce. Cucurbits. In: Vegetables: Characteristics, Production, and Marketing. New York: John Wiley & Sons, 1987, pp. 357–382.

40. AK Singh. Cytogenetics and evolution in the Cucurbitaceae. In: DM Bates, RW Robinson, PW Simmon. eds. Biology and Utilization of the Cucurbitaceae. Ithaca, NY: Cornell University Press, 1990, pp. 10–29.

41. RW Robinson, DS Decker-Walters. Evolution and exploitation. In: Cucurbits. Wallingford, U.K.: CAB International, 1997, pp. 23–38.

42. VE Rubatzky, M Yamaguchi. Cucumber, melons, watermelons, squashes and other cucurbits. In: World Vegetables Principles, Production, and Nutritive Values. 2nd ed. New York: Chapman & Hall, 1997, pp. 577–639.

43. DR Decoteau. Cucurbits. In: Vegetable Crops. Upper Saddle River, NJ: Prentice Hall, 2000, pp. 416–458.

44. RW Robinson, DS Decker-Walters. Major and minor crops. In: Cucurbits. Wallingford, U.K.: CAB International, 1997, pp. 58–112.

45. HL Chakravarty. Cucurbits of India and their role in the development of vegetable crops. In: DM Bates, RW Robinson, PW Simmins. eds. Biology and Utilization of the Cucurbitaceae. Ithaca, NY: Cornell University Press, 1990, pp. 325–334.

46. JG Vaugban, CA Geissler. Legumes. In: The New Oxford Book of Food Plants. 2nd ed. New York: Oxford, 1999, pp. 38–49.

47. VE Rubatzky, M Yamaguchi. Peas, beans, and other vegetable legumes. In: World Vegetables: Principles, Production, and Nutritive Values. 2nd ed. New York: Chapman & Hall, 1997, pp. 474–531.

48. LC Peirce. Legumes. In: Vegetables: Characteristics, Production, and Marketing. New York: John Wiley & Sons, 1987, pp. 333–356.

49. DR Decoteau. Legumes or pulse crops. In: Vegetable Crops. Upper Saddle River, NJ: Prentice Hall, 2000, pp. 343–367.

50. GE Gou. Pea. In: BF Hung. ed. Taiwan Agriculture Encyclopedia (Crop edition—2). Taiwan: Harvest Farm Magazine, 1995, pp. 445–450.

51. VE Rubatzky, M Yamaguchi. Tomatoes, peppers, eggplants, and other solanaceous vegetables. In: World Vegetables: Principles, Production, and Nutritive Values. 2nd ed. New York: Chapman & Hall, 1997, pp. 532–576.

52. LC Peirce. Solanaceous crops. In: Vegetables: Characteristics, Production, and Marketing. New York: John Wiley & Sons, 1987, pp. 309–332.

53. PW Bosland, EJ Votava. Introduction. In: Peppers: Vegetable and Spice Capsicums. Wallingford, U.K.: CABI Publishing, 2000, pp. 1–13.

54. PW Bosland, EJ Votava. Taxonomy, pod types and genetic resources. In: Peppers: Vegetable and Spice Capsicums. Wallingford, U.K.: CABI Publishing, 2000, pp. 14–39.

55. PW Bosland, EJ Votava. Production. In: Peppers: Vegetable and Spice Capsicums. Wallingford, U.K.: CABI Publishing, 2000, pp. 97–134.

56. VE Rubatzky, M Yamaguchi. Sweet corn. In: World Vegetables Principles, Production, and Nutritive Values. 2nd ed. New York: Chapman & Hall, 1997, pp. 235–252.

57. DR Decoteau. Sweet corn. In: Vegetable Crops. Upper Saddle River, NJ: Prentice Hall, 2000, pp. 368–379.

58. DT Zhang, SX Fan, JT Gu, DB Wang, PX Han, YR Xu, XQ Wang. The nutrition of vegetable sprouts. Agricultural World 173:61–64, 1998.

59. SJ Kays, JC Silva Dias. Names of cultivated vegetables. Economic Botany 49:115–152, 1995.

21 Nutritional Value of Vegetables

C. Alan Titchenal and Joannie Dobbs
Department of Human Nutrition, Food and Animal Sciences, University of Hawaii

CONTENTS

I. INTRODUCTION

Vegetables are considered a significant part of all major dietary guidance systems. Their many chemical elements and compounds are known to affect thousands of physiological functions and to promote health (1). This chapter provides an overview of nutrients and non-nutrient phytochemicals commonly found in vegetables, along with a description of the basic nutrient profile for vegetables in general. Factors affecting nutrient variations, both naturally occurring and due to processing, are summarized. Lastly, this chapter reviews many of the purported health benefits derived from various vegetable phytochemicals.

II. NUTRIENTS

A. NUTRIENTS

About a century ago, researchers observed that growth and survival of animals was directly affected by various individual components in foods. These components were termed nutrients and were to be considered required for normal growth and health. In the early 1900s, researchers began to focus on the disease-preventing properties of vegetables. McCollum and colleagues realized that the addition of vegetables to a seed diet was necessary to prevent deficiency conditions in omnivore species (2). Researchers then realized that a diet deficient in even a single essential nutrient (required from food), could result in a dietary deficiency disease or even death (3).

Strictly speaking, nutrients are compounds that cannot be synthesized by the human body from other chemicals or cannot be synthesized rapidly enough to meet the needs of the body. Thus, by the classical definition of nutrient, the term "essential nutrient" is redundant. However, the terms "non-essential nutrient" or "dispensable nutrient" are sometimes used to describe chemical compounds that are contained in foods and have a function in the body, but are typically synthesized by the body in adequate amounts.

As nutrition science evolved, a third category of nutrients has been identified as "conditionally essential." This terminology is used to describe substances that may become essential under specific conditions that reduce the body's capability to synthesize adequate amounts of the compound. This may be caused by changes in physiological demands due to a genetic defect, a disease condition, the stress of surgery, or the use of certain drugs such as statins and Co-enzyme Q10 (4,5).

Presently, there are approximately 50 individual food elements and chemical compounds identified as essential nutrients. These nutrients are classified into six broad chemical categories based on chemical structure and functions including water, proteins, fats, carbohydrates, vitamins, and minerals. Table 21.1 lists nutrients by essentiality category and the basic physiological functions of providing energy, structure, or regulation of the body's thousands of chemical reactions.

Nutrients frequently act in concert to regulate specific physiological functions. For example, calcium, magnesium, and potassium regulate muscle contraction and relaxation (7,8). Vitamins B-6, B-12, and folate function in concert to prevent the excessive accumulation of homocysteine, which in turn reduces the risk of coronary artery disease (9).

The proper proportion of specific nutrients is also important in maintaining health. For example, the ratio of omega-3 fatty acids (primarily from fish oils and some vegetable oils) to omega-6 fatty acids (primarily derived from many vegetable oils) is an example of the essentiality of correct nutrient proportions. Both types of fatty acid are essential for regulating eicosanoid synthesis which in turn affects physiological functions such as blood pressure, inflammation, and blood clotting. The appropriate proportion of omega-3 to omega-6 fatty acids is 1 to 4 up to 1 to 10. An imbalance of these fatty acids appears to be related to various chronic health problems (10).

Nutrients, even essential nutrients, are known to be harmful in excessive amounts. The Institute of Medicine has published both the recommended levels of intake and the tolerable upper intake levels for many nutrients. These recommendations provide guidelines on what constitutes generally safe ranges of intake and what levels of a nutrient may be excessive and even harmful to humans (11–14).

The use of certain drugs may require nutrient intake to be maintained within a more narrow range. For example, excess vitamin K intake, even from naturally occurring plant sources, can interfere with the function of common blood anticoagulant drugs (15).

B. NUTRIENT PROFILES

Foods from various common food groups (meat and poultry, milk products, fruits, vegetables, grains, and beans) have classic nutrient profiles or distinctive nutrient fingerprints. Typically, these nutrient profiles are expressed as the amount of various key nutrients typically contained in 100 grams of edible portion.

Compared to other food group nutrient profiles, vegetables provide the nutrient characteristics that most consumers perceive as health promoting (Table 21.2).

Vegetables contain no cholesterol, very little fat, sugar, and sodium, yet provide concentrated sources of many vitamins and minerals. There are literally hundreds of vegetables, with the majority of these cultivated in Asia (17). Table 21.3 presents representative nutrient ranges and means for 38 of the more commonly consumed vegetables in America (18).

C. FACTORS AFFECTING NUTRIENT COMPOSITION OF VEGETABLES

Biological, chemical, and physical factors all affect the nutrient composition of vegetables. For these reasons, nutrient values for any particular vegetable may differ significantly from published values commonly used in databases. Table 21.4 presents a partial list of factors that can significantly affect variability of nutrient content in foods. Comprehensive texts and research papers (as well as references cited within) are referenced in this table for those interested in a deeper understanding of any single production factor.

Because of the virtually endless possibilities of factor combinations, there is no definite set of rules dictating how the exact nutrient composition of any single plant may vary from the usual. Vitamins and minerals, rather than protein, fat, and carbohydrates, are the nutrients likely to have the greatest variation even within a single plant species.

Vitamins, functioning as cell regulating cofactors, will continue to be utilized by the plant even after being harvested (24). Other factors such as heating, acid, or alkaline exposure, and processing techniques that cause oxidation can decrease the vitamin concentration to a fraction of the initial value (25).

The content of some minerals in plants is dependent upon the amount of a particular element available in the soil for the growing plant. For example, depending upon the selenium content in the soil, plants may have very low levels of selenium or contain toxic amounts.(26).

D. BIOAVAILABILITY

Even though vegetables may contain ample quantities of nutrients and phytochemicals, some vegetables also contain chemicals that bind with nutrients and phytochemicals making the beneficial compounds unavailable for absorption. An understanding of these bioavailability considerations is essential to avoid using nutrient data of vegetables in a misleading way (27,28).

Nutrient antagonists can significantly decrease the bioavailability of nutrients from foods. High levels of one mineral may competitively reduce the absorption of another mineral element. For example, magnesium interferes with calcium absorption (29). Zinc also is known to interfere with magnesium absorption (30). Phytochemicals, like

TABLE 21.1
Human Essentiality and Physiological Function of Nutrients Found in Plants

Nutrient	Essentiality	Physiological Function			Examples of Key Specific Functions
		Energy	Structure	Regulation	
Water	Essential		x	x	Provides fluid structure for every cell
PROTEIN—AMINO ACIDS:					Source of kilocalories; protein structure of all cells; regulate chemical reactions through enzymes; necessary for DNA synthesis
Histidine, Isoleucine, Leucine, Lysine, Methionine	Essential	x	x	x	
Phenylalanine, Threonine, Tryptophan, Valine	Essential	x	x	x	
Alanine, Arginine, Asparagine, Aspartic Acid	Dispensable	x	x	x	
Glutamic Acid, Glycine, Proline, Serine	Dispensable	x	x	x	
Cysteine, Glutamine, Tyrosine	Conditional	x	x	x	
LIPID—FATTY ACIDS:					Source of calories; cell membrane structure; eicosanoid synthesis;
Linoleic: omega-6, alpha-Linolenic: omega-3	Essential	x	x	x	
Other Fatty Acids	Dispensable	x	x		
CARBOHYDRATES:					Energy source especially essential for red blood cells and brain
Glucose	Dispensable	x			
MINERAL ELEMENTS:					Bone and tooth structure Miscellaneous physiological and regulatory functions including: energy metabolism; synthesis and transport of red blood cells and hormones; water balance; and immune system functions
Calcium, Fluoride, Magnesium, Phosphorus	Essential		x	x	
Chloride, Chromium, Copper, Iodine	Essential			x	
Iron, Manganese, Molybdenum	Essential			x	
Potassium, Selenium, Sodium, Zinc	Essential			x	
Arsenic, Boron, Nickel, Silicon	Essential			x	Functions unclear
VITAMINS:					Miscellaneous regulatory functions including: preventing oxidation; energy metabolism; blood clotting; and eye health
Biotin, Choline, Folate, Niacin (B-3), Pantothenic acid	Essential			x	
Riboflavin (B-2), Pyridoxine (B-6), Thiamin (B-1)	Essential			x	
Vitamin A (carotenoids), Vitamin C (ascorbic acid)	Essential			x	
Vitamin E (tocopherol), Vitamin K	Essential			x	

Essential nutrients not present in vegetables include Vitamin D and Vitamin B12. Dietary fiber is commonly classified as a non-digestible form of carbohydrate. However, it is not a nutrient and has been included in Table 5 as a phytochemical.

Source: Ref. 6.

TABLE 21.2
Nutrient Profile of "Classic" Food Groups Based on 100 gram (g) Edible Material as Raw or Minimally Prepared for Consumption; Information is Based on USDA Nutrient Database Series 14 and Presented as Unrounded Range and Rounded Mean for Each Food Group

	Water (g)	Calories (kcal)	Total Fat (g)	Saturated Fat (g)	Cholesterol (mg)	Sodium (mg)	Carbohydrates (g)	Fiber (g)	Sugar (g)	Protein (g)	Vitamin A (IU)	Vitamin C (mg)	Calcium (mg)	Iron (mg)
Vegetables	64-96	5-145	0.04-0.7	0.0-0.17	0	2-201	2-24	0-5	0-6	0-5	0-19000	3-93	0-119	0.1-3.3
	90	35	0.25	0	0	35	7	2	1.5	2	1770	24	50	0.9
Fruits (not including avocado)	70-95	27-92	0.09-0.96	0-0.22	0	0-20	6-23	0-4	1-18	0-1	10-3800	4-98	4-40	0.1-0.6
	85	50	0.25	0	0	2	12	1.8	10	1	550	28	15	0.3
Grains—Cooked	65-90	43-135	0.16-1.08	0.2-2.0	0	1-35	9-30	0-7	0-1	1-4	0-98	0	1-13	0.2-1.5
	76	96	0.5	1	0	15	20	2.2	0.5	2.5	10	0	8	0.8
Beans—Cooked	61-70	118-173	0.38-8.98	0.05-1.32	0	1-13	10-28	2-9	0-3	7-17	0-9	0-2	14-142	1.1-5.2
	65	139	2.2	0.5	0	3	21	6	2	10	3	1	62	2.8
Nuts	2-47	224-718	1.12-76.5	0.16-29.7	0	0-38	12-73	0-11	0-13	3-26	0-1091	0-36	1-234	0.9-9.2
	12	533	45	7	0	9	28	5	4	13	130	8	74	3.2
Meat	47-76	110-274	1.25-21	0.33-8.54	41-440	39-102	0-6	0	0	17-32	0-35350	0-34	4-11	0.7-8.6
	66	173	8.5	3	100	68	0	0	0	22	2165	3	11	2.2
Eggs	70-75	149-185	10.0-13.8	3.1-3.7	425-933	125-150	0-1	0	0-1	13-14	300-1328	0	50-100	1.4-4.1
	73	170	12	3.5	790	140	1	0	1	13	820	0	67	3.3
Milk	81-91	35-108	0.18-7.01	0.12-4.6	2-27	44-52	4-5	0	4-5	3-6	126-205	1-4	119-193	0.0-0.1
	87	64	3	2	11	50	5	0	5	4	180	2	138	0.1

Source: Ref. 16.

TABLE 21.3
Vegetable Composition Based on 100 g Edible Portion as Raw or Minimally Prepared for Consumption. Range Information Based on Various Sources Including USDA Nutrient Database Series 14 and Others

Vegetable	Water (g)	kilocalories	Fat (g)	Protein (g)	Total Carbohydrates* (g)	Sugar (g)	Fiber (g)
Artichoke (globe)	80–86	17–70	0.3–0.4	0.5–4.5	13	2	0.8–5.4
Asparagus	92–93	9–27	0.2	2.2–3.9	4.6	1.3–2.3	0.0.7–2.1
Beet root	83–89	44–58	Tr - 0.7	1.3–1.8	10	6–7.3	0.6–3.1
Broccoli	89–91	28	Tr - 0.3	3.1–4.0	5.3	0.4–2	1.3–3
Brussels sprouts	84–89	16–58	Tr - 0.5	2.4–4.4	8.7	3.6–4	1.3–4.6
Cabbage	86–93	8–36	Tr - 0.7	1.4–3.3	5.4	2.7–3.8	0.6–3.4
Carrot	84–95	19–47	Tr - 0.7	0.6–2.0	10.1	5.4–7.5	0.6–2.9
Cassava	50–74	120–153	Tr - 0.7	0.7	27	1.2	0.6–1.7
Cauliflower	84–92	11–34	Tr - 0.3	1.8–3.4	5.2	2.4–2.6	0.8–2.4
Celery	89–96	5–22	Tr - 0.5	0.7–2.0	3.7	1–1.2	0.7–2.7
Chard	91–94	16–19	0.2–0.4	1.5–2.6	3.8	0.8–1.1	0.6–1.6
Chayote	74–95	24–29	0.1	0.8	5.1	–	0.4–0.6
Cucumber	91–97	9–16	Tr - 0.2	0.6–1.4	2.8	1.8–2.6	0.3–0.7
Eggplant	89–94	15–38	Tr - 0.7	0.7–2.4	6.7	2.1–4.2	0.9–2.5
Endive	93–94	11–24	Tr - 0.2	1.6–1.8	3.4	0.3–1.0	0.8–2.2
Leek	71–92	25–52	Tr - 0.4	1.3–2.5	7.6	1–4	1.0–3.3
Lettuce	92–97	11–27	Tr - 0.5	0.8–1.6	2.2	1.1–2.2	0.3–1.4
Mustard	68–89	10–28	Tr - 0.3	1.6–2.4	2.1	0.4–0.9	1.8–3.7
Onion	81–93	13–49	Tr - 0.35	0.9–2.2	8.6	5.2–6.7	0.5–1.7
Parsley	68–89	21–60	Tr - 1.0	3.7–5.2	6.9	Tr	0.9–9.1
Parsnip	79–83	56–83	Tr - 0.5	1.5–1.7	19.5	5.5–9.5	2.2–4.4
Pea	65–81	49–138	Tr - 0.8	4.6–8.2	15.6	2.3–7.4	1.8–5.5
Peppers	70–93	27–37	0.1–0.7	1.2–2.0	6.4	1.7–13.9	0.5–2.7
Plantain	58–74	116–128	0.05–0.8	1	31.2	5.6	0.3–2.3
Pumpkin	80–96	15–36	Tr - 0.2	0.6–1.8	4.9	2.5–3.2	0.5–1.3
Potato	71–85	75–109	Tr - 0.1	1.6–2.3	25.2	0.3–1.6	0.3–2.4
Radish	92–95	15–22	Tr - 1.1	0.7–1.2	3.6	2.0–3.4	0.5–1.0
Spinach	91–93	16–35	0.3	2.3–5.1	3.5	0.3–0.4	0.6–2.7
Summer squash	86–95	19–44	0.03–0.3	0.6–1.5	4.4	1.0–3.9	0.3–1.9
Sweet corn	57–80	86–142	0.8–2.1	2.9–4.5	19	3.2–5.2	0.6–3.2
Sweet potato	60–80	98–125	0.04–0.7	1.4–2.8	24.3	5.4–11.6	0.5–2.3
Taro	54–83	111–142	0.1–0.5	0.5–2.9	34.6	1	0.4–5.1
Tomato	90–96	14–23	Tr - 1.26	0.7–1.2	4.7	1.2–3.4	0.4–1.8
Turnip	87–93	11–35	Tr - 0.2	0.6–1.1	6.5	3.8–4.6	0.7–2.8
Watercress	90–94	11–29	Tr - 0.6	1.7–3.1	1.3	0.2–0.6	0.5–3.3
Yam	54–84	104–116	0.03 - 4	1.5–2.4	27.6	0.5	0.4–3.9
Zucchini	95–98	7–16	Tr	0.4	4	1.3–2.2	0.6–1.4

(Continued)

dietary fiber and phytic acid, can reduce the bioavailability of minerals such as iron or calcium.

Minerals are the nutrient class most commonly affected by decreased bioavailability. Most commonly, the low availability of the mineral to the body is due to the mineral's chemical form or to other components in the diet. Bioavailability for each mineral can vary extensively. For example, on the average, a human absorbs from the diet about 1 to 10% of the iron and manganese, 1 to 20% of the zinc, and 15 to 40% of the magnesium and calcium. These percentages will vary based on the quantity of food components such as dietary fiber and oxalic acid which bind with minerals making them unavailable

for absorption. Spinach is a good example of a vegetable with relatively high levels of calcium that are virtually unavailable to the body due to the high oxalate concentration in the spinach. Consequently, listing spinach as a food that is high in calcium is technically correct, however, it is deceiving because it is not a good source of calcium for humans (31).

Another factor that can affect the bioavailability of minerals is the physiological status of a person. For some minerals, the efficiency of absorption is increased (within certain limits) during times of dietary deficiency and the absorption efficiency is decreased during times of high intake (32).

TABLE 21.3
(Continued)

Vegetable	Ascorbic acid (mg)	Vitamin A (IU)	Thiamine (mg)	Riboflavin (mg)	Niacin (mg)	Folic Acid (µg)	Calcium (mg)	Iron (mg)
Artichoke (globe)	5–33	16	0.07–0.2	0.01–0.17	0.1–1.3	66	19–74	0.02–1.0
Asparagus	11–41	100–550	0.1–0.23	0.08–0.3	0.8–1.1	25–156	13–28	0.5–2.0
Beet root	Tr - 6	Tr - 35	0.01–0.03	0.01–0.06	0.06–0.4	20–80	15 32	0.4–2.8
Broccoli	40–93	700–1550	0.06–0.07	0.12–0.2	0.6	50–71	48–160	0.9–1.5
Brussels sprouts	35–128	50–720	0.06–0.13	0.08–0.19	0.4–1.04	14–86	10–53	0.1–2.5
Cabbage	20–220	Tr - 1330	0.03–0.17	0.03–0.21	0.15–1.55	20–37	30–204	0.5–1.9
Carrot	4–58	1660–28130	0.04–0.1	0.03–0.06	0.2–1.16	10–14	27–57	0.2–1.2
Cassava	9–48	10–240	0.04–0.23	0.02–0.1	0.25–1.4	22	23–91	0.6–3.6
Cauliflower	8–114	Tr - 20	0.04–0.13	0.04–0.06	0.25–0.89	30–48	13–43	0.2–1.9
Celery	5–15	Tr - 220	0.02–0.5	0.02–0.5	0.2–0.4	7–28	31–53	0.4–9.9
Chard	30–72	390–3300	0.04–0.07	0.06–0.14	0.61–1.14	14	51–176	1.4–4.0
Chayote	8–20	Tr - 50	0.01–0.03	0.02–0.04	0.4–0.45	18	12–13	0.3–0.4
Cucumber	5–19	Tr - 215	0.02–0.1	0.02–0.11	0.1–0.6	6–13	14–23	0.3–0.8
Eggplant	1–5	Tr - 65	0.05–0.08	0.02–0.04	0.5–0.8	14	6–36	0.4–1.0
Endive	7–12	560–2050	0.06–0.08	0.1–0.8	0.4	142	44–52	0.8–2.8
Leek	4–32	10–405	0.03–0.8	0.02–0.1	0.2–0.5	24	30–85	1–2
Lettuce	3–33	40–2200	0.04–0.14	0.03–0.1	0.2–0.5	20–73	17–107	0.05–4.0
Mustard	25–102	970–3030	0.04–0.09	0.06–0.2	0.36–0.8	29–73	65–220	0.7–4.5
Onion	6–10	Tr - 170	0.02–0.03	0.02–0.04	0.1–0.2	19	20–52	0.2–0.5
Parsley	90–200	1220–5200	0.08–0.2	0.11–0.6	0.53–1.8	40–183	130–325	2.3–19.2
Parsnip	10–18	Tr	0.07–0.11	0.05–0.09	0.2–0.7	20–58	36–57	0.6–1.5
Pea	12–35	50–600	0.25–0.52	0.06–0.15	1.3–3.3	8–63	13–52	1.2–3.6
Peppers	73–342	40–750	0.03–0.1	0.02–0.18	0.3–2.17	22	9–29	0.5–1.5
Plantain	6–54	15–910	0.02–0.1	0.01–0.1	0.16–1.4	26	2–23	0.1–2.1
Pumpkin	4–20	50–10820	0.03–0.05	0.03–0.08	0.4–0.9	9	15–66	0.3–0.8
Potato	8–64	Tr - 10	0.04–0.16	0.02–0.04	0.8–5.1	6–11	4–13	0.5–1.4
Radish	6–43	Tr - 10	Tr - 0.04	0.01–0.05	0.2–0.65	10–27	21–52	0.3–1.9
Spinach	1–59	800–6720	0.05–0.15	0.08–0.24	0.35–0.75	53–194	60–595	0.8–4.5
Summer squash	3–46	Tr - 1200	0.02–0.1	0.01–0.4	0.2–1.4	8–26	9–40	0.2–2.4
Sweet corn	7–10	Tr - 170	0.15–0.2	0.06–0.1	1.7	46	2–9	0.5–0.7
Sweet potato	7–68	3340–17050	0.1–0.15	0.03–0.14	0.41–1.56	10–11	14–45	0.6–1.3
Taro	3–8	Tr - 5	0.03–0.27	0.03–0.1	0.06–1.16	19	18–150	0.7–2
Tomato	19–48	50–625	0.04–0.11	0.02–0.12	0.45–0.91	5–15	5–14	0.4–1.2
Turnip	17–37	Tr - 5	0.03–0.07	0.03–0.06	0.4–0.94	4–15	30–65	0.01–0.5
Watercress	37–153	450–4700	0.05–0.2	0.09–0.3	0.2–1.38	9–50	63–222	1.3–5.1
Yam	Tr - 13	Tr - 200	0.05–0.15	0.01–0.03	0.1–0.55	16	8–37	0.5–1.2
Zucchini	2–5	240	Tr - 0.04	0.04	0.2–0.4	17	13–14	0.2–0.4

* USDA database values only — expressed as total carbohydrate by difference; includes sugar, starch, and dietary fiber. Tr = trace amount.
Source: Refs. 16, 18.

III. NON-NUTRITIVE PHYTOCHEMICALS

A. PHYTOCHEMICALS

Many components of foods are not strictly required by the body for growth and daily maintenance, yet some of these components may promote health and help prevent disease. It has become common to call these compounds by the general term phytochemicals when present in plant foods or zoochemicals when present in animal foods. Some phytochemicals are conspicuous by their colors (carotenoids) or flavors (tannins); however, the presence of many other phytochemicals is not as evident.

In 1919, E.V. McCollum wrote in his book *The Newer Knowledge of Nutrition*, "A plant structure, or an animal body is an exceedingly complex mixture of chemical substances many of which are themselves individually as complicated in their structure as the most complex machine. The first step in the direction of reaching an understanding of the chemistry in the living mass, must involve the separation and the study of the structural units of which the tissues are composed" (2, p. 2).

Although McCollum was likely writing this about nutrients, his statement is as true today as nearly a century ago. Presently the field of nutrition is identifying and quantifying thousands of non-nutritive phytochemicals.

TABLE 21.4

Factors That Can Affect Nutrient Content of Foods or Reported Nutrient Values

General References Relating to Multiple Factors (19–22)

Agriculture Production Genetics: species and plant variety	*Environmental* Geography, Altitude, Climate, Pest control, Season, Sunlight, Soil composition/fertilization, Water
Harvesting, Shipping, and Storage Plant maturity, harvesting time and method; Ripeness of plant, Harvesting time and temperature, Time before, during, and after processing	*Added Food Ingredients and/or Supplemented with Nutrients*
Level and Type of Processing Fresh, Canned, Frozen, Concentrated, Dehydrated, Dried, Fermented, Salted, Smoked, With/without sweeteners, salt, fat, added liquid	*Preparation Methods* Whole or cut, Cut/grind size, Mixed/whipped/blended, hot/cold preparation, Dry or moist heat frying, Cooled/frozen
Heat Processing Pasteurization, Irradiation, Ultra-high temperature, High-temperature short term, Microwave, Pressure	*Laboratory Analysis (23)* Sampling scheme, Chemical analysis methods, Laboratory procedures, Use of calibration standards, Intra-laboratory variation, Inter-laboratory variation, Data transcription

Source: Refs. 18–23.

Many of these plant chemicals have been identified as having health-promoting qualities. A partial list of vegetable phytochemicals linked to beneficial biological activities is presented in Table 21.5. Other phytochemicals have negative effects upon health either by inhibiting specific nutrient utilization or by being toxic (57).

B. PHYTOCHEMICAL PROFILES

The development of chemical profiles for vegetable phytochemicals is in its infancy. Due to the enormity of the task, it will likely be decades before good phytochemical profiles exist.

C. FACTORS AFFECTING PHYTOCHEMICAL COMPOSITION OF VEGETABLES

Many of the factors that affect nutrient composition (i.e., genetics, environmental factors, and processing) likely also affect the phytochemical composition of vegetables. This is especially true for the phytochemicals functioning as antioxidants. However, information on this topic is extremely limited.

IV. HEALTH BENEFITS DERIVED FROM VEGETABLES

Modern society has dramatically affected how we eat. Since the introduction of T.V. dinners, it appears that convenience greatly influences people's food choices. Researchers have found that monkeys or apes foraging in the wild appear to get far higher levels of many essential nutrients and beneficial phytochemicals relative to their body weight than the average American (58).

Without a doubt, vegetables can be considered more nutrient dense (nutrient content per kilocalorie of food) than foods from other food groups. However, the phytochemicals in vegetables may provide equally important benefits for the prevention of chronic diseases like cancer and heart disease (59).

Research on the purported health benefits of vegetables focuses on two main areas of study:

1) Maintenance of gastrointestinal tract health and
2) Reduction of chronic disease risk

A. GASTROINTESTINAL TRACT HEALTH

The gastrointestinal tract (GI-tract) is the gateway through which the body transports nutrients and phytochemicals into the circulation for delivery to body cells. A complex network of internal organs and tissues is responsible for the digestion or breakdown of food components into compounds and elements that can be absorbed into the body. In addition, the GI-tract serves as a protective barrier to prevent some substances from entering the body (60).

Due to the extremely active and chemically hostile internal environment necessary to accomplish the digestive process within the GI-tract, cells along the 25–30 feet of intestine are exposed to a great deal of chemical and physical damage. Consequently, many of these cells have only a three- to five-day life span. This constant turnover of GI-tract cells results in continuous cellular replacement and repair of damage.

TABLE 21.5
Some Important Non-Nutrient Phytochemicals in Vegetables

Phytochemical	Anti-cancer	Antioxidant	Anti-inflamatory	Blood Clotting	Detoxification	Eye Health	G.I.-Tract Health	Heart Health	Immune System	Osteoporosis	Examples of Food Sources	Ref.
Capsaicin	+/−			+							Hot chile peppers	33
Carotenoids alpha-carotene, beta-carotene, beta-cryptoxanthin, lutein, lycopene, zeaxanthin	+/−	+				+		+			Orange, yellow, & green vegetables	34–36
Curcumin (phenolic)	+	+	+								Turmeric, mustard	37
Coumarins		+		+					+		Vegetables, tonka bean, sweet clover, licorice	38,39
Dietary fiber	+						+	+			Wide variety of vegetable sources	33,40–43
Glucosinolates (glucobrassicin) Isothiocyanates (sulphorophane) Indoles (indole-3-carbinol)	+	+									Cruciferous vegetables, broccoli sprouts	36,37,40, 44–46
Inositol phosphates (phytate)	+	+									Whole grains, beans	47
Monoterpene (limonene)	+										Citrus fruit peel	36,37,40
Organosulfur compounds diallyl sulfide, allyl methyl disulfide, allyl methyl trisulfide, S-allyl cysteine, diallyl trisulfide, and others	+/−										Garlic, onions, and other allium vegetables; mustard and horseradish	33,48,49
Protease inhibitors	+/−										Legumes, cereals, vegetables	36,50
Tannins	+/−	+							+		Grapes, tea, lentils, wine	51,52
Flavonoids apigenin, catechins, chrysin, kaempferol, myricetin, quercetin	+	+	+	+				a		+	Green vegetables, onions, garlic, tea	40,47,48, 53
Isoflavonoids, biochanin A, daidzein, formononetin, genistein, glycitein	+/− −							+		+	soybeans, clover sprouts, alfalfa sprouts	54,55
Lignans	+										flaxseed, berries, whole grains	54,56
Coumestans	+										soybeans, clover sprouts, alfalfa, beans	54,56

There is a significant amount of nutrient recycling from injured GI-tract cells which allows many nutrients to be digested and absorbed along with new food components. This combination of recycled and dietary nutrients is utilized to support adequate replacement of the cell lining of the GI-tract.

Over the last decade there has been an increase in the number of reported cases of various gastrointestinal diseases. Two of the most common GI-tract diseases are diverticulitis (inflammation of small pouches formed along the gastrointestinal tract) and gastro-esophageal reflux disease (GERD), the common cause of indigestion which causes the pain popularly called "heartburn" (61). In fact, GERD is so common and chronic in the United States that Prilosec® was one of the world's top-selling drugs in the year 2000.

Diverticulitis and GERD have one significant dietary factor in common. Both of these conditions appear to be related to years of inadequate dietary fiber intake (61,62). Ironically, fiber is the most abundant phytochemical in vegetables.

Vegetables contain both soluble and insoluble forms of dietary fiber. The physiological effects of these two dietary fiber types have both similarities and some significant differences.

Both soluble and insoluble fiber types hold water and create bulk inside the GI-tract. Soluble fibers slow the rate of stomach emptying into the small intestine. It is thought that the stomach distension caused by fiber bulk and the slower stomach emptying produces an extended feeling of satiety after a meal (63,64). Intake of high soluble fiber also tends to decrease the overall nutrient absorption rate and may also reduce the amount of nutrients and phytochemicals absorbed. This can benefit those with problems in the management of blood glucose and may reduce the absorption of cholesterol (65). Excessively high intake of dietary fiber can interfere with the absorption of minerals.

B. IMMUNE SYSTEM HEALTH

The immune system is part of the body's natural defense system against disease and disease-producing conditions. Approximately 80 percent of the immune system is located directly adjacent to the GI-tract. Ordinarily, undigested food molecules, microorganisms, and many toxins cannot readily cross through the intestinal lining and do not enter the circulatory system. However, disruptions to the integrity of the GI-tract can challenge the immune system beyond its capacity to maintain health (60).

C. CHRONIC DISEASE

Many phytochemicals have been associated with preventing or decreasing the incidence of disease. Disease conditions and related mechanisms that are purported to be affected by various phytochemicals are summarized in Table 21.5.

No doubt there are numerous triggers in the initiation of cancer and heart disease. And although there may be many varied mechanisms of phytochemicals with anti-cancer and heart promoting properties, one mechanism may be related to the antioxidant property shared by many of these compounds. The process of normal cellular metabolism produces chemicals that are reactive oxygen species like hydrogen peroxide and the superoxide anion free radical. It is thought that free radical production causes a secondary oxidative stress whenever there is an imbalance of antioxidants to oxidants. This can occur with an excess of oxidation stress or an inadequate amount of antioxidants in the diet.

Research has shown that antioxidants are involved in delaying many diseases and conditions that are associated with aging such as cancer, heart disease, decreased immune functioning, and visual and cognitive impairment (66). A number of vitamins, minerals, and phytochemicals provide antioxidant protection in the body. Based on a per gram or per kilocalorie basis, vegetables contain significant amounts of antioxidants.

Dietary phytoestrogens may help reduce the risk of developing certain hormone-stimulated cancers such as breast and prostate cancers. However, much more research on this relationship is needed since some studies indicate that phytoestrogen compounds may stimulate progression of some types of cancer (67).

Flavonoids such as those found in onions, tea, and red wine also are under study for potential cancer prevention. The possible mechanisms of action may vary from one flavonoid to another. They may prevent cancer cell proliferation through specific enzyme inhibition (68).

V. SUMMARY

As a major category of foods, vegetables have a variety of qualities and characteristics that supports common recommendations to include them as a significant part of a balanced and varied diet. They serve as important sources of a wide variety of vitamins and minerals essential for normal human nutrition.

Vegetables supply these nutrients in forms that are generally low in energy and fat, making them more "nutrient dense" than most other food sources. The nutrient content of a particular vegetable can vary, with the extent dependent on the nutrient, and a variety of factors including plant genetics, agricultural factors, storage and handling, processing, packaging, and preparation. Nutrient content values in databases generally reflect averages.

The extent to which a vegetable food is a good source of a nutrient also depends on type of processing and the bioavailability of the nutrient. In some cases, a vegetable can contain high levels of a mineral such as calcium or iron, but the form of the mineral or interfering compounds in the vegetable allow very little of the mineral to be absorbed into the body. Some nutrients are not found in vegetables, including vitamins D and B-12 and the long chain omega-3 fatty acids commonly found in fish oils and some species of algae.

In addition to nutrients, vegetables provide a great variety of non-nutrient chemical compounds commonly called phytochemicals. The potential benefits and risks of various phytochemicals found in vegetables represent an increasingly active area of nutrition research. The body of scientific research to date supports the inclusion of a wide variety of vegetables in the human diet for reducing the risk of developing a number of disease conditions that tend to develop with age. Additional research is needed to clarify more specific risks and benefits of various types of chemical compounds found in vegetables.

ACKNOWLEDGMENT

The information in this chapter has been derived from "Nutritional Value of Vegetables," by C.A. Titchenal, J. Dobbs. In *Handbook of Vegetable Preservation and Processing*, edited by: Y.H. Hui et al., Marcel Dekker, New York, 2004.

REFERENCES

1. AS Truswell. Dietary goals and guidelines: national and international perspectives. In: ME Shils, JA Olson, M Shike, AC Ross. eds. Modern Nutrition in Health and Disease. 9th ed. Baltimore: Williams & Wilkins, 1999, pp. 1727–1741.
2. EV McCollum. The Newer Knowledge of Nutrition. New York: MacMillan, 1919, pp. 34–68; p. 2.
3. AE Harper. Defining the essentiality of nutrients. In: ME Shils, JA Olson, M Shike, AC Ross. eds. Modern Nutrition in Health and Disease. 9th ed. Baltimore: Williams & Wilkins, 1999, pp. 3–10.
4. BI Labow, WW Souba. Glutamine. World J Surg 24:1503–1513, 2000.
5. Anonymous. Extra co-enzyme Q10 for statin-users? Treatment Update. 13:4–7, 2001.
6. ME Shils, JA Olson, M Shike, AC Ross. eds. Modern Nutrition in Health and Disease. 9th ed. Baltimore: Williams & Wilkins, 1999, pp. 3–569.
7. HP Sheng. Sodium, chloride, and potassium. In: MH Stipanuk. ed. Biochemical and Physiological Aspects of Human Nutrition. Philadelphia: W.B. Saunders Company, 2000, pp. 686–710.
8. RK Rude. Magnesium. In: MH Stipanuk. ed. Biochemical and Physiological Aspects of Human Nutrition. Philadelphia: W.B. Saunders Company, 2000, pp. 671–685.
9. M Cattaneo. Hypercysteinaemia and atherothrombosis. Ann Med 32 (Suppl 1):46–52, 2000.
10. LS Harbige. Dietary n—6 and n—3 fatty acids in immunity and autoimmune disease. Proc Nutr Soc 57:555–562, 1998.
11. Food and Nutrition Board, Institute of Medicine. Dietary Reference Intakes for Calcium, Phosphorus, Magnesium, Vitamin D, and Fluoride. Washington, D.C.: National Academy Press, 1997.
12. Food and Nutrition Board, Institute of Medicine. Dietary Reference Intakes for Thiamin, Riboflavin, Niacin, Vitamin B-6, Folate, Vitamin B-12, Pantothenic Acid, Biotin, and Choline. Washington, D.C.: National Academy Press, 1998.
13. Food and Nutrition Board, Institute of Medicine. Dietary Reference Intakes for Vitamin C, Vitamin E, Selenium, and Carotenoids. Washington, D.C.: National Academy Press, 2000.
14. Food and Nutrition Board, Institute of Medicine. Dietary Reference Intakes for Vitamin A, Vitamin K, Arsenic, Boron, Chromium, Copper, Iodine, Iron, Manganese, Molybdenum, Nickel, Silicon, Vanadium, and Zinc. Washington, D.C.: National Academy Press, 2001.
15. WH Chow, TC Chow, TM Tse, YT Tai, WT Lee. Anticoagulation instability with life—threatening complication after dietary modification. Postgrad Med J 66:855–857, 1990.
16. U.S. Department of Agriculture, Agricultural Research Service. USDA Nutrient Database for Standard Reference, Release 14. Nutrient Data Laboratory Home Page, http://www.nal.usda.gov/fnic/foodcomp, 2001.
17. JS Siemonsma, K Piluek. eds. Plant Resources of South-East Asia. Bogor, Indonesia: Prosea Foundation, 1994.
18. RB Duckworth. Fruit & Vegetables. London: Pergamon Press, 1966, Appendix A, p. 280.
19. LW Aurand, AE Woods, MR Wells. Food Composition and Analysis. New York: Van Nostrand Reinhold Company, 1987.
20. PJ Fellows. Food Processing Technology, 2nd ed. Boca Raton, FL: CRC Press, 2000.
21. DK Salunkhe, SS Deshpande. eds. Foods of Plant Origin, Production, Technology, and Human Nutrition. New York: AVI, 1991.
22. E Karmas, RS Harris. eds. Nutritional Evaluation of Food Processing, 3rd ed. New York: Van Nostrand Reinhold, 1988.
23. Y Pomeranz, CE Meloan. Food Analysis Theory and Practice. 3rd ed. New York: Chapman & Hall, 1994.
24. WG Burton. Post-harvest Physiology of Food Crops. London: Longman, 1982.
25. RS Harris. General discussion on the stability of nutrients. In: E Karmas and RS Harris. eds. Nutritional Evaluation of Food Processing, 3rd ed. New York: Van Nostrand Reinhold, 1988, pp. 3–5.
26. M Simonoff, C Hamon, P Moretto, Y Llabador, G Simonoff. Selenium in foods in France. J Food Comp Anal 1:295–302, 1988.
27. D Southgate, I Johnson, GR Fenwick. Nutrient Availability: Chemical & Biological Aspects. Cambridge: The Royal Society of Chemistry, 1989.
28. CB Ammerman, DH Baker, AJ Lewis. eds. Bioavailability of Nutrients for Animals. San Diego: Academic Press, 1995.
29. JL Greger. Food, supplements, and fortified foods: scientific evaluations in regard to toxicology and

nutrient bioavailability. J Am Diet Assoc 87: 1369–1373, 1987.

30. H Spencer, C Norris, D Williams. Inhibitory effects of zinc on magnesium balance and magnesium absorption in man. J Am Coll Nutr 13:479–484, 1994.

31. RP Heaney, CM Weaver, RR Recker. Calcium absorbability from spinach. Am J Clin Nutr 47:707–709, 1988.

32. VF Fairbanks. Iron in medicine and nutrition. In: ME Shils, JA Olson, M Shike, AC Ross. eds. Modern Nutrition in Health and Disease. 9th ed. Baltimore: Williams & Wilkins, 1999, pp. 193–221.

33. TK Yun. Update from Asia. Asian studies on cancer chemoprevention. Ann N Y Acad Sci 889:157–192, 1999.

34. D Giugliano. Dietary antioxidants for cardiovascular prevention. Nutr Metab Cardiovasc Dis 10:38–44, 2000.

35. MA Eastwood. Interaction of dietary antioxidants in vivo: how fruit and vegetables prevent disease? QJM 92:527–530, 1999.

36. KA Steinmetz, JD Potter. Vegetables, fruit, and cancer prevention: a review. J Am Diet Assoc 96:1027–1039, 1996.

37. L Jaga, H Duvvi. Risk reduction for DDT toxicity and carcinogenesis through dietary modification. J R Soc Health 121:107–113, 2001.

38. M Makris, HG Watson. The management of coumarin-induced over-anticoagulation. Br J Haematol 114:271–280, 2001.

39. J Hirsh, J Dalen, DR Anderson, L Poller, H Bussey, J Ansell, D Deykin. Oral anticoagulants: mechanism of action, clinical effectiveness, and optimal therapeutic range. Chest 119:8S–21S, 2001.

40. JH Weisburger. Approaches for chronic disease prevention based on current understanding of underlying mechanisms. Am J Clin Nutr 71:1710S–1714S and discussion 1715S–1719S, 2000.

41. JW Anderson, TJ Hanna. Impact of nondigestible carbohydrates on serum lipoproteins and risk for cardiovascular disease. J Nutr 129:1457S–1466S, 1999.

42. VC Knauf, D Facciotti. Genetic engineering of foods to reduce the risk of heart disease and cancer. Adv Exp Med Biol 369:221–228, 1995.

43. BO Schneeman. Carbohydrates: significance for energy balance and gastrointestinal function. J Nutr 124:1747S–1753S, 1994.

44. G van Poppel, DT Verhoeven, H Verhagen, RA Goldbohm. Brassica vegetables and cancer prevention. Epidemiology and mechanisms. Adv Exp Med Biol 472:159–168, 1999.

45. DT Verhoeven, H Verhagen, RA Goldbohm, PA van den Brandt, G van Poppel. A review of mechanisms underlying anticarcinogenicity by Brassica vegetables. Chem Biol Interact 103:79–129, 1997.

46. RK Heaney, GR Fenwick. Natural toxins and protective factors in Brassica species, including rapeseed. Nat Toxins 3:233–237 and discussion 242, 1995.

47. W Mazur. Phytoestrogen content in foods. Baillieres Clin Endocrinol Metab 12:729–742, 1998.

48. C Borek. Antioxidant health effects of aged garlic extract. J Nutr 131:1010S–1015S, 2001.

49. H Amagase, BL Petesch, H Matsuura, S Kasuga, Y Itakura. Intake of garlic and its bioactive components. J Nutr 131:955S–962S, 2001.

50. AR Kennedy. Prevention of carcinogenesis by protease inhibitors. Cancer Res 54:1999S–2005S, 1994.

51. KT Chung, TY Wong, CI Wei, YW Huang, Y Lin. Tannins and human health: a review. Crit Rev Food Sci Nutr 38:421–464, 1998.

52. H Kolodziej, O Kayser, KP Latte, AF Kiderlen. Enhancement of antimicrobial activity of tannins and related compounds by immune modulatory effects. Basic Life Sci 66:575–594, 1999.

53. CD Humfrey. Phytoestrogens and human health effects: weighing up the current evidence. Nat Toxins 6:51–59, 1998.

54. MS Kurzer, X Xu. Dietary phytoestrogens. Annu Rev Nutr 17:353–381, 1997.

55. YH Ju, CD Allred, KF Allred, KL Karko, DR Doerge, WG Helferich. Physiological concentrations of dietary genistein dose-dependently stimulate growth of estrogen-dependent human breast cancer (MCF-7) tumors implanted in athymic nude mice. J Nutr 131:2957–2962, 2001.

56. T Arakawa, DK Chong, CW Slattery, WH Langridge. Improvements in human health through production of human milk proteins in transgenic food plants. Adv Exp Med Biol 464:149–159, 1999.

57. Committee on Food Protection, Food and Nutrition Board, National Research Council. Toxicants Occurring Naturally in Foods. Washington, D.C.: National Academy of Sciences, 1973.

58. K Milton. Nutritional characteristics of wild primate foods: do the diets of our closest living relatives have lessons for us? Nutrition 15:488–498, 1999.

59. B Stavric. Role of chemopreventers in human diet. Clin Biochem 27:319–332, 1994.

60. JS Bland, L Costarella, B Levin, D Liska, D Lukaczer, B Schiltz, MA Schmidt. Clinical Nutrition: A Functional Approach. Gig Harbor, WA: Institute for Functional Medicine, 1999, pp. 191–218.

61. SJ Sontag. Defining GERD. Yale J Biol Med 72:69–80, 1999.

62. SJ O'Keefe. Nutrition and gastrointestinal disease. Scan J Gastroenterol 220 (suppl):52–59, 1996.

63. SJ French, NW Read. Effect of guar gum on hunger and satiety after meals of differing fat content: Relationship with gastric emptying. Am J Clin Nutr 59:87–91, 1994.

64. RC Spiller. Pharmacology of dietary fibre. Pharmacol Ther 62:407–427, 1994.

65. CD Jensen, W Haskel, JH Shittam. Long-term effects of water-soluble dietary fiber in the management of hypercholesterolemia in healthy men and women. Am J Cardiol 79:34–37, 1997.

66. IS Young, JV Woodside. Antioxidants in health and disease. J Clin Pathol 54:176–186, 2001.

67. DF McMichael-Phillips, C Harding, M Morton, SA Roberts, A Howell, CS Potten, NJ Bundred. Effects of soy-protein supplementation on epithelial proliferation in the histologically normal human breast. Am J Clin Nutr 68:1431–1435, 1998.

68. 1. DF Birt, JD Shull, AL Yaktine. Chemoprevention of cancer. In: ME Shils, JA Olson, M Shike, AC Ross. eds. Modern Nutrition in Health and Disease. 9th ed. Baltimore: Williams & Wilkins, 1999, pp. 1263–1295.

22 Canned Vegetables: Product Descriptions

Peggy Stanfield
Dietetic Resources

CONTENTS

I. INTRODUCTION

This book is not the proper forum to present the manufacturing process for all categories of canned vegetables being marketed in the United States. This chapter provides a short description of requirements for the major commercial canned vegetables.

In the United States, two federal agencies have the responsibility to make sure that the canned vegetables in the market are safe and do not pose any economic fraud. The U.S. Food and Drug Administration issues regulations to achieve both goals. The U.S. Department of Agriculture issues voluntary guides to achieve the same goals. The information in this chapter has been modified from such regulations and guidelines.

II. CANNED CORN

Canned sweet corn is the product prepared from clean, sound kernels of sweet corn packed with a suitable liquid packing medium which may include water and the creamy component from corn kernels. The tip caps are removed. The product is of the optional styles.

III. CANNED GREEN BEANS AND CANNED WAX BEANS

A. GENERAL DESCRIPTION

Canned green beans and canned wax beans are the foods prepared from succulent pods of fresh green bean or wax bean plants conforming to the characteristics of *Phaseolus vulgaris* L. and *Phaseolus coccineus* L. Such food is so processed by heat, in an appropriate manner before or after being sealed in a container as to prevent spoilage.

Requirements are provided for optional color and varietal types; styles of pack; ingredients; and labeling.

Optional color types are Green or Wax. Optional varietal types include:

1. Round. Beans having a width not greater than 1-1/2 times the thickness of the bean; or
2. Flat. Beans having a width greater than 1-1/2 times the thickness of the bean.

Optional styles of pack:

1. Whole. Whole pods of any length.
2. Shoestring or sliced lengthwise or French style. Pods sliced lengthwise.
3. Cuts. Transversely cut pods not less than 19 mm (0.75 in) long as measured along the longitudinal axis, which may contain the shorter end pieces that result from cutting such pods.
4. Short cuts. Pieces of pods cut transversely of which 75 percent, by count, or more are less than 19 mm (0.75 in.) in length and not more than 1 percent by count are more than 32 mm (1-1/4 in) in length.
5. Diagonal cuts. Pods cut in lengths as specified, except the pods are cut at an angle approximately 45 deg. to the longitudinal axis.
6. Diagonal short cuts. Pods cut in lengths as specified, except the pods are cut at an angle approximately 45 deg. to the longitudinal axis.
7. Mixture. Any mixture of two or more of the styles specified.

Optional ingredients are:

1. Salt.
2. Monosodium glutamate.
3. Disodium inosinate.
4. Disodium guanylate.
5. Hydrolyzed vegetable protein.
6. Autolyzed yeast extract.
7. Nutritive carbohydrate sweeteners.
8. Spice.
9. Flavoring (except artificial).
10. Pieces of green or red peppers or mixtures of both, either of which may be dried, or other vegetables not exceeding in total 15 percent by weight of the finished product.
11. Vinegar.
12. Lemon juice or concentrated lemon juice.
13. Glucono delta-lactone.
14. Mint leaves.
15. Butter or margarine in a quantity of not less than 3 percent by weight of the finished product.
16. When butter or margarine is added, emulsifiers or stabilizers, or both, may be added.
17. No spice or flavoring simulating the color or flavor imparted by butter or margarine is used.

B. LABELING

The name of the food is "green beans" or "wax beans" as appropriate. Wax beans may be additionally designated "golden" or "yellow."

A declaration of any flavoring that characterizes the product:

1. A declaration of any spice, seasoning, or garnishing that characterizes the product, e.g., "with added spice," or, in lieu of the word "spice," the common name of the spice, e.g., "seasoned with green peppers."
2. The words "vacuum pack" or "vacuum packed" when the weight of the liquid in the container is not more than 25 percent of the net weight, and the container is closed under conditions creating a high vacuum in the container.
3. The name of the optional style of bean ingredient, if a product consists of a mixture of such styles, the words "mixture of" the blank to be filled in with the names of the styles present, arranged in the order of decreasing predominance, if any, by weight of such ingredients.
4. If the product consists of whole beans and the pods are packed parallel to the sides of the container, the word "whole" may be preceded or followed by the words "vertical pack," or if the pods are cut at both ends and are of substantially equal lengths, the words "asparagus style" may be used in lieu of the words "vertical pack."
5. If the product consists of short cuts or diagonal short cuts, a numerical expression indicating the predominate length of cut in the finished food may be used in lieu of the word "short," e.g., "1/2 inch cut."

The following may be included in the name of the food:

1. The word "stringless" where the beans are in fact stringless.
2. The name of the optional varietal type, or the specific varietal name, e.g., "Blue Lake Green Beans," or both.
3. If a term designating diameter is used, it should be supported by an exact graphic representation of the cross section of the bean pod or by a statement of the maximum diameter in common or decimal fractions of an inch and, optionally, by the millimeter equivalent stated parenthetically. The diameter of a whole, cut, diagonal cut, or short cut is determined by measuring the thickest portion of the pod at the shorter diameter of the bean perpendicular to the longitudinal axis.

IV. CANNED MUSHROOMS

A. Legal Requirement

The FDA has established a standard of identity for canned mushrooms. Some aspects are presented below.

1. Definition

Canned mushrooms is the food properly prepared from the caps and stems of succulent mushrooms conforming to the characteristics of the species *Agaricus (Psalliota) bisporus* or *A. bitorquis*, in one of the optional styles, packed with a suitable liquid medium which may include water; and may contain one or more safe and suitable optional ingredients. The food is sealed in a container and, before or after sealing, is so processed by heat as to prevent spoilage.

2. Styles

The optional styles of the mushroom ingredient are:

1. Buttons—consisting of whole mushrooms with attached stems not exceeding 5 millimeters (0.2 inch) in length, measured from the bottom of the veil.
2. Whole—consisting of whole mushrooms with attached stems cut to a length not exceeding the diameter of the cap, measured from the bottom of the veil.
3. Quarters—consisting of buttons or whole style cut into four approximately equal parts.
4. Slices or sliced—consisting of buttons or whole style of which not less than 50 percent are cut parallel to the longitudinal axis of the stem and 2 millimeters to 8 millimeters (0.08 inch to 0.32 inch) in thickness.
5. Random sliced—consisting of buttons or whole style sliced in a random manner.
6. Pieces and stems—consisting of pieces of caps and stems of irregular shapes and sizes.

3. Optional Ingredients

Optional ingredients are:

1. Salt.
2. Monosodium glutamate.
3. Disodium inosinate.
4. Disodium guanylate.
5. Hydrolyzed vegetable protein.
6. Autolyzed yeast extract.
7. Ascorbic acid (vitamin C) in a quantity not to exceed 132 milligrams for each 100 grams (37.5 milligrams for each ounce) of drained weight of mushrooms.
8. Organic acids (except no vinegar is permitted), only where the inside metal of the container is fully enamel-lined and in glass containers with fully enamel-lined caps. Ascorbic acid is an example.
9. Calcium disodium ethylenediaminetetraacetate ($CaNa_2$ EDTA) in a quantity not to exceed 200 parts per million for use to promote color retention.

4. Fill of Container

1. The fill of the mushroom ingredient and packing medium container is not less than 90 percent of the total capacity of the container.
2. The drained weight of the mushroom ingredient is not less than 56 percent of the water capacity of the container.

B. General Processing

Canned mushroom is considered a low acid canned food and there are stringent regulations govering its manufacture. This section provides some background information. A commercial processor must comply with basic federal requirements.

1. Types and Varieties

All cultivated mushrooms belong to the species *Agaricus campestris*. Various bracket fungi, puffballs, and other fungi have been used as food, but none has been grown commercially in this country. Mushrooms are classified as white, cream, or brown, depending on the color of the cap. Those grown for canning are almost exclusively of the white variety. In the East and Midwest the white variety is also the principal kind grown for fresh mushroom consumption, while in the West and in Canada a fair quantity of the cream variety is used. Of course, in the last two decades or so, many varieties of mushrooms are available from imports, e.g., countries in the Pacific Rim.

2. Growing Requirements

Since mushrooms, like all fungi, do not possess chlorophyll with which to manufacture carbohydrates from CO_2 absorbed from the air, they must obtain carbohydrates and other nutrients by growing on organic material containing these ingredients. Compost is the favorite growing medium in commercial mushroom houses.

Unlike plants possessing chlorophyll, mushrooms can grow in tare in darkness. A cool, moist atmosphere is most favorable for their development. Caves and abandoned mines have been used extensively for the growing of mushrooms.

Most mushrooms are grown in houses constructed especially for the purpose. Cinder blocks are a favorite construction material. The houses should be well insulated against cold in winter and heat in summer, and should have heating facilities for use in winter and means for keeping the air moist when the outside humidity becomes low.

Most houses produce two distinct crops a year. Each crop consists of several "breaks." After the mushrooms are harvested the north beds are covered with a new layer of "casing" soil and watered down for the next growth of mushrooms. After several such "breaks," the beds are cleaned out and filled with fresh compost. The entire cycle area may be completed in as little as three months or even less, up to as long as seven months, depending largely on temperature.

Higher temperatures usually mean a greater proportion of small land mushrooms.

Artificial air conditioning enables some growers to obtain three crops a year.

The months of October to May, inclusive, are the months of heaviest production. Harvesting is light during the warm weather months. A few growers maintain production during the summer by means of artificial air conditioning.

3. Harvesting and Delivery

Most canners grow the greater part of the mushrooms they use, purchasing the remainder of their requirements from other growers. Some canners grow for canning exclusively; others grow both for the fresh market and for processing.

Mushrooms are pulled from the beds with roots attached before the "veil" or membrane breaks open and exposes the "gills." Depending upon the contract between the packer and grower, the mushrooms may be delivered to the plant either with or without roots attached. In the latter case, the roots are cut from the mushrooms in the growing houses by the harvesters. In either case they are placed in baskets holding from three to as much as ten pounds for

delivery to the plant. Obviously, unlike small growers, large corporations use a more advanced system to handle this harvesting and delivery.

Freshly harvested mushrooms with the root portion attached will remain fresh longer than if the root portion has been removed. Mushrooms frequently grow in clusters, which may contain from three to five or more units. The units may vary in size from tiny to large in the same cluster that developed from one root.

Mushrooms deteriorate rapidly after picking, becoming discolored and wilted. They should be delivered to the cannery or processor promptly after picking. When mushrooms cannot be processed promptly after delivery to the cannery, they should be placed in a refrigerated room at a temperature of 36° to 37°F until needed. Refrigeration permits the supplies to be carried overnight to begin canning operations the following morning, or late weekend deliveries may be carried over to Monday morning.

Mushrooms must be handled carefully at all times to avoid bruising, which results in dark discolored areas.

C. Preparation and Canning

The following description of a canned mushroom operation is reasonably typical. The order, methods, and equipment may vary from plant to plant, especially a small versus a big one.

After delivery to the plant, mushrooms which cannot be processed immediately are placed in refrigerated storage until they can be processed.

The baskets of mushrooms are taken to the cutting line for removal of root stubs and stems. In most plants the cutting operation is performed mechanically, although some plants may still be cutting by hand. The stem may undergo one or two cuttings, depending on the style of mushrooms desired, whether whole or button.

In the case of whole mushrooms, only the root portion of the stem is removed by the mechanical cutter. If the style of buttons is desired, the cutters first remove the root portion of the stem which is carried away for waste. The rest of the stem is then removed by cutting immediately below the veil. This portion of the stem is used in the style of *stems and pieces*.

1. Washing, Trimming, and Sorting

After cutting, both the caps and stems are conveyed to a spray washer which removes the clinging bits of casing soil or other dirt. The mushrooms then pass over an inspection belt where seriously blemished mushrooms may be trimmed or sorted out. Misshapen, blemished, trimmed, and broken mushrooms are sorted out and placed with other mushroom material for the stems and pieces style.

Mushrooms with partially open veils may be placed with the pieces delivery material, or be added to the buttons or whole mushrooms intended for one of the sliced styles.

2. Sizing

Mushrooms intended for whole mushrooms or buttons are conveyed by means of water flume or other techniques to the sizers.

The mushrooms may be sized in a revolving drum sizer submerged in water. Rotary size graders which are not immersed in water may also be used. A submerged sizer minimizes bruising and gives the mushrooms an additional washing. The caps float upward from the sizer and each size is floated off into a separate holding tank.

The buttons may be separated into six different sizes. The larger sizes are generally sliced and the smaller sizes packed as buttons. Price lists of packers may quote sizes in terms of number of buttons per 8-ounce can as 20/40, 40/60, 60/80, or 100/120. The same size designations apply when the mushrooms are packed in smaller sized cans. For example, the 40/60 size would pack between 20 to 30 buttons in a 4-ounce can.

3. Slicing

Mushrooms intended for slicing are generally sliced prior to blanching; however, slicing may be performed after blanching. The mushrooms are passed through a mechanical slicer with circular knives which cut them into slices of predetermined thickness. A shaker screen removes the small pieces after slicing.

Three styles of sliced mushrooms are produced: 1) Sliced Whole; 2) Sliced Buttons; and 3) Random Sliced Whole.

"Sliced Whole" style is prepared by aligning the mushrooms prior to slicing so that the mushroom is sliced lengthwise from stem to apex.

"Sliced Buttons" style is prepared by positioning the mushrooms prior to slicing so that the mushroom is sliced parallel to the longitudinal axis.

"Random Sliced Whole" style is prepared by slicing the mushroom in any direction.

4. Blanching

The mushrooms are flumed from the holding tanks or slicer to the blancher. The purpose of blanching is to shrink the mushrooms in order to obtain the proper fill. Shrinkage is due to loss of mushroom juice. Mushrooms may shrink as much as 30 to 40 percent in size in blanching

Mushrooms may be blanched by immersing in water at a temperature of 200°F or more. The usual method, however, is to pass the mushrooms through a continuous steam blancher where they are exposed to live steam for a period of 5 to 8 minutes. In some cases the mushrooms may be filled into the cans and then blanched in the cans. Since iron tends to discolor mushrooms, the blancher should be made of stainless steel or other non-corrosive metal. During blanching, the color of some white varieties may change from near-white to a light tan or buff color.

5. Filling and Weighing

Whole or Button styles are generally filled into the can by hand while a semi-automatic filler is usually used for slices and piece pack. After filling, the cans are moved by belt conveyor in front of the weighers, who weigh the individual cans and adjust the fill so that the finished product will meet the required minimum drained weight.

As a safety factor, weighers generally overfill the cans, usually in accordance with a schedule of overfill weights which vary according to can size and style of pack.

Cans may vary considerably in weight, particularly in the smaller sizes. Deficient drained weights have been found to be due in some cases to the use of an unusually light can as tare by the weigher. The weigher should choose a tare can of average weight.

6. Brining and Cooking

After weighing, a salt tablet which may also contain ascorbic acid is added and cans are moved under taps of hot water, the temperature of which may range from 190° to 200°F. The taps are adjusted to fill cans to overflowing. A hot brine solution is sometimes used instead of the water and salt tablet. It is generally unnecessary to use an exhaust on the filled cans since a sufficiently high vacuum is obtained for most purposes by the addition of hot water.

After closing, the cans are processed in retorts under steam pressure. After processing, the cans may be cooled by water in the retort or a cooling tank. The cans should be cooled to 90° to 100°F, in order to check the cook but leave cans warm enough to dry off readily and prevent rusting.

7. Modern Technology and FDA Regulations

The information in this section on mushrooms must be interpreted in terms of the following premises:

1. Depending on the size and operation of a processor, the use of new equipment and machinery has eliminated a lot of problems that used to accompany the processing of mushrooms.
2. If used properly, food additives can contribute to the proper processing of mushrooms.
3. Always be concerned that mushrooms in a container are subject to the important regulations promulgated by the FDA for low acid canned and acidified foods.

V. CANNED ONIONS

A. PRODUCTION

1. Varieties

Yellow globe onions, a commercial term applied to several different varieties and strains of onions, are preferred by processors of onions. The more acceptable varieties are the Southport yellow globe and the yellow globe Danver. Western processors for the most part use only the yellow globe Danver.

2. Harvesting

The customary period at which to harvest onions for canning is in the fall when the tops of the onions have begun to turn greenish yellow. Usually the crop is dug by a hoe or an implement which turns the ground exposing the onions to the surface. After the onions are taken from the ground they are thrown in windrows or piles in the field, where they remain until the tops are completely dry. After curing sufficiently, the tops are cut or pulled off close to the bulbs. The onions are then placed in sacks or crates and are placed in storage or shipped.

B. PREPARATION AND CANNING

1. Receiving

Onions are usually delivered to the cannery in sacks or crates, and are placed in storage until used. Well-cured onions will keep for several months if stored in a well-ventilated place. In some areas it may be necessary to store them in an enclosed shed for protection against freezing. Onions will sprout within a few months if stored in a warm place. Badly spoiled onions become soft. The fresh fruit and vegetable inspection service inspects a large volume of onions for shippers and buyers at time of shipment or in receiving markets. Onions delivered to canners may or may not have been officially inspected.

Generally the onions are emptied from sacks onto a belt conveyor, carrying them to a sizer which eliminates over- and under-sized onions. From the sizer the onions are placed in buckets or pans on a "merry-go-round" sorting table where ends of the onions are trimmed and onions possessing rot, decay, or other serious defects are discarded.

2. Peeling

From the "merry-go-round" sorting table, the onions are conveyed to a carborundum peeler which tends to loosen the outer skin of the onion bulb. As the onions leave the carborundum peeler they pass through a continuous lye peeler containing a three to ten percent lye solution, depending upon the variety and character of the onions, which further loosens the outer scales of the onion bulb.

3. Washing

Following the peeling process, the onions pass through a rotary screen washer where adhering portions of the outer loosened scales are washed off under a strong spray of water. A closely controlled check is necessary to assure complete removal of the lye solution from the onion bulbs.

4. Pre-Removing of Blemishes and Defects

After washing, the onions are moved by conveyer belt to an inspection table where onions containing blemishes are removed.

5. Sizing

Normally onions are separated into three size classifications: tiny, small, and medium. Each processor has developed his own particular sizing operation. However, for the most part onions exceeding an inch and one-half in diameter and those with a diameter of less than 5/8 of an inch are not used for canning.

6. Final Removing of Blemishes and Defects

As the onions come from the sizer, they are conveyed onto a final inspection table where loosened scales, loose centers, onions possessing blemishes, or excessive discolored onions are removed.

7. Filling

The onions are then filled into cans or glass jars and a sufficient amount of hot brine is added for proper fill. After the cans or glass jars are filled they are quickly closed. In packing onions, the product is acidified to assure sterilization and to prevent spoilage. A pH of 4.5 is most desirable. The acid solution may be used as a dip, or may be added direct to the containers in the filling operations.

8. Defects

a. General
Immediately after ascertaining the uniformity of size and shape, segregate any defects in the following groups in accordance with the definitions outlined by the USDA.

b. Extraneous vegetable material
Remove from each container the pieces present and arrange all the extraneous material such as loose skins and dried onion tops. Extraneous vegetable material refers to harmless vegetable material and the material falling into this category is evaluated with respect to its effect on the overall requirements for the grade classification. No tolerance is provided for extraneous vegetable material of a different origin than the onion plants such as weeds and weed seeds. When such extraneous material is found the supervisor should be contacted.

c. Blemished onions

A blemished onion is one that is affected by surface or internal discoloration to such an extent that the appearance or eating quality is materially affected. The following are examples of onions scoreable as being blemished:

1. **Staining**. Onions that show brown or streaked discoloration from lying on the ground.
2. **Seed Stems**. Onions often throw up stalks on which to bear seeds during the later part of their growth. When harvested the seed stems are cut or broken off leaving thick tough stems extending through the centers of the onions. Onions possessing tough or woody seed stems should be considered blemished onions.
3. **Sunburn**. Sunburn is a green discoloration caused by exposure of the bulb to the sun and is normally present only on the outer scale of the onion bulb. This condition should not be confused with the natural greening of certain varieties of onions wherein the green color may be present in the outer scales of the onion bulbs.
4. **Sunscald**. This injury takes place at harvest time when the bulbs are exposed to heat and bright sunlight. The tissue of the exposed area of the bulb will scald and become soft and slippery. When temperatures are reduced and the onions are exposed to the air, the scalded tissue loses moisture by evaporation and leather-like areas are produced which may be bleached almost white.
5. **Freezing injury**. This injury is recognized by the watersoaked appearance, soft feel, and discoloration appearing in a portion of the scales or scales. The affected area normally has a translucent or paper-like appearance.
6. **Smudge**. Smudge is characterized by black blotches or aggregations of minute black or dark-green dots on the outer scales. These dots are often arranged in concentric rings. Generally the lesions are on the outer scales but they may be found on inner scales. On the fleshy scale of the bulb the fungus produces sunken yellowish spots.
7. **Surface Molds**. Surface molds may be black, blue, or gray in color and may be found growing either on the outer scales or frequently between the outer scales of the bulb.
8. **Rot**. Several types of rot may be present in onions, some of which are bacterial soft rot, blue mold rot, fusarium rot, and green mold rot. Normally onion bulbs affected by rot have a water-soaked appearance with various discolorations of outer or inner scales. Canned onions should not contain any units showing rot other than an accidental unit.

d. Seriously blemished onion

A seriously blemished onion is an onion that is affected by surface or internal discoloration to such an extent that the appearance or eating quality is seriously affected. Insect injury, wherever the insect bite extends through the scale of an onion bulb, is very noticeable and should be considered seriously blemished. Dark pathological areas which are unsightly are considered seriously blemished.

9. Mechanical Damage

Onion bulbs mechanically damaged by crushing, gouging, or trimming should be classified as damaged only when the condition materially affects the eating appearance or quality of the bulb.

10. Loose Scales or Pieces of Scales

Loose scales or pieces of scales are those not attached to an onion bulb. Do not aggregate pieces of scales to give the equivalent of one loose scale.

11. Detached Center

Detached center is when the center portion of the onion bulb has become detached. The onion bulb thus damaged is scored as a defect and the loose centers which have become detached are disregarded.

12. Well Trimmed

Determining whether onions are well trimmed is judged entirely on an appearance basis. In meeting the requirement for well trimmed the top and root of the onion should be neatly removed. Onion bulbs with off-slant cuts that materially affect the appearance of the unit are not considered well trimmed.

VI. CANNED PEAS AND DRY PEAS

Canned peas is the food prepared from fresh or frozen succulent seeds of the pea plant of the species *Pisum sativum* L. but excluding the subspecies *macrocarpum*. Only sweet wrinkled varieties, smooth-skin varieties, or hybrids thereof may be used. The product is packed with water or other suitable aqueous liquid medium to which may be added one or more of the other optional ingredients. Such food is sealed in a container and, before or after sealing, is so processed by heat as to prevent spoilage.

In addition to the optional packing media, the following safe and suitable optional ingredients may be used:

1. Salt.
2. Monosodium glutamate.
3. Disodium inosinate.

4. Disodium guanylate.
5. Hydrolyzed vegetable protein.
6. Autolyzed yeast extract.
7. One or any combination of two or more of the dry or liquid forms of sugar, invert sugar syrup, dextrose, glucose syrup, and fructose.
8. Spice.
9. Flavoring (except artificial).
10. Color additives.
11. Calcium salts, the total amount of which added to firm the peas should not result in more than 350 milligrams/kilogram (0.01 ounce/2.2 pounds) of calcium in the finished food.
12. Magnesium hydroxide, magnesium oxide, magnesium carbonate, or any mixture or combination of these in such quantity that the pH of the finished canned peas is not more than 8, as determined by the glass electrode method for the hydrogen ion concentration.
13. Seasonings and garnishes.
14. Pieces of green or red peppers or mixtures of both, either of which may be dried, or other vegetables not exceeding in total 15 percent of the drained weight of the finished food.
15. Lemon juice or concentrated lemon juice.
16. Mint leaves.
17. Butter or margarine in a quantity not less than 3 percent by weight of the finished food, or other vegetable or animal fats or oils in a quantity not less than 2.4 percent by weight of the finished foods.
18. When butter, margarine, or other vegetable or animal fats or oils are added, emulsifiers or stabilizers or both may be added, but no color, spice, or flavoring simulating the color or flavor imparted by butter or margarine may be used.

A. LABELING

The name of the food is "peas" and may include the designation "green." The term "early," "June," or "early June" should precede or follow the name in the case of smooth-skin peas or substantially smooth-skin peas, such as Alaska-type peas or hybrids having similar characteristics. Where the peas are of sweet green wrinkled varieties or hybrids having similar characteristics, the name may include the designation "sweet," "wrinkled," or any combination thereof. The term "petit pois" may be used in conjunction with the name of the food when an average of 80 percent or more of the peas will pass through a circular opening of a diameter of 7.1 millimeters (0.28 inch). If any color additive has been added, the name of the food should include the term "artificially colored."

The following should be included as part of the name or in close proximity to the name of the food:

1. A declaration of any flavoring that characterizes the food.
2. A declaration of any spice, seasoning, or garnishing that characterizes the product, e.g., "seasoned with green peppers," "seasoned with butter," "seasoned with _____ oil," the blank to be filled in with the common or usual name of the oil, "with added spice," or, in lieu of the word spice, the common or usual name of the spice.
3. The words "vacuum pack" or "vacuum packed" when the weight of the liquid in the container is not more than 20 percent of the net weight, and the container is closed under conditions creating a high vacuum in the container.

VII.   CANNED PUMPKIN AND CANNED SQUASH

A.   PRODUCTION

1.   Varieties

The names pumpkin and squash are popularly applied to the fruits of the species of the genus *Cucurbita*, namely *C. pepo*, *C. maxima*, and *C. moschata*. In general, the term pumpkin is applied to the late maturing or fall varieties of *C. pepo* and *C. maxima*. The principal varieties of *C. pepo* and *C. maxima* used for canning are the Connecticut field pumpkin, Dickinson pumpkin, Kentucky field pumpkin, the Boston marrow squash, and the Golden Delicious squash.

2.   Harvesting

Pumpkin and squash should not be harvested for canning until fully matured. Harvesting is usually done after the leaves begin to turn yellow. Mature pumpkin or squash have a hard rind which can be dented only with difficulty with the thumbnail. If picked too green the under portions of the pumpkin will have a greenish color and this may be carried over into the finished product. Pumpkin and squash are usually harvested starting approximately September 15 in the Midwest and Northeast States, and October 1 in the Pacific Northwest.

B.   PREPARATION AND CANNING

1.   Receiving

Pumpkin and squash are usually delivered as harvested and stored at the cannery until used. Well-matured pumpkin or squash will keep for several weeks if stored in a well-ventilated place. In some areas it may be necessary to store them in an enclosed shed for protection against freezing. Normally no inspection is made of pumpkin or squash received by the plants.

2. Washing

Whole pumpkins or squashes are fed by hand or conveyed into a combined tank and spray washer, consisting of a rotary drum partially submerged in a tank of water. The combined soaking and rotary motion loosens adhering dirt which is removed by strong sprays of water. Grit sometimes becomes embedded in the rind, necessitating thorough washing.

3. Trimming

From the washer the pumpkins or squash pass to the inspection belt where stems are knocked off by hand and blossom ends, scar tissue rot, and other blemishes are trimmed out.

4. Cutting

In some canneries the trimmers also cut the pumpkin or squash into halves or quarters with long knives and scrape out the seeds and stringy pulp by hand. In many plants mechanical cutters are used into which the whole units (or halves) are fed by a conveyor cutting the units in pieces. Strong sprays of water help knock out most of the seeds, which drop from the cutter through small perforations.

Where the units are cut and the seeds and pulp removed in separate operations, the cut pieces pass to a revolving drum where they are tumbled under strong sprays of water which remove most of the seeds and pulp.

Where seeds are to be saved for planting, they may undergo further washing to separate them from the pulp.

Cut pieces are in some cases passed over an inspection belt where imperfect pieces and internal rot, not visible from the outside, may be picked out by hand.

5. Wilting (Steaming)

The cut pieces are cooked in live steam until they are tender all the way through. The length of time necessary depends upon the size of the pieces and the nature of the equipment in which the steaming is done. The following are examples in which the wilting or steaming may be accomplished:

1. In metal baskets in retorts, either under pressure or at atmospheric pressure.
2. In continuous metal box wilters. The pieces are carried through on a continuous belt and are subjected to live steam.
3. In wilting towers. These are tall cylindrical silo-like structures into which the cut pieces are fed continuously at the top by conveyor and removed at the bottom by a screw conveyor. The pumpkin or squash is continuously treated with live steam as it passes through the wilting tower.

6. Pressing

The wilted pumpkin or squash is soggy with liquid which is a mixture of condensed steam and pumpkin or squash juice. The product is treated to remove excess liquid in order to attain the desired consistency in the canned product. This is done by putting the wilted pumpkin or squash through an adjustable press. In certain plants the pressing and wilting are done simultaneously by the use of augers inside of cone-shaped perforated screens.

7. Pulping

The pressed pumpkin or squash goes to the pulper or cyclone to remove hard particles, pieces of stems, seeds, fiber, and other extraneous material. In some cases the product is first put through a coarse, heavy cyclone to remove the bulk of extraneous material and an ordinary cyclone to reduce the size of the particles. For the latter a screen with perforations 1/8 inch in diameter is commonly used.

Some processors use what is commercially known as a Fitz mill. This machine, constructed with hammer and knife edges on opposite sides, reduces or pulps pumpkin by a combined impact mashing action.

8. Finishing

From the pulper the product goes to the finisher which removes the finer bits of seeds or other material and gives the final product the desired physical character. There is a difference of opinion among canners as to the most desirable size of the particles of pumpkin in the finished product. Some prefer a very smooth product which can be obtained by using a very fine finisher; others feel that the canned pumpkin or squash should have a noticeable amount of grainy structure and, therefore, use a finisher that is relatively coarse.

9. Preheating

The filling temperature of the prepared pumpkin or squash is an important part of processing. Heat penetration of the product is very slow because of its physical character, and the temperature at the beginning of the process is correspondingly important. By use of the preheater, it is possible to fill all of the cans at a uniform high temperature.

The preheater is usually a straight piece of pipe surrounded by a larger pipe. The product is pumped through the smaller internal pipe and the space between the two pipes is filled with steam, the temperature of which can be controlled. The rate of flow of the product through the pipe and the temperature of the steam determines the temperature at which it goes to the filler. The preheater normally raises the temperature of the product to 190–200°F. To prevent scorching the preheater is usually constructed so that it will shut off automatically if, for any reason, the flow through the inside pipe is stopped.

10. Filling

The hot pumpkin or squash goes directly to the filler and into cans. If the thickness of the product at this point is too great, the product may not be handled properly by the filler. If, for any reason, the filler or closing machine is forced to stop for any length of time all of the pumpkin material should be put back with the material going through the preheater. Pumpkin or squash has a corrosive action on tin-plate and should be packed in enamel-lined cans. It is important to fill the cans completely so that the product is in contact with the entire inner surface of the cover when the can is sealed. Even a small headspace may result in some discoloration after processing.

11. Processing

The filled cans should be processed promptly. High closing temperature may be offset by undue delay between closing and starting of the process time. A partially filled crate of cans should be sent at once to the retort rather than waiting any length of time for additional cans.

12. Cooling

Prompt and adequate cooling is especially important since canned pumpkin has a slow heating and cooling rate. Failure to cool the product promptly may result in overcooking and loss of color and may be directly responsible for spoilage by thermophilic bacteria. Cooling is usually accomplished by moving the metal retort baskets through a long tank of water by means of an overhead endless chain. The speed of the chain is regulated according to the degree of cooling desired. Cold water is kept continuously flowing into the tank to hold down the temperature. Immediately after cooking, while the cans are distended by heat and internal pressure, minute openings in the double seams may be present. Cooling water contaminated with bacteria may be drawn through seam openings as pressure in the cans is replaced by vacuum; therefore, water in the cooling tank should be kept clean. Some canners cool by means of a water spray in order to reduce the contamination hazard.

VIII. CANNED VEGETABLES

Additional production descriptions are provided for the following vegetables: artichokes, asparagus, bean sprouts, shelled beans, lima or butter beans, beets, beet greens, broccoli, Brussels sprouts, cabbage, carrots, cauliflower, celery, collards, dandelion greens, kale, mustard greens, leaves of the mustard plant, okra, onions, parsnips, peas, black-eye or black-eyed peas, field peas, green sweet peppers, red sweet peppers, pimientos (pimentos), potatoes, rutabagas, salsify, spinach, potatoes, sweet, Swiss chard, truffles, turnip greens, turnips.

Table 22.1 provides a basic description of each canned vegetable. Column I describes the canned vegetable. The vegetable ingredient in each such canned vegetable is obtained by proper preparation from the succulent vegetable described in column II of the table. If two or more forms of such ingredient are designated in column III of the table, the vegetable in each the form is an optional ingredient. To the vegetable additional ingredients (required or permitted) are added, and the food is sealed in a container and so processed by heat as to prevent spoilage.

Water is added to the vegetable ingredient may be added except that pimientos may be canned with or without added water, and sweet potatoes in mashed form are canned without added water. Asparagus may be canned with added water, asparagus juice, or a mixture of both. Asparagus juice is the clear, unfermented liquid expressed from the washed and heated sprouts or parts of sprouts of the asparagus plant, and mixtures of asparagus juice and water are considered to be water when such mixtures are used as a packing medium for canned asparagus. In the case of artichokes, a vinegar or any safe and suitable organic acid, which either is not a food additive as defined or if it is a food additive as so defined, is used in conformity with regulations established, is added in such quantity as to reduce the pH of the finished canned vegetable to 4.5 or below.

The following optional ingredients may be added in the case of the vegetables in Table 22.1.

An edible vegetable oil, in the case of artichokes and pimientos, and snaps, in the case of shelled beans, black-eyed peas, and field peas.

In the case of all vegetables (except canned mashed sweet potatoes), one or more of the following optional seasoning ingredients may be added in a quantity sufficient to season the food.

1. Refined sugar (sucrose).
2. Refined corn sugar (dextrose).
3. Corn syrup, glucose syrup.
4. Dried corn syrup, dried glucose syrup.
5. Spice.
6. A vinegar.
7. Green peppers or red peppers, which may be dried.
8. Mint leaves.
9. Onions, which may be dried.
10. Garlic, which may be dried.
11. Horseradish.
12. Lemon juice or concentrated lemon juice.
13. Butter or margarine in a quantity not less than 3 percent by weight of the finished food. When butter or margarine is added, safe and suitable emulsifiers or stabilizers, or both, may be added. When butter or margarine is added, no spice or flavoring simulating the color or flavor imparted by butter or margarine is used.

TABLE 22.1
Canned Vegetables, Source, and Optional Forms of Vegetable Ingredients

I—Name or Synonym of Canned Vegetable	II—Source	III—Optional Forms of Vegetable Ingredient
Artichokes	Flower buds of the artichoke plant	Whole; half or halves or halved; whole hearts; halved hearts; quartered hearts
Asparagus	Edible portions of sprouts of the asparagus plant, as follows:	
	3 and 3/4 in. or more of upper end;	Stalks or spears
	3 and 3/4 in. or more of peeled upper end	Peeled stalks or peeled spears
	Not less than 2 and 3/4 in. but less than 3 and 3/4 in. of upper end	Tips
	Less than 2 and 3/4 in. of upper end	Points
	Sprouts cut in pieces	Cut stalks or cut spears
	Sprouts from which the tip ha been removed, cut in pieces	Bottom cuts or cuts—tips removed
Bean sprouts	Sprouts of the Mung bean	
Shelled beans	Seed shelled from green or wax bean pods, with or without snaps (pieces of immature unshelled pods)	
Lima beans or butter beans	Seed shelled from the pods of the lima bean plant	
Beets	Root of the beet plant	Whole; slices or sliced; quarters or quartered; dice or diced; cut; shoestring or French style or julienne
Beet greens	Leaves, or leaves and immature root, of the beet plant	
Broccoli	Heads of the broccoli plant	
Brussels sprouts	Sprouts of the Brussels sprouts plant	
Cabbage	Cut pieces of the heads of the cabbage plant	
Carrots	Root of the carrot plant	Do
Cauliflower	Cut pieces of the head of the cauliflower plant	
Celery	Stalks of the celery plant	Cut; hearts
Collards	Leaves of the collard plant	
Dandelion greens	Leaves of the dandelion plant	
Kale	Leaves of the kale plant	
Mustard greens	Leave of the mustard plant	
Okra	Pods of the okra plant	Whole; cut
Onions	Bulb of the onion plant	Do
Parsnips	Root of the parsnip plant	Whole; quarters or quartered; slices or sliced; cut; shoestring or French style or julienne
Black-eye peas or black-eyed peas	Seed shelled from pods of the black-eye pea plant, with or without snaps (pieces of immature unshelled pods)	
Field peas	Seed shelled from pods of the field pea plant (other than the black-eye pea plant), with or without snaps (pieces of immature unshelled pods)	
Green sweet peppers	Green pods of the sweet pepper plant	Whole; halves or halved; pieces; dice or diced; strips; chopped
Red sweet peppers	Red-ripe pods of the sweet pepper plant	Do
Pimientos or pimentos	Red-ripe pods of the pimiento, pimento, pepper plant	Whole; halves or halved; pieces; dice or diced; slices or sliced; chopped
Potatoes	Tuber of the potato plant	Whole; slices or sliced; dice or diced; pieces; shoestring or French style or julienne; French fry cut

(Continued)

TABLE 22.1

(*Continued*)

I—Name or synonym of Canned Vegetable	II—Source	III—Optional Forms of Vegetable Ingredient
Rutabagas	Root of the rutabaga plant	Whole; quarters or quartered; slices or sliced; dice or diced; cut
Salsify	Root of the salsify plant	
Spinach	Leaves of the spinach plant	Whole leaf; cut leaf or sliced; chopped
Sweet potatoes	Tuber of the sweet potato plant	Whole; mashed; pieces or cuts or cut (longitudinally cut halves may be named on labels as halves or halved in lieu of pieces or cuts or cut)
Swiss chard	Leaves of the Swiss chard plant	
Truffles	Fruit of the truffle	
Turnip greens	Leaves of the turnip plant	
Turnips	Root of the turnip plant	Whole; quarters or quartered; slices or sliced; dice or diced; cut

In the case of all vegetables, the following optional ingredients may be added:

1. Salt.
2. Monosodium glutamate.
3. Disodium inosinate.
4. Disodium guanylate.
5. Hydrolyzed vegetable protein.
6. Autolyzed yeast extract.

In the case of all vegetables flavoring (except artificial) may be added.

In the case of bean sprouts, lima beans, carrots, green sweet peppers, red sweet peppers, and potatoes, any safe and suitable calcium salts may be added as a firming agent.

In the case of canned artichokes packed in glass containers, ascorbic acid may be added in a quantity not to exceed 32 milligrams per 100 grams of the finished food.

In the case of canned asparagus, ascorbic acid, erythorbic acid, or the sodium salts of ascorbic acid or erythorbic acid may be added in an amount necessary to preserve color in the "white" and "green-tipped and white" color types.

In the case of canned asparagus packed in glass containers, stannous chloride may be added in a quantity not to exceed 15 parts per million calculated as tin (Sn), except that in the case of asparagus packed in glass containers with lids lined with an inert material, the quantity of stannous chloride added may exceed 15 parts per million but not 20 parts per million calculated as tin (Sn).

In the case of canned black-eyed peas, disodium EDTA may be added in a quantity not to exceed 145 parts per million.

In the case of potatoes, calcium disodium EDTA may be added in a quantity not to exceed 110 parts per million.

A vinegar or any safe and suitable organic acid for all vegetables (except artichokes, in which the quantity of such optional ingredient is prescribed by the introductory text) in a quantity which, together with the amount of any lemon juice or concentrated lemon juice that may be added, is not more than sufficient to permit effective processing by heat without discoloration or other impairment of the article.

The name of each canned vegetable is designated in column I of the table.

When two or more forms of the vegetable are specified in column III of the table, the label should bear the specified word or words, showing the form of the vegetable ingredient present, except that in the case of canned spinach, if the whole leaf is the optional form used, the word "spinach" unmodified may be used in lieu of the words "whole leaf spinach."

If the optional ingredient specified is present, the label should bear the statement "_____ oil added" or "With added _____ oil," the blank being filled in with the common or usual name of the oil.

If asparagus juice is used as a packing medium in canned asparagus, the label should bear the statement "Packed in asparagus juice."

If the optional ingredient specified is present, the label should bear the statement "With snaps."

The name of the food should include a declaration of any flavoring that characterizes the product as specified, and a declaration of any spice or seasoning that characterizes the product; for example, "with added spice," "seasoned with red peppers," "seasoned with butter."

Wherever the name of the vegetable appears on the label so conspicuously as to be easily seen under customary conditions of purchase, the words and statements specified should immediately and conspicuously precede or follow such name, without intervening written, printed, or graphic matter, except that the varietal name of the vegetable may so intervene.

IX. CANNED CHILI SAUCE

Chili sauce is the product prepared from mature, clean, sound, tomatoes of the red or reddish varieties which are peeled and chopped or crushed, or all (or a portion) of the tomatoes may be chopped, crushed, or macerated and the peelings screened out in a manner so that at least a substantial portion of the seed remains in the product, to which is added salt, spices, vinegar, nutritive sweetening ingredients, and to which may be added vegetable flavoring ingredients such as chopped onion, chopped green or red pepper, chopped green tomatoes, chopped celery, and sweet pickle relish in such quantities as will not materially alter the appearance of the product with respect to the predominance of the tomato ingredient, and any other ingredients permissible under FDA regulations and standards. The chili sauce is processed in accordance with good commercial practice; is packed in hermetically sealed containers; and is sufficiently processed by heat, before or after sealing, to assure preservation of the product. The refractive index of the filtrate of the chili sauce at 20°C is not less than 1.3784.

A. INGREDIENTS

1. Tomato Pulp

The primary ingredient in chili sauce is red tomatoes. The tomatoes may be hand peeled and broken up by stirring or the tomatoes may be prepared by any one of a number of machines especially designed for the purpose, or there may be a combination of whole peeled tomatoes and more or less macerated tomatoes from which the peelings have been removed by screening. These machines are usually similar to the tomato pulper or finisher, except that the holes through which the tomato material is forced are usually quite large. They are not nearly as efficient as the usual finishing machine at removing the peeling and defects from the tomatoes. For economic reasons some manufacturers have resorted to using a large amount of cyclone pulp and a small amount of hand-peeled or mechanically peeled tomatoes or tomatoes which have been forced through small openings. In general the more of the larger pieces of tomato material present, the better the pulp is for chili sauce.

2. Sugar

The use of any of the nutritive sweetening ingredients is permitted in this product. The usual sweetener is sugar (sucrose). The solids of chili sauce are usually brought up higher by the use of sugar and lowered by concentrating the tomatoes than is usual with catsup. Some manufacturers use as much as 1/2 more sugar than they do with catsup yet finish at about the same point with respect to soluble solids.

3. Spices, Salt, and Acids

Most of the same spices are used in chili sauce as in the manufacture of catsup, except that garlic is seldom used in chili sauce. The proportions of the various spice ingredients are not standardized between manufacturers. Salt and vinegar are used in about the same proportions as with catsup.

4. Other Ingredients

The other ingredients, such as onion, bell peppers, celery, and sweet pickle relish, contribute to the flavor of the product and also provide body to the finished product; that is, they provide part of the consistency and most of the chewiness of the finished chili sauce. The ingredients used and the proportions of the ingredients used vary widely from packer to packer; therefore, quite a variety of flavors can be expected in chili sauces. The onion ingredient is often dehydrated onion flakes. Red or green diced dehydrated peppers are often used.

5. Manufacture

Most important in the manufacture of chili sauce is the preparation of the tomato pulp.

6. Tomato Pulp

Where peeled tomatoes are used for a part or all of the tomato pulp they are usually taken from the regular canning lines after at least a partial preparation by mechanical or hand peeling, trimming, and coring. There is usually some selection of the raw tomatoes that are to be run through chili sauce preparation machines. Some packers divert very ripe tomatoes that need no trimming to the chili sauce lines while others box-sort or load-sort the tomatoes and trim them on the conveyer belts. This trimming removes defective parts and stems that would become defects in the sauce. The trimmers may or may not remove most of the green portions of the tomatoes depending on the machinery used and the manufacturer's desires with respect to the appearance of chili sauce. If green pepper, pickle relish, or green tomatoes are added green shouldered tomatoes are not usually trimmed. Manufacture consists of combining the ingredients in a manner so that the finished chili sauce will have the desired qualities of color, consistency, finish, absence of defects, and flavor. The tomato pulp, whether from broken peeled tomatoes or from special chili sauce machines, or cyclone juice to which some tomato material containing tomato seed is added, is run to kettles, usually steam jacketed, and reduced by boiling to about one-half the original volume. Concentration in vacuum pans is particularly satisfactory for this operation.

7. Adding Other Ingredients

Onion is often added at the beginning of the boil. The other ingredients may be added at any time but the sugar is usually added late to prevent caramelization. Spices, if in the form of oils or cream of spice, are usually added late to prevent evaporation of the flavor ingredients.

8. The Finishing Point

Because of the nature of the ingredients there is no accurate means of determining a correct finishing point which will apply to all formulae. The first batches when starting, or after any major change in formula, are dropped when they appear to be about correct. As with tomato catsup the consistency of the hot sauce may be measured by any suitable device and the refractive index may be taken. Succeeding batches can then be adjusted by these instruments by increasing or decreasing the boiling or by adjusting the amounts of pulp and sugar to the desired result.

9. Processing

Chili sauce is usually closed at about 180°, at which temperature further processing is usually not necessary. Foaming may occur at higher temperatures and an additional process is usually given if the sauce is closed at lower temperatures.

X. CANNED TOMATOES

Canned tomatoes is the food prepared from mature tomatoes conforming to the characteristics of the fruit *Lycopersicum esculentum* P. Mill, of red or reddish varieties. The tomatoes may or may not be peeled, but should have had the stems and calicies removed and should have been cored, except where the internal core is insignificant to texture and appearance.

Canned tomatoes may contain one or more of the safe and suitable optional ingredients, be packed without any added liquid or in one of the optional packing media, and be prepared in one of the styles. Such food is sealed in a container and before or after sealing is so processed by heat as to prevent spoilage.

One or more of the following safe and suitable ingredients may be used:

1. Calcium salts in a quantity reasonably necessary to firm the tomatoes, but the amount of calcium in the finished canned tomatoes is not more than 0.045 percent of the weight, except that when the tomatoes are prepared in one of the styles specified the amount of calcium is not more than 0.08 percent of the weight of the food.
2. Organic acids for the purpose of acidification.
3. Dry nutritive carbohydrate sweeteners whenever any organic acid is used, in a quantity reasonably necessary to compensate for the tartness resulting from such added acid.

4. Salt.
5. Spices, spice oils.
6. Flavoring and seasoning.
7. Vegetable ingredients such as onion, peppers, and celery, that may be fresh or preserved by physical means, in a quantity not more than 10 percent by weight of the finished food.

A. PACKING MEDIA

Packing media includes:

1. The liquid draining from the tomatoes during or after peeling or coring.
2. The liquid strained from the residue from preparing tomatoes for canning consisting of peels and cores with or without tomatoes or pieces thereof.
3. The liquid strained from mature tomatoes (tomato juice).
4. Tomato paste, or tomato puree, or tomato pulp complying with the compositional requirements.

1. Styles

Styles may be:

(a) Whole.
(b) Diced.
(c) Sliced.
(d) Wedges.

2. Name of the Food

The name of the food is "tomatoes," except that when the tomatoes are not peeled the name is "unpeeled tomatoes."

The following should be included as part of the name or in close proximity to the name of the food.

(a) A declaration of any flavoring that characterizes the product as specified.
(b) A declaration of any added spice, seasoning, or vegetable ingredient that characterizes the product, (e.g., "with added _____" or, "with _____" the blank to be filled in with the word(s) "spice(s)," "seasoning(s)," or the name(s) of the vegetable(s) used or in lieu of the word(s) "spice(s)" or "seasoning (s)" the common or usual name(s) of the spice(s) or seasoning(s) used) except that no declaration of the presence of onion, peppers, and celery is required for stewed tomatoes.
(c) The word "stewed" if the tomatoes contain characterizing amounts of at least the three optional vegetables listed.

(d) The styles: "Diced," "sliced," or "wedges" as appropriate.

(e) The name of the packing medium: "tomato paste," "tomato puree," or "tomato pulp" or "strained residual tomato material from preparation for canning." The name of the packing medium should be preceded by the word "with."

(f) The following may be included as part of the name or in close proximity to the name:

The word "whole" if the tomato ingredient is whole or almost whole, and the weight of such ingredient is not less than 80 percent of the drained weight of the finished food as determined in accordance with the method prescribed.

The words "solid pack" when none of the optional packing media are used.

The words "in tomato juice" if the packing medium is used.

The name of each ingredient used should be declared on the label as required.

The standard of quality for canned tomatoes is as follows:

The drained weight is not less than 50 percent of the weight of water required to fill the container

The strength and redness of color is not less than that of the blended color of any combination of the color discs.

Blemishes per kilogram (2.2 pounds) of the finished food cover an area of not more than 3.5 cm (0.54 square inch) which is equivalent to 1.6 cm (0.25 square inch) per pound based on an average of all containers examined.

If the quality of canned tomatoes falls below standard with respect to only one of the factors of quality specified, there may be substituted for the second line of such general statement of substandard quality ("Good Food—Not High Grade") a new line to read as follows:

"Poor color" or
"Excessive peel" or
"Excessive blemishes."

3. Fill of Container

The standard of fill of container for canned tomatoes is a fill of not less than 90 percent of the total capacity of the container.

If canned tomatoes fall below the standard of fill of container, the label should bear the general statement of substandard fill

XI. CANNED TOMATO JUICE

Tomato juice is the food intended for direct consumption, obtained from the unfermented liquid extracted from mature tomatoes of the red or reddish varieties of *Lycopersicum esculentum* P. Mill, with or without scalding followed by draining. In the extraction of such liquid, heat may be applied by any method that does not add water thereto.

Such juice is strained free from peel, seeds, and other coarse or hard substances, but contains finely divided insoluble solids from the flesh of the tomato in accordance with current good manufacturing practice. Such juice may be homogenized, may be seasoned with salt, and may be acidified with any safe and suitable organic acid. The juice may have been concentrated and later reconstituted with water and/or tomato juice to a tomato soluble solids content of not less than 5.0 percent by weight.

The food is preserved by heat sterilization (canning), refrigeration, or freezing. When sealed in a container to be held at ambient temperatures, it is so processed by heat, before or after sealing, as to prevent spoilage.
The name of the food is:

1. "Tomato juice" if it is prepared from unconcentrated undiluted liquid extracted from mature tomatoes of reddish varieties.

2. "Tomato juice from concentrate" if the finished juice has been prepared from concentrated tomato juice as specified or if the finished juice is a mixture of tomato juice and tomato juice from concentrate.

Each of the ingredients used in the food should be declared on the label as required.

The standard of quality for tomato juice is as follows:

The strength and redness of color complies with specific requirement.

Not more than two defects for peel and blemishes, either singly or in combination, in addition to three defects for seeds or pieces of seeds, defined as follows, per 500 milliliters (16.9 fluid ounces):

(a) Pieces of peel 3.2 millimeters (0.125 inch) or greater in length.

(b) Blemishes such as dark brown or black particles (specks) greater than 1.6 millimeters (0.0625 inch) in length.

(c) Seeds or pieces of seeds 3.2 millimeters (0.125 inch) or greater in length.

If the quality of the tomato juice falls below the standard, the label should bear the general statement of substandard quality.

In lieu of such general statement of substandard quality when the quality of the tomato juice falls below the standard in one or more respects, the label may bear the alternative statement, "Below Standard in Quality _____," the blank to be filled in with the words:

(i) "Poor color"
(ii) "Excessive pieces of peel"
(iii) "Excessive blemishes."
(iv) "Excessive seeds" or "excessive pieces of seed."

The standard of fill of container for tomato juice is not less than 90 percent of the total capacity, except when the food is frozen.

If the tomato juice falls below the standard of fill, the label should bear the general statement of substandard fill.

XII. CANNED TOMATO CONCENTRATES, "TOMATO PUREE," "TOMATO PULP," OR "TOMATO PASTE"

Tomato concentrates are the class of foods each of which is prepared by concentrating one or any combination of two or more of the following optional tomato ingredients:

1. The liquid obtained from mature tomatoes of the red or reddish varieties (Lycopersicum esculentum P. Mill).
2. The liquid obtained from the residue from preparing such tomatoes for canning, consisting of peelings and cores with or without such tomatoes or pieces thereof.
3. The liquid obtained from the residue from partial extraction of juice from such tomatoes.

Such liquid is obtained by so straining the tomatoes, with or without heating, as to exclude skins (peel), seeds, and other coarse or hard substances in accordance with good manufacturing practice. Prior to straining, food-grade hydrochloric acid may be added to the tomato material in an amount to obtain a pH no lower than 2.0. Such acid is then neutralized with food-grade sodium hydroxide so that the treated tomato material is restored to a pH of 4.2 ± 0.2. Water may be added to adjust the final composition. The food contains not less than 8.0 percent tomato soluble solids as specified.

The food is preserved by heat sterilization (canning), refrigeration, or freezing. When sealed in a container to be held at ambient temperatures, it is so processed by heat, before or after sealing, as to prevent spoilage.

One or any combination of two or more of the following safe and suitable ingredients may be used in the foods:

1. Salt (sodium chloride formed during acid neutralization should be considered added salt).
2. Lemon juice, concentrated lemon juice, or organic acids.
3. Sodium bicarbonate.
4. Water.
5. Spices.
6. Flavoring.

The name of the food is:

1. "Tomato puree" or "tomato pulp" if the food contains not less than 8.0 percent but less than 24.0 percent tomato soluble solids.
2. "Tomato paste" if the food contains not less than 24.0 percent tomato soluble solids.
3. The name "tomato concentrate" may be used in lieu of the name "tomato puree," "tomato pulp," or "tomato paste" whenever the concentrate complies with the requirements of such foods, except that the label should bear the statement "for re-manufacturing purposes only" when the concentrate is packaged in No. 10 containers (3.1 kilograms or 109 avoirdupois ounces total water capacity) or containers that are smaller in size.
4. "Concentrated tomato juice" if the food is prepared from the optional tomato ingredient described and is of such concentration that upon diluting the food according to label directions as required, the diluted article will contain not less than 5.0 percent by weight tomato soluble solids.

The following should be included as part of the name or in close proximity to the name of the food:

1. The statement "Made from" or "Made in part from," as the case may be, "residual tomato material from canning" if the optional tomato ingredient is present.
2. The statement "Made from" or "Made in part from," as the case may be, "residual tomato material from partial extraction of juice" if the optional tomato ingredient present.
3. A declaration of any flavoring that characterizes the product and a declaration of any spice that characterizes the product, e.g., "Seasoned with _____," the blank to be filled in with the words "added spice" or, in lieu of the word "spice," the common name of the spice.

The label of concentrated tomato juice should bear adequate directions for dilution to result in a diluted article containing not less than 5.0 percent by weight tomato soluble solids, except that alternative methods may be used to convey adequate dilution directions for containers that are larger than No. 10 containers (3.1 kilograms or 109 avoirdupois ounces total water capacity).

A. Fill of Container

The standard of fill of container for tomato concentrate, as determined by the general method for fill of container, is not less than 90 percent of the total capacity, except when the food is frozen.

XIII. TOMATO CATSUP

Catsup, ketchup, or catchup is the food prepared from one or any combination of two or more of the following optional tomato ingredients:

1. Tomato concentrate as described.
2. Lemon juice, concentrated lemon juice, or safe and suitable organic acids may be used in quantities no greater than necessary to adjust the pH.

3. The liquid derived from mature tomatoes of the red or reddish varieties *Lycopersicum esculentum* P. Mill.

4. The liquid obtained from the residue from preparing such tomatoes for canning, consisting of peelings and cores with or without such tomatoes or pieces thereof.

5. The liquid obtained from the residue from partial extraction of juice from such tomatoes. Such liquid is strained so as to exclude skins, seeds, and other coarse or hard substances in accordance with current good manufacturing practice. Prior to straining, food-grade hydrochloric acid may be added to the tomato material in an amount to obtain a pH no lower than 2.0. Such acid is then neutralized with food-grade sodium hydroxide so that the treated tomato material is restored to a pH of 4.2 ± 0.2.

The final composition of the food may be adjusted by concentration and/or by the addition of water. The food may contain salt (sodium chloride formed during acid neutralization should be considered added salt) and is seasoned with optional ingredients (see above).

The food is preserved by heat sterilization (canning), refrigeration, or freezing. When sealed in a container to be held at ambient temperatures, it is so processed by heat, before or after sealing, as to prevent spoilage.

One or any combination of two or more of the following ingredients in each category is added to the tomato ingredients:

1. Vinegars.
2. Nutritive carbohydrate sweeteners.
3. Spices, flavoring, onions, or garlic.

4. Labeling.
5. The name of the food is "Catsup," "Ketchup," or "Catchup."

The following should be included as part of the name or in close proximity to the name of the food:

1. The statement "Made from" or "Made in part from," as the case may be, "residual tomato material from canning" if the optional tomato ingredient or tomato concentrate containing the ingredient is present.

2. The statement "Made from" or "Made in part from," as the case may be, "residual tomato material from partial extraction of juice" if the optional tomato ingredient or tomato concentrate containing the ingredient is present.

The name "tomato concentrate" may be used in lieu of the names "tomato puree," "tomato pulp," or "tomato paste" and when tomato concentrates are used.

A. FILL OF CONTAINER

The standard of fill of container for catsup is not less than 90 percent of the total capacity except when the food is frozen, or when the food is packaged in individual serving-size packages containing 56.7 grams (2 ounces) or less.

ACKNOWLEDGMENT

The information in this chapter is based on *Food Safety Manual*, published and copyrighted by Science Technology System, West Sacramento, California, 2004. Used with permission.

23 Frozen Vegetables: Product Descriptions

Peggy Stanfield
Dietetic Resources

CONTENTS

I. INTRODUCTION

This book is not the proper forum to discuss the manufacture of every processed vegetable available in the market. However, regulatory agencies such the Department of Agriculture (USDA) and the Food and Drug Administration (FDA) have issued some minimal criteria for each processed vegetable such as what they are, what types and styles are available and so on. The information in this chapter describes each available frozen vegetable product and has been modified from the product grades (USDA) and product standards (FDA). Product standards and product grades are established to achieve two objectives: assure product safety and minimize economic fraud.

The information provided here has one major objective: to remind a commercial processor what each frozen vegetable is and the applicable criteria for particular products.

II. FROZEN ASPARAGUS

Frozen asparagus consists of sound and succulent fresh shoots of the asparagus plant (*Asparagus officianalis*). The product is prepared by sorting, trimming, washing, and blanching as necessary to assure a clean and wholesome product. It is then frozen and stored at temperatures necessary for preservation.

1. TYPES

1. Green or all-green consists of units of frozen asparagus which are typically green, light-green, or purplish-green in color.
2. Green-white consists of frozen asparagus spears and tips which have typical green, light-green, or purplish-green color to some extent but which are white in the lower portions of stalk.

2. STYLES

Spears or stalks style consists of units composed of the head and adjoining portion of the shoot that are 3 inches or more in length. Tips style consists of units composed of the head and adjoining portion of the shoot that are less than 3 inches in length. Center cuts or cuts style consists of portions of shoots (with or without head material) that are cut transversely into units not less than one-half inch in length and that fail to meet the definition for cut spears or cuts and tips style.

Cut spears or cuts and tips style consists of the head and portions of the shoot cut transversely into units 2 inches or less but not less than one-half inch in length. To be considered this style head material should be present in these amounts for the respective lengths of cuts:

1. 1-1/4 inches or less. Not less than 18 percent (average), by count, of all cuts are head material.

2. Longer than 1-1/4 inches. Not less than 25 percent (average), by count, of all cuts are head material.

III. FROZEN LIMA BEANS

Frozen lima beans are the frozen product prepared from the clean, sound, succulent seed of the lima bean plant without soaking, by shelling, washing, blanching, and properly draining. They are then frozen in accordance with good commercial practice and maintained at temperatures necessary for the preservation of the product.

1. TYPES

1. Thin-seeded such as Henderson, Bush, and Thorogreen varieties.
2. Thick-seeded Baby Potato such as Baby Potato, Baby Fordhook, and Evergreen. Thick-seeded, such as Fordhook variety.

IV. FROZEN BEANS, SPECKLED BUTTER (LIMA)

Frozen speckled butter (lima) beans are the frozen product prepared from the clean, sound, freshly-vined (but not seed-dry) seed of the speckled butter (lima) bean plant (*Phaseolus limensis*). The skins of the seed are pigmented and the external colors range from variegated speckling of green, pink, red, and/or lavender to purple. The product is prepared by shelling the pods; by washing, blanching, and properly draining the seeds that have been sorted and blended or otherwise prepared in accordance with good commercial practice. They are frozen in accordance with good commercial practice and maintained at temperatures necessary for the preservation of the product.

V. FROZEN BROCCOLI

Frozen broccoli is the product prepared from the fresh, clean, sound stalks or shoots of the broccoli plant [*Brassica oleracea* (Italica group)] by trimming, washing, blanching, sorting, and properly draining. The product is frozen in accordance with good commercial practice and maintained at temperatures necessary for its preservation.

1. STYLES

1. Spears or stalks are the head and adjoining portions of the stem, with or without attached leaves, which may range in length from 9 cm (3.5 in.) to 15 cm (5.9 in.). The spears or stalks may be cut longitudinally.
2. Short spears or florets are the head and adjoining portions of the stem, with or without attached leaves, which may range in length from 2.5 cm (1 in.) to 9 cm (3.5 in.). Each short

spear or floret must weigh more than 6 g (0.2 oz). The short spears or florets may be cut longitudinally.

3. Cut spears or short spears are cut into portions which may range in length from 2 cm (0.8 in.) to 5 cm (2 in.). Head material should be at least 62.5 g (2.2 oz) per 250 g (8.8 oz) and leaf material should not be more than 62.5 g (2.2 oz) per 250 g (8.8 oz).

4. Chopped spears or short spears are cut into portions which are less than 2 cm (0.8 in.) in length. Head material should be at least 12.5 g (0.4 oz) per 50 g (1.8 oz) and leaf material should not be more than 12.5 g (0.4 oz) per 50 g (1.8 oz).

5. Pieces or random cut pieces are cut or chopped portions of spears or short spears or other units which do not meet the requirements for cut or chopped styles.

VI. FROZEN BRUSSELS SPROUTS

Frozen Brussels sprouts are the frozen product prepared from the clean, sound succulent heads of the Brussels sprouts plant (*Brassica oleracea* L. var. *gemmifera*) by trimming, washing, blanching, and properly draining. The product is frozen in accordance with good commercial practice and maintained at temperatures necessary for its preservation.

VII. FROZEN CARROTS

Frozen carrots are the clean and sound product prepared from the fresh root of the carrot plant (*Daucus carota*) by washing, sorting, peeling, trimming, and blanching, and are frozen in accordance with good commercial practice and maintained at temperatures necessary for the preservation of the product.

1. STYLES

Wholes (or whole carrots) retain the approximate confirmation of a whole carrot.

Halves or halved carrots are cut longitudinally into two units.

Quarters or quartered carrots are cut longitudinally into four approximately equal units. Carrots cut longitudinally or cut longitudinally and crosswise into six or eight units approximating the size and appearance of quartered carrots are also permitted in this style.

Slices or sliced carrots are sliced transversely to the longitudinal axis.

Diced carrots consist of approximate cube-shaped units.

Double-diced carrots consist of approximate rectangular shapes that resemble the equivalent of two cube-shaped units.

Strips are carrots that consists of approximate French-cut shapes, with flat-parallel or corrugated-parallel surfaces, one-half inch or more in length.

Chips are carrots that consist of predominately small-sized units (such as less than one-half cube) and variously shaped pieces or slivers in which the longest-edge dimension approximates not more than one-half inch.

Cut carrots consist of cut units that do not conform to any of the forgoing styles.

VIII. FROZEN CAULIFLOWER

Frozen cauliflower is prepared from fresh flower heads of the cauliflower plant (*Brassica oleracea botrytis*) by trimming, washing, and blanching, and is frozen and maintained at temperatures necessary for preservation of the product.

1. STYLES AND REQUIREMENTS

1. Clusters are individual segments of trimmed and cored cauliflower heads, which measure not less than 20 mm (0.75 in.) in the greatest dimension across the top of the unit. A maximum of 10%, by weight, of clusters less than 20 mm (0.75 in.) in the greatest dimension across the top of the unit are allowed.

2. Nuggets or small clusters are individual segments of trimmed and cored cauliflower heads, which measure from 6 mm (0.25 in.) to less than 20 mm (0.75 in.) in the greatest dimension across the top of the unit. A maximum of 20%, by weight, of clusters, 20 mm (0.75 in.) or greater, and a maximum of 10%, by weight, of clusters less than 6 mm in the greatest dimension across the top of the unit are allowed.

IX. FROZEN CORN ON THE COB

Frozen corn on the cob is the product prepared from sound, properly matured, fresh, sweet corn ears by removing husk and silk, by sorting, trimming, and washing to assure a clean and wholesome product. The ears are blanched, then frozen and stored at temperatures necessary for the preservation of the product.

1. STYLES

1. Trimmed. Ears trimmed at both ends to remove tip and stalk ends and or/cut to specific lengths.

2. Natural. Ears trimmed at the stalk end only to remove all or most of the stalk.

2. LENGTHS

1. Regular. Ears which are predominantly over 3-1/2 inches in length.
2. Ears which are predominantly 3-1/2 inches or less in length.

Colors of frozen corn on the cob: Golden (or yellow); white.

X. FROZEN LEAFY GREENS

Frozen leafy greens are the frozen product prepared from the clean, sound, succulent leaves and stems of any one of the plants listed below by sorting, trimming, washing, blanching, and properly draining. The product is processed by freezing and maintained at temperatures necessary for its preservation. Any functional, optional ingredient(s) permissible under the law may be used to acidify and/or season the product.

1. TYPES

Beet greens.
Collards.
Dandelion greens.
Endive.
Kale.
Mustard greens.
Spinach.
Swiss chard.
Turnip greens.
Any other "market accepted" leafy green.

2. STYLES

1. Leaf consists substantially of the leaf, cut or uncut, with or without adjoining portion of the stem.
2. Chopped consists of the leaf with or without adjoining portion of the stem that has been cut into small pieces less than approximately 20 mm (0.78 in.) in the longest dimension but not comminuted to a pulp or a puree.
3. Pureed consists of the leaf with or without adjoining portion of the stem that has been comminuted to a pulp or a puree.

XI. FROZEN OKRA

Frozen okra is the product prepared from the clean, sound, succulent, and edible fresh pods of the okra plant

(*Hibiscus esculentus*) of the green variety. The product may or may not be trimmed, is properly prepared and properly processed, and is then frozen and stored at temperatures necessary for preservation.

1. STYLES

1. Whole okra consists of trimmed or untrimmed whole pods of any length that may possess an edible portion of the cap. The length of a whole pod is determined by measuring from the outermost point of the tip end of the pod to the outermost point of the stem end of the pod, exclusive of any inedible stem portion that may be present.
2. Cut okra is trimmed or untrimmed whole pods, which may possess an edible portion of cap, and which have been cut transversely into pieces of approximate uniform length. The length of a unit of cut okra is determined by measuring the longitudinal axis of the unit.

XII. FROZEN ONION RINGS, BREADED, RAW OR COOKED

Frozen breaded onion rings, hereinafter referred to as frozen onion rings, is the product prepared from clean and sound, fresh onion bulbs (*Allium cepa*) from which the root bases, tops, and outer skin have been removed. The onion bulbs are sliced and separated into rings, coated with batter (or breaded), and may or may not be deep fried in a suitable fat or oil bath. The product is prepared and frozen in accordance with good commercial practice and maintained at temperatures necessary for the proper preservation of the product.

1. TYPES

The type of frozen onion rings applies to the method of preparation of the product, and includes:

1. French fried onion rings that have been deep fried in a suitable fat or oil bath prior to freezing.
2. Raw breaded onion rings that have not been oil blanched or cooked prior to freezing.

XIII. FROZEN PEAS

Frozen peas is the food in "package" form, prepared from the succulent seed of the pea plant of the species *Pisum sativum* L. Any suitable variety of pea may be used. It is blanched, drained, and preserved by freezing in such a way that the range of temperature of maximum crystallization is passed quickly. The freezing process should not be regarded as complete until the product temperature has reached −18°C (0°F) or lower at the thermal center, after thermal stabilization. Such food may contain one, or any combination of two or more, of the following safe and suitable optional ingredients:

XIV. PEAS, FIELD AND BLACK-EYE

Frozen field peas and frozen black-eye peas, hereafter referred to as frozen peas, are the frozen product prepared from clean, sound, fresh, seed of proper maturity of the field pea plant (*Vigna sinensis*), by shelling, sorting, washing, blanching, and properly draining. The product is frozen and maintained at temperatures necessary for preservation. Frozen peas may contain succulent, unshelled pods (snaps) of the field pea plant or small sieve round type succulent pods of the green bean plant as an optional ingredient used as a garnish.

XV. FROZEN PEPPERS, SWEET

Frozen sweet peppers are the frozen product prepared from fresh, clean, sound, firm pods of the common commercial varieties of sweet peppers, which have been properly prepared, may or may not be blanched, and are then frozen in accordance with good commercial practice and maintained at temperatures necessary for the preservation of the product.

1. TYPES

Type I, green.
Type II, red.
Type III, mixed (green and red).

2. STYLES

1. Whole stemmed: whole unpeeled pepper pods with stem and core removed.
2. Whole unstemmed: whole unpeeled pepper pods with stems trimmed to not more than 1/2 inch length.
3. Halved: whole stemmed, unpeeled pepper pods which have been cut approximately in half from stem to blossom end.
4. Sliced: whole stemmed, unpeeled pepper pods or pieces of pepper pods which have been cut into strips.
5. Diced: whole stemmed, unpeeled pepper pods or pieces of pepper pods which have been cut into approximate square pieces measuring 1/2 inch or less.
6. Unit: a whole unpeeled pepper pod or portion of a pepper pod in frozen sweet peppers.

XVI. FROZEN POTATOES, FRENCH FRIED

Frozen French fried potatoes are prepared from mature, sound, white or Irish potatoes (*Solanum tuberosum*). The potatoes are washed, sorted, and trimmed as necessary to assure a clean and wholesome product. The potatoes may or may not be cut into pieces. The potatoes are processed in accordance with good commercial practice which includes deep frying or blanching in a suitable fat or oil and which may include the addition of any ingredient permissible under the law. The prepared product is frozen and is stored at temperatures necessary for its preservation.

1. TYPES

Frozen French fried potatoes are of two types, based principally on intended use, as follows:

1. Retail type. This type is intended for household consumption. It is normally packed in small packages that are labeled or marked for retail sales. It may be otherwise designated for such use.
2. Institutional type. This type is intended for the hotel, restaurant, or other large feeding establishment trade. Primary containers, usually 5 pounds or more, are often not as completely labeled as for retail sales.

2. STYLES

Styles of potatoes are grouped into general, strips, slices, dices, and Rissolé.

The style of frozen French fried potatoes is identified by the general size, shape, or other physical characteristics of the potato units. Styles with cut units may be further identified by substyles as follows:

1. Straight cut refers to smooth cut surfaces and
2. Crinkle cut refers to corrugated cut surfaces.

The strips style consists of elongated pieces of potato with practically parallel sides and of any cross-sectional shape. This style may be further identified by the approximate dimensions of the cross-section, for example:

1/4 × 1/4 inch
3/8 × 3/8 inch
1/2 × 1/4 inch, or
3/8 × 3/8 inch

Shoestring refers to strip, either straight cut or crinkle cut, with a cross section predominantly less than that of a square measuring 3/8 × 3/8 inch.

Slices is a style that consists of pieces of potato with two practically parallel sides, and which otherwise conform generally to the shape of the potato. This style may also contain a normal amount of outside slices.

Dices consists of pieces of potato cut into approximate cubes.

Rissolé is a style that consists of whole or nearly whole potatoes.

Any other individually frozen French fried potato product may be designated as to style by description of the size, shape, or other characteristic that differentiates it from the other styles.

3. LENGTH DESIGNATIONS

The length designations described in this section apply to strip styles only.

Frozen French fried potato strips are designated as to length in accordance with the following criteria. Percent, as used in this section, means the percent, by count, of all strips of potato that are 1/2-inch in length, or longer.

1. Extra long. Eighty (80) percent or more are 2 inches in length or longer; and 30 percent or more are 3 inches in length or longer.
2. Long. Seventy (70) percent or more are 2 inches in length, or longer; and 15 percent or more are 3 inches in length or longer.
3. Medium. Fifty (50) percent or more are 2 inches in length or longer.
4. Short. Less than 50 percent are 2 inches in length or longer.

XVII. FROZEN POTATO, HASH BROWN

Frozen hash brown potatoes are prepared from mature, sound, white or Irish potatoes (*Solanum tuberosum*) that are washed, peeled, sorted, and trimmed to assure a clean and wholesome product. The potatoes so prepared are blanched, may or may not be fried, and are shredded or diced or chopped and frozen and stored at temperatures necessary for their preservation.

1. STYLES

1. Shredded. Shredded potatoes are cut into thin strips with cross-sectional dimensions from 1 mm by 2 mm to 4 mm by 6 mm and formed into a solid mass before freezing.
2. Diced. Diced potatoes are cut into approximate cube shape units from 6 mm to 15 mm on an edge and loose frozen. They contain not more than 90 grams, per sample unit, of units smaller than one-half the volume of the predominant size unit.

3. Chopped. Chopped potatoes are random cut pieces predominantly less than 32 mm in their greatest dimension and loose frozen.

XVIII. FROZEN VEGETABLES, MIXED

Frozen mixed vegetables consist of three or more succulent vegetables, properly prepared and properly blanched; may contain vegetables (such as small pieces of sweet red peppers or sweet green peppers) added as garnish; and are frozen and maintained at temperatures necessary for the preservation of the product.

1. KINDS AND STYLES OF BASIC VEGETABLES

It is recommended that frozen mixed vegetables, other than small pieces of vegetables added as garnish, consist of the following kinds and styles of vegetables as basic vegetables:

1. Beans, green or wax: Cut styles, predominantly of 1/2 inch to 1-1/2 inch cuts.
2. Beans, lima: Any single varietal type.
3. Carrots: Diced style, predominantly of 3/8 inch to 1/2 inch cubes.
4. Corn sweet: Golden (or Yellow) in whole kernel style.
5. Peas: Early type or sweet type.

2. RECOMMENDED PROPORTIONS OF INGREDIENTS

It is recommended that frozen mixed vegetables consist of three, four, or five basic vegetables in the following proportions:

1. Three vegetables. A mixture of three basic vegetables in which any one vegetable is not more than 40 percent by weight of all the frozen mixed vegetables.
2. Four vegetables. A mixture of four basic vegetables in which none of the vegetables is less than 8 percent by weight or more than 35 percent by weight of all the frozen mixed vegetables.
3. Five vegetables. A mixture of five basic vegetables in which none of the vegetables is less than 8 percent by weight or more than 30 percent by weight of all the frozen mixed vegetables.

ACKNOWLEDGMENT

The information in this chapter has been derived from *Food Safety Manual*, published and copyrighted by Science Technology System, West Sacramento, California, 2004. Used with permission.

24 Fruits: Horticultural and Functional Properties

Jiwan S. Sidhu
College for Women, Kuwait University

Sameer F. Al-Zenki
Department of Biotechnology, Kuwait Institute for Scientific Research

CONTENTS

I. INTRODUCTION

Fruits, either fresh or processed, form an important part of our daily diet, and demand is increasing in all affluent countries of the world. This has become possible because of the availability of the improved quality and extended variety of fruits throughout the year. Recent advances in agricultural technology have contributed significantly to the improved production of fruits throughout the world. In addition, the critical advances in fruit processing technologies, refrigeration, transportation, storage and distribution have made it possible for consumers to enjoy these products year-round. The emphasis in fruit processing is shifting now from traditional methods like canning, freezing and dehydration to "fresh cut" or "minimal processing." Because present-day consumers prefer food products that contain fruit, food processors are using more fruits as value-added ingredients (fruit concentrates, pulps, candied pieces, etc.) in their formulations, like snacks, baby foods, baked goods and many other processed foods. At the same time, the variety of fruits available for extended periods throughout the year in developed countries has increased. Many tropical fruits that were earlier considered exotic and expensive are now being commonly consumed as fresh produce.

Fruit consumption has witnessed unprecedented growth during the past few decades. Current nutrition studies are making consumers more informed about the health benefits of various fruit constituents. The importance of vitamins, minerals, antioxidants, dietary fiber and a long list of phytochemicals present in fruits are being discussed daily in the print and television media. Now, the idea of nutrient clusters also supports the need for a varied healthy diet that contains recommended servings of fruits and vegetables (1). A diet that lacks fruits and vegetables rarely supplies the levels of nutrients needed for optimal health. The world population is also ageing and life expectancy is increasing with every passing decade. This prompts us to understand the relationship of nutrition to ageing and to study the effect of dietary requirements on an aged population. The role of phytochemicals present in fruits and vegetables in promoting health and reducing the risk of various chronic diseases among the older adults is now attracting the attention of health professionals (2).

II. BIOLOGY OF FRUITS

Fruit, in strict botanical terms, is the fleshy or dry ripened ovary of a plant, which encloses the seed or seeds. Therefore, mangoes, apricots, bananas, grapes, bean pods, almonds, tomatoes and cucumbers are all technically fruits. However, the term fruit is restricted to the ripened ovaries that are sweet and either succulent or pulpy. A fruit, when developed from only the carpellary structures, is called a true fruit or, if it is developed from a superior ovary, a superior fruit. Fruits with accessory parts are called accessory fruits (grapes, dates and plums), or because of their frequent development from inferior ovaries, are called inferior fruits (bananas, pears and walnuts). Invariably, the true fruits develop from the superior ovaries of hypogynous or perigynous flowers, but the accessory fruits usually develop from the inferior or part-inferior ovaries of epigynous or semiepigynous flowers. The number of ovaries and flowers that constitute the fruits also characterizes fruits. A simple fruit is derived from one ovary (e.g., apples), whereas an aggregate fruit is developed from several ovaries of one flower (e.g., strawberries). A multiple or collective fruit is developed from the structures of ovaries and accessories of several flowers consolidated into a mass (e.g., figs and pineapples). Simple fruits are either true or accessory fruits, but the aggregate and multiple fruits are always accessory fruits.

The classification of fruits is based on numerous criteria, e.g., dehiscence versus indehiscence, dry versus fleshy, textural quality, morphology, development, relationship of ovary to other reproductive parts of the plant and number of carpels and seeds present therein. Fleshy fruits are generally indehiscent, but with a few exceptions. The major types of simple fleshy fruits include a pome with a thin inner part (endocarp) and fleshy outer part (e.g., pear and pomegranate); the latter is a leathery pome. The drupe (stone fruit, e.g., cherry, peach, plum) has an outer exocarp (skin) in the fruit wall, a central fleshy mesocarp (flesh) and an inner stony endocarp or stone. The berry has the entire center of fruit as fleshy (e.g., grapes, bananas, kiwi), whereas hesperidium, a modified berry, has a thick, leathery separate outer rind (e.g., citrus fruits).

Fruits are very perishable in nature because these are living and respiring tissues. Based on the post-harvest patterns of respiration, fruits are classified as climacteric and nonclimacteric (3). Climacteric fruits, such as mango, banana, pear, apricot, guava, kiwi, papaya, peach, fig, plum and apple, produce large amounts of carbon dioxide and ethylene; the production rates of these gases coincide with ripening. These fruits can be harvested at an early mature stage and ripened artificially with ethylene gas (4). The nonclimacteric fruits, such as the orange, strawberry, grape, lime, lemon, pineapple, grapefruit and cherry, show no change in their low production rates of these two gases during ripening and post-harvest storage. Nonclimacteric fruits, if picked too early, are generally sour and of poor quality because they ripen gradually over a long period of time. Environmental factors, like temperature, relative humidity and atmospheric gaseous composition, greatly influence the respiration rate and shelf life of fruits during post-harvest storage. Handling methods should be chosen carefully so that they maintain fruit quality and chemical composition. The delay between harvesting, cooling, processing and consumption may lead to direct losses in quality (water loss and decay) and indirect losses in flavor and nutritional quality. The harvesting at an appropriate stage of maturity is, therefore, important for better postharvest shelf life and final fruit quality (5).

III. EDIBLE FRUITS OF THE WORLD

Fruits are grown in temperate, subtropical and tropical climates of the world. Among the fruits grown in temperate and subtropical regions, oranges are the leading groups of fruit in terms of production, which are mainly processed into juice (Table 24.1). Bananas are the second leading fruits and are consumed mainly in fresh form. The major portion of grapes the third leading fruits, goes into juice, wine production and dried fruits, i.e., raisins (6). The major grape-growing countries of the world are Italy, France, the United States, Spain and Russia. The fourth leading group, apples, are mostly eaten as fresh, but reasonable quantities are also processed into juice, dried or canned. Kiwi is another fruit that has become increasingly popular in the international market. The production of fruits is increasing rapidly throughout the world and fruits are becoming great foreign exchange earners for the developing countries.

Banana, mango, papaya and pineapple are the important tropical fruits that have gained commercial importance in international trade (7). Mangoes and lychees are becoming immensely popular fruits among the Asian population all over the world. The United States is the leading producer of fruits in the world, is followed by Brazil, Italy, India, France, Russia and China (6, 8). A few of the important examples of fruits grown in each of the climatic regions of the world (9) are presented in Table 24.2.

IV. COMPOSITION OF FRUITS

Fruits and their processed products are not only colorful, flavorful and appealing to the eye, but are also vital sources of essential vitamins, minerals, dietary fiber and a host of important health-promoting phytochemicals (10). In addition to these nutrients, they also contain complex carbohydrates and proteins (Tables 24.3–24.5). Fruits are good sources of calcium, phosphorus, iron and magnesium. They also supply a major portion of vitamin C in our diets. Green-, yellow- and orange-colored fruits are rich sources of β-carotene (a provitamin A). A substantial portion of the complex carbohydrates in fruits is present as cellulose, hemicellulose, pectic substances and lignins, which serve as dietary fiber in our diets. Dietary fiber content and composition of some of the important fruits, determined by the Association of Official Analytical Chemists (AOAC) method (11) as well as the Uppsala method (12), are presented in Table 24.6. The dietary fiber constituents neutralize the acid produced by meats, milk products and other high protein foods in our diets. The presence of polyphenols, anthocyanins and phytochemical constituents is now being examined for their protective role against cardiovascular diseases and certain types of cancer (13).

Water is the most abundant constituent of most fresh fruits, at usually around 80%, but some fruits, like apples and oranges, may contain more than 90% water (15). Some

TABLE 24.1
World Production of Major Fruits (1000 MT)

Fruit	Production	Fruit	Production
Oranges	63,838	Plums	7,836
Bananas	58,975	Peaches	10,923
Grapes	58,466	Papayas	5,024
Apples	56,087	Strawberries	2,682
Mangoes	23,428	Apricots	2,295
Pineapples	12,794	Avocadoss	2,342
Pears	13,318	Grapefruits & Pomelos	5,038
Plantains	29,501	Raspberries	306

Source: Ref. 6.

TABLE 24.2
Classification of Fruits Based on Climatic Region

Temperate Region	Subtropical Region	Tropical Region
Pome fruits: Apple, Asian pear (*Nashpati*), European pear, quince	Citrus fruits: Orange, grapefruit, tangerine, mandarin, lemon, lime, pomelo	Major tropical fruits: Banana, mango, papaya, pineapple
Stone fruits: Peach, plum, nectarine, apricot, cherry, almond, chestnut, lychee, walnut, pecan	Non-citrus fruits: Kiwifruit, figs, olive, pomegranate, cherimoya, ber (*Zizyphus*), bael (*Aegle marmelos*), date fruit (*Phoenix dactylifera* L.), loquat (*Eribotrya japonica* Lindl.), persimmon (*Diospyros*), phalsa (*Grewia subinaegualis* L.), jamun (*Syzygium cuminii* Skeels)	Minor tropical fruits: Cashew apple, guava, carambola, durian, longan, passion fruit, mangosteen, rambutan, tamarind, sapota, coconut, amla (*Phyllanthus emlica* L.), jackfruit (*Artocarpus heterophyllus*)
Small fruits and berries: Grape, strawberry, raspberry, cranberry, blueberry, blackberry, currant, gooseberry		

Source: Ref. 9.

TABLE 24.3
Proximate Composition (%) of Major Fruits Grown in the World (Based on Total Edible Parts)

Fruit	Water	Energy	Protein	Fat	Carbohydrate	Minerals
Grapes	81.6	67	1.3	1.0	15.7	0.4
Oranges	86.0	49	1.0	0.2	12.2	0.6
Bananas	75.7	85	1.1	0.2	12.6	0.6
Apples	84.4	58	0.2	0.6	14.5	0.3
Mangoes	83.4	59	0.5	0.2	15.4	0.4
Pineapples	85.4	52	0.4	0.2	13.7	0.3
Pears	83.2	61	0.7	0.4	15.3	0.4
Plums	81.1	66	0.5	0.2	17.8	0.4
Peaches	89.1	38	0.6	0.1	9.7	0.5
Papayas	90.7	32	0.5	0.1	8.3	0.4
Apricots	85.3	51	1.0	0.2	12.8	0.7
Avocados	74.4	80.5	1.8	20.6	–	1.2
Strawberries	89.9	37	0.7	0.5	8.4	0.5

Source: Refs. 7, 8 and 10.

TABLE 24.4
Mineral Contents (mg/100 g of Total Edible Parts) of Major Fruits Grown in the World

Fruit	Calcium	Phosphorus	Iron	Magnesium
Grapes	16	12	0.4	13
Oranges	41	20	0.4	11
Bananas	8	26	0.7	33
Apples	7	10	0.3	8
Mangoes	12	12	0.8	–
Pineapples	18	8	0.5	–
Pears	8	11	0.3	7
Plums	18	17	0.5	9
Peaches	9	19	0.5	10
Papayas	20	13	0.4	–
Apricots	17	23	0.5	12
Avocados	14	27	0.7	23
Strawberries	21	21	1.0	12

Source: Refs. 7, 8 and 10.

Table 24.5
Vitamin Content (Per 100 g of Total Edible Parts) of Major Fruits Grown in the World

Fruit	Vitamin A (IU)	Thiamine (mg)	Riboflavin (mg)	Nicotinic acid (mg)	Ascorbic acid (mg)
Grapes	100	0.05	0.03	0.3	4
Oranges	200	0.10	0.04	0.4	50
Bananas	190	0.05	0.06	0.7	10
Apples	90	0.03	0.02	0.1	4
Mangoes	630	0.05	0.06	0.4	53
Pineapples	15	0.08	0.04	0.2	61
Pears	20	0.02	0.04	0.1	4
Plums	300	0.08	0.03	0.5	5
Peaches	1330	0.02	0.05	1.0	7
Papayas	110	0.03	0.04	0.3	46
Apricots	2700	0.03	0.04	0.6	10
Avocados	–	0.07	0.12	1.9	11
Strawberries	60	0.03	0.07	0.6	59

Source: Refs. 7, 8 and 10.

content could be in traces in cherries to more than 8% in ripe bananas and pineapples. Fructose, being sweeter than sucrose and glucose, has a desirable influence on the taste of fruits. Starch is present as small granules within the cells of immature fruits, which is converted to sugars as the fruit matures and ripens. Cellulose, hemicellulose, pectic substances and lignins are the other polysaccharides, which are the major constituents of cell walls. These compounds are broken down into simpler and more soluble components during fruit ripening (19).

Fruits contain less than 1% proteins, except in fruit nuts, such as almonds, pistachios and walnuts (~20% protein). It is mainly the enzymes that constitute this 1% protein, and these enzymes are responsible for catalyzing various metabolic processes involved in fruit ripening and senescence viz. polygalacturonase hydrolyzes pectic substances, resulting in fruit softening, and polyphenoloxidase catalyzes oxidation of phenolics, leading to browning of cut apples. Ascorbic acid oxidase catalyzes oxidation of ascorbic acid, and thus lowers the nutritional quality of fruits. Chlorophyllase removes the phytol ring from chlorophyll, which leads to loss of green color during ripening of fruits.

Most fresh fruits are low in lipids (0.1 to 0.2%), except avocados, nuts and olives. Lipids are present in the cell membranes, as a part of surface wax and cuticle. The surface wax contributes to fruit appearance, and the cuticle protects against water loss and pathogens. The type of fatty acids present determines the flexibility of cell membranes, with higher saturation resulting in rigid cells.

Organic acids are major intermediary products of metabolism and are further oxidized through the Krebs cycle to provide energy for the maintenance of cell integrity. The acidity of most fresh fruits is due to these organic acids. Certain fruits, like lemons, may contain as

fruits, like bananas, jackfruit, dates and grapes, are rich in carbohydrates (mainly sugars), whereas others, like nuts, dried apricots and figs, are good sources of proteins and amino acids. A few fruits, like avocados, olives and nuts, are exceptionally rich in oils and fats. In general, most fruits typically contain between 10 to 25% carbohydrates, less than 1% proteins and very small amounts (less than 0.5%) of fat. Some exceptions like dates have about 77.97 to 79.39% total sugars at the *kimri* stage of maturity (16), avocados have a fat content ranging from 15.5 to 23.4% (17) and olives have a fat content ranging from 15 to 30% (18).

Sucrose, glucose and fructose are the main sugars found in most fruits, although sorbitol is present in reasonable amounts in some fruits (cherry, plum and pear). The total sugars are present mainly in the cytoplasm, and range from 0.9% in limes to 16% in fresh figs. Sucrose

TABLE 24.6

Dietary Fiber Content and Composition of Fruits (g/100 g of Total Edible Parts)

Sample	Dry wt., FW	AOAC[a] Total fiber, FW	Uppsala Method[b]							
			Soluble Fiber				Insoluble Fiber			
			Total Fiber, FW	Neutral Sugars, DW	Uronic Acids, DW	Total, DW	Neutral Sugars, DW	Uronic Acids, DW	Klason Lignin, DW	Total, DW
Apples										
Applesauce, canned	11.5	1.4	1.2	1.0	1.5	2.5	6.5	1.3	0.4	8.2
Macintosh, unpeeled	15.3	2.3	1.8	0.4	1.7	2.1	7.0	1.7	1.3	10.0
Apricots										
Dried	69.4	7.7	7.1	0.9	2.1	3.0	5.3	1.3	0.7	7.3
Fresh, unpeeled	11.3	1.6	1.5	0.7	3.5	4.2	6.4	1.3	1.0	8.7
Berries										
Blackberry, frozen	17.9	7.0	6.5	0.9	1.9	2.8	13.5	3.3	16.5	33.4
Cranberry sauce, frozen	39.4	1.4	1.1	0.2	0.5	0.7	1.2	0.1	0.7	2.0
Raspberry, red, fresh	12.3	4.4	4.1	1.1	2.4	3.5	9.9	1.7	18.7	30.3
Strawberry, frozen	10.7	1.9	1.7	1.2	2.6	3.8	5.7	1.4	5.1	12.2
Grapes										
Black, seeded	21.5	1.0	0.9	0.2	0.1	0.3	1.3	0.9	1.5	3.7
Red, seedless	21.3	1.3	1.0	0.1	0.2	0.3	1.5	0.8	2.1	4.4
Oranges										
Mandarin, canned	16.1	0.3	0.2	0.2	0.1	0.3	0.6	0.4	0.2	1.2
Temple, fresh	14.7	1.7	1.5	0.7	1.5	2.2	4.8	2.8	0.5	8.1
Valencia, fresh	13.1	1.6	1.5	0.9	1.1	2.0	4.5	3.7	0.8	9.0
Peaches										
Canned in fruit juice	15.8	1.5	1.4	1.1	2.0	3.1	3.9	1.1	0.9	5.9
Fresh, unpeeled	13.3	1.9	1.7	1.5	3.0	4.5	6.5	1.0	1.1	8.6
Fresh, peeled	12.4	1.6	1.3	1.1	2.7	3.8	4.5	0.9	1.0	6.4
Plums										
Canned in heavy Syrup	27.0	2.1	1.8	1.0	1.5	2.5	2.9	0.5	0.8	4.2
Prunes	65.8	8.0	7.3	1.3	2.6	3.9	4.3	1.0	1.8	7.1
Prunes, fresh	16.6	2.2	1.9	0.7	2.1	2.8	4.3	1.4	2.6	8.3

[a]Mean of four measurements, [b]Mean of two measurements, FW = Fresh weight, DW = Dry weight.

Source: Ref. 14.

much as 4.17 to 4.64% acidity, citric acid being the predominant one (20). Malic and citric acids are the most abundant in most fruits, except the tartaric acid in grapes and the quinic acid in kiwi fruits. The titratable acidity of fruits plays an important role in determining the maturity of most of these fruits. Acid content of fruits usually decreases during the ripening process as these are used in respiration or converted to sugars (21).

Pigments are the chemicals responsible for the characteristic color of skin and the flesh of fruits. In general, peel tissues of white and yellow flesh nectarines and peaches, and yellow and red plums, contain higher levels of phenols; anthocyanins and flavonols are almost exclusively located in this tissue (22). Many changes occur in these pigments during maturation and ripening of fruits. Fruit color is, therefore, used as an index of maturity and stage of ripeness in many fruits. The color of fruits also changes during the period of post-harvest in cold storage. Changes in the color and anthocyanin content have been investigated during the development and ripening of strawberries and pomegranates (23, 24). An increase in phenylalanine ammonia lyase (PAL) activity correlates with anthocyanin production in strawberries. The anthocyanins increase in pomegranate and low bush blueberry fruits during cold storage (24, 25). PAL activity and anthocyanin concentration in the skin of harvested apples increases after irradiation with UV and white light (26). The anthocyanin content in apples is adversely affected by higher carbon dioxide levels (73%) during cold storage (27), but a moderate carbon dioxide atmosphere (10 kPa) prolongs the storage life and maintains the quality of pomegranate, including adequate red color intensity of the arils (28).

β-Carotene is a precursor of vitamin A, and not only imparts color to fruits, but is also important in terms of nutritional quality. Most of the carotenoid pigments are quite stable and remain intact in fruit tissues, even after senescence, processing and storage. The elucidation of biosynthesis pathway in plants has opened up new possibilities to manipulate/engineer fruit cultivars rich in provitamin A carotenoids (29). A combination of biochemical and genetic approaches has led to the isolation of a key gene, lycopene-epsilon-cyclase, responsible for the relative proportions of β-carotene and lycopene in tomato fruits (30). Among the phenolics, anthocyanins occur as glycosides and are water soluble, unstable during processing as well as to changes in pH. These glycosides are readily hydrolyzed by enzymes to free anthocyanins, which may be further oxidized by phenoloxidases to yield brown-colored oxidation products. The green color imparted to fruits by chlorophyll is influenced by pH changes, oxidation and the action of the enzyme chlorophyllase.

The plant polyphenols occur naturally in plant foods, like teas, fruits, juices and grape seeds. Grape seed tannins are known to exhibit remarkable antioxidant effects (31). The total phenolic compounds are higher in immature fruits than in the mature fruits, and usually range between 0.1 and 2% on a fresh weight basis. These include chlorogenic acid, catechin, epicatechin, leucoanthocyanidins, flavonols, cinnamic acid derivatives and simple phenols. Chlorogenic acid occurs widely in fruits and is responsible for the enzymatic browning of cut or damaged fruit tissues. The phenolic content of red grapes is about 20–50 times higher than of white grapes (32). Apart from nutritional significance, these polyphenols are associated with color in fruits and vegetables and contribute to flavor sensations like astringency and bitterness (33). Anthocyanins are responsible for the bright red and purple colors of fruits and flowers (34). The astringency is directly linked to the phenolic content and decreases during fruit ripening, as the phenolics are converted from soluble to insoluble, nonastringent form (35). These phenolic compounds are plant secondary metabolites and play an important role in plant-derived food quality, as they affect various quality attributes, such as appearance, flavor and health-promoting properties (36).

Fresh as well as processed fruits are important sources of vitamins in the human diet. Apricot, peach, papaya, cherry, orange, cantaloupe and watermelon are good sources of β-carotene (provitamin A), whereas Indian gooseberry, strawberry, orange, grapefruit, kiwi, papaya and cantaloupe are important sources of ascorbic acid. Peach, banana, orange, apricot, avocado, grapefruit and apple also contain appreciable amounts of certain B-complex vitamins. The levels of some of these vitamins may be reduced during processing into various products, as some of these are sensitive to heat, oxygen, light, pH and certain trace minerals. Banana, peach, orange and apple are rich in potassium, whereas orange, banana, peach, raisin and fig are rich in phosphorus. Citrus fruits, like tangerine, grapefruit and orange, contain good amounts of calcium, and strawberry, banana, apple and orange are rich in iron. On a fresh weight basis, the dietary fiber content of fruits ranges from 0.5 to 1.5%. The dietary fiber comprises cellulose, hemicellulose, lignin and pectin, which are derived from the cell wall and skin of fruits (9).

Chemical composition of fruits is affected by a number of preharvest and post-harvest factors. Among the preharvest factors, genetics (like cultivars and rootstocks) are known to influence raw fruit composition, durability and response to processing. As an example, several reports are available on the genetic improvements of grape vines (37, 38). Similarly, climatic factors, like light intensity, significantly affect the concentration of certain vitamins, and temperature influences mineral uptake and metabolism due to its effect on transpiration rate. Cultural practices like fertilizer application affect the mineral content of fruits while pruning/thinning influences nutritional composition by changing fruit density and size (39).

V. STRUCTURAL PROPERTIES OF FRUITS

Fruits are consumed not only for their nutritional value, but also for pleasure. The type of sensations one experiences as the fruit deforms and fractures during the initial stage of chewing determines our acceptance or rejection. Over the years, food processors have developed many methods to evaluate structural properties (such as modulus, fracture stress and strain) and to relate these parameters to the textural quality of fruits. Fruit firmness is another important mechanical property in determining the quality and ripeness behavior of fruits. A more fundamental understanding of the relationship between structural properties and microstructure of fruits is a prerequisite for any improvements in the textural qualities of these food products. Single edge notch bend tests were employed to relate mechanical properties to food texture (40). These workers reported good agreement between the measured (3.4 ± 0.3 MPa) and calculated (3.0) Young's modulus (E values) for apples. The fracture toughness, K_{Ic}, fracture energy, G_c, and yield stress, σ_y, values for apples were reported to be 10.1 ± 1.4 kPa m$^{1/2}$, 39.6 ± 10.5 Jm^{-2} and 0.3 ± 0.1 MPa, respectively. The firmness of pear fruit is a function of the mechanical properties of cell wall, cell properties like turgor and bonding between neighboring cells (41). A sigmoidal relationship between fruit firmness and tensile strength of tissue soaked in isotonic solutions is observed. The major mechanism of tissue failure involves cell wall failure and cell fracture at high firmness and intercellular debonding at low firmness. The stress-hardening of the cell wall in response to an increase in cell turgor increases the cell wall elastic modulus. Fruit firmness decreases from 100 to 20 N and from 60 to 25 N during the ripening of European and Asian pears, respectively. Tissue and cell extension at maximum force declines as fruit softens. During fruit ripening, the hydrolysis of pectins present in the middle lamella leads to tissue breakdown by cell-to-cell debonding rather than the cell wall rupture.

As the mechanical properties are a function of ripening, these parameters can be used to discriminate between batches of certain types of fruits based on their degree of ripeness. Mechanical parameters can be used in assessing the optimum stage of ripening for harvest of Burlat sweet cherries using a penetration test, a compression test between two plates, and a compression-relaxation test (42). Based on compression-relaxation data, the calculated "apparent secant modulus" seems to be the most useful single mechanical parameter to clearly classify batches and to distinguish different varieties. Data in Table 24.7 show that the maximum penetration force ranges from 6.2 N (for very green cherries) to 1.8 N (for purple cherries). The hardness decreases as the cherries mature, but a sharp reduction in force occurs between stages red and very red, which are used as optimum stages of harvesting.

Firmness is a critical parameter of textural quality of apples. Information on the mechanical properties of apple flesh and intact apples is required to develop suitable methods for the sorting of whole apples according to firmness. Apple firmness is affected by many factors such as pre-harvest factors (genetics, fertilizers and other nutrients, breeding for fruit size, use of plant regulators); and post-harvest factors (maturity at harvest, pre-storage treatment with calcium, heat, plant regulators, storage atmosphere) (43). Calcium chloride treatment (2%) is effective in firming the apples (44). After six months of storage, treated samples had textural characteristics values equal to or better than the control treated with water only. The involvement of calcium ions in the maintenance of apple tissue during storage is suggested (45). The infiltration with

calcium ions increases the tensile strength of tissue from air-stored apples to 85% of that of untreated controlled atmosphere-stored fruits. Both the movement of calcium ions from the middle lamella and loss of its binding sites occur during fruit softening, thus affecting the fruit texture. The softening of apricots during canning is accelerated when chelators, such as organic acid anions, remove structural calcium from the cell wall once the cell membrane is lyzed during heat processing (46). Infiltration of these apricot fruits, susceptible to softening, with calcium chloride before processing gives firmed canned products.

The stone cells also influence the firmness of Asian, European and Chinese pears (47). Fruit firmness increases with the increase in weight of stone cells, but soluble solid content is not affected. Weight of stone cells (per g of fruit) is negatively correlated with fruit size. Different cultivars show differences in the weight and size of stone cells. The degree of ripeness, specimen orientation and location within the apple tissue affect the failure stress, strain and energy and apparent modulus of elasticity (Young's modulus). Failure stress is the highest in vertical direction and lowest in tangential direction (48). Young's modulus is significantly ($p < 0.05$) higher in radial samples than in tangential and vertical samples. The bottom sections give the largest values for failure stress and Young's modulus, and the top sections give the lowest values for Young's modulus. A non-destructive method has been developed to determine fruit elasticity using the coefficient of elasticity (49). The coefficient of elasticity is the ratio of compressive stress to deformation. While using different types of penetrometers, coefficient of elasticity shows a close correlation with compressive stress and an acceptable correlation with rupture stress for apples. The coefficient of elasticity can be used to characterize stress-strain behavior of fruits, as it is a good indicator of firmness for both scientific and practical evaluation.

TABLE 24.7
Mechanical Parameters for Burlat Sweet Cherry with Skin (Mean Values)

Parameter	Very Green	Green	Red	Very Red	Purple
Penetration Test					
Max. penetration force, N	6.2 (1.1)	4.3 (0.6)	4.2 (0.6)	2.3 (0.4)	1.8 (0.2)
Compression test					
Force to bioyield, N	51.0 (10.6)	30.0 (5.3)	19.3 (1.7)	14.1 (1.9)	13.5 (1.2)
Terminal slope, N cm^{-1}	1.5 (0.4)	0.8 (0.2)	0.4 (0.1)	0.3 (0.0)	0.2 (0.0)
Compression-Relaxation Test					
Maximum force, N	6.1 (0.7)	4.7 (0.4)	3.5 (0.5)	2.0 (0.3)	1.4 (0.3)
Residual force, N	3.7 (0.5)	2.8 (0.3)	2.1 (0.3)	1.2 (0.2)	0.9 (0.2)
Residual force/Maximum force	0.61	0.60	0.60	0.60	0.64
Relaxed force, N	2.4 (0.2)	1.9 (0.1)	1.4 (0.2)	0.8 (0.1)	0.6 (0.1)
Apparent secant modulus, N	76 (8.6)	59 (5.0)	43 (5.8)	25 (3.6)	18 (3.6)

Mean values of 20 cherries, and, in parentheses, 95% confidence interval.

Source: Ref. 42.

Size of individual fruits among their class is an important parameter that determines the textural attributes and consumer acceptability. Among the three size classes, ≤ 8 mm, 9–10 mm and 11–12 mm of Maine wild blueberries, consumers prefer the largest size (50). The compression test using an Instron testing machine measuring force and deformation to the point of rupture of individual blueberries relates to consumer acceptance. The consumers prefer larger 11–12 mm berries as these show lower stress and strain values, i.e., easier to chew. The compression tests reveal significant differences among all three size classes with respect to apparent modulus. A linear relationship is observed between the sensory texture and the elastic modulus (Tables 24.8 and 24.9).

The curve generated by the texturometer by plotting force as a function of time is known as a texture profile. This curve when analyzed in conjunction with the sensory texture parameters defined by Szczesniak (51), such as fracturability, hardness, cohesiveness, adhesiveness, springiness, gumminess and chewiness, is known as texture profile analysis technique and still used for food samples. Mechanical parameters of food samples measured by a texturometer correlate well with the sensory scores obtained by using a trained texture profile panel. This correlation indicates that the food texturometers have the capability to measure certain characteristics in a similar manner to those perceived by the human mouth. This texture profile analysis technique has been employed in a number of fruits such as pears (52), peaches (53) and apples (54). A typical texture profile curve is presented in Figure 24.1. Five measured and two calculated parameters, originally suggested by Szczesniak (55) and Friedman et al. (56), modified by Bourne (57) are described as follows:

1. *Fracturability* (earlier called *brittleness*) is defined as the force at the first significant break in the first positive bite area (PA1).
2. *Hardness* is defined as the peak force (PP1) during the first compression cycle.
3. *Cohesiveness* is defined as the ratio of the positive force area during the second compression cycle to the positive force area during the first compression cycle, or PA2/PA1.
4. *Adhesiveness* is defined as the negative force area for the first bite (NA1), representing the work required to pull the plunger away from the food sample.
5. *Springiness* (originally called *elasticity*) is defined as the height to which the food recovers during the time that elapses between the end of the first bite and the start of the second bite.
6. *Gumminess* is defined as the product of hardness and cohesiveness.
7. *Chewiness* is defined as the product of gumminess and springiness.

Texture profile analysis (TPA) is a useful technique to evaluate such structural properties of fruits. For more information on TPA, the reader is referred to the book by Rao and Rizvi (58).

TABLE 24.8
Means Separation of Mechanical Tests for Engineering Stress and Strain and Modulus of Elasticity by Berry Size

Berry Size	Mechanical Test*		
	Peak Force, mN	Deformation, mm	Modulus of Elasticity, mN/mm²
8 mm	0.323a	0.00481a	25.72a
9–10 mm	0.307a	0.00455a	17.70a
11–12 mm	0.304a	0.00395b	14.49b

*Means with different letters are significantly different (p ≤ 0.05).

Source: Ref. 50.

TABLE 24.9
Regression Model Results of Panelist and Berry Size with Respect to Sensory and Mechanical Attributes

Attribute	Panelist	Berry Size	Model R-Square
Sensory Attribute			
Flavor	Y	Y	0.597
Texture	Y	Y	0.559
Overall	Y	Y	0.635
Mechanical attribute			
Peak force	Y	N	0.539
Deformation at peak force	Y	Y	0.561
Modulus of elasticity	Y	Y	0.685

Y indicates significance at the 0.05 level.

Source: Ref. 50.

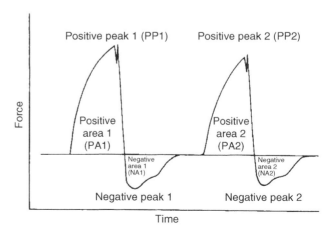

FIGURE 24.1 A typical texture profile curve with a two-bite compression cycle. (*Source*: Ref. 58.)

Fresh-cut fruit slices have become quite popular among consumers in the U.S. Apart from type of cultivars and storage conditions, fruit size and firmness are the other two important parameters that affect the quality of fresh-cut fruits. Among the factors affecting the quality of fresh-cut pears, fruit ripeness based on flesh firmness of 44 to 58 N is optimal for fresh-cut pear slice processing (59). The pear slices obtained from smaller size fruits (122–135 g) undergo a greater cut surface discoloration and deteriorate faster than slices obtained from larger fruits (152 g). Similarly, the optimal ripeness for preparing fresh-cut peach slices is the ripe stage having greater than 13–27 N flesh firmness (60). However, the optimal ripeness for preparing fresh-cut nectarine slices is the partially ripe (greater than 27–49 N) or ripe (greater than 13–27 N flesh firmness) stages. The size of fruits also determines their acceptance among consumer populations. Hampson et al. (61) reported that age groups differed slightly in apple fruit size preference. Fruit diameter considered ideal for dessert use ranged from 7.4 to 7.6 cm among various age groups.

Volatile compounds extracted from hyuganatsu fruits (*Citrus tamurana* Hort. ex Tanaka) vary with a fruit size of 100 to 350 g (62). Sesquiterpene contents are the highest in larger fruits, trans-beta-farnesene is lower in middle range fruits and l-carvone tends to increase with fruit size. As fruit size has a great influence on market price, processing quality and consumer acceptance, fruit breeders aim to produce larger fruits with better quality through the application of various plant growth regulators (63). The application of thidiazurin (TDZ) increases the fresh fruit weight and yield of kiwifruit nearly 13 and 22% with 2 and 10 ppm TDZ, respectively (64). A higher dose (10 ppm) gives slightly rounder fruits than the control and during ripening, no significant change in soluble solids, flesh firmness, glucose, fructose, sucrose and starch is observed. The application of CPPU [N-(2-chloro-4-pyridyl)-N′-phenyl urea] at concentration ranging from 4 to 8 mg/l increases maximum fruit size without causing fruit asymmetry in apples (65).

A number of chemical thinning treatments for apples are known to influence their ripeness and processing quality (66). Carbaryl alone, 2-1-naphthylacetic acid (NAA) and ethephon improve fruit size, but the benzyladenine/gibberellic acid is ineffective as a thinner and fruit size is not altered at harvest. Although ethephon shows promise as a fruitlet thinner and a promoter of ripeness in Paula red cv, these beneficial effects must be balanced against possible adverse effects on storage life of this fruit. The application of NAA (30 ppm) plus ethephon (500 ppm) is also beneficial in advancing fruit maturity, enhancing fruit color, increasing fruit size and providing better sensory quality with higher soluble solids and low acidity in pear (*Pyrus communis* L.) cv LeConte (67). As the source-sink balance is critical in the papaya fruit set, fruit development and sugar accumulation, defoliation and fruit removal can be employed to alter fruit size and quality (68). Fruit thinning increases the new fruit set and ripe fruit total soluble solids in papaya. Larger fruit size, faster fruit development and higher sugar contents are observed in immature fruits when old fruits are removed.

Porosity is another important physical property that plays a significant role during fruit processing operations, such as impregnation of fruit chunks in sugar syrups or their own juices. The porosity behavior of a few fruits (apple, strawberry, mango, peach and kiwi fruit) during vacuum impregnation treatments to determine deformation and impregnation levels through the hydrodynamic mechanism (HDM) and the deformation-relaxation phenomena (DRP) is important (69). Porosity and other physical characteristics of these fruits are presented in Table 24.10. The ratio of effective porosity (ε_e) to fruit porosity (ε) obtained from the density data is lower than 1 in almost all the fruits. This indicates that only a fraction of fruit pores is available to HDM action. DRP affects the volume

TABLE 24.10
Some Physical Characteristics of Fruits

Characteristic	Apple, cv Golden	Mango, cv Tommy Atkins	Strawberry, cv Chandler	Kiwi Fruit, cv Hayward	Peach, cv Miraflores
Fruit density[1]	0.787±0.014	1.022±0.005	0.984±0.009	1.051±0.006	1.038±0.005
Solid/liquid density[1]	1.0548±0.0008	1.13±0.02	1.05±0.009	1.076±0.006	1.0654±0.001
Fruit porosity	25.4±1.4	9.9±1.3	6.3±1.6	2.3±0.8	2.6±0.5
Water activity	0.985±0.00	0.9895±0.0007	0.9923±0.0015	0.992±0.000	0.9920±0.0010
Moisture content[2]	0.835±0.016	0.7868±0.0007	0.911±0.007	0.815±0.011	0.820±0.002
Ripeness index[3]	44.1±1.9	43.69±0.16	48.0±1.3	10.0±0.3	31±2
Soluble solids[4]	15.3±0.4	17.8±0.5	7.2±0.6	14.28±0.13	15±2
pH	3.833±0.012	4.29±0.00	3.36±0.02	3.527±0.008	3.91±0.14
Fruit acidity[5]	0.346±0.009	0.408±0.009	0.149±0.010	1.43±0.05	0.49±0.04

[1] (Kg/m^3), [2] (Kg water/Kg of sample), [3] (Soluble solids/fruit acidity), [4] (°Brix), [5] (Kg prevailing acid/100 Kg of sample).
Source: Ref. 69.

fraction of impregnated liquid in all fruits. Post-harvest fruit density can also be used in sorting fruits according to taste, because density is an indicator of dry matter, starch and sugars in unripe and in kiwifruit ripened during storage (70). The soluble solids (being mainly sugars) correlate to fruit density, and can be used for sorting kiwi fruit according to taste. The floating or sinking of this fruit in saline solutions could be used as a rapid method for this purpose.

VI.   MORPHOMETRIC PROPERTIES

Fruits come in various shapes, ranging from round to oval, oblique, oblong, oblate, obovate, elliptical, truncate, unequal, ribbed, regular, irregular, cylindrical, conical or pyramidal (71). The morphology of fruits can be evaluated by considering either bulk or individual units, but it is important to have information on the accurate estimate of shape, size, volume, specific gravity, surface area and other physical characteristics. Specific charts can be prepared for different fruits and using these charts, the shape of the fruit can be described either by a number on that chart or by the above-mentioned descriptive terms. The shape of fruits has significance in harvesting, handling, grading, processing and packaging operations. Most of the harvested fruits are graded roughly according to size and appearance. The size and shape of fruits are variable and depend upon the cultivars, climate and agricultural practices followed during growth of crops. Figure 24.2 shows an example of a standard chart describing shapes of fruits and vegetables (72).

VII.   MICROSCOPIC PROPERTIES

The study of physical properties of fruits requires some knowledge of their structure as well as their relationship to the chemical composition. As an example, citrus fruit consists of three distinctly different parts: the epicarp consists of the colored portion of the peel, called flavedo, and contains carotenoid pigments as well as oil glands (73). These oil glands contain essential oils characteristic of each citrus cultivar. Immediately under the epicarp is the mesocarp or albedo, a thick, white, spongy layer, rich in pectic substances and hemicelluloses. The combined albedo and flavedo are called the pericarp, but is commonly known as peel or rind. Next to the albedo is the edible portion of citrus fruits or the mesocarp. The mesocarp consists of many segments and, inside each segment, is located juice sacks or vesicles (Figure 24.3).

Many chemical components are distributed among various tissues of the citrus fruit. For example, flavanone glycosides are present in higher concentrations in the albedo than the juice sacks or the flavedo (74), and the bitter principles (limonin) are the highest in seeds and membranes (75). In contrast, grape berries always occur in clusters. A cluster consists of peduncle, capstem, rachis and berries. The grape bunch shape could be cylindrical, conical, pyramidal or globular. The grape berry consists of skin, pulp and seed. The seeds may vary from 0 to 4 per berry and are rich in tannins (5–8%) and oil (10–20%). The skin constitutes 5–12% of the mature grape berry and contains most of the aroma, coloring and flavoring components. The juice accounts for 80–90% of the grape berries.

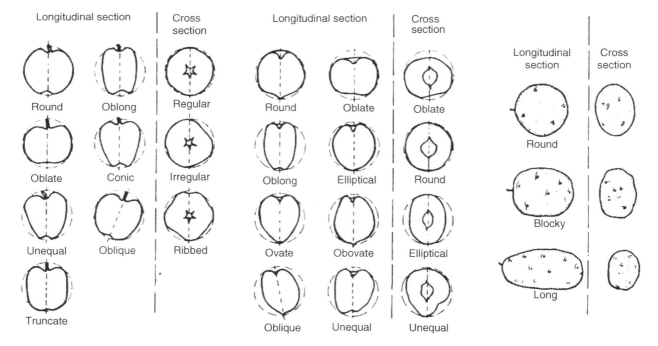

FIGURE 24.2 Example of charted standard for describing shape of fruits and vegetables. From left to right: apples, peaches, potatoes. (From Ref. 72.)

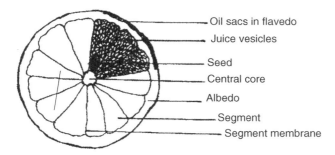

FIGURE 24.3 Cross section of a citrus fruit. (*Source:* Ref. 10.)

In physiological terms, a fruit can be defined as a structural entity arising from the development of the tissues that support the ovule. The basic function of fruit is the dispersal of seeds for the propagation of the species. Unripe fruits generally have rigid, well-defined structures, whereas ripe fruits have soft and diffused cell walls. An early model of the plant primary cell wall, in which cellulose fibrils are coated with hemicellulose and embedded in a matrix composed of pectin and protein (Figure 24.4), has been proposed by Keegstra et al. (76). This model has been further developed over the years and it provides an adequate basis to investigate fruit ripening.

The plant cell consists of a cytoplasm surrounded by a cell wall. Each cell is attached to adjacent cells by a pectin-rich middle lamella. The cytoplasms of these cells are interconnected with each other through plasmadesmata, which, in ripe fruits, provide a degree of cohesion. As long as the cell continues to register growth, its cell walls remain thinner. At this stage of fruit development,

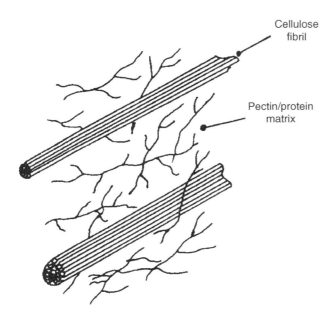

FIGURE 24.4 Idealized cell wall model. (*Source*: Ref. 76.)

it is known as the primary cell wall and consists of roughly 90% polysaccharides and 10% protein. The primary cell wall components can be further classified into pectic polysaccharides (34%), hemicellulose (24%), cellulose (23%) and hydroxy proline-rich glycoprotein (19%). The ratio of these constituents varies in cell walls of different plants (77). The way in which various components of the cell wall are linked with each other is not exactly known yet. It is believed that the various domains of pectic substances are covalently linked together to form complex molecules. It is suggested that the xyloglucan, which is the major hemicellulose in primary cell walls, is strongly held to the surface of cellulose fibers through hydrogen bonds. The glucuronoarabinoxylan may bind to themselves as well as to the cellulose in cell walls (78). Such interactions would help in the formation of cross-links of polymers in primary cell walls.

The hydroxyproline-rich glycoprotein has regions of helical conformation, which are likely to give a rod-like molecule to serve structural function in plant cells (79). It has also been proposed that glycoproteins could be held in the cell walls by phenolic cross-links, which may be glycoprotein-protein or glycoprotein-polysaccharide in nature (80). A number of phenolic materials, like ferulic acid, p-coumaric acid and other unidentified phenols, have been isolated from plant cell walls. Ferulic acid alone accounts for 0.5% of the cell wall and is suggested to be linked to the nonreducing termini of arabinose and/or galactose-containing regions of pectic substances. Such residues can cross-link to form diferuloyl bridges, which would reduce extensibility of plant cell walls and could also play a role in resistance to fungal pathogens (81).

In addition, a number of cell wall models have been proposed to account for some of the cell wall properties viz. their strength in withstanding turgor pressure; their ability to grow without loss of strength; and their behavior under chemical and enzymatic attack. A modified updated cell wall model is presented in Figure 24.5 (82). The major features of this model indicate that several layers of pectin form an outer network around the cell wall constituting the middle lamella. The pectic molecules are interconnected through covalent bonds as well as calcium bridges. Some regions of pectic molecules are strongly hydrogen bonded with xyloglucans, but the pectins also have some covalently linked glucose and xylose sugars. Under these pectin layers are several layers of cellulose fibers, which are noncovalently associated with xyloglucans. Xyloglucan-associated cellulose is cross-linked through hydroxyproline-rich glycoproteins in a noncovalent manner involving isodityrosine bridges (83).

Cell number, volume and weight that determine fruit weight are hormonally controlled during fruit growth. Most of the fruits develop by cell enlargement accompanied by cell division, which may continue briefly (e.g., in

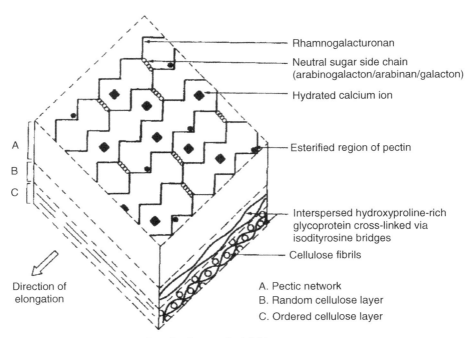

FIGURE 24.5   Modified model of primary cell wall. (*Source*: Ref. 82.)

peaches and other stone fruits) or until the end of fruit maturity (e.g., citrus fruits). Usually, all parts of the fruits do not grow at the same rate. In the case of apples, 25% of the total volume of fruit is contributed by the expansion of intercellular spaces. In the case of kiwi, the cells may enlarge more than 10–15 times. Some fruits (e.g., avocado) may increase 300,000 times in size compared with their flowers. Large fruits generally require additional anatomical features for nutrition or support or both for the developing seeds. Extra phloem in fruit vascular bundles and the increased amount of vascular tissues in the fruit wall and septa supply these nutrients to the developing seeds in large fleshy fruits. Collenchyma and sclerenchyma are common supportive and protective tissues, and the long axes of these cells are oriented crosswise to provide a mechanically strong structure to the fruits.

As large-sized fruits bring higher prices for the growers, the fruit breeders direct their research programs to achieve this objective (84). After the cessation of cell division, peach fruit growth depends mainly on cell enlargement. Mesocarp cells do not grow uniformly during the rapid fruit growth and maturation stage, and the length of radial cells near the stone is greater than that of the outer areas of the peach fruit. Flesh cell division continues 4–5 weeks after blooming, and increases in size only thereafter. In the case of the wild peach Ohatsumomo, cells divide more slowly than the commercial cultivars. This wild peach has the fewest and the smallest cells, thereby, giving a very small fruit. Similar

observations by Cano-Medrano and Darnell (85) on blueberry fruits indicated that the differences in final fruit size between pollinated and GA-induced parthenocarpic blueberry fruits were due to differences in cell enlargement rather than increase in cell numbers. Similarly, the size of apple fruits of Jonagold and Fuji cultivars is observed to be a function of cell numbers rather than cell diameter (86). However, in the case of early maturing American Summer Pearmain, Tsugaru and Senshu cultivars, fruit size correlates positively with cell diameter.

The texture of fruits is also affected by the changes in cell wall components that may take place during chilling or heat processing treatments. Various cytochemical and structural changes during cold storage affect the quality of peaches (87). Mealiness in fruits develops due to chilling injury as a result of separation of mesocarp paremchyma cells resulting in increased intercellular spaces and accumulation of pectic substances in the intercellular matrix. No structural change is observed in the cellulosic component of cell walls of peach fruit. In peaches having a leathery texture, mesocarp parenchyma cells collapse, the intercellular spaces increase and the pectin-positive staining in the intercellular matrix is significantly higher. As the internal breakdown progresses, dissolution of middle lamella, cell separation, irregular thickening of the primary cell wall and plasmolysis of the mesocarp parenchyma cells are observed. Addition to cell wall degradation leading to fruit softening, starch hydrolysis (possibly producing cell turgor changes) might also be involved in the softening of kiwifruit during storage at

0°C (88). As the softening of kiwi fruit progresses, more uronic acids and neutral sugars (galactose, arabinose and rhamnose) usually associated with pectic substances are detected.

Cell structure of fruits is related to their fracture behavior. Cell size and intercellular spaces influence the values of fracture toughness and fracture energy (40). In addition to cell size, cell wall chemistry also influences the mechanical properties of fruits and, hence, texture. Currently, there is a lot of interest in the mechanical properties of plant cell walls. Fruits derive their textural qualities from the strength and stiffness of these cell walls, bonding between the adjacent walls and the turgor pressure. Deformation of plant cells by a fine probe provides a measure of cell wall stiffness that is responsible for many of the mechanical properties of fruits (89).

Fruits are generally harvested at the fully mature stage, when the development and growth in size have ceased. In fully mature fruits, many physical as well as chemical changes take place that convert these fruits to a more palatable form. Astringency decreases due to reduced tannin content. Specific flavors are developed due to increased sweetness and lower acid content. The softening caused by breakdown of the cell wall structure in the pulp is often accompanied by a change in coloration. Chlorophyll in the chloroplasts of the outermost cells decreases while the carotenoids and anthocyanins develop in the fully mature fruits. Most of these changes are brought about by the coordinated action of a group of hydrolytic enzymes on the cell wall constituents. Apart from protein (mainly enzymes) synthesis, starch and pectic substances hydrolysis are the major biochemical changes occurring during fruit ripening. During normal ripening, polygalacturonase (PG) activity increases while the pectin esterase (PE) activity decreases. Any imbalance in their activity could lead to inadequate hydrolysis of pectic polymers, with increased accumulation of higher- molecular-weight pectin with low levels of esterification. The woolliness defect in nectarines is possibly due to the accumulation of these pectic polymers (90). Changes in cellulase (endo-β-1, 4-D-glucanase) activity are also associated with the modifications in cell wall structures during fruit ripening (91).

For further detailed description of the physical properties of fruits and food materials, the reader is referred to two excellent books in this area by Mohsenin (72) and Rao and Rizvi (58).

VIII. PROCESSING AND FUNCTIONAL PROPERTIES

Processing and functional properties of fresh fruits are of paramount importance because these affect the acceptability of fresh or processed fruit products by consumers. A set of quality characteristics important for consumer acceptance is associated with each fresh fruit or its processed products. A list of characteristics identified as important for consumer acceptance of fruits and vegetables is reviewed by Kader (92). Unfortunately, no single parameter/property can establish consumer acceptance forever since consumer tastes and preferences change with time and are also influenced by cultural factors. Careful evaluation of fruits in terms of consumer acceptance criteria is essential to identify target markets. As an example, German consumers prefer a fuller-flavored grapefruit, whereas French consumers prefer the one that is sweeter (93). Similarly, regional preferences exist for apples in the United States; New Englanders look for a tart taste, whereas Southerners prefer a sweeter one (94). Most packers and wholesale and retail dealers buy fruits on the basis of grades and standards established by the concerned agencies in each country.

IX. MATURITY INDICES

Maturity at harvest is one of the most important factors affecting the rate of change of quality during post-harvest handling and processing into finished products. Various biochemical and physiological changes occurring at the final stages of fruit development result in making these fruits palatable and acceptable to consumers. Maturity indices for fruits can be determined by estimating duration of development, measuring size, weight or density; physical attributes like color, firmness, moisture or total soluble solids content; chemical attributes like starch, sugar, acidity, flavor and aroma constituents; or the morphological characteristics (95, 96).

A. SIZE, MASS AND DENSITY

Size, mass and density can easily be employed as maturity indices. Each fruit becomes larger as it matures on the plant, although other production factors like moisture and soil fertility also affect the size of fruits. As an example, fruit size is considered the most effective method of segregating strawberries into different maturity classes (97). Similarly, specific gravity is used as an index of maturity in pineapples (98).

B. COLOR

Color is another useful measure of maturity in many fruits. Uniformity and intensity of color is important for appearance qualities and processing properties. Chlorophyll tends to disappear as the fruit matures on the plant as well as during handling and storage. On the other hand, anthocyanins are synthesized in light while fruits are attached to the plant, but are not affected greatly during post-harvest handling and storage. The pigments of grapes, anthocyanins (red, blue, purple and black), are modified by attachment of a glucose molecule. The basic part of grape pigments is made up of the five anthocyanins, namely, cyanidin, peonidin, delphinidin, petunidin and malvidin. The red pigments in grapes (anthocyanins) reach their full potential at complete maturity (99). Total anthocyanin content shows the greatest potential as a maturity index for raspberries (100). For the color measurement of horticultural crops, a number of techniques, like visual color matching charts, guides and dictionaries to match, light reflectance meter, light transmission meter, delayed light emission measurement and determination of various pigments (e.g., chlorophyll, carotene, lycopene, xanthophylls, anthocyanins), are now available. Standard color chips are now available for assessing the maturity of peaches (101). Colorimeters can also be used for this purpose (102). The technique of delayed light emission has the advantage of not being affected by orientation of multicolored fruits like papaya (103), cantaloupes (104) and peaches (105).

C. FIRMNESS

Firmness or softness of fruit is an important processing property that is affected by the stage of maturity and storage. Firmness is also an important textural quality attribute and is usually combined with other attributes, such as color and flavor, for use as an index of both maturity and processing quality of fruits. Use of firmness and total soluble solids as an index of maturity of kiwifruit, have been recommended by Crisosto et al. (106). Firmness can be measured using penetration force (Magness-Taylor pressure tester, Effegi penetrometer, Instron universal testing machine); fibrousness and toughness by shear force measurement using Instron, or resistance to cutting by a fibrometer or chemical analysis for crude fiber and lignin content; measurement of water content as an indication of succulence; measurement of extractable juice as an indication of juiciness; or by sensory evaluation for grittiness, crispness, mealiness, chewiness and oiliness. A nondestructive firmness tester is available for assessing the maturity of avacados (107). Firmness is a simple, rapid technique for measuring the harvest maturity of apples (108) and pears (109).

D. SOLIDS CONTENT

Moisture or solid contents are being used effectively as maturity indices of fruits for processing purposes. Iodine staining of starch has been used as a measure of assessing maturity in apples (110). Sugars are the industry standard to assess the maturity of cantaloupe and other melons. Soluble solids have been suggested as a maturity index for sweet cherries (111), and Brix-to-acid ratio for citrus fruits (112), whereas both soluble solids and acidity are used to assess maturity in grapes (113). Mango is another popular specialty fruit of great economic importance to the tropical regions, in which sugars and acids influence its consumer acceptability (114, 115). As a result of starch hydrolysis from increased amylase activity (116), sucrose

is the major sugar in ripe mango fruits. Among the reducing sugars, glucose is reported to be the major sugar by Selvaraj et al. (117), whereas fructose was identified as a predominant sugar by Medlicott and Thompson (118) and attributed this contradiction to the varying cultivars and storage conditions used by these workers.

E. FLAVOR

Flavor is another important processing property and consumption attribute critical to consumer acceptability and hidden attributes of fruits (119). Sweetness is a function of sugar concentration and sourness is a function of acidity, and their ratio determines the flavor of fruits because consumers perceive sweetness or sourness in terms of sugar:acid ratio. Sugar concentration is usually estimated by measuring the percentage of soluble solids (°Brix) using a refractometer (120) and acidity by titration against a standard base. The Brix-to-acid ratio (BAR) is used to assess the relative sweetness or sourness for most of the fruits for processing purposes. Lack of attention to flavor compounds in breeding programs has led to flavor mediocrity in many fruits. The lack of information on flavor compounds available to breeders on this complex trait is the main reason for this. Using gas chromatography, as many as 225 volatile compounds have been reported for grape cultivars (99, 121), although every particular cultivar emits a special aroma. Many fruits contain a single volatile compound, described as character impact compound, that imparts the flavor message by itself. Some examples of these character impact compounds given by Shewfelt (122) are ethyl-2-methylbutyrate in apples, γ-decalactone in peaches and isoamylacetate in bananas. However, the full aroma of any fruit is a subtle combination of many compounds, which makes it difficult for food scientists to duplicate fruit flavors in artificial beverages. A number of volatile compounds have been identified to be associated with the distinctive aroma of fresh as well as processed fruits. These aroma compounds, in combination with sweet, sour, salty, astringent and bitter sensations, endow characteristic flavors to various fruits and their products. The type of cultivars, post-harvest processing and storage treatments are some of the factors that affect the flavor properties of various fruits and their processed products (123, 124). The task of preserving and improving the aroma of fruits will probably be difficult. For example, some treatments currently used to prevent decay or to preserve texture and color can damage aroma quality. A higher concentration of carbon dioxide is usually used to reduce decay in strawberries and other similar crops, but it can induce fermentation (125). Similarly, lower oxygen levels, while extending the shelf life of apples and other pome fruits, can reduce aroma at stress levels, and may even cause off-flavors (126).

X. PROCESSING OF VARIOUS FRUITS

A. GRAPES

The grape cultivars are classified according to table, juice, wine and raisin purposes. Table grapes are consumed as fresh fruit or processed into juice. They should have large clusters and berries of appealing appearance, fine flesh with low acidity and high sugar content, and a few or no seeds (99). In the case of colored grapes, heating the crushed berries for 10–15 min at 60–63°C is necessary to extract the coloring matter (127). This heating step is not required in white grapes. Frozen grape juice concentrates are available commercially, but their production is less compared with orange juice concentrate. Wine grapes are processed into juice and fermented by yeast to make wine, or distilled to make a number of beverages (e.g., brandy). The wine grapes should have small clusters with round berries set compactly, with soft, juicy flesh of high acidity and low pH (128). After wine, raisins are the second most important product made from grapes (129). Raisin grapes are a special category of table grapes, having thin skin, firm flesh with higher sugar content and moderate to low acidity, with berries loosely attached in the clusters.

B. CITRUS FRUITS

Apart from consumption as fresh fruits, citrus fruits are processed mainly into juice, frozen concentrate, jam, marmalade, squash, candied peel and certain by-products, such as pectin, citric acid and peel oil. Juice is the most popular product prepared from citrus fruits and may be canned, frozen or chemically preserved (130). Frozen concentrated orange juice is by far the most important processed product from citrus in the U.S. The popularity of this product has been decreasing recently, as consumers prefer natural or minimally processed food products (131). Sound and mature fruits with the highest possible juice quality are desirable for producing orange juice. The color, flavor, yield and total soluble contents of the fruit increase with the maturity of oranges. The best quality orange juice can be produced if the Brix-acid ratio is between 13 and 19, 15 being the preferred one. Mid-season or late-season oranges give better yield and quality of juice than the early-season fruits (132). An excessive amount of peel oil in juice is undesirable. However, a certain amount of peel oil (0.01–0.02%) is considered to be necessary for obtaining maximum flavor (133).

C. DATE FRUIT

Date palm (*Phoenix dactylifera* L.) is an important food crop in the Middle Eastern countries. Rygg (134) reviewed the detailed description of the date growing regions of the world, date varieties and general cultivation practices. Four maturity stages have been recognized in date fruits, i.e., *kimri, khalal, rutab* and *tamer* (135). At the *kimri* stage, the fruit is hard in texture, green in color and can be used for making pickle, relish and chutney (16, 136). Depending upon the cultivar, the *khalal* stage fruit develops a yellow, red, purple or yellow-scarlet color, but retains a firm texture and can be used for making jam, butter, dates-in-syrup or for eating as fresh dates (137, 138). The *rutab* stage is characterized by softening of the half portion of the fruit, developing a dark brown color and increased sweetness and can be used for jam, butter, date bars, date paste or eaten as fresh (139). During the *tamer* stage, the whole of the fruit becomes soft in texture, wrinkled, relatively drier, and dark in color and attains maximum sweetness (140). The *tamer* fruits can be further dried for prolonged shelf life during storage. The chemical composition of date fruit varies with maturity. The total sugars in date fruits at the *kimri* stage range from 32.99 to 38.20%, but are increased to 77.97 to 79.39% at the *tamer* stage of maturity. The ranges of protein, fat, ash, pectin, tannin and crude fiber contents of *tamer* stage date fruits are 2.1–2.4, 0.1–0.2, 1.6–2.0, 1.3–1.9, 0.4–0.4 and 2.5–2.9%, respectively (141).

The majority of the date fruit is harvested at the *tamer* stage and enters the trade for consumption as such (142). Recently, the quantities of processed dates have been increasing rapidly as a result of encouragement and support being provided to the date fruit processing industry by governmental agencies. The development of newer processed date fruit products would increase the economic value of this crop immensely (143). Due to increased production and a decreased tendency towards direct consumption of date fruits, the introduction of processed products holds a great future for this important food crop of this arid region of the world.

D. BANANA

Bananas are one of the most important fruits grown in the tropics. About 50% of the bananas produced are consumed in Africa as a cooked vegetable and are often called plantains. A number of processed products, such as juice, pulp, puree, concentrate, canned slices, fruit bars, powder, wine, brandy and deep-fried chips, have been prepared from ripe as well as unripe bananas (144). Among all these products, banana puree is by far the most important processed product prepared from the pulp of ripe fruit. Puree finds uses in dairy desserts, bakery items, mixed fruit drinks, sauces and as a part of special diets in hospitals and nursing homes.

E. APPLE

Apples are processed into a variety of products, such as juice, concentrate, sauce, butter, preserve, vinegar, cider, wine, brandy, candy, jam, jelly and canned products. Apples are also dried as rings, chips or cubes. Edible pectin is also produced from the waste of the apple processing industry. Apple juice, in the form of clarified apple juice (made using pectinol enzymes), natural apple juice, pulpy apple juice and as fruit cocktail blends, is second only to orange juice in Europe and North America (145–147). Apple juice contains most of the soluble components of original apples, such as sugars, acids (mainly malic acid) and various other carbohydrates.

F. Mango

India contributes about 64% of the world production of mangoes. The mango fruit is highly perishable, highly susceptible to disease, extremes of temperature and physical injury, and international trade in fresh mango has been limited. However, a number of products, such as canned mango pulp, juice, nectar, squash, beverage, jam, chutney, pickle, mango leather and raw mango powder, are routinely prepared (6). Mango is one fruit that is processed and used at almost every stage of its growth. Raw mango fruit is mainly used for the preparation of raw mango powder, chutney and pickle (148, 149). Mango puree made from ripe mango is one of the most important processed products, which finds further utilization in various other products, such as nectar, squash, jam and ready-to-serve beverages. Puree is canned for long-term storage and marketing worldwide (150). Mango pulp can also be preserved using 350–700 ppm of sulfur dioxide, but there are reservations among consumers towards sulfited foods due to objectionable odor and toxicity (151). Mango fruit beverages are very nutritive drinks and are extremely popular in India and other Asian countries (152). Mango beverages with 20% puree in the formulation and with 20°Brix taste very sweet, so most of these mango drinks are adjusted to only 15°Brix, because less than 15% puree adversely affects the color and flavor of the mango beverages during storage.

Mango, being rich in a desirable strong flavor of its own, lends itself to be blended with a number of other fruits for the preparation of fruit juice cocktails (153). Blends of mango puree with papaya, orange, kinnow, apple, guava, pear, peach and apricot could be used in many foods (154). Peeled slices/cubes obtained from ripe or semiripe mango fruits can be preserved in sugar syrup, especially from some Indian mango cultivars, such as *Saheb Pasand*, having a TSS of 30°Brix that has bright-colored pulp and a firm texture (155). Mango leather, another popular product, is prepared by drying mango pulp to a final moisture content of about 15%. For the preparation of mango leather, an ideal ratio of 25:0.3 for TSS:acid has been suggested (156). Pectin when used at a rate of 0.5 to 0.75% improves the texture of mango leather.

G. Pineapple

The pineapple is one of the most important commercial fruits of the world, and is mainly used in processed form

as dessert fruits, or as canned pineapple in the form of slices, rings, chunks, fruit cocktails or in the preparation of juice and jams. Most of the world's pineapple production is canned, largely as slices, juice, chunks and diced pineapple (157). Pineapple juice contains neutral polysaccharides (mainly galactomannan), which are removed using pectinase, cellulase and hemicellulase enzymes (158). Pineapple juice stored at higher temperature (37°C) loses its color rapidly, but it can be stored at room temperature for 12–15 months without any serious loss in quality or nutritive value (159). Pineapple concentrate can also be prepared, which can be stored satisfactorily at 10–38°C by adding sulfur dioxide without any significant loss in color or flavor (160). Although attempts have been made to prepare pineapple juice powder by freeze-drying, the product has not become commercially viable (161).

H. Pear

Pears have been consumed primarily as fresh fruit, although a part of pear production has been processed into juice, wine, candy, dried and canned products (162). Pears are a good source of pectin, sugars and thiamine. Pear fruit is reported to help in maintaining a desirable acid/base balance in the human body. Because of its low sucrose content, pear fruit is also recommended for diabetics. The pear fruit is either canned as juice, or as chunks in fruit cocktail along with other fruits. Puree prepared from pear fruit finds uses in baby foods, pear butter and jams. Pear juice concentrate is finding wider applications in beverages and fruit spreads. Pear candy prepared from sand pear and Bagygosha cultivars are reported to retain about 50% of the ascorbic acid during 40 weeks of storage at room temperature (163). The stone pear is suitable for jam, chutney, clarified juice and preserve (164).

I. Plum

Plums are generally consumed as fresh fruit, and only a small quantity is used for canning, dehydration and beverages. Whole plums fruits with higher sugar content and firm flesh are dried and are called prunes. More than 50% of the total world production of plums comes from the U.S., the former U.S.S.R., China and Romania (6). Apart from canning, plums are used for the preparation of jam, jelly, beverages, wines and brandy. Prune juice produced from dried plums is rich in minerals and acts as a mild laxative. Use of pectolytic enzymes increases the yield of prune juice and aids in easy filtration (165). Pectolytic enzymes not only increase plum juice yield, but also drastically decrease the apparent viscosity and improve the color and clarity without affecting the flavor (166). A natural plum juice containing pulp has also been prepared recently (167). Being high in acidity, no more than 40% of plum juice can be used in the preparation of beverages like sweetened plum juice. About 20% of enzymatically extracted plum juice with 15°Brix has been found to be optimum for preparing nectar (168).

Preparation of plum juice concentrate is one of the best options of utilizing fruit during glut seasons. Plum juice can be concentrated under vacuum to 73°Brix. This juice concentrate has higher total soluble solids, reducing sugars, total solids, browning and viscosity, but the pectin content and acidity are slightly reduced (169). Firmer fruits are generally preferred for canning than softer fruits. Softening of ripe plums during canning can be prevented using 500 ppm of calcium chloride (170). About 75% of the world supply of dried prunes comes from California and the Pacific Northwest. Dried prunes, prune flakes, nuggets and granules are also produced commercially for use as fillings in bakery products. Low-moisture prune powder is also available for use as a sweetening and flavoring agent in whole wheat and rye bread formulations. The plum pulp is also utilized in ice cream mix, confectionery items and meat sauces (171). Wine or brandy prepared from fruits other than grapes are referred to by the name of that fruit used. Plum wines are quite popular in Germany and many Pacific coastal states of the U.S. The method for making plum wine or brandy is similar to that of grapes (172).

J. PEACH

Peach and its smooth-skin mutant nectarine are some of the most important stone fruits in temperate regions of the world. Apart from consumption as fresh fruit, peaches are usually canned. Only a small portion is utilized as frozen or dried or used as jams, peach conserve, marmalade, peach butter, fruit bar, pickle and beverages (173). Peach puree is the basic starting material for the preparation of many other products, such as jam, nectar, juice, baby foods and ready-to-serve beverages. Initial color and viscosity of puree have been considered as important quality characteristics for further processing (174). Commercial canning of peaches is the major industry in the world. Peaches can be canned as whole, halves, quarters or slices, usually in sugar syrup or juices of other fruits (175). The peach fruit for canning should be picked at or near optimum maturity and should be of uniform large size (a dia of 6.03 cm or more), good yellow color and of good cooking quality (176). Steep preservation is another simple technique that could be used for peaches (177).

K. BERRIES

Juices from berries are widely used for the manufacture of jams, jellies, beverages, wine, fruit yogurt and ice cream (178). To increase juice yield from berries, pectolytic enzymes are added to the pulp (0.1g/kg of fruit). The enzymes are allowed to act on the cell wall pectic substances to release juice. The juice could be preserved by the addition of antimicrobial agents (potassium benzoate or sodium sorbate) followed by pasteurization (179). The juice can also be concentrated, but the susceptibility to undesirable changes in flavor during storage has hindered its application in food and beverages (180). Wines from strawberry, raspberry and kiwifruit are also prepared (181–183). Use of pectolytic enzymes for increasing juice extraction yield is essential for making wine with desirable clarity, color and flavor.

L. APRICOT

All of the mechanically harvested apricots (roughly more than 50% of total production) in the U.S. are used for processing, mostly for canning. About 84% of the total production of apricots in the U.S. is canned, dried and frozen (184). The canning process for apricots is the one typically used for most stone fruits. The textural quality of canned apricots is affected by a number of factors, such as sterilization conditions, maturity of fruits and storage conditions. Even immature fruits can be canned after treating them with ethylene for two days (185). Dried apricots are another important snack, becoming popular with present-day consumers because of their desirable color, flavor and nutritive value. Dried apricots are produced from fully ripe and plump fruits (186). High natural sugar level and low pH of dried apricots prevents microbial spoilage and enzymatic deterioration in quality during storage. The apricot fruits unsuitable for canning are utilized for the preparation of juice and concentrates. The juice concentrate can be used for the preparation of nectar and baby foods. The concentrated juice can also be dried to obtain powder that can be used in bakery products, beverages, jellies and desserts (165). Because of excellent natural flavor, apricots are also processed to jams, jellies and preserves. Due to higher susceptibility to browning and oxidation during freezing, frozen apricots are not very popular.

M. BY-PRODUCTS OF THE FRUIT PROCESSING INDUSTRY

Fruits are marketed either as fresh produce or processed as frozen, dehydrated, canned, pureed, juices, jams, jellies, marmalades, pickles, chutney and in many more forms. During these processing operations, a large proportion of fruit ends up as residue that needs to be handled properly to avoid environmental pollution while generating additional revenue for the processing industry. The wastes arising out of the fruit processing industry can be utilized for the preparation of human food, animal feed, fertilizers, soil conditioners or for landfill (187).

Dietary fiber is extracted from apple and pear pomace to obtain a product containing 56 and 77% fiber, respectively. This product has the consistency of whole wheat flour with a bland taste and is utilized in baked goods, breakfast cereals, granola products, laxatives, pharmaceutical preparations and pet foods (188). Peels and cores from apples can be utilized to produce vinegar and jelly juice stock. Apple pomace can be extracted with liquid carbon dioxide to produce an intensely flavored fraction. Pectin is an important by-product from the apple processing waste. Different apple cultivars are reported to vary in pectin yield, jelly grade and other qualities of the extracted pectin (150). Pectin extracted with alcohol from apple pomace can be dried to 5% moisture content and used for jam and jelly-making. About 250 g of citric acid can be obtained by growing *Aspergillus niger* on apple pomace (one kg solids) under controlled conditions. Around 30–35% of the pear fruit ends up as waste during canning operations. The waste from pear fruit processing industries has been used in the preparation of vinegar, brandy, denatured alcohol and sugar syrup or has also been dried for use as cattle feed (170). Kiwifruit peel is another suitable source of citric acid production. In the presence of 2% methanol at 30°C, about 100 g of citric acid per kg of kiwifruit peel can be produced by solid-state fermentation using *Aspergillus niger* (193). Apple pomace can be used as animal feed, either fresh or as dried product (150).

Citrus fruit processing waste can be utilized for the production of citric acid, but the process is uneconomical because citric acid now produced by microbial fermentation is much lower in cost. Citrus peels contain 2.5 to 5.5% pectin, which can be extracted with acidified water. After centrifugation, the clarified pectin solution is dried to obtain pectin powder. By the cold pressing method, fresh orange peel also yields about 0.54% superior quality oil, which finds uses in juice and squash manufacture (199). Guava fruit is another important source of food-grade pectin. During the extraction of pectin by hot water-boiling, use of sodium hexametaphosphate or 1:1 mixture of ammonium oxalate and oxalic acid at 0.25–0.75% concentration gives higher yields of pectin with high jelly grade (200).

About 40 to 60% of the fruit intake ends up as waste in the mango processing factories. This fruit waste consists of 12–15% peel, 5–10% pulp waste and 15–20% mango seed kernel (160). The pectin obtained from mango peel is comparable with the pectin extracted from citrus peel (161). Mango peel is a very good source of sugars (48.1%), pectin (12.9%), protein (3.9%), fiber (8.4%), tannins (2.3%) and minerals (2.9%; all values on dry basis) and constitutes about 13% of the mango fruit (161). Good quality pectin obtained from mango peel can be used in the manufacture of jam, jelly, marmalades and many pharmaceuticals. Depending upon the cultivars, mango kernel (or stone) is about 45.7 to 72.8% of the mango fruit and is a good source of starch (57.8%), fat (13.7%), tannins (10.6%) and protein (7.1%) on a dry basis (162). Among the other by-products, mango kernel fat has attracted major attention because it could be a very good substitute for tallow and cocoa butter in soups and confectionery products (201, 202). Cake left after the extraction of kernel oil could substitute for wheat and maize flour in animal feed as it is a good source of many essential amino acids. Mango peel is also suitable as a supplement in fish feed. The waste from mango processing plants can be used for biogas production. Recently, a mixture of 5-(12-*cis*-hepta decenyl) and 5-pentadecyl resorcinol has been isolated from mango peel, and this has been found to be effective against *Alternaria alternata*, a fungus that causes black spot disease in mango fruit (163).

Guava seeds are usually discarded during processing, but these seeds are rich in oil (5–13%), which can be utilized in salad dressing. Guava seed oil is especially rich in essential fatty acids, such as oleic (54%) and linoleic (29%) acids (203).

Green banana fruit, pseudostems and foliage are good sources of energy and serve as cattle feed after supplementation with a protein source. About 1000 banana plants can yield 20–25 tonnes of pseudostems, which contain about 5% edible starch that finds a number of industrial uses (145). Banana stem waste is another important waste product that can be used for growing food yeast (146). The pineapple processing industry waste can be utilized for the preparation of several products, such as citric acid, cattle feed, sugar syrup, wine, bromolain enzyme, wax and sterols (169). Peach processing generates a lot of waste in the form of peel, seeds and trimmings, which contain proteins, polysaccharides, sugars, amino acids and pectin. After enzymatic treatment, peach solid waste may be utilized for ethanol production (186).

Production of citric acid from fruit processing solid wastes using *Aspergillus niger* in solid-state fermentation has been suggested (193). Apart from these specific by-products of commercial value, the waste from most of the fruit processing plants could be utilized in animal feeds and production of ethanol, biomass and many other chemicals.

XI. NUTRITIONAL AND HEALTH PROPERTIES

Consumption of fruits and vegetables by adults in the U.S. has not reached the recommended level suggested by nutritionists and other health professionals. Unfortunately, children consume even less. Various governmental agencies, professional associations, food processors and health organizations are making efforts to encourage increased consumption of fruits and vegetables (204), because intake of fruits and vegetables has an inverse association with the risk of cardiovascular diseases and mortality in the U.S. population (205). Fruits are rich not only in dietary fiber, vitamins and minerals, but a number of bioactive compounds present therein are strong antioxidants and function to modify the metabolic activation/detoxification of carcinogens.

A. FRUITS AND DIETARY FIBER

A low intake of dietary fiber is associated with a spectrum of degenerative diseases, such as constipation, diverticular disease, coronary heart disease, hiatus hernia, appendicitis, varicose veins, piles, diabetes, obesity, bowel cancer and gallstones (206). Soluble dietary fiber, including pectic substances and hydrocolloids, is present in fruits, vegetables, legumes and oat bran. By-products from fruit processing industries are potential sources of both soluble and insoluble dietary fiber in our diet (207). Association between fruit, vegetable and dietary fiber consumption and colorectal cancer risk in the U.S. population has been observed (208). The total fruit and vegetable consumption is inversely associated with colorectal cancer risk, but subanalyses show this association is largely due to fruit consumption. The association is stronger and the dose-response effect is more evident among those individuals who consume the lowest amounts of fruits and vegetables (less than 1.5 servings) compared with those who consume greater amounts (more than 2.5 servings/d).

To assess the role of certain tropical fruits, such as lychee, guava and ripe mango, in the prevention of cardiovascular diseases, contents of total and water-soluble dietary fiber are determined by Gorinstein et al. (209). Lychee, guava and ripe mango had a total fiber content of 2.2, 5.6 and 3.1 g/100 g fresh fruit and soluble fiber of 1.05, 2.7, 1.51 g/100 g fresh fruit, respectively. Use of lychee, guava and ripe mango could be suitable for the prevention of cardiovascular disease through dietary methods. The non-starch polysaccharides in Starkspur Supreme Delicious apples from Arkansas ranges from 1.41 to 1.98 g/100 g fresh fruit (210). Total fiber contents in four berries (blackberries, cranberries, red raspberries, strawberries) ranges from 1.0 to 7.0% fresh weight (14). Peeling and canning changes the uronic acid and neutral sugar contents of soluble and insoluble fiber fractions of several fruits.

Rosado et al. (211) analyzed 24 fruits for dietary fiber contents. The total dietary fiber (wet weight basis) ranged from 0.3 to 7%, and soluble fiber contents (% of total dietary fiber) ranged from 6 to 44%. The total dietary fiber contents in 47 Italian fruits range from 0.22 to 6.47 g/100 g for fresh fruits and 5.0 to 30.0 g/100 g for dry fruits (212). Marlett (213) analyzed 23 fruits and reported a mean dietary fiber content of 1.4 ± 0.7 g/100 g fresh weight, and 13 to 20% of this was soluble fiber fraction. Pectin constituted 15 to 30% of the total dietary fiber contents among fruits. The total dietary fiber contents of five fruits that are most commonly consumed in Malaysia range from 1.5 to 3.6% on a fresh weight basis (214). The incorporation of prunes in the diet as a source of dietary fiber lowers plasma low-density-lipoprotein cholesterol more significantly (3.9 mM) than when grape juice (4.1 mM) is consumed (215). Prunes also significantly lower fecal bile acid content of lithocholic acid. Fecal output is nearly 20% higher after consuming prunes, but the total bile acid content is unchanged.

B. PHYTOCHEMICALS IN FRUITS

Oxygen during normal metabolism yields a number of reactive oxygen species (ROS), most of which are free radicals having an odd number of electrons. These reactive species initiate lipid peroxidation, a chain reaction that can oxidize DNA, proteins (enzymes) and cell membranes (216). It is now proposed that oxygen free radicals are involved in several pathological conditions, such as oxidation of LDL and development of atherosclerosis, different stages of cancer development, autoimmune destruction of β cells leading to diabetes, inflammatory damage in asthma, in rheumatoid arthritis, age-related macular degeneration (AMD) and oxidation of lens proteins leading to cataracts (217). To neutralize these reactive species, the body's defense system is equipped with a few enzymes, some high-molecular-weight antioxidant proteins, and some low-molecular antioxidants, like ascorbate, vitamin E, β-carotene, glutathione and uric acid. If this balance is overwhelmed, oxidative stress builds up and this becomes the underlying cause of aging and some of the age-related diseases, such as cancer, cataracts, AMD and cardiovascular disease (218). Fruits have the ability to protect us against this free radical damage if consumed regularly. Fruits, like prunes, raisins, blueberries, cranberries and blackberries, have the highest antioxidant capacity, followed by strawberries, raspberries, plums, oranges, red grapes, red cherries, kiwi fruit, pink grapefruit, bananas and apples (219).

Many bioactive phytochemicals (or neutraceuticals) present in fruits have the ability to provide immense health benefits to us. These phytochemicals include terpenoids, phenolics, alkaloids and fiber. The role of these compounds against cancers, coronary heart disease, diabetes, hypertension, inflammation, microbial, viral and parasitic infections, ulcers, etc., has been recently reviewed (220). In addition to primary antioxidants, such as ascorbate, vitamin E and carotenes, most of the other phytochemicals present in fruits act as antioxidants to reduce the oxidative damage caused to lipids, proteins, nucleic acids and other cellular targets by reactive oxygen species (ROS). The effect of these antioxidants on changes in oxidative stress status associated with aging and other chronic conditions, like diabetes, cardiovascular diseases, cataracts and age-related macular degeneration, is being actively explored at Tufts Nutrition Antioxidant Research Laboratory (2). Although many other foods (such as vegetables, whole grains and whey proteins) also play an important role, the contribution of fruits to human nutrition and health is equally important.

C. FRUIT INTAKE AND CANCER RISK

The relation between cancer risk and the consumption of fruits and vegetables is now gaining a lot of attention

(221). Diets rich in fruits and vegetables are more strongly related to a lower risk of epithelial cancers of the respiratory and digestive tract. However, the intake of fruits and vegetables does not show a strong association with hormonally related cancers such as breast, endometrium, ovary and prostrate. No information is available on the total intake of phenolic phytochemicals. If this group includes anthocyanins, flavanols, isoflavones, phenolic acids and tannins, the total phenolic phytochemical intake may be up to hundreds of milligrams per day (222). This intake could be even higher in populations where red wine, soy products, lentils and beans are consumed. This information on the intake of phenolic phytochemicals would be useful because most of these phenolics have antioxidant properties with similar biological activities. Some of these phenolics trap nitrates and prevent the formation of mutagenic N-nitroso compounds in foods (223). The intake of these N-nitroso compounds is known to induce cancers of the nasopharynx, esophagus and stomach (224). In a recent study, regular consumption of fruits was strongly associated with reduced risk of many types of cancers (225). The strongest evidence correlates with the reduced risk of the mouth, esophagus, pharynx, lung, stomach and colon, whereas moderately strong evidence exists for cancers of the breast, pancreas and bladder.

D   ANTIOXIDANTS/PHYTOCHEMICALS IN FRUITS

Until recently, fruits were known only as a source of certain vitamins, minerals and dietary fiber, but now a number of nonessential bioactive compounds (phytochemicals) are attracting the attention of food scientists and health professionals. Among the vitamins present in fruits, ascorbic acid has been investigated extensively. Ascorbic acid is a water-soluble antioxidant, which can easily be oxidized to form a free radical semidehydroascorbic acid that is quite stable. As ascorbic acid can lose an electron very easily, it is a very effective antioxidant in cytoplasm of biological systems (226). Blood levels of vitamin C above 49 μmol/L have been associated with a 64% reduced risk of cataracts in a Mediterranean population (227). Although more than 600 carotenoids have been identified so far, only about 50 of these possess vitamin A activity. Carotenoids, being lipid-soluble, act as antioxidants to protect the cell membranes of biological systems by quenching singlet oxygen and scavenging free radicals. Lycopene has the greatest antioxidant activity, followed by α-carotene, β-carotene, lutein and cryptoxanthin (228). Autumn olive (*Elaeagnus umbellata* Thunb.) bears yellow or brilliant red berries, which are very rich in lycopene (229) containing 15 to 54 mg from naturalized plants and 17 to 48 mg/100 g of fresh fruit from four cultivars with red-pigmented fruit. In contrast, the fresh tomato fruit had only about 3 mg of lycopene per 100 g. In addition, this fruit also contained α-cryptoxanthin, β-carotene, lutein, phytoene

and phytofluene. This newly identified fruit (Autumn olive) can become an excellent source of lycopene and other carotenoids in our diet.

Lutein is a well-known carotenoid, whose intake has been shown to be inversely associated with ocular diseases, such as cataracts and age-related macular degeneration (230, 231). Lutein offers protection to the cells of the macula by acting as an antioxidant against the reactive oxygen species (232). The consumption of carotenoids from various sources does not reduce plasma carotenoid concentrations in the medium term, thus suggesting the eating of a diet rich in a variety of fruits and vegetables (233). Limonoids (terpenes) present in citrus fruits are shown to inhibit Phase I enzymes and induce Phase II detoxification enzymes in the liver and provide protection against cancer (234).Vitamin E is another major lipid-soluble antioxidant that protects the polyunsaturated fatty acids in cell membranes against free radicals and singlet oxygen species. Glutathione, selenium and flavonoids are the other water-soluble antioxidants. About 2000 chemical distinct flavonoids (flavonols, flavones, flavanones, isoflavones and flavanols) are present in fruits that may have antioxidant activity.

Phenolics, such as tannins and flavonoids, present in fruits have also been studied extensively as antioxidant protectants for humans. Plant phenolics are mostly produced through phenylpropanoid pathways and comprise a variety of compounds, such as cinnamic acids, benzoic acids, flavonoids, proanthocyanidins, stilbenes, coumarins, lignans and lignins. They are known to be strong antioxidants and prevent oxidative damage to DNA, lipids and proteins, which may play a role in chronic diseases like cancer and cardiovascular disease (235). Ferulic acid (a phenolic compound), a component of the plant cell wall, has the ability to mop up damaging free radicals and reactive oxygen species (236). One possible use for ferulic acid may be as a stimulant for sperm motility in fertility treatments or during *in vitro* fertilization. The polymeric tannins from grape seeds function as antioxidants and neutralize the effects of oxidative stress induced both by the deficiency of other vitamins and an atherogenic diet (31). Flavonoids are known to perform against free radicals, free radical-mediated cellular signaling, allergies, inflammation, platelets aggregation, ulcers, tumors, microbe viruses and hepatotoxins (237). Catechins and gallic acid present in grapes and berries have free radical scavenging activity, and inhibit eicosanoid synthesis and platelet aggregation.

Anthocyanidins are water-soluble flavonoids that are the principal pigments in fruits and are known to have antioxidative properties (238). Among the flavonoids, anthocyanins are reported to possess higher antioxidant activity as measured by oxygen radical absorbance capacity (ORAC) equivalents (239). On a fresh weight basis, the anthocyanin content in fruits, such as blackberries, blueberries, cranberries, raspberries, strawberries and boysenberries, may range from 200 to 4950 mg/kg. An intake of 100 to 150 g of these fruits could easily give us 100 to 200 mg of anthocyanins, which are well above the suggested levels (240). Intake of two to five servings of fruits and vegetables per day would result in 1200 to 1640 ORAC equivalents for the person and may be responsible for the health benefits achieved with increased consumption of these foods. The polyphenols from blueberries and cranberries possess antioxidative and anti-inflammatory activities in endothelial cells and are reported to be beneficial in reducing initiation or development of cardiovascular diseases (241).

E. STABILITY OF PHYTOCHEMICALS DURING PROCESSING

Food technologists are currently busy adding bioactive phytochemicals for developing new food products. These formulated foods will not only meet the nutritional needs of growth and maintenance, but are also expected to provide additional health benefits to consumers. Some of these targeted benefits are preventing disease and improving physical performance and the overall quality of life. The biochemical aspects, physiological effects and health benefits of phytochemicals in fruits were reviewed recently (242). The topics covered are characteristics of major fruit phytochemicals (phenols and carotenoids); physiological effects of phenols, carotenoids and other bioactive compounds (limonoids, ascorbate, limonene and folate) found in citrus fruits; evidence of health benefits, antioxidative and anticancer properties of bioactive compounds present in berries; and composition and physiological effects of phytochemicals in strawberries, apples, melons and some other fruits.

The antioxidant capacity of these phytochemicals is affected not only by various horticultural factors, but also by the food processing practices employed in the industry. The antioxidant capacity due to phenols in blueberries is decreased by food processing practices, such as heating and aeration (243). The composition, antioxidative capacity and levels of anthocyanins and total phenols in cultivated blueberries (*Vaccinium corymbosum* L.) and wild blueberries (*V. augustifolium* Aiton) are influenced by the method of extraction (244). The highest anthocyanin, total phenolic contents and antioxidative capacity are observed when aqueous methanol is used as a solvent. Irrespective of the solvent used, wild blueberries give higher values for these three parameters than the cultivated blueberries.

The temperature, pH and oxygenation during extraction of anthocyanins affect the antioxidative activity of extracted blueberries (245). Extraction of fruits at 60°C gives higher recovery of anthocyanins and antioxidant capacity than the extract obtained at 25°C, but subsequent loss in anthocyanins during room temperature storage

occurs only in the former. Antioxidant capacity is higher in pH 1 extracts than those at pH 4 and 7. Oxygenation is detrimental to both the anthocyanins and antioxidant capacity. The antioxidant capacity of these processed products is positively correlated with anthocyanin (R=0.92) and phenolic (R=0.95) contents, and negatively correlated with percentage polymeric color (R=0.64). In general, the higher the extent of processing treatment, the lower is the antioxidant capacity. Simple colorimetric tests for anthocyanins and phenols are available to evaluate their antioxidant capacity in processed food products.

The antioxidant capacity, ascorbic acid, phenolics and anthocyanins of small fruits (strawberries, raspberries, cultivated and wild blueberries) during storage at 0, 10, 20 and 30°C for up to eight days are investigated (246). These four fruits vary significantly in total antioxidant activity, which is strongly correlated with the total phenolics (R=0.83) and anthocyanins (R=0.90). Antioxidant capacity is three times higher in blueberry species than either strawberries or raspberries. Ascorbic acid contents differ significantly among these fruit species, strawberries and raspberries having almost four times more ascorbate than blueberries. No loss of ascorbate is observed after eight days of storage at any of the temperatures in strawberries or cultivated blueberries, but there are losses in two other fruit species. Storage at a temperature higher than 0°C increases antioxidant capacity of strawberries and raspberries, and it is accompanied by increases in anthocyanins in strawberries, and increases in anthocyanins and total phenols in raspberries. Ascorbic acid contributes very little (0.4–9.4%) to the total antioxidant capacity of these fruits. The increase in antioxidant capacity through post-harvest phenolic synthesis, therefore, indicates the possibility of enhancing the health benefits of these small fruit crops.

XII. FUTURE CONSIDERATIONS

Fruits are grown universally in almost every part of the world and serve as vital sources of essential vitamins, minerals, dietary fiber and many other bioactive compounds. Fruits are highly perishable in nature, and the growth of post-harvest technology is essential to minimize losses during their production, processing, handling and transportation. Fruits are processed into a variety of products, and are consumed either alone or in combination with grains, milk and milk products to provide maximum nutritional advantages to consumers.

Apart from a botanical basis, fruits have been classified solely on color or other physical properties. Most of these physical properties (viz. size, mass, total solids, firmness, density, color, specific gravity and porosity) are well correlated with the chemical composition, nutritional value and processing quality of finished products. The classification based on color serves as a useful indicator, not only for the fruit breeders, but also for the food scientists to look for many phytochemicals (e.g., carotenoids from yellow, orange fruits, anthocyanins from colored fruits). This has opened up a vast opportunity for fruit biotechnologists to pursue a significant area of health-based fruit quality modification to selectively increase levels of different vitamins and other phytochemicals in various fruit species in coming years. This will give another boost to the fruit-based agro-processing industry around the world. Considering the scope of functional foods based on phytochemicals, nowhere is the marketing transformation more visible than among the fruit growers and processors. As most fruits contain bioactive compounds that have extraordinary health-promoting characteristics, the growers, cooperatives and processors are quick to move these products to the frontline of their marketing programs.

While phytochemicals in fruits clearly show promise to prevent many diseases, important scientific questions are yet to be answered. We have to look for the answers to some of the questions like "Which of these phytochemicals are more effective, what is the mechanism of their action, and more importantly, how to preserve these bioactive compounds during processing?" We also need to identify and quantify these bioactive compounds in foods, their bioavailability, pharmacokinetics and metabolism in humans, determination of the relationship between molecular structure and antioxidant capacity, mutual interaction of these phytochemicals in the human digestive tract when consumed together, doses required for their effectiveness, and their stability during processing, storage and distribution of these food products right up to our dining table.

REFERENCES

1. Anon. Combining nutrients for health benefits. Food Technol 55(2):42–47, 2001.
2. J Blumberg, K Cappelland. Phytochemical research at Tufts Nutrition Labs. Food Technol 56(3):23, 2002.
3. JB Biale. Post-harvest biochemistry of tropical and sub-tropical fruits. Adv Food Res 10:293–354, 1961.
4. RM Smock. Controlled atmosphere storage of fruits. Hort Rev 1:301–304, 1979.
5. RL Shewfelt. Post harvest treatment for extending the shelf life of fruits and vegetables. Food Technol 40(5):70–74, 1986.
6. FAO. FAO Production Year Book: FAO Statistics Series No. 142, Vol. 51. Rome: Food and Agriculture Organization, 1997, pp 151–173.
7. LG Smith, SM Somerset. Fruits of temperate climate. In: R McRae, RK Robinson, MJ Saddler. eds. Encyclopedia of Food Science, Food Technology and Nutrition. London: Academic Press, 1993, pp 2083.
8. SJR Underhill. Fruits of tropical climate. In: R McRae, RK Robinson, MJ Saddler. eds. Encyclopedia of Food Science, Food Technology and Nutrition. London: Academic Press, 1993, p 2108.
9. AA Kader, DM Barrett. Classification, composition of fruits and post harvest maintenance of quality. In: LP Somogyi, HS Ramaswamy, YH Hui, eds. Processing Fruits: Science and Technology, Vol. I. Biology, Principles, and Applications. Lancaster/Basel: Technomic Publishing Co Inc, 1996, pp 2–3.
10. DK Salunkhe, SS Kadam. Introduction. In: DK Salunkhe, SS Kadam. eds. Handbook of Fruit Science and Technology: Production, Composition, Storage and Processing. New York: Marcel Dekker, 1995, pp 1–6.
11. L Prosky, NG Asp, TF Schweizer, JW DeVries, I Furda. Determination of insoluble, soluble and total dietary fiber in foods and food products: Interlaboratory study. JAOAC 71:1017–1023, 1988.
12. O Theander, P Aman, E Westerlund, H Graham. The Uppsala method for rapid analysis of total dietary fiber. In: I Furda. CJ Brine, eds. New Developments in Dietary Fiber. New York: Plenum Press, 1990, pp 273–281.
13. P Hollingsworth. Growing neutraceuticals. Food Technol 55(9):22, 2001.
14. JA Marlett, NW Vollendorf. Dietary fiber content and composition of different forms of fruits. Food Chem 51(1):39–44, 1994.
15. DK Salunkhe, HR Bolin, NR Reddy. Storage, processing and nutritional quality of fruits and vegetables, Vol. I. Fresh fruits and vegetables. Boca Raton, FL: CRC Press, 1991, pp 84–86.
16. SN Al-Hooti, JS Sidhu, J Al-Otaibi, H Al-Amiri, H Qabazard. Utilization of date fruits at different maturity stages for variety pickles. Adv Food Sci 19(1/2):1–7, 1997.
17. T Nogalingam. Avocado. In: R McRae, RK Robinson, MJ Saddler. eds. Encyclopedia of Food Science, Food Technology and Nutrition. London: Academic Press, 1993, pp 289–295.
18. DR Maestro. Relationship between the composition and ripening of the olive and quality of the oil. Acta Hort 286:441–446, 1990.
19. H Van Gorsel, C Li, EL Kerbel, M Smits, AA Kader. Compositional characteristics of prune juice. J Agric Food Chem 40:784–786, 1992.
20. WB Sinclair, ET Bartholomew, RD Ramsey. Analysis of the organic acids in orange juice. Plant Physiol 20:3–5, 1945.
21. Y Selvaraj, DK Pal, NG Diwakar, AG Purohit, SD Shikhamany. Sugars, organic acids and amino acids in Anab-e-Shahi grape during growth development. J Food Sci Technol 16:136–139, 1978.
22. FA Tomas-Barberan, MI Gil, P Cremin, AL Waterhouse, B Hess-Pierce, AA Kader. HPLC-DAD-ESIMS analysis of phenolic compounds in nectarines, peaches and plums. J Agric Food Chem 49(10):4748–4760, 2001.
23. NK Given, MA Venis, D Grierson. Phenylalanine ammonia lyase activity and anthocyanin synthesis in ripening strawberry fruit. J Plant Physiol 133:25–30, 1998.
24. M Gil, C Garcia-Viguera, F Artes, FA Tomas-Barberan. Changes in pomegranate juice pigmentation during ripening. J Sci Food Agric 68:77–81, 1995.

25. W Kalt, JE McDonald. Chemical composition of low bush blueberry cultivars. J Amer Soc Hort Sci 121:142–146, 1996.

26. Y Dong, D Mitra, A Kootsra, C Lister, J Lancaster. Post harvest stimulation of skin color in Royal Gala apple. J Amer Soc Hort Sci 120:95–100, 1995.

27. TY Lin, PE Koehler, RL Shewfelt. Stability of anthocyanin in the skin of Starkrimson apples stored unpackaged, under heat shrinkable wrap and in-package modified atmosphere. J Food Sci 54:405–407, 1989.

28. DM Holcroft, MI Gil, AA Kader. Effect of carbon dioxide on anthocyanins, phenylalanine ammonia lyase and glucosyltransferase in the arils of stored pomegranates. J Amer Soc Hort Sci 123(1):136–140, 1998.

29. JJ Giovannoni. Genetic control of fruit quality, and prospects for nutrient modification. Hort Science 37(3):453–456, 2002.

30. G Ronen, GL Carmel, D Zamir, J Hirschberg. An alternative pathway to beta-carotene formation in plant chloroplasts discovered by map-based cloning of Beta and old-gold color mutations in tomato. PNAS USA 97:11102–11107, 2000.

31. K Tebib, JM Rouanet, P Besancon. Antioxidant effects of dietary polymeric grape seed tannins in tissues of rats fed a high cholesterol-vitamin E deficient diet. Food Chem 59(1):135–141, 1997.

32. CM Hasler. Functional foods: Their role in disease prevention and health promotion. Food Technol 52(11):63–70, 1998.

33. CA Rice-Evans, NJ Miller, PG Bolwell, PM Bramley, JB Pridham. The relative antioxidant activities of plant-derived polyphenolic flavonoids. Free Radical Res 27:429–435, 1995.

34. NC Cook, S Sammon. Flavonoids- Chemistry, metabolism, cardio protective effects, and dietary sources. J Nutr Biochem 7:66–76, 1996.

35. E Haslam, TH Lilley. Natural astringency of foodstuffs — a molecular interpretation. Crit Rev Food Sci Nutr 27:1–40, 1988.

36. FA Tomas-Barberan, JC Espin. Phenolic compounds and related enzymes as determinants of quality in fruits and vegetables. J Sci Food Agric 81:853–876, 2001.

37. BN Shinde, VK Patil. Pollination studies in Anab-e-Shahi grape. Punjab Hort J 9(3/4):130–132, 1979.

38. LH Stover. Progress in the development of grape varieties for Florida. Proc Fl St Hort Soc 73:320–322, 1960.

39. WJ Conradie, D Saayman. Effect of long term nitrogen on chenin blanc vines. II. Leaf analysis and grape composition. Am J Enol Vitic 40(2):91–94, 1989.

40. MD Alvarez, DEJ Saunders, JFV Vincent, G Jeronimidis. An engineering method to evaluate the crisp texture of fruit and vegetables. J Text Studies 31:457–473, 2000.

41. ND Belie, IC Hellett, FR Harker, JD Baerdemaeker. Influence of ripening and turgor on the tensile properties of pears: A microscopic study of cellular and tissue changes. J Am Soc Hort Sci 125(3):350–356, 2000.

42. PL Marquina, J Burgos, R Oria. Application of a compression-relaxation test for the characterization of Burlat sweet cherry. J Text Studies 32:15–30, 2001.

43. JR DeEll, S Khanizadeh, F Saad, DC Ferree. Factors affecting apple fruit firmness — review. J Am Pomological Soc 55(1):8–27, 2001.

44. JA Abbott, WS Conway, CE Sams. Post harvest calcium chloride infiltration affects textural attributes of apples. J Am Soc Hort Sci 114(6):932–936, 1989.

45. J Stow. The involvement of calcium ions in maintenance of apple fruit tissue structure. J Exptl Bot 40(218):1053–1057, 1989.

46. DA French, AA Kader, JM Labavitch. Softening of canned apricots: a chelation hypothesis. J Food Sci 54(1):86–89, 1989.

47. JE Lee, WS Kim. Morphological characters of stone cells and their effect on fruit quality of pears. J Korean Soc Hort Sci 42(4):449–452, 2001.

48. JA Abbott, R Lu. Anisotropic mechanical properties of apples. Trans ASAE 39(4):1451–1459, 1996.

49. A Fekete. Non-destructive method of fruit elasticity determination. Hungarian Agril Eng 6:50–52, 1993.

50. DW Donahue, TM Work. Sensory and textural evaluation of Maine wild blueberries for the fresh pack market. J Text Studies 29:305–312, 1998.

51. AS Szczesniak. Classification of textural characteristics. J Food Sci 28:385–389, 1963.

52. MC Bourne. Texture profile of ripening pears. J Food Sci 33:223–226, 1968.

53. MC Bourne. Textural changes in ripening peaches. J Can Inst Food Sci Technol 7:11–15, 1974.

54. F Paoletti, E Moneta, A Bertone, F Sinesio. Mechanical properties and sensory evaluation of selected apple cultivars. Food Sci Technol 26:264–270, 1993.

55. AS Szczesniak. General Foods texture profile revisited — ten years perspective. J Texture Stud 6:5–17, 1975.

56. HH Friedman, JE Whitney, AS Szczesniak. The texturometer a new instrument for the objective texture measurement. J Food Sci 28:390–396, 1963.

57. MC Bourne. Texture profile analysis. Food Technol 32(7):62–66, 72, 1978.

58. VNM Rao, RAM Delaney, GE Skinner. Rheological properties of solid foods. In: MA Rao, SSH Rizvi. eds. Engineering Properties of Foods, 2nd Ed. New York: Marcel Dekker, Inc, 1995, pp 55–97.

59. JR Gorny, RA Cifuentes, B Hess-Pierce, AA Kader. Quality changes in fresh-cut pear slices as affected by cultivar, ripeness stage, fruit size, and storage regime. J Food Sci 65(3):541–544, 2000.

60. JR Gorny, B Hess-Pierce, AA Kader. Effect of fruit ripeness and storage temperature on the deterioration rate of fresh-cut peach and nectarine slices. HortScience 33(1):110–113, 1998.

61. CR Hampson, K Sanford, J Cline. Preference of Canadian consumers for apple fruit size. Can J Plant Sci 82(1):165–167, 2002.

62. SC Hyang, M Sawamura. Composition of *Citrus tamurana* Hort. ex Tanaka (Hyuganatsu) cold-pressed oils in different sized fruits. Food Sci Biotechnol 11(1):71–77, 2002.

63. NE Looney. Plant bioregulators in fruit production: an overview and outlook. J Korean Soc Hort Sci 39(1):125–128, 1998.

64. F Famiani, A Battistelli, S Moscatello, M Boco, T Gardi, S Proietti, E Antognozzi. Thidiazuron increases current-year fruit size and production in *Actinidia deliciosa* without decreasing return bloom. J Hort Sci Biotechnol 77(1):116–119, 2002.

65. DW Greene. CPPU influences fruit quality and fruit abscission of McIntosh apples. HortScience 36(7): 1292–1295, 2001.

66. CG Embree, DS Nichols, JM DeLong, RK Prange. Certain chemical thinning treatments advance maturity of Paula red apple. Can J Plant Sci 81(3):499–501, 2001.

67. P Singh, PS Kahlon, JS Bal. A note on the effect of NAA and ethephon on maturity and fruit quality in pear (*Pyrus communis* L.) cv LeConte. Haryana J Hort Sci 26(1/2):91–94, 1997.

68. L Zhou, DA Christopher, RE Paull. Defoliation and fruit removal effects on papaya fruit production, sugar accumulation, and sucrose metabolism. J Am Soc Hort Sci 125(5):644–652, 2000.

69. D Salvatori, A Andres, A Chiralt, P Fito. The response of some properties of fruits to vacuum impregnation. J Food Process Eng 21:59–73, 1998.

70. RB Jordan, EF Walton, KU Klages, RJ Seelye. Post harvest fruit density as an indicator of dry and ripened soluble solids of kiwifruit. Post Harvest Biol Technol 20(2):163–173, 2000.

71. NN Mohsenin. Terms, Definitions and Measurements Related to Mechanical Harvesting of Selected Fruits and Vegetables. Penn Agr Exp Sta 1965, Report No. 257.

72. NN Mohsenin. Physical Properties of Plant and Animal Materials, 2nd Ed. New York: Gordon and Breach Science Publishers, 1986, pp 22–54, 79–127, 383–479.

73. L Izquierdo, JM Sendra. Citrus: Composition and characterization. In: R McRae, RK Robinson, MJ Saddler. eds. Encyclopedia of Food Science, Food Technology and Nutrition. London: Academic Press, 1993, pp 999–1002.

74. R Hendrickson, JW Keterson. Hesperidin in Florida oranges. Fla Agr Expt Sta Tech Bull 614:3–5, 1964.

75. WC Scott. Limonene in Florida citrus fruits. Proc Fla St Hort Soc 83:270–272, 1970.

76. K Keegstra, KW Talmadge, WD Bauer, P Albersheim. The structure of plant cell walls. III. A model of the walls of suspension cultured sycamore cells based on the interactions of the macromolecular components. Plant Physiology 51:188–196, 1973.

77. M McNeil, A Darvill, P Albersheim. The structural polymers of the primary cell walls of dicots. Fortschr Chem Org Naturst 37:191–249, 1979.

78. WD Bauer, KK Talmadge, K Keegstra, P Albersheim. The structure of plant cell walls. II. The hemicellulose of the walls of suspension-cultured sycamore cells. Plant Physiol 51:174–187, 1973.

79. DTA Lamport, JW Catt. Structure and function of plant glycoproteins. In: W Tanner, FA Loewus. eds. Encyclopedia of Plant Physiology, Vol. 13B. Berlin and New York: Springer-Verlag, 1981, pp 133–165.

80. MA O'Neill, RR Selvendran. Glycoproteins from the cell wall of *Phaseolus coccineus*. Biochem J 187:53–63, 1980.

81. SC Fry. Feruloylated pectins from primary cell wall: Their structure and possible functions. Planta 157:111–123, 1983.

82. MA John, PM Dey. Post harvest changes in fruit cell wall. Adv Food Res 30:139–193, 1986.

83. DTA Lamport, L Epstein. A new model for the primary cell wall: A concatenated extensin-cellulose network. Curr Top Plant Biochem Physiol 2:73–83, 1983.

84. M Yamaguchi, T Haji, M Miyake, H Yaegaki. Varietal differences in cell division and enlargement periods during peach (*Prunus persica* Batsch) fruit development. J Japanese Soc Hort Sci 71(2):155–163, 2002.

85. R Cano-Medrano, RL Darnell. Cell number and cell size in parthenocarpic vs pollinated blueberry (*Vaccinium ashei*) fruits. Annals Bot 80(4):419–425, 1997.

86. H Fukuda, O Moriyamo. Relationship between cortical cell diameter, population and the harvest size of apple. J Japanese Soc Hort Sci 66(1):185–188, 1997.

87. JG Luza, RV Gorsel, VS Polito, AA Kader. Chilling injury in peaches: a cytochemical and ultra structural cell wall study. J Am Soc Hort Sci 117(1):114–118, 1992.

88. ML Arpaia, JM Labavitch, C Greve, AA Kader. Changes in the cell wall components of kiwifruit during storage in air or controlled atmosphere. J Am Soc Hort Sci 112(3):474–481, 1987.

89. GC Davies, S Hiller, DM Bruce. A membrane model for elastic deflection of individual plant cell walls. J Text Studies 29:645–667, 1998.

90. HW Zhou, L Sonego, A Khalchitski, R Ben-Arie, A Lers, S Lurie. Cell wall enzymes and cell wall changes in 'Flavortop' nectarines: mRNA abundance, enzyme activity, and changes in pectic and neutral polymers during ripening and in woolly fruit. J Amer Soc Hort Sci 125(5):630–637, 2000.

91. RL Fischer, AB Bennett. Role of cell wall hydrolases in fruit ripening. Annual Review of Plant Physiology and Plant Molecular Biology 42:675–703, 1991.

92. AA Kader. Quality factors: Definition and evaluation for fresh horticultural crops. In: AA Kader, ed. Post harvest Technology of Horticultural Crops. Berkeley: Agricultural and Natural Resources Publication, University of California, 1985, pp 118–121.

93. A Goldman, M Given. Taste preferences for grapefruit in Germany and France. Research report, Citrus Marketing Board of Israel. 1986, pp 143–148.

94. JC Moyer, HC Atkin. Apple juice. In: PE Nelson, DK Tressler. eds. Fruit and Vegetable Juice Processing Technology, 3rd ed. New York: AVI/Van Nostrand, 1980, pp 212–267.

95. M Rhodes. The maturation and ripening of fruits. In: KV Thimann. ed. Senescence in Plants. Boca Raton, FL: CRC Press, 1980, pp 157–205.

96. RL Shewfelt. Measuring quality and maturity. In: RL Shewfelt, SE Prussia. eds. Post Harvest Handling: A Systems Approach. New York: Academic Press Inc, 1993, pp 99–124.

97. WA Sistrunk, JR Morris. Strawberry quality: influence of cultural and environmental factors. In: HE Pattee. ed.

Evaluation of Quality of Fruits and Vegetables. New York: AVI/Van Nostrand Reinhold Inc, 1985, pp 217–256.

98. LG Smith. Indices of physiological maturity and eating quality in Smooth Cayenne Pineapples. I. Indices of physiological maturity. Queensland J Agric Anim Sci 45:213–218, 1988.

99. HP Olmo. Grapes, In: R McRae, RK Robinson, MJ Saddler. eds. Encyclopedia of Food Science, Food Technology and Nutrition. London: Academic Press, 1993, pp 2252–2253.

100. TM Sjulin, J Robbins. Effect of maturity, harvest date and storage time on post harvest quality of red raspberry fruit. J Amer Soc Hort Sci 112:481–487, 1987.

101. MJ Delwiche, RA Baumgardner. Ground color as a peach maturity index. J Amer Soc Hort Sci 110:53–57, 1985.

102. MJ Delwiche, S Tang, JW Rumsey. Color and optical properties of clingstone peaches related to maturity. Trans ASAE 30:1873–1879, 1987.

103. WR Forbus, SD Senter, HT Chan. Measurement of papaya maturity by delayed light emission. J Food Sci 52:356–360, 1987.

104. WR Forbus, SD Senter. Delayed light emission as an indicator of cantaloupe maturity. J Food Sci 54:1094–1095, 1989.

105. WR Forbus, GG Dull. Delayed light emission as an indicator of peach maturity. J Food Sci 55:1581–1584, 1990.

106. GU Crisosto, FG Mitchell, ML Arpaia, G Mayer. The effect of growing location and harvest maturity on the storage performance and quality of 'Hayward' kiwifruit. J Amer Soc Hort Sci 109:584–587, 1984.

107. K Pelag, U Ben-Hanan, S Hinga. Classification of avocado by firmness and maturity. J Text Stud 21:123–139, 1990.

108. PD Lidster, SW Porritt. Influence of maturity and delay of storage on fruit firmness and disorders in 'Spartan' apple. HortScience 13:253–254, 1978.

109. HA Quamme, JI Gray. Pear fruit quality and factors that condition it. In: HE Pattee. ed. Evaluation of Quality of Fruits and Vegetables. New York: AVI/Van Nostrand Reinhold Inc, 1985, pp 47–61.

110. MS Reid, CAS Padfield, CB Watkins, JE Harman. Starch iodine pattern as a maturity index for Granny Smith apples. I. Comparison with flesh firmness and soluble solids content. NZ J Agric Res 25:239–243, 1982.

111. SR Drake, JS Fellman. Indicators of maturity and storage quality of 'Ranier' sweet cherry. HortScience 22:283–285, 1987.

112. R Ben-Arie, S Lurie. Prolongation of fruit life after harvest. In: SP Monseliese. ed. CRC Handbook of Fruit Set and Development. Boca Raton, FL: CRC Press, 1986, pp 493–520.

113. JR Morris. Grape juice quality. In: HE Pattee. ed. Evaluation of Quality of Fruits and Vegetables. New York: AVI/Van Nostrand Reinhold Inc, 1985, pp 129–176.

114. S Mitra, EA Baldwin. Mango. In: S Mitra. ed. Post harvest physiology and storage of tropical and subtropical fruits. New York: CAB International, 1997, pp 85–122.

115. TMM Malundo, RL Shewfelt, GO Ware, EA Baldwin. Sugars and acids influence flavor properties of mango (*Mangifera indica*). J Amer Soc Hort Sci 126:115–121, 2001.

116. DK Tandon, SK Kalra. Changes in sugars, starch and amylase activity during development of mango fruit cv Dashehari. J Hort Sci 58:449–453, 1983.

117. Y Selvaraj, R Kumar, DK Pal. Changes in sugar, organic acids, amino acids, lipid constituents and aroma characteristics of ripening mango (*Mangifera indica* L.) fruit. J Food Sci Technol 26:308–313, 1989.

118. AP Medilcott, AK Thompson. Analysis of sugars and organic acids in ripening mango fruit (*Mangifera indica* L. var. Keitt) by high performance liquid chromatography. J Sci Food Agric 36:561–566, 1985.

119. TMM Malundo, EA Baldwin, GO Ware, RL Shewfelt. Volatile composition and interaction influence flavor properties of mango. Proc Fla State Hort Soc 109:264–268, 1996.

120. JA Ruck. Chemical Methods for Analysis of Fruits and Vegetables Products. Summerland, BC: Canadian Dept. Agric. Publ. No. SP50, 1969, pp 10–12.

121. P Schreier, F Drawert, A Junker. Identification of volatile constituents from grapes. J Agric Food Chem 24:331–336, 1976.

122. RL Shewfelt. Flavor and color of fruits as affected by processing. In: JG Woodroof, BS Luh. eds. Commercial Fruit Processing, 2nd ed. New York: AVI/Van Nostrand Reinhold Inc, 1986, pp 479–529.

123. JK Fellman, TW Miller, DS Mattinson, JP Mattheis. Factors that influence biosynthesis of volatile flavor compounds in apple fruits. HortScience 35:1026–1033, 2000.

124. CF Forney, W Kalt, MA Jordan. The composition of strawberry aroma is influenced by cultivar, maturity and storage. HortScience 35:1022–1026, 2000.

125. RM Beaudry. Effect of carbon dioxide partial pressure on blueberry fruit respiration and respiratory quotient. Post Harvest Biol Tech. 3:249–258, 1993.

126. A Brackmann, J Streif, F Bangerth. Relationship between a reduced aroma production and lipid metabolism of apples after long-term controlled atmosphere storage. J Amer Soc Hort Sci 118:243–247, 1993.

127. MA Joslyn. 1961. Fruit juices and concentrates. In: DK Tressler, MA Joslyn. eds. Fruit and Vegetable Juice Processing Technology. New York: AVI/Van Nostrand Reinhold Inc, 1961, pp 314–346.

128. ER Suresh, S Ethiraj. Effect of grape maturity on the composition and quality of wines made in India. Am J Enol Vitic 38:329–331, 1987.

129. KG Shanmugavelue. Post harvest handling and marketing of grapes. Vitic India 390, 1989.

130. Anon. Some Recent Developments, Central Food Technological Research Institute, Mysore, India, 1982, pp 1–9.

131. K Fox. Status update of the worldwide citrus industry. Citrus Engineering Conference, Fla. Sec. Amer. Soc. Mech. Eng. Miami, 1991, pp 10–14.

132. VS Govindarajan, S Ranganna, KV Ramana. Citrus Fruits. III. Chemistry, technology and quality evaluation.

C. Quality evaluation. CRC Crit Rev Food Sci Nutr 20:73–95, 1984.

133. DW Ruster, OG Draun, WE Pearce. Citrus Fruits. Food Ind 17:742–747, 1945.

134. GL Rygg. Date development, handling, and packing in the United States. Agricultural Handbook 482, Agricultural Research Service, USDA, Washington, D.C., 1975, pp 18–25.

135. F Hussein. Date culture in Saudi Arabia, Ministry of Agriculture and Water, Dept. of Research and Development, Saudi Arabia, 1970, pp 33–34.

136. SN Al-Hooti, JS Sidhu, J Al-Otaibi, H Al-Amiri, H Qabazard. Processing of some important date cultivars grown in United Arab Emirates into chutney and date relish. J Food Process Preserv 21:55–68, 1997.

137. SN Al-Hooti, JS Sidhu, J Al-Otaibi, H Al-Amiri, H Qabazard. Processing quality of important date cultivars grown in United Arab Emirates for jam, butter and dates-in-syrup. Adv Food Sci 19(1/2):35–40, 1997.

138. SN Al-Hooti, JS Sidhu, J Al-Otaibi, H Qabazard. Extension of shelf life of date fruits at the *khalal* stage of maturity. Indian J Hort 52(4):244–249, 1995.

139. SN Al-Hooti, JS Sidhu, J Al-Otaibi, H Al-Amiri, H Qabazard. Date bars fortified with almonds, oat flakes and skim milk powder. Plant Foods Human Nutrition 51:125–135, 1997.

140. SN Al-Hooti, JS Sidhu, H Qabazard. Objective color measurement of fresh date fruits and processed date products. J Food Quality 20:257–266, 1997.

141. SN Al-Hooti, JS Sidhu, H Qabazard. Physicochemical characteristics of five date fruit cultivars grown in the United Arab Emirates. Plant Foods Human Nutrition 50:101–113, 1997.

142. MS Mikki, AH Hegazi, AA Abdel-Aziz, SM Al-Taisan. Suitability of major Saudi date cultivars for commercial handling and packing. Proc. 2nd Symp. Date Palm in Saudi Arabia, Vol. II. 1986, pp 9–24.

143. AK Yousif, AM Hamad, WA Mirandella. Pickling of dates at the early *khalal* stage. J Food Technol 20:697–702, 1985.

144. Anon. Banana in India: Production, Preservation and Processing, Industrial Monograph Series, Central Food Technological Institute, Mysore, India, 1989, pp 1–27.

145. VL Bump. Apple processing and juice extraction. In: DL Downing. ed. Processed Apple Products. New York: AVI Van Nostrand Reinhold, 1981, pp 53–62.

146. CS Pederson. Apple juice. In: DE Nelson, DK Tressler. eds. Fruit and Vegetable Juice Processing Technology, 3rd ed. Westport, CT: AVI, 1980, pp 289–304.

147. SK Chauhan, BK Lal, VK Joshi. Development of protein rich apple beverage. Res & Ind 38:227–229, 1993.

148. RS Dabhade, DM Khedkar. Studies on drying and dehydration of raw mangoes for preparation of mango powder (*Amchur*). Indian Food Packer 34(3):18–21, 1980.

149. MV Sastry, U Habib. Studies on Indian pickles. V. Storage of raw mangoes for pickling. Indian Food Packer 33(6):10–15, 1979.

150. M Mahadeviah. Factors affecting tin pick-up in canned mango products. Indian Food Packer 30:92–95, 1976.

151. Anon. Food and Nutrition Research, Indian Council of Medical Research Publication, New Delhi, India, 1974, pp 1–3.

152. SK Kalra, DK Tandon, BP Singh. A glimpse of quality of market fruit drinks. Beverage and Food World 15(4):13–15, 1988.

153. KS Sandhu, JS Sidhu. Studies on the development of multi-fruit ready-to-serve beverages. J Plant Sci Res 8(1–4):87–88, 1992.

154. P Aggarwal, GS Padda, JS Sidhu. Standardization of jelly preparation from grape: guava blends. J Food Sci Technol 34(4):335–336, 1997.

155. IS Yadav, GC Sinha, S Rajan, SK Kalra. Saheb Pasand, a potential mango cultivar. Prog Hort 19(3/4):316–317, 1987.

156. V Satyaprakash Rao, SK Roy. Studies on dehydration of mango pulp. Indian Food Packer 34(3):64, 72, 1985.

157. SK Sen. Pineapple. In: TK Bose. ed. Fruits of India: Tropical and Sub-Tropical. Calcutta, India: Naya Prokash, 1985, pp 298–306.

158. K Chenchin, A Yugawa, HY Yamamoto. Enzymic degumming of pineapple and pineapple mill juices. J Food Sci 49:132–134, 1984.

159. JS Pruthi, G Lal. Varietal trials in canning of pineapple. Bull Central Food Technol Res Inst 4:284–286, 1954.

160. KS Sandhu, BS Bhatia, FC Shukla. Physico-chemical changes during storage of kinnow, mandarin, orange and pineapple juice concentrates. J Food Sci Technol 22(5):342–344, 1985.

161. HS Phanindrakumar, K Jayathilakan, TS Vasundhara. Factors affecting the quality of freeze-dried pineapple juice powder. J Food Sci Technol 28(6):391–393, 1991.

162. Anon. Wealth of India, Vol. 8. Raw Materials. Publication and Information Directorate, Council of Scientific and Industrial Research, New Delhi, 1969, pp 330–333.

163. U Rani, BS Bhatia. Studies on pear candy processing. Indian Food Packer 39(5):40–44, 1985.

164. Anon. Annual Report, Central Food Technol. Res. Inst. Mysore, India, 1975, pp 26–28.

165. DK Salunkhe, HR Bolin, K Salunkhe. High protein juice powders. Utah Sci 32(4):112–113, 1971.

166. VK Joshi, SK Chauhan, BB Lal. Extraction of juices from peaches, plums and apricots by pectolytic enzyme treatment. J Food Sci Technol 28:64–66, 1991.

167. MA Wani, SPS Saini. Processing of plums. J Food Sci Technol 27:304–306, 1990.

168. VK Joshi, SK Chauhan, BB Lal. Evaluation of enzymatically extracted plum juice for preparation of beverages. J Food Sci Technol 30:208–210, 1993.

169. W Aulch. Manufacture of concentrates of plum puree. German Democratic Republic Patent 138597, 1979.

170. IAG Weinert, J Solms, F Escher. Diffusion of anthocyanins during processing and storage of canned plums. Food Sci Technol 23:396–399, 1990.

171. VN Kozlov, AS Destik. Butter with apple and fruit fillers. Tovarovedenie 18:29–31, 1985.

172. VK Joshi, VP Bhutani. Evaluation of plum cultivars for wine preparation. XXIII International Horticulture Congress, Italy, 1990, Abstr. No. 3336.

173. JG Woodroof. History and growth of fruit processing. In: JG Woodroof, BS Luh. eds. Commercial Fruit Processing. 2nd ed. Westport, CT: AVI, 1986, pp 1–14.

174. AP Kuezynski, P Varoquax, F Voaroguex. Reflectometric method to measure the initial color and browning rate of white peach pulps. Sciences des Aliments 12(2):213–215, 1992.

175. KK Vyas, VK Joshi. Canning of fruits in natural fruit juices. I. Canning of peaches in apple juice. J Food Sci Technol 19(1):39–41, 1982.

176. SJ Leonard, BS Luh, CP Chichester, M Simone. Relationship of fresh clingstone peach color and grade after canning. Food Technol 15:492–496, 1961.

177. GS Mudahar, BS Bhatia. Steeping preservation of fruits. J Food Sci Technol 20(2):77–80, 1983.

178. SE Spayd, JR Morris. Influence of immature fruits on strawberry jam quality and storage stability. J Food Sci 46:414–416, 1981.

179. GM Sapers, SB Jones, GT Maher. Factors affecting the recovery of juice and anthocyanin from cranberries. J Am Soc Hort Sci 108:245–249, 1983.

180. DS Lundahl, MR McDaniel, RE Wrolstad. Flavor, aroma and compositional changes in strawberry juice concentrate stored at 20°C. J Food Sci 54:1255–1257, 1988.

181. L Pilando, RE Wrolstad, DA Healtherbell. Influence of fruit composition, maturity and mold contamination on the color and appearance of strawberry wine. J Food Sci 50:1121–1124, 1985.

182. A Rommel, DA Heatherbell, RE Wrolstad. Red raspberry juice and wine. Effect of processing and storage on anthocyanin pigment composition, color and appearance. J Food Sci 55:1101–1104, 1988.

183. LM Withy, N Lodge. Kiwi fruit wine: Production and evaluation. Am J Enol Vitic 33(4):191–193, 1982.

184. SA Paunovicz. Apricots. Second International Workshop on Apricot Culture and Decline. Acta Hort 209:23–24, 1988.

185. JK Brecht, AA Kader, CM Heintz, RC Norona. Controlled atmosphere and ethylene effects on quality of California apricots and clingstone peaches. J Food Sci 47:432–434, 1982.

186. EH Abdelhag, TP Labuza. Air drying characteristics of apricot. J Food Sci 52:342–344, 1987.

187. JD Mannapperuma. Residual management in fruit processing plants. In: LP Somogyi, HS Ramaswamy, YH Hui. eds. Processing Fruits: Science and Technology, Vol. I. Biology, Principles, and Applications. Lancaster/Basel: Technomic Publishing Co Inc, 1996, pp 461–499.

188. CE Morris. Apple and pear fiber. Food Eng 57:72–73, 1985.

189. TR Sharma, BB Lal, S Kumar, AK Goswami. Pectin from different varieties of Himachal Pradesh apples. Indian Food Packer 39(4):53–56, 1985.

190. YD Hang, BS Luh, EE Woodams. Microbial production of citric acid by solid state fermentation of kiwifruit peel. J Food Sci 52(1):226–228, 1986.

191. S Ranganna, VS Govindarajan, KV Ramanna. Citrus fruits. II. Chemistry, technology and quality evaluation. B. Technology. CRC Crit Rev Food Sci Nutr 19:1–98, 1983.

192. MK Dhingra, OP Gupta. Evaluation of chemicals for pectin extraction from guava (*Psidium guajava* L.) fruits. J Food Sci Technol 21(3):173–175, 1984.

193. SD Bhalerao, GV Mulmuley, SM Ananthakrishna, VH Potty. Waste and waste water management in food industry. I. Fruit and vegetable processing. Indian Food Packer 43(2):5–7, 1989.

194. OP Beerh. Utilization of mango waste: Peel as a source of pectin. J Food Sci Technol 13(2):96–98, 1976.

195. JS Pruthi, R Susheela. Studies on the utilization of mango waste kernels: Some chemical and technological aspects. Punjab J Hort 3(2–4):272–274, 1963.

196. BP Baliga, AD Shitole. Cocoa butter substitute from mango fat. J Am Oil Chem Soc 58(2):110–114, 1981.

197. YG Moharram, AM Moustafa. Utilization of mango seed kernel (*Mangifera indica*) as a source of oil. Food Chem 8(4):269–276, 1982.

198. M Cojocaru, S Droby, E Glotter, A Goldman, HE Gottlieb, B Jacoby, D Prusky. 5-(12-Heptaddcenyl)-resorcinol, the major component of the antifungal activity in the peel of mango fruit. Phytochemistry 25(5):1093–1095, 1986.

199. VVR Subramanyam, KT Achaya. Lesser-known Indian vegetable fats. 1. Oleic-rich fats. J Sci Food Agric 8:857–860, 1957.

200. HS Shantha, GS Siddappa. Physico-chemical nature of banana pseudostem starch. J Food Sci 35:72–75, 1970.

201. BL Singh, DS Johar. Note on the utilization of banana stem waste for growing food yeast. Bull Central Food Technol Res Inst (Mysore, India) 1(11):346–347, 1952.

202. G Joseph, M Mahadeviah. Utilization of waste from pineapple processing industries. Indian Food Packer 42:46–49, 1988.

203. DW Roberts, DJ Hills. Enzyme pretreatments of peach solid wastes used for ethanol fermentation. Agric Waste 12(2):173–176, 1985.

204. BP Klein, AC Kurilich. Processing effects on dietary antioxidants from plant foods. HortScience 35(4):580–584, 2000.

205. LA Bazzano, J He, LG Ogden, CM Loria, S Vupputuri, L Myers, PK Welton. Fruit and vegetable intake and risk of cardiovascular disease in U.S. adults: the first National Health and Nutrition Examination Survey Epidemiological Follow-up Study. Am J Clin Nutr 76:93–99, 2002.

206. TL Cleave. The neglect of natural principles in current medical practice. J Royal Navy Med Service 42:55–83, 1956.

207. LH McKee, TA Latner. Underutilized sources of dietary fiber: A review. Plant Foods Human Nutrition 55:285–304, 2000.

208. P Terry, E Giovannucci, KB Michels, L Bergkvist, H Hansen, L Holmberg, A Wolk. Fruits, vegetables, dietary fiber and risk of colorectal cancer. J Nat Can Inst 93(7):523–533, 2001.

209. S Gorinstein, M Zemser, R Haruenkit, R Chuthakorn, F Grauer, O Martin-Belloso, S Trakhtenberg. Comparative

content of total polyphenols and dietary fiber in tropical fruits and persimmon. J Nutr Biochem 10(6):367–371, 1999.

210. F Gheyas, E Young, SM Blankenship, RF McFeeters. Dietary fiber composition of Starkspur Supreme Delicious apple fruit as influenced by rootstock and growing region. Fruit Var J 50(1):35–41, 1996.

211. JL Rosado, P Lopez, Z Huerta, E Munoz, L Mejia. Dietary fiber in Mexican foods. J Food Comp Anal 6(3):215–222, 1993.

212. C Lintas, M Cappelloni. Dietary fiber content of Italian fruits and nuts. J Food Comp Anal 5(2):146–151, 1992.

213. JA Marlett. Content and composition of dietary fiber in 117 frequently consumed foods. J Am Dietet Assoc 92(2):175–186, 1992.

214. H Osman. Dietary fiber composition of common vegetables and fruits in Malaysia. Food Chem 37(1):21–26, 1990.

215. LF Tinker, BO Schneeman, PA Davis, DD Gallaher, CR Waggoner. Consumption of prunes as a source of dietary fiber in men with mild hypercholesterolemia. Am J Clin Nutr 53(5):1259–1265, 1991.

216. B Halliwell. Antioxidants and human disease: A general introduction. Nutr Rev 55:S44–S49, 1997.

217. P Knekt, J Kumpulainen, R Jarvinen, H Rissanen, M Heliovaara, A Reunanen, T Hakulinen, A Aromaa. Flavonoid intake and risk of chronic diseases. Am J Clin Nutr 76:560–568, 2002.

218. BP Yu. Aging and oxidative stress: Modulation by dietary restriction. Free Radical Biol Med 21:651–668, 1996.

219. RL Prior, G Cao. Antioxidant phytochemicals in fruits and vegetables: Diet and health implications. Hort Science 35(4):588–592, 2000.

220. CJ Dillard, JB German. Phytochemicals: nutraceuticals and human health – A review. J Sci Food Agric 80:1744–1756, 2000.

221. KA Steinmetz, JD Potter. Vegetables, fruits and cancer. I. Epidemiology. Cancer Causes Control 2:325–357, 1991.

222. KA Steinmetz, JD Potter. Vegetables, fruits and cancer. II. Mechanisms. Cancer Causes Control 2:427–442, 1991.

223. HF Stich, MP Rosin. Naturally occurring phenolics as antimutagenic and anticarcinogenic agents. Adv Exp Med 177:1–29, 1984.

224. H Bartsch, R Montesano. Relevance of nitrosamines to human cancer. Carcinogenesis 5(11):1381–1393, 1984.

225. MJ Wargovich. Anticancer properties of fruits and vegetable. HortScience 35(4):573–575, 2000.

226. T Byers, G Perry. Dietary carotenes, vitamin C and vitamin E as protective antioxidants in human cancers. Ann Rev Nutr 12:139–159, 1992.

227. MP Valero, AE Fletcher, B De Stavola, J Vioque, VC Alepuz. Vitamin C has also been associated with reduced risk of cataract in a Mediterranean population. J Nutr 132(6):1299–1306, 2002.

228. DC Liebler. Antioxidant reactions of carotenoids. Ann New York Acad Sci 691:20–31, 1993.

229. IM Fordham, BA Clevidence, ER Wiley, RH Zimmerman. Fruit of Autumn Olive: A rich source of lycopene. HortScience 36(6):1136–1137, 2001.

230. L Brown, EB Rimm, JM Seddon, EL Giovannucci, L Chasan-Taber, D Spiegelman, WC Willet, SE Hankinson. A prospective study of carotenoid intake and risk of cataract extraction in U.S. men. Am J Clin Nutr 70:517–521, 1999.

231. G Dagnelie, IS Zorge, TM McDonald. Lutein improves visual function in some patients with retinal degeneration: A pilot study via the Internet. Optometry 71:147–150, 2000.

232. LA Fullmer, A Shao. The role of lutein in eye health and nutrition. Cereal Foods World 46(9): 408–413, 2001.

233. V Tyssandier, N Cardinault, C Caris-Veyrat, MJ Amiot, P Grolier, C Bouteloup, V Azais-Braesco, P Borel. Vegetable-borne lutein, lycopene, and β-carotene compete for incorporation into chylomicrons, with no adverse effect on medium-term (3-week) plasma status of carotenoids in humans. Am J Clin Nutr 75:526–534, 2002.

234. N Uedo, M Tatsuta, H Iishi, M Baba, N Sakai, H Yano, T Otani. Inhibition by D-limonene of gastric carcinogenesis induced by N-methyl-N′-nitro-N-nitroguanidine in Wistar rats. Cancer Lett 137:131–136, 1999.

235. PCH Hollman. Evidence for health benefits of plant phenols: local or systemic effects? J Sci Food Agric 81:842–852, 2001.

236. C Faulds, B Clarke, G Williamson. Ferulic acid unearthed. Chem Britain 36(5):48–50, 2000.

237. JE Kinsella, E Frankel, B German, J Kanner. Possible mechanisms for the protective role of antioxidants in wine and plant foods. Food Technol 47:85–89, 1993.

238. BL Pool-Zobel, A Bub, N Schroder, G Rechkemmer. Anthocyanins are potent antioxidants in model system but do not reduce endogenous oxidative DNA damage in human colon cells. Eur J Nutr 38:227–234, 1999.

239. H Wang, G Cao, RL Prior. The oxygen radical absorbed capacity of anthocyanins. J Agric Food Chem 45:304–309, 1997.

240. MGL Hertog, PCH Hollman, MB Katan, D Kromhout. Intake of potentially anticarcinogenic flavonoids and their determinants in adults in the Netherlands. Nutr Cancer 20:21–29, 1993.

241. KA Youdim, J McDonald, W Kalt, JA Joseph. Potential role of dietary flavonoids in reducing microvascular endothelium vulnerability to oxidative and inflammatory insults. J Nutr Biochem 13(5):282–288, 2002.

242. W Kalt. Health functional phytochemicals of fruit. Hort Rev 27:269–315, 2001.

243. W Kalt, A Howell, JC Duy, CF Forney, JE McDonald. Horticultural factors affecting antioxidant capacity of blueberries and small fruits. Hort Technology 11(4):523–528, 2001.

244. W Kalt, DAJ Ryan, JC Duy, RL Prior, MK Ehlenfeldt, SP Vander-Kloet. Interspecific variation in anthocyanins, phenolics, and antioxidant capacity among genotypes of high bush and low bush blueberries (Vaccinium spp.). J Agric Food Chem 49(10):4761–4767, 2001.

245. W Kalt, JE McDonald, H Donner. Anthocyanins, phenolics, and antioxidant capacity of processed low bush blueberry products. J Food Sci 65(3):390–393, 2000.

246. W Kalt, CF Forney, A Martin, RL Prior. Antioxidant capacity, vitamin C, phenolics, and anthocyanins after fresh storage of small fruits. J Agric Food Chem 47(11):4638–4644, 1999.

25 Frozen Fruits: Product Descriptions

Peggy Stanfield
Dietetic Resources

CONTENTS

I. FROZEN FRUITS

A. APPLES

Frozen apples are prepared from sound, properly ripened fruit of *Malus sylvesfris (Pyrus malus);* are peeled, cored, trimmed, sliced, sorted, and washed; are properly drained before filling into containers; may be packed with or without the addition of a nutritive sweetening ingredient and any other legally permissible ingredients and are frozen in accordance with good commercial practice and maintained at temperatures necessary for the preservation of the product.

The term "slices" means frozen apples consisting of slices of apples cut longitudinally and radially from the core axis.

B. APRICOTS

Apricots are the food prepared from mature apricots of one of the optional styles specified, which may be packed as solid pack or in one of the optional packing media specified.

Such food may also contain one or any combination of two or more of the following safe and suitable optional ingredients:

1. Natural and artificial flavors.
2. Spice.
3. Vinegar, lemon juice, or organic acids.
4. Apricot pits, except in the case of unpeeled whole apricots and peeled whole apricots in a quantity not more than 1 apricot pit to each 227 grams (8 ounces) of finished frozen apricots.
5. Apricot kernels, except in the case of unpeeled whole apricots and peeled whole apricots, and except when an optional ingredient is used.
6. Ascorbic acid in an amount no greater than necessary to preserve color.

Such food is sealed in a container and before or after scaling is so processed by heat as to prevent spoilage.

1. Optional Styles of the Apricot Ingredients

The optional styles of the apricot ingredients arc peeled or unpeeled: (i) whole, (ii) halves, (iii) quarters, (iv) slices, (v) pieces or irregular pieces.

Each such ingredient, except in the cases of unpeeled whole apricots and peeled whole apricots, is pitted.

2. Packing Media

The optional packing media are (a) water, (b) fruit juice(s) and water, (c) fruit juice(s).

Such packing media may be used as such, or any one or any combination of two or more safe and suitable

nutritive carbohydrate sweetener(s) may be added. When a sweetener is added as a part of any such liquid packing medium, the density range of the resulting packing medium expressed as percent by weight of sucrose (degrees Brix) should be designated by the appropriate name for the respective density ranges, namely:

When the density of the solution is 10 percent or more but less than 16 percent, the medium should be designated as "slightly sweetened water" or "extra light syrup," "slightly sweetened fruit juice(s) and water" or "slightly sweetened fruit juice(s)," as the case may be.

When the density of the solution is 16 percent or more but less than 21 percent, the medium should be designated as "light syrup," "lightly sweetened fruit juice(s) and water," or "lightly sweetened fruit juice(s)," as the case may be. When the density of the solution is 21 percent or more but less than 25 percent, the medium should be designated as "heavy syrup," "heavily sweetened fruit juice(s) and water," or "heavily sweetened fruit juice(s)," as the case may be.

When the density of the solution is 25 percent or more but not more than 40 percent, the medium should be designated as "extra heavy syrup," "extra heavily sweetened fruit juice(s) and water," or "extra heavily sweetened fruit juice(s)," as the case may be.

3. Labeling Requirements

The name of the food is apricots. The name of the food should also include a declaration of any flavoring that characterizes the product and a declaration of any spice or seasoning that characterizes the product; for example, "Spice Added," or in lieu of the word "Spice," the common name of the spice, e.g., "Seasoned with Vinegar" or "Seasoned with Apricot Kernels."

When two or more of the optional ingredients specified are used, such words may be combined, as for example, "Seasoned with Cider Vinegar, Cloves, Cinnamon Oil, and Apricot Kernels."

The style of the apricot ingredient and the name of the packing medium preceded by "In" or "Packed in" or the words "Solid Pack," where applicable, should be included as part of the name or in close proximity to the name of the food, except that pieces or irregular pieces should be designated "Pieces," "Irregular Pieces," or "Mixed Pieces of Irregular Sizes and Shapes."

The style of the apricot ingredient should be preceded or followed by "Unpeeled" or "Peeled," as the case may be. "Halves" may be alternatively designated "Halved," "Quarters" as "Quartered," and "Slices" as "Sliced." When the packing medium is prepared with a sweetener(s) that imparts a taste, flavor, or other characteristic to the finished food in addition to sweetness, the name of the packing medium should be accompanied by the name of such sweetener(s), for example, in the case of a mixture of brown sugar and honey, an appropriate statement would be "_____syrup of brown sugar and honey" the blank to be filled in with the word "light," "heavy," or "extra heavy," as the case may be.

When the liquid portion of the packing media consists of fruit juice(s), such juice(s) should be designated in the name of the packing medium as follows.

In the case of a single fruit juice, the name of the juice should be used in lieu of the word "fruit."

In the case of a combination of two or more fruit juices, the names of the juices in the order of predominance by weight should be used in lieu of the word "fruit" in the name of the packing medium.

In the case of a single fruit juice or a combination of two or more fruit juices any of which are made from concentrate(s), the words "from concentrate(s)" should follow the word "juice(s)" in the name of the packing medium and in the name(s) of such juice(s) when declared as specified.

Whenever the names of the fruit juices used do not appear in the name of the packing medium, such names and the words "from concentrate," should appear in an ingredient statement.

4. Label Declaration

Each of the ingredients used in the food should be declared on the label.

Frozen apricots are prepared from sound, mature, fresh, peeled or unpeeled fruit of any commercial variety of apricot, which are sorted, washed, and may be trimmed to assure a clean and wholesome product. The apricots are properly drained of excess water before filling into containers; may be packed with the addition of nutritive sweetening ingredient(s) (including syrup and/or syrup containing pureed apricots) and/or suitable antioxidant ingredient(s) and/or any other legally permissible ingredients(s).

The apricots are prepared and frozen in accordance with good commercial practice and are maintained at temperatures necessary for the preservation of the product.

5. Styles of Frozen Apricots

(a) Halves are cut approximately in half along the suture from stem to apex and the pit is removed.

(b) Quarters are apricot halves cut into two approximately equal parts.

(c) Slices are apricot halves cut into sectors smaller than quarters.

(d) Diced are apricots cut into approximate cubes.

(e) Cuts are apricots that are cut in such a manner as to change the original conformation and do not meet any of the foregoing styles.

(f) Machine-pitted means mechanically pitted in such a manner as to substantially destroy the conformation of the fruit in removing the pit.

C. Berries

Frozen berries are prepared from the properly ripened fresh fruit of the plant (genus 48 *Rubus*); are stemmed and cleaned, may be packed with or without packing media, and are frozen and stored at temperatures necessary for the preservation of the product.

1. Types of Frozen Berries

(a) Blackberries
(b) Boysenberries
(c) Dewberries
(d) Loganberries
(e) Youngberries
(f) Other similar types, such as nectar berries

2. Blueberries

Frozen blueberries are prepared from sound, properly ripened fresh fruit of the blueberry bush (genus *Vaccinium*), including species or varieties often called huckleberries, but not of the genus *Gaylussacia;* they are cleaned and stemmed, are properly washed, are packed with or without packing media, and are frozen and maintained at temperatures necessary for the preservation of the product.

Types of frozen blueberries are (a) native or wild type; (b) cultivated type.

D. Red Tart Pitted Cherries

Frozen red tart pitted cherries are the foods prepared from properly matured cherries of the domestic *(Prunes cerasus)* red sour varietal group that have been washed, pitted, sorted, and properly drained; they may be packed with or without a nutritive sweetened packing medium or any other substance permitted under federal regulations and are frozen and stored at temperatures necessary for the preservation of the product.

II. FROZEN JUICES

A. Apple Juice

Frozen concentrated apple juice is prepared from the unfermented, unsweetened, unacidified liquid obtained from the first pressing of properly prepared, sound, clean, mature, fresh apples, and/or parts thereof by good commercial processes. The juice is clarified and concentrated to at least 22.9° Brix. The apple juice concentrate so prepared, with or without the addition of legal ingredients, is packed and frozen in accordance with good commercial practice and maintained at temperatures necessary for the preservation of the product.

The Brix value of the finished concentrate should not be less than the following for the respective dilution factor of frozen concentrated apple juice:

Dilution Factor Value of Concentrate: minimum Brix (degrees)

1 plus 1 22.9
2 plus 1 33.0
3 plus 1 42.2
4 plus 1 50.8
5 plus 1 58.8
6 plus 1 66.3
7 plus 1 73.3

B. LEMON JUICE (FOR PREPARING FROZEN CONCENTRATE FOR LEMONADE)

Lemon juice is the unfermented juice, obtained by mechanical process, from sound, mature lemons (*Citrus limon* (L.) Burm. f.), from which seeds (except embryonic seeds and small fragments of seed which cannot be separated by good manufacturing practice) and excess pulp are removed. The juice may be adjusted by the addition of the optional concentrated lemon juice ingredient in such quantity that the increase in acidity, calculated as anhydrous citric acid, does not exceed 15 percent of the acidity of the finished food. The lemon oil and lemon essence (derived from lemons) content may be adjusted in accordance with good manufacturing practice. The juice may have been concentrated and later reconstituted. When prepared from concentrated lemon juice, the finished food contains not less than 6 percent, by weight, of soluble solids taken as the refractometric sucrose value (of the filtrate), corrected to 20°C, but uncorrected for acidity, and has a titratable acidity content of not less than 4.5 percent, by weight, calculated as anhydrous citrus acid.

The food may contain one or any combination of the safe and suitable optional ingredients. Lemon juice may be preserved by heat sterilization (canning), refrigeration, freezing, or by the addition of safe and suitable preservatives. When sealed in a container to be held at ambient temperatures, it is preserved by the addition of safe and suitable preservatives or so processed by heat, before or after sealing, as to prevent spoilage.

1. Optional Ingredients

The optional safe and suitable ingredients are (i) concentrated lemon juice (lemon juice from which part of the water has been removed), (ii) water and/or lemon juice to reconstitute concentrated lemon juice in the manufacture of lemon juice from concentrate, and (iii) preservatives.

2. Labeling

The name of the food is "lemon juice" if the food is prepared from unconcentrated, undiluted liquid extracted from mature lemons; or if the food is prepared from unconcentrated, undiluted liquid extracted from mature lemons to which concentrated lemon juice is added to adjust acidity.

The name is "lemon juice from concentrate" or "reconstituted lemon juice" if the food is prepared from concentrated lemon juice and water and/or lemon juice; or if the food is prepared from lemon juice from concentrate and lemon juice.

Frozen concentrate for lemonade is the frozen food prepared from one or both of the lemon juice ingredients together with one or any mixture of safe and suitable nutritive carbohydrate sweeteners. The product contains not less than 48.0 percent by weight of soluble solids taken as the sucrose value.

When the product is diluted according to directions for making lemonade which should appear on the label, the acidity of the lemonade, calculated as anhydrous citric acid, should be not less than 0.70 gram per 100 milliliters, and the soluble solids should be not less than 10.5 percent by weight.

3. The Lemon Juice Ingredients

Lemon juice ingredients are lemon juice or frozen lemon juice or a mixture of these or concentrated lemon juice or frozen concentrated lemon juice or a mixture of these. For this purpose, lemon juice is the undiluted juice expressed from mature lemons of an acid variety, and concentrated lemon juice is lemon juice from which part of the water has been removed. In the preparation of the lemon juice ingredients, the lemon oil content may be adjusted by the addition of lemon oil or concentrated lemon oil in accordance with good manufacturing practice, and the lemon pulp in the juice as expressed may be left in the juice or may be separated.

Lemon pulp that has been separated, which may have been preserved by freezing, may be added in preparing frozen concentrate for lemonade, provided that the amount of pulp added does not raise the proportion of pulp in the finished food to a level in excess of that which would be present by using lemon juice ingredients from which pulp has not been separated. The lemon juice ingredients may be treated by heat, either before or after the other ingredients are added, to reduce the enzymatic activity and the number of viable microorganisms.

C. FROZEN CONCENTRATE FOR ARTIFICIALLY SWEETENED LEMONADE

Frozen concentrate for artificially sweetened lemonade conforms to the description for frozen concentrate for lemonade, except that in lieu of nutritive sweeteners it is sweetened with one or more of the artificial sweetening ingredients permitted by law, and the soluble solids specifications do not apply. When the product is diluted according to directions that should appear on the label, the acidity of the artificially sweetened lemonade, calculated as anhydrous citric acid, should be not less than 0.70 gram per 100 milliliters. It may contain one or more safe and suitable dispersing ingredients serving the function of distributing the lemon oil throughout the food. It may also contain one or more safe and suitable thickening ingredients. Such dispersing and thickening ingredients are not legal food additives.

The name of the food is "frozen concentrate for artificially sweetened lemonade." The words "artificially sweetened" should be of the same size and style of type as the word "lemonade." If an optional thickening or dispersing ingredient is used, the label should bear the statement "_____ added" or "with added _____," the blank being filled in with the common name of the thickening or dispersing agent used. Such statement should be set forth on the label with such prominence and conspicuousness as to render it likely to be read and understood by the ordinary individual under customary conditions of purchase.

D. FROZEN CONCENTRATE FOR COLORED LEMONADE

Frozen concentrate for colored lemonade conforms to the description for frozen concentrate for lemonade, except that it is colored with a safe and suitable fruit juice, vegetable juice, or any such juice in concentrated form, or with any other legal color additive ingredient suitable for use in food, including legal artificial coloring.

The name of the food is "frozen concentrate for_____lemonade," the blank being filled in with the word describing the color, for example, "frozen concentrate for pink lemonade."

E. GRAPEFRUIT JUICE

Grapefruit juice is the unfermented juice, intended for direct consumption, obtained by mechanical process from sound, mature grapefruit (*Citrus paradisi* Macfadven) from which seeds and peel (except embryonic seeds and small fragments of seeds and peel that cannot be separated by good manufacturing practice) and excess pulp are removed and to which may be added not more than 10 percent by volume of the unfermented juice obtained from mature hybrids of grapefruit. The juice may be adjusted by the addition of the optional concentrated grapefruit juice ingredients specified, but the quantity of such concentrated grapefruit juice ingredient added should not contribute more than 1 percent of the grapefruit juice soluble solids in the finished food. The grapefruit pulp, grapefruit oil, and grapefruit essence (components derived from grapefruit) content may be adjusted in accordance with good manufacturing practice. The juice may have been concentrated and later reconstituted with water suitable for the purpose of maintaining essential composition and quality factors of the juice. It may be sweetened with the dry nutritive sweeteners. If the grapefruit juice is prepared from concentrate,

such sweeteners in liquid form also may be used. When prepared from concentrated grapefruit juice, exclusive of added sweeteners, the finished food contains not less than 10 percent, by weight, of soluble solids taken as the refractometric sucrose value (of the filtrate), corrected to 20°C, and corrected for acidity by adding (0.012 + 0.193x- 0.0004x), where x equals the percent anhydrous citric acid in sample, to the refractometrically obtained sucrose value. Grapefruit juice, as defined in this paragraph, may be preserved by heat sterilization (canning), refrigeration, or freezing. When scaled in a container to be held at ambient temperatures, it is so processed by heat, before or after scaling, as to prevent spoilage.

1. Optional Ingredients

The optional ingredients are (a) concentrated grapefruit juice (grapefruit juice from which part of the water has been removed); (b) water and/or grapefruit juice to reconstitute concentrated grapefruit juice in the manufacture of grapefruit juice from concentrate; and (c) one or any combination of two or more of the dry or liquid forms of sugar, invert sugar syrup, dextrose, glucose syrup, and fructose.

The name of the food is "Grapefruit juice" if the food is prepared from unconcentrated, undiluted liquid extracted from mature grapefruit, or if the food is prepared from unconcentrated, undiluted liquid extracted from mature grapefruit to which concentrated grapefruit juice is added to adjust soluble solids.

"Grapefruit juice from concentrate" is the name if the food is prepared from concentrated grapefruit juice and water and/or grapefruit juice; or if the food is prepared from grapefuit juice from concentrate and grapefruit juice. The words "from concentrate" should be shown in letters not less than one-half the height of the letters in the words "grapefruit juice."

If any nutritive sweetener is added, the principal display panel of the label should bear the statement "sweetener added." If no sweetener is added, the word "unsweetened" may immediately precede or follow the words "grapefruit juice" or "grapefruit juice from concentrate."

F. ORANGE JUICE

Orange juice is the unfermented juice obtained from mature oranges of the species *Citrus sinensis* or of the citrus hybrid commonly called "Ambersweet" [1/2 *Citrus sinensis* × 3/8 *Citrus reticulata* × 1/8 *Citrus paradisi* (USDA Selection: 1-100-29: 1972 Whitmore Foundation Farm)]. Seeds (except embryonic seeds and small fragments of seeds that cannot be separated by current good manufacturing practice) and excess pulp are removed. The juice may be chilled, but it is not frozen.

The name of the food is "orange juice." The name "orange juice" may be preceded on the label by the varietal name of the oranges used, and if the oranges grew in a single State, the name of such State may be included in the name, as for example, "California Valencia orange juice."

G. PASTEURIZED ORANGE JUICE

Pasteurized orange juice is the food prepared from unfermented juice obtained from mature oranges, to which may be added not more than 10 percent by volume of the unfermented juice obtained from mature oranges of the species *Citrus reticulata* or *Citrus reticulata* hybrids. Seeds (except embryonic seeds and small fragments of seeds that cannot be separated by good manufacturing practice) are removed, and pulp and orange oil may be adjusted in accordance with good manufacturing practice. If the adjustment involves the addition of pulp, then such pulp should not be of the washed or spent type. The solids may be adjusted by the addition of one or more of the optional concentrated orange juice ingredients. One or more of the optional sweetening ingredients may be added in a quantity reasonably necessary to raise the Brix or the Brix-acid ratio to any point within the normal range usually found in unfermented juice obtained from mature oranges. The orange juice is so treated by heat as to reduce substantially the enzymatic activity and the number of viable microorganisms. Either before or after such heat treatment, all or a part of the product may be frozen. The finished pasteurized orange juice contains not less than 10.5 percent by weight of orange juice soluble solids, exclusive of the solids of any added optional sweetening ingredients, and the ratio of the Brix hydrometer reading to the grams of anhydrous citric acid per 100 milliliters of juice is not less than 10 to 1.

The optional concentrated orange juice ingredients are frozen concentrated orange juice and concentrated orange juice for manufacturing when made from mature oranges; but the quantity of such concentrated orange juice ingredients added should not contribute more than one-fourth of the total orange juice solids in the finished pasteurized orange juice.

The optional sweetening ingredients referred to are sugar, invert sugar, dextrose, dried corn syrup, and dried glucose syrup.

The name of the food is "pasteurized orange juice." If the food is filled into containers and preserved by freezing, the label should bear the name "frozen pasteurized orange juice." The words "pasteurized" or "frozen pasteurized" should be shown on labels in letters not less than one-half the height of the letters in the words "orange juice."

If the pasteurized orange juice is filled into containers and refrigerated, the label should bear the name of the food, "chilled pasteurized orange juice." If it does not purport to be either canned orange juice or frozen pasteurized orange juice, the word "chilled" may be omitted from the name. The words "pasteurized" or "chilled pasteurized" should be shown in letters not less than one-half the height of the letters in the words "orange juice."

H. FROZEN CONCENTRATED ORANGE JUICE

Frozen concentrated orange juice is the food prepared by removing water from the juice of mature oranges, to which may be added unfermented juice obtained from mature oranges of the species *Citrus reticulata,* other *Citrus reticulata* hybrids, or of *Citrus aurantiurn,* or both. However, in the unconcentrated blend, the volume of juice from *Citrus reticulata* or *Citrus reticulata* hybrids should not exceed 10 percent, and from *Citrus aurantium* should not exceed 5 percent. The concentrate so obtained is frozen. In its preparation, seeds (except embryonic seeds and small fragments of seeds that cannot be separated by good manufacturing practice) and excess pulp are removed, and a properly prepared water extract of the excess pulp so removed may be added. Orange oil, orange pulp, orange essence (obtained from orange juice), orange juice and other orange juice concentrate or concentrated orange juice for manufacturing (when made from mature oranges), water, and one or more of the optional sweetening ingredients may be added to adjust the final composition. The juice of *Citrus reticulata* and *Citrus aurantium,* as permitted by this paragraph, may be added in single strength or concentrated form prior to concentration of the *Citrus sinensis* juice, or in concentrated form during adjustment of the composition of the finished food. The addition of concentrated juice from *Citrus reticulata* or *Citrus aurantium,* or both, should not exceed, on a single-strength basis, the 10 percent maximum for *Citrus reticulata* and the 5 percent maximum for *Citrus aurantiumi* prescribed by this paragraph. Any of the ingredients of the finished concentrate may have been so treated by heat as to reduce substantially the enzymatic activity and the number of viable microorganisms. The finished food is of such concentration that when diluted according to label directions the diluted article will contain not less than 11.8 percent by weight of orange juice soluble solids, exclusive of the solids of added optional sweetening ingredients. The term "dilution ratio" means the whole number of volumes of frozen per volume of frozen concentrate required to produce orange juice from concentrate having orange juice soluble solids of not less than 11.8 percent by weight exclusive of the solids of any added optional sweetening ingredients.

The optional sweetening ingredients are sugar, sugar syrup, invert sugar, invert sugar syrup, dextrose, corn syrup, dried corn syrup, glucose syrup, and dried glucose syrup.

If one or more of the sweetening ingredients are added to the frozen concentrated orange juice, the label should bear the statement "_____added," the blank being filled in with the name or an appropriate combination of names of the sweetening ingredients used. However, the name "sweetener" may be used in lieu of the specific name or names of the sweetening ingredients.

The name of the food concentrated to a dilution ratio of is "frozen concentrated orange juice" or "frozen orange juice concentrate." The name of the food concentrated to a dilution ratio greater than 3 plus 1 is "frozen concentrated orange juice, _____ plus l" the blank being filled in with the whole number showing the dilution ratio; for example, "frozen orange juice concentrate, 4 plus 1." However, where the label bears directions for making 1 quart of orange juice from concentrate (or multiples of a quart), the blank in the name may be filled in with a mixed number; for example, "frozen orange juice concentrate, $4^1/_3$ plus 1." For containers larger than 1 pint, the dilution ratio in the name may be replaced by the concentration of orange juice soluble solids in degrees Brix; for example, a 62° Brix concentrate in 3⁄8 gallon cans may be named on the label "frozen concentrated orange juice, 62° Brix."

I. REDUCED ACID FROZEN CONCENTRATED ORANGE JUICE

Reduced-acid frozen concentrated orange juice is the food that complies with the requirements for composition and label declaration of ingredients prescribed for frozen concentrated orange juice except that it may not contain any added sweetening ingredient. A process involving the legal use of anionic ion-exchange resins is used to reduce the acidity of the food so that the ratio of the Brix reading to the grams of acid, expressed as anhydrous citric acid, per 100 grams of juice is not less than 21 to 1 or more than 26 to 1.

The name of the food is "reduced acid frozen concentrated orange juice."

J. ORANGE JUICE FOR MANUFACTURING

Orange juice for manufacturing is the food prepared for further manufacturing use. It is prepared from unfermented juice obtained from oranges as provided earlier, except that the oranges may deviate from the standards for maturity in that they are below the minimum for Brix and Brix-acid ratio for such oranges, and to which juice may be added not more than 10 percent by volume of the unfermented juice obtained from oranges of the species *Citrus reticulata* or *Citrus reticulata* hybrids (except that this limitation should not apply to the hybrid species). Seeds (except embryonic seeds and small fragments of seeds that cannot be separated by good manufacturing practice) are removed, and pulp and orange oil may be adjusted in accordance with good manufacturing practice. If pulp is added it should be other than washed or spent pulp. The juice or portions thereof may be so treated by heat as to reduce substantially the enzymatic activity and number of viable microorganisms, and it may be chilled or frozen, or it may be so treated by heat, either before or after sealing in containers, as to prevent spoilage.

The name of the food is "orange juice for manufacturing."

K. ORANGE JUICE WITH PRESERVATIVE

Orange juice with preservative is the food prepared for further manufacturing use. It complies with the requirements for composition of orange juice for manufacturing as specified, except that a preservative is added to inhibit spoilage. It may be heat-treated to reduce substantially the enzymatic activity and the number of viable microorganisms.

The preservatives referred to are any safe and suitable preservatives or combinations thereof.

The name of the food is "orange juice with preservative." Each of the ingredients used in the food should be declared on the label as required by regulations. In addition, the name of each preservative should be preceded by a statement of the percent by weight of the preservative used. If the food is packed in container sizes that are less than 19 liters (5 gallons), the label should bear a statement indicating that the food is for further manufacturing use only.

Wherever the name of the food appears on the label so conspicuously as to be easily seen under customary conditions of purchase, the statement for naming the preservative ingredient used should immediately and conspicuously precede or follow the name of the food, without intervening written, printed, or graphic matter.

L. CONCENTRATED ORANGE JUICE FOR MANUFACTURING

Concentrated orange juice for manufacturing is the food that complies with the requirements of composition and label declaration of ingredients prescribed, except that it is either not frozen or is less concentrated, or both, and the oranges from which the juice is obtained may deviate from the standards for maturity in that they are below the minimum Brix and Brix-acid ratio for such oranges: However, the concentration of orange juice soluble solids should not be less than 20° Brix.

The name of the food is "concentrated orange juice for manufacturing, _____" or "_____ orange juice concentrate for manufacturing," the blank being filled in with the figure showing the concentration of orange juice soluble solids in degrees Brix.

M. CONCENTRATED ORANGE JUICE WITH PRESERVATIVE

(a) Concentrated orange juice with preservative complies with the requirements for composition and labeling of optional ingredients prescribed for concentrated orange juice for manufacturing by Sec. 146.153, except that a preservative is added to inhibit spoilage. (b) The preservatives referred to in paragraph (a) of this section are any safe and suitable preservatives or combinations thereof. (c) The name of the food is "concentrated orange juice with preservative, _____," the blank being filled in with the figure showing the concentration of orange juice soluble solids in degrees Brix. (d) Label declaration. Each of the ingredients used in the food should be declared on the label as required by regulations. In addition, the name of each preservative should be preceded by a statement of the percent by weight of the preservative used. If the food is packed in container sizes that are less than 19 liters (5 gallons), the label should bear a statement indicating that the food is for further manufacturing use only.

N. PINEAPPLE JUICE

Pineapple juice is the juice, intended for direct consumption, obtained by mechanical process from the flesh or parts thereof, with or without core material, of sound, ripe pineapple *(Ananas comosus* L. Merrill). The juice may have been concentrated and later reconstituted with water suitable for the purpose of maintaining essential composition and quality factors of the juice. Pineapple juice may contain finely divided insoluble solids, but it does not contain pieces of shell, seeds, or other coarse or hard substances or excess pulp. It may be sweetened with any safe and suitable dry nutritive carbohydrate sweetener. However, if the pineapple juice is prepared from concentrate, such sweeteners, in liquid form, also may be used. It may contain added vitamin C in a quantity such that the total vitamin C in each 4 fluid ounces of the finished food amounts to not less than 30 milligrams and not more than 60 milligrams. In the processing of pineapple juice, dimethylpolysiloxane may be employed as a defoaming agent in an amount not greater than 10 parts per million by weight of the finished food. Such food is prepared by heat sterilization, refrigeration, or freezing. When sealed in a container to be held at ambient temperatures, it is so processed by heat, before or after sealing, as to prevent spoilage.

The name of the food is "pineapple juice" if the juice from which it is prepared has not been concentrated and/or diluted with water. The name of the food is "pineapple juice from concentrate" if the finished juice has been made from specified pineapple juice. If a nutritive sweetener is added, the label should bear the statement "sweetener added." If no sweetener is added, the word "unsweetened" may immediately precede or follow the words "pineapple juice" or "pineapple juice from concentrate."

Each of the ingredients used in the food should be declared on the label.

O. QUALITY

The standard of quality for pineapple juice is as follows: (a) The soluble solids content of pineapple juice (exclusive of added sugars) without added water should not be less than 10.5° Brix as determined by refractometer at 20°C uncorrected for acidity and read as degrees Brix on

International Sucrose Scales. Where the juice has been obtained using concentrated juice with addition of water, the soluble pineapple juice solids content (exclusive of added sugars) should be not less than 12.8° Brix, uncorrected for acidity and read as degrees Brix on the International Sucrose Scales. The acidity is not more than 1.35 grams of anhydrous citric acid per 100 milliliters of the juice. The ratio of the degrees Brix to total acidity is not less than 12. The quantity of finely divided "insoluble solids" is not less than 5 percent or more than 30 percent.

P. BLENDED GRAPE AND ORANGE JUICE

1. Product Description

Frozen concentrated blended grapefruit juice and orange juice is the frozen product prepared from a combination of concentrated, unfermented juices obtained from sound, mature grapefruit (*Citrus paradisi*) and from sound, mature fruit of the sweet orange group (*Citrus sinensis*) and Mandarin group (*Citrus reticulate*), except tangerines. The fruit is prepared by sorting and by washing prior to extraction of the juices to assure a clean product. The juices may be blended upon extraction of such juices or after concentration, and fresh orange juice extracted from sorted and washed fruit, as aforesaid, is admixed to the concentrate. It is recommended that the frozen concentrated blended grapefruit juice and orange juice be composed of the equivalent of not less than 50 percent orange juice in the reconstituted juice; however, in oranges yielding light-colored juice it is further recommended that as much as the equivalent of 75 percent orange juice in the reconstituted juice be used. The concentrated juice is packed in accordance with good commercial practice and is frozen and maintained at temperatures necessary for the preservation of the product.

2. Styles of Frozen Concentrated Blended Grapefruit Juice and Orange Juice

There are two styles: (a) Style I, without sweetening ingredient added. The Brix value of the finished concentrate should be not less than 40° or more than 44°; and (b) Style II, with sweetening ingredient added. The finished concentrate, exclusive of added sweetening ingredient, has a Brix value of not less than 38°; and the finished concentrate, including added sweetening ingredient, should have a Brix value of not less than 40° but not more than 48°.

ACKNOWLEDGMENT

The information in this chapter is based on *Food Safety Manual*, published and copyrighted by Science Technology System, West Sacramento, California, 2004. Used with permission.

26 Milk Proteins

Harjinder Singh and John Flanagan
Riddet Centre, Massey University

CONTENTS

I. INTRODUCTION

Bovine milk contains approximately 3.5% protein, and is an important protein source for both man and developing neonate. The protein concentration of milk may vary quite considerably due to a variety of factors; breed and age of cow, stage of lactation, number of lactations and diet of cow exert influence upon both the overall protein concentration of milk and the proportion of the individual milk proteins.

About 100 years ago it was shown that the proteins in milk could be fractionated into two well-defined groups. When the pH of raw milk is adjusted to 4.6 at ~30°C, a precipitate containing 80% of the total milk protein is formed. This fraction is called casein and the remaining soluble material under these conditions is referred to as whey or serum proteins or non-casein nitrogen. Both casein and whey proteins are quite heterogeneous, as outlined in Figure 26.1. These two classes of milk proteins are considered separately due to the large differences in their structures and physico-chemical properties. Many

reviews and monographs on the structures and properties of casein and whey proteins have been published (1–6). Most of the existing information on milk proteins has been compiled in the recently published Encyclopedia of Dairy Sciences (7).

This chapter provides an overview of the properties and structures of the main milk protein components. These topics have been covered in a greater detail in several text and reference books mentioned throughout this chapter.

II. CASEINS

For more than 50 years, it was believed that the casein fraction was a pure single entity. The application of moving boundary electrophoresis and sedimentation techniques in the late 1930s demonstrated the heterogeneity of the casein fraction. Three components were demonstrated and named α-, β- and γ-caseins in order of decreasing electrophoretic mobility and represented 75, 22 and 3%, respectively, of whole casein. In 1956, the α-casein

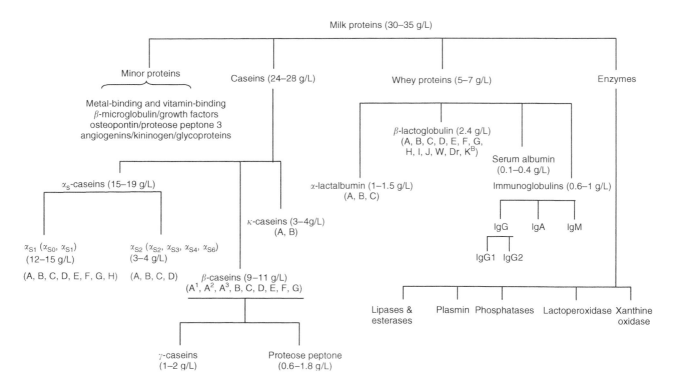

FIGURE 26.1 Distribution of fractions, and approximate concentrations and genetic variants of the major proteins in bovine milk. (Adapted from Ref. 3.)

fraction was shown to contain two proteins, one of which was precipitated by low Ca^{2+} concentration and was called α_s-casein, while the other, which was insensitive to calcium, was called κ-casein (8). α_s-Casein was later shown to consist of two proteins which are now called α_{S1}- and α_{S2}-caseins. Thus, bovine milk contains four major caseins, denoted as α_{S1}-casein, α_{S2}-casein, β-casein and κ-casein, which represent approximately 37, 10, 35 and 12% of the whole casein, respectively (9).

Minor components of the casein system are a heterogeneous group of proteins known as γ-caseins. These caseins occur as a result of limited proteolysis of the C-terminal of β-casein, caused by the action of the indigenous proteinase, plasmin (10). The γ-caseins are classified as γ^1-(β-casein f29-209), γ^2-(β-casein f106-209~11) and γ^3-(β-casein f108-209). The corresponding N-terminal portion of β-casein is the source of the so-called proteose peptones; PP5, PP8 fast and PP8 slow, i.e., β-CN f1-105/7, f1-28 and f29-105/7, respectively (see Figure 26.2). The proteose peptones elute in the whey fraction of milk.

Each of the four major caseins exhibits variability in the degree of phosphorylation and glycosylation. All caseins are phosphorylated: most of the α_{S1}-casein molecules contain 8 PO_4 residues but some contain 9; α_{S2}-casein contains 10, 11, 12 or 13 mol PO_4/mol; β-casein usually contains 5 mol PO_4/mol but occasionally 4 mol PO_4/mol; κ-casein contains 1 mol PO_4/mol but some molecules of κ-casein may contain 2 or 3 PO_4/mol. κ-Casein is the only casein which is normally glycosylated and contains galactose, galactosamine and N-acetyl neuraminic acid which occur as either trisaccharides or tetrasaccharides attached to threonine residues in the C-terminal region. κ-Casein may contain zero to four tri- or tetrasaccharide moieties, resulting in nine forms of κ-casein (4).

A further heterogeneity in caseins arises from the occurrence of genetic polymorphism, which is due to either substitutions or, rarely, deletions of amino acids in the caseins as a consequence of mutations causing changes in base sequences in the genes. Among the 21 variants in caseins (Figure 26.1), two are due to deletion of a segment in the α_{S1}-casein. The variants A and H of α_{S1}-casein differ from variant B by the absence of amino acid sequences 14–26 and 51–58, respectively. The deletion of residues 51–59 in α_{S2}-casein A leads to the occurrence of variant D. All other genetic variants of casein involve amino acid substitutions. As the casein system is very complex and heterogeneous, a logical nomenclature, recommended by the Nomenclature Committee of the American Dairy Science Association, has been adopted. The casein family is indicated by a Greek letter with a subscript (i.e., α_{S1}) followed by CN. The genetic variant is indicated by a Roman letter (A, B, C, etc.) with a superscript, if necessary (e.g., α_{S1}-CN A^2). The degree of phosphorylation is indicated as the number of phosphate residues, e.g., α_{S1}-CNB - 8P.

A. CASEIN STRUCTURES AND PROPERTIES

The primary structures of the major caseins have been known since the early 1970s and are shown in Figures 26.3 a–d. In comparison to typical globular proteins, the structures of caseins are quite unique. Each of the caseins has distinct areas of positively and negatively charged groups in their primary structures resulting in the amphiphilic nature of the individual proteins (Figure 26.4). In addition, the hydrophobicity of each of the caseins varies considerably as a function of position on the peptide chain (Figure 26.4).

The caseins, compared to typical globular proteins which have mainly α-helical and β-sheet structures, contain less secondary and tertiary structures. Most of the secondary structure is likely to be present in the hydrophobic domains.

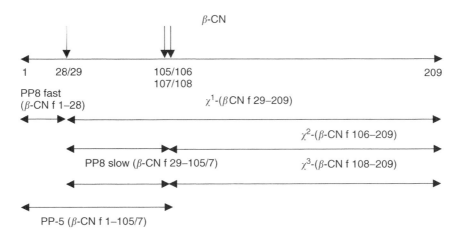

FIGURE 26.2 Principal plasmin cleavage sites on β-casein with resulting peptides.

```
                                                      10                                                        20
H.Arg – Pro – Lys – His – Pro – Ile – Lys – His – Gln – Gly – Leu – Pro – Gln – Glu – Val – Leu – Asn – Glu – Asn – Leu –
                                                      30                                                        40
   Leu – Arg – Phe – Phe – Val – Ala – Pro – Phe – Pro – Gln – Val – Phe – Gly – Lys – Glu – Lys – Val – Asn – Glu – Leu –
                                                      50                                                        60
   Ser – Lys – Asp – Ile – Gly – Ser(P) – Glu – Ser(P) – Thr – Glu – Asp – Gln – Ala – Met – Glu – Asp – Ile – Lys – Gln – Met –
                                                      70                                                        80
   Glu – Ala – Glu – Ser(P) – Ile – Ser(P) – Ser(P) – Ser(P) – Glu – Glu – Ile – Val – Pro – Asn – Ser(P) – Val – Glu – Gln – Lys – His –
                                                      90                                                        100
   Ile – Gln – Lys – Glu – Asp – Val – Pro – Ser – Glu – Arg – Tyr – Leu – Gly – Tyr – Leu – Glu – Gln – Leu – Leu – Arg –
                                                      110                                                       120
   Leu – Lys – Lys – Tyr – Lys – Val – Pro – Gln – Leu – Glu – Ile – Val – Pro – Asn – Ser(P) – Ala – Glu – Glu – Arg – Leu –
                                                      130                                                       140
   His – Ser – Met – Lys – Glu – Gly – Ile – His – Ala – Gln – Gln – Lys – Glu – Pro – Met – Ile – Gly – Val – Asn – Gln –
                                                      150                                                       160
   Glu – Leu – Ala – Tyr – Phe – Tyr – Pro – Glu – Leu – Phe – Arg – Gln – Phe – Tyr – Gln – Leu – Asp – Ala – Tyr – Pro –
                                                      170                                                       180
   Ser – Gly – Ala – Trp – Tyr – Tyr – Val – Pro – Leu – Gly – Thr – Gln – Tyr – Thr – Asp – Ala – Pro – Ser – Phe – Ser –
                                                      190                                                       199
   Asp – Ile – Pro – Asn – Pro – Ile – Gly – Ser – Glu – Asn – Ser – Glu – Lys – Thr – Thr – Met – Pro – Leu – Trp.OH
(a)
```

```
                                                      10                                                        20
H.Lys – Asn – Thr – Met – Glu – His – Val – Ser(P) – Ser(P) – Ser(P) – Glu – Glu – Ser – Ile – Ile – Ser(P) – Gln – Glu – Thr – Tyr –
                                                      30                                                        40
   Lys – Gln – Glu – Lys – Asn – Met – Ala – Ile – Asn – Pro – Ser – Lys – Glu – Asn – Leu – Cys – Ser – Thr – Phe – Cys –
                                                      50                                                        60
   Lys – Glu – Val – Val – Arg – Asn – Ala – Asn – Glu – Glu – Glu – Tyr – Ser – Ile – Gly – Ser(P) – Ser(P) – Ser(P) – Glu – Glu –
                                                      70                                                        80
   Ser(P) – Ala – Glu – Val – Ala – Thr – Glu – Glu – Val – Lys – Ile – Thr – Val – Asp – Asp – Lys – His – Tyr – Gln – Lys –
                                                      90                                                        100
   Ala – Leu – Asn – Glu – Ile – Asn – Glu – Phe – Tyr – Gln – Lys – Phe – Pro – Gln – Tyr – Leu – Gln – Tyr – Leu – Tyr –
                                                      110                                                       120
   Gln – Gly – Pro – Ile – Val – Leu – Asn – Pro – Trp – Asp – Gln – Val – Lys – Arg – Asn – Ala – Val – Pro – Ile – Thr –
                                                      130                                                       140
   Pro – Thr – Leu – Asn – Arg – Glu – Gln – Leu – Ser(P) – Thr – Ser(P) – Glu – Glu – Asn – Ser – Lys – Lys – Thr – Val – Asp –
                                                      150                                                       160
   Met – Glu – Ser(P) – Thr – Glu – Val – Phe – Thr – Lys – Lys – Thr – Lys – Leu – Thr – Glu – Glu – Glu – Lys – Asn – Arg –
                                                      170                                                       180
   Leu – Asn – Phe – Leu – Lys – Lys – Ile – Ser – Gln – Arg – Tyr – Gln – Lys – Phe – Ala – Leu – Pro – Gln – Tyr – Leu –
                                                      190                                                       200
   Lys – Thr – Val – Tyr – Gln – His – Gln – Lys – Ala – Net – Lys – Pro – Trp – Ile – Gln – Pro – Lys – Thr – Lys – Val –
                                                      207
   Ile – Pro – Tyr – Val – Arg – Tyr – Leu.OH
(b)
```

FIGURE 26.3 (a) Primary structure of bovine α_{S1}-casein B. (Source: Mercier et al., Structure primaire de la caséine α_{S1}-bovine. Eur J Biochem 25:505–514, 1972, Blackwell Publishing Ltd.); (b) Primary structure of bovine α_{S2}-casein A. (Source: Federation of the European Biochemical Societies, from: Complete amino acid sequence of α_{S2}-casein, by Brignon et al., FEBS Lett 76:274–279, 1977.)

1. α_{S1}- and α_{S2}-Caseins

The primary structure of α_{S1}-casein is shown in Figure 26.3a. The α_{S1}-casein molecule contains 199 amino acids and 8 phosphate groups that are esterified to serine groups. It has no cysteine residues. The molecule has a net charge of about −24 at pH 6.7; the sequence 45 →89 which contains 8 phosphate groups and 12 carboxyl groups, has a net charge of about −23 at pH 6.7. Three hydrophobic regions are located in the sequences 1–44, 90–113 and 132–199 (4). The molecule contains 17 proline residues which are almost randomly distributed within the hydrophobic portion of the molecule and these residues disrupt the formation of α-helices and β-sheet structures. Physical methods, such as circular dichroism (CD) or Raman spectral analysis indicate that there is a low level of either α-helix or β-sheet (about 30–40%) (16). Sequence predictions suggest that the likely positions for helix formation are near residues 60, 100 and 125.

α_{S2}-Casein contains 207 amino acids, including 10 proline residues and two cysteines at positions 36 and 40 (Figure 26.3b). Among the caseins, it is the least hydrophobic and most highly and variably phosphorylated. The degree of phosphorylation ranges from 10 to 13 phosphate groups, and these casein forms have been identified as α_{S2}-, α_{S3}-, α_{S4}-, α_{S5}- and α_{S6}-caseins (α_{S5}- is a dimer of α_{S3}- and α_{S4}-). These phosphate groups are located in three regions (7–31, 55–66 and 129–143) of the molecule. There are two large hydrophobic regions: residues 90–120 and 160–207 (4). The C-terminal 47-residue sequence has a net charge of +9.5 while the N-terminal 68-residue sequence has a net charge of −21. The C-terminal half probably has a globular conformation while the N-terminal region probably forms a randomly structured hydrophilic tail.

```
                                                              10                                                           20
H.Arg – Glu – Leu – Glu – Glu – Leu – Asn – Val – Pro –   Gly – Glu – Ile  – Val – Glu – Ser – Leu – Ser – Ser – Ser – Glu –
                                                              30                   P              P     P     P           40
Glu – Ser – Ile  – Thr – Arg – Ile  – Asn – Lys – Lys –   Ile – Glu – Lys – Phe – Gln – Ser – Glu – Glu – Gln – Gln – Gln –
                                                              50                   P                                      60
Thr – Glu – Asp – Glu – Leu – Gln – Asp – Lys – Ile  –    His – Pro – Phe – Ala – Gln – Thr – Gln – Ser – Leu – Val – Tyr –
                                                              70                                                          80
Pro – Phe – Pro – Gly – Pro – Ile  – Pro – Asn – Ser –    Leu – Pro – Gln – Asn – Ile – Pro – Pro – Leu – Thr – Gln – Thr –
                                                              90                                                         100
Pro – Val – Val – Val – Pro – Pro – Phe – Leu – Gln –     Pro – Glu – Val – Met – Gly – Val – Ser – Lys – Val – Lys – Glu –
                                                             110                                                         120
Ala – Met – Ala – Pro – Lys – His – Lys – Glu – Met –     Pro – Phe – Pro – Lys – Tyr – Pro – Val – Gln – Pro – Phe – Thr –
                                                             130                                                         140
Glu – Ser – Gln – Ser – Leu – Thr – Leu – Thr – Asp –     Val – Glu – Asn – Leu – His – Leu – Pro – Pro – Leu – Leu – Leu –
                                                             150                                                         160
Gln – Ser – Trp – Met – His – Gln – Pro – His – Gln –     Pro – Leu – Pro – Pro – Thr – Val – Met – Phe – Pro – Pro – Gln –
                                                             170                                                         180
Ser – Val – Leu – Ser – Leu – Ser – Gln – Ser – Lys –     Val – Leu – Pro – Val – Pro – Glu – Lys – Ala – Val – Pro – Tyr –
                                                             190                                                         200
Pro – Gln – Arg – Asp – Met – Pro – Ile  – Gln – Ala –    Phe – Leu – Leu – Tyr – Gln – Gln – Pro – Val – Leu – Gly – Pro –
                                                             209
Val – Arg – Gly – Pro – Phe – Pro – Ile  – Ile  – Val.OH
```

(c)

```
                                                              10                                                           20
PyroGlu – Glu – Gln – Asn – Gln – Glu – Gln – Pro – Ile  –   Arg – Cys – Glu – Lys – Asp – Glu – Arg – Phe – Phe – Ser – Asp
                                                              30                                                           40
Lys – Ile  – Ala – Lys – Tyr – Ile  – Pro – Ile  – Gln –    Tyr – Val – Leu – Ser – Arg – Tyr – Pro – Ser – Tyr – Gly – Leu –
                                                              50                                                           60
Asn – Tyr – Tyr – Gln – Gln – Lys – Pro – Val – Ala –       Leu – Ile – Asn – Asn – Gln – Phe – Leu – Pro – Tyr – Pro – Tyr –
                                                              70                                                           80
Tyr – Ala – Lys – Pro – Ala – Ala – Val – Arg – Ser –       Pro – Ala – Gln – Ile  – Leu – Gln – Trp – Gln – Val – Leu – Ser –
                                                              90                                                          100
Asp – Thr – Val – Pro – Ala – Lys – Ser – Cys – Gln –       Ala – Gln – Pro – Thr – Thr – Met – Ala – Arg – His – Pro – His –
                                                             110                                                          120
Pro – His – Leu – Ser – Phe – Met – Ala – Ile  – Pro –      Pro – Lys – Lys – Asn – Gln – Asp – Lys – Thr – Glu – Ile  – Pro –
                                                             130                                                          140
Thr – Ile  – Asn – Thr – Ile  – Ala – Ser – Gly – Glu –     Pro – Thr – Ser – Thr – Pro – Thr – Ile  – Glu – Ala – Val – Glu –
                                                             150                                                          160
Ser – Thr – Val – Ala – Thr – Leu – Glu – Ala – Ser –       Pro – Glu – Val – Ile  – Glu – Ser – Pro – Pro – Glu – Ile  – Asn –
                                                              P
                                                             169
Thr – Val – Gln – Val – Thr – Ser – Thr – Ala – Val.OH
```

(d)

FIGURE 26.3   (c) Primary structure of bovine β-casein A². (Source: Ribadeau-Dumas et al., Structure primaire de la caséine β-bovine: séquence complète. Eur J Biochem 25:505–514, 1972, Blackwell Publishing Ltd.) (d) Primary structure of bovine κ-casein B. (Source: Mercier et al., Structure primaire de la caséine κ-bovine: sequence complète. Eur J Biochem 35:222–235, 1973. Blackwell Publishing Ltd.)

2. β-Casein

β-Casein is made up of 209 amino acids and contains a high proportion of proline residues (35 residues), which are randomly distributed throughout the molecule. The molecule contains no cysteine residues and 5 phosphate groups each as a serine phosphate ester. There are 6 forms of β-casein with 0–5 phosphate groups attached to serine residues (3). It is the most hydrophobic of the intact caseins and has two large hydrophobic regions (55–90 and 130–209). The N-terminal 21-residue sequence has a net charge of −12, while the rest of the molecule is very hydrophobic and has no net charge (4). Consequently, this molecule is very amphipathic with a polar domain comprising one-tenth of the chains but carrying one-third of the total charge and a hydrophobic domain consisting of the C-terminal three-fourths of the molecule.

Theoretical calculations suggest that β–casein could have 10% of its residues in the α-helices, 17% in the β-sheets and 70% in unordered structures (17).

3. κ-Casein

κ-Casein consists of 169 amino acids and is the only protein of the casein family that is glycosylated. About half of the κ-casein molecules are glycosylated at positions 131, 133, 135 or 142, and most of the κ-casein molecules are phosphorylated at Ser 149. Like β-casein, the structure of κ-casein is highly amphipathic. The N-terminal domain comprising residues 1–105 (para-κ-casein) is highly hydrophobic and carries a net positive charge. The

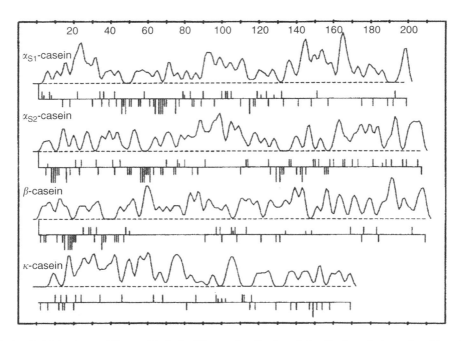

FIGURE 26.4 Hydrophobicity (curved lines with dashed line as baseline) and distribution of charged residues (vertical bars above and below the solid lines) as a function of sequence position of α_{S1}-casein B, α_{S2}-casein A, β-casein A^2 and κ-casein B. The vertical bars below the solid line indicate the phosphoserine (long bars), glutamic and aspartic acid side chains and the C-terminal group. The vertical bars above the solid line indicate the histidine (shorter bars), lysine and arginine side chains and the N-terminal groups (note that κ-casein has a pyroglutamate terminus). (Source: Casein and Caseinates, Swartz et al. In: Encyclopedia of Food Science and Technology. Copyright © (Wiley 1991). Reprinted by permission of John Wiley & Sons, Inc.)

C-terminal 53-residue sequence carries a net negative charge, with a preponderance of polar residues. These two domains are joined by a peptide (residues 96–112) that carries a net positive charge, which is generally predicted to be β-strand and contains a motif that is readily recognised by chymosin (4). Chymosin is able to cleave specifically the Phe105-Met106 bond to form two peptides: a large hydrophobic peptide (para-κ-casein, residues 1–105) and a smaller hydrophilic peptide (caseino-macropeptide, CMP, residues 106–169).

κ-Casein appears to be the most highly structured of the caseins, with 10–20% α-helix, 20–30% β-structure and 15–25% turns (16, 18). Several structural motifs have been suggested including possible anti-parallel and parallel β-sheets or $\beta\alpha\beta$ structure in the hydrophobic domain and a β-turn-β-strand-β-turn motif centered on the chymosin sensitive residues 105–106 (18).

B. SELF-ASSOCIATION OF CASEINS

Due to their peculiar charge distributions and large size of hydrophobic domains, the casein monomers cannot sufficiently remove their hydrophobic surfaces from contact with water. Consequently, the caseins associate with themselves and with each other. The association behavior of caseins has been covered in more detail in a number of reviews, including Rollema (19) and de Kruif & Holt (20).

At low ionic strength (0.003–0.01 M) and neutral or alkaline pH, α_{S1}-casein occurs as a monomer. As the pH is decreased and the ionic strength is increased, this protein shows progressive self-association to dimers, tetramers, hexamers, etc. Dynamic and static light scattering studies indicate that a rod-like chain polymer is formed (21).

The association behavior of monomeric α_{S2}-casein is similar to that of α_{S1}-casein, except for the effect of ionic strength. With increasing ionic strength, the extent of association first increases, but above 0.2 M, the degree of association decreases with a further increase in ionic strength (19). This peculiar behavior has been attributed to the non-uniform distribution of positive and negative charges along the polypeptide chain.

The self-association of β-casein is described by a monomer-polymer equilibrium:

$$n\beta\text{-}CN \rightleftharpoons \beta\text{-}CN_n$$

The association is characterized by formation of detergent-like micelles, with the critical micelle concentration ranging from 0.3 to 0.7 mg mL^{-1} depending on the temperature and ionic strength. The driving forces in micelle formation are the hydrophobic interactions between the C-terminal segments. At 4°C and low ionic strength, β-casein in solution exists as a monomer, but as the temperature and/or ionic strength is increased, the monomers associate to form polymers, with n ranging from 20–60. For the shape of the polymer, a thread-like structure, a spherical particle and an oblate ellipsoid approaching spherical shape have been proposed (22).

In unreduced form, κ-casein is present largely as disulfide-linked polymers. In a reduced form, κ-casein associates according to the monomer-polymer equilibrium in a similar manner to β-casein. At low protein concentrations, a critical micelle concentration (typically 0.2–0.5 mg mL⁻¹) is obser-ved which decreases with increasing ionic strength. At pH 7 and 20°C, the degree of polymerization is independent of temperature between 4 and 20°C and ionic strength between 0.1 and 1.0 M (23). In contrast to β-casein association, κ-casein polymers are of a fixed size irrespective of temperature or ionic strength.

C. CALCIUM BINDING AND PRECIPITATION OF CASEINS

All caseins are able to bind calcium, and the extent of binding is directly related to the number of phosphoserine residues in the molecule. Thus the calcium binding capacity follows the order: α_{S2}- > α_{S1}- > β- > κ-casein (19). Binding of calcium reduces the negative charge on casein molecules, diminishing electrostatic repulsions, and inducing precipitation.

At all temperatures, α_{S1}-casein B, α_{S1}-casein C and α_{S2}-caseins are insoluble in Ca^{2+} concentrations above about 4 mM. α_{S1}-Casein A, in which a relative hydrophobic region is deleted, is soluble at Ca^{2+} concentrations up to 0.4 M and temperatures below 33°C. Above 33°C, it precipitates but redissolves on cooling to 20°C. β-Casein is soluble at high concentrations of Ca^{2+} (0.4 M) at temperatures below 18°C, but above 18°C β-casein is very insoluble, even in the presence of low concentrations of Ca^{2+} (4 mM). κ-Casein, with only one phosphoserine, binds little calcium and remains soluble in Ca^{2+} at all concentrations. κ-Casein is also capable of stabilizing α_{S1}-, α_{S2}- and β-caseins against precipitation by Ca^{2+} and restricts the growth of the aggregates to colloidal dimensions (19).

D. CASEIN MICELLES

In normal milk, about 95% of the casein proteins exist as coarse colloidal particles, called micelles, with diameters ranging from 80 to 300 nm (average ~150 nm). These particles are formed within the secretory cells of the mammary gland and undergo relatively little change after secretion. On a dry weight basis, the micelles consist of ~94% protein and ~6% of small ions, principally calcium, phosphate, magnesium and citrate, referred to collectively as colloidal calcium phosphate (CCP). The κ-casein content of casein micelles is inversely proportional to their size, while the content of CCP is directly related to size. The composition

TABLE 26.1

Some Physicochemical Characteristics of Casein Micelles

Diameter	50–300 nm
Surface Area	8×10^{-10} cm²
Volume	2×10^{-15} cm³
Density	1.063 g cm⁻³
Molecular weight (hydrated)	1.3×10^9 Da
Voluminosity	4.4 cm³ per g protein
Hydration	2 g H_2O per g protein
Water content (hydrated)	63%

Source: Adapted from McMahon and Brown. J Dairy Sci 67:499–512, 1984. American Dairy Science Association.

and some of the physico-chemical characteristics of casein micelles are presented in Table 26.1. The structure and properties of casein micelle have been reviewed recently by de Kruif and Holt (20) and Horne (25).

The micelles are very open and highly hydrated structures containing about 2–4 g H_2O per g protein, depending on the method of measurement. The apparent zeta potential for casein micelles is about −19 mV at 25°C. The structure of the micelle is dynamic, e.g., cooling the milk to about 4°C causes solubilization of a significant proportion of β-casein and some κ-casein and much lower levels of α_{S1}- and α_{S2}-caseins. Almost complete disintegration of micelles occurs by addition of a calcium sequestrant such as EDTA or through the addition of high levels of urea or SDS (20).

The precise structure of the casein micelle is a matter of considerable debate at the present time. A number of models have been proposed over the past 40 years, but none of them can describe completely all aspects of casein micelle behavior. The models include coat-core models which postulate that the interior of the micelle is composed of proteins that are different from those on the exterior (26,27) and sub-unit structure models to which the term sub-micelle is attached (1,28,29).

In the sub-unit models (29), caseins are aggregated to form sub-micelles (10–15 nm in diameter). It has been suggested that sub-micelles have a hydrophobic core that is covered by a hydrophilic coat. The polar moieties of κ-casein molecules are concentrated in one area. The remaining part of the coat consists of the polar parts of other caseins, notably segments containing their phosphoserine residues. The sub-micelles are assumed to aggregate into micelles by CCP which would bind to α_{S1}-, α_{S2}- and β-caseins via their phosphoserine residues. Sub-micelles with no or low κ-casein are located in the interior of the micelle whereas κ-casein rich sub-micelles are concentrated on the surface.

Other models consider the micelle as a porous network of proteins (of no fixed conformation); the calcium phosphate nanoclusters are responsible for crosslinking the protein and holding the network together (2). More specifically there are no subunits because individual polypeptide chains with two or more phosphate centers provide a network of strong interactions that link together most of the Ca-sensitive caseins in a micelle. The surface layer is a natural extension of the internal structure. A recent model proposed by Horne (30) assumes that the assembly of the casein micelle is governed by a balance of electrostatic and hydrophobic interactions between casein molecules. As stated earlier, α_{S1}-, α_{S2}- and β-caseins consist of distinct hydrophobic and hydrophilic regions. Two or more hydrophobic regions from different molecules form a bonded cluster. Growth of these polymers is inhibited by the protein charge residues, the repulsion of which pushes up the interaction free energy. Neutralization of the phosphoserine clusters by incorporation into the CCP diminishes that free energy as well as producing the second type of cross-linking bridge. κ-Casein acts a terminator for both types of growth, as it contains no phosphoserine cluster or another hydrophobic anchor point.

A common factor in all models is that most of the κ-casein appears to be present on the surface of casein micelles. The hydrophilic, C-terminal part of κ-casein, is assumed to protrude 5 to 10 nm from the micelle surface into the surrounding solvent, giving it a "hairy" appearance and providing a steric stabilizing layer. The highly charged flexible "hairs" physically prevent the approach and interactions of hydrophobic regions of the casein molecules.

E. CASEIN MICELLE STABILITY

The micelles are stabilized by two principal factors: (1) a surface potential of C. -20 mV at pH 6.7 which alone is insufficient for colloidal stability and (2) steric stabilization due to protruding κ-casein hairs. Casein micelles can be caused to aggregate by several factors. Much attention has been focussed on the curd formation during cheese making brought about by the action of chymosin which destroys the stabilizing effect of κ-casein. Chymosin is highly specific in its action, splitting the κ-casein at the Phe105-Met106 bond, releasing the hydrophilic peptide and destabilising the micelles. This action results in a decrease in the micellar zeta potential from about -20 to -10 mV, and prior to aggregation a decrease in micellar hydrodynamic size as the hairy layer is cleaved off (20). Many other proteases with a more general action can also hydrolyze a specific bond of κ-casein, resulting in micelle aggregation.

Casein micelles aggregate and precipitate from solution when the pH is lowered to about pH 4.6. When the pH of milk is reduced, CCP is dissolved and the caseins are dissociated into the milk serum phase (31,32). The extent of dissociation of caseins is dependent on temperature of acidification; at 30°C, a decrease in pH causes virtually no dissociation; at 4°C about 40% of the caseins are dissociated in the serum at pH ~5.5 (32). Aggregation of

casein occurs as the isoelectric point (pH 4.6) is approached. Apparently little change in the average hydrodynamic diameter of casein micelles occurs during acidification of milk to pH~5.0 (31). The lack of change in the size of micelles on reducing the pH of milk to 5.5 may be due to concomitant swelling of the particles as CCP is solubilized. The mobility of casein micelles measured by nuclear magnetic resonance spectroscopy does not change with pH (33).

Casein micelles are very stable at high temperatures, but they can aggregate and coagulate after heating at 140°C for 15–20 min. Such coagulation results from a number of changes in milk systems that occur during heating, including a decrease in pH, denaturation of whey proteins and their association with κ-casein, transfer of soluble calcium and phosphate into colloidal state, dephosphorylation of caseins and a decrease in hydration (34,35).

The micelles are also destabilized by addition of about 40% ethanol at pH 6.7 and by lower concentrations if the pH is reduced. This is due to the collapse and folding of the hairy layer of κ-casein in the non-solvent mixture, allowing micelles to interact and aggregate (36).

Freezing of milk has been shown to cause destabilization of casein micelles which is due to a decrease in pH and an increase in the Ca^{2+} concentration in the unfrozen phase of milk.

III. WHEY PROTEINS

The whey protein fraction accounts for approximately 20% of total protein. Whey proteins are an even more heterogeneous group of proteins than the caseins, containing a greater number of individual proteins. The principal fractions of whey proteins are β-lactoglobulin, bovine serum albumin, α-lactalbumin and immunoglobulins which account for more than 95% of the proteins in the whey fraction (Figure 26.1). These proteins have been well characterized. Major reviews covering structures and properties of whey proteins have been published (5,6,9,37). Unlike the caseins, the whey proteins possess high levels of secondary, tertiary and in most cases, quaternary structures. Most are typical globular proteins and are denatured by heat treatments. Both β-lactoglobulin and α-lactalbumin are synthesized in the mammary gland whereas serum albumin is transported to the mammary gland via the blood serum.

A. β-LACTOGLOBULIN

β-Lactoglobulin is the most abundant whey protein which represents about 50% of the total whey protein in bovine milk. There are 13 known genetic variants of β-lactoglobulin: A, B, C, D, E, F, G, H, I, J, W, Dr and K^B (38). The A and B genetic variants are the most common and exist in almost the same frequency. The primary structure of

```
                                    10                                        20
H.Leu – Ile  – Val – Thr – Gln – Thr – Met – Lys – Gly – Leu – Asp – Ile  – Gln – Lys – Val – Ala – Gly – Thr – Trp – Tyr –
                                    30                                        40
Ser – Leu – Ala – Met – Ala – Ala – Ser – Asp – Ile  – Ser – Leu – Leu – Asp – Ala – Gln – Ser – Ala – Pro – Leu – Arg –
                                    50                                        60
Val – Tyr – Val – Glu – Glu – Leu – Lys – Pro – Thr – Pro – Glu – Gly – Asp – Leu – Glu – Ile  – Leu – Leu – Gln – Lys –
                                    70                                        80
Trp – Glu – Asn – Gly – Glu – Cys – Ala – Gln – Lys – Lys – Ile  – Ile  – Ala – Glu – Lys – Thr – Lys – Ile  – Pro – Ala –
                                    90                                        100
Val  – Phe – Lys – Ile  – Asp – Ala – Leu – Asn – Glu – Asn – Lys – Val – Leu – Val – Leu – Asp – Thr – Asp – Tyr  – Lys –
                                    110                                       120
Lys – Tyr – Leu – Leu – Phe – Cys – Met – Glu – Asn – Ser – Ala – Glu – Pro – Glu – Gln – Ser – Leu – Ala – Cys – Gln –
                                    130                                       140
Cys – Leu – Val – Arg – Thr – Pro – Glu – Val – Asp – Asp – Glu – Ala – Leu – Glu – Lys – Phe – Asp – Lys – Ala  – Leu –
                                    150                                       160
Lys – Ala – Leu – Pro – Met – His – Ile  – Arg – Leu – Ser – Phe – Asn – Pro – Thr – Gln – Leu – Glu – Glu – Gln – Cys –
                                    162
His – Ile.OH
```

(a)

```
                                    10                                        20
H.Glu – Gln – Leu – Thr – Lys – Cys – Glu – Val – Phe  – Arg – Glu – Leu – Lys – Asp – Leu – Lys – Gly – Tyr – Gly – Gly –
                                    30                                        40
Val – Ser – Leu – Pro – Glu – Trp – Val – Cys – Thr  – Thr – Phe – His – Thr – Ser – Gly – Tyr – Asp – Thr – Glu – Ala –
                                    50                                        60
Ile  – Val – Glu – Asn – Asn – Gln – Ser – Thr – Asp – Tyr  – Gly – Leu – Phe – Gln – Ile  – Asn – Asn – Lys – Ile  – Trp –
                                    70                                        80
Cys – Lys – Asn – Asp – Gln – Asp – Pro – His – Ser – Ser – Asn – Ile  – Cys – Asn – Ile  – Ser – Cys – Asp – Lys – Phe –
                                    90                                        100
Leu – Asn – Asn – Asp – Leu – Thr – Asn – Asn – Ile  – Met – Cys – Val – Lys – Lys – Ile  – Leu – Asp – Lys – Val – Gly –
                                    110                                       120
Ile  – Asn – Tyr – Trp – Leu – Ala – His – Lys – Ala – Leu – Cys – Ser – Glu – Lys – Leu – Asp – Gln – Trp – Leu – Cys –
                                    123
Glu – Lys – Leu.OH
```

(b)

FIGURE 26.5 (a) Primary structure of bovine β-lactoglobulin B. (Source: Braunitzer et al., Automatische sequenzanalyse eines proteins (β-lactoglobulin AB). H-S Z Physiol Chem 353: 832–834, 1972, Walter de Gruyter GmbH & Co. KG.) (b) Primary structure of bovine α-lactalbumin B. (Source: Brew et al., The complete amino acid sequence of α-lactalbumin. J Biol Chem 245:4570–4582, 1970, The American Society for Biochemistry and Molecular Biology.)

β-lactoglobulin is shown in Figure 26.5a. The β-lactoglobulin monomer comprises 162 amino acids with one free thiol group (Cys 121) and two disulfide bridges (Cys 106-Cys119 and Cys 66-Cys160) and has a molecular weight of 18,000 Da. The A and B variants differ at positions 64 and 118, where Asp and Val in β-lactoglobulin A are replaced by Gly and Ala in β-lactoglobulin B.

β-Lactoglobulin is a highly structured protein; optical rotary dispersion, circular dichroism, infrared spectroscopy and nuclear magnetic resonance show around 10% α-helix, 50% β-sheet and 40% unordered structure including β-turns. The tertiary structure of β-lactoglobulin consists of nine anti-parallel β-strands, of which eight are wrapped into a β-barrel (Figure 26.6) (40,41). β-Strands A-D form one side of the calyx, and β-strands E-H are also part of strand A from the opposite side. The ninth strand, I, is on the outside, on the opposite side of strand A to strand H. The three-turn α-helix is located on the outside of the barrel and aligned along strands A, G and H.

In milk, native β-lactoglobulin occurs as a dimer. The association behavior of this protein is dependent on several parameters, including pH, temperature, protein concentration and ionic conditions. Below pH 3.5, β-lactoglobulin dissociates into its monomers, whereas between pH 3.5 and 5.2 it reversibly forms tetramers/octamers. Above pH 7.5, it starts to unfold, with a concomitant increase in the reactivity of thiol group. The proportion of dimer increases with increasing protein concentration and ionic strength. At temperatures between 30 and 55°C, the β-lactoglobulin dimer dissociates into monomers and at higher temperature (above 60°C), the monomer unfolds resulting in an increased reactivity of the free thiol group (38).

The biological function of β-lactoglobulin remains unclear but it appears to have at least two roles. Firstly, β-lactoglobulin is capable of binding several hydrophobic molecules, including retinol (vitamin A) (38). Retinol is bound in a hydrophobic pocket of β-lactoglobulin and transported to the small intestine where it is transferred to a retinol-binding protein, which has a structure similar to β-lactoglobulin. This binding also protects retinol against oxidation. Secondly, through its ability to bind fatty acids, β-lactoglobulin stimulates lipase activity.

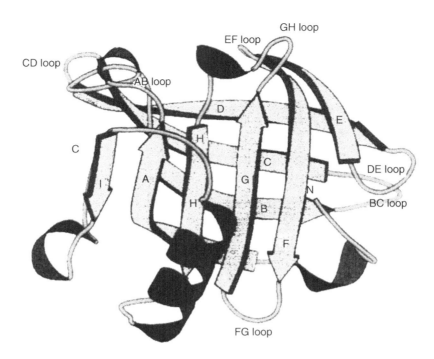

FIGURE 26.6   Ribbon diagram of a single subunit of β-lactoglobulin lattice X, with nine anti-parallel β-strands and with joining loops labeled. (Source: Structure, 5, Brownlow et al., Bovine β-Lg at 1.8Å resolution — still an enigmatic lipocalin, pp 481–495. Copyright (1997) Elsevier.)

B.   α-LACTALBUMIN

α-Lactalbumin accounts for about 20% of whey protein and has three known genetic variants. The primary structure of α-lactalbumin is shown in Figure 26.5b. α-Lactalbumin has a molecular weight of about 14,000 Da and contains four intrachain disulphide bonds. It is relatively rich in tryptophan (four residues per mole). There is a considerable similarity between the primary and tertiary structure of α-lactalbumin and chicken egg white lysozyme (43). Its secondary structure at physiological pH consists of 26% α-helix, 14% β-structure and 60% unordered structure. The approximate globular structure of α-lactalbumin (dimensions 23Å × 26Å × 40Å) includes three regular α-helices, two regions of 3_{10} helix, and a small 3-stranded anti-parallel β-pleated sheet separated by irregular β-turns. The bilobal structure is formed by segregation of α-helices in one lobe and a small β-sheet and irregular structures in the other (Figure 26.7).

α-Lactalbumin binds one Ca^{2+} per mole in a pocket containing four Asp residues (45). At pH below 5.0, the Asp residues become protonated which results in the loss of bound Ca^{2+} which makes this protein susceptible to denaturation. Under acidic conditions, α-lactalbumin undergoes a transconformation to a non-native (A state) with altered spectroscopic properties (46). In the A state, the secondary structure of α-lactalbumin is nearly as compact as the native protein but lacks a fixed tertiary structure; this state is commonly referred to as the molten globule state.

The biological function of α-lactalbumin is to modulate the substrate specificity of galactosyltransferase in the lactose synthetase complex which is responsible for the synthesis of lactose in the lactating mammary tissue (45). The concentration of lactose in milk is directly related to the concentration of α-lactalbumin; the milk of some marine mammals which contains no α-lactalbumin, co tains no lactose.

C.   SERUM ALBUMIN

Serum albumin isolated from milk is identical to the serum albumin found in the blood and represents about 5% of the total whey proteins. The protein is synthesized in the liver and gains entrance to milk through the secretory cells. The protein has the longest single polypeptide chain of the proteins found in milk consisting of 582 amino acid residues and has a molecular weight of 66,000 Da. It has 17 disulphide linkages, which hold the protein in a multi-loop structure, and one free thiol group. The secondary structure of serum albumin has 55% α-helix, 16% β-pleated sheet and 29% unordered structure. The current view of the three-dimensional crystal structure of serum albumin is that the molecule exists in three major domains, each consisting of two large double loops and a small double loop with an overall elliptical shape (47).

Serum albumin appears to function as a carrier of small molecules, such as fatty acids, but any specific role that it may play is unknown.

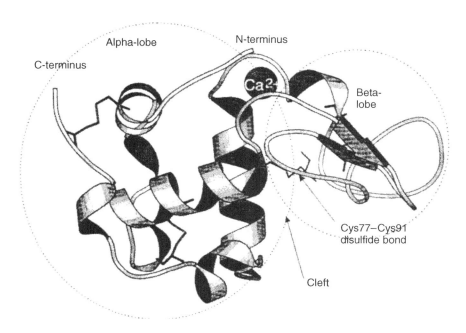

FIGURE 26.7 Tertiary structure of bovine α-lactalbumin, showing bilobal structure displayed using MOLSCRIPT. (Source: Brew, α-Lactalbumin, pp 387–421, 2003. In Advanced Dairy Chemistry Volume 1: Proteins, 3rd ed., Part A: Kluwer Academic/Plenum Publishers.)

D. IMMUNOGLOBULINS

Milk-borne immunoglobulins (Igs) provide the offspring with an immunological protection against microbial pathogens and toxins and protect the mammary gland against infection. Igs are divided into classes and subclasses; essentially there are 5 classes of Ig: IgA, IgG, IgD, IgE and IgM. IgA, IgG and IgM are present in milk. These occur as subclasses, e.g., IgG occurs as IgG_1 and IgG_2. IgG consists of two light (L) polypeptide chains and two heavy (H) polypeptide chains, of molecular weights 22,400 and 50–60,000 Da, respectively; these are linked together by disulphide bonds. IgA consists of two such units (i.e., 8 chains) linked together by a secretory component (SC) and a junction component (J) while IgM consists of five linked 4-chain units. The concentration of different Ig classes in milk and colostrum differs considerably depending on species, breed, age, stage of lactation and health status. As ruminant neonates are born virtually without Ig, ingested Igs are necessary for survival. Consequently, ruminants' colostrum contains considerably higher concentrations of Igs than human milk.

In addition to antigen binding, all Igs exhibit one or more effector functions by linking various parts of the immune system. For example, Igs may bind to leucocytes (which are an integral part of milk and of vital importance in defending the mammary gland against pathogens) or to host tissues. In addition, Igs can prevent the adhesion of microbes to surfaces, inhibit bacterial metabolism, agglutinate bacteria and neutralize toxins and viruses. Milk Igs have also been found to exert a synergistic effect on the activity of non-specific antimicrobial factors such as lactoferrin and lysozyme as well as lactoperoxidase. A more detailed discussion on the structure, origin, transfer and function of Igs has been published by Hurley (48).

IV. MINOR PROTEINS

Several proteins are found in relatively small quantities in the whey fraction of milk. These proteins are referred to as minor protein. They include metal- and vitamin-binding proteins, β_2-microglobulin and growth factors.

A. METAL BINDING PROTEINS

Human milk contains 2–4 mg mL^{-1} of lactoferrin which is specifically involved in metal-binding. Lactoferrin, which appears identical to transferrin found in blood, has also been detected at quite low concentrations in bovine milk (49). Lactoferrin has the ability to bind iron very strongly, indicating that the protein is involved in iron absorption and protection against enteric infection in the neonate (49). Considerable interest has been expressed in supplementing bovine milk-based infant formulae with lactoferrin, as bovine milk contains much lower levels of lactoferrin than human milk and lactoferrin, isolated from human milk, can bind 2 moles of iron per mole of protein (50). The biological importance of lactoferrin has been reviewed recently by Lönnerdal (51).

B. VITAMIN BINDING PROTEINS

Milk contains an array of vitamin-binding proteins, including Vitamin B_{12}-binding protein, folate-binding protein, Vitamin D-binding protein and riboflavin-binding protein. These proteins occur at low concentrations, but may play a significant role in the uptake of vital vitamins from the diet (52,53).

Three different proteins are required for the uptake of Vitamin B_{12} in the gastro-intestinal tract. The milk of several mammalian species (human, rat, pig and rabbit) has been shown to contain one of these proteins (haptocorrin), whereas bovine milk contains a different Vitamin B_{12}-binding protein (transcobalamin) (54).

Milk also contains folate-binding proteins; these proteins are specifically involved in the uptake of folate from the intestine. *In vivo* studies on rats have shown that protein-bound folate is absorbed at a lower rate than free folate, resulting in increased retention time of folate, allowing it to reach its target tissues. Folate-binding protein also reduces the availability of folate to bacteria in the gut and hence may have antibacterial properties (55).

Raw bovine milk contains a riboflavin binding protein (56) and riboflavin bound to this milk protein has been shown to have similar antioxidant activities to riboflavin bound to egg white riboflavin binding protein (57).

C. GROWTH FACTORS

Highly potent hormone-like polypeptides, termed growth factors, which play a significant role in the regulation and differentiation of a variety of cells, can be found in milk. These growth factors may modulate growth and differentiation of a variety of cell types, modulate mammary development, and may also modulate neonatal development of the gastrointestinal (GI) tract. The growth factors are predominantly found in developing glands and colostrum, while milk may also contain comparatively lower concentrations of growth factors, depending on stage of lactation.

Growth factors and hormones identified in mammary secretions include lactoferrin (58), epidermal growth factor (EGF), transforming growth factor α (α-TGF) and

β (β-TGF), insulin-like growth factor (IGF), insulin (59), basic fibroblast growth factor (basic FGF) (60) and prolactin (61). It is unclear whether many of these growth factors are targeted to promote growth of the mammary gland or the intestinal cells of the recipient neonate.

D. OTHER MINOR PROTEINS

Several other minor proteins, including $β_2$-microglobulin, osteopontin, proteose peptone 3, angiogenins, kininogen and milk glycoproteins, have been identified in the whey fraction of milk. At present, relatively little information is available on the biological activities and functions of these proteins.

V. MILK ENZYMES

Milk contains in the region of 60 indigenous enzymes, approximately 20 of which have been isolated and characterized in great detail. The remaining 40 enzymes, whose presence has been demonstrated via their activity, are of little or no technological interest. The principal milk enzymes of technological importance are discussed below, and the details of these and other milk enzymes are detailed in Table 26.2. The reader is directed to Chapter 27 (this volume, "Enzymes of Significance to Milk and Dairy Products") for a comprehensive review of this area.

A. LIPASES AND ESTERASES

The ability of milk lipase (EC 3.1.1.) to hydrolyze triglycerides to form fatty acids is well known, and is responsible for the onset of rancidity in milk and milk products. Milk lipase is a lipoprotein lipase, and is similar to the lipoprotein lipase found in the mammary gland, suggesting that it may be transferred to milk from the mammary gland. In bovine milk, about 80% of milk lipase is associated with the casein micelles by electrostatic bonding

TABLE 26.2
Some Enzymes Present in Bovine Milk

| Name | EC Number | Optimum | | Inactivation[1] |
		pH	Temperature (°C)	
Xanthine oxidase	1.1.3.22	~8	37	7 min 73°C
Sulphydryl oxidase	1.8.?	~7	~45	3 min 73°C
Catalase	1.11.1.6	7	37?	2 min 73°C
Lactoperoxidase	1.11.1.7	6.5	20	10 min 73°C
Superoxidase dismutase	1.15.1.1	?	?	70 min 76°C
Lipoprotein lipase	3.1.1.34	~9	33	30 s 73°C
Alkaline phosphatase	3.1.3.1	~9	37	20 s 73°C
Ribonuclease	3.1.27.5	7.5	37	?
Plasmin	3.4.21.7	8	37	40 min 73°C

[1] Heat treatment required to reduce activity to approximately 1%.
Source: Ref. 62, page 92, by courtesy of Marcel Dekker, Inc.

between negatively charged phosphates on the caseins and positively charged amino acid residues in the heparin-binding sites of milk lipase (63).

Milk lipase is a glycoprotein which is optimally active at pH 9.2 and 37°C, and has a native molecular mass of 100 kDa. Milk lipase is strongly inhibited by the products of its activities (64), i.e., long-chain fatty acids; therefore blood serum albumin (BSA) and Ca^{2+} enhance the activity of milk lipase as BSA and Ca^{2+} bind free fatty acids. The enzyme is inactivated by ultraviolet light, heat, acid and oxidizing agents. Less than 10% of milk lipase remains active after pasteurization.

In milk triglycerides, long-chain fatty acids are attached to the glycerol at the 1 and 2 positions, while shorter-chain fatty acids are found at the 3 position. Milk lipase liberates fatty acids from the 1,3 positions in milk triglycerides. Lipolysis increases the levels of short-chain, volatile fatty acids present in milk. This results in rancid, butyric, bitter, soapy or astringent flavors that render milk and milk products unacceptable for consumption.

Increased lipolysis can result from vigorous agitation or homogenization of milk which causes damage to the milk fat globule membrane and leaves it vulnerable to the action of milk lipase. The extent of lipolysis may be reduced on strict temperature control (< 5°C) and avoiding excessive agitation prior to pasteurization (64).

Milk also contains three types of esterases. These are A-type carboxylic ester hydrolase (which hydrolyzes aromatic residues); B-type esterase (which hydrolyzes aliphatic esters rapidly and aromatic esters slowly); and C-type esterase (which are active on alkaline esters) (65).

B. PLASMIN

Plasmin (EC 3.4.21.7), the principal proteolytic enzyme in milk, is mainly found in the form of the inactive zymogen, plasminogen. Through a system of plasmin inhibitors and plasminogen activators (along with their associated inhibitors), plasminogen is converted to active plasmin (10). Plasmin is a serine proteinase with a high specificity for peptide bonds to which lysine or arginine supplies the carboxyl group. β- and α_{S1}-caseins are most susceptible to plasmin hydrolysis; α_{S2}-casein is also attacked, while κ-casein is relatively resistant to hydrolysis. Plasmin cleavage of β-casein yields γ-casein and proteose-peptones (66,67) (see Figure 26.2).

Severe heat treatment of milk, such as ultrahigh temperature (UHT), reduces plasmin activity due to inactivation of plasmin by thiol-disulphide interchange reactions between plasmin and the highly reactive thiol groups of β-lactoglobulin (68). However, high-temperature-short-time (HTST) pasteurized milk stored at 20–37°C displayed significantly increased plasmin activity as storage time increased (69). This increase in plasmin activity, concomitant with a decrease in plasminogen activity, is due to denaturation of inhibitors of plasminogen activator (10).

Plasmin activity may influence the quality of dairy products, such as cheeses, UHT-treated milk products and milk protein products. Increased plasmin activity in cheese has been shown to improve the flavor and overall quality of certain cheeses. Plasmin may also play a role in the age gelation of UHT-treated milk.

C. PHOSPHATASES

Bovine milk contains a number of indigenous phosphatases; the two principal types which have been shown to have a technological significance in milk are milk alkaline phosphatase (EC 3.1.3.1) and milk acid phosphatase (EC 3.1.3.2).

1. Alkaline Phosphatase (ALP)

ALP occurs in all mammalian milk; in bovines milk levels vary between cows and also within the lactation period. The activity of ALP is used as an index of the efficiency of milk pasteurization, because ALP is slightly more resistant to heat than *Mycobacterium tuberculosis* (70). However, the activity of ALP may not always be an accurate indicator of HTST pasteurization of milk for a number of reasons. Under certain conditions, reactivation of ALP may occur, complicating interpretation of test results. The enzyme also appears to be fully inactivated at sub-pasteurization conditions and in addition the relationship between $\log_{10}$ % initial activity and pasteurization equivalent (PE) is less linear than the relationship between PE and lactoperoxidase or γ-glutamyl transpeptidase activities in milk (53). Furthermore, ALP is only partially inactivated during ultra-high pressure treatment of milk, rendering the ALP test an unsuitable indicator of effectiveness of the ultra-high pressure treatment process.

2. Acid Phosphatase (ACP)

The concentration of ACP in milk is dependent on stage of lactation and increased levels have been observed in mastitic milk; however, the activity of ACP is much lower than that of ALP. ACP is a very heat stable enzyme which is not affected by HTST pasteurization, but is completely inactivated following UHT treatment (72).

ACP may play a role in the heat stability of dairy products. As the caseins are phosphoproteins and are good substrates for ACP, the micellar integrity of caseins may be lost on dephosphorylation of casein serine residues. ACP may also influence cheese flavor; several partially dephosphorylated phosphopeptides have been isolated from different cheese types and have been attributed to ACP activity (73,74).

D. LACTOPEROXIDASE

Lactoperoxidase (LPO; EC 1.11.1.7) is a broad specificity peroxidase which is present in high concentrations in bovine milk compared to human milk. LPO exhibits antibacterial activity in the presence of H_2O_2 and thiocyanate (SCN^-), in which SCN^- is converted to hypothiocyanate ($OSCN^-$) (75). Inactivation of eight different bacteria including *E. coli, Pseudomonas fluorescens, S. aureus, Enterococcus faecalis, Listeria innocua* and *Lactobacillus plantarum*, has been shown by LPO (76). LPO may also be used as an indication of mastitic activity, as LPO levels increase during mastitis. Research has focused on activation of the indigenous enzyme for cold pasteurization of milk and protection of the mammary gland against mastitis, and also on addition of isolated LPO to calf or piglet milk to protect against enteritis.

E. XANTHINE OXIDASE

Bovine milk xanthine oxidase (EC 1.1.3.22) is a dimeric metallo-flavoprotein with a molecular mass of approximately 300 kDa and is a major component of the milk fat globule membrane. It is a non-specific oxidoreductase that plays a metabolic role in purine catabolism, catalyzing the oxidation of hypoxanthine to xanthine, and xanthine to uric acid, with the concomitant reduction of O_2 to H_2O_2. Activity levels of xanthine oxidase differ between species; human milk contains approximately 1–6% of the activity of bovine milk (35 mg/L) (77). About 33% of the iron and all of the molybdenum in human milk is found in xanthine oxidase.

VI. INDUSTRIAL MANUFACTURE OF MILK PROTEINS

A range of protein products can be obtained from milk, and the more commonly used methods for obtaining these products are described in Figure 26.8. The production and utilization of milk proteins has been reviewed recently by Mulvihill and Ennis (78).

A. CASEIN PRODUCTS

The manufacture of this protein family of products from milk involves centrifugal separation of the skim milk from the cream, followed by pasteurization. The caseins are then precipitated either by the action of a coagulant such as rennet or by a reduction in pH to the isoelectric point (4.6) by fermentation or direct addition of mineral acid. The coagulated protein is heated to form the curd, and the curd is then separated from the whey by filtration or centrifugation, in combination with countercurrent washing with water. The curd may then be dried as insoluble casein, or first be reacted with alkali, e.g., sodium hydroxide, followed by drying to produce a water-soluble caseinate. A protein product including both the casein and the whey proteins, known as total milk proteinate, may be manufactured by a variation of the process described in Figure 26.8.

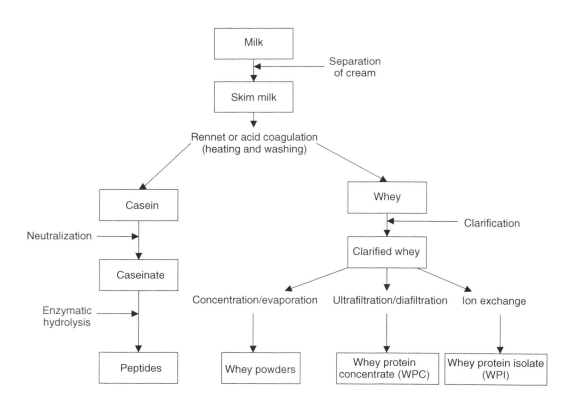

FIGURE 26.8 Outline of principal processes used for the manufacture of casein and whey proteins products.

B. WHEY PRODUCTS

Whey is produced as a by-product of cheese and casein manufacture. There are many possible products and manufacturing processes, some of which are outlined in Figure 26.8. The first step involves separation and selective concentration of residual fat and casein by centrifugation. This is followed by concentration of the whey proteins by the use of membrane separation (ultrafiltration and diafiltration). The protein stream is further concentrated by evaporation and then spray-dried to produce whey protein concentrate, with an approximate protein concentration of 85%. Alternatively, further fractionation and concentration of the whey proteins may be performed using ion exchange to produce whey protein isolates (containing approximately 95% protein).

The protein products described have a wide range of food ingredient and industrial applications, many utilizing the emulsifying, water- and fat-binding, and nutritional properties of the proteins. The decision to incorporate whey protein isolate ahead of whey protein concentrate into a food matrix is based on a balance of cost, fat content, and functional properties differences, among others, between the products.

VII. FUNCTIONAL PROPERTIES OF MILK PROTEINS AND FOOD USES

Protein functionality has been broadly defined as any physiochemical property which affects the processing and behavior of proteins, as judged by the quality attributes of the final product (79). These attributes may include structure, appearance, texture, viscosity and mouthfeel (80). Milk proteins possess functional properties which provide desirable textural or other attributes to the final product and for this reason have found numerous applications in traditional dairy products and in other foods (Table 26.3).

The functional properties of proteins are governed by intrinsic properties, i.e., their structural characteristics, e.g., size and surface hydrophobicity. These intrinsic properties are themselves affected by many extrinsic or environmental factors, such as pH, ionic strength and temperature, and also by interactions between the proteins and other materials in the food system. Not only does milk comprise various proteins with unique intrinsic properties, the milk proteins themselves are commercially available in many different forms. Furthermore, milk proteins may be modified by physical, chemical or enzymatic means, possibly resulting in significant improvements in one or more functional properties (Table 26.4). However, physical and enzymatic methods of modification are currently preferred over chemical methods, mainly due to consumers' concerns over "added chemicals" and the potential risk of occurrence of toxic side-reactions.

A. SOLUBILITY

Protein-water and protein-protein interactions in aqueous systems are vitally important and control the dispersibility, viscosity and solubility properties of proteins (81). A sensitive balance between repulsive and attractive intermolecular forces, which are in turn controlled by protein and water structures and affected by environmental factors, controls solubility (82). Generally, proteins are soluble in water and electrostatic and/or hydration repulsion between proteins is greater than the driving forces for hydrophobic interactions. Thus, the polar and ionizable groups of proteins largely confer water solubility (79).

Solubility is often used as a key indicator of a protein's ability to exhibit other functional properties such as

TABLE 26.3
Functional Properties of Milk Proteins Exploited in Food Systems

Functional Property	Potential Food Applications
Solubility	Nitrogen fortification of low pH beverages
Emulsification	Pastries, coffee creamers, milk beverages, milk shakes, high fat powders, butter-like spreads, cheese fillings and dips
Foaming	Egg replacer, whipped toppings, fizzy drinks, ice cream, mousses, meringues, sponge cakes
Heat stability	Imitation pasta, meat products, marshmallow and nougat
Aggregation/Coagulation/Gelation	Cultured milk products, comminuted meat products
Viscosity	Cake mixes, milk-based flavored beverages, frozen desserts
Water-binding and hydration	Imitation cheeses, toffees, fudges

TABLE 26.4

Methods Used to Improve the Functionality of Milk Proteins

Method	Treatments
Physical	Heat, pH, high pressure
Chemical	Phosphorylation, deamidation, glycosylation, covalent attachment of hydrophobic groups, acylation, reduction of disulphide bonds
Enzymatic	Hydrolysis, cross-linking with transglutaminase, glycosylation, phosphorylation, deamidation

emulsifying, foaming and gelation properties, although this general rule may not always apply, particularly in the case of highly hydrolyzed milk proteins. Solubility may be generally defined as the amount of protein that goes into solution or into colloidal dispersion under specified conditions (e.g., pH, ionic strength, protein concentration and temperature) until a maximum concentration is reached, after which the soluble concentration remains constant and a solid phase appears (83).

Solution conditions, such as pH, ionic strength and temperature, also affect the amount of water associated with proteins (82). Solution pH, for example, affects the amount of water associated with proteins by influencing the net charge of the protein. Ionic strength affects the solubility of proteins depending on the number of hydrophobic groups exposed on the protein's surface.

Unlike whey proteins, which exhibit excellent solubility over the entire pH range, caseinates (alkali dispersions of casein which are used in commercial applications) are almost completely insoluble in the region of their isoelectric point (pI: pH 4.0–5.0). However, outside of this region, caseinates possess excellent solubility, resulting in a U-shaped pH-solubility profile (84). Enzymatic hydrolysis has been frequently applied for improving solubility of caseinates in the pI region. Improved solubility is mainly due to a reduction in the molecular weight, increased exposure of polar groups and decreased secondary structure of the peptides formed upon hydrolysis of the intact protein. Enzymatic hydrolysis of food proteins has been thoroughly described by Adler-Nissen (85).

Casein and caseinates are utilized for their high solubility at highly acidic pH values (pH 2–3.5) in fruit juices and carbonated beverages (86), and may also be used for the nitrogen fortification of low pH beverages.

B. Interfacial Properties

Milk proteins have found numerous applications in food systems due to their ability to form and stabilize emulsions. Caseins possess high surface hydrophobicity with a well-balanced distribution of hydrophilic and hydrophobic domains and possess a high degree of conformational flexibility, which allows them to interact strongly at the oil-

water interface (87). However, the caseins have high aggregative tendencies and low solubilities around their pI (88). Whey proteins also adsorb rapidly to, unfold and reorientate at oil-water and air-water interfaces, forming emulsions which are only slightly less stable than those formed with casein under the same conditions. Emulsions formed with pure β-lactoglobulin may increase in stability over time, due to intermolecular linking of disulphide groups which are in close proximity at the oil-water interface.

Due to the excellent surface activity of milk proteins, they have found numerous applications in several food products in which incorporation of oil/water/air into the continuous system is required. Examples of these include salad dressings, mayonnaise, liqueurs, meringues, soufflés, whipped toppings, confectionary, sponge cakes, etc. Caseinates generally give emulsions with increased droplet coverage and high foam expansion but produce less stable emulsions and foams than those formed with whey protein concentrate (WPC). Preheat treatment may be used to improve the emulsifying and foaming characteristics of WPC, while enzymatic hydrolysis to different extents has been shown to significantly improve both the emulsifying and foaming properties of sodium caseinate-stabilized emulsions and foams at certain pH values (84). However, extensive hydrolysis generally results in the loss of emulsifying and foaming activity. Combinations of enzymatic hydrolysis and cross-linking, using a novel cross-linking enzyme transglutaminase, have resulted in products which exhibit significantly greater emulsifying properties than the products of hydrolysis or cross-linking per se (89).

The foaming and emulsifying properties of milk proteins are also affected by many extrinsic or environmental factors, such as protein concentration, energy input, state of protein aggregation, pH, ionic strength, temperature, calcium ion concentration and the presence of contaminants which may destabilize the oil-water or air-water interface. In addition, the ratio of oil:water phase used during emulsion formation is of major importance to emulsion properties.

C. Heat Stability

Due to their limited secondary structure, the caseins possess excellent heat stability. Na, K and NH_4 caseinates are extremely heat stable and aqueous solutions of Na caseinate may be heated up to 140°C for 60 min without precipitation; however, Ca caseinate has much lower heat stability by comparison. Consequently, caseinates may be used in food products which experience thermal treatments, such as soups and sauces. The effects of heating on sodium caseinate have been extensively studied (90–92). Whey proteins, on the other hand, are readily denatured above 70°C, leading to aggregation and, depending on pH and protein concentration, precipitation or gelation. Factors such as pH, protein concentration, total solids content and the presence of sugar may influence the denaturation of milk proteins.

A common method for measurement of heat stability involves heating a protein solution of known concentration and pH, in an oil bath or autoclave for a given period of time at defined temperatures. Changes in free amino nitrogen, soluble ammonia, turbidity, and trichloroacetic acid soluble and pH 4.6 soluble amino nitrogen have been attributed to the effects of heating on protein solutions. Enzymatic modification with transglutaminase has been shown to improve the heat stability of both reconstituted skim milk (93) and Na caseinate (94).

D. AGGREGATION/COAGULATION/GELATION

Milk proteins also have the ability to form rigid, heat-induced irreversible gels that hold water and fat, and provide structural support (80). Coagulation and/or gelation are required in some cultured milk products, and may be brought about on addition of acid or rennet to milk to form casein gels. Caseinates per se are rarely used as gelling agents in formulated food products; however, the ability of whey proteins to form gels under a range of conditions have found many applications in food products.

Gelation of whey proteins occurs on heating (usually in the range 80–100°C) depending on the concentration (normally above 8%) and purity of the whey protein. The initial steps of gelation include unfolding of the globular protein molecules, followed by aggregation in the aqueous medium. Once aggregation exceeds a certain level, a three-dimensional self-supporting network is formed which traps the solvent within the system, resulting in an irreversible thermo-induced gel.

While Ca caseinate solutions at concentrations greater than 15% form reversible gels on heating to 50–60°C, Na caseinate may also be used to form gels in conjunction with κ-carrageenan (95). The introduction of covalent cross-links using transglutaminase has also been used to induce gelation in Na caseinate (96,97).

Important attributes of gels are gelling time, opacity (or lack of) and gel hardness and strength which may be measured using rheological methods; these are affected by extrinsic factors such as pH and ionic salt concentration. Lipids and lactose may adversely affect whey protein gelation.

Further applications of milk protein gels include the immobilization of enzymes or entrapment of drugs or bioactive peptides for the purpose of oral drug delivery systems.

E. VISCOSITY

Milk proteins, either in solution or incorporated into a food matrix, provide physical stability to emulsions and to other suspended particles in foods by influencing the viscosity of the system, whilst also contributing to mouthfeel (98). The viscosity of a protein system depends on the proteins' intrinsic properties such as heterogeneity, size, shape and charge; these properties are further affected by extrinsic conditions, such as temperature, concentration, pH, ionic strength and previous processing history. Randomly coiled structures, such as caseins, generally display greater viscosity in solution than whey proteins which have a compact globular structure.

Na caseinate solutions are highly viscous at 15% concentrations and display pseudoplasticity above this concentration. Viscosity of Na caseinate solutions increases exponentially with protein concentration, and generally decreases with increasing temperature, depending on concentration. Viscosity of Na caseinate solutions is also highly dependent on pH, with minimum viscosity observed at pH 7. Native whey protein solutions have very low viscosities compared to caseinates; however, viscosity increases at higher temperatures (>70°C) due to unfolding and aggregation of the globular whey protein. The viscosity of milk protein solutions is usually expressed as relative or apparent viscosity and may be measured using a variety of viscometers.

F. WATER-BINDING AND HYDRATION

The ability of proteins to hydrate and entrap water without syneresis is utilized in many food applications. Water molecules bind to both polar and non-polar groups in proteins to different extents, depending on the charge and polarity of the amino groups. Due to the globular tertiary structure of the whey proteins, the majority of the amino acid residues are buried within the protein interior. Thus, the hydration capacity of the whey proteins arises predominantly from binding of water to amino acid residues on the protein surface. Hydration values for native individual whey proteins range from 0.3 to 0.6 g H_2O per g protein (99,100). Casein micelles, on the other hand, can bind up to 4 g H_2O per g protein, mainly due to the enormous amount of void space within the casein micelles' structure and binding of water to the hydrophilic surface of the micelles.

Solution conditions, such as pH, ionic strength, and temperature, affect hydration of proteins (101). Hydration capacity is minimal at the pI, where protein-protein interactions are favored over protein-water interactions. Low salt concentrations can also increase the hydration capacity of proteins.

Milk proteins have found numerous applications in food products due to their ability to bind water and swell, thereby resulting in an increase in viscosity in the food system. Whey proteins are used as water-binders in food systems which will receive sufficient heat treatment to denature the globular protein and increase its hydration capacity. These food systems include meat patties, sausages, bread and cakes. Caseins and caseinates have found application in products such as imitation cheeses, confectionary and comminuted meat products.

Aside from hydration capacity of proteins, large amounts of water may also be held within a food matrix such as a gel. This water mainly includes physically entrapped water and it is this water which provides juiciness and tenderness to the final product.

VIII. MILK PROTEIN-DERIVED BIOACTIVE PEPTIDES

In addition to the biologically active proteins indigenous to milk, all the principal milk proteins contain sequences which, when released on proteolysis, exhibit biological activity. These biological activities include opiate, antithrombotic, antihypertensive, immunomodulatory, metal-binding and antimicrobial activities (Table 26.5).

A. Opioid Activities

Opioid peptides are short peptides (5–10 amino acids) termed casomorphins or exorphins for their ability to bind opioid receptors on intestinal epithelial and other cells (103) and have an opiate-like effect. The major opioid milk peptide β-casomorphin is a fragment of the β-casein sequence 60–70, while α_{S1}-casein (α-casomorphin), β-lactogobulin (β-lactorphin) and α-lactalbumin (α-lactorphin) also contain peptides which display opiate-like activity. Although opioid peptides derived from milk may be generated by proteolytic digestion of milk proteins *in vitro*, only β-casomorphin has been found in digesta after *in vivo* digestion of milk in calves (104) but not in humans (105). Milk protein-derived opioid peptides prolong gastrointestinal transit time (106), exert anti-diarrhoeal action

(107), modulate intestinal transport of amino acids (108) and influence postprandial metabolism by stimulating secretion of insulin (109) and somatostatin (110).

B. Opioid Antagonist Activities

Opioid antagonistic peptides are also found within the structure of milk proteins. Termed casoxins and lactoferroxins, they are derived from peptic digestion of κ-casein and lactoferrin, respectively. Opioid antagonists may antagonize the inhibition of gut motility as induced by casomorphins (111). Opioid antagonists have been found in bovine and human κ-casein (111) and in human α_{S1}-casein (112).

C. Inhibition of Angiotensin-I-Converting Enzyme (ACE)

The casein-derived ACE inhibitors, or casokinins, have been isolated from bovine α_{S1}- and β-casein and from human β- and κ-casein (103,114). Opioid fragments relating to β-casomorphin-7 (115) and β-lactorphin (116) have also been identified as ACE inhibitory peptides with moderate activities. ACE is a multifunctional enzyme that is located in different body tissues and is associated with the renin-angiotensin system, which regulates peripheral blood pressure. Inhibition of ACE has been shown to block the conversion of angiotensin-I to angiotensin-II, a potent vasoconstrictor.

D. Immunomodulatory Effects

α-Lactalbumin, β- and α_{S1}-casein-derived immunopeptides have been found to enhance phagocytosis and modulate proliferation and differentiation of lymphocytes (117). Immunomodulation appears to be a particularly important bioactivity of the developing, involuting or inflamed mammary gland. Hormones, growth factors and cytokines found in milk also appear important in immunomodulation and immuno-development (111).

E. Antithrombotic Effects

Casoplatelins, peptides derived from the C-terminus of bovine κ-casein, have been shown to exhibit antithrombotic activity, i.e., inhibition of blood clotting. These peptides function by inhibiting the aggregation of ADP-activated platelets as well as binding of human fibrinogen γ-chain to a specific receptor site on the platelet surface (118).

F. Mineral Binding Properties

While intact casein has been shown to bind zinc and calcium, tryptic hydrolysates of α_{S1}-, α_{S2}-, β- and κ-casein also display mineral binding properties. Termed caseinophosphopeptides (CPPs), these peptides can bind and solubilize high concentrations of calcium due to their highly polar acidic domain. Consumption of high concentrations

TABLE 26.5
Bioactive Peptides Derived from Milk Proteins

Bioactive Peptide	Protein Precursor	Bioactivity
Casomorphins	α_{S1}-, β-Casein	Opioid agonist
α-Lactorphin	α-Lactalbumin	Opioid agonist
β-Lactorphin	β-Lactoglobulin	Opioid agonist
Lactoferroxins	Lactoferrin	Opioid antagonist
Casoxins	κ-Casein	Opioid antagonist
Casokinins	α_{S1}-, β-Casein	ACE-inhibitory
Lactokinins	α-Lactalbumin, β-Lactoglobulin, serum albumin	ACE-inhibitory
Immunopeptides	α_{S1}-, β-Casein	Immunomodulatory
Lactoferricin	Lactoferrin	Antimicrobial
Casoplatelins	κ-Casein	Antithrombotic
Phosphopeptides	α_{S1}-, β-Casein	Mineral binding

Source: Fitzgerald and Meisel, Milk protein hydrolysates and bioactive peptides, pp 675–698, 2003. In Advanced Dairy Chemistry Volume 1: Proteins, 3rd ed., part A. Kluwer Academic/Plenum Publishers.

of calcium in early life contributes to development of maximal bone density, which in turn can prevent osteoporosis in later life (102). In addition, calcium-binding CPPs can have an anticariogenic effect in that they inhibit caries lesions through recalcification of the dental enamel (119).

G. ANTIMICROBIAL ACTIVITY

Lactoferrin is an iron-binding glycoprotein present in the whey fraction in milk from which antimicrobial peptides have been derived (120). It is considered to be an important component of the host defense against microbial infections. The antimicrobial ability of lactoferricin may be correlated with the net positive charge of the peptides. These cationic peptides kill sensitive microorganisms by increasing cell membrane permeability (121). Lactoferricin displayed antimicrobial activity against yeast, filamentous fungi (122), *Escherichia coli, Listeria monocytogenes* (123) and clinical isolates of *E. coli* 0157:H7 (124). Recently, fragments from α_{S1}- and α_{S2}-casein have been found to inhibit the growth of *E. coli* (125) and *Staphylococcus aureus* (126).

IX. CONCLUSION

Bovine milk protein fulfills important nutritional, functional and physiological roles in both the developing neonate and man. From a nutritional viewpoint, milk protein is a balanced source of all the essential amino acids. The functional properties of milk proteins are exploited in many food products and the ability of milk protein to act as surface active agents, contribute to texture or to bind water or fat, is determined, in part, by its unique structure. Milk also contains an array of enzymatic activities; these enzyme activities are important from both a functional and physiological perspective. Finally, all the principal milk proteins contain sequences which, when released on proteolysis, may confer beneficial physiological effects.

REFERENCES

1. P Walstra. On the stability of casein micelles. J Dairy Sci 73:1965–1979, 1990.
2. C Holt. Structure and stability of bovine casein micelles. Adv Prot Chem 43:63–151, 1992.
3. HE Swaisgood. Chemistry of the caseins. In: PF Fox. ed. Advanced Dairy Chemistry – 1: Proteins. London: Elsevier, 1992, pp 63–110.
4. HE Swaisgood. Chemistry of the Caseins. In: PF Fox, PLH McSweeney. eds. Advanced Dairy Chemistry – 1: Proteins. 3rd ed., Part A. New York: Kluwer Academic/Plenum Publishers, 2003, pp 63–110.
5. JE Kinsella, DM Whitehead. Proteins in whey: Chemical, physical and functional properties. Adv Food Nutr Res 33:343–438, 1989.
6. SG Hambling, AS McAlpine, L Sawyer. β-Lactoglobulin. In: PF Fox. ed. Advanced Dairy Chemistry – 1: Proteins. London: Elsevier, 1992, pp 141–190.
7. H Roginski, JW Fuquay, PF Fox. eds. Encyclopedia of Dairy Sciences. London: Academic Press, 2003.
8. DF Waugh, PH von Hippel. κ-Casein and the stabilisation of casein micelles. J Am Chem Soc 78, 45–167, 1956.
9. HE Swaisgood. Chemistry of Milk Proteins. In: PF Fox. ed. Developments in Dairy Chemistry – 1. London: Applied Science, 1982, pp 1–61.
10. ED Bastian, RJ Brown. Plasmin in milk and dairy products: an update. Int Dairy J 6:435–457, 1996.
11. JC Mercier, F Grosclaude, B Ribadeau-Dumas. Structure primaire de la caséine α_{S1}-bovine. Eur J Biochem 23: 41–51, 1971.
12. G Brignon, B Ribadeau-Dumas, JC Mercier, JP Pélissier, BC Das. Complete amino acid sequence of α_{S2}-casein. FEBS Lett 76:274–279, 1977.
13. B Ribadeau-Dumas, G Brignon, F Grosclaude, JC Mercier. Structure primaire de la caséine β-bovine: séquence complète. Eur J Biochem 25:505–514, 1972.
14. JC Mercier, G Brignon, B Ribadeau-Dumas. Structure primaire de la caséine κ-bovine: séquence complète. Eur J Biochem 35:222–235, 1973.
15. M Swartz, N Walker, L Creamer, C Southward. Casein and caseinates. In: Encyclopedia of Food Science and Technology. New York: Wiley, 1991, pp 310–318.
16. DM Byler, HM Farrell Jr., H Susi. Raman spectroscopy study of casein structure. J Dairy Sci 71, 2622–2629, 1988.
17. ERB Graham, GN Malcolm, HA McKenzie. On the isolation and conformation of bovine β-casein A1. Int J Biol Macromol 6, 155–161, 1984.
18. J Rapp, KET Kerling, HJ Freeman, S Visser. Peptide substrates for chymosin (rennin): Conformational studies of κ-casein-related oligopeptides by circular dichroism and secondary structure prediction. Arch Biochem Biophys 221, 117–124, 1983.
19. HS Rollema. Casein association and micelle formation. In: PF Fox. ed. Advanced Dairy Chemistry – 1: Proteins. London: Elsevier, 1992, pp 111–140.
20. CG De Kruif, C Holt. Casein micelle structure, functions and interactions. In: PF Fox, PLH McSweeney. eds. Advanced Dairy Chemistry – 1: Proteins. 3rd ed., Part A. New York: Kluwer Academic/Plenum Publishers, 2003, pp 233–276.
21. A Thurn, W Burchard, R Niki. Structure of casein micelles. II. αS1-casein. Colloid and Polymer Sci 265, 897–902, 1987.
22. K Kajiwara, R Niki, H Urakawa, Y Hiragi, N Donkai, M Nagura. Micellar structure of β-casein observed by small angle X-ray scattering. Biochim Biophys Acta 955, 128–134, 1988.
23. HJ Vreeman, JA Brinkhuis, JA, C van der Spek. Some association properties of bovine SH-κ-casein. Biophys Chem 14, 185–193, 1981.
24. DJ McMahon, RJ Brown. Composition, structure and integrity of casein micelles. A review. J Dairy Sci 67, 499–512, 1984.

25. DS Horne. Ethanol Stability. In: PF Fox, PLH McSweeney. eds. Advanced Dairy Chemistry – 1: Proteins. 3rd ed., Part B. New York: Kluwer Academic/Plenum Publishers, 2003, pp 975–1000.

26. DF Waugh, RW Noble Jr. Casein micelles. Formation and structure II. J Am Chem Soc 87:2246–2257, 1965.

27. S Hansen, R Bauer, SB Lomholt, K Bruun Qvist, JS Pederson, K Mortensen. Structure of casein micelles studied by small-angle neutron scattering. Eur Biophys J 24:143–147, 1996.

28. CW Slattery. Casein micelle structure: An examination of models. J Dairy Sci 59:1547–1556, 1976.

29. DG Schmidt. Association of caseins and casein micelle structure. In: PF Fox. ed. Developments in Dairy Chemistry – 1. London: Applied Science, 1982, pp 61–86.

30. DS Horne. Casein interactions: casting light on the *black boxes*, the structure in dairy products. Int Dairy J 8:171–177, 1998.

31. SPFM Roefs, P Walstra, DG Dalgleish, DS Horne. Preliminary note on the changes in casein micelles caused by acidification. Neth Milk Dairy J 39:119–122, 1985.

32. DG Dalgleish, AJR Law. pH-induced dissociation of bovine casein micelles. I. Analysis of liberated caseins. J Dairy Res 55:529–538, 1988.

33. HS Rollema, JA Brinkhuis. A 1H-NMR study of bovine casein micelles; influence of pH, temperature and calcium ions on micellar structure. J Dairy Res 56:417–425, 1989.

34. PF Fox. Heat-induced coagulation of milk. In: PF Fox. ed. Developments in Dairy Chemistry – 1. London: Applied Science, 1982, pp 189–228.

35. H Singh, LK Creamer. Heat Stability of Milk. In: PF Fox. ed. Advanced Dairy Chemistry – 1: Proteins. London: Elsevier, 1992, pp 621–656.

36. DS Horne. Ethanol Stability. In: PF Fox. ed. Advanced Dairy Chemistry – 1: Proteins. London: Elsevier, 1992, pp 657–690.

37. RMCL Whitney. Proteins of milk. In: NP Wong, R Jenness, M Keeney, EM Marth. eds. 3rd ed. Funda-mentals of Dairy Science. Westport, CT: AVI, 1988, pp 81–169.

38. L Sawyer. β-Lactoglobulin. In: PF Fox, PLH McSweeney. eds. Advanced Dairy Chemistry – 1: Proteins. 3rd ed., Part A. New York: Kluwer Academic/Plenum Publishers, 2003, pp 319–386.

39. G Braunitzer, R Chen, B Schrank, A Strangl. Automatische Sequenzanalyse eines Proteins (β-lac-toglobulin AB). H-S Z Physiol Chem 353:832–834, 1972.

40. MZ Papiz, L Sawyer, EE Eliopoulos, ACT North, JBC Findlay, R Sivaprasadarao, TA Jones, ME Newcomer, PJ Kraulis. The structure of β-lactoglobulin and its sim-ilarity to plasma retinol-binding protein. Nature 324:383–385, 1986.

41. S Brownlow, JHM Cabral, R Cooper, DR Flower, SJ Yewdall, I Polikarpov, ACT North, L Sawyer. Bovine β-lactoglobulin at 1.8 Å resolution – still an enigmatic lipocalin. Structure 5:481–495, 1997.

42. K Brew, FJ Castellino, TC Vanaman, RL Hill. The com-plete amino acid sequence of α-lactalbumin. J Biol Chem 245:4570–4582, 1970.

43. K Brew, TC Vanaman, RL Hill. Comparison of the amino acid sequences of bovine α-lactalbumin and hen's egg white lysozyme. J Biol Chem 242: 3747–3749, 1967.

44. PJ Kraulis. MOLSCRIPT: A program to produce both detailed and schematic plots of protein structure. J Appl Crystallogr 24:946–950, 1991.

45. K Brew. α-Lactalbumin. In: PF Fox, PLH McSweeney. eds. Advanced Dairy Chemistry – 1: Proteins. 3rd ed., Part A. New York: Kluwer Academic/Plenum Publishers, 2003, pp 387–421.

46. MJ Kronman. Metal-ion binding and the molecular confirmation properties of α-lactalbumin. Crit Rev Biochem Mol Biol 24:564–667, 1989.

47. DC Carter, JX Ho. Structure of serum albumin. Adv Prot Chem 45:153–203, 1994.

48. WL Hurley. Immunoglobulins in mammary secretions. In: PF Fox, PLH McSweeney. eds. Advanced Dairy Chemistry – 1: Proteins. 3rd ed., Part A. New York: Kluwer Academic/Plenum Publishers, 2003, pp 421–447.

49. B Reiter. Protective proteins in milk–Biological signifi-cance and exploitation. Intern Dairy Fed Bull 191:1–35, 1985.

50. WR Bezwoda, N Mansoor. Isolation and characterisa-tion of lactoferrin separated from human whey by absorption chromatography using Cibacron Blue F3 G-A linked affinity adsorbent. Clin Chim Acta 157: 89–94, 1986.

51. B Lönnerdal. Lactoferrin. In: PF Fox, PLH McSweeney. eds. Advanced Dairy Chemistry – 1: Proteins. 3rd ed., Part A. New York: Kluwer Academic/Plenum Publishers, 2003, pp 449–466.

52. KJ Anderson, G von der Lippe. The effect of proteolytic enzymes on the vitamin B_{12}-binding proteins of human gastric juice and saliva. Scand J Gastroent 18:833–838, 1979.

53. DN Salter, A Mowlem. Neonatal role of milk folate-binding proteins. Studies on the course of digestions of goat's milk folate binder in the 6-d child. Brit J Nutr 50, 589–596, 1983.

54. DP Sandberg, JA Begley, CA Hall. The content, bind-ing, and forms of Vitamin B_{12} in milk. Am J Clin Nutr 34, 1717–1724, 1981.

55. JE Ford. Some observations on the possible nutritional significance of vitamin B12 and folate-binding protein in milk. Br J Nutr 31, 243, 257, 1974.

56. C Kanno, N Kanehara. Influence of riboflavin-binding protein in raw cow milk. Proc Ann Meeting Soc Heric Chem Jpn, 1985, p 718.

57. T Toyosaki, T Mineshita. Antioxidant effect of protein-bound riboflavin and free riboflavin. J Food Sci 53:1851–1853, 1988.

58. BL Nichols, KS McKee, JF Henry, HA Heubers, M Putman. Human lactoferrin stimulates thymidine incor-poration into the DNA of rat crypt cells. Pediatr Res 21:563–567, 1987.

59. O. Koldovsky. The potential physiological significance of milk-borne hormonally active substances for the neonate. J Mammary Gland Biol 1:17–323, 1996.

60. T Hironaka, H Ohishi, T Masaki. Identification and partial purification of a basic fibroplast growth factor-like growth factor derived from bovine colostrum. J Dairy Sci 80:488–495, 1997.

61. R Kooijman, EJ Scholtens, GT Rijkers, BJ Zegers. Prolactin, growth hormone, and insulin-like growth factor-I in the immune system. Adv Immunol 63:377–454, 1996.

62. P Walstra, TJ Geurts, A Noomen, A Jellema, MAJS van Boekel. Dairy Technology. New York: Marcel Dekker, 1999, p 92.

63. PF Fox, M Yaguchi, NP Tarassuk. Distribution of lipase in milk proteins. II. Dissociation from κ-casein with dimethylformamide. J Dairy Sci 50:307–312, 1967.

64. T Olivecrona, S Vilaro, G Olivecrona. Lipases in Milk. In: PF Fox, PLH McSweeney. eds. Advanced Dairy Chemistry – 1: Proteins. 3rd ed., Part A. New York: Kluwer Academic/Plenum Publishers, 2003, pp 473–494.

65. Shakeel-ur-Rehman, NY Farkye. Lipases and Esterases. In: H Roginski, JW Fuquay, PF Fox. eds. Encyclopedia of Dairy Sciences. London: Academic Press, 2003, pp 926–929.

66. AT Andrews. The composition, structure and origin of proteose-peptone component 5 of milk. Eur J Biochem 90:59–65, 1978.

67. AT Andrews. The composition, structure and origin of proteose-peptone component 8F of milk. Eur J Biochem 90:67–71, 1978.

68. A Kennedy, AL Kelly. The influence of somatic cell count on the heat stability of bovine milk plasmin activity. Int Dairy J 7:717–721, 1997.

69. BC Richardson. The proteinases of bovine milk and the effect of pasteurisation on their activity. NZ J Dairy Sci Technol 18:233–245, 1983.

70. GK Murthy, DH Kleyn, T Richardson, RM Rocco. Alkaline phosphatase methods: In: RT Marshall. ed. Standard Methods for the Examination of Dairy Products, 15th ed. Washington D.C.: American Public Health Association, 1993, pp 413–431.

71. Shakeel-ur-Rehman, NY Farkye. Phosphatases. In: H Roginski, JW Fuquay, PF Fox. eds. Encyclopedia of Dairy Sciences. London: Academic Press, 2003, pp 934–938.

72. AT Andrews, M Anderson, PW Goodenough. A study of the heat stabilities of a number of indigenous milk enzymes. J Dairy Res 54:237–246, 1987.

73. F Addeo, L Chianese, R Sacchi, SS Musso, P Ferranti, A Malorni. Characterisation of the oligopeptides of Parmigiano Reggiano cheese soluble in 120 g trich-loroacetic acid/L. J Dairy Res 61:365–374, 1994.

74. P Ferranti, F Barone, L Chianese, F Addeo, A Scaloni, L Pellegrino, P Resmini. Phosphopeptides from Grano Padano cheese: nature, origin and changes during ripening. J Dairy Res 64:601–615, 1997.

75. K Pruitt. Lactoperoxidase. In: PF Fox, PLH McSweeney. eds. Advanced Dairy Chemistry – 1: Proteins. 3rd ed. Part A. New York: Kluwer Academic/Plenum Publishers, 2003, pp 563–570.

76. C Garcia-Graells, I Van Opstal, SCM Vanmuysen, CW Michiels. The lactoperoxidase system increases efficacy of high-pressure inactivation of foodborne bacteria. Int J Food Micro 81:211–221, 2003.

77. P Walstra, R Jenness. Dairy Chemistry and Physics. New York: John Wiley, 1980.

78. DM Mulvihill, MP Ennis. Functional milk proteins: production and utilization. In: PF Fox, PLH McSweeney. eds. Advanced Dairy Chemistry – 1: Proteins. 3rd ed., Part B. New York: Kluwer Academic/Plenum Publishers, 2003, pp 1175–1228.

79. JE Kinsella. Functional properties of proteins in foods: A survey. Crit Rev Food Sci 7:219–280, 1976.

80. H Singh. Milk proteins: Functional Properties. In: H Roginski, JW Fuquay, PF Fox. eds. Encyclopedia of Dairy Sciences. London: Academic Press, 2003, pp 1976–1982.

81. JE Kinsella. Milk proteins: physicochemical and functional properties. Crit Rev Food Sci 21:197–262, 1984.

82. JE Kinsella, DM Whitehead, J. Brady, NA Bringe. Milk proteins: Possible relationships of structure and function. In: PF Fox. ed. Developments in Dairy Chemistry, Vol. 4. New York: Elsevier Science, 1989, pp 55–96.

83. F Vojdani. Solubility. In: GM Hall. ed. Methods of Testing Protein Functionality. London: Blackie Academic & Professional, 1996, pp 11–60.

84. J Flanagan, RJ FitzGerald. Functionality of Bacillus proteinase hydrolysates of sodium caseinate. Int Dairy J 12:737–748, 2002.

85. J Adler-Nissen. Enzymic Hydrolysis of Food Proteins. London: Elsevier Applied Science Publishers, 1986.

86. CR Southward. Uses of caseins and caseinates. In: PF Fox. ed. Developments in Dairy Chemistry, Vol. 4. New York: Elsevier Applied Science, 1989, pp 173–244.

87. DG Dalgleish. Structure-function relationships of caseins. In S Damodaran, A Paraf. eds. Food Proteins and Their Applications, New York: Marcel Dekker, 1997, pp 199–224.

88. KP Das, JE Kinsella. Stability of food emulsions: Physicochemical role of protein and nonprotein emulsifiers. In: JE Kinsella. ed. Advances in Food and Nutrition Research, Vol. 34. London: Academic Press, 1990, pp 82–201.

89. J Flanagan, RJ FitzGerald. Functional properties of Bacillus proteinase hydrolysates of sodium caseinate incubated with transglutaminase pre- and post-hydrolysis. Int Dairy J 13:135–143, 2003.

90. MR Guo, PF Fox, A Flynn, PS Kindstedt. Heat-induced modifications of the functional properties of sodium caseinate. Int Dairy J 6:473–483, 1996.

91. JCA Hustinx, TK Singh, PF Fox. Heat-induced hydrolysis of sodium caseinate. Int Dairy J 7:207–212, 1997.

92. F Jahaniaval, Y Kakuda, V Abraham, MF Marcone. Soluble protein fractions from pH and heat treated sodium caseinate: physicochemical and functional properties. Food Res Int 33:637–647, 2000.

93. MM O'Sullivan, PC Lorenzen, JE O'Connell, AL Kelly, E Schlimme, PF Fox. Influence of transglutaminase on

the heat stability of milk. J Dairy Sci 84:1331–1334, 2001.

94. J Flanagan, Y Gunning, RJ FitzGerald. Effect of cross-linking with transglutaminase on the heat stability and some functional characteristics of sodium caseinate. Food Res Int 36:267–274, 2003.

95. D Oakenfull, E Miyoshi, K Nishinari, A Scott. Rheological and thermal properties of milk gels formed with kappa-carrageenan. I. Sodium caseinate. Food Hydrocolloid 13:525–533, 1999.

96. M Nonaka, H Sakamoto, S Toiguchi, H Kawajiri, T Soeda, M Motoki. Sodium caseinate and skim milk gels formed by incubation with microbial transglutaminase. J Food Sci 57:1214–1218, 1241, 1992.

97. E Dickinson, Y Yamamoto. Rheology of milk protein gels and protein-stabilized emulsion gels cross-linked with transglutaminase. J Agric Food Chem 44:1371–1377, 1996.

98. TW Schenz, CV Morr. Viscosity. In: GM Hall. ed. Methods of Testing Protein Functionality. London: Blackie Academic & Professional, 1996, pp 61–75.

99. DM Mulvihill. Milk protein products. In: PF Fox. ed. Advanced Dairy Chemistry – 1: Proteins. London: Elsevier, 1992, pp 369–404.

100. AJ Carr, CR Southward, LK Creamer. Protein hydration and viscosity of dairy fluids. In: PF Fox, PLH McSweeney. eds. Advanced Dairy Chemistry – 1: Proteins. 3rd ed., Part B. New York: Kluwer Academic/Plenum Publishers, 2003, pp 1289–1323.

101. S Damodaran. Food Proteins: An Overview. In: S Damodaran, A Paraf. eds. Food Proteins and Their Applications, New York: Marcel Dekker, 1997, pp 1–24.

102. RJ FitzGerald, H Meisel. Milk protein hydrolysates and bioactive peptides. In: PF Fox, PLH McSweeney. eds. Advanced Dairy Chemistry – 1: Proteins. 3rd ed., Part B. New York: Kluwer Academic/Plenum Publishers, 2003, pp 675–698.

103. E Schlimme, H Meisel. Bioactive peptides derived from milk proteins. Structural, physiological and analytical aspects. Nahrung 39:1–20, 1995.

104. H Teschemacher, G Koch. Opioids in the milk. Endocr Reg 25:147–150, 1991.

105. H Teschemacher, M Umbach, U Hamel, K Praetorius, G Ahnert-Hilger, V Brantl, F Lottspeich, A Hanschen. No evidence for the presence of β-casomorphins in human plasma after ingestion of cows' milk or milk products. J Dairy Res 53:135–138, 1986.

106. H Daniel, M Vohwinkel, G Rehner. Effect of casein and β-casomorphins on gastrointestinal motility in rats. J Nutr 120:252–257, 1990.

107. H Daniel, A Wessendorf, M Vohwinkel, V Brantl. Effect of D-Ala^{2,4}, Tyr^5-β-casomorphin-5-amide on gastrointestinal functions. In: F Nyberg, V Brantl. eds. β-Casomorphins and related peptides. Uppsala: Fyris-Tryck AB, 1990, pp 95–104.

108. M Brandsch, P Brust, K Neubert, A Ermisch. β-Casomorphins – chemical signals of intestinal transport systems. In: V Brantl, H Teschemacher. eds.

β-Casomorphins and Related Peptides: Recent Developments. Weinheim: VCH, 1994, pp 207–219.

109. V Schusdziarra, R Schick, A de la Fuente, J Specht, M Klier, V Brantl, EF Pfeiffer. Effect of β-casomorphins and analogs on insulin release in dogs. Endocrinology 112:885–889, 1983.

110. V Schusdziarra, R Schick, A de la Fuente, A Holland, V Brantl, EF Pfeiffer. Effect of β-casomorphins on somatostatin release in dogs. Endocrinology 112:148–151, 1983.

111. FL Schanbacher, RS Talhouk, FA Murray, LI Gherman, LB Willet. Milk-borne bioactive peptides. Int Dairy J 8:393–403, 1998.

112. H Chiba, F Tani, M Yoshikawa. Opioid antagonist peptides derived from k-casein. J Dairy Res 56:363–366, 1989.

113. M Yoshikawa, F Tani, H Shiota, H Usui, K Kurahashi, HD Chiba. Casoxin D, an opioid antagonist/ileum-contracting/vasorelaxing peptide derived from human α$_{s1}$-casein. In: V Brantl, H Teschemacher. eds. β-Casomorphins and Related Peptides: Recent Developments. Weinheim: VCH, 1994, pp 43–48.

114. A-M Fiat, D Migliore-Samour, P Jollès. Biologically active peptides from milk proteins with emphasis on two examples concerning antithrombotic and immuno-modulating activities. J Dairy Sci 76:301–310, 1993.

115. H Meisel, E Schlimme. Inhibitors of angiotensin-converting-enzyme derived from bovine casein (casokinins). In: V Brantl, H Teschemacher. eds. β-Casomorphins and Related Peptides: Recent Developments. Weinheim: VCH, 1994, pp 27–33.

116. MM Mullally, H Meisel, RJ FitzGerald. Synthetic peptides corresponding to α-lactalbumin and β-lactoglobulin sequences with angiotensin-I-converting enzyme inhibitory activity. Biol Chem H-S 377:259–260, 1996.

117. H Kayser, H Meisel. Stimulation of human peripheral blood lymphocytes by bioactive peptides derived from bovine milk proteins. FEBS Lett 383:18–20, 1996.

118. P Jollès, S Lévy-Toledano, AM Fiat, C Soria, D Gillessen, A Thomaidis, FW Dunn, JB Caen. Analogy between fibrinogen and casein. Eur J Biochem 158:379–384, 1986.

119. RJ FitzGerald. Potential uses of caseinophosphopeptides. Int Dairy J 8:451–457, 1998.

120. M Tomita, W Bellamy, M Takase, K Yamauchi, H Wakabayashi, K Kawese. Potent antibacterial peptides generated by pepsin digestion of bovine lactoferrin. J Dairy Sci 74:4137–4142, 1991.

121. Bellamy, H Wakabayashi, M Takase, K Kawase, S Shimamura, M Tomota. Role of cell-binding in the antibacterial mechanism of lactoferricin. B J Appl Bacteriol 75:48–484, 1993.

122. W Bellamy, M Takase, K Yamauchi, K Kawase, S Shimamura, M Tomita. Identification of the bactericidal domain of lactoferrin. Biochim Biophys Acta 1121:130–136, 1992.

123. DA Dionysius, JM Milne. Antibacterial peptides of bovine lactoferrin: purification and characterizaton. J. Dairy Sci 80:667–674, 1998.

124. K Shin, K Yamauchi, S Teraguchi, H Hayasawa, M Tomita, Y Otsuka, S Yamazaki. Antibacterial activity of bovine lactoferrin and its peptides against enterohaemorragic *E. coli* O157:H7. Lett Appl Microbiol 26:407–411, 1998.

125. HD Zucht, M Raida, K Andermann, H-J Mägert, WG Forssman. Casocidin-I: α casein-α_{s2} derived peptide exhibits antibacterial activity. FEBS Lett 372:185–188, 1995.

126. E Lahov, W Regelson. Antibacterial and immunostimulating casein-derived substances from milk: casesidin, isracidin peptides. Food Chem Toxic 34:131–145, 1996.

27 Enzymes of Significance to Milk and Dairy Products

A.L. Kelly and P.L.H. McSweeney
Department of Food and Nutritional Sciences, University College Cork

CONTENTS

I. INTRODUCTION

When considering the processing and quality of milk and dairy products, a number of enzymes are of significance. These fall broadly into 3 categories:

1. Indigenous enzymes: Fresh raw bovine milk contains a heterogeneous group of enzymes, derived from various sources. While different authors may use different nomenclature to indicate the origin of enzymes, in this chapter, enzymes of bovine origin that are found in milk will be referred to as indigenous. While the complement of milk enzymes has not been completely classified, and gaps in knowledge and understanding clearly occur, the principal classes of enzymes include proteolytic and lipolytic enzymes, phosphatases, antimicrobial enzymes, e.g., lysozyme and lactoperoxidase, and a number of other enzymes, such as xanthine oxidase. Approximately 60 indigenous enzyme activities have been reported in bovine milk, of which ca. 20 have been characterized (1, 2). The milk of mammals other than the cow probably contains similar enzyme profiles, although most have not been studied in detail (2).

2. Exogenous enzymes: A number of enzymes are added to milk during processing (3); these will be referred of hereafter as exogenous. The oldest example of such use of an enzyme in the dairy industry is the application of extracts of stomachs of calves, kids or lambs (containing chymosin) to coagulate milk in cheesemaking. Today, a range of milk coagulants is used (e.g., rennet extracts, recombinant calf chymosin, microbial rennets, etc.). Other enzymes that are commercially available today can be used to manipulate and accelerate cheese ripening (e.g., added protease and lipase preparations), to hydrolyze lactose in milk (lactases or β-galactosidases) and, most recently, to manipulate the

texture of milk products through the creation of new covalent inter-protein cross-links (transglutaminase).

3. Endogenous enzymes. Endogenous enzymes in this case refer to those that are present in a food but are not part of it, e.g., enzymes produced by microorganisms that grow in milk, either as natural contaminants (e.g., psychrotrophic bacteria, mastitis pathogens) or following deliberate inoculation (e.g., the lactic acid bacteria used in the manufacture of fermented dairy products). While such microorganisms possess a wide range of enzymes, which can contribute either negatively (e.g., lipases and proteases of *Pseudomonas*) or positively (e.g., the proteolytic system of *Lactococcus*) to the characteristics of dairy products, they will not be considered in this chapter. The reader is directed to reviews in this area (4–8).

In this chapter, the indigenous and exogenous enzymes of importance to milk and dairy products will be discussed. The significance of these enzymes to dairy product manufacture and quality will be emphasized.

II. INDIGENOUS ENZYMES

It has long been recognized that there is a significant and heterogeneous mixture of enzymes in fresh milk. Today, many of these enzymes have been characterized but our understanding of the significance of all these enzymes for product quality is incomplete.

In terms of indigenous enzymes, the key questions to be considered may be summarized as follows:

(i) What enzymes are present and from where do they originate?

As stated already, a number of enzyme activities have been identified in milk, which will be listed and described in detail below; however, it is unlikely that all enzymes in milk have been identified. Indigenous enzymes differ in their origin (e.g., blood or lysosomes of somatic [white blood] cells) and distribution in milk. Indigenous enzymes in milk originate from:
(a) Blood (via leaky junctions between mammary secretory cells)
(b) Somatic cells, particularly during mastitic infection
(c) Mammary cell cytoplasm, as a result of the way in which milk is expressed in the udder
Indigenous enzymes in milk are found in, or associated with, casein micelles, the milk fat globule membrane (most enzymes), milk serum or somatic cells.

One of the major challenges in studies of indigenous milk enzymes is the requirement for suitable methodologies and assays to allow evaluation of their nature and significance.

(ii) At what level are these enzymes found, and what factors affect their activity?

The enzyme complement in raw milk is far from constant, and may vary qualitatively and quantitatively due to several factors, including individual variation between cows, health status (particularly incidence of mastitis), stage of lactation, nutritional status, breed and physiological or nutritional stress. Thus, fresh milk as a raw material for production of dairy products may exhibit considerable, potentially significant, variation in its complement of indigenous enzymes. For some indigenous enzymes (e.g., plasmin), the factors affecting its activity in milk are quite well defined; in the cases of many other enzymes, such as the acid protease cathepsin D, this information is incomplete. Many of these factors, where known, will be discussed in the relevant section for each enzyme hereafter.

(iii) What is their significance in dairy products?

The most significant features of indigenous enzymes with respect to dairy products are (2):
(a) Indices of animal health (especially mastitis)
(b) Indices of the thermal history of milk
(c) Deterioration of product quality
(d) Desirable changes in dairy products
(e) Protective (antibacterial) effects.

This review will concentrate on the effects of indigenous enzymes on the technological properties of milk and dairy products.

Perhaps the principal issue to be addressed in terms of evaluating the significance of indigenous milk enzymes for the majority of modern dairy products is whether the activity remains following pasteurization, which is the primary processing step commonly applied to most milk. Many studies have shown that milk is not rendered enzymatically inert by such thermal processing. Indeed, the activity of the principal proteolytic enzyme in milk, plasmin, may be increased during storage of milk post-pasteurization, as will be discussed below. Post-pasteurization, the residual activity of indigenous enzymes have been linked to a wide range of positive or negative effects in dairy products (e.g., in the case of plasmin, from the ripening of cheese to coagulation and instability of UHT milk products). Furthermore, when it occurs, inactivation of enzymes by pasteurization or other processing steps may not be sufficient to eliminate completely the activity of certain enzymes in milk; in many cases, the enzymes already have had significant opportunity to act on milk constituents (e.g., to hydrolyze casein in such a manner as to affect product quality) prior to pasteurization, either rapidly at temperature near their optimum (i.e., in the udder at 37°C, prior to milking) or more slowly during refrigerated storage at the farm or factory.

In the following sections, the significance of indigenous enzymes will be discussed in the above light, under each of the major groups known to be present in raw milk.

A. INDIGENOUS LIPASE ACTIVITY IN MILK

Lipoprotein lipase (LPL) is found as an indigenous enzyme in the milk of all mammals, although its level varies from species to species; LPL is the only indigenous lipase in bovine milk (9–11). It plays an important role in milk production in the udder, as the products of its action on triglycerides in lipoproteins, i.e., fatty acids and monoglycerides, are taken into the cell for the production of energy, synthesis of tissue components or milk lipids, or storage. LPL activity in the mammary gland is low before and during pregnancy but increases soon after parturition and remains high throughout lactation (12). This elevated LPL activity means that triglycerides are diverted to the mammary gland for the synthesis of milk lipids. LPL is probably synthesized mainly and secreted into milk together with the casein micelles; some transfer of LPL to the milk fat globules may occur, particularly after milking (9). To date, no role has been proven for LPL in milk utilization by the neonate; Olivecrona et al. (9) speculated on possible roles for this enzyme, including assisting with the binding of milkfat to the intestinal mucosa, catalysis of the transfer of lipids into cells, facilitating the action of pancreatic lipase by partial hydrolysis of milkfat and perhaps an anti-parasitic function.

Bovine LPL is a non-covalent homodimer of glycosylated subunits containing 450 residues, 5 disulphide bridges and 2 oligosaccharide chains. The structure of LPL has been deduced by comparison of its sequence with that of the closely related pancreatic lipase (9). The active site of the enzyme is in a hydrophobic pocket protected by a surface loop ("lid"). LPL requires apolipoprotein CII (apoCII) for activity on lipoprotein substrates; apoCII is not related to the co-lipase needed for the action of pancreatic lipase. The exact mechanism by which apoCII activates LPL is unknown, but it has been speculated that it helps to orientate the lipase molecule at the oil-water interface at which the enzyme acts (9).

LPL binds strongly to heparin and related polysaccharides (13) *via* a groove on the side of the enzyme opposite the active site. The role of heparin binding appears to be to anchor the enzyme to heparin sulphate proteoglycans of the vascular endothelium (9). The catalytic mechanism of LPL is similar to that of pancreatic lipase and it preferentially releases fatty acids from the *sn*-1 and *sn*-3 positions of mono-, di- and triglycerides in emulsified lipid substrates. Since short- and intermediate-chain fatty acids are esterified mainly at these positions, the action of LPL results, in particular, in the release of these fatty acids. The apparent pH optimum of LPL on milk fat globules as substrate is ca. pH 8 (9).

In common with many lipases, LPL is subject to strong product inhibition (9). Since LPL can also catalyze the synthesis of ester bonds between fatty acids and partial glycerides, if the products of the hydrolysis (fatty acids) are not removed or complexed, LPL will spend much time producing fatty acids by hydrolysis and then using them as substrates for synthesis. In addition, fatty acids interfere with the binding of the enzyme to lipid droplets (14).

LPL in milk is associated mainly (>80%) with the casein micelles and its presence is of significance for lipolysis in milk and dairy products (9). Lipolysis occurs slowly in milk during storage, principally due to the action of LPL; it is only on prolonged storage or in cases of poor hygiene that bacterial lipases become important. Under ideal conditions (37°C, pH 7, in the presence of activators), raw milk should become rancid within a few minutes (9). Lipolysis in milk may be classified as spontaneous (i.e., without mechanical damage) or induced. Most milks do not exhibit spontaneous lipolysis. The incidence of induced lipolysis in milk has been reduced by improvement in design and operation of mechanical pipeline milking systems to avoid foaming or excessive shear forces during pumping. However, lipolysis may remain a problem if the milk is held for a long period before being transported to the dairy for processing.

LPL may cause lipolysis in raw milk but, since this enzyme is largely inactivated by pasteurization, its contribution to lipolysis in products made from pasteurized milk is minor. It is essential to pasteurize milk either before, or immediately after, homogenization, as the changes to the milk fat globule membrane would facilitate rapid lipolysis unless LPL is inactivated (9, 11).

LPL plays a role in lipolysis during ripening of cheese made from raw milk, or from sub-pasteurized milk (15). The presence of active LPL in raw milk cheese is one of the factors responsible for the difference in flavor between cheeses of the same variety made from raw or pasteurized milk, although heat-induced changes to the indigenous microflora of the cheesemilk are probably of greater importance (16).

A second lipase, bile salt-stimulated (or activated) lipase (BSSL), is found in the milks of humans and some primates, but not in those of domesticated milk-producing animals. BSSL is also present in pancreatic juice where it is referred to as "non-specific lipase" or "cholesteryl ester hydrolase." BSSL is found at high concentrations in human milk, where it is thought to improve the utilization of milk lipids by the neonate. Efforts are under way to produce this enzyme by fermentation with a view to supplementing infant formulae (9).

B. INDIGENOUS PROTEINASES IN MILK

1. The Plasmin/Plasminogen System

Babcock and Russel (17) first recognized the presence of indigenous proteolytic activity in raw milk. Today, the principal indigenous proteinase in milk is recognized to be the alkaline proteinase, plasmin (EC 3.4.21.7), which was first identified in milk by Kaminagowa et al. (18). Several reviews of the nature and significance of plasmin in milk have been published in recent years (19–23).

Plasmin is identical to the enzyme of the same name (which is also known as fibrinolysin) found in blood. That enzyme is a key element of the blood clotting mechanism (its role is in dissolving blood clots), and in that role its activity is, perhaps unsurprisingly, under the control of a complex and interconnected system of activators and inhibitors (24). It is thought that plasmin in milk originates from blood through leakage across the mammary gland secretory cell membranes, and to date almost all of the components of the blood plasmin system have also been found in milk, presumably through leakage (23). The principal elements of the plasmin system in milk are:

- Plasmin, the active enzyme, a serine proteinase of molecular weight 88,092 Da
- Plasminogen, its inactive zymogen (precursor)
- Plasminogen activators (PA), which proteolytically cleave plasminogen to yield active plasmin; there are two classes of PA in milk: tissue-type PA (tPA) and urokinase-type PA (uPA)
- Inhibitors of plasminogen activators (PAI)
- Inhibitors of plasmin (PI)

The properties of these elements of the plasmin system, where known, are summarized in Table 27.1. All the parts of the plasmin system listed above are indigenous to milk. In addition, some pathogenic bacteria associated with mastitis, i.e., infection of the mammary gland, such as *Streptococcus uberis*, possess PA activity, which they use to accelerate proteolysis in the infected udder (25). Furthermore, the proteolytic activity of some psychrotrophic bacteria can release plasmin from the casein micelles, where it is normally located, into the serum phase of milk, or whey (26, 27).

a. Proteolysis of Milk Proteins by Plasmin

There are two principal classes of proteins in milk. The caseins (α_{s1}-, α_{s2}-, β- and κ-) are relatively hydrophobic proteins which occur, in milk, in the form of spherical micelles containing thousands of molecules of each casein, plus nanoclusters (small particles) of (colloidal) calcium phosphate; the structure of the caseins has been described as rheomorphic, which means that they have a high degree of conformational flexibility (28). The casein micelles are stabilized in the aqueous environment of milk by a "hairy layer" comprising the hydrophilic C-terminal glycoprotein moiety of κ-casein. The second class of milk proteins, the whey proteins, are globular proteins, the principal of which are β-lactoglobulin and α-lactalbumin.

Plasmin is an alkaline serine proteinase, with a temperature optimum of 37°C and a pH optimum of 7.5. It preferentially hydrolyzes peptide bonds of the type Lys-X and, to a lesser extent, Arg-X; of the caseins (CN), β-CN is its preferred substrate. Hydrolysis of this protein by plasmin yields three polypeptide products known as the γ-caseins (β-CN f29-209, f106-209, f108-209), as well as proteose peptones (PP) PP 5 (β-CN f1-105/7), PP8 fast (f1-28) and PP8 slow (f29-105/7) (29). In solution, plasmin also readily degrades α_{s2}-CN (30, 31), but peptides derived from it have not been identified in milk. While plasmin acts more slowly on α_{s1}-CN (32), a number of α_{s1}-CN-derived peptides, collectively known as the λ-caseins, have been identified in milk (33). κ-CN is resistant to hydrolysis by plasmin. The whey proteins are also resistant to proteolysis by plasmin, and β-lactoglobulin can, in fact, act as an inhibitor of plasmin activity.

b. Factors Affecting Plasmin Activity in Milk

Plasmin activity is usually measured in a citrate dispersion of milk or cheese, using either a fluorogenic or chromogenic substrate (34–36). Total activity (plasminogen plus plasmin) is measured after activation of plasminogen by added urokinase, and the level of plasminogen calculated by difference. Assays have also been described for activity of PA (37); the ratio of plasminogen to plasmin in milk is also frequently used as an indication of the extent of plasminogen activation.

One problem with enzymatic assays for plasmin is the presence of protease inhibitors in milk. Some methods for assaying this activity avoid such interference by centrifugation of plasmin, bound to casein, from milk and re-suspending the pellet in a buffer containing ε-amino-caproic acid, which releases the enzyme from the micelles, prior to assay (37). A new modified method uses a clarifying

TABLE 27.1
Principal Constituents of the Plasmin System in Milk

Constituent	Function	Location
Plasmin	Active enzyme	Casein micelle
Plasminogen	Inactive zymogen	Casein micelle
Plasminogen activators (PA)		
Tissue-type (tPA)	Convert plasminogen to plasmin	Milk serum
Urokinase-type (uPA)	Convert plasminogen to plasmin	Somatic cells
Plasminogen activator inhibitors (PAI)	Inhibition of PA	Milk serum
Plasmin inhibitors (PI)	Inhibition of plasmin	Milk serum

reagent to reduce the turbidity of milk before fluorimetric analysis, without the need for more complex sample preparation (38). Alternatively, ELISA methods have been used to quantify plasmin levels in milk (39). However, different approaches will yield different information, for example, the exact concentration of plasmin in milk versus its actual proteolytic potential, as determined by all inhibitory substances present.

The activity of plasmin in milk is not constant, but varies due to a number of factors. Furthermore, there are several mechanisms by which plasmin activity can be modulated in milk, which leads to a complex multi-factorial system influencing the net plasmin activity in fresh raw milk.

The two principal routes by which plasmin activity in milk may be increased are (40):

- Increased transport of active plasmin from blood
- Increased conversion of plasminogen to plasmin by PA

These two routes are not independent; the increased permeability of the blood/milk barrier which facilitates the first route also increases the levels of PAs (41, 42). For example, somatic cells in milk possess PA activity, and can thereby activate plasminogen.

The principal factors which affect plasmin activity in milk are summarized in Table 27.2.

When milk is refrigerated, proteolysis is reduced greatly, although β-casein dissociates from the casein micelles into the serum (43), which should, in theory, facilitate proteolysis. However, at 4°C, no activation of plasminogen occurs and the activity of plasmin decreases over time (44).

Plasmin activity is further affected by the processing of raw milk. The effect of pasteurization on plasmin activity in milk is complex. The heat treatment per se (typically heating to 72–74°C for 15–30 s in a plate heat exchanger) slightly reduces the activity of plasmin. However, inhibitors of PA are believed to be inactivated by pasteurization, which accelerates the subsequent conversion of

plasminogen to plasmin (in the absence of down-regulation by these inhibitors), and eventually causes a net increase in plasmin activity in pasteurized milk relative to raw milk (45).

More severe heat treatments than pasteurization result in far more significant inactivation of plasmin in milk. In general, the inactivation of plasmin in milk is thought to be linked to the denaturation of the whey protein, β-lactoglobulin (β-lg); thermal denaturation of the latter protein exposes a highly reactive sulphydryl group, which can undergo disulphide-sulphydryl interchange reactions with disulphide bonds which are key structural features of the molecular conformation of plasmin. In the absence of β-lg, plasmin is very heat resistant, and will refold to an active state after thermal unfolding; however, in the presence of β-lg, heat-induced formation of heterologous disulphide-linked complexes prevents such refolding, and leads to loss of enzyme activity. In ultra-high-temperature (UHT)-treated milk, for example, plasmin activity is very low (46, 47).

In fact, heating milk to a temperature sufficient to denature β-lg reduces proteolysis therein by two mechanisms: enzyme inactivation, as discussed above, and complexation of denatured β-lg with casein micelles, which may sterically hinder access of the enzyme to cleavage sites on the caseins (48).

c. Significance of Plasmin in Milk and Dairy Products

In pasteurized liquid milk, proteolysis of casein by plasmin during storage has little direct impact: while, in principle, such action could result in physical instability (as will be discussed below for UHT milk) or development of bitterness (through the liberation of small hydrophobic peptides), the growth of psychrotrophic bacteria, such as *Bacillus* species, is generally the principal determinant of shelf life (49).

However, in long shelf-life milk products (such as UHT milk), where bacterial growth and activity do not occur, and the product is often stored at ambient temperature, even the low residual activity of plasmin remaining

TABLE 27.2
Farm-level Factors Affecting Plasmin Activity in Milk

Factor	Comments on Known Effects
Stage of lactation	Plasmin activity generally increases in late lactation
Mastitis	Plasmin activity is generally well correlated with milk somatic cell count (SCC); levels of protease inhibitors in milk also increase mastitis
Diet	Restricted diets increase plasmin activity, especially in late lactation
Breed of cow	Milk from Fresian cows has higher plasmin activity than that of Jersey cows
Age of cow	Plasmin activity is higher in milk from older cows
Genotype	Milk with different genotypes of β-lactoglobulin can vary in plasmin activity
Hormone usage	Somatotrophin suppresses plasmin in milk; estrogen increases activation of plasminogen to plasmin.

after the severe heat treatment applied (typically, 135–140°C for 2–4 sec) can contribute to proteolysis, albeit at a very low level, during storage. Furthermore, it has been suggested that such slow hydrolysis of caseins may be linked to the occurrence of physical changes in the milk, such as irreversible gelation during storage (46, 47).

Plasmin activity can potentially influence cheese quality in two main ways. Firstly, pre-manufacture hydrolysis of the caseins has been shown to affect the rennet coagulation properties of milk (50, 51); while rennet coagulation times can actually be reduced by plasmin action, gels formed from hydrolyzed milk are weaker than those from control milk (although these effects may be confounded by other changes in milk with elevated plasmin activity, such as late lactation or mastitic milk). Secondly, plasmin in curd is an important contributor to primary proteolysis of the caseins during cheese ripening. The activity of plasmin in cheese is directly affected by the cheese manufacture protocol (e.g., a high curd cooking temperature increases the relative contribution of plasmin to ripening) and the physicochemical environment of the cheese (e.g., pH, temperature, etc.). Studies involving either inhibition or augmentation of plasmin activity in cheese (the latter to investigate the possibility of using plasmin to accelerate cheese ripening) have shown that it probably does not contribute directly to cheese flavor, being principally involved in production of large polypeptides, rather than amino acids (52).

2. Other Indigenous Proteinases in Milk

Milk from a healthy cow contains a low level (<200,000 cells/ml) of white blood (somatic) cells. On mastitic infection, the somatic cell count (SCC) of milk increases rapidly and markedly, principally due to a massive influx of one type of white blood cell, polymorphonuclear leucocytes (PMN). Somatic cells in milk possess lysosomes which contain a range of proteolytic and other enzymes, the significance of which for the quality of dairy products is ill-defined (21).

Proteolytic activity in milk is correlated with its SCC; while part of this is unquestionably due to increased plasmin activity (Table 27.2), it is acknowledged that lysosomal proteinases contribute to proteolysis. This can be estimated by using specific assays for a range of proteolytic enzymes, or by examining the nature and origin of hydrolytic products in milk samples with different SCC (53, 54).

The second proteinase to be identified conclusively in milk was the lysosomal aspartic proteinase cathepsin D (55, 56). This enzyme is present in a number of different molecular forms in milk, not all of which are proteolytically active, and is located in the serum phase of milk (57). Cathepsin D activity in milk may be assayed using haemoglobin or synthetic chromogenic peptides as substrate; its activity is actually quite low, relative to that of

plasmin (proteolysis patterns in fresh milk quite closely reflect those of the latter enzyme). Cathepsin D at least partially survives pasteurization (58, 59).

The proteolytic activity of cathepsin D and chymosin on α_{s1}-casein are very similar; cathepsin D is quite active on this substrate (60, 61). β-Casein is also hydrolyzed readily by cathepsin D, yielding a pattern similar, but not identical, to those produced by chymosin (60, 61). The action of cathepsin D on bovine α_{s2}-casein produces a hydrolysis pattern quite different from that produced from this substrate by chymosin (60, 61). As for plasmin, the whey proteins are relatively resistant to the action of cathepsin D, compared with the caseins (60).

κ-Casein, the micelle-stabilizing protein, is hydrolyzed by cathepsin D at the Phe_{105}-Met_{106} position, the bond cleaved by chymosin during the rennet coagulation of milk (60, 61). Thus, it might be expected that cathepsin D could coagulate milk; however, exogenous cathepsin D coagulates milk very slowly (60, 61). The ability of cathepsin D to coagulate milk is strongly pH-dependent and is faster at lower pH, reflecting the low pH optimum of the enzyme. The level of indigenous cathepsin D in milk (ca. 0.4 µg ml^{-1}) is much lower than that required to cause coagulation of milk within a reasonable time, even under ideal conditions; thus, the action of indigenous cathepsin D probably does not significantly influence rennet coagulation, particularly if cheese is made from pasteurized milk (60). However, the enzyme may contribute to the degradation of κ-casein in other dairy products during prolonged storage.

In terms of the significance of cathepsin D for other products, most studies to date have focused on cheese, where it is extremely difficult to discern its contribution due to its close resemblance to chymosin. However, evidence of its activity has been reported in Swiss cheese and, most significantly, in Feta-like cheese made from thrice-pasteurized milk without the use of rennet (59) and in Quarg made from pasteurized milk without use of rennet (62).

Cathepsin D is probably only one of a number of lysosomal proteolytic enzymes in milk; it seems almost inevitable that other enzymes from this source are present in milk, at levels proportional to the SCC of milk. However, this area has received little attention to date. Many lysosomal proteinases are cysteine proteinases (including cathepsins B, L and H); cysteine proteinase activity in milk, due to the presence of at least two separate enzymes, and strongly correlated with SCC, has been reported by two independent groups (63, 64). The presence of immunoreactive cathepsin B in normal milk has been demonstrated (63). The specificity of cathepsin B on the caseins has also been determined recently (65).

The principal serine proteinase in the polymorphonuclear leucocytes (PMN), the principal type of somatic cell found in milk during mastitis (66), is elastase, an inhibitor of which has been found in milk (67); another important somatic cell proteinase is cathepsin G. There have also been sporadic reports of other indigenous proteolytic enzymes in bovine milk, such as an indigenous lysine aminopeptidase (68), but the presence of this enzyme has not been confirmed.

In general, it may be argued that the levels of proteinases other than plasmin in normal milk are too low to have an influence on the quality of dairy products; however, this area warrants further attention.

C. ENZYMES INVOLVED IN PHOSPHORYL TRANSFER

Four categories of enzymes are involved in the transfer of the phosphoryl group: phosphatases (EC 3.1.3…), phosphodiesterases (EC 3.1.4…), kinases (EC 2.7.1…– EC 2.7.6…) and phosphorylases (EC 2.4.1… and EC 2.4.2…). The most important phosphohydrolases in milk are two types of phosphomonoesterases (phosphatases), alkaline phosphatase and acid phosphatase. A number of other activities have been found in milk, including 5′-nucleotidase, glucose-6-phosphatase, phosphodiesterase I, deoxyribonuclease (DNase), ribonuclease (RNase), inorganic pyrophosphatase, adenosine triphosphatase and nucleotide pyrophosphatase. This class of enzymes in milk has been reviewed regularly (69–71).

The major indigenous phosphomonoesterase in milk is alkaline phosphatase (EC 3.1.3.1). This enzyme is a dimeric glycoprotein (85 kDa subunits), requiring 4 Zn atoms per molecule for activity; it is activated by divalent metal ions (Ca^{2+}, Mn^{2+}, Zn^{2+}, Co^{2+}, Mg^{2+}) and inhibited by metal chelators and orthophosphates. The enzyme is present mainly in the milk fat globule membrane. Alkaline phosphatase is optimally active in the pH 9–10.5 range and at 37°C (70).

The thermal inactivation kinetics of alkaline phosphatase have been studied thoroughly as residual alkaline phosphatase activity is widely used as an index of pasteurization (72). The enzyme is slightly more heat-resistant than *Mycobacterium tuberculosis*, which for many years was the most heat-resistant vegetative pathogen known in milk and the target organism for pasteurization. Results of "phosphatase tests" below certain limits are required for certification of pasteurized milk in many countries. However, the use of alkaline phosphatase as a marker enzyme for pasteurization suffers from a number of drawbacks (73):

- Some microorganisms in certain types of cheese (e.g., some lactic acid bacteria and *Penicillium roqueforti*) have alkaline phosphatase activity and thus certain cheeses, made from properly pasteurized milk, may exhibit a positive phosphatase test.
- Reactivation of alkaline phosphatase can occur following certain heat treatments equivalent to,

or greater than, pasteurization (e.g., temperatures of 82–180°C for milk or 74–180°C for cream for a short time).
- The enzyme appears to be inactivated fully by sub-pasteurization conditions (70°C × 16 s).
- The relationship between pasteurization equivalent and log (% residual activity) is less linear for alkaline phosphatase than for some other indigenous enzymes in milk (e.g., lactoperoxidase or γ-glutamyl transpeptidase).

The major technological importance of alkaline phosphatase is its use as a marker enzyme for pasteurization; no other technological roles have been confirmed (70).

An indigenous acid phosphatase (EC 3.1.3.2) in milk was reported first in the 1940s. A high proportion of the total acid phosphatase activity in milk is in skim milk, although cream contains a higher specific activity. This enzyme is a glycoprotein with a molecular mass of ca. 42 kDa and a pI of 7.9, containing a high level of basic amino acids but lacking methionine. It is inhibited by several heavy metals, F^-, oxidizing agents, orthophosphates and polyphosphates, activated by thiol reducing agents and ascorbate and is unaffected by metal-chelating agents (70). The enzyme is active against phosphoproteins, including the caseins, and is quite heat-stable, surviving HTST pasteurization but being inactivated by UHT treatments. Although a lower level of acid phosphatase activity than alkaline phosphatase activity is found in milk, acid phosphatase may be technologically important, due to its lower pH optimum (ca. 3.5–5), which is closer to the pH of many fermented dairy products (70).

There have been reports that milk contains more than one indigenous acid phosphatase (70), although it is likely that this heterogeneity is due to leukocyte enzymes from somatic cells, some of which are always present in milk.

As discussed by Shakeel-Ur-Rehman et al. (70), several small partially dephosphorylated peptides have been isolated from a number of cheese varieties, although it is not entirely clear whether indigenous or endogenous (starter) phosphatases are responsible for their production. However, the activity of the indigenous acid phosphatase is thought to be important.

Milk also contains two indigenous acid phosphatases of leukocyte (somatic cell) origin; the acid phosphatase activity of milk increases 4–10 fold during mastitis (74–76).

Nucleases are particular types of phosphodiesterases which hydrolyze the phosphodiester linkages in nucleic acids. As reviewed by Stepaniak et al. (77), milk is a rich source of RNase, which is almost entirely located in the serum phase, and is optimally active at ~pH 7.5. A number of isoenzymes of RNase are present in milk, principally RNase A (which is identical to pancreatic RNase A) and RNase B, in a ratio of about 4:1. Bovine milk contains approximately 3 times as much RNase as human, ovine or caprine milk. Most of the RNase activity in milk survives HTST pasteurization, although activity is essentially completely lost on UHT treatment. There has also been one report of indigenous DNase activity in milk (77).

D. LACTOPEROXIDASE

Milk contains natural inhibitors ("lactenins") of the growth of susceptible strains of starter bacteria. Further study has shown the lactenins to be antibodies (which cause susceptible bacteria to aggregate and localized acid production) and lactoperoxidase. Lactoperoxidase, an oxidoreductase, is a glycoprotein consisting of a single peptide chain with a molecular weight of 78,000 Da; it is a haem protein, with one iron molecule bound per mole of enzyme, and its stability depends on binding of a chelated calcium ion (78–80).

This enzyme catalyzes the following reactions:

$$(1) \qquad H_2O_2 + 2HA \rightarrow 2H_2O + 2A \qquad (27.1)$$

where the substrate, HA, can be one of several compounds, including aromatic amines, phenols, vitamin C.

$$(2) \text{ oxidation of thiocyanate (CNS}^-\text{) by } H_2O_2 \quad (27.2)$$

The products of reaction 27. 2, particularly the hypothiocyanate anion (OSCN⁻), inhibit many bacteria; this inhibition is particularly effective against bacteria which produce H_2O_2, such as lactic acid bacteria. It is believed that hyopthiocyanate can oxidize vital bacterial enzymes and sulphydryl groups in the cytoplasmic membrane, impairing its transport properties (81). Lactoperoxidase itself has no antibacterial action, but merely catalyzes the formation of antibacterial substances (e.g., the hypothiocyanate anion) from precursors.

The inhibition may be temporary (especially for Gram-positive bacteria such as streptococci and lactobacilli) or permanent and lethal (for Gram-negative catalase-positive bacteria such as *E. coli*, *Salmonellae* and *Pseudomonas* spp.) (78, 82).

However, while there is always a relatively constant and high level of lactoperoxidase in milk (30 mg/L, a 30-fold excess of the minimum required to achieve microbial inhibition), the concentrations in milk of other critical components and substrates of the system can vary widely (79). For example, the level of thiocyanate is generally limiting and depends on the availability of precursor substances (such as cyanoglucosides) in the feed (plants of the brassica family, e.g., cabbage, are rich in these); the origin of the very low level of H_2O_2 naturally present in milk is unclear, but may be related to the action of milk leucocytes and mammary tissues, the presence of catalase-positive microorganisms or the action of xanthine oxidase (79). The total antibacterial action is proportional to the production of the inhibitory end-products, and hence this can also vary (78).

The lactoperoxidase system can be exploited to prevent the spoilage of raw milk by adding thiocyanate (typically 10 mg kg⁻¹ of a powdered preparation), followed by thorough mixing and addition of a small amount of H_2O_2 (often in the form of granular sodium carbonate peroxyhydrate) (83). This method has particular applications in countries with a warm climate, where it can allow milk to be stored at a relatively high temperature (e.g., 30°C for 7–8 hours, or 20°C for 16–17 hours) (84). This allows producers without cooling facilities to transport milk to central cooling and processing centers, and has significant economic implications for milk-producing farmers in developing countries. A Code of Practice for the application of this method for preserving milk was approved by the FAO/WHO Expert Committee on Food Additives in 1989 and by the Codex Alimentarius Commission in 1991. Ideally, the natural thiocyanate content of the milk should be determined, in a centralized testing facility, before determining the level of thiocyanate to be added.

The effectiveness of the lactoperoxidase system can also be enhanced by adding xanthine oxidase to milk, an indigenous oxidizing enzyme which can produce H_2O_2 from substances such as xanthine and hypoxanthine.

Lactoperoxidase treatment of milk is not regarded as a treatment suitable for liquid milk, but rather as a processing aid which merely enhances a naturally occurring functionality of the milk; quality of the raw milk must still be good. The lactoperoxidase system has also been exploited in mastitis therapy during the dry period, control of post-fermentation acidification of yoghurt, preservation of HTST pasteurized milk and stabilization of dairy emulsions. The system has also been applied in cosmetics, ophthalmic solutions, dental and wound treatments, toothpastes and mouth rinses, and anti-tumor, anti-bacterial and anti-viral products (for a review of applications of lactoperoxidase, see Ref. 85).

Lactoperoxidase is considerably more heat-resistant than, for example, alkaline phosphatase, having a D-value at 80°C of 4 sec, and a very high Q_{10} value (72, 86).

E. OTHER INDIGENOUS ENZYMES

Approximately 60 enzyme activities have been identified in milk, although most have not been studied in detail. As discussed by Fox (2) and Farkye (87), some indigenous enzymes present at low levels in milk have an established function for the development of the neonate, while others may be present in milk simply because of the way in which it is synthesized in the udder or through leakage from the blood. A partial list of minor enzyme activities identified in milk is shown in Table 27.3; most of these enzymes have no technological significance.

Putative roles have been suggested by Farkye (87) for some indigenous enzymes in milk present at low concentrations, although it should be stressed that many of these

TABLE 27.3
Partial List of Minor Enzyme Activities in Milk (Modified from Ref. 87)

EC No.	Enzyme	Reaction Catalyzed	Location in Milk
1.1.1.14	L-Iditol dehydrogenase	L-Iditol + NAD^+ $\leftrightarrows$ L-sorbose + NADH	SM
1.1.1.27	L-Lactate dehydrogenase	L-lactate + NAD^+ $\leftrightarrows$ pyruvate + NADH + H^+	?
1.1.1.37	Malate dehydrogenase	Malate + NAD^+ $\leftrightarrows$ oxaloacetate + NADH	SM
1.1.1.40	Malic enzyme (oxaloacetate-decarboxylating) ($NADP^+$)	Malate + $NADP^+$ $\leftrightarrows$ pyruvate + CO_2 + NADPH	SM
1.1.1.42	Isocitrate dehydrogenase ($NADP^+$)	Isocitrate + $NADP^+$ $\leftrightarrows$ 2-oxogluterate + CO_2 + NADPH	SM
1.1.1.44	Phosphogluronate dehydrogenase (decarboxylating)	6-Phospho-D-gluconate + $NADP^+$ $\leftrightarrows$ D-ribulose 5-phosphate + CO_2 + NADPH	SM
1.1.1.49	Glucose-6-phosphate dehydrogenase	D-Glucose-6-phosphate + $NADP^+$ $\leftrightarrows$ D-glucono-1,5-lactone 6-phosphate + NADPH	SM
1.1.3.22	Xanthine oxidase	Xanthine + H_2O + O_2 $\leftrightarrows$ uric acid + $O_2^{(-)}$ Xanthine + NAD^+ + H_2O $\leftrightarrows$ uric acid + NADH	FGM
1.4.3.6	Amine oxidase (Cu-containing)	RCH_2NH_2 + H_2O + O_2 $\leftrightarrows$ RCHO + NH_3 + H_2O_2	SM
–	Polyamine oxidase	Spermine $\rightarrow$ spermidine $\rightarrow$ putrescine	SM
–	Sulphydryl oxidase	$2RSH$ + O_2 $\rightarrow$ RSSR + H_2O_2	SM
–	Fucosyltransferase	Catalyzes transfer of fucose from GDP L-fucose to specific oligosaccharides and glycoproteins	SM
1.6.99.3	NADH dehydrogenase	NADH + acceptor $\leftrightarrows$ NAD^+ + reduced receptor	FGM
1.8.1.4	Dihydrolipomide dehydrogenase (diaphorase)	Dihydrolipomide + NAD $\leftrightarrows$ lipoamide + NADH	SM/FGM
1.11.1.6	Catalase	$2H_2O_2$ $\leftrightarrows$ $2H_2O$ + O_2	SM/FGM
1.11.1.9	Glutathionine peroxidase	$2GSH$ + H_2O_2 $\rightarrow$ GSSH + $2H_2O$	SM
1.15.1.1	Superoxide dismutase	$2O_2^{(-)}$ + $2H^+$ $\rightarrow$ H_2O_2 + $O_2^{\bullet}$	SM
2.3.2.2	γ-Glutamyl transferase	(5L-Glutamyl)-peptide + amino acid $\leftrightarrows$ peptide + 5-L-glutamyl-amino acid	SM/FGM
2.4.1.22	Lactose synthetase A protein UDP-galactose: D-glucose, 1-galactosyl-transferase B protein: α-lactalbumin	UDP galactose + D-glucose $\leftrightarrows$ UDP + lactose	SM
2.4.1.38	Glycoprotein 4-β-galactosyltransferase	UDP galactose + N-acetyl-D-glucosaminyl-glycopeptide $\leftrightarrows$ UDP + 4-β-D-galactosyl-N-acetyl-D-glucosaminylglycopeptide	FGM
2.4.1.90	N-Acetyllactosamine synthase	UDP galactose + N-acetyl-D-glucosamine $\leftrightarrows$ UDP + N-acetyllactosamine	
2.4.99.6	CMP-N-acetylneuraminate-galactosyldiacyl-glycerol α-2,3-sialyltransferase	CMP-N-acetylneuraminate + β-D-galactosyl-1,4-N-acetyl-D-glucosaminyl-glycoprotein $\leftrightarrows$ CMP + α-N-acetylneuraminyl 1-2,3-β-D-galactosyl-1,4-N-acetyl-D-glucosaminyl-glycoprotein	SM
2.5.1.3	Thiamin-phosphate pyrophosphorylase	2-Methyl-4-amino-5-hydroxy-methylpyrimidinediphosphate + 4-methyl-5-(2-phosphonooxyethyl)-thiazole $\leftrightarrows$ pyrophosphate + thiamine monophosphate	FGM
2.6.1.1	Aspartate aminotransferase	L-Aspartate + 2-oxoglutarate $\leftrightarrows$ oxaloacetate + L-glutamate	SM
2.6.1.2	Alanine aminotransferase	L-Alanine + 2-oxoglutarate $\leftrightarrows$ pyruvate + L-glutamate	SM
2.7.7.49	RNA-directed DNA polymerase	n Deoxynucleoside triphosphate $\leftrightarrows$ n pyrophosphate + DNA_n	SM
2.8.1.1	Thiosulphate sulphurtransferase	Thiosulphate + cyanide $\leftrightarrows$ sulphite + thiocyanate	SM
3.1.1.8	Cholinesterase	An acylcholine + H_2O $\leftrightarrows$ choline + a carboxylic acid anion	FGM
3.1.3.4	Phosphatidate phosphatase	A 3-sn-phosphatidate + H_2O $\leftrightarrows$ a 1,2-diacyl-sn-glycerol + orthophosphate	FGM
3.1.3.5	5'-Nucleotidase	5'-Ribonucleotide + H_2O $\leftrightarrows$ ribonucleoside + Pi	FGM
3.1.3.9	Glucose-6-phosphatase	D-Glucose 6-phosphate + H_2O $\leftrightarrows$ D-glucose + Pi	FGM
3.1.4.1	Phosphodiesterase I	Removes 5'-nucleotides successively from the 3'-hydroxy terminal of 3'-hydroxy-terminated oligonucleotides	FGM
3.1.6.1	Arylsulphatase	A phenol sulphate + H_2O $\leftrightarrows$ a phenol + sulphate	
3.2.1.1	α-amylase	Hydrolyzes 1,4-α-D-glucosidic linkages in polysaccharides containing at least three 1,4-α-linked D-glucose units	?

(Continued)

TABLE 27.3   (Continued)

EC No.	Enzyme	Reaction Catalyzed	Location in Milk
3.2.1.17	Lysozyme	Cleaves 1,4-β-linkages between N-acetylmuramic acid and N-acetyl-D-glucosamine residues in peptidoglycan	?
3.2.1.21	β-Glucosidase	Hydrolysis of terminal non-reducing β-D-glucose	FGM
3.2.1.23	β-Galactosidase	Hydrolysis of terminal non-reducing β-D-galactosides	FGM
3.2.1.24	α-Mannosidase	Catalyzes the hydrolysis of terminal, non-reducing residues from α-D-mannosides	SM
3.2.1.30	N-Acetyl-β-D-glucosaminidase	Hydrolysis of terminal non-reducing N-acetyl-β-D-glucosamine residues from glycoproteins	SM??
3.2.1.31	β-Glucuronidase	β-D-glucuronoside + $H_2O \leftrightarrows$ alcohol + D-glucuronic acid	?
3.2.1.51	α-L-Fucosidase	An α-L-fucoside + $H_2O \leftrightarrows$ alcohol + L-fucose	—
3.4.11.1	Cystol aminopeptidase (leucine aminopeptidase)	Aminoacyl-peptide + $H_2O \leftrightarrows$ amino acid + peptide	SM
3.4.11.3	Cystinyl-aminopeptidase (oxytocinase)	Cystinyl-peptide + $H_2O \leftrightarrows$ amino acid + peptide	SM
3.4.21.4	Trypsin	Hydrolyzes peptide bonds, preferentially Arg-X, Lys-X	SM
3.6.1.1	Inorganic pyrophosphatase	Pyrophosphate + $H_2O \leftrightarrows$ 2 orthophosphate	SM/FGM
3.6.1.3	Adenosine triphosphatase	ATP + $H_2O \rightarrow$ ADP + Pi	FGM
3.6.1.6	Thiamine pyrophosphatase (nucleoside diphosphatase)	A nucleoside diphosphate + $H_2O \leftrightarrows$ a nucleotide + orthophosphate	FGM
3.6.1.9	Nucleotide pyrophosphatase	A dinucleotide + $H_2O \leftrightarrows$ 2 mononucleotides	SM/FGM
4.1.2.13	Fructose-biphosphate aldolase	D-Fructose-1,6-biphosphate $\leftrightarrows$ glycerol phosphate + D-glyceraldehyde-3-phosphate	SM
4.2.1.1	Carbonate dehydratase	$H_2CO_3 \leftrightarrows CO_2 + H_2O$	SM
5.3.1.9	Glucose-6-phosphate isomerase	D-Glucose 6-phosphate $\leftrightarrows$ D-fructose 6-phosphate	SM
6.4.1.2	Acetyl-CoA carboxylase	ATP + acetyl-CoA + $HCO_3^- \leftrightarrows$ ADP orthophosphate + malonyl-CoA	FGM

SM = skim milk; FGM = fat globule membrane.

hypotheses are highly speculative and that further research is necessary for their validation.

Some of these are summarized below:

- L-Lactate dehydrogenase, catalase, β-glucuronidase and N-acetyl-β-D-glucoseaminidase have been suggested as marker enzymes for mastitis.
- Inactivation of α-mannosidase has been suggested as a method to monitor heat treatment of milk at a temperature between 80 to 90°C.
- Glutathione peroxidase is a selenoenzyme and thus is a source of Se in milk.
- Indigenous lysozyme may have an antibacterial effect. Lysozymes (muramidase, peptidoglycan-N-acetylmuramoyl hydrolase) cleave the glycosidic linkage between N-acetylmuramic acid and N-acetyl-D-glucosamine in the peptidoglycan of bacterial cell walls.
- Sulphydryl oxidase in milk produces H_2O_2, which may be involved in the antibacterial lactoperoxidase system in milk.
- Superoxide dismutase may play a role in maintaining the oxidative stability of milk by scavenging the superoxide ions produced by xanthine oxidase.

- Xanthine oxidase, one of the most well-studied indigenous enzymes in milk, plays a role in the metabolism of purines, catalyzing the oxidation of hypoxanthine to xanthine, of xanthine to uric acid and the superoxide anion. It has been suggested that xanthine oxidase might be involved in the development of a spontaneous oxidized flavor in milk, although studies disagree on its role in this defect. It had been suggested that xanthine oxidase plays a role in the development of atherosclerosis, but this hypothesis has been disproved.
- Catalase, which contains iron, may act non-enzymatically to promote lipid oxidation.

III. EXOGENOUS ENZYMES

A. MILK COAGULANTS

It is speculated that rennet-coagulated cheese developed accidentally, due to the separation into curds and whey of milk stored in bags made from animal stomachs. Scientific study of this phenomenon revealed that such stomachs contain enzymatic activity with milk-clotting activity (MCA). The nature and composition of this activity changes with age of the cow; an extract of calf contains predominantly the aspartic proteinase, chymosin, with a small amount of pepsin. With increasing age, however, the proportion of chymosin decreases, while that of pepsin increases.

While many proteinases will coagulate milk under suitable conditions, many decades of investigation of other enzymes suitable for coagulation of milk for industrial cheesemaking failed to uncover an enzyme better than chymosin. The first commercially available standardized calf-derived coagulant preparation was produced by Christian Hansen in 1874. Rennet was the first enzyme industrially produced and sold with a standardized enzyme activity. The characteristics of chymosin as a milk coagulant have been reviewed (88–93).

Calf chymosin has a very high specificity for the Phe_{105}-Met_{106} bond of bovine κ-casein; this is thought to be partly due to electrical attraction between the positively charged region of the protein from residues 98 to 111 and the negatively charged active site of the enzyme, and also to structural conformation of the binding pocket of the enzyme relative to this region of the substrate protein. Cleavage of this bond removes the glycosylated region of the protein (glycomacropeptide, GMP); the remainder of the molecule is referred to as para-κ-casein (κ-CN f1-105). The enzymatic reaction is first-order and diffusion-limited in nature; the velocity of the reaction depends greatly on pH and temperature.

The portion of the molecule removed by chymosin, known as the caseinomacropeptide (CMP), stabilizes the hydrophobic caseins as micelles in the aqueous environment of milk, by mutual electrostatic and steric repulsion of individual micelles. Removal of the GMP reduces the zeta potential of casein micelles, and greatly destabilizes them. When denuded of a critical level (~80%) of this protective coating, in the presence of a sufficient level of calcium and at a temperature above 18°C, the casein micelles begin to aggregate, at first into chains and clusters, but finally coalescing into a three-dimensional network, which results in the gelation of the milk (for a review of the manner in which coagulants destabilize the casein micelle, see Ref. 94).

Chymosin is an aspartic proteinase (MW 35,600 Da) with a pH optimum for proteolytic activity around 4. Chymosin has been very well characterized at the enzymatic and molecular levels. While it exhibits a very high specificity for the Phe_{105}-Met_{106} bond of κ-casein, chymosin is also generally proteolytically active on the caseins. However, during the coagulation of milk, the reaction which causes milk coagulation occurs at such a relatively rapid rate that very little additional proteolysis occurs during the course of cheesemaking; hence, the loss of peptides in whey is very low. This unusually low level of non-specific proteolysis during cheesemaking (in comparison to other milk coagulants) is the main reason why chymosin is regarded as such an ideal milk coagulant (95).

While most of the chymosin added to milk in cheesemaking is lost in the whey, some adsorbs onto the caseins and is incorporated into the cheese curd; in addition, some is retained in the serum phase (whey) within the cheese (96). Along with plasmin, chymosin is one of the most significant agents during the early stages of ripening of many cheese varieties, hydrolyzing the caseins to large polypeptides that are further degraded by starter bacterial proteinases and peptidases. Chymosin hydrolyzes α_{s1}- and β-caseins quite readily (95). The hydrolysis of β-casein at pH 6.5 is strongly inhibited by increasing salt concentration, due to hydrophobic interactions, which shield chymosin-sensitive peptide bonds; this inhibitory effect is reduced at lower pH values. Chymosin principally hydrolyzes α_{s1}-casein at the Phe_{23}-Phe_{24} bond, yielding the peptides α_{s1}-CN (f1-23) and α_{s1}-CN (f24-199; sometimes known as α_{s1}-I-casein); this cleavage reaction plays a role in the initial softening of cheese texture during ripening (97). However, several other bonds in α_{s1}-casein are also cleaved by chymosin in cheese. α_{s2}-Casein is relatively resistant to hydrolysis by chymosin (95).

The activity of chymosin is generally evaluated by activity tests which measure the ability of an extract or preparation containing the enzyme to coagulate milk under controlled conditions (temperature, pH, etc.). More recently, a more sensitive and objective method was developed in the authors' laboratory; this test uses reversed-phase high-performance liquid chromatography (RP-HPLC) to measure the hydrolysis of a synthetic heptapeptide substrate by chymosin (98).

The optimum temperature for the coagulation of milk by chymosin is 45°C, but at temperatures above 50°C the enzyme is rapidly inactivated (99). This inactivation is responsible for the low chymosin activity in Swiss-type cheese, which is cooked during manufacture at around 55°C; the resultant lack of primary proteolysis of α_{s1}-casein in these cheeses during ripening contributes to their rubbery and elastic texture. Pasteurization of whey almost completely inactivates the enzyme, facilitating further processing of this by-product of cheese manufacture.

In the 1970s, the availability of calf stomachs became limited due to increased demand for rennets and reduction in the number of calves slaughtered, leading to an intense search for novel milk coagulants. An ideal alternative to chymosin as a coagulant for milk would:

- Be an acid proteinase capable of hydrolyzing κ-casein at approximately the same position as chymosin
- Possess a similar ratio of MCA to overall proteolytic activity
- Have an MCA that is not very pH dependent in the region 6.5–6.9
- Have thermostability comparable to that of calf rennet at the pH values and temperatures used during cheesemaking

- Have low thermostability during whey processing
- Possess the ability to produce desired flavor, body and texture characteristics in the finished cheese (100)

One result of this search was the identification of a number of microbial coagulants, as will be discussed below; the other was the application of the developing discipline of biotechnology to the production of pure chymosin (fermentation-produced chymosin, FPC) from genetically manipulated microorganisms, such as *E. coli*, *Aspergillus niger* and *Kluyveromyces lactis* (101, 102). More recent public concerns over bovine-related health issues (such as BSE and foot-and-mouth disease) have further increased demand for FPC and other alternatives to traditional rennets.

Among the principal advantages of FPC today are:

- Constant, controlled activity of a very pure enzyme
- Guaranteed supply
- Suitability for vegetarian, Kosher or Halal cheese

FPCs are identical in amino acid sequence to calf chymosin, and differences from the latter enzyme may occur only due to differing degrees of glycosylation by the host microorganism; such changes, however, have not been found to influence the properties of the enzyme. FPCs have been intensively studied in cheesemaking trials and generally found to give very satisfactory results (103), and are now widely used commercially in many countries.

Substitutes for chymosin used as coagulants include pepsins (bovine, porcine and to a lesser extent, chicken) and microbial proteinases from *Rhizomucor miehei*, *R. pusillus* and *Cryphonectria parasitica*. However, the fungal rennet substitutes are now used most commonly. Interestingly, *C. parasitica* proteinase cleaves κ-casein at Ser_{104}-Phe_{105} rather than at the Phe_{105}-Met_{106} bond, which is cleaved by chymosin, pepsins and the other fungal proteinases. *C. parasitica* proteinase has relatively high heat stability. The use of coagulants more heat stable than calf rennet should be avoided; otherwise, excess proteolytic activity may remain in the curd and may result in excessive proteolysis and bitterness unless ripening times and/or cooking temperatures are changed to compensate for the more rapid rate of proteolysis (96).

Plant rennets have a long history; the use of fig rennet was mentioned in Homer's *Iliad*. However, most plant coagulants are too proteolytic relative to their MCA, resulting in a reduced yield of curd and the development of bitterness during ripening. An exception is a protease from dried flowers of the cardoon thistle, *Cynara cardunculus*, which contain two enzymes, cardosins A and B,

and which have been used successfully for many centuries in the Iberian Peninsula for the manufacture of some traditional cheeses, e.g., Serra da Estrela, La Serena, Los Pedroches (104).

Commercial rennet extracts are free from lipolytic activity. However rennet paste, which does contain lipolytic activity, is used in the manufacture of some hard Italian varieties (e.g., Provolone, Pecorino Romano and many Pecorino cheeses). Rennet pastes are prepared from the abomasa of calves, kids or lambs slaughtered after suckling. The abomasum and contents are partially dried and ground into a paste, which is slurried in milk before being added to the milk from which cheese is to be made. Rennet paste contains a lipase, pregastric esterase (PGE), which is highly specific for short-chain acids esterified at the *sn*-3 position. Suckling stimulates the secretion of PGE by glands at the base of the tongue, and it is washed into the abomasum with the milk. Due to concerns regarding the hygienic quality of rennet pastes, research has been focused on exogenous lipases which could be blended with rennet extracts to produce substitutes for rennet pastes; certain fungal lipases may be acceptable alternatives, as are semi-pure preparations of PGE (100).

B. ACCELERATION OF CHEESE RIPENING AND ENZYME-MODIFIED CHEESES

In addition to their use as coagulants, exogenous enzymes have been investigated as possible agents to accelerate the ripening process of cheese. Cheese ripening is a slow, and consequently expensive, process in which the bland-flavored immature curd develops the flavor and texture characteristic of the mature cheese. Although soft (high moisture) varieties ripen quickly, the ripening period of hard cheeses is quite long (e.g., 6–24 months for Cheddar). A number of strategies have been investigated to reduce this ripening period, including the use of an elevated temperature, exogenous enzymes, slurry systems, adjunct cultures and high pressure treatment (105–108).

Proteinases, peptidases and lipases have been added individually, or in various combinations, to cheese with the objective of accelerating ripening. However, the use of exogenous enzymes to accelerate ripening suffers from a number of drawbacks, which have limited the commercial use of this approach. Probably the most serious limitation of the use of exogenous enzymes to accelerate ripening is that cheese flavor is the result of a wide range of sapid compounds produced by a number of enzyme-catalyzed pathways. Thus, addition of specific enzymes will not accelerate all pathways simultaneously and equally and thus can result in unbalanced flavor. In the case of exogenous proteinases, reduction in yield, textural problems and the development of bitterness have been reported (although the last defect can be ameliorated by the use of selected peptidase preparations). A second major drawback to the use of exogenous enzymes is that most of the enzyme added to the cheesemilk is lost in the whey. Enzymes can be added more efficiently to varieties such as Cheddar by mixing with the dry salt, but problems with uniform distribution of enzyme have been reported. Encapsulation of enzymes (e.g., in milk fat or liposomes) has been used in attempts to overcome some of these problems, but with limited success (106).

Enzyme-modified cheeses (EMCs) are concentrated cheese flavors produced by the enzyme-catalyzed hydrolysis of cheese curd or other ingredients (109, 110). EMCs are produced by adding exogenous enzymes, e.g., exogenous proteinase, peptidase and/or lipase preparations, to a pasteurized slurry of emulsified cheese curd and incubating under controlled conditions (typically 30–45°C for 24–72 h). The product is then heat treated (70–85°C) to inactivate the added enzymes. EMCs are sold as pastes (40–60% moisture) or, after drying, as powders. EMCs may be manufactured using one-step or component approaches; in the latter approach, several different flavor fractions (e.g., produced by lipolysis or proteolysis) are then blended to give the final product.

Flavor generation in EMCs is principally *via* lipolysis and proteolysis of the base material using exogenous enzymes. EMCs contain high levels of free fatty acids, peptides and amino acids, far in excess of those of natural cheese. The extensive proteolysis of the caseins during the manufacture of EMCs often leads to bitterness unless proteolytic enzymes are carefully selected or other debittering strategies are adopted. The flavor of EMCs may be augmented by the addition of flavor enhancers such as monosodium glutamate, yeast extract, NaCl, organic acids or starter distillates.

A wide range of exogenous lipases, proteinases (e.g., from *Bacillus* or *Aspergillus* spp.) and peptidases (e.g., from *Aspergillus*, *Rhizomucor* or *Lactococcus* spp.) are used in the manufacture of EMCs. Most lipases used are derived from animal or microbial sources; the most commonly used animal lipase is PGE. PGE preferentially liberates strongly flavored fatty acids. A range of microbial lipases is also available; they tend to be cheaper than animal lipases and may have broader specificity. In addition, microbial lipases have vegetarian status and are free from amylase activity, which otherwise may cause problems in foods to which EMCs are added, many of which may contain starch.

Proteinases used in the manufacture of EMCs are generally derived from microbial sources (e.g., *Bacillus* spp. or *Aspergillus* spp.) and are used to develop rapidly an intense savory background flavor. Peptidase preparations, derived from fungal or bacterial sources, are used to enhance flavor and/or to control bitterness. Peptidase preparations contain a range of enzymes, including endopeptidases, aminopeptidases and proline-specific peptidases.

EMCs have the advantages over other sources of cheese flavors in the intensity and range of flavors available, reduced production costs and extended shelf-life. Because of their high flavor intensity, only small amounts of EMCs (ca. 0.1%, w/w) are needed to impart a cheese flavor to products in which they are used (e.g., processed cheese, cheese analogues, cheese spreads, snack foods, soups, sauces, cookies, dips and pet foods).

C. β-GALACTOSIDASE

Hydrolysis of the milk sugar, the disaccharide lactose (4-*O*-β-D-galactopyranosyl-D-glucopyranose), yields two monosaccharides, D-glucose and D-galactose (111). Hydrolysis of lactose may be achieved either chemically, by acidification to low pH values, or enzymatically. The enzymes capable of catalyzing the latter hydrolysis reaction are collectively known as β-galactosidases or, more simply, lactases (although, strictly speaking, many β-galactosidases, especially those of plant origin, cannot degrade lactose) (112, 113).

A large proportion of the world's population suffers from lactose intolerance, leading to varying degrees of gastrointestinal distress if dairy products are consumed. The two products of the hydrolysis of lactose, however, are more readily metabolized; glucose and galactose are also sweeter than the parent sugar.

Lactose also has a number of other properties that cause difficulty in the processing of dairy products. Among these is its tendency to form large crystals on cooling of concentrated solutions of the sugar; galactose and, to an even greater extent, glucose, are more soluble than lactose (112). Thus, for example, hydrolysis of whey concentrates offers the possibility of preserving such products through increasing osmotic pressure while maintaining physical stability. Industrial applications of lactose hydrolysis have, in fact, focused to a large extent on treatment of whey to produce lactose-hydrolyzed whey concentrates or syrups (112).

Other applications of lactose hydrolysis include production of low-lactose market milk (114); this may even be achieved domestically by addition of a commercial preparation of β-galactosidase to fresh milk and incubation in the refrigerator. For long shelf-life products (such as UHT milk), β-galactosidase may be added to the package at a very low level and allowed to work slowly during storage. Lactose hydrolysis also has applications in ice cream manufacture, where it can reduce the incidence of sandiness (due to lactose crystallization) during storage and, due to the enhanced sweetness, permit the reduction of sugar content. Use of lactose-hydrolyzed milk can also accelerate the acidification of yoghurt (112).

Several sources of β-galactosidase (including yeasts, fungi and bacteria) have been identified, including *E. coli*, *Aspergillus niger*, *A. oryzae* and *Kluyveromyces lactis*

(111–113). The enzyme from the latter yeast is active at 4°C, which raises interesting possibilities in dairy processing (for example, it could be added to milk before cold storage in silos, removing the need for holding at a higher temperature with concomitant problems of microbial control). There is also much current interest in the use of β-galactosidase from thermophilic bacteria, which could permit operation of reactors at a high temperature, resulting in high rates of hydrolysis without the risk of growth of contaminating microorganisms (115). The principal criterion for acceptability of a microbial β-galactosidase is that the source should be safe and acceptable to regulatory authorities; genes for some microbial β-galactosidases have been cloned into safe hosts for expression and recovery for this reason.

The activity of β-galactosidase is generally monitored either by measuring disappearance of lactose or production of galactose and glucose (measurement of product monosaccharides is easier and more common, e.g., by HPLC or commercial enzymatic assay kits) (112). Synthetic substrates may also be used for assays of activity. In milk, simple and rapid estimation of hydrolysis of lactose may be achieved by monitoring the freezing point: freezing point; depression is linearly correlated with the degree of hydrolysis. However, many assay methods are complicated in cases where production of side-products (oligosaccharides) is significant.

For hydrolysis of lactose in milk, β-galactosidase may simply be added in free solution, allowed sufficient time to react typically, for most enzymes, at a temperature from 10 to 35°C, and inactivated by heat-treatment of the product. In an attempt to control the reaction and prevent uneconomical single-use of the enzyme, immobilized enzyme technologies have been studied widely (116, 117). In such systems, β-galactosidase may be immobilized on inorganic supports (which can change its kinetic properties) or entrapped within gels or fibers, such as those of cellulose acetate. One of the earliest systems, developed by the Corning Glass Company in the U.S., used covalent enzyme attachment to microporous silica beads (112). In entrapment-based systems, the porosity of fibers allows inward and outward diffusion of reaction products, but does not allow the enzyme to escape. The enzyme is, in effect, in solution within the fibers, and its enzymatic characteristics are not affected. Batchwise systems based on cellulose acetate membranes capable of processing 10,000 L milk per day have been developed. Overall, however, few immobilized systems for lactose hydrolysis are used commercially, the main limitations being the poor mechanical properties of supports and other technological problems with the process.

In an alternative approach, after hydrolysis of lactose, β-galactosidase may be recovered from milk or whey by ultrafiltration and reused, which combines the kinetic advantages of using the soluble enzyme with the economical benefits of recycling of the enzyme.

A new technique with potential for application in lactose hydrolysis processes is the use of permeabilized cells of bacteria or yeast (e.g., *Kluyveromyces lactis*) with β-galactosidase activity (118). These cells are treated, e.g., with ethanol, to allow diffusion of substrate and reaction products across the damaged cell membrane; the cell itself becomes the immobilization matrix and the enzyme is active in its natural cytoplasmic environment. Permeabilization may provide a crude but convenient and inexpensive enzyme utilization strategy.

Lactose hydrolysis reactions rarely lead to complete conversion of lactose to monosaccharides, for two reasons (112). Firstly, the galactose produced in the reaction can inhibit the enzyme in a feedback inhibition mechanism. Secondly, side-reactions (such as transferase reactions) often occur, resulting in the production of isomers of lactose and oligosaccharides. While initially thought to be an undesirable by-product of lactose hydrolysis, galacto-oligosaccharides, it is now recognized, may actually act as bifidogenic factors, enhancing the growth of desirable probiotic bacteria in the intestines of consumers and depressing the growth of harmful anaerobic colonic bacteria.

Overall, despite considerable interest, industrial use of lactose hydrolysis by β-galactosidases has not been widely adopted (119).

D. TRANSGLUTAMINASE

Transglutaminase (TGase) can modify the properties of many proteins through the formation of new cross-links, incorporation of an amine or deamidation of glutamine residues (120). To create protein cross-links, TGase catalyzes an acyl-group transfer reaction between the γ-carboxyamide group of peptide-bound glutamine residues and the primary amino group of a variety of amine compounds, including lysine residues in proteins. TGase (protein-glutamine: amine γ-glutamyl-transferase) type-enzymes are widespread in nature. For example, blood factor XIIIa, or fibrinoligase, is a TGase-type enzyme, and TGase-mediated cross-linking is involved in cellular and physiological phenomena such as cell growth and differentiation, as well as blood clotting and wound healing. TGase enzymes have been identified in animals, plants, fish and microbes (e.g., *Streptoverticillium mobaraense*); the latter is the source of much of the TGase used in food studies. TGase from different sources may either be calcium-independent (most microbial enzymes) or calcium-dependent (typical for mammalian enzymes) in mode of action.

TGase-catalysed cross-linking can alter the solubility, hydration, gelation, rheological, emulsifying, rennetability and heat stability properties of a variety of food proteins. Not all proteins are similarly affected by the action of TGase; the structure of individual proteins determines whether cross-linking by TGase is possible.

Perhaps not surprisingly, in recent years a number of studies have explored the potential applications of TGase in dairy protein systems. The caseins are good substrates for TGase, due to their open structure (121, 122). Treatment of casein micelles with TGase stabilizes them to the action of dissociating agents, such as calcium chelators or urea. In contrast, the whey proteins, due to their globular structure, require modification, for example heat-induced denaturation, to allow cross-linking.

A number of studies have shown clear effects of TGase treatment on the properties of milk and dairy products (123, 124). For example, TGase treatment of fresh raw milk increases its heat stability (125); however, if milk is pre-heated under conditions where whey protein denaturation occurs prior to TGase treatment, the increases in heat stability are even more marked. This is probably due to the formation of cross-links between the caseins and unfolded denatured whey proteins, brought into close proximity by formation of disulphide bridges between β-lactoglobulin and micellar κ-casein. When the whey proteins in milk are in the native state, the principal cross-linking reactions involve the caseins; heat-induced denaturation renders the whey proteins susceptible to cross-linking, both to each other and to casein molecules.

There has been considerable interest in the effects of TGase treatment on the cheesemaking properties of milk, in part due to the potential for increasing cheese yield. Some commercial reports have indicated that treatment, either of milk before renneting, or of curd if TGase is added during the cheesemaking process itself, can achieve this effect. However, a number of recently published studies (124, 126) have indicated that the rennet coagulation properties of milk and syneretic properties of TGase-crosslinked rennetted milk gels, as well as the proteolytic digestibility of casein, are impaired by cross-linking of proteins, which may alter cheese manufacture and ripening. Further studies are required to evaluate whether limited, targeted cross-linking may give desirable effects.

Other potential benefits of TGase treatment of dairy proteins include physical stabilization and structural modification of products such as yoghurt, cream and liquid milk products, particularly in formulations with a reduced fat content, and the production of protein products, such as caseinates or whey protein products, with modified or engineered functional properties (127–129).

Overall, it appears clear that TGase may have commercial applications in modifying the functional characteristics of milk and dairy products. However, some issues remain to be clarified; for example, control of the reaction in milk, to fix the exact extent of cross-linking of proteins to achieve desired properties, requires understanding of the heat inactivation kinetics of TGase in milk, which have not been reported. Further research is also required on the effect of variables such as temperature, pH and other operating conditions on the nature and rate of cross-linking reactions. Finally, a clear commercial advantage of using TGase over other methods of manipulating the structure and texture of dairy products (such as addition of proteins or hydrocolloids) must be established definitively.

E. MISCELLANEOUS EXOGENOUS ENZYMES

There are also some additional enzymes that may be added exogenously to milk (130), although their commercial application is limited. These are summarized below.

(i) Since human milk contains significantly more indigenous lysozyme than bovine milk, the supplementation of milk-based infant formulae with lysozyme has been proposed. It has been claimed that supplementation of such formulae with egg-white lysozyme gives beneficial results, especially with premature infants, but results are equivocal. Lysozyme is effective at killing *Clostridium* cells and preventing the outgrowth of their spores and thus it also has been studied as an alternative to nitrate for preventing the growth of *C. tyrobutyricum* in cheese and the butyric acid fermentation which leads to late-gas blowing. Lysozyme has also been shown to be quite effective against *Listeria monocytogenes* and other bacteria involved in food-borne illness and spoilage (130).

(ii) Glucose oxidase (GO) catalyzes the oxidation of glucose to gluconate *via* gluconic acid-δ-lactone (Figure 27.1). Glucose oxidase has four principal uses in the food industry, viz, removal of trace levels of glucose, removal of trace levels of O_2, generation of H_2O_2 *in situ* and production of gluconic acid *in situ*. However, GO is not commercially very significant, particularly in the dairy industry (131).

(iii) Superoxide dismutase (SOD) catalyzes the reduction of superoxide anions to H_2O_2 and O_2. It has been suggested that SOD together with catalase may be useful as an antioxidant in dairy products, although as far as we know, it is not used commercially for this purpose (130).

(iv) Sulphydryl oxidase, which catalyzes the oxidation of sulphydryl groups to disulphides

$$i.e., 2RSH + O_2 \rightarrow RSSR + H_2O$$

has been shown to ameliorate the cooked flavor of UHT milk, although, as far as we know, the enzyme is not used commercially for this purpose (132).

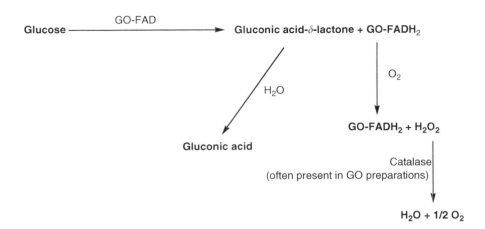

FIGURE 27.1   Reactions catalysed by glucose oxidase (GO).

(v) Catalase catalyzes the decomposition of H_2O_2 to H_2O and O_2. Produced H_2O_2 may be used for the cold-sterilization of milk and excess H_2O_2 may be destroyed by the use of exogenous catalase (130).

(vi) Exogenous β-lactamase, which degrades β-lactam antibiotics (e.g., penicillin), has been shown to be able to render milk contaminated with penicillin suitable for cheese manufacture (133).

IV. CONCLUSIONS

In summary, the two classes of enzymes considered in this chapter, i.e., indigenous and exogenous enzymes, are of great significance to the dairy industry, and an area of ongoing research and study, for two major reasons.

Firstly, milk is not an enzymatically inert raw material; on the contrary, it possesses a heterogeneous and highly variable complement of enzymes of many different types, the exact definition of which remains unclear, as does the significance of many of these enzymes for dairy product quality.

Secondly, the dairy industry is and remains a significant consumer of large quantities of commercially produced enzymes (e.g., the world market of commercial rennet is $\sim 30 \times 10^6$ liters per annum, representing one of the largest commodity enzymes in use today). Identification of novel sources of enzymes (e.g., the search for more thermostable β-galactosidases, which would allow operation at temperatures which would inhibit microbial growth), and optimization of the application and control of the activity of existing enzymes remain key food biotechnological goals. In parallel, demand for new dairy products drives the study of novel enzymatic reactions that can be harnessed to manipulate the flavor, texture or other characteristics of milk and dairy products.

REFERENCES

1. PF Fox. Significance of indigenous enzymes in milk and dairy products. In JR Whitaker, AGJ Voragen, DWS Wong, eds. Handbook of Food Enzymology. New York: Marcel Dekker, 2003, pp. 255–277.

2. PF Fox. Indigenous enzymes in milk. In: PF Fox and PLH McSweeney, eds. Advanced Dairy Chemistry. 1. Proteins, 3rd ed. New York: Kluwer Academic/Plenum Publishers, 2003, pp. 467–471.

3. PF Fox. Exogenous enzymes in dairy technology. In JR Whitaker, AGJ Voragen, DWS Wong, eds. Handbook of Food Enzymology. New York: Marcel Dekker, 2003, pp. 279–301.

4. RC McKellar (ed). Enzymes of Psychrotrophs in Raw Food. Boca Raton: CRC Press, 1989.

5. PF Fox, PLH McSweeney. Proteolysis in cheese during ripening. Food Rev. Int. 12: 457–509, 1996.

6. ERS Kunji, I Mierau, A Hagting, B Poolman, WN Koning. The proteolytic systems of lactic acid bacteria. Antonie van Leeuwenhoek 70: 187–221, 1996.

7. J Law and A Haandrikman. Proteolytic enzymes of lactic acid bacteria. Int. Dairy J. 7: 1–11, 1997.

8. JE Christensen, EG Dudley, JA Pederson, JL Steele. Peptidases and amino acid catabolism in lactic acid bacteria. Antonie van Leeuwenhoek 76: 217–246: 1999.

9. T Olivecrona, S Vilaró, G Olivecrona. Lipases in milk. In: PF Fox and PLH McSweeney, eds. Advanced Dairy Chemistry. 1. Proteins, 3rd ed. New York: Kluwer Academic/Plenum Publishers, 2003, pp. 473–494.

10. T Olivecrona, G Bengtsson-Olivecrona. Indigenous enzymes in milk II, Lipase. In: PF Fox, ed. Food Enzymology. London: Elsevier Appl. Sci. 1991, pp. 62–78.

11. T Olivecrona, S Vilaró, G Bengtsson-Olivecrona. Indigenous enzymes in milk. II. Lipases in milk. In: PF Fox, ed. Advanced Dairy Chemistry. 1. Proteins. London: Elsevier Appl. Sci. 1992, pp. 292–310.

12. MC Barber, RA Clegg, MT Travers and RG Vernon. Lipid metabolism in the lactating mammary gland. Biochim. Biophys. Acta 1347: 101–126, 1997.

13. A Lookene, O Chevreuil, O Ostergaard and G Olivecrona. Interaction of lipoprotein lipase with heparin fragments and with heparan sulfate: stoichiometry, stabilization and kinetics. Biochemistry 35: 12155–12163, 1996.

14. G Bengtsson and T Olivecrona. Lipoprotein lipase. Mechanism of product inhibition. Eur. J. Biochem. 106: 557–562, 1980.

15. YF Collins, PLH McSweeney and MG Wilkinson. Lipolysis and free fatty acid catabolism in cheese: A review of current knowledge. Int. Dairy J. 13: 841–866, 2003.

16. PF Fox, PLH McSweeney and CM Lynch. Significance of non-starter lactic acid bacteria in Cheddar cheese. Aust. J. Dairy Technol. 53: 83–89, 1998.

17. SM Babcock, HL Russel. Unorganized ferments of milk: a new factor in the ripening of cheese. Wisc. Agr. Exp. Stat. 22: 161, 1897.

18. S Kaminogawa, H Mizobuchi, K Yamauchi. Comparison of bovine milk protease with plasmin. Agric. Biol. Chem. 36: 2163–2167, 1972.

19. ED Bastian, RJ Brown. Plasmin in milk and dairy products: an update. Int. Dairy J. 6: 435–457, 1996.

20. MB Grufferty, PF Fox. Milk alkaline proteinase. J. Dairy Res. 55: 609–630, 1988.

21. AL Kelly, PLH McSweeney. Indigenous proteolytic enzymes in milk. In: PF Fox and PLH McSweeney, eds. Advanced Dairy Chemistry. 1. Proteins, 3rd ed., New York: Kluwer Academic, pp. 495–521.

22. SS Nielsen. Plasmin system and microbial proteases in milk: Characteristics, roles and relationship. J. Agric. Food Chem. 50: 6628–6634, 2002.

23. SS Nielsen. Plasmin system in milk. In: H Roginski, JW Fuquay, PF Fox, eds. Encyclopedia of Dairy Sciences. London: Academic Press, 2002. Vol. 2, pp. 929–934.

24. FJ Castellino. Recent advances in the chemistry of the fibrinolytic system. Chem. Rev. 81: 431–446, 1981.

25. JA Leigh. Activation of bovine plasminogen by *Streptococcus uberis*. FEMS Microbiol. Lett. 114: 67–72, 1993.

26. CE Fajardo, SS Nielsen. Effect of psychrotrophic microorganisms on the plasmin system in milk. J. Dairy Sci. 81: 901–908, 1998.

27. CE Fajardo-Lira, M Oria, KD Hayes, SS Nielsen. Effect of psychotrophic bacteria and of an isolated protease from *Pseudomonas fluorescens* M3/6 on the plasmin system of fresh milk. J. Dairy Sci. 83: 2190–2199, 2000.

28. CG DeKruif, C Holt. Casein micelle structure, functions and interactions. In: PF Fox, PLH McSweeney, eds. Advanced Dairy Chemistry-1. Proteins, 3rd ed. New York: Kluwer Academic, 2003, pp. 233–276.

29. WN Eigel, JE Butler, CA Ernstrom, HM Farrell, VR Harwalkar, R Jenness, RMcL Whitney. Nomenclature of the protein of cow's milk. 5th revision. J. Dairy Sci. 67: 1599–1631, 1984.

30. S Visser, KJ Slangen, AC Alting, HJ Vreeman. Specificity of bovine plasmin in its action on bovine α_{s2}-casein. Milchwissenschaft 44: 335–339, 1989.

31. D Le Bars, J-C Gripon. Specificity of plasmin towards bovine α_{s2}-casein. J. Dairy Res. 56: 817–821, 1989.

32. PLH McSweeney, NF Olson, PF Fox, A Healy, P Højrup. Proteolytic specificity of plasmin on bovine α_{s1}-casein. Food Biotechnol. 7: 143–158, 1993.

33. WR Aimutis, WN Eigel. Identification of λ-casein as plasmin-derived fragments of bovine α_{s1}-casein. J. Dairy Sci. 65: 175–181, 1982.

34. BC Richardson, KN Pearce. The determination of plasmin in dairy products. N.Z. J. Dairy Sci. Technol. 16: 209–220, 1981.

35. HS Rollema, S Visser, JK Poll. Spectrophotometric assay of plasmin and plasminogen in bovine milk. Milchwissenschaft 38: 214–217, 1983.

36. I Politis, B Zavizon, DM Barbano, RC Gorewit. Enzymatic assay for the combined determination of plasmin plus plasminogen in milk: revisited. J. Dairy Sci. 76: 1260–1267, 1993.

37. DD Lu, SS Nielsen. Assays for native plasminogen activators in bovine milk. J. Dairy Sci. 76: 3362–3368, 1993.

38. T Saint-Denis, G Humbert, JL Gaillard. Enzymatic assays for native plasmin, plasminogen and plasminogen activators in bovine milk. J. Dairy Res. 68: 437–447, 2001.

39. D Dupont, C Bailly, J Grosclaude, J-C Collin. Differential titration of plasmin and plasminogen in milk using sandwich ELISA with monoclonal antibodies. J. Dairy Res. 64: 77–86, 1997.

40. I Politis, E Lachance, E Block JD Turner. Plasmin and plasminogen in bovine milk: a relationship with involution? J. Dairy Sci. 72: 900–906, 1989.

41. I Politis. Plasminogen activator system: implications for mammary cell growth and involution. J. Dairy Sci. 79: 1097–1107, 1996.

42. I Politis, DM Barbano, RC Gorewit. Distribution of plasminogen and plasmin in fractions of bovine milk. J. Dairy Sci. 73: 1402–1410, 1990.

43. DG Dalgleish, AJR Law. pH-induced dissociation of bovine casein micelles. II. Mineral solubilisation and its relation to casein release. J. Dairy Res. 56: 727–735, 1989.

44. P Guinot-Thomas, M Al Ammoury, Y LeRoux, F Laurent. Study of proteolysis during incubation of raw milk at 4°C: effect of plasmin and microbial proteinases. Int. Dairy J. 5: 658–697, 1995.

45. BC Richardson. The proteinases of bovine milk and the effect of pasteurisation on their activity. N.Z. J. Dairy Sci. Technol. 18: 245–252, 1983.

46. KL Kohlmann, SS Nielsen, MR Ladisch. Effect of a low concentration of added plasmin on ultra-high temperature processed milk. J. Dairy Sci. 74: 1151–1156, 1991.

47. E Enright, AP Bland, EC Needs, AL Kelly. Proteolysis and physicochemical changes in milk on storage as affected by UHT treatment, plasmin activity and KIO_3 addition. Int. Dairy J. 9: 581–591, 1999.

48. E Enright, AL Kelly. The influence of heat treatment of milk on susceptibility of casein to proteolytic attack by plasmin. Milchwissenschaft 54: 491–493, 1999.

49. L Meunier-Goddik, S Sandra. Liquid milk products: pasteurized milk. In: H Roginski, JW Fuquay, PF Fox, eds. Encyclopedia of Dairy Sciences. London: Academic Press, 2002. Vol. 3, pp. 1627–1632.

50. O Mara, C Roupie, A Duffy, AL Kelly. The curd-forming properties of milk as affected by the action of plasmin. Int. Dairy J. 8: 807–812, 1998.

51. M Srinivasan, JA Lucey. Effects of added plasmin on the formation and rheological properties of rennet-induced skim milk gels. J. Dairy Sci. 85: 1070–1078, 2002.

52. NY Farkye, PF Fox. Contribution of plasmin to Cheddar cheese ripening: Effect of added plasmin. J. Dairy Res. 59: 209–216, 1992.

53. BM O'Driscoll, FP Rattray, PLH McSweeney, AL Kelly. Examination of protease activities in raw bovine milk using a synthetic heptapeptide substrate. J. Food Sci. 64: 606–611, 1999.

54. JM Somers, B O'Brien, WJ Meaney, AL Kelly. Heterogeneity of proteolytic enzyme activities in milk samples of different somatic cell count. J. Dairy Res. 70: 45–50, 2003.

55. S Kaminogawa, Yamauchi, K. Acid protease of bovine milk. Agric. Biol. Chem. 36: 2351–2356, 1972.

56. MJ Hurley, LB Larsen, AL Kelly, PLH McSweeney. The milk acid proteinase cathepsin D: a review. Int. Dairy J. 10: 673–681, 2000.

57. LB Larsen, TE Petersen. Identification of five molecular forms of cathepsin D in bovine milks. In: K. Takahashi, ed. Aspartic Proteinases: Structure: Structure, Function, Biology, and Biomedical Implications. New York: Plenum Press, 1995, pp. 279–283.

58. MG Hayes, MJ Hurley, AA Magboul, LB Larsen, CW Heegard, JC Oliveira, PLH McSweeney, AL Kelly. Thermal inactivation kinetics of bovine cathepsin D. J. Dairy Res. 68: 267–276, 2001.

59. LB Larsen, H Wium, C Benfeldt, CW Heegaard, Y Ardö, KB Qvist, TE Petersen. Bovine milk procathepsin D: presence and activity in heated milk and extracts of rennet free UF-Feta. Int. Dairy J. 10: 67–73, 2000.

60. LB Larsen, C Benfeldt, LK Rasmussen, TE Petersen. Bovine milk procathepsin D and cathepsin D: coagulation and milk protein degradation. J. Dairy Res. 63: 119–130, 1996.

61. PLH McSweeney, PF Fox, NF Olson. Proteolysis of bovine caseins by cathepsin D: preliminary observations and comparison with chymosin. Int. Dairy J. 5: 321–336, 1995.

62. MJ Hurley, LB Larsen, AL Kelly, PLH McSweeney. Cathepsin D activity in quarg-type cheese. Int. Dairy J. 10: 453–458, 2000.

63. AAA Magboul, LB Larsen, PLH McSweeney, AL Kelly. Cysteine protease activity in bovine milk. Int. Dairy J. 11: 865–872, 2001.

64. J Suzuki, N Katoh. Cysteine protease in bovine milk capable of hydrolyzing casein as the substrate and elevation of the activity during the course of mastitis. Jpn. J. Vet. Sci. 52: 947–954, 1990.

65. T Considine, A Healy, AL Kelly, PLH McSweeney. Hydrolysis of caseins by cathepsin B, a cysteine proteinase indigenous to milk. Int. Dairy J. 14: 117–124, 2003.

66. K Ostensson. Total and differential leucocyte counts, N-acetyl-β-D-glucosaminidase activity, and serum albumin content in foremilk and residual milk during endotoxin-induced mastitis in cows. Am. J. Vet. Res. 54: 231–238, 1993.

67. S Christensen, T Wiegers, J Hermansen, L Sottrup-Jensen. Plasma-derived protease inhibitors in bovine milk. Int. Dairy J. 5: 439–449, 1995.

68. EH Reimerdes. New aspects of naturally occurring proteases in bovine milk. J. Dairy Sci. 66: 1591–1600, 1983.

69. AT Andrews. Indigenous enzymes in milk: phosphatases. In: PF Fox, ed. Advanced Dairy Chemistry. 1. Proteins, 2nd ed. London: Elsevier Applied Science Publishers, 1992, pp. 322–331.

70. Shakeel-ur-Rehman, CM Fleming, NY Farkye, PF Fox. Indigenous phosphatases in milk. In: PF Fox and PLH McSweeney, eds. Advanced Dairy Chemistry. 1. Proteins, 3rd ed. New York: Kluwer Academic/Plenum Publishers, 2003, pp. 523–543.

71. Shakeel-Ur-Rehman, NY Farkye. Phosphatases. In: H Roginski, JW Fuquay, PF Fox, eds. Encyclopedia of Dairy Sciences. London: Academic Press, 2002. Vol. 2, pp. 934–938.

72. WL Claeys, LR Ludikhuyze, AM Van Loey, ME Hendrickx. Inactivation kinetics of alkaline phosphatase and lactoperoxidase, and denaturation kinetics of beta-lactogloblin in raw milk under isothermal and dynamic temperature conditions. J. Dairy Res. 68: 95–107, 2001.

73. RC McKellar, HW Modler, H Couture, A Hughes, D Mayers, T Gleeson, WH Ross. Killing time. Dairy Int. Int. 58(10): 49–51, 1994.

74. AT Andrews. Further studies on acid phosphatase of leucocyte origin in normal and mastitic bovine milks. J. Dairy Res. 43: 127–131, 1976.

75. AT Andrews, E Alichanidis. The acid phosphatases of bovine leukocytes, plasma and the milk of healthy and mastitic cows. J. Dairy Res. 42: 391–400, 1975.

76. M Anderson, BE Brooker, AT Andrews, E Alichanidis. Membrane material in bovine skim-milk from udder quarters infused with endotoxin and pathogenic organisms. J. Dairy Res. 42: 401–417, 1975.

77. L Stepaniak, CM Fleming, M Gobbetti, A Corsetti, PF Fox. Indigenous nucleases in milk. In: PF Fox and PLH McSweeney, eds. Advanced Dairy Chemistry. 1. Proteins, 3rd ed., New York: Kluwer Academic/Plenum Publishers, 2003, pp. 545–561.

78. Shakeel-Ur-Rehman, NF Farkye. Lactoperoxidase. In: H Roginski, JW Fuquay, PF Fox, eds. Encyclopedia of Dairy Sciences. London: Academic Press, 2002. Vol. 2, pp. 938–941.

79. KD Kussendrager, ACM van Hooijdonk. Lactoperoxidase: physico-chemical properties, occurrence, mechanism of activation and applications. Brit. J. Nutr. 84: S19–S25, 2000.

80. K Pruitt. Lactoperoxidase. In: PF Fox and PLH McSweeney, eds. Advanced Dairy Chemistry. 1. Proteins, 3rd ed., New York: Kluwer Academic/Plenum Publishers, 2003, pp. 563–570.

81. KM Pruitt, B Reiter. Biochemistry of peroxidase system: Antimicrobial effects. In: KM Pruitt and JO Tenovuo, eds. The Lactoperoxidase System. Chemistry and Biological Significance. New York: Marcel Dekker Inc., 1985, pp. 143–178.

82. WM Pitt, TJ Harden, RR Hull. Investigation of the antimicrobial activity of raw milk against several food-borne pathogens. Milchwissenschaft 55: 249–252, 2000.

83. MS Haddadin, SA Ibrahim, RK Robinson. Preservation of raw milk by activation of the natural lactoperoxidase system. Food Control 7: 149–152, 1996.

84. L Björk, O Claesson, W Schultes. The lactoperoxidase/thiocyanate/hydrogen peroxide system as a temporary preservative for raw milk in developing countries. Milchwissenschaft 34: 726–729, 1979.

85. JN de Wit, ACM Van Hooydonk. Structure, functions and applications of lactoperoxidase in natural antimicrobial systems. Neth. Milk Dairy J. 50: 227–244, 1996.

86. M Blel, MF Guingamp, JL Gaillard, G Humbert. Improvement of a method for the measurement of lactoperoxidase activity in milk. Int. Dairy J. 11: 795–799, 2001.

87. NY Farkye. Other enzymes. In: PF Fox and PLH McSweeney, eds. Advanced Dairy Chemistry. 1. Proteins, 3rd ed., New York: Kluwer Academic/Plenum Publishers, 2003, pp. 571–603.

88. A Andrén. Rennets and coagulants. In: H Roginski, JW Fuquay, PF Fox, eds. Encyclopedia of Dairy Sciences. London: Academic Press, 2002. Vol. 1, pp. 281–286.

89. S Chitpinityol, MJC Crabbe. Chymosin and aspartic proteinases. Food Chem. 61: 395–418, 1998.

90. B Foltman. General and molecular aspects of rennets. In: PF Fox, ed. Cheese: Chemistry, Physics and Microbiology, Vol. 1, 2nd ed., London: Elsevier Sciences, 1993, pp. 37–68.

91. PF Fox, PLH McSweeney. Rennets: their role in milk coagulation and cheese ripening. In: BA Law, ed. Microbiology and Biochemistry of Cheese and Fermented Milk, 2nd ed., London: Chapman and Hall, 1997, pp. 1–49.

92. TP Guinee, MG Wilkinson. Rennet coagulation and coagulants in cheese manufacture. J. Soc. Dairy Technol. 45: 94–104, 1992.

93. M Harboe, P Budtz. The production, action and application of rennets and coagulants. In: BA Law, ed. Technology of Cheesemaking. London: Blackie Academic and Professional, 1998, pp. 33–65.

94. DB Hyslop. Enzymatic coagulation of milk. In: PF Fox and PLH McSweeney, eds. Advanced Dairy Chemistry. 1. Proteins, 3rd ed., New York: Kluwer Academic/Plenum Publishers, 2003, pp. 839–878.

95. PF Fox, PLH McSweeney. Proteolysis in cheese during ripening. Food Rev. Int. 12: 457–509, 1996.

96. PF Fox, PLH McSweeney. Rennets: their role in milk coagulation and cheese ripening. In: Advances in the Microbiology and Biochemistry of Cheese and Fermented Milk, BA Law, ed., London: Blackie Academic and Professional, 1997, pp. 1–49.

97. LK Creamer, NF Olson. Rheological evaluation of maturing Cheddar cheese. J. Food Sci. 47: 631–636, 1982.

98. MJ Hurley, BM O'Driscoll, AL Kelly, PLH McSweeney. Novel HPLC assay for determining residual milk coagulants in cheese. Int. Dairy J. 9: 553–558, 1999.

99. MG Hayes, JC Oliveira, PLH McSweeney, AL Kelly. Thermal inactivation kinetics of chymosin in model systems and under cheese manufacturing conditions. J. Dairy Res. 69: 269–279, 2002.

100. PF Fox, TP Guinee, TM Cogan, PLH McSweeney. Fundamentals of Cheese Science. Gaithersburg, MD: Aspen Publishers, 2000.

101. AK Mohanty, UK Mukhopadhyay, S Grover, VK Batish. Bovine chymosin: production by rDNA technology and application in cheese manufacture. Biotechnol. Adv. 17: 205–217, 1999.

102. M Teuber. Production of Chymosin (EC 3.4.23.4) by Microorganisms and Its Use for Cheesemaking. Bulletin 251. Brussels: IDF, 1990, pp. 3–15.

103. VE Bines, P Young, BA Law. Comparison of Cheddar cheese made with a recombinant calf chymosin and with standard calf rennet. J. Dairy Res. 56: 657–664, 1989.

104. MJ Sousa, Y Ardo, PLH McSweeney. Advances in the study of proteolysis in cheese during ripening. Int. Dairy J. 11: 327–345, 2001.

105. M El Soda Accelerated cheese ripening. In: H Roginski, JW Fuquay, PF Fox, eds. Encyclopedia of Dairy Sciences. London: Academic Press, 2002. Vol. 1, pp. 281–286.

106. VK Upadhyay, PLH McSweeney. Acceleration of cheese ripening. In: G Smit, ed. Dairy Processing: Maximizing Quality, Cambridge: Woodhead Publishing, pp. 419–447.

107. MG Wilkinson. Acceleration of cheese ripening. In: PF Fox, ed. Cheese: Chemistry, Physics and Microbiology, 2nd ed., vol. 2, London: Chapman and Hall. 1993, pp. 523–555.

108. CE O'Reilly, AL Kelly, PM Murphy, TP Beresford. Effect of high pressure on proteolysis during ripening of Cheddar cheese. Innov. Food Sci. Emerg. Technol. 1: 109–117, 2000.

109. MG Wilkinson, KN Kilcawley. Enzyme-modified cheese. In: H Roginski, JW Fuquay, PF Fox, eds. Encyclopedia of Dairy Sciences. London: Academic Press, 2002. Vol. 1, pp. 434–438.

110. KN Kilcawley, MG Wilkinson, PF Fox. Enzyme-modified cheese. Int. Dairy J. 8: 1–10, 1998.

111. RR Mahoney. Lactose: enzymatic modification. In: PF Fox, ed. Advanced Dairy Chemistry, Vol. 3, Lactose, Salts, Water and Vitamins. London: Chapman and Hall, 1997, pp. 77–126.

112. RR Mahoney. Enzymes exogenous to milk in dairy technology: Beta-D-Galactosidase. In: H Roginski, JW Fuquay, PF Fox, eds. Encyclopedia of Dairy Sciences. London: Academic Press, 2002. Vol. 2, pp. 907–914.

113. JR Whitaker. β-Galactosidase. In: Principles of Unzymology for the Food Sciences. New York: Marcel Dekker Inc., 1994, pp. 419–423.

114. HW Modler, A Gelda, M Yamaguchi, S Gelda. Production of fluid milk with a high degree of lactose hydrolysis. In: Lactose Hydrolysis, IDF Bulletin 289. Brussels: IDF, 1993, pp. 57–61.

115. T Vasiljevic, P Jelen. Production of β-galactosidase for lactose hydrolysis in milk and dairy products using thermophilic lactic acid bacteria. Innov. Food Sci. Emerg. Technol. 2: 75–85, 2001.

116. JM Obon, MR Castellar, JL Iborra, A Manjøn. β-Galactosidase immobilisation for milk lactose hydrolysis: a simple experimental and modelling study of batch and continuous reactors. Biochem. Educ. 28: 164–168, 2000.

117. M Becerra, B Baroli, AM Fadda, JB Méndez, MI Gonzaléz-Siso. Lactose bioconversion by calcium-alginate immobilisation of *Kluyveromyces lactis* cells. Enzyme Microb. Technol. 29: 506–512, 2001.

118. EAF Fontes, FML Passon, FJV Passos. A mechanistical mathematical model to predict lactose hydrolysis by β-galactosidase in a permeabilised cell mass of *Kluyveromyces lactis*: variability and sensitivity analysis. Process Biochem. 37: 267–274, 2001.

119. JG Zadow. Economic considerations related to the production of lactose and lactose by-products. In: Lactose Hydrolysis, IDF Bulletin 289. Brussels: IDF, 1993, pp. 10–15.

120. M Motoki, K Seguro. Transglutaminase and its use for food processing. Trends Food Sci. Technol. 9: 204–210, 1998.

121. K Ikura, T Komitani, M Yoshikawa, R Sasaki, H Chiba. Crosslinking of casein components by transglutaminase. Agric. Biol. Chem. 44: 1567–1573, 1980.

122. R Sharma, PC Lorenzen, KB Qvist. Influence of transglutaminase treatment of skim milk on the formation of ε-(γ-glutamyl) lysine and the susceptibility of individual proteins towards crosslinking. Int. Dairy J. 11: 785–793, 2001.

123. PC Lorenzen, E Schlimme. Properties and Potential Fields of Application of Transglutaminase Preparations in Dairying. Bulletin 332. Brussels: International Dairy Federation, 1998, pp. 47–53.

124. MM O'Sullivan, AL Kelly, PF Fox. Influence of transglutaminase treatment on some physicochemical properties of milk. J. Dairy Res. 69: 433–442, 2002.

125. MM O'Sullivan, AL Kelly, PF Fox. Effect of transglutaminase on the heat stability of milk: a possible mechanism. J. Dairy Sci. 85: 1–7, 2002.

126. PC Lorenzen. Renneting properties of transglutaminase-treated milk. Milchwissenschaft 55: 433–437, 2000.

127. M Færgamand, J Otte, KB Qvist. Emulsifying properties of milk proteins cross-linked with microbial transglutaminase. Int. Dairy J. 8: 715–723, 1998.

128. M Færgamand, KB Qvist. Transglutaminase: effect on rheological properties, microstructure and permeability of set-style skim milk gel. Food Hydrocolloids 11: 287–292, 1998.

129. E Dickinson, Y Yamamoto. Rheology of milk protein gels and protein-stabilised emulsion gels cross-linked with transglutaminase. J. Agric. Food Chem. 44: 1371–1377, 1996.

130. PF Fox. Exogenous enzymes in dairy technology. In: JR Whitaker, AGJ Voragen, DWS Wong, eds. Handbook of Food Enzymology. New York: Marcel Dekker, 2003, pp. 279–301.

131. AJ Vroemen. Glucose oxidase. In: JR Whitaker, AGJ Voragen, DWS Wong, eds. Handbook of Food Enzymology. New York: Marcel Dekker, 2003, pp. 425–432.

132. PF Fox, PA Morrissey. Indigenous enzymes of bovine milk. In: GG Birch, N Blakeborough and KJ Parker, eds. Enzymes and Food Processing. London: Applied Science Publishers, 1981, pp. 213–238.

133. M Korycka-Dahl, T Richardson, RL Bradley. Use of microbial β-lactamase to destroy penicillin added to milk. J. Dairy Sci. 68: 1910–1916, 1985.

28 Meat: Chemistry and Biochemistry

Fidel Toldrá
Instituto de Agroquímica y Tecnología de Alimentos (CSIC)

CONTENTS

I. INTRODUCTION

Meat quality is very important for all segments of the industry from producers to consumers. There are many aspects such as source, cost, ethical factors, religion, production systems and safety that affect meat acceptability by consumers. Other quality factors perceived by consumers are related to sensory characteristics (i.e., color, tenderness and flavor), nutritional properties (i.e., calories, vitamins content, fatty acids profile, etc.) and appearance (i.e., exudation, marbling, amount of fat, etc.). One of the major concerns for consumers is the variability in meat quality; this constitutes a problem to solve within the meat industry. The composition, structure and metabolic status of the muscle have a great influence on numerous chemical and biochemical changes affecting meat quality characteristics such as tenderness in beef or exudation in pork and poultry. This chapter summarizes the chemistry and biochemistry of meat, taking into account how all these factors interact during postmortem stages and thus how they affect the final meat quality. A better understanding of these reactions and changes is essential for the standardization and improvement of production processes to obtain a high quality meat.

II. MUSCLE STRUCTURE

Skeletal, smooth and cardiac constitute the main types of muscles. However, from the point of view of meat, skeletal muscle is the most important because it represents a high percentage of the total body weight. Skeletal muscle is voluntary (the organism can contract it voluntarily), striated (cross striations may be observed under the microscope due to the alternance of dark and light bands) and multinucleated (several nuclei located peripherally in the cell). The muscle is covered by a sheath of connective tissue, the epimysium. There are several bundles of fibers inside the muscle which are covered by thin connective tissue layers, the perimysium, and each individual fiber is wrapped by thin collagen, the endomysium (see Figure 28.1). Each muscle fiber may contain about 1,000

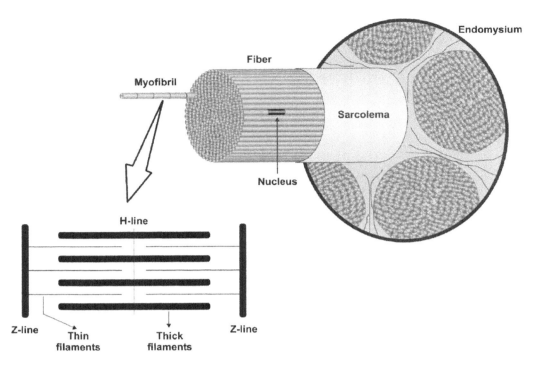

FIGURE 28.1 Scheme of the organization and structure of skeletal muscle.

myofibrils, which are arranged in a parallel way, and are responsible for the contraction of the muscle (1). Fibers have an approximate diameter of around 50 μm and may vary in length from a few milimeters up to several centimeters (2). They contain myofibrils, composed of thick and thin filaments arranged in an array and responsible for muscle contraction and relaxation, giving rise to alternating dark (A) and light (I) bands. The Z and M lines bisect each I and A band, respectively (see Figure 28.1). The M lines connect the center of the thick filaments to keep the structure (3). The Z line appears as a zigzag structure and has diverse properties such as resistance to physical forces but, on the other hand, it is susceptible to protease action (4). The sarcomere, usually in the range of 2–3 μm in length, is defined as the distance between two consecutive Z lines. The thick and thin filaments are composed of myofibrillar proteins (see Table 28.1). Actin filaments extend into Z lines at one end and extend between thick filaments at the other end (5). Thick filaments are mainly composed of myosin with minor presence of other proteins. The fibers are embebbed in a liquid or cytoplasm, also known as sarcoplasm, that contains mitochondria, lysosomes, enzymes, lipids, glycogen, myoglobin, ATP and creatine. As most of these proteins are soluble in water and are present in the sarcoplasm, they are known as sarcoplasmic proteins. The scanning electron microscopy of skeletal muscle reveals details of the muscle fiber structure in a three-dimensional image. An example of a micrograph from the scanning electron micro-scope is shown in Figure 28.2.

Muscles present different appearances and have been traditionally classified as red or white based on the color properties that are dependent on the proportion of the muscle fiber types. Other classifications based on the amount of released water have not been used widely. The red color is related to the content in myoglobin, naturally present in the muscle, and hemoglobin from remaining blood. Differences between red and white muscles are especially evident in pork and poultry while differences in color are relatively masked in beef due to its higher content in myoglobin. Based on histochemical properties, muscle fibers have been classified as red, intermediate and white (6). Red fibers contain higher amounts of myoglobin, are better capillarized, are oxidative in metabolism, and can function over a long period of time but are slower contracting than white fibers that are mainly glycolytic (7). Intermediate fibers have oxidative and glycolytic activity. Thus, red muscles contain a higher proportion of red fibers and are mostly related to locomotion while white muscles have a higher proportion of white fibers and are mostly related to support tasks (8). Other classifications of muscle fibers are based on the contraction speed (9): slow twitch oxidative (type I), fast twitch oxidative type (IIA) and fast twitch glycolytic type (IIB). So, the response of slow twitch muscles to a stimulus is slower and once the stimulus is finished the relax is also slower than fast twitch muscles.

Differences between red and white muscles are also significant during meat processing because large variations are found in sensory properties such as tenderness, juiciness, flavor (10) as well as physicochemical (11) and

TABLE 28.1
Location and Functions of Major Meat Proteins (Adapted from Refs. 2, 9, 24, 151)

Protein	Type	Function
Myosin	Myofibrillar	Major contractile
Actin	Myofibrillar	Major contractile
Tropomyosin	Myofibrillar	Regulatory
Troponins T, C, I	Myofibrillar	Regulatory
α and β actinin	Myofibrillar	Regulatory
Titin	Myofibrillar	Cytoskeletal
Nebulin	Myofibrillar	Cytoskeletal
Filamin,synemin, vinculin, zeugmatin, Z nin	Myofibrillar	Z-line
C, H, X, F, I proteins	Myofibrillar	Thick filaments
Desmin	Myofibrillar	Myofibrils union at Z-line level
Creatin kinase	Myofibrillar	M-line
Myomesin	Myofibrillar	M-line
M protein	Myofibrillar	M-line
Mithocondrial enzymes	Sarcoplasmic	Respiration
Lysosomal enzymes	Sarcoplasmic	Intracellular digestion
Other cytosolic enzymes	Sarcoplasmic	Glycolysis, gluconeogenesis, citric acid cycle, neutral proteolysis
Myoglobin	Sarcoplasmic	Natural pigment
Hemoglobin	Sarcoplasmic	Pigment from residual blood
Cytochrome	Sarcoplasmic	Respiratory pigment
Collagen	Connective	Structure resistance
Reticulin	Connective	Elasticity
Elastin	Connective	Structure resistance
Proteoglycans and glycoproteins	Connective	Ground substance

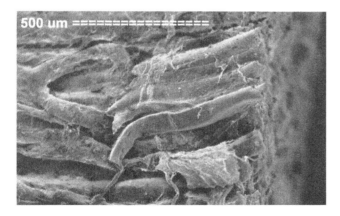

FIGURE 28.2 Scanning electron micrograph of porcine muscle fibers in porcine muscle (Toldrá and Voyle, 1987, unpublished).

biochemical characteristics like enzyme activity (12, 13), lipid composition (14, 15) and content in free amino acids and dipeptides (16–18). These variations may be attributed to certain differences in the biochemical and functional properties of myofibrillar proteins associated with the type of fiber (9, 19).

III. MEAT COMPOSITION

Meat presents a complex structure with water, proteins and lipids present in higher amounts. Water is the most abundant compound in meat (within the range of 65–80%) and has an important influence on juiciness, color, texture and surface appearance. The rest of the composition of meat can be divided into nitrogenous and non-nitrogenous compounds. Nitrogenous compounds are mainly composed of proteins (myofibrillar, sarcoplasmic and connective), peptides (carnosine, anserine and balenine), free amino acids, nucleotides/nucleosides (ATP-derived compounds) and water-soluble vitamins (group B vitamins). In addition to water, non-nitrogenous compounds include lipids (triacylglycerols, phospholipids and cholesterol), minerals (iron, phosphorus, sodium, potassium, etc.), trace elements (zinc, selenium, etc.), carbohydrates (glycogen, glucose, etc.) and fat-soluble vitamins (vitamins A, D, E and K). The main groups of compounds are described below.

A. PROTEINS

After water, protein is the major component of meat, in the range of approximately 15–22 g/100 g. Proteins are very important in postmortem conversion of muscle to meat, in changes affecting tenderness during meat processing and for the nutritional quality of the diet. Meat proteins are considered of high biological value because they provide relatively high percentages of all the essential amino acids (20). There are three categories in meat: myofibrillar, sarcoplasmic and connective (listed in

Table 28.1), in an approximate ratio 60/30/10, with each category having specific roles (7).

Myofibrillar proteins are the main constituents of the structure of the myofibrils. They are soluble in high ionic strength buffers and its content is around 9.5 g/100 g. Myosin and actin provide the structural backbone of the myofibril. Myosin is the major myofibrillar protein and, in fact, is the predominat protein of thick filaments. It is a large molecule composed of two heavy chains of 220 kDa and four light chains within the range of 16–22 kDa (9). The actin monomer, G-actin, has a globular shape and, in the presence of ATP, polymerizes to form filamentous F-actin. The thin filaments ensure by the helical arrangement of F-actin molecules twisted around each other (21). Two extremely large proteins, titin and nebulin, also known as gap filaments, ensure the longitudinal continuity and integrity of the structure (22, 23). Proteins in the Z-line area are involved in the linkage of thin filaments of adjacent sarcomeres while desmin connects adjacent myofibrils at the level of the Z-line. Regulatory proteins like tropomyosin and troponin, which has three subunits (Tn-T, Tn-C and Tn-I), are involved in the muscle contraction mechanism (9).

Sarcoplasmic proteins, around 9 g/100 g, constitute a varied group consisting of proteins soluble in low ionic strength buffers or even water. Myoglobin is the major sarcoplasmic protein responsible for the red color of meat. Myoglobin content in meat is variable, depending on the animal species (high in beef or lamb, low in pork and very low in poultry) and age (increases with the age of the animal). More or less hemoglobin may remain in meat depending on the efficiency of blood draining from muscle during bleeding. The rest of sarcoplasmic proteins consist of metabolic enzymes located in mitochondrias, lysosomes, microsomes, and nucleus and free in the cytosol.

Connective proteins, around 3 g/100 g consisting basically of collagen and elastin, are insoluble and contribute to the skeletal framework (strength, support and shape) of the muscle but also to certain toughness of the meat when consumed. In fact, collagen becomes tougher with the age of animal due to the progressive increase in the number of cross-links. Collagen is rich in hydroxyproline, a low biological value amino acid. There are different types of collagen (8). Type I is found in tendons, type II in cartilages and type III in skin and vascular tissues. Types IV and V form fine networks in the basement membranes around the muscle (24). Elastin is more elastic and is mainly involved in tissues requiring a certain degree of flexibility such as skin, tendons, ligaments, muscle and the walls of large arteries (24).

B. LIPIDS

The lipids content of muscle is variable (in the range of 1.5–17 g/100 g) and mainly depends on the degree of fattening and amount of adipose tissue. The main classes of lipids are non-hydrolyzable lipids (fatty acids, aldehydes, aliphatic hydrocarbons, sterols), neutral fats (mono, di and triacylglycerols and sterol esters) and phospholipids. The relative proportion varies depending on the species, the developmental stage and physiological status of the animal (8). Main locations of lipids are intramuscular, intermuscular and in adipose tissue. Intramuscular lipids are mainly composed of triacylglycerols, stored in fat cells, and phospholipids, located in cell membranes. Cholesterol is the only sterol found in meat; the cholesterol ester comprises about 90% of the total cholesterol content (25). Intermuscular and adipose tissue lipids are mainly composed of triacylglycerols and contain a small amount of cholesterol (below 60 mg/100 g).

Triacylglycerols are major constituents of reserve fats and have fatty acid composition that varies widely with species and diet. There are three possible pathways for the biosynthesis of triacylglycerols: the glycerol-3-phosphate, the dihydroxyacetone phosphate and the monoacylglycerol pathway (8). The type and fatty acid composition of feeds has a strong influence on the fatty acids profiles of fats, especially in monogastric animals (26, 27). Thus, the effects of different feeds on fatty acid composition of pork and poultry fats have been extensively reported in the literature (27–32) following consumer demands for higher unsaturated fats (26). In the case of ruminants, fat hydrolysis and hydrogenation of unsaturated fatty acids by the microbial population of the rumen somehow tend to standardize the final composition in fatty acids and certain changes in the diet fed to cattle may also change the content of the fat in the meat. For instance, dietary full-fat canola or even full-fat soybeans have been reported to alter the fatty acid composition of intramuscular and subcutaneous lipids of beef (33). The type of diet may have important consequences for the sensory quality of meat, especially its flavor (34). So, changes in the fatty acid composition of phospholipids have been reported to give significant differences in flavor characteristics of forage and grain-fed beef (35). It must be pointed out that meat from ruminants represents a major dietary source of conjugated linoleic acids (CLA), a group of C18 isomers of linoleic acid with conjugated double bonds in the cis or trans configurations at positions 10 and 12 or 9 and 11 (36). CLA content in meat is in the range of 3–6 mg/g of fat. CLA have been reported to have some health-promoting biological activity such as inhibition of tumor growth and reduction of atherosclerotic risk (36, 37). The composition in fatty acids determines main fats properties. So, fats with excessive polyunsaturated fatty acids, like linoleic (typical of feeds rich in corn, for instance) and linolenic acids, tend to be softer, have an oily appearance and are more susceptible to oxidation. This is the reason why meats with a high percentage of polyunsaturated fatty acids are not preferred for further meat processing.

Phospholipids are present in minor amounts but due to their particular fatty acid composition, which is richer in polyunsaturated fatty acids, they have an important role in flavor development and oxidation in postmortem meat. Major constituents are phosphatidylcholine (lecithine) and phosphatidylethanolamine while phosphatidylserine and sphingomyelin are present in minor amounts. Some variability in phospholipids has been reported depending on the genetic type of the animal and anatomical location of the muscle (38). For instance, the amount of phopholipids tends to be higher in red oxidative muscles than in white glycolytic muscles (15).

C. MINOR COMPOUNDS

Meat constitutes a good source of group B vitamins that, although present in low concentrations, contribute significantly to the daily intake requirements (39, 40). Pork meat is particularly rich in thiamin. However, the amount of fat-soluble vitamins in meat is rather poor or even almost negligible. Only vitamin E is significant in those animals with specific supplementation in the diet. Feed enrichment with vitamin E, at levels above dietary requirements (i.e., 200 mg/kg feed), is a relatively new practice, expanded in recent years, to protect unsaturated lipids from oxidation and obtain other benefits like better color stability of fresh beef (41, 42) and improved water retention in pork meat (43). The content in carbohydrates is rather poor, around 1.5 g/100 g, although it depends on the previous exercise of the animal prior to slaughtering. Meat also constitutes a good source of dietary iron, with the additional advantage that a good percentage is in the absorbable form of heme iron (44), and trace elements like zinc, selenium, magnesium, manganesum, etc. (40, 45–48). The mineral content is around 1 g/100 g.

IV. THE MEAT ENZYME SYSTEMS INVOLVED IN MAJOR BIOCHEMICAL CHANGES

Skeletal muscle contains a wide variety of enzymes involved in multiple metabolic pathways. Some of the most important, shown in Figure 28.3, are related to carbohydrate metabolism (glycolytic enzymes), protein breakdown (endo-peptidases), generation of small peptides (tri and dipeptidylpeptidases) and free amino acids (aminopeptidases and carboxypeptidases), hydrolysis of triacylglycerols and phospholipids (lipases and phospholipases) and transformation of ATP into numerous derived compounds. Most of these enzymes remain active in postmortem muscle, playing important roles in glycolysis, proteolysis, lipolysis and transformation of nucleotides that are essential for the development of meat quality. The location of these enzymes may vary. Some are located in organules like lysosomes while others are bound to membranes or free in the cytosol (49). A brief description of the proteolytic and lipolytic enzymes that play an important role in meat quality is given below.

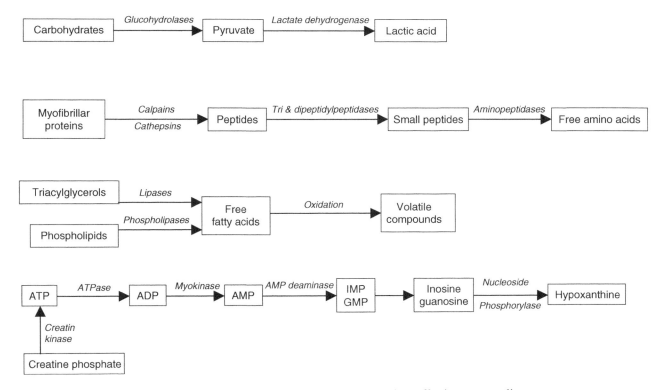

FIGURE 28.3 Scheme showing some of the most important enzymatic reactions affecting meat quality.

A. PROTEASES

Lysosomes are organules containing a large number of hydrolytic enzymes, including proteases. Cathepsins B, H and L, which are cysteine proteinases, and cathepsin D, an aspartate proteinase, are the main lysosomal proteinases. In general, these enzymes are small, 20–40 kDa (see Table 28.2), which allow their penetration into the myofibrillar structure. However, although the anaerobic glycolysis in postmortem muscle generates the adequate environment, such as pH drop, for cathepsin activity (50), the enzymes probably play a minor role in meat texture development during meat ageing as there is little or no degradation of myosin and actin, two important proteins very sensitive to cathepsins (51).

Cathepsins D and L are able to degrade myosin heavy chains, titin, M and C proteins, tropomyosin and troponins T and I (52–54). Cathepsin L is very active on both titin and nebulin. Cathepsin D may be quite inactive at refrigeration tenperatures (53) but can act during cooking because of its thermostability (55). On the other hand, cathepsin B is able to degrade myosin heavy chains, actin and even collagen but has no effect on myosin light chains and troponin C (56, 57), and cathepsin H shows both endo and aminopeptidase activity, being classified as an aminoendopeptidase (58). Cathepsin activity is regulated by cystatins, a family of cysteine peptidase inhibitors which are predominantly extracellular and have been isolated from different animal species (59, 60). Four families of cystatins have been reported in the literature based on their primary structure (51). Optimal pH for cathepsin D is acid (in the range of 3.0–5.0), slightly acid for cathepsins B and L (around 6.0) and near neutrality (6.8) for cathepsin H (61–64).

Calpains, a group of cystein endopeptidases, are located in the cytosol especially in the Z-line area. They have different names in the literature such as calcium-activated neutral proteinase, calcium-dependent protease or

TABLE 28.2
Main Characteristics of Meat Proteolytic Enzymes (Adapted from Refs. 51–84)

Enzyme	Classification	Location	Substrates	Optimal pH
Cathepsin B (EC 3.4.22.1.)	Cystein	Lysosome	Myosin, actin, collagen	5.5–6.0
Cathepsin D (EC 3.4.23.5.)	Aspartyl	Lysosome	Myofibrillar proteins	4.0
Cathepsin H (EC 3.4.22.16.)	Cystein	Lysosome	Myofibrillar proteins	6.8
Cathepsin L (EC 3.4.22.15.)	Cystein	Lysosome	Myofibrillar proteins, collagen	5.5–6.0
μ-Calpain (EC 3.4.22.17.)	Cystein/metallo	Z-line	Myofibrillar proteins	7.5
m-Calpain (EC 3.4.22.17.)	Cystein/metallo	Z-line	Myofibrillar proteins	7.5
20S proteasome	Ntn-hydrolase	Cytosol	Myofibrillar proteins	7.0–7.5
DPP I (EC 3.4.14.1)	Cystein	Lysosome	Polypeptides	5.5
DPP II (EC 3.4.14.2.)	Serin	Lysosome	Polypeptides	5.5
DPP III (EC 3.4.14.4.)	Serin	Cytosol	Polypeptides	8.0
DPP IV (EC 3.4.14.5.)	Serin	Membrane	Polypeptides	7.5–8.0
TPP I (EC 3.4.14.9.)	Serin	Lysosome	Polypeptides	4.0
TPP II (EC 3.4.14.10.)	Serin	Cytosol	Polypeptides	6.5–7.5
Alanyl aminopeptidase (EC 3.4.11.14.)	Cystein/metallo	Cytosol	Amino terminus of peptides	6.5
Arginyl aminopeptidase (EC 3.4.11.6.)	Cystein/metallo	Cytosol	Amino terminus of peptides	6.5
Methionyl aminopeptidase (EC 3.4.11.18.)	Cystein	Cytosol	Amino terminus of peptides	7.5
Leucyl aminopeptidase (EC 3.4.11.1.)	Metallo	Cytosol	Amino terminus of peptides	9.0
Pyroglutamyl aminopeptidase (EC 3.4.19.3.)	Cystein	Cytosol	Amino terminus of peptides	8.5
Carboxypeptidase A (EC 3.4.16.1.)	Serin	Lysosome	Carboxy terminus of peptides	5.2–5.5
Carboxypeptidase B (EC 3.4.18.1.)	Cystein	Lysosome	Carboxy terminus of peptides	5.0

calcium-activated factor. Calpain I or μ-calpain requires 50–70 μM of Ca^{2+} for activation and calpain II or m-calpain requires 1–5 mM of Ca^{2+}. Optimal pH for calpain activity is 7.5 (see Table 28.2) but poor activity is observed below pH 6.0, reaching negligible activity at pH 5.5 (65). Calpains are heterodimers of 110 KDa composed of an 80 KDa catalytic subunit responsible for the peptidase activity and a 30 KDa regulatory subunit which is common for both enzymes (66). Calpain I can be autolyzed in the presence of Ca^{2+} and usually shows a poor stability in meat while calpain II may be stable for a few weeks (67). Calpains have shown ability to degrade titin, nebulin, troponins T and I, tropomyosin, C-protein, filamin, desmin and vinculin but cannot degrade myosin, actin, α-actinin and troponin C (68, 69). The endogenous inhibitor calpastatin regulates calpain activity in post-mortem muscle. Calpastatin is destroyed by autolysis after a few days postmortem (67).

The proteasome complex is a large protease with multiple catalytic sites such as a chymotrypsin-like activity, a trypsin-like activity and a peptidyl-glutamyl hydrolyzing activity (70, 71). The proteasome 20S can be associated with large regulatory complexes, like one or two 19S complexes, or one or two 11S activator complexes or even other activator complexes like PA700 or PA28 (51). The 20S proteasome can degrade myofibrils and affect M and Z lines, especially in high pH meats and slow-twitch oxidative muscles and thus could have a role in tenderness in those specific muscles (72, 73).

Peptidases constitute a large group of proteases. The most important found in meat are tripeptidylpeptidases (TPP) and dipeptidylpeptidases (DPP). TPP I, a lysosomal enzyme, shows optimal activity at acid pH and TPP II is most active at neutral pH. Both enzymes are able to hydrolyze different tripeptides from the amino termini of peptides, like Gly-Pro-Phe and Ala-Ala-Phe, respectively (74, 75). DPP I and II are located in the lysosomes and have optimal acid pH. DPP I has special preference for hydrolyzing dipeptides Ala-Arg and Gly-Arg from the amino termini of peptides and DPP II for Gly-Pro. DPP III is found in the cytosol and DPP IV is linked to the plasm membrane, both enzymes having optimal pH in the range of 7.8–8.0 (76–79). DPP III has a preference for hydrolyzing dipeptides Arg-Arg and Ala-Arg and DPP IV for Gly-Pro. Dipeptidases catalyze the hydrolysis of dipeptides and their names vary depending on the preference for certain amino acids. For instance, cysteinylglycine dipeptidase is specific for the dipeptide Cys-Gly and arginin dipeptidase has a special preference for basic amino acids (80).

Aminopeptidases constitute a group of exopeptidases able to release a free amino acid from the amino termini of peptides and proteins. They have a large molecular mass and a complex structure (62). Major aminopeptidases in skeletal muscle are: arginyl, alanyl, pyroglutamyl, leucyl and methionyl aminopeptidases. All of them are active at neutral or basic pH (see Table 28.2) and their names are related to the preference or requirement for a specific N-terminal amino acid although they can hydrolyze other amino acids at slower rates. Alanyl aminopeptidase, which mainly hydrolyzes alanine, is considered the major aminopeptidase in postmortem muscle. This enzyme is able to hydrolyze a wide spectrum of amino acids such as aromatic, aliphatic and basic aminoacyl-bonds (81). Arginyl aminopeptidase, also known as aminopeptidase B, hydrolyzes basic amino acids such as arginine or lysine (82). Methionyl aminopeptidase, a calcium-activated enzyme, has a wide spectrum of activity with preference for methionine, alanine, lysine and leucine (83). Leucyl and pyroglutamyl aminopeptidases are active at basic pH and play a minor role in meat (84). Carboxypeptidases are lysosomal enzymes with optimal activity at acid pH and able to generate free amino acids from the carboxy termini of peptides and proteins. Carboxypeptidase A has a preference for hydrophobic amino acids while carboxypeptidase B has a wider spectrum of activity (80).

B. LIPASES

Major lipolytic enzymes in muscle are lysosomal acid lipase and phospholipase A (see Table 28.3). Both enzymes

TABLE 28.3
Main Characteristics of Meat Lipolytic Enzymes (Adapted from Refs. 61, 62, 86, 88, 89, 92)

Enzyme	Location	Substrate	Optimal pH
Lysosomal acid lipase	Lysosome	Long chain tri and diacylglycerols	5.0
Neutral lipase	Membrane	Long chain tri and diacylglycerols	7.5
Phospholipase A	Lysosome	Phospholipids	5.0
Muscle acid esterase	Lysosome	Short chain tri and diacylglycerols	5.0
Muscle neutral esterase	Cytosol	Short chain tri and diacylglycerols	7.5
Hormone-sensitive lipase	Adipose tissue	Long chain tri, di and monoacylglycerols	7.0
Monoacylglycerol lipase	Adipose tissue	Long chain monoacylglycerols	7.0
Lipopotein lipase	Adipose tissue	Lipoproteins	8.5
Acid esterase	Adipose tissue	Short chain tri and diacylglycerols	5.0
Neutral esterase	Adipose tissue	Short chain tri and diacylglycerols	7.5

are located in the lysosomes and are responsible for the generation of long chain free fatty acids in meat. Lysosomal acid lipase hydrolyzes primary ester bonds of tryacylglycerols at acid pH (4.5–5.5). This enzyme can also hydrolyze di and monoacylglycerols although at a slower rate (85, 86). Phospholipase A hydrolyzes phospholipids, at positions 1 or 2. The order of preference for fatty acids, especially polyunsaturated C18, esterified to phospholipids as a result of *in vitro* assays, is as follows: Linoleic acid > Oleic acid > Linolenic acid > Palmitic acid > Stearic acid > Arachidonic acid. The activity of lipases, phospholipase A and lysophospholipases is quite a bit higher in oxidative than in glycolytic muscles (15, 87). Acid and neutral esterases, able to hydrolyze short chain fatty acids from tri, di and mono acylglycerols, have been identified in the lysosomes and cytosol, respectively (88). In general, lipases prefer long chain fatty acids while esterases are especially active against short chain fatty acids.

There are three lipases in adipose tissue (see Table 28.3): hormone-sensitive lipase, monoacylglycerol lipase and lipoprotein lipase with optimal pH in the neutral/basic range (62, 89). The hormone-sensitive lipase (HSL) has a high specificity for the hydrolysis of diacylglycerols. The triacylglycerol hydrolysis by this enzyme is the rate-controlling step in the lipolysis phenomena in adipose tissue (90). The monoacylglycerol lipase (MGL) hydrolyzes 1 or 2 monoacylglycerols with no positional specificity, releasing medium and long chain monoacylglycerols (91).

Lipoprotein lipase is located in the capillary endothelium and hydrolyzes the acylglycerol components at the luminal surface of the endothelium (92). This enzyme has a preference for fatty acids at position 1 over those at position 3 (93, 94). Acid and neutral esterases are also present in adipose tissue (62, 88).

V. CHEMISTRY OF THE CONVERSION OF MUSCLE TO MEAT

Multiple reactions involved at the early postmortem are briefly summarised in Figure 28.4. It is important to emphasize that not all muscles, or even parts within the same muscle, change in an uniform way because these changes will depend on the respective ratios of white and red fibers. Additionally, the rate of these changes also depends on the temperature achieved within each muscle. Twelve moles of ATP are produced per mole of glucose under aerobic conditions like those usually found in living muscle. The first important change in the muscle following death consists of its inability to synthesize or to remove certain metabolites (see Figure 28.5). The supply of oxygen is cut off once the blood circulation ceases and then there is a progressive decrease in oxygen concentration in the muscle cell and a reduction of the redox potential towards anaerobic values (95). The lack of available oxygen stops the activity of the mitochondria system and cell respiration is progressively stopped. Once in anaerobic

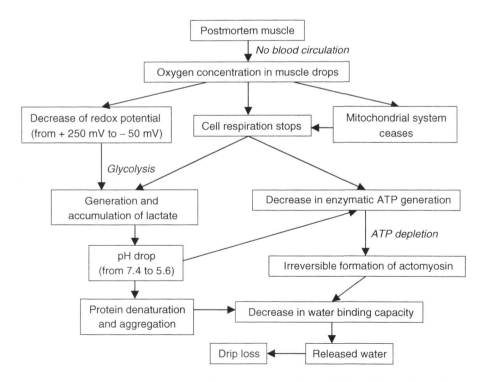

FIGURE 28.4 Scheme summarizing early post-mortem changes in muscle. From Toldrá, "Muscle foods: Water, structure and functionality," Food Sci Tech Int 9, 173–177, 2003.

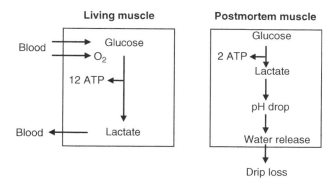

Living muscle

Postmortem muscle

FIGURE 28.5 Main differences between living and post-mortem muscle. From Toldrá, "Muscle foods:Water, structure and functionality." Food Sci Tech Int 9, 173–177, 2003.

conditions, lactic acid is produced from glucose through glycolysis, but the efficiency is lower than under aerobic conditions because only 2 moles of ATP are produced per mole of glucose. The generation of ATP is necessary in the muscle to provide the required energy to drive the Na/K pump of the membranes, to drive the calcium pump in the sarcoplasmic reticulum and to provide energy for muscle contraction. ATP may also be formed from ADP and crea-tine phosphate through the action of the enzyme phospho-creatin kinase (96). ATP is also necessary for muscle contraction-relaxation where it acts as a lubricant but, once ATP is fully exhausted, the muscle remains contracted (rigor mortis). This is related to the formation of acto-myosin and the loss of extensibility (97).

An important consequence of lactic acid accumula-tion is the pH drop to acid values (5.6 to 5.9) within a few hours postmortem. The pH drop rate depends on the meta-bolic status of the muscle and glycogen availability. As pH approaches the isoelectric point of myofibrillar pro-teins (pH values around 5.0), their charges move towards neutrality and water binding decreases rapidly, the struc-ture tightens and myofibrillar proteins are partially dena-tured (98). Thus, the water binding depends on the ultimate pH in the muscle and the amount of released water, lost as dripping, increases when the ultimate pH is lower (99). Important muscle soluble compounds like myoglobin, lysosomal enzymes, nucleotides and nucleo-sides, free amino acids, vitamins and minerals are partly lost in the drip, affecting the final quality. Pork carcasses during early postmortem are shown in Figure 28.6.

There are many and relevant biochemical changes dur-ing early postmortem and ageing of meat with important consequences for quality. Most of these changes are enzy-matic in nature either affecting meat tenderness due to structural protein breakdown or generating a substantial number of new compounds with direct influence on taste and/or aroma. The trend towards rapid lean growth in cat-tle, pigs and poultry increases the relative proportion of

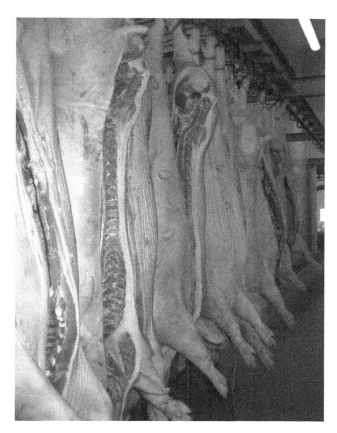

FIGURE 28.6 Pork carcasses at early postmortem in the slaughterhouse. Image courtesy of Industrias Cárnicas Vaquero SA, Madrid, Spain.

meat quality defects, mainly related to color and water-holding capacity (100).

A. GLYCOLYSIS

Main reactions for glycolysis are schematized in Figure 28.3. Key enzymes in the glycolytic chain are phosphory-lase, phosphofructokinase and pyruvic kinase. Lactate dehydrogenase is involved in the last step, consisting of the conversion of pyruvic acid into lactic acid. The gener-ation and accumulation of lactic acid in the meat causes the pH to drop from neutral (pH around 7.2) to acid val-ues (below 5.8). If the reserves of glycogen are rather poor prior to slaughter, the final pH will not experience such an intense drop and will remain above 6.0. The pH limit for the DFD pork meat condition (dark, firm and dry) is con-sidered around 5.9 at 24 h. The ultimate pH depends on the type of muscle, animal species and physiological state. The rate of glycolysis also depends on the temperature. Minimum pH drop is observed at 10–12°C but if temper-ature decreases down to 0°C too early, there is a release of calcium ions into the myofibrillar space that activates ATPase. Under these circumstances and if there is still some available ATP, an extra contraction of actomyosin is produced, resulting in a tight structure phenomenon known as cold shortening (97, 101). Cold shortening is mainly observed in beef, lamb and turkey, and with less intensity in pork (102). Prevention of cold shortening may be achieved by keeping carcasses above 15°C until the pH reaches 6.0. Another important alteration, known as thaw rigor or thaw shortening, is produced when thawing meat that was frozen in the prerigor state (still keeping a substantial amount of ATP). Under these circumstances, calcium is released and moves is into the intracellular spaces, causing an extensive contraction (101).

Exudation constitutes one of the major problems in pork quality. This condition, is known as pale, soft and exudative (PSE), is characterized by its pale color, soft texture and high drip loss (103). Another type of exudative meat, known as red, soft and exudative (RSE), is characterized by similar defects although this meat keeps its normal color (104), making it difficult to differentiate from normal meats (105). Finally, another defective meat with lower incidence is known as dark, firm and dry (DFD) due to its darker color, firm texture and dry appearance on the external surface. Pork meat classification is usually based on pH, color and drip loss (106, 107). Exudative (PSE and RSE) meats are characterized by a low pH value at early postmortem (i.e., pH below 5.8 at 2 h), a pale color reflected in a L value higher than 50 (only for PSE) and drip loss higher than 6%. Figure 28.7 shows a typical pH drop profile for normal, DFD and PSE pork meats. The negative effects of exudative meats may be reduced significantly with some preventive measures such as appropiate pre-transport handling, lairage, stunning, postmortem temperature and chilling rate. The incidence of exudative pork meat is still significant. For instance, a 1992 survey of the pork supply in the U.S. revealed that 16% was PSE and 10% was DFD (108). Only 16% was considered to be of ideal quality (RFN) while the remainder was found to be of somewhat questionable quality (RSE), indicating very little progress in the elimination or minimization of the problem (108).

B. NUCLEOTIDE BREAKDOWN

ATP is the main source of energy for the biochemical reactions in postmortem muscle. However, its content rapidly decreases from an initial 5–8 μmol/g muscle to final negligible values (rigor state). Initially, some ATP may be formed through creatin kinase acting on creatin phosphate and through anaerobic glycolysis (96) but, once creatin phosphate and glycogen are exhausted or the involved enzymes inactivated, ATP drops in a few hours to near zero values through conversion into ADP, AMP and other derived compounds (see Figure 28.10 for an example on pork meat). The concentrations of ADP and AMP decrease to negligible values after 24–48 hours postmortem. 5'-inosin-monophosphate (IMP) is formed from AMP deamination by the action of AMP deaminase, an enzyme very active at pH near 6.2. Some IDP, generated from ADP, may be temporarily detected although it is depleted in a few days. IMP can be further degraded into inosine and hypoxanthine, both compounds experiencing a substantial increase as meat is aged (see Figure 28.8). Similar reactions, although at minor concentrations, are also observed for 5'-guanosin monophosphate (GMP). The rate for all these reactions varies depending on the metabolic status of the animal prior to slaughter as well as the pH and temperature of the meat (109, 110).

C. PROTEOLYSIS

Proteolysis consists of the progressive enzymatic degradation of major meat proteins, especially myofibrillar

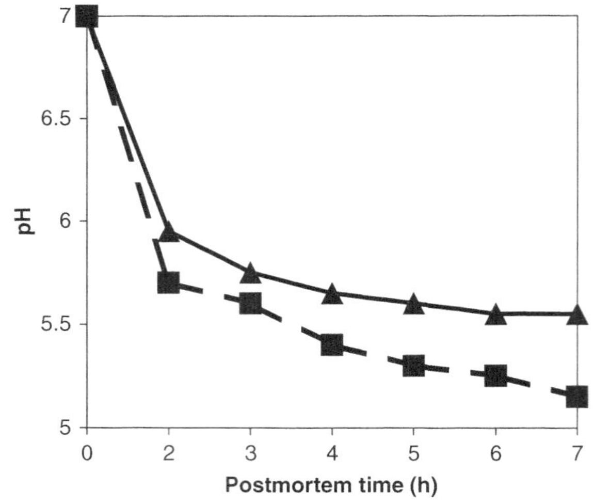

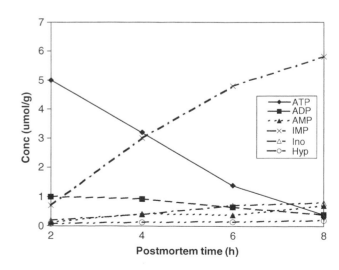

FIGURE 28.7 Example of pH fall of normal (—■—) and pale, soft, exudative (PSE) (▲) pork meat (Toldrá, 2000, unpublished).

FIGURE 28.8 ATP depletion and evolution of ATP-derived compounds in aged pork meat (adapted from Ref. 109).

proteins, and the subsequent generation of peptides and free amino acids. The breakdown of structural proteins results in a weakening of the myofibrillar network and a sensible improvement in meat tenderness. There are many muscle endopeptidases (mostly calpains and cathepsins) and exopeptidases (mostly tri and dipeptidylpeptidases and aminopeptidases) involved in proteolysis (see Figure 28.3). Main properties of these enzymes have been described above (see Table 28.2). The extent of proteolysis and thus the tenderness and generation of taste compounds depend on many factors (111). The activity of endogenous muscle enzymes may vary depending on the genetics (112, 113) and the age of the animals (114, 115). Furthermore, the action of these enzymes also depend on the processing technology. For instance, major or minor action of the enzymes may be expected depending on the temperature and time of ageing. These enzymes are also regulated by certain agents like salt (63, 64, 116, 117).

In general, the amount of peptides increases during meat ageing as reported for beef, pork, chicken and rabbit (118). Some characteristic peptides have been described in postmortem meat and some of them are related to meat tenderness or have flavor properties, for instance, the 30 kDa peptide originating from troponin T through the action of calpain (119) which is related to meat tenderization (120–124), a 110 kDa polypeptide from C protein (125) and some peptides corresponding to 1282.8 Da from the sarcoplasmic protein glyceraldehyde 3-phosphate dehydrogenase, 1734.8 Da from troponin T and 5712.9 Da from creatine kinase (125). Recently, a 32 kDa peptide derived from troponin T has been reported to increase during 20 days of ageing (111). Several small peptides were also isolated from pork meat and some of them were proposed as predictors of pork meat quality (126–128). The generation of these peptides may be depressed if some salt, which inhibits muscle peptidases, is added (62). The activity of endogenous muscle aminopeptidases is quite relevant and, in fact, a significant amount of released free amino acids that contribute to meat taste may be found after several days of meat ageing (129–132).

D. LIPOLYSIS

Lipolysis consists of the breakdown of triacylglycerols by lipases and phospholipids by phospholipases resulting in the generation of free fatty acids (see Figure 28.3). Some of these fatty acids may contribute to taste but, most important, unsaturated fatty acids may contribute to the generation of aroma compounds through further oxidative reactions. Main lipolytic enzymes, located in muscle and adipose tissue and involved in these phenomena, are listed in Table 28.3. These enzymes show good stability and, although their activity depends on pH, salt concentration and water activity, the conditions during meat ageing favor their action (88, 133). The generation rate of free fatty acids increases with length of ageing. In the case of intramuscular lipids, most of the released fatty acids proceed from phospholipid degradation while in adipose tissue they proceed almost exclusively from triacylglycerols (134, 135).

The generated mono and polyunsaturated fatty acids are susceptible to further oxidative reactions to give volatile compounds (136). The beginning of lipid oxidation is correlated with flavor development but an excess of oxidation may lead to off-flavors, one of the main mechanisms responsible for quality deterioration in meat and meat products. Warmed-over flavor (WOF) is recognized as a sensory defect that has been described as the rapid onset of off-notes developed in cooked meat after refrigeration storage (137). WOF is characterized by a decrease in fresh meatiness and the development of cardboard and rancid/painty notes in beef, pork and chicken, that may be detected even after 48 hours (137).

The beginning of lipid oxidation consists of the formation of free radicals, reactions catalyzed by muscle oxidative enzymes, like peroxydases and ciclooxygenases, external light, heating and the presence of moisture and/or metallic cations. The next step in oxidation is the formation of peroxide radicals (propagation), by reaction of free radicals with oxygen. The hydroxyperoxides (primary oxidation products) formed are flavorless but very reactive (136) giving secondary oxidation products that contribute to flavor (138). The oxidation is finished when free radicals react with each other. Unsaturated fatty acids, especially those of phospholipids, are prone to oxidation. The oxidation rate depends on the level of unsaturated fatty acids and number of unsaturations. For instance, arachiconid acid (C20:4) is oxidized faster than linolenic acid (C18:3), and this faster than linoleic acid (C18:2) and oleic acid (C18:1). An example of the evolution of oxidation during refrigerated storage of pork meat is shown in Figure 28.9. Typical volatile compounds resulting from lipid oxidation (139) are aliphatic hydrocarbons (poor contribution to flavor), alcohols (high odor threshold), aldehydes (low odor threshold) and ketones.

VI. DEVELOPMENT OF SENSORY QUALITY

The chemical and biochemical changes taking place during the refrigerated storage of meat are intimately linked to the development of specific sensory properties of meat like color, texture and flavor which are basic to quality. An example of meat conditioning is shown in Figure 28.10.

A. COLOR

The protein myoglobin constitutes the major pigment in meat, from 50 to 80% of the total pigment content (Miller, 1994). Myoglobin is composed of globin, a protein moiety,

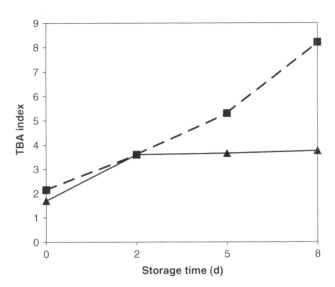

FIGURE 28.9 Example of lipid oxidation, measured through the thiobarbituric acid (TBA) index, during the refrigerated storage of pork meat (▲) and adipose tissue (—■—) (Toldrá, 2000, unpublished).

and an iron-containing heme group. When the heme iron exists in a reduced ferrous form, it is called deoxymyoglobin and gives a purplish-red color (140). When oxygen occupies the sixth ligand by oxygenation under high oxygen tension, it is called oxymyoglobin, and gives a cherry-red color. These two myoglobin forms may be oxidixed to metmyoglobin, which gives an undesirable brownish-red color (140). Metmyoglobin may be formed at high temperature, low pH and under exposure to UV light. Some bacteria may also favor its formation (97) while some lactic acid bacteria have shown ability to reduce metmyoglobin to myoglobin (141). When oxygen tension is low, oxygen dissociates from the heme and gives myoglobin. The content in myoglobin varies depending on the species. So, beef meat (containing about 5 mg of myoglobin per g of muscle) has the darkest color, followed by lamb (about 2.5 mg/g) and pork (about 1 mg/g) (142). Myoglobin content also varies depending on the physiological role (muscles with higher content of red fibers are darker) and age (myoglobin content increases with age) (16). In general, a better red color may be found in meats from mature animals than in meats from younger animals.

FIGURE 28.10 Pork meat (loins) at slaughterhouse before distribution to retailers. Image courtesy of Industrias Cárnicas Vaquero SA, Madrid, Spain.

Color stability is very important for fresh meat marketability. Color may be influenced by drop in pH rate and is more stable at relatively higher ultimate pH values. The oxidation of myoglobin is accelerated by increases in temperature. The partial oxygen pressure is very important to the balance between the three myoglobin forms. Finally, light may produce meat discoloration as well as bacterial contamination (140).

B. TEXTURE

Calpains play an important role in proteolysis and tenderness development during early postmortem while cathepsins play a minor role (143). Calpains are activated in postmortem meat by the increased calcium concentration as a consequence of calcium release from the sarcoplasmic reticulum and mitochondria and cause an intense breakdown of the myofibrillar structure, especially around the Z-line area. Further evidence has been obtained by addition of specific cathepsin inhibitors, observing a similar degree of meat tenderization and myofibrillar fragmentation (144) or even acceleration of the tenderization rate when calcium salts are added (145). The need for increased tenderness and optimized ageing processes prompted the development of tenderization models based on the activity of calpains (146). However, other factors must be considered when comparing proteolytical enzyme levels in different species (beef, pork, lamb and poultry) and respective rates of tenderization (147). Even non-enzymatic mechanisms regarding depolymerization of intermediate filaments under non-physiological conditions have been proposed for meat tenderization (148). Calpastatin and cystatins regulate the activity of calpains and cathepsins, respectively, and their content varies with species. For instance, pork muscle has lower calpastatin level (149) and lower calpain II activity than beef and lamb but at 1 day postmortem pork meat was the most tender (150). Thus, calpastatin and cystatins, or even the enzyme/inhibitor ratios, appear to be better predictors of meat quality than the assays of enzyme activity alone (151).

Changes in rate of tenderization may be due to different ultimate pH values (value at 24 h postmortem). So, preslaughter stress and consequent glycogen depletion may raise the ultimate pH to intermediate values (around 6.0) and give tougher meat at first day postmortem while lower and higher ultimate pH give tender meat (152). Myofibrillar protein extractability is lower in PSE pork meat than in normal meat and this may change the susceptibility of myofibrils to proteolysis (153). In fact, major changes by calpains are observed in DFD and normal meats while the action of cathepsins remains similar in both normal and PSE types of meats (154). Proteolysis and ultrastructural breakdown has been reported to be faster in fast glycolyzing muscles. Higher calpain I activity and lower calpastatin activity

(high enzyme/inhibitor ratio) confirms that calpain I has an important role in tenderness even in meats with lower pH values (155).

C. FLAVOR

Raw meat has little aroma but meat flavor is developed as a consequence of a good number of compounds produced in postmortem muscle. The most important non-volatile compounds with taste properties are free amino acids, peptides, inosine and hypoxanthine, lactic and succinic and other acids, sugars, and the sodium salts of glutamic and aspartic acids (156). Flavor enhancers such as 5′-inosin- and 5′-guanosin-monophosphate, glutamic acid and monosodium glutamate are also important for the final flavor of meat (157, 158). Free amino acids contributing to meat taste have been reported in beef, rabbit and pork (130, 131, 159, 160). Peptides generated in aged meat also make an important contribution to taste. An octapeptide, Lys-Gly-Asp-Glu-Glu-Ser-Leu-Ala, was isolated from beef after digestion with papain (161, 162). This peptide was named the beefy meaty peptide (BMP) or delicious peptide because of its taste-enhancing properties. This octapeptide exhibits sourness and astringency at pH 3.5 and umami at pH 6.5 which is enhanced in the presence of salt and monosodium glutamate (163). Other tripeptides like Ala-Asp-Glu, Ala-Asp-Glu, Asp-Glu-Glu and Ser-Pro-Glu and dipeptides like Glu-Glu and Glu-Val, with taste-enhancing properties, have been isolated from chicken meat treated with bromelain (164). The production of peptides with desirable flavors is favored within the pH range 5.0–6.0 in beef (165). The division of generated peptides in aged beef into three fractions revealed that those with molecular mass of 500–1000 kDa and higher than 10,000 kDa had a negligible effect on taste while those within the range 1,000–10,000 kDa suppressed sourness, probably by inhibition of the binding of lactic acid to membranes, and enhanced umami taste (118). In a similar way, small peptides in the range 2,700 to 4,500 Da or even below 2,700 Da, have been detected in postmortem pork meat and some of them gave characteristic brothy and umami tastes (166).

Volatile compounds are generated with aroma properties belonging to the following groups: aldehydes, ketones, esters, hydrocarbons, acids, alcohols, lactones, furanes, pyrroles, pyridines, pyrazines, non-heterocyclic sulphur compounds, thiophenes and thiazoles (167). Further generation of these taste and aroma compounds and interactions among them take place during meat processing and cooking (157, 168). For instance, the optimal flavor quality of aged top round beef meat was found after 4 days of ageing (165). The main reactions involved during cooking are: pyrolysis of amino acids and peptides, carbohydrate degradation, Maillard reactions, Strecker degradations, degradation of thiamin and lipid degradation (157). Depending on the balance and relative intensity of all these reactions, the flavor may change. For instance, some pyrazines, thiophenes and thiazoles are responsible for the roasted flavor. Thus, the different flavors for different meats depend on the balance of the non-volatile and volatile compounds and the way they interact (167, 169).

In summary, the chemistry and biochemistry of meat are quite complex and involve numerous chemical reactions (i.e., lipid oxidation, Maillard reactions, Strecker degradations, etc.) and biochemical reactions related to indigenous enzymes (i.e., glycohydrolases, proteases, lipases, etc.). Knowledge of these reactions is very important in order to obtain standardized high quality meats because all related chemical and biochemical changes have a strong effect on final quality and consumer acceptability.

REFERENCES

1. RG Cassens. Structure of muscle. In: JF Price, BS Schweigert, eds. The Science of Meat and Meat Products. Westport, CT: Food & Nutrition Press, 1987, pp. 11–59.

2. KO Honikel. The biochemical basis of meat conditioning. In: JM Smulders, F Toldrá, J Flores, M Prieto, eds. New technologies for meat and meat products. Nijmegen, the Netherlands: Audet, 1992, pp. 135–161.

3. PJ Bechtel. Muscle development and contractile proteins. In: PJ Bechtel, ed. Muscle as food. Orlando, FL: Academic Press, 1986, pp. 1–35.

4. A Okitani, U Matsukura, H Kato, M Fujimaki. Purification and some properties of a myofibrilar protein-degrading protease, cathepsin L from rabbit skeletal muscle. J Biochem 87: 1133–1143, 1980.

5. M Yamaguchi, H Kamisoyama, S Nada, S Yamano, M Izumimoto, Y Hirai, RG Cassens, H Nasu, M Mugurama, T Fukuzawa. Current concepts of muscle ultrastructure with emphasis on Z-line architecture. Food Microstructure 5: 197–205, 1986.

6. WG Moody, RG Cassens. Histochemical differentiation of red and white muscle fibers. J Anim Sci 27: 961, 1968.

7. RG Cassens. Meat Preservation. Westport, CT: Food & Nutrition Press, 1994, pp. 11–32.

8. K Urich. Comparative Animal Biochemistry. Berlin: Springer Verlag, 1994, pp. 526–623.

9. AM Pearson, RB Young. Muscle and Meat Biochemistry. San Diego, CA: Academic Press, 1989, pp. 1–261.

10. C Valin, C Touraille, P Vigneron, CR Ashmore. Prediction of lamb meat quality traits based on muscle biopsy fiber typing. Meat Sci 6: 257–263, 1982.

11. G Monin, A Ouali. Muscle differentiation and meat quality. In: R Lawrie, ed. Developments in Meat Science 5. London: Elsevier Applied Science, 1991, pp. 89–157.

12. M Flores, C Alasnier, MC Aristoy, JL Navarro, G Gandemer, F Toldrá. Activity of aminopeptidase and lipolytic enzymes in five skeletal muscles with various oxidative patterns. J Sci Food Agric 70: 127–130, 1996.

13. D Laborde, A Talmant, G Monin. Activités enzymatiques métaboliques et contractiles de 30 muscles du porc. Relations avec le pH ultime atteint après la mort. Reprod Nutr Develop 25: 619–628, 1985.

14. A Leseigneur-Meynier, G Gandemer. Lipid composition of pork muscle as related to metabolic types of fibres. Meat Sci 29: 229–241, 1991.

15. P Hernández, JL Navarro, F Toldrá. Lipid composition and lipolytic enzyme activities in porcine skeletal muscles with different oxidative pattern. Meat Sci 49: 1–10, 1998.

16. MC Aristoy, F Toldrá. Concentration of free amino acids and dipeptides in porcine skeletal muscles with different oxidative patterns. Meat Sci 50: 327–332, 1998.

17. M Cornet, J Bousset. Free amino acids and dipeptides in porcine muscles: Differences between red and white muscles. Meat Sci 51: 215–219, 1999.

18. KM Chan, EA Decker. Endogenous skeletal muscle antioxidants. Crit Rev Food Sci Nutr 34: 403–426, 1994.

19. YL Xiong. Myofibrillar protein from different muscle fiber types: Implications of biochemical and functional properties in meat processing. Crit Rev Food Sci Nutr 34: 293–320, 1994.

20. M Reig, F Toldrá. Protein nutritional quality of muscle foods. Recent Res Devel Agric Food Chem 2: 71–78, 1998.

21. HJ Swatland. Structure and Development of Meat Animals and Poultry. Lancaster, PA: Technomics Pub. Co., 1994, pp. 229–286.

22. RM Robson, E Huff-Lonergan, FC Parrish Jr, CY Ho, MH Stromer, TW Huiatt, RM Bellin, SW Sernett. Postmortem changes in the myofibrillar and other cytoskeletal proteins in muscle. Proceedings of the 50th Annual Reciprocal Conference. Vol. 50, Ames, Iowa, 1997, pp. 43–52.

23. RH Locker. The role of gap filaments in muscle and in meat. Food Microstructure 3: 17–32, 1984.

24. E Bandman. Chemistry of animal tissues. Part 1 — Proteins. In: JF Price, BS Schweigert, eds. The Science of Meat and Meat Products. Westport, CT: Food & Nutrition Press, 1987, pp. 61–102.

25. LR Dugan Jr. Chemistry of animal tissues. Part 2 — Lipidss. In: JF Price, BS Schweigert, eds. The Science of Meat and Meat Products. Westport, CT: Food & Nutrition Press, 1987, pp. 103–113.

26. K Jakobsen. Dietary modifications of animal fats: status and future perspectives. Fett/Lipid 101:475–483, 1999.

27. F Toldrá, M Reig, P Hernández, JL Navarro. Lipids from pork meat as related to a healthy diet. Recent Res Devel Nutr 1: 79–86, 1996.

28. CA Morgan, RC Noble, M Cocchi, R McCartney. Manipulation of the fatty acid composition of pig meat lipids by dietary means. J Sci Food Agric 58: 357–368, 1992.

29. JR Romans, DM Wulf, RC Johnson, GW Libal, WJ Costello. Effects of ground flaxseed in swine diets on pig performance and on physical and sensory characteristics and omega-3 fatty acid content of pork: II. Duration of 15% dietary flaxseed. J Anim Sci 73: 1987–1999, 1995.

30. C Lauridsen, G Andersen, M Andersson, V Danielsen, R Engberg, K Jakobsen. Effect of dietary fish oil supplied

to pigs from weaning to 60 kg liveweight on performance, tissue fatty acid composition and palatability of pork when slaughtered at 100 kg liveweight. J Anim Feed Sci 8: 441–456, 1999.

31. NG Marriott, JE Garrett, MD Sims, JR Abril. Composition of pigs fed a diet with docosahexanoic acid. J Muscle Foods 13: 265–277, 2002.

32. M Enser, RI Richardson, JD Wood, BP Gill, PR Sheard. Feeding linseed to increase the n-3 PUFA of pork: fatty acid composition of muscle, adipose tissue, liver and sausages. Meat Sci 55: 201–212, 2000.

33. DC Rule, JR Busboom, CJ Kercher. Effect of dietary canola on fatty acid composition of bovine adipose tissue, muscle, kidney and liver. J Anim Sci 72: 2735–2744, 1994.

34. SL Melton. Effects of feeds on flavor of red meat: a review. J Anim Sci 68: 4421–4435, 1990.

35. DK Larick, BE Turner. Flavor characteristics of forage and grain-fed beef as influenced by phospholipid and fatty acid compositional differences. J Food Sci 55: 312–317, 368, 1990.

36. NT Dunford. Health benefits and processing of lipid-based nutritionals. Food Technol 55: 38–44, 2001.

37. YL Ha, NK Grimm, WM Pariza. Newly recognized anticarcinogenic fatty acids: Identification and quantification in natural and processed cheeses. J Agric Food Chem 37: 75–81, 1989.

38. E Armero, JL Nnavarro, MI Nadal, M Baselga, F Toldrá. Lipid composition of pork muscle as affected by sire genetic type. J Food Biochem 26: 91–102, 2002.

39. M Reig, F Toldrá. Pork meat as a source of vitamins. Recent Res Devel Nutr Res 2: 29–34, 1998.

40. KS Rhee, HA Griffith-Bradle, YA Ziprin. Nutrient composition and retention in browned ground beef, lamb and pork. J Food Comp Anal 6: 268–277, 1993.

41. A Asghar, JI Gray, AM Booren, EA Gomaa, MM Abouzied, ER Miller, DJ Buckley. Influence of supranutritional dietary vitamin E levels on subcellular deposition of alpha-tocopherol in the muscle and on pork quality. J Sci Food Agric 57: 31–41, 1991.

42. DJ Buckley, PA Morrisey, JI Gray. Influence of dietary vitamin E on the oxidative stability and quality of pig meat. J Anim Sci 73: 3122–3130, 1995.

43. K Rosenvold, HJ Andersen. Factors of significance for pork quality — a review. Meat Sci 64: 219–237, 2003.

44. B Worthington-Roberts, ER Monsen. Iron. In: AM Pearson, TR Dutson, eds. Meat and Health. London: Elsevier Applied Science, 1990, pp. 185–235.

45. K Ono, BW Berry, E Paroczay. Contents and retention of nutrients in extra lean and regular ground beef. J Food Sci 50: 701–706, 1985.

46. AE Hortin, PJ Bechtel, DH Baker. Efficacy of pork loin as a source of zinc and effect of added cysteine on zinc bioavailability. J Food Sci 56: 1505–1507, 1991.

47. HH Sanstead, LS Darnell, JC Wallwork. Role of zinc and the contribution of meat to human nutrition. In: AM Pearson, TR Dutson, eds. Meat and Health. London: Elsevier Applied Science, 1990, pp. 237–274.

48. MJ Marchello, WD Slanger, DB Milne. Macro and micro minerals from selected muscles of pork. J Food Sci 50: 1375–1378, 1985.

49. NF Haard. Enzymes from food myosystems. J Muscle Foods 1: 293–338, 1990.

50. DJ Etherington. Conditioning of meat factors influencing protease activity. In: A Romita, C Valin, AA Taylor, eds. Accelerated Processing of Meat. London: Elsevier Applied Science, 1987, pp. 21–28.

51. MA Sentandreu, G Coulis, A Ouali. Role of muscle endopeptidases and their inhibitors in meat tenderness. Trends Food Sci Technol 13: 398–419, 2002.

52. U Matsukura, A Okitani, T Nishimura, H Katoh. Mode of degradation of myofibrillar proteins by an endogenous protease, cathepsin L. Biochim Biophys Acta 662: 41–47, 1981.

53. MG Zeece, K Katoh. Cathepsin D and its effects on myofibrillar proteins: A review. J Food Biochem 13: 157–178, 1989.

54. MC Hughes, A Healy, PLH McSweeney, EE O'Neill. Proteolytic specificity of cathepsin D on bovine F-actin. Meat Sci 56: 165–172, 2000.

55. AM Draper, MG Zeece. Thermal stability of cathepsin D. J Food Sci 54: 1651–1652, 1989.

56. WN Schwartz, JWC Bird. Degradation of myofibrillar proteins by cathepsins B and D. Biochem J 167: 811–820, 1977.

57. MC Hughes, EE O'Neill, PLH McSweeney, A Healy. Proteolysis of bovine F-actin by cathepsin B. Food Chem 64: 525–530, 1999.

58. A Okitani, T Nishimura, H Katoh. Characterization of hydrolase H, a new muscle protease possesing aminoendopeptidase activity. Eur J Biochem 115: 269–274, 1981.

59. A Ouali, P Rouchon, M Zabari, M Berri, F Zamora, C Tassy. Natural serine and cysteine proteinase inhibitors in bovine skeletal muscle. In: A Ouali, D Demyer, FJM Smulders, eds. Expression of Tissue Proteinases and Regulation of Protein Degradation as Related to Meat Quality. Nijmegen, the Netherlands: Audit, 1995, pp. 173–198.

60. MG Zeece, TL Woods, MA Keen, WJ Reville. Role of proteinases and inhibitors in postmortem muscle protein degradation. Proc Reciprocal Meat Conf, Colorado State Univ 45: 51–61, 1992.

61. F Toldrá. Dry-Cured Meat Products. Trumbull, CT: Food & Nutrition Press, 2002, pp. 7–26.

62. F Toldrá. The enzymology of dry-curing of meat products. In: JM Smulders, F Toldrá, J Flores, M. Prieto, eds. New Technologies for Meat and Meat Products. Nijmegen, the Netherlands: Audet, 1992, pp. 209–231.

63. E Rico, F Toldrá, J Flores. Activity of cathepsin D as affected by chemical and physical dry-curing parameters. Z Lebensm Unters Forsch 191: 20–23, 1990.

64. E Rico, F Toldrá, J Flores. Effect of dry-curing process parameters on pork muscle cathepsins B, H and L activities. Z Lebensm Unters Forsch 193: 541–544, 1991.

65. DJ Etherington. The contribution of proteolytic enzymes to postmortem changes in muscle. J Anim Sci 59: 1644–1650, 1984.

66. JS Bond, PE Butler. Intracellular proteases. Ann Rev Biochem 56: 333–364, 1987.

67. M Koohmaraie, SC Seideman, JE Schollmeyer, TR Dutson, JD Grouse. Effect of postmortem storage on

Ca^{2+} dependent proteases, their inhibitor and myofibril fragmentation. Meat Sci 19: 187–196, 1987.

68. DE Goll, Y Otsuka, PA Nagainis, JD Shannon, SK Sathe, M Muguruma. Role of muscle proteinases in maintenance of muscle integrity and mass. J Food Biochem 7: 137–177, 1983.

69. M Koohmaraie. Muscle proteinases and meat ageing. Meat Sci 36: 93–104, 1994.

70. E Seemuller, A Lupas, D Stock, J Lowe, R Huber, W Baumeister. Proteasome from Thermoplasma acidophilum: a threonine protease. Science 268: 579–592, 1995.

71. O Coux, K Tanaka, A Goldberg. Structure and function of the 20S and 26S proteasomes. Ann Rev Biochem 65: 801–847, 1995.

72. D Dutaud, RG Taylor, B Picard, A Ouali. Le protéasome: une nouvelle protéase impliquée dans la maturation de la viande. Viandes Prod Carnés 17: 333–335, 1996.

73. A Ouali, MA Sentandreu. Overview of muscle peptidases and their potential role in meat texture development. In: F Toldrá, ed. Research Advances in the Quality of Meat and Meat Products. Trivandrum, India: Research Signpost, 2002, pp. 33–63.

74. P Blanchard, M Ellis, C Maltin, G Falkous, JB Harris, D Mantle. Effect of growth promoters on pig muscle structural protein and proteolytic enzyme levels in vivo and in vitro. Biochimie 75: 839–847, 1993.

75. Y Sanz, MA Sentandreu, F Toldrá. Role of muscle and bacterial exopeptidases in meat fermentation. In: F Toldrá, ed. Research Advances in the quality of Meat and Meat Products, Trivandrum, India: Research Signpost, 2002, pp. 143–155.

76. MA Sentandreu, F Toldrá. Biochemical properties of dipeptidylpeptidase III purified from porcine skeletal muscle. J Agric Food Chem 46: 3977–3984, 1998.

77. MA Sentandreu, F Toldrá. Purification and biochemical properties of dipeptidylpeptidase I from porcine skeletal muscle. J Agric Food Chem 48: 5014–5022, 2000.

78. MA Sentandreu, F Toldrá. Importance of dipeptidylpeptidase II in postmortem pork muscle. Meat Sci 57: 93–103, 2001.

79. MA Sentandreu, F Toldrá. Dipeptidylpeptidase IV from porcine skeletal muscle: Purification and biochemical properties. Food Chem 75: 159–168, 2001.

80. JK McDonald, AJ Barrett, eds. Mammalian Proteases. A Glossary and Bibliography. Volume 2. Exopeptidases. London: Academic Press, 1986.

81. M Flores, MC Aristoy, F Toldrá. HPLC purification and characterization of soluble alanyl aminopeptidase from porcine skeletal muscle. J Agric Food Chem 44: 2578–2583, 1996.

82. M Flores, MC Aristoy, F Toldrá. HPLC purification and characterization of porcine muscle aminopeptidase B. Biochimie 75: 861–867, 1993.

83. M Flores, M Marina, F Toldrá. Purification and characterization of a soluble methionyl aminopeptidase from porcine skeletal muscle. Meat Sci 56: 247–254, 2000.

84. F Toldrá, MC Cerveró, C Part. Porcine aminopeptidase activity as affected by curing agents. J Food Sci 58: 724–726, 747, 1992.

85. T Imanaka, M Yamaguchi, S Ahkuma, T Takano. Positional specifity of lysosomal acid lipase purified from rabbit liver. J Biochem 98: 927–931, 1985.

86. SD Fowler, WJ Brown. Lysosomal acid lipase. In: B Borgström, HL Brockman, eds. Lipases. Amsterdam, the Netherlands: Elsevier, 1984, pp. 329–364.

87. Alasnier, Gandemer 2000.

88. MJ Motilva, F Toldrá, J Flores. Assay of lipase and esterase activities in fresh pork meat and dry-cured ham. Z Lebensm Unters Forsch 195: 446–450, 1992.

89. P Belfrage, G Fredrikson, P Stralfors, H Tornqvist. Adipose tissue lipases In: B Borgström, HL Brockman, eds. Lipases. Amsterdam, the Netherlands: Elsevier, 1984, pp. 365–416.

90. G Fredrikson, P Stralfors, NO Nilson, P Belfrage. Hormone-sensitive lipase of rat adipose tissue. Purification and some properties. J Biol Chem 256: 6311–6320, 1981.

91. H Tornqvist, P Nilsson-Ehle, P Belfrage. Enzymes catalyzing the hydrolysis of long-chain monoacylglycerols in rat adipose tissue. Biochim Biophys Acta 530: 474–486, 1978.

92. LC Smith, HJ Pownall. Lipoprotein lipase. In: Lipases. B Borgström, HL Brockman, eds. Elsevier, Amsterdam, the Netherlands, 1984, pp. 263–305.

93. CJ Fielding, PE Fielding. Characteristics of triacylglycerol and partial acylglycerol hydrolysis by human plasma lipoprotein lipase. Biochim Biophys Acta 620: 440–446, 1980.

94. CH Miller, JW Parce, P Sisson, M Waite. Specificity of lipoprotein lipase and hepatic lipase toward monoacylglycerols varying in the acyl composition. Biochim Biophys Acta 665: 385–392, 1981.

95. F Toldrá. Muscle foods: Water, structure and functionality. Food Sci Technol Int 9: 173–177, 2003.

96. ML Greaser. Conversion of muscle to meat. In, PJ Bechtel, ed. Muscle as Food. Orlando, FL: Academic Press, 1986, pp. 36–102.

97. NAM Eskin. Biochemical changes in raw foods: Meat and fish. In: Biochemistry of Foods. 2nd ed. San Diego, CA: Academic Press, 1990, pp. 3–68.

98. G Offer, J Trinick. On the mechanism of water holding in meat: The swelling and shrinking of myofibrils. Meat Sci 8: 245–281, 1983.

99. J Wismer-Pedersen. Water. In: JF Price, BS Schweigert, eds. The Science of Meat and Meet Products. Westport, CT: Food & Nutrition Press, 1987, pp. 141–154.

100. S De Smet, E Claeys, D Demeyer. Muscle enzymes in relation to meat quality and muscularity. In: F Toldrá, ed. Research Advances in the Quality of Meat and Meat Products. Trivandrum, India: Research Signpost, 2002, pp. 123–142.

101. AM Pearson. Physical and biochemical changes ocurring in muscle during storage and preservation. In: PJ Bechtel, ed. Muscle as Food. Orlando, FL: Academic Press, 1986, pp. 103–134.

102. CL Davey, RJ Winger. Muscle to meat (biochemical aspects). In: HR Cross, AJ Overby, eds. Meat Science, Milk Science and Technology. Amsterdam, the Netherlands: Elsevier Science Pub. BV, 1988, pp. 3–31.

103. RG Kauffman, RG Cassens, A Scherer, DL Meeker. Variations in pork quality. Des Moines, IA: National Pork Producers Council Publications, 1992.

104. RD Warner, RG Kauffman, RL Russell. Muscle protein changes post mortem in relation to pork quality traits. Meat Sci 45: 339–372, 1997.

105. F Toldrá, M Flores. The use of muscle enzymes as predictors of pork meat quality. Food Chem 69: 387–395, 2000.

106. RG Kauffman, W Sybesma, FJM Smulders, G Eikelenboom, B Engel, RLJM Van Laack, AH Hoving-Bolink, P Sterrenburg, EV Nordheim, P Walstra, PG Van der Wal. The effectiveness of examining early post-mortem musculature to predict ultimate pork quality. Meat Sci 34: 283–300, 1993.

107. RD Warner, RG Kauffman, RL Russell. Quality attributes of major porcine muscles: a comparison with the *Longissimus lumborum*. Meat Sci 33: 359–372, 1993.

108. RG Cassens. Historical perspectives and current aspects of pork meat quality in the USA. Food Chem 69: 357–363, 2000.

109. N Batlle, MC Aristoy, F Toldrá. Early postmortem detection of exudative pork meat based on nucleotide content. J Food Sci 65: 413–416, 2000.

110. N Batlle, MC Aristoy, F Toldrá. ATP metabolites during aging of exudative and nonexudative pork meats. J Food Sci 66: 68–71, 2001.

111. T Okumura, R Yamada, T Nishimura. Survey of conditioning indicators for pork loins: changes in myofibrils, proteins and peptides during postmortem conditioning of vacuum-packed pork loins for 30 days. Meat Sci 64: 467–473, 2003.

112. E Armero, M Flores, F Toldrá, JA Barbosa, J Olivet, M Pla, M Baselga. Effects of pig sire types and sex on carcass traits, meat quality and sensory quality of dry-cured ham. J Sci Food Agric 79: 1147–1154, 1999.

113. E Armero, JA Barbosa, F Toldrá, M Baselga, M Pla. Effect of the terminal sire and sex on pork muscle cathepsin (B, B+L and H), cysteine proteinase inhibitors and lipolytic enzyme activities. Meat Sci 51: 185–189, 1999.

114. F Toldrá, M Flores, MC Aristoy, R Virgili, G Parolari. Pattern of muscle proteolytic and lipolytic enzymes from light and heavy pigs. J Sci Food Agric 71: 124–128, 1996.

115. CM Rosell, F Toldrá. Comparison of muscle proteolytic and lipolytic enzyme levels in raw hams from Iberian and White pigs. J Sci Food Agric 76: 117–122, 1998.

116. F Toldrá, E Rico, J Flores. Activities of pork muscle proteases in cured meats. Biochimie 74: 291–296, 1992.

117. CM Rosell, F Toldrá. Effect of curing agents on m-calpain activity throughout the curing process. Z Lebensm Unters Forsch 203: 320–325, 1996.

118. T Nishimura. Influence of peptides produced during postmortem conditioning on improvement of meat flavor. In: F Toldrá, ed. Research Advances in the Quality of Meat and Meat Products. Trivandrum, India: Research Signpost, 2002, pp. 65–78.

119. H Negishi, T Yamamoto, T Kuwata. The origin of the 30 kDa component appearing during post-mortem ageing of bovine muscle. Meat Sci 42: 289–303, 1996.

120. DG Olson, FC Parrish Jr. Relationship of myofibril fragmentation index to measures of beef steak tenderness. J Food Sci 42: 506–511, 1977.

121. DG Olson, FC Parrish Jr, WR Dayton, DE Goll. Effects of postmortem storage and calcium activated factors on the myofibrillar proteins of bovine skeletal muscle. J Food Sci 42: 117–124, 1977.

122. IF Penny, E Dransfield. Relationship between toughness and troponin T in conditioned beef. Meat Sci 3: 135–141, 1979.

123. G Whipple, M Koohmaraie, ME Dikeman, JD Crouse, MC Hunt, RD Klemm. Evaluation of attributes that affect *Longissimus* muscle tenderness in *Boss Taurus* and *Bos Indicus* cattle. J Anim Sci 68: 2716–2728, 1990.

124. MA McBride, FC Parrish. The 30,000 dalton component of tender bovine Longissium muscle. J Food Sci 42: 1627–1629, 1977.

125. S Stoeva, CE Byrne, AM Mullen, DJ Troy, W Voelter. Isolation and identification of proteolytic fragments from TCA soluble extracts of bovine M. Longissimus dorsi. Food Chem 69: 365–370, 2000.

126. VJ Moya, M Flores, MC Aristoy, F Toldrá. Nitrogen compounds as potential biochemical markers of pork meat quality. Food Chem 69: 371–377, 2000.

127. VJ Moya, M Flores, MC Aristoy, F Toldrá. Evolution of hydrophobic polypeptides during the ageing of exudative and non-exudative pork meat. Meat Sci 57: 395–401, 2001.

128. VJ Moya, M Flores, MC Aristoy, F Toldrá. Pork meat quality affects peptide and amino acid profiles during the ageing process. Meat Sci 58: 197–206, 2001.

129. A Göransson, M Flores, A Josell, JM Ferrer, MA Trelis, F Toldrá. Effect of electrical stimulation on the activity of muscle exoproteases during beef ageing. Food Sci Tech Int 8: 285–289, 2002.

130. T Nishimura, MR Rhue, A Okitani, H Kato. Components contributing to the improvement of meat taste during storage. Agric Biol Chem 52: 2323–2330, 1988.

131. FC Feidt, A Petit, F Bruas-Reignier, J Brun-Bellut. Release of free amino acids during ageing in bovine meat. Meat Sci 44: 19–25, 1996.

132. MC Aristoy, F Toldrá. Deproteinization techniques for HPLC amino acid analysis in fresh pork muscle and dry-cured ham. J Agric Food Chem 39: 1792–1795, 1991.

133. MJ Motilva, F Toldrá. Effect of curing agents and water activity on pork muscle and adipose subcutaneous tissue lipolytic activity. Z Lebensm Unters Forsch 196: 228–231, 1993.

134. MJ Motilva, F Toldrá, P Nieto, J Flores. Muscle lipolysis phenomena in the processing of dry-cured ham. Food Chem 48: 121–125, 1993.

135. MJ Motilva, F Toldrá, MC Aristoy, J Flores. Subcutaneous adipose tissue lipolysis in the processing of dry-cured ham. J Food Biochem 16: 323–335, 1993.

136. LH Skibsted, A Mikkelsen, G Bertelsen. Lipid-derived off-flavours in meat. In: F Shahidi, ed. Flavor of Meat, Meat Products and Seafoods. London: Blackie Academic & Professional, 1998, pp. 217–256.

137. DV Byrne, WLP Bredie. Sensory meat quality and warmed-over flavour — a review. In: F Toldrá, ed.

Research Advances in the Quality of Meat and Meat Products. Trivandrum, India: Research Signpost, 2002, pp. 95–121.

138. DA Lillard. Chemical changes involved in the oxidation of lipids in foods. In: MK Supran, ed. Lipids as a source of flavor. Washington, D.C.: ACS Symp. Series 75, 1978, pp. 68–80.

139. M Flores, AM Spanier, F Toldrá. Flavour analysis of dry-cured ham. In: F Shahidi, ed. Flavor of Meat M Products and Seafoods. London: Blackie Academic & Professional, 1998, pp. 320–341.

140. C Faustman, RG Cassens. The biochemical basis for discoloration in fresh meat: a review. J Muscle Foods 1: 217–243, 1990.

141. JKS Moller, JS Jensen, LH Skinsteid, S Knöchel. Microbial formation of nitrite-cured pigment, nitrosylmyoglobin, from metmyoglobin in model systems and smoked fermented sausages by Lactobacillus fermentum strains and a commercial starter culture. Eur Food Res Technol 216: 463–469, 2003.

142. RG Kauffman and BB Marsh. Quality characteristics of muscle as food. In JF Price and BS Schweigert, eds. The Science of Meat and Meat Products. 3rd ed. Westport, CT: Food & Nutrition Press, 1987, pp. 349–369.

143. DL Hopkins, JM Thompson. Inhibition of protease activity. I. The effect on tenderness and indicators of proteolysis in ovine muscle. Meat Sci 59: 175–185, 2001.

144. JA Mestre-Prates, AMR Ribeiro, AA Dias-Correia. Role of cysteine endopeptidases (EC 3.4.22) in rabbit meat tenderisation and some related changes. Meat Sci 57: 283–290, 2001.

145. AD Alarcón Rojo, E Dransfield. Alteration of post-mortem ageing in beef by the addition of enzyme inhibitors and activators. Meat Sci 41: 163–178, 1995.

146. E Dransfield. Optimisation of tenderisation, ageing and tenderness. Meat Sci 36: 105–121, 1994.

147. PJ Blanchard, D Mantle. Comparison of proteolytic enzyme levels in chicken, pig, lamb and rabbit muscle at point of slaughter: role in meat tenderisation post mortem. J Sci Food Agric 71: 83–91, 1996.

148. K Takahashi. Structural weakening of skeletal muscle tissue during postmortem ageing of meat: the non-enzymatic mechanism of meat tenderization. Meat Sci 43: s67–s80, 1996.

149. A Ouali, A Talmant. Calpains and calpastatin distribution in bovine, porcine and ovine skeletal muscles. Meat Sci 28: 331–348, 1990.

150. M Koohmaraie, G Whipple, DH Kretchman, JD Crouse, HJ Mersmar. Postmortem proteolysis in Longissiums muscle from beef, lamb and pork carcasses. J Anim Sci 69: 617–624, 1991.

151. C Valin, A Ouali. Proteolytic muscle enzymes and post-mortem tenderization. In: JM Smulders, F Toldrá, J Flores, M Prieto, eds. New technologies for meat and meat products. Nijmegen, the Netherlands: Audet, 1992, pp. 163–179.

152. A Watanabe, CC Daly, CE Devine. The effects of ultimate pH of meat on the tenderness changes during ageing. Meat Sci 42: 67–78, 1995.

153. M Gil, M Hortós, C Sárraga. Calpain and cathepsin activities, and protein extractability during ageing of longissimus porcine muscle from normal and PSE meat. Food Chem 63: 385–390, 1998.

154. M Hortós, M Gil, C Sárraga. Effect of calpain and cathepsin activities on myofibrils from porcine longissimus muscle during conditioning of normal and exudative meat. Sci Aliment 14: 503–515, 1994.

155. GR O'Halloran, DJ Troy, DJ Buckley, WJ Reville. The role of endogenous proteases in the tenderisation of fast glycolysing muscle. Meat Sci 47: 187–210, 1997.

156. H Kato, MR Rhue, T Nishimura. Role of free amino acids and peptides in food taste. In: R Teranishi, RG Buttery, F Shahidi, eds. Flavor Chemistry. Trends and Development. Washington, D.C.: ACS Symposium Series, 388, 1989, p. 158.

157. DS Mottram. Meat. In: H Maarse, ed. Volatile Compounds in Foods and beverages. New York: Marcel Dekker Inc. 1991, pp. 107–177.

158. M Flores, E Armero, MC Aristoy, F Toldrá. Sensory characteristics of cooked pork loin as affected by nucleotide content and post-mortem meat quality. Meat Sci 51: 53–59, 1999.

159. F Toldrá, M Flores, MC Aristoy. Enzyme generation of free amino acids and its nutritional significance in processed pork meats. In: G Charalambous, ed. Food Flavors: Generation, Analysis and Process Influence. Amsterdam, the Netherlands: Elsevier Science Publishers BV, 1995, pp. 1303–1322.

160. AM Mullen, S Stoeva, K Laib, G Gruebler, W Voelter, DJ Troy. Preliminary analysis of amino acids at various locations along the M. Longissimus dorsi in aged beef. Food Chem 69: 461–465, 2000.

161. Y Yamasaki, K Maekawa. A peptide with delicious taste. Agric Biol Chem 42: 1761–1765, 1978.

162. Y Yamasaki, K Maekawa. Synthesis of a peptide with delicious taste. Agric Biol Chem 44: 93–97, 1980.

163. K Wang, JA Mega, PJ Bechtel. Taste properties and synergism of beefy meaty peptide. J Food Sci 61: 837–839, 1996.

164. K Maehisa, M Matsuzaki, Y Yamamoto, S Udaka. Isolation of peptides from enzymatic hydrolysate of food proteins and characterization of their taste properties. Biosci Biotechnol Biochem 63: 555–559, 1999.

165. AM Spanier, M Flores, KW McMillin, TD Bidner. The effect of post-mortem aging on meat flavor quality in Brangus beef. Correlation of treatments, sensory, instrumental and chemical descriptors. Food Chem 59: 531–538, 1997.

166. MC Aristoy, F Toldrá. Isolation of flavor peptides from raw pork meat and dry-cured ham. In: G Charalambous, ed. Food Flavors: Generation, Analysis and Process Influence. Amsterdam, the Netherlands: Elsevier Science Publishers BV, 1995, pp. 1323–1344.

167. F Toldrá, M Flores. Meat quality factors. In: L Nollet, ed. Handbook of Food Analysis. New York: Marcel Dekker Inc. 2003, pp. 1961–1977.

168. F Shahidi, LJ Rubin. Meat flavor volatiles: a review of the composition, techniques of analysis, and sensory evaluation. CRC Crit Rev Food Sci Nutr 24: 141–243, 1986.

169. DS Mottram, RA Edwards. The role of triglycerides and phospholipids in the aroma of cooked beef. J Sci Food Agric 34: 517–522, 1983.

29 Chemical Composition of Red Meat

Baowu Wang
Department of Food and Nutritional Sciences, Tuskegee University

CONTENTS

I. INTRODUCTION

Red meat refers to the meat from mammalian skeletal muscle tissue with distinctive red color including beef, pork, and lamb. Although muscle and meat are used interchangeably on many occasions, there are differences between the two terms. Muscle refers to a tissue responsible for contraction and movement in live animals, while meat is a broad term referring to edible tissues from animals consisting of muscle, adipose, and other connective tissues (1). The major components of meat include water, proteins, lipids, carbohydrates, minerals, soluble non-protein substances, vitamins, and some incidental compounds such as feed additives or contaminants (Table 29.1). The composition of meat is dependent on the species, breed, sex, age, activity, the anatomical location of the cut, the relative proportions of tissues in the retail cut, and other factors. However, the composition of lean meat is fairly consistent even across different species (Table 29.2). Hence, in later discussions, the chemical composition of red meat is not separated into species.

II. WATER IN MEAT

Generally, water is the most abundant component in lean meat, ranging from 65% to 80%. However, if the meat contains excessive adipose tissue, fat may be the predominant component (Table 29.3). Water is not randomly distributed in meat. At the time of slaughter, approximately 85% water in muscle is located intracellularly. The remaining 15% water is located in the extracellular spaces. The water in the muscle is withheld through different mechanisms, less than 15% tightly bound to proteins, another 15% loosely bound to proteins, and the remaining 70% by capillary forces (6). Since most of the water is distributed in the spaces among myofibrils, swelling or shrinkage of myfibrils alters the distribution of water within the muscle but does not necessarily affect the muscle volume as a whole (7).

The level of water in meat has a direct impact on cooking yield as well as on tenderness and juiciness of meat products. Hence, it is desirable to improve water binding capacity of meat through breeding, slaughtering, post mortem handling, formulation, and further processing such as mixing, tumbling, and other procedures.

TABLE 29.1

Composition of Typical Mammalian Muscle*

Component	Wet %
Water	75.0
Protein	19.0
Lipids	2.5
Carbohydrates	1.2
Non-protein nitrogenous compounds	1.65
Inorganic	0.65
Vitamins and other minor components	Minimal

* Compiled from Ref. 2.

TABLE 29.2

Composition of Separable Red Lean Meat from Different Species (%)

	Water	Protein	Lipids	Ash
Beef	71	21	5.8	1.0
Pork	72	21	5.9	1.0
Lamb	73	20	5.2	1.0

Compiled from Refs. 3–5.

TABLE 29.3

Composition of Red Meat with Adipose Tissues (%)

	Water	Protein	Lipids	Ash
Beef	60	18	20	1
Pork	42	12	43	1
Lamb	62	17	18	1

Compiled from Refs. 3–5.

III. MEAT PROTEINS

For lean meat, proteins constitute 16% to 22% of the meat mass. Meat proteins can be divided into three groups based on their solubility: sarcoplasmic proteins (soluble in aqueous solutions with an ionic strength of 0.15 or less), myofibrillar proteins (soluble in aqueous solutions with an ionic strength of sodium or potassium ions at least 0.3), and stromal proteins (insoluble even in high ionic strength solutions of sodium or potassium ions) (2).

A. SARCOPLASMIC PROTEINS

The sarcoplasmic proteins contribute to about 30% of the total protein, corresponding to 5.5% of lean meat. The sarcoplasmic proteins include a mixture of about 50 components. The major components are glycolytic enzymes, myoglobin, cytochromes, and flavoproteins (2). It should be noted that glycolytic enzymes are not randomly suspended in the sarcoplasm. Instead, they are bound to the myofibrillar protein (actin). This feature may assist in the muscular metabolism and physiological function. In addition, the proportion of the bound glycolytic enzymes

increases in electrically stimulated glycolysis and decreases when the stimulation stopped (2). Glycolytic enzymes also bind to other sites in muscle cell, including the sarcolemma, the sarcoplasmic reticulum, and the membranes of nuclei and mitochondria. These glycolytic enzymes play a critical role during post mortem glycolysis. The myoglobin, and to a lesser extent, hemoglobin, are responsible for the typical red color of meat. The amount of myoglobin is determined by the metabolic characteristics of the muscle. For instance, red meat contains high levels of myogolbin to provide more oxygen for the synthesis of ATP. In contrast, white meat contains low levels of myoglobin because its energy is generated primarily through glycolysis. Generally, sarcoplasmic proteins have limited functionalities in water-binding, gel-forming, and emulsifying capacity.

B. MYOFIBRILLAR PROTEINS

Myofibrillar proteins constitute about 60% of total muscle proteins, corresponding to about 11.5% of lean meat. Myofibrillar proteins can be further divided into three subgroups including contractile proteins, regulatory proteins, and cytoskeletal proteins (Table 29.4). The major contractible proteins are myosin and actin. The major regulatory proteins are tropomyosin, troponin, actinins, and other minor regulatory proteins. Cytoskeletal proteins include a diverse group of proteins such as titin, nebulin, desmin, filamin, vinculin, and synemin. The myofibrillar proteins construct the thick filament, thin filament, Z-line, and M-line which can be observed under the microscope or electron microscope.

1. Myosin

Myosin is the most abundant myofibrillar protein, contributing to abut 40% of the total myofibrillar protein or about 5.5% of lean meat. Myosin contains six subunits with two identical heavy chains and four light chains (2). There are three kinds of light chains, i.e., DTNB light chain (MW 18,000 D), alkaline light chain 1 (MW 25,000 D), and alkaline light chain 2 (MW 16,000 D). The names of the light chains come from the reagents used to release them from myosin, either sulfhydryl agent 5,5-dithio-bis(2-nitrobenzoic acid) (DTNB) or alkaline solution. One myosin molecule contains two identical DTNB light chains and two identical alkaline light chains (either 1 or 2). The six subunits form two identical units which form a complete myosin molecule with a length of 1500 Å (2). A whole myosin molecule looks like a golf club with the N-terminus in the head region. The four light chains and ATPase activity are located at the head. Many myosin molecules aggregate at the tail to form myosin filament (thick filament) which in turn forms myofibrils with other proteins (2, 9). Another protein component for thick filament, titin, will be discussed later.

TABLE 29.4
Some Characteristics of Myofibrillar Proteins from Vertebrate Skeletal Muscle

Protein	MW (KD)	%*	Location	Function
Contractile				
Myosin	500	43	Thick filament	Contraction
Heavy chain	220		(A-band)	
Light chain	16/18/25			
Actin (G-form)	42	22	Thin filament	Contraction
			(I-band)	
Regulatory				
Tropomyosin	70	8	Thin filament	Regulates contraction
α-chain	34			
β-chain	36			
Troponin	74	5	Thin filament	
Troponin-C	18			Ca^{2+}-binding
Troponin-I	21			Inhibits myosin-actin interaction
Troponin-T	35			Binds to tropomyosin
α-actinin	95	2	Z-disk	Fastens thin filaments to Z-disk
β-actinin	130	0.1	Thin filament	Regulates thin filament length
γ-actinin	35	0.1	Thin filament	Inhibits G-actin
Eu-actinin	42	0.3	Z-disk	Density
C-protein	140	2	Thick filament	Adheres to thick filament
M-protein	165	2	M-line	Binds to myosin
X-protein	152	0.2	Thick filament	Binds to myosin
H-protein	69	0.18	Thick filament	Adheres to C-protein & myosin
Paratropomyosin	35	0.15	Edges of A-band	Involving postmortem changes
Creatine kinase	42	0.1	M-line	Binds to M-protein
Cytoskeletal				
Titin	>1000	8	Entire scaromere	Holds thick filaments & links them to Z-disks
Nebulin	600	3	N-line	Binds & holds thin filaments
Desmin	550	0.18	Z-disk	Links neighboring Z-disks
Filamin	230	0.1	Z-disk	Binds & holds titin
Vimentin	58	0.1	Z-disk	Links Z-disk in periphery
Synemin	220	0.1	Z-disk	Binds to desmin & vimentin
Zeugmatin	550	0.1	Z-disk	Links thin filaments to Z-disk

*Percentage of total myofibrillar protein
Compiled from Ref. 8.

2. Actin

The other important contractile protein is actin, contributing to about 20% of total myofibrillar proteins or about 2.5% of lean meat (Table 29.4). Actin contains a single polypeptide chain. Each actin molecule forms a globe that is called G-actin. A series of G-actin aggregate linearly to form a fibrous structure that is called F-actin. F-actin has a double stranded right-handed helical structure with a half pitch consisting of 13 monomers (10). The polymerization of G-actin to F-actin (G-F transformation) is thought to be similar to the process of crystallization (11). It occurs only above a critical concentration of actin at which F-actin is in equilibrium with G-actin. F-actin, tropomyosin, troponin, and nebulin are the major components for the thin filaments in myofibrils.

3. Tropomyosin

Tropomysoin contributes to about 8% of myofibrillar proteins. It is an α-helical molecule approximately 41 nm long. It is so named because its amino acid composition is similar to that of myosin (12). Tropomyosin consists of two subunits with a molecular weight of approximately 37,000 daltons. The two subunits are α and β which can be separated by sodium docecyl sulfate gel electrophoresis or by ion-exchange chromatography.

4. Troponin

Troponin is a protein of MW 80,000 consisting of three subunits that are named I, T, and C. Troponin C is an acidic protein that can bind Ca^{++} with four calcium binding sites on each troponin C (13). Troponin I is a basic protein that inhibits the actin-myosin interaction in the presence of ATP. The presence of tropomyosin greatly enhances this inhibition (14). Troponin T binds strongly to tropomyosin periodically at 40 nm intervals along the entire length of the thin filament (15). Since each troponin molecule must regulate seven actin molecules, it is believed that this must be mediated via a dislocation of the filamentous tropomyosin molecule along the groove of actin filaments (16).

5. Actinins

Actinins are proteins that play a role in regulating the physical state of actin. Four classes of actinins are known, α-actinin, β-actinin, γ-actinin, and eu-actinin. α-actinin is the major actinin found in skeletal muscle, contributing to about 1–2% of myofibrillar proteins. It is an acidic protein located in Z-lines, probably participating in cementing the components of the Z-line (17). Mild treatment of myofibrils with proteases results in a marked decrease in the density of Z-lines with a release of intact α-actinin. The decrease in Z-line density and the loss of register of Z-lines in adjacent myofibrils are characteristic of post-mortem muscle. It is believed that the release of α-actinin contributes to the tenderness of postmortem meat (18). β-actinin is a protein contributing to less than 0.01% of myofibrillar proteins. β-actinin is present at the free end of actin filaments to prevent actin from binding to another actin filament (19). γ-Actinin is a protein contributing to less than 0.01% of myofibrillar proteins. It inhibits the polymerization of G-actin. Eu-actinin contributes to about 0.3% of myfibrillar proteins. It is located at Z-lines to interact with both α-actinin and actin.

6. Other Regulatory Proteins

Other regulatory proteins include M-protein, C-protein, and F-protein, among other minor components. M-protein contributes to about 0.5% of myfibrillar proteins. It is located at the M-line of the thick filaments. Other proteins found at the M-line include myomesin and creatine kinase (20–22). C-protein comprises 2% of the myofibrillar protein with a relatively high proline content. C-protein copolymerizes with myosin filaments. F-protein binds to myosin filament. I-protein is located at the A-band. It is suggested that I-protein inhibits the unnecessary splitting of ATP in relaxed muscle (9).

C. Cytoskeletal Proteins

Cytoskeletal proteins include titin (connectin), nebulin, desmin (skeletin), and other minor components. Titin is the largest protein molecule with a MW of over 1,000,000. Titin contributes to about 10% of myofibrillar proteins. It seems that titin forms a three-dimensional net of very thin filaments to link the neighboring Z-lines (23). It extends longitudinally in each half sarcomere from the M-line to the Z-disk as a third filament of the myofibril. Titin and C-protein bind to the outside shaft of the thick filament. They encircle and stabilize the thick filament and hence should be considered components of thick filament. It is believed that titin is responsible for the resting tension associated with each sarcomere. Nebulin constitutes approximately 4% of myofibrillar proteins. It is located close and parallel to the thin filament. Nebulin extends longitudinally along the entire length of the thin filament from the A-band to the Z-disk. In mature muscle, it serves as a template for assembly and/or scaffold for stability of thin filaments. It may also help to anchor thin filaments to Z-disks (1). Desmin contributes to less than 0.2% myofibrillar proteins. It is located at the periphery of the Z-disk and also in the filaments that link neighboring Z-disks. Other minor proteins contributing to the cytoskeleton include filamin, vimentin, synemin, and paranemin (1).

D. Stromal or Connective Tissue Proteins

Stomal proteins include collagen, elastin, and other insoluble proteins. Connective tissue proteins play an important role in physiological functions as well as in determining the eating quality of meat. Their physiological functions include covering the body, protecting the body from damage, and connecting muscles, organs, and other structures to the skeleton and to each other (24).

Collagen is a major structural component of all connective tissues including tendon, bone, cartilage, skin, vascular tissues, and basement membranes. It is the most abundant protein in animal bodies constituting 20–25% of the total protein. Different tissues have different types of collagens (Table 29.5). Distribution of collagen is not uniform among skeletal muscles with the amount generally paralleling physical activity of the muscle. Hence, muscles of limbs contain more collagen than those around the spinal column. Consequently, the former are tougher than the latter. At a level of 33%, glycine is the most abundant amino acid in collagen, followed by proline and hydroxyproline comprising another one-third of the amino acids of collagen. Since hyroxyproline is a relatively constant component of collagen (13–14%) and does not occur to a significant extent in other animal proteins, chemical analysis of hydroxyproline is commonly used to determine the amount of collagen in tissues. In addition, collagen is a glycoprotein in that it contains a small quantity of galactose and glucose (24).

Tropocollagen is the structural unit of the collagen fibril. Tropocollagen molecules are composed of three α-chains that form a triple helix, with each α-chain forming a left-handed helix and three of the left-handed α-chains form a right-handed supercoil. Following synthesis of tropocollagen in fibroblasts, they are secreted

TABLE 29.5
Distribution and Molecular Properties of Genetically Distinct Collagens

Type	Molecular composition	Tissue location
I	$[\alpha1(I)]_2\alpha2(I)$	Skin, tendon, bone, dentine
II	$[\alpha1(II)]_3$	Cartilage, disc, vitreous, notocord
III	$[\alpha1(III)]_3$	Vascular system, skin, intestine
IV	$[\alpha1(IV)]_2\alpha2(IV)+\alpha3(IV)$	Basement membrane
V	$[\alpha1(V)]_2\alpha2(V)+\alpha1(V)\alpha2(V)$	Embryonic tissue, skin, vascular system
	$\alpha3(V)+$	Other combinations
VI	$[\alpha1(VI)_2 \alpha2(VI)\alpha3(VI)]$	Vascular system
VII	$[\alpha1(VII)]_3$	Skin amniotic membrane
VIII	$[\alpha1(VIII)]_3 + [\alpha2(VIII)]_3$	Aortic intima
IX	$[\alpha1(IX)\alpha2(IX)\alpha3(IX)]$	Cartilage
X	$[\alpha1(X)]_3$	Cartilage
XI	$\alpha1(XI)\alpha2(XI) \alpha3(XI)$	Cartilage

Compiled from Refs. 24–27.

into the intercellular matrix where they are assembled into collagen fibrils. During fibril assembly, tropocollagen molecules are aligned longitudinally end to end and laterally in a slightly less than one-fourth overlapping stagger. The overlapping stagger gives rise to the unique striated appearance of collagen fibrils. It should be pointed out that only type I and type III collagen fibrils can form collagen fibers. Type I collagen forms large fibers while type III collagen forms fine fibers. In fibrous collagens, cross-linkages are formed via intermolecular or intramolecular cross-links. The number of cross-links depends on the load and stress of the muscle and also on the age of the animal. Limb muscle and aged animals generally have more crosss-links, resulting in tougher meat than meat from loin or young animals. The cross-links result from covalent bonding of hydroxyprolines, deaminated lysine, hydroxylysine, or sulfhydryl groups. The enzymes responsible for the modification of proline and lysine are located in fibroblasts and the modifications occur post-translation of the polypeptides.

Elastin is a much less abundant connective tissue protein than collagen. Its ultrastructural characteristics are not well known. Elastin is a rubbery protein present throughout the body in ligaments and arterial walls, as well as in the framework of a number of organs including muscle. Elastin fibers can be easily stretched and, when tension is released, return to their original length. Elastin contains eight amino acid residues with glycine being the most abundant. There are two unique amino acid residues in elastin, desmosine and isodesmosine. Elastin is highly resistant to digestive enzymes and cooking has little solubilizing effect on it. Thus, elastin contributes little to the nutritive value of meat (1).

IV. LIPIDS

Lipids is the component with the highest variability for meat, ranging from 1.5% to 13.0% (28), but lipids content can be as high as 43% if the meat contains excessive adipose tissue (3–5). The variability of lipids arises primarily from the differences in neutral fat, or triacylglycerides. Other lipid components such as phospholipids, cerebrosides, and cholesterol are fairly constant among different meat cuts. The differences in triacylglycerides reside in the fatty acids. The common fatty acids found in meat include stearic, palmitic, oleic, and linolenic (Table 29.6). Feed has an impact on the composition of fatty acids in meat. This is particularly obvious for pork. Bacon and other meat products from hogs that have ingested flax seed or fishy residue may develop painty or fishy flavors. Dietary fatty acids have less impact on the fatty acid profile of ruminant animals because the ruminant bacteria convert unsaturated fatty acids to saturated fatty acids through hydrogenation (28).

The level of phospholipids in muscle tissues is generally in the range of 0.5–1%. Most of the phospholipids are phosphoglycerides, i.e., phosphotidylcholine, phosphotidylethanolamine, and phosphotidylserine. Since phospholipids contain relatively high levels of polyunsaturated fatty acids, they tend to be oxidized to generate off-flavor. Meat also contains a small amount of cholesterol, generally in the range of 100 mg/100 g (3–5).

V. CARBOHYDRATES

Carbohydrates and related compounds contribute to about 1.0% of meat weight (22). The major components are glycogen and glucose. Other components such as triose

TABLE 29.6
Fatty Acids Composition of Animal Fats

Fatty Acids	Pork Lard	Beef Tallow	Mutton Tallow
Lauric (C12:0)	Trace	<0.2	Trace
Myristic (C14:0)	0.7–4.0	2–8	1–4
Palmitic (C16:0)	26–32	24–33	20–28
Stearic (C18:0)	12–16	14–29	25–32
Arachidic (C20:0)	Trace	0.4–1.3	Trace
Total saturated	*40–48*	*40–56*	*46–60*
Myristoleic (C14:1)	<0.3	<0.6	Trace
Palmitoleic (C16:1)	2–5	1.9–2.7	Trace
Oleic (C18:1)	41–51	39–50	36–47
Linoleic (C18:2)	3–14	<5	3–5
Linolenic (C18:3)	<1	<0.5	Trace
Arachidonic (C20:4)	<3	<0.5	Trace
Total unsaturated	*52–60*	*44–60*	*40–54*

Compiled from Refs. 3–5, 28.

phosphates and lactic acid arise from the metabolism of glucose or glycogen. The level and metabolism of carbohydrates determine, to a great extent, the eating quality of meat because during postmortem glycolysis, glucose is converted to lactic acid and ATP, both of which have significant impact on postmortem changes. Other important carbohydrates are bound to proteins which are called proteoglycans (protein accounting for 5–15% and carbohydrate accounting for 85–95%) and glycoproteins (protein being the major component and carbohydrate being the minor component).

VI. OTHER COMPONENTS

The mineral content in meat is generally low, with potassium 0.355%, sodium 0.07%, and phosphorus 0.19% (Table 29.7). However, meat provides some essential trace elements (Fe, Zn, Cu, etc.) that have higher absorption than food of plant origins.

Non-protein nitrogenous (NPN) substances contribute to about 1.5% of meat weight. These substances include creatine, creatine phosphate, nucleotides, free amino acids, peptides, creatinine, etc. The level of NPN may have a significant impact on the flavor of meat. Meat also contains significant amount of vitamins, especially vitamin B1 and niacin (Table 29.8).

TABLE 29.7
Mineral Content of Separable Red Lean Meat (mg/100 g)

	Beef	Pork	Lam
Potassium	350	384	280
Phosphorus	200	220	170
Sodium	63	54	66
Magnesium	22	23	26
Calcium	6	17	10
Zinc	4.0	2.0	4.0
Iron	2.0	0.9	1.8

Compiled from Refs. 3–5.

TABLE 29.8
Vitamin Content of Separable Red Lean Meat (mg/100 g)

	Beef	Pork	Lamb
Vitamin B1	0.1	0.98	0.13
Vitamin B2	0.18	0.27	1.23
Niacin	3.59	4.8	6.0
Pantothenic acid	0.36	0.79	0.70
Vitamin B6	0.44	0.51	0.16
Folic acid	0.007	0.005	0.023
Vitamin B12	0.003	0.0007	0.003

Compiled from Refs. 3–5.

REFERENCES

1. ED Aberle, JC Forrest, DE Gerrard, EW Mills, HB Hedrick, MD Judge, RA Merkel. Principles of Meat Science. 4th ed. Dubuque, IA: Kendall/Hunt Publishing Company, 2001, pp 1–44.
2. RA Lawrie. Meat Science. 5th ed. Oxford, U.K.: Pergamon Press, 1991, pp 27–79.
3. USDA Composition of Foods: Lamb, veal and game products; raw, processed, prepared. In: USDA Agricultural Handbook No. 8–17. Washington, D.C.: U.S. Department of Agriculture, 1989.
4. USDA Composition of Foods: Beef products; raw, processed, prepared. In: USDA Agricultural Handbook No. 8–13. Washington, D.C.: U.S. Department of Agriculture, 1990.
5. USDA Composition of Foods: Pork products; raw, processed, prepared. In: USDA Agricultural Handbook No. 8–10. Washington, D.C.: U.S. Department of Agriculture, 1992.
6. RLJM van Laack. The role of proteins in water-holding capacity of meat. In: YL Xiong, CT Ho, and F Shahidi. eds. Quality Attributes of Muscle Foods. New York: Kluwer Academic/Plenum Publishers, 2001, pp 309–318.
7. G Offer, P Knight. The structural basis of water-holding in meat. In: R Lawrie. ed. Developments in meat science — 4. London, U.K.: Elsevier Applied Science, 1988, pp 63–243.
8. YL Xiong Structure-functionality relationships of muscle proteins. In: S Damodaran and A Paraf. eds. Food Proteins and Their Applications. New York: Marcel Dekker, 1997, pp 341–389.
9. E Bandman. Chemistry of animal tissues. In: JF Price, BS Schweigert. eds. The Science of Meat and Meat Products. 3rd ed. Westport, CT: Food & Nutritional Press, 1987, pp 61–101.
10. PB Moore, HE Huxley, DJ Derosier. Three-dimensional reconstruction of F-actin, thin filaments and decorated thin filaments. J Mol Biol 50:279–295, 1970.
11. PC Leavis, J Gergely. Thin filament proteins and thin filament-linked regulation of vertebrate muscle contraction. CRC Crit Rev Biochem 16:235–305, 1984.
12. AM Gordon, M Regnier, E Homsher. Skeletal and cardiac muscle contractile activation: tropomyosin "rocks and rolls." News Physiol Sci 16:49–55, 2001.
13. PC Leavis, SS Rosinfeld, J Gergely, Z Grabarik, W Drabikosky. Proteolytic fragments of troponin C. J Bio Chem 253:5452–5459, 1978.
14. JM Wilkinson, SV Perry, HA Cole, IP Trayer. The regulatory proteins of the myofibril. Biochem J 127:215–228, 1972.
15. S Ebashi. Separation of troponin into its three components. J Biochem 72:787–789, 1972.
16. FM Clarke, SJ Lovell, CJ Masters, DJ Winzor. Beef muscle troponin: evidence for multiple forms of troponin-T. Biochim Biophys Acta 427:617–626, 1976.
17. C Knupp, PK Luther, JM Squire. Titin organisation and the 3D architecture of the vertebrate-striated muscle I-band. J Molecular Biol 322:731–739, 2002.

18. E Hugg-Lonergan, SM Lonergan. Postmortem mechanism of meat tenderization. In: YL Xiong, CT Ho, and F Shahidi. eds. Quality Attributes of Muscle Foods. New York: Kluwer Academic/Plenum Publishers, 2001, pp 229–251.

19. MO Steinmetz, A Hoenger, D Stoffler, AA Noegel, U Aebi, CA Schoenenberger. Polymerization, Three-dimensional structure and mechanical properties of *Dictyosteliumversus* rabbit muscle actin filaments. J Molecular Biol 303:171–184, 2000.

20. T Masaki, O Takaitai. M-protein. J Biochem 75:367–380, 1974.

21. BK Grove, V Kurer, C Lehner, TC Doetschman, J-C Perriadrd, HM Eppenburger. A new 5,000-dalton skeletal muscle protein detected by monoclonal antibodies. J Cell Biol 98:518–524, 1984.

22. TM Byrem, GM Strasburg. Chapter 22 Red meat. In: GL Christen, JS Smith. eds. Food Chemistry: Principles and Applications. West Sacramento, CA: Science Technology System, 2000, pp 365–398.

23. K Maruyama, S Kimura, K Ohashi, Y Kuwano. Connectin, an elastic protein of muscle. Identification of "titin" with connectin. J Biochem 89:701–709, 1981.

24. AJ Bailey. The biological diversity of collagen: A family of molecules. In: Pearson AM, Dutson TR, and Bailey AJ. eds. Advances in Meat Research. New York: Van Nostrand Reinhold Company, 1985, pp 1–17.

25. PC Marchisio, O Cremona, P Savoia, G Pellegrini, JP Ortonne, P Verrando, RE Burgeson, R Cancedda, MD Luca. The basement membrane protein bm-600/nicein codistributes with kalinin and the integrin $\alpha 6\beta 4$ in human cultured keratinocytes. Exp Cell Res 205:205–212, 1993.

26. NS Greenhill, BM Ruger, O Hasan, PF Davis. The $\alpha 1$(VIII) and $\alpha 2$(VIII) collagen chains form two distinct homotrimeric proteins in vivo. Matrix Biol 19:19–28, 2000.

27. M Moradi-Ameli, BD Chassey, J Farjanel, MVD Rest. Different splice variants of cartilage $\alpha 1$(XI) collagen chain undergo uniform amino-terminal processing. Matrix Biol 17:393–396, 1998.

28. LR Dugan, Jr. Part 2 — Fats. In: JF Price, BS Schweigert. eds. The Science of Meat and Meat Products. 3rd ed. Westport, CT: Food & Nutritional Press, 1987, pp 103–113.

30 Meat Species Identification

Y.-H. Peggy Hsieh
Department of Nutrition, Food and Exercise Sciences, Florida State University

CONTENTS

I. INTRODUCTION

Meat species identification has been an active area of research for the past three decades. Identification of the animal origin is important for fair trade, for ensuring compliance with labeling regulations, and for other issues such as wild life management and conservation. Initially, method development for species identification was mainly for the legal enforcement of regulations governing the import of raw meats at ports of entry, since species substitutions, such as the substitution of horse or kangaroo meat for beef (1, 2), and pork for beef or sheep meat (3), had been reported in several countries. Methods that give a clear qualitative result, verifying and identifying the species of origin, were sufficient at the time. However, as processed meat and prepared ready-to-eat products have become increasingly available to consumers, the possibility of fraudulent adulteration and substitution of the expected species with other meats has also increased.

Widespread problems due to mixing undeclared meat species have been documented among fresh and processed ground meat products in retail markets as either a consequence of improper handling or economic fraud (4, 5). Whether this is due to accidental contamination of low levels of undeclared meat or intentional adulteration involving significant amounts and/or multiple species, such practices pose a substantial concern to consumers in terms of economic loss, food allergies, religious observance, loss of traceability, and food safety (6). It has been observed that the adulteration problem occurs more frequently in precooked meats than in fresh meat, possibly due to the lack of reliable and economical analytical methods for cooked meats (7). Wherever the law enforcement is inadequate with regard to meat species monitoring programs, the rate of adulteration increases substantially. Therefore, the recent focus of species detection has been on the content of various processed and precooked ground and comminuted meat products. The development of reliable analytical methods that can sensitively identify and quantify the unknown species in processed and composite mixtures has thus become more important and, at the same time, more complicated. Research efforts have concentrated on searching for species markers that are not only unaffected by the processing conditions, such as cooking temperature, but can also be used to quantitatively assess the proportion of the target tissue present in meat samples (6).

Recently, an emerging issue concerning the transmission of the fatal neurodegenerative disease, Bovine Spongiform Encephalopathy (BSE, commonly known as mad cow disease), has made the science of species detection even more demanding and challenging. Most scientists agree that the BSE epidemic originated from the practice of feeding cattle with rendered animal protein derived from scrapie-infected sheep tissue, and the disease is further spread by recycling meat and bones from infected animals back into cattle feed (8). Etiologically linked to BSE, the recent occurrence of a new variant of Creutzfeldt Jakob Disease (nv CJD) in humans is believed to result from consumption of beef from BSE-infected cattle (9). Ultimately, food safety is the threshold issue for consumers' fear of BSE. To prevent the spread of the disease in animals and reduce the potential risk of BSE transmission to humans, stringent feed control is essential. The use of rendered protein supplement derived from ruminants was banned in ruminant feed in the European Union (EU) in 1994 (10) and in the U.S. in 1997 (11). Since 1996 the World Health Organization (WHO) has recommended that all countries ban the use of ruminant tissue in ruminant feed (12). The EU has introduced a total ban on the feeding of processed animal protein to all animals which are for human consumption under the new processed Animal Protein Regulations, while blood, milk and gelatin are exempt from the feed ban (13). This total feed ban has been in force since 2000. While the practice of adding rendered animal by-products, such as meat and bone meal (MBM) as a protein supplement to non-ruminant animal feed and pet food continues in many BSE-free countries, different regulatory emphases are placed on specific animal species and the materials that are permissible for use or prohibited. Therefore, methods that can reliably detect prohibited animal species in MBM and feedstuffs are crucial for effective implementation and enforcement of the preventive measures for BSE, as well as other Transmissible Spongiform Encephal-opathies. The requirement of adequate sensitivity and reliability of the assay to not only detect prohibited species but also differentiate the prohibited tissues from allowed animal materials, such as blood, milk and gelatin of the same species, and without cross reaction with plant materials in severely heat-processed and highly complex feed samples has greatly increased the level of the challenge involved in method development.

In this chapter, the author presents a brief overview of the techniques that are currently used to identify meat species and/or quantify the species content. These methods are summarized in Figure 30.1 and the currently available commercial assays for meat species identification are listed in Table 30.1. The term "meat species" is used in this chapter to refer to a broad range of animal species including mammalian, avian and marine animals. The intent is not to provide an exhaustive review of the analytical methods in this area but to describe the trend of method development and to discuss the principles, usefulness and limitations of the most commonly used techniques illustrated by using exemplary studies. More detailed reviews of the methods used for meat species identification in food or feed products at various developmental stages can be found in a number of articles in the literature (6, 14–22). The classic methods such as electrophoresis, chromatography and immunodiffusion usually depend on the stability of the soluble proteins and are generally applied to raw meat products, although some have also been applied to cooked meat with limited success. Since the recent development of new techniques has centered on protein-based enzyme immunoassay and DNA-based Polymerase Chain Reaction (PCR) analyses in heat-processed products, essential factors and considerations important to their assay development are discussed. An overall comparison between these two approaches is made in terms of specificity, sensitivity, quantitative measure and convenience of the assay.

II. CURRENTLY AVAILABLE METHODS

A. Electrophoresis

Electrophoresis is a powerful technique for the separation of soluble proteins into distinctive banding patterns. In general, most electrophoretic methods use sarcoplasmic proteins for species identification in raw meat, because heat denatures and insolubilizes most of the native sarcoplasma proteins, protein extracts of heat-processed meat result in only a few faint bands. Analysis of meat samples by electrophoretic methods must be made by comparing the patterns obtained to those of authentic samples run simultaneously. Usually, the complex protein banding fingerprint makes electrophoresis unsuitable for the analysis of meat mixtures. Several electrophoretic techniques are described below. They are commonly used to differentiate animal species, mostly in raw samples, although a few heat-processed sample treatments are also included.

1. Sodium Dodecyl Sulfate-Polyacrylamide Gel Electrophoresis (SDS-PAGE)

SDS-PAGE is the most widely used technique for the separation of soluble proteins based on their molecular sizes.

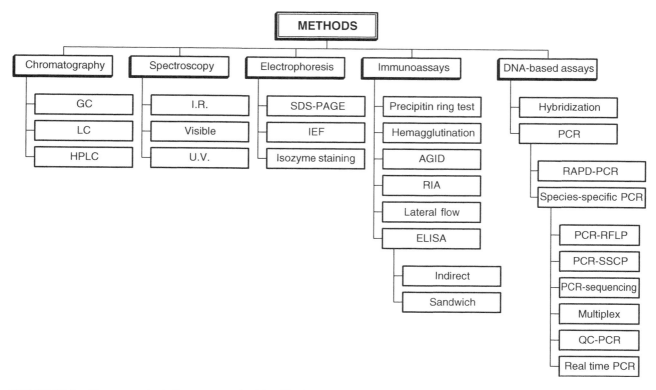

FIGURE 30.1 Current methods for meat species identification.

This technique has been successfully used to detect differences in native and heat-treated muscle proteins of various animals (23–25). Separation of different muscle proteins by SDS-PAGE usually results in relatively uniform patterns, therefore, this method is less reliable for meat species identification (26–28). Using more sensitive silver staining for visualization of the SDS-PAGE protein bands, Zerifi et al. (29) reported that this method detected species adulteration in cooked meat at concentrations of 10% (w/w) in a binary meat mixture. However, many factors other than the animal species, such as the amount of protein loaded on the gel, the freshness of the meat, the age and sex of the animal, the residual blood content, the degree of heat processing and the staining techniques, may all affect the protein-banding patterns. Thus, the lack of sensitivity and reproducibility of the assay and the difficulty of the gel interpretation are the main drawbacks limiting the use of SDS-PAGE for meat species identification.

2. Isoelectric Focusing (IEF)

IEF separates proteins into characteristic patterns based on differences in the isoelectric points of their protein bands. IEF was first used by Tinbergen and Olsman (30) for species identification. It has since been extensively used and officially recommended for the identification of fish species (31–34). The IEF protein banding profiles for many species are available from the U.S. Food and Drug Administration (http://vm.cfscan.fda.gov). It is also used in identifying animal species in either raw or cooked meats (35–39). Although the resolution is better than SDS-PAGE, the patterns of the total protein profiles obtained by IEF are much more complicated and less consistent (40). The technique may be useful for identifying individual species within families or genera, but the large number of protein bands makes the interpretation of the results impossible in meat mixtures or in uncommon meat samples.

3. Isozyme Staining

Another possible approach is to use isozyme staining to improve the sensitivity of electrophoretic assays in raw meat. Isozymes are different enzyme proteins that catalyze the same reaction. After electrophoretic separation of meat protein extracts, the gel is stained for a particular enzymatic reaction. The staining makes the isozymes catalyze the formation of colored compounds via a set of coupled reactions. For most meat extracts, isozyme staining will lead to several different protein bands on the gel at different positions, which correspond to the different enzyme proteins that are capable of catalyzing the same enzymatic reaction. The relative positions of the isozyme markers are characteristic of the species. Several staining systems using isozymes, such as esterase (41, 42), phosphoglucomutase (43), creatine kinase (44, 45), lactate dehydrogenase (40, 46) and peroxidase (47) have been employed for species

TABLE 30.1

Commercial Assay Products for Meat Species Identification

Company	Product Name	Type of Test	Species	Conditions	References
Adgen	DNAnimal Consensus	PCR	B, C, S, P or T	Raw, cooked, boiled, smoked, gelatin, processed	http://www.adgen.co.uk/index.php?area=foodfeed&kword=meat%20speciation&formaction=get_products&referrerArea=speciation&intro=meat_spec
	BOS Ident		B		
	BOS Quant		B	MBM and feed	
	Ruminant MBM tests (Neogen tests)	Lateral flow strip tests	Rum		
Alcum	Standard Animal-Kits	PCR	C, T, B, P, Go, Do or S	Raw, boiled, cooked and sausage	http://www.alcum.de/engl/index.html
	Extra Animal-Kits		C, T, P, B or H	Highly heated canned foods or products	
Biotools B&M Labs, S.A.	Biofood identification kit	PCR-RFLP	Vertebrates (e.g. Fish, P, B, C, T, S, Go, R, H, Dog, Cat, Du or G)	Raw and processed	http://www.biotools.net/eng/productos/f12.htm
	Biofood mixed kit	PCR	H, S, B, Go, C, or P	Raw and processed	http://www.biotools.net/eng/productos/f13.htm
Cibus Biotech	CIB-A-Kits (standard)	PCR	C, B, Do, Go, P, S or T C-T-B-P (mix kit)	Raw, boiled and cooked	http://www.cibus-biotech.de/products/products.html#2.1
	CIB-A-Kits (extra)	PCR	C, B, H, O, P or T C-T-B-P (mix kit)	Extremely processed and canned	
Coring System Diagnostic GmbH	PCR-standard-kits	PCR	Do, C, T, B, S, P or Go B-P-C-T (mix kit)	Raw and cooked	http://www.coring.de/eng/pcr_uk.htm#tierart
	PCR-extra-kits	PCR	C, H, T, O, P or Rum B-P-C-T (mix kit)	Processed products	
ELISA Technologies	ELISA-TEK microplate kits	ELISA	C-P-Po or C-T-S B-P-Po or S-H-D	Raw Cooked	http://www.elisa-tek.com/
	MELISA-TEK Meat Species Kit	ELISA	Rum or P	MBM, feed, cooked and raw	
r-Biopharm	DTEK immunosticks	Immunosticks	B, P, S, H, Go, R, K, Wb or Po	Raw	http://www.r-biopharm.com/food-andfeed/pdf/surefood_elisa.pdf
	Surefood	PCR/ELISA	B, P, S, Go, C, G, T, Du or D B-S-Go, C-G-T-Du, B-P-T-C, B-P, C-T or C-P	Raw and processed	
Neogen	Reveal ruminant feed Reveal ruminant MBM	Lateral flow strip tests	Rum	MBM and finished feed	http://www.neogen.com/bse.htm
Strategic Diagnostics Inc.	FeedChek	Lateral flow test	Mam/avian/fish, Mam only	Raw and finished feed	http://www.sdix.com/ProductSpecs.asp?nProductID=40
Tepnel	BioKits Animal Speciation Testing	ELISA/ Immunosticks Immunosticks PCR	B, P, S, H or Po B, P, S or Po C, T, K, R, H, Go or Bu B, P, S, C, H, T, R or Go	Cooked Raw Raw Cooked and raw	http://www.tepnel.com/ag_bio_and_food_testing/animal_speciation_testing.asp

B = Beef	D = Deer	G = Goose	K = Kangaroo	O = Ostrich	R = Rabbit	T = Turkey
Bu = Buffalo	Do = Donkey	Go = Goat	Mam = Mammalian	P = Pork	Ru = Ruminant	Wb = Water buffalo
C = Chicken	Du = Duck	H = Horse	MBM = Meat & bone meal	Po = Poultry	S = Sheep	

identification of meat after electrophoresis. Although isozyme patterns are essentially the same for all members within a species, there are distinctive patterns between each species (40) and some variations within species age and sex groups may also occur (41). Since the proteins must retain their activity for the staining process, it is essential that the isozyme markers do not denature during extraction and electrophoresis (43, 46). As a result, this method is less reliable due to the difficulty of controlling the enzyme activity of the unknown samples and its application is thus limited to the identification of species in raw meat.

4. Capillary Electrophoresis (CE)

Capillary electrophoresis is a sensitive separation technique that combines the electrophoresis principle with chromatographic methods for protein analysis. A sodium dodecyl sulfate polymer-filled capillary gel electrophoresis (CE-SDS) method was developed by Cota-Rivas and Vallejo-Cordoba (48) for species identification of raw beef, pork and turkey meat. The CE-SDS sarcoplasmic protein profiles that resulted were specific for each animal species both qualitatively and quantitatively. The same authors (49) later developed a pattern recognition statistical model that utilized linear discrimination analysis to interpret the CE-SDS meat protein profiles. This method is sensitive enough to differentiate between mechanically recovered chicken meat and hand-deboned chicken breast meat based on the difference in their hemoglobin (50). In general, however, this level of sensitivity is not desirable for routine meat species identification but only serves to complicate the results. Although fast separation, automation and on-line data analysis are major advantages of the technique, investment in an expensive instrument is required. It is also extremely difficult to interpret the results, especially when mixtures of multiple species or protein additives are involved.

B. Chromatography

Chromatographic methods such as gas chromatography (GC), liquid chromatography (LC) and high performance liquid chromatography (HPLC) have been applied to identify species in meat samples based on an examination of their fatty acid composition (51), histidine dipeptides (52, 53) or protein profiles (54, 55). Among these techniques, HPLC has been the most frequently used method by researchers. For example, a reverse phase high-performance liquid chromatography (RP-HPLC) method has been used to identify several animal species in raw and heated meat based on species-dependent histidine peptides, specifically the ratio of carnosine to serine (C/A) (53). In another study a size-exclusion HPLC column was used to examine differences in the myofibrillar protein profiles of fresh meat samples (55). Although the chromatographic patterns were similar for different muscles within species,

there were several unique proteins and the percentage area under several protein peaks varied (54, 55), which may present difficulties for data interpretation. Based on the rationale that fat is not affected by heating, an LC method was developed for the detection of pork and lard in fresh and heat-processed meats based on the increased ratio of the triglyceride containing saturated fatty acid to the triglyceride containing unsaturated fatty acid at the C-2 position after derivatization (56). However, since the fat content in meat products varies widely, it is difficult to quantify meat adulteration from the fat profiling methods alone. As with electrophoretic methods, chromatographic methods may be capable of differentiating between individual meat species, but they are less effective in detecting adulterated species in meat mixtures or cooked meat because of the increased complexity of the chromatographic patterns. In addition, the requirements of expensive instruments and laborious sample preparation procedures have restricted their use for regulatory purposes.

C. Spectroscopy

Spectroscopic methods are based on the light absorption at selective wavelength of the electromagnetic spectrum by the molecules in the samples. Spectroscopies using mid-infrared (2000–800 cm^{-1}), near-infrared (750–2498 nm) and visible (400–750 nm) reflectance spectra of meat samples for both discrimination and quantification of species content have been reported (57, 58). These spectral ranges can be used alone and in combination. Data in each spectral region are related but not identical and their combination may provide a synergistic advantage to spectroscopic analysis (59). A near-infrared spectroscopic technique was developed to distinguish between beef and kangaroo meat (60) and detect beef hamburgers adulterated with 5–25% mutton, pork, skim milk powder or wheat flour with an accuracy of up to 92.7% (61). A feasibility study on the application of mid-infrared spectroscopy has been used for quantification of chicken/turkey blends (62). A combined visible and near-infrared spectroscopy has been applied to identify species in raw homogenized meats (63) and to detect MBM in fish meal (64). When an adulterant is detected, the adulteration level can be predicted by using calibration equations for each adulterant. However, the performance of the calibration equations may be affected by several factors, including spectral scatter, derivative treatment and even sample presentation methods. The position of the spectral peaks of absorption bands may shift not only due to adulteration with other meat, but also with different food additives, fat contents, residual blood and moisture levels and cooking methods (61). In addition, this spectroscopic technique requires advanced knowledge of using statistical models for data processing and different models may be required for each possible blend of meat (58). Thus, the application of this technique to identify meat species in highly processed products presents serious difficulties and it is neither a common nor a convenient method for the routine analysis of meat origin.

D. IMMUNOASSAYS

Ever since the beginning of the 20th century, immunological approaches based on specific antibody-antigen reactions have been applied in meat species identification (65). Classical immunological procedures that use antispecies antisera include the precipitin ring test (66), hemagglutination inhibition tests (67) and the agar gel immunodiffusion (AGID) technique (68). Advances in immunochemical techniques have led to new types of immunoassays, including radioimmunoassays, enzyme immunoassays and non-enzymatic chromatographic immunoassays (lateral flow), with greatly improved sensitivity and accuracy. Radioimmunoassay is commonly used only in clinical settings, as the hazardous radioactive materials involved and the requirement for expensive and delicate scintillation counting equipment have restricted its use in routine and field tests of meat species. Two immunoassays, agar gel immunodiffusion (AGID) and the more recent enzyme-linked immunosorbent assay (ELISA), both of which are widely used for meat identification, are described in more detail in the following sections.

1. Agar Gel Immunodiffusion

Agar gel immunodiffusion (AGID), a double immunodiffusion technique originally described by Ouchterlony (68), involves the diffusion of antigens and antibodies in a semisolid agar gel. After overnight incubation, a visible opaque band is formed at the point where the antibody and its correspondent antigen have met. The modification of this technique using stabilized reagent paper discs and pre-prepared agar plates has led to the development of convenient field test kits such as ORBIT (Overnight Rapid Bovine Identification Test, 69), PROFIT (Poultry Rapid Overnight Field Indentification Test, 70), PRIME (Porcine Rapid Overnight Field Identification Method, 71), SOFT (Serological Ovine Field Test, 72), REST (Rapid Equine Serological Test, 73), DRIFT (Deer Rapid Identification Field Test, 74) and MULTI-SIFT (MultiSpecies Identification Field Test) for meat speciation by USDA-FSIS meat inspectors (75). These field tests are mainly based on the detection of serum proteins and are suitable for testing intact pieces of raw meat. Antisera against plasma proteins for raw meat species identification are available commercially. The detection limit of the assay for the target species in a meat admixture relies on the quality of the antispecies antisera. With traditional AGID, the detection limit of the assay is usually in the region of 3–10% (17, 76). In most cases, standardization of the commercial antisera against each type

of sample is required. Although AGID is relatively simple to perform, it requires a substantial amount of antisera and the variable sensitivity, possible interferences by non-meat ingredients and the requirement for overnight incubation have restricted AGID to qualitative assays of whole pieces of fresh meat.

2. Enzyme-Linked Immunosorbent Assay (ELISA)

ELISA has gained widespread acceptance for meat speciation applications due to its simplicity, specificity and sensitivity and is now recognized as a suitable analytical method for quality control and enforcement of muscle food safety and labeling regulations. It can be used for assaying various analytes in complex mixtures with minimal sample preparation requirements. ELISA does not need major scientific equipment, is easy to perform, uses only small quantities of immunoreagents, and has large-scale screening and field test capacity. However, the success of the assay primarily relies on the quality of the detecting antibodies that capture the target protein antigen in a sample extract. Both polyclonal (Pabs) and monoclonal (Mabs) antibodies have been employed in various formats of ELISA for the detection of species adulteration. Traditionally, Pabs obtained from the antisera of immunized animals have been used in ELISA. More recently, however, several Mabs against muscle proteins have been developed for the identification of raw meat (77–81) and for heat-processed meats and feedstuffs (6, 28, 82–85). A comprehensive review of studies published up to 1998 of ELISAs that utilize Pabs and Mabs for species identification of raw and cooked meat is provided in Hsieh et al. (6).

The two ELISA formats most commonly used for meat speciation are indirect ELISA and double sandwich ELISA. Indirect ELISA involves the adsorption of a fixed amount of meat proteins that may or may not contain the antigen molecules of a target species onto a microtiter plate. An antispecies antibody is then used to bind the antigen to the solid phase. The immunoreaction between the bound antigen and the antibody can be detected by a secondary anti-immunoglobulin enzyme conjugate, and subsequently color is developed by the addition of the enzyme substrate. The color intensity is proportional to the amount of antigen present in the protein extract. Indirect ELISA is often used to determine the titers and specificity of an antibody reagent. However, it is neither a convenient nor a reliable assay format for the routine analysis of unknown samples because the protein concentration for each meat extract must be determined before the sample can be properly diluted and coated on the microtiter plate. The dilution and composition of the meat extract affects the antibody binding, and thus the ELISA results. Sandwich ELISA employs an antibody immobilized on the solid phase as the capture antibody and another antibody as the detecting antibody to form a sandwich with the antigen in the middle and two antibodies attached on the different epitopes of the antigen molecule. This is a more user-friendly format that is widely used for commercial test kits because properly diluted sample extracts can be directly added to the assay plates which are pre-coated with the first capturing antibody reagent. To develop a sandwich ELISA, if Pabs are used in the assay, the same Pab reagent can be used for both the capturing and detecting antibodies due to its heterogenous nature. If Mabs are used, however, two different antibodies with similar specificity and affinity that bind to different epitopes are required. A combination of Pab and Mab is also commonly used in a sandwich ELISA.

3. Factors to Be Considered in Immunoassay Development

a. Species markers

To identify an animal species using an immunoassay, a suitable species marker must be chosen as the antigen for antibody development. For most raw meat identification, serum proteins have been used as antigens to develop the immunoassays (2, 86–88). Serum proteins are water soluble and easy to extract, thus the sample preparation is simple. However, the presence of serum proteins may not necessarily denote the presence of muscle tissues due to variations in the residual blood content of the muscle tissues. Such assays would not be reliable for quantifying adulteration levels of extraneous muscle tissues (89). Moreover, serum proteins are susceptible to heat denaturation; the reliability of using serum proteins for detecting species origin would be greatly reduced in cooked meats (90). Any antigens used for cooked meat identification must either be able to withstand cooking or maintain their antigenicity after heating.

Assays based on the detection of heat-resistant, species-specific muscle proteins are more indicative for a quantitative measure of lean meat, as well as supporting the assay in both raw and cooked meat mixtures (77, 82). Several researchers have attempted to resolve the thermal-stable components of different meat species. Milgrom and Witebsky (91) described antigens from the adrenal gland that are suitable for species identification. Those antigens, designated as BE, retained their immunogenic properties even after being subjected to boiling and autoclaving, and can be precipitated with ethanol. Hayden (92) developed polyclonal antisera to adrenal BE antigens for species identification using an immunodiffusion assay, which enabled the detection of meat from different species at 5–10% levels in cooked beef sausages. Using isoelectric focusing, Jones and Mortimer (37) demonstrated that for the thermal-stable muscle proteins (TSMP) eluted in a low pH range (3.5–6.5), the characteristic pattern of thermal-stable proteins from different species were not notably different. Sherikar et al. (93) later reported that "troponin T," with a molecular weight of 36 kD, was the specific antigenic fraction of the TSMPs. Assays based on these TSMP markers showed more or less cross-reactivity to certain non-specific proteins. ELISA protocols currently used by the USDA-FSIS for the identification of cooked meats utilize Pabs against heat-resistant muscle glycoproteins (94, 95). Several commercial sandwich ELISA kits for cooked meat speciation have also been produced based on the detection of the glycoproteins (Table 30.1). These commercial kits are able to analyze meats cooked under normal conditions, although the ELISA signal decreases rapidly when the meat is cooked above 100°C.

Antisera raised against crude thermal-stable muscle proteins according to the method of Kang'ethe and Gathuma (96) have been used to detect ruminant proteins in rendered animal materials heated to >130°C (97). However, the ELISA based on these antisera requires a lengthy procedure to remove gelatin, which interferes with the measurement, and to concentrate sample proteins in order to boost the assay sensitivity. The assays also exhibit cross-reactivity with plant protein present in the feedstuff (98, 99). In our own laboratory, troponin I (TnI), a subunit of troponin which is a contractile regulatory protein in the muscle thin filament, has been identified as a suitable species-specific and thermal-stable biomarker for meat species identification in raw, cooked and autoclaved meats (100, 101). Mabs developed against TnI could detect and quantify muscle protein heated up to 132°C for 2 hours without compromising any of the reaction signals (85). An indirect ELISA based on the Mabs raised against porcine TnI was developed to quantify pork skeletal muscle tissue in a meat admixture, with a detection limit of 0.5% (w/w) (28). Sandwich ELISAs based on TnI-specific Mabs have also been developed for the detection of prohibited animal proteins, such as ruminant, mammalian and all animal species, in rendered MBM and/or in feeds with a detection limit of 5 ng/ml of TnI, or at least 0.05% of the adulteration meat species in feed (102). In addition, the abundance of TnI in muscle tissue and its excellent extractability, even after severe heating, offers advantages for a sensitive detection method with a simple sample extraction procedure. The lateral flow strip test kits marketed by a U.S. company (Table 30.1) are based on the detection of the ruminant TnI antigen, and are currently being used internationally for BSE surveillance.

b. Antibodies

Once a suitable antigen has been selected, the most important criterion for the successful development of enzyme immunoassays for meat speciation is the production of species-specific antibodies raised against the antigen. The antibodies are the key immunoreagents that differentiate individual species. The performance of ELISA depends on the nature, quality and availability of the antibody used and both Pabs and Mabs have been used in immunoassays for species identification. Pabs are antibodies obtained from the antiserum produced by an immunized animal in response to an antigen. They are relatively quick and easy to develop and are heterogeneous in nature, with subpopulations binding to either species-specific or non-species-specific epitopes; hence cross-reactivity of the antisera with closely related species is commonly observed (103). However, the preparation of species-specific antisera requires immunoaffinity adsorption of cross-reactivity, which is a costly and time-consuming procedure. Moreover, variations in specificity and affinity between batches of antisera are the major concerns when developing standardized procedures (15). In contrast, Mabs are produced by a chemical fusion of antibody-producing cells (B-lymphocytes) and myeloma cells. They offer advantages over Pabs due to their homogeneous nature and biologically well-defined characteristics. Although the initial development costs of Mabs are higher than for Pabs, the use of Mabs in immunoassays ensures a continuous supply of a uniform immunoreagent and will eventually reduce the cost of the analysis (6, 77). Since every Mab has unique binding properties, ELISA procedures for each Mab must be optimized individually to achieve the most accurate analysis and the lowest detection limit.

Usually, IgG is the class of Mabs that is preferred for use in immunoassays, as it has been reported that IgM Mabs frequently participate in unexpected cross-reactions (104). IgM Mabs that are high-molecular-weight molecules are also more difficult to purify and store than IgGs (105). The most convenient way to avoid obtaining IgMs is to screen hybridoma clones with detection antibodies specific to the IgG γ-chain.

4. Specificity

Immunoassays for species identification are typically developed for a specific animal species and cross-reactivity of the antibody reagent to closely related species is often a major concern. As mentioned previously, the preparation of species-specific Pab reagents requires immunoaffinity absorption of the cross reactive components. Usually, pure antigen is required to immunize animals in order to increase the chance of producing more specific Pabs in the antiserum. Developing Mabs does not require the use of a pure antigen and crude antigens could theoretically be used for the production of species-specific Mabs. However, we found this to be ineffective, as the chance of selecting a specific clone by immunizing and screening with crude antigen is remote. The development of mono-specific Mabs is much more difficult than that of group-specific Mabs. This is mainly because species-specific antigenic determinants on the crude protein antigens are much rarer than those determinants shared by zoologically related species. The use of a pure antigen with known species-specific antigenic

determinants substantially increases the chances of eliciting specific antibodies.

Developing antibodies with broad specificity is also important for the initial screening of samples for the detection of species adulteration or substitution in meat products. Currently available commercial ELISA kits for meat species identification are designed for qualitative tests of a single species at a time. For regulatory purposes, it is very expensive and time-consuming to test a large number of samples for multiple species using these ELISA kits, and it would be much more cost- and labor-effective for a single screening to be used to distinguish between different classes of meat. Mabs developed to recognize common mammalian species in cooked poultry products (83) and to detect poultry meat in cooked mammalian meat (84) have been reported. More recently, Chen et al. (85, 102) developed ruminant-specific, mammalian-specific and all animal-specific Mab-based immunoassays for the detection of ruminant, mammalian and animal proteins, respectively, in feedstuffs. These assays do not differentiate between individual species within the group but detect the presence of animal proteins of the target group.

The specificity requirement of an assay to differentiate allowed animal proteins from prohibited tissue proteins to ensure compliance with the BSE surveillance regulations presents fresh challenges for the development of species identification immunoassays. Specificity of the antibodies to muscle proteins seems to be a prerequisite for the development of such assays. Immunoassays using skeletal-muscle-specific Mabs that are able to detect severely heat-treated target meat with no cross-reactivity to blood and food proteins, including milk proteins, egg albumin, soy proteins and gelatin, have been reported (102, 106). The muscle-specificity of the assay is also important for food testing because food proteins are frequently used as additives in commercially prepared meat products.

E. DNA-BASED ASSAYS

Immunoassays have been extensively used for authentication of animal species in raw meat for decades, but the non-availability of antibodies or cross-reactions of the antibodies to proteins from closely related animal species in highly processed and heat-treated meat is the major reason behind recent efforts to develop nucleic acid-based methods as a alternative approach. In general, DNA is both more stable and more heat-resistant than proteins and the information content of DNA is greater than that of proteins due to the degeneracy of the genetic code. For these reasons, DNA-based methods are now being developed to counter the challenges that currently limit immunoassay techniques. DNA hybridization and polymerase chain reactions (PCR) are the two major DNA-based analytical approaches to meat species identification. DNA hybridization techniques are generally time-consuming and complicated. In contrast, the more recent PCR techniques, which easily amplify target regions of template DNA with or without prior knowledge of the genetic information, have proved to be more sensitive and rapid than DNA-based techniques for meat species identification. Lockley and Bardsly (20) have reviewed DNA-based methods for food authentication.

1. Hybridization

The initial studies using DNA for meat speciation were based on hybridization of labeled DNA probes to samples. Either genomic DNA or cloned DNA was hybridized with target genomic DNA that had been covalently attached to nylon membranes in a slot- or dot-blot format and detected by color development or autoradiography (107–111). This had the advantage that preparation of probes from genomic DNA did not require prior knowledge of the DNA sequences. Utilizing hybridization based on a total genomic probe, a cross-reaction between cattle, sheep and goats was observed, reflecting some degree of homology in the sequences of the satellite DNA in these closely related species (109). Modified DNA hybridization for reducing cross-reaction by the addition of unlabeled DNA from the cross-hybridizing species enabled differentiation between sheep and goat with about a 10% detection limit (111). Improved assay specificity was also achieved by using probes derived from published satellite sequence information. Wintero et al. (108) compared a probe based on a 2.7 kb porcine specific satellite fragment (112) with labeled total genomic DNA, and found the former to be more specific. The use of species-specific satellite DNA probes for the unequivocal identification of raw meat from pigs, cattle, deer, chickens, turkeys, rabbits, sheep and goats has been reported (113–115). As the species-specific probes tend to be relatively short oligonucleotides of less than 100 bases, hybridization is possible even after DNA degradation has occurred. These methods are specific and useful for the identification of cooked meat species, but the procedure is complex, time-consuming and inadequate for complex sample matrices or for quantification of adulteration levels.

2. Polymerase Chain Reaction (PCR)

PCR methods have gained tremendous popularity in recent years because the amplification power of the PCR technique enables the detection of target DNA sequences when sample quantity is limited. A wide variety of PCR-based methods for the identification of meat species in food and feed products have been developed in the past decade. All of these PCR methods can be categorized into two approaches, Random Amplified Polymorphic DNA (RAPD) and species-specific PCR. RAPD amplifies multiple unidentified sequences using non-specific primers, leading to species-specific fingerprints of PCR products visualized by gel electrophoresis. No prior knowledge of the DNA sequences is required. Species-specific PCR uses either conserved or specific oligonucleotide primer pairs targeting species-distinguishing sequences in genomic or mitochondrial DNA. The prior knowledge on the DNA sequences is required for primer design. The amplified PCR products can then be discriminated according to their sizes, sequencing or further analyses such as Restriction Fragment Length Polymorphism (RFLP) or Single Strand Conformational Polymorphism (SSCP). Advances in modern PCR techniques have emphasized improving the efficiency, reproducibility and speed of detection.

a. Random Amplified Polymorphic DNA (RAPD)

Using arbitrary primers based on short oligonucleotide sequences, the RAPD method amplifies numerous unidentified sequences simultaneously. After gel electrophoresis, the PCR products generate fingerprint patterns that contain features unique to a particular species. The discriminating ability of the RAPD-PCR is virtually unlimited because there is an unlimited choice of arbitrary primers. However, not all random primers can adequately distinguish between species. A careful screening and selection of the primer used is important for the successful application of the technique (116). RAPD has been employed to differentiate species in domestic animals (117), various meat and meat products (116, 118) and feedstuffs (119). RAPD has also been shown to produce clear fingerprints from processed products in which DNA has been slightly degraded, such as smoked or salted fish products (120). Although the technique generates informative fingerprints in a relatively short time, the reproducibility of the patterns is unpredictable due to various factors, such as changes in cycling conditions or intra-species polymorphisms. Use of longer primers and higher stringency amplification conditions may improve the assay reproducibility and resolution (121). Therefore, RAPD assay protocols must be optimized for each application and must be stringently followed to ensure assay repeatability. The DNA molecules are usually degraded into smaller fragments in severely processed products; RAPD analysis thus cannot reliably be used to analyze canned or sterilized samples. In addition, RAPD may not be practical for identifying species of origin in products containing 50–50% mixtures of species that can be interbred, because the pattern of a 50–50% meat mixture cannot be distinguished from that of a hybrid (120). Thus, RAPD is useful as a rapid, qualitative method for meat speciation, but known standards must be run simultaneously each time a sample is tested (117). A review of the principles and applications of RAPD assay for genetic analysis of livestock species was published by Cushwa and Medrano (16).

b. Species-specific PCR

Species-specific PCR for species identification has been developed to target a DNA segment with sufficient species-specific variation. The forward and reverse primers are designed to be specific to each species based on the alignment of available DNA sequences from selected genes. Under stringently defined reaction conditions, such primers generate an amplicon only in the presence of DNA from a given species. Complete sequence information permits the size of the product to be predicted, so that the identification can be confirmed if an appropriately sized amplicon appears on the gel. Mitochondrial genes such as the ATPase subunit 8 and subunit 6 (122, 123), D-loop (124) and cytochrome b (Cyt b) genes (125–129), satellite DNA (130), actin genes (131, 132), Art2 short and CR1 long interspersed repetitive elements in genomic genes (133) and growth hormone gene (134) have been studied for the purpose of identifying animal species, with most of the methods concentrating on the Cyt b gene as a target sequence. The specificity of PCR primer pairs that encoded the Cyt b gene sequence has permitted the amplification of degraded tuna DNA for the identification of cooked and canned tuna fish species in commercial preparations (135). Tartaglia et al. (122) developed a bovine-specific PCR assay using bovine-specific mitochondrial DNA sequence, which allowed the detection of bovine meat and bone meal in feedstuffs at the 0.125% level. By amplifying the satellite DNA using a bovine-specific primer pair, Guoli et al. (130) was able to identify raw, cooked (100°C, 30 min) and autoclaved (120°C, 30 min) beef without cross-amplification with other animal species tested. Multiplex PCR allows simultaneous identification of multiple species with one PCR by using one universal primer from a conserved DNA sequence in the gene paired with multiple primers target to hybridize on species-specific sequences for each species (127, 136). All these species-specific PCR products were obtained without the need to adopt other secondary associated techniques such as, RFLP, SSCP or DNA sequencing.

More recently, several real-time PCR methods have been developed in order to shorten the assay time by eliminating the need for post-PCR processing, such as electrophoresis associated with conventional PCR. For real-time PCR using TaqMan™ technology (137), one of the primer probes is labeled with a reporter fluorescence dye and a quencher dye. When both dyes are attached to the probe, the fluorescence is quenched by the quencher dye so that negligible fluorescence from the reporter dye's emission is observed. Once the PCR amplification begins, DNA polymerase cleaves the labeled probe and the reporter dye is released from the probe. The separation of the reporter dye from the quencher dye during each amplification cycle generates a sequence-specific fluorescent signal. The signal increases in real time as the PCR cycles progress, as the intensity of the fluorescence is a function of the number of cycles. Real-time PCR, therefore, can be used to monitor the PCR product accumulation as the amplification cycle proceeds, allowing the detection of the target sequence with a high sensitivity. Since the analysis and detection take place in a closed reaction vessel, this has the advantage of minimizing carry-over contamination and reducing the incidence of false-positive results. TaqMan™ technology amplifying species-specific primers has been developed for the detection of beef or pork in foods with a detection limit of 0.1% to 0.01% of the adulteration level (138–140). An alternative real-time PCR system using LightCycler™ technology has been used for the detection of trace amounts of tiger bone, with a detecting power of 10 substrate molecules (141). In this system, fluorescence is emitted when labeled probes are hybridized to newly synthesized DNA (142).

3. Factors to Be Considered in the Development of PCR Methods

a. DNA probes

The specific interaction between the sequence of the DNA probe and the complementary sequence in the DNA segment of interest determines the assay outcome. PCR allows a particular sequence of DNA in samples to be targeted by primers and amplified. Selection of the primer sequence for PCR amplification depends on the sequence variation in primers that subsequently and adequately produce amplicons unique to each animal species. Primers used will affect the sensitivity and accuracy of the PCR assay. Total genomic probes can be used to identify distantly related species, but tailored oligonucleotide probes need to be designed for differentiation of closely related species (17). Most strategies to date have targeted the Cyt b gene in the mitochondrial DNA sequences because of the high number of copies per cell in animal tissues (143), inherent variability (144) and the difference in its gene arrangement between plants and animals (145). It has been shown that each cell may contain up to 1000 copies of Cyt b locus and Cyt b sequences differ by at least a few nucleotides even in very closely related species (146). PCR assays based on the amplification of Cyt b have the advantage of increased sensitivity compared to single or low copy nuclear DNA targets (147). The repetitive sequence in genomes can also be markers for sensitive species identification because these repetitive elements are present in more copies than mitochondrial DNA. Using short and long interspersed nuclotide elements, Tajima et al. (133) reported a PCR assay with improved sensitivity. Their primers were able to detect DNA in feed containing 0.01 to 0.001% commercial MBM. However, the quantity of genomic DNA or mitochondrial DNA per gram present in different types of tissues varies (148), which may affect the detection limit of the assay or a quantitative estimation of the target species in a meat mixture (136). For identification of hybridized animals, assays based on the maternally transmitted mitochondrial DNA are invalid because only the maternal lineage can be identified. Species origin of a hybrid animal can only be verified by analysis of nuclear DNA (149).

Although DNA is more heat stable than most proteins, DNA is also degraded by heat or the action of radicals. Severe heat treatment or prolonged processing of the meat product will increase the degradation of DNA; thus the recovery of analyzable DNA can be difficult or uneven from different species (127). The fragment sizes of DNA from meat heated to 100°C is reduced from ~1100 bp to ~300 bp (110), while the DNA extracted from canned tuna meat was degraded to an average size of ~100 bp. In order to confirm the utility of the PCR method for analyzing heat-processed tissues, the amplification should be carried out on DNA derived from larger portions that were subject to longer heating times (147). In other words, the length of the DNA fragments should be long enough to distinguish species variation and at the same time short enough to allow amplification of highly degraded DNA. RAPD analysis does not seem to be reliable for analyzing canned or sterilized samples. The specie-specific oligonucleotide probes which recognize relatively short sequences of DNA with adequate sequence variation between species, on the other hand, are able to accommodate a considerable amount of DNA degradation without influencing assay specificity. In addition, PCR fragments generated from mitochondrial DNA seem to be more successful than nuclear DNA for speciation of heat-processed samples because mitochondrial DNA, being circular in shape, is more resistant to heat disintegration (150). Most recently developed PCR methods (123, 138, 151–154) for the detection of bovine tissue in feedstuffs are based on the amplification of the ATPase subunits 8 and 6 of the bovine mitochondrial DNA sequences, which was firstly described by Tartaglia et al. (122).

b. Secondary analyses of PCR products

For species identification, several secondary analyses have been applied to PCR amplified products of which each targets a conserved region of the DNA sequence. These methods vary in their complexity, utility and cost due to the nature of each assay.

1. PCR-RFLP

PCR analysis with subsequent restriction fragment length polymorphism is the most widely used method of identifying meat and fish species (19). PCR-RFLP allows the genetic variation between species to be distinguished by digesting PCR amplified fragments from a conserved region of DNA with restriction enzymes, which act on DNA at specific sites. Based on the sequence variability among species, these enzyme-digested products can be visualized by agarose or polyacrylamide gel electrophoresis as a DNA fingerprint unique to each species. The banding pattern varies when different restriction enzymes are employed. It is important to use appropriate restriction enzymes and to ensure the complete digestion of all the DNA fragments analyzed. The enzymes selected should be available commercially, economically priced, reasonably active in the PCR mix and able to maximally differentiate

between the species analyzed. PCR-RFLP has been extensively used for meat species identification in food and feed samples (149, 154–160). Partis et al. (147) evaluated this DNA fingerprinting method for determining the species origin of raw and cooked meats by amplifying a fragment within the Cyt b gene, and concluded that although the PCR-RFLP is a suitable method for identifying species in raw and cooked pure animal tissues, the assay is not suitable for analyzing mixtures since the results may not be representative of the true components present in the mixture due to differential template amplification. The general applicability of RFLP may also be hampered by intraspecies DNA sequence polymorphism or point mutations that affecting the typical RFLP pattern of a species. To overcome this drawback, the use of two restriction enzymes for the identification of an unknown sample may be sufficient because no individual identified as having two different RFLP patterns compared to other individuals of the same species has been observed (156).

2. Sequencing

If information on the DNA sequence is available from databases, individual species may be identified through a given sequence of digestions with specific restriction enzymes (155). Direct sequencing of the PCR products is an ideal confirmation test and allows an assignment to a species even if there is no reference material available. Comparing Cyt b sequences from the database Brodmann et al. (5) reported that vertebrates of different classes showed correspondence of at the most 80%, and animals of the same genus showed correspondence above 94%. Correspondences of more than 99% generally indicate the same species. Traditionally, sequencing has been considered to be time-consuming and expensive and to require data handling skills, but due to recent advances in the nucleotide sequencing process, this method is nowadays relatively simple and fast. Since sequencing PCR fragments has become a standard procedure in laboratories working with recombinant DNA technologies, it has been suggested that a DNA sequence database for unambiguous authentication of animal species should be constructed (19). However, it is still difficult to apply sequencing to mixtures of different species.

3. PCR-SSCP

In comparisons involving high homology DNA sequences, further analysis of PCR products may be accomplished using Single Strand Conformational polymorphism (SSCP), which can be used to analyze the polymorphism at single loci. The PCR-SSCP technique is based on the principle that single-stranded DNA molecules take on specific sequence-dependent secondary structure under non-denaturing conditions. After performing the PCR, the amplicons are denatured to single strands. Single-stranded molecules differing by as little as a single base substitution will form different conformers and migrate differently in a non-denaturing gel electrophoresis (161). This technique has been applied to identify fish species (162–165) as well as differentiate between samples of species of pig and wild boar meat (166). Stringent conditions must be maintained for intra-base pairing, as this affects the electrophoretic mobility and reference material must be treated in the same way and run alongside the unknown sample. Intraspecies variability of single-strand DNA patterns may also cause some confusion in identifying an unknown sample. In such cases, different regions of the DNA probe can be used for SSCP, or use of RFLP analysis or sequencing of the amplicons (163).

F. OVERALL COMPARISON OF IMMUNOASSAY AND PCR METHODS

Immunoassay systems are suitable for use in the laboratory for routine analyses or large-scale sample screening, as well as for development into convenient field test kits. These assays usually only require simple sample preparation and need no major instrumentation. The overall assay time can be as short as 30 minutes. However, immunological approaches depending on antibodies often suffer from loss of reactivity due to heat treatment of the sample and cross-reactions of proteins from closely related species. Availability of suitable antibody reagents is the major limiting factor for the application of immunoassay methods. Immunoassays based on the detection of serum proteins are limited to qualitative analysis only because the amount of residual blood does not parallel the quantity of meat tissue present in a sample. In order to achieve a quantitative analysis, the assay must target an abundant antigen with an even distribution in muscle tissues from different parts of the animal, so that the amount of antigen measured by the assay corresponds to the amount of the target muscle tissue in the sample, regardless of the location of the cut. Once developed, the antibodies can be applied in various immunoassays for maximum success.

It is a common belief that PCR-based techniques offer a high detection sensitivity and specificity. They can be applied in both raw and highly processed products even with extensive protein denaturation; thus most of the recently developed methods for meat species differentiation in feedstuffs are PCR-based techniques (see Table 30.2). Since DNA can potentially provide more information through the acquisition of sequence database, differentiation of closely related species is less difficult than in an immunoassay, which relies on the availability of specific antibodies. However, PCR-based methods are technically demanding and prone to contamination; they also require expensive instruments and dedicated facilities. Moreover, PCR based methods for quantification of the extent of sample adulteration are complex and the data interpretation is difficult. Current DNA-based techniques provide no satisfactory answer to the proportional amount of a particular species for

the following reasons: 1) the difference in DNA quantity and extractability in different tissues (113); 2) differential template amplification resulted from primer mismatches (147); and 3) the ubiquity of DNA in all types of cells. Although quantitative PCR detection of porcine DNA has been reported (167, 168), the results only refer to the DNA content over a certain limited range, which cannot be translated into the content of fat or lean meat. DNA based methods are not able to distinguish between different tissues or materials (21). Therefore it is impossible to use DNA-based methods to differentiate prohibited animal tissue from the allowed blood or milk in feedstuffs. In addition, most PCR methods require the extraction of nucleic acids from the sample tissue, which limits its application for large-scale practice and the development of field testing kits. For all the above reasons, PCR-based techniques have not been adopted for routine analysis, while faster and more specific DNA-based technologies are developing rapidly. Accumulation of an extensive database of DNA sequences from different animal species will facilitate the design of primers, and thus the development and usefulness of PCR methods.

III. FINAL CONSIDERATIONS

Reliable analytical methods are indispensable for the accurate labeling of food and feed products. Detection of species adulteration requires an assay capable of working in complex and variable matrices. Hence, the challenges in developing antibody-based immunoassay or PCR methods for meat species identification lie in overcoming the potential cross-reactivity with other species and food additives. Usually, the judgment of the violation samples is limited to determining the minimum level that the method could achieve. For practical purposes, it is necessary to set a cutoff value for judging violations. Hsieh et al. (4, 7) applied 1% as their criterion for reporting the violation rate of species adulteration in official meat samples, because adulteration at such a low level would not confer any economic incentive. An assay capable of detecting down to the 1% adulteration level thus seems to be adequate for routine analysis. The assay sensitivity of both modern immunoassays and PCR methods are comparable, and either can achieve this generally acceptable detection limit of 1% or below for the adulteration level in food products. As the minimum safe level to prevent transmission of BSE in feedstuffs has not been established, no agreed sensitivity value of the assay has been established. A detection limit at a lower level than 1% is generally expected for safety reason. It is also crucial that the assay conditions are properly controlled in order to preclude incidences of false positive and false negative results.

It is necessary to optimize and standardize the conditions for protein or DNA extraction from a variety of samples. Due to the variation in sample composition, factors affecting the recoveries of antigen or DNA from samples,

TABLE 30.2
PCR and ELISA Methods Used to Identify Animal Species in Feedstuffs

References	Methods	Target Species	Probes	Detection Limit	Test of Industrial Samples No. Correctly Identified/No. Tested
159	PCR-RFLP	Dog or cat	Cyt b mt DNA	0.01% in rendered meat mixtures (121°C, 30 min)	
123	PCR	Bovine, ovine, swine or chicken	mtDNA*	0.01% in ref feedstuffs	
134	TaqMan™ real-time PCR	Mammal orbBovine (cross react w/Cervidae)	Growth hormone genes	0.02 ng or 0.01% DNA 1–5% in MBM	4/7 bovine in MBM 5/7 mammalian in MBM
158	PCR-RFLP	Cattle, sheep, goats, deer, elk	mtDNA	Not reported	
139	Real-time PCR	Cattle or pig	mtDNA	0.1–0.5% in feed	
168	PCR	Beef	Satellite DNA	1% bMBM (120°C, 30 min) in feed	
138	Real-time PCR	Bovine	mtDNA*	0.001% in LSR	4/6
133	PCR	Ruminants, pigs, chickens	Genomic DNA	0.01% in feed	
154	PCR-RFLP	Sheep, pork, poultry	mtDNA*	0.125% in LSR 1–5% in industrial MBM	3/7
157	PCR-RFLP	Ruminant or nonruminant	Cyt b mtDNA	Not reported	
153	PCR	Bovine	mtDNA*	0.125% in feed	False-negative 1.25% (3/240) False-positive 0.83%
152	PCR	Bovine, ovine or porcine	mtDNA*	0.3% (bovine/ovine) 1% (porcine) in LSR	Amplified 5/7 samples with accuracy of 72.5% and 60% for 2 extraction methods, failed to amplify 2/7 samples
151	PCR	Bovine	mtDNA	0.125% bMBM in feed	
122	PCR	Bovine	mtDNA*	0.125% bMBM in feed	
102	Sandwich ELISA	Ruminant	Tn I-specific Mabs	5 ng/ml TnI or 0.05% in feed	
85	Indirect ELISA	All animal, mammalian and ruminant species	Tn I-specific Mabs	0.1% (all animal) 0.3% (mammalian) 2% (ruminant) in feed	
98	Sandwich ELISA	Ruminant and porcine	Rabbit antisera	1250 ppm proteins after gelatin removal	
97	Sandwich ELISA	Ruminant	Rabbit antisera	166 ppm proteins after gelatin removal	

* Primer design according to Tartaglia et al., 1998 (Ref. 122)
bMBM: bovine meat and bone meal
Cyt b: cytochrome b
LSR: laboratory scale rendered samples

Mabs: monoclonal antibodies
MBM: meat and bone meal
mtDNA: mitochondrial DNA

PCR: polymerase chain reaction
RFLP: restriction fragment length polymorphism
TnI: troponin I

such as the extraction method, pH, salt content and heating conditions of the sample and sample matrices, need to be carefully controlled, studied and considered in interpretation of results. For validation of an assay, the lab-formulated meat mixtures might not sufficiently represent the vast variety of commercial products. Therefore, conducting trials on a variety of commercially available meat and feed products is important for assessing the validity of a new assay.

Ideal analytical methods for meat species identification and detection of species adulteration need to be specific, sensitive, rapid, affordable, of high throughput, able to analyze heat-processed as well as raw products and provide quantitative measures. No single method can meet all these requirements for all types of samples at all times. Selection of an assay depends on many factors, such as the purpose of the assay, nature of the sample, sample size and numbers, specificity and sensitivity required, turnaround time, cost, availability of facilities and equipment, etc. Although many challenges have yet to be fully met by any laboratory or diagnostic service, most assays mentioned in this chapter may be used complementarily to each other. To safeguard consumers, the integrity of the food chain is non-negotiable. As the problems and trends of species adulteration change in the meat and/or feed industries, in order to ensure compliance with the corresponding regulations, our analytical skills will continue to face challenges in this area. New techniques emphasizing faster and more convenient assays, such as one-step assays, biosensors, microarray technology, and automated systems based on antibodies, DNA or both, will provide the weapons for the next generation's fight to protect consumers and safeguard our food supply.

REFERENCES

1. C R-A Martin. Sale of horse flesh. British Food J 83:101–102, 1981.
2. R G Whittaker, T L Spencer, J W Copland. An enzyme-linked immunosorbent assay for species identification of raw meat. J Sci Food Agric 34:1143–1148, 1983.
3. L Rugraff, A Karleskind. Analysis of animal fat mixtures-application in checking that taflows and subsidiary raw or cooked meat products and derivatives are free from pork fat. Revue Française des Corps Gras 30: 323–325, 1983.
4. Y-H P Hsieh, B B Woodward, S H Ho. Detection of species substitution in raw and cooked meats using immunoassays. J Food Prot 58:555–559, 1995.
5. P D Brodmann, G Nicholas, P Schaltenbrand, E C Ilg. Identifying unknown game species: experience with nucleotide sequencing of the mitochondrial cytochrome b gene and a subsequent basic local alignment search tool search. Eur Food Res Technol 212:491–496, 2001.
6. Y-H P Hsieh, F-C Chen, N Djurdjevic. Monoclonal antibodies against heat-treated muscle proteins for the species identification and endpoint temperature determination of cooked meats. In: Quality Attributes of Muscle Foods. Y L Xiong, C T Ho, F Shahidi (eds). New York: Plenum Publishing Co, 1999, pp. 287–307.
7. Y-H P Hsieh, M A Johnson, C J Wetzstein, N R Green. Detection of species adulteration in pork products using agar gel immunodiffusion and enzyme linked immunosorbent assay. J Food Qual 19:1–13, 1996.
8. J W Wilesmith, G A H Wells, M P Cranwell, B M Ryan. Bovine spongiform encephalopathy: epidemiological studies. Vet Rec 123:638–644, 1988.
9. P Brown, R G Will, R Bradley, D Asher, L Detwiler. Bovine spongiform encephalopathy and variant Creutzfeldt-Jacob disease: background, evolution, and current concerns. Emerging Infectious Diseases 7:6–16, 2001.
10. European Commission (EC). Commission Decision 94/381/EC of 27 June 1994 concerning certain protection measures with regard to bovine spongiform encephalopathy and the feeding of mammalian derived protein. Off J Eur Comm L. 172, 7 July, 23–24, 1994.
11. FDA. Substances prohibited from use on animal food or feed; animal proteins prohibited in ruminant feed; final rule. 21 Code of Federal Regulations, Part 589, 2000, 1997.
12. World Health Organization (WHO). Variant Creutzfeldt-Jacob disease. http://www.who.int/mediacentre/factsheets/fs180/en/; accessed on January 23, 2004.
13. European Commission. Commission Decision of 29 December 2000 concerning control measures required for the implementation of Council Decision 2000/766/EC concerning certain protection measures with regard to transmissible spongiform encephalopathies and the feeding of animal protein. Off J Eur Comm, L002:32–40, 2001.
14. E K Kang'ethe. Use of immunoassays in monitoring meat protein additives. In: Development and Application of Immunoassay for Food Analysis. J H Rittenburg (ed.). Elservier Applied Science, New York: 1990, pp. 127–139.
15. R L S Patterson, S J Jones. Review of current techniques for the verification of the species origin of meat. Analyst 115: 501–506, 1990.
16. W T Cushwa, J F Medrano. Applications of the random amplified polymorphic DNA (RAPD) assay for genetic analysis of livestock species. Animal Biotechnol 7:11–31, 1996.
17. I D Lumley. Authenticity of Meat and Meat Products. New York: Blackie Academic & Professional, 1996, pp. 109–139.
18. I M Mackie. Authenticity of Fish. In: Food Authentication. P R Ashurst, M J Dennis (eds.). London: Blackie Academic & Professional, 1996, pp. 141–170.
19. P Bossier. Authentication of seafood products by DNA pattern. J Food Sci 64:1899–1993, 1999.
20. A K Lockley, R G Bardsley. DNA-based methods for food authentication. Trends. P R Ashurst, M J Dennis (eds.). London: Food Sci Technol 11:67–77, 2000.

21. D Moncilovic, A Rasooly. Detection and analysis of animal materials food and feed. J Food Prot 63:1602–1609, 2000.

22. G Gizzi, L W D van Raamsdonk, V Baeten, I Murray, G Berben, G Brambilla, C von Holst. An overview of tests for animal tissues in feeds applied in response to public health concerns regarding bovine spongiform encephalopathy. Rev Sci Tech Off Int Epiz 22:311–331, 2003.

23. T Kato, M Deki. 1977. Cited by K Hofmann. In: Biochemical Identification of Meat Species. R L S Patterson (ed.). New York: Elsevier Science Publishing, 1985, pp. 9–31.

24. R J McCormick, G R Reeck, D H Kropf. Separation and identification of porcine sarcoplasmic proteins by reversed-phase high-performance liquid chromatography and polyacrylamide gel electrophoresis. J Agric Food Chem 36:1193, 1988.

25. A Craig, A H Ritchie, I M Mackie. Determining the authenticity of raw reformed breaded scampi (Nephrops norvegicus) by electrophoretic techniques. Food Chem 52:451–454, 1995.

26. K Hofmann. Principle problems in the identification of meat species of slaughter animals using electrophoretic methods. In Biochemical Identification of Meat Species. R L S Patterson (ed.). New York: Elsevier Applied Science Publishers, 1985, pp. 9–31.

27. K Hofmann. Fundamental problems in identifying the animal species of muscle meat using electrophoretic methods. Fleischwirtschaft 67:820, 1987.

28. F-C Chen, Y-H P Hsieh, R C Bridgman. Monoclonal antibodies to porcine thermal-stable muscle protein for detection of pork in raw and cooked meats. J Food Sci 63:201–205, 1998.

29. A Zerifi, C Labie, G Bernard. SDS-PAGE technique for the species identification of cooked meat. Fleischwirtschaft 71:1060–1062, 1991.

30. B J Tinbergen, W J Olsman. Isoelectric focusing as a species identification technique in the inspection of food products. Fleischwirtschaft 10:1501, 1976.

31. H Rehbein. Electrophoretic techniques for species identification of fishery products. Z Lebensm Unters Forsch 191:1–10, 1990.

32. H Rehbein. Parvalbumins as marker proteins for the fish species in fishery products. In: Quality Assurance of the Fish Industry. Amsterdam: Elsevier Science, 1992, pp. 399–405.

33. T-S Huang, M R Marshall, C-I Wei. Identification of Red Snapper (Lutjanus campechanus) using electrophoretic techniques. J Food Sci 60:279–283, 1995.

34. Y-H P Hsieh, F-C Chen, M Nur. Rapid species identification of cooked red snapper using isoelectric focusing. J Food Sci 62:15–19, 1997.

35. K P Kaiser, G Matheis, C Knita-Durrmann. Qualitative and quantitative analysis of raw binary meat mixtures by means of isoelectric focusing. Z Lebensm Unters Forsch 171:415–419, 1980.

36. A J Sinclair, W J Slattery. Identification of meat according to species by isoelectric focusing. Aust Vet J 58:79, 1982.

37. S J Jones, R H Mortimer. Species identification of cooked meats by isoelectrofocusing: Preliminary studies to resolve heat-stable components isolated from adrenal and muscle tissue. In: Biochemical Identification of Meat Species. R L S Patterson (ed.). New York: Elsevier Science Publishing Inc., 1985, pp. 118–128.

38. L A Shelef. Characterization and identification of raw beef, pork, chicken and turkey meats by isoelectrophoretic patterns of the sarcoplasmic proteins. J Food Sci 51:731, 1986.

39. H J Skarpeid, K Kvaal, K I Hildrum. Identification of animal species in ground meat mixtures by multivariate analysis of isoelectric focusing protein profiles. Electrophoresis 19:3103–3109, 1998.

40. W J Slattery, A J Sinclair. A comparison of electrophoretic techniques for the species identification of meat. Food Technology in Australia 39:105–108, 1987.

41. H H Heinart, A Klinger. Tierartpezifische Eiweissdifterentzierung: Protein und enzymuster bei Reh und Hirsch. Fleischwirtsch 60:1682–1685, 1980.

42. V Prasad, D Misra. Differentiation of meats of different species of animals by muscle esterase pattern in different age and sex groups. Indian J Anim Sci 51:211–214, 1981.

43. N L King, L Kurth. Analysis of raw beef samples for adulteration meat species by enzyme-staining of isoelectric focusing gels. J Food Sci 47:1608–1612, 1982.

44. H Kim, L A Shelef. Characterization and identification of raw beef, pork, chicken and turkey meats by electrophoretic patterns of their sarcoplasmic proteins. J Food Sci 51:735–741, 1986.

45. R J McCormick, D A Collins, R A Field, T D Moore. Identification of meat from game and domestic species. J Food Sci 57:516–523, 1992.

46. W J Slattery, A J Sinclair. Differentiation of meat according to species by the electrophoretic separation of muscle lactate dehydrogenase and esterate isoenzymes and isoelectric focusing of soluble muscle proteins. Aust Vet J 60:47, 1983.

47. F Bauer, K Hofmann. Improving the sensitivity of electrophoretic determination of animal species of meat by means of peroxidase staining of myoglobins. Fleischwirtschaft 67:861, 1987.

48. M Cota-Rivas, B Vallejo-Cordoba. Capillary electrophoresis for meat species differentiation. J Capillary Electrophoresis 4:195–199, 1997.

49. B Vallejo-Cordoba, M Cota-Rivas. Meat species identification by linear discriminant analysis of capillary electrophoresis protein profiles. J Capillary Electrophoresis 5:171–175, 1998.

50. L Day, H Brown. Detection of mechanically recovered chicken meat using capillary gel electrophoresis. Meat Sci 58:31–37, 2001.

51. R Verbeke, H D Brabander. Differentiation of meat species in processed meat products through identification of animal fat species. In: Biochemical Identification of Meat Species. R L S Patterson (ed.). New York: Elsevier Science Publishing, Inc., 1985, pp. 145–154.

52. P R Carnegie, M Z Illic, MO Etheridge, M G Collins. Improved high performance liquid chromatographic method for analysis of histidine dipeptides anserine, camosine and balenine present in fresh meat. J Chromatogr 261:153–157, 1983.

53. G-S Chung, M-H Lee, J-M Kim, J M Park. Differentiation the species of origin of meats on the basis of the contents of histidine dipeptides in muscle. J Vet Sci 40:1–6, 1998.

54. S H Ashoor, W G Monte, P G Stiles. Liquid chromatographic identification of meats. J Assoc Off Anal Chem 71:397–403, 1998.

55. R-M Toorop, S J Murch, R O Ball. Development of a rapid and accurate method for separation and quantification of myofibrillar proteins in meat. Food Res Int 30:619–627, 1997.

56. T Saeed, S G Ali, H A A Rahman, W N Sawaya. Detection of pork and lard as adulterants in processed meat: Liquid chromatographic analysis of derivatized triglycerides. J Assoc Off Anal Chem 72:921–925, 1989.

57. H Rannou, G Downey. Discrimination of raw pork, chicken and turkey meat by spectroscopy in the visible, near- and mid-infrared ranges. Anal Comm 34:401–404, 1997.

58. G Downey, J McElhinney, T Fearn. Species identification in selected raw homogenized meats by reflectance spectroscopy in the mid-infrared, near infrared and visible ranges. Appl Spectrosc 54:894–899, 2000.

59. J McElhinney, G Downey, C O'Donnell. Quantitation of lamb content in mixtures with raw minced beef using visible, near and mid-infrared spectroscopy. J Food Sci 64:587–591, 1999.

60. H B Ding, R J Xu. Differentiation of beef and kangaroo meat by visible/near-infrared reflectance spectroscopy. J Food Sci, 64:814–817, 1999.

61. H B Ding, R J Xu. Near-infrared spectroscopic technique for detection of beef hamburger adulteration. J Agric Food Chem 48:2193–2198, 2000.

62. O Al-Jowder, E K Kemsley, R H Wilson. Mid-infrared spectroscopy and authenticity problems in selected meats: a feasibility study. Food Chem 59:195–201, 1997.

63. J McElhinney, G Downey. Chemometric processing of visible and near infrared reflectance spectra for species identification in selected raw homogenized meats. J Near Infrared Spectrosc 7:145–154, 1999.

64. I Murray, L S Aucott, I H Pike. Use of discriminant analysis on visible and near infrared reflectance spectra to detect adulteration of fish meal with meat-bone-meal. J NIRS 9:297–311, 2001.

65. P Uhlenhuth. Die Unterscheidung des Fleisches verschiedener Tiere mithilfe spezieller Sera und die praktische Anwendung der Methode in der Fleischbeschau. Dt Med Wschr 27:780, 1901.

66. F C Pinto. Serological identification of ox, buffalo, goat and deer flesh. Brit Vet J 117:540–544, 1961.

67. T Kamiyama, Y Katsube, K Imaizumi. Serological identification of animal species of meats by a passive hemagglutination inhibition test using cross-reacting anti-serum albumin antiserum. Jap J Vet Sci 40:653–661, 1978.

68. O Ouchterlony. In vitro method for testing the toxin-producing capacity of diphteria bacteria. Acta Pathol Microbiol Scand 25:186–191, 1948.

69. R P Mageau, M E Cutrufelli, B Schwab, R W Johnston. Development of an overnight rapid bovine identification test (ORBIT) for field use. J Assoc Off Anal Chem 67:949–954, 1984.

70. M E Cutrufelli, R P Mageau, B Schwab, R W Johnston. Development of poultry rapid overnight field identification test (PROFIT). J Assoc Off Anal Chem 69:483–487, 1986.

71. M E Cutrufelli, R P Mageau, B Schwab, R W Johnston. Development of porcine rapid identification method (PRIME) by modified agar-gel immunodiffusion. J Assoc Off Anal Chem 71:444–445, 1988.

72. M E Cutrufelli, R P Mageau, B Schwab, R W Johnston. Development of serological ovine field test (SOFT) by modified agar-gel immunodiffusion. J Assoc Off Anal Chem 72:60–61, 1989.

73. M E Cutrufelli, R P Mageau, B Schwab, R W Johnston. Development of a rapid equine serological test (REST) by modified agar-gel immunodiffusion. J Assoc Off Anal Chem 74:410–412, 1991.

74. M E Cutrufelli, R P Mageau, B Schwab, R W Johnston. Development of a deer rapid identification field test (DRIFT) by modified agar-gel immunodiffusion. JAOAC Int 75:74–76, 1992.

75. M E Cutrufelli, R P Mageau, B Schwab, R W Johnston. Development of a multispecies identification field test by modified agar-gel immunodiffusion. JAOAC Int 76:1022–1026, 1993.

76. C H S Hitchcock, A A Crimes. Methodology for meat species identification: A review. Meat Sci 15:215–224, 1985.

77. R Martin, R J Wardale, S J Jones, P E Hernandez, R L S Patterson. Production and characterization of monoclonal antibodies specific to chicken muscle proteins. Meat Sci 25:199–207, 1989.

78. B Gibbins, K Pickering, B Scanlon, E E Billett. A pork specific murine monoclonal antibody to desmin to be used in meat speciation. In: Food Safety and Quality Assurance Application of Immunoassay Systems. M R A Morgan, C J Smith, P A Williams (eds). New York: Elsevier Science Publishing, Inc., 1992, pp. 71–74.

79. P Morales, T Garcia, I Gonzalez, I Martin, B Sanz, P E Hernandez. Monoclonal antibody detection of porcine meat. J Food Prot 57:146–149, 1994.

80. T Garcia, R Marin, P Morales, A I Haza, G Antigua, I Gonzalez, B Sanz, P E Hernandez. Production of a horse-specific monoclonal antibody and detection of horse meat in raw meat mixtures by an indirect ELISA. J Sci Food Agric 66:411–415, 1994.

81. C H Wang, D M Smith. Lactate dehydrogenase monoclonal antibody immunoassay for detection of turkey meat in beef and pork. J Food Sci 60:253–256, 1995.

82. E E Billett, R Bevan, B Scanlon, K Pickering, B Gibbons. The use of a poultry specific murine monoclonal antibody directed to the insoluble muscle protein desmin in meat speciation. J Sci Food Agric 70:396–404, 1996.

83. Y-H P Hsieh, F-C Sheu, R C Bridgman. Development of monoclonal antibody specific to cooked mammalian meats. J Food Prot 61:476–481, 1998.

84. S-C Sheu, Y-H P Hsieh. Production and partial characterization of monoclonal antibodies specific to cooked poultry meat. Meat Sci 50:315–320, 1998.

85. F-C Chen, Y-H P Hsieh, R C Bridgman. Monoclonal antibodies against troponin I for the detection of rendered muscle tissues in animal feedstuffs. Meat Sci 62:405–412, 2002.

86. M K Ayob, A A Ragab, J C Allen. An improved rapid ELISA technique for detection of pork in meat products. J Sci Food Agric 49:103–116, 1989.

87. R M Patterson, R G Whittaker, T L Spencer. Improved species identification of raw meat by double sandwich enzyme-linked immunosorbent assay. J Sci Food Agric 35:1018–1023, 1984.

88. S J Jones, R L S Patterson. A modified indirect ELISA procedure for raw meat speciation using crude anti-species antisera and stabilized immunoreagents. J Sci Food Agric 37:767–775, 1986.

89. N M Griffiths, M J Billington, A A Crimes. An assessment of commercially available reagents for an enzyme-linked immunosorbent assay of soya protein in meat products. J Sci Food Agric 35:1255–1260, 1984.

90. B Dincer, J L Spearow, R G Cassens, M L Greaser. The effects of curing and cooking on the detection of species origin of meat products by competitive and indirect ELISA techniques. Meat Sci 20:253–265, 1987.

91. F Milgrom, E Witebsky. Immunological studies on adrenal glands. I. Immunization with adrenals of foreign species. Immunology 5:46–66, 1962.

92. A R Hayden. Use of antisera to heat-stable antigens of adrenals for species identification in thoroughly cooked beef sausages. J Food Sci 46:1810–1813, 1981.

93. A T Sherikar, U D Karkare, J B Khot, B M Jayarao, K N Bhilegaonkar. Studies on thermostable antigens, production of species-specific antiadrenal sera and comparison of immunological techniques in meat speciation. Meat Sci 33:121–136, 1993.

94. R G Berger, R P Mageau, B Schwab, R W Johnston. Detection of poultry and pork in cooked and canned meat foods by enzyme-linked immunosorbent assays. J Assoc Off Anal Chem 71:406–409, 1988.

95. C D Andrews, R G Berger, R P Mageau, B Schwab, R W Johnston. Detection of beef, sheep, deer and horse meat in cooked meat products by enzyme-linked immunosorbent assay. J Assoc Off Anal Chem 75:572–576, 1992.

96. E K Kang'ethe, J M Gathuma. Species identification of antoclaved meat samples using antisera to thermostable muscle antigens in an enzyme immunoassay. Meat Sci 19:265–270, 1987.

97. M Ansfield. Production of a sensitive immunoassay for detection of ruminant proteins in rendered animal material heated to >130°C. Food Agric Immunol 6:419–433, 1994.

98. M Ansfield, S D Reaney, R Jackamn. Production of a sensible immunoassay for detection of ruminant and porcine proteins, heated to >130°C at 2.7 bar, in compound animal feedstuff. Food Agric Immunol 12:273–284, 2000.

99. M Ansfield, S D Reaney, R Jackamn. Performance assessment and validation of a sensitive immunoassay for detection of ruminant and porcine heat stable proteins in compound animal feedstuffs. Food Agric Immunol 12:285–297, 2000.

100. F-C Chen, Y-H P Hsieh. Separation and characterization of a porcine-specific thermostable muscle protein from cooked pork. J Food Sci 66:799–803, 2001.

101. F-C Chen, Y-H P Hsieh. Porcine troponin I: A thermostable species marker protein. Meat Sci 61:55–60, 2002.

102. F-C Chen, Y-H P Hsieh, R C Bridgman. Monoclonal antibodies-based sandwich enzyme-linked immunosorbent assay for sensitive detection of prohibited ruminant proteins in feedstuffs. J Food Prot, In press. 2004.

103. A R Hayden. Detection of chicken flesh in beef sausages. J Food Sci 42:1189–1192, 1977.

104. P Casali, A L Notikins. Probing the human B-cell repertoire with EBV: polyreactive antibodiesad CD5+B lymphocytes. Annual Review of Immunology 7:513–522, 1989.

105. A M Campbell. Assay Techniques. Monoclonal antibody and immunosensor technology, P C Van der Vliet (ed.). Amsterdam: Elsevier Science, 1991, pp. 51–115.

106. F-C Chen, Y-H P Hsieh. A monoclonal antibody-based ELISA for detection of pork in heat-processed meat products. JAOAC Intern 83:79–85, 2000.

107. C Baur, J Teifelgreding, E Liebhardt. Identification of heat processed meat by DNA analysis. Arch Lebensmittelhyg 38:172–174, 1987.

108. A K Wintero, P D Thomsen, W Davis. A comparison of DNA-hybridization, immunodiffusion, countercurrent immunoelectrophoresis and isoelectric focusing for detecting the admixture of pork to beef. Meat Sci 27:75–85, 1990.

109. K Chikuni, K Ozutsumi, T Koishikawa, S Kato. Species identification of cooked meats by DNA hybridization assay. Meat Sci 27:119–128, 1990.

110. K F Ebbehoj, P D Thomsen. Species differentiation of heated meat products by DNA hybridization. Meat Sci 30:221–234, 1991.

111. K F Ebbehoj, P D Thomsen. Differentiation of closely related species by DNA hybridization. Meat Sci 30:359–366, 1991.

112. W Davies, I Harbitz, R Fries, G Stranziger, J G Hauge. Porcine malignant hyperthermia carrier detection and chromosomal assignment using a linked probe. Anim Genet 19:203–212, 1988.

113. D J Hunt, H C Parkes, I D Lumley. Identification of the species of origin of raw and cooked meat products using oligonucleotide probes. Food Chem 60:437–442, 1997.

114. J B Buntjer, N Haagsma, J A Lenstra. Rapid species identification by using satellite DNA probes. Z Lebensm Unters Forsch 201:577–582, 1995.

115. J B Buntjer, A Lamine, N Haagsma, J A Lenstra. Species identification by oligonucleotide hybridization: The influence of processing meat products. J Food Sci 79:53–57, 1999.

116. R Saez, Y Sanz, F Toldrá. PCR-based fingerprinting techniques for rapid detection of animal species in meat products. Meat Sci 66:659–665, 2004.

117. M C Koh, C H Lim, S B Chua, S T Chew, S T W Phang. Random amplified polymorphic DNA (RAPD) fingerprints for identification of red meat animal species. Meat Sci 48:275–285, 1998.

118. I Martinez, M Yman. Species identification in meat products by RAPD analysis. Food Res Int 31:459–466, 1999.

119. F Bellagamba, F Valfrè, S Panseri, V Moretti. Polymerase chain reaction-based analysis to detect terrestrial animal protein in fishmeal. J Food Protein 66:682–685, 2003.

120. I Martinez. DNA typing of fish products for species identification. In: Seafood from Product to Consumer: Integrated Approach to Quality. J Luten, T Borresen, J Oehlenschlager (eds.). Amsterdam: Elsevier Science, 1997, pp. 497–506.

121. E Desmarais, I Lanneluc, J Lagne. Direct amplification of length polymorphism (DALP) or how to get and characterize new genetic markers in many species. Nucleic Acids Res 26:1458–1465, 1998.

122. M Tartaglia, E Saulle, S Pestalozza, L Morelli, G Antonucci, P Battaglia. Detection of bovine mitochondrial DNA in ruminant feeds: A molecular approach to test for the presence of bovine-derived materials. J Food Prot 61:513–518, 1998.

123. P Krcmar, E Rencova. Identification of species-specific DNA in feedstuffs. J Agric Food Chem 51:7655–7658, 2003.

124. B W Murray, R A McClymont, C Strobeck. Forensic identification of ungulate species using restriction fragment digests of PCR-amplified mitochondrial DNA. J Forensic Sci 40:943–951, 1995.

125. T D Kocher, W K Thomas, A Meyer, S V Edwards, S Pääbo, F X Villablanca, A C Wilson. Dynamics of mitochondrial DNA evolution in animals: amplification and sequencing with conserved primers. Proc Natl Acad Sci USA 86:6196–6200, 1989.

126. M Burgener, P Hübner. Mitochondrial DNA enrichment for species identification and revolutionary analysis. Z Lebensm Unters Forsch 207:261–263, 1998.

127. T Matsunaga, K Chikuni, R Tanabe, S Muroya, K Shibata, J Yamada, Y Shimura. A quick and simple method for the identification of meat species and meat products by PCR assay. Meat Sci 51:143–148, 1999.

128. F Colombo, R Viacava, M Giaretti. Differentiation of the species ostrich (Struthio camelus) and emu (Dromaius novaehollandiae) by polymerase chain reaction using an ostrich-specific primer pair. Meat Sci 56:15–17, 2000.

129. L Herman. Determination of the animal origin of raw food by species-specific PCR. J Dairy Res 68:429–436, 2001.

130. Z Guoli, Z Mingguang, Z Zhijiang, O Hongsheng, L Qiang. Establishment and application of a polymerase chain reaction for the identification of beef. Meat Sci 51:233–236, 1999.

131. K S Fairbrother, A J Hopwood, A K Lockley, R G Bardsley. Meat speciation by restriction fragment length polymorphism analysis using an α-actin cDNA probe. Meat Sci 50:105–114, 1998.

132. A J Hopwood, K S Fairbrother, A K Lockley, R G Bardsley. An actin gene-related polymerase chain reaction (PCR) test for identification of chicken in meat mixtures. Meat Sci 53:227–231, 1999.

133. K Tajima, O Enishi, M Amari, M Mitsumori, H Kajikawa, M Kurihara, S Yanai, H Matsui, H Yasue, T Mitsuhashi, T Kawashima, M Matsumoto. PCR detection of DNAs of animal origin in feed by primers based on sequences of short and long interspersed repetitive elements. Biosci Biotechnol Biochem 66(10):2247–2250, 2002.

134. P D Brodmann, D Moor. Sensitive and semi quantitative TaqMan real time polymerase chain reaction systems for the detection of beef (Bos taurus) and the detection of the family mammalia in food and feed. Meat Sci 65:599–607, 2003.

135. M Unseld, B Beyermann, P Brandt, R Hiesel. Identification of the species origin of highly processed meat products by mitochondrial DNA sequences. PCR Met Appl 4:241–243, 1995.

136. M A Rodriguez, T Garcia, I Gonzalez, L Asensio, B Mayoral, I Lopez-Calleja, P E Hernandez, R martin. Identification of goose, mule duck, turkey, and swine in foie grass by species-specific polymerase chain reaction. J Agric Food Chem 51:1524–1529, 2003.

137. P M Holland, R D Abramson, R Watson, D H Gelfand. Detection of specific polymerase chain reaction product by utilization the 5′ to 3′ exonuclease activity of Thermus aquaticus. Proc Natl Acad Sci USA 88:7276–7280, 1991.

138. S Lahiff, M Glennon, J Lyng, T Smith, N Shilton, M Maher. Real-time polymerase chain reaction detection of bovine DNA in meat and bone meal samples. J Food Prot 65:1158–1165, 2002.

139. M Dubois, O Fumière, C Holst, G Brambilla, G Berben. Meat and bone meal detection in feed by real time PCR with specific hybridization probes. FDA/AAFCO BSE Workshop for the Detection of Animal Proteins Prohibited in Ruminant Feed (http://www.aafco.org/FDA_AAFCO_BSE_Workshop_Jan_2003.html), 2003.

140. L Laube, A Spiegelberg, A Butschke, J Zagon, M Schauzu, L Kroh, H Broll. Methods for the detection of beef and pork in foods using real-time polymerase chain reaction. Int J Food Science Technol 38:111–118, 2003.

141. J H Wetton, C S F Tsang, C A Roney, A C Spriggs. An extremely sensitive-specific ARMS PCR test for the presence of tiger bone DNA. Forensic Sci Int 126:137–144, 2002.

142. C A Heid, S J Stevens, K J Livak, P M Williams. Real time quantitative PCR. Genome Res 6:986–994, 1996.

143. E D Robin, R Wong. Mitochondrial DNA and virtual number of mitochondria per cell in mammalian cells. J Cell Physiol 136:507–513, 1988.

144. W M Brown, M George, Jr, A C Wilson. Rapid evolution of animal mitochondrial DNA. Proc Natl Acad Sci USA 76:1967–1971, 1979.

145. D R Wolstenholme. Animal mitochondrial DNA: structure and evolution. Int Rev Cytol 141:173–216, 1992.

146. A P Martin and S R Palumbi. Protein evolution in different cellular environments: cytochrome b in sharks and mammals. Mol Biol Evol 10:873–891, 1993.

147. L Partis, D Croan Z Guo, R ClarkT, Coldham, J Murby. Evaluation of a DNA fingerprinting method for determining the species origin of meat. Meat Sci 54:369–376, 2000.

148. P L Altman, D D Katz. Cell Biology: Biological Handbook 1. Bethesda, MD: Federation of American Societies for Experimental Biology, 1976.

149. E L C Verkaar, I J Nijman, K Boutaga, J A Lenstra. Differentiation of cattle species in beef by PCR-RFLP of mitochondrial and satellite DNA. Meat Sci 60:365–369, 2002.

150. R Borgo, C Souty-Grosset, D Bouchon, L Gomot. PCR-RFLP analysis of mitochondrial DNA for identifica-tion of snail meat species. J Food Sci 61:1–4, 1996.

151. R-F Wang, M J Myers, W Campbell, W-W Cao, D Paine, CE Cerniglia. A rapid method for PCR detection of bovine material in animal feedstuffs. Mol Cell Probes 14:1–5, 2000.

152. S Colgan, L O'Brien, M Maher, N Shilton, K McDonnel, S Ward. Development of DNA-based assay for species identification in meat and bone meal. Food Res Int 34:409–414, 2001.

153. M J Myers, S L Friedman, D E Farrell, D A Dove-Pettit, M F Bucker, S Kelly, S Madzo, W Campbell, R-F Wang, D Paine, C E Cerniglia. Validation of a polymerase chain reaction method for the detection of rendered bovine-derived materials in feedstuffs. J Food Prot 64:564–566, 2001.

154. S Lahiff, M Glennon, L O'Brien, J Lyng, T Smith, M Maher, N Shilton. Species-specific PCR for the identification of ovine, porcine, and chicken species in meat and bone meal (MBM). Mol Cell Probes 15:27–35, 2001.

155. R Meyer, C Höfelein, J Lüthy, U Candrian. Polymerase chain reaction – Restriction fragment length polymorphism analysis: A simple method for species identification in food. JAOAC Int 78:1542–1551, 1995.

156. C Wolf, J Rentsch, P Hübner. PCR-RFLP analysis of mitochondrial DNA: A reliable method for species identification. J Agric Food Chem 47:1350–1355, 1999.

157. F Bellagamba, V M Moretti, S Comincini, F Valfre. Identification of species in animal feedstuffs by polymerase chain reaction-restriction freagment length polymorphism analysis of mitochondrial DNA. J Agric Food Chem 49:3775–3781, 2001.

158. M J Meyer, H F Yancy, D E. Farrell. Characterization of a ppolymerase chain reaction-based approach for the simultaneous detection of multiple animal-derived materials in animal feed. J Food Protec 66:1085–1089, 2003.

159. A Abdulmawjood, H Schönenbrücher, M Bülte. Development of a polymerase chain reaction system for the detection of dog and cat meat in meat mixtures and animal feed. J Food Sci 68:1757–1761, 2003.

160. Y-L Sun, C-S Lin. Establishment and application of a fluorescent polymerase chain reaction-restriction fragment length polymorphism (PCR-RFLP) method for identifying porcine, caprine, and bovine meats. J Agric Food Chem 51:1771–1776, 2003.

161. M Orita, Y Suzuki, T Sekiya, K Hayashi. Rapid and sensitive detection of point mutations and DNA polymorphisms using the polymerase chain reaction. Genomics 5:874–879, 1989.

162. A Céspedes, T Garcia, E Carrera, I Gonzalez, A Fernández, P E Hernández, R Martin. Application of polymerase chain reaction-single strand conformational polymorphism (PCR-SSCP) to identification of flatfish species. JAOAC Int 82:903–907, 1999.

163. H Rehbein, G Kress, T Schmidt. Application of PCR-SSCP to species identification of fishery products. J Sci Food Agric 74:35–41, 1997.

164. H Rehbein, I M Mackie, S Pryde, C Gonzales-Sotelo, R I Peréz-Martín, J Quintero, M Rey-Mendez. Comparison of different methods to produce single strand DNA for identification of canned tuna by single-strand conformation polymorphism analysis. Electrophoresis 19:1381–1384, 1998.

165. H Rehbein, I M Mackie, S Pryde, C Gonzales-Sotelo, R I Peréz-Martín, J Quintero, M Rey-Mendez. Fish species identification in canned tuna by PCR-SSCP: validation of a collaborative study and investigation into inter-species variability of the DNA patterns. Food Chem 64:263–268, 1999.

166. S Rea, K Chikuni, P Avellini. Possibility of using single strand conformation polymorphism (SSCP) analysis for discriminating European pig and wild boar meat samples. Ital J Food Sci 3:211–220, 1996.

167. C Wolf, J Luthy. Quantitative competitive (QC) PCR for quantification of porcine DNA. Meat Sci 57:161–168, 2001.

168. J H Calvo, R Osta, P Zaragoza. Quantitative PCR detection of pork in raw and heated ground beef and pate. J Agric Food Chem 50:5265–5267, 2002.

31 Poultry: Chemistry and Biochemistry

Christine Z. Alvarado
Department of Animal and Food Sciences, Texas Tech University

Casey M. Owens
Department of Poultry Science, University of Arkansas

CONTENTS

I. INTRODUCTION

The conversion of muscle into meat is a complex process that involves an understanding of muscle components as well as metabolic reactions. This chapter will focus on the chemical components of the live muscle and chemical and biochemical reactions leading to the conversion of muscle into meat.

II. COMPOSITION AND CHEMISTRY

A. WATER

One of the most abundant and important components of meat is water. Poultry meat contains approximately 75% water by weight. Water has several functions within meat, one of which is a medium for transportation of nutrients, hormones, metabolites, and waste to and from cells. It also provides a medium for chemical reactions and metabolic processes. Three states of water exist in muscle: bound, immobilized, and free. Bound water is very tightly bound to proteins and can only be removed by ashing. Immobilized water has weaker interactions than the bound water and is associated with ions and proteins. This water, held by ionic interactions, may be released during cooking or heat application. Free water is loosely held in the cell, and is susceptible to loss known as drip or purge.

B. CARBOHYDRATES

Skeletal muscle does not have an abundant supply of carbohydrates. Glycogen, the storage form of glucose, is the major carbohydrate found in muscle and can be up to 0.5 to 1.3% of the weight of the muscle (1). It is important in providing energy for metabolism, contraction, and relaxation. Other carbohydrates include intermediate substances and products of cell metabolism.

C. LIPIDS

Poultry muscle contains several types of fatty acids including saturated, unsaturated, acylglycerols or neutral lipids, and phospholipids. The neutral lipids are the most abundant. These fats are composed of fatty acids and a glycerol backbone. They consist of mono-, di-, and triglycerides, depending upon how many fatty acids are bound to the glycerol backbone. Phospholipids are mainly found in the cell membranes and contain both hydrophobic and hydrophilic sites. Lipids have many functions including providing energy for the muscle cell, metabolic functions, and cell membrane structure and function.

D. PROTEINS

Protein constitutes approximately 16% to 22% of the muscle, second in abundance only to water (1). Muscle contains several classes of proteins including myofibrillar, sarcoplasmic, and connective tissue proteins. The myofibrillar proteins are long, fibrous, charged, and are salt soluble in elevated ionic concentrations of 0.3 M or greater (<1.5% NaCl) (2). These myofibrillar proteins are responsible not only for contraction and relaxation, but also water holding capacity and protein functionality. The myofibrillar proteins can be further divided into three functional categories: contractile (myosin, actin), regulatory (tropomyosin, troponin) and cytoskeletal proteins (titin, connectin, C-protein, and desmin). Of these proteins, myosin and actin are considered to be the most abundant and the most functional, especially in food complexes.

Sarcoplasmic proteins are mainly globular and function as enzymes and cofactors involved in energy metabolism. Many of these proteins share common properties such as high isoelectric points, globular structures, and low molecular weights. With these properties, the sarcoplasmic proteins are water soluble and can be extracted in low salt solutions with an ionic strength of less than 0.15 M.

Connective tissue proteins provide strength and support for the muscle in such ways as tendons and ligaments. Within the interstitial space of the muscle, the connective tissues consist of collagen, reticulin, and elastin along with other supporting proteins termed ground substance. Connective tissue proteins are very fibrous and insoluble in high ionic strength solutions.

E. INORGANIC SUBSTANCES

Most of the inorganic constituents consist of cations and anions used in muscle metabolism, contraction, and relaxation. Calcium is required for contraction to occur and is stored within the muscle cells. Other inorganic substances are potassium, sodium, magnesium, chloride, and iron.

III. SKELETAL MUSCLE

A. ULTRASTRUCTURE

Skeletal muscle is a complex structure that is a major component of the body and has been reviewed by several authors (3–7). The muscle is surrounded by a thick connective tissue sheath known as the epimysium which is continuous with the tendon (Figure 31.1). The muscle is then divided into bundles of fibers surrounded by the perimysium. The connective tissue surrounding individual muscle fibers is the endomysium.

Avian skeletal muscle fibers are long, unbranched, narrow, and multinucleated cells (4–6). These fibers can vary in length from several millimeters to more than 30 cm and have a diameter of 10 μm to 100 μm. Surrounding the muscle fiber is the sarcolemma, an elastic plasma membrane composed mainly of proteins and lipids. The sarcolemma not only surrounds the contractile units of the muscle, but also regulates uptake and release of molecules by the cell. The most distinguishing feature of the sarcolemma is its ability to depolarize during a nerve impulse. Invaginations of the sarcolemma form a network of tubules known as the transverse tubule (t-tubule) system. When an action potential reaches the myoneural junction, the t-tubule system aids in the progression of this impulse longitudinally along the sarcolemma in both directions along the entire length of the fiber.

The sarcoplasmic reticulum (SR) is an intracellular membrane structure separate from the sarcolemma and t-tubule system. The SR is responsible for the release and sequestration of calcium involved in contraction (3). Small structures called "feet" bridge the gap between the t-tubules and the SR. When the muscle cell is stimulated, the action potential reaches the sarcoplasmic reticulum through the t-tubule system causing the release of stored Ca^{+2} for muscle contraction initiation (4).

The basic contractile unit of the muscle is the sarcomere which is mainly composed of the myofibrillar proteins myosin and actin (Figure 31.2). These proteins are arranged parallel to the muscle fiber and overlap in certain regions. This overlap accounts for the banding pattern of the myofibril. The protein-dense bands where actin and myosin overlap are referred to as the A bands because they are anisotropic in polarized light. The less dense area is known as the I band since it is isotropic in polarized light.

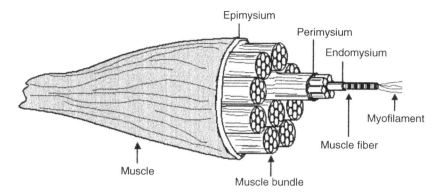

FIGURE 31.1 Diagram of gross muscle structure indicating muscle and connective tissue components. (Modified from Bechtel, 1986, and Gualt, 1992.)

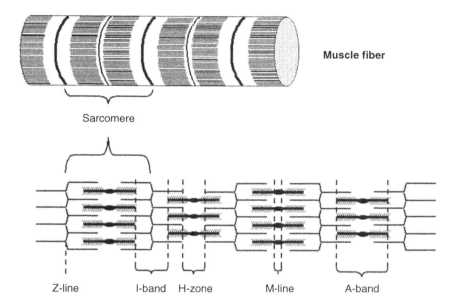

FIGURE 31.2 Diagram of the striated muscle fiber and the structure of the sarcomere.

B. MUSCLE PROTEINS

The muscle is made up of three major types of proteins: myofibrillar (or contractile), sarcoplasmic, and stromal (or connective). The myofibrillar proteins make up approximately 50–60% of total muscle protein and include proteins that are involved in the contraction-relaxation process (5, 6, 9). Sarcoplasmic proteins comprise approximately 30–35% of the muscle proteins and include the enzymes involved in muscle metabolism (5, 9). Connective tissue is made of stromal proteins and comprises approximately 3–6% of total muscle protein (9).

1. Thick Filament

Myosin is a globular and filamentous protein, which is the basis for the thick myofilament. Myosin makes up approximately 45–50% of total myofibrillar protein (6, 10). It is also one of most important proteins, along with actin, that is involved in muscle contraction. The protein consists of two globular heads attached to a long α-helical-like filamentous tail (Figure 31.3). Myosin is a large molecule of approximately 520 kD and is made up of six subunits. There are two heavy chains, approximately 220 kD, that make up the fibrous portion of the molecule, and two sets of light chains, approximately 17–22 kD, that are found in the globular regions of the molecules (5). Furthermore, the myosin molecule can be divided into two sections: heavy meromyosin (HMM) and light meromyosin (LMM). The globular heads, located in HMM, contain the adenosine triphosphate (ATP)-binding site and the actin-binding region, which are necessary for muscle contraction. The HMM section also contains a portion of the fibrous myosin. The LMM section, a portion of the fibrous myosin, is the area of the molecule that is packed into the thick filament. It is thought that the myosin molecule has two hinge points, one between

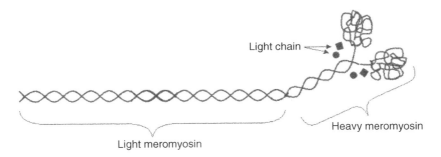

FIGURE 31.3   Diagram of myosin, a component of the thick filament. (Modified from Vander et al., 2001.)

HMM and LMM and the other between the fibrous myosin and globular myosin, so that it can function properly and effectively in the contraction-relaxation process. Approximately 200 myosin molecules aggregate along with other structural proteins to form the thick myofilament (7, 8). During aggregation, the myosin heads point toward the Z-lines and the tails toward the M-line. The thick filament is approximately 1.5 μm in length and 14–16 nm in diameter (4). The primary structural proteins are called C-proteins and M-proteins. The C-proteins are thought to hold the myosin filament together by wrapping around the myosin filament (11). There are seven bands of C-protein around the thick filament on each side of the H-zone (4, 5). The M-protein and myomesium are thought to adjoin the two myosin filaments at the tail region of myosin in the center of the sarcomere, or at the M-line (3). At the M-line, creatine kinase is also present, but its role in the structure of the thick filament is not known (3, 11). Creatine kinase is important to muscle metabolism. It is used in the formation of ATP from creatine, which is a short term energy supply for the muscle. Other proteins are also associated with the thick filament including F-protein, H-protein, and I-protein although their role in structural integrity of the thick filament is not known. It is thought that the I-protein inhibits myosin ATP-ase activity, an enzyme involved in ATP hydrolysis (11).

2.   Thin Filament

The actin protein is made up of globular molecules, approximately 42 kD, that form a filamentous protein which is the basis for the thin filament (Figure 31.4). Actin comprises approximately 20% of the total myofibrillar proteins and is essential to the muscle contraction process (5). Approximately 200 globular molecules, G-actin, are bound together by ionic and hydrophobic bonds to form each filamentous actin, or F-actin. Two strands of F-actin along with two strands of filamentous tropomyosin and associated troponin (globular) are twisted together to form the thin (actin) filament. There are approximately 13 G-actin molecules per strand per twist of F-actin. The tropomyosin protein is made up of two α-helical polypeptide chains that twist around each

other forming a filamentous rope-like structure. Tropomyosin, approximately 41 nm in length and 71 kD, lies near the groove of the F-actin filament (11). In conjuction with tropomyosin is the globular protein, troponin, which appears every seven G-actin molecules. Troponin is made up of three subunits: troponin I (21 kD), troponin T (37 kD), and troponin C (15 kD). Each subunit has a different function that is important in the contraction process. Troponin-T binds to tropomyosin, troponin-I inhibits actomyosin interactions by binding to actin, and troponin-C binds to calcium. These functions will be discussed later in this chapter. The thin filament, made of actin and the tropomyosin-troponin complex, is approximately 6–8 nm in diameter and extends approximately 1 μm from the Z-line toward the thick filament where a portion of the thin filament overlaps with the thick filament at the A band. The I band of the sarcomere consists of the thin filament alone.

In addition to actin, tropomyosin, and troponin, there are other proteins also present that are associated with the thin filament. γ-Actinin and β-actinin are present along the thin filament and at the end of the filament, respectively. It is thought that these proteins aid in regulating the length of the thin filament, thereby stabilizing the structure. Furthermore, β-actinin may inhibit interfilament intereactions thereby allowing it to smoothly slide during contraction and relaxation (5).

3.   Z-Line and Gap Filaments

Each sarcomere is made up of thick filaments, thin filaments, and other proteins located near or at the Z-line and either as an integral part or on the periphery, the beginning and end of each sarcomere. Some of the Z-line proteins include desmin, vimentin, synemin, α-actinin, Eu-actinin, vinculin and zeugmatin (5, 10). Nebulin is also present near the Z-line in the N-line. Other myofibrillar proteins that are present include Z-protein and tensin, located in the integral, and filamin, plectin, spectrin, and ankyrin, located in the periphery; however, the role of these proteins in muscle is not fully understood.

Desmin is generally located around the periphery of the Z-line, running transversely, indicating that this protein acts

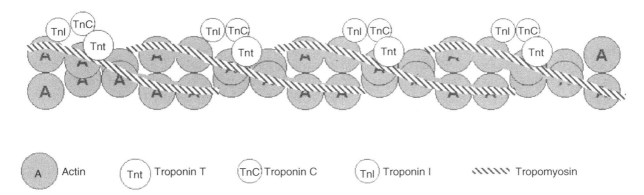

(A) Actin   (Tnt) Troponin T   (TnC) Troponin C   (TnI) Troponin I   〰〰〰 Tropomyosin

FIGURE 31.4 Diagram of thin filament. Actin, tropomyosin, and troponin make up the thin filament (Drawn by E. M. Hirschler; Modified from Cohen, 1975).

to tie the adjacent myofibrils together by forming a filamentous network. Furthermore, desmin may also link myofibrils to subcellular organelles, nuclei and mitochondria, and to the cellular membrane (10). Vimentin and synemin, like desmin, are also involved in forming a network around and between adjacent myofibrils. The role of these proteins is to provide structural integrity to not only the single myofibril, but also to a group of myofibrils, or muscle fiber. α-Actinin is a protein that ties actin into the Z-line, or Z-disk. This protein is an integral component of the Z-disk and is located in the interior. In addition to its role in structural integrity, α-actinin is thought to play a role in the formation of actin (i.e., direction of forming filament, length of filament). Although not well understood, zeugmatin and Eu-actinin are thought to link actin to the Z-disk (5). Vinculin is thought to attach the myofibrils to the sarcolemma; however, its function is not fully understood (5, 11). Nebulin was previously thought to be associated with the N-lines within the sarcomere and to control the geometric organization of the thin filament (12). However, more recent evidence suggests that nebulin is an elongated filamentous protein that runs parallel to the thin filament binding to both F-actin and α-actinin, thereby suggesting that nebulin aids in stabilizing the thin filament (10, 12, 13). Nebulin is also thought to serve as a template for the thin filament during formation. In addition to these proteins, there is another major protein present in the muscle that aids in structural integrity known as titin. Titin, a gap filament, is the third most abundant protein in the muscle, comprising approximately 8% of the myofibrillar proteins. Titin is a highly elastic filamentous protein that is located throughout the sarcomere, extending longitudinally from the Z-line to the M-line (10). Titin is thought to serve as a template for the formation of thick and thin filaments. It also serves to keep the thick filaments aligned in striated muscle (5, 10).

4. Stromal Proteins (Connective Tissue)

There are two types of connective tissue found in the body: connective tissue proper and supportive connective tissue. While these types differ in their function, they are very similar in composition. Connective tissue that covers the muscle, muscle bundle, and muscle fiber (epimysium, perimysium, and endomysium, respectively) is known as connective tissue proper (4). It is this type of connective tissue that can influence the tenderness of meat. In contrast, connective tissue in bones and cartilage provides structural support; therefore this type is known as supportive connective tissue. Connective tissue is made up of a non-structured ground substance which contains carbohydrates, proteins, and lipids (14). There is also an extracellular matrix which is fibrous in structure and made up of a class of proteins called stromal proteins (5). The stromal proteins consist primarily of collagen and elastin, and aggregation of these proteins make up the extracellular fibers that are embedded in the ground substance. Unlike any other aggregation of proteins, these have high tensile strength once a fiber is formed. Several authors have compiled a comprehensive review of connective tissue (5, 15, 16).

5. Collagen

Collagen makes up the majority of the stromal proteins and is considered the most abundant protein in the body, comprising up to one third of the total body protein (3, 14). It is not only found in muscle, but also in bone, skin, tendons, cartilage, and the vascular system (4, 14). Collagen has a unique structure. The collagen molecule is made up of three polypeptide chains that form into a triple helix known as *tropocollagen,* the structural unit of a collagen fibril (Figure 31.5). Globular domains also exist on the collagen molecule and are referred to as non-triple helical domains (15). These domains are important in the association of multiple collagen molecules. The polypeptide chains are made up of repeating amino acid sequences of Gly-X-Y, where X and

FIGURE 31.5 Diagram of tropocollagen, the collagen molecule made up of three polypeptide chains that form a triple helix.

Y can be any amino acid except tryptophan. Most often the X and Y are proline and hydroxyproline, respectively (5, 15). The amino acid glycine comprises one third of the amino acids found in collagen. Hydroxyproline and hydroxylysine are also present in high proportions within collagen, and are generally only found in collagen. There can be at least 19 variations of the polypeptide chains. Fifteen identified types of collagen can form from various combinations of the individual polypeptide chains that make up the tropocollagen molecules (16). Types I, III, IV, V, and VII are associated with connective tissue in skeletal muscle (4, 14). Type I collagen is located in the epimysium and perimysium, type III in the perimysium and endomysium, and types IV and V in the endomysium (16). It is thought that type III collagen plays a major role in meat tenderness when connective tissue is a factor (14).

Tropocollagen molecules, 300 nm in length, are bound together to form *collagen fibrils* with a striated appearance in types I, II, III, V, and XI. Fibrils are assembled by the tropocollagen molecules aligning adjacently end to end. The molecules align in a quarter-stagger parallel pattern with an end overlap of 25 nm, and are stabilized by ionic and hydrophobic interactions (5, 16). This quarter-stagger and overlapping pattern that repeats every 67 nm results in the striated appearance of the *collagen fiber* (Figure 31.6). The collagen fibers have a distinctive crimp (fold) that is observed once the fiber is formed; however, the crimp disappears when the muscle is under tension (Figure 31.7). It is thought that this *planar crimping* serves as a shock absorber to take up strain before tension is applied to the muscle (15, 16).

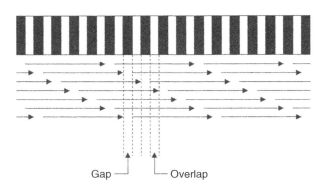

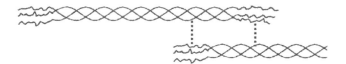

FIGURE 31.6 Diagram of collagen fibril where the light segments represent overlapping collagen molecules and the dark segments represent areas where a gap is present. (Modified from Sims and Bailey, 1992.)

FIGURE 31.7 Diagram of intermolecular crosslinking between two collagen molecules. (Modified from Bailey and Light, 1989.)

The fibrous structure of collagen has high tensile strength due to its enzyme-induced intermolecular (between molecules) crosslinks (Figure 31.7). These crosslinks are covalent bonds that can occur in the carboxy- and amino-terminal ends of the tropocollagen, depending on the collagen type. Because type III collagen is the predominant collagen type that can play a role in meat quality, only the crosslinks of this type will be discussed. However, the crosslinking mechanism is similar in other collagen types.

Three types of crosslinks can occur in the formation of stable collagen fibers. First, disulfide bonds are formed in type III and IV collagen. These types of collagen contain the amino acid, cysteine, whereas the remaining types do not. The disulfide bonds are formed near the carboxy-terminal end of a tropocollogen molecule and can occur both intra- (within molecule) or intermolecularly between α-chains of tropocollagen. Secondly, lysine-derived reducible divalent crosslinks can be formed during fiber synthesis, both intra- and intermolecularly. The third type of crosslink that can occur in collagen is a trivalent crosslink that forms as the animal ages. This type of crosslink is usually referred to as *mature crosslinks*. Mature crosslinks are heat stable and are the cause of toughness due to connective tissue associated with mature animals. In the latter two types of crosslinks, the enzyme lysyl oxidase plays a major role in the crosslink formation.

Lysyl oxidase binds to α-chains in the tropocollagen molecule in either the amino- or carboxy-terminal end. Lysyl oxidase reacts with and converts the lysyl group into an aldehyde group. Two aldehyde groups can further react to form either an intramolecular crosslink, known as an aldol, or the aldehyde can react with hydroxylysine to form an aldimine or oxo-imine (or keto-imine) bond (15). The aldimine bond is heat labile while the oxo-imine is heat stable. Both of these bonds form intermolecularly at either the amino- or carboxy-terminal end of the tropocollagen molecule. As the animal ages, nonreducible trivalent bonds can form from these existing divalent bonds. There is much less information available on the mechanism of mature crosslink formation. However, it is known that the trivalent bonds increase the tensile strength of collagen. Furthermore, the mature crosslinks are heat stable. Therefore, upon cooking of meat from a mature animal, the crosslinks will not break and the network of connective tissue remains intact resulting in decreased tenderness of the meat.

The tropocollagen molecules found in type IV collagen do not form collagen fibrils, but form a more open network of tropocollagen that is hexagonal in shape, resembling chicken wire. The molecules found in type IV collagen are 400 nm in length and, due to the location of the glycine residues and the charge profile, the molecules are more flexible and form a thin open structure upon aggregation (16). Type IV collagen is often found in basement membranes. In skeletal muscle, it is one of the types of collagen found in the endomysium.

6. Elastin

In addition to collagen, elastin also makes up the stromal proteins of connective tissue. However, elastin is much less abundant than collagen and plays less of a role in meat quality except in instances where elastin content is high in certain muscles. Elastin is generally found in arterial walls and ligaments in the body. It is a rubbery protein that is insoluble in water or salt solutions, is very heat stable, and is resistant to digestive enzymes.

C. CONTRACTION/RELAXATION

Contraction and relaxation of the muscle are both active processes which have been reviewed by several authors (4–6, 17, 18). The act of contraction begins when an action potential received from a motor neuron at the motor end plate depolarizes the sarcolemma, allowing a rapid influx of Na^+ and efflux of K^+, and causing a membrane polarity reversal. When a threshold of -70 mV is reached, this action potential is propagated in both directions along the sarcolemma down the length of the entire muscle, finally reaching the sarcoplasmic reticulum through the t-tubule system. Once the action potential reaches the sarcoplasmic reticulum, the sequestered Ca^{+2} is released into the sarcoplasmic fluid. This release increases the free Ca^{+2} concentration from 10^{-7} moles/L normally present within the muscle to 10^{-6} or 10^{-5} moles/L (4). The free Ca^{+2} then binds to the regulatory protein troponin-C causing a change in configuration of the troponin-I subunit, which releases the inhibition of tropomyosin, exposing the actin-binding site to myosin. This release of tropomyosin allows myosin to bind to actin and form actomyosin crossbridges. The myosin ATPase is then activated and hydrolyzes ATP into ADP and inorganic phosphates, thereby releasing the energy required to tilt the myosin head (Figure 31.8). This action pulls the actin filament toward the center of the sarcomere, resulting in a shortened sarcomere (Z-lines are closer together). During the resulting contraction, actomyosin crossbridges are continually broken and formed to allow for sliding of the filaments. In cases of severe muscle contraction, the actin filaments may overlap. However, it is important to note that during contraction, the actual length of the myosin and actin filaments do not change.

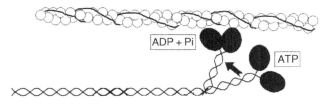

FIGURE 31.8 Diagram of myosin heads coupling with actin and ratcheting releasing ADP and Pi.

Relaxation is measured by a decrease in muscle tension (4). In order for relaxation to occur, the membranes must become repolarized, Ca^{+2} must be resequestered within the sarcoplasmic reticulum, and ATP must be regenerated through a series of reactions. Membrane repolarization is due to the Na^+/K^+ ATPase pump re-establishing a resting membrane potential of -90 mV through the active transport of Na^+ out of the cell and K^+ into the cell (17). The resequestration of Ca^{+2} is accomplished by activation of an ATPase, which aids in pumping Ca^{+2} back into the sarcoplasmic reticulum.

Both muscle contraction and relaxation require energy in the form of ATP for re-establishment of the electrochemical gradient through the Na^+/K^+ pump, for breaking and forming actomyosin bonds, and for pumping Ca^{+2} into the sarcoplasmic reticulum (4). Normally, muscle contains approximately 2 to 4 mM of ATP (18). Due to the fact that muscle cannot store a sufficient amount of ATP for the above conditions to occur, a rapid source and an efficient method of rephosphorylating ADP to ATP must be available.

D. ENERGY METABOLISM

The synthesis of ATP required for these processes to occur has been reviewed by several authors (3, 4, 6). The most rapid source of energy is through phosphocreatine, a sarcoplasmic component, which, when combined with ADP, is converted to ATP and creatine by the catalytic enzyme creatine kinase. During extensive use of ATP within the muscle, creatine is depleted and must be regenerated at the mitochondrial membrane during rest.

$$\text{ADP + Phosphocreatine} \xrightarrow{\text{Creatine Kinase}} \text{ATP + Creatine}$$

Aerobic metabolism is the method that generates the most ATP (Figure 31.9). This series of reactions utilizes carbohydrates, proteins, and lipids, which are degraded to carbon dioxide and water while releasing energy as ATP. Glucose is broken down into pyruvate through glycolysis, netting three ATP molecules per molecule of glucose. In the presence of oxygen, pyruvate then enters the tricarboxylic acid cycle (TCA) in the mitochondria, releasing hydrogen ions. These ions then enter into the electron transport chain and through oxidative phosphorylation net 34 ATP molecules per molecule of glucose (4). Therefore a total of 37 ATP molecules are produced during aerobic metabolism.

Anaerobic glycolysis is a less efficient method of producing ATP, with three molecules of ATP produced per glucose molecule. In anaerobic metabolism, there is a lack of oxygen and pyruvate cannot enter into the TCA cycle. Instead, the combination of pyruvic acid and H^+, both by-products of glycolysis, form lactic acid. In a normal functioning homeostatic system, lactic acid is removed

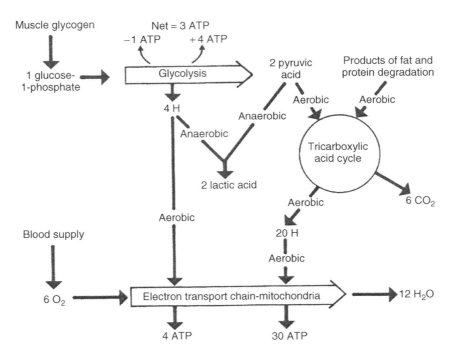

FIGURE 31.9 Pathways that supply energy for muscle function. One molecule of glucose 1 – phosphate is split from glycogen and is degraded to CO_2 and H_2O in the aerobic pathway (sarcoplasm). Then energy yield in terms of ATP is indicated at each step. When oxygen is limited, energy is supplied by glycolysis and conversion of pyruvic acid to lactic acid. (Courtesy of W. H. Freeman and Company.)

through the blood stream. However, during poultry processing, exsanguination, occurs, leading to a build-up of lactic acid in the muscle. This increase in lactic acid post-mortem is important in the development of rigor mortis as will be discussed later.

E. GLYCOGEN CATABOLISM

Homeostasis can be defined as the state of equilibrium in an organism. Homeostasis is maintained by the cyclic nature of providing energy to the muscle cells as well as removal of waste (Figure 31.10). Glucose is absorbed by the gastrointestinal tract into the blood stream where it is either absorbed by the liver for storage as glycogen or carried to the muscle cell for utilization or storage as glycogen. Glycogen is the major storage form of glucose in the muscle and can be 0.5 to 1.3% of the weight of the muscle (4).

In times of high muscle activity, liver glycogen can be hydrolyzed into glucose and transported via the blood for utilization by the muscle cell (Figure 31.10). The regulation of glycogen breakdown into glucose in the muscle cell is controlled through phosphorylase (19, 20). Phosphorylase is the enzyme controlling the conversion of glycogen into glucose-1-phosphate for ATP generation in glycolysis. In resting muscle, phosphorylase activity is low. However, in an active muscle, phosphorylase is activated through a process of phosphorylation to allow breakdown of glycogen for ATP production.

There are several different control mechanisms for phosphorylase, including external regulators, hormones and calcium concentration. Phosphorylase can be activated by an increased amount of ATP breakdown products (inorganic phosphate, AMP, and IMP) which are indicative of an active muscle. Hormones such as epinephrine and adrenaline can also activate this cascade. During stress, glycogen breakdown is required for generation of ATP for the "fight or flight" response.

Calcium concentrations can also stimulate glycogen catabolism. Calcium is required for muscle contraction. When the muscle receives a nervous impulse, Ca^{+2} is released from the sarcoplasmic reticulum increasing the cellular concentration to 10^{-6} M. This concentration is required not only for contraction via myofibrillar ATPase activity, but is also the same concentration required for activation of phosphorylase. Therefore, both nervous and hormonal changes aid in concert to increase the breakdown of glycogen to ATP for energy.

Once glycogen has been catabolized into glucose, the muscle cell utilizes glucose to form ATP. Glycolysis yields 3 ATP, pyruvate and two molecules of lactic acid. Pyruvate can then enter the TCA cycle in the mitochondria and yield CO_2 and H^+. The H^+ then enters into the mitochondrial electron transport chain yielding water, oxygen, 34 ATP, and heat.

Metabolic waste such as lactic acid, heat, CO_2, and water are removed from the cell by the circulatory system

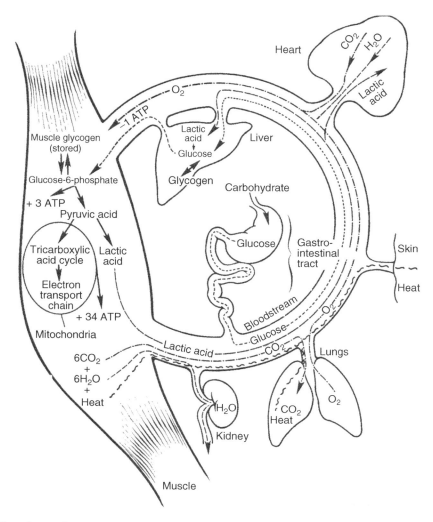

FIGURE 31.10 Cyclic pathways that provide energy for muscle contraction and relaxation. (Courtesy of W. H. Freeman and Company.)

and removed from the body via the lungs and kidneys. Lactic acid can be metabolized into CO_2 and water by the liver or it can be re-synthesized into glucose for storage. During times of increased activity, a build-up of lactic acid can occur and can cause acidosis. However, following a rest period, the lactic acid is removed via the blood and the muscle can return to its resting state.

F. RIGOR MORTIS

Rigor mortis or "stiffness of death" is the process of converting muscle into meat through a series of biochemical, physical, and structural changes. These changes begin with exanguination at which time there is a loss of both oxygen transportation to the muscle and a removal of metabolic waste such as lactic acid from the muscle. When stores of creatine phosphate have been depleted, glycogen stores are used for further phosphorylation of ADP. Aerobic metabolism continues until oxygen is depleted. Anaerobic metabolism is then utilized for the production of ATP until lactic

acid accumulates and pH decreases to a level (approximately pH 5.9) that prevents glycolysis. However, ATP is still present within the muscle cell. Therefore, any stimulation to the muscle such as deboning prior to the completion of rigor mortis will increase actomyosin bond formation and sarcomere shortening, resulting in decreased tenderness. Due to this objectionable toughness associated with early deboning, poultry carcasses must be aged for 4–6 hours to allow for rigor mortis development (21, 22). This phase of oxygen depletion and muscle extensibility is referred to as the onset of rigor mortis (Figure 31.11).

Reduced extensibility begins the onset phase and continues until the muscle is completely inextensible and rigor mortis is complete. During the completion phase, 90% or more available actomyosin bonds are formed compared with only 20% in the living muscle (4). An ATP concentration of 1 μM/g is required for muscle function to occur. When the concentration of ATP decreases to below 1 μM/g, the muscle is no longer extensible (Figure 31.12).

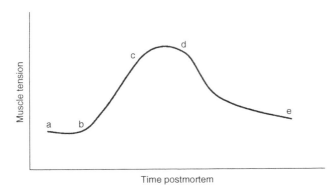

FIGURE 31.11 Phases of rigor mortis development. a–b delay phase; b–c development of rigor; c–d completion phase; d–e resolution phase. (Reprinted with permission from S. Barbut, Poultry Processing Products, An Industry Guide. Boca Raton, FL: CRC Press, 2002, p. 58.)

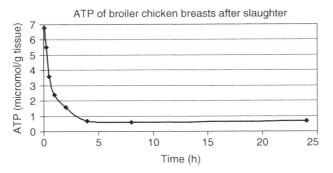

FIGURE 31.12 ATP concentration in broiler muscle during rigor mortis development.

The final stage of rigor, resolution, is characterized by a decrease in structural integrity of the muscle during postmortem storage. This decrease in structural integrity is due to proteolytic degradation of certain myofibrillar Z disk proteins such as desmin, titin, and nebulin by proteases such as calpain. Calpains improve meat tenderness by degrading Z disk proteins, thus increasing myofibrillar fragmentation. Also, ionic interactions may affect the postmortem tenderization of meat. Ionic strength increases in postmortem muscle due to the release of Ca^{+2} from the sarcoplasmic reticulum and the accumulation of phosphate from ATP degradation. This increased ionic strength decreases the sphere of charge surrounding each protein and weakens the structural integrity of the myofibrils, resulting in decreased toughness (23).

G. METABOLIC DIFFERENCES BETWEEN RED AND WHITE FIBERS

Muscle fiber types differ among species and also among muscles within a single animal due to genetic expression, function, and stage of growth. The four basic fiber types include: slow-twitch oxidative (type I, red), fast-twitch

oxidative and glycolytic (type IIA, red), fast-twitch glycolytic (type IIB, white), and intermediate (type IIC). Broiler pectoralis muscles, for example, contain 100% white fibers, while Pekin duck pectoralis contain around 84% red fibers (24–26). Intermediate muscles contain a mixture of both red and white fibers.

Red fibers contain more myoglobin, are more vascularized, and are able to utilize oxidative metabolism as a source of energy, while white fibers mainly utilize glycolytic enzymes (Table 31.1) (5, 27). As a result of the increased oxidative metabolism in the red fibers, they contain not only more but larger mitochondria. When comparing red muscles of the broiler leg to white muscles of the broiler breast during rigor development, the white muscles have an increased accumulation of lactic acid due to their ability to use stored muscle glycogen in the glycolytic pathway for energy (Figure 31.13). Without oxygen, the red fibers cannot utilize the oxidative pathways and energy replenishment decreases.

White fibers are able to contract more rapidly and in short bursts since they mainly utilize glycogen rather than fat stores and have a more developed sarcoplasmic reticulum and t-tubule system (6). White fibers are also more easily fatigued compared to red fibers, which contract slower and for a longer duration without fatigue (27).

Red fibers develop rigor mortis at a faster rate compared to white fibers. No biochemical changes occurred after 2 hours postmortem in red muscles; however, the white muscle fibers display metabolic changes up to 8 hours postmortem. The red muscle fibers of the duck pectoralis have a faster rate of pH decline than the white muscle fibers of the broiler pectoralis, indicating a more rapid onset of rigor mortis (24). Red fibers are generally smaller in diameter when compared to white fibers, and have

TABLE 31.1
Relative Comparisons of Red and White Fibers in Poultry Muscle

Parameter	White	Red
Myoglobin	Low	High
Color	White	Red
Contraction Speed	Fast	Slow
Fatigue Resistance	Low	High
Contractile Action	Phasic	Tonic
Capillary Density	Low	High
Energy Source	Glycolytic	Oxidative
Mitochondrial Size	Small	Large
Mitochondria Number	Low	High
SR and T-tubules	More Developed	Less Developed
Fiber Diameter	Larger	Smaller
Connective Tissue	More	Less
Rigor Development	Slow	Fast
Glycogen Content	High	Low
Lipid Content	Low	High

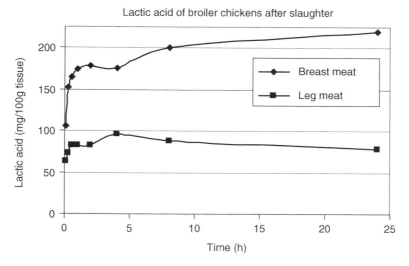

FIGURE 31.13 Comparison of lactic acid accumulation in red- and white-fibered muscles in broilers during rigor development.

proportionally more connective tissue surrounding each fiber as compared to white fibers (5). Thus, tenderness decreases with an increase in red fiber content within specific muscle groups.

IV. MEAT QUALITY CHARACTERISTICS

The inability of the muscle cells to rid themselves of metabolic by-products such as lactic acid causes several postmortem metabolic and structural changes within the muscle, the most important of which is a decrease in pH (28). This decrease in pH is the most significant postmortem change and can affect important meat quality attributes such as color, water holding capacity, and texture (29, 30). These three attributes are used to evaluate meat quality by both processors and consumers. Two conditions caused by the rate of pH decline include dark, firm, and dry (DFD) and pale, soft, and exudative (PSE) meat.

Dark, firm, and dry meat develops when muscle glycogen is depleted prior to slaughter, resulting in high muscle pH from reduced postmortem glycolysis (4, 6, 31). Dark, firm, and dry meat is characterized as having a high water holding capacity, even though the meat appears dry (5).

Pale, soft, and exudative meat is characterized as having a pale color, soft texture when cooked, and a low water holding capacity. This condition develops due to an accelerated postmortem metabolism which leads to a rapid decline in postmortem muscle pH (4–6). Rapid postmortem glycolysis has been observed in both swine and turkeys in which pH of PSE muscles was less than 5.8 within 45 min postmortem in swine and 15 min postmortem in turkeys. This would be compared to normal muscle pH at this postmortem time of greater than 6.0 (32, 33). This rapid decline in pH occurring while muscle temperatures are still elevated denatures proteins and causes a

decrease in solubility and enzymatic activity (34, 35). Porcine muscles with pH values below 6.0 at 45 min postmortem had a higher ATPase activity, indicating a more rapid glycolytic rate, and were found to produce poor meat quality (36). Authors have reported that rabbit muscle kept at 37°C for 6 hours postmortem resulted in a rapid pH decline to below 5.8 and a loss of half Mg-ATPase activity compared to muscles incubated at 34°C (37).

A. COLOR

Color is an important quality attribute as consumers are often willing to pay more for poultry products based on color. Several factors can influence meat color including pH, myoglobin concentration, and nitrites (4). Even though myoglobin has been shown to be important in determining raw meat color, it is less important in broiler and turkey breast meat meat simply because there is less myoglobin than in other meats (beef, pork).

Pinking is an important problem in turkey and broiler meat. Pinking can result from several factors such as undercooking meat, contamination with nitrites, addition of ingredients such as peppers, improper stunning, and several antemortem stressors. There are several problems that can arise from pinking such as food safety issues with undercooked meat, consumer complaints, and a decreased purchasing of poultry products by consumers. Probably one of the main reasons for pinking in white poultry meat is the addition of nitrite. Nitrite is an ingredient that is normally added to cured products and produces a characteristic pink cured color upon heating. Normally, nitrite is not added to products made with white meat but can inadvertently be added through contamination from water sources or human error.

In cooked products, several pigments have been linked to pinking in poultry white meat. Myoglobin facilitates the transfer of oxygen and waste to and from muscles from the blood. Denaturation of myoglobin is related to pH, time, and cooking temperature. Undenatured myoglobin due to improper heating of high pH that prevent denaturation at adequate cooking temperatures can reault in pinking of white meat. This is especially true in turkey breast meat, which has a higher concentration of myoglobin than broiler white meat. Cytochrome c is another important pigment in meat which can lead to undesired pinking since it has a higher denatutaion point that myoglobin. Cytochrome c is a heme protein responsible for transport of electrons in the mitochondria. Levels of this protein have been elevated in stressed animals.

B. WATER HOLDING CAPACITY

The state of water in striated muscle has been reviewed by several people (3, 4, 38). Striated muscle contains approximately 75% water, which exists as three forms in the muscle: bound, immobilized and free. Since water is a polar compound, it can bind with other water molecules as well as charged protein groups. Bound or constitutional water is less than 1% of muscle water and is located within the protein molecules. This water has such a strong protein-water interaction that it cannot be lost except during ashing of the meat. The second form of water is immobilized or interfacial water and is approximately 10–15% of water in meat. Immobilized water is attracted to the bound water layer, creating multilayers of water each more loosely bound as the distance from the bound water increases. Due to the strong water-water and water-protein interactions, immobilized water is typically lost with cooking. Free water accounts for the remaining portion of water in meat tissues and is associated with the extracellular space. Free water is held loosely through capillary forces and can be lost easily through mechanical actions such as cutting, grinding, cooking, and storage of meat.

Water binding capacity of meat is altered in two ways: by the net charge effect and the steric effect. As a polar molecule, water can bind to other charged amino acid side groups. The amount and type of charge on a protein changes with pH. As pH decreases, the number of reactive groups available for water binding decreases. The point at which water binding is minimal on a protein is referred to as the isoelectric point or pI. Since actin and myosin are the most predominant proteins in the muscle and since they are most responsible for water holding capacity, their pI is the pH at which the meat's water holding capacity is the least. The pI of muscle is approximately 5.1 where the number of positive charges equals the number of negative charges resulting in a net zero charge or the pH at which the meat's water holding capacity is minimal (17).

The steric effect or degree of contraction has the greatest effect on the water holding capacity of meat. As the amount of space between the muscle protein structures decreases with contraction, less space is available for water around the proteins. Contractile state and pH of the muscle can influence the amount of interstitial space. If the muscle is in a contracted state, there is less space within the muscle to hold water intracellularly due to the shortening of the sarcomeres. Therefore, water is expelled into the extracellular space.

Muscle pH can also affect the amount of space to bind water molecules. If repulsion between charged groups is increased, as occurs in higher pH muscle, the protein network is enlarged and allows an increased amount of water holding capacity. In PSE meat, when the pH is closer to the pI of the myofibrillar proteins, attraction between charged groups increases and the protein network shrinks. Therefore, part of the immobilized water becomes free water, which may be lost as drip (39).

Myofibrillar proteins such as myosin, the predominant muscle protein, have a large amount of water holding capacity. Any changes to this protein can decrease the ability of the muscle to retain water. Denaturation of myosin has been found to decrease water holding capacity (35, 40). In PSE muscle the myosin head shrinks from 19 nm in normal muscle to 17 nm (40). This shrinkage of the protein lattice causes expulsion of intracellular water into the extracellular space and decreases water holding capacity. The extent of myosin shrinkage is also dependent upon the rate of pH decline, ultimate pH, and temperature during chilling with the faster rate of decline and higher temperatures early postmortem, leading to increased denaturation and shrinkage.

C. TEXTURE

Protein gels are formed by intermolecular crosslinks resulting in an ordered three-dimensional network of proteins. The two primary steps involved in thermal gelation are denaturation of native myosin and aggregation of the partially unfolded myosin molecules to form the protein gel. Myosin denaturation can decrease the strength of heat-induced gelation. There are two transition temperatures (T_m) of myosin that are important in gel formation. Chicken breast myosin Tm_1 at 47.5°C is associated with the aggregation of the globular heads through disulfide bond formation while Tm_2 at 54°C is more associated with the network formation by the unfolding of the helical tail portion (41). However, turkey breast myosin is more temperature sensitive with the Tm_1 in turkey breast being only 40°C at pH 6–12 (42). These researchers also found that there was full reversibility of turkey breast myosin denaturation when heated for 5–30 min at 40°C and 5 min at 50°C followed by incubation at 4°C for 24 hours.

Gel strength is negatively correlated with cook loss and meat color, with higher cook loss and paler meat resulting in decreased gel strength. This negative correlation is probably due to the decreased solubility of myosin in PSE meat as well as fewer charges available for water-

water and protein-protein interactions. Extraction of salt soluble proteins from PSE meat is decreased compared to that of normal meat and gel strength is significantly less from product made with PSE meat. It has been postulated that the precipitation of phosphorylase onto the myofibrils at the Z line and A band results in a decreased solubility of myosin (43).

V. CONCLUSION

Muscle is a complex and highly specialized tissue that is able to convert chemical energy into mechanical energy for locomotion. The biochemical reactions that allow the muscle to complete these highly specialized tasks are the same reactions which cause the conversion of muscle into meat. The loss of the circulatory system is responsible for the anoxic conditions and allows the build-up of lactic acid which begins the process of rigor development. Meat quality characteristics can be affected by the rate of rigor mortis development. Once rigor mortis is complete, the muscle has been converted into meat.

REFERENCES

1. ED Aberle. Structure and Composition of Animal Tissues. In: Principles of Meat Science. 4th ed. Dubuque, IA: Kendall/Hunt Publishing Company, 2001, pp 9–41.
2. YL Xiong. Meat Processing. In: Shuryo, Nakai, HW Modler. eds. Food Proteins Processing Applications. New York: Wiley-VCH, 2000, pp 89–147.
3. PJ Bechtel. Muscle development and contractile proteins. In: PJ Bechtel. ed. Muscle as Food. New York: Academic Press, 1986, pp 1–35.
4. HB Hedrick, ED Aberle, JC Forrest, MD Judge, RA Merkel. Principles of Meat Science. 3rd ed. Dubuque, IA: Kendall/Hunt Publishing Co., 1989.
5. AM Pearson, RB Young. Muscle and Meat Biochemistry. San Diego, CA: Academic Press, 1989.
6. G Offer, P Knight, R Jeacocke, R Almond, T Cousins, J Elsey, N Parsons, A Sharp, R Starr, P Purslow. The structural basis of the water-holding, appearance and toughness of meat and meat products. Food Microstruct 8:151–170, 1989.
7. AC Guyton, JE Hall. Textbook of Medical Physiology. 9th ed. Philadelphia, PA: W B Saunders Co., 1996.
8. RA Lawrie. Lawrie's Meat Science. 6th ed. Cambridge, England: Woodhead Publishing Limited, 1998.
9. DM Smith. Functional properties of muscle proteins in processed poultry products. In: AR Sams. ed. Poultry Meat Processing. Boca Raton, FL: CRC Press, 2001, pp 181–194.
10. RM Robson, TW Huiatt, FC Parrish Jr. Biochemical and structural properties of titin, nebulin, and intermediate filaments in muscle. Recip Meat Conf Proc 44:7–20, 1991.
11. NFS Gualt. Structural aspects of raw meat. In: DA Ledward, DE Johnston, MK Knight. ed. The Chemistry of Muscle-Based Foods. Cambridge, England: The Royal Society of Chemistry, 1992, pp 79–105.
12. K Wang. Sarcomere-associated cytoskeletal lattices in striated muscle. Review and hypothesis. In: JW Shay. ed. Cell and Muscle Motility. Vol 6. New York: Plenum Publishing, 1985, pp 315–369.
13. DO Furst, M Osborn, R Nave, K Weber. The organization of titin filaments in the half-sarcomere revealed by monoclonal antibodies in immunoelectron microscopy: A map of ten nonrepetitive epitopes starting at the Z-line extends close to the M-line. J Cell Biol 106:1563–1572, 1988.
14. EA Foegeding, TC Lanier, HO Hultin. Characteristics of edible muscle tissues In: OR Fennema. ed. Food Chemistry. 3rd ed. New York, Marcel Dekker, Inc., 1996, pp 879–938.
15. AJ Bailey, ND Light. Connective Tissue in Meat and Meat Products. New York: Elsevier Science Publishing Co., 1989.
16. TJ Sims, AJ Bailey. Structural aspects of cooked meat. In: DA Ledward, DE Johnston, MK Knight. eds. The Chemistry of Muscle-Based Foods. Cambridge: The Royal Society of Chemistry, 1992, pp 106–127.
17. JR Bendall. Postmortem changes in muscle. In: GH Bourne. ed. The Structure and Function of Muscle. Vol. 2, Part 2. 2nd ed. New York: Academic Press, 1973, pp 244–309.
18. JM Murray, A Weber. The cooperative actions of muscle proteins. Sci Am 230:59–63, 1974.
17. WF Ganong. Excitable tissue: Muscle. In: Review of Medical Physiology. 17th ed. Norwalk, CT: Appleton and Lange, 1995, pp 56–67.
18. AJ Vander, JH Sherman, DS Luciano. Human Physiology: The Mechanisms of Body Function. 8th ed. New York: McGraw Hill Book Co., 2001.
19. AL Lehninger, DL Nelson, MM Cox. Integration and hormonal regulation of mammalian metabolism. In: Principles of Biochemistry. 2nd ed. New York: Worth Publishers, 1993, pp 736–787.
20. CK Matthews, KE Van Holde. Biochemistry. 2nd ed. Menlo Park, CA: Benjamin Cummings Publishing Co., Inc., 1996.
21. de Fremery, MF Pool. Biochemistry of chicken muscle as related to rigor-mortis and tenderization. Food Res 25:73–87, 1960.
22. PL Dawson, DM Janky, MG Dukes, LD Thompson, SA Woodward. Effect of postmortem boning time during simulated commercial processing on the tenderness of broiler breast meat. Poultry Sci 74:2035–2040, 1987.
23. Y Wu, and SB Smith. Ionic strength and myofibrillar solubilization. J Anim Sci 65:597–603, 1987.
24. DP Smith, DL Fletcher, CM Papa. Duckling and chicken processing yields and breast meat tenderness. Poultry Sci 71:197–202, 1992.
25. AR Sams, DM Janky. Research Note: Simultaneous histochemical determination of three fiber types in single sections of broiler skeletal muscles. Poultry Sci 69:1433–1436, 1990.
26. DP Smith, DL Fletcher, RJ Buhr, and RS Beyer. Pekin duckling and broiler chicken pectoralis muscle structure and composition. Poultry Sci 72:202–208, 1993.
27. JC George, AJ Berger. Avian Myology. New York: Academic Press, 1966, pp 177–183.

28. M Judge, ED Aberle, JC Forrest, HB Hedrick, RA Merkel. Principles of Meat Science. 2nd ed. Dubuque, IA: Kendall/Hunt Publishing Co., 1989.

29. PR Ferket, EA Foegeding. How nutrition and management influence PSE in poultry meat. In: Proceedings from BASF Technical Symposium, Multi-State Poultry Feeding and Nutrition Conference, Indianapolis, IN, 1994, pp 64–78.

30. AM Pearson. Introduction to quality attributes and their measurement in meat, poultry and fish products. In: AM Pearson, TR Dutson. eds. Quality Attributes and Their Measurement in Meat, Poultry and Fish Products. Glasgow, U.K.: Blackie Academic & Professional, 1994, pp 1–17.

31. NG Gregory. Preslaughter handling, stunning and slaughter. Meat Sci 36:45–56, 1994.

32. AC Enfalt, K Lundstrom, U Engstrand. Early post-mortem pH decrease in porcine M. Longissimus of PSE, normal, and DFD quality. Meat Sci 34:131–143, 1993.

33. BM Rathgeber, JA Boles, PJ Shand. Rapid postmortem pH decline and delayed chilling reduce quality of turkey breast meat. Poultry Sci 78:477–484, 1999.

34. EJ Briskey, J Wismer-Pedersen. Biochemistry of pork muscle structure. I. Rate of anaerobic glycolysis and temperature change verses the apparent structure of muscle tissue. J Food Sci 26:297–305, 1961.

35. IF Penny. Protein denaturation and water holding capacity in pork muscle. J Food Technol 4:269–273, 1969.

36. T Wismer-Pedersen. Quality of pork in relation to rate of pH change post-mortem. Food Res 24:711–727, 1959.

37. IF Penny. The effect of post-mortem conditions on the extractability and adenosine triphosphate activity of myofibrillar proteins of rabbit muscle. J Food Technol 2:325–338, 1967.

38. KO Honikel, R Hamm. Measurements of water-holding capacity and juiciness. In: AM Pearson, TR Dutson. eds. Quality Attributes and Their Measurement in Meat, Poultry and Fish Products. Glasgow, U.K.: Blackie Academic & Professional, 1994, pp 125–161.

39. R Hamm. Function properties of the myofibrillar system. In: Muscle as Food. Orlando, FL: Academic Press, Inc., 1986, pp 135–182.

40. G Offer. Modeling of the formation of pale, soft, and exudative meat: effects of chilling regime and rate and extent of glycolysis. Meat Sci 30:157–184, 1991.

41. AB Smyth. Heat induced gelation properties of muscle proteins. Ph.D. Dissertation. University College, Cork, Ireland, 1996.

42. GE Arteaga, S Nakai. Thermal denaturation of turkey breast myosin under different conditions: effect of temperature and pH, and reversibility of the denaturation. Meat Sci 31:191–200, 1992.

43. MM Pietrzak, L Greaser, AA Sosnicki. Effect of rapid rigor mortis processes on protein functionality on pectoralis major muscle of domestic turkeys. J Anim Sci 75:2106–2116, 1997.

32 Chemical Composition of Poultry Meat

Tomasz Lesiów
Department of Quality Analysis, University of Economics

CONTENTS

Poultry, especially chicken broilers and turkey, is one of the most widely consumed muscle foods in the world. It is an important source of dietary energy and nutrients, such as high quality proteins, essential fatty acids, vitamins and highly bio-available minerals [1]. In south-east and east Asia, as well as in eastern and western Europe, ducks and geese also play an important role because of their tasty meat. The world consumption of poultry meat in the year 2001 exceeded 69 949 thousand tons, ranked between production of beef and veal (56 647 thousand tons) and pig meat (91 188 thousand tons) [2]. The increase in muscle proportion and the reduction in carcass fat content by selection and careful restriction are major attempts to improve carcass quality of poultry and the nutritional value of meat [3–7]. However, concern has been raised over its high consumption and the fat content, in particular saturated fatty acids, which can greatly increase the risk of cardiovascular diseases and some type of cancer [8,9].

The chemical properties of poultry meat (or muscle) have been studied intensely. These studies were primarily carried out on whole poultry carcasses and/or specific muscles and included the examination of variables such as breed (genetics), diet formulations, age, gender, housing (live bird production) and general management practices (short-term antemortem stress) on composition, nutritive value, and quality of meat [10–13]. The present review will focus on the impact of muscle type on the nutritional value of poultry meat.

I. CHEMICAL COMPOSITION

Information about body composition can be important for those producing and selling animal products and nutritionists. Producers need information about body composition to produce leaner meat animals, sellers need information to determine how much of the energy that an animal eats is captured as growth or other forms of production [10].

The chemical composition of poultry breast (B) and thigh/leg (T/L) muscles is presented in Tables 32.1 through 32.3. The richest in protein were breast muscles of turkeys, broilers, geese, and ducks. The T/L muscles of

TABLE 32.1
Approximate Chemical Composition Profile for Breast (B) and Thigh/Leg (T/L) Poultry Muscles

Poultry Type	Moisture (%)		Protein (%)		Total Lipid (%)		Ash (%)		Reference
Muscle/Meat	B	T/L	B	T/L	B	T/L	B	T/L	
Chicken									
Broiler (6 wk) M	74.36	73.21	22.80	19.14	1.58	6.65	1.26	1.05	[11,12,14–18]
	(0.52)	(0.41)	(0.92)	(1.05)	(0.61)	(1.23)	(0.27)	(0.09)	
Broiler (8 wk)	75.37	74.66	22.39	19.00	1.48	5.33	0.61	0.51	[13*,19]
	(0.24)	(1.92)	(0.01)	(0.01)	(0.03)	(1.23)	(0.00)	(0.00)	
Hens (64 wk)**	73.21	74.04	–	–	1.51	4.49	1.08	1.06	[20]
Turkey (22 wk) M	72.74	72.24	23.36	19.54	1.63	4.84	1.18	1.09	[21–23]
	(2.10)	(1.03)	(1.37)	(0.08)	(0.35)	(1.09)	(0.02)	–	
Turkey (15 wk) F	73.51	72.91	23.29	19.52	1.25	6.28	1.17	1.06	[21,22,24]
	(0.56)	(24.0)	(1.14)	(0.31)	(0.59)	(0.80)	(0.05)	(0.02)	
Duck									
Pekin (7 wk) M	76.82	75.80	21.20	20.90	1.31	2.00	0.99	0.80	[25–27]
	(1.32)	(1.41)	(1.57)	(1.65)	(0.82)	(0.62)	(0.13)	(0.00)	
Pekin (8 wk) M	77.17	76.85	20.87	19.35	1.60	3.45	–	–	[12,26,28,29]
	(1.53)	(0.49)	(0.40)	(0.35)	(0.87)	(2.47)	–	–	
Muscovy (12 wk) M	76.43	76.06	20.89	20.31	1.43	3.43	1.07	–	[29–33]
	(0.39)	(0.48)	(0.67)	(0.27)	(0.47)	(0.61)	(0.08)	–	
Mule (12 wk)	74.55	74.50	21.78	21.40	2.41	2.70	1.15	1.20	[4,34,35]
	(0.67)	(0.00)	(1.29)	(0.00)	(0.38)	(0.00)	(0.07)	(0.00)	
Geese									
White Italian (16 wk) M	71.07		22.26		4.84		1.50		[36,37]
	(0.96)		(0.65)		(0.48)		(0.16)		
White Italian (17 wk)	72.36	71.55	22.48	20.38	3.11	6.51	1.18	1.00	[38,39]
	(0.08)	(2.81)	(0.62)	(0.49)	(0.18)	(3.27)	(0.11)	(0.03)	

M = male, F = female, * = drumstick, ** = white, dark muscles.

all kinds of poultry contained approximately 0.4–3.8% less protein (Table 32.1). Some authors found higher differences in protein content between breast and thigh muscles of broilers (23.80 vs. 18.30% [16]), 22 wk male turkeys (24.51 vs. 19.60% [22]), 16 wk female turkeys (25.24 vs. 21.29% [43] or 23.96 vs. 18.92% [45]) (Table 32.3), and 14 wk geese (23.02 and 19.39% [46]).

The fat content of breast muscles, in ascending order, was turkey females, Pekin and Muscovy ducks, broilers, hens, turkey males, Mule ducks, and geese; for T/L muscle, it was Pekin, mule, and Muscovy ducks, hens, turkey (Table 32.1). The fat content for the breast muscles from all poultry types was lower than for the L/T muscles.

Moisture content for Pekin and Muscovy ducks was greater than for other kinds of poultry. Moisture was comparable for turkey and geese and it was lower than in broilers, hens, and Mule ducks. Broilers, Pekin ducks, and goose breast muscles had higher percentage of moisture than the T/L muscles. The higher content of moisture in broiler breast muscles than in thigh muscle (73.74 vs. 73.22%) was also found by Gornowicz and Dziadek [15] but it was not significantly different (Table 32.3). However, Biliński et al. [38] found about 1% lower moisture content in 17 wk goose breast muscle compared to thigh muscle (72.31 vs. 73.54%).

The content of ash in breast muscle of chickens, Pekin ducks, and geese was higher than in thigh muscles while it was comparable both brest & thigh muscles for hens, turkeys and Mule ducks.

A. CHEMICAL COMPOSITION—AGE, SEX, STRAIN

The influence of age and sex on chemical composition of poultry meat is presented in Tables 32.2 and 32.3. In earlier studies as the broiler increased in age from 6 to 8 wk protein content in light male and female meat increased by 0.52 and 0.80% and fat in male white and dark meat increased by 1.32 and 1.66% [47]. The protein content increased with age to the detriment of water content in 12 vs. 14 wk female turkey breast and thigh muscles (23.60 vs. 24.80% and 20.70 vs. 22.40% [41]) and Pekin and Mule duck breast muscles [4,26] (Table 32.2). In 16–18 wk female turkey muscles the protein (breast) and moisture (breast and thigh) contents were comparable, while in thigh muscles protein content decreased after 16 wk [41]. During the growth from 2 to 5 wk Pekin duck breast muscles decreased in protein content from 21.5 to 20.0% and then after 7 wk increased to 21.9% while the leg muscle protein content was not influenced by age [25]. With advancing age increased fat content was observed in turkey breast muscle [40]; female turkey

TABLE 32.2

Influence of Age on Approximate Chemical Composition Profile for Poultry Breast (B) and Thigh/Leg (T/L) Muscles

Poultry Type	Moisture (%)		Protein (%)		Total Lipid (%)		Ash (%)		Reference
Muscle/Meat	B	T/L	B	T/L	B	T/L	B	T/L	
Turkey (16 wk)	73.74		23.98		0.18		1.04		[40]
Turkey (20 wk)	73.52		23.85		0.47		1.00		[40]
Turkey (12 wk) F	74.70	75.20/	23.60	20.70/	1.50	3.70/			[41]
Turkey (16 wk) F	73.60	72.80/	24.30	20.10/	1.90	6.30/			[41]
Turkey (18 wk) F	73.50	72.90/	24.10	20.60	1.90	5.50/			[41]
Duck									
Pekin (7 wk)	77.50	76.80/	19.40	19.00/	0.40	1.50/			[26]
Pekin (8 wk)	76.00	76.50/	21.30	19.60/	0.60	1.70/			[26]
Pekin (9 wk)				21.30	20.20/	1.50	3.20		[6]
Pekin (12 wk)				22.00	19.60	2.10	3.20		[6]
Muscovy (10.5 wk)			19.90	20.30/	1.40	1.90/			[6]
Muscovy (15 wk)			21.00	20.50/	1.30	1.70/			[6]
Mule (8 wk)			19.20	20.40/	1.00	1.60/			[6]
Mule (14 wk)			22.00	20.40/	1.40	1.80/			[6]
Mule (10 wk) M	75.60		21.84		2.09		1.10		[4]
Mule (12 wk) M	74.10		22.53		2.83		1.20		[4]
Geese (10 wk)	75.14	75.78/	20.77	19.27/	2.61	3.45/	0.99	0.79/	[38]
Geese (17 wk)	72.31	73.54/	22.04	20.73/	3.24	4.20/	1.10	0.98/	[38]
Geese (33 wk)	72.13	73.32/	20.92	19.57/	4.12	5.73/	1.19	1.09/	[38]
Geese (15 wk)*	71.69	/70.73	21.53	/20.39	5.87	/8.61	1.18	/1.01	[42]
Geese (24 wk)**	71.56	/71.35	21.67	/20.34	5.17	/7.12	1.06	/1.06	[42]

M = male, F = Female, * = intensive, ** = semi-intensive system.

thigh muscle [41]; Pekin breast [6]; Pekin thigh muscles [26]; and Mule duck breast and thigh muscles [4,6]. However, less fat content was found in 15 vs. 10.5 wk Muscovy ducks [6] and 24 vs. 15 wk geese [42]. According to Bieliński et al. [38] the protein and fat content in goose breast and thigh muscles increased with age from 10 to 17 wk, remained comparable between 17 and 25 wk, and after 33 wk protein content decreased and fat content increased, respectively. Moreover, in muscles of 10 wk geese the moisture content was the highest and the ash content was the lowest and they did not change with age (Table 32.2). Friend et al. [48] found no effect of age on geese breast muscles protein and fat contents.

The differences in chemical composition between males (M) and females (F) were found for broilers, turkeys, and ducks (Table 32.3). Evans et al. [47] found that fat content was higher in male broiler light (white, breast) meat than in light females (16.18 vs. 14.66%) and the protein content of dark meat of males compared with females was higher (18.32 vs. 17.60%) but the moisture (64.37 vs. 66.62%) and fat (11.85 vs. 13.99%) contents were lower. Gornowicz and Dziadek [15] found only a higher content of moisture and ash in broiler male muscles compared to female muscles (Table 32.3). The breast muscles of 22/24 wk male turkeys contained less moisture

[22,23,45] and more fat than those of 15/16 wk females [21–23,43,45]. However, Faruga et al. [43] noticed higher amounts of moisture in 24 wk turkey males both in breast and thigh muscles than in 16 wk females. Lower moisture content and higher fat content were also observed in male Mule duck breast compared with females [4]. The reverse trend, i.e., higher moisture and lower lipid content, was found for male and female breast muscles of Pekin ducks [28]. Muscovy duck [28] and goose [36,44] male breast muscles were characterized by higher fat content than females. The thigh muscles of turkey and male Pekin duck had lower lipid levels than female thigh muscle [22,23,27,43,45] (Table 32.3). At the same age (14 wk) male turkeys deposited in breast and thigh muscles less total lipid content than females, i.e., 0.96 vs. 1.32% and 2.26 vs. 2.88%, respectively [49]; this was in line with lower fat content in male turkey thigh muscles than female at different ages (22/24 vs. 15/16 wk). Male Turkeys had higher ash content in the breast muscles compared to females (1.11 vs. 0.93% [40]).

Other authors found no differences in moisture, fat, and protein contents based on sex for broiler muscles [15] and Pekin duck [25] and goose [48] breast and/or leg muscle protein and fat; broiler breast [14], turkey breast [40] and Muscovy duck [29] and 12/16 wk goose [50]

TABLE 32.3
Influence of Sex on Approximate Chemical Composition Profile for Poultry Breast (B) and Thigh/Leg (T/L) Muscles

| Poultry Type | Moisture (%) | | Protein (%) | | Total Lipid (%) | | Ash (%) | | |
Muscle/Meat	B	T/L	B	T/L	B	T/L	B	T/L	Reference
Broiler (6 wk) M	73.74	73.22/	21.49	18.34/	0.88	6.73/	1.79	1.15/	[15]
Broiler (6 wk) F	70.44	70.17/	21.67	18.15/	0.71	6.67/	1.35	0.91	[15]
Turkey (22wk) M	73.95		21.85		1.57		1.20		[21]
Turkey (15 wk) F	74.13		22.43		0.88		1.22		[21]
Turkey (24 wk) M	72.35	72.51/	24.64	22.31/	2.09	4.39/	1.12	1.09/	[43]
Turkey (16 wk) F	70.24	68.65/	25.24	21.29/	1.17	7.42/	1.12	1.06/	[43]
Turkey (22 wk) M	70.32	72.97/	24.51	19.60/	1.32	4.07/	1.17	1.09/	[22]
Turkey (15 wk) F	73.04	72.74/	24.58	19.74/	0.93	5.72/	1.13	1.08/	[22]
Turkey (22 wk) M	73.96	71.52/	23.73	19.49/	2.01	5.61/			[23]
Turkey (16 wk) F	74.60	71.61/	23.96	18.92/	0.76	8.61			[23]
Turkey M	73.70		23.81		0.31		1.11		[40]
Turkey F	73.56		24.02		0.34		0.93		[40]
Duck									
Pekin (7 wk) M	75.30	74.80/	22.30	21.70/	1.50	2.70/	0.90	0.80/	[27]
Pekin (7 wk) F	75.70	75.10/	21.00	20.50/	2.10	3.40/	1.10	1.00/	[27]
Pekin (8 wk) M	76.60		20.80		2.10				[28]
Pekin (8 wk) F	74.00		20.50		2.60				[28]
Muscovy (12 wk) M	76.13	/75.72	21.32	/20.12	2.09	/3.86			[29]
Muscovy (10 wk) F	76.63	/75.62	21.20	/19.95	1.90	/3.96			[29]
Muscovy (11 wk) M	76.50		20.20		2.50				[28]
Muscovy (9 wk) F	76.30		19.60		1.60				[28]
Mule (10 wk) M	75.60		21.84		2.09		1.10		[4]
Mule (10 wk) F	76.35		21.66		1.69		1.11		[4]
Mule (12 wk) M	74.10		22.53		2.83		1.20		[4]
Mule (12 wk) F	75.02		22.27		2.26		1.24		[4]
Geese (16 wk) M	70.39		22.72		5.18		1.39		[37]
Geese (16 wk) F	70.45		21.64		4.32		1.38		[37]
Geese (16.6 wk) M	73.10		22.70		6.10		1.60		[44]
Geese (16.6 wk) F	73.70		22.60		5.30		1.40		[44]

M = male, F = Female.

muscles; turkey thigh [22,23,45] and goose [36] breast muscle protein and moisture; and Mule duck breast muscle [4] mineral content.

Differences in the moisture, protein, and fat content of pullet and cockerel breast and thigh muscles or broiler breast muscles were associated with strain crosses [13,15]. Strain also influenced the protein percentage and fat in broiler thigh muscles but no strain-related differences were found in moisture content. The small differences in muscle chemical composition among strain crosses may slightly alter the nutritional value of broiler meat [13]. Puchajda et al. [22,45] found that turkey medium-heavies' genetic lines influenced the differences in breast protein content of 22 wk males and in thigh muscle fat content of 15/16 wk females. However, another survey found no influence of genetic lines of heavies turkey males (22 wk) on muscle protein and fat content

[23]. Filus et al. [21] did not show any significant indication of the dependency of hybrid turkey heavies and medium-heavies on the chemical composition of meat.

Górska and Górski [26] reported differences among duck crossbreds in breast and thigh muscle moisture and protein contents with no apparent species-fat content relationship in the case of both muscles. Nutritive values of breast and thigh muscles of SW (Small White), Synta (Pekin) ducks and their reciprocal crosses showed a tendency of paternal effect on protein and fat contents in breast and thigh muscles; in ash this was only evident in thigh muscles [27]. The strain had also a significant impact on the protein [39,50], moisture, and/or ash content in goose breast and leg muscles [39]. According to Friend et al. [48] strain influenced the fat content in goose breast muscles but had no influence on protein content.

II. AMINOACIDS AND COLLAGEN

Poultry meat is an important source of high biological value proteins providing all of the indispensable (essential) amino acids [44,51,52]. On average, 40% of the amino acids present in meat are indispensable for human health [9]. Dietary proteins are the only source of amino acids that we need. Our bodies require nine essential amino acids that animal protein contains in the best "proportion" [1]. The high lysine content of meat protein is important nutritionally because it counter-balances the low lysine content of cereal proteins when they are eaten together in a mixed diet [9].

The content, type, and cross-links in collagen influence nutritional and dietetic values of meat and its tenderness [53,54]. Poultry breast muscle was found to contain less collagen than thigh muscle (Table 32.4). The same trend was observed when collagen was expressed in relation to total protein content in the particular kind of poultry meat with the exception of 8 week Pekin ducks for which breast protein contained 1% more collagen than thigh muscle protein. As a protein of lower value collagen was the lowest in turkey and geese, and higher in broiler an Pekin duck muscles.

III. HEME PIGMENTS

Primary heme pigments in poultry meat include myoglobin, hemoglobin, and cytochrome c. The quantity of myoglobin greatly influences the appearance of poultry meat. Hemoglobin is another pigment of importance since about 20 to 30% remains in the carcass of a well-bled bird, thus influencing final carcass coloration [57]. Heme pigment content and "free iron ions" were associated with occurrence of lipid oxidation [19,58].

Table 32.5 shows total heme and heme pigments in poultry muscles. Goose and duck breast muscles contained considerably more heme pigments than the breast muscles of turkeys, hens, and broilers. The same trend was observed in T/L muscle; however, differences in heme pigment content (except for young and adult layer) were less pronounced among different poultry types. Nishida et al. [62] found different amounts of myoglobin in adult layer leg muscles, i.e., from 4.44 to 5.82 mg/g in adductores, 2.53 mg/g in sartorius, and 0.57 mg/g in biceps femoris, which was greater than for young layer, amounted to 0.33 mg/g of myoglobin in biceps femoris. The broiler, hen, and turkey breast muscles had from 1.4 to 6.4 times lower concentration of heme pigments, hemoglobin, myoglobin, and cytochrome (broilers) than those for T/L muscles (Table 32.5). These differences were smallest broilers and greatest for hens. In duck and goose breast muscles the heme pigments content was 14 to 79% greater than that in the leg muscles. However, total pigment concentration in Muscovy ducks and hemoglobin content in Pekin ducks were not significantly different in both muscles.

The mg of total pigment per gram of muscle increased in the following order: broiler breast, hen breast, turkey breast, broiler thigh/leg, hen leg, turkey leg, duck leg, goose leg, duck breast, and goose breast.

A. HEME PIGMENTS—AGE, SEX, AND STRAIN

With advancing age (18 vs. 28 wk) myoglobin concentration significantly increased in male turkey breast muscles

TABLE 32.4
Collagen Content for Poultry Breast (B) and Thigh (T) Muscles

Poultry Type	Collagen		Collagen/Protein (%)		
Muscle	B	T	B	T	Reference
Broiler	3.12 (mg/g)				[55]
Broiler	1.27 (mg/g)				[12]
Broilers	0.54 (%)	1.05 (%)	2.34	5.31	[53]
Broilers M	0.733 (%)	1.04 (%)			[56]
Broilers F	0.62 (%)	0.783 (%)			[56]
Turkey (22 wk) M	385 (mg%)	572 (mg%)	1.63	2.94	[23]
Turkey (16 wk) F	429 (mg%)	484 (mg%)	1.80	2.55	[45]
Turkey (16 wk) F	358 (mg%)	839 (mg%)	1.48	4.17	[41]
Duck					
Pekin	1.75 (mg/g)				[12]
Pekin (8 wk)			5.0	4.05	[26]
Muscovy (12 wk)	2.52 (%)				[33]
Geese					
White Italian (14 wk)	340 (mg%)	670 (mg%)	1.45	2.83	[36]
White Italian (17 wk)	400 (mg%)	600 (mg%)	1.81	2.89	[38]

M = male, F = Female.

TABLE 32.5
Total Heme, Hemoglobin, and Myoglobin Content in Poultry Breast (B) and Thigh/Leg (T/L) Muscles

Poultry Type	Total Pigment (mg/g)		Hemoglobin (mg/g)		Myoglobin (mg/g)		Cytochrome (mg/g)		Reference
Muscle/Meat	B	T/L	B	T/L	B	T/L	B	T/L	
Broiler*	0.32	0.59/	0.17	0.38/	0.15	0.21/	13.71	37.38/	[59]
Broiler**	0.44	0.79/	0.28	0.48/	0.16	0.30/	27.15	65.99/	[59]
Broiler	0.24	/1.09	0.24	0.75	–	0.34			[60]
Broiler (8 wk)	0.43	/1.75	0.12	/0.58	0.31	/1.17			[61]
Hen (60 wk)	0.46	/2.49	0.13	/0.80	0.33	/1.69			[61]
Turkey	0.51		0.06		0.45				[40]
Turkey (24 wk) M	0.74	/2.66	0.16	/1.02	0.58	/1.64			[61]
Duck									
Pekin (8 wk)	3.59	/2.91	1.19	/1.17	2.40	/1.74			[61]
Pekin (8 wk)	4.31	/3.54							[29]
Muscovy (12 wk) M	3.90	/3.02							[29]
Muscovy (10 wk) F	3.68	/2.79							[29]
Goose (16 wk)	6.47	/3.80	1.71	/1.14	4.76	/2.66			[61]

M = male, F = Female, * = ice slush, ** = air chilling.

and male and female thigh muscles with no changes in the breast muscles from female turkeys [63].

Male turkeys exhibited significantly higher myoglobin concentration than females [63] and male Muscovy ducks had higher total heme pigment concentration than females (Table 32.5) [29].

IV. VITAMINS

Poultry meat is rich in niacin (PP), an essential vitamin that plays a role in many metabolic cycles. Moreover, it is also an important source of vitamins from the B group, like thiamine (B_1) and riboflavin (B_2), both important in energy metabolism, and B_{12}, which is necessary to the nervous system and exclusively present in foods of animal origin (not available in plants) [1]. Depending on the kind of diet, broiler and turkey muscles, hens, ducks, and goose meat can be also a supplementary source of vitamins diluted in lipids, i.e., vitamins A, D, and E [64,65].

The content of vitamins in poultry muscles is presented in Table 32.6. Thiamine content (B_1) was the highest in duck flesh and substantially lower, 2.79 times, in goose flesh, 5.1 times in broiler breast, and 5.6 times in turkey white meat [52]. The content of vitamin B_1 was comparable in broiler breast and T/L muscles and turkey white and dark meat, respectively. The increasing order of the amount of riboflavin (B_2) in poultry meat was as follows: broiler breast, turkey white, turkey breast, hen breast, broiler leg, turkey dark, duck and goose flesh. The broiler muscles had two times more niacin (PP) than turkey light and dark meat and 2–3 times more than hen, duck, and goose flesh. The richest in vitamin B_6 were

broilers, then geese and turkey, while duck content of this vitamin was the lowest.

A. VITAMINS—AGE, SEX, AND STRAIN

Riboflavin (B_2) content in breast broiler muscles decreased with age from 7 to 12 wk (0.093 vs. 0.086 mg/100 g) with no changes in niacin (PP) and vitamin B_6 [66]. In contrast, Singh and Essary [67] reported that with advancing age of broilers from 8 to 10 wk the content of thiamine (B_1) and riboflavin (B_2) increased in breast (0.032 vs. 0.045 and 0.040 vs. 0.050 mg/100 g) and thigh (0.059 vs. 0.066 and 0.096 vs. 0.113 mg/100 g) while the amount of niacin (PP) decreased in thigh muscles (6 vs. 5.6 mg/100 g) and did not change in breast muscles (10.4 vs. 10.2 mg/100 g).

Ang and Hamm [14] stated no significant differences due to sex in riboflavin (B_2), niacin (PP), and vitamin B_6 in the breast of 7 wk broilers. It was in line with results of Singh and Assary [67] who found that only male broiler thigh contained significantly more thiamine (B_1) and riboflavin (B_2) than female thigh muscles, i.e., 0.065 vs. 0.060 and 0.111 vs. 0.101 mg/100 g, respectively.

V. MINERALS

Minerals influence palatability, acidity of meat, biological activity of different enzymes, and osmolarity of meat. Iron is an important nutrient for human beings because it plays a part in the process of oxygen transport from lungs to various tissues by means of hemoglobin to which it is linked. Iron functions as a catalyst in many metabolic reactions. Its absence provokes anaemia [1]. Preponderance of haem

TABLE 32.6
Approximate Analysis of Vitamins in Poultry Breast (B) and Thigh/Leg (T/L) Muscles

Poultry Type	Thiamine (B₁) (mg/100 g)		Riboflavin (B₂) (mg/100 g)		Niacin (PP) (mg/100 g)		B₆ (mg/100 g)		
Muscle/Meat	B	T/L	B	T/L	B	T/L	B	T/L	Reference
Broiler			0.093		12.12		0.84		[66]
Broiler			0.086		11.98		0.824		[14]
Broiler	0.070	0.076/	0.092	0.188/	11.194	6.328/	0.55	0.33/	[52]
Broiler	0.090	/0.080	0.153	/0.226	12.44	/2.78			[65]
Hen**	0.083		0.159		5.16				[65]
Turkey*	0.064	0.081	0.122	0.221	5.844	3.075	0.56	0.36	[52]
Turkey	0.036		0.150		4.92				[65]
Duck**	0.360		0.450		5.300		0.34		[52]
Duck**	0.177		0.226		3.45				[65]
Goose**	0.129		0.377		4.278		0.64		[52]
Goose**	0.120		0.330		6.40				[65]

* = light and dark meat, ** = flesh.

iron in meat, which is absent from plant sources, makes the iron from meat more bioavailable [9]. Zinc is important because it is involved in several metabolic reactions and meat is its main source. Its deficiency reduces the immunological defenses of the organism [1,68].

Table 32.7 shows the mineral content in poultry meat. The broiler breast muscles contained more Mg, K, P, and Li (18.2 vs. 5.8 µg/g [69]), less Cu, Fe, Zn, and Na, and a comparable level of Ca than T/L muscles. Goluch-Koniuszy et al. [70,71] found no difference in Cu and Mg content between broiler breast and leg muscles and Kunachowicz et al. [65] found lower Ca content in broiler breast than thigh muscles. Turkey breast muscles were characterized by higher content of K and P and lower content of remaining minerals when compared with thigh muscles [41]. However, Posati [52] showed higher Mg content in light than in dark turkey muscles. Goose breast muscles had a higher content of Fe and lower Ca than thigh muscles. The higher content of Fe in broiler and turkey T/L muscles as well as in goose breast muscle was related to their greater content of myoglobin and hemoglobin than in corresponding breast and thigh muscles, respectively (Table 32.5). Higher content of Zn in T/L muscles can be explained by their greater metabolic activity.

The iron content in goose muscles was substantially higher than in broiler and turkey muscles and in hen, duck, and goose flesh (Table 32.7). The richest in zinc were turkey thigh muscles. The average zinc content was in duck flesh and broiler T/L muscles, and the lowest was in turkey and broiler breast muscles. The Mg content was rather uniformly distributed in broiler and turkey muscles and its content in duck, hen, and goose flesh was between that of broilers and turkeys. It was difficult to estimate the

order of Na, K, and P contents in poultry meat on the basis of different author results presented in Table 32.7.

A. MINERALS—AGE, SEX, AND STRAIN

In broiler breast and thigh muscles sex influenced Fe, Zn, and Na levels. Fe content was lower in breast and thigh muscles of broiler males than females while Zn content was higher in males than females, but differences were not so high as for Fe content [16]. According to Goluch-Koniuszy et al. [71], sodium content was higher in female breast muscles and in male leg muscles, respectively. Other authors found no sex influence on the level of nutrients (Cu, Fe, Zn, Mg, Ca, Na, K, P, and Li) in broiler cockerels and pullets [69,70].

Strain influenced the level of Mg, Ca, and K [16] as well as Ca and Li levels [69] in broiler breast and thigh muscles.

VI. LIPID FRACTIONS CONTENT

Lipids play a key role in many quality traits of meat products including nutritional value and sensory properties, mainly flavor because they are both solvent and precursors of aroma compounds. Intramuscular lipids refer to lipids contained in both intramuscular adipose tissue and muscle fibers. The intramuscular adipose tissue comprises cells located along the fibers and in the interfascicular area. The fat cells contain almost exclusively triacylglycerols (TAG). The lipids of the fibers consist of cytosolic droplets of TAGs and membrane lipids, phospholipids (PL), and cholesterol. The amount of TAGs in the fibers only accounts for a small part of the total intramuscular TAGs [74].

TABLE 32.7
Minerals in Poultry Breast (B) and Thigh/Leg (T/L) Muscles (Wet Weight Basis)

Poultry Type Muscle	Cu B	Cu T/L	Fe B	Fe T/L	Zn B	Zn T/L	Mg B	Mg T/L	Ca B	Ca T/L	Na B	Na T/L	K B	K T/L	P B	P T/L	Mn B/T	Reference R
Broiler	0.51	0.68	6.81	10.70	6.65	15.27	247	216	39.00	42.00	456	620	2099	1835	2479	1829		R
	(0.03)	(0.02)	(1.70)	(3.28)	(0.07)	(1.01)	(73.76)	(60.62)	–	–	(88.84)	(39.00)	(627)	(461)	(339)	(127)		
Broiler	0.41	0.65	7.20	10.30	8.00	19.85	280	235	110	105	650	860/	2550	2300	1960	1675	0.18/0.20	[52]
Broiler			4.00	7.00/			330	230/	50.00	90.00/	550	850/	3850	3000/	2400	1960/		[65]
Turkey F 0.41	0.96/	5.01	11.87/	9.08	26.03	97.99	129/	40.95	51.83/	630	880/	3780	3410/	2830	2630/	0.19		[41]
Turkey	0.57	0.98/	8.44	16.40/	9.23	24.27												[73]
Turkey*	0.75	1.47	11.90	17.50	16.20	32.2	270	220	120	170	630	770	3050	2860	2040	1840	0.19/0.22	[52]
Turkey			5.00				350		20.00		470		4600		2380			[65]
Goose			55.00	50.00/					155	230								[37]
Flesh Hens			16.00				190		110		660		3070		1620			[65]
Duck	2.53		21.00–24.00		19.00		140–190		80–110		660–740		2420–2710		1490–2030		[65–52]	
Goose	3.06		24.00–25.70		–		180–240		50–130		480–870		2430–4200		1520–3120		[65–52]	
Influence of Sex																		
Broiler M 0.53	0.67	4.46	6.13	6.70	14.10	162	/153			363	/581	1626	/1462				[70,71]	
Broiler F 0.57	/0.73	4.10	/5.89	6.63	13.12	164	/167			399	/552	1634	/1474				[70,71]	

M = male, F = Female, * = Light, Dark; R = [11,58,68–72].

TABLE 32.8

Total Lipid Content and Lipid Class Composition of Poultry Breast (B) and Thigh/Leg (T/L) Muscles

Poultry Type	Total Lipids (g/100 g)		TAG* (g/100 g)		PL** (g/100 g)		FFA (g/100 g)		
Muscle/Meat	B	T/L	B	T/L	B	T/L	B	T/L	Reference
Broiler			0.24	/0.70	0.50	/0.64	0.024	/0.033	[75]
Broiler		0.90	2.20	0.37	0.73/	0.61	0.26/		[76]
Broiler M	0.90	2.30/	0.35	0.76/	0.62	0.23/			[77]
Broiler F	0.90	3.20/	0.43	0.83/	0.55	0.16/			[77]
Broiler (11 wk)	0.97	/2.10	0.22	/1.08	0.68	/0.90			[78]
Broiler (11.7 wk)	0.87	2.60/	0.35	1.84/	0.52	0.76/			[64]
Turkey	1.21	2.03/	0.58	1.14/	0.50	0.76/	0.015	0.026/	[79]
Duck									
Muscovy (12 wk) M	1.82		0.56		1.12				[32]
Mule (10/12 wk) M	2.09/2.83		0.88/1.65		1.12/1.09				[4]
Mule (10/12 wk) F	1.69/2.26		0.58/1.11		0.98/1.0				[4]
Landaise Goose (24 wk)			3.88		0.98		0.04		[80]

M = male, F = Female, * = TAG (triacylglycerols), ** = PL (phospholipids).

Table 32.8 shows that the TAG content was the lowest in broiler breast, average in turkey and Muscovy duck breast, highers in male mule duck, and the highest in goose breast muscles. The PL content in broiler and turkey breast muscles was lower by nearly half of its level in duck and goose breast muscles.

Broiler, hen [81], and turkey breast muscles contained less total lipids, TAGs, and PL than thigh muscles. The high level of PL is characteristic of red, oxidative muscles. Therefore breast, glicolytic muscles of broilers and turkeys contained less PL than T/L contra partners as well as breast muscles of ducks and geese which mainly comprised red fibers [12,82–84]. Surprisingly, some authors found that PL was higher in the lipids of broiler breast than thigh muscle lipids [76,77]. In both broiler and turkey muscle types, free fatty acids were present in only trace amounts. The FFA concentration was higher in broiler leg muscles by 37% [85] and turkey thigh muscles by 73% [79] compared to corresponding breast muscles.

Broiler muscle lipid fraction contained more FFA amounts than turkey muscles. The broiler and Muscovy and 10 wk Mule duck breast muscles contained more PL than TAG. The reverse was true for goose breast and 12 wk male Mule duck muscles while in turkey breast and 12 wk mule female duck the level of the main components of lipids was comparable. On the other hand, in broiler and turkey T/L muscles PL content was lower than the TAG content.

The fatty acid composition of the different lipid classes of broiler and turkey muscles is shown in Tables 32.9 and 32.10. There were only small differences between broiler and turkey breast and leg TAG fatty acid composition (Table 32.9). According to Pikul et al. [78] in broiler muscles palmitic (C16:0), oleic (C18:1), linoleic (C18:2n6), and linolenic (C18:3n3) acids in TAG accounted for about 26%, 37%, 22%, and 1%, respectively. Ahn et al. [85] and Sklan and Tenne [75] found that broiler breast TAG contained less oleic acid (C18:1) and more linoleic acid (C18:2n6) and linolenic acid (C18:3n3) than leg muscles. Sklan and Tenne [79] found lower content of palmitic acid (C16:0) and higher content of linoleic acid (C18:2n6) in turkey breast TAG than in turkey thigh TAG. There were no arachidonic acid (C20:4n6) and polyunsaturated PUFA n-3 in turkey muscle TAGs fraction. The decreasing percentage of the fatty acid groups in TAGs was monounsaturated fatty acids (MUFA), saturated fatty acids (SFA), and PUFA for broiler muscles [64,75,78,85] and SFA, MUFA, and PUFA for turkey muscles [79].

The PL fatty acid composition of broiler and turkey breast muscles was different from T/L muscles (Table 32.10). The PL fraction of broiler and turkey breast contained more palmitic acid (C16:0) and oleic acid (C18:1) and less stearic acid (C18:0) and linoleic acid (C18:2n6) than PL from T/L muscles [64,75,78]. The above pattern was also valid for phosphatidyl choline (one apart phosphatidyl ethanolamine major PL) with the one exception of similar or higher values of linoleic acid (C18:2n6) in breast and T/L broiler muscles [75,85]. The broiler breast and T/L muscles contained a higher level of arachidonic acid (C20:4n6) in PL fraction than corresponding turkey muscles by 6.5 and 7.0%, respectively. The relative percentage of PUFA was the same in the PL from broiler breast and leg muscles while for turkey PL the percentage of PUFA was lower in breast than thigh muscles. Compared to phosphatidyl choline (PC) phosphatidyl ethanolamine (PE) in broilers contained more PUFAs. Turkey muscles lacked PUFA n-3 in the PL fraction, likewise in the TAGs fraction.

TABLE 32.9

Fatty Acid Composition (%) of the TAG Fraction of Lipids from Broiler and Turkey Breast (B) and Thigh/Leg (T/L) Muscles

Reference	[75]	[85]	[78]	[75]	[85]	[78]	[79]	[79]
Poultry Type	Broiler			Broiler			Turkey	
Muscle	B	B	B (11 wk)	T	L	L (11 wk)	B	T
FFA profile (%)								
C14:0		0.80	0.82		1.02	0.83		
C16:0	25.10	21.42	26.01	25.20	21.22	25.65	29.30	32.60
C18:0	6.50	5.96	6.36	5.80	5.45	5.81	9.00	9.40
C20:0		0.81	0.28			0.28		
C22:0			0.28			0.39		
C14:1			0.20			0.12		
C16:1	8.00	4.93	5.21	7.90	5.60	5.73	3.10	5.00
C18:1	43.00	46.35	37.31	44.60	52.08	36.41	30.20	30.30
C20:1			0.72			0.44		
C18:2n6	17.30	17.15	21.39	16.20	13.03	22.12	27.60	23.80
C20:2n6		0.41	0.21		0.29	0.32		
C20:4n6	0.10		0.70	0.30		1.08		
C18:3n3		1.46	1.25		0.69	1.24		
C20:5n3	0.00	0.00			0.19			
SFA	31.60	28.98	33.75	31.10	27.68	32.96	38.30	42.00
MUFA	51.00	52.00	42.72	52.50	58.13	42.26	33.30	35.30
PUFA	17.40	19.02	23.55	16.50	14.18	24.76	27.60	23.80
n-6	17.40	17.56	22.30	16.50	13.31	23.52	27.60	23.80
n-3		1.46	1.25		0.87	1.24		
n-6/n-3		12.03	17.84		15.30	18.97		

The decreasing percentage of the fatty acids groups in PL for broiler muscles, i.e., PUFA, SFA, and MUFA (The reverse when compared with TAGs) differed from turkey muscles: SFA, PUFA, and MUFA [64,75,78].

The fatty acid composition of TAGs was different from the fatty acid composition of PL (Tables 32.9 and 32.10). The PL fraction from broiler and turkey muscles contained more PUFA and SFA and less MUFA than the TAGs fraction. The arachidonic acid content in broiler breast and leg muscles was substantially higher in PL than in TAG. The broiler breast and leg PUFA n-6/n-3 ratio in PL was two times lower than in TAG (2.04 and 2.11) [78].

A. LIPID FRACTIONS CONTENT—AGE, SEX, AND STRAIN

The TAG content of Mule duck increased with age and this correlated with the increase in lipid content (Table 32.7) [4].

There was no change in the content or class composition of the lipids with sex of broilers [77]. At any given age, the TAG content was higher in male Mule duck breast compared with the females but this difference was not significant [4].

VII. CHOLESTEROL

Determination of cholesterol in food is important for consumer health [86]. High dietary cholesterol intake is considered to be one of the risk factors for human atherogenesis [87]. The higher cholesterol concentration reduces membrane fluidity, lowers Ca^+-ATPase activity, and regulates contraction and relaxation rates [88]. Cholesterol content in chicken tissue is possible to be influenced by fatty acid composition of the diet [3] or by the dietary garlic and copper content [88].

Table 32.11 presents cholesterol content expressed in mg/100 g of poultry meat. The cholesterol content in poultry breast white muscles, in ascending order, was as follows: broilers, hens and turkeys, Muscovy ducks, goose, Pekin and Mule ducks, and ranged from 41.0 to 123 mg/100 g. The cholesterol content in different poultry T/L muscles was on similar level with one exception of higher content in hen dark meat, and ranged from 64.0 to 101 mg/100 g. Cholesterol is solely a membrane lipid in meat, and is also found in cell membranes of adipose tissue and fatty tissue [91]. Cholesterol is usually associated with adipose tissue, which is more abundant in thigh than in broiler and turkey breast muscles (Table 32.1). Moreover,

TABLE 32.10

Fatty Acid Composition (%) of the PL Fraction and Its Classes (PE* and PC**) of Lipids from Broiler and Turkey Breast (B) and Thigh/Leg (T/L) Muscles

Reference	[75]	[75]	[85]	[85]	[75]	[75]	[85]	[85]	[78]	[78]	[79]	[79]
Poultry Type	Broiler										Turkey	
Muscle	B/PE	B/PC	B/PE	B/PC	T/PE	T/PC	L/PE	L/PC	B/PL	L/PL (11 wk)	B/PL	T/PL
FFA profile (%)												
C14:0			0.80	0.48			0.51	0.48	0.15	0.18		
C16:0	16.00	35.00	7.61	26.28	16.70	18.90	7.96	23.9	20.36	16.82	25.60	19.70
C18:0	26.60	11.00	19.21	10.58	24.10	33.70	19.99	15.99	12.76	20.09	22.50	24.30
C20:0			0.24	0.25			0.32	0.47	0.24	0.32		
C22:0									1.37	1.09		
C24:0									0.40	0.61		
C14:1									0.06	0.07		
C16:1	2.10	1.70	0.58	0.85	2.80	1.30	0.48	0.82	0.45	0.71		
C18:1	17.60	24.00	20.06	26.06	17.80	16.60	16.57	23.18	18.06	13.67	21.20	13.60
C20:1			0.72	0.46			0.76	0.38				
C22:1			0.29	0.51			0.45	1.83	2.52	1.92		
C18:2n6	6.80	13.60	14.54	19.15	9.10	10.80	15.61	19.54	10.95	14.99	16.70	26.00
C20:2n6			2.00	1.98			1.39	1.64	0.37	0.40		
C20:3n6			2.27	2.21			1.28	1.34				
C20:4n6	12.60	5.20	17.07	6.21	11.10	10.80	20.13	5.98	20.02	19.71	13.50	12.70
C22:2n6			0.52	0.21								
C22:4n6			3.93	1.31			4.73	1.05	5.03	4.98		
C18:3n3			0.47	0.19			0.34	0.21	0.09	0.31		
C20:3n3			0.35	0.24			0.30	0.25				
C20:5n3	0.20	2.40	1.28	0.42	2.40	1.40	0.93	0.42				
C22:3n3			1.59	0.47			1.54	0.54				
C22:5n3	6.20	3.30	2.73	0.92	4.00	3.10	3.07	0.75	2.27	1.39		
C22:6n3	11.90	3.70	3.78	1.24	11.80	3.40	3.66	1.29	2.71	1.76		
SFA	42.60	46.00	27.86	37.58	40.80	52.60	28.78	40.88	35.28	39.11	48.10	44.00
MUFA	19.70	25.70	21.64	27.88	20.60	17.90	18.25	26.21	21.09	16.37	21.20	13.60
PUFA	37.70	28.20	49.69	34.55	38.40	29.50	52.98	32.92	41.44	43.54	30.20	38.70
n-6	19.40	18.80	39.80	31.07	20.20	21.60	43.14	29.54	36.37	40.08	30.20	38.70
n-3	18.30	9.40	10.69	3.48	18.20	7.90	9.84	3.38	5.07	3.46		
n-6/n-3	1.06	2.00	3.72	8.93	1.11	2.73	4.38	8.74	7.17	11.58		

* = PE (phosphatidyl ethanolamine), ** = PC (phosphatidyl choline).

slow-twitch fibers of thigh muscles have many more mitochondria, their mitochondria are bigger, and the metabolic rate in muscles is faster in comparison to the fast-twitch fibers of breast muscles [88]. Therefore, the cholesterol content in T/L or dark meat was higher by 17.0–48.3% in broilers, by 50.2% in hens and by 20.3–37.3% in turkeys (range from 63.7 to 78.9 mg/100 g) compared to breast or white meat (range from 40.9 to 58.2 mg/100 g). In contrast, the cholesterol level in goose breast muscles was higher by 15.3% than in thigh muscles.

The cholesterol content expressed as a percentage of total lipids in broiler breast muscles (2–2.7%) was two to three times higher than in thigh muscles (1.0%) [17,77]. In contrast, the cholesterol concentration in total lipids of turkey male breast and thigh muscles was not significantly

different (4.07 vs. 3.10%) [90]. Irrespective of the differences between muscles, cholesterol concentration was substantially higher in total lipids of turkey muscles than in chicken muscles. This can be explained by lower total lipid content in turkey breast and thigh muscles (1.47 and 2.45%) (Table 32.1) than in breast and thigh broiler muscles (1.80 and 7.30%) [17,90].

A. Cholesterol—Age, Sex, and Strain

The cholesterol content decreased with age: in 7 vs. 9 wk broiler breast muscle by 33.30% [66], in 5 vs. 13 wk broiler breast muscle by 8.40%, and in thigh muscle by 23.57% [92], in 10 vs. 25 wk male turkey breast muscles by 20.97%, and in thigh muscles by 23.76% [49], and in

10 vs. 12 wk male Mule duck breast muscles of males by 13.22% and females by 13.68% [4]. In 9–11 wk broiler breast muscles there was no age dependency on cholesterol content and after 12 wk its content increased to the level of 7 wk broiler breast muscle [66]. The cholesterol content in breast and thigh muscles of female turkeys (10 vs. 18 wk) was entirely independent of age [49].

At the comparable age (14 wk) male turkeys had higher cholesterol content than females in breast and thigh muscles (Table 32.11) [49]. The same trend was observed for goose and male and female Mule duck breast muscles but differences were not significant [4].

VIII. FFA

To prevent serious chronic diseases of humans, it is necessary to consider both the balance intake of fatty acids [8,93] and the intake of cholesterol [86] in poultry meat. A substantial reduction in carcass fats and cholesterol and improvement of the fatty acid make-up in poultry muscles, such as omega-3 fatty acids, bring about nutritional and economic benefits to consumers and producers alike [3]. Fat deposition is controlled by the calorie: protein ratio of the diet, and the fatty acid composition is

controlled by type and amount of dietary fat by adding linoleic (LA, C18:2n6) and linolenic (LNA, C18:3n3) acids, vegetable oils, fish meal, fish oils, beef tallow and marine algae [3,8,85,87,94–99]. For example, the composition of fatty acids in chicken carcass can be modified through feeding because in the digestive system of chickens, lipids are absorbed and deposited in tissue in unchanged form. The concentration of fatty acids in tissue is closely correlated with their dietary content, in contrast to SFA and MUFA acids which can be synthesisted de novo from simple precursors such as glucose or amino acids [5,8,94,100]. Linoleic acid (C18:2n6) and α-linolenic acid (C18:3n3), the precursors of the n-6 and n-3 family of fatty acids, respectively, are essential fatty acids and have to be supplied by the diet [100].

The fatty acid composition of muscle tissue plays a major role in lipid stability and product quality. Lipid oxidation is one of the main causes of deterioration in the quality of meat during storage and processing. Lipid oxidation is a major problem in poultry meat due to the high content of polyunsaturated fatty acids (PUFA) and low level of natural antioxidants such as tocopherol [8,64,85,94,101]. However, introducing antioxidants to the diet, especially vitamin E, efficiently protects the carcass from this process [102,103].

Okuyama et al. [104] recommended the decrease of polyunsaturated (PUFA) n-6/n-3 ratio in diet and the separate evaluation of the content of α-linolenic acid (LNA, C18:3n3; the basic fatty acid and precursor of PUFA n-3 family), arachidonic acid (AA, C20:4n6; a key metabolite in the PUFA n-6 family), eicosapentaenoic acid (EPA, C20:5n3), and docosahexaenoic acid (DHA, C22:6n3) in foods, because the physiological activity of EPA+DHA is five times higher in comparison with LNA. Another dietary factor influencing the risk of atherosclerosis in humans is the ratio of saturated (SFA), monounsaturated (MUFA), and polyunsaturated (PUFA) fatty acids [8].

Some long chain PUFAs (i.e., dihomo-α-linolenic acid, AA and EPA) are precursors of eicosanoids — important metabolites in the control of cell metabolism [105]. In contrast to PUFA n-6 arachidonic acid (C20:4n6), dietary PUFA n-3 decrease production of pro-inflammatory eicosanoids and have a positive effect on cardiovascular–coronary heart disease, autoimmune, and other chronic diseases, including cancer [8,100,106]. The incidence of coronary heart disease has been said to be dependent upon two different processes – atherosclerosis and trombosis – where atherosclerosis relates to the thickening of the arterial wall and trombosis relates to formation of a clot that occludes the artery, causing heart attack [8,107]. The DHA has an important role in the development of the central nervous system of the newborn while the EPA is involved in blood clotting and the inflammatory response [9]. In view of physiological effects of arachidonic acid (AA), i.e., an increased synthesis of pro-inflammatory prostaglandins,

TABLE 32.11
Cholesterol Content in Poultry Breast (B) and Thigh/ Leg (T/L) Muscles

Poultry Type	Cholesterol (mg/100 g)		
Muscle/Meat	B	T/L	Reference
Broiler	42.40	63.70/	[17]
Broiler	43.40	/84.00	[89]
Broiler	47.41		[12]
Broiler	51.00		[66]
Broiler (11 wk)	40.90	/77.50	[78]
Broiler*	59.40	71.60	[3]
Average	47.42 (6.93)	74.20 (8.64)	
Hens*	50.07	100.61	[20]
Turkey	45.10	/71.90	[89]
Turkey (20 wk) M	47.40	70.00/	[49]
Turkey (20 wk) M	58.20	73.00/	[90]
Turkey (14 wk) M	52.70	78.90/	[90]
Turkey (14 wk) F	48.20	72.30/	[49]
Average for M	50.85 (5.84)	73.45 (3.84)	
Pekin duck	123		[91]
Pekin duck	99.11		[12]
Average	111.06 (16.89)		
Muscovy duck (M)	67.00		[32]
Mule duck (10/12 wk) M	121/105		[4]
Mule duck (10/12 wk) F	117/101		[4]
Goose	80.70	70.00	[89]
Goose (16.6 wk) M/F	88/82		[44]
Average	84.35 (5.16)	70.00	

M = male, F = female, * = white, dark muscles.

TABLE 32.12
Free Fatty Acid (FFA) Profile of Broiler Breast (B) or White (W) and Thigh/Leg (T/L) or Dark (D) Muscles

Reference	[3]	[111]	[101]	[85]	[17,112]	[105]	[77]	Average	[3]	[111]	[101]	[85]	[17,112]	[105]	[77]	Average
Muscle	W	B	B	B	B	B	B (M/F)	Average	D	T	L	L	T	L	T (M/F)	Average
FFA (%)																
C12:0		0.47						0.47		0.31						0.31
C14:0		0.82		0.61	0.50	0.66		0.65		1.05		0.37	0.60	0.69		0.68
C15:0		0.14						0.14		0.13						0.13
C16:0	18.10	23.43	20.40	19.46	22.80	22.62	23.8/21.9	21.08	18.40	21.77	19.30	18.92	22.80	22.00	22.60/22.00	20.83
C17:0		0.30				0.93		0.61		0.30				1.18		0.74
C18:0	12.50	13.88	10.40	8.32	6.85	9.92	7.50/7.00	9.91	10.90	9.90	9.70	6.68	6.00	9.75	7.60/6.30	8.65
C20:0		0.14		0.27		0.93		0.45		0.16		0.21		2.04		0.80
C22/24:0		0.30						0.30		0.19						0.19
C16:1		1.52	2.45	4.47	5.80	3.96	4.50/4.60	3.78		3.44	3.35	5.88	6.90	4.61	6.30/7.30	5.08
C18:1	33.50	26.02	24.55	39.97	38.90	36.66	29.10/28.00	32.67	37.40	31.98	28.25	44.17	41.15	36.35	32.00/36.10	35.90
C20:1		0.34		0.66	0.50	0.59	0.50/0.60	0.52		0.47		0.63	0.50	0.56	0.50/0.60	0.53
C22:1							0.40/0.50	0.40							0.60/0.20	0.60
C24:1			1.73					1.73		0.46						0.46
C18:2n6	18.40	13.38	17.20	17.88	18.60	14.33	17.80/17.00	16.80	18.50	17.23	20.20	18.43	18.55	14.41	18.30/18.90	17.95
C18:3n6			0.5/0.6			0.17		0.33					0.18			0.18
C20:2n6			0.67		0.74		0.14	0.52		0.52		0.31	0.36			0.40
C20:3n6					0.92		0.83	0.87				0.28		0.55		0.41
C20:4n6	8.00	3.65	5.45	3.15	2.10	3.11	5.00/4.00	4.35	5.70	2.10	3.90	1.24	0.90	3.06	3.70/2.50	2.94
C22:4n6			0.76	0.51	1.79			1.02		0.21		0.31	0.21	0.95		0.49
C22:5n6						0.10		0.10		0.05			0.05			0.05
C18:3n3	1.20	0.52	3.40	1.21	1.35	1.38	0.70/0.80	1.39	1.20	0.82	5.25	1.76	1.55	1.31	0.70/0.90	1.80
C20:5n3 (EPA)	0.80	0.62	1.50	0.28	0.30	0.59	0.90/1.70	0.71	0.50	0.48	0.9	0.09	0.10	0.63	0.60/0.30	0.47
C22:5n3 (DPA)	2.00	1.91	3.10	0.59	0.60	0.86		1.51	1.50	0.96	1.90	0.23	0.20	1.06	0.50/0.40	0.91
C22:6n3 (DHA)	2.50	2.95	2.25	0.72	0.90	0.69	1.80/3.20	1.68	2.30	1.45	1.20	0.30	0.30	0.49	1.00/0.60	1.01
SAT	30.80	39.46	35.05	28.67	30.20	34.13	33.50/31.20	33.12	29.60	33.81	31.65	26.38	29.35	34.48	32.20/30.10	31.07
MUFA	35.60	29.62	27.45	45.10	45.20	41.21	34.50/34.50	36.95	40.10	35.20	32.10	50.67	48.55	41.52	39.40/44.20	41.08
PUFA	33.10	23.19	36.00	26.25	24.60	23.73	32.00/34.30	28.41	30.20	23.08	35.25	22.95	22.05	22.82	28.50/25.60	26.41
Total n-6	27.10	17.69	25.75	23.45	21.45	20.21	27.40/27.20	23.29	24.80	19.85	25.95	20.57	19.90	19.33	25.10/23.30	22.21
Total n-3	6.40	5.50	10.25	2.80	3.15	3.52	4.50/7.10	5.16	5.40	3.23	9.30	2.38	2.15	3.49	3.40/2.40	4.19
n-6/n-3	4.23	3.22	2.51	8.38	7.25	5.74	6.09/3.83	5.35	4.59	6.14	2.80	8.64	9.25	5.54	7.38/9.71	6.33

M = male, F = female.

leukotrienes and platelet-activating factor which is connected with cancer and autoimmune diseases, the decrease of its intakes is recommended [108–110]. Generally, high intakes of EPA+DHA and AA are considered important positive and negative aspects for human nutrition, respectively [49,87,109,110].

The percentage representation of fatty acids in lipids from poultry breast and T/L muscles is presented in Tables 32.12–32.15. The main SFA fatty acids in poultry breast and T/L muscles were palmitic acid (C16:0) and stearic acid (C18:0), with minor quantity of myristic acid (C14:0), and for duck and goose breast muscles also lauric acid (C12:0). The stearic acid (C18:0) is not thought to raise blood cholesterol level while the myristic acid (C14:0), appears the most atherogenic and has four times the cholesterol-raising effect of palmitic acid [107]. Kelly [115] showed that stearic acid (C18:0) in the diet had beneficial effects on thrombogenic and atherogenic risk factors in males. The predominant MUFA fatty acids in the poultry for both muscles were oleic acid (C 18:1) and palmitoleic acid (C16:1). In the PUFA fatty acids group linoleic acid (C18:2n6) dominated followed by arachidonic acid (C20:4n6), α-linolenic acid (C18:3n3) and DHA (C22:6n3, except duck muscles and goose leg muscles). In all tissues the principal fatty acid was oleic (C18:1), followed by palmitic acid (C16:0) and/or linoleic acid (C18:2n6).

Broiler, hen and goose breast, or white muscle lipids contained more SFA, PUFA n-6, and PUFA n-3, and total PUFA but less MUFA than T/L or dark muscle lipids (Tables 32.12, 32.13, and 32.15). However, some authors found in broiler breast muscles, when compared with T/L muscles, less PUFA n-6 by 2.16% [111] or almost the same percentage of SFA [3,17,105], MUFA, and PUFA n-3 [105]. The nutritionally significant PUFA n-6/PUFA n-3 ratio was lower (more favorable) in broiler breast muscle (5.35) compared with thigh muscle (6.33). For hens the ratio of PUFA n-6/PUFA n-3 was slightly higher (by 0.32%) in white than in dark smuscles.

TABLE 32.13
Free Fatty Acid (FFA) Profile of Hen and Turkey Breast (B) or White (W) and Thigh (T) or Dark (D) Muscles

Reference	[20]	[20]	[90]	[49]	[49]	[90]	[49]	[49]
Muscle	Hen W 64 wk	Hen D	Turkey B 20 wk M	B 20 wk M	B 14 wk F	Turkey T 20 wk M	T 20 wk M	T 14 wk F
FFA (%)								
C14:0	0.67	1.53	0.99			0.99		
C16:0	23.01	21.38	24.32	22.40	20.80	24.41	22.20	20.20
C18:0	10.32	8.87	9.95	7.70	11.30	10.49	9.80	8.90
C16:1	2.48	3.78	6.14			5.84		
C18:1	32.38	39.26	28.48	36.60	32.10	28.45	32.70	32.60
C20:1	0.28	0.36	0.30			0.33		
C18:2n6	12.62	15.36	21.54	21.30	21.00	22.58	22.50	24.90
C18:3n6			0.11			0.12		
C20:2n6	0.39	0.24						
C20:3n6	0.45	0.26						
C20:4n6	8.11	3.27	4.15	1.40	3.00	3.59	2.60	2.30
C22:4n6	0.76	0.50	1.03			0.74		
C22: 5n6			0.27			0.19		
C18:3n3	0.75	1.99	0.89	2.80	2.00	0.94	2.50	2.70
C20:5n3 (EPA)	0.00	0.03	0.19			0.18		
C22:5n3 (DPA)	0.52	0.18	0.63			0.43		
C22:6n3 (DHA)	1.58	0.56	1.01	1.60*	3.20*	0.72	2.10*	2.20*
SAT	34.01	31.79	35.26	30.10	32.10	35.89	32.00	29.10
MUFA	35.13	43.40	34.92	36.60	32.10	34.62	32.70	32.60
PUFA	25.57	22.38	29.82	27.10	29.20	29.49	29.70	32.10
Total n-6	22.71	19.63	27.10	22.70	24.00	27.22	25.10	27.20
Total n-3	2.86	2.75	2.72	4.40	5.20	2.27	4.60	4.90
n-6/n-3	8.01	7.69	9.96	5.16	4.62	11.99	5.46	5.55

M = male, F = female, * = EPA + DHA.

TABLE 32.14
Free Fatty Acid (FFA) Profile of Duck Breast (B) and Thigh (T) Muscles

Reference	[12]	[32]	[113]	[113]	[6]	[6]	[6]
Muscle	B Pekin 7 wk	B Muscovy 12 wk	B A44 8 wk	T A44 8 wk	T Pekin 9/12 wk	T Muscovy 10.5/15 wk	T Mule 8/14 wk
FFA (%)							
C12:0	1.72			1.09/0.94	1.20		1.18
C14:0	1.51	1.20	1.20	0.90	0.70/0.67	0.55/0.53	0.63/0.57
C15:0		1.80	0.80	0.30			
C16:0	28.23	22.40	27.80	23.90	23.80/23.10	25.00/22.00	25.70/21.60
C17:0		0.30		0.20			
C18:0	14.01	13.30	11.40	7.50	5.40/5.40	8.00/7.40	6.90/6.90
C14:1		0.50	0.20	0.10			
C16:1	2.20	1.90	3.40	4.50	3.50/2.20	2.10/1.50	3.00/1.70
C17:1		0.40		0.10			
C18:1	32.41	28.40	34.80	48.40	48.80/45.40	41.30/40.60	43.90/43.80
C20:1		0.60		0.70	0.81/0.93	0.52/0.62	0.56/0.77
C18:2n6	13.12	14.90	11.40	10.10	11.50/17.50	17.20/20.00	14.90/19.10
C20:2n6		1.20					
C20:3n6		0.50					
C20:4n6	3.91	12.60	6.90	2.50			
C18:3n3		1.30	0.60	0.80	0.94/0.69	0.88/0.91	0.91/0.77
SAT	45.46	38.70	41.50	32.80	30.99/30.11	34.75/29.93	34.41/29.07
MUFA	34.61	30.80	39.40	53.80	51.11/48.53	43.92/42.72	47.46/46.27
PUFA	17.03	30.50	18.90	13.40	12.44/18.19	18.08/20.91	15.81/19.87
Total n-6	17.03	29.20	18.30	12.60	11.50/17.50	17.20/20.00	14.90/19.10
Total n-3	1.30		0.60	0.80	0.94/0.69	0.88/0.91	0.91/0.77
n-6/n-3		22.46	30.5	15.75	12.23/25.36	19.55/21.98	16.37/24.81

Broiler, hen, duck and goose breast muscles were characterized by a higher proportion of stearic acid (C18:0) and lower proportion of oleic acid (C18:1) than thigh muscles. Lipids associated with broiler or hen breast meat contained less linoleic acid (C18:2n6) and linolenic acid (C18:3n3), but more arachidonic acid (C20:4n6) and eicosapentaenoic EPA (C20:5n3—no difference in hens), docosapentaenoic DPA (C22:5n3) and docosahexaenoic DHA (C22:6n3) than lipids associated with T/L muscles. The level of EPA, DPA, and DHA in broiler breast lipids was at least one and a half that of thigh muscles lipids and DHA exceeded EPA in both breast and thigh muscles lipids by a factor of two and a half. Kralik and Ivankovic [111] found higher content of EPA, DPA, DHA, and total n-3 fatty acids but less n-6 fatty acids in broiler breast muscles compared with thigh muscles which indicated that the percentage of PUFA in both kinds of muscles was comparable. Others found no difference in linoleic acids (C18:2n6) [3,17] or in fatty acid profiles between broiler white and dark muscles [105]. The level of DPA and DHA in hen breast muscles was 2.8 times higher than in thigh muscles [20]. In goose breast muscles, likewise in broilers

and hens, the proportion of linolenic acid (C18:3n3) was lower than in leg muscles [42]. In contrast, goose breast muscle lipids were characterized by the presence of higher levels of linoleic acid (C18:2n6) and the same values of arachidonic acid (C20:4n6) as in leg muscles, and according to Biesiada-Drzazga et al. [42], by the absence of EPA, DPA, and DHA in both muscles. The proportion of linoleic acid (C18:2n6) in Pekin [6,12] and in Muscovy duck [6,32] breast muscles compared with thigh muscle was higher and lower, respectively.

Breast and thigh muscle lipids of 20 wk male turkeys were comparable in total values of the main fatty acids fractions [49] or were different in fatty acid composition [90]. Therefore, turkey breast muscles were characterized by a higher proportion of linolenic acid (C18:3n3) and lower proportions of SFA, linoleic acid (C18:2n6), and arachidonic acid (C20:4n6) compared to thigh muscles [49,79] which was in accordance with data for chicken and hen only for linoleic acid (C18:2n6). According to Komprda et al. [90], turkey breast muscles had slightly higher arachidonic acid (C20:4n6) and DHA (C22:6n3) percentages than thigh muscles which corresponded with broilers. However, higher or

TABLE 32.15
Free Fatty Acid (FFA) Profile of Goose Breast (B) and Leg (L) Muscles

Reference	[80]	[114]	[114]	[42]	[42]
Muscle	B 24 wk	B 16 wk M/F	B 26 wk M/F	B 15*/24** wk	L 15*/24** wk
FFA (%)					
C12:0	0.13				
C14:0	0.67	2.20	1.40	0.07/0.08	0.06/0.06
C15:0	0.82				
C16:0	24.87	24.50/26.40	25.10/26.20	24.76/27.47	24.27/20.40
C18:0	6.82	10.60	8.80	3.16/4.35	3.02/2.58
C20:0	0.15				
C22:0	0.09				
C24:0	0.17				
C16:1	3.96	4.10	4.60	1.55/2.05	1.73/1.96
C18:1	43.40	49.80/46.30	50.30/50.20	61.19/58.30	63.20/67.89
C20:1	0.22	0.80-0.90	0.80-0.90	0.06/0.08	0.07/0.07
C22:1	0.02				
C18:2n6	15.00	6.90	6.10	8.76/7.38	7.40/6.76
C20:2n6	0.29	0.02/0.05	0.01/0.02		
C20:3n6				—/0.03	0.03/—
C20:4n6	2.31	0.70	0.50	0.24/0.12	0.07/0.12
C18:3n3	0.66	0.50-0.60	0.50	0.08/0.06	0.07/0.07
C22:5n3 (DPA)	0.13				
C22:6n3 (DHA)	0.25				
SAT	32.31	37.00/40.30	36.10/36.40	27.99/31.90	27.35/23.04
MUFA	47.60	55.00/51.30	56.30/57.00	62.80/60.43	65.00/69.92
PUFA	18.64	8.10	7.10	9.10/7.64	7.58/6.97
Total n-6	17.60	7.60	6.60	9.02/7.58	7.51/6.90
Total n-3	1.04	0.50	0.50	0.08/0.06	0.07/0.07
n-6/n-3	16.92	15.20	13.20	112.7/112.6	107.3/98.57

M = male, F = female, * = intensive system, ** = semi-intensive system.

the same MUFA percentage and lower or the same PUFA percentage in male turkey breast than thigh muscles were not in line with broilers and hens. The PUFA n-6/n-3 ratio was comparable in turkey muscles and hens. A comparison of fatty acid composition in male turkeys and broiler breast and thigh muscles revealed that in turkey muscles the ratio of SFA was higher by 5.06/6.59%; MUFA was lower by 10.28/14.08%; PUFA was higher by 4.60/7.49%; and arachidonic acid (C20:4n6) was higher by 2.05/2.69% [17,90]. Therefore, turkey meat provided substantially less MUFA (a desirable fraction from the viewpoint of human nutrition) and more arachidonic acid (undesirable fraction) compared to broiler meat.

Duck breast muscles contained more SFA than other kinds of poultry and less PUFAs than broilers, hens, and turkeys. The fatty acid contents of duck and goose muscles were very similar and contained approximately 50% SFA, 33% MUFA, and 16% PUFA (Tables 32.12–32.15).

The interpretation of fatty acid composition in poultry meat depends on the presentation method. As a percentage of total fatty acids, broiler thigh SFA were not different (30.60 vs. 31.27%), MUFA was higher (49.06 vs. 43.31%), and PUFA was lower (15.51 vs. 18.87%) than breast muscles of the corresponding fatty acid groups [58]. In contrast, when fatty acid content was expressed in mg/100 g of muscles, broiler thigh muscles contained more SFA (1530 vs. 300 mg/100 g), MUFA (2460 vs. 410 mg/100 g) and PUFA (780 vs. 180 mg/100 g). Likewise, in turkey thigh muscles the sum of SFA, MUFA (725 vs. 441 mg/100 g), PUFA, and EPA and DHA (18.2 and 14.6 mg/100 g) and arachidonic acid (C20:4n6) (72.7 vs. 50.3 mg/100 g) was substantially higher than in breast muscles, due to the higher total lipid content in thigh compared to breast muscles (2.45 vs. 1.47%) [90]. These values differ from that expressed as a percentage of total fatty acids for turkey muscles as shown in Table 32.12. Turkey breast muscles contained 5% less SFA, nearly 40% less MUFA, and approximately the same amount of PUFA compared to broiler breast muscles [17,90]. The EPA+DHA values for turkey and chicken breast muscles were similar. However, turkey thigh muscles contained less EPA+DHA than broiler thigh muscles (18.2 vs. 31 mg/100 g) due to the substantially lower total lipid content, i.e., 2.45 vs. 7.30%, respectively. The content of arachidonic acid (C20:4n6) in turkey breast muscles (50.3 mg/100 g) was higher by nearly 60% in comparison to chicken breast muscles (32.1 mg/100 g).

A. FFA—AGE, SEX, AND STRAIN

Fatty acid composition of broilers, turkeys, ducks, and geese was affected by age and sex. A comparison of 13 wk fast growing broilers with 5 wk broilers showed that older birds had significantly lower MUFA content in breast muscles, and the levels of PUFA and arachidonic acid (C20:4n6) were higher in breast muscles and lower in thigh muscles, respectively [92]. Advancing age of male and female turkey was accompanied by increased MUFA and decreased PUFA percentage in breast and thigh muscles while the percentage of SFA decreased in breast muscles and increased in thigh muscles, respectively (Table 32.13) [49]. Moreover, with increasing age the content of sum of EPA+DHA decreased in both male muscles, but did not differ in female muscles. The arachidonic acid (C20:4n6) content decreased with age in breast muscles of turkeys of both sexes, but not in thigh meat. With age duck thigh muscle lipids had a lower level of MUFA and higher levels of PUFA and linoleic acid (C18:2n6). Age had no influence on SFA content in Pekin duck thigh muscles, but in Muscovy and Mule duck the SFA level decreased with age (Table 32.13). During the time of rearing of geese from 6–30 wk the fat of male and female breast, muscles decreased gradually with the content of SFA by 3.0–3.4% and stearic acid (C18:0) by 4.9%. The share of MUFA and palmitoleic acid (C16:1) increased by 1.1–3.0% and by 1.1%, respectively (Table 32.14) [114]. However, the PUFA, linoleic acid (C18:2n6), and arachidonic acid (C20:4n6) were not influenced by age. Friend et al. [48] found no differences due to age in goose fatty acid composition.

The male broiler breast muscles concentration of total PUFA and PUFA n-3 was lower than in female breast muscles while the male thigh muscle concentration of MUFA was lower and total PUFA and PUFA n-3 were higher than in female thigh muscles. The level of arachidonic acid (C20:4n6) in male broiler muscles was higher than for female muscles [77]. At the same age, male turkey breast muscles were characterized by lower MUFA content and thigh muscles had lower contents of both MUFA and PUFA than corresponding female muscles [49].

The breast muscle lipids of 16 wk male geese males were characterized by more favorable composition of fatty acids compared to females due to the higher share of MUFA and lower level of SFA (Table 32.14) [114].

Geese strains influenced the composition of the following fatty acids: palmitic (C16:0), palmitoleic (C16:1),

stearic (C18:0), oleic (C18:1), linoleic (C18:2n6), and arachidonic (C20:4n6) [48]. Batura et al. [50] also found geese strain dependent on differences in the level of myristic acid (C14:0), linoleic acid (C18:2n6), and arachidonic acid, (C20:4n6).

IX. CONCLUSIONS

Muscles highest in protein content were turkey, broiler and goose breast muscles while the lowest in fat were breast muscles of turkeys, broilers, and Pekin-Muscovy ducks. The best proportion of protein to fat was in the duck thigh muscles. Goose and turkey muscles had the lowest moisture content.

The broiler muscles were the highest in niacin. Duck and goose flesh were the best sources of thiamine (B₁) and riboflavin (B₂). The broiler and turkey thigh/leg or dark muscles contained more riboflavin (B₂) and less niacin (PP) and vitamin B₆ than breast/light muscles. Poultry meat is also an important source of several minerals, especially iron (goose muscles, turkey dark), zinc (turkey dark), potassium and phosphorus (goose flesh), and other trace elements such as copper.

Lipids of white poultry meat (broilers, hens, geese) were richer in SFA and PUFA and the lipids of red meat were richer in MUFA. Therefore, poultry consumption, especially breast muscle, could provide an important additional source of nutritionally important unsaturated fatty acids (PUFA).

Poultry breast muscles have higher nutritional and dietetic values than thigh muscles (lower lipid and collagen content and higher protein content).

REFERENCES

1. A D'Amicis, A Turrini. The role of meat in human nutrition: The Italian case. Proceedings of 48th International Congress of Meat Science and Technology, Rome, 2002, Vol. 1, pp 117–119.
2. Statistical Yearbook of the Republic of Poland. LXII ed. Central Statistical Office, Warszawa, 2002, pp 683.
3. AO Ajuyah, KH Lee, RT Hardin, JS Sim. Changes in the yield and in the fatty acid composition of whole carcass and selected meat portions of broiler chickens fed full-fat oil seeds. Poult Sci 70:2304–2314, 1991.
4. E Baeza, MR Salichon, G Marche, N Wacrenier, B Dominguez, J Culioli. Age and sex effects on the technological and chemical characteristics of mule duck meat. Proceedings of XIVth European Symposium on the Quality of Poultry Meat, Bologna, 1999, pp 135–142.
5. PS Hargis, ME Van Elswyk. Manipulating the fatty acid composition of poultry meat and eggs for the health conscious consumer. World's Poult Sci J 49:251–264, 1993.
6. M Golze, H Pingel. Carcass composition and meat quality of different duck species. Proceedings of 2nd World Conference on Waterfowl, Alexandria, 2003, (in press).

7. H Pingel, U Knust. Review on duck meat quality. Proceedings of XIth European Symposium on the Quality of Poultry Meat, Tours, 1993, pp 26–43.

8. CO Leskanich, RC Noble. Manipulation of the n-3 polyunsaturated fatty acid composition of avian eggs and meat. World's Poult Sci J 53:155–183, 1977.

9. F Robinson. The nutritional contribution of meat to the Brit diet: recent trends and analyses. Brit Nutr Foundation Nutr Bull 24:283–293, 2001.

10. JD Latshaw, BL Bishop. Estimating body weight and body composition of chickens by using noninvasive measurements. Poult Sci 80:868–873, 2001.

11. M Qiao, DL Fletcher, JK Northcutt, DP Smith. The relationship between raw broiler breast meat color and composition. Poult Sci 81:422–427, 2002.

12. DP Smith, DL Fletcher, RJ Buhr, RS Beyer. Pekin duckling and broiler chicken *Pectoralis* muscle structure and composition. Poult Sci 72:202–208, 1993.

13. YL Xiong, AH Cantor, AJ Pescatore, SP Blanchard, ML Straw. Variations in muscle chemical composition, pH, and protein extractability among eight different broiler crosses. Poult Sci 72:583–588, 1993.

14. CYW Ang, D Hamm. Comparison of commercial processing method vs hot-deboning of fresh broilers on nutrient content of breast meat. J Food Sci 48:1543–1544, 1565, 1983.

15. E Gornowicz, K Dziadek. Variability in chemical composition of breast and thigh muscles depending on the origin of broiler chickens (English abstr.). Roczniki Naukowe Zootechniki 28(2):89–100, 2001.

16. D Hamm, GK Searcy, AA Klose. Mineral content and proximate analysis of broiler meat from two strains and three regions of production. J Food Sci 45:1478–1480, 1980.

17. T Komprda, J Zelenka, P Tieffova, M Stohandlova, J Foltyn. Effect of the growth intensity on cholesterol and fatty acids content in broiler chicken tissues. Arch Geflügelk 63:36–43, 1999.

18. SK Williams, BL Damron. Sensory and objective characteristics of broiler meat from commercial broilers fed rendered whole-hen meal. Poult Sci 77:329–333, 1998.

19. C Castellini, C Mugnai, A Dal Bosco. Effect of organic production system on broiler carcass and meat quality. Meat Sci 60:219–225, 2002.

20. AO Ajuyah, RT Hardin, K Cheung, JS Sim. Yield, lipid, cholesterol and fatty acid composition of spent hens fed full-fat oil seeds and fish meal diets. J Food Sci 57:338–341, 1992.

21. K Filus, J Jankowski, Z Meller, T Rotkiewicz. Meat quality and quantity of different hybrids of slaughter turkeys. Proceedings of XIIth European Symposium on the Quality of Poultry Meat, Zaragoza, 1995, pp 165–171.

22. H Puchajda, A Faruga, K Pudyszak. Effect of turkey line on meat quality. Proceedings of XIIth European Symposium on the Quality of Poultry Meat, Poznań, 1997, pp 53–57.

23. H Puchajda, A Faruga, D Klossowska, J Batura, G Elminowska-Wenda. Characteristics of meat quality of slaughter turkeys from three different genetic groups (English abstr). Roczniki Naukowe Zootechniki 8:166–170, 2000.

24. A Faruga, K Pudyszak. The effect of adding herb mixture to turkey feeds on meat quality. Proceedings of XIIth European Symposium on the Quality of Poultry Meat, Poznań, 1997, pp 144–149.

25. A Bons, R Timmler, H Jeroch. Changes in body composition and content of fat and protein in carcass of male and female Pekin ducks during growth. Zeszyty Naukowe. Przeglad Hodowlany. PTZ. Chów i Hodowla Drobiu 36:165–175, 1998.

26. A Górska, J Górski. The changes of the total protein, collagen and fat content in Pekin duck crossbreds at the end of rearing period. Proceedings of XIIth European Symposium on the Quality of Poultry Meat, Poznań, 1997, pp 334–337.

27. E Koci, J Baumgartner, V IIIes, O Palanska. Carcass and nutritive value of the small white broiler duck and its crosses. Arch Geflügelk 46:157–161, 1982.

28. G Paci, M Bagliacca, M Marzoni, CF Avanzi. Meat quality of Italian strains of muscovy, common and muscovyxcommon ducks bred under two different technologies. Proceedings of XIIth European Symposium on the Quality of Poultry Meat, Tours, 1993, pp 66–73.

29. J Pikul, W Doruchowski, S Tański, T Reksiński. Slaughter yields, carcass composition, chemical analysis and technological properties of Muscovy and Pekin ducks (English abstr). Zeszyty Naukowe Drobiarstwa IV:73–92, 1987.

30. H Kontecka, J Pikul, E Wencek, K Hońownia. Meat traits of Polish Muscovy ducks. Proceedings of XIIth European Symposium on the Quality of Poultry Meat, Poznań, 1997, pp 237–212.

31. I Romboli, C Russo, S Zanobini. Effect of dietary vitamin E on chemical composition and meat colour in heat stressed muscovy duck. Proceedings of XIIth European Symposium on the Quality of Poultry Meat, Poznań, 1997, pp 205–211.

32. MR Salichon, E Baeza, B Leclerco. Biochemical characteristics of Muscovy duck breast. Sciences des Aliments 17:227–233, 1997.

33. RM Turi, P Sacchi, I Romboli. Carcass composition and meat quality on Muscovy ducks in response to clenbuterol administration. Arch Geflügelk 58:257–261, 1994.

34. A Auvergne, R Babile, M Bouillier-Oudot, H Manse, G Latil. Influence of two feeding rates on muscular and liver composition in forced-fed mule ducks. Proceedings of XIIth European Symposium on the Quality of Poultry Meat, Zaragoza, 1995, pp 181–188.

35. J. Woloszyn. The physicochemical and technological characteristic of muscles from force fed ducks (English abstract). Prace Naukowe nr 921. Monografie i Opracowania nr 145: Wydawnictwo AE, 2002, pp. 53.

36. K Bielińska, K Bieliński, L Skarzyński. The effect of the intensity of additional feeding at rearing on pasture on the fattening performance of 4 month old geese (English abstr). Roczniki Naukowe Zootechniki 11:91–104, 1984.

37. K Bielińska, L Skarzyński, K Bieliński. The effect of the level of concentrate intake on the fattening performance of 4-month old pasture-raised geese (English abstr). Roczniki Naukowe Zootechniki 11:185–196, 1984.

38. K Bieliński, K Bielińska, L Skarzyński, K Traczykiewicz. The effect of age on the productivity, slaughter value and

meat and fat quality in oat geese (English abstr). Rocniki Naukowe Zootechniki 10:21–35, 1983.

39. K Pudyszak, H Puchajda, A Faruga. Meat quality in the geese Bińgorajska, Italian white, and their hybrids. Proceedings of XIIth European Symposium on the Quality of Poultry Meat, Poznań, 1997, pp 243–246.

40. DA Ngoka, GW Froning, SR Lowry, AS Babji. Effects of sex, age, preslaughter factors, and holding conditions on the quality characteristics and chemical composition of turkey breast muscles. Poult Sci 61:1996–2003, 1982.

41. U Bojarska, J Batura. Nutritive value of muscles of female turkey WAMA-1. Prace IZZ 93:84–88, 1998.

42. B Biesiada-Drzazga, J Górski. Effect of raising system and age on chemical composition of breast, thigh and drumstick muscles in meat type geese (English abstr). Zeszyty Naukowe. Przeglad Hodowlany. PTZ. Chów i Hodowla Drobiu 36:367–375, 1998.

43. A Faruga, J Jankowski, I Sobina. Meat quality of young market turkeys reared on different floor types (English abstr). Acta Acad Agricult Techn Olst. Zeszyty Naukowe AR-T Olsztyn. Zootechnika 31:205–214, 1988.

44. T Skrabka-Blotnicka, A Rosiński, E Przysiężna, J Woloszyn, G Elminowska-Wenda. The effect of dietary formulation supplemented with herbal mixture on the goose breast muscle quality. Report 1: The effect on the chemical composition. Arch Geflügelk 61:135–138, 1997.

45. H Puchajda, A Faruga, D Klosowska, J Batura, Z Meller. Nutritive and technological value of meat of slaughter turkeys of various origin. Zeszyty Naukowe. Przeglńd Hodowlany. PTZ. Chów i Hodowla Drobiu 45:463–469, 1999.

46. H Puchajda, A Faruga, K Pudyszak. Effect of silages on the yield and quality of meat from two lines of goose. Pol. J. Food Nutr. Sci 6/47:141–147, 1997.

47. DG Evans, TL Goodwin LD Andrews. Chemical composition, carcass yield and tenderness of broiler as influenced by rearing methods and genetic strains. Poult Sci 55:748–755, 1976.

48. DW Friend, JKG Kramer, A Fortin. Effect of age, sex and strain on the fatty acid composition of goose muscle and depot fats. J Food Sci 48:1442–1444, 1983.

49. T Komprda, I Sarmanova, J Zelenka, P Bakaj, M Fialova, E. Fajmonova. Effect of sex and age on cholesterol and fatty acid content in turkey meat. Arch Geflügelk 66:263–273, 2002.

50. J Batura, M Karpińska, U Bojarska. Nutritive and technological value of meat from four experimental strains of geese (English abstr). Zeszyty Naukowe. Przeglńd Hodowlany. PTZ. Chów i Hodowla Drobiu 36:357–366, 1998.

51. D Hamm. Amino acid composition of breast and thigh meat from broilers produced in four locations of the United States. J Food Sci 46:1122–1124, 1981.

52. L Posati. Composition of Foods. Poultry Products. Raw-Processed-Prepared. Agriculture Handbook No. 8–5. Science and Education Administration. United States Department of Agriculture, 1979, pp 65–293.

53. W Stoltman, J Gardzielewska. Collagen content in the breast and thigh muscles of six weeks old broilers grown under uniform management conditions in successive production cycles. Proceedings of XIIth

European Symposium on the Quality of Poultry Meat, Poznań, 1997, pp 366–370.

54. YL Xiong. Structure-function relationships of muscle proteins. In: Food Proteins and Their Application. Eds. S Damodaran and A Paraf. New York: Marcel Dekker, 1997, pp 356–359.

55. B Ruantrakool, TC Chen. Collagen contents of chicken gizzard and breast meat tissues as affected by cooking methods. J Food Sci 51:301–304, 1986.

56. W Gawęcki, E Gornowicz. Ocena podstawowego skńadu chemicznego miesni kurczat brojlerów pochodzacych z róznych hodowli zagranicznych. Gospodarka Miesna LII(7):42–44, 2001.

57. GW Froning. Color of poultry meat. Poultry Avian Biol Rev 6:83–93, 1995.

58. KS Rhee, LM Anderson, AR Sams. Lipid oxidation potential of beef, chicken, and pork. J Food Sci 61:8–12, 1996.

59. BK Fleming, GW Froning, TS Yang. Heme pigment levels in chicken broilers chilled in ice slush and air. Poult Sci 70:2197–2200, 1991.

60. RW Kranen, THVAN Kuppevelt, HA Goedhart, CH Veerkamp, E Lambooy, JH Veerkamp. Hemoglobin and myoglobin content in muscles of broiler chickens. Poult Sci 78:467–476, 1999.

61. A Niewiarowicz, J Pikul, P Czjka. Gehalt an Myoglobin and Hämoglobin im Fleisch verschiedener Geflügelarten. Fleischwirtschaft 66:1281–1282, 1986.

62. J Nishida, T Nishida. Relationship between the concentration of myoglobin and parvalbumin in various types of muscle tissues from chickens. Brit Poult Sci 26:105–115, 1985.

63. GW Froning, J Daddario, TE Hartung. Color and myoglobin concentration in turkey meat as affected by age, sex and strain. Poult Sci 47:1827–1835, 1968.

64. C Alasnier, A Meynier, M Viau, G Gandemer. Hydrolityc and oxidative changes in the lipids of chicken breast and thigh muscles during refrigerated storage. J Food Sci 65:9–14, 2000.

65. I Kunachowicz, I Nadolna, K Iwanow, B Przygoda. Wartość odzywcza wybranych produktów spozywczych i typowych potraw. 3rd ed. Warszawa: Wydawnictwo Lekarskie PZWL, 2002, pp 34–36.

66. D Hamm, CYW Ang. Effect of sex and age on proximate analysis, cholesterol and selected vitamins in broiler breast meat. J Food Sci 49:286–287, 1984.

67. SP Singh, EO Essary. Vitamin content of broiler meat as affected by age, sex, thawing and cooking. Poult Sci 50:1150–1155, 1971.

68. T Hazell. Iron and zink compounds in the muscle meats of beef, lamb, pork and chicken. J Sci Food Agric 33:1049–1056, 1982.

69. J Gardzielewska, A Sochacka, Z Goluch, A Cyran, W Natalczyl-Szymkowska. The Mg, Na, K, Ca, P and Li content in muscles of broiler chickens kept under farm conditions. Zeszyty Naukowe AR Szczecin. Zootechnika 34:33–38, 1997.

70. Z Goluch-Koniuszy, J Gardzielewska, T Karamucki, M Jakubowska, M Pulwer-Kaca. The Cu, Fe and Zn content in muscles of Isa Vedette broiler chickens (English abstr). Zeszyty Naukowe. Przeglńd

Hodowlany. PTZ. Chów i Hodowla Drobiu 36:383–389, 1998.

71. Z Goluch-Koniuszy, J Gardzielewska, M Jakubowska, T Karamucki. The effect of starvation period before slaughter on Mg, K and Na content in muscles of broiler chickens Isa Vedette (English abstr). Zeszyty Naukowe. Przeglńd Hodowlany. PTZ. Chów i Hodowla Drobiu 45:383–389, 1999.

72. D Han, KW McMillin, JS Godber, TD Bidner, MT Younathan, DL Marshall, LT Hart. Iron distribution in heated beef and chicken muscles. J Food Sci 58:697–700, 1993.

73. OC Zenoble, JA Bowers. Copper, zinc and iron content of turkey muscles. J Food Sci 42:1408–1409, 1412, 1977.

74. G Gandemer. Lipids in muscles and adipose tissues, changes during processing and sensory properties of meat products. Meat Sci 62:309–321, 2002.

75. D Sklan, Z Tenne. Changes in the lipid fractions and bacteriological counts in chilled broiler meat. Poult Sci 63:76–81, 1984.

76. HW Hulan, RG Ackman, WMN Ratnayake, FG Proudfoot. Omega-3 fatty acid levels and general performance of commercial broilers fed practical levels of redfish meal. Poult Sci 68:153–162, 1989.

77. WMN Ratnayake, RG Ackman, HW Hulan. Effect of redfish meal enriched diets on the taste and n-3 PUFA of 42-day-old broiler chickens. J Sci Food Agric 49:59–74, 1989.

78. J Pikul, DE Leszczynski, FA Kummerow. Relative role of phospholipids, triacylglycerols, and cholesterol esters on malonaldehyde formation in fat extracted from chicken meat. J Food Sci 49:704–708, 1984.

79. D Sklan, Z Tenne., P Budowski. Simultaneous lipolytic and oxidative changes in turkey meat stored at different temperatures. J Sci Food Agric 34:93–99, 1983.

80. E Baeza, G Guy, MR Salichon, H Juin, D Rousselot-Pailley, D Klosowska, G Elminowska-Wenda, M Srutek, A Rosiński. Influence of feeding system, extensive vs intensive, on fatty liver and meat production in geese. Arch Geflügelk 62:169–175, 1998.

81. JO Igene, AM Pearson, RA Merkel, TH Coleman. Effect of frozen storage time, cooking and holding temperature upon extractable lipids and TBA values of beef and chicken. J Anim Sci 49:701–707, 1979.

82. E Baeza, MR Salichon, G Marche, N Wacrenier. Age and sex effects on muscular development of Muscovy ducks. Proceedings of XIVth European Symposium on the Quality of Poultry Meat, Bologna, 1999, pp 129–134.

83. G Elminowska-Wenda, A Rosiński, D Kńosowska, G Guy. Effect of feeding system (intensive vs. semi-intensive) on growth rate, microstructural characteristics of *pectoralis* muscle and carcass parameters of the white Italian geese. Arch Geflügelk 61:117–119, 1997.

84. D Klosowska, A Rosiński, G Elminowska-Wenda, B Klosowski. Effect of preslaughter stress on glycogen content in muscle fibers of white Italian geese. Proceedings of XIIth European Symposium on the Quality of Poultry Meat, Zaragoza, 1995, pp 341–347.

85. DU Ahn, FH Wolfe, JS Sim. Dietary α-linolenic acid and mixed tocopherols, and packaging influences on lipid stability in broiler chicken breast and leg muscle. J Food Sci 60:1013–1018, 1995.

86. LL Rudel, JS Parks, CC Hedrick, M Thomas, K Williford. Lipoprotein and cholesterol metabolism in diet-induced coronary artery atherosclerosis in primates. Role of cholesterol and fatty acids. Prog Lipid Res 37:353–370, 1998.

87. S Lopez-Ferrer, MD Baucells, AC Barroeta, MA Grashorn. N-3 enrichment of chicken meat. 1. Use of very long chain fatty acids in chicken diets and their influence on meat quality: fish oil. Poult Sci 80:741–752, 2001.

88. VH Konjufca, GM Pesti, RI Bakalli. Modulation of cholesterol levels in broiler meat by dietary garlic and copper. Poult Sci 76:1264–1271, 1997.

89. KO Honikel, W Arneth. Cholesteringehalt in Fleisch und Eiern. Fleischwirtschaft 76:1244–1253, 1996.

90. T Komprda, J Zelenka, A Jarosova, M Fialova, E Blazkova, E Fajmonova. Cholesterol and fatty acid content in breast and thigh meat of turkeys growing with different intensity. Arch Geflügelk 65:258–264, 2001.

91. KO Honikel, W Arneth. Cholesterol content of various meat species and its relation to fat content. Proceedings of 42nd ICoMST, Lillehammer, 1996, pp 214–215.

92. T Komprda, J Zelenka, P Tieffova, M Stohandlova, J Foltyn, E. Fajmonova. Effect of age on total lipid, cholesterol and fatty acids content in tissues of fast and slow growing chickens. Arch Geflügelk 64:121–128, 2000.

93. BA Griffin. Lipoprotein atherogenicity: an overview of current mechanisms. Proc Nutr Soc 58:163–169, 1999.

94. AO Ajuyah, DU Ahn, RT Hardin, JS Sim. Dietary antioxidants and storage affect chemical characteristics of ω-3 fatty acid enriched broiler chicken meats. J Food Sci 58:43–46, 61, 1993.

95. M Du, DU Ahn. Effect of dietary conjugated linoleic acid on the growth rate of live birds and on the abdominal fat content and quality of broiler meat. Poult Sci 81:428–433, 2002.

96. A Grau, F Guardiola, S Grimpa, AC Barroeta, R Codony. Oxidative stability of dark chicken meat through frozen storage: Influence of dietary fat and α-tocopherol and ascorbic acid supplementation. Poult Sci 80:1630–1642, 2001.

97. S Lopez-Ferrer, MD Baucells, AC Barroeta, MA Grashorn. Influence of vegetable oil sources on quality parameters of broiler meat. Arch Geflügelk 29–35, 1999.

98. JW Mooney, EM Hirschler, AK Kennedy, AR Sams, ME Van Elswyk. Lipid and flavour quality of stored breast meat from broilers fed marine algae. J Sci Food Agric 78:134–140, 1998.

99. M Pietras, T Borowicz, R Gasior. The effect of vegetable fat supplements on carcass quality and fatty acid profile of meat in broiler chickens. Roczniki Naukowe Zootechniki 27:209–219, 2000.

100. SSD Nair, JW. Leitch, J Falconer, ML Garg. Prevention of cardiac arrythmia by dietary (n-3) polyunsaturated fatty acids and their mechanism of action. J Nutr 127:383–393, 1997.

101. G Cherian, RK Selvaraj, MP Goeger, PA Stitt. Muscle fatty acid composition and thiobarbituric acid-reactive substances of broilers fed different cultivars of sorghum. Poult Sci 81:1415–1420, 2002.

102. C Jensen, C Lauridsen G. Bertelsen. Dietary vitamin E: Quality and storage stability of pork and poultry. Trends J Food Sci Tech 9:62–72, 1998.

103. KT Nam, HA Lee, BS Min, CW Kang. Influence of dietary supplementation with linseed and vitamin E on fatty acids, α-tocopherol and lipid peroxidation in muscles of broiler chicks. Anim Feed Sci Technol 66:149–158, 1997.

104. H Okuyama, T Kobayashi, S Watanabe. Dietary fatty acids—The n-6/n-3 balance and chronic elderly diseases. Excess linoleic acid and relative n-3 deficiency syndrome seen in Japan. Prog Lipid Res 35:409–457, 1997.

105. B Krasicka, GW Kulasek, E Swierczewska, A Orzechowski. Body gains and fatty acid composition in carcasses of broilers fed diets enriched with full-fat rapeseed and/or flaxseed. Arch Geflügelk 64:61–69, 2000.

106. JE Kinsella, B Lokesh, RA Stone. Dietary n-3 polyunsaturated FA and amelioration of cardiovascular disease: possible mechanisms. J Food Sci Tech 52:1–28, 1990.

107. TLV Ulbricht, DAT Southgate. Coronary heart disease: seven dietary factors. Lancet 338:985–992, 1991.

108. YY Fan, RS Chapkin. Importance of dietary α-linolenic acid in human health and nutrition. J Nutr 128:1411–1414, 1998.

109. D Li, A Ng, NJ Mann, AJ Sinclair. Contribution of meat fat to dietary arachidonic acid. Lipids 33:437–440, 1998.

110. L Taber, C-H Chiu, J Whelan. Assessment of the arachidonic acid content in foods commonly consumed in the American diet. Lipids 33:1151–1157, 1998.

111. G Kralik, S Ivanković. The profile of fatty acids in intramuscullar fat of chickens. Proceedings of International Congress of Meat Science and Technology, Rome, 2002 pp 996–997.

112. T Komprda, J Zelenka, P Tieffova, M Stohandlova, J Foltyn, E. Fajmonova. Kubis. Meat quality of broilers fattened deliberately slow by cereal mixtures to higher age. 2. Total lipid, cholesterol and fatty acid content. Arch Geflügelk 64:38–43, 2000.

113. J Batura, W Korzeniowski, R Bochno. Effect of duck limited feeding on fatty acids composition of the deposited and muscle fats (English abstr). Przegląd Naukowej Literatury Zootechnicznej. PTZ. Zeszyt Specjalny XXXV:133–140, 1990.

114. J Batura, M Karpińska, U Bojarska. Fatty acid composition of fat in breast muscles of geese (English abstr). Zeszyty Naukowe. Przeglńd Hodowlany. PTZ. Chów i Hodowla Drobiu 45:471–481, 1999.

115. FD Kelly, AJ Sinclair, NJ Mann, AH Turner, L Abedin, D Li. A stearic acid-rich diet improves thrombogenic and atherogenic risk factor profiles in healthy males. Eur J Clin Nutr 55:88–96, 2001.

33 Poultry Processing Quality

Christine Z. Alvarado
Department of Animal and Food Sciences, Texas Tech University

CONTENTS

I. INTRODUCTION

Per capita consumption of poultry has increased dramatically during the last 40 years with poultry meat ranking as the most consumed muscle food per capita in the United States. This increased consumption in poultry compared to other meats can be attributed to vertical integration, an increase in value-added product offerings, and nutritional quality. In vertically integrated companies, the same company owns several or even all of the process from live production through slaughter, and distribution to retail or foodservice. Vertical integration has improved product uniformity and increased profit margins for the poultry industry compared to other meat industries. The poultry industry has also increased the production of value-added poultry products to meet consumer demands for convenience, versatility, and variety. Also, nutritionally, the fat in both chicken and turkey meat is easily removed compared to other meats, enabling consumers to adopt a more low-fat type of meat into their diets. The process of converting the live animal into meat is complex. Many steps are implemented to ensure uniformity and high quality for the consumer. This chapter will detail the steps required to convert a live bird into a convenient and versatile product for consumers.

II. SLAUGHTER

Poultry slaughter involves six primary unit operations: preslaughter, immobilization, feather removal, evisceration, chilling, and further processing. In each of these processes, bird uniformity and automation can affect both quality and efficiency (yield). Normally, plants process birds at 70–140 birds per minute depending on the inspection system used, the type of birds (broilers versus turkeys), and the uniformity of the birds.

A. PRESLAUGHTER

The United States Department of Agriculture (USDA) has a "Zero Tolerance" for fecal contamination of poultry carcasses in the Pathogen Reduction/Hazard Analysis and Critical Control Point System (HACCP) (1). Therefore, birds are removed from feed, but allowed access to water 8–12 hours prior to slaughter to allow for clearing of the intestinal tract (2). This time for clearing of the gastrointestinal tract helps prevent some fecal contamination of carcasses due to intestinal rupture by the automated evisceration/processing equipment. Feed withdrawal fewer than eight hours can result in fecal contamination and full crops, which can lead to contamination of the carcass during evisceration and possible condemnations (3). Feed withdrawal greater than 12 hours prior to slaughter can result in loose feces, green gizzards, and bloated intestines, which leads to downgrades and meat yield loss for processors. Also, the longer the feed withdrawal period, the more water weight is lost, resulting in a decreased yield for processors. Therefore, feed withdrawal should be within the 8–12 hours prior to slaughter to allow for the clearing of the intestinal tract, and to minimize yield losses (4).

Antemortem handling of the birds preslaughter can affect meat quality and consumer acceptability of the product. The largest meat quality determinants at this antemortem stage are handling and stress to the bird. Improper handling can result in bruises, broken and dislocated bones, and variation in breast meat color, all resulting in decreased yield for the processor through carcass downgrading. The areas most frequently bruised are the breast, wings, and legs (5). An estimate of 90–95% of all bruises found on broiler carcasses occurs during the final 12 hours prior to slaughter (6). This period is normally when the birds are caught, cooped, transported to the plant, and unloaded for slaughter. Ages of bruises are easily determined and can be used at the plant to determine problem areas either at the farm or during catching, transportation, or unloading. During the initial formation of a bruise, the area appears bright red, followed by purple, yellow, green, and orange before returning to the normal color of the tissue (7, 8).

Increased stress due to catching and transportation may also lead to poor meat quality and reduced yield. Most birds are usually caught and cooped during the evening to early morning hours to ensure cooler temperatures and to reduce stress. Several broiler companies use automated methods to catch birds. These machines "scoop" birds from the floor of the house into coops minimizing bruising and broken bones. However, most turkey facilities are still completely manual when catching birds due to their large size. Transportation of the birds may lead to increased stress and can result in poor meat quality. This will be discussed in more detail later in the chapter.

B. IMMOBILIZATION – STUNNING, EXSANGUINATION

Following arrival at the processing plant, the birds are unloaded from the transportation trucks onto a conveyor line through an automated "dumping" mechanism. However, turkeys are normally unloaded from the trucks by hand. Both methods can cause bruising and broken bones if the animal is handled improperly. Once on the conveyor, the birds enter the plant and are hung on shackles prior to slaughter. The hanging room is usually a dark room with red or black lights to offer a calming effect on the birds to reduce stress. Once shackled, the birds are electrically stunned in a saline (approximately 1% NaCl) water bath to render the bird unconscious. Electrical stunning is the most common method of bird immobilization in the U.S. because it is inexpensive, convenient, and safe (9, 10).

Electrical stunning produces a uniform heartbeat for better bleeding, immobilizes the bird for slaughter, and relaxes the feather follicles for better picking. Normally, the birds are stunned for 10–12 seconds (10–20 mA per broiler; 20–40 mA per turkey) to produce a state of unconsciousness for 60–90 seconds (11). Stunning parameters with excessive amperage can cause downgrades, while too low of an amperage can cause poor bleeding, poor meat quality, and improperly killed birds. Therefore, proper stunning amperages are important determinants of good quality meat.

Stunning parameters and methods vary from country to country. For example, the European Economic Community requires birds to be irreversibly stunned by using saline bath electrical stunning methods that deliver approximately 100 mA per bird. This high amperage can cause broken clavicles, blood splash, rupture femoral arteries, and other downgrades (12). Brazil and some European countries have replaced high amperage electrical stunning with gas stunning. Gas stunning utilizes argon and carbon dioxide mixtures to displace oxygen and cause hypoxia in birds. Meat quality from gas stunned birds and low amperage stunned birds is better in comparison to high amperage electrical stunning because of the prevention of blood splash and broken bones (13, 14).

To reduce blood splash and ruptured arteries, bleed out must be performed within 10 seconds of low amperage electrical stunning. Exsanguination (or bleed out) is the period of blood removal which usually lasts 1.5 to 3 minutes. Following stunning, the head of the bird is guided through a set of bars for proper presentation to the cutting blade (Figure 33.1). Most of these automated cutting blade machines use a single unilateral neck cut which severs the right carotid artery and jugular vein. However, some processors use a rotating blade to sever both carotid arteries and jugular veins for a more complete bleeding efficiency. Either way, the blood volume lost is 30–50%, mainly from the major arteries and veins (11). This loss of blood volume causes brain failure and eventually death to the bird. Insufficient bleeding can result in poor meat quality and discoloration of the skin during scalding. Flavor is the most affected quality parameter associated with improper bleeding with the development of a gamey flavor due to the residual blood remaining in the muscles.

FIGURE 33.1 Killing machine indicating the bicycle wheel and guide bars used for alignment. Reprinted with permission from Poultry Meat Processing, 2002. Ed. AR Sams, Copyright CRC Press, Boca Raton, Florida.

C. FEATHER REMOVAL – SCALDING, PICKING

Feather removal is a two-step process – scalding and picking. Scalding is time and temperature dependent with two variations, soft scald and hard scald, depending upon the intended use of the carcass or parts. Soft scald is immersion of the carcasses in 53.35°C (128°F) water for 120 seconds (11). Soft scalding loosens the feathers but does not disrupt the outer skin layer or the cuticle (waxy, yellow-pigmented outer layer). Thus, a yellowish coating is retained on the skin of the bird. Soft scalded birds can be difficult to pick because the feather follicle is not loosened fully. Also, a quality problem can exist in further processed products with soft scalded birds because the cuticle prevents coating adhesion on batter and breaded products.

A hard scald is immersion of the carcass in 61–63°C (140–145°F) water for 45 seconds. The cuticle layer is removed through this hard scald process. Feathers are also easier to remove compared to the soft scald. Also, there are fewer quality problems with hard scalding since coated products have better batter adhesion without the cuticle layer. However, appearance may be a problem for those consumers that prefer the "yellow" tinted soft scalded birds.

Feather removal (picking) is completed by rotating rubber fingers which grasp the feathers and remove them (Figure 33.2). Proper picking is dependent upon the time the carcass spends in the picker as well as the speed of the rotating fingers. Over picking may cause downgrades and mutilations (carcass that have no salvageable parts) while under picking may leave feathers on the carcass resulting in downgrading further down the processing line. Therefore, feather removal is important in maximizing quality and yield of the carcass.

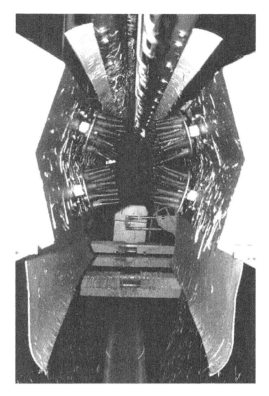

FIGURE 33.2 Picking cabinet with rubber fingers used to remove feathers. Reprinted with permission from Poultry Meat Processing, 2002. Ed. AR Sams, Copyright CRC Press, Boca Raton, Florida.

D. EVISCERATION – VISCERA REMOVAL, INSPECTION

Prior to actual evisceration, the head, feet, and preen gland (oil gland located at the base of the tail) are removed. Evisceration, or the process of removing viscera from the carcass, is normally automated in chicken plants but is still performed manually in most turkey plants. With either method, the viscera is exposed and removed from the internal body cavity. Once exposed, the USDA inspector examines the carcass for field or plant condemnations and fecal contamination. Condemned birds are usually those with obvious signs of disease as well as cadavers (birds that have died for reasons other than exsanguinations). These birds are disposed of and do not enter the production chain. Fecal contaminated birds must be reprocessed and or trimmed prior to re-entering the production chain. The inedible viscera is then removed from the carcass and discarded while the edible viscera (heart, liver, and gizzard) are collected, cleaned, chilled, and packaged for retail or fast food restaurants. Necks are removed from the birds and lungs are vacuumed out of the body cavity by automated machines. Birds without their viscera are then visually inspected (final inspection) by trained plant personnel for such things as surface lesions, tumors, and bruising. Any imperfections will be trimmed and washed prior to the bird re-entering production.

To ensure high quality of meat, the most important parameter in evisceration is dependent upon the uniformity of the birds and proper machine adjustment. Improperly adjusted machines or flocks with very little uniformity in size or shape can cause an increase in number of mutilations and downgrades. Both of these scenarios cause decreased yield and profit margins for the processor. For this reason, processors utilize specific genetic lines of broilers or turkeys to minimize size variation within the plant.

E.   CHILLING

Poultry meat must be chilled to 4.4°C within 4 hours of slaughter for 4 lb. broilers, 6–8 hours for 4 to 8 lb broilers and within 8 hours for broilers greater than 8 pounds and for turkeys. In order to accomplish this, two methods are utilized, immersion or air chilling. Air chilling is not the most common method in the United States for poultry carcasses; however, it is used extensively in Europe, South America, and Canada. With air chilling, the birds remain on the shackles following evisceration and enter a room with temperatures ranging from −7°C to 2°C (15). The carcasses remain in this room for 1–3 hours and may have a continual spray mist to help reduce temperatures of the carcass as well as prevent extra moisture loss and reduction in carcass yield. Even with misting, air chilled birds normally have a dry appearance to their skin which disappears during rehydration. However, air chilled birds normally have a lower pathogen load and have an increased shelf-life when compared to immersion chilled carcasses (16, 17).

Immersion chilling is the most common method of chilling poultry in the U.S. Carcasses are removed from the shackle following evisceration and are placed in staged water tanks for a period of about 80 minutes (sometimes longer for turkeys). During immersion chilling, the carcasses are moved through a continuous chilling system by paddles or an auger, through increasingly colder and cleaner water (counter-current flow system) (Figure 33.3). An air bubble agitation system is also employed that decreases the thermal layering effect cooling the carcasses at a faster rate (Figure 33.4). This counter-current flow method of chilling increases water uptake, increases heat exchange, and provides a method of cleaning the bird. Immersion chilled birds have a lower

FIGURE 33.4   Water immersion chilling tank showing air hoses used to agitate water. Reprinted with permission from Poultry Meat Processing, 2002. Ed. AR Sams, Copyright CRC Press, Boca Raton, Florida.

total microbial count than air chilled carcasses due to the washing effect of the immersion. However, there are an increased number of pathogen-positive birds due to cross-contamination issues related to tank sharing during the production day. It is important to note that antimicrobials are used during the chilling process to decrease bacteria, especially pathogens. Chlorine is the most common antimicrobial used in immersion chilling at a level of 20–50 ppm as allowed by FSIS.

Immersion chilling involves three steps. The first stage is referred to as pre-chilling and can be a separate tank in some processing plants. This separate tank acts as a "bird wash" to decrease microbial load and debris in the subsequent tanks. The temperature of the pre-chill is around 12°C (55°F) while the other stages are 4–7°C (40–45°F) and finally 1°C (30–34°F) prior to exit of the birds from the chiller and into second processing. During the pre-chill stage, birds absorb some amount of water in their skin while the final stage allows pores in the skin to close trapping the water inside and increasing the weight of the bird.

Postmortem temperature is an important processing factor involved in determining meat quality. Improper chilling of the bird can cause color defects in the meat

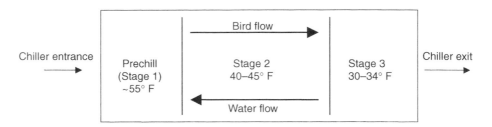

FIGURE 33.3   Immersion chiller system showing the counter-current flow of water and birds.

know as pale, soft, and exudative (PSE) meat. The development of PSE meat is caused by protein denaturation resulting from a rapid rate of pH decline while carcass temperatures are still elevated. The elevated carcass temperatures may have a more damaging effect when meat pH is below 6.2 (18). Carcasses with a normal pH decline may develop PSE meat if improperly chilled (19, 20). Rapid chilling decreases protein denaturation and can significantly reduce the development of PSE meat. Therefore, processors should chill carcasses rapidly early postmortem to prevent poor meat quality problems. Achieving a breast muscle temperature of less than 36°C (95°F) by 60 minutes postmortem and 28°C (82°F) by 90 minutes postmortem may reduce the PSE-like characteristics in turkeys (21).

A recent change in the poultry industry has occurred with a new regulation regarding moisture absorption and retention. The Food Safety Inspection Service has issued a final rule requiring that plants produce poultry products with either no retained water or only the minimum amount required to meet food safety requirements (22). The reasons for this rule deals with both complaints from consumer groups and inconsistencies with red meat processing. Consumer groups have long argued that retained water in poultry meat and subsequent leakage from the meat into packages could lead to spillage and contamination in the home. This increased contamination could result in an increase in food-borne illnesses from *Salmonella* and *Campylobacter*. The inconsistencies in meat processing have focused on the different methods of chilling carcasses. Meat carcasses (beef, pork, and lamb) are air chilled not immersion chilled so water is not retained in these meat products as in poultry carcasses. Actually, water (moisture) is reduced due to shrinking that occurs with air chilling these carcasses. Therefore, the red meat industry has argued that poultry meat is "adulterated" because water has been added to increase its bulk weight and therefore consumers are paying for water along with meat weight. If water is not regulated to be at a minimum uptake during chilling, then the product is not only adulterated but misbranded. Therefore, FSIS has proposed this regulation to help make the meat processing and poultry processing more consistent.

F. SECOND PROCESSING

Following temperature reduction of the carcasses, the birds are hung on shackles and either packaged as whole birds or cut into parts through automated processes. Adding value to carcasses by cutting them into parts has revolutionized the poultry industry (Table 33.1). In 2000, the predominant form of chicken marketed in the United States was parts (11). This trend started more than 30 years ago when consumers demanded more versatility and variety in chicken meat. At this time, consumers were mostly made up of two income families and there was less time for preparation of meals and cutting up of whole birds. Therefore, as we have entered into the 21st century, this trend of increasing versatility and variety has continued. From a processor stand point, adding value by cutting whole carcasses into parts increases profit margins and consumers are willing to pay an increased price for convenience.

TABLE 33.1
Commonly Used Configurations for Parts of a Chicken Carcass in the U.S.

Part	Description
Half Carcass	Carcass split evenly into right and left halves
Breast Quarter	Anterior right or left quarter containing half of the spine, the ribs, the pectoralis muscles (major and minor), and the attached wing
Leg Quarter	Posterior right or left quarter containing half of the spine, the thigh, and the drumstick
Wing	The three segments of the wing with a variable amount of the breast meat (depending on the customer)
Breast	The major and minor pectoralis muscles with or without rib and sternum bones or skin
Thigh	The upper part of the leg containing the femur
Drumstick	The lower part of the leg containing the tibia and fibula
Drumette	The inner portion of the wing
Wing Portion	The middle section of the wing, with or without the outer "flipper or wing tip" portion still attached
Whole Breast	The anterior half of the carcass without wings, with both breasts still connected in front and with or without the spine connecting them in the back
Keel Piece	The pointed posterior tip of the whole breast before splitting (approximately one third of the whole breast)
Breast Piece	After the removal of the keel piece from the whole breast, the remaining part is split into right and left halves
Whole Leg	Drum and thigh with no spine
Back or Strip Back	Spine and pelvis, production of quarters puts the back as part of the respective quarters
Breast Half or Front Half	The entire, intact, anterior half of the carcass
Leg Half, Back Half, or Saddle	The entire, intact, posterior half of the carcass

Source: Reprinted with permission from poultry meat processing, 2002. Ed. AR Sams, Copyright CRC Press, Boca Raton, Florida.

G. DEBONING

Following second processing, any birds not sold as whole carcasses or parts for retail are usually stored in tubs on ice in a 4°C cooler for 8–12 hours. This storage time allows for the development of rigor mortis and helps to decrease the toughness associated with early deboning. Once aged, the carcass can be either deboned manually or automatically by specialized equipment. Deboning method is the same for either automatic or manual operations: the breast fillet is stripped from the carcass. The wings are then sold as parts and the butterfly can either then be sold or split into two fillets as a less expensive part.

Deboned broiler beast meat is the most valued portion of the carcass and has the highest scrutiny from the consumer. Since this product is normally free of skin, all discolorations and blemishes (bruises) are evident and highly scrutinized by consumers. The three toughest challenges to the processor with deboned broiler breast fillets are portion control, uniformity, and toughness. Portion control is important in the food service industry (restaurants, hotels, etc.) where every consumer should receive the same amount of meat to allow for better cost estimation and meat ordering. In order to accomplish this portioning, scales are used in the deboning section of plants so all deboned broiler breast fillets are automatically weighed and sold based on uniformity of weight.

To ensure uniformity of size, the breast fillets can also be hand trimmed of excess fat, connective tissue, and even meat. Several restaurants require the meat to be a specific shape and size, so, either manually or by specialized equipment, the breast fillet is cut either horizontally or vertically to achieve the desired shape as defined by the customer. Automated equipment is now available to quickly create specific dimensions of the fillets by water knives. This specialized sizing is costly to the consumer because it is very labor intensive.

Uniform tenderness is a very challenging consumer concern for the poultry industry. Rigor mortis development is discussed in detail in other chapters. However, the development of rigor mortis takes 4–6 hours in broilers. Any stimulation to the muscle prior to the development of rigor mortis can cause an increase in toughness. For this reason, carcasses, or even front halves, are aged on the bone in a cooler for a minimum of 4 hours to overnight to prevent toughening. This aging time is expensive and labor intensive and can even cause a decrease in yield from water loss up to 2–3% (23).

To alleviate this toughness associated with early deboning, several plants have implemented electrical stimulation of the carcass following death or marination techniques following chilling. Electrical stimulation (ES) is different from stunning in that ES requires higher amperage and it is applied to the carcass immediately after death. When applied, electrical stimulation causes muscle contractions which uses energy stored in the muscle and allows rigor mortis to develop at a faster rate. Therefore, storing carcasses to prevent toughness associated with early deboning is no longer needed. Another method used to alleviate toughness is marination or the addition to salt and phosphates to increase juiciness of the meat. This increase in juiciness results in a more tender product. Marination will be discussed further in this chapter.

III. GRADING

A. CLASSIFICATION

Each species of poultry (chickens, ducks, geese, guineas, and pigeons) is divided into classes by their physical appearance mainly associated with age and sex. Based on these classes, quality grades are then established based on the quality of individual carcass and parts as will be discussed later in the chapter.

B. STANDARDS FOR GRADING

One way to add value other than cutting whole carcasses into parts is to grade carcasses or sort them by specific conditions and quality characteristics. The Agricultural Marketing Service (AMS) is a branch of the USDA responsible for poultry grading. Following mandatory inspection for wholesomeness (Figure 33.5), each bird is examined to determine eating quality and uniformity. Grading is voluntary, unlike inspection by FSIS. Therefore, the processing plant must pay for personnel from AMS to grade carcasses, thus increasing the price of the graded product for consumers. However, consumers are willing to pay for the added increase to ensure good eating quality and uniformity with tenderness, juiciness,

FIGURE 33.5 USDA inspection shield for wholesomeness.

color, and meatiness. Grading has become an industry standard and is almost expected from consumers.

Once graded by an authorized grader, the official USDA grade mark is used on packages and is easily identified by consumers (Figure 33.6). The highest quality grade is USDA Grade A, followed by USDA Grade B and then USDA Grade C. The standards for USDA Grade A, B, and C carcasses and bone in parts are listed in Table 33.2 (24). USDA Grade A is usually in retail packages and consumers are mostly familiar with this grade. Downgraded carcasses, USDA Grades B and C, are usually further processed because of some deformities or defects. One way to add value to downgraded carcasses is to cut them into parts for retail.

IV. QUALITY CHARACTERISTICS

Three main characteristics of poultry meat determine overall meat quality: tenderness (texture), water holding capacity, and color.

A. TENDERNESS

Tenderness is one of the most important meat quality characteristics. Several factors influence the tenderness of whole muscle meat products. These factors include the contractile state of the muscle, the amount of connective tissue, and juiciness. In market age broilers (6 weeks), probably the most important influence is the contractile state of the muscle. Most of the tenderness variation due to contractile state in meat from young broilers is related to the conversion of muscle to meat (rigor mortis development). During this conversion, which begins at the time of slaughter, muscle pH declines due to an accumulation of lactic acid in the muscle. In addition, ATP content declines as the muscle shifts from aerobic to anaerobic metabolism. This rigor mortis period takes approximately 4–6 hours in broilers (25, 26). If the muscle is stimulated by deboning or extreme cold temperatures (cold shortening) prior to rigor completion, the muscle can have some degree of contraction possibly without enough energy present for muscle relaxation (depending on what time the stimulation occurred). Therefore, the muscle would shorten thus altering the state of contraction; the denser the muscle, the tougher it will feel to consumers.

The connective tissue component of meat tenderness does not play a major role in young broilers. However, it does affect older animals (such as spent fowl) to a greater extent because as the animal ages, heat-stable crosslinks in the collagen form that will not melt during cooking. Juiciness is important in meat tenderness as well because it provides lubrication and mouth feel which are important from a consumer sensory perception. Cooking method is the primary factor impacting juiciness. For example, overcooking which can cause excess moisture loss can decrease tenderness or perceived tenderness by consumers. Any cooking method in which the product can lose excess moisture (example: uncovered grilling compared to covered baking) can decrease the juiciness and therefore decrease tenderness of the product.

B. WATER HOLDING CAPACITY

Water holding capacity (WHC) is another important characteristic of meat quality. Water holding capacity can be defined as the ability to retain inherent water in the meat or added water (observed in further processed items). Water can be lost from meat through gravitational (storage, drip loss), mechanical (cutting), or thermal (cooking) forces. Differences in meat quality are directly related to how the meat can handle the application of these forces.

Water exists as three forms in the muscle: bound, immobilized, and free. Bound water is closely associated with the muscle proteins. Because water molecules are polar, they associate with the electrically charged reactive groups of the proteins. This water layer is so tightly bound that it can only be removed by incineration (high temperatures). The second form of water is known as immobilized. This water layer is attracted to the bound layer of water, but the attraction is much weaker. The attraction also decreases as the distance to the proteins increase. The third form of water is known as free water and accounts for the majority of the water in meat. Free water is loosely held by capillary forces and is easily lost during processing procedures such as cutting, grinding, storage (drip), and cooking.

Water holding capacity is affected by pH (net charge effect) and the amount of space between the muscle protein structures (steric effect). The postmortem decline in pH results in a loss of reactive groups to bind water due to reduced net protein charge and reduced protein solubility. As pH decreases in meat, it nears the isoelectric point (pI) of muscle proteins (approximately 5.1). The closer the pH is to the pI of the meat proteins, the number of charged sites on the proteins that normally bind water decreases. Examples of changes in WHC due to pH are pale, soft,

FIGURE 33.6 Grade mark from USDA Agricultural Marketing Service.

TABLE 33.2

Summary of Specifications for Grading A, B, and C Grade Carcasses

Ready-to-Cook Poultry — A Quality
Summary of Specifications for Standards of Quality for Individual Carcasses and Parts
Effective April 29, 1998 (Not All Inclusive — Minimum Requirements and Maximum Defects Permitted)

A Quality

Conformation:	Normal
Breastbone	Slight curve or dent
Back	Slight curve
Legs and Wings	Normal
Fleshing:	Well fleshed, considering kind and class
Fat Covering:	Well-developed layer — especially between heavy feathers tracts

Defeathering:	**Turkeys** (feathers less than 3/4 in.)		**Ducks and Geese**[1] (feathers less than 1/2 in.)		**All Other Poultry** (feathers less than 1/2 in.)	
	Carcass	**Parts**	**Carcass**	**Parts**	**Carcass**	**Parts**
Free of protruding feathers and hairs	4	2	8	4	4	2

Exposed Flesh:[2]

Weight Range		**Carcass**		**Large Carcass Parts**[3] (halves, front and rear halves)		**Other Parts**[3]
Minimum	Maximum	Breast and Legs	Elsewhere	Breast and Legs	Elsewhere	
None	2 lbs.	1/4 in.	1 in.	1/4 in.	1/2 in.	1/4 in.
Over 2 lbs.	6 lbs.	1/4 in.	1 1/2 in.	1/4 in.	3/4 in.	1/4 in.
Over 6 lbs.	16 lbs.	1/2 in.	2 in.	1/2 in.	1 in.	1/2 in.
Over 16 lbs.	None	1/2 in.	3 in.	1/2 in.	1 1/2 in.	1/2 in.

Discolorations: Carcass

		Lightly Shaded		**Moderately Shaded**[4]	
		Breast and Legs	Elsewhere	Hock of leg	Elsewhere
None	2 lbs.	3/4 in.	1 1/4 in.	1/4 in.	5/8 in.
Over 2 lbs.	6 lbs.	1 in.	2 in.	1/2 in.	1 in.
Over 6 lbs.	16 lbs.	1 1/2 in.	2 1/2 in.	3/4 in.	1 1/4 in.
Over 16 lbs.	None	2 in.	3 in.	1 in.	1 1/2 in.

Discolorations: Large Carcass Parts (halves, front and rear halves)

		Lightly Shaded		**Moderately Shaded**[4]	
		Breast and Legs	Elsewhere	Hock of leg	Elsewhere
None	2 lbs.	1/2 in.	1 in.	1/4 in.	1/2 in.
Over 2 lbs.	6 lbs.	3/4 in.	1 1/2 in.	3/8 in.	3/4 in.
Over 6 lbs.	16 lbs.	1 in.	2 in.	1/2 in.	1 in.
Over 16 lbs.	None	1 1/4 in.	2 1/2 in.	5/8 in.	1 1/4 in.

Discolorations: Other Parts

		Lightly Shaded	**Moderately Shaded**[4]
None	2 lbs.	1/2 in.	1/4 in.
Over 2 lbs.	6 lbs.	3/4 in.	3/8 in.
Over 6 lbs.	16 lbs.	1 in.	1/2 in.
Over 16 lbs.	None	1 1/4 in.	5/8 in.

Disjointed and Broken Bones:	Carcass—1 disjointed and no broken bones. Parts—Thighs with back portion, legs, or leg quarters may have femur disjointed from the hip joint. Other parts—none.
Missing Parts:	Wing tips and tail. In ducks and geese, the parts of the wing beyond the second joint may be removed if removed at the joint and both wings are so treated. Tail may be removed at the base.
Freezing Defects:	Slight darkening on back and drumstick. Overall bright appearance. Occasional pock-marks due to drying. Occasional small areas of clear, pinkish, or reddish-colored ice.

[1] Hair or down is permitted on the carcass or part, provided the hair or down is less than 3/16 inch in length, and is scattered so that the carcass or part has a clean appearance, especially on the breast and legs.

[2] Maximum aggregate area of all exposed flesh. In addition, the carcass or part may have cuts or tears that do not expand or significantly expose flesh, provided the aggregate length of all such cuts and tears does not exceed a length tolerance equal to the permitted dimensions listed above.

[3] For all parts, trimming of skin along the edge is allowed, provided at least 75 percent of the normal skin cover associated with the part remains attached, and the remaining skin uniformly covers the outer surface and does not detract from the appearance of the part.

[4] Moderately shaded discolorations and discolorations due to flesh bruising are free of clots and limited to areas other than the breast and legs except for the area adjacent to the hock.

Source: USDA, 1998.

TABLE 33.2 (*Continued*)

Ready-to-Cook Poultry — B Quality

Summary of Specifications for Standards of Quality for Individual Carcasses and Parts

Effective April 29, 1998 (Not All Inclusive — Minimum Requirements and Maximum Defects Permitted)

B Quality

Conformation:	Moderate deformities
Breastbone	Moderately dented, curved, or crooked
Back	Moderately crooked
Legs and Wings	Moderately misshapen
Fleshing:	Moderately fleshed, considering kind and class
Fat Covering:	Sufficient fat layer—especially on breast and legs

Defeathering:	**Turkeys**		**Ducks and Geese**[1]		**All Other Poultry**	
A few scattered protruding	(feathers less than 3/4 in.)		(feathers less than 1/2 in.)		(feathers less than 1/2 in.)	
feathers and hairs	**Carcass**	**Parts**	**Carcass**	**Parts**	**Carcass**	**Parts**
	6	3	10	5	6	3

Exposed Flesh:

Weight Range

Minimum:	Maximum:	**Carcass**	**Parts**
None	2 lbs.	No part on the carcass (wings, legs, entire back,	No more than 1/3 of the flesh normally
Over 2 lbs.	6 lbs.	or entire breast) has more than 1/3 of the flesh exposed	covered by skin exposed
Over 6 lbs.	16 lbs		
Over 16 lbs.	None		

Discolorations:[2]

Carcass		**Carcass**	
		Lightly or Moderately Shaded Discolorations	
		Breast and Legs	Elsewhere
None	2 lbs.	1 1/4 in.	2 1/4 in.
Over 2 lbs.	6 lbs.	2 in.	3 in.
Over 6 lbs.	16 lbs.	2 1/2 in.	4 in.
Over 16 lbs.	None	3 in.	5 in.

Discolorations:[2]

Large: Carcass Parts		**Large Carcass Parts**	
(halves, front and rear halves)		Lightly or Moderately Shaded Discolorations	
		Breast and Legs	Elsewhere
None	2 lbs.	1 in.	1 1/4 in.
Over 2 lbs.	6 lbs.	1 1/2 in.	1 3/4 in.
Over 6 lbs.	16 lbs.	2 in.	2 1/2 in.
Over 16 lbs.	None	2 1/2 in.	3 in.

Discolorations:[2]

Other Parts		**Other Parts**
		Lightly or Moderately Shaded Discolorations
		Breasts, Legs, and Parts
None	2 lbs.	3/4 in.
Over 2 lbs.	6 lbs.	1 in.
Over 6 lbs.	16 lbs.	1 1/2 in.
Over 16 lbs.	None	1 3/4 in.

Disjointed and Broken Bones:	Carcass—2 disjointed and no broken bones, or 1 disjointed and 1 non-protruding broken bone. Parts—may be disjointed, no broken bones; wing beyond second joint may be removed at a joint.	
Missing Parts:	Wing tips, 2nd wing joint, and tail.	
Trimming:	**Carcass**	**Parts**
	Slight trimming of the carcass is permitted provided the meat yield of any part on the carcass is not appreciably affected. The back may be trimmed in an area not wider than the base of the tail to the area halfway between the base of the tail and the hip joints.	A moderate amount of meat may be trimmed around the edge of a part to remove defects.
Freezing Defects:	May lack brightness. Few pockmarks due to drying. Moderate areas showing a layer of clear, pinkish, or reddish-colored ice.	

[1] Hair or down is permitted on the carcass or part, provided the hair or down is less than 3/16 inch in length, and is scattered so that the carcass or part has a clean appearance, especially on the breast and legs.

[2] Discolorations due to flesh bruising shall be free of clots and may not exceed one-half the total aggregate area of permitted discoloration.

TABLE 33.2 *(Continued)*

Ready-to-Cook Poultry — C Quality
Summary of Specifications for Standards of Quality for Individual Carcasses and Parts
Effective April 29, 1998 (Not All Inclusive) (Minimum Requirements and Maximum Defects Permitted)

C Quality

Conformation:	Abnormal
Breastbone	Seriously curved or cooked
Back	Seriously crooked
Legs and Wings	Misshapen
Fleshing:	Poorly fleshed
Fat Covering:	Lacking in fat covering over all parts of carcass

Deathering:	**Turkeys**		**Ducks and Geese**[1]		**All Other Poultry**	
Scattering of protruding	(feathers less than 3/4 in.)		(feathers less than 1/2 in.)		(feathers less than 1/2 in.)	
feathers and hairs	**Carcass**	**Parts**	**Carcass**	**Parts**	**Carcass**	**Parts**
	8	4	12	6	8	4

Exposed Flesh:
Weight Range

Minimum:	Maximum:	**Carcass**	**Parts**
None	2 lbs.		
Over 2 lbs.	6 lbs.	No limit	
Over 6 lbs.	16 lbs		
Over 16 lbs.	None		

Discolorations:[2]
Carcass

		Carcass
		Breast and Legs Elsewhere
None	2 lbs.	No limit
Over 2 lbs.	6 lbs.	on size, number of areas, or intensity of discolorations
Over 6 lbs.	16 lbs	and flesh bruises if such areas do not render
Over 16 lbs.	None	any part of the carcass unfit for food.

Discolorations:[2]
Parts
(includes large carcass parts)

		Parts
		Breasrs, Legs, and Parts
None	2 lbs.	No limit
Over 2 lbs.	6 lbs.	on size, number of areas, or intensity of
Over 6 lbs.	16 lbs.	discolorations and flesh bruises if such areas
Over 16 lbs.	None	do not render any part unfit for food.

Disjointed and Broken Bones:	No limit
Missing Parts:	Wing tips, wings, and tails.
	Backs shall include all meat and skin from pelvic bones, except that the meat contained in the ilium (oyster) may be removed.
	The vertebral ribs and scapula with meat and skin and the backbone located anterior (for ward) of ilia bones may also be removed (front half of back).

Trimming:	**Carcass**	**Parts**
	Trimming of the breast and legs is permitted, but not to the extent that the normal meat yield is materially affected.	
	The back may be trimmed in an area not wider than the base of the tail and extending from the tail to the area between the hip joints.	

Freezing Defects:	Numerous pockmarks and large dried areas.

[1] Hair or down is permitted on the carcass or part, provided the hair or down is less than 3/16 inch in length, and is scattered so that the carcass or part has a clean appearance, especially on the breast and legs.

exudative (PSE) meat, and dark, firm, and dry (DFD) meat conditions. Because the pH of PSE meat is closer to pH 5.1, it will have lower water holding capacity partly due to its lower pH resulting in fewer charges to bind water; however, DFD has high water holding capacity because its high pH is further away from the pI. Meat with high pH has a pH that is further away from the pI of myofibrillar proteins increasing the number of charged groups; therefore, the proteins have more reactive groups available to hold water.

Water holding capacity is also affected by a steric effect, or the amount of interstitial space between muscle proteins. The amount of this space can be influenced by pH and contractile state of the muscle. At higher muscle pH, further away from the pI, there are more charged ions in the muscle. These charged ions separate muscle proteins by repulsive force which then allows more physical space available to hold water. The contractile state of the muscle can also affect this space. For example, if muscle is in a contracted state, there is less interstitial space available to hold water. Any factor contributing to muscle shortening in the prerigor state such as early deboning can affect WHC.

C. COLOR

Color is an important meat quality attribute that can be affected by several factors including myoglobin concentration, oxidation state of the iron within the myoglobin, and muscle pH. Pinking in poultry has become a problem in recent years because consumers seem to associate the "pink" color to a food safety problem (undercooking of the chicken or turkey meat). However, pinking can occur as a result of addition of ingredients such as nitrite, improper stunning causing petechial hemorrhaging, and undenatured myosin following improper heating. Nitrites are normally added to further processed products to add color and for food safety measures. However, during heating, a characteristic pink color develops in the product, which can sometimes be confused with undercooking. Insufficient heating can also cause some undenatured myoglobin pigments to retain a "pinkish" color which could present a quality problem to consumers. Another common reason for pinking is contamination of the meat with nitric dioxide and carbon dioxide from oven gasses. These combinations can cause pinking in meat often leaving the consumer wondering if the product is fully cooked. Pinking in poultry meat can be avoided by cooking meat to an internal temperature of 71–73°C, adding compounds that scavenge undenatured myoglobin components that cause pinking, and keeping burners cleaned and running efficiently (27).

Another common quality problem with color in poultry meat is pale, soft, and exudative meat. Denaturation of proteins, specifically the sarcoplasmic proteins, can cause increased scattering of light in the muscle resulting in lighter (or paler) meat. Shrinkage of myofibrils at low muscle pH levels causes greater scattering of light at the myofibril surface. The transmittance of individual muscle fibers is decreased at low pH resulting in less light absorption and paler meat. Furthermore, myofibrils are birefringent, or have two refractive indices, which cause light to take two different paths as it travels through the myofibrils. Muscle pH strongly affects the difference between the two paths with increased light scattering at low pH levels.

D. RELATIONSHIP BETWEEN COLOR AND WATER HOLDING CAPACITY

Color is also related to water binding capacity of the meat. Color of meat is discussed further in Chapter 31, "Poultry: Chemistry and Biochemistry." In general, pale, soft, and exudative (PSE) meat has a low pH; therefore, water binding is low because more water is contained in the extracellular space rather than intracellular space. With more water in the extracellular space, light will be reflected rather than absorbed. In poultry, muscle pH is highly correlated with L* value, a measurement of lightness. In the case of dark, firm, and dry (DFD) meat, meat color is darker due to the high pH. The high pH causes the meat to bind more water, and because of the high water binding, more light is absorbed rather than reflected and results in a darker color.

V. MARINATION

The easiest way to improve quality for consumers and improve the profit margins for processors is to marinate poultry parts, especially breast fillets. Marination of poultry breast meat continues to grow as the demand for further processed products increases. Marinades can be incorporated into meat by tumbling, mixing, or massaging the meat at low temperatures, thereby facilitating tenderization through disintegration of the muscle fiber sheath and stretching of the myofibrils. Commercial methods used to marinate meat including tumbling, blending, and injection. Each method has its advantages and disadvantages. Tumbling promotes rapid and consistent pickup at controlled temperatures, the ability to marinate large quantities, and the capability to handle many different products and sizes. Blending allows for finer control of product mixing as compared to tumbling, and the ability to directly apply refrigerant. Injection marination is beneficial for its relative consistency of marinade application on large and complex products, and reduction of labor and speed of marination.

The two key ingredients in commercial poultry marinades are salt and phosphate. Marination with a variety of combinations of salt and phosphates has been used as means to improve taste, tenderness, and protein functionality of broiler breast fillets. Marination has also been used to improve protein functionality losses imparted by the PSE condition (28).

One of the most important properties of poultry meat is its water holding capacity (ability to bind and retain innate water, as well as added water during marination). Pale, soft and exudative meat has poor water holding capacity which results in an economic loss for processors, as well as a decrease in consumer acceptance. Marination has been used as a method to increase the water holding capacity, thereby improving the quality and increasing the yield of the meat. This increase in functional property is due to the marinade solution maintaining a higher pH postmortem.

Myofibrillar proteins, such as actin, myosin, and the actomyosin complex, are primarily responsible for WHC and marinade pick-up and retention. The salt and sodium tripolyphosphates commonly used in poultry meat marination work synergistically to increase water binding by increasing pH and ionic strength, combined with the dissociation of actomyosin, exposing more water binding sites (29). Basically, the salt and phosphate marinade uptake causes the tissue fibers to swell, resulting in decreased cooking loss and increased juiciness and tenderness of the meat.

Salt can affect proteins in many ways. At a low concentration, salt increases the WHC of proteins due to hydrated salt ions binding to charged groups of proteins. This resultant increase in water binding can be attributed to the water associating with bound ions. When salt binds to proteins, electrostatic repulsion causes the protein structure to loosen and allow more water binding. Salt also increases marinade pick-up by solubilizing the actin and myosin proteins which increases the space between the thick and thin filaments to pick up and retain marinade solution. Phosphates also increase WHC by increasing the number of charged sites on the protein for water binding to bind. The most common phosphates used in the poultry industry are sodium tripolyphosphates. However, several other phosphates are available with differing solubility, pH, and functional properties. An increased WHC allows for better uptake and retention of the marinade solution itself, as well as increasing the retention of the meat's own moisture, consequently increasing yield in an inexpensive manner.

The effect of various polyphosphate and salt (NaCl) solutions on myofibril protein extraction has been studied (30). In the absence of phosphates, no significant swelling or any other changes were noted at salt concentrations of 0.4 M or less. When salt concentrations were increased to 0.5 M and 0.6 M, myofibrils started to enlarge transversely and protein extraction became significantly noticeable.

The addition of polyphosphates induces changes in the protein extraction pattern. It is thought that polyphosphates possess an ATP-like property that allows polyphosphates to extract myosin and disintegrate part of the myofibril (30). Actomyosin is formed during rigor mortis and creates a state of permanent muscle contraction that leads to tough meat. Polyphosphates have the ability to dissociate this actomyosin complex, enabling myofibril lattices to expand laterally, resulting in an increase in water uptake. Tripolyphosphates were also shown to have similar effects. The researchers concluded that both poly- and tripolyphosphates are ionic species that dissociate myofilaments, depolarize thick filaments, and remove the

actomyosin structural barricade, thereby enhancing cooking yield and juiciness.

VI. CONCLUSION

The process of converting muscle into meat is highly complex. The poultry industry has reduced this complexity some by vertically integrating the production and processing stages. This integration has helped improve uniformity and quality in poultry meat. However, as discussed in this chapter, there are very intricate steps in the conversion of the live animal into meat for consumers and quality can be affected at each step.

REFERENCES

1. USDA, HACCP-based Inspection Models, Backgrounders, Food Safety and Inspection Service, U.S. Department of Agriculture, Washington, D.C., 1998, 1.
2. CJ Wabeck. Feed and water withdrawal time relationship to processing yield and potential fecal contamination of broilers. Poult Sci 51:1119–1124, 1972.
3. JD May, BD Lott, JW Deton. The effect of light and environmental temperatures on broiler digestive tract contents after feed withdrawal. Poult Sci 69:1681–1685, 1990.
4. JK Northcutt, RJ Buhr. Maintaining broiler meat yields: longer feed withdrawal can be costly. Broiler Ind 60(12):28–31, 1997.
5. JK Northcutt. Preslaughter factors affecting poultry met quality. In: AR Sams. ed. Poultry Meat Processing. Boca Raton, FL: CRC Press, 2001, pp. 5–18.
6. MK Handy, LE Kunkle, FE Deatherage. Bruised tissue II: Determination of the age of a bruise. J Anim Sci 16:490–494, 1957.
7. JK Northcutt, RJ Buhr. Management guide to broiler bruising. Broiler Ind 61(10): 18–23, 1998.
8. JK Northcutt, RJ Buhr, GN Rowland. Relationship of the age of the broiler bruise, skin appearance, and tissue histological characteristics. J Appl Poult Res 9:13–16, 2000.
9. SF Bilgili. Electrical Stunning of broilers-basic concepts and carcass quality implications: A review. J Appl Poult Res 1:135–146, 1992.
10. DL Fletcher. Stunning of broilers. Broiler Ind 56:40–42, 1993.
11. AR Sams. First Processing: Slaughter Through Chilling. In: AR Sams. ed. Poultry Meat Processing. Boca Raton, FL: CRC Press, 2001, pp. 19–34.
12. NG Gregory, LJ Wilkins. Cause of downgrades. Broiler Ind 56(4):42–45, 1993.
13. GH Poole, DL Fletcher, Comparison of a modified atmosphere stunning-killing system to conventional electrical stunning and killing on selected broiler breast muscle rigor development and meat quality attributes. Poult Sci 74:342–347, 1998.
14. AB Mojan Raj, TC Grey, AR Audsely, NG Gregory. Effect of electrical and gaseous stunning on the carcass

and meat quality of broilers. Br Poult Sci 31:725–730, 1990.

15. CH Veerkamp. Chilling, freezing and thawing. In: GC Mead. ed. Processing of Poultry. London: Elsevier Science, 1989, 103–112.

16. MX Sanchez, WM Fluckey, MM Brashears, SR McKee. Microbial profile and antibiotic susceptibility of Campylobacter spp. and Salmonella spp. in broilers processed in air-chilled and immersion-chilled environments. J Food Prot 65(6):948–956, 2002.

17. CZ Alvarado, CD Carroll, HM Buses, KD Paske, LD Thompson. Comparison of Air and Immersion Chilling on Meat Quality and Shelf Life of Broiler Breast Fillets. Accepted abstract International Poultry Scientific Forum, Atlanta, 2004.

18. AW Khan, AR Frey. A simple method for following rigor mortis development in beef and poultry. Can Inst Food Technol 4:139–142, 1971.

19. G Offer. Modeling of the formation of pale, soft, and exudative meat: effects of chilling regime and rate and extent of glycolysis. Meat Sci 30:157–184, 1991.

20. X Fernandez, A Forslid, E Tornberg. The effect of high postmortem temperature on the development of pale, soft, and exudative pork: Interaction with ultimate pH. Meat Sci 37:133–147, 1994.

21. CZ Alvarado, AR Sams, 2002. The role of carcass chilling rate in the development of pale, soft, and exudative turkey pectoralis. Poult Sci 81:1365–1370.

22. USDA, Retained Water in Raw Meat and Poultry Products: Poultry Chilling. Final Rule 9 CFR Parts 381

and 441. U.S. Department of Agriculture, Washington, D.C., 1998.

23. EM Hirschler, AR Sams. Commercial scale electrical stimulation of poultry: the effects on tenderness, breast meat yield, and production costs. J Appl Poult Res 7:99–103, 1998.

24. USDA, United States Classes, Standards, and Grades for Poultry, AMS 70.200 et seq. Agricultural Marketing Service, Poultry Programs, U.S. Department of Agriculture, Washington, D.C., 1998.

25. D de Fremery, MF Pool. Biochemistry of chicken muscle as related to rigor-mortis and tenderization. Food Res 25:73–87, 1960.

26. PL Dawson, DM Janky, MG Dukes, LD Thompson, SA Woodward. Effect of postmortem boning time during simulated commercial processing on the tenderness of broiler breast meat. Poult Sci 74:2035–2040, 1987.

27. KE Friesen, JA Marcy. Pinking in Poultry, Ohio, Proceedings of the 53rd Reciprocal Meat Conference, 2000, pp. 2–4.

28. CZ Alvarado, AR Sams. Injection marination strategies for remediation of PSE broiler breast meat. Poult Sci 79:98 (Suppl. 1) (Abstr.). 2000.

29. DWS Wong. Additives. In: Mechanism and Theory in Food Chemistry. New York: Van Nostrand, Reinhold, 1989, pp. 314–349.

30. YL Xiong, DR Kupski, Monitoring phosphate marinade penetration in tumbled chicken filets using thin-slicing, dye-tracing method. Poult Sci 78:1048–1052, 1999.

34 Fats and Oils: Science and Applications

Jan Pokorný
Department of Food Chemistry and Analysis, Prague Institute of Chemical Technology

CONTENTS

I. DEFINITIONS OF FATS, OILS, AND LIPIDS

In the scientific and even professional literature, the term lipids is more and more widely used. Lipids are classes of fatty acid derivatives. Their nomenclature is defined by the joint IUPAC-IUB standard (1). Fatty acids (aliphatic monocarboxylic acids) of 4 and more carbon atoms are usually bound as esters in plant and animal tissues, and only rarely as amides or free acids. Triacylglycerols, waxes, phospholipids, glycolipids, mucolipids, and lipoproteins are the most important lipid representatives. For many authors, especially in medical or biological sciences, lipids are exclusively naturally occurring fatty acid derivatives, but this definition is not useful for food science and technology because many closely related compounds, such as hydrogenated oils, structured lipids, fatty acid methyl or ethyl esters, and many oleochemicals do not occur in nature, but have been produced industrially. Aliphatic fatty acids are not the only organic acids bound in lipids because alicyclic or even phenolic acids were detected in natural lipids.

Substances like psychosin or lysoplasmalogens are included as lipids even when they do not contain any fatty acids. Long-chain fatty alcohols naturally occur in the liposoluble fraction of foods. Their properties and chemical structures are close to those of fatty acids, and therefore they are often treated as lipids. The same is true of sterols, but it is preferable to classify steroes as terpenic derivatives or as a separate class of compounds. Sterols are often esterified with fatty acids so that sterol esters are formed. They are classified as lipids because they contain bound fatty acids. Ethyl or higher esters of fatty acids (4–12 carbon atoms) are often present as natural components in fruits or are produced by fermentation in alcoholic beverages. They have specific aromas. They are, however, not considered lipids. It is evident from this discussion no generally accepted definition of lipids exists.

Fats and oils are lipophilic products obtained by processing natural materials of both plant and animal origin. Fats are usually of animal origin, and most oils are of plant origin, but animal oils such as fish oils exist, too. Fats are solid at room temperature while oils are liquid. The classification depends on the ambient temperatures; some products of tropical trees, such as palm or coconut oils, are liquid in the country of origin, but are solid in a temperate climate. Some semisolid lipid products are called butters, such as cocoa butter or shea butter, because their consistency is similar to butter in the country of origin. Officially, only a product of milk fat may be called butter; butters of vegetable origin should be better called fats.

Fats and oils are not pure compounds because they consist of all liposoluble substances extracted during processing of biological materials. They mostly consist of triacylglycerols (more than 95%), which are lipids, but they are accompanied by other liposoluble nonlipidic products, such as sterols, hydrocarbons, or liposoluble vitamins. Essential oils may be present in traces, but they are not lipids as they mainly consist of terpenes. For this reason, it would be preferable to use the terms fats and oils only for industrial products, and to use the term lipids for classes of pure substances. Of course, professionals in English-speaking countries often are not very careful concerning terminology.

II. FATTY ACIDS

A. DEFINITION

Fatty acids bound in lipids are mostly monocarboxylic acids with an aliphatic straight hydrocarbon chain. Branched fatty acids are rare, and are present almost exclusively as minor components. Odd carbon number fatty acids are also present only exceptionally. Fatty acids differ in the number of carbon atoms and double bonds. Some fatty acids are substituted by oxygen groups and even by other functional groups. Fatty acids with less than 4 carbon atoms have not been found in natural lipids.

B. SATURATED FATTY ACIDS

Saturated fatty acids have no double bond in their hydrocarbon chain. They have both systematic and trivial names, usually reflecting their origin (Table 34.1). The most common saturated fatty acid is palmitic acid, present in all lipids, at least in a small amount. Even carbon-number saturated fatty acids are mostly present in natural lipids, while odd carbon-number acids are present only as traces or as no more than minor acids in some fats. Short chain acids (1–3 carbon atoms) occur in nature, but are not bound in natural lipids. They may be found in lipids from some industrial products. Medium chain saturated acids (4–10 carbon atoms) are liquid at room temperature. Higher saturated acids are solid with their melting points increasing with the increasing carbon number.

C. MONOUNSATURATED FATTY ACIDS

Monounsaturated fatty acids contain a double bond in their hydrocarbon chain. They have both systematic and trivial names. In the case of unsaturated fatty acids, isomerism is possible. The double bond exists in cis (Z) or trans (E) configuration, and the double bond may be located at different carbon atoms (Table 34.2). Natural unsaturated fatty acids are mostly of the cis-configuration. Traces of trans-unsaturated fatty acids (0.04–0.05%) are detected even in cold-pressed edible oils (2). The position of double bonds is usually counted from carboxyl carbon, but in texts dealing with nutrition, calculation is often from the final methyl group. In such cases, they are defined, e.g., as an n-6 or ω-6 acid, if the double bond is located at the 6th carbon atom from the final methyl group. The most common unsaturated fatty acid is oleic acid (an n-9 fatty acid), which is present in nearly all lipids at least in small amounts. Monounsaturated acids

TABLE 34.1

The Most Important Saturated Fatty Acids (Compiled from Beilstein and Chemical Abstracts Data Bases)

Systematic Name	Trivial Name	Number of Carbon Atoms	Molecular Weight	Melting Point [°C]
Butyric	Butyric	4	88.1	−4.6
Hexanoic	Caproic	6	116.2	−1.5
Octanoic	Caprylic	8	144.2	16.3
Decanoic	Capric	10	172.3	32.4
Dodecanoic	Lauric	12	200.3	43.8
Tetradecanoic	Myristic	14	228.4	54.4
Hexadecanoic	Palmitic	16	256.4	62.6
Octadecanoic	Stearic	18	284.5	70.4
Eicosanoic	Arachic	20	312.5	75.8
Docosanoic	Behenic	22	340.6	80.2
Tetracosanoic	Lignoceric	24	368.6	84.2
Hexacosanoic	Cerotic	26	396.7	87.7

TABLE 34.2

The Most Important Monounsaturated Fatty Acids (Compiled from Beilstein and Chemical Abstracts Data Bases)

Systematic Name	Trivial Name	Number of Carbon Atoms	Molecular Weight	Melting Point [°C]
9-*cis*-Hexadecenoic	Palmitoleic	16	254.4	34.5
6-*cis*-Octadecenoic	Petroselinic	18	282.5	31.5
9-*cis*-Octadecenoic	Oleic	18	282.5	16
9-*trans*-Octadecenoic	Elaidic	18	282.5	45.5
11-*trans*-Octadecenoic	Vaccenic	18	282.5	39
13-*cis*-Docosenoic	Erucic	22	338.6	33.5
13-*trans*-Docosenoic	Brassidic	22	338.6	60.6

containing a triple bond are very rare, and are found only in fats for nonedible uses.

Unsaturated fatty acids have lower melting points than the respective saturated fatty acids, and are better soluble in organic solvents. Trans unsaturated acids have higher melting points than the respective *cis* acids (Table 34.2).

D. POLYUNSATURATED FATTY ACIDS

Polyenoic unsaturated fatty acids contain 2–6 double bonds. Many isomers are possible, but only a few are really found in nature. The majority among them belong to essential fatty acids as they cannot be synthetized in the human body [3]. Most natural polyunsaturated fatty acids have trivial names, which are more widely used than the systematic names (Table 34.3). Melting points of polyenoic fatty acids are lower than 0°C; therefore, they are not given in Table 34.3. An exception is eleostearic acid – because of the presence of trans double bonds (α-eleostearic acid = 49°C, β-eleostearic acid = 71°C). The allylic (pentadienoic) configuration is most frequent, -CH=CH-CH$_2$-CH=CH-, where the double bonds are separated by a methylene group. Their structures (4) are shown in Figure 34.1. Both n-6 and

n-3 polyunsaturated fatty acids belong to the essential fatty acids. They are enzymatically transformed into eicosanoids (5). The n-3 polyenoic acids are appreciated as they neutralize unfavorable effects of the excessive n-6 polyunsaturated fatty acid intake in modern diet of developed countries [6]. The balance between n-6 and n-3 polyunsaturated fatty acids should be maintained in the diet (7).

Conjugated unsaturated acids, -CH=CH-CH=CH- are rather rarely found, e.g., in milk fat or in some nonedible oils. In the most common fatty acids, the first double bond is located at the 9th or 6th carbon atoms (from the carboxyl group) or at the 3rd or 6th carbon atom (from the methyl group). Pentaenoic and hexaenoic n-3 fatty acids are typical for marine oils. They belong to the important essential fatty acids.

III. LIPIDS

A. ESTERS OF GLYCEROL

Fatty acids are mostly bound as glycerol esters in natural material. Glycerol (propantriol, Figure 34.2.A) contains three hydroxyl groups, each of which could be esterified with a fatty acid residue. Monoacylglycerols (formerly monoglycerides) contain only one fatty acid residue in the molecule, and exist in two isomeric forms (Figure 34.2.B and 34.2.C). The former one is more stable. The 1-acyl isomer has an unsymmetrical carbon atom, so that two optical isomers exist. Diacylglycerols (formerly diglycerides) are formed by substitution of two hydroxyl groups with an acyl group (Figure 34.2.D and 34.2.E). The 1,2-isomer has an asymmetrical carbon atom. It is easily isomerized into its more stable 1,3-isomer. The most common glycerol esters are triacylglycerols (formerly triglycerides), where all hydroxyl groups of glycerol are substituted with fatty acids (Figure 34.2.F). Monoacyl and diacylglycerols are present only in small amounts as intermediary metabolic products.

In simple triacylglycerols, all hydroxyl groups may be substituted with the same fatty acid (Figure 34.2.F), but in most cases, mixed triacylglycerols exist in nature, where two or three different fatty acids are bound on the same

TABLE 34.3

The Most Important Polyunsaturated Fatty Acids (Compiled from Beilstein and Chemical Abstracts Data Bases)

Systematic Name	Trivial Name	Number of Carbon Atoms	Number of Double Bonds	Melting Weight
9-*cis*, 12-*cis*-Octadecadienoic	Linolenic	18	2	280.4
9-*cis*, 12-*cis*, 15-*cis*-Octadecatrienoic	Linolenic	18	3	278.4
6-*cis*, 9-*cis*, 12-*cis*-Octadecatrienoic	γ-Linolenic	18	3	278.4
9-*trans*, 11-*trans*, 13-*trans*-Octadecatrienoic	Eleostearic	18	3	278.4
5,8,11,14-*all-cis*-Eicosatetraenoic	Arachidonic	20	4	304.6
5,8,11,14,17-*all-cis*-Eicosapentaenoic	EPA	20	5	302.4
4, 7, 10, 13, 16, 19-*all-cis*-Docosahexaenoic	DHA	22	6	328.5

$$R\text{-}CH_2\text{-}CH_2\text{-}COOH \rightarrow R\text{-}CH\text{-}CH_2\text{-}COOH \rightarrow R\text{-}CO\text{-}CH_3 + CO_2 \quad [1]$$
$$\underset{\displaystyle OOH}{\vert}$$

$$R^* + O_2 \rightarrow R\text{-}O\text{-}O^* \quad [2]$$

$$R\text{-}O\text{-}O^* + R\text{-}H \rightarrow R\text{-}O\text{-}OH + R^* \quad [3]$$

$$R\text{-}O\text{-}O\text{-}H \rightarrow R\text{-}O\text{-}O^* + H^* \text{ or } R\text{-}O^* + H\text{-}O^*$$

$$\text{or } 2\,R\text{-}O\text{-}O\text{-}H \rightarrow R\text{-}O\text{-}O^* + R\text{-}O^* + H_2O \quad [4]$$

$$\text{-}CH\text{=}CH\text{-}C^*\text{-}CH\text{=}CH\text{-} + O_2 \rightarrow \text{-}CH\text{=}CH\text{-}CH\text{=}CH\text{-}CH\text{-} \text{ or}$$
$$\underset{\displaystyle OOH}{\vert}$$

$$\text{-}CH\text{-}CH\text{=}CH\text{-}CH\text{=}CH\text{-} \quad [5]$$
$$\underset{\displaystyle OOH}{\vert}$$

$$2\,R^* \text{ or } R^* + R\text{-}O\text{-}O^* \text{ or } R^* + R\text{-}O^* \text{ or } 2\,R\text{-}O^* \rightarrow \text{ Relatively stable products} \quad [6]$$

$$R\text{-}O\text{-}O\text{-}H + Me^{2+} \rightarrow R\text{-}O\text{-}O^* + Me^+ + H^+ \quad [7]$$

$$R\text{-}O\text{-}O\text{-}H + Me^+ \rightarrow R\text{-}O^* + H\text{-}O^- + Me^{2+} \quad [8]$$

$$R\text{-}O^* + R^* \rightarrow R\text{-}O\text{-}R \quad [9]$$

FIGURE 34.1 Chemical structures of polyenoic fatty acids.

glycerol molecule. If the carbon atoms 1 and 3 are occupied by different fatty acids, the carbon atom 2 becomes asymmetrical; if the stereospecificity has to be evident, it is expressed by means of the *sn* system. The carbon numbers of glycerol are numbered stereospecifically (1). The carbon atom that appears on top in that Fischer projection that shows a vertical carbon chain with the hydroxyl group at carbon-2 to the left is designated as C-1. To differentiate such numbering from the conventional numbering, the prefix *sn* is used, e.g., *sn*-1-palmitoyl, 2-linoleoyl, 3-oleoylglycerol. Physical properties of optical isomers are not very different.

The number of triacylglycerol isomers is theoretically very high, but it is usually substantially restricted in natural fats and oils. Triacylglycerols are formed in natural food raw materials by esterification of glycerol under catalytic action of lipases. Lipases possess certain selectivity so that in most natural vegetable fats and oils the carbon atom *sn*-1 is occupied by palmitic acid or other saturated acids, and the carbon atom *sn*-2 by linoleic acid or linolenic acid, less often by oleic acid. The carbon atom *sn*-3 may be substituted with any fatty acid, most often unsaturated fatty acids.

In some plant or animal raw materials fatty acids are bound to monohydroxylic aliphatic alcohols or sterols. They are called waxes (8). The most important wax is bees wax. Their importance in the human diet is low.

Fatty esters of sugars, e.g., sucrose, are produced as fat replacers [9] as they are not cleaved by natural lipases, and cannot thus be utilized as a source of energy by humans.

More information on physical and chemical characteristics of oils, fats, and waxes are obtained from the literature (10).

B. PHOSPHOLIPIDS

Phospholipids consist not only of fatty acids and an alcohol, but also contain a phosphoryl group, usually ionized (1). The most common phospholipids are esters of glycerol; therefore, they are called glycerophospholipids. They are derivatives of 1,2-diacylglycerol, where the phosphoryl group is bound to the carbon atom *sn*-3. Such a derivative is called a phosphatidyl (Figure 34.3.A). If no other residue is bound to the phosphoryl group, phosphatidic acids are formed (Figure 34.3.B). They may exist as calcium or magnesium or other salts.

Very often, the aminoalcohol choline is bound to the phosphoryl group, and the resulting compound is phosphatidylcholine (earlier lecithin) (Figure 34.3.C), most often existing as an inner salt. The phospholipid containing another amino alcohol — ethanolamine — is called phosphatidylethanolamine — earlier known as colamine (Figure 34.3.D). Another important phospholipid class contains bound amino acid serine — phosphatidylserine (Figure 34.3.E). Other phospholipids may not contain any nitrogen, e.g., they contain bound myoinositol (hexahydroxycyclohexane); such phospholipids — phosphatidylinositols (Figure 34.3.F) — may be esterified by other phosphoryl residues. The phosphoryl group may be substituted by a glycerol (Figure 34.3.G) or a diacylglycerol (Figure 34.3.H).

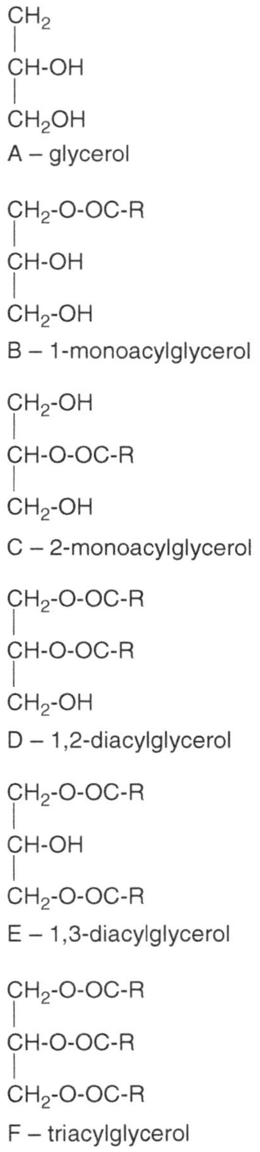

CH₂
|
CH-OH
|
CH₂OH

A – glycerol

CH₂-O-OC-R
|
CH-OH
|
CH₂-OH

B – 1-monoacylglycerol

CH₂-OH
|
CH-O-OC-R
|
CH₂-OH

C – 2-monoacylglycerol

CH₂-O-OC-R
|
CH-O-OC-R
|
CH₂-OH

D – 1,2-diacylglycerol

CH₂-O-OC-R
|
CH-OH
|
CH₂-O-OC-R

E – 1,3-diacylglycerol

CH₂-O-OC-R
|
CH-O-OC-R
|
CH₂-O-OC-R

F – triacylglycerol

FIGURE 34.2 Chemical structure of glycerol and glycerol esters.

Phosphatidylinositols, among other functions, diminish the postprandial oxidation of triacylglycerols, thus increasing the feeling of satiety, and decreasing the weight gain (11).

In natural phospholipids the fatty acid residue in the position *sn*-2 may be cleaved off by action of phospholipases, and lysophospholipids are formed (Figure 34.3.J). Plasmalogens are phospholipids, where a fatty acid is replaced by an aldehyde in the form of a hemiacetal, usually in its dehydrated form as the respective 2-unsaturated alcohol (Figure 34.3.K).

Some phospholipids do not contain any bound glycerol. Fatty acids are bound to a long-chain alcohol, such as sphingosine in animal tissues (Figure 34.3.L) or phytosphingosine in plant tissues (Figure 34.3.M). They are not bound as esters but as amides, and the hydroxyl group is esterified by a molecule of phosphoric acid,

which may contain bound choline or other compounds. Such lipids are called sphingolipids (Figure 34.3.N).

Phospholipids are present in all food materials at least in small amounts (12). Their content in oilseeds varies between 1–3% of the oil basis. The phospholipids fraction is present in crude oils obtained by extraction of oilseeds with nonpolar. It is precipitated from crude oils by action of water, or better by phosphoric or citric acid. The precipitate contains about 60% phospholipids. It is called lecithin. Lecithins of acceptable sensory properties, good functional properties, and reasonable availability are obtained only from soybeans or egg yolk, but the latter are more expensive. For most edible purposes, it is bleached and/or modified, e.g., by addition of free fatty acids. Lecithins enriched in phospholipids or phoshatidylcholine are available on the market. Lecithin is highly appreciated as an emulsifier or for many other purposes. Lower quality products are used for nonedible purposes. For more information about phospholipids see References 13–15.

C. GLYCOLIPIDS

Glycolipids are fatty acid derivatives containing bound sugars, most often D-galactose or D-glucose. The simplest glycolipids are derived from 1,2-diacylglycerols by substitution of the remaining hydroxyl group with a galactosyl (Figure 34.4.A) or a digalactosyl (Figure 34.4.B) residue. More complicated derivatives were identified, e.g., in oat lipids (16).

Galactosyldiacylglycerols are present in plants as a part of membranes for storage of starch (17). Emulsions containing galactolipids are components of fat replacers as they evoke the sense of fullness.

Cerebrosides are glycosides derived from sphingosine amides — ceramides (Figure 34.4.C).

Glycolipids contain sulphuric acid, sometimes bound to the glycoside residue (Figure 34.4.D). Gangliosides are complex phospholipids containing bound sialic acid (Figure 34.4.E), and usually also one or several residues of bound sugars. They were earlier called mucolipids.

D. LIPOPROTEINS

Lipids form macromolecular complexes with protein, where lipids are bound to proteins by multiple physical forces. They are present either as dispersible aggregates, soluble in water, or as membranes. Covalent bonds are found only exceptionally in natural lipoproteins, but may be formed by interactions of oxidized lipids with proteins.

In water-soluble lipoproteins, the lipid moiety is surrounded by a layer of hydrated proteins (Figure 34.5.A). The contact between the lipid and the protein moieties is effected by a layer of emulsifiers, chiefly sterols and phospholipids. The lipophilic, hydrophobic hydrocarbon chains of the emulsifiers are oriented inside the oil droplet while the hydrophilic parts are oriented towards the relatively polar and hydrophilic protein layer. The stability of

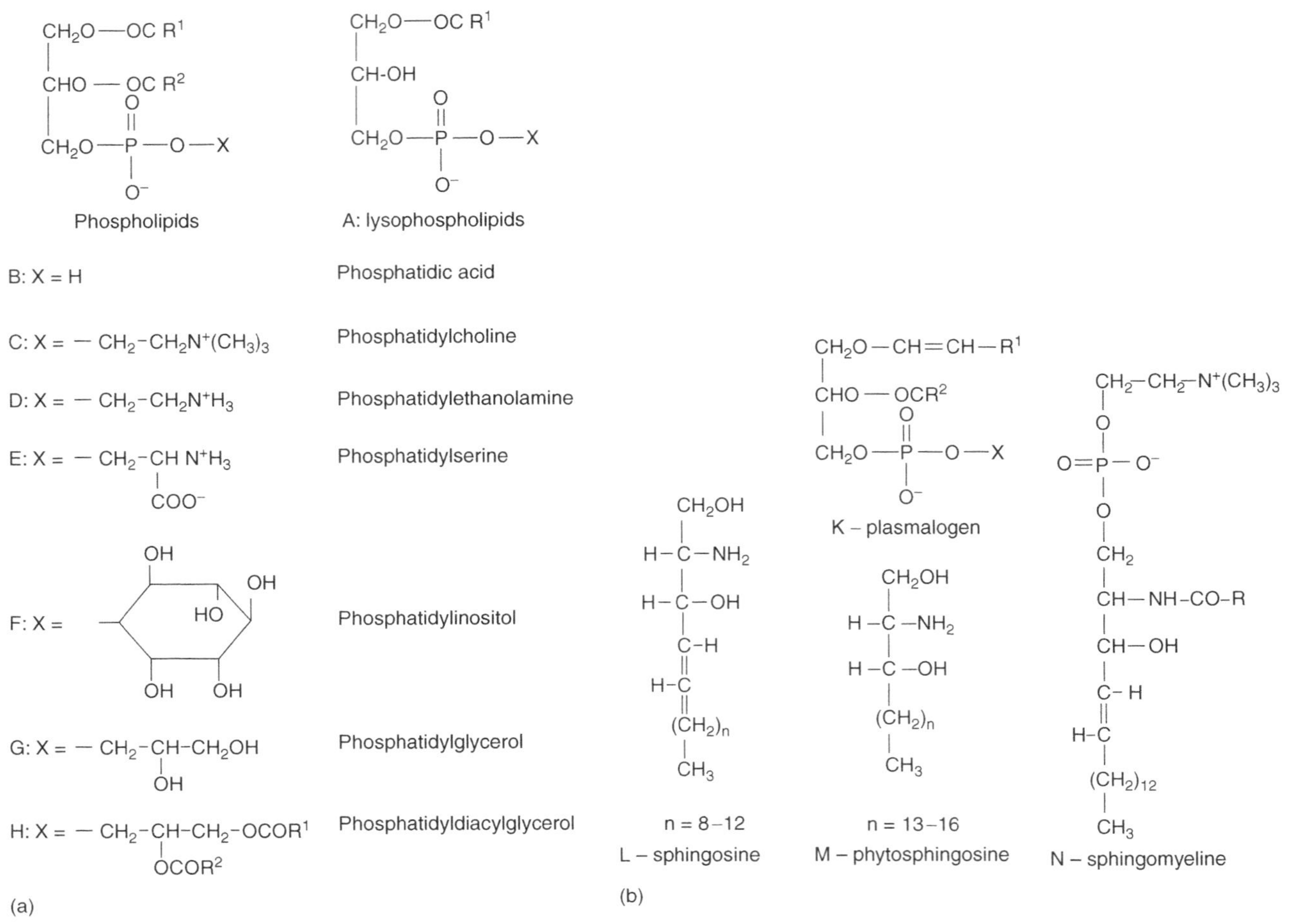

FIGURE 34.3   Chemical structures of phospholipids.

the dispersions of lipoproteins in water depends on the ratio of lipids:proteins. More information on lipoproteins is available from specialized literature (18, 19).

The most widely studied dispersed lipoproteins are those of blood plasma, which belong to the following classes according to their behavior under centrifugation, where they are separated on the basis of their density (specific gravity):

a.   VLDL — very low density lipoproteins;
b.   LDL — low density lipoproteins;
c.   HDL — high density lipoproteins.

The content of hydrophilic components and the stability of lipoprotein dispersion increases with their increasing density.

Lipoproteins forming membranes regulate the permeation of water molecules into cells and subcellular particles. They mostly consist of a double layer of lipoproteins. The polar moieties are oriented towards the water phases on both sides of the membrane, while the non-polar moieties form multiple physical bonds between the two lipid layers

of the membrane (Figure 34.4.B). Both phospholipids and sterols are important parts of membrane lipoproteins.

Lipids form complexes with starch and other macromolecular carbohydrates as well as with proteins (20). Three types of these interactions exist:

a.   Complexes consisting of lipid inclusion compounds inside an amylose helix or short helices inside amylopectin straight-chain oligosaccharide branches.
b.   Complexes, where lipids are sorbed on the surface of carbohydrate particles.
c.   Complexes, where lipids are located in capillaries between carbohydrate particles.

IV.   OCCURRENCE OF LIPIDS IN PLANT AND ANIMAL FOOD MATERIALS

Lipids are present in almost all food materials of both animal and plant origin (21). They are necessary for the existence of living tissues, even when mostly only in small amounts of 0.5 to 3.0%. These lipids are mainly located in

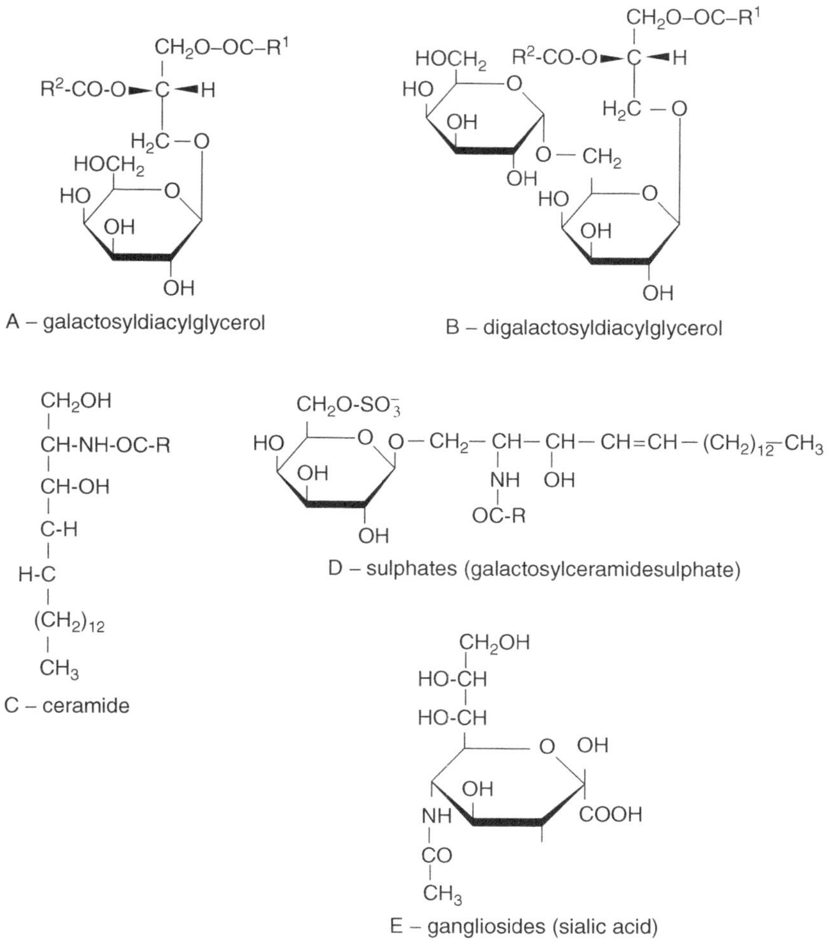

A – galactosyldiacylglycerol

B – digalactosyldiacylglycerol

C – ceramide

D – sulphates (galactosylceramidesulphate)

E – gangliosides (sialic acid)

FIGURE 34.4 Chemical structures of glycolipids.

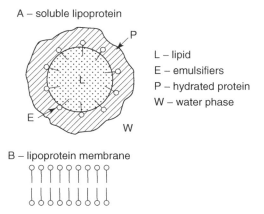

A – soluble lipoprotein

L – lipid
E – emulsifiers
P – hydrated protein
W – water phase

B – lipoprotein membrane

FIGURE 34.5 Chemical structures of lipoproteins.

cell membranes and in intracellular membranes, and mainly consist of phospholipids, glycolipids, and lipoproteins. The triacylglycerol fraction is relatively low in these tissues. The lipids are mostly bound to proteins and other hydrophilic components so that they are extractable only with solvent mixtures containing polar components, such as mixtures of chloroform and methanol or diethyl ether and ethanol.

In addition to their function in the metabolism of living organisms, lipids are deposited as energy reserves. The reserve lipids are very important raw materials in the food industry. They consist mostly of relatively non-polar triacylglycerols. Therefore, they are extractable with hydrocarbon solvents. Plant seeds contain either macromolecular carbohydrates or lipids as a source of energy for the germinating organism. In those plants, where the energy is stored in lipids, the content of seed lipids (called mostly oils) may be 30–60% dry weight (Table 34.4). In some plants, energy is stored both as lipids and as starch, such as in soybeans, where the lipid content is about 20%. In some seeds, lipids are stored also in the pericarp, e.g., in olives, avocado, or oil palm fruits. The fatty acid composition of storage lipids may be very different from that of membrane lipids.

Seed oils have different fatty acid composition from pericarp oils, e.g., palm oil has a fatty acid composition close to that of lard, while the palm kernel oil has the fatty acid composition similar to that of coconut oil (Table 34.5).

TABLE 34.4
Content of Plant Lipids (15)

Plant Name	Systematic Name	Lipid Source	Lipid Content [% Dry Weight]
Soya	*Soja hispida*	Beans	16–22
Sunflower	*Helianthus annuus*	Seed	42–62
Peanut	*Arachis hypogaea*	Seed	45–50
Rape	*Brassica napus*	Seed	40–48
Cocoa	*Theobroma cacao*	Seed	53–59
Almonds	*Prunus amygdalus*	Seed	60–65
Sesame	*Sesamum indicum*	Seed	50–55
Cotton	*Gossypium hirsutum*	Seed	20–24
Oil palm	*Elaeis guineensis*	Pericarp	30–40
Cocos palm	*Cocos nucifera*	Copra	63–70
Olive	*Olea europaea*	Pericarp	13–50
Rice	*Oryza sativa*	Bran	8–15
Wheat	*Triticum aestivum*	Germ	7–12
Corn	*Zea mays*	Germ	14–19

Examples of fatty acid composition of the most important fats and oils are shown in Table 34.5 (trace fatty acids are not included).

Even in plants using starch as a source of energy for germinating organism, at least the germ is rich in lipids so that it may be used for industrial processing, e.g., in the case of corn or wheat germs (Table 34.4). During the germination, oil is gradually used up as a source of energy, or it is converted into other compounds, chiefly cellulose.

Animal tissues also consist of two types of lipids. Lipid membranes and dispersible lipoproteins are present only in limited amounts of about 1–2% dry weight in the respective tissue. They consist mainly of phospholipids and glycolipids. Animals store energy in carbohydrates only in very small amounts; therefore, only energy reserves stored as triacylglycerols are important for the organism and in the industry. Surprisingly, in some tissues the amount of lipids may be much higher than the amounts of proteins. The fatty acid composition of reserve (depot) fat is different from the composition of polar lipids as polar lipids are rich in linoleic acid and more unsaturated polyenoic acids. The fatty acid composition of depot fat in farm animals depends partially on the composition of feed lipids, and similar relations exist in other animals. A typical example are lipids of fish and other aquatic animals as the fatty acid composition is influenced by that of algae and small crustaceans, which are their main source of nutrition. Polar lipids bound in membranes are not substantially affected by fatty acid composition of feed lipids.

The fatty acid composition of the triacylglycerol fraction of fats and oils is very different, and it is specific for each species. Examples of fatty acid composition of the most important fats and oils are shown in Table 34.5. (Trace fatty acids are not included and may be found in the original literature). The fatty acid composition of vegetable oils

is very variable. In some species oleic acid prevails, in other it is linoleic acid, and in another group linolenic acid is present, too. In palm seed lipids the major fatty acids are lauric, myristic, and palmitic acids. Triacylglycerols of land animals mostly consist of palmitic, stearic, oleic, and linoleic acids while polyunsaturated fatty acids are major components of marine oils (22).

The traditional fatty acid composition may be substantially modified by breeding, genetic manipulations, or even climatic conditions. Modified soya cultivars yield oil with high saturated fatty acid content, suitable as transfree replacers of hydrogenated oils, or canola oil with 40% lauric acid is suitable for nonedible uses (23). In animals it is affected by feed lipids. The novel modified oils usually have higher oleic acid content and lower polyunsaturated acid content so that they are more resistant against oxidation on heating or long storage.

V. CHEMICAL CHANGES DURING INDUSTRIAL FAT AND OIL EXTRACTION AND PROCESSING

A. FAT AND OIL EXTRACTION FROM NATURAL SOURCES

Oilseeds are the most important raw material for the production of edible oils. Soybeans, followed by palm fruits, are the chief oilseeds worldwide, but rapeseed and sunflower seed are also important in Europe, followed by olives and animal raw materials (24). Seeds are first crushed, and the resulting meal is heated by steam application. During the process, heat denaturation of the protein moiety destroys lipid membranes and other lipoproteins so that the yield of oil substantially increases in comparison to the cold extraction. This process is called conditioning.

Conditioned oilseed meals of oilseeds containing 40–60% oil are then fed to expeller presses, where oil is extracted from the meal under high pressure and temperatures up to 100°C. Crude oil is removed and collected in a tank, and the pressed material (cakes), still containing about 12–20% oil, is cooled to the ambient temperature. Soybeans have only about 20% oil so that the cake has a lower concentration of oil or is treated by solvent extraction before the previous expeller pressing. Rice brans or corn germs are not expeller pressed because of low oil content, but are treated directly with solvents. Olives are cold-pressed in special crushers at temperatures below 40°C with production of virgin olive oils (25, 26).

The cakes are then extracted using solvents, most often hexane, pentane, and their isomers, or other hydrocarbons of similar boiling temperatures. Continuous processes are mostly used, and the resulting extracted meal is then separated from the solution of oil in the extraction solvent (micella). Crude oil is then obtained by

TABLE 34.5
Fatty Acid Composition of Fats and Oils (66)

A. Linoleic Acid Oils

Fatty Acid Code	Sunflower Oil	Peanut Oil*	Safflower Oil	Sesame Oil	Cottonseed Oil**
16:00	5–8	8.3–14	5.3–8.0	7.9–10.2	21.4–26.4
16:01	<0.5	<0.2	<0.2	0.1–0.2	<1.2
18:00	2.5–7	1.9–4.4	1.9–2.9	4.8–6.1	2.1–3.3
18:01	13–40	36.4–67.1	8.4–21.3	35.9–42.3	14.7–21.7
18:02	40–74	14.0–43.0	67.8–83.2	41.5–47.9	46.7–58.2
18:03	<0.3	trace	trace	0.3–0.4	<0.4
20:00	<0.5	1.1–1.7	0.2–0.4	0.3–0.6	0.2–0.5
20:01	<0.5	0.7–1.7	0.1–0.3	<0.3	trace
>20	<1.5	3–6	<2.0	<0.5	<0.1

Note: * = also 22:0, 2.1–4.4%, and 24:0, 1.1–2.2%; ** = also 14:0 0, 6–1.0%.

B. Oils Containing Linolenic Acid and Cereal Oils

Fatty Acid Code	Soybean Oil	Rapeseed (Canola) Oil	Linseed Oil	Corn Oil	Rice Bran Oil
16:00	9.7–13.3	3.3–6.0	7	10.7–16.5	16–28
16:01	<0.2	0.1–0.6	trace	<0.3	0.5
18:00	3.0–5.4	1.1–2.5	4	1.6–3.3	2–4
18:01	17.7–25.1	52.0–66.9	20	24.6–42.2	42–48
18:02	49.8–57.1	16.1–24.8	17	39.4–60.4	16–36
18:03	5.5–9.5	6.4–14.1	52	0.7–1.3	0.2–1.0
20:00	0.1–0.6	0.2–0.8	trace	0.3–0.6	0.5–0.8
20:01	<0.3	0.1–3.4	trace	0.2–0.4	0.3–0.5
>20	<1.2	<1.3*	trace	<0.9	<1.0

Note: * = mostly erucic acid.

C. Oils from Palms, Examples of Vegetable Butters and Oleic Acid Oils

Fatty Acid Code	Palm Oil	Palmkernel Oil	Coconut Oil	Cocoa Butter	Olive Oil*
8:00	0	2.1–4.7	4.6–9.4	0	0
10:00	0	2.6–4.5	5.5–7.8	0	0
12:00	trace	43.6–53.2	45.1–50.3	0	0
14:00	0.7–1.3	15.3–17.2	16.8–20.6	0.1	trace
16:00	40.1–46.3	7.1–10.0	7.7–10.2	25–27	7.5–20
18:00	4.0–6.5	1.3–3.0	2.3–3.5	33–37	0.5–5.0
18:01	36.7–40.9	11.9–19.3	5.4–8.1	34–35	55–83
18:02	9.4–12.1	1.4–3.3	1.0–2.1	3–4	3.5–21
20:00	0.1–0.7	<0.7	<0.2	0.2–1.0	<0.8
>20	<0.4	<0.8	<0.2	trace	<0.3

Note: * = also 16:1 0.3–3.5% and 18:3 <1.5%.

D. Fats of Farm Animals

Fatty Acid Code	Cow Milk Fat*	Chicken Fat	Pork Lard	Beef Tallow	Mutton Tallow
12:00	2.2–4.5	0.1	0	0	0
14:00	5.4–14.6	0.9	trace	1–6	2–4
14:01	0.6–1.6	trace	0.5–2.5	<1	trace, low
16:00	25–41	22	20–32	20–37	20–27
16:01	2–6	6	1.7–5.0	1–9	1.4–4.5
18:00	6–12	6	35–62	25–40	22–34
18:01	18.7–33.4**	37	35–62	31–50***	30–42***

(Continued)

TABLE 34.5   *(Continued)*

	D. Fats of Farm Animals				
Fatty Acid Code	Cow Milk Fat*	Chicken Fat	Pork Lard	Beef Tallow	Mutton Tallow
18:02	0.9–3.7	20	3–16	1–5	1.9–2.4
20:00	1.2–2.4	trace	<1.0	trace	trace
>20	0.8–3.0	trace	<3.0	trace	trace

Notes: * = also 4:0, 2.8–4.0%; 6:0, 1.4–3.0%; 8:0, 0.5–1.7%; 10:0, 1.7–3.2%; ** = Including 2–3% trans fatty acids; *** = Including minor trans fatty acids.

	E. Fish Oils			
Fatty Acid Code	Cod Liver Oil	Herring Oil	Carp Oil	Menhaden Oil*
14:00	3–5	3–10	3	6–12
16:00	10–14	13–25	17	14–23
16:01	6–12	5–8	17	7–15
18:00	1–4	1–4	4	2–4
18:01	19–27	9–22	28	6–16
18:02	1–2	1–2	13	1–2
18:04	–	1–5	–	1–5
20:01	7–15	9–15	4	0.5–2
20:2–4	0.8–3.0	0.8–1.2	3	1–4
20:05	8–14	–	3	12–18
22:01	4–13	12–27	–	0.2–0.4
22:06	6–17	4–10	–	2–4

Note: * = also 16:2–16:4, 1.8–6.2%; 24:0, 4–15%.

Expressed as weight % total fatty acids; trace fatty acids are omitted; fatty acid codes: number of carbon atoms: number of double bonds.

distilling off the solvent. The last solvent residues are removed by distillation with steam. The resulting crude oil is stored in a separate tank or mixed with oil obtained by expeller pressing.

During the industrial extraction of fats and oils, other lipophilic substances, such as sterols or tocopherols, come into the extract, even when they may be originally not present in oil droplets of seed cells but in other parts of the seed (27).

The extracted meal from the solvent extraction is treated in a toaster at temperatures of about 100°C or higher to liberate the residual solvent, to deactivate enzymes, and to detoxicate extracted meal. The last solvent traces are removed by steaming. Meal is then cooled down and stored in elevators. The extracted meal is used for feeding purposes.

B. Crude Oil Refining

Crude vegetable oil contains various minor components, such as oxidation products of triacylglycerols and terpenes, polar lipids, trace metal derivatives, which deteriorate its sensory and functional properties. Therefore, it is processed by refining. Good detailed information on vegetable oil processing techniques for human nutrition is available (28–30). The first refining step is the degumming. Oil is treated with hot water, usually containing phosphoric or citric acid. Most phospholipids present in crude oil are hydrated and become insoluble in oil. Some

phospholipids are not precipitated unless special procedures are used, such as superdegumming. The precipitate, containing coprecipitated components other than phospholipids and some oil, is removed, dried, and used as commercial lecithin. The membrane filtration is another approach to degumming (31).

The degummed product may be treated in two ways. If the free fatty acid content is high, it is alkali refined by a solution of sodium hydroxide or, less often, by sodium carbonate.

Free fatty acids are converted into water soluble sodium salts, which are washed out of oil with hot water. Natural pigments and other impurities are partially removed, too. After the alkali refining, oil is dried by heating at reduced pressure, and treated with bleaching earth or a mixture of bleaching each and with active carbon. In the process of bleaching, natural pigments (mainly carotenoids, pheophytins and chlorophylls) and the last traces of sodium salts are removed. Dimers of polyunsaturated fatty acids or sterols and trans-isomers may be formed in the course of bleaching (32). More information on bleaching is available (33).

Bleached oil is deodorized by treatment with overheated steam under reduced pressure in nitrogen at temperatures of 220–250°C. Volatile substances, formed by oxidation of unsaturated fatty acids during seed storage or seed processing, are removed during the process, and both the sensory value and the resistance against oxidative sensory deterioration (called rancidity) are thus substantially improved. Other relatively volatile substances are also removed at least partially, such as sterols or tocopherols. The deodorized oil has a bland neutral flavor.

Crude oils containing less than about 1% free fatty acids may be refined in a simpler way, i.e., by physical refining (34). After degumming, crude oil is deodorized in a similar way as in the case of alkali refined oils to remove all relatively volatile components, including free fatty acids. The resulting oil is bleached. The alkali refining step is thus eliminated, which is advantageous from the environmental standpoint. The resulting refined oil is of about the same quality as alkali-refined oil, e.g., as in the case of rapeseed oil (35).

During the process of deodorization *cis,cis*-diunsaturated fatty acid bound in triacylglycerols is partially isomerized into *cis,trans* and *trans,cis*-dienoic isomers in the case of linoleic acid (36). Several other trienoic isomers are formed in oils containing linolenic acid, such as soybean or rapeseed oil. As the nutritional value of these isomers is doubtful, the deodorization temperature should be lower than 240°C to minimize the isomerization. The best results are obtained using thin-film deodorization. In this process the temperature may be lower and the heating time shorter (37).

Vapors removed during deodorization are collected as deodorization sludges. They contain free fatty acids, sterols, and tocopherols so that they can be used for the production of tocopherol concentrates suitable as antioxidants. Sterols may be isolated, too, and used either directly or after hydrogenation in stanols in margarines as an additive lowering blood pressure and decreasing the cholesterol content in blood plasma (38).

Refined oils are either used directly as salad oils or frying oils, or after emulsification as mayonnaise and salad dressings, or are added to margarines (39). If fresh fish oils are properly refined (40), they are acceptable for margarines even without hydrogenation (41), even when their oxidation stability may still be a problem (40).

C. PRODUCTION OF LECITHIN

Crude lecithin is obtained in the process of crude oil degumming (39) as explained in Section 34.V.B. It is mostly used for feed or other nonedible purposes; only soybean or egg lecithin are used for edible purposes. Typical properties of soybean lecithin are shown in Table 34.6. They are used as

TABLE 34.6
Properties of Food Lecithin (8)

Component	Content [%]
Acetone insolubles	≥ 65
Toluene insolubles	max. 0.3
Moisture	max. 0.3
Free fatty acids*	max. 15

Note: Free fatty acids may be added to change the consistency.

natural surface active agents for many purposes in the food industry (42). Lecithin may be modified in different ways (43). For use in light-colored food products, it is bleached by hydrogen peroxide. For some purposes concentrated phospholipids are necessary; therefore, oil is removed from commercial lecithin by membrane filtration or selective extraction, e.g., with acetone or propane, which is a more acceptable solvent for environmental reasons (44). The most important component of soy phospholipids is phosphatidylcholine. Soy phospholipid concentrate may be enriched to high levels of phosphatidylcholine by interesterification with choline in the presence of phospholipases (45). Fractions enriched with phosphatidylcholine and in phosphatidylinositol may be obtained from lecithin by fractionation with 90% aqueous ethanol (46).

D. INTERESTERIFICTION, ESTER INTERCHANGE, AND SAPONIFICATION

Fats and oils are essentially mixtures of triacylglycerols. They may be converted into other esters by interesterification (47) with methanol or higher alcohols (Figure 34.6.A). The process is called alcoholysis, and is catalyzed by small amounts of alkaline hydroxides or alcoholates, produced *in situ* by dissolution of metallic sodium in alcohol. The conversion of triacylglycerols into methyl esters is used for analytical purposes and for diesel fuels.

The alcoholysis of triacylglycerols with glycerol — glycerolysis — is of technical importance. Solid fats, such as fully hydrogenated oils, are commonly used. They are heated with glycerol to high temperatures in the presence of small amounts of sodium hydroxide. A mixture of monoacylglycerols and diacylglycerols results (Figure 34.6.B), which are used as emulsifiers. They may be fractionated into the monoacylglycerol fraction and the diacylglycerol fraction using short space vacuum distillation. The monoacylglycerol fraction is particularly useful as an emulsifier for the production of margarines and other emulsified fats and oils.

Another procedure for production of partial glycerol esters is the treatment of triacylglycerols with water in the presence of lipases, most often immobilized on a solid support (45).

Tricylglycerols of natural fats and oils possess specific distribution of fatty acids. The distribution may be randomized by interesterification of the particular fat and oil or a mixture (ester interchange, Figure 34.6.C) or of a mixture of different tricylglycerols (Figure 34.6.D). The reaction is carried out again in the presence of sodium hydroxide, metallic sodium, or sodium methoxide as a catalyst. Immobilized lipases may be used as catalysts, too. The reaction proceeds at ambient or moderately increased temperatures. The resulting products may be tailored to specific properties, especially rherological properties (sensory texture or consistency). Low-caloric structured lipids are produced in this way, containing

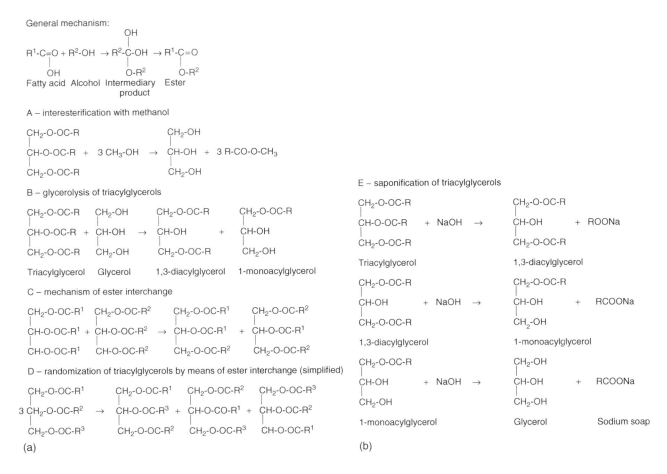

FIGURE 34.6 Esterification reaction of fats and oils.

long-chain, medium-chain, and short-chain fatty acids (48). In contrast, the stability against oxidative rancidity is often decreases (49).

Natural fats and oils may be fully hydrogenated and the resulting trisaturated triacylglycerols are then interesterified with non-hydrogenated oils (50). Plastic solid fats are thus produced, containing no *trans*-unsaturated fatty acids. The topic of structurally modified food fats has been reviewed (51).

As some consumers would like to decrease their energy consumption of fats without affecting the sensory properties of food and decreasing the agreeable fatty taste, some undigestible fat replacers have been introduced to the market, such as Olean, Salatrim, and Caprenin. In these products, esterified fatty acids cannot be split off by lipases (52).

Fats and oils are very rich sources of energy; therefore, their consumption may result in obesity. Fats with lower energy content are produced by interesterification of natural oils with stearic or behenic acid, which are not completely utilized in the metabolism, and medium-chain fatty acids, which have moderately lower energy content and are not deposited in the fatty tissues. These products are marketed as structured fats.

E. HYDROLYSIS OF FATS AND OILS

Triacylglycerols are hydrolyzed into fatty acids and glycerol. The reaction with sodium hydroxide was used to produce soap; therefore, the process is still called saponification (Figure 34.6.E). Saponification proceeds by mixing fat with a solution of sodium hydroxide at the boiling temperature. The first stage, i.e., the cleavage of a triacylglycerol molecule into a diglycerol and soap, is slow as the reactants are immiscible and the reaction proceeds only on the interphase. The reaction products act as emulsifiers so that the second stage of saponification is fast. After saponification, sodium chloride is added to the reaction mixture in order to decrease the solubility of soaps in the aqueous phase. The lower aqueous layer also contains glycerol, which is isolated, and distilled from impurities, especially water. The separation of soaps from the water phase containing glycerol by salting is still not complete.

Saponification is now carried out on the plant scale mostly by simply heating fats or oils with water under pressure to high temperature, sometimes in the presence of metallic oxides as catalysts. Fatty acids are gradually cleaved from the original glycerol esters. Free fatty are then purified by vacuum distillation. They are then used for soap production, production of metallic soaps, or for other purposes. Glycerol obtained in this way is less contaminated than in the case of saponification with sodium hydroxide.

Lipids may be hydrolyzed with immobilized lipases, too (45). Depending on the origin of lipase, the reaction may be stereospecific.

F. Hydrogenation of Fats and Oils

At the beginning of the 20th century, there was an excess of oils on the market, but consumers required solid fats, similar to lard or butter. Hydrogenation was a suitable solution. The unsaturated fatty acids bound in triacylglycerols are converted into less unsaturated or even saturated fatty acids by the addition of hydrogen. Triacylglycerols of saturated fatty acids are solid, unlike triacylglycerols of unsaturated fatty acids. However, triacylglycerols containing three saturated fatty acids in the molecule have too high melting points (about 70°C). They remain solid at body temperature; therefore, they are not attacked by lipases, and their digestibility is only very low. They have a strong tallowy taste, and are thus unsuitable for human nutrition. Therefore, only one or two fatty acids in a triacylglycerol molecule should be converted into a saturated fatty acid. Solid fats with melting points corresponding to lard are thus obtained.

Prerefined edible vegetable oils or fish oils are used as raw material. They are heated to 160–180°C in the atmosphere of hydrogen using nickel as a catalyst. Nickel is deposited on the surface of kieselguhr or another suitable inert substrate; mixtures of nickel with nickel oxide are preferred. Other metals, such as palladium, rhodium, cobalt, or mixtures of nickel with copper also have catalytic qualities, but nickel is usually used. The pressure may be between 0.15–0.5 MPa. Free fatty acids, phospholipids, soap or other surface active compounds, and sulphur derivatives act as catalytic poisons, so they should be removed from oil before the reaction, usually by refining processes. More information is available on both the theory and practice of hydrogenation (53). Partially hydrogenated oils are chiefly solid; therefore, they can be used for the production of shortenings (cooking fats). Fluid shortenings are available on the market, mainly for use in the baking industry (54).

During the hydrogenation reaction polyunsaturated fatty acids are first converted into monounsaturated fatty acids (Figure 34.7.A). The formation of saturated fatty acids (Figure 34.7.B) is slower. The ratio of reaction rates $k_1:k_2$ is the selectivity of hydrogenation (55), which depends on the catalyst and the reaction conditions. The reaction rate constant k_1 defines the rate of hydrogenation of dienoic acids into monoenoic acids, while the constant k_2 defines the rate of hydrogenation of monoenoic fatty acids into saturated acids. Low hydrogen pressure, low temperature, and low catalyst content determine the selectivity. Because hydrogenation is an exothermic reaction, heat is produced and the reactor has to be cooled. The reaction is usually stopped at the stage when the melting point reaches the required value, usually between 30–45°C, depending on the purpose of the product.

An important side reaction takes place during hydrogenation, i.e., the isomerization of the original cis double bond into a trans double bond. The trans monounsaturated fatty acids have higher melting points than the corresponding cis fatty acids so that the desired melting point is already attained at a higher degree of unsaturation. The low hydrogen pressure, lower content of the catalyst, and higher temperature favor the formation of trans fatty acids. The trans fatty acids are now considered undesirable for human nutrition (36, 56). Therefore, hydrogenation conditions have to be adapted to obtain products with low content of trans fatty acids or hydrogenated oils are replaced with other solid fats. The cis,trans isomerization is accompanied by positional isomerization of double bonds.

Hydrogenated oils are cooled after the reaction, filtered to remove the catalyst, and refined to remove impurities. They may be used as shortenings or cooking fats, or added to emulsified fats, such as margarines. There is now a tendency to replace hydrogenated oils with palm oil fractions or other solid fats free of trans fatty acids.

Free fatty acids may be fully hydrogenated too, e.g., for the production of metallic and alkaline soaps or solid free fatty acids, but higher hydrogen pressure and higher content of catalyst are needed.

At very high hydrogen pressures of 20–50 MPa, higher temperature, and using special catalysts containing copper and chromium, not only double bonds, but also the carbonyl double bond in the carboxyl or ester group are hydrogenated, and fatty alcohols result which are useful for the production of surfactants.

G. Oxidation Reactions

Unsaturated fatty acids bound in lipids are oxidized on storage using several mechanisms (58). Different types of oxidation processes occur in unsaturated fats and oils (59). The spontaneous oxidation by air triplet oxygen is called autoxidation, and it is usually initiated by free radicals or by singlet oxygen. Singlet oxygen is produced in course of photooxidation of unsaturated lipids in the presence of photosensitizers. Several enzymes present in oilseeds or animal tissues, such as lipoxygenases, catalyze oxidation reactions.

The most important oxidation mechanisms are shown in Table 34.7. Enzyme-catalyzed oxidation occurs even in seeds or fruits and other edible parts of raw materials of both plant and animal origin. Lipoxygenases are the most important representatives of this group of enzymes (60). For this reason, even fresh edible oils contain at least minute traces of oxidation products. The oxidation occurring spontaneously in the presence of oxygen is autoxidation. In both cases unsaturated hydroperoxides are the primary reaction products.

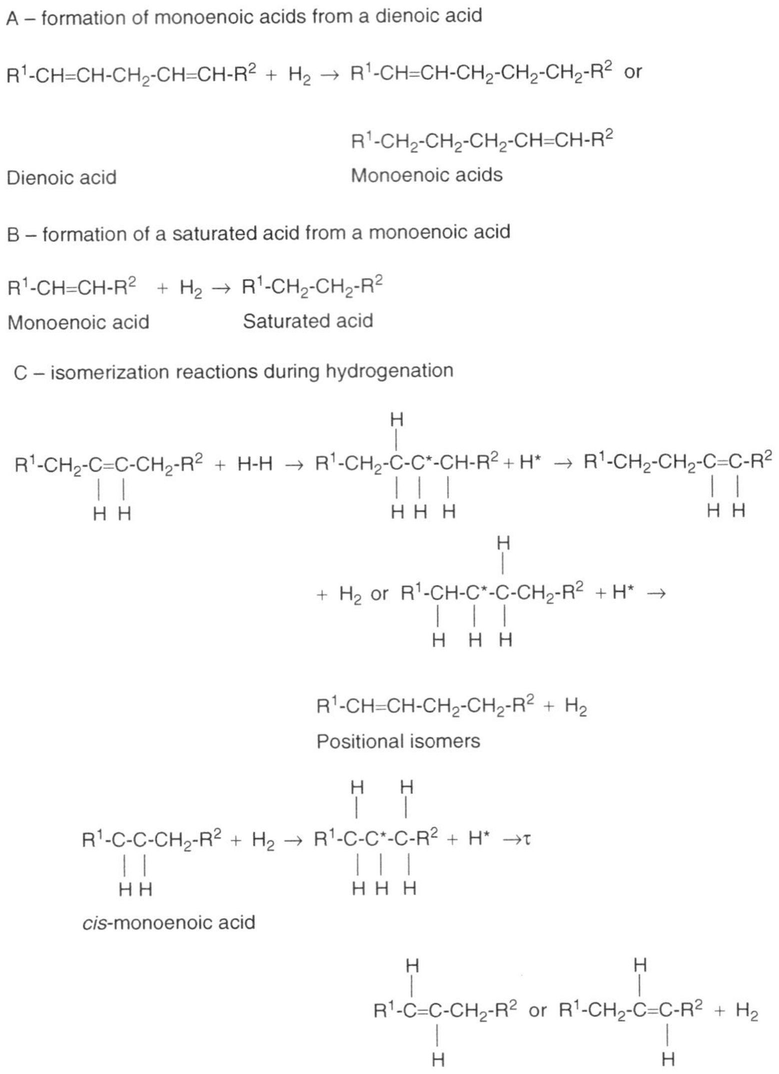

A – formation of monoenoic acids from a dienoic acid

R^1-CH=CH-CH$_2$-CH=CH-R^2 + H$_2$ → R^1-CH=CH-CH$_2$-CH$_2$-CH$_2$-R^2 or

R^1-CH$_2$-CH$_2$-CH$_2$-CH=CH-R^2

Dienoic acid   Monoenoic acids

B – formation of a saturated acid from a monoenoic acid

R^1-CH=CH-R^2 + H$_2$ → R^1-CH$_2$-CH$_2$-R^2

Monoenoic acid   Saturated acid

C – isomerization reactions during hydrogenation

R^1-CH$_2$-C=C-CH$_2$-R^2 + H-H → R^1-CH$_2$-C-C*-CH-R^2 + H* → R^1-CH$_2$-CH$_2$-C=C-R^2

+ H$_2$ or R^1-CH-C*-C-CH$_2$-R^2 + H* →

R^1-CH=CH-CH$_2$-CH$_2$-R^2 + H$_2$

Positional isomers

R^1-C-C-CH$_2$-R^2 + H$_2$ → R^1-C-C*-C-R^2 + H* →τ

cis-monoenoic acid

R^1-C=C-CH$_2$-R^2 or R^1-CH$_2$-C=C-R^2 + H$_2$

FIGURE 34.7   Hydrogenation of fats and oils.

TABLE 34.7
Mechanism of Lipid Oxidation

Type of Oxidation	Precursors	Primary Products
Lipoxygenase catalyzed	Linoleic, linolenic acids	Conjugated hydroperoxides
Autoxidation	Unsaturated fatty acids	Hydroperoxides
Photooxidation	Unsaturated fatty acids	Hydroperoxides
In vivo oxidation	Essential fatty acids	Eicosanoids
Hydrogen peroxide oxidation	Unsaturated fatty acids	Hydroxy acids

The oxidation is a free radical chain raction, proceeding after the following mechanism (Figure 34.8). The methylene groups adjacent to a double bond or located between two double bonds are the primary site of attack (Figure 34.8.A). Free radicals produced in this way add a molecule of oxygen with formation of free peroxy radicals (Figure 34.8.B).

These radicals can abstract hydrogen from another molecule of an unsaturated fatty acid with formation of a hydroperoxide and another free radical (Figure 34.8.C). Such a reaction chain can be repeated up to several hundred times before the reaction is stopped by a termination reaction (Figure 34.8.D). The reaction is efficiently terminated by interaction of free R-O* or R-OO* radicals with

A – formation of lipid free radicals (initiation reaction)

R-H → R* H*

Lipid   Lipid free radical

B – formation of a peroxy radical

R* + O$_2$ → R-OO*

C – formation of a hydroperoxide (propagation step)

R-OO* + R-H → R-OOH + R*

D – termination reactions

R-O* or R-OO* or R* → Non-radical stable compounds

E – rearrangement of a pentadienoic system during the propagation step

R^1-CH=CH-CH$_2$-CH=CH-R$_2$ → R^1-CH=CH-C*H-CH=CH-R^2 Free radical

R^1-C*H-CH=CH-CH=CH-R^2 or R^1-CH=CH-CH=CH-C*H-R^2

Conjugated dienoic free radicals

↓ + O$_2$

R^1-CH-CH=CH-CH=CH-R^2 or R^1-CH=CH-CH=CH-CH-R^2
      | |
     OO*   OO*

Free peroxy radicals

↓ + R-H

R^1-CH-CH=CH-CH=CH-R^2 or R^1-CH=CH-CH=CH-CH-R^2
      | |
    OOH   OOH

Isomeric conjugated lipid hydroperoxides

FIGURE 34.8 Mechanism of lipid autoxidation.

antioxidants (61), which are discussed in detail elsewhere in this book. Rearrangement of the double bond and the pentadienoic double bond systems (Figure 34.8.E) accompanies the formation of free radicals. Products with a conjugated double bond system are produced, which contain *trans* double bonds, at least partially. The reaction mixture consists of two to four isomers, the proportions of which depend on reaction conditions. In the case of enzyme-catalyzed reactions, selective oxidation takes place so that certain isomers prevail.

The autoxidation rate increases with increasing temperature. At room temperature linoleic and linolenic acids are oxidized at a much faster rate than monoenoic fatty acids, but at high temperatures, monoenoic fatty acids and even saturated fatty acids can be oxidized, especially in the presence of metallic catalysts. The relative reaction rates depend

on the reactive system, e.g., the stability of fatty acids in bulk oils decreases with increasing degree of unsaturation. In contrast, the oxidation stability increases with the increasing degree of unsaturation in water micelles (62).

The lipid hydroperoxides can be oxidized into diperoxides of different structures, usually peroxohydroperoxides. Hydroperoxides are very unstable, particularly at higher temperatures, being dissociated after two mechanisms (Figure 34.9.A,B). The cleavage into alkoxy free radicals is more probable. The degradation is accelerated in the presence of heavy metal compounds with transient valency, such as copper or iron ions (Figure 34.9.C,D). During the reaction the metal ion is reduced into its lower valency state and oxidized again into its higher valency state (61). As the decomposition is again a chain reaction, one metal ion can catalyze the decomposition of many hydroperoxide

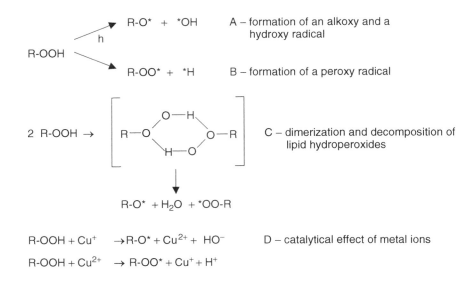

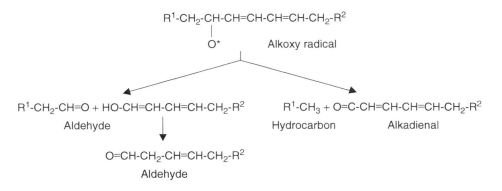

FIGURE 34.9 Decomposition of lipid hydroperoxides into nonvolatile compounds.

molecules. Each reaction produces two free radicals, initiating further oxidation chain reaction. Therefore, heavy metals are very efficient oxidation catalysts.

Free radicals are eliminated by reaction of two free radicals, e.g., with formation of a dimer (Figure 34.9.E), or by reaction with antioxidants, as explained in another Chapter. The dimeric compounds are transformed in free antioxidant radicals of very low reactivity. However, large excess of free radicals becomes harmful in biological systems (63).

Polymers produced during the autoxidation are mainly dimers, where the fatty acid chains are bound by C-C, C-O-C, or C-O-O-C bonds, their ratios depending on the access of oxygen during oxidation. Multiple bonds may be formed in case of polyenoic fatty acids so that lipids oxidized to an advanced degree always contain cyclic compounds. In addition to cyclic oligomers, cyclic monomers are also produced by oxidation (64). The amount of polymers may be high, up to 10%, in frying oils used for a repeated deep frying.

Another reaction of unsaturated lipid hydroperoxides is their decomposition by rearrangement and chain cleavage with formation of both volatile and non-volatile compounds, such as shown in Figure 34.10.A. Aldehydes, alcohols, hydrocarbons, and ketones are produced in this way. They are very sensory active, especially the unsaturated derivatives, and impart to fats and oils a characteristic off-flavor called a rancid flavor. Hexanal, 2-hexenal, 2-octenal, or 2,4-decadienal (Figure 34.10.C) are typical rancidity products.

Another type of oxidation proceeds on light in the presence of photosensitizers, such as chlorophylls or pheophytins. They convert the ordinary triplet oxygen present in air into singlet oxygen, which is several hundred times more reactive than triplet oxygen. It is added to double bonds with the formation of hydroperoxides. Edible oils and foods nearly always contain minute traces of chlorophyll pigments; therefore, the exposure of oils to light should be avoided. The concentration of chlorophylls is particularly high in virgin olive oil which is rather sensitive to singlet oxygen oxidation.

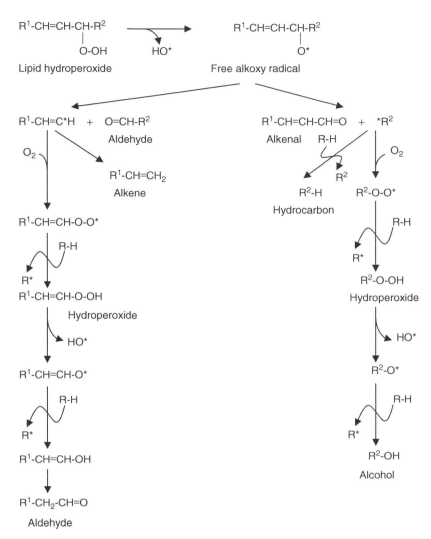

FIGURE 34.10 Cleavage of monoenoic lipid hydroperoxides into volatile compounds.

Oxidation reactions proceed rapidly at high temperatures, such as during deep fat frying (65, 66) or microwave heating (67).

Oxidation is desirable for some industrial purposes. Dry films are formed from thin layers of oil applied on a metallic or wooden surface. Such oils are called drying oils, e.g., linseed or tung oil belong to this group. In the formation of coatings containing linseed oil, and in artistic painting, metal salts are often added to hasten the drying reaction.

H. CHEMICAL CHANGES IN THE PRODUCTION OF OLEOCHEMICALS FROM FATS AND OILS

Lipids are important sources of oleochemicals. Alkaline soaps have been already mentioned. Salts of other metallic cations, such as calcium salts, are also produced for various purposes, and are called metallic soaps. They are usually produced from solutions of alkaline or ammonium salts of fatty acids by precipitation with metallic anions. Metallic soaps are used for many purposes. Aluminium or zinc stearates are used as lubricants, as paint thickeners, or in the cosmetic and pharmaceutical industries. Salts of heavy metals (such as manganese or cobalt) are used in paint dryers and as additives in plastic materials.

Fatty acids are used as raw materials in other products, mainly surfactants, such as copolymerates with ethylene oxide (Figure 34.11.A) or propylene oxide.

Very important intermediary products are fatty alcohols, produced by high pressure hydrogenation of fats or fatty acids (explained in Section 34.V.E). They may also form copolymers with ethylene or propylene oxides (Figure 34.11.B) or they are sulphated with sulphuric trioxide into sulphates. Alkaline salts of alkyl sulphates are used as detergents.

Fatty acids of fats can be converted into amides by reaction with amoniac (Figure 34.11.C). Amides are dehydrated into nitriles (Figure 34.11.D), which are hydrogenated into alkyl amines (Figure 34.11.E). Salts of

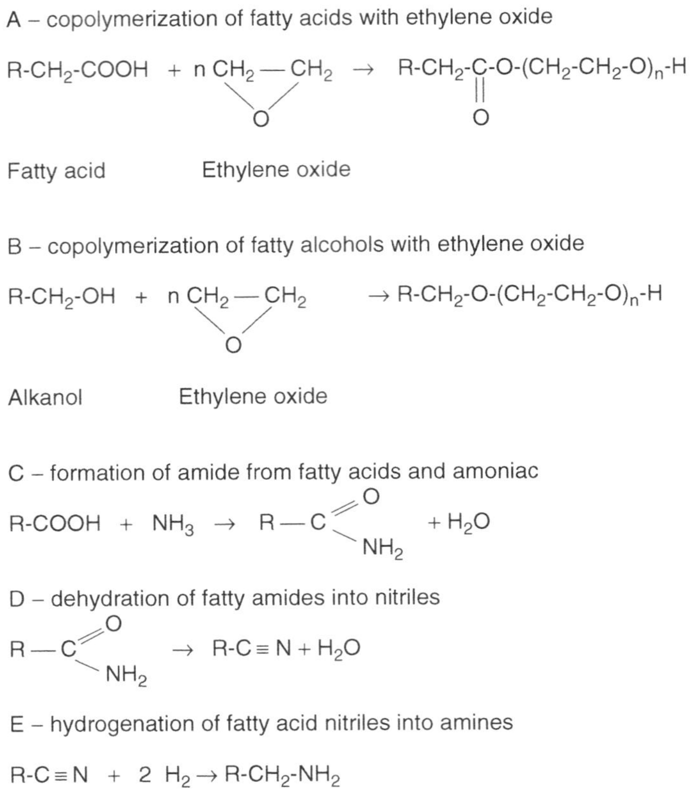

A – copolymerization of fatty acids with ethylene oxide

$$R\text{-}CH_2\text{-}COOH \; + \; n\, CH_2 \!-\! CH_2 \; \rightarrow \; R\text{-}CH_2\text{-}\underset{\underset{O}{\|}}{C}\text{-}O\text{-}(CH_2\text{-}CH_2\text{-}O)_n\text{-}H$$
$$\underset{O}{\diagdown\diagup}$$

Fatty acid   Ethylene oxide

B – copolymerization of fatty alcohols with ethylene oxide

$$R\text{-}CH_2\text{-}OH \; + \; n\, CH_2 \!-\! CH_2 \qquad \rightarrow R\text{-}CH_2\text{-}O\text{-}(CH_2\text{-}CH_2\text{-}O)_n\text{-}H$$
$$\underset{O}{\diagdown\diagup}$$

Alkanol   Ethylene oxide

C – formation of amide from fatty acids and amoniac

$$R\text{-}COOH \; + \; NH_3 \; \rightarrow \; R-C\!\!\overset{\displaystyle \diagup O}{\diagdown NH_2} \; + H_2O$$

D – dehydration of fatty amides into nitriles

$$R-C\!\!\overset{\displaystyle \diagup O}{\diagdown NH_2} \; \rightarrow \; R\text{-}C \equiv N + H_2O$$

E – hydrogenation of fatty acid nitriles into amines

$$R\text{-}C \equiv N \; + \; 2\,H_2 \rightarrow R\text{-}CH_2\text{-}NH_2$$

FIGURE 34.11 Formation of surfactants from fats, oils and fatty acids.

alkyl amines (usually alkylated) are technically important surface active agents — inversion salts. Quarternary ammonium salts are particularly useful.

Many other oleochemicals can be manufactured from fats and oils, but they are a topic for special monographs.

VI. PHYSICAL CHANGES OF FATS AND OILS

A. EMULSIFICATION

Fats and oils are insoluble in water, but may form emulsions. Two types of emulsions occur in foods: oil-in-water emulsions (O/W), where water is the continuous phase and oil is the dispersed phase, and water-in-oil emulsions (W/O), where water is the dispersed phase and oil is the continuous phase. Mayonnaise and cream belong to the O/W type, while butter and margarine belong to the W/O type. Mixed emulsions also exist (31), e.g., in margarines or cosmetic emulsions, where drops of the dispersed aqueous phase may contain dispersed tiny oily droplets.

Emulsions are unstable unless they are protected by emulsifiers. Emulsifiers are semipolar compounds, consisting of a polar group and a non-polar hydrocarbon chain. On the water and oil interface they are oriented towards the water phase with their polar groups and towards the oil phase with their hydrocarbon chains

(Figure 34.12). The phases are thus protected against coalescence. Even stabilized emulsions are not equilibriated systems, and still have a tendency to partial coalescence, especially if the size of droplets of the dispersed phase is large (68).

The choice of suitable emulsifers is limited; they should be natural food components and harmless to human health. Phospholipids are natural emulsifiers as they act as emulsifiers in blood plasma and other tissues in the organism, and in cream or butter. However, the amount of phospholipids — mostly soybean lecithin — available on the market is not sufficient for the industrial production of food emulsions. Another choice are monoacylglycerols. They are natural metabolites of fats and oils easily produced by glycerolysis of fats and oils in the industry, and the reaction mixture may be used either directly or after fractionation into monoacylglycerols and diacylglycerols. Most margarines and bread spreads contain monoacylglycerols as emulsifiers. The amount of the emulsifier depends on the composition of the water and oil phases, on their ratio, and on the size of dispersed particles. The chemical structures of emulsifiers are similar, consisting of a polar functional group and a long nonpolar chain. The ratio of the polar and the nonpolar moieties indicates the emulsifying capacity, and is defined as the hydrophilic-lipophilic balance (HLB). A higher HLB

A – Oil–in–water (o/w) emulsions

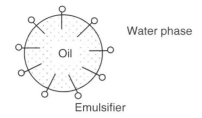

Water phase

Oil

Emulsifier

B – Water–in–oil (w/o) emulsions

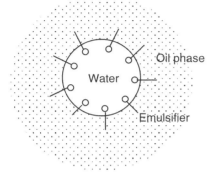

Oil phase

Water

Emulsifier

FIGURE 34.12 Role of emulsifiers in the stabilization of an emulsion.

value of an emulsifier enhances the formation of O/W emulsions. In low-fat emulsified products the emulsion stability may be enhanced by additions of ingredients increasing the viscosity of the aqueous phase, such as modified starches or carbohydrate gums. Other emulsifiers are manufactured for nonedible uses. More information may be obtained from specialized literature (69–71).

B. FRACTIONATION OF FATS AND OILS

Physical properties, mostly the texture (formerly consistency), and the nutrition value, are changed by fractionation into a higher melting and a low melting (or even liquid) fraction. Either dry process or fractionation in the presence of emulsifiers may be used. The proper procedure of crystallization and the crystalline modifications obtained are of great importance (72). The process is used for the preparation of stearin and olein, fractionation of milk fat (73) or palm oil, e.g., for cocoa butter replacements (74). Palm stearin and palm olein are important ingredients for the production of margarines (75).

VII. CONCLUSIONS AND FUTURE TRENDS

New raw materials for edible and speciality fats and oils are constantly being sought, and other new oils are developed by conventional breeding or genetic manipulation from traditional oilseeds. They have fatty acid composition and

properties tailored for specific uses. Another trend is to modify the fatty acid and triacylglycerol composition of conventional fats and oils or phospholipids by treatment with lipases or phospholipases or by ester interchange. Minor components may be removed from natural fats and oils by modern technologies, such as membrane filtration. New culinary equipment such as microwave heating affects fats and oils in ways not completely understood, and should be studied. The stability of fats and oils against oxidation is still a problem, and new methods of stabilization, especially new natural antioxidants, are being studied. Fats and oils may be stabilized against oxidation, too, by preventing the air access.

VIII. SUGGESTIONS FOR FURTHER STUDY OF FATS AND OILS

More systematic information on fats and oils may be obtained in general compendia on fats and oils (76–79), or in specialized monographs, such as on soybean processing (39), applications to functional foods (80), and lipid chemistry (81). Tables provide useful information about lipid analysis (82, 83). Data on fatty acid composition of natural lipids have been reviewed recently (21, 82, 84).

REFERENCES

1. IUPAC-IUB Information Bulletin No. 67. Nomenclature of Lipids. Oxford, U.K.: IUPAC, 1977.
2. L Brühl. Determination of trans fatty acids in cold pressed oil. Eur J Med Res 1: 89–93, 1995/6.
3. AA Spector. Essentiality of fatty acids. Lipids 34S: 51–53, 1999.
4. DS Nichols, K Sanderson. The nomenclature, structure, and properties of food lipids. In: ZE Sikorski, A Kolakowska, eds. Chemical and Functional Properties of Food Lipids. Boca Raton, FL: CRC Press, 2002, pp 29–60.
5. RD Riemersma, R Armstrong, RW Kelly, R Wilson. Essentiality of Fatty Acids and Eicosanoids. Champaign, IL: AOCS Press, 1999.
6. DS Kelley, PC Taylor, GJ Nelson, PC Schmidt, A Ferretti, KL Erickson, R Yu, RK Chandra, BE Mackey. Docosahexaenoic acid ingestion inhibits natural killer cell activity and production of inflammatory mediators in young healthy men. Lipids 34: 317–324, 1999.
7. LS Harbige. Fatty acids, the immune response, anti autoimmunity: A question of n-6 essentiality and the balance between n-6 and n-3. Lipids 38: 323–341, 2003.
8. RJ Hamildon. Waxes: Chemistry, Molecular Biology and Functions. Dundee, U.K.: The Oily Press, 1996.
9. S Roller, S Jones. Handbook of Fat Replacers. Paris: Lavoisier, 1996.
10. D Firestone. Physical and Chemical Characteristics of Oils, Fats, and Waxes. Champaign, IL: AOCS Press, 1999.
11. T Yanagita. Nutritional functions of dietary phosphatidylinositol. INFORM 14: 64–66, 2003.

12. JL Weihrauch, YS Soon. The phospholipid contents of foods. J Am Oil Chem Soc 60: 1971–1978, 1983.

13. BF Szuhaj, GR List. Lecithins. Champaign, IL: AOCS Press, 1985.

14. SH Zeisel, BF Szuhaj. Choline, Phospholipids, Health and Disease. Champaign, IL: AOCS Press, 1999.

15. G Cevc, F Paltauf. Phospholipids: Characterization, Metabolism, and Novel Biological Applications. Champaign, IL: AOCS Press, 1995.

16. M Hamberg, E Liepinsh, G Otting, W Griffiths. Isolation and structure of a new galactolipid from oat seeds. Lipids 33: 355–363, 1998.

17. BC Herslöf. From drug delivery to functional foods – a lipid story. INFORM 11: 1109–1115, 2000.

18. EG Perkins. Lipoproteins. Champaign, IL: AOCS Press, 1993.

19. DE Vance, JE Vance. Biochemistry of Lipids, Lipoproteins and Membranes. 4th ed. Amsterdam: Elsevier, 2002.

20. R Hoover. Starch-Lipid Inteactions. Polysaccharide Association Structures in Food. New York, NY: Marcel Dekker, 1998.

21. Fatty Acids: Supplement to McCance & Widdowson's The Composition of Foods. London: Ministry of Agriculture, Fisheries and Food, 1998.

22. ZE Sikorski, A Kolakowska. Chemical and Functional Properties of Food Lipids. Boca Raton, FL: CRC Press, 2003.

23. A Spurling. New refining techniques described at Cancan. INFORM 12: 183–192, 2001.

24. AJ Dijkstra. Edible oils in Europe. INFORM 11: 386–394, 2000.

25. M Servili, P Piacquadio, G DiStefano, A Taticchi, V Sciancalepore. Influence of new crushing technique on the composition of the volatile compounds and related sensory quality of virgin olive oil. Eur J Lipid Sci Technol 104: 483–489, 2002.

26. D Boskou. Olive Oil: Chemistry and Technology. Champaign, IL: AOCS Press, 1996.

27. H Yoshida, S Takagi, H Ienaga, C Isuchiya. Regional distribution of tocopherols and fatty acids within soybean seeds. JAOCS 75: 767–774, 1998.

28. R Przybylski, BE McDonald. Development and Processing of Vegetable Oils for Human Nutrition. Champaign, IL: AOCS Press, 1995.

29. RD O'Brien. Fats and Oils: Formulating and Processing for Applications. Lancaster, PA: Technomic Publishing, 1998.

30. W Farr, RD O'Brien, P Wan. Introduction to Fats and Oils Technology. 2nd ed. Champaign, IL: AOCS Press, 2000.

31. S Koseoglu. Advantages of membrane degumming – real or imagined? Eur J Lipid Sci Technol 104: 317–318, 2002.

32. W Zschau. Bleaching of edible fats and oils. IX. Legal and analytical aspects of bleaching. Eur J Lipid Sci Technol 103: 117–122, 2001.

33. HBW Patterson. Bleaching and Purifying Fats and Oils: Theory and Practice. Champaign, IL: AOCS Press, 1993.

34. J Čmolík, J Pokorný. Physical refining of edible oils. Eur J Lipid Sci Technol 102: 472–486, 2000.

35. J Čmolík, W. Schwarz, S Svoboda, J Pokorný, Z Réblová, M Doležal, H Valentová. Effects of plant scale

36. J Fritsche, H Steinhart. Analysis, occurrence, and physiological properties of trans fatty acids with particular emphasis on conjugated linoleic acid isomers. Fett 100: 190–210, 1998.

37. O Stenberg, P Sjöberg. Thin-film deodorizing of edible oils. INFORM 7: 1296–1304, 1996.

38. RA Moreau, RA Norton, KB Hicks. Phytosterols and phytostanols lower cholesterol. INFORM 10: 572–577, 1999.

39. DE Erickson. Practical Handbook of Soybean Processing and Utilization. Champaign, IL: AOCS Press, 1995.

40. UN Wanasundara, F Shahidi, R Amarowicz. Effect of processing on constituents and oxidative stability of marine oils. J Food Lipids 5: 29–41, 1998.

41. FVK Young, SM Barlow, J Madsen. Using unhydrogenated fish oil in margarine. INFORM 1: 731–741, 1990.

42. M Schneider. Phospholipids for functional food. Eur J Lipid Sci Technol 103: 98–101, 2001.

43. R Ziegelitz. Lecithin processing possibilities. INFORM 6: 1224–1230, 1995.

44. E Weidner, Z Zhang, B Czech, S Peter. Entölung von Rohlecithin mit Propan. Fat Sci Technol 95: 347–351, 1993.

45. WU Yingzi, T Wang. Soybean lecithin fractionation and functionality. JAOCS 80: 319–326, 2003.

47. J Davídek, J. Velíšek, J. Pokorný. Chemical Changes during Food Processing. Amsterdam: Elsevier, 1990, pp 169–229.

48. X Xu. Enzymatic production of structured lipids: Process reactions and acyl migration. INFORM 11: 1121–1131, 2000.

49. WE Neff, MA El-Agaimy, TL Mounts. Oxidative stability of blends and interesterified blends of soybean oil and palm olein. J Am Oil Chem Soc 71: 1116–1116, 1994.

50. GR List, T Pelloso, F Orthoffer, K Warner, WE Neff. Soft margarines from lipid stearic acid soybean oils. JAOCS 78: 103–104, 2001.

51. A Christophe. Structured Modified Food Fats: Synthesis, Biochemistry, and Use. Champaign, IL: AOCS Press, 1998.

52. C Watkins. AHA speaks out about fat replacers. INFORM 13: 624, 2002.

53. HBW Patterson. Hydrogenation of Fats and Oils: Theory and Practice. Champaign, IL: AOCS Press, 1994.

54. AG Herzing. Fluid shortenings in bakery products. INFORM 7: 165–167, 1996.

55. AJ Dijkstra. Hydrogenation revisited. INFORM 8: 1150–1158, 1997.

56. JL Sébédio, WW Christie. Trans fatty acids in human nutrition. Dundee, U.K.: The Oily Press, 1998.

57. WMN Ratnayake, G Pelletier. Positional and geometrical isomers of linoleic acid in partially hydrogenated oils. J Am Oil Chem Soc 69: 95–105. 1992.

58. EN Frankel. Lipid Oxidation. Dundee, U.K.: The Oily Press, 1998.

59. J Pospíšil, PP Klemchuk. Oxidative processes in organic materials. In: Oxidation Inhibition in Organic Materials, Vol. I. Boca Raton, FL: CRC Press, 1989, pp 1–11.

60. G Piazza. Lipoxygenase and Lipoxygenase Pathway Enzymes. Champaign, IL: AOCS Press, 1996.

61. J Pokorný. Major factors affecting the autoxidation of lipids. In: HWS Chan, ed. Autoxidation of Unsaturated Lipids. London: Academic Press, 1987, pp 141–206.

62. K Miyashita. Polyunsaturated lipids in aqueous systems do not follow our preconceptions of oxidative stability. Lipid Technol Newsletter 4: 35–41, 2002.

63. M Roberfroid, PBU Calderon. Free Radicals and Oxidation Phenomena in Biological Systems. Basel: Dekker, 1997.

64. JL Sébédio, J Prévost, A Grangirard. Heat treatment of vegetable oils. I. Isolation of the cyclic fatty acid monomers from heated sunflower and linseed oils. J Am Oil Chem Soc 64: 1026–1032, 1987.

65. MC Dobarganes, G Márquez-Ruiz, O Berdaux, J Velasco. Determination of oxidation compounds and oligomers by chromatographic techniques. In: D Boskou, I Elmadfa, eds. Frying of Food. Lancaster, PA: Technomic Publishing, 1999, pp 143–162.

66. CJK Henry, C Chapman. The Nutrition Handbook for Food Processors. Cambridge: Woodhead Publishing, 2002, pp 247–264.

67. CP Tan, YB CheMan, S Jinap, MSA Yusoff. Effects of microwave heating on changes in chemical and thermal properties of vegetable oils. JAOCS 78: 1227–1232, 2001.

68. DG Dalgleish. Food Emulsions. In: J. Sjöblom, ed. Encyclopedic Handbook of Emulsion Technology. New York, NY: Marcel Dekker, 2001, pp 287–325.

69. GL Hasenhuettl, R Hartel. Food Emulsifiers and Their Applications. New York, NY: Chapman & Hall, 1997.

70. SE Friberg, K Larsson. Food Emulsions. 3rd ed. New York, NY: Marcel Dekker, 1997.

71. DJ McClements. Lipid-based emulsions and emulsifiers. In: CC Akoh, DB Min, eds. Food Lipids. New York, NY: Marcel Dekker, 1998.

72. N Widlak, R Hartel, S Narine. Crystallization and Solidification Properties of Lipids. Champaign, IL: AOCS Press, 2001.

73. E Deffense. Milk fat fractionation today: A review. J Am Oil Chem Soc 70: 1193–1201, 1993.

74. EJ Wilson, JJ Pease. Confectonery fats from palm and lauric oils revisited. In: EC Leonard, EG Perkins, A Cahn, eds. Proceedings of the World Conference on Palm and Coconut Oils for the 21th Century. Champaign, IL: AOCS Press, 1998, pp 93–101.

75. EC Leonard, EG Perkins, A Cahn. Proceedings of the World Conference on Palm and Coconut Oils for the 21st Century. Champaign, IL: AOCS Press, 1998, pp 67–93.

76. YH Hui. Bailey's Industrial Oil and Fat Products, 5th ed. New York, NY: John Wiley, 1996.

77. M Bockisch. Fats and Oils Handbook. Champaign, IL: AOCS Press, 1998.

78. RD O'Brien, W Farr, PJ Wan. Introduction to Fats and Oils Technology. 2nd ed, Champaign, IL: AOCS Press, 2000.

79. J Graille. Lipides et corps gras alimentaires. London, Paris. Lavoisier, 2003.

80. FD Gunstone. Lipids for Functional Foods and Nutriceuticals. Dundee, U.K.: The Oily Press, 2003.

81. ZE Sikorski, A Kolakowska. Chemical and Functional Properties of Food Lipids. Boca Raton, FL: CRC Press, 2002

82. A Dieffenbacher, WD Pocklington, eds. IUPAC Standard Methods for the Analysis of Oils, Fats and Derivatives. 1st Suppl. to the 3rd ed. Oxford, U.K.: Blackwell, 1992.

83. AOCS Official Methods and Recommended Practices of the AOCS. Champaign, IL: AOCS, 1998.

84. K Aitzetmüller, B Matthäus, S Friedrich. A new database for seed oil fatty acids – the database SOFA. Eur J Lipid Sci Technol 105: 92–103, 2003.

35 Fish Biology and Food Science

R. Malcolm Love
Consultant, East Silverburn, Kingswells

CONTENTS

I. INTRODUCTION

The science of fish as food usually concentrates on the deterioration that occurs after death. Even when packed in ice, the dead fish are still attacked by spoilage bacteria. If they are frozen immediately after catching and cold-stored, the texture of the thawed, cooked product gradually toughens with storage time, while the flavour will become rancid unless special precautions are taken.

While investigating cold-storage phenomena, the writer became aware that natural variations in the raw material could sometimes be more significant than the changes resulting from refrigeration, which had been the focal point of the study. This finding indicated a prior need for an investigation of 'variation,' the role of season and fishing ground, and ultimately their effects on the suitability of a batch of fish as a foodstuff.

Anecdotal evidence existed long before any systematic work had been undertaken in this field. For example, fishermen from the Moray Firth (north of Aberdeen, Scotland) used to risk damaging their nets by fishing as close as possible to stony ground, since experience had taught them that fish caught there were firm-fleshed. Those caught on a soft ground 'had a soft texture,' which precluded their being transported to Aberdeen because they decayed so rapidly. Similar conclusions were derived from the nature of the diet of the fish at the time. Cod (*Gadus morhua* L.) which were consuming soft and fatty sand-eels (*Ammodytes* spp.), 'became soft themselves,' while those with shellfish in their stomachs ('hard-feeding') were firmer.

These observations, based on a lifetime's experience at sea, were of course reliable; the interpretations were not. In fact, the basis for the observations was almost certainly the nutritional status of the fish. Most species starve during the winter, and those that spawn in late winter, developing gonads while starving, drain their resources further. Since they deplete their own body proteins, the flesh becomes soft. When feeding resumes, the fish cram themselves with whatever food has become available — in the case of cod, fatty sand-eels. However, at this point they have not yet recovered, and when the fishermen examine them, they are still soft. Additionally, digestive enzymes are found in abundance in stomachs full of food. If the fish are not sufficiently washed after gutting, some autodigestion could also take place, leading to further softening. Later in the summer, the fish become more choosey and prefer shrimps — and their flesh by now is firmer.

Nearly 50 years ago, a scientific report (1) hinted that the fishing grounds themselves might influence the quality of the fish. It was stated that cod caught in the Faroes kept better in melting ice than did those from other grounds. This is now known to be a pH effect, governed by the carbohydrate reserves of the fish, and will be fully described later.

In the following account, we shall describe some individual features of the fish and how or why they change with the seasons and the locality. Shulman (2) described them collectively as the 'syndrome' of the fish: it is the integrated features which govern the overall acceptability of the fish as food. The fish type used for study has mostly been the Atlantic cod along with lesser consideration of other gadoids, fatty fish, and salmonids. Observations made with one species do not necessarily apply to others.

II. FEATURES OF THE FISH

A. SKIN COLOUR

The skin colour of many species of fish reflects that of the sea-bottom. Thus, cod from the north of Iceland, where the bottom is mostly of black volcanic ash, are the darkest of all that we have encountered. Cod from the fjords along the coast of Norway live amongst weeds

and are often of a rich gold colour. Those from the Faroe Bank (60–53 N 08–20 W), which is composed of gleaming white shells, are extremely pale, as are all other species from that ground.

The fish change their colour according to stimuli received from their eyes, so if there is a black fish in a shoal of normally-coloured fish, that fish is blind. An experienced buyer on the fish-market can often pin-point where any batch was caught, so is able to choose those which he most favours.

There are so many variables involved in animal biology that apparently simple relationships do not necessarily apply at all times. In the present instance, the adaptability of fish skin colour to background colour is limited. When some pale-coloured cod from the Faroe Bank were brought back alive to Aberdeen (3) and placed in an aquarium together with darker-coloured cod from the Aberdeen Bank (57–05 N 01–15 W), the skins of the two groups of fish tended to change towards the intermediate colour of their new surroundings, *but not completely*. After as much as 16 weeks in the same environment, the two groups of fish could still easily be distinguished by colour, though not as strikingly as at first. This could indicate either a genetic difference between the two stocks, or different, limited ranges of colours being assigned to the two groups early in life as, for example, are the numbers of vertebrae in herrings (*Clupea harengus* L.), which become established in the young fry of a specific age according to the environmental temperature (4).

B. FLESH COLOUR

1. Non-Fatty Fish

Figure 35.1 shows the appearance of a cod with the skin removed. The lateral dark area represents 'red muscle,' the remainder 'white muscle.' The former is more fatty and more vascular than the latter and is rich in myoglobin and mitochondria, characteristics typical of very active muscle. Its metabolism is aerobic, and its purpose is to enable the fish to cruise for long periods without resting. The white muscle operates anaerobically and is used for a sudden dash in pursuit or escape; its poor vascularity and lack of haem pigments result in the need for a recovery period between bursts of activity to restore the energy

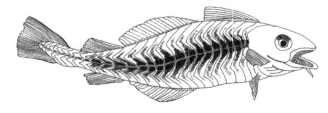

FIGURE 35.1 A cod with skin removed, showing the lateral red muscle. (Drawn by Eva Parsons. Crown copyright.)

compounds. The actual proportion of red muscle between different species of fish reflects their customary physical activity; flat fish which spend much of their time at rest have hardly any of it.

The most active species of the gadoid family is the saithe (*Pollachius virens* L.), so its musculature contains a greater proportion of red muscle than that of cod or whiting (*Merlangius merlangus* L). It can make the fillet look rather dirty, for which reason it fetches a lower price on the market. This can have important commercial consequences, as the following account shows.

A certain company bought the total catch of cod from a trawler, without prior inspection. When filleted, the flesh was found to be unacceptably dark for processing into the frozen cod fingers for which they had been purchased. It was realised that there would be complaints and possible litigation so, rather than scrap the whole batch, they made it into fish-cakes, a lower-priced product. The exact source of the fish was unknown, so an extensive survey of cod from different grounds was undertaken at Torry Research Station (5).

The actual *proportion* of red muscle was found to differ little between cod caught on different grounds, but the *intensity* of the red colour was greater in the fish from two localities at Svalbard, the most northerly grounds investigated. The Svalbard cod are unique in swimming great distances each year, from the Lofoten Islands off Norway, where they spawn in February, to Svalbard, where they arrive in summer to feed. Another feature which makes the Svalbard cod unique (Figure 35.2) is the distribution

of red muscle colour between the individual fish of each sample. In the fish from grounds other than Svalbard, the distribution was Gaussian — a symmetrical shape, with values greater and less than the median tapering off in each direction. No such shape was seen in the samples from the two Svalbard grounds, where values ranged haphazardly from pale to intense. Examination of the same race during the spawning season off Lofoten again revealed deep chocolate-brown lateral muscle.

The most reasonable interpretation of Figure 35.2 is that, while the red muscle in cod from Svalbard was on average darker than that from other grounds, the fish with the most intense colour had just arrived from their long journey, while the pale ones had reached Svalbard some time previously and were now less active. Subsequent experiments with cod caught near Aberdeen showed that after 28 days of activity, swimming round a circular tank (5), their red muscle had become significantly darker than that in fish from the same batch, which had been rested for the same period; during this resting time, the colour had faded appreciably. Thus, the intensity of colour in red muscle adapts to activity level, rather than being a fixed characteristic of a species.

In a seasonal survey of cod from Aberdeen Bank, the red muscle colour showed a smooth variation during the year (Figure 35.3), the minimum value in April being just 63% of the maximum in August. Since changes in pigmentation follow physical activity, a 'swimming activity curve' would probably lie somewhat to the left. Be that as it may, the more deeply pigmented cod must have been more energetic than usual, presumably because of increased feeding activity.

2. Fatty Fish

All species of fish carry triacyl glycerols as reserves of energy, but non-fatty fish, such as cod, carry virtually all of it in the liver, and fatty fish, such as herring (*Clupea* spp.) and salmonids, distribute it throughout the flesh. Since fatty species are active swimmers, their musculature is usually dark-coloured, but this fact does not actually worry the consumer. The point is that, because of its content of flavourous substances, the red-coloured muscle is more tasty than the white muscle anyway. In a trial at sea with two senior Japanese fishery scientists (6), European species of non-fatty fish were tasted, immediately after catching, as *O-Sashimi*, i.e., raw, with *Wasabi* sauce. The somewhat despised saithe was here considered the most desirable, better even than prime fish such as lemon sole (*Microstomus kitt* Walbaum).

The lipid content of the muscle of fatty fish is the major factor influencing quality. Since it decreases markedly at and following spawning, there is therefore a seasonal variation in the acceptability of these fish. When the proportion of lipid is low, the cut surface of the fillet is matt instead of

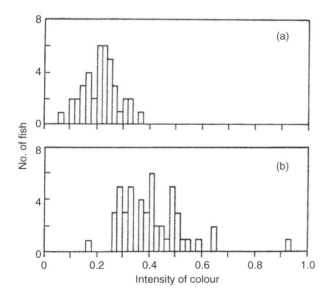

FIGURE 35.2 Distribution of intensity of red muscle colour in batches of 50 cod caught (a) on the Faroe Bank and (b) off West Svalbard. Faroe Bank fish are a stationary stock, Svalbard fish are migratory. The values on the abscissa are optical densities at 512 nm of a 4 cm light path of acid-acetone extracts. (Reference 5.)

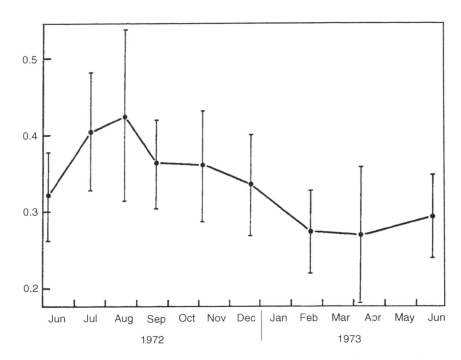

FIGURE 35.3   Changes in the concentrations of total haem pigments in the red muscle of cod over a 12-month period. Units as for abscissa in Figure 35.2. (Reference 5.)

glossy, it does not smoke satisfactorily, and the texture is 'dry' or fibrous in the mouth. The colour is not affected.

3.   Salmonids

The pink colour of salmon and trout flesh reveals the presence of carotenoids, mostly astaxanthin and canthaxanthin. As far as the consumer is concerned, the colour is a desirable feature, but why is it present in these species and not in others? For a long time, carotenoids were considered to be a 'playful diversion of Nature' (7) of no real use to the fish except as precursors of vitamin A, but in salmonids they are closely tied to the reproductive cycle. The fish obtain them from their food, some being deposited unchanged while others are converted into other carotenoids before being laid down in the tissues (8). During the feeding season, they accumulate in the liver, flesh, skin, and fins, but accumulation in the flesh is negligible until maturation has definitely started (P.N. Lewtas, personal communication, 1977). As the gonads grow larger, their demand for carotenoids exceeds the dietary intake, and pigment is then increasingly transferred to them from the flesh. The process is induced by 17-methyl testosterone (9) and halted if the fish are castrated (10).

There is therefore a seasonal variation in the amount of pigment in salmonid flesh, which drains almost to zero around the spawning time. Figure 35.4 shows the changes in farmed rainbow trout (*Salmo gairdnerii* Richardson), which occur despite the fact that because the fish were farmed, they were receiving a continuous supply of

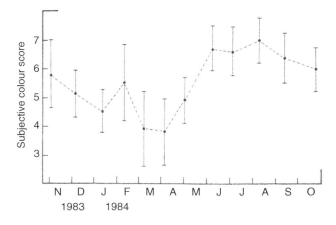

FIGURE 35.4   Seasonal variation in the flesh colour of rainbow trout from one farm, assessed by a panel on a subjective scale. (After Mochizuki and Love, unpublished. Crown copyright.)

canthaxanthin. Studies on chum salmon (*Oncorhynchus keta* Walbaum) during their spawning migration (11) showed that the carotenoid concentration in the blood serum ('in transit') rises steeply in the pre-spawning and near-spawning phases, but drops sharply when spawning actually starts.

A number of functions has been suggested for carotenoids in salmonids: as hormones and as assistants for fertility and embryonic development among other ideas. However, trout embryos with the orange oil droplet removed can develop normally (summarised 7). M. Hata (personal communication, 1977) successfully reared rainbow trout embryos which were free from carotenoids. The main function of carotenoids may well be to protect the eggs from the harmful effects of sunlight, since salmonids lay them in shallow water.

C. CHANGES IN THE MAIN CONSTITUENTS

1. Lipids

All mature fish undergo a regular cycle of depletion and restitution. This is the background to most of the phenomena, important in food science, described in the present account. It is based on the fact that ripe gonad tissue in most fish, particularly the females, occupies a relatively large part of the body cavity, and represents a huge synthesis of new protein and transfer of lipid. In most cases, the amount of food that the fish eats is quite inadequate to supply all this material plus the energy required for swimming, so the fish must perforce break down much of its own musculature ('endogenous feeding' - 12). As triacyl glycerols in the muscle of fatty fish are used up for gonad synthesis, the relative proportion of water in the tissue rises. This inverse relationship was called the 'fat-water line' by Brandes and Dietrich (13), who found that the percentage of muscle lipids in fatty fish could be assessed more conveniently just by measuring the water content.

In cod and similar low-fat fish, triacyl glycerols are virtually absent from the white muscle. The total lipid content is only between 0.5% and 0.6%, made up of 'structural' components, phospholipids and cholesterol and derivatives (14), the latter being about 10% of the total lipid. These membrane lipids are not available for mobilisation unless the muscle itself is broken down. Stored triacyl glycerols are removed from the liver instead.

There is some evidence that maturation, as distinct from simple starvation, mobilises polyunsaturated fatty acids selectively from the reserves for transfer to the gonads. An early report (15) stated that the lipids remaining in the bodies of herrings at maturity were less unsaturated than those from fish in the early stages of maturation. Studies on capelin (*Mallotus villosus* Müller) also showed (16) that polyunsaturated fatty acids tended to be mobilised from the body lipids and the more saturated fatty acids tended to be left behind. Neither study compared the changes in maturing fish with those which were not maturing under the same conditions. However, more fatty acid C22:6 (docosahexaenoic acid) has been found to be removed from the livers of starving cod which were actively maturing than from similar fish which had been castrated (17). This fatty acid is the most important one in the gonads of both sexes.

Some activities, such as maturation and migration which deplete the lipid levels in the fish, actually require a certain level of lipid reserves before they can take place. Thus, when young Atlantic salmon are starved on alternate

weeks in the springtime, reducing their lipid stores, maturation is suppressed (18). Knowledge of this phenomenon can help the economics of fish farms, since the expensive fodder is directed towards profitable body growth, rather than to gonads which represent waste.

Anchovy (*Engraulis encrasicholus* L) overwinter by migrating from the Sea of Azov in September to warmer water, but must first accumulate a critical level of lipid. This 'triggers' migration at a particular range of water temperatures. Those which fail to exceed 14% lipid during their summer feeding do not migrate at all and die when this shallow sea freezes (19, 20).

2. Proteins

a. Muscle Tissue

In the muscle of non-fatty fish there is a significant 'protein-water line' (21), but in this case the water content is not just relative: extra water has entered the tissue. Figure 35.5

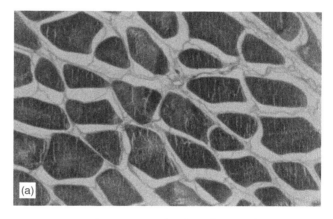

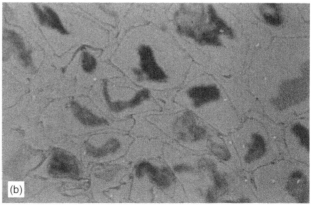

FIGURE 35.5 Cross sections of the white muscle of starving cod. (a) Moderate starvation, water content 83.3%. Some diminution of the solid contractile tissue can be seen, and the collagen sheath of each cell is separated from it by a layer of fluid. (b) Very severe starvation, water content 95.3%. The original outlines of the cells are still delineated by the thin lines of connective tissue but most of the contractile tissue has disappeared. Magnification: 120 times. (After Lavéty, unpublished. Crown copyright.)

shows a cross section of the muscle of a much-depleted cod, compared with a less-depleted counterpart. It will be seen that, while much of the contractile muscle tissue has been removed, the cells still retain roughly the same shape as before, the vacant space now being occupied by fluid.

This observation shows the main weakness of the classical 'condition factor,' used extensively at one time to assess the nutritional status of fish. The weights of fish of the same length were compared, using the formula (W/L^3), where W is the weight of the fish and L the length. Figure 35.5 shows that measuring the loss in weight during starvation or maturation under-estimates the actual loss of protein. In the case of extreme emaciation, cod do actually appear thinner (22) as seen in Figure 35.6, but the loss of protein in the earlier stages is not revealed. The concurrent loss of lipids from the liver can be seen in its diminishing size and its change of colour from creamy-yellow to red.

More than 40 years ago, a simple survey of the proportion of water in the white muscle of cod during the year (23) provided more information than expected (Figure 35.7). The water content of sexually immature cod was seen to increase in the spawning season, though to a lesser extent than in mature fish. This shows that the shortage of food in winter depletes every fish, not just those which synthesise gonads. In addition, fish which have spawned several times are more depleted than first-time spawners. In the author's laboratory (unpublished), it was later shown that the water content of the white muscle of cod held without food in an aquarium could increase to 86% in young fish before death ensued. That of large cod, however, could rise to as much as 96%, so it is clear that larger fish adapt to the greater drain on their resources. As fish grow, the proportion of gonads produced as a percentage of the body weight increases steadily. For example, the burden of spawning in hake (*Merluccius merluccius* L.) doubles for every 10 cm increase of body length (24). Eventually, the fish become so depleted that they cannot recover from spawning and die (25).

The relevance of these observations to food science is that while many species of fish go through a season of wateriness, which makes them unsuitable as food, small fish are less likely to be affected.

b. Connective tissue

The glistening sheets of material which bind individual muscle cells together and join blocks of muscle to the vertebral column are constructed of collagen, a protein rich in proline and hydroxyproline. It appears not to be mobilised to supply energy during starvation but, as described later, its physical properties change with the season.

3. Carbohydrates

a. Their role and origins

Carbohydrates are stored in the liver as glycogen, a 'polyglucose,' which is released into the blood as free glucose and transported to the muscle as required. On arrival, it is either used immediately to supply energy, or resynthesised into muscle glycogen for temporary storage. Although carbohydrates make up only a small percentage of the weight of the fish at any time, they are probably the most important of all constituents in the context of food science, since they are responsible for changes in the texture of the cooked product and in the way the fillets hold together. Their behaviour will therefore be described in some detail.

Carnivorous species of fish can acquire appreciable quantities of glycogen from the livers of their prey. Vegetarian fish on the other hand receive little or none of it in this manner, and indeed all species continually synthesise most or all of what they need from protein and lipid precursors ('gluconeogenesis'). They do, however, maintain certain levels of it which vary according to the general nutritional status of the fish, the glycogens of liver and muscle varying in tandem with each other (26). Figures 35.8 and 35.9 illustrate these relationships. There have been particular problems in studying the glycogen of white muscle. While there is enough of it in the liver to be measured by standard methods, this is not possible in white muscle because of the low levels present and their

FIGURE 35.6   Severely starved cod (upper), showing overall change in shape compared with a fed specimen (lower). (Reference 21.)

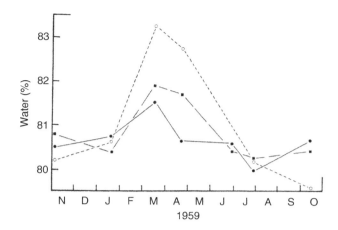

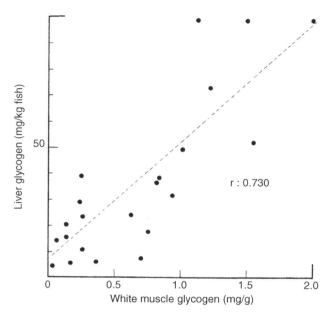

FIGURE 35.7 Changes in the water content of cod white muscle during a year in the wild. Solid circles: immature fish. Squares: first-time spawners. Hollow circles: spawned more than once. Large fish not available in June. (Reference 22, redrawn in Reference 41.)

FIGURE 35.9 Relationships between the glycogen contents of liver and muscle in rested cod of various nutritional states. (Reference 25.)

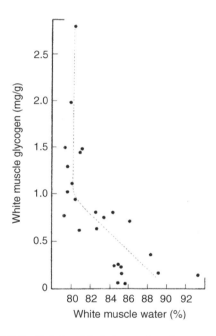

FIGURE 35.8 Relationship between the glycogen content of the white muscle of cod and its nutritional state as indicated by the water content. (Reference 25.)

ephemeral nature. Glycogen fuels all muscular activity, so it is rapidly consumed by the thrashing about which accompanies capture, and indeed its concentration in the muscle can be reduced by half after only 15 seconds of struggling (reviewed p 423 of Reference 8). Attempts to measure it in the muscle of newly-captured or frozen fish are therefore pointless.

The best that can be done in the way of direct assessment of glycogen in muscle is to stun rested fish by a blow on the head before they have had time to struggle. Small samples of muscle are then rapidly excised and dropped into liquid air for subsequent analysis. As it is not possible even with these precautions to avoid all struggling, the levels as measured vary more than those from the liver.

b. The pH of muscle after death
i. Its derivation and measurement

As soon as a fish dies, oxygen no longer circulates to the muscle and glycogen breakdown stops at the lactic acid stage, through the Embden-Meyerhof-Parnas pathway. Some of it takes another path and is broken down into glucose by the action of an amylase present in the muscle (reviewed 27), so any variation in the proportion of the lactic acid and amylolytic pathways would affect the 'final' pH of the muscle (the pH after carbohydrate degradation is complete, usually measured 24 h after death), since lactic acid lowers it and glucose does not. It has been shown that the initial glycogen concentration strongly influences the 24 h post-mortem pH value of the white muscle of cod, whether fully fed, starved, or starved and refed. Possible effects of variations in the pathway therefore seem unimportant (28).

One question remains. Does the amount of struggling undergone by the fish at death influence the final pH? While the lactic acid formed during exercise is rapidly released into the blood system from the muscle of mammals (29), very little is released from fish muscle (30). The stress which accompanies some modes of exercise seems to cause the fish muscle to retain its lactic acid, probably under the influence of the catecholamine hormones (31). The lactic acid generated by violent exercise will therefore supplement that generated spontaneously after death, so that the 24 h post-mortem pH values should be the same, however long the fish struggled before death. Experiments have confirmed this, the final pH of the muscle of cod removed quickly from a tank and stunned being similar to that of those previously exercised stressfully (32).

The measurement of pH after the completion of glycolysis therefore constitutes a simple method of assessing the carbohydrate level of the flesh (28) and, by the relationship shown in Figure 35.9, that of the liver also.

Struggling can, arguably, confer a certain benefit. *Rigor mortis* sets in as soon as the residual glycogen falls below a critical level after death. Since struggling greatly reduces the level of glycogen in the muscle, the fish enters *rigor* more quickly, and the condition lasts for a shorter time, than in a fish which dies without stress (33). This benefits farmed salmon, which should not be handled or filleted in *rigor* because it causes gaping; when they have become flaccid again after *rigor* (the 'resolution of *rigor*') they are suitable for filleting. It may take several inconvenient days before this state is reached, so some struggling before death can save money. There seem to be no advantages to processing or handling salmon by prolonging the times before or in *rigor* after harvesting, except where the salmon are to be sold intact to a customer, where the state of *rigor mortis* indicates freshness (34).

ii. Seasonal variation

It is reasonable to expect that the final pH of fish muscle should be high during the winter, because food is scarce and little carbohydrate is present in the muscle to form lactic acid after death. The fish feed continuously during the summer, so the final pH should then be consistently low. However, experimental findings do not bear this out. Figure 35.10 shows that, over a wide range of fishing

grounds, the pH of cod muscle after death is high during most of the year, but that around June most of the fish exhibit low values for a short period, after which high values are restored. The approximate date when low values occur varies somewhat from year to year, but the principle is the same (35). The phenomenon appears not to occur in haddock (*Melanogrammus aeglefinus* L.) (31), but a short-term minimum pH value has been observed in June in farmed Atlantic salmon (36).

iii. Experimental starvation and refeeding

Studies of the three main constituents of cod tissues during starvation (37) have shown that they are mobilised for energy purposes in a definite order (Figure 35.11). The integrity of white muscle is more important to the survival of the fish than are the lipid reserves of the liver, so its proteins are not mobilised to supply energy until most of the liver lipids have disappeared. There is therefore a hiatus of several weeks, longer at lower temperatures and *vice versa*, before any change is seen in the protein content of the white muscle during starvation. Red muscle is generally more important to the fish than is white muscle, since it enables the fish to 'cruise' without fatigue. It therefore retains its glycogen for several weeks after the beginning of starvation, while depletion begins immediately in white muscle.

It is again reasonable to expect that, with the decline of available carbohydrate in starving cod, the activities of the enzymes that convert protein and lipid to glycogen (gluconeogenesis) would become more active, to redress the situation. However, it has been shown (38) that in fact the enzymes involved, phosphoenol pyruvate carboxykinase and alanine aminotransferase in the liver, and the fructose diphosphatase in liver, red muscle and white muscle, become steadily *less* active during starvation, though there can be a transient increase in activity during the early stages.

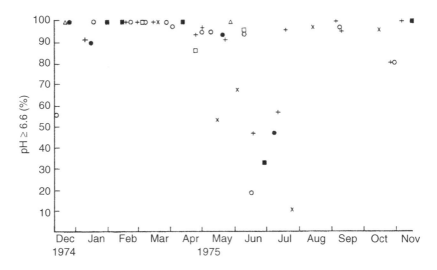

FIGURE 35.10 Proportions of batches of 20 cod, caught on various northern grounds, with post-mortem pH in the white muscle of 6.6 or more. (Reference 34.)

The starving cod adapt to decreasing glycogen resources by reducing their swimming activity, spending long hours motionless on the bottom of the aquarium. In contrast, starving rainbow trout (*Salmo gairdnerii* Richardson) do increase the activity of their gluconeogenetic enzymes, so that reasonable levels of glucose in the blood and muscle are maintained. The trout is a more physically active fish and continues to swim during starvation.

On refeeding, the sequence of change illustrated in Figure 35.11 is reversed. The muscle proteins are restored first, red muscle before white. Only after this do the liver lipids return to normal values (26).

The restoration of glycogen, however, is remarkable. There is enormous over-compensation, both in liver and muscle, during refeeding. A 20-fold increase above non-starving values of liver glycogen is possible (39). Figure 35.12 shows the effect in cod liver (26). It is noteworthy that the value after 195 days has dropped spontaneously to normal, despite the continuation of the feeding regime. Similar rises and subsequent falls are shown in red and white muscle (Figure 35.13).

The large increases in the levels of glycogen in the three tissues of starving-refed fish, compared with the level in fish fed continuously during the experiment, almost seem to indicate a loss of control or a metabolic imbalance, but studies with the DNA/RNA ratio, which varies in proportion to the vigour of protein synthesis, suggest that the over-compensation is a necessary part of the restorative process (26). The glycogen level in the red muscle reaches a maximum value after 60 days of refeeding, compared with 105 days in white muscle. The DNA/RNA ratios reach maxima at the same two points. Perhaps the energy required for protein resynthesis comes

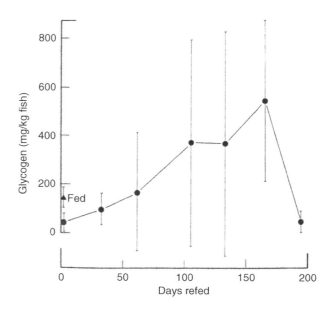

FIGURE 35.12   The excessive increase in liver glycogen during refeeding after starvation. The triangular point shows the level in fish fed throughout the experiment (never starved). (Reference 25.)

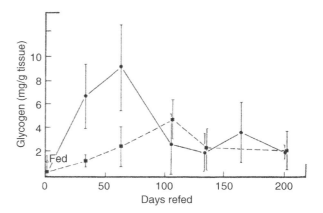

FIGURE 35.13   The excessive compensation of glycogen in red muscle (circles) and white muscle (squares) of cod, refed after starvation. Note how the maxima differ between the two types of muscle and (Figure 35.12) the liver. (Reference 25.)

from this glycogen. The restoration of red muscle protein has priority over that of white muscle.

A smaller glycogen overshoot is seen in fish previously starved for a shorter period, and the type of food proffered for refeeding also influences the phenomenon (26). Figure 35.14 shows that a diet of squid during refeeding results in a bigger overshoot than that resulting from a diet of herrings.

Figure 35.15 shows the corresponding final pH of the white muscle during starving and refeeding. A refeeding period of around 100 days was chosen to correspond with the glycogen maximum (Figure 35.13). A final pH lower than that usually found in fish from the

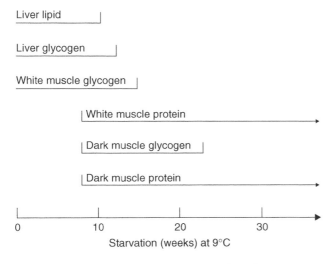

FIGURE 35.11   Diagrammatic representation of the sequence in which the principal constituents of liver and muscle are mobilised during the starvation of cod at 9°C. Time values are approximate. (Reference 25.)

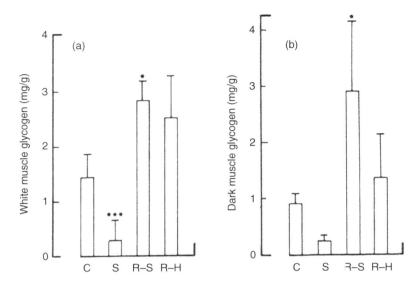

FIGURE 35.14   The effect of diet on the concentrations of glycogen in (a) white muscle and (b) red muscle in cod starved for 77 days and refed for 97 days. Asterisks show the degrees of significance from fed controls. C = control; S = starved; R-S = refed on squid muscle; R-H = refed on herring muscle. (Reference 25.)

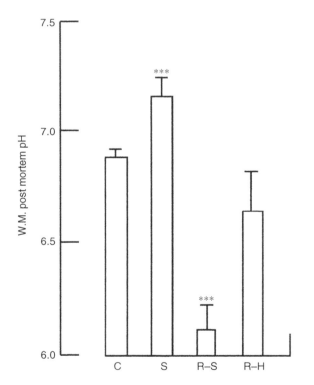

FIGURE 35.15   The final pH of white muscle in cod. Conditions and key as in Figure 35.14. (Reference 25.)

sea can be seen in the fish refed on squid. This result is thought to mirror the phenomenon seen in Figure 35.10 in free-living cod caught around June. Using the period of 100 days, one could speculate that these fish had started to feed in March (the stock used spawns around the second week in March). However, the results show

too much scatter to predict the date of resumption of feeding from year to year.

III. BIOLOGICAL PHENOMENA AND FOOD SCIENCE

A. GAPING

1. Anatomical Background

Figure 35.16 shows the appearance of the cut surface of a cod fillet. The pattern of lines shows the cut edges of connective tissue sheets (*myocomma*; plural: *myocommata*) which merge with the skin on the lower surface and are joined to the vertebrae on the upper. They are made of the protein collagen (non-contractile) and bind blocks of muscle tissue (*myotomes*) together, transmitting the force of the muscular contractions used in swimming.

In the muscle tissue of warm-blooded animals such as beef, the connective tissue toughens as the animal ages, eventually resulting in a material which is a challenge to eat, even after long cooking. Fish connective tissue is much more 'frail,' and dissolves into gelatin at temperatures well below that of boiling water. It is therefore never a problem as regards the texture of the cooked product. Most of the potassium of muscle tissue is found within each contractile cell, while sodium is principally in the spaces between the cells and in the connective tissue. Figure 35.16 shows that there is a far greater proportion of connective tissue at the caudal end of the fillet, so consumers on a low-sodium diet should perhaps avoid this part.

Figure 35.17 shows (magnified) the junction between the ends of some white muscle cells on each side of a sheet

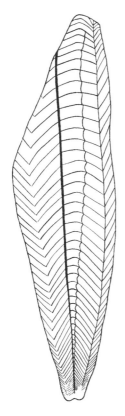

FIGURE 35.16 Drawing of the cut surface of a cod fillet (musculature next to the bone). The thin lines indicate the cut ends of the myocommata. (Reference 39.)

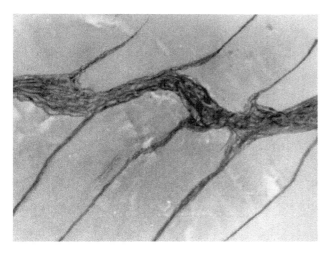

FIGURE 35.17 Photomicrograph of the junction of 4 individual muscle cells (pale areas) with each side of a myocomma (thick black stripe). The cells are about 100 microns across, and the connective tissue tubes separating each from its neighbour are shown as thin dark lines. (Author's picture. Crown copyright.)

of connective tissue, shown in black. The light grey areas are longitudinal sections of individual muscle cells, and it can be inferred that each cell is surrounded by a 'tube' of connective tissue which merges with the myocomma itself.

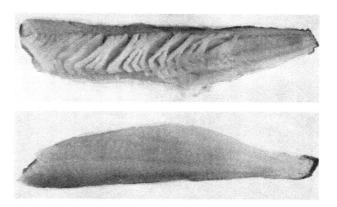

FIGURE 35.18 A bad case of gaping (upper), compared with a normal (lower) fish. Both fish were frozen 'round,' thawed and filleted, but the good specimen was frozen before *rigor mortis* and the gaping one had been preserved for 8 days in melting ice before freezing. (Crown copyright.)

It is an elegant mode of attachment, but when this junction breaks, gaping occurs (Figure 35.18).

2. Causes of Gaping

As a general rule, gaping is a problem of frozen fish. More specifically, it can be seen in fish which have been frozen intact, with or without guts in, then thawed and filleted. It is not usually a problem when they are filleted after the resolution of *rigor mortis* before freezing. Gaping is of great economic significance: a gaping fillet cannot be sliced, smoked — or sold. The difficulties associated with gaping and its commercial significance were brought home to the writer at a large processing plant, the owners of which owned the fishing boats which supplied it. At the time (June), their haddock were gaping so badly after filleting that they had to be minced and sold as a low-priced product which represented financial loss for the company. The management were in a position to control all handling procedures aboard the ships, but nothing they requested improved the situation. This fact triggered an eight-year investigation at Torry Research Station, Aberdeen.

Folk-lore from the fishermen has it that fish stuffed with food ('feedy fish') gape. This suggests that the soft flesh seen in early summer contains weak connective tissue, but experiments again showed otherwise (40). Figure 35.19 shows that it is the best-nourished fish which gape, the starved ones do not. The gaping score was assessed subjectively: a value of '1' signified a single longitudinal split in the fillet, and higher scores were based on the number of gaps between myotomes (41). The score figures are not mathematically related to one another, but the method is still a useful research tool. Figure 35.20 suggests that pH could be the factor responsible rather than softness as such, because the gaping follows the seasonal pattern of pH (42). The relationship was confirmed when

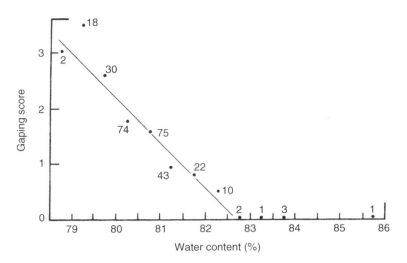

FIGURE 35.19 The relationship between the gaping of cod, frozen whole, thawed and filleted, and the water content of the white muscle. Numbers show the size of each sample wherein the water contents differed by not more than 0.5%. (Reference 41, redrawn in Reference 39.)

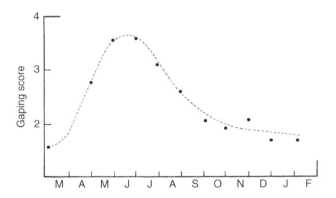

FIGURE 35.20 Seasonal variation in the gaping of cod muscle (1969–1970). Note that the peak corresponds with the period of minimum pH. (Reference 41.)

isolated myocommata, suspended in buffers of various pH values and subjected to increasing tension until they broke, became increasingly frail as the pH decreased (Figure 35.21). The effect was reversible: myocommata which had been weakened in a buffer of low pH, then transferred to one of neutral pH, were found to have regained their strength (43). A similar relationship between season, pH and gaping has been found in farmed Atlantic salmon, the highest gaping score being in June and the lowest in January (36).

B. THE FREEZING PROCESS ITSELF

The time between the death of the fish and freezing is important. Figure 35.22 shows that gaping is minimal in whole fish, frozen before the onset of rigor mortis and thawed before filleting. It rises when the fish have been frozen *in rigor* and rises further when frozen after the fish

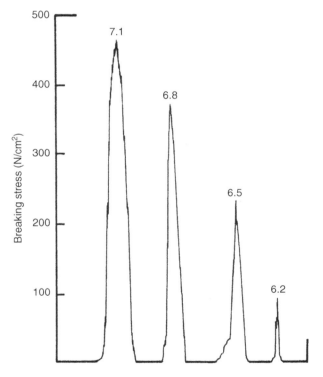

FIGURE 35.21 Tracings showing the force required to break strips of myocomma buffered at various pH values (shown above each peak) at 0. (Reference 42.)

have become limp again (41).The phenomenon has been seen in several species of fish, but there are differences in degree (41). Haddock (*Melanogrammus aeglefinus* L.) gape the most, followed in sequence by cod, saithe (*Pollachius virens* L.), redfish (*Sebastes marinus* L.), halibut (*Hippoglossus hippoglossus* L.), and lemon sole (*Microstomus kitt* Walbaum).

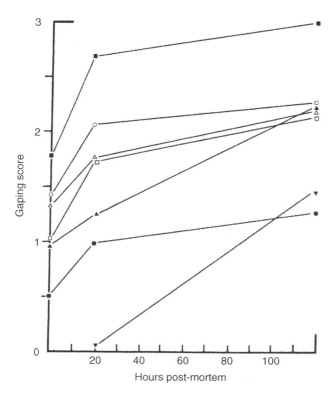

FIGURE 35.22 Gaping in fillets made from different fish species frozen at different times after death. All species were pre-*rigor* at 0 h, in *rigor* at 20 h and post-*rigor* at 120 h. Species from the top downwards: haddock, cod, saithe, redfish, halibut, lemon sole, plaice. (Reference 40.)

The lesson is clear: freeze whole fish as soon and as quickly as possible after death, bearing in mind that if they are frozen slowly, the effect is the same as that of prolonging the period preceding freezing.

The mechanism of gaping from this cause is interesting. The surface of a fillet cut before the onset of *rigor mortis* is dry to the touch, while if it is taken from a fish actually in *rigor*, it feels and looks wet. Freezing results in the solidification of this 'free' water, together with some of the water more closely associated with the contractile proteins. The frozen water becomes physically separated from the muscle cells, now dehydrated, in bodies of protein-free ice, faster freezing generating more numerous, smaller ice crystals and *vice versa*. Some tissue water is so tightly bound to the protein that it never freezes, but the proportion of freezable water is smaller in *pre-rigor* muscle than in muscle in or beyond *rigor*. Measurements on cross-sections of frozen cod muscle (44) show that the area attributable to ice is 46% of the total area in cod rapidly frozen *pre-rigor*, while in that frozen in *rigor* or after its resolution the figure is 57%. In addition, when fish are kept for longer periods in melting ice, water from outside steadily diffuses into the muscle tissue (45), resulting in further break-up of the myocommata on freezing (Figure 35.23).

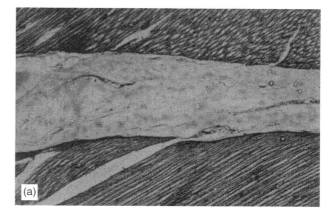

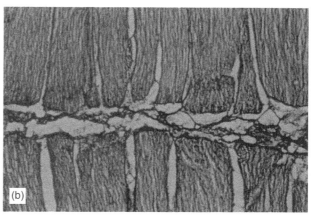

FIGURE 35.23 Sections through frozen cod muscle (small pale areas represent ice crystals). Both specimens frozen very rapidly at –80°C, but specimen (a) frozen 1 day after death, (b) after the whole, gutted fish had been held in melting ice for 8 days before freezing. The band across the middle is the myocomma, with muscle cells on either side. The tissues in (a) appear almost as fresh muscle. The myocomma in (b) is completely disrupted by ice crystals; fish in this condition gape badly. (Reference 44, Crown copyright.)

C. HANDLING

pH is not the sole arbiter of gaping. The intrinsic strengths of the collagen membranes vary between species. In a comparison of hake (*Merluccius merluccius* L.), cod and catfish (*Anarhichas lupus* L.), hake were found to gape more readily than the other two species and catfish did not gape under any experimental conditions, including very rough handling (46). The mean breaking stresses of myocommata were found to be 30 (hake), 87 (cod) and 142 (catfish) N/cm³, the final pH values of all the fish being similar. The breaking stresses of skin samples were greater, but differed between the species in the same sequence as above.

In *rigor mortis* of whole fish, the muscle masses on each side of the fish contract strongly against each other, resulting in an unyielding rigidity. If the fish is curved as it enters *rigor*, this shape becomes fixed, and clearly any attempt to straighten it before filleting would cause severe gaping in species other than catfish. Similarly, throwing rigid fish to other operatives or dropping them from a height would also cause gaping. This is common sense, but it still happens in practice.

Incidentally, if a fish is filleted before *rigor mortis* has set in, the musculature is now free to contract as it enters *rigor*. The shortened fillets, which take on a ribbed appearance, are tough to eat after cooking. If the *pre-rigor* fillet is dropped straight into a hot pan, it contracts even more and is virtually inedible because of its very rubbery texture.

D. TEMPERATURE

As stated, fish collagens dissolve as gelatin at much lower temperatures than the collagens of warm-blooded animals. The effect can be seen in Figure 35.24, where gaping increases to a maximum value when freshly-killed cod enter *rigor mortis* at 25°C. Controls at iced temperature do not gape at all (47). During heavy fishing in the summer months, the temperature of the fish could easily rise sufficiently to cause ruinous gaping if freezing were delayed. It may, however, be possible to retrieve the situation (43). Figure 35.25 shows that myocommata break more at higher temperatures, but that they are less easily broken if they are cooled to 0°C before measurement. Hence, it is vital to cool fish before further handling if they have been lying in the sun.

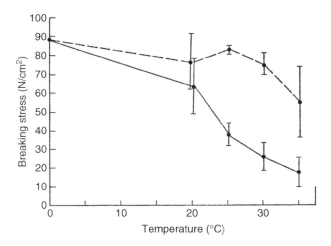

FIGURE 35.25 Breaking stress of isolated myocommata from cod kept at various temperatures for 1 h. Continuous line: measured at the actual experimental temperature. Broken line: collagen specimen cooled to 0°C before being stressed. (Reference 42.)

Rainbow trout also gape more as they enter *rigor* at higher temperatures, but *rigor* at 26°C in this species does not cause gaping: high scores require temperatures at or above 35°C. The higher water-temperatures tolerated by this species during life seem to engender a greater thermal stability in their collagen (36).

E. SIZE

Figure 35.26 shows that small cod gape more than large. The relationship is seen only in summer and autumn, however, disappearing or even being reversed in the winter and spring (48). Two factors are at work here: the pH of larger cod can be lower than that of smaller, varying with the season, and can over-ride the size effect.

Do any of these observations help to explain the industrial problem with haddock, described earlier? Fish of this

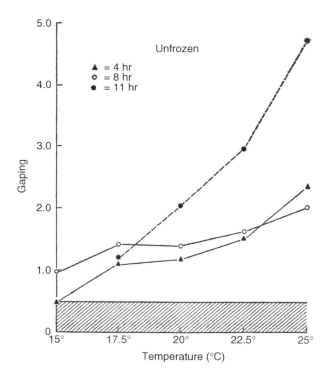

FIGURE 35.24 Gaping after filleting whole, gutted cod kept at different temperatures after death. The hatched area shows the unchanging state of controls kept in melting ice throughout the same period. (Reference 46.)

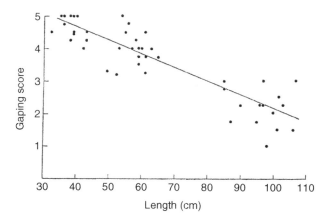

FIGURE 35.26 Influence of body length on gaping in cod caught in June 1968, frozen, thawed and filleted. r = 0.899. (Reference 47.)

species have been found to gape more than other species investigated (41), and the industrial problem was encountered in June, when the final pH values are often low. Isolated myocommata from haddock are in fact stronger than those of cod (43), but the final pH of this species has been observed to be intrinsically low, even as late as October (49), almost certainly accounting for their greater tendency to gape. The reason for the low pH is unknown.

There is scant advice for mitigating severe gaping in haddock. The fish should be put into the freezer before the onset of *rigor* if at all possible and any additional fish chilled *at once* and handled gently. Otherwise, it is better not to freeze them whole around June — though such advice may be impractical.

F.   TEXTURE

1.   pH

Although the tough texture sometimes found in cooked beef is never found in fish, the latter, stored in the frozen state for too long or at too high a temperature (or both), yields a product which, after cooking, is somewhat difficult to swallow and can leave fibrous strands stuck between the teeth of the consumer. The sensation is of a dry, fibrous product and is unpleasant, especially if coupled with a rancid taste. Here we examine the texture of fish that has not been frozen, which can range between sloppy and firm.

The relationship (50) between the final pH of cod muscle and the texture as eaten is shown in Figure 35.27. The water contents of the muscle of the different fish fell within the narrow range of 80.0 to 80.9%, which is normal for well-fed cod (23). The softest fish were therefore not watery. This finding casts an interesting light on the texture of acutely starving fish, which are also sloppy and can, after cooking, be sucked through the teeth (not pleasant). The very slight effect of water content at constant pH on texture is shown in Figure 35.28. It is clear that pH is the over-riding factor governing the texture of the cooked product. Its importance in assessing the suitability of fish for processing was recognised earlier by Cowie and Little (51), who selected fish on the market for processing solely

on the basis of pH, using a probe pH electrode pushed straight into the wet tissue. The dividing line between tough and acceptable frozen cod fillets has been found to apply also to fish *minces* from 16 Australian species caught by mid-water trawling and cooked after storage for up to a year at −18°C (52).

2.   Cold Storage

There is little to add to what has been said already. Free water and some water associated with the protein structures of the muscle separate out as ice as the fish freezes. As cold storage continues, the individual muscle cells are less and less able to resorb the melt-water, after thawing. More water therefore drips out of the thawed fillets and the sensation of the cooked product becomes increasingly dry or fibrous.

The rate of deterioration is governed by the storage temperature; it is progressively slower at lower temperatures, but also varies with the species. Studies carried out at −14°C showed that the whiting (*Merlangius merlangus* L.) deteriorated the most quickly, reaching its limit after 10 weeks (53), whereas the lemon sole (*Microstomus kitt* Walbaum) required over 17 years to reach the same degree of deterioration (54). For this to happen, the muscle fibres must be dehydrated by the formation of ice bodies within the tissue. Frozen cod muscle deteriorates very quickly at −1.5, but no change occurs in supercooled muscle stored at the same temperature with no ice present (55).

The consequence of these phenomena is that fish which are already firm-textured through having a low final pH soon become unacceptable as a foodstuff if they are subsequently cold stored. More interestingly, high-pH fish which are sloppy-textured can actually be improved by a short period of frozen storage.

IV.   THE SIGNIFICANCE OF GEOGRAPHY

A.   INTRODUCTION

We have seen earlier that the colour of the red muscle of one particular stock of cod which swim great distances (the Svalbard-Lofoten stock) is more intense than that of

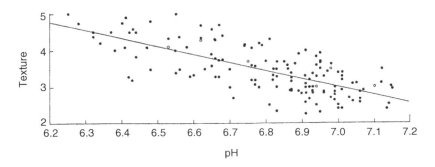

FIGURE 35.27   Influence of final pH on the texture of cooked cod fillets. Water contents of all samples limited to 80.0–80.9%. Texture scores above 3 represent firm or tough flesh, below 3 soft or sloppy. Two identical values are shown as hollow symbols. (Reference 49.)

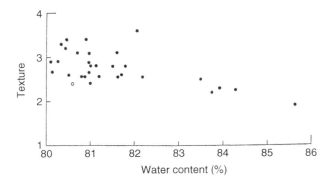

FIGURE 35.28 The influence of muscle water content on the texture of cooked cod muscle as eaten. All pH values were within range of 7.0–7.1. (Reference 49.)

FIGURE 35.29 A cod from the Faroe Bank (length: 51 cm). (Author's picture. Crown copyright.)

more sedentary stocks. As regards food science, the effect is largely cosmetic but can lead to financial loss. We now consider whether the characteristics of any grounds are such as to affect the desirability of the fish as food.

It is easy to imagine that fish from widely-spaced enclosed bodies of water might differ from one another because of disparities in temperature, water-chemistry, identity of creatures consumed, etc. The chances of finding important differences between fish from widely spaced oceanic locations seemed much less promising, and a detailed survey was undertaken without much optimism (56). However, the results amply justified the enterprise, some characteristics of cod from the Faroe Bank (60-53 N 08-20 W) being significantly different from those of cod from the other grounds investigated.

B.   THE FAROE BANK COD

1.   The Fish Themselves

Figure 35.29 shows the fine appearance and corpulence of a Faroe Bank cod, quantified in Figure 35.30. Only the neighbouring Faroe Plateau cod are comparable. The livers were very large and creamy, showing how well the fish had been nourished. Early work on cod from Aberdeen Bank (57-05 N 01-15 W) showed that the water content of the muscle ranged from about 80% to 80.9% in well-fed fish during a span of twelve months (Figure 35.7), a value of about 81% or more signifying early stages of starvation (23). The white muscle of spring-caught Faroe Bank cod seems to be unique in having less than 80% of water (Figure 35.31) and more protein nitrogen (Figure 35.32) than cod from other grounds. Values for liver glycogen are high though not remarkable (56), but the final pH of the muscle is lower than in any other group (Figure 35.33). These fish were caught in the spring of 1966. Those caught in the autumn of 1968, when all the fish were sated, still maintained the uniquely low level of muscle water content, but the protein nitrogen and pH values were not remarkable. The others had caught up. The low value of muscle

water in Faroe Bank cod was observed again during surveys in September 1971 and September 1972.

In a small independent experiment (57), the total lipid content of the white muscle of Faroe Bank cod caught in the spring was 0.63%, compared with a value of 0.55% in Aberdeen Bank cod, while in the autumn the corresponding figures were 0.78% and 0.67%. This small difference appears to be important, as we shall see.

2.   Consequences for Cold-Stored Cod

It has been concluded in a well-reasoned article (58) that the term 'quality' is often over-used and made to cover a variety of observations. Preferably, one should specify the parameter studied. Here we study the texture, flavour and appearance of the thawed, filleted and cooked product. Just looking at the superb appearance of the fish lying on the deck at 3 A.M. or so (night-fishing is the rule on the Faroe Bank), one instinctively feels that their overall 'quality' as an item of food must be at the top of the scale. In our survey (56), the fish were frozen whole very soon after capture, stored at −30°C for three months, thawed at low air temperatures, filleted and examined before and after cooking. These conditions are as near ideal as one can provide — but the quality scores for all three parameters were uniformly low.

a.   Texture and Gaping

Because of the strong link between pH and texture, it has been suggested that the fish most suitable for long-term storage should have a pH not less than 6.6 (59) or 6.7 (60). In many of the Faroe Bank cod caught in the spring, the pH was lower than 6.6. As a result, the texture of the cooked product as tasted by a panel was firm, but that of the same fish after 3 months at −30°C, thawed and cooked, was judged to be unacceptably tough. (50). Similarly, because of the low pH of the muscle, the thawed fillets gaped. The fact of unacceptability in each case casts doubt on the suitability of these fish for freezing and cold-storage.

b.   Flavour

The off-flavour developed by fish muscle during cold-storage (rancidity) has been likened to wet cardboard, boiled

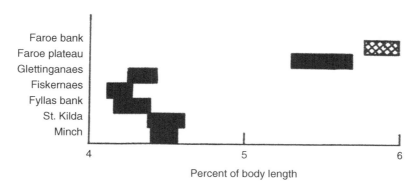

FIGURE 35.30 Corpulence of cod caught on different grounds in spring 1966, shown as the maximum diameter of the caudal peduncle expressed as a percentage of body length. Bars represent 95% confidence limits. (Reference 54.)
Map references: Faroe Bank: 60-53N 08-20W, Faroe Plateau: 62-34N 06-24W, Glettinganaes (SE Iceland): 65-27N 13-08W, Fiskernaes (Greenland): 63-15N 52-40W, Fyllas Bank: 63-55N 52-53W, St. Kilda (Scotland): 57-45N 08-40W, Minch: 58-13N 05-38W

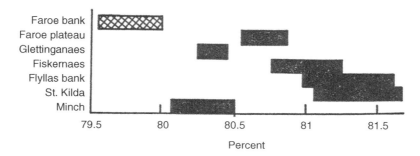

FIGURE 35.31 Water content of the white muscle of cod caught on different grounds. Legend as in Figure 35.30. (Reference 54.)

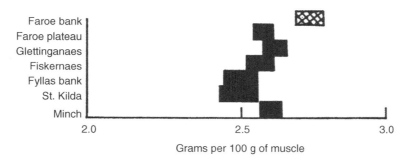

FIGURE 35.32 Total protein nitrogen in the white muscle of cod. Legend as in Figure 35.30. (Reference 54.)

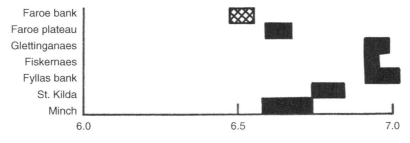

FIGURE 35.33 Final pH of white muscle of cod. Legend as in Figure 35.30. (Reference 54.)

TABLE 35.1

Taste-panel assessment of cold-store off-flavour and off-odour of cod caught in spring 1970 on different grounds, gutted and stored for 3 months at $-30°C$. The fish were filleted and steam-cooked without seasoning before tasting. 0 = absent; 5 = very strong, the upper limit of commercial acceptability being about 3. Comparing the five grounds by analysis of variance by the F test showed that the mean results for the Faroe Bank differed significantly from the others for flavour ($P = 0.01$) and odour ($P = 0.05$). (Reference 64.)

Fishing Ground	Map Reference	Cold Store Flavour		Cold Store Odour	
		X	SD	X	SD
Aberdeen Bank	57-05 N 01-15 W	1.68	0.60	1.32	0.51
Faroe Bank	60-53 N 08-20 W	3.02	0.95	2.29	0.84
Faroe Plateau	62-34 N 06-24 W	1.45	0.63	0.91	0.51
SE Iceland	65-27 N 13-08 W	1.70	0.49	1.04	0.35
NW Iceland	65-35 N 25-00 W	1.37	0.37	0.84	0.24

clothes and other poetic imagery. It results mostly from the oxidation of polyunsaturated fatty acids located primarily in the phospholipids, and has been identified as hept-cis-4 enal (61–63). Many factors govern the rate of the reaction, and the chemistry is complex: the subject has been reviewed recently in detail (64). Since the phospholipids are part of the structure of muscle cell membranes, they present a large surface area for oxidation, compared with the neutral lipids (triacyl glycerols) which are more 'compact' and contain a smaller proportion of polyunsaturated fatty acids. They are the main constituents of the fatty deposits used as stores of energy. The spatial distribution of the two types of lipid is important (64) and may help to explain inter-species differences.

Since the lipid content of cod muscle is usually less than 1%, it might be supposed that it would develop negligible rancidity compared with that found in more fatty species on cold-storage, but this is not necessarily so. The most likely reason is that the lipids of cod muscle consist almost entirely of phospholipids — triacyl glycerols make up only about 1% of the total (65).

In small samples of Faroe Bank cod, the white muscle was found to contain about 20% more total lipid than that in Aberdeen Bank cod, and this probably explains the fact that cold-storage off-flavour (and off-odour) was significantly greater in Faroe Bank cod than in cod from four other grounds (66) and considered unacceptable by the tasters (Table 35.1). Might it be possible to reduce the cold-storage off-flavour of cod by reducing their total lipid content? A further factor which may govern the propensity of frozen fish to become rancid is geographic latitude, which affects the temperature of the sea-water. The lipids of fish become progressively more unsaturated as the water becomes colder (more likely to become rancid), and *vice versa* (21, 67, 68). The purpose appears to be to ensure that the melting-points of structural lipids are below that of the environmental temperature so that they remain flexible.

Experimental starvation of Aberdeen Bank cod for 2 months (69) resulted in a water-content of 84% and some

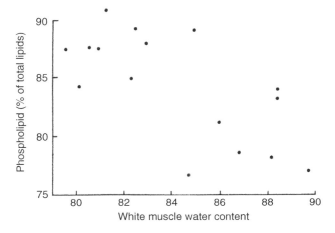

FIGURE 35.34 The decrease in proportion of phospholipids in the lipids of cod white muscle during starvation, shown by the increase in water content. (Reference 65.)

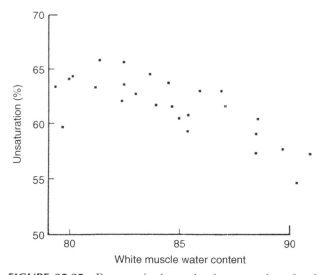

FIGURE 35.35 Decrease in the total polyunsaturation of cod white muscle lipids during starvation. Unsaturation represented as the sum of fatty acids 22:6, 22:5, 20:5, and 20:4 (% of total fatty acids). (Reference 65.)

TABLE 35.2

The effect of moderate starvation of cod on the development of off-odours and off-flavours during cold-storage at −10°C. (Reference 65.)

	Odour		Flavour	
	5 weeks	10 weeks	5 weeks	10 weeks
Fed controls (5 fish)	1.5	1.55	3.43	3.55
Starved fish (5 fish)	0.55	0.4	1.28	1.8
Difference	0.95	1.15	2.15	1.75
Significance level	1%	5%	0.1%	5%

Cis-4-heptenal values were as follows: starved cod muscle, 3.5 nmol/1000g wet muscle; fed cod muscle, 23.0 nmol/1000 g wet muscle.

reduction in the lipids of the muscle. The proportion of phospholipids (Figure 35.34) and the degree of unsaturation in the residual lipids (Figure 35.35) were also reduced. Freezing followed by cold-storage at −10°C resulted in a much reduced development of off-flavour and off-odour (Table 35.2). Analysis of hept-cis-4-enal confirmed the finding. Several factors may be involved here, although the results appear to be a simple cause and effect.

It is improbable that deliberate starvation will ever be used in practice to reduce the deterioration of flavour in cold-stored cod, but, as a water-content of 84% or more is often found naturally in late winter in this species, it suggests that advantage might be taken of the likely seasonal variation in off-flavour.

It should now be obvious that the difference between Faroe Bank cod and the others originates in an unusually rich food supply. There is a deep oceanic channel which keeps the fish separate from neighbouring stocks. We found that they were not eating particularly fatty prey, but that the stomachs were filled with echinoids, crustaceans, and sometimes fish.

3. Chilled Fresh Fish

One feature of Faroe Bank cod does favour them as an item of food, when compared with cod from at least one other ground. It keeps for a longer period in melting ice (1). This is clearly a result of the lower pH, which inhibits the activity of spoilage bacteria (70).

V. ACKNOWLEDGEMENT

The complex interactions described in this chapter have been supplemented and confirmed in species other than gadoids in a large number of reports published over 24 years by Professor Anna Kolakowska and her co-workers (71). It is a pleasure to pay tribute to the fine work of a colleague whom I have never met.

VI. CAVEAT LECTOR

The influences of geographical location on cod regarded as a foodstuff seem to be straightforward enough, but one can never assume that other species will behave in the same way. Cold-storage off-flavours develop strongly in herrings (*Clupea harengus* L.) but the off-flavour in cold-stored Atlantic salmon, another fatty species, seems to develop more slowly — salmon keep well in the deep-freezer. Triacyl glycerols in salmon muscle are found in the myocommata, so perhaps they protect the phospholipids within the myotomes from oxidation: it would be difficult to prove. Again, the starvation of rainbow trout results in a net increase in the unsaturation of the fatty acids of the flesh, but the flesh of the starving fish containing the highest concentration of docosa-hexaenoic acid does not develop more cold-storage off-flavour than those containing less (72). However, the apparent rises and falls of docosahexaenoic acid in this species are merely the results of outflow and inflow of triacyl glycerols.

There are usually traps for the unwary who try to derive generalised relationships from individual dynamic interactions. This is the way of much biological research.

BIBLIOGRAPHY

1. GA Reay. Factors affecting initial and keeping quality. Food Invest Bd DSIR Ann Rep 1957, p 3.
2. GE Shulman. Life Cycles of Fish. Physiology and Biochemistry. Moscow. Translated from Russian by N Kaner. New York and Toronto: John Wiley & Sons, 1974.
3. RM Love. Colour stability in cod (*Gadus morhua* L.) from different grounds. J Cons Int Explor Mer 35: 207–209, 1974.
4. G Hempel, JHS Blaxter. The experimental modification of meristic characters in herrings (*Clupea harengus* L.). J Cons Perm Int Explor Mer 26: 336–346, 1961.
5. RM Love, LJ Munro, I Robertson. Adaptation of the dark muscle of cod to swimming activity. J Fish Biol 11: 431–436, 1977.
6. RM Love. Eating raw fish in Europe. Fishing News Internat, March 1974: 47 only, 1974.
7. J Deufel. Physiological effect of carotenoids on salmonidae. Hydrologie 37: 244–248, 1975.
8. RM Love. The Chemical Biology of Fishes. 2. London: Academic Press, 1980, p 144.
9. S Ando, F Yamazaki, M Hatano, K Zama. Deterioration of chum salmon (*Oncorhynchus keta*) muscle during migration — III. Changes in protein composition and protease activity of juvenile chum salmon muscle upon treatment with sex hormones. Comp Biochem Physiol 83B: 325–330, 1986.
10. EM Donaldson, UHM Fagerlund. Effect of sexual maturation and gonadectomy at sexual maturity on cortisol secretion rate in sockeye salmon (*Oncorhynchus nerka*). J Fish Res Bd Can 27: 2287–2296, 1970.

11. T Kitahara. Behaviour of carotenoids in the chum salmon (*Oncorhynchus keta*) during anadromous migration. Comp Biochem Physiol 76B: 97–101, 1983.

12. GE Shulman, RM Love. The Biochemical Ecology of Marine Fishes. London: Academic Press, 1999. Advances in Marine Biology, AJ Southward, ed., Vol 36, p 106.

13. CH Brandes, R Dietrich. Observations on the correlations between fat and water content and the fat distribution in commonly eaten fish. Veröff Inst Meeresforsch Bremerh 5: 299–305, 1958.

14. MD Garcia, JA Lovern, J Olley. The lipids of fish. 6. The lipids of cod flesh. Biochem J 62: 99–107, 1956.

15. JA Lovern. Fat metabolism in fishes. XII. Seasonal changes in the composition of herring fat. Biochem J 32:676–680, 1938.

16. RJ Henderson, JR Sargent, CCE Hopkins. Changes in the content and fatty acid composition of lipid in an isolated population of capelin (*Mallotus villosus*) during sexual maturation and spawning. Mar Biol 78: 255–263, 1984.

17. K Takama, RM Love, GL Smith. Selectivity in mobilisation of stored fatty acids by maturing cod, *Gadus morhua* L. Comp Biochem Physiol 80B: 713–718, 1985.

18. DK Rowe, JE Thorpe. Suppression of maturation in male Atlantic salmon (*Salmo salar* L.) parr by reduction in feeding and growth during spring months. Aquaculture 86: 291–313, 1990.

19. GE Shulman. Characteristics of the chemical composition of Azov anchovy during spring and wintering migrations (in Russian). Rybnoye Khozyaistvo 8: 68–70, 1957.

20. GE Shulman. Dynamics of chemical composition of Azov Sea anchovy in relation to its biology (in Russian). Trudy Azovsko-chernomorskogo Nauchno-issledovatelnogo Instituta morskogo Rybno Khozyastva i Oceanografii 18: 130–144, 1960.

21. RM Love. The Chemical Biology of Fishes. Vol. 1. London: Academic Press, 1970, Fig. 85, p 229.

22. RM Love. Studies on the North Sea cod. III. Effects of starvation. J Sci Food Agric 9: 617–620, 1958.

23. RM Love. Water content of cod (*Gadus callarias* L.) muscle. Nature, Lond 185: 692 only, 1960.

24. CF Hickling. The natural history of the hake. Fishery Invest, Lond, Ser 2, 12(1): 78, 1930.

25. JH Orton. Reproduction and death in invertebrates and fishes. Nature, Lond 123: 14–15, 1929.

26. D Black, RM Love. The sequential mobilisation and restoration of energy reserves in tissues of Atlantic cod during starvation and refeeding. J Comp Physiol 156B: 469–479, 1986.

27. JR Burt. The course of glycolysis in fish muscle. In: JM Leitch, ed. Food Science and Technology, vol 1, Chemical and physical aspects of food. Proceedings of 1st International Congress on Food Science and Technology. London: Gordon and Breach, 1969, pp 193–198.

28. D Black, RM Love. Estimating the carbohydrate reserves in fish. J Fish Biol 32: 335–340, 1988.

29. RS Batty, CS Wardle. Restoration of glycogen from lactic acid in the anaerobic swimming muscle of plaice, *Pleuronectes platessa* L. J Fish Biol 15: 509–519, 1979.

30. PR Dando. Lactate metabolism in fish. J Mar Biol Ass UK 49:209–223, 1969.

31. CS Wardle. Non-release of lactic acid from anaerobic swimming muscle of plaice *Pleuronectes platessa* L.: a stress reaction. J Exp Biol 77: 141–155, 1978.

32. RM Love, M Muslemuddin. Protein denaturation in frozen fish. XII. The pH effect and cell fragility determinations. J Sci Food Agric 23: 1229–1238, 1972.

33. T Berg, U Erikson, TS Nordtvedt. Rigor mortis assessment of Atlantic salmon (*Salmo salar*) and effects of stress. J Food Sci 62: 439–446, 1997.

34. P Howgate. Post-harvest handling and processing. In: SM Stead, L Laird, eds. Handbook of Salmon Farming. London: Springer, in association with Chichester, U.K., Praxis Publishing, 2002, pp 187–202.

35. RM Love. The post-mortem pH of cod and haddock muscle and its seasonal variation. J Sci Food Agric 30: 433–438, 1979.

36. J Lavéty, OA Afolabi, RM Love. The connective tissues of fish. IX. Gaping in farmed species. Internat J Food Sci Tech 23: 23–30, 1988.

37. D Black. The metabolic response to starvation and refeeding in fish. Ph.D. dissertation, Aberdeen (Scotland) University, 1983.

38. RM Love, D Black. Dynamics of stored energy in North Sea cod (*Gadus morhua* L.) and cultured rainbow trout (*Salmo gairdneri* Richardson). In: J Mellinger, ed. Animal Nutrition and Transport Processes. 1. Nutrition in wild and domestic animals. Comp Physiol. Basel: Karger, 1990, pp 193–202.

39. SK Kamra. Effect of starvation and refeeding on some liver and blood constituents of Atlantic cod (*Gadus morhua* L.). J Fish Res Board Can 23: 975–982, 1966.

40. RM Love, I Robertson. The connective tissues of fish. I. The influence of biological condition in cod on gaping in frozen-thawed muscle. J Food Technol 3: 215–221, 1968.

41. RM Love, J Lavéty, PJ Steel. The connective tissues of fish. II. Gaping in commercial species of frozen fish in relation to rigor mortis. J Food Technol 4: 39–44, 1969.

42. RM Love. The Food Fishes. Their Intrinsic Variation and Practical Implications. London: Farrand Press, 1988, Fig. 86, p 166.

43. RM Love, J Lavéty, NG Garcia. The connective tissues of fish. VI. Mechanical studies on isolated myocommata. J Food Technol 7: 291–301, 1972.

44. RM Love. Protein denaturation in frozen fish. XI. The proportion of tissue water converted to ice. J Sci Food Agric 17: 465–471, 1966.

45. RM Love, J Lavéty. The connective tissues of fish. VII. Post-mortem hydration and ice-crystal formation in myocommata, and their influence on gaping. J Food Technol 7: 431–441, 1972.

46. K Yamaguchi, J Lavéty, RM Love. The connective tissues of fish. VIII. Comparative studies on hake, cod and catfish collagens. J Food Technol 11: 389–399, 1976.

47. RM Love, MA Haq. The connective tissues of fish. III. The effect of pH on gaping in cod entering rigor mortis at different temperatures. J Food Technol 5: 241–248, 1970.

48. RM Love, MA Haq, GL Smith. The connective tissues of fish. V. Gaping in cod of different sizes as influenced by a seasonal variation in the ultimate pH. J Food Technol 7: 281–290, 1972.

49. RM Love, MA Haq. The connective tissues of fish. IV. Gaping of cod muscle under various conditions of freezing, cold-storage and thawing. J Food Technol 5: 249–260, 1970.

50. RM Love, I Robertson, GL Smith, KJ Whittle. The texture of cod muscle. J Texture Studies 5: 201–212, 1974.

51. WP Cowie, WT Little. The relationship between the toughness of cod stored at −29C and its muscle protein solubility and pH. J Food Technol 1: 335–343, 1966.

52. HA Bremner, GM Laslett, J Olley. Taste panel assessment of textural properties of fish minces from Australian species. J Food Technol 13: 307–318, 1978.

53. RM Love, J Olley. Cold-storage deterioration in several species of fish, as measured by two methods. In: R Kreuzer ed. The Technology of Fish Utilisation. London: Fishing News (Books) Ltd, 1965, pp 116–117.

54. H-K Kim, I Robertson, RM Love. Changes in the muscle of lemon sole (*Pleuronectes microcephalus*) after very long cold-storage. J Sci Food Agric 28: 699–700, 1974.

55. RM Love. New factors involved in the denaturation of frozen cod muscle protein. J Food Sci 27: 544–550, 1962.

56. RM Love, I Robertson, J Lavéty and GL Smith. Some biochemical characteristics of cod (*Gadus morhua* L.) from the Faroe Bank compared with those from other fishing grounds. Comp Biochem Physiol 47B: 149–161, 1974.

57. RM Love, R Hardy, J Nishimoto. Lipids in the flesh of cod (*Gadus morhua* L.) from Faroe Bank and Aberdeen Bank in early summer and autumn. Mem Fac Fish, Kagoshima Univ 24: 123–126, 1975.

58. HA Bremner. Understanding the concepts of quality and freshness of fish. In: HA Bremner, ed. Safety and Quality Issues in Fish Processing. Boca Raton, FL: CRC Press, Cambridge: Woodhead Publishing Ltd., 2002, pp. 163–172.

59. KO Kelly. Factors affecting the texture of frozen fish. In: R Kreuser, ed. Freezing and Irradiation of Fish. London: Fishing News (Books) Ltd., 1969, pp 339–342.

60. TR Kelly. Quality in frozen cod and limiting factors on its shelf life. J Food Technol 4: 95–103, 1969.

61. AS McGill. An investigation into the chemical composition of the cold storage flavour components of cod. IFST mini-symposium on freezing. Inst Food Sci Technol U.K., 1974, pp 24–26.

62. AS McGill, R.Hardy, JR Burt, FD Gunstone. Hept-cis-4-enal and its contribution to the off-flavour in cold-stored cod. J Sci Food Agric 25: 1477–1489, 1974.

63. AS McGill, P Howgate, AB Thomson, G Smith, A Ritchie, R Hardy. The flavour of white fish and the relationship between the chemical analysis and sensory data. In: J Adda, ed. Proceedings of the 4th Weurman Flavour Research Symposium, Dourdon, France. Amsterdam: Elsevier Science Publishers, 1985, pp 149–164.

64. IP Ashton. Understanding lipid oxidation in fish. In: HA Bremner. ed. Safety and Quality Issues in Fish Processing. Boca Raton, FL: CRC Press; Cambridge: Woodhead Publishing Ltd., 2002, pp 254–285.

65. DA Ross. Lipid metabolism of the cod *Gadus morhua* L. Ph.D. Dissertation, 1977, Aberdeen (Scotland) University.

66. RM Love. Variability in Atlantic cod (*Gadus morhua*) from the northeast Atlantic: a review of seasonal and environmental influences on various attributes of the flesh. J Fish Res Board Can 32: 2333–2342, 1975.

67. GA Dunstan, J Olley, DA Ratkowsky. Major environmental and biological factors influencing the fatty acid composition of seafood from Indo-Pacific to Antarctic waters. Recent Res Devel Lipids Res., 3: 63–86, 1999.

68. MV Bell, RJ Henderson, JR Sargent. The role of polyunsaturated fatty acids in fish. Comp Biochem. Physiol 83B: 711–719, 1986.

69. DA Ross, RM Love. Decrease in the cold store flavour developed by frozen fillets of starved cod (*Gadus morhua* L.). J Food Technol 14: 115–122, 1979.

70. JM Jay. Modern Food Microbiology. New York: Van Nostrand Reinhold Company, 1970, pp 26–28.

71. A Kolakowska, J Olley, GA Dunstan. Fish Lipids. Chapter 12. In: ZE Sikorski, A Kolakowska, eds. Chemical and Functional Properties of Food Lipids. Boca Raton, FL: CRC Press, 2003, pp 221–264.

72. L Ludovico-Pelayo, A Hume, RM Love. Seasonal variations in flavour change of cold-stored rainbow trout. In: P Zeuthen, JC Cheftel, C Eriksson, M Jul, H Leninger, P Linko, G Varela, G Vos, eds. Thermal Processing and Quality of Foods. London and New York: Elsevier Applied Science, 1984, pp 659–663.

36 Edible Shellfish: Biology and Science

Natalie A. Moltschaniwskyj
Tasmanian Aquaculture and Fisheries Institute, University of Tasmania

CONTENTS

I. INTRODUCTION

Commercially important edible shellfish include marine and freshwater animals that belong to two major taxonomic groups: the Mollusca and the Crustacea. The hard external shell is a common external characteristic that often results in the two groups being given the common name shellfish. Both groups are invertebrates that have no internal skeleton or vertebrae, and in most cases the external shell provides protection, support to soft body tissues, and a mechanism to deal with changes in the environment. The cephalopods (squid, cuttlefish, and octopus) do not possess an external shell, but are grouped with the shellfish by virtue of their molluscan taxonomic status.

This chapter will describe the general biology of edible shellfish species that are commonly eaten. The two major taxonomic groups will be described separately because their biology is so different. Given the importance of these species in harvest and aquaculture industries this provides the focus of research activities. The range of topics covered particularly relate to those aspects of the biology that are relevant to these animals as food, in particular the lifecycle, reproductive and feeding biology, movement, and behaviour.

II. MOLLUSCAN SHELLFISH

Molluscan shellfish have no typical shape or form and the body plan is changed and adapted to the environment (1). Edible mollusc predominantly belong to three broad groups: bivalves (e.g., oysters, mussels, and scallops), gastropods (e.g., abalone and *Trochus*), and cephalopods (e.g., squid, cuttlefish, and octopus), according to the number and arrangement of the shell(s). Bivalve molluscs have two symmetric or asymmetric shells joined by a hinge, while the gastropod molluscs have a single shell, and most of the cephalopods have no external shell. Most of the edible molluscan shellfish are aquatic, mainly marine or estuarine, and relatively sedentary. Commonly harvested and cultured species include the ubiquitous Pacific oyster (*Crassostrea gigas*), the flat oysters (*Ostrea* spp.), scallops (*Pecten* and *Astropecten* spp.), a variety of mussel species (*Perna* and *Mytilus* spp.) and the small burrowing clam species (*Mercenaria* spp. and *Mya arenaria*), abalone (*Haliotis* spp.) and snails (*Trochus* spp.). The cephalopods either have an internal calcareous cuttlebone (cuttlefish), an internal chitinous pen (squid), or no shell (octopus). The only terrestrial edible mollusc is the land snail (*Helix*).

A. GENERAL BIOLOGY

The crystalline calcareous shell of the bivalves and gastropods is present from the larval form and provides protection from environmental changes, e.g., temperature, salinity and aerial exposure, and predators. Some species are attached to a hard substrate as adults by either a cement-like substance (e.g., oysters) or a byssus thread (e.g., mussels). The size and extent of musculature in bivalve molluscs is varied; oysters have small amounts of muscle tissue while scallops have a very large adductor muscle. Bivalves that burrow in soft sediments have an extendable muscular foot which they use to pull themselves into the sediment. Some species have limited mobility, for example, scallops can rapidly clap the two shells together which can result in the rapid ejection of water and using this jet propulsion small distances (<1 m) can be moved. Small clam species that burrow in soft sediment move by rolling around in the waves and then re-burrow using the muscular foot. Gastropods, which are more mobile than bivalves, have a large powerful muscular foot beneath the single shell which is used to pull the animal along hard substrates. The muscle tissue of scallops and abalone is the primary tissue eaten, with the gonad and digestive tissue removed, although the scallop may be marketed as "roe-on." In contrast oysters and mussels are eaten whole, typically with the gonad and digestive system as well as the small muscle. The athletes of the molluscan world are squid, which may undertake extensive migrations; the muscular body is essential for movement, respiration, and structural support.

B. LIFE-HISTORY

Most molluscs have a bipartite lifecycle with a relatively short planktonic free-living veliger followed by the benthic adult phase (Figure 36.1). Individuals hatch as a trochophore and within 24 hours a larval shell develops. This is followed by the development of a veliger (also referred to as D-veliger due to the distinctive D shape), which lasts between several days to a month. A short planktonic phase (<5 days) is typical of abalone species and the veligers are non-feeding. A longer veliger stage (c. 20 days) is more typical of many bivalve molluscs and the veligers actively

feed on phytoplankton using the velum, a fringe of beating cilia. The velum also provides some mobility in the water column, allowing the veligers to adjust their position in the water column. The planktonic phase is important for a number of reasons as it allows offspring to colonise new areas and also for these individuals to avoid the risk of predation close to the reef. Once the veliger is ready to settle onto the substrate, a change in morphology begins and a 'pediveliger' develops, which has a foot that extends out of the shell and is able to test the substrate before deciding to settle (Figure 36.1). Once a suitable place for settlement has been selected the individual secretes either a cement or byssal threads to attach itself. The pediveliger finally undergoes metamorphosis into the adult form and takes up a sedentary lifestyle.

In some species the female brood the veligers inside her shell, e.g., the flat oyster (*Ostrea* sp.). Fertilisation occurs within the shell environment of the female, using sperm released into the water by males. Veligers are attached by the velum to the female ctenidia (gills) and they use the food filtered by the mother's ctenidia. Shortly before metamorphosis veligers are dislodged and expelled out of the mother.

The selection of settlement sites by the larvae is critical for species with a sedentary adult phase, as conditions for feeding and reproducing must ensure survival. The site must provide water currents for delivery of food and removal of faecal wastes and there must be individuals of the same species in close proximity for reproduction. Selection of settlement sites can range from general to specific, and is generally species-specific. The presence of conspecific adults can be important as this suggests a suitable environment for growth and reproduction (2). Characteristics of the rock surface, e.g., rugosity or presence of algal and bacteria

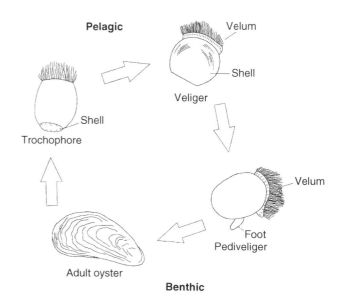

FIGURE 36.1 Lifecycle of an oyster.

species (3), or sediment characteristics of soft shores may be cues for settlement. Factors affecting settlement are of interest to ecologists, particularly with respect to human impacts on shore environments that may modify the substrate and make it become less suitable for settlement by juveniles. Many aquaculture ventures rely on collection of wild spat for on-growing to adults and are exploring suitable materials to enhance settlement rates (4). Hatcheries also need to use suitable surfaces to maximise settlement rates of juveniles. It is possible to induce settlement of pediveligers in culture conditions by exposing them to neuroactive compounds, e.g., L-DOPA. This induces settlement and the metamorphosis of the pediveliger into a spat, without the pediveliger going through the process of selecting a suitable substrate (5). The use of these compounds by shellfish hatcheries allows efficient management of stock by forcing settlement to occur when the hatchery is ready to deal with large numbers of juveniles and it also promotes synchronous settlement of larvae.

C. REPRODUCTION

All molluscs reproduce sexually, with separate sexes in most species (dioecious), e.g., mussels and abalone. However, some species have both sexes present simultaneously (monoecious or hermaphrodism), e.g., scallops have a creamy coloured testis and orange coloured ovary present at the same time. In a few species sex change can occur (sequential hermaphrodism), with sperm being produced in smaller younger individuals, then a change to female in some bigger and older individuals. Many *Crassostrea* oyster species are hermaphroditic or will undergo sex change, which is a function of both secondary genes and/or environmental conditions (6). In oysters and mussels the reproductive tissue is not contained within a discrete organ or region of the body. Instead, gametes are produced in tissue surrounding the digestive system. Other shellfish, e.g., abalone and scallops, have a discrete organ for gamete production which is clearly identifiable.

Spawning in most temperate molluscs is seasonal, either in the spring/summer, e.g., oysters and scallops, or winter, e.g., mussels. Many tropical species may not show distinct spawning seasons, but a component of the population will always have some individuals that are reproductively mature and spawning. Prior to egg and sperm production individuals build up a store of energy reserves, usually glycogen. At some point during the year an environmental trigger, usually water temperature or day length, will stimulate the use of these glycogen reserves to produce gametes (7). Once gametes start to be produced individuals undergo a period of maturation before being ready to spawn and at this point the gonad may constitute most of the individuals' body mass. Gametes are released either in a single spawning episode or in a series of spawning episodes over several days to weeks. After the release of

gametes there is a dramatic decrease in the mass of soft tissue and the flesh is flaccid and watery. As the tissue is unsuitable for consumption animals are not harvested for approximately a month after spawning to allow accumulation of carbohydrate reserves to begin.

As many molluscs are sedentary, gametes are released into the water column and fertilisation of eggs by sperm is external; this is referred to as broadcast spawning. Spawning in the population is co-ordinated to ensure that males and females release gametes simultaneously and that the density of gametes in the water is high enough to ensure high rates of fertilisation. The co-ordination of broadcast spawning within the population may be triggered by factors such as changes in water temperature or salinity, lunar and tidal cycles, and increasing or decreasing day length.

The squid, octopus, and cuttlefish have a more complex reproductive system in which, often following extensive courtship, the male passes packages of sperm (spermatophores) to the female (8). The female fertilises each egg and packages it in a jelly-like substance that provides protection for the developing embryo. Eggs are either attached to the reef or macroalgae individually (e.g., octopus and cuttlefish), laid in finger-like strands with multiple eggs in each strand (e.g., reef-associated squid) or unattached large balloon-like masses that float in ocean currents (e.g., oceanic squid) (8). Female octopus will guard and care for the eggs until they hatch, as miniature adults that are capable of jetting, inking, capturing prey, and avoiding predators. The squid and cuttlefish do not provide any parental care of the eggs or the juveniles.

D. TRIPLOIDY PRODUCTION

Oysters, mussels, and clams are eaten whole without the gonad and digestive tissue removed prior to consumption. Taste tests have demonstrated that consumers prefer to eat oysters when the tissue is full and creamy and full of glycogen reserves, but before the animal is ripe with gametes (9). Given that individuals have high levels of glycogen for relatively short periods this means that marketable stock may only be available seasonally. Over the past 10 years there has been interest in the production of sterile oysters, i.e., individuals that are unable to produce gametes. In sterile individuals glycogen reserves are accumulated but not used for reproduction, resulting in the production of stock that are suitable for consumption over an extended period of the year. An additional benefit of producing sterile animals is that exotic aquaculture species may be farmed in new areas without the risk of introducing a species that may be detrimental to native flora and fauna (10).

In molluscs sterile animals have been obtained through the production of triploid individuals (11), which have 50% more chromosomal material than ordinary diploid individuals. Currently, triploid Pacific oysters are being produced by the aquaculture sector in the U.S. and

Australia (see review 12). Triploid oysters usually exhibit reduced gonad development and acceptable meat condition through the inhibition of spawning and faster growth rates (12). Currently the most popular and successful method of producing triploid molluscs is by blocking the formation and release of a polar body in the newly fertilised egg (11). The additional chromosomal material in cells prevents or limits the process of cell division associated with gamete production (meiosis), thereby causing an extra set of chromosome to be retained. Methods used to induce triploidy in oysters are either physical, e.g., temperature and pressure, or chemical, e.g., caffeine. Immersion of newly fertilised eggs in cytochalasin B, a fungal antibiotic, is currently the most effective method and is commonly used by commercial hatcheries.

Methods of triploidy induction in the aquaculture industry need to ensure a high percentage of triploids (ideally 100%), high survival rates and low rates of abnormality in the veligers, and consider operator safety and consumer acceptance. Unfortunately cytochalasin B is classified as a carcinogen and is a potential hazard to operators at bivalve hatcheries. The future use of cytochalasin B is in doubt, both because of its toxicity and because triploidy induction is not 100% effective, usually about 80%. Current research is exploring methods of producing triploids commercially that are potentially less hazardous and more reliable. One recent approach has been to cross tetraploids, individuals with double the normal genetic complement, with diploids (13). This method has successfully produced 99.9% triploids and the veligers have survivorship rates that are comparable with normal diploid oysters. Furthermore, these triploid individuals are produced without the use of artificial treatments and toxic substances.

E. FEEDING

Bivalve shellfish (oysters, mussels, clams, and scallops) are filter feeders, using specialised gill structures (ctenidia) to selectively remove phytoplankton and organic matter from the water. The ctenidia have cilia that generate current and the movement of water into the animal as an inhalant flow. Each species is able to select particles within a very narrow size range (3–24 μm). Particles that are too small or too large are rejected by the ctenidia, bound in mucus, and expelled in a strand through an exhalent flow as pseudofaeces. Particles that are suitable for ingestion are passed to the mouth (labial palps) using the cilia on the surface of the ctenidia. Ingested food is bound in a strand of mucus and enters the digestive system by being drawn in by a crystalline style, which releases digestive enzymes. Once the digestive process has been completed faeces are released into the exhalent current and moved away from the animal.

Oysters can filter several litres of seawater daily and the advanced filter feeding mechanism allows bivalves to regulate the efficiency of particle retention and absorption. The rate of pumping and retention of food particles is modified in response to the density of particles in the water while maintaining respiratory functions. If the density of particles in the water is too high the ctenidia become clogged and rates of pseudofaeces production increases. Other factors that affect feeding rates in bivalves are water current, water temperature, salinity, turbidity, and dissolved oxygen (14).

Most edible gastropod molluscs are herbivorous grazers (e.g., abalone), but there are a small number that are carnivorous predators (e.g., trochus, conch, and whelks). Grazing molluscs use a radula, a protrusible tongue-like structure with a complex ribbon of teeth, with which they scrape algae and biofilm off rocks or tear and cut macroalgae. As teeth at the front of the radula wear out they are replaced by secretion of new teeth at the back of the radula. Some of the carnivorous molluscs have specialisations of the radula that allow them to bore holes through the shell of prey or harpoon prey. After maceration of food the radula carries particles of food backwards and into the digestive tract. Digestion is usually extracellular in the stomach and digestive gland.

Squid, octopus, and cuttlefish are voracious carnivorous predators. Squid and cuttlefish predominantly eat crustaceans and fish which are captured using contractile tentacles (the longest of the arms). Octopus species eat predominantly crustaceans and molluscs and they are able to deal with the hard outer parts by either drilling through the shell or in the case of bivalves pulling apart the two valves (15). Members of this group have a parrot-like beak which is used to tear tissue into small pieces and the salivary gland secretes enzymes that are used to break down flesh prior to ingestion. Once in the stomach enzymes secreted by the digestive gland continue digestive processes.

F. SHELLFISH-ASSOCIATED DISEASE OUTBREAKS

Ingested particles, including bacteria and viruses, are digested by bivalves and then either absorbed into the tissues or excreted. As result of pathogenic micro-organisms being retained and absorbed molluscan shellfish become vectors of bacterial and viral pathogens. The rate of pathogenic micro-organism uptake and retention is a function of the density of micro-organisms in the water being filtered. Oysters may accumulate pathogens to levels as much as four times greater than levels in the water from which food is being removed (16). If shellfish (e.g., oysters) are consumed raw and whole with the digestive system still intact the pathogenic microbes present in the tissue and gut pose a health risk to the consumer. In the U.S. from 1991–1998 the consumption of raw or partially cooked shellfish resulted in more than 2,000 illnesses.

Viral agents that are of chief concern in world shellfish industries are human enteric virus, Norwalk virus, and hepatitis A. All cases of food-borne viral diseases from shellfish have occurred due to human faecal contamination in areas where shellfish are harvested and the consumption of shellfish that is raw, steamed, incompletely cooked, or frozen. Bacterial agents, particularly *Vibrio* spp. have been identified as being pathogenic or potentially pathogenic to humans (17). Unlike virally associated disease outbreaks, contamination by *Vibrio* tends to be more sporadic and involve individual cases (18). Where outbreaks have occurred they have been associated with *V. vulnificus* septicaemia with 50% mortality rates (19), or epidemics of cholera caused by consumption of raw shellfish contaminated with *V. cholerae* 01 (20). *Vibrio* spp. naturally occur in estuarine and marine waters and are not associated with faecal contamination; however, numbers of *Vibrio* in shellfish can increase in improperly stored shellfish (21). Some pathogenic bacteria may not naturally occur in marine and estuarine environments, but are associated with incorrect storage, faecal pollution, or infected food handlers may contaminate shellfish. Enteric bacterial pathogens that have been implicated in shellfish associated disease outbreaks are *Clostridium perfringens*, *Salmonella*, and *Shigella* (22).

A factor influencing the timing and occurrence of shellfish-related outbreaks is the ability of shellfish to selectively accumulate viruses. Selective accumulation can be attributed to the feeding mechanism when there is ionic bonding of viral particles to the shellfish mucus. There is evidence that the seasonal occurrence of shellfish-related illnesses by enteric viruses may be due to oysters undergoing seasonal physiological changes that affect their ability to accumulate viral particles (16).

Current practice to remove pathogenic micro-organisms is to put shellfish through a depuration process after harvest. This process provides conditions for shellfish to purge their digestive system of their gastrointestinal contents, thereby supposedly removing the micro-organisms that had been taken up during filter feeding. Depuration is typically conducted in an isolated system, with temperature controlled re-circulating seawater. The seawater should be continually cleaned, e.g., using a UV steriliser attached to the re-circulating system. The temperature of the system needs be stable and set at a level that encourages the shellfish to filter the clean seawater.

The ability of depuration to remove pathogens is dependent upon a number of factors. (1) The molluscs must feed normally in the system; if active pumping and filtering of seawater do not occur then microbes present in the gut will not be purged. (2) Variability in the loads of micro-organisms among individual animals may result in differential removal of pathogens. (3) The depuration conditions (water temperature and salinity) that are suitable for normal feeding are species specific. (4) Microbes that have been incorporated into body tissues will not be removed, only those pathogens currently resident in the gut and on the

gills will be removed. (5) The ability of the disinfection technique to inactivate the purged microbes; if purged microbes are not killed by the disinfection system then re-infection of animals in the depuration system is likely.

G. SHELLFISH TOXICITY

Paralytic shellfish poison (PSP), amnesic shellfish poison (ASP), and diarrheic shellfish poisoning (DSP) are caused by naturally occurring biotoxins that accumulate in molluscan shellfish (review 23). These biotoxins are caused by microscopic toxin-producing dinoflagellate phytoplankton that naturally occur in marine waters, normally in amounts too small to be harmful. However, on occasion, a combination of warm temperatures, sunlight, and nutrient-rich waters can cause rapid plankton reproduction, or "blooms." The toxins in the microalgae ingested by shellfish build up and become concentrated in the gut and somatic tissues. This may result in mass mortalities either through toxins affecting the shellfish, or high densities of phytoplankton clogging the ctenidia and causing asphyxia. The toxins also pose a health hazard to humans consuming contaminated shellfish. As cooking does not break down the toxins and many shellfish are eaten raw, the toxin is ingested by humans and other predators. Although first recognised and described in Canada, PSP and ASP have been found worldwide (24).

Paralytic shellfish poisoning is caused by a suite of neurotoxins (saxitoxins) produced by species such as *Alexandrium* spp. and *Gymnodinium catenatum*. The type and storage of paralytic shellfish toxins in bivalves species vary considerably. Mussels, clams, and scallops appear to accumulate high levels of saxitoxins, while in oysters the levels of the toxins are low or absent (23). Amenesic shellfish poisoning is linked to the presence of domoic acid produced by the diatoms *Pseudonitzschia* spp. and *Nitschia* (24). Shellfish appear to concentrate the toxin and again the response to the toxin is species specific. Scallops and mussels appear to be unaffected, while oysters become physiologically stressed. Diarrheic shellfish poisoning occurs when shellfish containing okadaic acid are eaten. Okadaic acid and its derivatives are produced by the dinoflagellates *Dinophysis* spp. and *Prorocentrum lima* (25). As with other toxins there are differential effects among the bivalve species and seasons and the length of time the toxins remain in the tissue. Blue mussels in Sweden can retain toxins for up to five months after accumulation, although high levels of toxins are not necessarily associated with any known health effects (23).

The economic cost of both human pollutants and naturally occurring biotoxins is high for countries that have shellfish harvest and aquaculture industries. The presence of toxic algae has been responsible for the collapse of bivalve populations in Alaska, and fisheries and aquaculture are closed for extended periods in countries such as Sweden,

Norway, the U.S., Spain, and Australia (23). The costs incurred with the occurrence of toxic algae blooms are associated with (1) the need to have expensive shellfish monitoring programs to assess the presence of contaminants, (2) the cessation of harvesting and selling of produce, and (3) the development and running of depuration systems. Current research is focussed on how effective the depuration process is at removing the toxins and how the toxins are removed from different organs. Understanding how toxins are accumulated, transformed, and eliminated allows the time course of the toxic episode to be predicted and hence how long harvest of animals should be suspended. It is possible that toxins are transformed in the body tissues and then excreted from the animal over time, although there is evidence that metabolism of the PSP toxins is more complex than just a transformation of toxic compounds (26).

H. BIOACCUMULATION AND BIOMONITORING

As a result of the relatively sedentary lifestyle of many shellfish and their modes of feeding (filter feeding and deposit feeding) many species ingest or uptake and retain trace metals present in the environment. Molluscan shellfish can accumulate heavy metals (e.g., copper) and organic contaminants (e.g., pesticides) in body tissues. Marine molluscs tend to accumulate arsenic, cadmium, copper, lead, mercury, silver, and zinc, but have a low tendency to accumulate chromium. As a result of the accumulation, concentrations of these trace metals in body tissues can be many times higher than present in the environment (27). This accumulation of heavy metals and contaminants has two problems. The first is that many of these animals are prey of higher order predators and as a result serious pollutants enter the food chain and are present in higher concentrations further up the food chain (biological amplification). The second problem is that many shellfish species and their predators are a food source for humans and as a result are a health hazard.

One advantage of sedentary molluscs accumulating heavy metals, viruses, and bacteria is that they provide a time-integrated measure of the bioavailability of these contaminants (see review 28). As such, some bivalves are used as sentinel species to monitor or assess concentrations of contaminants available for uptake in the environment. Such biomonitoring involves assessing the effects and levels of contaminants in the environment on animals. Uptake of contaminants varies among and within species as a function of factors such as size, age, sex, and among geographic locations due to environmental factors such as temperature and salinity. However, it is possible to move healthy individuals into cages at sampling locations and assess the levels of contaminants after a period of time. For example, mussel species (*Mytilus edulis* and *M. californicus*) are commonly used around the U.S. coastline as sentinel species for biomonitoring because they are endemic, abundant on many coastlines, and tolerate translocation. Another example, is the use of oysters to assess the bioavailability of tributyltin (29), a compound has been implicated as a cause of shell thickening in many oyster species (e.g., 30).

III. CRUSTACEAN SHELLFISH

Edible crustaceans all belong to a group known as decapods which are the largest and most specialised of the crustacean species. They are characterised by a heavily segmented body and a chitinous exoskeleton which provides an outer protective shell that is articulated like body armour. All edible crustaceans are aquatic, with most occupying marine and estuarine habitats, but some crayfish and prawns are found in freshwater. Crustaceans are benthic but highly mobile, e.g., prawns swim regularly and some lobsters undertake long migrations. Commonly harvested and cultured edible crustaceans include prawns (shrimps), both freshwater (e.g., *Macrobrachium* spp.) and marine (e.g., *Penaeus* spp. *Metapenaeus* spp.), crabs (e.g., *Callinectes sapidus, Scylla serrata*), clawed lobsters (e.g., *Homarus* spp. *Nephrops* spp.), spiny lobsters (e.g., *Palinurus* spp., *Panulirus* spp., and *Jasus* spp.) and crayfish (crawfish and yabbies).

The common names used to describe edible crustaceans are often confusing. The distinction between prawns and shrimps may be based upon the taxonomic group and the habitat of the adults (31). Freshwater species, e.g., *Macrobrachium,* are often referred to as prawns, while marine and estuarine species (e.g., penaeids) are shrimps. Alternatively, size of the adults is often used to distinguish among the two names; with shrimps being small species and larger species prawns. Similarly, there is often confusion over use of the common names lobster and crayfish. Again the distinction is made taxonomically, but generally lobsters are marine (this includes both clawed and non-clawed species), and crayfish or crawfish are freshwater.

A. GENERAL BIOLOGY

The general body plan is similar among the decapod crustaceans with two sections making up the body: the fused head and thorax (cephalothorax) and the tail (abdomen). Each section is made up of a series of segments, but the number of segments and specialisation of segments varies among species. The cephalothorax is completely fused with no external segmentation visible, the shell (carapace) surface of the cephalothorax may be smooth or covered with spines depending on the species. In contrast, the abdomen is distinctly segmented. Attached to both sections are specialised paired appendages, the number of which depends on taxonomy and function of the appendage. Around the head and mouth appendages are modified for food capture and feeding (mandibles, maxillae, and maxillipeds). The head also has antennae, antennules, and a pair of stalked compound eyes. The corneal surface of the eyes is convex and, when on a stalk, the cornea may cover an arc of $>180°$. The remaining appendages (pereiopods) on the cephalothorax are used in crawling or walking. The first pair of pereiopods in lobsters and crabs is modified as a claw (chela), which may be large and distinctively coloured. Appendages attached to the abdomen (pleopods) are used for swimming, as well as egg attachment in some species, e.g., crabs and *Macrobrachium*. The last pair of pleopods (uropods) and the telson, at the terminal end of the abdomen, forms a tail fan that can be used for locomotion using a rapid flexing motion. Appendages may be specialised in some species for fighting, courting, and egg handling.

Prawns in the genus *Penaeus* and *Macrobrachium* are commercially the most important in the world. They are cylindrical with a well-developed abdomen and an exoskeleton that is thin and flexible. Many penaeid shrimps use the pleopods to excavate shallow burrows in soft bottoms during periods of inactivity. Shrimps move predominantly by rapidly beating the large fringed pleopods, but rapid flexion of the abdomen and the tail fan will allow fast backward movement.

Lobsters and crabs have a dorso-ventrally flattened body, with a heavier and stronger exoskeleton, and the strong claws (chelipeds) have a lot of musculature which is a commercially valuable part of the animal. The abdomen in crabs is reduced and folded under the cephalothorax, the uropods are absent, but large and strong legs on the cephalothorax are used for walking which is the primary mode of locomotion. Reduction of the abdomen allows rapid crawling and they commonly move sideways. In contrast to crabs, lobsters have a very well-developed tail (abdomen), which has a high monetary value given the high tail to body ratio. The legs allow lobsters to crawl while the muscular tail allows fast flexing of the abdomen resulting in rapid backward movement. Spiny lobsters (*Jasus, Palinurus,* and *Panulirus* spp.), present in both tropical and temperate waters, do not have chelipeds, and it is the meat in the tail that is prized. The shovelnose or slipper lobsters (*Scyllarus* and *Thenus* spp.) have a dorso-ventrally flattened body with short, flattened antennae, compared with the cylindrical body and long antennae in clawed and spiny lobsters.

B. Life History

Crustaceans have a more complex life history than molluscs and each stage has distinct behavioural and ecological characteristics (32). Most crustaceans have separate sexes and generally hold their eggs, either in brood sacs or attached to the abdominal appendages. Like many marine invertebrates the crustaceans have a bipartite life history, with a free-living, planktonic larval phase, followed by a benthic adult phase. The stages, forms, and time spent as

larvae are highly variable among the decapod crustaceans, often depending on how much development occurs in the egg. However, all the decapod larvae undergo a series of developmental stages during which the larvae metamorphoses into a more advanced form until the final adult form is developed. The different stages of the life history are often associated with different and distinct habitats.

Penaeid prawns undergo several distinct larval and juvenile phases that are associated with different habitats (33). The embryonic phase is short and, as a result, the newly hatched larvae (nauplii) are less morphologically developed than some of the newly hatched forms of other decapod crustaceans (Figure 36.2). The nauplius is the first larval phase and it has only three pairs of appendages which are all used for swimming. Furthermore, the nauplii do not feed and are supported by the maternal yolk reserves that are present when they hatch. The nauplii metamorphose first into feeding protozoea and then a mysis (Figure 36.2), both of which live in offshore waters. Metamorphosis of the mysis produces a megalopa which migrates to brackish inshore waters. The megalopa undergoes metamorphosis into a benthic juvenile which uses estuaries as a nursery habitat. Adults then move from the estuaries back to deeper and full salinity water offshore.

Freshwater prawns, such as *Macrobrachium*, and crabs hatch out as planktonic zoea, advanced larval forms that use thoracic appendages to swim upside down (Figure 36.3). The freshwater *Macrobrachium* have a zoea that lives in estuarine environments as it needs brackish water (34); they are carnivorous, eating zooplankton, worms, and larval forms of other invertebrates. Zoea undergoes a series of developmental stages before becoming a postlarva (*Macrobrachium* prawns) or megalopa (crabs). *Macrobrachium* pelagic postlarvae move upstream towards less saline water swimming with the dorsal side uppermost. During this migration the postlarvae start to undergo the transition to the adult benthic habit. The size at which postlarvae start the upstream

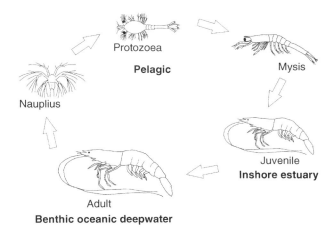

FIGURE 36.2 Lifecycle of a penaeid prawn.

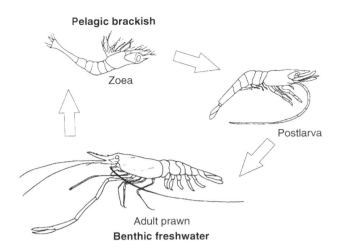

Pelagic brackish

Zoea

Postlarva

Adult prawn

Benthic freshwater

FIGURE 36.3 Lifecycle of the freshwater prawn *Macrobrachium*.

migration is thermally driven and low temperatures can bring about migration in small individuals.

The larval and post larval phase of *Homarus* lobsters is about 6–8 weeks long. They have a very short nauplius phase and quickly metamorphose into a larval form; the first three larval stages are very similar to the zoea phase of the crabs and are sometimes called mysid larvae (35). The zoea of *Homarus* lobsters undergoes a series of developmental stages, ultimately becoming a postlarva (equivalent to the megalopa). Postlarvae undertake the transition from a planktonic to a settling and finally a benthic juvenile through behavioural response to light, gravity, and water pressure. The early benthic juvenile phase is highly cryptic as these individuals use shelters until they are big enough to avoid predation.

The life history of spiny lobsters (palinurids) differs from the other decapod Crustacea in that the nauplius stage is very short (several hours) before development into a larvae (phyllosoma). The phyllosoma is dorso-ventrally flattened, transparent, and very thin (36), a body form that is suitable for the passive dispersal of these larvae in ocean water currents. The phyllosoma phase is very long, lasting as much as 391 days and potentially larvae are carried considerable distances (>1000 km). This extended dispersal phase makes it difficult to locate and collect the phyllosoma in oceanic waters and as a result little is known about their biology. There are 7–13 phyllosoma stages and the last phyllosoma stage metamorphoses into a non-feeding, transparent, and free-swimming puerulus (postlarvae). Puerulus use energy stores acquired as phyllosoma until metamorphosis into a feeding post-puerulus or juvenile. Benthic puerulus are vulnerable to predation and therefore initially hide in cracks and crevices, or in burrows. As a result of this cryptic behaviour it has been difficult to determine the cues important in the selection of settlement sites and habitats. Once juveniles are large enough to protect themselves from predators they begin to adopt a more typical adult lifestyle and a scavenging and omnivorous diet.

C. GROWTH AND ECDYSIS

The hard exoskeleton of the crustaceans is a non-living layer that plays a role in protection, gaseous exchange, and support. However, it is unable to increase in size, and therefore growth is constrained by this hard exoskeleton. An increase in size occurs only after the old exoskeleton has been shed (moult) and a new exoskeleton has formed and hardened. The process of moulting is called ecdysis and as a result the process of growth is incremental rather than continuous. During the moulting process the animal increases in size by absorption of water, but somatic growth occurs between moults. Many aspects of the life of crustaceans, including growth and reproduction, are directly under the control of the physiological changes associated with the moulting cycle.

The process of moulting can be divided into five distinct stages (37):

1. Premoult. Animals are getting ready to discard the old exoskeleton by starting to break down the exoskeleton. Enzymes are released that start dissolving the old skeleton, and calcium and other materials are absorbed from the old shell. The epidermal cells beneath the cuticle increase in size and begin to secrete the new exoskeleton which is deposited beneath the old exoskeleton.
2. Moult. As the animal increases in size through ingestion of water the internal pressure causes the weakened old exoskeleton to split at the membrane between the cephalothorax and the abdomen. The animal pulls itself out of the old exoskeleton and emerges out of the original shell. The new exoskeleton is present, but is soft and pliable and the animal is defenceless until it hardens. Water continues to be absorbed to increase body size.
3. Postmoult. The new exoskeleton hardens by the re-deposition of calcium and other soluble materials that were stored from the dissolution of the old endoskeleton. The exoskeleton is still soft and animals are vulnerable to predation.
4. Intermoult. This is the period between moults during which time the water absorbed by the animal during the moult is replaced by somatic tissue. In the early stages of the lifecycle, when the larvae and juveniles are growing quickly and undergoing metamorphosis, the intermoult periods are relatively short. However, once the adult phase is reached, moulting occurs less frequently and the intermoult periods are longer.

Crustaceans may lose appendages through accidents or shed appendages voluntarily in a process called autotomy (38). In the decapod crustaceans there is a specific site on an appendage at which autotomy can occur. This means that, regardless of where the damage has occurred, the appendage will always be dropped off at that point. Once an appendage has been shed cells at the breakpoint begin to enlarge and a regenerated appendage is formed, complete with exoskeleton. Regeneration can only occur during the premoult phase; therefore the animal cannot form a new limb until it is passes through the next moult cycle. If an individual has lost a large number of appendages then the intermoult phase may be shortened and the next moult cycle will start earlier (38).

Growth rates of many crustacean species have largely been described under culture conditions. However, models of population dynamics and stock assessment required for fisheries management rely heavily on accurate estimates of growth rates of wild animals. In fish, hard structures like scales and ear bones (otoliths) grow in such a way as to leave a record of somatic growth. However, the lack of permanent hard structures in crustaceans that contain a record of somatic growth is problematic when estimates of age are need. Tagging studies on wild populations have been used to estimate growth rates (e.g., 39); however, this relies on adequate recovery rates of tagged individuals and retention of tags during moulting cycles. Recently, it has been discovered that both freshwater and marine crustaceans have deposits of an autofluorescent neurolipofuscin that accumulates in the eyestalk ganglion and the concentration of which is correlated to the physiological age of the individual (40, 41). The neurolipofuscin pigment can be extracted from the tissue using solvents and the intensity of fluorescence is used as a measure of neurolipofuscin concentration (42). Alternatively, tissue sections prepared histologically can be viewed under a specialised microscope and the density of fluorescing granules estimated (41). As deposition rates of neurolipofuscin are related to the physiological, not chronological, age of individuals the rates of deposition are modified by environmental factors such as temperature (43). Despite this lipofuscin concentration has the potential to be used to estimate growth rates and determine year-class strength in populations for fisheries management.

D. HORMONAL CONTROL OF MOULTING AND REPRODUCTION

The cyclic processes of moulting and reproduction have a major impact on adult physiology and are under the control of hormones (44). The neurosecretory X-organ, located in the eyestalk of many decapod crustaceans, produces moult-inhibiting hormone (MIH) and vitellogenesis-inhibiting hormone (VIH). These hormones once released by the X-organ are sent to a sinus gland, also in the eyestalk, and then released into the hemolymph (blood). If the

concentration of moult-inhibiting hormone decreases in the hemolymph this promotes the release of moulting hormones (ecdysteroids) from the Y-gland, located near the mandible muscles. Low concentrations of moulting hormones are present during postmoult and intermoult periods, but they increase during early premoult which starts the processes of moulting, followed by a decrease prior to moulting. Likewise, low concentrations of VIH result in the release of reproductive hormones and the process of egg production begins.

Although the moulting cycle is controlled hormonally factors that initiate moulting are often external, e.g., food, temperature, and day length. Given that aquaculture requires the control of all aspects of an animal lifecycle, including growth and reproduction, there is some understanding of the hormonal control of moulting and how this can be manipulated. In the 1970s it was found that destroying the eye stalk (ablation) will induce non-gravid female shrimp to mature and produce eggs. Eyestalk ablation will reduce the intermoult phase, induce stimulation of ovarian development, and accelerate the rate of ovarian development due to the absence of the moult-inhibiting and vitellogenesis-inhibiting hormones (45). Today eyestalk ablation is used in almost every marine and seawater shrimp aquaculture facility to shorten the intermoult phase, accelerate growth rates, and to produce animals with soft shells for market. In aquaculture the ability to control reproductive activities and ensure the production of eggs and sperm when required has many advantages; (1) it allows development of selective breeding programs, (2) it is possible to promote reproductive development and not be seasonally dependent on natural reproductive cycles, and (3) control spawning activities which can increase the proportion of females that spawn at any time. Therefore, hatcheries use eyestalk ablation as a way to advance reproductive activities and synchronise spawning.

E. REPRODUCTION

The sexes are separate in the decapod crustaceans; in females a pair of ovaries and in males a fused pair of testis is located in the cephalothorax. In some species, shortly after the female becomes sexually mature she must undergo a moult at which time she is able to mate and receive sperm from males. Males have an opening (gonopore) on the last pair of walking legs through which sperm enclosed in a package (spermatophore) is deposited between the fourth pair of walking legs on the female thorax. In prawns, females have a spermatophore receptacle called a thelycum. Females lay eggs through a gonopore after sperm deposition and the sperm is used to fertilise the eggs.

Penaeid prawns release the fertilised eggs into the ocean, but most species transfer eggs to the underside of the abdomen. The egg brood is kept aerated and clean of debris by the fanning movement of the pleopods. The eggs develop here until the larvae hatch out. A female carrying a brood of eggs is described as being in berry and the eggs can be seen as a mass of orange due to the presence of carotenoids. As the eggs develop they change colour from orange to brown and then finally grey several days before hatching. Larvae hatch from the eggs and remain attached to the brood chamber for up to 24 hours. The female dislodges the larvae by lifting her tail and vigorously beating the pleopods. Larvae are usually released at night to minimise risk of predation and on a high tide to ensure the transport of larvae away from the reef. Generally newly released larvae respond negatively to gravity and positively to light such that they move up in the water column into surface waters.

F. FEEDING

Larvae and postlarvae are predators, feeding actively on phytoplankton and invertebrate zooplankton (46). They are able to feed on suspended particles and will actively chase and capture zooplankton. However, they are largely opportunistic feeders and may be cannibalistic when held in high densities. Among the adult forms there is a diversity of feeding modes, but many of the edible crustaceans are scavengers and/or predators and many species are omnivorous. The diet of scavengers (e.g., prawns) includes a range of dead plant and animal matter including detrital aggregates. The prey of predators (e.g., lobsters and crabs) includes worms, crustaceans, molluscs, and fish. Cannibalism may occur at very high densities in culture conditions, particular in crabs and especially when individuals have just moulted and are soft-shelled. Food detection is primarily through chemosensory structures on the head. The antennae and antennules can detect low concentrations of chemicals and are used for distance chemoreception, while appendages around the mouth are used for contact chemoreception and are able to detect high concentrations of organic compounds (33).

Once food is captured or found the maxillipeds are used to hold and crush, and the mandibles and maxillae are used for ingestion. At this point food is broken into fine pieces before being passed into the foregut. In decapod crustaceans the muscular foregut is divided into two chambers; a cardiac stomach and a pyloric stomach. In the cardiac stomach a gastric mill with chitinous teeth is used to further grind food down before it is passed into the pyloric stomach. Digestive processes are initiated in the foregut with the release of enzymes secreted by a digestive gland. Partially digested food is then passed from the foregut through to the mid-gut which is the primary site of enzyme activity and nutrient absorption and the final stages of digestion occur. Enzymes are produced by digestive tubules that form a glandular appendage (digestive gland), which is involved in enzyme synthesis and secretion, nutrient absorption, and lipid storage.

Although toxic poisoning in humans through the consumption of crustaceans is not typically associated in the same way that molluscan shellfish are, there is evidence that crustaceans may accumulate toxins in their tissues (review 47). Uptake of toxins by crustaceans occurs when they consume bivalves that have toxins and toxins are accumulated in the hepatopancreas (48). However, poisoning of humans rarely occurs because the muscle tissue of crustaceans is predominantly eaten, but if the whole animal is cooked (e.g., crab soup) or the digestive gland is eaten then toxins accumulated in this gland can be transferred to humans. In crabs there is evidence that toxicity may be the direct result of the consumption of the macroalgae *Jania* (47).

G. MOVEMENT AND MIGRATION

For many crustaceans planktonic larvae are typically the dispersal phase of the life history, in those species which have a very long larval phase, e.g., spiny lobster, phyllosoma, can be dispersed considerable distances. Movement patterns of phyllosoma are poorly known because of difficulties in sampling animals that occur at low densities in large oceanic water masses. More recently the approach to studying movement patterns of these larvae has involved integrating oceanographic circulation patterns with larval distribution. In some cases there is evidence that phyllosoma may be retained within gyre systems ensuring that they return to the reef. Although dispersion of larvae and phyllosoma is affected by current systems, they can actively orientate themselves in the water column and effectively control some of their movement. Many species undertake vertical migrations in the water column, thereby using water currents at different depth strata to allow some control in their return to the reef (49). For example, the Western Australian spiny lobster early in the larval phase stays in surface waters which ensures movement offshore away from the reef, but when mid- and late-stage phyllosoma avoid surface waters they are more affected by subsurface circulation which returns them back to the coast (49).

Adult lobster species undergo movements that can occur on a range of spatial scales from 100s of metres to 100s of kilometres (32). Some of these movements are temporally and spatially predictable, with directional migration involving thousands of individuals as seen in some of the spiny lobsters (50). The reasons for the movements are varied and in many cases unknown (36). However, they may be related to spawning activities, redistribution of juveniles, movement out of sub-optimal environments, facilitating exchange of genetic material, or environmental factors, e.g., temperature. In some cases during the migrations lobsters follow predictable routes in single file for 2–4 days, which can make them vulnerable to over-fishing. On the Scotian shelf tagged adult *Homarus* lobster have recorded migrations in excess of

200 km over a year, but they often return to the same area, suggesting long-range homing behaviour (32). The mechanisms used by spiny lobsters to orientate themselves and be able to undertake directional migrations and display homing behaviour are unclear. Recent work has explored the use of magnetic orientation by spiny lobsters through experiments that relocate animals and use magnets to modify the magnetic field around the individual. It appears that spiny lobsters (*Panulirus argus*) do use magnetic information to orientate themselves and be able to return home. Interestingly, individuals appear to use their relative position to the home site to orientate; in other words, they use a geomagnetic map (51).

H. BEHAVIOUR

Unlike largely sedentary molluscan shellfish, many edible crustaceans, particularly lobsters and crabs, display advanced social and reproductive behaviour (32). However, much of what is understood about decapod behaviour has been obtained in aquaculture conditions, where animals are held in high densities and inter-individual interactions are frequent. In nature most decapods are largely solitary, nocturnal, and remain hidden. Spacing and occupancy of shelters is a major aspect of their social behaviour (52). Lobsters at high densities will obtain and defend mates and shelters through dominance hierarchies. In particular, dominant males are able to evict subordinate males and are able to gain and retain mates. In contrast, at low densities dominance hierarchies are not formed, but individuals are highly territorial. Although the differences in behaviour under conditions of high and low density are evident in culture conditions, these may also be seen in the wild associated with ontogenetic changes in behaviour. For example, juvenile spiny lobsters are solitary and cryptic, but intermediate-sized individuals will aggregate together in shelters.

The use of the claws in behaviour is diverse, e.g., male fiddler crabs wave their claw to entice females into the burrow for mating, and in contrast, some lobsters and crabs will use the well developed claws in aggressive interactions. Some factors that affect aggressive interactions and their outcome are size, moult stage, and gender of the individuals involved (53). The nature of dominance interactions can range from ritualised displays to physical fights which can result in the loss of limbs. Typically individuals that are bigger and with larger claws will have a greater chance of winning encounters. However, there are distinct changes in aggression during the moult cycle. An individual may maintain a high level of aggressiveness until the point that the old shell has been moulted, possibly so shelter that will provide protection during the soft-shell state can be obtained and maintained. Recently moulted individuals will be less aggressive as the soft-shell provides little protection during interactions.

IV. CONCLUSION

The shellfish represent a biologically diverse group of marine invertebrates that includes very important harvest and aquaculture species world-wide. The sedentary lifestyle of many species makes populations vulnerable to changes in the environment that will affect recruitment of juveniles into adult populations and the quality of adults as a food source. Aspects of biology, ie growth, ecology, reproduction, feeding, and movement that have been studied in detail are often related to our need to manage wild stocks and for the successful culture of new species. Given that these are invertebrates and many of these species are low in the food chain, it may be considered that they will be less vulnerable to over-exploitation. However, the advanced behaviour and extended pelagic larval phase of some lobster species, about which we know little, means that over-fishing is possible and aquaculture of these species will be challenging.

ACKNOWLEDGMENTS

Thanks to Dr Danielle Johnston for providing invaluable expertise and discussion about crustacean biology and Dr Keith Martin-Smith for constructive review of the chapter.

REFERENCES

1. J Morton. Molluscs. London: Hutchinson & Co, 1979, pp 264.
2. MJ Keough. Responses of settling invertebrate larvae to the presence of established recruits. J Exp Mar Biol Ecol 231:1–19, 1998.
3. R Roberts. A review of settlement cues for larval abalone (*Haliotis* spp.). J Shellfish Res 20:571–586, 2001.
4. J Holliday. Effects of surface orientation and slurry coating on settlement of Sydney rock, *Saccostrea commercialis*, oysters on PVC slats in a hatchery. Aquac Eng 15:159–168, 1996.
5. SL Coon, D Bonar. Induction of settlement and metamorphosis of the Pacific oyster, *Crassostrea gigas* (Thunberg), by L-DOPA and cetecholamines. J Exp Mar Biol Ecol 94:211–221, 1985.
6. X Guo, D Hedgecock, W Hershberger, K Cooper, S Allen. Genetic determinants of protandric sex in the Pacific oyster, *Crassostrea gigas* Thunberg. Evolution 52:394–402, 1998.
7. PA Gabbott. Storage cycles in marine bivalves: a hypothesis concerning the relationship between glycogen metabolism and gametogenesis. In: H Barnes. ed. Ninth European Marine Biol. Symposium Aberdeen. Aberdeen: Aberdeen University Press, 1975, pp 191–211.
8. R Hanlon, J Messenger. Cephalopod behaviour. Cambridge: Cambridge University Press, 1996, pp 232.
9. SK Allen Jr, SL Downing. Consumers and experts prefer the taste of sterile triploid over gravid diploid Pacific oysters (*Crassostrea gigas*, Thunberg, 1793). J Shellfish Res 10:19–22, 1991.

10. E Grosholz. Ecological and evolutionary consequences of coastal invasions. Trends Ecol Evol 17:22–27, 2002.

11. AR Beaumont, JE Fairbrother. Ploidy manipulation in molluscan shellfish: a review. J Shellfish Res 10:1–18, 1991.

12. J Nell. Farming triploid oysters. Aquaculture 210:69–88, 2002.

13. X Guo, GA DeBosse, SK Allen Jr. All-triploid Pacific oysters (*Crassostrea gigas* Thunberg) produced by mating tetraploid and diploids. Aquaculture 142:149–161, 1996.

14. B Bayne. The physiology of suspension feeding by bivalve molluscs: an introduction to the Plymouth "TROPHEE" workshop. J Exp Mar Biol Ecol 219:1–19, 1998.

15. MA Steer, JM Semmens. Pulling or drilling, does size or species matter? An experimental study of prey handling in *Octopus dierythraeus* (Norman, 1992). J Exp Mar Biol Ecol 290:165–178, 2003.

16. W Burkhardt III, KR Calci. Selective accumulation may account for shellfish-associated viral illness. Appl Environ Microbiol 66:1375–1378, 2000.

17. MT Kelly, FW Hickman-Brenner, JJ Farmer. *Vibrio*. In: A Balows, WJ Hausler, KL Herrmann, HD Isenberg and HJ Shadomy. eds. Manual of clinical microbiology. Washington, D.C.: American Society for Microbiology, 1991, pp 384–395.

18. PM Desmarchelier. *Vibrio cholerae* and other vibrios. In: KA Buckle, A Davey, MJ Eyles, AD Hocking, KG Newton and EJ Stuttard. eds. Foodbourne microorganisms of public health significance. Sydney: AIFST (NSW Branch) Food Microbiology Group, 1989, pp 167–176.

19. CO Tacket, TJ Barrett, JM Mann, MA Roberts, PA Blake. Wound infections caused by *Vibrio vulnificus*, a marine *Vibrio*, in inland areas of the United States. J Clinical Micro 19:197–199, 1984.

20. KC Klontz, S Rippey. Epidemiology of molluscan-bourne illnesses. In: WS Otwell, GE Rodrick and RE Martin. eds. Molluscan shellfish depuration. Boca Raton: CRC Press, 1991, pp 47–58.

21. NT Son, GH Fleet. Behaviour of pathogenetic bacteria in the oyster, *Crassostrea commercialis*, during depuration, re-laying, and storage. Appl Environ Microbiol 40:994–1002, 1980.

22. JE Kvenberg. Nonindigenous bacterial pathogens. In: DR Ward and C Hackney. eds. Microbiology of Marine Food Products. New York: Van Nostrand Reinhold, 1991, pp 267–284.

23. SE Shumway. A review of the effects of algal blooms on shellfish and aquaculture. J World Aquac Soc 21:65–104, 1990.

24. G Hallgraeff. A review of harmful algal blooms and their apparent global increase. Phycologia 32:79–99, 1993.

25. JH Landsberg. The effects of harmful algal blooms on aquatic organisms. Rev Fish Sci 10:113–390, 2002.

26. K Sekiguchi, T Ogata, S Kaga, M Yoshida, M Fukuyo, M Kodama. Accumulation of paralytic shellfish toxins in the scallop *Patinopecten yessoensis* caused by the dinoflagellate *Alexandrium catenella* in Otsuchi Bay, Iwate Prefecture, northern Pacific coast of Japan. Fish Sci 67:1157–1162, 2001.

27. M Depledge, P Rainbow. Models of regulation and accumulation of trace metals in marine invertebrates. Comp Biochem Physiol 97C:1–7, 1990.

28. D Boening. An evaluation of bivalves as biomonitors of heavy metals pollution in marine waters. Environ Monit Assess 55:459–470, 1999.

29. H Phelps, D Page. Tributyltin biomonitoring in Portuguese estuaries with the Portuguese oyster (*Crassostrea angulata*). Environ Technol 18:1269–1276, 1997.

30. M Almeida, J Machado, J Coimbra. Growth and biochemical composition of *Crassostrea gigas* (Thunberg) and *Ostrea edulis* (Linne) in two estuaries from the North of Portugal. J Shellfish Res 18:139–146, 1999.

31. AW Fast. Introduction. In: AW Fast and LJ Lester. eds. Marine shrimp culture: principles and practices. Amsterdam: Elsevier, 1992, pp 1–7.

32. P Lawton, KL Lavalli. Postlaval, juvenile, adolescent, and adult ecology. In: JR Factor. ed. Biology of the Lobster *Homarus americanus*. San Diego: Academic Press, 1995, pp 47–88.

33. JH Bailey-Brock, SM Moss. Panaeid taxonomy, biology and zoogeography. In: AW Fast and LJ Lester. eds. Marine shrimp culture: principles and practices. Amsterdam: Elsevier, 1992, pp 9–27.

34. D Ismael, M New. Biology. In: M New and W Valenti. eds. Freshwater prawn culture. Oxford: Blackwell Science, 2000, pp 18–40.

35. JR Factor. Introduction, anatomy, and life history. In: JR Factor. ed. Biology of the Lobster *Homarus americanus*. San Diego: Academic Press, 1995, pp 1–11.

36. RN Lipcius, DB Eggleston. Ecology and fishery biology of spiny lobsters. In: BF Phillips and J Kittaka. eds. Spiny Lobsters: Fisheries and Culture. 2000.

37. DM Skinner. Moulting and regeneration. In: DE Bliss and LH Mantel. eds. Biology of Crustacea. New York: Academic Press, 1985, pp 43–146.

38. P Hopkins, C-K Chung. Regeneration in the fiddler crab, *Uca pugilator*: histological, physiological, and molecular considerations. Am Zool 39:513–526, 1999.

39. IF Sommers, GP Kirkwood. Population ecology of the grooved tiger prawn *Penaeus semisulcatus*, in the northwestern Gulf of Carpenteria, Australia: growth, movement, age structure and infestation by the bopyrid parasite *Epipenaeon ingens*. Aust J Mar Freshw Res 42:349–367, 1991.

40. MRJ Sheehy. The potential of morphological lipofuscin age-pigment as an index of crustacean age. Mar Biol 107:439–442, 1990.

41. MRJ Sheehy, RCA Bannister, JF Wickins, PMJ Shelton. New perspectives on the growth and longevity of the European lobster, *Homarus gammarus*. Can J Fish Aquatic Sci 56:1904–1915, 1999.

42. S-J Ju, DH Secor, HR Harvey. Growth rate variability and lipofuscin accumulation rates in the blue crab *Callinectes sapidus*. Mar Ecol Prog Ser 244:197–205, 2001.

43. MRJ Sheehy, RCA Bannister. Year-class detection reveals climatic modulation of settlement strength in the European lobster, *Homarus gammarus*. Can J Fish Aquatic Sci 59:1132–1143, 2002.

44. ES Chang, SA Chang, EP Mulder. Hormones in the lives of crustaceans: an overview. Am Zool 41:1090–1097, 2001.

45. T Okumura, K Aida. Effects of bilateral eyestalk ablation on molting and ovarian development in the giant freshwater prawn, *Macrobrachium rosenbergii*. Fish Sci 67:1125–1135, 2001.

46. GP Ennis. Larval and postlarval ecology. In: JR Factor. ed. Biology of the Lobster *Homarus americanus*. San Diego: Academic Press, 1995, pp 23–46.

47. SE Shumway. Phycotoxin-related shellfish poisoning: bivalve molluscs are not the only vectors. Rev Fish Sci 3:1–31, 1995.

48. H Oikawa, T Fujita, M Satomi, T Suzuki, Y Kotani, Y Yano. Accumulation of paralytic shellfish poisoning toxins in the edible shore crab *Telmessus acutidens*. Toxicon 40:1593–1599, 2002.

49. BF Phillips. The circulation of the southeastern Indian ocean and the planktonic life of the western rock lobster. Oceanogr Mar Biol Annu Rev 19:11–39, 1981.

50. WF Hernkind. Movement patterns and orientation. In: F Vernberg and W Vernberg. eds. The Biology of Crustacea: Behaviour and Ecology. New York: Academic Press, 1983, pp 41–106.

51. L Boles, K Lohmann. True navigation and magnetic maps in spiny lobsters. Nature 421:60–63, 2003.

52. M Salmon, G Hyatt. Communication. In: F Vernberg and W Vernberg. eds. The biology of Crustacea: Behaviour and Ecology. New York: Academic Press, 1983, pp 1–40.

53. J Atema, R Voight. Behaviour and sensory biology. In: JR Factor. ed. Biology of the Lobster *Homarus americanus*. San Diego: Academic Press, 1995, pp 313–348.

37 Aquaculture of Finfish and Shellfish: Principles and Applications

C.G. Carter
Tasmanian Aquaculture and Fisheries Institute, University of Tasmania

CONTENTS

I. INTRODUCTION

Aquaculture has been described as both the art and science of growing aquatic animals and plants. It has been practiced for thousands of years by different societies using a wide variety of approaches to growing aquatic organisms in water. The origins of aquaculture will probably never be known because there are no ancient aquaculture-specific artifacts or even the remains of ponds or dams that can be distinguished from other uses such as water storage or for growing crops (1). However, there is some historical evidence from around the world that shows aquaculture has existed for thousands of years and in several different places. There is a bas-relief of fishing, probably for *Tilapia*, from fish ponds in ancient Egypt 4000–4500 years ago (1). Several types of integrated aquaculture/agriculture systems were known in South America (1) and there is the 1500–1800-year-old Ahupua'a marine aquaculture in Hawaii (2). Fish ponds were well known in Europe during the Roman Empire and Middle Ages (3). In many ways China could be considered the head and heart of traditional aquaculture, certainly in freshwater, since it is here that large scale aquaculture has the longest history and has shown the most evolution. Pond culture of common carp was recorded over 3000 years ago and about 2500 years ago Fan Li, considered the father of Chinese fish culturists, wrote "Yang Yu Ching" or a "Treatise on Pisciculture" to detail practical methods for freshwater aquaculture (4, 5). Recently, within the last half of the twentieth century, aquaculture has shifted into an industrial phase and global production has increased dramatically. Currently, aquaculture of finfish, molluscs and crustaceans (shellfish) produces 37.5 million tonnes per year and accounts for 29% of the total global fishery harvest (6). Aquaculture continues to expand and has increased its share of the global fishery from less than 4% in 1970 (6). Aquaculture has great potential to expand further and to meet an increasing human demand for protein. To accomplish this dramatic changes in current structures and practice may be necessary. The debate on sustainable aquaculture is only just beginning (7–10).

There are many ways to farm fish: they may be housed in ponds, tanks, cages and raceways; held inside or outside in salinities from freshwater through to seawater; and grown with or without other fish, animals or plants that are also available for harvesting. Aquaculture can be divided very broadly into extensive and intensive forms. It can be argued that intensive aquaculture is distinct from other forms, whereas there is a continuum from extensive to semi-intensive systems. Under intensive aquaculture, water provides physiological support for the fish but all other means of sustaining life are provided from external sources, the most obvious being the supply of nutritionally complete feeds. Extensive aquaculture is viewed as a system which manages the natural productivity of water to grow products that can be used. The level of management, the types and magnitude of inputs and the diversity of production all contribute to the complexity of non-intensive systems. Thus, Chinese polyculture of up to eight species of finfish is a good example of semi-intensive aquaculture at one end of the continuum. Annual gross yields in Chinese polyculture are reported to reach 20 tonnes per hectare although the median is six to eight tonnes (11). In contrast, extensive systems at the other end of the continuum, such as managed lakes, would rarely exceed 0.5 tonnes per hectare per year (see p. 37-10).

Carp species account for by far the largest portion of global finfish production with the majority of these grown in China (6). Production is based around polyculture within ponds and their integration within wider agriculture systems (11). Outside of China, carp are produced in many countries and systems, including intensive pond and tank production of common carp in Europe and Israel (12) and semi-intensive pond polyculture of common, Indian and Chinese major carp in India. Aquaculture of salmonid fishes, including Atlantic salmon, rainbow trout and Pacific salmon, is the largest intensive finfish aquaculture system in the world and has now overtaken channel catfish aquaculture, one of the first intensively farmed finfish species. Many countries have some salmonid aquaculture and the major producers are Norway, the United Kingdom, Canada and Chile. Nevertheless, the various carp species with more than 15 million tonnes per year dwarf salmonid culture with one tenth of this production (Figure 37.1). The other most important finfish are *Tilapia* and milkfish (6). *Tilapia* species (1.05 million tonnes) are cultured around the world under different systems: they are the mainstay of aquaculture in Africa where they are mainly grown extensively in small ponds; they are used in semi-intensive freshwater polyculture in China, as well as being grown intensively in tanks and ponds in Israel and the United States. Milkfish (0.46 million tonnes) is a major brackish water aquaculture species in South East Asia and a large expansion occurred after the development of commercially effective artificial propagation techniques in Taiwan (13). Species new to aquaculture are constantly under development with considerable focus on higher value marine species. The major hurdle to overcome with most marine species is closure of the life-cycle, which is often technically difficult due to the small size, fragility and unknown feeding and husbandry requirements of marine larvae. Wild-caught fry or juveniles are still used in the aquaculture of many species but the long-term sustainability of this practice is questionable. This is a major challenge that may take many years to solve for some species (see p. 37-6).

Finfish account for approximately half of aquaculture production with crustaceans and molluscs accounting equally for the majority of the remainder (6). Of the top 29 aquaculture species three bivalve molluscs are in the top ten by production with over 8 million tonnes whereas the predominant crustaceans are prawns with about 1 million tonnes per year (Figure 37.1). The monetary value reflects the socioeconomic and technical basis of particular aquaculture systems so that high value prawns and salmonids have a far larger share of the total monetary value of aquaculture production than of the production weight (Figure 37.2). Although aquaculture production is based on at least 210 different plant and animal species the majority comes from the few groups discussed above (6). In 2000 (6) nine countries produced more than half a million tonnes of aquaculture product, including plants, and were headed by China (32 million tonnes), India (2 million tonnes), Japan (1.3 million tonnes) and the Philippines (1 million tonnes).

The aim of this chapter is to provide an overview of the range of aquaculture species and systems found. A more detailed discussion of the principles governing aquaculture practice will use selected examples taken from intensive and semi-intensive aquaculture.

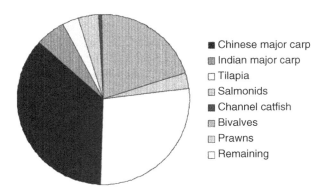

FIGURE 37.1 Distribution (% of total production weight) of major aquaculture groups in 2000 (35). Categories detailed in Table 37.1.

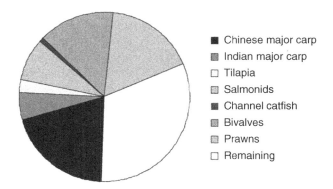

FIGURE 37.2 Distribution (% of total US$ value) of major aquaculture groups in 2000 (35). Categories detailed in Table 37.1.

II. INTENSIVE AQUACULTURE SYSTEMS

The principles that drive intensive aquaculture are based around maximising production in the shortest length of time. Intensive aquaculture is most often based on monoculture of high value species in developed countries. Animals may be contained in a wide variety of structures including net-cages (Figure 37.3), tanks, raceways and earthen ponds (Figure 37.4). Fish are held at high densities and fed nutritionally complete feeds, usually at maximum rations. As has been found in intensive agriculture industries, fish are sensitive to disease and periods of high mortality have been associated with many intensive aquaculture industries.

Reproduction and propagation of major freshwater finfish (i.e., salmonids, carps and catfish) is relatively straightforward and achieved with a high success rate. One of the important features of these finfish groups is the large

FIGURE 37.3 Use of cages in different forms of aquaculture a) 24-m² cages for marine Atlantic salmon farming, b) ring-cages for marine Atlantic salmon farming, c) small 4-m² cages for grouper farming, d) small 2-m² cages for barramundi grow-out in freshwater ponds.

FIGURE 37.4 Fish holding in (a) concrete tanks used for marine finfish, (b) concrete raceways for rainbow trout, (c) indoor fibreglass tanks for rainbow trout and (d) a drained earthen pond for freshwater silver perch.

size and robust nature of eggs and the ease of feeding compound feeds immediately at, or soon after, first-feeding. This is in marked contrast to marine species in which far greater investment in technologies for rearing larvae and for supplying live feeds has been made. It should be pointed out that some industries, such as Asian sea bass (14), are adopting extensive practices to produce feeding fry for intensive grow-out (see p. 37-6).

Nutrition and feed development are critical issues at present. Aquafeeds use large amounts of valuable fish meal and fish oil and considerable effort is being directed at developing alternative ingredients (15–17). The proportion of the global fish meal supply used in aquafeeds is reported to have increased from 10% (1988) to 35% (1998) (9). These authors also point out that this is due to a reallocation of a relatively static global harvest of fish meal from other feeds to aquafeeds; aquaculture has not caused any increase in fish meal production. Successful experimental feeds that are free of marine products have been developed for larger channel catfish, and following on from this the total animal meal now used in commercial catfish feeds is less than 2% (18). However, the omnivorous channel catfish is one of the few non-carnivorous finfish farmed intensively and the complete removal of marine ingredients from feeds for carnivorous species poses more difficulties. For example, salmonids have limited ability to use dietary carbohydrate (19), and this places constraints on the type of plant-based ingredients that can be used since raw meals contain large amounts of carbohydrates. A likely trend will be the development of high protein ingredients from plant and microbial sources. Products from grains and legumes such as soybean, lupins, canola and peas and microbial sources such as bacteria are currently being investigated (20, 21). Commercial Atlantic salmon feeds can contain over 38% fish oil, making the sector the major user of global fish oil production. This level of use and the probability of increased competition for fish oil from other sectors (e.g., nutraceuticals) have the potential to severely restrict further expansion of salmon aquaculture. Fortunately, it now appears feasible to replace up to 50% of the fish oil in Atlantic salmon feeds with plant oils (16), although there may be salmon health implications under some circumstances (22).

Maintaining animal health and disease control are of major importance in all sectors of aquaculture. There are examples of severe disease outbreaks that have led to huge losses in production. The effects of viruses, including white spot syndrome, monodon baculovirus and yellow head virus, have almost decimated the marine prawn industry; losses up to 1996 were estimated to have reached US$ 3 billion (23). The Atlantic and Pacific salmon industries have suffered from major viral (e.g., IPN, infectious pancreatic necrosis; ISA, infectious salmon anaemia), bacterial (e.g., furunculosis; bacterial

kidney disease) and parasitic (e.g., sea lice; ameobic gill disease) diseases. There was a major outbreak of furunculosis in the early 1990s that resulted in yearly losses of US$ 77 million. Fortunately, the disease has declined since 1993 due to the use of effective vaccines (24). Vaccination against a variety of potential pathogens is now a major management procedure in the Norwegian salmon industry and over 90% of all stocks are vaccinated by injection into the intraperitoneal (visceral) cavity (24). Vaccination is only a part of the health care management programs now in place in the salmon industry. These recognise the need for trained personnel, routine monitoring and quick diagnosis; to minimise stress through appropriate stocking densities, careful and minimal handling; site rotation to break the disease cycle; cooperation between farms to ensure single-year class stocking at a location in order to prevent vertical transfer and break disease cycles (24). Aquaculture is also vulnerable to environmental impacts that include predators, blooms of toxic algae, contamination from land run-off and disasters such as oil spills. Aquatic animals are bathed in the contaminated water and it is often much more difficult to move them away from an aquatic threat compared to terrestrial situations.

Offshore marine finfish aquaculture is now being developed in response to human-related pollution and other stresses on the marine coastal environment as well as user conflicts with commercial and recreational groups (25). Technology required for holding and servicing stocks must be far more resilient than for inshore farming and greater mechanisation is needed to reduce the need for manual intervention (25). Assessment of health and growth status, removal of dead fish and feeding are required on a regular basis; grading and harvesting should be possible in any weather. This involves greater use of technology, it is more expensive to purchase and has higher running costs which must be balanced by increased production efficiency (26). There is increasing evidence that growth is faster and more efficient in larger cages (27). Large submersible cages for offshore locations are under development for several aquaculture sectors including salmon and flatfish (28). One example was the Tension Leg Cage, which could be submerged in rougher weather to reduce wave damage at the surface (28). In addition to these open production systems there have been significant advances in closed production system technology. Closed systems are usually land based, use tanks and rely on technology and management to maximise water quality and minimise water use through reuse. This is achieved with water reticulation and physical filtration systems that aid the removal of solid and suspended organic material, heat exchangers to maintain water temperature and reduce heating costs, biofilters containing a microbial flora that removes various harmful nitrogenous compounds and UV filters to reduce bacterial loads.

A. SALMONIDS

Around ten salmonid species (members of the family Salmonidae) are farmed in 60 countries (29) and over 90% of aquaculture is based on Atlantic salmon, rainbow trout and coho salmon. Salmonid species of interest are naturally found in temperate areas of the northern hemisphere, *Oncorhynchus* species from the Pacific and *Salmo* species from the Atlantic. Demand from recreational fisheries and aquaculture places them as global species with a considerable southern hemisphere presence (30). Rainbow trout have been cultured for many years. Denmark pioneered pond-based production of plate-sized fish at the end of the nineteenth century (30). In the last ten years Atlantic salmon has become the major salmonid species due to a huge expansion in sea-cage farming in Norway followed by Scotland, Canada and Chile. Small juvenile Atlantic salmon, called parr, have brown sides with complex patterns of spots and darker stripes. Adults are typically streamlined and silver scaled with prominent dorsal, pectoral and pelvic fins; the tail should be distinct and slightly forked although farmed fish often have worn fins. Rainbow trout has been described as the Pacific cousin of Atlantic salmon due to the similarities in shape, patterns and silvery colour as well as similar reproductive characteristics (31). Coho salmon are also known as silver salmon. Immature fish have a metallic blue dorsal surface that silvers on the sides; mature males have bright red sides and bright green heads and backs (32).

Atlantic salmon are typically anadromous (return from the sea to spawn in freshwater) with freshwater and sea-water phases in their life-cycle. Mature males and females return to freshwater sometime in the 12 months before they spawn. These large impressive fish of up to 30 kilogram famously migrate up the rivers and streams that they last swam down as immature parr several years previously. Once in the spawning grounds the female makes a hollow (redd) in gravelly stream beds where the male fertilises the eggs as they are released. The buried eggs hatch into a yolk-sac stage (alevin) and emerge as fry that start feeding on animal prey. The fry grow into parr that then undergo smoltification, a metamorphosis taking several months, to enable migration into the sea. After two to five years at sea (sea-winters) the fish return as mature adults. Some fish mature and return after one sea-winter and are called grilse. Aquaculture initially recreated this natural life-cycle but varying degrees of manipulation are now used to promote rapid and uniform growth, minimise maturation and maximise harvest over as much of the year as possible.

Broodstock are often removed from a production run on the basis of size and external appearance. They are then conditioned prior to spawning. Selective breeding is used. In Norway it is estimated that 65% of the Atlantic salmon and rainbow trout produced originate from the National Breeding Program (33). This program has incorporated

growth, age at sexual maturation, disease resistance and flesh quality as selection characteristics (33). Broodstock conditioning is best in freshwater and synchronous maturation is achieved through the use of hormonal preparations as well as keeping the fish under the same conditions, sometimes males and females together or sometimes in recirculating water allowing chemicals released by the fish to act as they would in the wild (29). Hand "stripping" of eggs and milt, by applying firm pressure along the abdomen, followed by gentle mixing, fertilises the eggs. Hand-stripped Atlantic salmon and rainbow trout can be re-conditioned for the next season. When larger numbers of eggs and milt are required they are removed directly following euthanasia. This procedure has to be adopted with Pacific salmon which only spawn once (30). Sperm are inactive until they touch water so contact is minimised until mixing with eggs. Eggs absorb water on fertilisation, become larger and "sticky" and then harden. Straightforward procedures are followed to ensure maximum fertilisation rates that typically exceed 95%. Fertilised eggs are then incubated under dim or red lights in gently flowing water. Adequate water flow is required to ensure good supply of oxygen and the removal of soluble wastes as well as debris. Incubators are of different designs that vary between deeper cylindrical upwellers to shallow troughs. The California or undercurrent system uses hatching trays positioned in shallow troughs and is considered the most effective design (30). On hatching the alevins use their yolk-sac before being weaned directly onto compound feeds and the fry stage is reached on loss of the yolk-sac. There is considerable individual variation in feeding success and growth rate, so size-grading is used to control size distribution and prevent cannibalism (amongst the smaller stages). Development now proceeds from the parr to the smolt stage. Attention has been focused on controlling this process in order to manage the supply of fish into the major production stage. All in all there has been a highly effective transfer of scientific and technical principles reflected by 80–90% survival from hatch to smolt (30).

Smolt usually have to be transported from the hatchery to the grow-out site; this can be by land, air or sea and care is taken to reduce stress by providing dark aerated conditions and to transfer smolt via pipes directly into the cages. The "smoltification window" describes a period during the season when parr must be of a certain size to start the process of smoltification. It is normally in the spring for Atlantic salmon but more variable for Pacific salmon. In contrast, successful sea-water transfer of rainbow trout, a non-smolting species, is related to larger size (29). The majority of Atlantic salmon on-growing is conducted in sea-cage systems. These are essentially large bag-nets held on floating frames that are anchored to ensure the frames stay in the same place. Bag-nets are five to 20 metres deep and their shape is maintained by devices such as metal rings around the circumference of the net, weights and lead-core ropes (29). Groups of cages are usually held and anchored together and, depending on the design, they can be joined by walkways or only accessed individually by boat. Galvanised steel square-cages are typically available in 12 to 24 metre square sections. A 24 metre section would consist of a 15 by 15 metre net surrounded by walkways (Figure 37.3a). Each section incorporates floats under the walkways and sections are hinged together to expand a system and to provide flexibility in rougher seas. The other main type of sea-cage is the circular ring-cage in which a buoyant circular ring structure is used to hold a circular bag-net, mooring cables and other ancillary structures such as bird netting or feeders (Figure 37.3b). These structures can range in circumference from 60 to over 120 metres. Compared to square-cages they are usually placed further apart, allow greater water flow through a group of cages and are easier to handle independently of each other. There are a number of commercial variations of square- and ring-cages holding from a few tonnes to over 150 tonnes, approximately 40000 fish (29).

Considerable intervention has been used to manage smoltification and maturation. Controlling the supply of smolt enables stocking over more of the year and more even production throughout the year. This is particularly important when a large proportion of fish mature within one sea-winter as grilse which are smaller than older salmon (29). One-year smolt is the normal age category for smolt but half-year, one-and-a-half and two-year smolt are also produced and used (30). One-year smolt (S1) are exposed to a natural photoperiod and are transferred in spring after one year in freshwater; one-and-a-half year smolt are essentially delayed S1 and transferred in the autumn rather than in the spring like S1; Half-year smolt are transferred in autumn prior to S1 and are produced by photo-manipulation of the photoperiod that accelerates "spring." Mature salmon are not desirable in a production run. Mortality is higher in seawater; they partition feed resources into unwanted reproductive growth rather than somatic growth and develop many poor external and flesh quality characteristics that reduce marketability (29). Whether maturation occurs is highly influenced by size and nutritional status so that faster growing fish, often in warmer temperatures, will mature relatively quickly but be of a smaller size. Strategies to control the effects of maturation include the production of sterile triploid fish or the use of all female stock, since females show lower rates of maturity than males.

Selective breeding has been used as a strategy to improve Atlantic salmon and rainbow trout in Norway since 1971 (33). Initially selection was based on growth, then the frequency of grilse was incorporated to increase the age at maturation. More recent selection strategies have used disease challenge to increase disease resistance and measurements of flesh colour, fat content and fat distribution to improve meat quality (33). There has also

been development and testing of genetically modified or transgenic fish. Genetically modified Atlantic salmon parr containing a growth hormone transgene (chinook salmon growth hormone gene attached to an antifreeze protein promoter sequence from ocean pout) grew at over two and half times the rate of control fish due mainly to increased feed intake (34).

B. Marine Finfish

In the majority of developed countries that use intensive aquaculture there is a premium on marine rather than freshwater finfish. Of course, not all marine finfish command the same price or kudos associated with yellowtail, tuna, halibut or grouper, for example. As yet, there is no intensive aquaculture of high value marine finfish on the scale or with the current rate of increase of Atlantic salmon. The large and important Japanese yellowtail industry produced 137000 tonnes in 2000 (35) but this was below production at the start of the 1990s. Farming yellowtail in Japan developed from holding wild-caught fish and intensified in the 1970s. Too rapid expansion and limitations due to disease and markets have led to greater controls on the industry and a reduction in production (36). Although hatchery-based propagation is possible the Japanese industry is still largely based on small (<10 gram) wild-caught fingerlings that are grown to 50–100 grams before being sold for on-growing for about 12 months to about three kilograms (37). Bluefin tuna are very valuable fish and attempts at forms of aquaculture have been under way for many years in Japan, North America, Europe and Australia (38–40). The few commercial tuna farms, mainly located in Australia and the Mediterranean, on-grow large wild-caught juvenile tuna. In Australia, for example, juvenile southern bluefin tuna shoals are caught using a purse-seine, towed back in specially designed ring-cages and transferred to moored cages for a four- to eight-month grow-out (40). The tuna are around 20 kilograms at catch and controlled grow-out allows a high level of value adding to a fishery resource. farmed tuna can treble in weight and larger tuna are more valuable per kilogram as well as on a whole-fish basis. Recently there are indications that aquaculture based on a closed life-cycle of bluefin tuna is possible; successful larval production from northern bluefin tuna that had themselves been grown in culture from larvae has been achieved (41). The research program was started over 25 years prior to successful spawning of the wild tuna in 1995–96 and indicates the high level of complexity and need for a considerable economic and time investment to achieve success. Further development will be required because there may be key differences between wild-caught and domestic broodstock that could result in poor larval quality and a low success rate in the production of viable juveniles from this second generation.

Good examples of intensive marine aquaculture in which the life-cycle is closed and that have a high production are the European sea bass and gilthead sea bream in the Euro-Mediterranean region (42), red drum in the southern United States (43), red sea bream in Japan and the Asian sea bass in South East Asia (14). European sea bass production has increased steadily over the last ten years and all aspects of production, from larval rearing to broodstock management, are considered to be under control (44). Commercial hatcheries produce in excess of 180 million juveniles for sea-based grow-out. Propagation is based on a relatively standard larval rearing protocol supplying a sequence of live feeds, rotifer followed by brine shrimp, before weaning onto a compound feed (44). European sea bass larvae first feed four or five days after hatching when they are between four and six millimetres in length. After three to four weeks they reach ten millimetres and weaning onto a high protein compound feed begins and is usually complete by 40 days. An interesting development is the successful use of a compound feed immediately at first-feeding and for the entire larval period. Consideration of supplying essential nutrients in a form that can be readily assimilated is the key to this success and achieved using ingredients such as phospholipids and hydrolysed proteins (44). Rotifers and brine shrimps form the basis of most larval rearing protocols. Rotifers are smaller and always fed first, then with brine shrimp in order to provide food for smaller individuals before only brine shrimp are used. Other variations include "greenwater" techniques, whereby microalgae are also grown because they appear to benefit both the live feed and the finfish larvae. Red sea bream are fed microalgae (day three to 25), rotifers (day three to 33), brine shrimp (day 20 to 40) and compound feed (day 20 to 60). Live feeds are often "enriched" by feeding them commercial preparations to increase concentrations of specific nutrients, particularly polyunsaturated fatty acids and vitamins.

The aquaculture of Asian sea bass or barramundi provides an interesting view of how one species has been highly adaptable and successful under many systems (14). Its natural range encompasses the northern Indian and tropical western Pacific Oceans and it is found from Iran to Australia (14). Although aquaculture production is relatively small (20000 tonnes in 1999) there is great potential for a species that can be cultured using intensive and extensive methods, indoors or outdoors, and that can be grown over the full range of salinity (from fresh to seawater) and even in brackish bore waters far from the sea. Tucker *et al.* (2002) have recently reviewed barramundi aquaculture: barramundi are catadromous (opposite to salmon) and sea water is needed for the broodstock, eggs and the first half of the larval rearing cycle. The species is also a protandrous hermaphrodite so that individuals first mature into males (after two years) and then into females (after three to five years). Barramundi can be spawned in tanks or strip spawned and this can be achieved with or without hormonal manipulation. Ambient conditions are very important for maturation and spawning. Spawning will occur regularly under summer photoperiod and temperatures: in Australia these parameters are artificially controlled in enclosed tanks to produce a regular supply of larvae from a small broodstock population (14). In more tropical locations farmed broodstock kept under natural conditions at high temperatures (27–34°C) will spawn regularly in tanks. Spawning occurs on the full moon and can be enhanced by first decreasing (also increasing temperature) and then increasing tank water depth (decreasing temperature) to recreate a high tide. Barramundi are very fecund and females produce hundreds of thousands of eggs per kilogram on each spawning. Males are stocked with females and the floating fertilised eggs are collected by nets or from the outflow water. The larvae are 1.5 millimetres when they hatch and have a yolk sac and oil globule as food reserves that are fully depleted after six days. Typically, larvae first-feed after two to three days (2.6 millimetres length) and take around 25 days to metamorphose into juveniles (17 millimetres length). There are many approaches to larval rearing that range from intensive to extensive. Intensive procedures can be carried out in small tanks using a rotifer and brine shrimp sequence, rotifers from day two to day 15 and brine shrimp from day ten. Production methods may also incorporate a greenwater approach with the use of microalgae over the first part of larval rearing. Extensive procedures are carried out in large earthen ponds relying on natural plankton blooms initiated by fertilising the pond. Juveniles are easily weaned onto compound feeds and transferred from the nursery to grow-out stage. In Southeast Asia grow-out uses small ponds (0.08 to two hectares), coastal impoundments or smaller cages (one to 300 m^3). Several approaches to grow-out are used in Australia. These include open freshwater ponds, small cages held in freshwater ponds (Figure 37.3d), large marine cages and, because barramundi command a high market price, indoor tanks in more southerly non-tropical regions. Production is based on plate-size fish of around 400 to 700 grams and larger fish of around two to three kilograms for fillets or as "banquet" fish.

C. ABALONE

Abalone are herbivorous gastropod molluscs that graze, usually nocturnally, on microalgae (attached to surfaces) and macroalgae (seaweed) (4). They have one shell with several holes along the edge for water exchange and a famously pearly inner surface. Their large muscular foot is an expensive delicacy around the world. Aquaculture started in Japan about 50 years ago and numerous *Haliotis* species are now grown commercially around the world. Production is led by China and Taiwan with Australia considered to be leading industry development through research into areas such as feeds and nutrition, health and grow-out technologies (45). Abalone culture has been reviewed recently by Viana (2002). Farm-raised broodstock are readily available and synchronous reproduction is usually managed through the control of water temperature, water quality and high feed availability. Spawning can be induced by manipulation of temperature and light: temperature shock stimulation of spawning is created by raising water temperature to a target level and then dropping it suddenly and shifting to a dark period. Fertilised eggs hatch into non-feeding larvae which then undergo metamorphosis and leave the water column to settle on the tank floors. Diatoms (microalgae) are grown on hard surfaces and supplied for several months for the post-larvae to graze on before they grow larger and the radula becomes hard enough to graze on macroalgae. This switch takes place at about one centimetre length and abalone from one to three centimetres are then ready for grow-out to about seven centimetres. Broodstock and post-larval stages are often maintained in land-based facilities whereas grow-out may be sea- or land-based. Sea-based systems are designed to provide shelter and good water flow but feeds still have to be supplied. Abalone in land-based farms can be held in ponds, tanks, raceways or other types of enclosure. Shallow tanks with laminar water flow to minimise water use are suitable in conjunction with compound feeds but greater tank depth and water volumes are required when macroalgae are the food. Large sectors of the industry are based on the use of macroalgae as the principal and only food source for grow-out and the regular provision of large volumes of macroalgae is a major operational issue. However, abalone can still be grown intensively on macroalgae. For example, in some intensive Taiwanese farms abalone are housed in banks of many small containers that are lifted out from the water by overhead cranes, packed by hand with macroalgae and returned. Abalone are slow growing and will take up to five years to reach market size. In Australia the use of macroalgae is not thought economic and there has been a focus on developing a complete nutritionally balanced feed. As a result the time taken to reach market size has been reduced from five to less than four years. Abalone are slow feeders and feeds remain in the water for long periods of time which means significant leaching of nutrients can occur (46). A variety of technologies have been explored and include the use of high concentration of ingredients that act as binders and as nutrients (*e.g.*, wheat and maize gluten), combinations of binders and the use of microencapsulation for highly soluble nutrients (46). Growth variation is large and selective breeding programs for growth and growth efficiency are seen to be an important area for future development (45). A variety of traits such as growth rate, growth efficiency and marketable characteristics have been suggested and research has already established that heritability for survival and shell length is high enough for use in selective breeding programs (47).

III. SEMI-INTENSIVE AND EXTENSIVE AQUACULTURE SYSTEMS

Semi-intensive and extensive culture of fish in ponds is fundamentally different from intensive aquaculture. This form of pond culture uses a more holistic approach by exploiting the biological characteristics of the immediate aquatic ecosystem in fish production (48). The principles are based on the management of a pond's trophic web through alterations to the natural progression of the species balance in order to maximise conditions for fish production (48). Such alterations include efficient use of external inputs, principally organic fertilisers, the removal of species to shorten food chains or that are trophic "dead-ends" (*e.g.*, macrophytes), supplementary feeding and complex harvesting and re-stocking protocols. Pond-based polyculture, of mainly carp species, that has been refined in China and the pond-based monoculture of prawns provide examples of semi-extensive aquaculture. Large-scale changes in the types of aquaculture practiced in China are under way and intensive systems are being developed for freshwater and marine species (personal observation). Prawns are also farmed under intensive, extensive, polyculture and integrated aquaculture systems (49).

A. CHINESE FINFISH POLYCULTURE

As described above the most significant contribution to global aquaculture production is made by finfish cultured using Chinese pond-based polyculture systems. Although largely based on knowledge handed down by farmers without them necessarily understanding the scientific basis of management strategies (50) there has been considerable work by provincial fisheries bureaus to document information as a basis for making improvements through a scientific approach (51). There have been dramatic increases in production over recent years. Although aquaculture is thousands of years old it is only since 1957 that Chinese major carp fry have been artificially propagated. Apart from increases in the number of fish and ponds available other areas where huge improvements have been made include training and technology transfer, effective pond design, placing greater emphasis on polyculture, increasing stocking density and increasing production through multiple harvesting and re-stocking (51, 52).

The finfish used in polyculture can be divided into four groups based on their principal food and feeding habits: plankton, macrophytes, detritus or aquatic animals (53). The major species used in polyculture are silver carp (phytoplankton), bighead carp (zooplankton), grass carp (macrophytes), mud carp (detritus) and black carp (molluscs); common carp (omnivorous feeding) are also used in high numbers. The former group of carp species are known as the Chinese major carp (Table 37.1). Other species such as the blunt nosed bream or Wuchang fish (macrophytes),

TABLE 37.1
Major Aquaculture Species with Top 20 Rank by Production Weight in 2000 (35)

Group	Name (Rank)	Scientific Name	Water, Feeding Mode
Finfish			
Chinese major carp	Silver carp (2)	*Hypophthalmichthys molitrix*	FW, filter feeder
	Grass carp (3)	*Ctenopharyngodon idella*	FW, herbivore
	Bighead carp (6)	*Hypophthalmichthys nobilis*	FW, filter feeder
	Mud carp	*Cirrhinus molitorella*	FW, detritivore
	Black carp	*Mylophryngodon piceus*	FW, carnivore
Indian major carp	Rohu (11)	*Labeo rohita*	FW, omnivore
	Catla (12)	*Catla catla*	FW, filter feeder
	Mrigal (13)	*Cirrhinus mrigala*	FW, detritivore
Other carp	Common carp (4)	*Cyprinus carpio*	FW, detritivore
	Crucian carp (7)	*Carassius carassius*	FW, detritivore
Other finfish	Tilapia (9)	*Oreochromis niloticus*	FW, omnivore
	Milk fish (16)	*Chanos chanos*	B, herbivore
	Channel catfish (20)	*Ictalurus punctatus*	FW, omnivore
	Yellowtail	*Seriola quinqueradiata*	M, carnivore
Salmonids	Atlantic salmon (10)	*Salmo salar*	M, carnivore
	Coho salmon	*Oncorhynchus kisutch*	M, carnivore
	Rainbow trout (18)	*Oncorhynchus mykiss*	FW, carnivore
Shellfish			
Bivalves	Pacific oyster (1)	*Crassostrea gigas*	B, filter feeder
(Molluscs)	Small neck clam (5)	*Ruditapes philippinarum*	M, filter feeder
	Giant ezo scallop (8)	*Patinopecten yessoensis*	M, filter feeder
	Blue mussel (17)	*Mytilus edulis*	M, filter feeder
Prawns	Tiger (14)	*Penaeus monodon*	B & M*, detritivore
(Crustaceans)	Oriental	*Penaeus chinensis*	B & M*, detritivore
	White	*Penaeus vannamei*	B & M*, detritivore
	Giant freshwater	*Macrobrachium rosenbergii*	FW & B*, detritivore

FW = freshwater, B = brackish, M = marine, * = during reproduction and larval stages.

crucian carp (detritus) and *Tilapia* species (plankton and detritus) are also important in more complex polyculture systems. Chinese finfish polyculture has been divided into two main types: the "feeding model" and the "filter-feeding model" (51). The feeding model is based on grass, black and or common carp whereas the filter-feeding model makes more use of silver and bighead carp and rarely uses black carp. Although both models are widely used the balance differs between provinces. The feeding model is prevalent in Zhejiang (89%) and Jiansu (89%) compared to Hubei (25%) and Shandong (25%) (51). The number and mix of the principal species and the use of additional species is dependent on the province and on the farm (11). Polyculture in provinces such as Zhejiang has been practiced for thousands of years. The climate is ideal for extended production over a large part of the year and the province is wealthy and very close to the huge marketplace of Shanghai. Consequently, conditions favour the feeding model and the production of species (grass, black and common carp) that are preferred in the market place. Thus, the complexity of the polyculture practiced depends on geographical location, which influences the growing season; on the historical and technological basis of aquaculture, which influence expertise and technical support; as well as on socioeconomic factors, which influence the mix of species and the inclusion of more valuable species (11).

Broodstock are grown in special ponds for four to seven years and to weights in excess of five to ten kilograms depending on the species (50). Broodstock are placed in monoculture for a pre-spawning phase where water quality and feeding are managed. Species other than common carp normally spawn in flowing rivers so the maintenance of good water quality with high oxygenation is important in these ponds. Hormonal injections are used to induce spawning and male and females are placed together in circular concrete tanks where spawning and fertilisation occur (50). The fertilised eggs sink and are carried out of the tanks to be collected from the outflow and placed into incubation systems. Large circular incubation tanks, constructed from bricks and cement, are stocked at around 800000 eggs per cubic metre of water. Once the swim bladder is formed the larvae can be removed and stocked into the nursery ponds. Rearing progresses over the summer and the first stage lasts for around 30 days. Different carp are usually kept under monoculture due to the similarity in larval diets. Soya milk is supplied directly to the pond for feeding the larvae and early fry. Limited polyculture may be used in the later phases of fry production. Polyculture protocols use three to eight centimetre fry in different combinations of the main carp species. Stimulation of phyto- and then zooplankton blooms is managed through the application of organic fertilisers to provide food for the growing fry.

Rectangular ponds are recommended and are of different dimensions depending on the production stage: for example, fry ponds are 1.2 metre deep and less than a fifth of a hectare in area; fingerling ponds are 1.5 metre deep and up to a third of a hectare in area; grow-out ponds are two to three metre deep and up to two thirds of a hectare in area. The most efficient grow-out systems follow multiple-batch harvesting and re-stocking protocols, sometimes called "multi-grade conveyor culture," which coordinate several harvests and restocking of both fingerlings and of larger fish over the growing season. For example, in Guangdong Province 35% of ponds may be allocated to fingerling production and the rest to grow-out. The grow-out ponds will be divided for different sizes of fish. The final or "fattening" pond contains mainly bighead, grass, mud and silver carp, to be grown up to harvest size over different periods of time, as well as some common and black carp, Wuchang fish, tilapia and even snakehead (Table 37.2). In hilly regions where there are fewer ponds there is an emphasis on mixed-age culture within the same ponds. Chinese finfish polyculture is dependent on large inputs of organic fertilisers (mainly manure and composts) as well as some feed sources not available in the pond, especially terrestrial plant material for grass carp. Traditional fish farms are usually part of a larger integrated aquaculture-agriculture farm. Integrated farming, the integration of agriculture and aquaculture activities (Figure 37.5a), has several forms in China involving combinations of fish with ducks, pigs, chickens, cows and silk-worms.

TABLE 37.2
Stocking and Harvest Weights of "Fattening" Ponds in a Polyculture System in Use in Guangdong Province, China

Species	Stock Weight (Grams per Fish)	Harvest Weight (Grams per Fish)	Density* (Fish per Hectare)	Rearing Period (Days)
Bighead carp	500	1000–1500	330	40
Grass carp	250–500	1300–1500	600–1200	60–180
Mud carp	50	125	14250	180
Silver carp	250–600	700–1000	300–600	90–180
Common carp			300	
Tilapia			7500–15000	
Wuchang fish	100–250		750	
Black carp			75–150	

* = Based on 15 mu per hectare.

The integration of fish with pigs and with ducks are considered the most successful systems (54). In one documented example (55) 70 hectares of ponds produced 800 tonnes of fish (based on eight species polyculture), 400000 ducks, 1060 pigs, 123 cows and chickens to give an overall annual production of 13.5 tonnes per hectare. In fish-silk culture mulberry bushes (Figure 37.5b) are grown by fish ponds and provide leaves for silk-worms which produce manure and protein from the pupa.

Variations of finfish polyculture are found throughout the world and suit different socioeconomic situations. For example, a system of polyculture was developed in India around the Indian major carp (Table 37.1) and it now incorporates other carp species. In Bangladesh, Indian and Chinese major carp are grown in ponds under polyculture systems and sold as a cash crop. It has been shown that if smaller pond fish species are also included they provide a vital protein source for the farmer's family whereas the carp are treated only as a cash crop (56).

B. PRAWNS

Penaeid shrimps are the most important farmed "prawns" and over twenty species are farmed (4). The majority of production is of *Penaeus monodon* (570000 tonnes) with a sizable contribution from *P. chinensis* (219000 tonnes) and *P. vannamei* (144000 tonnes) (35). The giant freshwater prawn, *Macrobrachium rosenbergii*, is the fourth most important prawn (119000 tonnes), the majority of production being from China (48%) and Bangladesh (37%) (49). There are many similarities in aquaculture techniques for the different prawn species although there are also important differences, not least of which between the freshwater and marine species (54).

The current status of freshwater prawn aquaculture and techniques have been recently detailed in depth (49). Wild female *M. rosenbergii* migrate into estuaries where the fertilised eggs they are carrying hatch. Larvae metamorphosise through 11 stages before the post-larvae settle on the estuary bottom and migrate into freshwaters. The discovery that the larvae needed a brackish water environment for successful development is considered a major advance in the aquaculture of this species (4). Reproduction and larval rearing are now well understood. Seawater can be trucked inland to hatcheries and siting farms away from coastal areas is viewed as a major advantage of the industry (49). World production has stabilised but aquaculture may yet have great potential because there has been limited development in South and Central America or in Africa and the species characteristics are more favourable to lower intensity farming and to developing polyculture with finfish. Polyculture with finfish in ponds offers an opportunity to increase pond yields with little increased cost. Prawns feed on bottom detritus and do not compete with the finfish (49). A range of production

FIGURE 37.5 Chinese aquaculture showing a) view of integrated fish ponds and agriculture (photograph by Z-Y He), b) municipal fish ponds in Zhejiang Province with mulberry bushes on pond banks.

systems from extensive to intensive are used although the majority of the industry is based on semi-intensive grow-out. *M. rosenbergii* aquaculture provides a good example where the different aquaculture systems can be related to key aspects of farming. Extensive farming uses either dedicated ponds or impounded areas where there is another primary purpose such as rice fields or irrigation ditches; no feed is added; there is no control of water quality, predator or competitor species; stocking is 1–4 per square metre and production is less than 500 kilograms per hectare per year; harvesting is difficult because the water cannot be drained or seined. Intensive farming uses small concrete ponds; high water quality is maintained through high water exchange and continuous aeration; predator and competitor species are removed; nutritionally complete compounded feeds are used; stocking density is high at 20 per square meter and production is in excess of five tonnes per hectare per year; ponds are drain harvested (there are few commercial examples of intensive aquaculture). Semi-intensive aquaculture relies on daily management of water quality and water productivity to supply natural food sources; compound feeds are used to supplement pond-based food; stocking density is four to 20 per square meter and production is up to five tonnes per hectare per year (57). However, *M. rosenbergii* is territorial and density has a major effect on growth. Under semi-intensive conditions densities from four to 12 per square metre resulted in the most marked reduction in growth (57). Consequently, there has to be a balance between average growth rate and the total biomass available for harvest. An efficient semi-intensive operation would reach market weight of 30 to 60 grams in six to eight months with a survival of 50 to 80% (57).

Much of the research and development in marine prawn farming has been related to controlling spawning and larval rearing (54). Maturation, spawning and early larval stages of marine prawn species occur during the marine phase of the life-cycle, whereas the brackish waters of estuaries act as feeding grounds for post-larval and juvenile stages (4). Penaeid aquaculture was originally based on collection from the wild of either gravid females, which had mated and would then produce larvae, or post-larvae

and juveniles. Hatchery techniques that allow the control and management of maturation, spawning and the fertilisation of eggs are now established (54). One of the key techniques is the removal of one eyestalk (unilateral ablation) from females. This decreases the amount of gonad-inhibiting hormone produced and therefore promotes maturation and spawning, particularly in females. The level of management is species dependent so that *P. monodon* requires ablation. Ablation is used with *P. vannamei* but it is not essential and species such as *P. japonicus* are responsive to environmental manipulation and ablation is not used (4). Broodstock diet is important and although compound feeds could be used there is a strong belief that factors contained within fresh or frozen animal food and not in compound feeds are required. Broodstock diets often contain polychaete worms, squid or bivalves, trash fish or crustacean waste. Males and females are stocked in equal numbers in spawning tanks. Eggs are collected and removed to the hatchery. Larval rearing relies on a controlled environment and maintenance of high quality seawater. A sequence of live-food starting with algae, rotifers and then brine shrimp is used. The "Galveston" method was developed in the U.S. and is more intensive; small larval rearing tanks are stocked at high densities and live-feeds supplied from separate tanks. Post-larval stages are thinned down and transferred to larger tanks or ponds. The "community culture" method originates in Japan. It is based on larger tanks and relies on promoting the growth of live feed species within the same body of water as the larvae.

Grow-out may also be conducted under intensive, semi-intensive and extensive systems: intensive (>200 prawns per square metre) practices tend to use tanks, raceways or smaller concrete ponds whereas extensive (<1 prawn per square metre) practices usually rely on larger earthen ponds or impounded areas (4). Semi-intensive management strategies are broadly similar to those described above for *M. rosenbergii* and typical prawn ponds are rectangular and of one to three hectares, although some ponds in South America are as large as 20 hectares, and around one metre deep (54). Water circulation is vital to managing water quality and food supply. Regular water exchange is practiced along with direct aeration and circulation of pond water to ensure nutrients are re-suspended for assimilation by plankton. Production is around two to four tonnes per hectare per year. In contrast, intensive farming can be as high as 28 tonnes per hectare per year but has proved very vulnerable to disease problems (54).

IV. PACIFIC OYSTER FARMING

Pacific oyster farming has the highest production of any single aquaculture species. Production in 2000 was nearly four million tonnes and about 11% of total global aquaculture (35). Pacific oysters, originally from Japan, are very adaptable to different environmental conditions and are farmed throughout the world, having been introduced to the United States, Europe, South America, Africa and Australasia (4). They are bivalves so that a soft body is enclosed within two shells (valves) that are joined at a pointed end. The lower valve is cupped and normally the site of attachment to a substrate. The shape of the shell is very variable and heavily influenced by the environment: smooth and elongated shells result from growth on a soft substrate whereas a hard or gravelly substrate will cause flutes and corrugations as well as a deeper rounder shape (58). They inhabit brackish waters such as estuaries and feed by filtering nutrients out of the water. Consequently growth is highly dependent on the nutrient supply in the waters of the farm as well as on water temperature and quality. It takes fifteen to eighteen months to reach market size (about 100 grams) under natural conditions.

Males and females are separate and discharge sperm or eggs into water where fertilisation takes place. Between seasons they may changes sex from male to female (58). Spawning is stimulated by warming waters in the spring and summer and it may occur throughout the year at high temperatures (*e.g.*, 30–33°C in the Philippines). The larvae feed on microalgae in the water column before they metamorphosise into spat that settle out. Traditional Japanese oyster culture relied on the collection of wild spat on bamboo sticks and then on collectors suspended from rafts. Hatchery production has become more prominent although wild spat are still used. An important advantages of a hatchery-based industry is the relative ease of organising a genetic improvement program, as has been initiated in Tasmania (Australia) (59). The spat are grown until winter when they are graded and taken for one-year or two-year grow-out. Suspension of oysters in cultches and bags from floating rafts is the most common method in Japan, suspension from long-lines is more common in rougher deeper water. One-year oysters are transferred to productive waters after winter and grow rapidly. The two-year oysters are "hardened" over the first season on wooden racks positioned intertidally so that oysters are subjected to waves and air exposure. They are transferred to the grow-out areas the next season and are larger than the one-year oysters on harvest (4). Due to economic and legal restrictions on floating

structures many farms still adopt bottom culture, in which the oysters are grown directly on the sea bottom (54). Off-bottom structures that are located intertidally and built into the bottom include stakes (placed vertically) or sticks (placed horizontally), stone or concrete slabs placed in bridges and wooden rack systems that support trays and bags or are used to suspend ropes carrying the oyster cultch. Suspended systems such as rafts or long-lines are placed further offshore and carry suspended trays, lines and bags. The location of oyster farms is crucial and efficient grow-out depends mainly on understanding the carry capacity of the water to maximise the use of nutrients and avoid overstocking. Minimising grading and replanting is also important. Depuration is particularly important to ensure oysters are safe to eat. They are eaten raw and being filter feeders can concentrate pathogenic bacteria, viruses, natural toxins (notably from microalgae) and pollutants.

V. SUMMARY

On the order of 300 aquatic species are cultured throughout the world and many species that are new to aquaculture will be under investigation at any one time (and often rejected after some period of research and development). In this overview I have concentrated on major species and groups, particularly on a few finfish, bivalve molluscs and decapod crustaceans (prawns). Large amounts of seaweed are also farmed. There is significant commercial farming of other vertebrate (*e.g.*, frogs, soft-shelled turtles) and invertebrate (*e.g.*, echinoderms, sea cucumbers) groups. Intensive and semi-intensive approaches were described and they emphasise the scope of aquaculture practice as well as how systems need to be appropriate to specific socioeconomic circumstances. Important challenges face aquaculture and ensuring it is sustainable. These will partly be met by increased understanding through research and the development of technological solutions. Best practice clearly does not imply only the use of intensive aquaculture; considerable improvements can be made to all systems and approaches can be transferred. Whichever system is appropriate, more emphasis will be placed on increasing efficiency and maximising the use of valuable resources. A broader view of resources will encompass multiple use of location and the environmental impact of aquaculture, disease prevention rather than control and limiting the use of chemical or antibiotic solutions, the sustainable use of feed ingredients and decreasing reliance on marine products. Biotechnology may offer increased opportunity; there is already perceived but uneven market resistance to genetically modified products. Global forces such as climate change will have important consequences in relation to which species are farmed and where species are farmed. Increased water temperatures may allow species to be grown in new regions but also end the culture of other species. The importance of the contribution that aquaculture makes to human nutrition will continue to increase and considerable work is being done to ensure its effectiveness.

ACKNOWLEDGEMENTS

My sincere thanks go to Z.-Y. He, Zhejiang Provincial Fisheries Bureau for providing detailed information on Chinese aquaculture and for hosting my visits to his wonderful province.

REFERENCES

1. MCM Beveridge, DC Little. The history of aquaculture in traditional societies. In: BA Costa-Pierce. ed. Ecological Aquaculture: The Evolution of the Blue Revolution. Oxford: Blackwell Science, 2002, pp 1–29.

2. BA Costa-Pierce. The Ahupua'a aquaculture ecosystems in Hawaii. In: BA Costa-Pierce. ed. Ecological Aquaculture: The Evolution of the Blue Revolution. Oxford: Blackwell Science, 2002, pp 30–43.

3. M Huet. Textbook of Fish Culture: Breeding and Cultivation of Fish. Second Edition. Farnham, Surrey: Fishing News Books, 1986, pp. 438.

4. M Landau. Introduction to Aquaculture. New York: John Wiley & Sons, 1991, pp. 440.

5. S Li. Introduction: freshwater fish culture. In: S Li and J Mathias. eds. Freshwater Fish Culture in China: Principles and Practice. Amsterdam: Elsevier, 1994, pp 1–25.

6. FAO. The State of World Fisheries and Aquaculture. Rome: Food and Agriculture Organisation of the United Nations, 2002, pp. 150.

7. JE Bardach. ed. Sustainable Aquaculture. New York: John Wiley & Sons, 1997, pp. 251.

8. RL Naylor, RJ Goldburg, JH Primavera, N Kautsky, MCM Beverage, J Clay, C Folke, J Lubchenco, H Mooney, M Troell. Effects of aquaculture on world fish supplies. Nature 405 : 1017–1024, 2000.

9. JH Tidwell, GL Allan. Fish as food: aquaculture's contribution. World Aquacult 33 (3) : 44–48, 2001.

10. BA Costa-Pierce. ed. Ecological Aquaculture: The Evolution of the Blue Revolution. Oxford: Blackwell Science, 2002, pp. 382.

11. H Chen, B Hu, AT Charles. Chinese integrated fish farming: a comparative bioeconomic analysis. Aquacult Res 26 : 81–94, 1995.

12. R Billard, J Marcel, Y Racape. On-growing in ponds. In: R Billard. ed. Carp: Biology and Culture. Berlin: Springer-Verlag, 1995, pp 157–215.

13. IC Liao. Achievements and prospects of fisheries research in Taiwan. In: IC Liao and J Baker. eds. Aquaculture and Fisheries Resources Management: Proceedings of the Joint Taiwan-Australia Aquaculture and Fisheries Resources and Management Forum. Keelung, Taiwan: Taiwan Fisheries Research Institute, 2001, pp 15–29.

14. JW Tucker, DR Russel, MA Rimmer. Barramundi culture: a success story for aquaculture in Asia and Australia. World Aquacult 33 (3) : 53–59, 2002.

15. RW Hardy. Alternate protein sources for salmon and trout diets. Anim Feed Sci Technol 59 : 71–80, 1996.

16. JG Bell. Current aspects of lipid nutrition in fish farming. In: KD Black and AD Pickering. eds. Biology of Farmed Fish. Sheffield: Sheffield Academic Press, 2000, pp 114–145.

17. S Refstie, T Storebakken, G Baeverfjord, AJ Roem. Long-term protein and lipid growth of Atlantic salmon (Salmo salar) fed diets with partial replacement of fish meal by soy protein products at high lipid level. Aquaculture 193 : 91–106, 2001.

18. EH Robinson, MH Li. Channel catfish, Ictalurus punctatus. In: CD Webster and C Lim. eds. Nutrient Requirements and Feeding of Finfish for Aquaculture. Wallingford, U.K.: CABI Publishing, 2002, pp 293–318.

19. GI Hemre, K Sandnes, Ø Lie, O Torrissen, R Waagbø. Carbohydrate nutrition in Atlantic salmon, Salmo salar L.: growth and feed utilization. Aquacult Res 26 : 149–154, 1995.

20. T Storebakken, IS Kvein, KD Shearer, B Grisdale-Helland, SJ Helland, GM Berge. The apparent digestibility of diets containing fish meal, soybean meal or bacterial meal fed to Atlantic salmon (Salmo salar): evaluation of different faecal collection methods. Aquaculture 169 : 195–210, 1998.

21. CG Carter, RC Hauler. Fish meal replacement by plant meals in extruded feeds for Atlantic salmon, Salmo salar L. Aquaculture 185 : 299–311, 2000.

22. CG Carter, M Bransden, T Lewis, P Nichols. Potential of thraustochytrids to partially replace fish oil in Atlantic salmon feeds. Mar Biotechnol 5 : 480–492, 2003.

23. PJ Walker. Regional cooperation in controlling prawn viral diseases — application of molecular technologies. In: IC Liao and J Baker. eds. Aquaculture and Fisheries Resources Management: Proceedings of the Joint Taiwan-Australia Aquaculture and Fisheries Resources and Management Forum. Keelung, Taiwan: Taiwan Fisheries Research Institute, 2001, pp 59–62.

24. JA Holm. Disease prevention and control. In: S Willoughby. ed. Manual of Salmon Farming. Oxford: Blackwell Science, 1999, pp 195–259.

25. CJ Bridger. Sustainable offshore aquaculture development in the Gulf of Mexico. World Aquacult 32 (3) : 28–33 & 60, 2001.

26. B Myrseth. Open production systems: status and future challenges. In: H Reinertein, LA Dahle, L Jørgensen, K Tvinnereim. eds. Fish Farming Technology. Rotterdam: A.A. Balkema, 1993, pp. 5–16.

27. B Guldberg, A Kittelsen, M Rye, T Asgard. Improved salmon production in large cage systems. In: H Reinertein, LA Dahle, L Jørgensen, K Tvinnereim. eds. Fish Farming Technology. Rotterdam: A.A. Balkema, 1993, pp 241.

28. E Lien. Tension Leg Cage — A new net pen cage for fish farming. In: H Reinertein, LA Dahle, L Jorgensen, K Tvinnereim. eds. Fish Farming Technology. Rotterdam: A.A. Balkema, 1993, pp 251–258.

29. J Purser, N Forteath. Salmonids. In: J Lucas and P Southgate. eds. Aquaculture: Farming of Aquatic Animals and Plants. Oxford: Blackwell Science, 2003, pp 295–320.

30. S Willoughby. Manual of Salmonid Farming. Oxford: Fishing News Books, 1999, pp. 329.

31. EL Brannon. Rainbow trout culture. In: RR Stickney. ed. Culture of Salmonid Fishes. Boca Raton: CRC Press, 1991, pp 22–55.

32. RR Stickney. Salmonid life histories. In: RR Stickney. ed. Culture of Salmonid Fishes. Boca Raton: CRC Press, 1991, pp. 1–20.

33. T Gjedrem. Genetic improvement of cold-water fish species. Aquacult Res 31 : 25–33, 2000.

34. JT Cook, MA McNiven, GF Richardson, AM Sutterlin. Growth rate, body composition and feed digestibility/ conversion of growth-enhanced transgenic Atlantic salmon (*Salmo salar*). Aquaculture 188 : 15–32, 2000.

35. FAO. The State of the World Fisheries and Aquaculture 2002. Rome: Food and Agricultural Organisation of the United Nations, 2000, pp. 158.

36. F Doumenge. Aquaculture in Japan. In: G Barnabe. ed. Aquaculture, Vol. 2. New York: Ellis Horwood, 1990, pp 849–945.

37. T Masumoto. Yellowtail, *Seriola quinqueradiata*. In: CD Webster and C Lim. eds. Nutrient Requirements and Feeding of Finfish for Aquaculture. Wallingford, U.K.: CABI Publishing, 2002, pp 131–146.

38. FG Carey, JW Kanwisher, ED Stevens. Bluefin tuna warm their viscera during digestion. J Exp Biol 109 : 1–20, 1984.

39. T Kaji, M Tanaka, Y Takahashi, M Oka, N Ishibashi. Preliminary observations on development of Pacific bluefin tuna *Thunnus thynnus* (Scombridae) larvae reared in the laboratory, with special reference to the digestive system. Mar Freshwater Res 47 : 261–269, 1996.

40. B Glenncross, C Carter, J Gunn, R van Barneveld, K Rough, S Clarke. Southern bluefin tuna, *Thunnus maccoyii*. In: CD Webster, C Lim. eds. Nutrient Requirements and Feeding of Finfish for Aquaculture. Wallingford, U.K.: CABI Publishing, 2002, pp 159–171.

41. Anon. Complete cultivation if bluefin tuna acheived. Kippo News, Available from: <http://www.kippo.or.jp/ KansaiWindowsHtml/News/2002-e/20020717_NEWS. html> 2002.

42. Y Harache, P Paquotte. European marine fish farming: an emerging industrial activity. World Aquaculture 29 (3) : 42–48, 1998.

43. DM Gatlin. Red drum, *Sciaenops ocellatus*. In: CD Webster, C Lim. eds. Nutrient Requirements and Feeding of Finfish for Aquaculture. Wallingford, U.K.: CABI Publishing, 2002, pp 147–158.

44. SJ Kaushik. European sea bass, *Dicentrachus labrax*. In: CD Webster and C Lim. eds. Nutrient Requirements and Feeding of Finfish for Aquaculture. Wallingford, U.K.: CABI Publishing, 2002, pp 28–39.

45. MT Viana. Abalone aquaculture, an overview. World Aquacult 33 (1) : 34–39, 2002.

46. AE Fleming, RJ van Barneveld, PW Hone. The development of artificial diets for abalone: a review and future directions. Aquaculture 140 : 5–53, 1996.

47. NG Elliott. Genetic improvement programmes in abalone: what is the future? Aquacult Res 31 : 51–59 : 2000.

48. J Marcel. Fish culture in ponds. In: G Barnabe. ed. Aquaculture, Vol. 2. New York: Ellis Horwood, 1990, pp 593–627.

49. NB New, WC Valenti. eds. Freshwater Prawn Culture. Oxford: Blackwell Science, 2000, pp 464.

50. J Marcel. Aquaculture in China. In: G Barnabe. ed. Aquaculture, Vol. 2. New York: Ellis Horwood, 1990, pp 946–967.

51. H-L Chen, AT Charles, B-T Hu. Chinese integrated fish farming. In: JA Mathias, AT Charles, H Baotong. eds. Integrated Fish Farming. Boca Raton: CRC Press, 1998, pp 97–108.

52. JA Mathias. The importance of integrated fish farming to world food supply. In: JA Mathias, AT Charles, H Baotong. eds. Integrated Fish Farming. Boca Raton: CRC Press, 1998, pp 3–18.

53. S Li. Fish species cultured. In: S Li and J Mathias. eds. Freshwater Fish Culture in China: Principles and Practice. Amsterdam: Elsevier, 1994, pp 27–50.

54. TVR Pillay. Aquaculture: Principles and Practices. Oxford: Fishing News Books, 1990, pp 575.

55. G Barnebe. Extensive culture of fish in ponds. In: G Barnebe. ed. Aquaculture: Biology and Ecology of Cultured Species. New York: Ellis Horwood, 1994, pp 333–348.

56. MA Wahab, MM Rahman, A Milstein. The effects of common carp, *Cyprinus carpio*, and mrigal, *Cirrhinus mrigala*, as bottom feeders in Indian carp polyculture. World Aquacult 32 (4) : 50–52, 2001.

57. WC Valenti, NB New. Grow-out systems — monoculture. In: NB New and WC Valenti. eds. Freshwater Prawn Culture. Oxford: Blackwell Science, 2000, pp 157–176.

58. DB Quayle, GF Newkirk. Farming Bivalve Molluscs: Methods for Study and Development. Baton Rouge: World Aquaculture Society, 1989, pp 294.

59. RD Ward, LJ English, DJ McGoldrick, GB Maguire, JA Nell, PA Thompson. Genetic improvement of the Pacific oyster *Crassostrea gigas* (Thunberg) in Australia. Aquacult Res 31: 35–44, 2000.

38 Frozen Seafood Products: Description

Peggy Stanfield
Dietetic Resources

CONTENTS

This book is not the proper forum to discuss the manufacture of every frozen seafood product available on the market. However, regulatory agencies such as the National Marine Fisheries Service (NMFS) have issued some minimal criteria for several frozen seafood and seafood products: what they are, what types and styles are available, and so on. This chapter describes each available frozen seafood product based on the product grades issued by the NMFS. A product grade is established to achieve two objectives: ensure product safety and to minimize economic fraud.

I. FROZEN HEADLESS DRESSED WHITING

A. Description of the Product

The product described in this section consists of clean, wholesome whiting (silver hake) *Merluccius bilineraris*, *Merluccius albidus*, completely and cleanly headed and adequately eviscerated. The fish are packaged and frozen in accordance with good commercial practice and are maintained at temperatures necessary for the preservation of the product.

B. Grades of Frozen Headless Dressed Whiting

U.S. Grade A is the quality of frozen headless dressed whiting that possesses a good flavor and odor.

U.S. Grade B is the quality of frozen headless dressed whiting that possesses at least reasonably good flavor and odor.

Substandard or Utility is the quality of frozen headless dressed whiting that otherwise fails to meet the requirements of U.S. Grade B.

C. Determination of the Grade

Good flavor and odor (essential requirements for a U.S. Grade A product) means that the cooked product has the typical flavor and odor of the species and is free from rancidity, bitterness, staleness, and off-flavors and off-odors of any kind.

Reasonably good flavor and odor (minimum requirements of a U.S. Grade B product) means that the cooked product is lacking in good flavor and odor but is free from objectionable off-flavors and off-odors of any kind.

Arrangement of product refers to the packing of the product in a symmetrical manner, bellies or backs all facing in the same direction, and fish neatly dovetailed.

Condition of the packaging material refers to the condition of the cardboard or other packaging material of the primary container.

If the fish is allowed to stand after packing and prior to freezing, moisture from the fish will soak into the packaging material and cause deterioration of that material.

Dehydration refers to the presence of dehydrated (water-removed) tissue on the exposed surfaces of the whiting. Slight dehydration is surface dehydration which is not color-masking. Deep dehydration is color-masking and cannot be removed by scraping with a fingernail.

Minimum size refers to the size of the individual fish in the sample. Fish 2 ounces or over are considered acceptable. Smaller fish cannot be cooked uniformly with acceptable size fish.

Heading refers to the condition of the fish after they have been headed. The fish should be cleanly headed behind the gills and pectoral fins. No gills, gill bones, or pectoral fins should remain after the fish have been headed.

Evisceration refers to the cleaning of the belly cavities of the fish. All spawn, viscera, and belly strings should be removed.

Scaling refers to the satisfactory removal of scales from the fish.

Color of the cut surfaces refers to the color of the cut surfaces of the fish after heading and other processing.

Bruises and broken or split skin refers to bruises over one-half square inch in area and splits or breaks in the skin more than one-half inch in length which are not part of the processing.

Texture defects refers to the absence of normal textural properties of the cooked fish flesh, which are tenderness, firmness, and moistness without excess water. Texture defects are dryness, softness, toughness, and rubberiness.

II. FROZEN HALIBUT STEAKS

A. PRODUCT DESCRIPTION

Frozen halibut steaks are clean, wholesome units of frozen raw fish flesh with normally associated skin and bone and are 2 ounces or more in weight. Each steak has two parallel surfaces and is derived from whole or subdivided halibut slices of uniform thickness which result from sawing or cutting perpendicular to the axial length, or backbone, of a whole halibut. The steaks are prepared from either frozen or unfrozen halibut (*Hippoglossus* spp.). They are processed and frozen in accordance with good commercial practice and are maintained at temperatures necessary for the preservation of the product.

B. STYLES OF FROZEN HALIBUT STEAKS

The individual steaks of Style I, random weight pack, are of random weight and neither the weight nor the range of weights is specified.

All steaks of Style II, uniform weight or portion pack, in the package or in the lot are of a specified weight or range of weights.

C. RECOMMENDED DIMENSIONS

(a) The recommended dimensions of frozen halibut steaks are not incorporated in the grades of the finished product since dimensions, as such, are not factors of quality for the purpose of these grades. However, the degree of uniformity of thickness among units of the finished product is rated since it is a factor affecting the quality and utility of the product.

(b) It is recommended that the thickness (smallest dimension) of individually frozen halibut steaks be not less than ½ inch and not greater than inches.

Percentage glaze on halibut steak means the percent by weight of frozen coating adhering to the steak surfaces and includes the frost within the package.

Uniformity of thickness means that the thickness is substantially the same for one or more steaks within a package or sample unit.

D. COLOR DEFECTS

(a) Discoloration of drip liquor means that the free liquid which drains from the thawed steaks is discolored with blood residue usually from the dorsal aorta of the halibut.

(b) Discoloration of light meat means that the normal flesh color of the main part of the halibut steak has darkened due to deteriorative influences.

(c) Discoloration of the dark meat means that the normal color of the surface fat shows increasing degrees of yellowing due to oxidation.

(d) Non-uniformity of color refers to noticeable differences in color on a single steak or between adjacent steaks in the same package.

(e) Dehydration refers to the appearance of a whitish area on the surface of a steak due to the removal of water or drying of the affected area.

(f) Honeycombing refers to the visible appearance of numerous discrete holes or openings of varying size on the steak surface.

(g) Workmanship defects refers to appearance defects that were not eliminated during processing and are considered either objectionable or poor commercial practice.

(h) Texture defect refers to an undesirable increase in toughness and/or dryness, fibrousness, and watery nature of halibut examined in the cooked state.

III. FROZEN SALMON STEAKS

A. PRODUCT DESCRIPTION

Frozen salmon steaks are clean, wholesome units of frozen raw fish flesh with normally associated skin and bone and are 2.5 ounces or more in weight. Each steak has two parallel surfaces and is derived from whole or subdivided salmon slices of uniform thickness which result from sawing or cutting dressed salmon perpendicularly to the axial length, or backbone. The steaks are prepared from either frozen or unfrozen salmon (*Oncorhynchus* spp.) and are processed and frozen in accordance with good commercial practice and are maintained at temperatures necessary for the preservation of the product. The steaks in an individual package are prepared from only one species of salmon.

B. SPECIES

Frozen salmon steaks covered huiby are prepared from salmon of any of the following species:

Silver or coho (*O. kisutch*)
Chum or keta (*O. keta*)
King, chinook, or spring (*O. tshawytscha*)
Red, sockeye (*O. nerka*)
Pink (*O. gorbuscha*)

C. STYLES

The individual steaks of Style I, random weight pack are of random weight and neither the individual steak weight nor the range of weights is specified. The steaks in the lot represent the random distribution cut from the head to tail of a whole dressed salmon.

The individual steaks of Style II, random weight combination pack, are of random weight and neither the individual steak weight nor the range of weights is specified. The steaks in the lot represent a combination of cuts from selected parts of the whole dressed salmon.

All steaks of Style III, uniform weight or portion pack, in the package or in the lot are of a specified weight or range of weights.

D. RECOMMENDED DIMENSIONS

It is recommended that the thickness (smallest dimension) of individually frozen salmon steaks be not less than 1/2 inch and not greater than 1 1/2 inches.

General appearance defects refer to poor arrangement of steaks, distortion of steaks, wide variation in shape, between steaks greater than normal number of head and/or tail pieces, imbedding of packaging material into fish flesh, inside condition of package, frost deposit, excessive or non-uniform skin glaze, and undesirable level of natural color.

Dehydration refers to the appearance of a whitish area on the surface of a steak due to the evaporation of water or drying of the affected area.

Uniformity of thickness means that the steak thickness is within the allowed manufacturing tolerance between the thickest and thinnest parts of the steaks within a package or sample unit.

Workmanship defects refers to appearance defects that were not eliminated during processing and are considered objectionable or poor commercial practice. They include the following: Blood spots, bruises, cleaning(refers to inadequate cleaning of the visceral cavity from blood, viscera and loose or attached appendages), cutting (refers to

irregular, inadequate, unnecessary, or improper cuts and/or trimmings), fins, foreign material (refers to any loose parts, of fish or other than fish origin), collar bone, girdle(refers to bony structure adjacent to fin), loose skin, pugh marks, sawdust, and scales.

E. COLOR DEFECTS

Discoloration of fat portion means that the normal color of the fat shows increasing degrees of yellowing due to oxidation.

Discoloration of lean portion means that the normal surface flesh color has faded or changed due to deteriorative influences.

Nonuniformity of color refers to noticeable differences in surface flesh color on a single steak or between adjacent steaks in the same package or sample unit. It also includes color variation of the visceral cavity and skin watermarking.

Honeycombing refers to the visible appearance on the steak surface of numerous discrete holes or openings of varying size.

Texture defect refers to an undesirable increase in toughness and/or dryness, fibrousness, and watery nature of salmon examined in the cooked state.

IV. FROZEN FISH FILLET BLOCKS

A. PRODUCT DESCRIPTION

Frozen fish blocks are rectangularly shaped masses made from a single species of fish flesh. They are made from fillets or fillet pieces that are either skin-on and scaled or skinless. Blocks processed from skin-on fish flesh should be so labeled. The blocks should not contain minced or comminuted fish flesh. The blocks should not be made by restructuring (reworking) pieces of fish blocks into the shape of a fish block.

Dehydration is a defect that refers to loss of moisture from the surface of a fish block during frozen storage. Affected areas have a whitish appearance.

Moderate dehydration masks the surface color of the product and affects more than 5 percent up to and including 15 percent of the surface area. If more then 15 percent of the surface area is affected, each additional 15 percent of surface area affected is another instance. Moderate dehydration can be readily removed by scraping with a blunt instrument.

Excessive dehydration masks the normal flesh color and penetrates the product. It affects more than 5 percent up to and including 10 percent of the surface area. If more than 10 percent of the surface area is affected, each additional 10 percent of surface area affected is another instance. Excessive dehydration requires a knife or other sharp instrument to remove.

Uniformity of block size. This defect refers to the degree of conformity to the declared size. It includes deviations from the standard length, width or thickness. Only one deviation for each dimension should be counted.

Moderate means a deviation of length and width of 1/8 inch (0.32 cm) or more up to and including 1/4 inch (0.64 cm). A deviation of thickness of 1/16 inch (0.16 cm) or more up to and including inch 1/8 (0.32 cm).

Excessive means if over ¼ inch (0.64 cm), each additional inch (0.32 cm) of length and width is another instance. If over (0.32 cm), each additional 1/16 inch (0.16 cm) of thickness is another instance.

Underweight refers to underweight deviations from the stated weight.

Slight means from 0.1 ounce (2.84 g) up to and including 1.0 ounce (28.35 g).

Moderate means over 1.0 ounce (28.35 g) up to and including 4.0 ounces (113.4 g).

Excessive means if over 4.0 ounces (113.4 g), each additional 1.0 ounce (28.35 g) is another instance.

An acceptable edge angle is an angle formed by two adjoining surfaces whose apex (deviation from 90 degrees) is within 0.95 cm off a carpenter's square placed along its surfaces. An acceptable corner angle is an angle formed by three adjoining surfaces whose apex is within 0.95 cm of a carpenter's square.

Improper fill is a defect that refers to voids, air packets, ice pockets, ragged edges, bumps, depressions, damage, and embedded packaging material, each of which is greater than 1/8 inch (0.32 cm) in depth, and which would result in product loss after cutting. It is estimated by determining the minimum number of 1-ounce (28.35 g) model units that could be affected adversely. For the purpose of estimating product loss, the 1-ounce (28.35 g) model unit should have the dimensions $4 \times 1 \times 5/8$ inch (10.16 $\times$ 2.54 $\times$ 1.59 cm). The total number of model units that would be affected adversely is the number of instances.

Belly flaps (napes) may be either loose or attached to a fillet or part of a fillet. The maximum amount of belly flaps should not exceed 15 percent by declared weight of the block if this amount does exceed 15 percent, each additional 5 percent by declared weight is another instance.

Each lump or mass of clotted blood greater than 3/16 inch (0.48 cm) up to and including 3/8 inch (0.95 cm) in any dimension is an instance of a blood spot. If a blood spot is larger than 3/8 inch (0.95 cm), each additional 3/16 (0.48 cm) is another instance.

Bruises include distinct, unnatural, dark, reddish, grayish, or brownish off-colors due to diffused blood. Each instance is each bruise larger than 0.5 square inch (3.32 cm^2) and less than 1.5 square inch (9.68 cm^2). For each bruise 1.5 square inch (9.68 cm^2) or larger, each additional complete 1.0 square inch (6.45 cm^2) is another instance.

Discoloration refers to deviations from reasonably uniform color characteristics of the species used, such as

melanin deposits, yellowing, rusting or other kinds of discoloration of the fish flesh.

Moderate discoloration is a noticeable but moderate degree which is greater than 0.5 square inch (3.23 cm^2) up to and including 1.5 square inch (9.68 cm^2) is one instance. If the discoloration is greater than 1.5 square inch (9.68 cm^2), each additional complete 1.0 square inch (6.45 cm^2) is another instance.

An excessive degree of discoloration is greater than 0.5 square inch (3.23 cm^2) up to and including 1.5 square inch (9.68 cm^2). If the discoloration is greater than 1.5 square inch (9.68 cm^2) each additional complete 1.0 square inch (6.45 cm^2) is another instance.

Viscera and roe refer to any portion of the internal organs. Each occurrence of viscera and roe is an instance. Lace (frill) is a piece of tissue adhering to the edge of a flatfish (Order Pleuronectifonnes) fillet. For each lace, each 1/2 inch (1.27 cm) is an instance.

In skinless fish blocks, each piece of skin larger than 0.5 square inch (3.23 cm^2) up to and including 1.0 square inch (6.45 cm^2) is an instance. For each piece of skin that is larger than 1.0 square inch (6.45 cm^2), each additional complete 0.5 square inch (3.23 cm^2) in area is another instance. For pieces of skin smaller than 0.5 square inch (3.23 cm^2), the number of 0.5-square-inch (3.23 cm^2) squares fully or partially occupied after collecting these pieces on a grid is the number of instances.

Each piece of membrane (black belly lining) larger than 0.5 square inch (3.23 cm^2) up to and including 1.5 square inch (9.68 cm^2) is an instance. For pieces of membrane (black belly lining) that are larger than 1.5 square inch (9.68 cm^2), each additional complete 0.5 square inch (3.23 cm^2) in area is another instance.

For skin-on fillets that have been scaled, an instance is an area of scales over 0.5 square inch (3.23 cm^2) up to and including 1.5 square inch (9.68 cm^2). If the area is greater than 1.5 square inch (9.68 cm^2), each additional complete 1.0 square inch (8.45 cm^2) is another instance. Loose scales are counted and instances are deducted in the same manner as for skinless fillets.

For skinless fillets, the first five to ten loose scales is an instance. If there are more than ten loose scales, each additional complete count of five loose scales is another instance.

Any harmless material not derived from fish, such as packaging material, is foreign material. Each occurrence is an instance.

Bones (including pin bone and fin bone):

(i)   Each bone defect to a bone or part of a bone whose maximum profile is 3/16 inch (0.48 cm) or more in length, or at least 1/32 inch (0.08 cm) in shaft diameter or width, or, for bone chips, a longest dimension of at least 3/16 inch (0.48 cm).

(ii) An excessive degree of bone defect is each bone whose maximum profile can not be fitted into a rectangle, drawn on a flat, solid surface, that has a length of 1 3/16 inch (3.02 cm) and a width of ? inch (0.95 cm).

Fins or part fins is a defect that refers to two or more bones connected by membrane, including internal or external bones, or both, in a cluster.

(i) Moderate occurrence: Connected by membrane in a cluster, no internal bone.
(ii) Excessive occurrence: Connected by membrane in a cluster with internal bone.

Parasites are of two types:

(i) Metazoan parasites. Each such parasite or fragment of such a parasite that is detected is an instance.
(ii) Parasitic copepods. Each such parasite or a fragment of such a parasite that is detected is an instance.

Texture means that the cooked product has the textural characteristics of the indicated species of fish. It does not include any abnormal textural characteristics such as mushy, soft, gelatinous, tough, dry or rubbery.

(i) Moderate means moderately abnormal textural characteristics.
(ii) Excessive means excessively abnormal textural characteristics.

V. FROZEN MINCED FISH BLOCKS

A. PRODUCT DESCRIPTION

Frozen minced fish blocks are uniformly shaped masses of cohering minced fish flesh. A block may contain flesh from a single species or a mixture of species with or without food additives. The minced flesh consists entirely of mechanically separated fish flesh processed and maintained in accordance with good commercial practice. This minced flesh is made entirely from species which are known to be safe and suitable for human consumption.

B. PRODUCT FORMS

Types are as follows.
Unmodified means food additives are used.

(i) Single species
(ii) Mixed species

Modified means contains food additives.

(i) Single species
(ii) Mixed species

Color classifications include:

(1) White
(2) Light
(3) Dark

Texture is described as:

(1) Coarse—Flesh has a fibrous consistency.
(2) Fine—Flesh has a partially fibrous consistency because it is a mixture of small fibers and paste.
(3) Paste/Puree—Flesh has no fibrous consistency.

C. DEFINITIONS OF DEFECTS

Deteriorative color refers to discoloration from the normal characteristics of the material used. Deterioration can be due to yellowing of fatty material, to browning of blood pigments, or other changes.

(i) Slight deteriorative discoloration—refers to a color defect that is slightly noticeable but does not seriously affect the appearance, desirability, or eating quality of the product.
(ii) Moderate deteriorative discoloration—refers to a color defect that is conspicuously noticeable but does not seriously affect the appearance, desirability, or eating quality of the product.
(iii) Excessive deteriorative discoloration—refers to a defect that is conspicuously noticeable and that seriously affects the appearance, desirability, or eating quality of the product.

Dehydration refers to a loss of moisture from the surfaces of the product during frozen storage.

(i) Slight dehydration—is surface color masking, affecting more than 5 percent of the area, which can be readily removed by scraping with a blunt instrument.
(ii) Moderate dehydration—is deep color masking penetrating the flesh, affecting less than 5 percent of the area, and requiring a knife or other sharp instrument to remove.
(iii) Excessive dehydration—is deep color masking penetrating the flesh, affecting more than 5 percent of the area, and requiring a knife or other sharp instruments to remove.

Uniformity of size refers to the degree of conformity to the declared contracted dimensions of the blocks. A deviation is considered to be any deviation from the contracted length, width, or thickness; or from the average dimensions of the blocks, physically determined, if no dimensions are contracted. Only one deviation from each dimension may be assessed. Two readings for length, three readings for width, and four readings for thickness will be measured.

(i) Slight—two or more deviations from declared or average length, width, and thickness up to ± 1/8 inch.
(ii) Moderate—two or more deviations from declared or average length, width, and thickness from ± 1/8 inch to ± xx inch (variable, depending on products).
(iii) Excessive—two or more deviations from declared or average length, width, and thickness over ± 3/8 inch.

Uniformity of weight refers to the degree of conformity to the declared weight. Only underweight deviations are assessed.

(i) Slight—any minus deviation of not more than 2 ounces.
(ii) Excessive—any minus deviation over 2 ounces.

An acceptable edge angle is an angle formed by two adjoining surfaces of the fish block whose apex is within 3/8 inch of a carpenter's square placed along the surfaces of the block. For each edge angle, three readings will be made and at least two readings must be acceptable for the whole edge angle to be acceptable. An acceptable corner angle is an angle formed by 3 adjoining surfaces whose apex is within 3/8 inch of the apex of a carpenter's square placed on the edge surfaces. Any edge or corner angle which fails to meet these measurements is unacceptable.

(i) Slight—two unacceptable angles.
(ii) Moderate—three unacceptable angles.
(iii) Excessive—four or more unacceptable angles.

Improper fill refers to surface and internal air or ice voids, ragged edges, or damage. Improper fill is measured as the minimum number of 1-ounce units that would be adversely affected when the block is cut. For this purpose, the dimensions of a 1-ounce unit are $4 \times 1 \times 5/8$ inch.

(i) Slight—1 to 3 units adversely affected.
(ii) Excessive—over 3 units adversely affected.

Blemishes refer to pieces of skin, scales, blood spots, nape (belly) membranes (regardless of color), or other harmless extraneous material. One instance means that the area occupied by a blemish or blemishes is equal to a 1/4 inch square. Instances are prorated on a per pound basis.

(i) Slight—5 to 15 instances per pound.
(ii) Moderate—more than 15 but less than 30 instances per pound.
(iii) Excessive—30 or more instances per pound.

Bones refer to any objectionable bone or piece of bone that is 1/4 inch or longer and is sharp and rigid. Perceptible bones should also be checked by their grittiness during the normal evaluation of the texture of the cooked product (10). Bones are prorated on a five pound sample unit basis.

(i) Slight—1 to 2 bones per five pound sample unit.
(ii) Moderate—3 to 4 bones per five pound sample unit.
(iii) Excessive—over 4 bones, but not to exceed 10 bones, per five pound sample unit.

Flavor and odor are evaluated organoleptically by smelling and tasting the product after it has been cooked.

Good flavor and odor (essential requirements for a Grade A product) means that the cooked product has the flavor and odor characteristic of the indicated species of fish and is free from staleness, bitterness, rancidity, and off-flavors and off-odors of any kind.

Reasonably good flavor and odor (minimum requirements of Grade B product) means that the cooked product is moderately absent of flavor and odor characteristic of the indicated species. the product is free from rancidity, bitterness, staleness, and off-flavors and off-odors of any kind.

Minimal acceptable flavor and odor (minimum requirements of a Grade C product) means that the cooked product has moderate storage induced flavor and odor, but is free from any objectionable off-flavors and off-odors that may be indicative of spoilage or decomposition.

Texture defects are judged on a sample of the cooked fish.

(i) Slight—flesh is fairly firm, only slightly spongy or rubbery. It is not mushy. There is no grittiness due to bone fragments.
(ii) Moderate—flesh is mildly spongy or rubbery. Slight grittiness may be present due to bone fragments.
(iii) Excessive—flesh is definitely spongy, rubbery, very dry, or very mushy. Moderate grittiness may be present due to bone fragments.

D. ADDITIVES

Minced fish blocks may be modified with food additives as necessary to stabilize product quality in accordance with the federal requirements.

The fish material should be processed and maintained in accordance with federal hygiene requirements.

VI. FROZEN RAW FISH PORTIONS

A. DESCRIPTION OF THE PRODUCT

The product described in this section consists of clean, wholesome, shaped masses of cohering pieces (not ground) of fish flesh. The fish portions are cut from frozen fish blocks, and are packaged in accordance with good manufacturing practice. They are maintained at temperatures necessary for the preservation of the product. All fish portions in an individual package are prepared from the flesh of one species of fish.

B. STYLE

Style I, Skinless portions, means portions prepared from fish blocks which have been made with skinless fillets.

Style II, Skin-on portions, means portions prepared from fish blocks which have been made from demonstrably acceptable skin-on fillets.

C. TYPES

Type I, Uniform shaped, means all portions in the sample are uniformly shaped.

Type II, Specialty cut, is all portions not covered in Type I.

Dehydration refers to the presence of dehydrated (water-removed) tissue in the portions. Slight dehydration is surface dehydration which is not colormasking. Deep dehydration is color masking and cannot be removed by scraping with a blunt instrument.

Uniformity of size refers to the degree of uniformity in length and width of the frozen portions. Deviations are measured from the combined lengths of the two shortest and/or the combined widths of the two widest minus the combined widths of the two narrowest in the sample.

Uniformity of weight refers to the degree of uniformity of the weights of portions. Uniformity is measured by the combined weight of the two heaviest portions divided by the combined weight of the two lightest portions in the sample. No deductions are made for weight ratios less than 1.2 for Type I.

Blemishes refers to skin (except for Style II), blood spots or bruises, objectionable dark fatty flesh, or extraneous material. Instances of blemishes refer to each occurrence measured by placing a plastic grid marked off in 1/4-inch squares 1/16 square inch) over the defect area. Each square is counted as 1 whether it is full or fractional.

Bones means the presence of potentially harmful bones in a portion. A potentially harmful bone is one that after being cooked is capable of piercing or hurting the palate.

Texture defects of the fish flesh and texture of skin in Style II refers to the absence of the normal textural properties of the cooked fish flesh and to the absence of tenderness of the cooked skin in Style II.

Normal textural properties of cooked fish flesh are tenderness, firmness, and moistness without excess water. Texture defects of the cooked flesh are dryness, mushiness, toughness, and rubberiness. Texture defects of the

cooked skin in Style II are mushiness, rubberiness, toughness, and stringiness.

D. GENERAL DEFINITIONS

Small (overall assessment) refers to a condition that is noticeable but is only slightly objectionable.

Large (overall assessment) refers to a condition that not only is noticeable but is seriously objectionable.

Minor (individual assessment) refers to a defect that slightly affects the appearance and/or utility of the product.

Major (individual assessment) refers to a defect that seriously affects the appearance and/or utility of the product.

The net weight of the portions if glazed should be determined by the following method:

(i) Weigh the portions with the glaze intact, which gives the gross weight.
(ii) Thaw the glaze from the surfaces of the product with flowing tap water.
(iii) Gently wipe off the excess water from the surfaces with a single water saturated paper towel.
(iv) Weigh the deglazed portions, which gives the net weight.

VII. FROZEN RAW BREADED FISH STICKS

A. DESCRIPTION OF THE PRODUCT

Frozen raw breaded sticks are clean, wholesome, rectangular-shaped unglazed masses of cohering pieces (not ground) of fish flesh coated with breading. The sticks are cut from frozen fish blocks; are coated with a suitable, wholesome batter and breading; are packaged; and frozen in accordance with good commercial practice. They are maintained at temperatures necessary for preservation of the product. Frozen raw breaded fish sticks weigh up to and including 1½ ounces; are at least 3/8 inch thick; and their largest dimension is at least 3 times the next largest dimension. All sticks in an individual package are prepared from the flesh of one species of fish.

Frozen raw breaded fish sticks should contain 72 percent by weight of fish flesh determined by the official end-product method. Fish flesh content may be determined by the on-line method provided, That the results are consistent with the fish flesh content requirement of 72 percent by weight when verified by the official end-product method. Production methods employed in official establishments should be kept relatively constant for each production lot so as to minimize variation in any factors which may affect the relative fish flesh content.

B. DEFINITIONS

Selection of the sample unit: The sample unit should consist of 10 frozen raw breaded fish sticks taken at random from one or more packages as required. The fish sticks are spread out on a flat pan or sheet and are examined.

Examination of sample, frozen state:

Condition of package refers to the presence in the package of loose breading and/or loose frost.

Ease of separation refers to the difficulty of separating sticks from each other or from packaging material that are frozen together during the freezing.

Broken stick means a stick with a break or cut equal to or greater than one-half the width of the stick.

Damaged stick means a stick that has been mashed, physically or mechanically injured, misshaped, or mutilated to the extent that its appearance is materially affected. The amount of damage is measured by using a grid composed of squares ¼ inch (that is, squares with an area of 1/16 square inch each) to measure the area of the stick affected. Deductions are not made for damage less than 1/16 square inch.

Uniformity of size refers to the degree of uniformity in length and width of the frozen sticks. Deviations are measured from the combined lengths of the two longest minus the combined lengths of the two shortest and/or the combined widths of the two widest minus the combined widths of the two narrowest. Deductions are not made for overall deviations in length or width up to 1/4 inch.

Uniformity of weight refers to the degree of uniformity of the weights of the sticks. Uniformity is measured by the combined weight of the two heaviest sticks divided by the combined weight of the two lightest sticks. No deductions are made for weight ratios less than 1.15.

Cooked state means the state of the product after cooking in accordance with the instructions accompanying the product. However, if specific instructions are lacking, the product for inspection is cooked as follows: Transfer the product, while still in frozen state, into a wire mesh fry basket large enough to hold the fish sticks in a single layer and cook by immersing 2–3 minutes in 375°F. liquid or hydrogenated cooking oil. After cooking, allow the fish sticks to drain 15 seconds and place the fish sticks on a paper napkin or towel to absorb excess oil.

Examination of sample, cooked state:

Distortion refers to the degree of bending of the long axis of the stick. Distortion is measured as the greatest deviation from the long axis. Deductions are not made for deviations of less than 1/4 inch.

Coating defects refers to breaks, lumps, ridges, depressions, blisters, or swells and curds in the coating of the cooked product. Breaks in the coating are objectionable bare spots through which the fish flesh is plainly visible. Lumps are objectionable outcroppings of breading on the stick surface.

Ridges are projections of excess breading at the edges of the fish flesh.

Depressions are objectionable visible voids or shoulder areas which are lightly covered by breading. Blisters

are measured by the swelling or exposed area in the coating resulting from the bursting or breaking of the coating. Curd refers to crater-like holes in the breading filled with coagulated albumin. Instances of these defects are measured by a plastic grid marked off in ¼-inch squares (1/16 square inch). Each square is counted as 1 whether it is full or fractional.

Blemishes refers to skin, blood spots or bruises, objectionable dark fatty flesh, or extraneous material. Instances of blemishes refer to each occurrence measured by placing a plastic grid market off in ¼-inch squares (1/16 square inch) over the defect area. Each square is counted as 1 whether it is full or fractional.

Bones means the presence of potentially harmful bones in a stick. A potentially harmful bone is one that after being cooked is capable of piercing or hurting the palate.

Texture defects of the coating refers to the absence of the normal textural properties of the coating which are crispness and tenderness. Coating texture defects are dryness, sogginess, mushiness, doughyness, toughness, pastiness as sensed by starchiness or other sticky properties felt by mouth tissues and/or mealiness.

Texture defects of the fish flesh refers to the absence of the normal textural properties of the cooked fish flesh which are tenderness, firmness, and moistness without excess water. Texture defects of the flesh are dryness, mushiness, toughness, and rubberiness.

VIII. FROZEN RAW BREADED FISH PORTIONS

A. DESCRIPTION OF THE PRODUCT

Frozen raw breaded portions are clean, wholesome, uniformly shaped, unglazed masses of cohering pieces (not ground) of fish flesh coated with breading. The portions are cut from frozen fish blocks; are coated with a suitable, wholesome batter and breading; and are packaged and frozen in accordance with good commercial practice. They are maintained at temperatures necessary for the preservation of the product. Frozen raw breaded fish portions weigh more than 1-1/2 ounces, and are at least 3/8-inch thick. Frozen raw breaded fish portions contain not less than 75 percent, by weight, of fish flesh. All portions in an individual package are prepared from the flesh of one species of fish.

B. STYLES

Style I, Skinless portions, are portions prepared from fish blocks which have been made with skinless fillets.

Style II, Skin-on-portions, are portions prepared from fish blocks which have been made with demonstrably acceptable skin-on fillets.

Composition of the product.

(a) Frozen raw breaded fish portions should contain 75 percent by weight of fish flesh. Fish flesh content may be determined by the on-line method provided that the results are consistent with the fish flesh content requirement of 75 percent by weight, when verified by the official end-product method.

(b) Production methods employed in official establishments should be kept relatively constant for each production lot so as to minimize variation in any factors which may affect the relative fish flesh content.

Examination of sample, frozen state:

(1) Condition of package refers to the presence in the package of loose breading and/or loose frost.

(2) Ease of separation refers to the difficulty of separating the portions from each other or from the packaging material.

Broken portion means a portion with a break or cut equal to or greater than one-half the width or length of the portion.

Damaged portion means a portion that has been mashed, physically or mechanically injured. misshaped, or mutilated to the extent that its appearance is materially affected. The amount of damage is measured by using a grid composed of squares ¼ inch × ¼ inch (that is, squares with an area of 1/16 square inch each) to measure the area of the portion affected. No deductions are made for damage of less than 1/16 square inch.

Uniformity of size refers to the degree of uniformity in length and width of the frozen portions. Deviations are measured from the combined lengths of the two longest minus the combined lengths of the two shortest and/or the combined widths of the two widest minus the combined widths of the two narrowest portions in the sample. Deductions are not made for overall deviations in length or width up to 1/4 inch.

Uniformity of weight refers to the degree of uniformity of the weights of the portions. Uniformity is measured by the combined weight of the two heaviest portions divided by the combined weight of the two lightest portions in the sample. No deductions are made for weight ratios less than 1.2.

Cooked state means the state of the product after being cooked in accordance with the instructions accompanying the product.

C. EXAMINATION OF SAMPLE, COOKED STATE

(1) Distortion refers to the degree of bending of the long axis of the portion. Distortion is measured as the greatest deviation from the long axis. Deductions are not made for deviations of less than ¼ inch.

(2) Coating defects refers to breaks, lumps, ridges, depressions, blisters, or swells and curds in the coating of the cooked product. Breaks in the coating are objectionable bare spots through which the fish flesh is plainly visible. Lumps are objectionable outcroppings of breading on the portion surface. Ridges are projections of excess breading at the edges of the portions.

Depressions are objectionable visible voids or shouldow areas that are lightly covered by breading. Blisters are measured by the swelling or exposed area in the coating resulting from the bursting or breaking of the coating. Curd refers to crater-like holes in the breading filled with coagulated white or creamy albumin. Instances of these defects are measured by a plastic grid marked off in 1/4-inch squares (1/16 square inch). Each square is counted as 1 whether it is full or fractional.

(3) Blemishes refers to skin (except for Style II), blood spots or bruises, objectionable dark fatty flesh, or extraneous material. Instances of blemishes refers to each occurrence measured by placing a plastic grid marked off in 1/4-inch squares (1/16 square inch) over the defect area. Each square is counted as 1 whether it is full or fractional.

(4) Bones means the presence of potentially harmful bones in a portion. A potentially harmful bone is one that after being cooked is capable of piercing or hurting the palate.

(5) Texture defects of the coating refers to the absence of the normal textural properties of the coating which are crispness and tenderness. Defects in coating texture are dryness, sogginess. mushiness, doughyness, toughness, pastyness, as sensed by starchiness or other sticky properties felt by mouth tissues and/or mealiness.

(6) Texture defects of the fish flesh and texture of skin in Style II refers to the absence of the normal textural properties of the cooked fish flesh and to the absence of tenderness of the cooked skin in Style II.

Normal textural properties of cooked fish flesh are tenderness, firmness, and moistness without excess water. Texture defects of the cooked fesh are dryness, mushiness, toughness, and rubberiness. Texture defects of the cooked skin in Style II are mushiness, rubberiness, toughness, and stringiness.

Minimum fish flesh content—End-product determination refers to the minimum percent, by weight, of the average fish flesh content of three frozen raw breaded portions (sample unit for fish flesh determination).

IX. FROZEN FRIED FISH STICKS

A. DESCRIPTION OF THE PRODUCT

Frozen fried fish sticks are clean, wholesome, rectangular-shaped unglazed masses of cohering pieces (not ground) of fish flesh coated with breading and partially cooked. The sticks are cut from frozen fish blocks; are coated with a suitable, wholesome batter and breading; are fried, packaged, and frozen in accordance with good manufacturing practices. They are maintained at temperatures necessary for preservation of the product. Frozen fried fish sticks weigh up to and including 1½ ounces; are at least three-eighths of an inch thick; and their largest dimension is at least three times the next largest dimension. All sticks in an individual package are prepared from the flesh of one species of fish.

Frozen fried fish sticks should contain 60 percent by weight of fish flesh. Fish flesh content may be determined by the on-line method provided, that the results are consistent with the fish flesh content requirement of 60 percent by weight, when verified by the official end-product method.

Production methods employed in official establishments should be kept relatively constant for each production lot so as to minimize variation in any factors which may affect the relative fish flesh content.

Definitions of factors for point deductions are as follows:

B. EXAMINATION OF SAMPLE, FROZEN STATE

(1) Condition of package refers to the presence in the package of free excess oil and/or loose breading and/or loose frost.

(2) Ease of separation refers to the difficulty of separating sticks from each other or from packaging material that are frozen together after the frying operation and during the freezing.

(3) Broken stick means a stick with a break or cut equal to or greater than one-half the width of the stick.

(4) Damaged stick means a stick that has been mashed, physically or mechanically injured, misshaped or mutilated to the extent that its appearance is materially affected. The amount of damage is measured by using a grid composed of squares ¼ inch (that is, squares with an area of 1/16 square inch each) to measure the area of the stick affected. Deductions are not made for damage less than 1/16 square inch.

(5) Uniformity of size refers to the degree of uniformity in length and width of the frozen sticks. Deviations are measured from the combined lengths of the two longest minus the combined lengths of the two shortest and/or the combined widths of the two widest minus the combined widths of the two narrowest. Deductions are not made for overall deviations in length of width up to ¼ inch.

(6) Uniformity of weight refers to the degree of uniformity of the weights of the sticks. Uniformity is measured by the combined weight of the two heaviest sticks divided by the combined weight of the two lightest sticks. No deductions are made for weight ratios less than 1.15.

Examination of sample, cooked state:

Distortion refers to the degree of bending of the long axis of the stick. Distortion is measured as the greatest deviation from the long axis. Deductions are not made for deviations of less than 1/4 inch.

Coating defects refers to breaks, lumps, ridges, depressions, blisters, or swells and curds in the coating of the cooked product. Breaks in the coating are objectionable bare spots through which the fish flesh is plainly visible. Lumps are objectionable outcroppings of breading on the stick surface.

Ridges are projections of excess breading at the edges of the fish flesh.

Depressions are objectionable visible voids or shoulddow areas which are lightly covered by breading. Blisters are measured by the swelling or exposed area in the coating resulting from the bursting or breaking of the coating. Curd refers to crater-like holes in the breading filled with coagulated albumin. Instances of these defects are measured by a plastic grid marked off in ¼-inch squares (1/16 square inch). Each square is counted as one whether it is full or fractional.

Blemishes refers to skin, blood spots, or bruises, objectionable dark fatty flesh, carbon specks or extraneous material. Instances of blemishes refers to each occurrence measured by placing a plastic grid marked off in ¼ inch squares (1/16 square inch) over the defect area. Each square is counted as one whether it is full or fractional.

Bones means the presence of potentially harmful bones in a stick. A potentially harmful bone is one that after being cooked is capable of piercing or hurting the palate.

Texture defects of the coating refers to the absence of the normal textural properties of the coating which are crispness and tenderness. Coating texture defects are dryness, sogginess, mushiness, doughiness, toughness, pastiness, as sensed by starchiness or other sticky properties felt by mouth tissues; oiliness to the degree of impairment of texture; and/or mealiness.

Texture defects of the fish flesh refers to the absence of normal textural properties of the cooked fish flesh, which are tenderness, firmness, arid moistness without excess water. Texture defects of the flesh are dryness, softness, toughness, and rubberiness.

X. FROZEN FRIED FISH PORTIONS

A. DESCRIPTION OF THE PRODUCT

Frozen fried fish portions are clean, wholesome, uniformly shaped, unglazed masses of cohering pieces (not ground) of fish flesh coated with breading and partially cooked. The portions are cut from frozen fish blocks; coated with a suitable, wholesome batter and breading; are fried, packaged, and frozen in accordance with good manufacturing practices. They are maintained at temperatures necessary for preservation of the product. Frozen fried fish portions weigh more than 11/2 ounces and are at least three-eighths of an inch thick. All portions in an individual package are prepared from the flesh of one species of fish.

Frozen fried fish portions should contain 65 percent by weight of fish flesh. Fish flesh content may be determined by the on-line method, provided, that the results are consistent with the fish flesh content requirement of 65 percent by weight, when verified by the official end-product method.

Production methods employed in official establishments should be kept relatively constant for each production lot so as to minimize variation in any factors which may affect the relative fish flesh content.

Ease of separation refers to the difficulty of separating portions from one another or from packaging material that are frozen together after the frying operation and during the freezing.

Broken portion means a portion with a break or cut equal to or greater than one-half the width or length of the portion.

Damaged portion means a portion that has been mashed, physically or mechanically injured, misshaped or mutilated to the extent that its appearance is materially affected. The amount of damage is measured by using a grid composed of squares 1/4 inch (that is, squares with an area of 1/16 square inch each) to measure the area of the portion affected. Deductions are not made for damage less than 1/16 square inch.

Uniformity of size refers to the degree of uniformity in length and width of the frozen portions. Deviations are measured from the combined lengths of the two longest minus the combined lengths of the two shortest and/or the combined widths of the two widest minus the combined widths of the two narrowest. Deductions are not made for overall deviations in length or width up to ¼ inch.

Uniformity of weight refers to the degree of uniformity of the weights of the portions. Uniformity is measured by the combined weight of the two heaviest portions divided by the combined weight of the two lightest portions. No deductions are made for weight ratios less than 1.20.

XI. FRESH AND FROZEN SHRIMP

A. PRODUCT DESCRIPTION

The products are clean wholesome shrimp that are fresh or frozen, raw or cooked. Product forms are:

1. Types

(1) Chilled, fresh (not previously frozen).
(2) Unfrozen, thawed (previously frozen).
(3) Frozen individually (IQF), glazed or unglazed.
(4) Frozen solid pack, glazed or unglazed.
(b) Styles. (1) Raw (uncoagulated protein).

2. Blanched (Parboiled)

Blanched means heated for a period of time such that the surface of the product reaches a temperature adequate to coagulate the protein.

Cooked-heated for a period of time such that the thermal center of the product reaches a temperature adequate to coagulate the protein.

3. Market Forms

(1) Heads on (head, shell, tail fins on).
(2) Headless (only head removed: shell, tail fins on).
(3) Peeled, undeveined, round, tail on (all shell removed except last shell segment and tail fins, with segments unslit].
(4) Peeled, undeveined, round, tail off (all shell and tail fins removed, with segments unslit).
(5) Peeled and deveined, round, tail on (all shell removed except last shell segment and tail fins, with segments shouldowly slit to last segment).
(6) Peeled and deveined, round, tail off (all shell and tail fins removed, with segments shouldowly slit to last segment).
(7) Peeled and deveined, fantail or butterfly, tail on (all shell removed except last shell segment and tail fins,with segments deeply slit to last segment).
(8) Peeled and deveined, fantail or butterfly, tail off (all shell and tail fin removed, with segments deeply slit to last segment).
(9) Peeled and deveined, western (all shell removed except last shell segment and tail fins, with segments split to fifth segment and vein removed to end of cut).
(10) Other forms of shrimp as specified and so designated on the label.

B. EXAMINATION IN THE FROZEN STATE

Dehydration refers to a general drying of the shrimp flesh that is noticeable after any glaze and shell are removed. It includes any detectable change from the normal characteristic, bright appearance of freshly caught, properly iced or properly processed shrimp.

Slight dehydration means scarcely noticeable drying of the shrimp flesh that will not affect the sensory quality of the sample.

Moderate dehydration means conspicuous drying of the shrimp flesh that will not seriously affect the sensory quality of the sample.

Excessive dehydration means conspicuous drying that will seriously affect the sensory quality of the sample.

Examination in the fresh or thawed state indicates the following.

Uniformity of size refers to the degree of uniformity of the shrimp in the container to determine their conformity to the declared count.

Black spots, improperly headed (throats), and improperly cleaned ends refer to the presence of any objectionable black or darkened area that affects the desirability or sensory quality of the shrimp, whether the market form is shell-on or peeled. Objectionable black spot refers to more than three instances of penetrating black spot that is visible but difficult to measure because of its small size (approximately the size of a pencil point): or any areas larger than a pencil point that penetrates the flesh: or aggregate areas of non-penetrating surface black spot on the shell or membrane that is equal to or greater than 1/3 the area of the smallest segment.

Assessments are made on individual shrimp:

Throats are those portions of flesh and/or extraneous material from the head (cephalothorax) that remain attached to the first segment after heading.

Pieces of shrimp, broken or damaged shrimp:

Piece means for a count of 70 or less unglazed shrimp per pound (0.45 kg) any shrimp that has fewer than five segments, with or without tail fins attached: or, for a count of more than 70 unglazed shrimp per pound (0.45 kg), any shrimp that has fewer than four segments: or, any whole shrimp with a break in the flesh greater than 2/3 of the thickness of the shrimp where the break occurs.

Broken shrimp means a shrimp having a break in the flesh greater than 1/3 of the thickness of the shrimp.

Damaged shrimp means a shrimp that is crushed or mutilated so as to materially affect its appearance or useability.

Unusable material includes the following:

Legs refer to walking legs only, whether attached or not attached to the body (heads-on market from excepted).

Loose shell and antennae are any pieces of shell or antennae that are completely detached from the shrimp.

Flipper refers to any detached tail fin with or without the last shell segment attached, with or without flesh inside.

Extraneous material means any harmless material in a sample unit that is not shrimp material.

Unacceptable shrimp refers to abnormal or diseased shrimp.

Head refers to the cephalothorax, except for heads-on shrimp.

Inadvertently peeled and improperly peeled shrimp refer to the presence or absence of head, shell segment, swimmeret, or tail fin, which should or should not have been removed of certain market forms. (Shell-on shrimp with tail fins and/or telson missing is inadvertently peeled, but if the last segment of flesh is missing, the shrimp is damaged.)

Improperly deveined shrimp refers to the presence of dark vein (alimentary canal) containing sand or sediment or roe which should have been removed for peeled and deveined market forms. For shrimp of 70 count per pound (0.45 kg) or less, aggregate areas of dark vein or roe is a defect that are longer than one segment is a defect. For shrimp of 71 to 500 count per pound (0.45 kg), aggregate areas of dark vein or roe defect that are longer than two segments are a defect.

Note: This does not pertain to the last segment. For shrimp of over 500 count per pound (0.45 kg), dark vein or roe of any length is not a defect.

Examination in the cooked state:

Texture. The texture of cooked shrimp should be firm, slightly resilient but not tough, moist but not mushy. Texture as a defect refers to an undesirable toughness, dryness, or mushiness which deviated from the normal characteristics of the species when freshly caught, properly processed, and cooked.

Slight means slightly tough, dry, but not mushy.

Moderate means moderately tough, dry or mushy.

Excessive means excessively tough, very dry or very mushy.

XII. FROZEN RAW BREADED SHRIMP

The U.S. FDA has provided the following standards for frozen raw breaded shrimp.

A. DESCRIPTION

Frozen raw breaded shrimp are whole, clean, wholesome, headless, peeled shrimp which have been deveined where applicable of the regular commercial species, coated with a wholesome, suitable batter and/or breading. Whole shrimp consist of five or more segments of unmutilated shrimp flesh. They are prepared and frozen in accordance with good manufacturing practice and are maintained at temperatures necessary for the preservation of the product.

Frozen raw breaded shrimp is the food prepared by coating one of the optional forms of shrimp with safe and suitable batter and breading ingredients. The food is frozen.

The food tests not less than 50 percent of shrimp material as determined by prescribed method

The term shrimp means the tail portion of properly prepared shrimp of commercial species. Except for composite units, each shrimp unit is individually coated. The optional forms of shrimp are:

(1) Fantail or butterfly: Prepared by splitting the shrimp; the shrimp are peeled, except that tail fins remain attached and the shell segment immediately adjacent to the tail fins may be left attached.
(2) Butterfly, tail off: Prepared by splitting the shrimp; tail fins and all shell segments are removed.
(3) Round: Round shrimp, not split; the shrimp are peeled, except that tail fins remain attached and the shell segment immediately adjacent to the tail fins may be left attached.
(4) Round, tail off: Round shrimp, not split; tail fins and all shell segments are removed.
(5) Pieces: Each unit consists of a piece or a part of a shrimp; tail fins and all shell segments are removed.

The above information is categorized as follows.

1. Styles

Style I, Regular Breaded Shrimp, are frozen raw breaded shrimp containing a minimum of 50 percent of shrimp material.

Style II, Lightly Breaded Shrimp, are frozen raw breaded shrimp containing a minimum of 65 percent of shrimp material.

2. Types

Type I-Breaded fantail shrimp subtypes are:

Subtype A. Split (butterfly) shrimp with the tail fin and the shell segment immediately adjacent to the tail fin.

Subtype B. Split (butterfly) shrimp with the tail fin but free of all shell segments.

Subtype C. Split (butterfly) shrimp without attached tail fin or shell segments.

Type II-Breaded round shrimp subtypes are:

Subtype A. Round shrimp with the tail fin and the shell segment immediately adjacent to the tail fin.

Subtype B. Round shrimp with the tail fin but free of all shell segments.

Subtype C. Round shrimp without attached tail fin or shell segments.

Type III-Breaded split shrimp.

3. Definitions and Methods of Analysis

(a) Fantail shrimp:
This type is prepared by splitting and peeling the shrimp except that for Subtype A the tail fin remains attached and the shell segment immediately adjacent to the tail fin remains attached.

For Subtype B, the tail fin remains, but the shrimp are free of all shell segments.

For Subtype C, the shrimp are free of tail fins and all shell segments.

(b) Round shrimp: This type is the round shrimp, not split. The shrimp are peeled except that for Subtype A, the tail fin remains attached and the shell segment immediately adjacent to the tail fin remains attached.

For Subtype B, the tail fin remains, but the shrimp are free of all shell segments.

For Subtype C, the shrimp are free of all shell segments and tail fins.

B. COMPOSITE UNITS

Each unit consists of two or more whole shrimp or pieces of shrimp, or both, formed and pressed into composite units prior to coating; tail fins and all shell segments are removed; large composite units, prior to coating, may be cut into smaller units.

The batter and breading ingredients referred to are the fluid constituents and the solid constituents of the coating around the shrimp. These ingredients consist of suitable substances which are not food additives as defined by regulations. If they are food additives as so defined, they are used in conformity with established regulations. Batter and breading ingredients that perform a useful function are regarded as suitable, except that artificial flavorings, artificial sweeteners, artificial colors, and chemical preservatives, other than those specifically permitted are not suitable ingredients of frozen raw breaded shrimp. Chemical preservatives that are suitable are:

1. Ascorbic acid, which may be used in a quantity sufficient to retard development of dark spots on the shrimp; and
2. The antioxidant preservatives listed in the regulations that may be used to retard development of rancidity of the fat content of the food, in amounts within the limits prescribed.

The label should name the food, as prepared from each of the optional forms of shrimp specified, and following the numbered sequence of the following data

(1) "Breaded fantail shrimp." The word "butterfly" may be used in lieu of "fantail" in the name.
(2) "Breaded butterfly shrimp, tail off."

(3) "Breaded round shrimp."
(4) "Breaded round shrimp, tail off."
(5) "Breaded shrimp pieces."
(6) Composite units:

If the composite units are in a shape similar to that of breaded fish sticks the name is "Breaded shrimp sticks"; if they are in the shape of meat cutlets, the name is "Breaded shrimp cutlets."

If prepared in a shape other than that of sticks or cutlets, the name is "Breaded shrimp _____," the blank to be filled in with the word or phrase that accurately describes the shape, but which is not misleading.

The word "prawns" may be added in parentheses immediately after the word "shrimp" in the name of the food if the shrimp are of large size; for example, "Fantail breaded shrimp (prawns)." If the shrimp are from a single geographical area, the adjectival designation of that area may appear as part of the name; for example, "Breaded Alaskan shrimp sticks."

The names of the optional ingredients used should be listed on the principal display panel or panels of the label with such prominence and conspicuousness as to render them likely to be read and understood by the ordinary individual under customary conditions of purchase. If a spice that also imparts color is used, it should be designated as "spice and coloring," unless the spice is designated by its specific name. If ascorbic acid is used to retard development of dark spots on the shrimp, it should be designated as "Ascorbic acid added as a preservative" or "Ascorbic acid added to retard discoloration of shrimp."

If any other antioxidant preservative is used, such preservative should be designated by its common name followed by the statement "Added as a preservative."

Frozen raw lightly breaded shrimp complies with the provisions of frozen raw breaded shrimp except that it contains not less than 65 percent of shrimp material and that in the name prescribed the word "lightly" immediately precedes the words "breaded shrimp."

Factors affecting qualities that are measured on the product in the unbreaded or thawed debreaded state are degree of deterioration, dehydrations, sand veins, black spot, extra shell, extraneous material, and swimmerets.

Dehydration refers to the occurrence of whitish areas on the exposed ends of the shrimp (due to the drying of the affected area) and to a generally desiccated appearance of the meat after the breading is removed.

Deterioration refers to any detectable change from the normal good quality of freshly caught shrimp. It is evaluated by noting in the thawed product deviations from the normal odor and appearance of freshly caught shrimp.

Extraneous material consists of nonedible material such as sticks, seaweed, shrimp thorax, or other objects that may be accidentally present in the package.

Slight: Slight refers to a condition that is scarcely noticeable but does affect the appearance, desirability, and/or eating quality of breaded shrimp.

Moderate: Moderate refers to a condition that is conspicuously noticeable but that does not seriously affect the appearance, desirability, and/or eating quality of the breaded shrimp.

Marked: Marked refers to a condition that is conspicuously noticeable and that does seriously affect the appearance, desirability, and/or eating quality of the breaded shrimp.

Excessive: Excessive refers to a condition that is very noticeable and is seriously objectionable.

Halo: Halo means an easily recognized fringe of excess batter and breading extending beyond the shrimp flesh and adhering around the perimeter or flat edges of a split (butterfly) breaded shrimp.

Balling up: Balling up means the adherence of lumps of the breading material to the surface of the breaded coating, causing the coating to appear rough, uneven, and lumpy.

Holidays: Holidays means voids in the breaded coating as evidenced by bare or naked spots.

Damaged frozen raw breaded shrimp: Damaged frozen raw breaded shrimp means frozen raw breaded shrimp that have been separated into two or more parts or that have been crushed or otherwise mutilated to the extent that their appearance is materially affected.

Black spot: Black spot means any blackened area that is markedly apparent on the flesh of the shrimp.

Sand vein: Sand vein means any black or dark sand vein that has not been removed, except for that portion under the shell segment adjacent to the tail fin when present.

Extra shell: Extra shell means any shell segment(s) or portion thereof, contained in the breaded shrimp except the first segment adjacent to the tail fin for Type I, Subtype A, and Type II, Subtype A.

XIII. FROZEN RAW SCALLOPS

A. DESCRIPTION OF THE PRODUCT

Frozen raw scallops are clean, wholesome, adequately drained, whole or cutadductor muscles of the scallop of the regular commercial species. The portion of the scallop used should be only the adductor muscle eye whichcontrols the shell movement. Scallops should be washed, drained, packed, andfrozen in accordance with good manufacturing practices and are maintained attemperatures necessary for the preservation of the product. Only scallops of asingle species should be used within a lot.

1. Styles

Style I are solid pack scallops are frozen together into a solid mass.

(1) Substyle a. Glazed.
(2) Substyle b. Not glazed. (b) Style II. Individually quick frozen pack (IQF) scallops are individually quick frozen. Individual scallops can be separated without thawing.

(1) Substyle a. Glazed.
(2) Substyle b. Not glazed.

2. Types

(a) Type 1. Adductor muscle.
(b) Type 2. Adductor muscle with catch (gristle or sweet meat) portion removed.

Dehydration refers to the loss of moisture from the scallops surface during frozen storage. Small degree of dehydration is color-masking but can be easily scraped off. Large degree of dehydration is deep, color-masking, and requires a knife or other instrument to scrape it off.

Extraneous materials are pieces or fragments of undesirable material that are naturally present in or on the scallops and which should be removed during processing.

An instance of minor extraneous material includes but is not limited to each occurrence of intestines, seaweed, etc., and each aggregate of sand and grit up to ½-inch square and located on the scallop surface. Deduction points should be assessed for additional instances of intestines, seaweed, etc., and aggregates of sand and grit up to ½-inch square.

An instance of major extraneous material includes but is not limited to each instance of shell or aggregate of embedded sand or other extraneous embedded material that affects the appearance or eating quality of the product.

Texture refers to the firmness, tenderness, and moistness of the cooked scallop meat, which is characteristic of the species.

Net weight means the total weight of the scallop meats within the package after removal of all packaging materials, ice glaze, or other protective materials.

XIV. FROZEN RAW BREADED SCALLOPS FROZEN FRIED SCALLOPS

A. PRODUCT DESCRIPTION

Frozen raw breaded scallops are:

(1) Prepared from wholesome, clean, adequately drained, whole or cut adductor muscles of the scallop of the regular commercial species, or scallop units cut from a block of frozen scallops that are coated with wholesome batter and breading;
(2) Packaged and frozen according to good commercial practice and maintained at temperatures necessary for preservation; and
(3) Composed of a minimum of 50 percent by weight of scallop meat.

Frozen fried scallops.
Frozen fried scallops are:

(1) Prepared from wholesome, clean, adequately drained, whole or cut adductor muscles of the scallop of the regular commercial species, or scallop units cut from a block of frozen scallops that are coated with wholesome batter and breading;
(2) Precooked in oil or fat;
(3) Packaged and frozen according to good commercial practice and maintained at temperatures necessary for preservation; and
(4) Composed of a minimum of 50 percent by weight of scallop meat.

The styles of frozen raw breaded scallops and frozen fried scallops include the following.
Style I Random pack:
Scallops in a package are reasonably uniform in weight and/or shape. The weight or shape of individual scallops is not specified.
Style II Uniform pack:
Scallops in a package consist of uniform shaped pieces that are of specified weight or range of weights.

1. Types

(a) Type 1. Adductor muscle.
(b) Type 2. Adductor muscle with catch (gristle or sweet meat) portion removed.

Appearance refers to the condition of the package and ease of separation in the frozen state and continuity and color in the cooked state.

"Condition of the package" refers to freedom from packaging defects and the presence in the package of oil, and/or loose breading, and/or frost. Deduction points are based on the degree of the improper condition as small or large.

"Ease of separation" refers to the difficulty of separating scallops that are frozen together after the frying operation and during freezing.

"Continuity" refers to the completeness of the coating of the product in the cooked state. Lack of continuity is exemplified by breaks, ridges and/or lumps of breading. Each 1/16 square inch area of any break, ridge, or lump of breading is considered an instance of lack of continuity. Individual breaks, ridges, or lumps of breading measuring less than 1/16 square inch are not considered objectionable. Deduction points are based on the percentage of the scallops within the package that contain small and/or large instances of lack of continuity.

Workmanship defects refer to the degree of freedom from doubled and misshaped scallops and extraneous material. The defects of doubled and misshaped scallops are determined by examining the frozen product, while the defects of extraneous materials are determined by examining the product in the cooked state. Deduction points are based on the percentage by count of the scallops affected within the package.

Doubled scallops. Two or more scallops that are joined together during the breading and/or frying operations

Misshaped scallops. Elongated, flattened, mashed, or damaged scallop meats.

Extraneous material. Extraneous are pieces or fragments of undesirable material that are naturally present in or on the scallops and which should be removed during processing.

Examples of minor extraneous material include intestines, seaweed, and each aggregate of sand and grit within an area of 1/2-inch square.

Examples of major extraneous material include shell, aggregate of embedded sand or other extraneous embedded material that affects the appearance or eating quality of the product.

Texture in the cooked state
Texture of the coating:
Firm or crisp, but not tough, pasty, mushy, or oily
Moderately tough, pasty, mushy, or oily
Excessively tough, pasty, mushy, or oily
Texture of the scallop meat
Firm, but tender and moist
Moderately tough, dry, and/or fibrous or mushy
Excessively tough, dry, and/or fibrous or mushy
Character.

Character refers to the texture of the scallop meat and of the coating and the presence of gristle in the cooked state.

(1) *Gristle.* Gristle (type 2 only) is the tough elastic tissue usually attached to the scallop meat. Each instance of gristle is an occurrence.

(2) *Texture* refers to the firmness, tenderness, and moistness of the cooked scallop meat and to the crispness and tenderness of the coating of the cooked product. The texture of the scallop meat may be classified as a degree of mushiness, toughness, and fibrousness. The texture of the coating may be classified as a degree of pastiness, toughness, dryness, mushiness, or oiliness.

XV. FROZEN NORTH AMERICAN FRESHWATER CATFISH AND CATFISH PRODUCTS

A. SCOPE AND PRODUCT DESCRIPTION

The descriptions apply to products derived from farm-raised, or from rivers and lakes, North American freshwater catfish of the following common commercial species and hybrids thereof:

(1) Channel catfish (*Ictalurus punctatus*)
(2) White catfish (*Ictalurus catus*)

(3) Blue catfish (*Ictalurus furcatus*)
(4) Flathead catfish (*Pylodictis olivaris*)

Fresh products will be packaged in accordance with good commercial practices and maintained at temperatures necessary for the preservation of the product. Frozen products will be frozen to 0°F (-18°C) at their center(thermal core) in accordance with good commercial practices and maintained at temperatures of 0°F (-18°C) or less.

The product may contain bones when the principle display panel clearly shows that the product contains bones. Product presentation.

Catfish products may be presented and labeled as follows:

1. Types

(1) Fresh, or
(2) Frozen.

2. Styles

(1) Skin on, or
(2) Skinless.

Market forms include but are not limited to the following:

(1) Headed and gutted.
(2) Headed and dressed are headed and gutted usually with fins removed. This form may be presented with or without the dorsal spine and with or without the collar bone.
(3) Whole fillets are practically boneless pieces of fish cut parallel to the entire length of the backbone with the belly flaps and with or without the black membrane.
(4) Trimmed fillets are whole fillets without belly flaps.
(5) Fillet strips are strips of fillets weighing not less than ¾ ounce.
(6) Steaks are units of fish not less than 1 1/2 ounces in weight which are sawn or cut approximately perpendicular (30 degrees to 90 degrees) to the axial length or backbone. They have two reasonably parallel surfaces. The number of tail sections that may be included in the package must not exceed the number of fish cut per package).
(7) Nuggets are pieces of belly flaps with or without black membrane and weighing not less than ¾ ounce.

3. Bone Classifications

(1) Practically boneless fillet.
(2) Bone-in (fillet cut, with bones).

Dehydration applies to all frozen market forms. It refers to the loss of moisture from the surface resulting in a whitish, dry, or porous condition:

Slight: surface dehydration which is not color masking (readily removed by scraping) and affecting 3 to 10 percent of the surface area.

Moderate: deep dehydration which is color masking, cannot be scraped off easily with a sharp instrument, and affects more than one percent but not more than 10 percent of the surface area.

Excessive: deep dehydration which is color masking, and cannot be easily scraped off with a sharp instrument and affects more than 10 percent of the surface area.

Condition of the product applies to all market forms. It refers to freedom from packaging defects, cracks in the surface of a frozen product, and excess moisture (drip) or blood inside the package. Deduction points are based on the degree of this defect.

Slight refers to a condition that is scarcely oticeable but that does not affect the appearance, desirability or eating quality of the product.

Moderate refers to a condition that is conspicuously noticeable but that does not seriously affect the appearance, desirability, or eating quality of the product.

Excessive refers to a condition that is conspicuously noticeable and that does seriously affect the appearance, desirability or eating quality of the product.

Discoloration applies to all market forms. It refers to colors not normal to the species. This may be due to mishandling or the presence of blood, bile, or other substances.

Slight: 1/16 square inch up to and including one square inch in aggregate area.

Moderate: greater than one square inch up to and including 2 square inches in aggregate area.

Excessive: over 2 square inches in aggregate area. Also, each additional complete one square inch is again assessed points under this category.

Uniformity will be assigned in accordance with weight tolerances as follows:

Weight of portion: 0.75 to 4.16 ounces

Moderate: Over 1/8 ounce but not over 1/4 ounce above or below declared weight of portion

Excessive: In excess of 1/4 ounce above or below declared weight of portion 4.17 to 11.20 ounces

Moderate: Over 1/8 ounce but not over 1/2 ounce above or below declared weight of portion

Excessive: In excess of 1/2 ounce above or below declared weight of portion 11.21 to 17.30 ounces

Moderate: Over 1/8 ounce but not over 1/8 ounce above or below declared weight of portion

Excessive: In excess of 1/8 ounce above or below declared weight of portion

Skinning cuts apply to skinless market forms. It refers to improper cuts made during the skinning operation as evidenced by torn or ragged surfaces or edges, or gouges in the flesh which detract from a good appearance of the product.

Slight: 1/16 square inch up to and including 1 square inch in aggregate area.

Moderate: Over one square inch up to and including 2 square inches in aggregate area.

Excessive: Over 2 square inches in aggregate area. Also, each additional complete one square inch is again assessed points under this category.

Heading applies to the presence of ragged cuts or pieces of gills, gill cover, pectoral fins or collar bone after heading. Deduction points also will be assigned when the product is presented with the collar bone and it has been completely or partially removed.

Slight: 1/16 square inch up to and including one square inch in aggregate area.

Moderate: Over one square inch up to and including 2 square inches in aggregate area.

Excessive: Over 2 square inches in aggregate area. Also, each additional complete one square inch is again assessed points under this category.

Evisceration applies to all market forms. It refers to the proper removal of viscera, kidney, spawn, blood, reproductive organs, and abnormal fat (leaf). The evisceration cut should be smooth and clean. Deduction points are based on the degree of defect.

Slight: 1/16 square inch up to and including 1 square inch in aggregate area.

Moderate: Over 1 square inch up to and including 2 square inches in aggregate area.

Excessive: Over 2 square inches in aggregate area. Also, each additional complete one square inch is again assessed points under this category.

Fins refer to the presence of fins, pieces of fins or dorsal spines. It applies to all market forms except headed and gutted or headed and dressed catfish or catfish steaks. Deduction points also will be assigned when the product is intended to have the dorsal spine but it has been completely or partially removed.

Slight: Aggregate area up to including one square inch.

Moderate: Over one square inch area up to and including 2 square inches.

Excessive: Over 2 square inches in aggregate area. Also, each additional complete one square inch is again assessed points under this category.

Bones (including pin bone) apply to all fillet and nugget market forms. Each bone defect is a bone or part of a bone that is 3/16 inch or more at its maximum length or 1/32 inch or more at its maximum shaft width, or for bone chips, a length of at least 1/16 inch. An excessive bone defect is any bone which cannot be fitted into a rectangle, which has a length of 1 9/16 inch and a width of 1/8 inch. In market forms intended to contain bones, the presence of bones will not be considered a physical defect.

Skin refers to the presence of skin on skinless market forms. For semi-skinned forms, a skin defect is the presence of the darkly pigmented outside layers. Points will be assessed for each aggregate area greater than 1/2 square inch up to and including one square inch.

Bloodspots refer to the presence of coagulated blood.

Bruises refer to softening and discoloration of the flesh. Both bloodspots and bruises apply to all market forms. Points will be assessed for each aggregate area of bloodspots or bruises greater than 1/2 square inch up to and including one square inch.

Foreign material refers to extraneous material, including packaging material, not derived from the fish that is found on or in the sample. Each occurrence will be assessed.

Texture applies to all market forms and refers to the presence of normal texture properties of the cooked fish flesh, i.e., tender, firm, and moist without excess water. Texture defects are described as dry, tough, mushy, rubbery, watery, and stringy.

Moderate: Noticeably dry, tough, mushy, rubbery, watery, stringy.

Excessive: Markedly dry, tough, mushy, rubbery, watery, stringy.

ACKNOWLEDGMENT

The information in this chapter is based on *Food Safety Manual*, published and copyrighted by Science Technology System, West Sacramento, California, 2004. Used with permission.

39 Freezing Seafood and Seafood Products: Principles and Applications

Shann-Tzong Jiang
Department of Food Science, National Taiwan Ocean University

Tung-Ching Lee
Department of Food Science, Rutgers University

CONTENTS

GENERAL PRINCIPLES FOR THE FREEZING, STORAGE AND THAWING OF SEAFOOD

I. INTRODUCTION

Fish and shellfish are perishable and, as a result of a complex series of chemical, physical, bacteriological, and histological changes occurring in muscle, easily spoil after harvesting. These interrelated processes are usually accompanied by the gradual loss or development of different compounds which affect fish quality. The quality changes are highly influenced by many factors, the most important of which is temperature. If fresh fish is not properly stored, exposure to ambient temperature can cause serious deterioration in fish quality. Commercially, icing or chilling continues to play a major role in slowing down bacterial and enzymatic degradation of fish muscle. However, this process is not designed to totally eliminate changes in quality, since it only offers protection for 2–3 weeks, depending on the species.

Freezing preservation of food is an excellent method of preservation with wide applications. Freezing inhibits the activity of food spoilage and food poisoning organisms and the low storage temperature greatly slows down the enzymatic and biochemical reactions which normally occur in unfrozen foods. Freezing accomplishes these objectives in two ways: the lowering of the temperature of the food and the removal of water by converting it into ice. Lowering the temperature to below freezing point inhibits the growth and activity of many, but not all, microorganisms. Converting most of the water into ice with the concomitant increase in concentration of the dissolved substances reduces the water activity of the food to the point where no microorganisms can grow. Although biochemical reactions slow down at lower temperature, they will, unlike microbiological activities, progress even at low commercial freezer storage temperatures. In addition, conversion of water into ice initiates complex physical and physicochemical changes that can cause general deteriorative quality changes not ordinarily occurring in fresh foods. Pre-freezing processing, such as blanching, freezing and storage conditions should therefore be selected, individually, for each product to minimize the effect of these deteriorative reactions.

In most foods frozen commercially, water is the major component. Most of the water in the tissue dissolves soluble cell components, while a small part is bound up in hydrates and in macromolecular colloidal complexes.

In addition, much of the aqueous solution is part of the gel-like or fiber-like structures in the cell. The most obvious change that occurs on freezing is the solidification of water, which means that water is removed from its normal position within the tissues. It appears that removal of water from its normal position is only partly reversible upon thawing, leading to "drip" and other changes. "Drip" is the exudate from thawed tissue which is difficult in practice to distinguish from any superficial moisture or "glaze." There is sometimes an apparent enhanced susceptibility to invasion by microorganisms owing to the moist surfaces which occur during thawing. The conversion of water into ice increases the concentration of soluble cell components (in some cases to the point where they become saturated and precipitate), changes the pH of the aqueous solution and consequently affects the amount of water that is involved in the colloidal complexes and in the gel-like and fiber-like structures. The concentration of cell components leads to a high concentration of electrolytes, some of which interpose themselves in the polypeptide chains of proteins, leading to protein denaturation. In living cells this often leads to death (for example, freezing and frozen storage causes a slight reduction in number of most microorganisms), but in foods, which usually consist of dead tissue prior to freezing, it can lead, during storage, to irreversible changes in texture (e.g., toughness in fish) and to undesirable biochemical reactions (enzymatically produced off-flavors). An understanding of freezing therefore involves physical, physico-chemical, and biochemical aspects.

As mentioned above, freezing is an excellent process for keeping the original quality of foods, such as fish, for longer periods of time (commercially, up to 12 months or more). Freezing and subsequent frozen storage are particularly useful in making seasonal species of fish, like herring and mackerel, available all year round. In addition, freezing preservation is also applied in a number of different products made from various fish species. For example, tuna is frozen on board large commercial fishing vessels, brought to land, and then thawed for canning process. In the production of various value-added fish products, freezing is applied to breaded and battered fish sticks, fillets, steaks, or nuggets. Likewise, high-quality fish are usually filleted, frozen, and eventually sold to consumers.

Ideally, there should be no distinguishable differences between fresh fish and frozen fish after thawing. If kept under appropriate conditions, fish in the frozen state can be stored for several months or more without appreciable changes in quality. However, it is now well recognized that deteriorative changes take place in fish and seafood during freezing, frozen storage and thawing, which influence the quality of final products. Considerably more knowledge of the basic structure of fish muscle and its chemical composition is essential to understanding these changes that occur during processing.

II. NATURE OF FISH MUSCLE

Fish muscle has a unique arrangement of muscle fibers. It is divided into a number of segments called myotomes, which are separated from one another by a thin sheath of connective tissue called the myocomma or myoseptum. The number of myotomes in fish is dependent on the size of fish, while their diameters vary from head to tail (1). There are two major types of fish skeletal muscles, white and red. The red or dark muscle lies along the side the body next to the skin, particularly along the lateral lines, and may comprise up to 30% of fish muscle, depending on the species (2). Cells in red or dark muscle contain more lipids than those in white muscle (3, 4); they are basically employed for sustained swimming activities, functioning aerobically using lipids for fuel. In addition, red muscle has more mitochondria (5) but less sarcoplasmic reticulum than white muscle (6). It has a large supply of oxygen and a high content of myoglobin, the colored compound that gives its red color. These characteristics, coupled with the presence of the large amount of lipid, particularly among the fatty species, present a serious problem on preservation because of increased susceptibility of this muscle to lipid oxidation. The red muscle of some species has also been reported to contain enzymes that are responsible for chemical reactions such as lipid oxidation and the conversion of trimethylamine oxide (TMAO) to dimethylamine (DMA) and formaldehyde (FA) (7, 8). The shape of red muscle area in different species varies considerably. Lean fish such as flounder, hake, sole, cod, pollock, and whiting have a very small amount of red muscle, which lies along the fish skin, whereas the fatty and semi-fatty fish species have larger areas of red muscle.

White muscle, on the other hand, constitutes the majority of fish muscle. Unlike red muscle, it has minimal myoglobin and a restricted blood supply (5). Often referred to as the "fast" tissue (9), it is used for anaerobic activities such as short bursts of swimming activity. This muscle exhibits rapid, powerful contractions, the energy for which is produced by reducing glycogen to lactic acid anaerobically (5).

Intermediate between these two types of muscle are intermixed red and white muscle, commonly referred to as "mosaic" muscle (10). In some fish, this is a thin layer of muscle that separates the red from white muscle. However, in other fish, such as salmon, carp, and trout, this muscle is scattered throughout the body of the fish.

The chemical composition of fish varies, depending on several factors, such as age, species, gender, maturity, method of catch, fishing grounds, and other seasonal and biological factors. Even within the same species, chemical composition may vary significantly. Generally, fish contain a considerable amount of protein, lipid, and water, and small amounts of vitamins and minerals. Other components such as non-protein nitrogenous compounds are also present in the muscle. These include urea, taurine, peptides, free amino acids, and nucleotides such as inosine and hypoxanthine (11). These compounds, together with the macronutrients found in fish muscle, may be particularly important to fish processors, since they are frequently used as spoilage indices.

III. PHYSICAL ASPECTS OF FREEZING

A. FORMATION OF ICE

From a physical point of view, fish, land animal, and vegetable tissues can be roughly considered as dilute aqueous solutions. When they are chilled below 0°C, ice crystals form at a temperature characteristic of the product and the initial freezing point (FT), which is also the temperature at which the last ice crystals melt on thawing. The freezing point directly depends on the molar concentration of dissolved substances presented, but not on the water content. Fruits, for example, have high water content and a freezing point of −2 to −3°C, while fish contain less water, yet have a freezing point of about −1 to −2°C. The difference is due to the high sugar and acid content in fruits as compared with the low solute content of fish meat. Ice formation occurs during freezing only after a certain degree of supercooling (supercooling is the phenomenon of reducing the temperature of a solution or material below its freezing point without crystallization occurring) has been achieved, and the formation of ice is accompanied by a heating up of the supercooled product close to the freezing point. In commercial practice, the amount of supercooling is usually insignificant.

As the products are progressively cooled below their initial freezing point, more and more water will be turned into ice and the residual solutions will become more and more concentrated. If, at any time, the products are heated, some of the ice will be turned to water that will then dilute the residual solutions. The ratio of ice to residual solution in frozen foods is a function of temperature and initial concentration of solutes. At a temperature lower than −40°C, there is little or no measurable change in the amount of ice presented in most frozen foods. The percentage ratio of freezing (RF) of frozen foods is usually estimated as follows:

$$\text{RF (\%)} = 100 - [(\text{FT/temp. frozen food}) \times 100]$$

where RF represents the percentage ratio of freezing and FT represents the freezing point of the frozen food.

B. ICE CRYSTAL SIZE

Once water has started to freeze, the rate of ice formation is a function of the rate of heat removal, as well as of the rate of diffusion of water from the surrounding solutions or gels to the surface of the ice crystals. At slow rates of cooling few crystallization centers are formed and the ice crystals grow to a relatively large size. The water in the cell diffuses through the cell wall, leaving the cells in a collapsed condition. Very large ice crystals (few crystals) can lead to mechanical damage to the food product. The cells become physically separated over relatively long distances. As the freezing rate increases, the number of ice crystals increases while their size decreases. Many studies have been done on the effects of size and location of ice crystals on the quality of frozen food. It appears that, for most foods, the size and distribution of ice crystals, encountered in commercial practice, have relatively little effect on organoleptic quality. However, very slow freezing results in undesirable effects like "drip" on thawing, while very fast freezing may improve the texture of some products.

C. DIMENSIONAL CHANGES

The volume change accompanying the conversion of pure water into ice is about 9%. The volume change of foods as a result of ice formation is less, about 6%, because only part of the water present is frozen and because some foods contain spaces. This volume change has to be taken into account in equipment design. In very fast freezing (for example, immersion of large items in liquid nitrogen), it can lead to the build-up of excessive pressure inside the product, causing breaking and shattering.

D. COMPLETION OF FREEZING

The freezing process is, for practical purposes, completed when most of the freezable water at the thermal center of the product has been converted into ice, which coincides for most products with the temperature at the thermal center becoming colder than −10°C. Removal of the product from the freezing equipment before this point is reached may result in slow freezing at the thermal center. It is preferable to freeze the product until the equilibrium temperature (average temperature) is −18°C or colder.

E. DESICCATION OF FROZEN FOODS

1. During Freezing

It is inevitable that a proportion of water of a product without packaging will evaporate during freezing. The faster the freezing, the smaller the amount of evaporated water. If the product is enclosed in a water-vapor-proof package before freezing, the moisture that escapes from the packet will be nil, but when there is an air gap (on the order of millimeters) between the surface of the product and the internal surface of the package frost may be deposited inside the package to the same extent as moisture evaporates from the product.

For products frozen unpackaged, moisture loss varies from 0.5 to 1.5% or more, depending on the temperature, rate, and method of freezing, as well as the type of product. The colder the air temperature, the less moisture the air can absorb before it is saturated. Faster freezing methods lower the surface temperature of the product quickly to a value where the rate of moisture evaporation or sublimation is small. Where the surface of a product consists of a moisture-resistant layer (skin of the fish or fat on beef, for example), moisture losses are reduced in comparison with products with cut surfaces (fish fillets, hamburger patties, for example). Proper freezer design for a given product is, therefore, an important factor in minimizing moisture loss during freezing.

2. During Storage

Moisture loss during frozen storage is a more serious problem because of the length of storage usually involved. Tight-fitting water-vapor-proof packaging avoids all apparent moisture loss. Many frozen foods, however, are still stored unpackaged or packaged in water-vapor permeable materials. In these cases, moisture loss depends on the average ambient temperature and the temperature of the evaporator, as well as on the temperature fluctuations occurring during storage, and increases with increasing storage temperature, increasing frequency, and amplitude of temperature fluctuations, and with increasing difference between the storage temperature and the lower temperature reached by the evaporator. It should be noted that the saturated vapor pressure of frozen foods is equal to that of pure ice at the same temperature.

If a water-vapor-proof packaging does not fit tightly around the product, desiccation of the product still occurs, but the water removed remains inside the package as frost. The mechanism appears to be as follows:

a. The layer of air between product and packaging is subject to temperature variations. As the outside temperature decreases, the temperature of the inside surface of the packaging at a certain moment drops below the product surface temperature and ice on or in the product will sublime and condense on the inside of the package.

b. When the ambient temperature increases, the process is reversed. However, the water vapor will condense on the product surface rather than in the cellular structure from which it evaporated.

c. As the cooling-heating cycle recurs, the crystals on the product surface tend to follow package temperature more closely than the mass of the product, and this results in further sublimation of ice from the product.

Frost in packages of frozen foods can amount to several percent of the product weight. Because it leads to ready access of oxygen into the product, frost formation may, with some foods, increase quality deterioration.

The effects of temperature fluctuation depend on the average storage temperature. At warmer storage temperatures, a given temperature fluctuation results in a much larger change in ice vapor pressure than at colder temperatures. As a result the effect of temperature fluctuations on desiccation increases with a warmer storage temperature.

Excessive drying, in addition to leading to undesirable loss of weight, can accelerate oxidative changes by causing the loss of an added glaze, and also by causing the removal of ice from the superficial parts of the frozen products, thus allowing a free access of oxygen to the internal tissues. Some parts of the surface of protein foods may be highly desiccated and their structure even irreversibly deteriorated; light spots known as "freezer burn" occur on the surface and the appearance of produce may become unacceptable. Animal foods (fish, poultry, game) in particular can be affected severely by freezer burn.

F. Change in Ice Crystal Size in Frozen Foods during Storage

The changes in shape and size of the ice crystals in frozen foods are caused by periodic variations in temperature experienced during storage; the greater the amplitude of these variations, the greater will be the changes.

G. Thermal Radiation in Frozen Food Storage

Thermal radiation has a significant effect on frozen foods in open display cabinets. In these, the top layer of packages may reach a temperature up to 10°C warmer than the average cabinet temperature leading to quality losses. The temperature of the packages in the top layer represents a thermal equilibrium between the energy transferred by radiation and the energy transferred by conduction and convection. The effect of radiation depends on the emissivity of the radiating surfaces, e.g., the package and the ceiling or walls. (Emissivity characterizes the surface state as far as radiation is concerned. Emissivity reaches a maximum equal to 1 in the case of an ideally absorbing and emitting body (black body) and is zero in the case of a perfect reflector; the latter does not emit or absorb any radiative energy.) The important radiation is that in the far infrared range (wavelength 8 to 10.10 m) and not that of visible light. A reflecting canopy placed about the open area of the cabinet or packaging in bright metallic foil reduces radiation energy gain markedly. Bright metallic foil packaging may reduce product temperature at the top layer of display cabinets by as much as 6–8°C.

IV. PHYSICO-CHEMICAL ASPECTS OF FREEZING

A. Composition and pH Changes during Freezing

Freezing converts a large proportion of the water present in foods into ice and hence makes the remaining solution more concentrated in dissolved, colloidal, and suspended substances. This increased concentration causes a change in acid-base equilibrium (pH) important in the stability of many colloids and suspensions. Shifts in pH (usually towards the acid side) of up to 1 pH unit have been observed under these conditions.

A second result of this increased concentration is the precipitation of salts and other compounds that are only slightly soluble, such as phosphate. This can result in drastic pH changes (up to 2 pH units) and changes the salt composition of the aqueous solution in foods. These changes often affect the physico-chemical systems in food irreversibly. It has been shown, for example, that lactic dehydrogenase, a muscle enzyme, and lipoproteins, an important egg yolk constituent, are irreversibly damaged by a pH decrease from 7 to 5 and by increased phosphate concentration during freezing.

B. Physico-Chemical Changes in Frozen Foods

Textural properties and the initiation and acceleration of several biochemical reactions depend on the physical chemistry of food constituents and hence are affected by the physico-chemical changes brought about by freezing. Loss of water binding properties, resulting in drip, is an example of textural changes, while removal of enzymes from cell particles, allowing them free access to substrates in other parts of the cell, is an example of biochemical reactions initiated and accelerated by freezing. Other physico-chemical changes in frozen foods are actomyosin changes in muscle, leading to toughening (fish) or dryness (poultry), loss of turgor in fresh fruits and vegetables, and gelation of egg yolk.

Many physico-chemical changes increase with increased salt concentration in the unfrozen phase, but will decrease with decreasing temperature as a result of the lower mobility of the salt in the unfrozen phase and the general effect of temperature on chemical reactions. Consequently, physico-chemical changes are most damaging in the range between the freezing point of a food and about −10°C. It is important therefore to expose frozen foods for as short a time as possible to this temperature range, both during freezing and during thawing.

C. Effects of Preparation and Packaging on Frozen Fish

Product preparation and packaging significantly affect the quality and shelf life of frozen fish. If not properly controlled, these processes result in some deleterious effects after prolonged storage.

1. Product Preparation

Product preparation, in particular, produces a considerable effect on shelf stability of frozen fish. Whole and eviscerated fish have longer shelf stability than fillets, while minces can usually only be stored for a much shorter period of time. Crawford et al. (12–14) observed this difference during several studies using hake. Minced blocks exhibited reduced quality and accelerated deterioration during storage when compared to intact fillets. This characteristic of minces, which is more apparent among the gadoids, is probably due to the mincing action applied to the fish flesh, which results in tissue damage and subsequently more rapid deterioration. In addition, mixing of red and white muscle during mincing may also result in the dispersion of lipids and some of the enzymes present in the red muscle, leading to greater susceptibility of the minced tissue to deteriorative changes.

2. Packaging Materials and Methods

An efficient packaging system is essential to offset the detrimental quality changes that occur during frozen storage. Packaging materials and methods are obviously designed not only to protect the product from microbial and chemical contamination, dehydration, and physical damage, but also to protect the environment from the packaged product. Fish and seafood can leak gases or unsightly fluids, which may have unpleasant odors. Therefore, the choice of appropriate packaging materials and methods for frozen fish is a critical factor in terms of shelf-life extension.

Studies have shown that packaging systems affect the quality and shelf stability of frozen fish. For instance, vacuum packaging is well established as a method to provide an oxygen-free environment to minimize the problems associated with lipid oxidation and dehydration during frozen storage.

Several studies have shown the effectiveness of this method for frozen storage of some species of fish. For example, it has been reported that frozen blocks of fillets vacuum packed in moisture-proof films showed high degrees of acceptance and desirable frozen characteristics (12). Likewise, Santos and Regenstein (15) reported the effectiveness of vacuum packaging for inhibiting lipid oxidation in frozen mackerel fillets. Ahvenainen and Malkki (16) examined the influence of packaging on frozen herring fillets stored at different temperatures. They found that vacuum-packed product covered with metallized cardboard had a longer shelf life than a product vacuum packed and stored without cardboard. Vacuum packaging, on the other hand, need not be used if lipid oxidation is not the limiting factor affecting the shelf life of a product. Although the effect or absence of oxygen in packages on some fish species must be considered, other packaging methods such as glazing and the use of heat-sealable packaging films should also be considered. Pacific hake minced blocks stored in moisture-proof, vapor-proof packaging films exhibited superior quality over glazed samples (12). Likewise, Colokoglu and Kundacki (17) observed frozen mullet packed in plastic films with low permeability to oxygen and moisture to

have a longer shelf life than when unpacked in the glazed form. However, it should be noted that glazing is still considered to be the cheapest means of protecting frozen fish during storage and transport. Glazing provides a continuous film or coating that adheres to the frozen product, which retards moisture loss and the rate of oxidation.

Many different glazes are available, including (a) those with inorganic salt solutions of disodium acid phosphate, sodium carbonate, and calcium lactate, (b) alginate solution, otherwise known as the "Protan" glaze, (c) antioxidants such as ascorbic and citric acids, glutamic acid, and monosodium glutamate, and (d) other edible coatings such as corn syrup solids (18). Ice glaze is particularly important in handling frozen fish in developing countries. For products intended for short-term storage, glazing can be practically utilized as a viable alternative to storage without a protective covering. For instance, Jadhav and Magar (19) concluded that glazing was a cheaper alternative to expensive packaging systems for glazed Indian mackerel (*Rastrelliger kanagurta*) stored at $-20°C$. Glazed samples had a shelf life of 6 months, while samples without a protective covering lasted only 3–4 months.

3. Effects of Freezing, Frozen Storage, and Thawing on Color, Appearance, and Consumer Acceptance

One problem encountered during handling, freezing, and storage of fish is the difficulty in retaining the color and appearance of the meat. Changes in color and appearance of fish occur even immediately after catch. Blood pigments become noticeably discolored to various degrees after some period of time. The natural oils in fish play an important role in these color changes. The color of these oils is produced by the colored pigments dissolved in them which vary from one species to another. These pigments are subjected to considerable oxidation when the fish is frozen and stored. This then results in meat color darkening to either dark brown or, in some cases, black. This discoloration occurs especially when the fish is stored for an extended period of time. Some fish, like tuna, develop discoloration during frozen storage, reportedly due to oxidation of myoglobin to met-myoglobin in fish blood (20). Other species, such as salmon, swordfish, and shark, also exhibit color changes during storage. Salmon has a pink meat, but when subjected to oxidation its color slowly fades and, in extreme cases, may completely disappear after prolonged storage. Swordfish, on the other hand, develops green discoloration beneath its skin during frozen storage which, according to Tauchiya and Tatsukawa (21), is due to the development of sulf-hemoglobin, a product of oxidation. Shark flesh also discolors and occasionally develops off-odors during storage, most probably as a result of the presence of high amounts of trimethylamine oxide. Interestingly, these marked differences in the color and appearance of frozen fish are quite noticeable in fish sold either as steaks or as fillets, especially when cross-sectional cuts of the fish are made, which permits a comparison of the color of the exposed fish surface with that of the inner portion.

In shrimp, the rapid formation of black pigments, widely known as "melanosis," occurs within a few hours after death and is enhanced by exposing the shrimp to air (oxygen). It can occur within just 2–12 hours of exposure. The oxidation reaction leading to the formation of these black pigments can occur at 0°C; however, at −18°C, no visible spots were detected at up to 3 months of storage (22). Below this temperature, it is believed that melanosis can still positively occur. It should be noted, however, that although black spots do not necessarily make shrimp unfit for human consumption, such discoloration is usually associated with spoilage, resulting in a decrease in market value. In other shellfish, such as crab and lobster, the development of blue or black discoloration, otherwise known as "blueing," is one of the most troublesome problems. Blueing may occur after freezing or during frozen storage, or it may appear after thawing and subsequent air exposure or even shortly after cooking. Needless to say, these changes in color and appearance of fish and shellfish significantly affect consumer acceptance. When consumers select frozen fish, if these products can be seen through the packaging material used, the color and appearance of the frozen product provide an indication as to its degree of quality. As shown in Table 39.1, undesirable appearance and discoloration of samples have been observed in different frozen whole fish and fillets obtained from Singapore supermarkets (23). Preventing such quality changes is of great commercial importance, since they

detract not only from the consumer acceptability of the products but their shelf stability as well.

Thawing also influences the color and appearance of frozen fish and, inevitably, its consumer acceptability. Depending on the thawing technique used, discoloration may occur in fish and other seafood. For instance, when shrimp are thawed at temperatures higher than 0°C, black discoloration or melanosis may occur. This is due to the unnecessary exposure of the shrimp to air, leading to oxidation. A phenomenon known as "shimi" occurs in frozen-thawed fish meat. Shimi are the undesirable blood spots observed in the belly portion of carp on thawing and are also the distinguishable spots tainting frozen-thawed tuna meat (24). The latter condition is probably due to the blood vessels that remain in unbled tuna meat prior to freezing. When thawed, these blood vessels produce unsightly spots in the meat.

It is possible to determine if the product has been properly thawed and then refrozen. This is particularly noticeable in packaged frozen fish, where spaces on the sides of the package may be filled with a frozen cloudy liquid, known as thaw drip. Such muscle drip was originally attributed to the rupturing of cell walls caused by ice crystal formation during freezing, resulting in excess drip during thawing. However, it has been postulated that drip or exudate formation is directly related to the capacity of the fish protein to hold moisture (25). This unsightly exudate from fish muscle indicates, among other things, inappropriate handling, prolonged ice storage prior to freezing, frozen storage at inappropriate cold-storage temperatures, or improper thawing. If not properly controlled, freezing, frozen storage, and thawing generally result in quality changes in fish and seafood that in most cases render the product unacceptable to consumers.

TABLE 39.1
Characteristics of Some Frozen Fish Purchased in Singapore Supermarkets

Fish	Thawed-State Characteristics
Herring, whole	Skin and meat show rusting
Mackerel, whole	Surface dehydrated, skin and meat show rusting, spongelike meat
Mackerel, whole	Rancid smell in skin and meat
Chinese Pompret, whole	Dehydration at lower part of belly and fin
Chinese Pompret, whole	Head and belly parts yellowish discolored, spongelike meat
White pompret, whole	Skin and meat show rusting, spongelike meat
Jew fish, whole	Slight rancid smell in skin
Lemon sole, whole	Surface dehydrated, spoiled and rancid smell, spongelike meat
Haddock, fillet	No smell, spongelike meat, cracks
Cod, fillet	No smell, spongelike meat
Flounder, fillet	No smell

Source: Ref. 23.

4. Effects of Freezing, Frozen Storage, and Thawing on Palatability Attributes

Changes in the texture, odor, and flavor of fish and seafood affect their palatability. Fresh fish have a distinct succulence and a delicate odor and flavor, which are characteristic of the species. These attributes change noticeably when fish is frozen and stored for prolonged periods of time. Interestingly, the changes that influence the palatability of frozen fish and seafood can all be measured organoleptically and, to some extent, chemically.

a. Change in texture
Frozen fish gradually loses its juiciness and succulence after freezing and subsequent frozen storage. Such textural changes, reportedly caused by protein denaturation (26–29), are more pronounced in some species of fish, specifically the gadoids. In these species, the chemical breakdown of TMAO to DMA and FA and the subsequent cross-linking of FA to muscle protein (30) produce the

textural breakdown in the gadoids and result in a "cottony" or "spongy" texture. Fish muscle that has undergone such changes tends to hold its free water loosely like a sponge. When eaten, the fish muscle loses all its moisture during the first bite, and subsequent chewing results in a very dry and cottony texture.

In some species devoid of TMAO-degradation products, muscle fibers also tend to toughen and to become dry during freezing and storage. This is particularly true for most of the nongadoid species and for crab, shrimp, and lobster when stored for prolonged periods. In contrast, the effect of the thawing method on the texture of fish muscle basically depends on the product form. For instance, whole fish, when thawed, exhibits less textural change than filleted fish, basically as a result of the presence of the backbone, which serves as structural support for the flesh. In terms of the effect of the thawing method, it has been reported that microwave thawing results in higher gel strength of minced samples, when compared to samples thawed under running water (20°C) and samples thawed at room temperature (31). Consequently, the extent of textural changes depends upon the species of fish and upon the condition of handling, freezing, duration of frozen storage, and the thawing method used.

Several methods have been developed to objectively measure such textural changes, in addition to the gathering of comparative data from sensory evaluations. From texture analysis of minced fish, Borderias et al. (32) concluded that hardness as measured by the Kramer Shear cell and puncture (penetration) tests was highly correlated with the sensorial perceived firmness of raw samples, while a compression test was found to be a valuable technique for characterizing the cohesiveness and elasticity of both raw and cooked fish minces.

Alterations in the texture of frozen fish fillets, on the other hand, are difficult to measure objectively, mainly due to the textural variability that exists within the fish fillets, which is associated with the flakiness and the orientation of the muscle fibers (33). Several attempts have been made to determine the extent of textural changes in fish fillet, including those tested using fish minces (32). However, significant correlations were not obtained.

An instrumental method that may work on fish fillets is the deformation test using the Instron Universal Testing Machine equipped with a flat compression plate. As a nondestructive test (34), it can potentially be modified to conform to the irregular shape and the segmented structural orientation of fish fillets.

b. Changes in odor and flavor
Other important changes that affect the palatability of frozen fish include changes in the flavor and odor of fish and seafood. Fish are often described as having a "fishy" odor and flavor. Although the term sounds unpleasant, it can also be used to describe the pleasing taste and odor

characteristics of freshly caught fish. Such pleasant, palatable characteristics may be retained as long as the fish are promptly and properly frozen, stored, and thawed. However, the transformation of these attributes to unpleasant and unacceptable traits occurs very rapidly in some fish species, particularly the fatty fish species.

Changes in the delicate flavor of fish and seafood generally occur in three distinct phases during frozen storage: (a) the gradual loss of flavor due to loss or decrease in concentration of some flavor compounds (35, 36), (b) the detection of neutral, bland, or flat flavor, and (c) the development of off-flavors due to the presence of compounds such as the acids and carbonyl compounds that are products of lipid oxidation. These phases, however, only apply to those species with originally delicate, sweet, and meaty flavors. Other species, such as hake, have an originally bland flavor (35), but develop off-flavors during prolonged frozen storage.

Changes in odor occur in two phases: the loss of characteristic odor and the development of off-odors, which render the frozen product unacceptable. Generally, fish and seafood initially have a fresh, seaweed odor, which can be retained even after freezing and frozen storage. However, gradually such odor is lost, and eventually an unpleasant odor is given off, particularly when abused with inappropriate storage temperature. The development of unpleasant odor is due either to lipid oxidation, a reaction more apparent among the fatty fish species that results in the production of a strong oily, blow oily, or rancid odor, or to the degradation of TMAO, which leads to the production of an unpleasant ammonia odor. Other species such as white hake (*Urophysus tenuis*) initially give off weak odors of sweet, boiled milk, but when frozen storage is extended, hake assumes weak off-odors (often described as milk jug odor) followed by a sour milk odor.

V. BIOCHEMICAL ASPECTS OF FREEZING

A. POST MORTEM GLYCOLYSIS AND LIPID OXIDATION

Fish muscle obtains energy by hydrolyzing adenosine triphosphate (ATP). At any one moment, its concentration is relatively small. During life it is quickly re-synthesized using the energy produced when glycogen is oxidized to carbon dioxide and water. On death of the fish metabolism in the muscle continues for some time. Post mortem glycolysis, however, is a relatively inefficient process and it cannot maintain ATP at its *in vivo* level. Once ATP has fallen to a critical concentration it can no longer prevent the major proportion of the muscle actin and myosin from cross-linking. This causes the loss of elasticity known as rigor mortis and usually a slow irreversible contraction. The continuing production of lactate and H^+ ions causes the pH of the muscle to fall from its *in vivo* value of about

7.2 to the so-called ultimate pH, which is usually about 5.5. A pH of 5.5 is near the isoelectric point of the muscle proteins, at which they have minimum water holding capacity and a consequent relatively high tendency to drip on thawing. A higher ultimate pH, therefore, means a greater water holding capacity than at a lower pH. The quantity of glycogen present in the muscle at the moment of slaughtering will clearly determine how far the pH will fall during post mortem glycolysis. Like most chemical reactions post mortem glycolysis is temperature dependent. It is generally found that the lower the temperature at which this process occurs, the slower is its rate. Thus if the carcass is maintained at body temperature after death, the rate of pH fall, of ATP depletion, and of rigor mortis onset is fast. If, however, the muscle is chilled quickly, these changes are slowed down and the water holding capacity of the muscle remains relatively high.

There is no practical "cold shortening" problem with fish properly chilled after catching. Fish muscle shows the least shrinkage if held at about 0°C. At warmer temperatures the shrinkage and weight loss are greater and they may be quite substantial for a fillet removed from the skeleton pre-rigor and kept at room temperature. One qualitative difference between fish and meat is the generally lower glycogen content in fish than in meat animals rested before death. Consequently, the post mortem fall of pH in fish is smaller and the resistance against surface bacterial growth less than in meat. In many fish species, therefore, bacterial spoilage is an overwhelming factor.

The fat composition of fish differs markedly from that of meat because fish fat contains a higher proportion of polyunsaturated fatty acids. Although this factor may vary with species and is also influenced by dietary fat intake, it nevertheless implies that fish, in particular fatty fish, are very prone to development of rancidity by auto-oxidation. Such rancidity may even develop in fatty fish held before freezing, but it is particularly during storage of frozen fish that great care in packaging and the use of low temperatures are necessary to preserve quality.

B. DENATURATION OF MUSCLE PROTEINS

The proteins of fish muscle differ from those of meat especially in their higher susceptibility to cold store damage. Frozen storage of fish causes an increase of drip loss on thawing, toughness, coarseness, and dryness on cooking, and loss of the desired glossy pellicle on smoking. These changes are highly associated with the so-called protein denaturation caused by freezing and subsequent storage. They are temperature dependent, with the maximum rate of development being in the range −1 to −5°C. They are considerably slowed down by colder storage temperatures. Many techniques have been used to measure these changes, such as extractable protein in salt solutions (ionic strength 0.5–1.0) which has been most widely used. The

changes are mostly in the myofibrillar protein of fish muscle. In general, the sarcoplasmic proteins seem to be more stable on freezing and subsequent storage. This kind of "protein denaturation" is associated with the reaction of certain free fatty acids or their oxidized products on the myofibrillar proteins. Recently it has been found that the ultimate pH attained by fish can considerably affect texture. Thus, low pH in cod is associated with more pronounced toughness and larger drip loss on thawing.

Drip loss, some changes in flavor and taste, and an undesirable softening occur in freeze-thawed fish muscle. When the frozen and thawed fish was cooked, the succulence and water holding capacity greatly decreased and some undesirable changes in texture such as toughness, coarseness, and dryness occurred. Compared with unfrozen fresh meat, the functional properties such as emulsifying capacity, lipid binding properties, water holding or hydrating capacities and gel forming ability were lower in the frozen stored fish muscle. Most of the studies indicated that denaturation of muscle proteins plays a dominant role in the quality changes of frozen stored fish muscle. The fish muscle proteins have been found to be much less stable than those of beef, pig, and poultry muscles (38). The amount of extractable actomyosin decreased with the duration of storage, while no significant change in sarcoplasmic proteins was observed during frozen storage of cod and other fish (36–38). Since the decrease in soluble actomyosin correlated well with palatability scores, it was proposed that denaturation of actomyosin is the major cause for the decrease in eating quality of frozen fish. Although the change in extractable actomyosin is regarded as the primary criterion of freeze denaturation, it still must be noted that extractability data cannot indicate precisely how much protein is denatured and how much is native. According to previous studies, results from electron microscopic analyses (39), decreases in actomyosin peak (20s–30s) areas on ultracentrifugal analysis (40, 41) and viscosity of soluble actomyosin with duration of storage (41, 42) suggested the aggregation of muscle proteins occurred during frozen storage. In addition to aggregation, dissociation of f-actomyosin into f-actin and myosin also occurred. It appeared that the dissociated F-actin, as thin filaments, became entangled and aggregated and that the dissociated myosin monomers folded into globular form. At advanced stages of freeze denaturation, large masses with diffuse outlines were frequently found, indicating the formation of aggregation complex of actin and myosin (43).

ATPase activity of actomyosin and myosin, another property of myosin related to its contractile function, also decreased with the increase of frozen storage (40–42, 44–47). During frozen storage, changes in isolated actomyosin and myosin have been sought in the number of −SH groups (40–42, 44–47), titratable acid groups (48), and net charge (49), and in the salting-out profiles (50, 51). Connell (52) attributed the insolubilization of frozen stored cod actomyosin to the denaturation of myosin rather than actin. However, isolated carp actin denatured progressively with myosin during frozen storage as demonstrated by SDS-PAGE (53). During the initial frozen storage, it appears that both myosin and actin undergo denaturation, while denaturation of tropomyosin and troponin was observed during elongated frozen storage (53).

Decreases in the solubility, viscosity, ATPase activity, and number of SH groups of frozen stored rabbit, mackerel, milkfish, amberfish, tilapia, and trout were observed (44–47, 54, 55). Although Connell (56) ascribed the intramolecular aggregation of muscle proteins to the formation of non-covalent bonds (57) rather than to the formation of disulfide bonds, the involvement of SH group in the denaturation of muscle proteins during frozen storage has been emphasized by Buttkus (54, 55) and Jiang et al. (44–47). From the studies thus far reported, the crosslinkage of myosin is ascribed to the formation of disulfide bonds, hydrophobic bonds and hydrogen bonds during frozen storage. Free SH groups are firstly oxidized to disulfide bonds. However, only a small decrease was found in the number of free SH groups during frozen storage. Therefore, the changes appear to be the result of rearrangements of disulfide bonds from intra-molecular to intermolecular through a sulfhydryl-disulfide interchange reaction.

Myofibrils, a systematically organized complex of myofibrillar proteins, undergo some structural changes during frozen storage of fish. The most noticeable change is the fusion of the myofibrils as illustrated by cell fragility method (58, 59) and fragmentation into short pieces at the Z-bands (60–63). More recently, studies have been done on the denaturation of enzymes during frozen storage (64, 65). Inactivation of enzymes with globular molecule was considered to be due to the unfolding of intra-molecular structure (66).

Many hypotheses have been proposed to explain the denaturation of muscle proteins (67–70). They include: 1) the effect of inorganic salts concentrated into the liquid phase of the frozen system; 2) water-activity relations; 3) reactions with lipids; 4) reaction with formaldehyde derived from trimethylamine (in fish); 5) auto-oxidation; 6) surface effects at the solid-gas interface; 7) effects of heavy metals; and 8) effects of other water-soluble proteins (such as protease). Among these hypotheses, effects of lipids (67–72), formaldehyde (73–77), and gas-solid interface of myofibrillar proteins caused by free fatty acids and/or lipid peroxides must occur during frozen storage. Jarenback and Liljemark have shown by electron microscopy that, in muscle frozen stored with added linoleic and linolenic hydroperoxides, myosin became resistant to extraction with salt solution (78). However, recent studies on isolated muscle protein indicate that proteins undergo denaturation in the absence of lipids, formaldehyde, heavy metals and water-soluble proteins. Another popular view is the so-called "salt-buffer hypothesis" which gives attention to

the effects of highly concentrated salt solution in the unfrozen phase of frozen muscle proteins. The concentrated salt solution may denature the proteins (67–72).

One of the most prevalent chemical reactions to occur in fish muscle during freezing and frozen storage is the complex phenomenon of protein denaturation. It has been postulated that the rupturing of different bonds in the native conformation of proteins in frozen fish is followed by side-by-side aggregation of myofibrillar proteins, specifically myosin, brought about by the formation of intermolecular cross-linkages (27, 79). It is also believed that the significant decrease observed in the center-to-center distance between the thick filaments of the A-band of the sarcomere after prolonged frozen storage favors the formation of cross-linkages between molecules and stiffens the fibers (78). Such intermolecular cross-linkages result in aggregation (30), which leads to the formation of high-molecular-weight polymers (80, 81) and subsequent denaturation of myosin during frozen storage.

Several relevant theories on protein denaturation in relation to fish moisture and freezing damage have been formulated. One theory worthy of note is that of protein denaturation being affected by the freezing out of water. The conformation of most native proteins has the hydrophobic side chains buried inside the protein molecule. However, some of these hydrophobic side chains are exposed at the surface of the molecule itself. It has been suggested that the water molecules arrange themselves around these exposed hydrophobic side chain groups so as to minimize the energy of the oil/water interface and, at the same time, act as a highly organized barrier, which mediates the hydrophobic/hydrophilic interactions between protein molecules (81). These water molecules form a network of hydrogen bonds, which contribute to the stability of the highly organized three-dimensional structure of the proteins. As water molecules freeze out, they migrate to form ice crystals, resulting in the disruption of the organized H-bonding system that stabilizes the protein structure. As the freezing process continues, the hydrophobic as well as the hydrophilic regions of the protein molecules become exposed to a new environment, which may allow the formation of intermolecular cross-linkages (30), either within the same protein molecule, causing deformation of the three-dimensional structure of the protein, or between two adjacent molecules, leading to protein-protein cross-links.

Freezing also concentrates solids, including mineral salts and small organic molecules, within the remaining unfrozen aqueous phase in the cell (82), which results in changes in ionic strength and possibly pH, leading to the denaturation of the protein molecule (83). Love (84) considered this concentrated salt in the unfrozen phase to be the main protein denaturant in the frozen muscle system. If proteins are denatured over time in the presence of concentrated solutes, it is reasonable to believe that longer exposure of protein molecules to these denaturants (e.g., slow freezing) should be avoided. However, further work must be conducted to determine the effect of the rate of freezing on shelf life of frozen fish as related to the solute concentration effect.

Several methods have been established to determine the extent of protein denaturation during frozen storage of fish and seafood. According to Jiang and Lee (85), protein quality is more sensitively reflected by the enzymatic activities in the muscles than by its extractability, since small microstructural changes in protein molecules can cause more alterations in the enzymatic activities than in extractability. For example, the actomyosin Ca ATPase, which measures the activity of myosin, can be used as an index of protein quality. Since this ATPase is capable of hydrolyzing the terminal end phosphate group of ATP to give ADP (68), this particular enzymatic activity can be determined by measuring changes in the amount of inorganic phosphate present in the muscle. The loss of enzymatic activity reflects the extent of freeze damage and alteration of the protein structure in the muscle system. Connell (79) reported a loss in Ca ATPase activity in muscle during frozen storage. In a more recent study using mackerel, Jiang and Lee (85) observed a loss of ~66% of the original Ca ATPase activity of actomyosin after 6 weeks of storage at $-20°C$.

Visual examination under a transmission or scanning electron microscope is a powerful technique used in the determination of textural changes in fish muscle due to denaturation. The electron microscopic studies of Matsumoto (30) were able to detect damage to the native structure of the protein: aggregation and an entangled mass were observed. However, results from this technique have to be interpreted cautiously since the fixing processes of tissue or any tissue section may create artifacts by altering the ultrastructural images or by masking the microchanges in the muscle tissue.

The extent of protein denaturation in frozen fish muscle can also be determined by conducting several tests of protein functionality. The physicochemical properties that affect the behavior of protein molecules during processing are defined as the functional properties of the fish myosystem, which include protein homogenate solubility, emulsifying and water-retention properties, gelation, and viscosity (86). The most popular tests to determine the extent of protein denaturation during frozen storage of fish, in relation to its functionality, are determination of the loss in solubility or extractability of proteins and measurement of the water-retention properties of the fish muscle system.

C. EFFECTS OF FREEZING, FROZEN STORAGE, AND THAWING ON NUTRITIONAL VALUE

Considerable emphasis has been given to the influence of freezing, frozen storage, and thawing on quality indices such as appearance/color, texture, flavor, odor, and the chemical reactions that accompany such organoleptic changes. Less attention has been given to yet another useful area, i.e., the influence of such treatments on the nutritional value of frozen fish and seafood.

Put simply, considerable attention is given to sensorial perceived attributes because if consumers reject a frozen product on display, it is not purchased or eaten regardless of its nutritional value. Conversely, if consumers are attracted to a frozen product, they tend to buy it whether it has the needed nutrients or not. However, as the market shifts to the development and merchandising of products to meet the demands of health-conscious consumers, the nutritional value of frozen fish becomes of great importance.

When fish and seafood are frozen, and subsequently stored and thawed, protein denaturation occurs in muscle tissues. As a result, formation of thaw drip becomes apparent and consequently leads to the leaching out of dissolved materials. Likewise, there is an increase in the release of a watery "cook liquor" when the product is heated. Such water losses result in the loss of water-soluble proteins; however, such losses do not result in any measurable decrease in the nutritive value of the protein (87). However, such losses lower the proportion of sarcoplasmic proteins in the fish tissue and may also lead to a small loss of water-soluble vitamins and minerals.

Other quality changes, such as lipid oxidation, can also influence the nutritional value of frozen products. Oxidized fish lipids, such as lipid hydroperoxides, may induce oxidative changes in sulfur-containing proteins, producing significant nutritional losses (88).

D. EFFECTS OF FREEZING, FROZEN STORAGE, AND THAWING ON INTRINSIC CHEMICAL REACTIONS

When frozen fish are subjected to excessively prolonged cold storage at temperatures above $-30°C$, a series of intrinsic chemical reactions occurs in fish tissues. These reactions include protein denaturation, breakdown of TMAO, and lipid oxidation.

1. Breakdown of Trimethylamine Oxide

Quite obviously, protein denaturation during frozen storage produces extensive textural changes and deterioration in fish. These changes are more pronounced in some species of fish, specifically the gadoids, and are related to another intrinsic chemical reaction, the breakdown of TMAO.

TMAO is commonly found in large quantities in marine species of fish. It is believed that these species use TMAO for osmoregulation (89). Among the marine species, the elasmobranches contain more TMAO than the teleosts. Among the teleosts, the gadoids have more TMAO than the flatfish. Except for burbot, freshwater species have a negligible amount of TMAO in their muscles, since they do not take in TMAO in their diet beyond their bodies nutritional requirements, and they promptly excrete any excess.

After death, TMAO is readily degraded to DMA and FA through a series of reactions. This conversion of TMAO to DMA and FA is typically observed in frozen gadoid species such as cod, hake, haddock, whiting, red hake, and pollock (7).

The presence of air (oxygen) affects DMA and FA formation. It has been suggested that oxygen may actually inhibit the reaction by interacting with metal ions, which otherwise would accelerate the TMAO degradation (90). Lundstrom et al. (91) observed that red hake (*Urophysis chuss*) minces stored in the absence of oxygen showed more rapid DMA and FA formation than red hake fillets stored in air. Likewise, the presence of air (oxygen) in packaged white hake (*Urophysis tenuis*) significantly prolonged the shelf life of the frozen samples (15).

TMAO degradation to DMA and FA was enhanced by the presence of an endogenous enzyme (TMAOase) in the fish tissues, as observed in cod muscles by Amano and Yamada (92). They also found an enzyme in the pyloric ceca of Alaskan pollock (*Pollachius virens*), which was believed to cause DMA and FA formation in this species (93). However, evidence also exists which demonstrates that breakdown of TMAO to DMA and FA is nonenzymic in nature (94, 95). The breakdown of TMAO, whether enzymatically or nonenzymatically induced, is believed to produce destabilization and aggregation of proteins.

TMAO has been postulated to be responsible for stabilizing proteins against conformational changes and thermal denaturation (96). However, the conversion of TMAO to DMA and FA has been implicated in gadoid textural problems during frozen storage (12, 97, 98).

It has been suggested that TMAO's breakdown product, FA, may produce cross-linking of muscle proteins (30) due to its high reactivity: FA can covalently bond with various functional groups of proteins, such as the amino, imino, guanido, phenolic, imidazole, and indole residues. This reaction induces both intra- and intermolecular cross-linkages of the molecules, thus producing conformational changes.

However, textural changes may also occur during frozen storage for fish species devoid of the TMAO-enzyme system (99). Such textural changes must then be attributed to another type of mechanism that does not involve the cross-linking of protein molecules due to the presence of FA. Gill et al. (99) reported that the presence of FA in red hake resulted in the covalent cross-linking of troponin and myosin light chains, forming high-molecular-weight aggregates. However, when haddock, a species that does not produce FA, was examined, the same cross-linkages were not found at the molecular level, although textural toughening was observed, but not as pronounced as that in red hake. Based on these observations, they suggested that textural changes in haddock

were probably due to secondary bonds, such as hydrogen or electrostatic bonds, and not due to FA cross-links.

Clearly, the presence of FA is not the only factor involved in textural changes during frozen storage. However, with certain species of fish, it appears to be of primary importance.

To objectively determine the extent of textural deterioration due to DMA and FA formation and subsequent reactions, the measurement of DMA content is recommended. Due to the equimolar formation of DMA and FA in fish muscle and the observed high reactivity of FA, DMA content is routinely used as an index. Consequently, the DMA test indirectly measures the FA value in fish muscle. However, use of this test is limited to those species known to produce DMA and FA during frozen storage.

2. LIPID OXIDATION

Another chemical reaction generally associated with quality changes during freezing, frozen storage, and thawing is lipid oxidation. This phenomenon most commonly occurs in fatty fish and is considered one of the major causes of frozen shelf-life reduction.

Lipid oxidation results in the development of a condition described as "oxidative fat rancidity." The extent of oxidation in fish lipids varies with the quantity and the type of lipids in the fish muscle, i.e., fatty species are more prone to oxidation than lean species, and species with more highly unsaturated fatty acids are less stable than the other species. When oxidative rancidity progresses sufficiently, it leads to the development of obvious off-taste and odor, resulting in reduced shelf life.

Changes in fish lipids may be related to changes in protein during frozen storage. Several reports indicate that the unstable free radical intermediates formed during autoxidation attack the protein molecules, leading to the formation of protein free radicals (88). These protein free radicals may cross-link with other proteins to form protein-protein aggregates and with lipids to form protein-lipid aggregates (7).

Another possible mechanism for reaction between oxidized lipids and proteins occurs through stable oxidation products such as malonaldehyde, propanal, and hexanal (26), which covalently react with specific functional groups on protein side chains, including the –SH group of cysteine, the amino group of lysine, and the N-terminal amino group of aspartic acid, tyrosine, methionine, and arginine (11). Such interactions increase the hydrophobicity of proteins, making them less water soluble. Free fatty acids (FFA) formed during autoxidation produce indirect effects on textural degradation by promoting protein denaturation (86). FFA are believed to bind myofibrillar proteins, specifically actomyosin, rendering it unextractable (26, 29). According to Sikorski et al. (29), when the hydrophobic sites of FFA interact with protein molecules, the protein molecules become surrounded with a more hydrophobic environment, which subsequently results in a decrease in protein extractability. This interaction may occur through hydrophilic and hydrophobic forces (29).

Several techniques have been developed to assess the extent of lipid oxidation in fish muscle. The most common techniques include (1) the peroxide value (PV) test, which measures the amount of hydroperoxides or peroxides formed during autoxidation (this test provides only a means for predicting the risk of rancidity development) and (2) the thiobarbituric acid (TBA) test, which measures the amount of malonaldehyde formed upon the decomposition of hydroperoxides during the second stage of oxidative rancidity. Other methods are also undoubtedly available. Therefore, the choice of techniques depends on several factors, such as the accuracy required and the availability of equipment.

VI. MICROBIOLOGY

Most matters of animal and plant origin used as human food are subject to microbiological attack as well as chemical, biochemical, and physical changes. At room temperatures the microbial attack is often so rapid that all the other changes play only a minor role. Microorganisms in all food raw material release enzymes into substrates during their growth. Changes brought about by the activities of these microbial enzymes will alter the odor, flavor, texture, and appearance of the product. Occasionally this is advantageous but in general it causes deterioration and spoilage. The purpose of preservation, however it is accomplished, is to prolong the storage life of the particular food and this is done either by killing the microorganisms or by inhibiting their activity and multiplication.

Freezing and subsequent storage will kill some of the microorganisms present in the unfrozen material, but this is a slow and variable process depending, in part, upon the nature of the food. Thus freezing cannot be relied upon to substantially reduce bacterial contamination present in the foodstuff. The hygienic state of the product before freezing is consequently all-important. Storage at temperatures colder than $-12°C$ inhibits microbial growth and therefore is one effective method of preserving food against microbial spoilage.

Three aspects of microorganisms in frozen foods will be considered.

A. THE RESISTANCE OF MICROORGANISMS AGAINST FREEZING AND FROZEN STORAGE

Some pathogens are more resistant to freezing than are ordinary spoilage organisms. A direct examination for common or expected pathogens should therefore be carried out. Most of the common pathogenic bacteria are Gram-negative. This group is more sensitive to freezing, frozen storage, and thawing than are the Gram-positive spoilage organisms.

B. MULTIPLICATION OF MICROORGANISMS IN FROZEN FOODS

Even when microbial growth is completely inhibited, the frozen product can still deteriorate due to the activity of the released microbial enzymes which can still catalyze undesirable biochemical reactions in the food. When the handling of fish before freezing is improper, there is the danger that microorganisms may have released sufficient enzymes and toxin to affect the quality of the frozen product. For example, if lipases are produced before freezing, they can cause marked hydrolysis of fats in fatty fish even when stored at $-30°C$. If fish has been held at relatively high temperatures before freezing, any pathogens present could multiply and some may produce toxins. The latter will survive freezing and constitute a health hazard. A product destined for freezing should receive the same degree of hygienic handling as that which is to be stored at chill temperature.

Several psychrotrophic microorganisms can multiply at freezing temperatures. In practice, bacterial growth does not occur below temperatures of $-10°C$. This is probably due to the increasing concentration of soluble salts and organic compounds in the unfrozen water which will decrease the water activity of this fraction. Only the most drought-resistant microorganisms such as fungi and yeasts can grow in these physiologically very dry substrates and this is why these organisms are the ones which are still capable of growing at temperatures colder than those at which bacteria can grow. Yeasts are not reported to multiply below $-12°C$ and fungi not below $-18°C$. It must, however, be noted that microbial growth is extremely slow at these temperatures and, for practical purposes, can be disregarded below $-10°C$. During any long retention in the upper freezing range down to $-10°C$ yeasts or fungi may develop and form visible colonies on the surface of the frozen substrate.

C. MICROBIOLOGY OF THAWED FOODS

On thawing, frozen foods will spoil almost at the same rate as would be expected from unfrozen products with the same microbial population maintained at similar temperatures. Condensation of moisture on the surface of the product should be avoided as during thawing it may cause a speeding up of microbial growth.

Pathogenic organisms may grow and produce toxin in food without rendering the food unpalatable. They will be occasionally observed in any food even hygienically prepared. Contamination even with small numbers of pathogenic bacteria during preparation of foods for freezing should therefore be avoided as far as practicable.

Competition between different types of microorganisms is important if food that will be further prepared after thawing is stored in the thawed state before such preparation. A food lacking a normal flora of spoilage organisms but contaminated with a few pathogens is more likely to present a health hazard than the same food contaminated to the same degree with normal spoilage flora. In the case of frozen foods allowed to thaw slowly, the psychrotrophic flora is likely to dominate and may so alter the substrate as subsequently to inhibit or slow down the multiplication of any pathogens present when thawing is complete. Packaging exerts little effect on the spoilage pattern; even vacuum packing causes a negligible increase in the growth rate of anaerobes like *Clostridium botulinum* during storage after thawing.

D. Effects of Freezing, Frozen Storage, and Thawing on Microbiological Quality and Safety

It is readily apparent that spoilage changes in fresh fish occur most commonly as a result of bacterial activity. The species of bacteria vary according to storage temperature. In fish stored in ice, *Alteromonas*, *Achromobacter*, and *Flavobacter* spp. predominate. At temperatures between 35 and 55°C, *Micrococcus* and *Bacillus* spp. constitute the main microflora. Some of these microorganisms produce very active proteolytic enzymes, which produce odor, flavor, and textural problems.

When fish and seafood are frozen, the microorganisms present in their tissues are generally inactivated. Thus, during frozen storage, microbiological changes in fish tissue are usually minimal. Microorganisms not destroyed by the freezing process generally do not grow and in some cases die off slowly. Although some microorganisms survive storage at very low temperatures, their activities are suppressed, and bacterial numbers may be considerably reduced if recommended temperatures are maintained (100). The temperature below which microbial growth is considered minimal ranges from −10 to −12°C (101). Microorganisms, however, that survive and remain inactivated during frozen storage resume growth when the fish is thawed and may then lead to microbial spoilage of the thawed product.

Frozen fish are far from sterile and cannot therefore be considered a microbiologically safe product. The microbial activities in fish after thawing depend on the degree of freshness of the raw material, the natural microflora in the fish tissues, and the thawing technique utilized.

1. Stability of Frozen Products

The effects of various freezing conditions on quality and shelf stability of frozen fish and seafood have received considerable attention recently. Studies have dealt with either the stability of the frozen product as related to storage temperature and fluctuation in storage temperature or the effectiveness of food additives in providing shelf stability to frozen products.

a. Effects of storage temperature

The apparent effects of storage temperature on shelf-life stability of frozen fish are related to protein denaturation and lipid oxidation. The effects of temperature on protein denaturation have been comprehensively studied (37, 102). Maximum denaturation is reported to occur at −4°C in cod muscle (36), while changes in extractable proteins in haddock have been found to be greatest at −2 to −6°C (103).

The rate of lipid oxidation and the accumulation of FFA were observed to increase with temperature (77). In a study using various species of fish, it was observed that maximum production of FFA due to enzymic activities of lipases occurred at −12 to −14°C (104), while the maximum rate of lipid hydrolysis was detected at temperatures just below freezing (105).

Storage at much lower temperatures can, therefore, prolong the shelf life of frozen fish. For example, cod stored at −160°C showed no detectable deterioration after 6 months of storage (77). Even at −65 and −50°C, frozen samples exhibited very few changes after 9 months of storage. Such observations also suggest that low storage temperatures limit the problems associated with protein denaturation and lipid oxidation during frozen storage.

Several studies have been conducted in an attempt to determine the shelf life of frozen fish at different temperatures and to establish storage temperatures that can minimize quality deterioration in specific groups of fish. Poulter (106) reported that *Rastrelliger brachysoma* (club mackerel) stored at −10°C remained acceptable until the ninth month of storage, whereas samples kept at −30°C were rejected after 12 months of storage. *Scomber scombrus* (Atlantic mackerel) stored unwrapped at −18°C were rejected after 3 months of storage, while samples at −26°C remained acceptable until the sixth month of storage (107). Early rejection of fatty species at relatively low temperatures is reportedly due to the development of rancid flavor and odor. Several studies have also reported the same dependence of shelf life for different fish species on temperature (15, 108, 109).

Clearly, fish composition has an appreciable effect on shelf-life stability of frozen fish. For instance, in a comprehensive study using different fish species, it was found that fatty fish such as mackerel, salmon, herring, sprat, and trout had a shelf life of 2–3 months at −18°C, whereas lean fish such as cod, flounder, haddock, ocean perch, and pollock exhibited storage stability of up to 4 months at the same storage temperature (110).

Based on several studies, it is recommended that those species most susceptible to oxidative rancidity be stored at very low temperatures (at least −29°C) while species less susceptible to rancidity should be stored at temperatures between −18 and −23°C (18). For species with textural problems due to the TMAO breakdown, the storage temperature must be below $-30°C$.

b. Effects of fluctuations in temperature

Fluctuations in storage temperatures affect the shelf-life stability of frozen products due to an increase in the size of the ice crystals formed in fish tissues (26). With slight increases in temperature, small ice crystals melt faster than larger ones, so that when the temperature drops again, the melted ice refreezes around the large ice crystals, forming larger crystals. These large crystals accelerate freezing damage, leading to shorter storage stability.

c. Use of food-grade additives

The effectiveness of different food-grade additives has also received considerable attention recently. The most commonly used types of additives for fish and seafoods function either as antimicrobial agents or as antioxidants.

i. Antimicrobial agents

Additives are commonly used in the food industry to prevent the growth of bacteria, yeast, and molds. The selection of an antimicrobial agent or any combination of agents is rather complicated, especially when dealing with fish. The effectiveness of an antimicrobial agent depends on several factors, such as the moisture content of the product and the presence of other microbial inhibitors like smoke and salt.

Several antimicrobial agents have been tested for fishery products. For instance, the sorbic acid salt, potassium sorbate (KS), has been found useful in extending the shelf life of fresh fish. Studies have demonstrated that KS, when applied as part of the ice, increased ice storage stability of red hake and salmon up to 28 and 24 days, respectively (111, 112). KS, in combination with modified atmosphere packaging (MAP), was also determined to be an effective method for prolonging the shelf life of fresh whole and filleted haddock on ice (113).

The shelf life of fresh fish may also be extended under refrigerated conditions with the use of Fish Plus, which exhibits its preservative effect due to the combined action of components such as citric acid, polyphophates, and potassium sorbate. Citric acid lowers the muscle pH, which consequently creates an optimum environment for potassium sorbate to exhibit its antimicrobial effects. Dipping in Fish Plus has been found to extend the shelf life of lingcod on ice to as much as a week (114). Fish Plus may also be used on frozen fish.

ii. Antioxidants

An antioxidant is a substance capable of delaying or retarding the development of rancidity or other flavor deterioration due to oxidation. It is normally used in conjunction with freezing to reduce the rate of autoxidation during frozen storage. Antioxidants delay the development of rancidity by either interfering with the initiation step of the free radical reaction or by interrupting the propagation of the free radical chain reaction (115).

The kinetic of antioxidative action was considered to be that antioxidants act as hydrogen donors or free radical acceptors (AH) and react primarily with $ROO·$, not with $R·$ radicals.

$$ROO· + AH \longrightarrow ROOH + A·$$

A low concentration of this chain-breaking antioxidant (AH) can interfere with either chain or initiation, producing nonradical products:

$$A· + ROO· \longrightarrow$$
$$A· + A· \longrightarrow \text{nonradical products}$$

Different versions of the antioxidant mechanism have been suggested by different authors (100, 115).

Other antioxidants may function as metal-complexing agents, which partly deactivate the trace metals, often present as salts of fatty acid (100), which would otherwise promote the oxidative reaction. Citric, phosphoric, ascorbic, and erythorbic (isoascorbic) acids are typical metal-chelating agents.

Among these antioxidants, erythorbic acid was used in studies by Kelleher et al. (116) and Licciardello et al. (35) of shelf-life stability of frozen fish. This antioxidant was emphasized due to encouraging results with the use of its salt, sodium erythorbate, in retarding oxidation in whiting, chub mackerel, and white bass fillets (35, 117, 118). Licciardello et al. (35) demonstrated the effectiveness of erythorbic acid in the retardation of oxidative rancidity in fillet blocks of Argentine hake stored at $-18°C$.

However, the use of erythorbic acid is limited to fish species in which rancidity is the main problem. Kelleher et al. (116) demonstrated the effect of this compound on the frozen storage of red hake (*Urophysis chuss*), a gadoid species, in which lipid oxidation is not the limiting factor for shelf-life extension. They found that the rate of DMA formation at $-18°C$ in samples dipped in erythorbate solution was significantly greatly than the rate in untreated samples. Such effect of erythorbic acid on DMA formation may be explained by the fact that this acid acts as an alternative and preferred scavenger of oxygen, leaving metal ions that would otherwise bind to oxygen and be inactivated, available to catalyze the degradation of TMAO to DMA and FA (119).

APPLICATIONS

I. HYGIENE IN THE PREPARATION OF FROZEN SEAFOOD

Most foods and food products are susceptible to attack by microorganisms and they are always contaminated by a variety of such organisms present in the food production chain. Foodstuffs are subjected to further contamination during preparation for freezing as a result of contact with the hands of factory staff during preparation, packaging and transport, and with air or water.

In view of the hazards to health and the effect of microbial contamination on quality, every effort must be made to reduce such contamination to a reasonable level during the preparation of foodstuffs for freezing. Throughout the world frozen foods have very seldom been the cause of food poisoning incidents.

A. HUMAN CONTAMINATION

As pathogenic bacteria like *Salmonella* and *Staphylococcus* frequently derive from human sources, it is of vital importance that factory employees are aware of the basic concepts of good personal hygiene: the need for frequent washing and the wearing of clean clothes, overalls, hair covering, etc. The use of rubber gloves and a protective mask for the mouth may be desirable in some instances. When gloves are worn they must be thoroughly cleaned and inspected before use. Medical supervision is advisable and in some cases should be made compulsory. Notices in lavatories should draw attention to personal hygiene, especially the need for hand washing. Soaps, hand creams, or dips containing antiseptic agents should be readily available.

B. BUILDINGS AND EQUIPMENT

Design of the building should ensure that both the buildings and drains are vermin proof. Interior walls, floors, and ceilings should be finished with a non-flaking surface capable of withstanding detergents and sanitizers. All corners should be rounded to facilitate cleaning. The building should be large enough to house production equipment so that all sides of the equipment are accessible for cleaning.

Entrance to the process area should be supplied with adequate washing facilities with foot-operated taps. Wood, which is almost impossible to sanitize, should not be used in contact with food. All windows should be both bird and fly proof.

Equipment usually becomes soiled with organic residues, which act as carriers of microorganisms. It should be designed and constructed to prevent hygienic hazard and permit easy and thorough cleaning. All surfaces should have a smooth, hard, waterproof finish. Cutting boards should be of a hard material; plastic is preferable to wood. Cleaning and disinfection of the food handling area, including equipment and utensils, should be carried out at frequent and regular intervals. Waste materials should be frequently removed, in covered containers, from the working area during factory operation. Processes should be so separated — either in space or time — as to avoid recontamination of products in which the "bacterial load has already been reduced." For cleaning purposes an ample supply of potable water should be available. Chlorinated water is effective both for in-plant use (when concentra-

tions of around 5 to 10 ppm are appropriate) and for sanitation of equipment and surfaces (when concentrations of around 100 to 200 ppm are used) but this should be followed by a rinse. Organic residues inactivate chlorine which, therefore, should only be used to sterilize already clean surfaces. Chlorine can be responsible for flavor loss or taint (due to the formation of chloramines or chlorophenols). Removal of the chlorine (by thiosulphate addition, often combined with treatment in activated carbon towers) is practiced, especially in ice cream producing plants.

C. CROSS-CONTAMINATION

During the preparation of food for freezing, all efforts should be taken to avoid a build-up of an undesirable microbial population. For some foods, handling should take place at sub-ambient temperature in temperature-regulated rooms, and where a heat treatment is a part of the processing this should be so severe that most of the microorganisms are killed. After heat treatment, the food should be promptly cooled to avoid multiplication of the surviving bacteria in the critical zone between 50 and 10°C. Cooling water, if used, should be chlorinated.

D. BACTERIOLOGICAL CONTROL

Proper organization of the various processes from the hygienic point of view is essential and a constant watch should be kept for lapses in hygiene. This should include a bacteriological control of the various stages in the processing line. Bacteriological methods are now available that give a good estimate of the bacterial load of the raw material and of food contact surfaces. Methods that give a rapid result are especially useful, as they supply plant management with information on the bacteriological state of products actually under preparation.

The results of the examinations should be shown to the factory staff in order to make them comprehend the vital importance of hygiene in food production. Preferably, courses in food hygiene should be held at regular intervals for employees. The aim should be to give those engaged in food production a thorough understanding of the hazard involved.

The above considerations concerning personal hygiene, equipment, and preparation of foods also applies to handling of frozen foods in catering establishments. Thawing of frozen foods in these establishments should be completed as quickly as possible, and any storage of the food after thawing should be in a refrigerator.

II. PACKAGING

A. GENERAL REQUIREMENTS

Not only must packaging used for frozen foods meet all the requirements of normal packaging but it must also meet requirements of packaging suitable for food such as:

- Chemical inertness and stability;
- Freedom from taint and odor;
- Freedom from toxic materials which may migrate into the food;
- Impermeability, or nearly so, to water vapor and other volatile constituents as well as to any odors from the surroundings;
- Suitability for use in automatic packaging systems;
- Suitable size and shape for display in retail cabinets;
- Protection from bacterial contamination and filth;
- Ease of opening; and
- An attractive appearance.

In addition to these general requirements for food packages, frozen food packages should also:

- Be of such shape as to allow rapid freezing except for I.Q.F. (Individually Quick Frozen);
- Permit volume expansion in the freezing process;
- Be impermeable to liquids and have good wet strength and resistance to water and weak acid;
- Be able to withstand low temperatures, not becoming excessively fragile at cold temperatures encountered during the freezing process;
- Not adhere to the contents in the frozen condition;
- Have a high reflectivity to reduce heat gain by radiation during display in retail cabinets;
- Be impervious to light as far as practicable; and
- Surround the product closely, leaving the minimum of air entrapped, thus limiting sublimation during storage.

B. PACKAGING MATERIALS

A wide variety of materials have been used in devising packaging systems for various frozen foods, e.g., tinplate, paper, paper-board with a wax or plastic coating, aluminum foil, plastic film, thermoformed plastics, and laminated combinations of these materials.

Low permeability to water vapor is an important characteristic of packaging materials for frozen foods. Table 39.2 compares the permeability of commercially available packaging materials.

1. Paper-Board Packages

Paper-board package for foods is generally in the form of folded cartons, either directly printed or provided with printed wrappers on the outside and in some cases with

TABLE 39.2
Water Vapor Permeability*

Film Type, 0.025 mm (1 mil)	Transmission Rate at 38°C (100°F), 90% RH
Polyvinylchloride	120–190 g/m^2.24 h
Polyamid (Nylon)	120g/m^2.24h
Polyester (Mylar)	25 g/m^2.24 h
Polyethylene, low density	19 g/m^2.24 h
Polyethylene, high density	6g/m^2.24h
Cellophane MST-type	5–23 g/m^2.24 h
Polyvinylidene chloride (Saran)	1.5–5 g/m^2.24 h

* The data given in this table refer to a test temperature of 38°C and the ranking order between different materials in respect to water vapor permeability. Water vapor permeability of a good package should not exceed about 0.2–0.5g/m^2.24h at −20°C and 75% RH. The important factor, however, is not just the water vapor permeability of the packaging material, but that of the complete package.

plastic coated liners. The following coating or laminating materials are commonly used:

- Wax blends (paraffin and micro-crystalline compositions);
- Plastics, e.g., polyethylene or polypropylene (on one or both sides);
- Aluminum foil.

2. Wrappers and Bags

Materials most commonly used are: waxed paper; hot melt or plastic coated paper; aluminum foil; coated cellulose films such as MSAT (moisture-proof, scalable, anchored, and transparent); and plastic films, such as polyethylene (PE), polypropylene (PP), and polyvinylidene chloride (PVDC) films. Also of importance are the laminated materials built up from two or more of the above-mentioned materials or other films. Common combinations are cellulose and PE films, sometimes with a PVDC coating.

These materials are used as over wraps, liners, and as single or double wall bags. The bags are either of the prefabricated type or are formed from roll stock on a filling machine.

Particularly important are shrink-wrap materials because of their ability to adhere close to the product, leaving few if any air pockets. Shrink-wrap bags require evacuation of entrapped air before shrinking. Some of these bags can withstand boiling water and, therefore, the package can be used for end-cooking of the product before serving.

3. Wooden Boxes

Often used for fish, wooden boxes require an inner liner or glaze on the product to guard against desiccation.

4. Rigid Aluminum Foil Packaging

These packages, in the form of trays, dishes, and cups, are generally covered with a crimped-on aluminum sheet or a sheet of aluminum foil laminated to paper-board. Normally used for prepared foods and pastries, etc., they allow rapid heating of the product in the package before serving.

5. Semi-Rigid Plastic Packages

These are mostly manufactured from high density PE or PP in the form of trays and plates, covered by a lid; as with aluminum foil, these can also be used for prepared foods requiring heating before serving, providing only gentle heat, such as steaming, is employed.

6. Tin and Composite Containers

These are used mainly for frozen juices which often have a mobile liquid phase even at cold store temperatures. A more recent development is to use coated paper-board in the body and aluminum for the ends, coupled with an easy opening device.

7. Shipping Containers

These are normally manufactured from different materials such as solid, corrugated fiber-board or vulcanized fiber-board paper, and plastics. They are often good heat insulators.

C. PACKAGING MACHINERY/PACKAGING SYSTEMS

An essential requirement of any package used in modern industry is that it should form a part of a system which enables the packages to be formed, filled, sealed, and handled mechanically on an integrated packaging line.

1. Form-Fill-Seal Machines

These machines form pouch-shaped or tray-shaped packages from heat-scalable plastic films or laminates or plastic-coated papers in roll form. The packages are formed and filled in the machine simultaneously or consecutively; these machines can work either in a vertical or a horizontal plane.

2. Cartoning System

These can be top filled, end filled, or side filled but irrespective of these differences each machine should perform the operations of erecting, filling, and sealing.

3. Shrink Film Wrapping Equipment

These machines apply shrink film materials from rolls around a given number of consumer-sized packages to form a unit, often replacing cases or boxes. After the application of the film, mostly in the form of a sleeve wider than the width of the contents, the unit is passed quickly through a hot air oven which shrinks the film tightly around the unit.

III. BULK PACKAGING

The practice of storing frozen food in bulk has increased considerably for the following reasons:

- The economy of storage space thus achieved;
- The ability to separate an intricate labor-intensive further processing packaging operation from the essential processing and freezing operation carried out when the raw material is available;
- Flexibility in final package sizes of various produces.

Bulk packaging is extensively applied to fruit and vegetables and to a lesser extent to meat, fish and poultry. Individually frozen products, the form of freezing particularly applied to vegetables, is most suitable for bulk storage. Products may also be bulk frozen into blocks, this method is used primarily for fish and meat.

After freezing, vegetables such as peas, corn, beans and sprouts can be stored on site in silos holding one or more hundreds of tons. Bins of corrugated board, metal or timber construction, with polyethylene liners providing a moisture vapor barrier and protection against dirt, can be used for storage or shipping. Smaller containers may be multi-wall paper sacks, corrugated boxes or fiber drums provided with polyethylene liners. Storage temperatures should be constant to prevent formation of clumps which have to be removed during repacking. This operation normally consists of tipping the contents out of the bulk container, breaking any clumps before passing the product over a screen or through an air-cleaner to remove small pieces prior to visual inspection and repacking, care being exercised over the hygiene requirements of this operation.

Frozen-at-sea whole fish is frozen in blocks or individually. In both cases, the fish, if not packaged, should be glazed prior to storage to minimize desiccation. Some fish is slabbed as skin-on fillets or made into blocks of skinned and boned fish for later cutting; both packs should be cartoned or bagged to minimize desiccation.

IV. FREEZING

Freezing is simply the crystallization of ice in muscle tissue and includes the consecutive processes of *nucleation* and *growth*. These processes are central to the effects of different freezing rates and subsequent effects on meat quality. Meat does not freeze immediately when its temperature drops below the freezing point and the latent heat (i.e., heat required during the phase change during crystal formation) has been removed. In other words there is a degree of *supercooling*. The greater the supercooling, the greater the number of nuclei formed. The number of nuclei is greatest in the extracellular space, and they are only formed within the cell when the rate of heat removal is higher. As soon as the nuclei form, they begin to grow by the accumulation of molecules at the solid/liquid interface. However, the way they grow depends on the microgeometry and the temperature distribution ahead of the freezing front, in a complex way, as a consequence of dendrite formation with supercooling in front of the dendrite growth. An important concept is *characteristic freezing time*, which is a measure of the local freezing rate and is defined as the time during which the point under consideration decreases from $-1°C$ (freezing commences) to $-7°C$ (when 80% of the water is frozen). The growth of extracellular ice crystals also takes place at the expense of intracellular water. This leads to partial dehydration of the muscle fibers and subsequent distortion. At high characteristic times (slow freezing), the ice crystals are larger and the tissue distortion is greater.

The freezing process can rapidly minimize physical, biochemical, and microbiological changes in the food. This preservative effect is maintained by subsequent storage of the frozen food at a sufficiently cold temperature.

A. FREEZING PROCESS

The freezing process can be divided into three stages:

Stage 1: Cooling down from the initial temperature of the product to the temperature at which freezing begins. It must be borne in mind that the act of placing a product in a freezing apparatus does not render it "safe." Time will elapse before warm food passes out of the microbiologically hazardous temperature zone; this is particularly the case if freezing is carried out in slowly moving air as in the freezing of bulk products such as berries for subsequent jam manufacture.

Stage 2: This step covers the formation of ice in the products and extends from the initial freezing point to a temperature about $5°C$ colder at the center of the product. The major part of the freezable water will be converted to ice and this quite small reduction in temperature is accompanied by a massive enthalpy change.

Stage 3: Cooling down to the ultimate temperature for storage. When leaving the freezer, the frozen product will have a non-uniform temperature distribution: warmer in the center and coldest at the surfaces. Its average temperature will correspond to the value reached when the temperature of the product is allowed to equalize. In general, it is recommended to cool the product in the freezer to an equilibrium temperature of $-18°C$ or colder. Product leaving the freezer with a warmer temperature will be stored for some time in relatively unfavorable conditions. Cooling down to storage temperature may take days or weeks.

B. FREEZING TIME

The effective freezing time is determined not only by the initial and final temperature of the product and its change in enthalpy but also by the temperature of the heat transfer medium. The dimensions (especially the thickness) and shape of the product unit affect the overall heat transfer, which includes the surface heat transfer coefficient α and the heat conductivity λ characteristic of the product. When freezing by air blast α depends on the air velocity and the shape of the product. In an air blast freezer, the rate of freezing increases with increasing air velocity to an optimum value. The refrigeration load necessary to remove the heat produced by the fans increases with the cube of the air velocity; this factor should be taken into consideration when designing air blast freezers. It is important to direct the air circulation in such a way that all the product is equally exposed to the air current. In packaged food the packaging material presents a resistance to the heat transfer, depending on its thickness and conductivity. This resistance is increased considerably if air is trapped between the package and the product.

The freezing time as a function of the thickness of fish fillets in packages frozen in a plate freezer ($\alpha = 200$ kcal/m^2.°C including the packaging) and in a blast freezer with medium air velocity ($\alpha = 20$ kcal/m^2.°C) with heat removed from both sides of the package, is shown in Figure 39.1(a) (120). This graph indicates that during plate freezing the heat conductivity of the product is the main factor determining freezing time; it also shows that during air freezing the heat resistance of the surface (including packaging material) plays a dominant role for the product thickness encountered in practice.

Figure 39.1(b) (120) shows the freezing time for 450 g fish fillet packs as a function of the overall heat transfer, including the influence of some types of packages used in contact freezing. This graph indicates that the type of packaging alone may increase the freezing time in a plate freezer by 2.5 times, and the surface heat transfer resistance by some 4 times. The freezing of packaged foods takes longer in an air blast freezer than in a plate freezer under comparable conditions. In the freezing of packaged food, where the λ-value is influenced by the air inside the package, the difference in freezing rate between plate and blast freezing diminishes as does the influence of packaging material.

C. FREEZING RATE

Freezing must always be fast enough to minimize the development of microbiological and enzymatic changes in the product. A freezing process which occupies a matter of days will, in most cases, lead to deterioration in the frozen foodstuffs.

In the past, the beneficial effect of very rapid freezing on the quality of frozen foods has been overestimated: within certain limits the rate of freezing does not

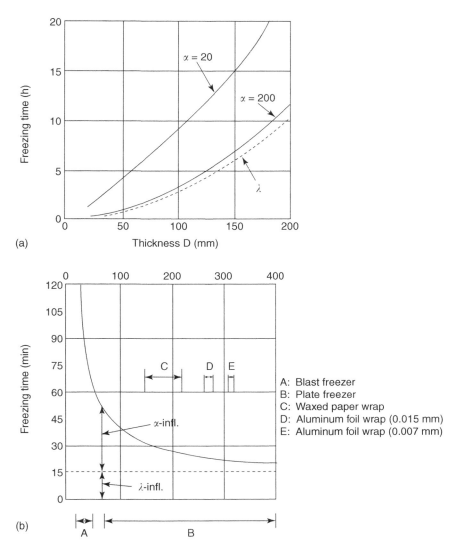

FIGURE 39.1 (a) Freezing time in hours as a function thickness D, of a slab of fish fillets frozen by removal of heat from two opposite sides of the package, for two values of the surface heat transfer coefficient $\alpha=20$ and $\alpha=200$ kcal/m². °C. A temperature of -30°C is assumed for the cooling medium (air, cold plates) and the process is considered to be completed when a temperature at the thermal center of -15°C is reached. The total freezing time is divided into two parts, one due to the influence of the internal conduction resistance ("λ-infl."), the other to the surface heat resistance, including package ("α-infl."). (b) Freezing time in minutes for a 32 mm thick 450 g package of fish fillets as a function of the surface heat transfer coefficient. The total time is divided according to the influence of conduction resistance ("λ-infl.") and surface resistance, including package ("α-infl."). The normal range of blast freezers and plate freezers is indicated. The influence of some types of packages in plate freezing is also shown.

materially affect the quality of most foods. This should not be interpreted to mean that the rate of freezing has no effect on the quality of frozen foods: most foods suffer from being frozen very slowly; a few foods demand ultra-rapid freezing. Fish and poultry seem to be more vulnerable to very slow freezing than most other foods, and meat (beef, pork, lamb) rather less. Strawberries and beans have a better texture and water holding ability if frozen ultra-rapidly while fruits and vegetables with a higher starch content such as peas are not as sensitive to freezing speed.

In commercial practice mean freezing rates vary between 0.2 and 100cm/h; 0.2cm/h (slow freezing) for bulk freezing in blast rooms, 0.5 to 3 cm/h (quick freezing) for retail packages in air blast or plate freezers, 5 to 10 cm/h (rapid freezing) for individual quick freezing of small-sized products, e.g., in a fluidized bed and 10 to 100 cm/h (ultra rapid freezing) by spraying with or immersion in liquid gases. For freezing of retail packages freezing rates faster than 0.5 cm/h and for I.Q.F. products rates faster than 5 cm/h are considered satisfactory in most cases. Only very susceptible foods (such as tomatoes) may be improved by increasing the freezing to above 10 cm/h. At these rates care should be taken to avoid cracking. When freezing larger units, such as beef quarters, with a mean freezing rate of 0.1 cm/h a freezing time of 3 to 5 days is unavoidable and times up to 5 days are quite common.

The rate at which freezing takes place can be considered both at micro and macro levels. At the micro level, freezing rate is described in terms of the speed with which the freezing front moves through the freezing object. At the macro level, the rate at which any given part of the object is cooled determines the temperature profile for that part, and thus has an important bearing on the biochemistry and microbiology of that part.

The undesirable changes in meat during freezing are associated with formation of large ice crystals in extracellular locations, mechanical damage by the ice crystals to cellular structures through distortion and volume changes, and chemical damage arising from changes in concentrations of solutes. The fastest freezing rates are associated with the least damage (121). Differences in freezing rate modify meat properties. Ice crystallization and its growth in meat tissues are discussed by Calvell (122).

Freezing commences when the surface temperature of the meat reaches its freezing temperature. A continuous freezing front forms and proceeds from the exterior to the interior. Extracellular water freezes more readily than intracellular water because of its lower ionic and solute concentration. Slower freezing favors the formation of pure ice crystals and increases the concentration of solutes in unfrozen solutions. Intracellular solutions are often deficient in the nucleation sites necessary to form small ice crystals. Such conditions favor the gradual movement of water out of the muscle cells, resulting in a collection of large extracellular ice crystals and a concentration of intracellular solutes. Freezing damage arises from massive distortion and damage to cell membranes. Such effects have implications during thawing as the large extracellular ice crystals produce drip during thawing. The structural changes that occur also obliterate the recognizable muscle structure.

Fast freezing results in small ice crystal formation in both intracellular and extracellular compartments of the muscle and very little translocation of water. Drip loss during thawing is thus considerably reduced, and the surface reflects more light than that of slowly frozen meat. Consequently, the cut surface appearance is more acceptable.

D. Freezing Methods and Equipment

Freezing equipment may be divided into the following main groups with regard to the medium of heat transfer: the metal group includes plate freezers and air (gaseous medium) blast freezers the liquid group includes immersion freezers and the evaporating liquid group includes liquid nitrogen and liquid fluorocarbon equipment.

While blast freezers are used for all kinds of products, packed or unpacked, blocks or I.Q.F. products, the Plate freezer and Immersion freezer accept only packaged product, and evaporating liquid freezers are used only for I.Q.F. products.

1. Plate Freezers

In a plate freezer the product is pressed by a hydraulic ram between metal plates which have channels for the refrigerant. This arrangement gives very good heat transfer of metal contact. This high thermal efficiency is reflected in short freezing times, provided the product itself is a good heat conductor, as is the case with fish fillets or chopped spinach. It is important that the packets are well filled and the metal trays that are used to carry the packets are not distorted.

The advantage of good heat transfer at the surface is gradually reduced with increasing thickness of the product. For this reason the thickness is often limited to a maximum of 50 mm.

The pressure from the plates maintained throughout the freezing process practically eliminates the "bulging" that may occur in air blast tunnels; the frozen packets will maintain their rectangular shape within close tolerances.

There are two main types of plate freezer: horizontal plate freezers and vertical plate freezers.

a. Horizontal plate freezer
Usually this type has 15–20 plates (Figure 39.2). The product is placed on metal trays, which are pushed in between the plates manually. This calls for a high labor content in the loading and unloading operation.

In order to obtain automatic operation of a horizontal plate freezer, the whole battery of plates is movable up and down in an elevator system. At the level of a loading conveyor the plates are separated. Packages which have been accumulated on the conveyor are pushed in between these plates, simultaneously discharging a row of frozen packages at the opposite end of the plates. This cycle is repeated until all frozen packages have been replaced. Then the space between the plates is closed and all plates are indexed up.

b. Vertical plate freezer
The vertical plate freezer was developed mainly for freezing fish at sea. It consists of a number of vertical freezing plates forming partitions in a container with an open top. The product is simply fed from the top. The frozen block is discharged either to the side, upwards, or down through the bottom. Usually this operation is mechanized; the discharge of product often being assisted by a short hot gas defrost period at the end of the freezing cycle and the use of compressed air to force the product out.

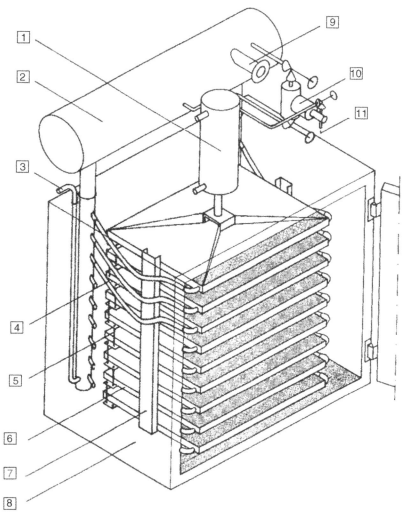

FIGURE 39.2 Horizontal plate freezer. (1. Hydraulic cylinder, 2. Liquid separator, 3. Hot gas defrost, 4. Flexible hoses, 5. Link bolts, 6. Freezing plate, 7. Guide, 8. Insulated cabinet, 9. Suction outlet, 10. Float valve, 11. Liquid inlet.)

2. Air Blast Freezers

Some foods, mainly bulk products such as beef quarters and fruits, for further processing are frozen in rooms with or without forced air circulation. Unless the room has been designed for freezing and equipped with suitable coolers and fans the freezing rate is very slow, resulting in an inferior quality for practically all products. If the room is also used for storage of frozen products the temperature of these products may rise considerably and the evaporators may frost up so quickly that the total refrigeration capacity is reduced below what is required to maintain the temperature of the store.

Good commercial practice for freezing in air blast uses include tunnel freezers, belt freezers, and fluidized bed freezers.

a. Tunnel freezers

In tunnel freezers the product is placed on trays, which stand in or pass through the tunnel in racks or trolleys one behind the other or singly. An air space is left between the trays.

The racks or trolleys are moved in and out of the freezer by manual power or by a forklift truck (stationary tunnels), pushed through the tunnel with a pushing mechanism (push-through tunnel) or are carried through by driving equipment, chain drive, etc. (carrier freezer) or slid through (sliding tray freezer). Tunnels are also used for freezing hanging meat carcasses mostly carried on a suspension conveyor.

Tunnel freezers are equipped with refrigeration coils and fans which circulate the air over the product in a controlled way (see Figure 39.3). Guide devices, properly locating the trays of food, lead to uniform freezing.

Tunnel freezers are very flexible freezers. Products of every size and shape, packaged or unpacked, can be frozen in stationary and push-through tunnels. They are used primarily for freezing packaged products. Unpacked products tend to stick to the trays, which may cause

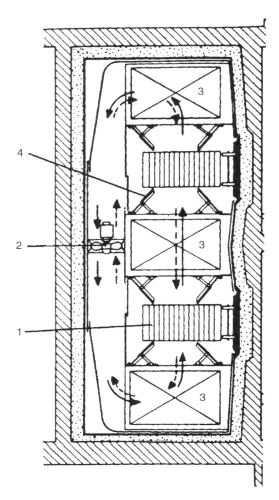

FIGURE 39.3 Sectional drawing of a push-through tunnel freezer. (1. Trolleys with trays, 2. Reversing fans, 3. Air coolers, 4. System of baffles which allows adjustment of the air flow.)

weight losses and time-consuming handling in releasing, cleaning, and transport of the trays. To obtain free flow products, improved handling, and an increase in the freezing rate, individual quick freezing (I.Q.F.) is preferred.

b. Belt freezers

Belt freezers are provided with a single belt (single-belt freezers, see Figure 39.4) or with belts positioned above each other which may run in the same or in opposite directions to increase throughputs and to reduce floor space (multi-belt-freezers) or as a spiral belt wound round a rotation drum stacking up to 30 tiers of the belt above each other (spiral-belt freezers). The belt, generally made of wire mesh, remains inside the freezer so that ancillary equipment for in and out feeding is necessary. Alternatively, the belt is carried to the outside as in some spiral-belt freezers. This arrangement has the advantage that the products can be placed on the belt in the processing room, where the operation can be supervised, before entering the freezer, and the product will remain undisturbed until removed at

the outlet (Figure 39.4). The belt is supported by rails and driven by passing around the rotating drum.

Modern belt freezers have vertical air flow so that the air is forced through the product layer. In freezing small products such as beans or cherries good contact with all product particles is thus created. In single-belt freezers with high air velocities the products may agitate. In all belt freezers care should be taken to spread the product uniformly across the total belt width to avoid "channeling," where the air stream bypasses the product.

Belt freezers are used mainly for freezing unpackaged products, e.g., I.Q.F. products. They are especially suitable for foods that need careful handling.

c. Fluidized bed freezer

Fluidization occurs when particles of fairly uniform shape and size are subjected to an upward air stream. At an air velocity depending on the characteristics of the product, the particles will float in the air stream, each one separated from the other, but surrounded by air and free to move. In this state the mass of particles behaves like a fluid. If the product is contained in an inclined trough which is fed at the higher end the fluidized mass moves towards the lower end, as long as more product is added. The product is thus frozen and simultaneously conveyed by air without the aid of a mechanical conveyor (Figure 39.5).

The use of the fluidization principle has the following advantages when compared with a belt freezer:

1. The product is always truly individually frozen (I.Q.F.). This applies even to products with a tendency to stick together, e.g. French style (sliced) green beans, sliced carrots, and sliced cucumber.
2. Independence of fluctuations in load. If partly loaded the air distribution will be the same as for full load, i.e., no hazard of channeling. If over-loaded no product flows onto the floor.
3. Reliability is improved when freezing wet products because the deep fluidized bed can accept products with more surplus water.

An important factor in the overall operation economy of a blast freezer is the weight losses during freezing. Improperly designed equipment will have losses of 5% or more whilst a "well-designed" freezer normally operates with only 0.5 to 1.5% loss for unpackaged products. Part of the weight losses are dehydration losses, which require particular consideration. Weight loss is minimized by low air temperatures and good heat transfer, i.e., high air velocities.

A freezing tunnel that is intended for packaged products should not, without due consideration, be used for thin unpackaged products, e.g., fillets of fish. The result may be that the relation of coil surface to product surface is put out of balance so that air temperature in the tunnel rises with resulting high weight losses. The coil may not be able to accommodate sufficient quantities of frost

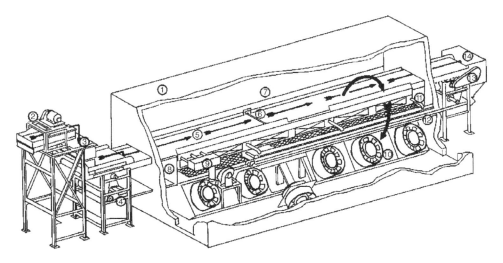

FIGURE 39.4 Single belt freezer. 1. Insulated wall of the tunnel, 2. De-watering vibrator, 3. Loading hopper, 4. Belt drying system, 5. Variable speed belt (open mesh belt), 6. Product spreader, 7. Air agitation zone, 8. Evaporator, 9. High velocity air, 10. Variable air flow fans, 11. Defrost water, 12. Refrigerant piping, 13. Belt speed changer, 14. Unloading hopper.

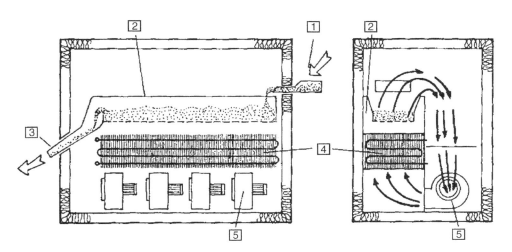

FIGURE 39.5 Fluidized bed freezer. (1. Unfrozen product conveyor, 2. Product trough, 3. Frozen product discharge, 4. Air coolers, 5. Fan.)

which results in reduced heat transfer or reduced air flow, both contributing to high weight losses.

It is important to note that in a vapor tight package containing a product that is not homogeneous, e.g., beans or broccoli, the heat transfer inside the package is carried out by air. The heat transfer is very poor, because there is no air circulation. The result is evaporation of moisture, which actually may be greater than it would have been without the package. This moisture remains as frost on the inside surfaces of the package, so that it is not usually recorded as a weight loss. The influence on product quality is, of course, the same whether the dehydration is recorded or not.

Higher velocities of air give better heat transfer. However, it is not sufficient just to increase the fan power. The most important factor is to direct the air circulation in

such a way that every product particle is efficiently and equally exposed to the air current. It is also important to study the conditions of the individual particles because a close study may reveal surprisingly uneven air flows.

3. Immersion Freezer

For irregularly shaped products, e.g., chicken, the best heat transfer is achieved in an immersion freezer. This consists of a tank with a cooled freezing medium, e.g., a salt or propylene glycol solution. The product is immersed in this brine or sprayed while being conveyed through the tank.

Immersion freezers are most commonly used for surface freezing of poultry to obtain a good color. The final freezing is effected in a separate blast tunnel or cold store.

The latter alternative, however, involves quality hazards because of slow freezing of the core.

The product must be protected by an absolutely tight, high quality packaging material. The brine on the package is washed off with water at the exit of the freezer.

4. Evaporating Liquid Freezers

Mainly two liquids or freezants are used: liquid nitrogen (LN2) and liquid fluorocarbon freezant (LFF).

a. LN2 freezer

Liquid nitrogen at −196°C is sprayed onto a single belt freezer. The nitrogen evaporates and is allowed to escape to the atmosphere after the vapors have been used for pre-cooling of the products (Figure 39.6).

The very high freezing rate results in improved textures, particularly in certain fruits and vegetables while with other products there seems to be little quality advantage compared with other freezing methods. LN2-freezing may result in cracking of the product surface if sufficient precautions are not taken.

Like immersion freezers LN2 freezers are often used only for surface freezing. If final freezing is to be carried out the LN2 consumption is of the order of 1.0–1.5 kg per kg of product which makes the operation rather expensive. In spite of this, the low investment and simple operation make this method economical for certain productions, especially in-line processes.

b. LFF system

The freezant is a specially purified dichlorodifluoromethane (fluorocarbon) which has a boiling point of −30°C at atmospheric pressure. The equipment consists of a container with openings at the top. The product is introduced into the container and dropped into a flowing stream of freezant (Figure 39.7). Owing to the extremely good heat

transfer the surface is frozen instantaneously so the product may be stacked on the horizontal freezing belt, where it is sprayed with freezant until finally frozen. A discharge conveyor brings the product up and out of the freezer. It is claimed that fluorocarbon leaves only small residues in most products. Experiments in this area are continuing.

On contact with product the freezant evaporates. The vapors are recovered (with only a slight loss) by condensation on the surfaces of the refrigerator, the latter remaining in the container with only small losses to the atmosphere. There is no measurable product weight loss due to dehydration using this method.

V. STORAGE

If the quality of frozen food is to be maintained during its storage life, the correct temperature must be selected for the expected period of storage. During the storage period, the following hazards to quality must be avoided:

1. A low relative humidity in the cold store.
2. Retention beyond the expected storage life.
3. Fluctuations in temperature (both during storage and in the process of loading, unloading, and dispatching vehicles).
4. Physical damage to the product or packaging during the course of storage or handling.
5. Contamination of the product by foreign bodies or vermin.

These hazards can be avoided by ensuring:

a. That the design of the cold store is appropriate to the duty it will be required to perform, and is such that these hazards are, to the greatest extent possible, eliminated at the design stage.

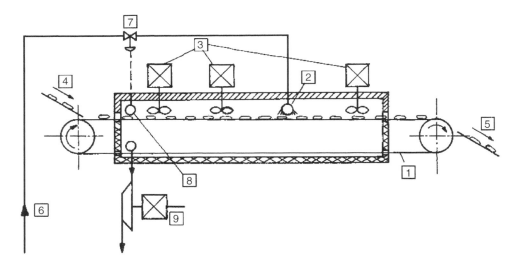

FIGURE 39.6 Liquid nitrogen freezer. (1. Belt, 2. Spraying nozzles, 3. Fans, 4. Inlet, 5. Outlet, 6. Nitrogen tank supply line, 7. Regulating valve, 8. Temperature sensing unit, 9. Nitrogen gas exhauster.)

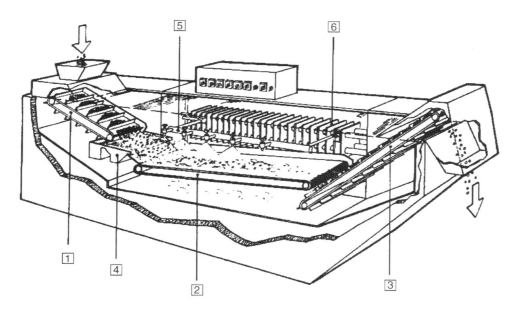

FIGURE 39.7 Liquid fluorocarbon freezer. (1. Product input conveyor, 2. Freezing conveyor, 3. Frozen product exit conveyor, 4. I.Q.F. bath, 5. Spray nozzles, 6. Condenser.)

b. That operation methods, designed to avoid such dangers, are laid down and strictly adhered to.

Small fluctuations in temperature are normal and unavoidable. They should, however, be kept at a minimum both in amplitude and duration in order to minimize the amount of weight loss by drying and in-package desiccation.

A.   COLD STORE DESIGN

The general design of a cold store is determined by the requirements for effective and safe handling of the merchandise, and a suitable storage climate for the products. The normal arrangement is that rooms are built side by side between road and railway loading banks; thus, all rooms can communicate directly with the loading banks and traffic yards. Today cold stores are frequently built with prefabricated concrete or steel structures. The insulation can be placed on the outside or the inside of the structure. Internal structure means that the insulation will form an unbroken envelope around the building. The insulation is well protected by the structure, internal installations are easy to fix, there is no hung insulated ceiling which can cause problems, and extensions are very simple to carry out.

It is essential that considerable thought should go into the definition of the duties the cold store has to perform. A clear statement has to be prepared of the maximum and average daily activity expected to take place in the cold store:

1. Quantity of each product to be received.
2. Temperature at which each product will be received.

3. Maximum number of operatives and trucks working in the cold store at any one time.
4. Number of anticipated door openings.
5. Maximum quantity to be out-loaded at any one time.

These considerations must be taken into account when calculating the maximum expected heat load. The temperature difference between the surface area of the cooling coils and the required room temperature should be as small as possible and not more than about 6°C.

1.   Frost Heave

Frost heave under cold stores is prevented by a special under-floor heating system or a ventilated space under the floor. The heating system may consist of an electrical mat or a pipe grid cast into the sub-floor; glycol or oil is circulated in the pipes. The liquid is often heated by surplus heat from the refrigeration plant.

2.   Insulation

The insulation represents a large percentage of the total cost for a normal cold store. It is, therefore, very important that it is designed from an economical point of view. However, one must also consider that the insulation value has an influence on the storage climate in that the transmission losses mean dry heat is entering the cold room. The choice of insulation system must be carried out carefully. The vapor barrier on the warm side must be completely water vapor tight, the insulation should contain no heat bridges, and the internal cladding must be hard, hygienic, and give a pleasant appearance. Today most cold store insulations are carried out with prefabricated panels, slabs of polyurethane foam, expanded polystyrene, mineral fiber, or cork. Where special attention must be given to the risk of fire, the insulation is combined with a special fire wall or the insulation is carried out with fiber glass between special insulation studs. The vapor barriers may consist of thin gauge aluminum, galvanized steel sheets, or heavy gauge polyethylene sheets. The joints are sealed with special sealing compounds. The internal cladding may be either profiled plastic, laminated galvanized steel sheet, or aluminum sheet. Good concrete kerbing and, in some cases, dunnage battens protect the internal finish and ensure that the merchandise is not stacked directly against the wall.

3. Refrigeration System

The refrigeration system must be designed with regard to the requirements of the climatic conditions for the stored merchandise. It must be adequate to allow for sufficient safety on peak days and summer conditions. The air coolers must be designed and located so that an even temperature can be maintained throughout the cold store even under severe conditions and without generating high air velocities in the cold store. Large evaporator surfaces and air distribution through air ducts or false ceilings will normally ensure this. Air ducts may be omitted if the cooling surface is divided on several cooler units distributed in the room so that the air velocity from the cooler fans is kept at a moderate level.

The most common refrigeration system for large cold stores is a two-stage compressor system with pump circulation of the cold refrigerant to the air coolers. The most common refrigerant is ammonia but halogenated hydrocarbons have also been used in some cases. For small cold stores a direct expansion, one-stage compressor system using halogenated hydrocarbons is widely used. In order to improve safety and make control easier and cheaper most modern refrigeration plants are automated. The degree of automation may vary but normally the room temperature, compressor capacity, lubrication, cooling water, defrosting, pumps, fans, current and voltage of the main supplies, etc. are controlled and supervised by a central control panel in the engine room.

4. Lighting

A cold store is a working place for fork lift drivers and others concerned with the handling of the products. Thus the lighting in the cold store must be good but at the same time it must be remembered that the lighting is adding to the heat load in a cold store. Lamps with a very high power/lighting ratio should be used. Mercury lamps are superior from this point of view and they are often used even if they can cause a slight discoloring of meat products during long storage. A normal cold store should have an average lighting of 100 lux at floor level and of 200 lux in break-up areas.

5. Layout

The layout of the storage space should be such as to reduce to the maximum extent possible the ingress of warm air and the exposure of product to atmospheric temperatures. Where possible, product should be conveyed from factory areas into cold store by means of conveyors in insulated tunnels. There should be no facility for any accumulation of product in ambient temperature. If the operation is a palletized one, then palletization of the product should take place in the cold store in an area set aside for this purpose. Port doors should be provided so that the maximum amount of traffic in and out is handled in this fashion and the product is completely protected from temperature changes during loading/unloading operations.

For safety reason, no glass should be allowed inside the cold store in any unprotected position. Translucent plastic visors should be placed around lamps or any other essential glass.

6. Jacketed Stores

Jacketed stores allow storage at near 100% relative humidity and at uniform and constant temperatures. These conditions, which greatly reduce weight losses of unpackaged foods and frost formation inside packaged frozen foods, are obtained by circulating the refrigerated air in a jacket around the load space to absorb the heat conducted through the insulation before it can enter the load space (Figure 39.8). This technique also increases the life and reduces the maintenance of the structure by preventing condensation and frost formation in the insulation.

7. Equipment

In equipping the store care should be taken to choose equipment which is suitable to the product being handled and which minimizes the possibility of damage or contamination; thus, timber pallets are suitable for properly packed products but lightly packed semi-processed stock may need a pallet constructed in metal or some similar washable and less easily damaged material.

It is likely, for economy reasons, that the store will be designed to maximize the use of height, and to this end some means of support for the product must be provided, e.g., racks, pallet posts, or pallet cages. The layout of pallets in the cold store should be such that damage to the products is minimized. Whilst accepting the need for maximum utilization of space, gangways and turnings should be wide enough for product to be moved without damage, while space should be allowed between lanes of pallets to permit the withdrawal or placing of a pallet when the adjacent lanes are full.

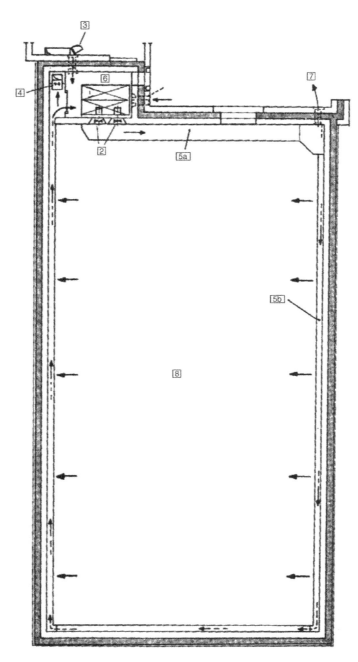

FIGURE 39.8 Jacketed store. [1. Air coolers, 2. Fans, 3. Fresh air duct, 4. Air vent, 5a. Air ducts, 5b. Jacket, 6. Air cooler enclosure, 7. Cooling orifice to antechamber, 8. Cold room. This type of jacketed store serves two purposes thanks to the two-speed fans: (a). At the lower speed, the air only circulates in the jacket. This is the classic operation of jacketed stores (arrows marked thus). (b). At the higher speed, the air enters the store through a system of movable vents which open via the effect of the increased air pressure. Through this means, one can complete the cooling of foodstuffs which may have been subjected to warming up prior to being introduced into the cold store (arrows marked thus).]

8. Operating Methods

It is important that everyone working in a cold store always bear in mind the prime objective of minimizing the exposure of products to ambient temperatures. Methods of handling and routes should be laid down which do not permit the product being placed in ambient temperature.

If it is not possible to load a vehicle by means of a port door or some similar method which gives complete protection and the only alternative is to traverse a loading bank, then the complete vehicle load should be assembled inside the cold store and conveyed direct to the vehicle without being placed on the loading bank. A similar procedure should apply in reverse for unloading. Doors should never be left open other than when personnel or goods are passing through them, and duration should be as short as practicable.

VI. THAWING

Most frozen food processors find it necessary to thaw stock of frozen material in some of their operations, and if thawing is not carried out carefully, quality and yield can suffer. This section sets out the broad principles involved in the thawing techniques available, and indicates some of the problem areas. Irrespective of the procedure involved, heat energy must be supplied, most of it being required to melt the ice in the food. About 300 kJ are required to thaw 1 kg of white fish from a starting temperature of $-30°C$. The figure for fatty herrings is smaller, about 250 kJ, because of the lower water content of herrings. Thawed materials spoil in the same way as their unfrozen equivalents and must be kept chilled until required; this can often be achieved conveniently by removing the product from the defroster just before thawing is complete so that the product has its own small reserve of "cold."

There are two principal groups of thawing methods: those in which heat is conducted into the product from the surface and those in which heat is generated within the product. In the first group, heat is applied to the surface of the product by exposing it to sources such as hot radiating surfaces, warm air, warm water, heated metal plates, or steam under vacuum. In the second group, heat is generated within the product by such means as electrical resistance, dielectric, or microwave heating. Surface heating methods are much more commonly used than are internal heating methods.

A. SURFACE HEATING METHODS

When using surface heating methods, thawing time for a product decreases with:

a. Decrease in physical size of the product;
b. Increase in thermal conductivity (or, more precisely thermal diffusivity) of the thawed product;
c. Increase in temperature difference between the surface of the product and its surroundings;
d. Increase in the movement of the surrounding medium relative to the product surface; and
e. Increase in humidity of the surroundings.

Since the thermal diffusivity of thawed product is less than that of frozen, surface thawing methods suffer from the inherent disadvantage that resistance to heat transfer increases progressively once thawing has started.

All surface heating methods can take advantage of a programmed temperature difference between the surface and the surroundings; the temperature of the surroundings is arranged to start high, and to decrease as the surface warms up to a predetermined level, usually below the temperature where bacterial activity or surface damage could be a hazard to the quality of the food. Thawing times are greatly increased if the product is encased in packaging material. Thus packaging material should be removed where possible.

B. STILL AIR THAWING

If thawing is conducted in still air, the air temperatures should not exceed $20°C$ and facilities for supplying heat to the room in which the product is laid out to thaw may be required. Air temperatures greatly in excess of the above should be avoided since the outer layer will warm up and spoil before the center is completely thawed. A typical block of sea frozen whole cod 9 cm thick will take up to 20 h to thaw under these conditions. This time can be reduced by separating the fish as soon as they can be separated without damage. Single fish, 10 cm thick, will take about 8 to 10 h to thaw.

1. Air Blast Thawing

A relative humidity of greater than 90% is advantageous both in reducing weight loss or shrinkage and also in obtaining a high level of heat transfer. Air velocities of 12-18 m/min at a temperature of $6–8°C$ for 3–5 days or 100 m/min for 2–2.5 days are needed for packages of boneless meat, whereas pork sides are normally thawed at $4–5°C$ for 2–4 days. Air speeds of the order of about 300 meters per minute at temperatures not exceeding $20°C$ with the air fully saturated with moisture will thaw sea frozen fish blocks 10 cm thick in 4 h. Higher air velocities at cool temperatures lead to surface desiccation while any higher temperature will lead to microbial growth on the heated surface.

C. WATER THAWING

This method is not normally applicable to meat and with fish there is a risk that fillets or cut surfaces will become waterlogged and lose flavor but water thawing can be used satisfactorily for frozen whole fish, even though there may be a slight loss of pigments. Usually there is a slight gain in weight, which is lost again when the fish is filleted.

The temperature of the water being circulated around the frozen fish or sprayed onto the fish should be no warmer than $20°C$ and the water itself should flow at not less than 30 cm per minute so as to obtain rapid thawing. The thawing time for a block of whole cod 10 cm thick in water at $20°C$ moving at about 120 cm per minute is similar to that in an air blast defroster using humid air at the same temperature, i.e., about 4 h.

When frozen fish blocks are thawed in still water, water temperatures may, in the initial stages, marginally exceed 20°C, but the thawing should be arranged so that the fish surface temperature does not exceed 20°C.

D. VACUUM THAWING

In this method the product lies on racks inside a container from which the air has been evacuated. Water, usually at about 18°C, is allowed to evaporate freely from heated vessels inside the container. In the absence of air, transfer of water vapor from a heated vessel to the product occurs readily, the water vapor giving up its latent heat on condensation. The advocates of this method claim faster thawing than other surface heating methods for products less than about 10 cm thick.

E. DOUBLE CONTACT THAWING

Plate frozen raw material lends itself particularly to plate thawing in an arrangement similar to that of a multi-plate freezer, with a liquid circulating through the plates (at a temperature not exceeding 20°C providing the necessary heat. A 10 cm block of whole cod when thawed between plates at 20°C for 5 h is ready for filleting 3.5 h later, making a total of 8.5 h for complete thawing. Care must be taken not to allow distortion of the blocks to occur during cold storage since this will lead to poor contact with the plates during thawing. Thawing fluid or semi-fluid food in a vertical plate apparatus may be carried out using temperatures as high as 40–50°C as long as the melted material is allowed to run away from the plates continuously.

F. INTERNAL HEATING METHODS

Internal heating methods rely on the use of applied electric fields which cause movement of the electric charges inherent in all products. The molecules of the product take up this energy of movement and the food warms up. The amount of heat generated in this way is strongly dependent on the electrical characteristics of the product. Since food is not usually homogeneous, there can be marked variations in the rate of heating of different parts of the food. Furthermore, for any particular component in the food, the rate of heating usually increases as the product thaws, making runaway heating a hazard. If these factors can be accommodated, the great advantage to be gained is extremely rapid, uniform thawing.

G. ELECTRICAL RESISTANCE THAWING

In this method, the product is sandwiched between electrodes and an electric current is passed through the product. Some preliminary warming is usually necessary to achieve good electrical contact and a satisfactorily high starting current. In practice this method has so far been used for thawing blocks of fish fillets up to 5 cm thick and weighing about 3 kg but it has not been found suitable for thicker blocks of fillets, blocks of whole fish (except herring), or single whole fish.

H. HIGH FREQUENCY THAWING

In the dielectric method, a high frequency electric field is applied to electrodes astraddle the product, but not physically in contact with it. The commonly used frequencies are either in the range 27 to 100 MHz (dielectric or high frequency heating) or 915 to 2450 MHz (microwave heating, where the energy is directed at the product enclosed in a chamber). The product must be reasonably homogeneous and regular in shape to achieve uniform heating. If the block is not homogeneous, or is irregular in shape, some parts may become overheated before the remainder is thawed. It has been found that if irregular blocks of fish are first immersed in water, thawing becomes uniform. The time taken for a 10 cm block of whole cod is typically just less than 1 h. Partial thawing by microwave is also used, thereby increasing the capacity of the thawing equipment. By going to the higher frequencies, the field strength can be substantially increased and thawing time reduced to a matter of minutes. Penetration into the food mass decreases so that the thickest block of meat which can be completely thawed at 2450 MHz is 3 to 4 cm.

In summary, freezing, frozen storage, and thawing affect the quality and shelf stability of fish and seafood. If kept under appropriate conditions, fish and seafood can be stored in the frozen state for several months without appreciable changes in quality. During frozen storage, microbiological changes in fish and seafood are very minimal. On the other hand, a series of changes such as protein denaturation, lipid oxidation, texture deterioration, loss of fresh odor and flavor, various enzymatically induced reactions, loss of volatile constituents, nutritional losses, and changes in moisture take place in fish and seafood when subjected to excessively prolonged frozen storage. Likewise, such changes may also occur in freeze-thawed fish and seafood. Quantitative evaluation of the influence of freezing, frozen storage, and thawing on fish and seafood is rather complex. The different variables that influence quality are related to one another. Therefore, it becomes almost impossible to describe some quality changes without actually discussing the other related changes that occur in fish tissues.

ACKNOWLEDGMENT

The information in this chapter is based on "Freezing seafood and seafood products: Principles and applications," by S. T. Jiang and T. C. Lee, in *Handbook of Frozen Foods*, edited by Y. H. Hui et al., Marcel Dekker, New York, 2004.

REFERENCES

1. M Love. Studies on the North Sea cod. I. Muscle cell dimensions, J. Sci. Food Agric. 9:609–622, 1958.

2. M Green-Walker, G Pull. A survey of red and white muscles in marine fish, J. Fish Biol. 7:295–300, 1975.

3. J George. A histological study of the red and white muscle of mackerel, Am. Midland Naturalist 68:487–494, 1962.

4. H Buttkus, N Tomlinson. Some aspects of post-mortem changes in fish muscle. In: The Physiology and Biochemistry of Muscle as a Food (E Briskey, R Cossers, T Trautman, eds.), University of Wisconsin Press, Madison, WI, 1966, pp. 197–203.

5. T Pitcher, P Hart. Fisheries Ecology, AVI Publishing Co., Westport, CT, 1982.

6. S Patterson, G Goldspink. The effect of starvation on the ultrastructure of red and white myotomal muscle of Crucian carp (*Carassius carassius*), Zellforschung 146:375–384, 1973.

7. C. Castells, W. Neal, J. Date. Comparison of changes in TMA, DMA, and extractable protein in iced and frozen stored gadoid fillets, J. Fish. Res. Bd. Can. 30:1246–1250 1973.

8. WJ Dyer, D Hiltz. Sensitivity of hake muscle to frozen storage, Halifax La. Fish. & Mar. Ser. Nova Scotia Circ. 45, Halifax, Nova Scotia, 1974.

9. R Shewfelt. Fish muscle hydrolysis—a review, J. Food Biochem. 5:79–94, 1980.

10. R Boddeke, E Slijper, A Van Der Stelt. Histological characteristics of the body musculature of fishes in connection with their mode of life, Konik. Ned. Akad. Wetenschappen Ser. C. 62:576–588, 1959.

11. S Konosu, K Watanabe, T Shimizu. Distribution of nitrogenous constituents in the muscle extracts of 8 species of fish, Bull. Jap. Soc. Sci. Fish. 40:909–915, 1974.

12. D Crawford, D Law, J Babbitt, L McGill. Comparative stability and desirability of frozen Pacific hake fillet and minced flesh blocks, J. Food Sci. 44(2): 363–367, 1979.

13. D Crawford, D Law, J Babbitt. Yield and acceptability of protein interactions during storage of cod flesh at –14°C, J. Sci. Food Agric. 16:769–772, 1972.

14. D Crawford, D Law, J Babbitt. Shelf-life stability and acceptance of frozen Pacific hake (*Merluccius productus*) fillet portions, J. Food Sci. 37:801–802, 1972.

15. E Santos, J Regenstein. Effects of vacuum packaging, glazing, and erythorbic acid on the shelf-life of frozen white hake and mackerel, J. Food Sci. 55:64–70, 1990.

16. R Ahvenainen, Y Malkki. Influence of packaging on shelf-life of frozen foods. II. Baltic herring fillets, J. Food Sci. 50:1197–1199, 1985.

17. M Colokoglu, A Kundacki. Hydrolytic and oxidative deterioration in lipids of stored frozen mullet (*Mugil cephalus* L.), Proceedings of the 6th World Congress of Food Science and Technology, Dublin, Ireland, 1983.

18. F Wheaton, A Lawson. Processing Aquatic Food Products, John Wiley & Sons, New York, 1985.

19. M Jadhav, N Magar. Presevation of fish by freezing and glazing. II. Keeping quality of fish with particular reference to yellow discoloration and other organoleptic changes during prolonged storage, Fish Technol. 7:146–149, 1970.

20. M Bito. Studies on the retention of meat color by frozen tuna. I. Absorption spectra of the aquaeous extract of frozen tuna meat, Bull. Jap. Soc. Sci. Fish. 30: 847–857, 1964.

21. Y Tauchiya, Y Tatsukawa. Green meat of swordfish, Tohotu J. Agric. Res. 4:183–190, 1954.

22. PJA Reilly, M Bernarte, E Dangla. Storage stability of brackish water prawn during processing for export, Food Technol. Aust. (May–June): 3–14, 1984.

23. C Ng, C Tan, S Nikkoni, Y Chin, S Yeap, M Bito. Studies on quality assessment of frozen fish. II. K-value, volatile bases, TMA-N as freshness indices and peroxide value and TBA number in rancidity of skin portion, Refrigeration 57(662): 117–118, 1982.

24. M Bito. The observation on blood spots 'shimi' in the frozen-thawed carp meat, Bull. Tokai Reg. Fish. Res. Lab. 113:1–5, 1984.

25. A Ciarlo, R Boeri, D Giannini. Storage life of frozen blocks of Patagonian hake (*Merluccius hubbis*) filleted and minced, J. Food Sci. 50:723–726, 1985.

26. S Shenouda. Theories of protein denaturation during frozen storage of fish flesh, Adv. Food Res. 26:275–311, 1980.

27. Z Sikorski. Protein changes in muscle foods due to freezing and frozen storage, Int. J. Ref. 1(3): 173–210, 1978.

28. Z Sikorski. Structure and protein of fish and shellfish, Part II. In: Advances in Fish Science and Technology (J Connell, ed.), Fishing News (Books) Ltd., Surrey, England, 1980, pp. 78–91.

29. Z Sikorski, S Kostuch, J Lolodziejska. Denaturation of protein in fish flesh, Nahrung 19:997–1010, 1975.

30. J Matsumoto. Denaturation of fish muscle during frozen storage. In: Protein at Low Temperature (O Fennema, ed.), ACS Symposium Series #180, ACS, Washington, D.C., 1979.

31. S Jiang, M Ho, T Lee. Optimization of the freezing conditions on mackerel and amberfish for manufacturing minced fish. J. Food Sci. 50:727–732, 1985.

32. A Borderias, M Lamua, M Tejada. Texture analysis of fish fillets and minced fish by both sensory and instrumental methods, J. Food Technol. 18:85–95, 1983.

33. E Johnson, M Peleg, R Segars, J Kapsalis. A generalized phenomenological rheological model for fish flesh, J. Text. Stud. 12:413–425, 1981.

34. M Bourne. Food Texture and Viscosity, Academic Press, New York, 1983.

35. J Licciardello, E Ravesi, M Allsup. Extending the shelf-life of frozen Argentine hake, J. Food Sci. 45:1312–1517, 1980.

36. WJ Dyer. Protein denaturation in frozen and stored fish, Food Res. 16:522–528, 1951.

37. WJ Dyer, ML Morton. Storage of frozen plaice fillets, J. Fish. Res. Bd. Can. 13:129–134, 1956.

38. WJ Dyer, ML Mortom, DI Fraser, EG Bligh. Sortage of frozen rosefish fillets, J. Fish. Res. Bd. Can. 13:569–573, 1956.

39. M Ohnishi, T Kubo, JJ Matsumoto. Bull. Jpn. Soc. Sci. Fish. 44:755–762, 1978.

40. S Noguchi, JJ Matsumoto. Studies on the control of the denaturation of fish muscle proteins during frozen storage, Bull. Jap. Soc. Sci. Fish. 36:1078–1083, 1970.

41. M Oguni, T Kubo, JJ Matsumoto. Studies on the denaturation of fish muscle proteins. I. Physicochemical and electron microscopical studies of freeze-denatured carp actomyosin, Bull. Jap. Soc. Sci. Fish. 41:1113–1119, 1975.

42. T Ueda, Y Shimizu, W Simidu. Studies on muscle of aquatic animals, XXXX, Bull. Jap. Soc. Sci. Fish. 28:1010–1017, 1962.

43. JJ Matsumoto. Chemical deterioration of muscle proteins during frozen storage. In: Chemical Deterioration of Muscle Proteins, ACS Symp. Series 123, ACS, Washington, D.C., 1980, pp. 95–124.

44. ST Jiang, DC Hwang, CS Chen. Denaturation and change in SH group of actomyosin from milkfish (Chanos chanos) during storage at –20°C, J. Agric. Food Chem. 36: 433–437, 1988.

45. ST Jiang, DC Hwang, CS Chen. Effect of storage temperatures on the formation of disulfide and denaturation of milkfish actomyosin (Chanos chanos), J. Food Sci. 53: 1333–1335, 1988.

46. ST Jiang, PC San, S Lenda Japit. Effect of storage temperatures on the formation of disulfide and denaturation of tilapia hybrid actomyosin (Tilapia nilotica X T. aurea), J. Agric. Food Chem. 37: 633–636, 1989.

47. CS Chen, DC Hwang, ST Jiang. Effect of storage temperatures on the formation of disulfide and denaturation of milkfish myosin (Chanos chanos), J. Agric. Food Chem. 37: 1228–1232, 1989.

48. JJ Connell, PF Howgata. Changes in ATPase activity in cod and haddock during frozen storage, J. Food Sci. 29:717–722, 1964.

49. M Migita, S Otaka. Studies on the effect of lethal conditions on the muscle proteins. I, Bull. Jap. Soc. Sci. Fish. 22:260–267, 1956.

50. M Migita, S Otaka. Studies on the effect of lethal conditions on the muscle proteins. II, Bull. Jap. Soc. Sci. Fish. 27:327–338, 1961.

51. T Ueda, Y Shimizu, W Simidu. Studies on muscle of aquatic animals. XXXI, Bull. Jap. Soc. Sci. Fish. 28:1005–1009, 1962.

52. JJ Connell. Changes in amount of myosin extractable from cod flesh during storage at –14°C, J. Sci. Food Agric. 13:607–611, 1962.

53. Y Irisa, M Ohnishi, T Tsuchiya, JJ Matsumoto. Denaturation of carp muscle protein during frozen storage, presented at Annual Meeting Japanese Society of Scientific Fisheries, Tokyo, April 3, 1978.

54. H Buttkus. Accelerated denaturation of myosin in frozen solution, J. Food Sci. 35:558–562, 1970.

55. H Buttkus. The sulfhydryl content of rabbit and trout myosins in relation to protein stability, Can. J. Biochem. 49:97–103, 1971.

56. JJ Connell. Aggregation of cod myosin during frozen storage, Nature (London), 183:664–669, 1959.

57. JJ Connell. The use of sodium dodecyl sulfate in the study of protein interactions during the storage of cod flesh at –14°C, J. Sci. Food Agric. 16:769–775, 1965.

58. RH Love, EH Mackay. Protein denaturation in frozen fish. II, J. Sci. Food Agric. 13:200–206, 1962.

59. RH Love, MM Aref, MK Elerian, JIM Ironside, EH Mackay, MG Varela. Protein denaturation in frozen fish. X, J. Sci. Food Agric. 16:259–264, 1965.

60. ST Jiang, YT Wang, BS Gau, CS Chen. Role of pepstatin-sensitive proteases on the postmortem changes of tilapia (Tilapia nilotica X T. aurea) muscle myofibrils, J. Agric. Food Chem. 38: 1464–1468, 1990.

61. ST Jiang, YT Wang, CS Chen. Lysosomal enzyme effect on the postmortem changes in tilapia (Tilapia nilotica X T. aurea), J. Food Sci. 57: 277–279, 1992.

62. L Jarenbäck, A Liljemark. Ultrastructural changes during storage of cod. II, J. Food Technol. 10:309–313, 1975.

63. T Tokiwa, H Matsumiya. Fragmentation of fish myofibril, Effect of storage condition and muscle cathepsin. Bull. Jap. Soc. Sci. Fish. 35:1099–1104, 1969.

64. AL Tappel. Denaturation of enzmes during frozen storage, In: Cryobiology. (HT Merymann, ed.), Academic Press, London, 1966, pp. 163–178.

65. E Gould. Denaturation of enzymes of frozen fish, In: Technology of Fish Utilization (R Kreuzer, ed.), Fishing News (Books) Ltd., London, 1965, pp. 126–145.

66. N Hanafusa. Protein denaturation of frozen fish, Refrigeration (Reito) 48:713–718, 1973.

67. OR Fennema, WD Powrie, EH Marth. Low Temperature Preservation of Foods and Living Matter, Marcel Dekker Inc., New York, 1973, pp. 577–583.

68. WJ Dyer, JR Dingle. Fish protein with special reference to freezing. In: Fish as Food (G Borstrom, ed.), Academic Press, New York, 1961, pp. 275–284.

69. RM Love. Protein denaturation in frozen fish, In: Cryobiology (HT Meryman, ed.), Academic Press, London, 1966, pp. 317–335.

70. Z Sikorski, J Olley, S Kostuch. Protein changes in frozen fish, Critical Reviews in Food Science and Nutrition, 8:97–146, 1976.

71. S Noguchi. Proteins of Fish Muscle (Jap. Soc. Sci. Fish, Ed.), Koseisha Koseikaku K. K., Tokyo, 1977, p. 99.

72. SWF Manson, J Olley. In: The Technology of Fish Utilization (R Kreuzer, ed.), Fishing News (Books) Ltd., London, 1965, p. 111.

73. WJ Dyer. Protein denaturation in frozen fish, Refrigeration (Reito) 48:38–43, 1973.

74. CH Castell, B Smith, WJ Dyer. Effect of formaldehyde on salt extractable proteins of gadoid muscle, J. Fish. Res. Bd. Can. 30:1205–1209, 1973.

75. JR Dingle, JA Hines. Protein instability in minced flesh fillets and frames of several commercial Atlantic fishes during storage at –5°C, J. Fish. Res. Bd. Can. 32:775–781, 1974.

76. T Tokunaga. The effect of decomposed products of trimethylamine oxide on quality of frozen Alaska Pollack fillet, Bull. Jap. Soc. Sci. Fish. 40:167–172, 1974.

77. JJ Connell. The effect of formaldehyde as a protein cross-linking agent acting during the frozen storage of cod, J. Sci. Food Agric. 26:1925–1930, 1975.

78. L Jarenback, A Liljemark. Ultrastructural changes during storage of cod, III. Effect of linoleic acid and linoleic acid hydroperoxides on myofibrillar proteins, J. Food Technol. 10:437–445, 1975.

79. JJ Connell. Studies on the protein of fish skeletal muscle. VII. Denaturation and aggregation of cod myosin, Biochem. J. 75:530–535, 1960.

80. E Childs. Interaction of formaldehyde with fish muscle in vitro, J. Food Sci. 38:1009–1011, 1973.

81. S Lewin. Displacement of Water and Its Control of Biochemical Reactions, Academic Press, London, 1974.

82. D Heldman. Food properties during freezing, Food Technol. 36(2): 92–98, 1982.

83. F Ota, T Tanaka. Some properties of the liquid portion in the frozen fish muscle fluid, Bull. Jap. Soc. Sci. Fish. 44:59–62, 1978.

84. M Love. Protein denaturation in frozen fish, J. Sci. Food Agric. 13:197–200, 1962.

85. ST Jiang, TC Lee. Changes in free amino acids and protein denaturation of fish muscle during frozen storages, J. Agric. Food Chem. 33:839–844, 1985.

86. F Colmonero, A Borderias. A study of the effects of frozen storage on certain functional properties of meat and fish protein, J. Food Technol. 18:731–737, 1983.

87. M Jul. The Quality of Frozen Foods, Academic Press, London, 1984.

88. M Karel, K Schaich, R Roy. Interaction of peroxidizing methyl linoleate with some proteins and amino acids, J. Agric. Food Chem. 23:159–163, 1975.

89. K Yamada. Occurrence and origin of TMAO in fishes and marine invertebrates, Bull. Jap. Soc. Sci. Fish. 33: 591–603, 1967.

90. National Marine Fisheries Services (NMFS), Fish News, New England Fish Development Foundation, Inc., Boston, 1986.

91. R Lundstrom, F Correia, K Wilhelm. DMA and formaldehyde production in fresh red hake (Urophysis chuss). In: The Effect of Packaging Materials, Oxygen Permeability, and Cellular Damage, Int. Inst. Ref., Boston, 1981.

92. K Amano, K Yamada. The biological formation of formaldehyde in cod fish. In: The Technology of Fish Utilization (R Kreuzer, ed.), Fishing News (Books) Ltd., London, 1965, pp. 73–87.

93. K Amano, K Yamada. Studies on the biological formation of formaldehyde and dimethylamine in fish and shellfish. V. On the enzymatic formation in the pyloric caeca of Alaskan pollack, Bull. Jap. Soc. Sci. Fish. 31:60–65, 1965.

94. H Tarr. Biochemistry of fishes, Ann. Rev. Biochem. 27:2223–2230, 1958.

95. J Spinelli, B Koury. Non-enzymatic formation of dimethylamine in dried fishery products, J. Agric. Food Chem. 27:1104–1110, 1979.

96. P Yancey, G Somero. Counteraction of urea destabilization of protein structure by methylamine regulatory compounds of elasmobrach fishes, Biochem. J. 183:317–320, 1979.

97. K Yamada, K Harada, K Amano. Biological formation of formaldehyde and DMA in fish and shellfish. VIII. Requirement of cofactor in the enzyme systems, Bull. Jap. Soc. Sci. Fish. 35:227–231, 1969.

98. C Castells, B Smith, W Neal. Production of dimethylamine in muscle of several species of gadoid fish during frozen storage, especially in relation to presence of dark muscle, J. Fish. Res. Bd. Can. 28:1–10, 1971.

99. T Gill, R Keith, B Lall. Textural deterioration of red hake and haddock muscle in frozen storage as related to chemical parameters and changes in the myofibrillar protein, J. Food Sci. 44:661–667, 1979.

100. H Hultin. Characteristics of muscle tissue. In: Food Chemistry, 2nd ed. (O Fennema, ed.), Marcel Dekker, New York, 1985, pp. 725–789.

101. C Dellino. Influence of different freezing techniques freezer types, and storage conditions on frozen fish. Info. Fish Market. Digest 2:40–44, 1986.

102. S Hanson, J Olley. Technology of Fish Utilization (R Kreuzer, ed.), Fishing News (Books) Ltd., London. 1965, pp. 111–115.

103. G Reay. The influence of freezing temperatures on haddock's muscle. Part 2, J. Soc. Chem. Ind. 53:265–270, 1983.

104. J Olley, R Pirie, H Watson. Lipase and phospholipase activity in fish skeletal muscle and its relationship to protein denaturation, J. Sci. Food Agric. 13:501–508, 1962.

105. J Lovern, J Olley. Inhibition and promotion of post-mortem lipid hydrolysis in the flesh of fish, J. Food Sci. 27:551–559, 1962.

106. R Poulter. Quality changes in fish from the South China Sea. II. Frozen storage of chub mackerel, Paper presented at IPFC/FAO Conference on Fish Utilization, Technology and Marketing. Manila, Philippines, 1978.

107. P Ke, D Nash, R Ackman. Quality preservation in frozen mackerel, J. Inst. Can. Sci. Technol. Aliment. 9(3):135–138, 1976.

108. N Screenivasan, G. Hiremath, S. Dhananjaya, H. Shetty. Studies on the changes in Indian mackerel during frozen storage and on the efficacy of protective treatments in inhibiting rancidity, Myosore J. Agric. Sci. 10:296–305, 1976.

109. D King, R Poulter. Frozen storage of Indian mackerel and big eye, Trop. Sci. 25:79–90, 1985.

110. F Bramnaes. Quality and stability of frozen seafood. In: Foods: Time-Temperature Tolerance and Its Significance (W VanArsdel, M Copley, R Olson, eds.), Wiley Interscience, New York, 1969.

111. M Fey. Extending the shelf-life of fresh by potassium sorbate and modified atmosphere at 0–1°C, Ph.D. dissertation, Cornell University, Ithaca, NY, 1980.

112. M Fey, J Regenstein. Extending the shelf-life of fresh red hake and salmon using a carbon dioxide modified atmosphere and potassium sorbate ice at 1°C, J. Food Sci. 47:1048–1054, 1982.

113. J Regenstein. The shelf-life extension of haddock in carbon dioxide atmosphere with and without potassium sorbate, J. Food Qual. 5:285–300, 1982.

114. W Nawar. Lipids. In: Food Chemistry, 2nd ed. (O Fennema, ed.), Marcel Dekker, New York, 1985.

115. N Uri. Mechanism of antioxidation. In: Autoxidation and Antioxidants (W Wundberg, ed.), Interscience Publishers, New York, 1960, pp. 133–169.

116. S Kelleher, E Buck, H Hultin, K Park, J Licciardello, R Damon. Chemical and physiological changes in red hake blocks during frozen storage, J. Food Sci. 46:65–70, 1981.

117. R Greig. Extending the shelf-life of frozen chub fillets through the use of ascorbic acid dips, Fish. Ind. Res. 4:23–29, 1967.

118. R Greig. Extending the shelf-life of frozen white bass through the use of ascorbic acid dips, Fish. Ind. Res. 4:30–35, 1967.

119. J Regenstein, C Regenstein. An Introduction to Fish Science and Technology, Cornell University, Ithaca, NY, 1985.

120. S. Kato. Theory and Application of Food Freezing (in Japanese), 5th Ed., Kohrin Kabusiki Kaisha, Tokyo, Japan, pp. 267–268.

121. P Gruji, L Petrovi, B Pikula, L Amilzic. Definition of the optimum freezing rate — 1. Investigation of structure and ultrastructure of beef *M. longissimus dorsi* frozen at different freezing rates, Meat Sci. 33:301, 1993.

122. A Calvello. Recent studies on meat freezing in developments in meat science — 2. (R Lawrie, ed.), Applied Science Publishers, London, 1981, p. 125.

40 The Application of Gene Technology in the Wine Industry

Miguel A. de Barros Lopes, Eveline J. Bartowsky, and Isak S. Pretorius
The Australian Wine Research Institute

CONTENTS

I. INTRODUCTION

Wine plays a major role in the economies of many nations. The world's annual wine production from about 8 million hectares of vineyards totals around 27 billion litres (1). Shifting consumer preferences, globalisation and other economic factors have forced an evolution of the international wine industry from a "cottage industry" of independent producers to global networks of consumer-conscious enterprises (2,3).

An increasing gap between wine production and wine consumption has given rise to an annual oversupply of 15–20% in the global market. There is a growing demand for cost-effective production of wine with minimised resource inputs, improved product quality, increased health benefits and low environmental impact. It is widely expected that advances in molecular biology and bioinformatics will help equip the wine industry with the tools to tailor grapevines and microbial starter strains, enhancing wine quality, purity, uniqueness and diversity (1,2,4).

Grape and wine research, fueled by greater understanding of basic cellular and molecular biology governing targeted traits and by considerations of future use, promises to be a powerful dynamo of technological progress in this increasingly market-oriented industry (2). It is therefore crucial that basic and applied research not be treated as separate ventures. Rather, grape and wine research, both in problem selection and experimental design, should be aimed at increasing fundamental understanding in a context responsive to the applied needs of producers and consumers.

This review passes familiar light through new prisms to demonstrate that ignoring gene technology imperils the international wine industry, despite the current vocal opposition to genetically modified organisms (GMOs) and products (1–5). This perspective is supported by examples of genetically improved grapevine prototypes showing increased productivity, efficiency, sustainability and environmental friendliness, particularly with regard to improved pest and disease control, water use efficiency and grape quality. Examples of genetically tailored microbial starter strains include those that could play a role in improving the fermentation, processing and preservation of wines, as well as those with the capacity to enhance the wholesomeness and sensory quality of wine.

II. THE GENETIC IMPROVEMENT OF GRAPEVINES FOR WINE PRODUCTION

A. GRAPEVINE SPECIES AND CULTIVARS

Grapevine belongs to the genus *Vitis*, consisting of two sub-genera, *Euvitis* and *Muscadinia*. The preferred wine grape species, *Vitis vinifera*, originated in Europe and consists of about 5000 cultivars (6). However, only a few select and ancient cultivars are relied on for commercial wine production. As a result of the wine industry's reliance on established varietal names and predictable wine styles to sell its products, there has not been a great incentive to breed new *V. vinifera* cultivars. Nevertheless, breeding programmes significantly impacted on the development of rootstock varieties resistant to soil-borne pests and pathogens, as well as to negative abiotic conditions (7). Improvements to rootstock and scion cultivars initially relied largely on arbitrary selections of natural mutations that enhanced cultivation or some aspect of fruit and/or wine quality and were later followed by the more directed, clonal selection schemes (5,8).

B. GENETIC FEATURES AND TECHNIQUES FOR THE ANALYSIS AND DEVELOPMENT OF GRAPEVINES

A dramatic new day in plant improvement is dawning, warmed by molecular biology, genetic transformation and functional genomics. Several plant genomes have now been fully sequenced, and though the accessibility of the grapevine genome is restricted by size and complexity, there are now intense multinational studies underway of the *Vitis* genome.

A growing number of plant species are becoming viable candidates for genetic transformation through *Agrobacterium*-mediated and biolistic bombardment technologies. The grapevine, however, has been resistant to genetic transformation: difficulties include finding tissue culture systems that can withstand the new techniques and subsequent selection regimes (5,8,9). Nevertheless, there are today a few grapevine scion and rootstock cultivars of commercial importance that can be genetically transformed with relatively little difficulty. The emphasis is gradually shifting from developing the technology to implementing it to generate useful plant lines.

C. TARGETS FOR THE GENETIC IMPROVEMENT OF GRAPEVINE VARIETIES

The genetic improvement of grapevine cannot occur in the absence of knowledge of the fundamental processes supporting the physiological responses to be altered. In the early days of limited genetic resources, genes with known functions were introduced into plant species in the hope of developing improved phenotypes. This approach, although problematic, demonstrated the value of adding application to theory. It is an exciting time, as the plant sciences enter a new era and the list of gene sequences, including those of grapevine, grows and becomes available. Potential areas for the genetic improvement of grapevine are discussed below and summarised in Figure 40.1.

1. Improving Disease and Pest Resistance

As genetic engineering of crop plants evolves, its primary focus remains upon enhanced disease tolerance. Single genes can confer disease resistance in plants, making individual gene transfers into plant genomes perhaps the best approach to control fungal, viral, bacterial and insect pathogens. Almost all of the approaches to enhanced disease tolerance in plants take advantage of the natural interactions between host and pathogen (10). In the battle for survival, host and pathogen evolve simultaneously, making those interactions fluid and complex.

There are currently two major approaches to manipulating disease tolerance in plants. The first is introducing a gene product with known anti-pathogen activity at high

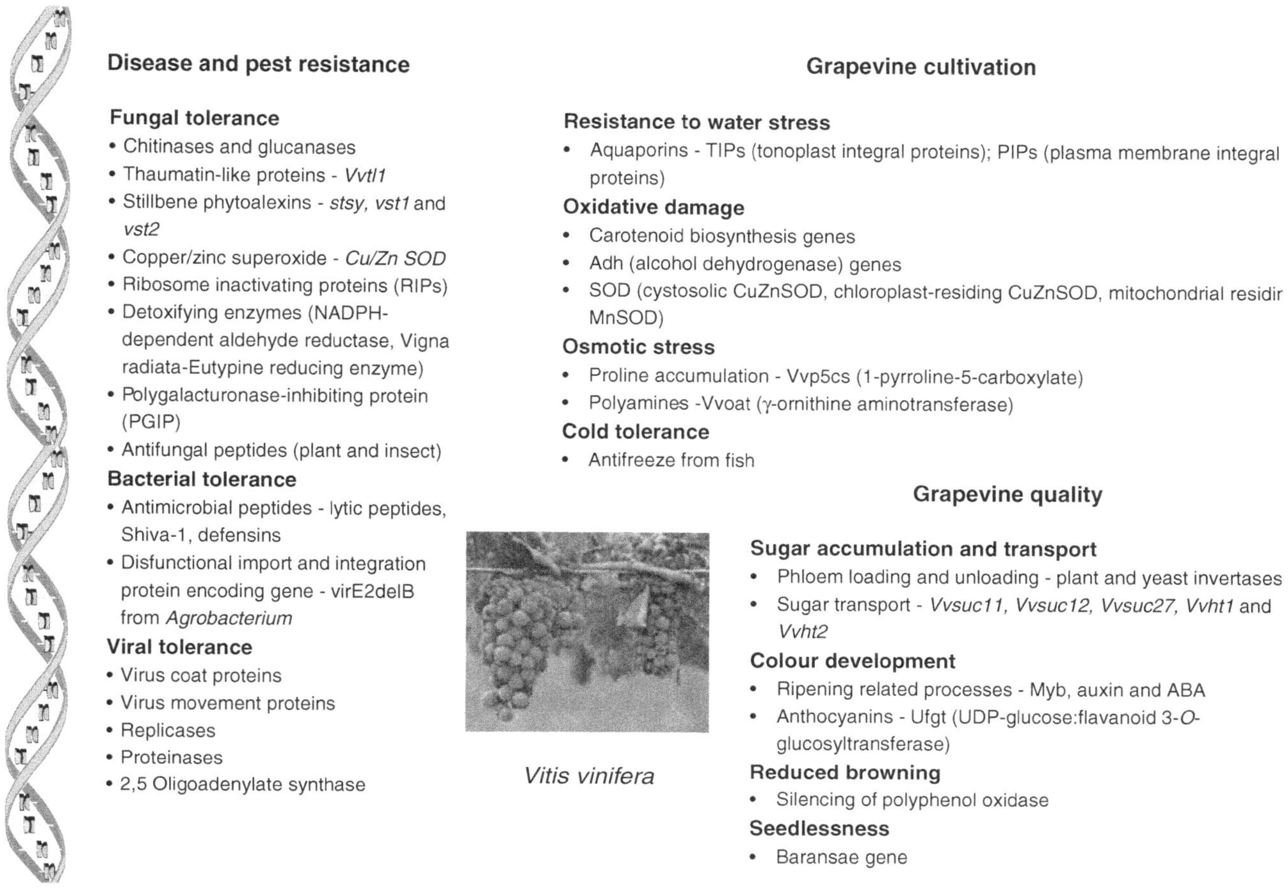

Disease and pest resistance

Fungal tolerance
- Chitinases and glucanases
- Thaumatin-like proteins - *Vvtl1*
- Stillbene phytoalexins - *stsy, vst1* and *vst2*
- Copper/zinc superoxide - *Cu/Zn SOD*
- Ribosome inactivating proteins (RIPs)
- Detoxifying enzymes (NADPH-dependent aldehyde reductase, Vigna radiata-Eutypine reducing enzyme)
- Polygalacturonase-inhibiting protein (PGIP)
- Antifungal peptides (plant and insect)

Bacterial tolerance
- Antimicrobial peptides - lytic peptides, Shiva-1, defensins
- Disfunctional import and integration protein encoding gene - virE2delB from *Agrobacterium*

Viral tolerance
- Virus coat proteins
- Virus movement proteins
- Replicases
- Proteinases
- 2,5 Oligoadenylate synthase

Grapevine cultivation

Resistance to water stress
- Aquaporins - TIPs (tonoplast integral proteins); PIPs (plasma membrane integral proteins)

Oxidative damage
- Carotenoid biosynthesis genes
- Adh (alcohol dehydrogenase) genes
- SOD (cystosolic CuZnSOD, chloroplast-residing CuZnSOD, mitochondrial residir MnSOD)

Osmotic stress
- Proline accumulation - Vvp5cs (1-pyrroline-5-carboxylate)
- Polyamines -Vvoat (γ-ornithine aminotransferase)

Cold tolerance
- Antifreeze from fish

Grapevine quality

Sugar accumulation and transport
- Phloem loading and unloading - plant and yeast invertases
- Sugar transport - *Vvsuc11, Vvsuc12, Vvsuc27, Vvht1* and *Vvht2*

Colour development
- Ripening related processes - Myb, auxin and ABA
- Anthocyanins - Ufgt (UDP-glucose:flavanoid 3-*O*-glucosyltransferase)

Reduced browning
- Silencing of polyphenol oxidase

Seedlessness
- Baransae gene

Vitis vinifera

FIGURE 40.1 Methods for the improvement of *Vitis vinifera.*

copies or in an inducible manner into the host to optimise the plant's innate defence responses. The other approach relies upon pathogen-derived resistance (PDR): a pathogen-derived gene is expressed inappropriately in time, form or amount during the infection cycle, preventing the pathogen from maintaining infection. PDR is at the root of most antiviral strategies and much of the activity in the genetic transformation of grapevine varieties.

Transgenic grapevines have been generated for providing viral resistance (10); in most of these cases expressing the virus coat protein achieved PDR. More recently, resistance to virus infection has also been achieved by expressing anti-sense to virus movement proteins (11) and replicase proteins.

Various studies have examined the expression of grapevine chitinases, β-1,3-glucanases, thaumatin-like proteins and stillbene synthetic enzymes with regard to fungal infection and grape ripening (12–14). Several of these enzymes have been shown to possess antifungal activity (15–18) and it has been demonstrated that in some cases, transgenic expression of genes encoding the proteins leads to increased resistance (18,19). Research has also shown that transgenic expression of a detoxifying enzyme

enhances resistance to *Eutypa lata* (20). In addition, a gene from the American wild grape species *Muscadinia rotundifolia* has been introgressed into a succession of pseudo back crosses of *V. vinifera*. Using this strategy, resistance to *Oidium tuckerii* (powdery mildew) has continued to segregate as a single gene, thereby making the gene an important candidate for the development of a transgenic method to confer powdery mildew resistance in *V. vinifera*.

Obtaining transgenic plants resistant to pathogenic bacteria has been less successful; the expression of the lytic peptide Shiva-1 has been reported (21), and induced expression of several defence genes have been detected in response to bacterial pathogens (13,22).

We are witnessing the onset of a new era in plant cultivation, as old problems are being addressed in new ways. Transgenic grapevines expressing heterologous antiviral and antifungal genes are currently undergoing field testing, the first 'prototypes' of manipulated disease tolerance in grapevine. The technology will undoubtedly become more sophisticated, raising the possibilities of multiple gene transfers and long-term and stable expression of transgenes along with the use of highly specific inducible regulatory sequences.

The process of generating and analysing transgenic plants has yielded considerable knowledge about the nature of plant-pathogen interactions and the disease resistance pathways that operate in plants. Model plants transformed with the various targeted genes become important resources when the nature of the manipulations and their effect *in planta* are further analysed with state-of-the-art technologies, such as transcriptomics, proteomics and metabolomics (23). A range of *Arabidopsis thaliana* mutants blocked in certain pathways of pathogen defence also provide extremely valuable information regarding the functions of genes (24). The disease pathways are now fairly well characterised and much emphasis is currently being placed on clarifying the trigger systems of defence and the subsequent signal transduction processes leading to the various forms of defence.

2. Improving Grapevine Cultivation

Genetic transformation technology carries with it the tantalising prospect of developing plant lines able to adapt to adverse climatic conditions, enhanced by greater understanding of stress tolerance in plants and basic knowledge of key aspects of plant growth and development. Ongoing efforts to develop transgenic grapevines with improved cultivation prospects are focussing on processes such as carbon-partitioning, modes of sugar translocation, water transport and the role of aquaporins, as well as the regulation of these processes. These efforts also deal with important limitations to cultivation such as drought and salt stress, photo-damage and freezing tolerance (25).

To date, a transgenic grapevine expressing antifreeze genes from Antarctic fish has been reported as a mechanism to provide cold tolerance (25). However, plant stress responses are complex pathways of interacting proteins driven by a range of signals attenuated or amplified by equally complex processes. This biological interaction is more difficult to manipulate with single or even multiple gene additions; knowledge of the control mechanisms and alterations thereof might prove more feasible. With this view, the accumulation of proline and polyamines are two examples in grapevine that have been studied. The regulation of key genes in these biosynthetic pathways is providing insight into their involvement in abiotic stress (26,27). Furthermore, the expression of several stress related genes has been shown to be activated during the grape ripening (28,29).

Crop prediction is another area of attention. One of the most difficult issues facing viticultural production is the understanding and management of crop load and quality in the face of seasonal and environmental variation and change in market demand. Most recently, a study of how related genes in grapevine are organised and interact was made possible by the identification of the genes involved in flowering and fruitfulness in *A. thaliana*. For example,

the chimera that results in pinot meunier can be separated into a conventional pinot and a mutant pinot form in which fruitfulness is dramatically increased even in juvenile plants. This dramatic change is the result of a single DNA base change in a single gene affecting vegetative and floral development of the vine (30).

3. Improving Grape Quality

Winemakers want small grapes of specific colour and ripeness as measured by the indicators of sugar, acids and phenolics. Researchers are investigating the basic processes of berry ripening and, particularly, ripening signals. Grapevine, a non-climacteric fruit, is studied for the biochemical, hormonal and environmental signals that influence ripening processes such as pigment production, sugar accumulation, transport and the formation of aroma components. The means of glucose/fructose accumulation during ripening is coming to light with the identification and analysis of grape berry genes encoding invertases and sugar transporters (31). The expression of flavenoid biosynthetic genes, responsible for colour development, coincide with hexose accumulation in berries (32–34). The importance of UDP glucose flavanoid-3-glucosyl transferase (UFGT) in the control of berry colour has been highlighted by comparison of gene expression in red and white grapes (35,36), and recent results indicate that Myb genes are involved in regulating UFGT (37). A number of genes that influence grape berry softening have also been isolated (38–40). Auxin and abscisic acid (natural hormones regulating growth and physiology) affect the expression of genes involved in the ripening process and have been implicated in the control of grape berry ripening (41). The aim of this approach is to meet the quality parameters of grapes with the formation of desirable or novel products by changing the metabolic flux through the important biosynthetic pathways active in the ripening berry.

To reach these goals grapevine biotechnology will have to draw upon considerably more knowledge of the underpinning processes as well as upon improvements in transformation technology. Targeted gene insertion and deletion technologies will make these and other innovative prospects more feasible.

III. THE GENETIC IMPROVEMENT OF WINE YEAST FOR ALCOHOLIC FERMENTATION

A. YEAST SPECIES AND STRAINS

Saccharomyces cerevisiae is unquestionably the most important yeast species in winemaking, but it competes with many other species for dominance. The ubiquitous fruit yeast, *Hanseniaspora uvarum* (anamorph *Kloeckera apiculata*), is the most common yeast isolated from grapes, and many other non-*Saccharomyces* species are also present in the initial stages of spontaneous alcoholic ferments. As the ethanol concentration increases and other conditions change, various yeasts prevail in sequence, until *S. cerevisiae* multiplies to be the dominant species (42).

Not surprisingly, in such a complex environment the yeast ecology is highly variable and dependent on geographic location, viticulture and winemaking practices. Over the last decade, the pace of microbial ecology research has been accelerated by the application of molecular methods. A widely used rapid species identification method is PCR-RFLP (*p*olymerase *c*hain *r*eaction-derived *r*estriction *f*ragment *l*ength *p*olymorphism) of the ribosomal RNA genes (43). Using this method highlights the unpredictability of wine yeast ecology. In some wines for example, there is an almost total absence of apiculate yeast (*Hanseniaspora* sp.), yielding to *Candida stellata, Metschnikowia pulcherrima* or even *S. cerevisiae* during the initial stages of fermentation (44). In other cases non-*Saccharomyces* species persist to the end of fermentation (45). Molecular methods have also begun to accent the role of other *Saccharomyces* sensu stricto species, as well as interspecific hybrids of *Saccharomyces* yeasts in vinification (46–48).

Recently developed molecular methods, in particular mitochondrial DNA RFLP, have been used to analyse fermentation ecology at the species as well as strain level. The most unexpected finding is the number of strains of the same species coexisting during fermentation, with some wines showing over 100 different *S. cerevisiae* strains at the end of fermentation (44,45). Other technologies such as denaturing gradient gel electrophoresis (DGGE) have been developed that no longer require the plating of yeast prior to identification. Using this method new non-culturable species have been discovered in wine (49).

Wines made from spontaneous ferments are often described as more complex and fuller than inoculated wines. It is common practice, nevertheless, in many wineries to inoculate with a specific strain of *S. cerevisiae*, for rapid fermentation and a more consistent product with a reduced possibility of microbial spoilage. It also allows winemakers to use preferred strains to produce wines of a chosen style. With the future availability of yeast strains that can improve multiple facets of the winemaking process, the advantages offered to winemakers performing inoculated ferments with both *Saccharomyces* and non-*Saccharomyces* strains will expand.

B. GENETIC FEATURES AND TECHNIQUES FOR THE ANALYSIS AND DEVELOPMENT OF WINE YEASTS

Several genetic methods are available for the improvement of wine yeast. These include the selection of mutants with the desired properties, the combination of traits by mating and sporulation/dissection of *S. cerevisiae* strains, and the use of protoplast fusion to introduce novel traits of other

species (1). Although these classic genetic methods have been used successfully for the development of new strains, they lack the precision and capability of gene cloning.

Specific characteristics of *S. cerevisiae* make it a model experimental organism (50). *S. cerevisiae* multiplies rapidly, shares many cellular regulatory mechanisms with humans and has a stable haploid and diploid life cycle. It has numerous suitable markers, plasmids and promoters for the regulated expression of chosen genes and undergoes efficient homologous recombination, permitting the precise deletion of selected genes. The *S. cerevisiae* genome was the first eukaryotic genome to be completely sequenced and this, along with its facile genetics, has made it an excellent research organism in the post-genomic era (51,52).

There have been major technical developments since the complete *S. cerevisiae* DNA sequence was published. Yeast deletion libraries are available in different mating types and ploidy that possess a set of approximately 6000 yeasts strains, each with a different single gene deleted. Phenotypic and chemical screens of these libraries make clear the biological function of each of the 6000 genes (53,54). The transcriptional response of each gene to different environmental conditions using microarrays is identifying genes that are important to wine fermentation [reviewed in (55)]. These conditions include the response to ethanol, osmotic stress, high and low temperature, high and low pH, copper, limited nitrogen and sugar, anaerobicity and progression into stationary phase (56–61). Microarray experiments are also being used to compare genome structure and gene expression in different grapevine isolates and commercial wine yeast (62–64). Proteomic approaches are being used in parallel to uncover the post-transcriptional changes that occur in different environmental conditions and genetic backgrounds in yeast (65). Of particular importance to wine is the emergence of metabolomics (66,67), which attempts to analyse all the metabolites produced by an organism in response to environmental or genetic changes. This will be fundamental to further understanding of how genetic and environmental changes impact on flavour and aroma.

The opportunity now exists to exploit these research findings and technological developments to produce genetically improved wine yeast strains of great value to the wine industry.

C. TARGETS FOR THE GENETIC IMPROVEMENT OF WINE YEAST STRAINS

Molecular genetics in wine yeast is being used to improve several aspects of winemaking, including fermentation performance, processing efficiency, sensory attributes and wine wholesomeness. These are summarised in Figure 40.2. Many of these aspects have been described in recent reviews (1,3,68), and the emphasis in this section is on current advances in this area as detailed in the latest literature.

Fermentation performance

Dessication tolerance

- Increased trehalose and glycogen accumulation - *nth1Δ, ath1Δ* and ↑*GSY2*
- Increased expression of aquaporins - ↑*AQY1* and ↑*AQY2*
- Increased accumulation of proline and charged amino acids - *put1Δ,* ↑*PRO1* and *car1Δ*

Fermentation stress

- Osmotic tolerance by modifying glycerol metabolism - ↑*GPD1,* ↑*GPD2,* ↑*GPP2*
- Ethanol tolerance by increasing sterol accumulation and ATPase activity - ↑*SUT1,* ↑*SUT2,* ↑*PMA1,* ↑*PMA2*

Nutrition

- Improved sugar transport - ↑*HXT3,* ↑*HXT6,* ↑*HXT7,* ↑*SNF3* and *FSY1*
- Improved nitrogen utilisation - *ure2Δ,* ↑*PUT1* and ↑*PUT4*

Control of indigenous microorganisms

- Increased sulfur dioxide - *met2Δ, met10Δ* and ↑*MET14*
- Hydrogen peroxide production - *GOX1*
- Expression of zymocins and bacteriocins - *PED1* and *LCA1*
- Expression of lysozyme, chitinases and glucanses - *HEL1, CTS1* and *EXG1*

Processing

Protein clarification

- Expression of yeast haze protection factors - invertase, *HPF1* and *HPF2*

Cell floculation and flotation

- Controlled cell sedimentation by regulating expression of flocculins *FLO1* and *FLO11*
- Vellum formation - *FLO11/MUC1*

Polysaccharide clarification

- Glucanases, pectinases, xylanases, arabinofuranosidases - *END1, EXG1, CEL1, BGL1, PEL5, PEH1, XYN1–5, ABF2* and ↑*PGU1*

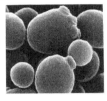

Saccharomyces cerevisiae

Wine wholesomeness

Resveratrol

- Increased resveratrol by grape stillbene synthesis - *4CL9/216, Vst1*

Ethyl carbamate and biogenic amines

- Decreased ethyl carbamate by decreasing urea formation - *car1Δ, URE1*
- Decreased biogenic amines by inhibiting bacterial growth

Sensory Attributes

Grape derived flavours

- Release of colour and flavour trapped in skin by expressing polysaccharide-degrading enzymes
- Release of terpenols by the expression of glycosidases - *END1, EXG1* and *BEG1*
- Modified terpenol concentrations by altering ergosterol biosynthesis and terpenol biotransformation
- Release of volatile thiols

Yeast secondary metabolites

- Enhanced production of desired esters by modifying transferases and esterases - ↑*ATF1* and ↑*IAH2*
- Optimised higher alcohol production modification of *BAT1, BAT2, ILE, VAL* and *LEU* genes
- Low ethanol wine yeast - ↑*GPD1,* ↑*GPD2, ald6Δ* and *GOX1*
- Modified sulfur metabolism - *met10Δ met14Δ, mxr1Δ,* ↑*MET25,* ↑*MET17* and ↑*SSU1*
- Malolactic fermentation - *mleS, mae1 mae2* and *LDH1*
- Optimised phenol production - *PAD1*

FIGURE 40.2 Methods for strain development of wine yeast. Photograph kindly provided by Dr Alan Wheals.

1. Improving Fermentation Performance

Sluggish and stuck ferments remain a major concern of the wine industry. The wine environment is very stressful for yeast and harsh conditions must be overcome to produce high-quality wines (69). Like all living organisms, yeast has mechanisms in place allowing it to respond quickly to a changing environment. A general environmental stress response (ESR) participates in a wide range of cellular functions, including cell wall modification, fatty acid metabolism, protein chaperone expression, DNA repair, detoxification of reactive oxygen species and energy generation and storage (57). In addition to the general stress response, specific strategies to combat distinct stresses are essential for the survival of yeast in the fermenting grape must environment.

a. Desiccation stress

The desiccation process, part of the production of active dried yeast, challenges the wine yeast to a mixed stress that, although not well defined, appears to share some properties with freezing and osmotic stress. Several metabolites increase the survival of *S. cerevisiae* cells exposed to physical or chemical stresses and have been implicated in the efficiency of reactivating dried wine yeast starter cultures. As a result, there is strong incentive to develop wine yeast strains that accumulate these metabolites.

Disabling the trehalose hydrolysis pathway, thereby increasing cellular trehalose concentrations by deleting the *NTH1* or *ATH1* (neutral and acidic trehalase) genes has been shown to increase freezing and dehydration tolerance in a laboratory and commercial baker's yeast (70,71). The build-up of a second carbohydrate storage molecule, glycogen, is thought to provide the yeast with a readymade energy source upon reactivation of dried yeast. It has been reported that a wine strain overexpressing the *GSY2* (glycogen synthase) gene accumulates glycogen and has enhanced viability under glucose limitation conditions (72). Overexpression of the *AQY1* and *AQY2* (aquaporin) genes also confers freeze tolerance upon both laboratory and commercial baking strains (73). Whether these changes prove to be an advantage to active dried yeast remains to be determined.

It has been shown that proline and charged amino acids provide desiccation and freeze tolerance. Deletion mutations in the *PUT1* gene, encoding proline oxidase, and a dominant mutation in the proline biosynthetic *PRO1* gene (γ-glutamyl kinase), increase intracellular proline and show higher desiccation, freeze and/or osmo-tolerance (74,75). A deletion mutation in the arginine degrading enzyme *CAR1* (arginase) increases arginine and glutamic acid levels and provides freeze tolerance (71).

b. Fermentation stress

The high concentration of sugar in grape juice imposes an osmotic stress on yeast. As indicated above, proline and trehalose accumulation both provide osmotolerance to yeast. The main osmolyte in yeast, however, is glycerol. In response to an osmotic stress, a MAPK cascade is activated and the two key genes in glycerol biosynthesis *GPD1* (glycerol-3-phosphate dehydrogenase) and *GPP2* (glycerol-3-phosphatase) are rapidly and transiently induced greater than 50-fold (61). Mutations in these genes are osmosensitive whereas mutations that increase their expression enhance osmotolerance (76). It has been reported that commercial wine yeast strains overexpressing either *GPD1* or *GPD2* have a slight growth advantage at the beginning of fermentation (77,78).

The primary cause of most sluggish and stuck fermentations is a high concentration of ethanol, an effect that can be augmented by a number of intrinsic and environmental factors. The physiological basis of ethanol toxicity is complex and not fully understood (59). A major target appears to be cell membranes, in which ethanol increases membrane fluidity and permeability, and impairs the transport of sugars and amino acids. The modification of *SUT1*, *SUT2*, *PMA1* and *PMA2* genes results in increased sterol accumulation and ATPase activity, thereby increasing the resistance to ethanol.

Zymocidal wild yeast may also inhibit the growth of the inoculated wine yeast strain and contribute to sluggish or stuck fermentation (79). Rapid progress in understanding sensitivity to killer toxins is being made, encouraging the development of broad-spectrum zymocidal resistance in wine yeast (80–82).

c. Utilisation of nutrients

Sugar uptake appears to limit complete sugar utilisation during vinification and is strongly influenced by conditions such as ethanol concentration and nitrogen availability. The low affinity hexose transporter Hxt3p and high affinity transporters Hxt6p and Hxt7p play particularly important roles in wine fermentation (83). It is possible that increased expression of these transporters will decrease the occurrence of stuck fermentation. Two hexose transporter homologues, Snf3p and Rgt2p, are required for glucose sensing. Snf3 is specifically required for inducing a number of *HXT* genes under low glucose conditions. Dominant *SNF3* mutants constitutively express hexose transporters and are resistant to translational inhibition upon glucose withdrawal (84,85), providing a potential mechanism for wine yeast improvement.

Nitrogen is the nutrient most often limiting wine fermentations; its deficiency can lead to cessation of fermentation as well as to the production of off-flavours such as hydrogen sulfide. A wine yeast strain carrying a mutation in the *URE2* gene, which represses expression of proline transport and metabolic genes, increases the availability of proline and arginine as nitrogen sources (86,87). However, *ure2Δ* strains possess pleotropic phenotypes. A more specific method may be to specifically target the proline permease and utilisation proteins (encoded by the *PUT* genes) (88). Global gene expression studies of wine yeast growing under differing nitrogen conditions will be important for identifying other genes that can improve fermentation under limiting nitrogen conditions (56,58).

An alternative source of nitrogen in vinification is from autolysis of the yeasts themselves (89). It is possible that a subset of yeast could be targeted to lyse toward the end of fermentation by adjusting the regulation of the cell integrity pathway (90).

d. Control of indigenous microorganisms

Uncontrolled microbial growth can alter the chemical composition of wine and detract from its sensory properties. The excessive use of chemical preservatives to control the growth of unwanted microbes can affect the quality of wine; it also faces increasing consumer resistance. As a response, wine yeast starter cultures that express antimicrobial enzymes or peptides are being developed.

Wine yeast producing increased sulfur dioxide (SO_2) concentrations could be useful for suppressing the growth of indigenous microbes, providing a means of reducing SO_2 as an antimicrobial and antioxidation agent in wine. Decreasing Met10p (sulfite reductase) and Met2p (serine acetyl transferase) activity or increasing Met14p (adenosine 5′ phosphosulfate kinase) activity leads to increased SO_2 production and has been shown to provide flavour stability to beer (91–93). Expression of hen-egg lysozyme or the *Aspergillus niger* glucose oxidase gene (*GOX1*) in yeast offers additional alternatives (94). The expression of *GOX1* in a wine yeast resulted in the production of hydrogen peroxide that can lead to oxidation toxicity of bacteria (95).

An alternative method is the use of a wine yeast with broad spectrum zymocidal activity. Whereas *S. cerevisiae*'s zymocins have a narrow killing range, the zymocins of *Pichia anomala*, *Willopsis saturnus* and *Kluyveromyces lactis* have been shown to be active on many species common in grape juice, including spoilage yeasts such as *Dekkera bruxellensis* (96). Several of the zymocins have been cloned in *S. cerevisiae;* the mechanisms of action are being established (80,97). Although these zymocins are generally less active at low pH, continuing advances in understanding the pH dependence of protein stability should make it possible to engineer more suitable zymocins for winemaking (98).

The zymocin zygocin, produced by the salt-tolerant yeast *Zygosaccharomyces bailli*, is also active against filamentous fungi (99). However, heterologous expression in *S. cerevisiae* causes the yeast to commit suicide. Some success in producing yeast that kill filamentous fungi by attacking the cell wall has been achieved by expressing the *CTS1* chitinase and the *EXG1* endoglucanase genes (100). Although zymocidal yeasts have also been shown to be active on bacteria, the focus in wine research has been on the production of strains that secrete bacteriocins or bacteriolytic enzymes (e.g., lysozyme) to suppress growth of undesirable bacteria. Secretion of the *Pediococcus acidilactici* and *Lactobacillus plantarum* bacteriocins in *S. cerevisiae* produced a yeast that killed sensitive bacteria (101,102).

2. Improving Wine Processing

Following alcoholic fermentation wine is further processed to achieve clarity and physiochemical stability. The fining and clarification processes often involve expensive and laborious practices that generate large volumes of lees for disposal. This causes wine loss and may remove important aroma and flavour compounds from the remaining wine. To minimise the impact of these practices an increasing spectrum of commercial enzyme preparations are being added to grape must and wine. Generating yeast that remove proteins and polysaccharides and causes cells to flocculate offers an alternative strategy to the addition of costly enzymes.

a. Protein clarification

Heat-induced protein haze is caused by thaumatin-like proteins and chitinases, which are pathogenesis-related grape proteins (103). These proteins slowly denature and aggregate, resulting in light dispersing particles forming in wine. Under winemaking conditions, proteases have been unsuccessful in degrading haze proteins (104). However, a number of glycoproteins have been found to visibly reduce haze formation in wine, including yeast invertase (105) and two mannoproteins from *S. cerevisiae* known as haze protection factors (HPF) (106).

b. Cell flocculation and flotation

Rapid settling of yeast is advantageous to post fermentation processing. Yeast flocculation, which entails an interaction between cell surface lectins and mannans, involves many genes in *S. cerevisiae* (107). *FLO1* has been the best studied and shown to impart flocculation to beer and wine strains (108,109). Given that the timing of flocculation is important, *FLO1* and *FLO11* were expressed from the *HSP30* promoter, linking flocculation to a heat shock towards the end of fermentation (110).

In sherry, the yeast trap carbon dioxide and float to the surface forming a vellum. Several cell wall proteins have been implicated in vellum formation but the process appears complex and is likely to be multigenic (111). The similarities between vellum and biofilm formation point to Flo11p/Muc1p as a candidate gene in the process (112).

3. Improving Wine Sensory Attributes

The endless variety of wine flavours stems from complex interactions among hundreds of metabolites. *S. cerevisiae* accounts for the major changes between grape must and wine, modifying the chemical, colour, mouth-feel and flavour complexity of wine by assisting in the extraction of compounds from solids present in grape must, modifying grape derived molecules, and producing yeast metabolites (113).

a. Grape derived flavours

(i) Polysaccharide degrading enzymes. Polysaccharide degrading enzymes facilitate wine clarification and increase juice yield; they can also lead to the release of colour and flavour compounds trapped in the grape skins. A wide variety of heterologous genes encoding polysaccharide degrading enzymes have been expressed in *S. cerevisiae* (114). Pectin degradation was increased by yeast co-expressing two bacterial pectinase genes, pectate lyase from *Erwinia chrysanthemi* and polygalacturonase from *Erwinia carotovora* (115), or the pectate lyase gene from *Fusarum solani* (116). The overexpression of the endopolygalacturonase-encoding gene (*PGU1*) from *S. cerevisiae* in a wine yeast strain resulted in a higher concentration of terpenols (nerol and geraniol) in the wines, which displayed sensory differences to wines made with the parent yeast (117).

A number of glucanase genes from bacteria, yeast and filamentous fungi have been expressed, either on their own or together in commercial wine strains (114). These yeasts were able to degrade glucans effectively. Similarly, a number of xylanases have been expressed in *S. cerevisiae*. Although the levels of secreted enzymes are still below the concentrations required for the effective removal of polysaccharides, a degree of clarification has already been achieved. Preliminary trials also indicate that some of the modified yeast lead to the release of colour and flavour compounds entrapped in the grape skins.

(ii) Glycosidases. Yeast can increase wine flavour by releasing terpenols present as non-volatile glycosides in grapes. Expression of a β-1,4-endoglucanase gene from the filamentous fungus *Trichoderma longibrachiatum* in a wine yeast produced a wine with increased aroma intensity (118). The impact on flavour release of co-expressing three glucanase genes from *S. cerevisiae* (*EXG1*), *Bacillus subtilis* (*END1*) and *Butyrivibrio fibrisolvens* (*BEG1*) in a yeast remains to be determined (119).

Yeast can influence the concentration of terpenols by two other means: first, strains containing mutations in ergosterol biosynthesis have been shown to produce geraniol, citronelol and linalool (120), and second, it has been shown that yeast are able to convert one terpenol into another. As the terpenols have distinct aromas and sensory thresholds, these biotransformations might have a significant effect on wine sensory properties (121,122).

(iii) Volatile thiols. A number of potent thiol compounds have been shown to provide the basis for the varietal aromas of Sauvignon Blanc and Scheurebe wines (123), and are present in wines made from other cultivars. The sulfur-containing volatiles are present as a cysteine conjugate in grape juice and are released during fermentation by the action of yeast. Release is strain dependent, indicating that the concentrations of the thiols in wine can be regulated by genetically modifying the yeast (124).

b. Yeast secondary metabolites

(i) Esters. The characteristic fruity aromas of wine are caused mainly by the acetate esters of higher alcohols and the C_4-C_{10} ethyl esters. Overexpression of alcohol acetyl transferase genes (*ATF*) has a marked affect on ester formation (125–127). In wine, the concentrations of ethyl acetate, iso-amyl acetate, and 2-phenylethyl acetate increased as much as 10-fold, and the acetic acid concentration decreased by more than half in an *ATF1* overproducing strain (126). In saké strains, isoamyl acetate (banana-like aroma) concentrations have been modified by adjusting the *ATF1/IAH2* (isoamyl acetate esterase) balance (128).

(ii) Alcohols. Higher alcohols can contribute positively to wine complexity, but at excessive levels are regarded to have a negative influence on wine quality. They are also important precursors to ester formation. They are produced either anabolically or catabolically, by the breakdown of branched chain amino acids (129). The role of the anabolic pathway has been recently studied by deleting the aminotransferase genes *BAT1* and *BAT2*, the mutations leading to a decreased formation of isobutanol, isoamyl and active amyl alcohols (127,130).

(iii) Low ethanol wine yeast. High ethanol can affect the sensory properties of wine, giving it a perceived 'hotness' as well as suppressing overall aroma and flavour. Moreover, health-conscious consumers are demanding lower alcohol content in wines. Diverting the flow of sugar away from ethanol synthesis and into the glycerol pathway has been achieved by overexpressing the glycerol phosphate dehydrogenase genes, *GPD1* and *GPD2*, in wine strains (77,78,131). Acetic acid (vinegar) concentrations in these strains are increased to unacceptable levels. The acetaldehyde dehydrogenase activity encoded by the *ALD6* gene appears to be the main contributor to the oxidation of acetaldehyde during fermentation (132). A laboratory yeast overexpressing *GPD2* and lacking *ALD6* had the desired effect of producing more glycerol and less ethanol, but without the increase in acetic acid (133). A 'metabolic snapshot' (67) of the glycerol overproducing ferments also demonstrated how seemingly unrelated biochemical pathways can be modified by the change in a single gene (133).

A second strategy used to decrease ethanol is the expression of the *A. niger* glucose oxidase gene (*GOX1*) into *S. cerevisiae*, resulting in a 2% decrease in ethanol

(95). The glucose in grape juice is thought to be converted to D-glucono-δ-lactone and gluconic acid, and is thus not available for conversion to ethanol.

(iv) Sulfur metabolism. Due to its low sensory threshold, the rotten egg aroma of hydrogen sulfide (H_2S) is highly undesirable in wine. Modification of genes required for sulfur metabolism leads to a significant decrease in hydrogen sulfide production (134–136). In *SSU1* overexpressing strains, a plasma membrane protein specifically for the efflux of sulfite from yeast (137), the sulfite is secreted prior to reduction to sulfide (93). Increases in *SSU1* expression also confer SO_2 resistance to *S. cerevisiae* strains. Many wine yeast strains that show natural resistance to sulfide have undergone chromosome translocation, positioning the *SSU1* gene downstream of a stronger promoter, and consequently causing its increased expression (138).

(v) Malolactic fermentation. During malolactic fermentation (conducted by certain species of lactic acid bacteria) L-malic acid is decarboxylated to L-lactic acid, which reduces wine acidity. *S. cerevisiae* is unable to transport malic acid into the cell and is inefficient in metabolising malic acid. The construction of a *S. cerevisiae* strain which is able to deacidify wine has been successfully demonstrated by expressing the malolactic gene (*mleS*) from *Lactococcus lactis* and the malate permease gene (*mae1*) from *Schizosaccharomyces pombe* (139).

In an attempt to redirect glucose carbon to lactic acid, the lactate dehydrogenase-encoding genes from *Lactobacillus casei*, the filamentous fungus *Rhizopus oryzae* and bovine muscle were expressed in yeast. As much as 20% of the glucose was converted into lactic acid in these strains (140,141).

(vi) Phenols. The decarboxylation of phenolic acids to volatile phenols can make a positive contribution to wine when present in appropriate concentrations. Although *S. cerevisiae* possesses a phenolic acid decarboxylase, *POF1* (*PAD1*), it displays low activity. Expressing the phenolic acid decarboxylase or *p*-coumaric acid decarboxylase from *Bacillus subtilis* and *Lactobacillus plantarum*, respectively, gave an approximate twofold increase in volatile phenol formation in a laboratory strain (142).

4. Improving Wine Wholesomeness

During the last few years it has become widely accepted that wine contains protective compounds that when consumed in moderate quantities reduce the likelihood of contracting certain diseases. However, a number of unwanted compounds are also present in wine. Generating improved yeasts that produce the correct balance of these compounds will be important for enhancing the health benefits of wine.

a. Resveratrol

Resveratrol, a polyphenolic phytoalexin found mainly in grape skins, has been associated with a large number of health benefits, including the decreased risk of coronary heart disease, cancer prevention and treatment, and neuro-protection (60). Expression of the *Candida molisciana bgiN* gene, encoding a β-glucosidase, showed an increase in resveratrol in white wine. Release of glucose moieties from the glucoside form of resveratrol was the suggested mechanism (116). Also, yeast with altered phenyl-propanoid metabolism, expressing the coenzyme A lyase gene and the grape stillbene synthase gene (*Vst1*), can synthesise resveratrol (143).

b. Ethyl carbamate
Ethyl carbamate, a suspected mammalian carcinogen, is formed through the chemical reaction of ethanol and citrulline, urea or carbamyl phosphate. In a saké strain disrupted for the *CAR1* arginase gene, no urea or ethyl carbamate was produced (144).

c. Biogenic amines
Biogenic amines are neurotoxins that can trigger hypoten-sion and migraines, lead to histamine toxicity and produce carcinogenic nitrosamines (145). These biogenic amines originate from decarboxylation of amino acids by bacte-ria, including malolactic species (146,147). Wine yeast strains that inhibit bacterial growth may offer a solution.

IV. THE GENETIC IMPROVEMENT OF WINE BACTERIA FOR MALOLACTIC FERMENTATION

Malolactic fermentation (MLF), conducted by malolactic bacteria, is an important step in the grape vinification process, particularly in red wines. Most often MLF will occur after the alcoholic fermentation; however, it is not limited to this stage of winemaking. The role of MLF is threefold: wine deacidification by the conversion of L-malic acid to the 'softer' L-lactic acid, microbial stabil-ity and wine flavour modification.

This section will not elaborate on the biochemistry of MLF. Rather it will discuss the bacteria involved in the process, summarise the genetics of the malolactic bacteria and postulate potential genes that could be manipulated in order to improve the malolactic reaction, increase stress tol-erance of the bacteria, and/or favourably alter the sensory profile of the wine. The ability to genetically alter the mal-olactic bacterial genome will depend upon the development of a suitable genetic transfer system (transformation, con-jugation or transduction), which currently is unavailable.

A. LACTIC ACID BACTERIA SPECIES AND STRAINS

The wine bacteria associated with MLF belong to the fam-ily of lactic acid bacteria (LAB). This group of bacteria is involved with the fermentation of a range of food products, including milk, vegetables, meat and fruit, especially grapes.

The malolactic bacteria are encompassed in four genera, *Lactobacillus (Lb.)*, *Leuconostoc (Lc.)*, *Oenococcus (O.)* and *Pediococcus (P.)* from within the larger group of LAB. The species in these genera can be characterised by their ability to tolerate low pH, high ethanol concentration and by their ability to grow in wine. Those most commonly associ-ated with wine are *Lb.brevis*, *Lb. plantarum*, *Lb. hilgardii*, *Lc. mesenteroides*, *O. oeni*, *P. damnosus* and *P. pen-tosaceus*. *Oenococcus oeni*, formerly known as *Leuconostoc oenos* (148), is the LAB species most commonly associated with wine, as it is particularly well adapted to the harsh wine environment (low pH, high ethanol content, low nutrients) (149). For a more detailed description of LAB taxonomy the reader is referred to several reviews [(150,151); *Bergey's Manual of Determinative Bacteriology*, 1986)].

Even though it is postulated that species of *Lactobacillus* and to a lesser extent *Pediococcus* species may conduct the deacidification reaction in spontaneous MLF, species of these two genera are more likely to be associated with spoilage of wine than with positive sen-sory attributes.

B. GENETIC FEATURES AND TECHNIQUES FOR THE ANALYSIS AND DEVELOPMENT OF LACTIC ACID BACTERIA

The *O. oeni* genome has been sequenced in its entirety by two different groups (University of California, Davis with the group of D. Mills and at ESBANA, Dijon, France with the groups of J. Guzzo and A. Lonvaud-Funel). This sequence information will greatly enhance the initial work on the *O. oeni* genome (150–153) and add to the limited number of genes that have been characterised. Though *O. oeni* is an important organism in winemaking, knowledge of its genetics is limited. The current lack of a genetic transfer mechanism into *O. oeni* further hampers genetic characterisation of this organism.

Considerable research has been done on other LAB, particularly those from the dairy industry. Substantial work has been devoted to the genetics of *Lactobacillus* sp. but to a lesser extent in *Pediococcus* sp. Numerous vectors have been constructed to introduce modified genes into *Lactobacillus* species and strains. These vec-tors are designed to enable easy movement between Gram-positive and Gram-negative organisms utilising dual replicons (origin of replication) and antibiotic mark-ers. Also available are temperature-sensitive features on a few of these plasmids. Some of these plasmids/vectors also function in *Leuconostoc* sp., which is the closest LAB genus to *Oenococcus*. Many of these vectors may be suitable for *O. oeni*.

Another approach to improving industrially important *O. oeni* strains is the use of a new technology known as genome shuffling (154,155). This technique involves using a classical strain improvement method to generate populations with subtle improvements. Next, these populations are shuffled by recursive pool-wise protoplast fusions. Genome shuffling has been successfully applied to improve acid tolerance in a poorly characterised industrial *Lactobacillus* strain (156) and appears to be broadly useful for the rapid development of tolerance and other complex phenotypes in industrial organisms.

C. TARGETS FOR THE GENETIC IMPROVEMENT OF MALOLACTIC BACTERIAL STRAINS

Potential improvements to MLF by the genetic modification of *O. oeni* are presented in Figure 40.3. It would be of obvious interest to construct an *O. oeni* strain which is able to ward off potential competitors, improve its ability to cope with the harsh wine environment, increase its efficiency in the bioacidification of wine-conversion of malic acid to lactic acid, and/or to provide mechanisms to improve the

organoleptic qualities of wine. Such an organism would not necessarily possess all these attributes, but generating a selection of improved *O. oeni* would be of great benefit to the wine industry.

1. Improving Fermentation Performance

a. Adaptation to environmental stress

It has been demonstrated that *O. oeni* responds to various environmental stresses, such as high alcohol, acid and sulfur dioxide (SO$_2$) concentrations, by producing heat shock and stress proteins (*hsp18*, *clpX* and *trxA*) (157). The manipulation of these genes could lead to improved tolerance of *O. oeni* to wines with conditions at the upper limit of *O. oeni* tolerance. The elevated expression of these heat and stress proteins may also aid the commercial production of *O. oeni* for direct inoculation into wine, by better preparing the bacterial cells for the harsh wine environment.

Fermentation performance

MLF efficiency
- Malolactic enzyme
- (*mleR*, *mleA*, *mleP*)
- Increase the efficiency of malate metabolism

Stress
- Heat shock and stress proteins
- (*hsp18*, *clpX*, *trxA*)
- Regulation of production could lead to improved tolerance to wine conditions, especially alcohol (high EtOH, 14–15%)

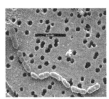

Oenococcus oeni

Wine wholesomeness

Arginine / Ethyl carbamate
- *Arc* cluster (arginine metabolism)
- Arginine metabolism leads onto ethyl carbamate (animal carcinogen)
- Manipulation of *arc* cluster could lead to ↓ ethyl carbamate production

Biogenic amines
- ↓ histindine decarboxylase (*hdc*) activity to reduce the concentration of histidine in wine

Antimicrobial
- ↑ bacteriocin production (pediocin, lactocin, nisin) might result in↑natural removal of selected spoilage LAB during MLF
- Cyclic peptides produced by *Lb. plantarum* and *P. pentosaceus*; ↑natural removal of selected spoilage fungi during MLF

Sensory attributes

Diacetyl
- Buttery, nutty, butterscotch notes
- *alsS, alsD* (α-acetolactate synthase and decarboxylase)
- ↑↓ synthesis of diacetyl
- Δ *ldh* (drives reaction towards pyruvate and onto diacetyl)
- Modulation of aroma and flavour in wine

Esters
- ↑ acyl transferases (*atf*) and ↓ esterase activity
- ↑ aroma profile of wine

Glycosidase
- *bgl* (β-glucosidase)
- Clone other genes required for sequential release of disaccharide bound aglycon; ↑ aroma and flavour

Mouth-feel
- Polysaccharides β(1→3)glucanase
- Other mouth-feel contributors
- (glycerol, mannoproteins)

FIGURE 40.3 Methods for strain development of lactic acid bacteria. Photograph kindly provided by Dr Jeffery Broadbent.

b. Improved efficiency of malate catabolism

The genes for malate metabolism have been cloned from *O. oeni* and three genes *mleR* (regulator), *mleA* (enzyme) and *mleP* (permease), have been identified (139). In order for malate metabolism to be initiated and to proceed efficiently in wine, a bacterial population density of at least one million cells/mL is needed. To increase the conversion efficiency of L-malate to L-lactate, it is necessary to understand the regulation of *mleA* by *mleR* and determine the rate limiting step for malate metabolism, especially important at low cell density. A rapid adaptation of the *O. oeni* cell to its harsh wine environment may also ultimately enhance the catabolism of L-malate.

2. Improving Wine Wholesomeness

a. Arginine/ethyl carbamate

The role that MLF plays in ethyl carbamate formation remains unclear. Arginine, a quantitatively important amino acid of grape must and wine, is a precursor to ethyl carbamate. Lactic acid bacteria vary in their ability to degrade arginine; experiments conducted in a synthetic and a laboratory vinified wine demonstrated a correlation between arginine degradation, citrulline production and ethyl carbamate formation during MLF conducted by an *O. oeni* and *Lb. buchneri* strain (158–160). The arginine catabolism (*arc*) gene cluster of *O. oeni* (161) has been cloned and characterised, thus providing a basis for manipulating the *arc* genes and reducing the potential of ethyl carbamate production.

b. Biogenic amines

Biogenic amines have undesirable physiological effects when consumed at high concentrations. The major biogenic amines in wine are histamine, phenylethylamine, putrescine and tyramine (162–164). Their concentration is lowest after alcoholic fermentation and increases variably in most wines during MLF (165). Wine-associated LAB, including *O. oeni*, have been shown to decarboxylate amino acids to their corresponding amines (166). This decarboxylation reaction is purported to favour growth and survival in acidic media, since it induces an increase in pH and can also provide energy to the LAB (167). LAB vary in their ability to produce the various amines.

The *O. oeni* histidine decarboxylase gene (*hdc*) has been cloned and characterised (168). A PCR-based test has also been developed for the detection of amino acid decarboxylating genes in LAB (169). The manipulation of the *hdc* gene in *O. oeni* strains with other desirable characteristics would ensure that reduced concentrations of histidine are present in wine.

c. Antimicrobial activity

The use of bacteriocin-producing LAB species/strains in other food industries, especially the dairy industry, has met with considerable success. A pediocin-producing *Lb. plantarum* strain was shown to efficiently combat the spoilage of cheese by *Listeria monocytogenes* (170). Furthermore, the expression of pediocin PA-1 from *Pediococcus acidilactici* or plantaricin 423 from *Lb. plantarum* by the introduction of the respective genes into *S. cerevisiae* has been shown to effectively eliminate LAB from an alcoholic fermentation (101). A similar strategy could be used to introduce the necessary genes into *O. oeni*.

3. Improving Wine Sensory Attributes

a. Diacetyl

One of the most important flavour compounds associated with MLF is diacetyl (a diketone, 2,3-butanedione), which can impart a 'buttery' or 'butterscotch' flavour to wine (171–173). Diacetyl is principally formed during MLF by the bacterial metabolism of citric acid. This diketone is also an important flavour compound in the dairy industry, providing the characteristic 'buttery' flavour of many fermented milk products.

The metabolism of diacetyl is well understood (174–176) and the environmental factors that influence its formation and degradation in wine have been established (177–179). The diacetyl pathway has been amenable to genetic manipulation, leading to overproduction of diacetyl in *Lactococcus lactis* (180). With the inactivation of the lactate dehydrogenase gene (*ldh*) in *L. lactis*, there was an accompanying alteration to the metabolic flux, eliminating lactic acid as a metabolic end product and producing ethanol, formate and acetoin. Acetoin is a degradation product of diacetyl and is considered flavourless in wine because of its high aroma threshold. The overexpression of α-acetolactate synthase (*ilvBN* genes in *L. lactis*) leads to an increased production of acetoin (the reaction is driven towards acetoin and away from diacetyl), whereas the inactivation of the *aldB* gene (encoding α-acetolactate decarboxylase) resulted in an increased production of α-acetolactate and diacetyl at the expense of acetoin. The latter scenario is quite desirable in the dairy industry. The analogous genes [*alsS* (α-acetolactate synthase) and *alsD* (α-acetolactate decarboxylase)] have been cloned and sequenced from *O. oeni* (181), providing a means of altering diacetyl concentrations in wine. An alternative strategy would be to inactivate the citrate permease gene (*citP*), thus removing the initial substrate for diacetyl. Such a natural mutant of *O. oeni* has been isolated and is commercially available (MT01, Lallemand).

b. Glycosidases

Many potential aroma and flavour compounds are found in grapes and wine as glycosidically bound aglycons (monoterpenes, norisoprenoids, benzene derivatives and aliphates). Though β-glucosidase activity has been demonstrated in *S. cerevisiae* and *O. oeni* (182), both have limited ability to release the disaccharide glycosides.

Improving release of glycosides in *O. oeni* strains following MLF using similar methods to those described in yeast could lead to enhanced grape variety aroma in the wine.

c. Esterases

Various sensory studies pre and post MLF have shown that the fruity qualities of a wine may be enhanced after MLF (183,184). An improved understanding of the formation and further metabolism of esters [acyl alcoholtransferase (ester synthesising enzymes) and esterases (ester catabolising enzymes)] in *O. oeni* could lead to the enhancement of specific, desirable esters.

d. Bitterness

Bitterness is a spoilage problem, primarily in red wine, that can be associated with LAB, including *O. oeni* strains. The fermentation of glycerol can lead to the formation of acrolein, which when it reacts with phenolic hydroxyl groups, results in wine bitterness. The manipulation of the pathway of glycerol catabolism, for example the glycerol dehydratase, may lead to reduced acrolein formation.

The presence of certain peptides is also a potential cause of bitterness in wine. Bitterness due to proteolytic action and formation of short peptides has been studied extensively in dairy LAB. There appears to be a minimal proteolytic activity associated with *O. oeni* and the peptide transport system of *O. oeni* is poorly understood. A better understanding of potential bitter wine peptides and their formation could reduce the occurrence of bitterness in some wines.

e. Mouth-feel properties

Numerous MLF sensory studies and anecdotal evidence point to changes in the texture and body of the wine following MLF, with reports indicating a fuller, richer, longer aftertaste (183). The chemical changes contributing to these favourable mouth-feel properties are poorly understood. The deacidification process itself contributes substantially to changes in mouth-feel, with the consequent increase of pH and decrease in titratable acidity. In addition, the L-lactic acid feels softer than L-malic acid. Other contributors to wine mouth-feel or taste perception have been suggested, including polysaccharides, glycerol and mannoproteins. The contribution of MLF in this area remains to be studied.

MLF has great potential to further enhance wine qualities by retaining or altering the aroma/flavour profile of the wine as well as by conferring microbial stability. However, the genetics of *O. oeni* for all these processes are still not well understood. With the availability of the complete *O. oeni* genome sequence, the development of an efficient gene transfer system into *O. oeni* and the understanding of the various pathways, 'tailor-made' *O. oeni* strains will become possible.

V. THE FUTURE OF GENETICALLY IMPROVED GRAPEVINES, YEASTS AND BACTERIA IN THE WINE INDUSTRY

Molecular genetic research has much to offer the wine industry. It is a powerful technology for studying the regulation of pathways in grapevine, yeast and bacteria, thus providing an understanding of how viticulture and wine-making practices impact on grape and wine quality. In some cases, especially yeast and bacteria, identifying the important genes will provide non-GM improvement strategies. Molecular techniques are also starting to dominate systematics, simplifying *Vitis* varietal identification and wine microbial ecological studies.

This review has focused upon the use of molecular techniques to produce GM grapevines and wine microbes that can provide major advantages to the wine industry and wine consumer. Several obstacles, however, must be overcome before these techniques can be put to use. These include scientific and technical issues, a number of regulatory and economic concerns and the public perception of GM foods (5).

A. SCIENTIFIC AND TECHNICAL OBSTACLES

The bacterium *Escherichia coli* and plants such as *Zea mays* and *Arabidopsis thaliana* have been used as experimental model organisms for many decades, but the study of important wine bacterial species and *Vitis vinifera* is much more recent. Similarly, although laboratory strains of *S. cerevisiae* are easily manipulated, wine yeast have characteristics such as homothallism, polyploidy, and the lack of auxotrophic markers that make them more difficult to manipulate. There is increasingly rapid progress, however, in the molecular improvement of these organisms, and as important genes continue to be identified, the potential for use of GMOs in the wine industry will continue to expand.

B. REGULATORY, ECONOMIC AND POLITICAL OBSTACLES

Most countries' legislation and regulations applying to the use of GMOs and the approval of GM foods are now broadly similar and fall into two categories. The approach exemplified by the regulations of the United States of America takes the view that each case of a GMO needs to be considered on its merit and there is no *a priori* reason to assume that the use of GM plants and microbes is of itself more risky than conventional methods of introgressing new genes into organisms and products. The arguments used in this approach are those of 'substantial equivalence' and statutory approval usually requires several obvious assurances, such as that there be no additional threat to human health or the environment. The second approach is exemplified by the European Union's regulatory system that takes the view that GM material has an intrinsic level of risk beyond that accepted in non-GM products. The regulations are framed around this philosophy and the requirements to demonstrate the properties of GMO-based material are substantially more rigorous than those placed upon the introduction of food material bred by conventional genetic means.

While genetically improved grapevines, yeast and bacteria need some form of economic protection, patents covering many of the tools used in genetic engineering, including the genes themselves, leave little 'freedom to operate' (185). If commercialisation of GMOs is to be viable, it is imperative that intellectual property issues be addressed.

There is also a belief that patents on genetically engineered organisms give an unfair advantage to certain large multinational producers, thereby concentrating economic power in their hands. With the visibility of the anti-globalisation movement and a surplus of wine in some countries, it is possible that the commercialisation of improved GM wines could be misused to justify technical barriers to free trade.

Bottle labelling is another hurdle. The marketing of wine relies to a great extent on label integrity and product identity, and it is hoped that wines exhibiting improved flavour and colour characteristics will be able to retain the established varietal names. It may also become obligatory to label GM wines as such, and it is not clear whether this will be detrimental to the sale of these wines (186). For example, the European Union and Japan have recently introduced new legislation such that all food products with more than 0.9% and 0.5% GM content, respectively, will have to be labelled as GM. Any GM food product derived from GM ingredients but whose presence is undetectable in the product will also have to be labelled.

Much of the wine industry is bound by tradition and regional culture, making it particularly unreceptive to technological change. In addition, there is a concern that GM wines will become standardised, and lose their mystique and romanticism. Quite to the contrary, gene technology will allow winemakers to diversify their products and provide even greater consumer choice.

C. PUBLIC PERCEPTION OBSTACLES

The public perception of GM foods has been, so far, that the potential risks outweigh the benefits. Sensationalist reporting has increased public fears of 'Frankenfoods,' which of course spread far more readily than good sense or wise science. Ironically the potential advantages to consumers and the environment are numerous, and include a healthier and better product and agricultural sustainability. To reverse negative perceptions it is essential that scientists ensure the trust of the public by providing balanced, understandable information on the safety and environmental risks associated with GMOs (187).

It should be remembered that the improvement of foods has been going on for many thousands of years, initially by selection and later by selective breeding, and unwanted and indeterminate changes have been routinely transferred along with the desired modifications. These methods are completely acceptable to consumers, if they are even aware of them. Genetic engineering provides a more precise means of bringing about the intended changes, which together with recent developments in the field of metabolomics, offers techniques to produce foods that comply with the test of 'substantial equivalence' (188,189).

Evaluating potential environmental risks of GMOs is more difficult, and will have to be examined on a case-by-case basis (190). Meanwhile, improvements in the technology continue to reduce the potential of risk (191). Guidelines for the release of GMOs in most countries require the absence of any selective advantage conferred by the transgenic organism that could allow it to become dominant in natural habitats. Again, improved molecular techniques such as Real Time PCR should assist in evaluating competitiveness (192,193).

The nature of the modification will also influence consumer acceptance. Whereas some modifications do not add foreign DNA, others require the insertion of antibiotic or herbicide resistant markers often considered undesirable. Some genetic modifications cross species barriers; these are more likely to generate debate and allow objectors to pose religious and moral questions.

In winemaking the yeast and bacteria are not present in the final product, and the clarification of wine removes nucleic acid, including that of the grapes. This should allay consumer fears that they are ingesting modified DNA (194).

VI. CONCLUSIONS AND OUTLOOK

In many respects wine is no longer seen as a dietary beverage, but as a non-essential luxury product, offered to consumers along with many other luxury products. The international wine industry is obviously in business to attract a fair proportion of the consumers' disposable income in competition with other luxury goods and services. To do so it must offer products that exhibit desirable and pleasurable characteristics to the consumer, continue reducing its impact on the environment, and offer a competitive quality/price ratio while remaining profitable for the producers.

Competitors of the wine industry, e.g., producers of other alcoholic beverages, do not hesitate to employ new technology as it becomes available. Winemakers must become more sophisticated about the application of new scientific and technological knowledge while still respecting the cultural roots and traditions associated with winemaking. The ongoing research into the genetic improvement of grapevines and wine microbes as outlined in this chapter provide the global wine sector with an enormous opportunity to improve the quality/price ratio of wine by embracing biotechnological innovations.

In the medical world the uses of GM products are accepted and widespread. In agriculture the uptake in the field crop industries has been steadily increasing to the degree that in 2002 almost 60 million hectares of GM field crops were being grown worldwide. And this trend toward greater acceptance is likely to continue. With the rapid growing power of bioinformatics and the dawn of the 'omics' era in molecular biology it is widely expected that high quality information and 'precision' gene technology will increasingly allow grape and wine biotechnology to be harnessed for the good of the producer, consumer and environment. That is why some optimists even claim that gen*omics*, transcript*omics*, prote*omics* plus metabol*omics* equal econ*omics*!

Reality looms in the form of agronomic, business, regulatory and social hurdles currently blocking commercial availability of GM grapes and wine. But the smart money is saying that the benefits to the industry such as minimised resource inputs, improved product quality, increased health benefits and low environmental impact will ultimately put gene technology in the winner's circle.

ACKNOWLEDGMENTS

Research conducted at The Australian Wine Research Institute is supported by Australia's grapegrowers and winemakers through their investment body the Grape and Wine Research and Development Corporation, with matching funds from the Australian Government.

The information in this chapter is based on "The application of gene technology in the wine industry," in: *Wine Biotechnology Manual*, copyright ©2003 by Isak S. Pretorius. Used with permission.

REFERENCES

1. IS Pretorius. Tailoring wine yeast for the new millennium: novel approaches to the ancient art of winemaking. Yeast 16: 675–729, 2000.
2. IS Pretorius. The genetic analysis and tailoring of wine yeasts. in: JH de Winde (Ed.), Topics in Current Genetics. Functional Genetics of Industrial Yeasts. Springer-Verlag, Heidelberg, 2003, pp 99–142.
3. IS Pretorius, FF Bauer. Meeting the consumer challenge through genetically customized wine-yeast strains. Trends Biotechnol 20: 426–432, 2002.
4. IS Pretorius. The genetic improvement of wine yeasts. in: D Arora, PD Bridge, D Bhatnagar (Eds.), Handbook of Fungal Biotechnology. (2nd ed.) Marcel Dekker, Inc., New York, 2004, pp 209–232.
5. MA Vivier, IS Pretorius. Genetically tailored grapevines for the wine industry. Trends Biotechnol 20: 472–478, 2002.
6. RS Jackson. Grapevine species and varieties. in: Wine Science: Principles and Application. Academic Press, New York, 1994, pp 11–31.
7. MG Mullins, A Bouquet, LE Williams: Biology of the Grapevine, Cambridge University Press, Cambridge, 1992.
8. MA Vivier, IS Pretorius. Genetic improvement of grapevine: tailoring grape varieties for the third millennium. S Afr J Enol Vitic 21: 5–26, 2000.
9. P Iocco, T Franks, MR Thomas. Genetic transformation of major wine grape cultivars of *Vitis vinifera* L. Transgenic Res 10: 105–112, 2001.
10. V Colova-Tsolova, A Perl, S Krastanova, I Tsvetkov, A Atanassov. Genetically engineered grape for disease and stress tolerance. in: KA Roubelakis-Angelakis (Ed.), Molecular Biology and Biotechnology of the Grapevine. Kluwer Academic Publishers, Dordrecht, 2001, 411–432.
11. L Martinelli, E Candioli, D Costa, A Minafra. Stable insertion and expression of the movement protein gene of grapevine Virus A (GVA) in grape (*Vitis rupestris* S.). Vitis 41: 189–193, 2002.
12. A Bezier, B Lambert, F Baillieul. Study of defense-related gene expression in grapevine leaves and berries infected with *Botrytis cinerea*. European J Plant Pathol 108: 111–120, 2002.
13. N Robert, J Ferran, C Breda, P Coutos-Thevenot, M Boulay, D Buffard, R Esnault. Molecular characterization of the incompatible interaction of *Vitis vinifera* leaves with *Pseudomonas syringae* pv. *pisi*: expression of genes coding for stillbene synthase and class 10 PR protein. European J Plant Pathol 107: 249–261, 2001.
14. DB Tattersall, KF Pocock, Y Hayasaka, K Adams, R van Heeswijck, EJ Waters, PB Høj. Pathogenesis related proteins — their accumulation in grapes during berry growth and their involvement in white wine heat instability. Current knowledge and future perspectives in relation to winemaking practices. in: KA Roubelakis-Angelakis (Ed.), Molecular Biology and Biotechnology of the Grapevine. Kluwer Academic Publishers, Dordrecht, 2001, pp 183–201.
15. C Giannakis, CS Bucheli, KGM Skene, SP Robinson, NS Scott. Chitinase and β-1,3–glucanase in grapevine leaves. Austral J Grape Wine Res 4: 14–22, 1998.
16. RA Salzman, I Tikhonova, BP Bordelon, PM Hasegawa, RA Bressan. Coordinate accumulation of antifungal proteins and hexoses constitutes a developmentally controlled defense response during fruit ripening in grape. Plant Physiol 117: 465–472, 1998.
17. JR Kikkert, MR Thomas, BI Reisch. Grapevine genetic engineering. in: KA Roubelakis-Angelakis (Ed.), Molecular Biology and Biotechnology of the Grapevine. Kluwer Academic Publishers, Dordrecht, 2001, 393–410.
18. P Coutos-Thevenot, B Poinssot, A Bonomelli, H Yean, C Breda, D Buffard, R Esnault, R Hain, M Boulay. *In vitro* tolerance to *Botrytis cinerea* of grapevine 41B rootstock in transgenic plants expressing the stilbene synthase *Vst1* gene under the control of a pathogen-inducible PR 10 promoter. J Exp Bot 52: 901–910, 2001.

19. A Schouten, L Wagemakers, FL Stefanato, RM van der Kaaij, JAL van Kan. Resveratrol acts as a natural profungicide and induces self-intoxication by a specific laccase. Mol Microbiol 43: 883–894, 2002.

20. V Legrand, S Dalmayrac, A Latche, JC Pech, M Bouzayen, J Fallot, L Torregrosa, A Bouquet, JP Roustan. Constitutive expression of *Vr-ERE* gene in transformed grapevines confers enhanced resistance to eutypine, a toxin from *Eutypa lata*. Plant Sci 164: 809–814, 2003.

21. R Scorza, JM Cordts, DJ Gray, D Gonsalves, RL Emershad, DW Ramming. Producing transgenic 'Thompson Seedless' grape (*Vitis vinifera* L.) plants. J Am Soc Hort Sci 121: 616–619, 1996.

22. N Robert, K Roche, Y Lebeau, C Breda, M Boulay, R Esnault, D Buffard. Expression of grapevine chitinase genes in berries and leaves infected by fungal or bacterial pathogens. Plant Sci 162: 389–400, 2002.

23. PM Schenk, K Kazan, I Wilson, JP Anderson, T Richmond, SC Somerville, JM Manners. Coordinated plant defense responses in *Arabidopsis* revealed by microarray analysis. Proc Natl Acad Sci USA 97: 11655–11660, 2000.

24. EB Holub. The arms race is ancient history in *Arabidopsis*, the wildflower. Nat Rev Genet 2: 516–527, 2001.

25. IJ Tsvetkov, AI Atanassov, VM Tsolova. Gene transfer for stress resistance in grapes. Acta Hort 528: 389–396, 2000.

26. R van Heeswijck, AP Stines, J Grubb, IS Moller, PB Høj. Molecular biology and biochemistry of proline accumulation in developing grape berries. in: KA Roubelakis-Angelakis (Ed.), Molecular Biology and Biotechnology of the Grapevine. Kluwer Academic Publishers, Dordrecht, 2001, 87–108.

27. KA Paschalidis, A Aziz, L Geny, NI Primikirios, KA Roubelakis-Angelakis. Polyamines in grapevine. in: KA Roubelakis-Angelakis (Ed.), Molecular Biology and Biotechnology of the Grapevine. Kluwer Academic Publishers, Dordrecht, 2001, pp 109–151.

28. C Davies, SP Robinson. Sugar accumulation in grape berries. Cloning of two putative vacuolar invertase cDNAs and their expression in grapevine tissues. Plant Physiol 111: 275–283, 1996.

29. R Pratelli, B Lacombe, L Torregrosa, F Gaymard, C Romieu, JB Thibaud, H Sentenac. A grapevine gene encoding a guard cell K(+) channel displays developmental regulation in the grapevine berry. Plant Physiol 128: 564–577, 2002.

30. PK Boss, MR Thomas. Association of dwarfism and floral induction with a grape 'green revolution' mutation. Nature 416: 847–850, 2002.

31. L Fillion, A Ageorges, S Picaud, P Coutos-Thevenot, R Lemoine, C Romieu, S Delrot. Cloning and expression of a hexose transporter gene expressed during the ripening of grape berry. Plant Physiol 120: 1083–1094, 1999.

32. PK Boss, C Davies, SP Robinson. Analysis of the expression of anthocyanin pathway genes in developing *Vitis vinifera* L. cv Shiraz grape berries and the implications for pathway regulation. Plant Physiol 111: 1059–1066, 1996.

33. F Sparvoli, C Martin, A Scienza, G Gavazzi, C Tonelli. Cloning and molecular analysis of structural genes involved in flavonoid and stillbene biosynthesis in grape (*Vitis vinifera* L.). Plant Mol Biol 24: 743–755, 1994.

34. CM Ford, PK Boss, PB Høj. Cloning and characterization of *Vitis vinifera* UDP-glucose: flavonoid 3-O-glucosyltransferase, a homologue of the enzyme encoded by the maize bronze-1 locus that may primarily serve to glucosylate anthocyanidins *in vivo*. J Biol Chem 273: 9224–9233, 1998.

35. PK Boss, C Davies, SP Robinson. Expression of anthocyanin biosynthesis pathway genes in red and white grapes. Plant Mol Biol 32: 565–569, 1996.

36. S Kobayashi, M Ishimaru, CK Ding, H Yakushiji, N Goto. Comparison of UDP-glucose: flavonoid 3-O-glucosyltransferase (UFGT) gene sequences between white grapes (*Vitis vinifera*) and their sports with red skin. Plant Sci 160: 543–550, 2001.

37. S Kobayashi, M Ishimaru, K Hiraoka, C Honda. Myb-related genes of the Kyoho grape (*Vitis labruscana*) regulate anthocyanin biosynthesis. Planta 215: 924–933, 2002.

38. C Davies, SP Robinson. Differential screening indicates a dramatic change in mRNA profiles during grape berry ripening. Cloning and characterization of cDNAs encoding putative cell wall and stress response proteins. Plant Physiol 122: 803–812, 2000.

39. KJ Nunan, C Davies, SP Robinson, GB Fincher. Expression patterns of cell wall-modifying enzymes during grape berry development. Planta 214: 257–264, 2001.

40. L Barnavon, T Doco, N Terrier, A Ageorges, C Romieu, P Pellerin. Involvement of pectin methyl-esterase during the ripening of grape berries: partial cDNA isolation, transcript expression and changes in the degree of methyl-esterification of cell wall pectins. Phytochemistry 58: 693–701, 2001.

41. C Davies, PK Boss, SP Robinson. Treatment of grape berries, a nonclimacteric fruit with a synthetic auxin, retards ripening and alters the expression of developmentally regulated genes. Plant Physiol 115: 1155–1161, 1997.

42. G Fleet, G Heard. Yeasts–growth during fermentation. in: G Fleet (Ed.), Wine Microbiology and Biotechnology. Harwood Academic, Reading, 1993, pp 27–54.

43. B Esteve-Zarzoso, C Belloch, F Uruburu, A Querol. Identification of yeasts by RFLP analysis of the 5.8s rRNA gene and the two ribosomal internal transcribed spacers. Int J Syst Bacteriol 49: 329–337, 1999.

44. PV Pramateftaki, P Lanaridis, MA Typas. Molecular identification of wine yeasts at species or strain level: a case study with strains from two vine-growing areas of Greece. J Appl Microbiol 89: 236–248, 2000.

45. MJ Torija, N Rozes, M Poblet, JM Guillamon, A Mas. Yeast population dynamics in spontaneous fermentations: comparison between two different wine-producing areas over a period of three years. Antonie van Leeuwenhoek 79: 345–352, 2001.

46. I Masneuf, J Hansen, C Groth, J Piskur, D Dubourdieu. New hybrids between *Saccharomyces* sensu stricto

yeast species found among wine and cider production strains. Appl Environ Microbiol 64: 3887–3892, 1998.

47. S Redžepovic, S Orlic, S Sikora, A Majdak, IS Pretorius. Identification and characterization of *Saccharomyces cerevisiae* and *Saccharomyces paradoxus* strains isolated from Croatian vineyards. Lett Appl Microbiol 35: 305–310, 2002.

48. GI Naumov, I Masneuf, ES Naumova, M Aigle, D Dubourdieu. Association of *Saccharomyces bayanus* var. *uvarum* with some French wines: genetic analysis of yeast populations. Res Microbiol 151: 683–691, 2000.

49. DA Mills, EA Johannsen, L Cocolin. Yeast diversity and persistence in Botrytis-affected wine fermentations. Appl Environ Microbiol 68: 4884–4893, 2002.

50. MM Barr. Super models. Physiol Genomics 13: 15–24, 2003.

51. K Dolinski, R Balakrishnan, KR Christie, MC Costanzo, SS Dwight, SR Engel, DG Fisk, JE Hirschman, EL Hong,, L Issel-Tarver, A Sethuraman, CL Theesfeld, G Binkley, C Lane, M Schroeder, S Dong, S Weng, R Andrada, D Botstein, JM Cherry. *Saccharomyces* genome database. http://genome-www. stanford.edu/*Saccharomyces*/, 2003.

52. A Goffeau, BG Barrell, H Bussey, RW Davis, B Dujon, H Feldmann, F Galibert, JD Hoheisel, C Jacq, M Johnston, EJ Louis, HW Mewes, Y Murakami, P Philippsen, H Tettelin, SG Oliver. Life with 6000 genes. Science 274: 546, 563–574, 1996.

53. EA Winzeler, DD Shoemaker, A Astromoff, H Liang, K Anderson, B Andre, R Bangham, R Benito, JD Boeke, H Bussey, AM Chu, C Connelly, K Davis, F Dietrich, SW Dow, M El Bakkoury, F Foury, SH Friend, E Gentalen, G Giaever, JH Hegemann, T Jones, M Laub, H Liao, RW Davis, et al. Functional characterization of the *S. cerevisiae* genome by gene deletion and parallel analysis. Science 285: 901–906, 1999.

54. D Delneri, FL Brancia, SG Oliver. Towards a truly integrative biology through the functional genomics of yeast. Curr Opin Biotechnol 12: 87–91, 2001.

55. JE Pérez-Ortin, J Garcia-Martinez, TM Alberola. DNA chips for yeast biotechnology. The case of wine yeasts. J Biotechnol 98: 227–241, 2002.

56. VD Marks, GK van der Merwe, HJ van Vuuren. Transcriptional profiling of wine yeast in fermenting grape juice: regulatory effect of diammonium phosphate. FEMS Yeast Res 3: 269–287, 2003.

57. AP Gasch, PT Spellman, CM Kao, O Carmel-Harel, MB Eisen, G Storz, D Botstein, PO Brown. Genomic expression programs in the response of yeast cells to environmental changes. Mol Biol Cell 11: 4241–4257, 2000.

58. LE Backhus, J DeRisi, PO Brown, LF Bisson. Functional genomic analysis of a commercial wine strain of *Saccharomyces cerevisiae* under differing nitrogen conditions. FEMS Yeast Res 1: 111–125, 2001.

59. H Alexandré, V Ansanay-Galeote, S Dequin, B Blondin. Global gene expression during short-term ethanol stress in *Saccharomyces cerevisiae*. FEBS Lett 498: 98–103, 2001.

60. SH Yang, JS Kim, TJ Oh, MS Kim, SW Lee, SK Woo, HS Cho, YH Choi, YH Kim, SY Rha, HC Chung, SW An. Genome-scale analysis of resveratrol-induced gene expression profile in human ovarian cancer cells using a cDNA microarray. Int J Oncol 22: 741–750, 2003.

61. M Rep, M Krantz, JM Thevelein, S Hohmann. The transcriptional response of *Saccharomyces cerevisiae* to osmotic shock. Hot1p and Msn2p/Msn4p are required for the induction of subsets of high osmolarity glycerol pathway-dependent genes. J Biol Chem 275: 8290–8300, 2000.

62. N Hauser, K Fellenberg, R Gil, S Bastuck, J Hoheisel, J Pérez-Ortin. Whole genome analysis of a wine yeast strain. Comp Func Genomics 2: 69–79, 2001.

63. D Cavalieri, JP Townsend, DL Hartl. Manifold anomalies in gene expression in a vineyard isolate of *Saccharomyces cerevisiae* revealed by DNA microarray analysis. Proc Natl Acad Sci USA 97: 12369–12374, 2000.

64. N Rachidi, P Barre, B Blondin. Examination of the transcriptional specificity of an enological yeast. A pilot experiment on the chromosome-III right arm. Curr Genet 37: 1–11, 2000.

65. L Trabalzini, A Paffetti, A Scaloni, F Talamo, E Ferro, G Coratza, L Bovalini, P Lusini, P Martelli, A Santucci. Proteomic response to physiological fermentation stresses in a wild-type wine strain of *Saccharomyces cerevisiae*. Biochem J 370: 35–46, 2003.

66. J Allen, HM Davey, D Broadhurst, JK Heald, JJ Rowland, SG Oliver, DB Kell. High-throughput classification of yeast mutants for functional genomics using metabolic footprinting. Nat Biotechnol 21: 692–696, 2003.

67. LM Raamsdonk, B Teusink, D Broadhurst, N Zhang, A Hayes, MC Walsh, JA Berden, KM Brindle, DB Kell, JJ Rowland, HV Westerhoff, K van Dam, SG Oliver. A functional genomics strategy that uses metabolome data to reveal the phenotype of silent mutations. Nat Biotechnol 19: 45–50, 2001.

68. S Dequin. The potential of genetic engineering for improving brewing, wine-making and baking yeasts. Appl Microbiol Biotechnol 56: 577–588, 2001.

69. C Ivorra, JE Perez-Ortin, M del Olmo. An inverse correlation between stress resistance and stuck fermentations in wine yeasts. A molecular study. Biotechnol Bioeng 64: 698–708, 1999.

70. J Kim, P Alizadeh, T Harding, A Hefner-Gravink, DJ Klionsky. Disruption of the yeast *ATH1* gene confers better survival after dehydration, freezing, and ethanol shock: potential commercial applications. Appl Environ Microbiol 62: 1563–1569, 1996.

71. J Shima, A Hino, C Yamada-Iyo, Y Suzuki, R Nakajima, H Watanabe, K Mori, H Takano. Stress tolerance in doughs of *Saccharomyces cerevisiae* trehalase mutants derived from commercial baker's yeast. Appl Environ Microbiol 65: 2841–2846, 1999.

72. R Pérez-Torrado, JV Gimeno-Alcaniz, E Matallana. Wine yeast strains engineered for glycogen overproduction display enhanced viability under glucose deprivation conditions. Appl Environ Microbiol 68: 3339–3344, 2002.

73. A Tanghe, P van Dijck, F Dumortier, A Teunissen, S Hohmann, JM Thevelein. Aquaporin expression correlates with freeze tolerance in baker's yeast, and overexpression improves freeze tolerance in industrial strains. Appl Environ Microbiol 68: 5981–5989, 2002.

74. Y Morita, S Nakamori, H Takagi. L-proline accumulation and freeze tolerance of *Saccharomyces cerevisiae* are caused by a mutation in the *PRO1* gene encoding gamma-glutamyl kinase. Appl Environ Microbiol 69: 212–219, 2003.

75. H Takagi, K Sakai, K Morida, S Nakamori. Proline accumulation by mutation or disruption of the proline oxidase gene improves resistance to freezing and desiccation stresses in *Saccharomyces cerevisiae*. FEMS Microbiol Lett 184: 103–108, 2000.

76. S Hohmann. Osmotic stress signaling and osmoadaptation in yeasts. Microbiol Mol Biol Rev 66: 300–372, 2002.

77. S Michnick, JL Roustan, F Remize, P Barre, S Dequin. Modulation of glycerol and ethanol yields during alcoholic fermentation in *Saccharomyces cerevisiae* strains overexpressed or disrupted for *GPD1* encoding glycerol 3–phosphate dehydrogenase. Yeast 13: 783–793, 1997.

78. M de Barros Lopes, A-U Rehman, H Gockowiak, A Heinrich, P Langridge, P Henschke. Fermentation properties of a wine yeast over-expressing the *Saccharomyces cerevisiae* glycerol 3–phosphate dehydrogenase gene (*GPD2*). Austral J Grape Wine Res 6: 208–215, 2000.

79. F Pérez, M Ramirez, JA Regodon. Influence of killer strains of *Saccharomyces cerevisiae* on wine fermentation. Antonie van Leeuwenhoek 79: 393–399, 2001.

80. L Fichtner, F Frohloff, K Burkner, M Larsen, KD Breunig, R Schaffrath. Molecular analysis of *KTI12/TOT4*, a *Saccharomyces cerevisiae* gene required for *Kluyveromyces lactis* zymocin action. Mol Microbiol 43: 783–791, 2002.

81. F Breinig, DJ Tipper, MJ Schmitt. Kre1p, the plasma membrane receptor for the yeast k1 viral toxin. Cell 108: 395–405, 2002.

82. N Page, M Gerard-Vincent, P Menard, M Beaulieu, M Azuma, GJ Dijkgraaf, H Li, J Marcoux, T Nguyen, T Dowse, AM Sdicu, H Bussey. A *Saccharomyces cerevisiae* genome-wide mutant screen for altered sensitivity to k1 killer toxin. Genetics 163: 875–894, 2003.

83. K Luyten, C Riou, B Blondin. The hexose transporters of *Saccharomyces cerevisiae* play different roles during enological fermentation. Yeast 19: 713–726, 2002.

84. MP Ashe, SK De Long, AB Sachs. Glucose depletion rapidly inhibits translation initiation in yeast. Mol Biol Cell 11: 833–848, 2000.

85. S Ozcan, J Dover, AG Rosenwald, S Wolfl, M Johnston. Two glucose transporters in *Saccharomyces cerevisiae* are glucose sensors that generate a signal for induction of gene expression. Proc Natl Acad Sci USA 93: 12428–12432, 1996.

86. O Martin, MC Brandriss, G Schneider, AT Bakalinsky. Improved anaerobic use of arginine by *Saccharomyces cerevisiae*. Appl Environ Microbiol 69: 1623–1628, 2003.

87. JM Salmon, P Barre. Improvement of nitrogen assimilation and fermentation kinetics under enological conditions by derepression of alternative nitrogen-assimilatory pathways in an industrial *Saccharomyces cerevisiae* strain. Appl Environ Microbiol 64: 3831–3837, 1998.

88. K Poole. Enhancing yeast performance under oenological conditions by enabling proline utilisation. Ph.D. thesis, University of Adelaide, Adelaide, 2002.

89. AJ Martinez-Rodriguez, MC Polo. Characterization of the nitrogen compounds released during yeast autolysis in a model wine system. J Agric Food Chem 48: 1081–1085, 2000.

90. A Lagorce, NC Hauser, D Labourdette, C Rodriguez, H Martin-Yken, J Arroyo, JD Hoheisel, J Francois. Genome-wide analysis of the response to cell wall mutations in the yeast *Saccharomyces cerevisiae*. J Biol Chem 278: 20345–20357, 2003.

91. J Hansen, MC Kielland-Brandt. Inactivation of *MET10* in brewer's yeast specifically increases SO_2 formation during beer production. Nat Biotechnol 14: 1587–1591, 1996.

92. J Hansen, MC Kielland-Brandt. Inactivation of *MET2* in brewer's yeast increases the level of sulfite in beer. J Biotechnol 50: 75–87, 1996.

93. UE Donalies, U Stahl. Increasing sulphite formation in *Saccharomyces cerevisiae* by overexpression of *MET14* and *SSU1*. Yeast 19: 475–484, 2002.

94. HR Ibrahim, T Matsuzaki, T Aoki. Genetic evidence that antibacterial activity of lysozyme is independent of its catalytic function. FEBS Lett 506: 27–32, 2001.

95. DF Malherbe, M du Toit, RR Cordero Otero, P van Rensburg, IS Pretorius. Expression of the *Aspergillus niger* glucose oxidase gene in *Saccharomyces cerevisiae* and its potential applications in wine production. Appl Microbiol Biotechnol 61: 502–511, 2003.

96. NA Yap, M de Barros Lopes, P Langridge, PA Henschke. The incidence of killer activity of non-*Saccharomyces* yeasts towards indigenous yeast species of grape must: potential application in wine fermentation. J Appl Microbiol 89: 381–389, 2000.

97. KF Lowes, CA Shearman, J Payne, D MacKenzie, DB Archer, RJ Merry, MJ Gasson. Prevention of yeast spoilage in feed and food by the yeast mycocin HMK. Appl Environ Microbiol 66: 1066–1076, 2000.

98. M Tollinger, KA Crowhurst, LE Kay, JD Forman-Kay. Site-specific contributions to the pH dependence of protein stability. Proc Natl Acad Sci USA 100: 4545–4550, 2003.

99. F Weiler, K Rehfeldt, F Bautz, MJ Schmitt. The *Zygosaccharomyces bailii* antifungal virus toxin zygocin: cloning and expression in a heterologous fungal host. Mol Microbiol 46: 1095–1105, 2002.

100. M Carstens, MA Vivier, P van Rensburg, IS Pretorius. Overexpression, secretion and antifungal activity of the *Saccharomyces cerevisiae* chitinase. Ann Microbiol 50: 15–28, 2003.

101. H Schoeman, MA Vivier, M Du Toit, LMT Dicks, IS Pretorius. The development of bactericidal yeast strains by expressing the *Pediococcus acidilactici* pediocin gene (*ped*A) in *Saccharomyces cerevisiae*. Yeast 15: 647–656, 1999.

102. CA van Reenen, ML Chikindas, WH van Zyl, LMT Dicks. Characterization and heterologous expression of a class IIa bacteriocin, plantaricin 423 from *Lactobacillus*

plantarum 423, in *Saccharomyces cerevisiae*. Int J Food Microbiol 81: 29–40, 2003.

103. KF Pocock, Y Hayasaka, MG McCarthy, EJ Waters. Thaumatin-like proteins and chitinases, the haze-forming proteins of wine, accumulate during ripening of grape (*Vitis vinifera*) berries and drought stress does not affect the final levels per berry at maturity. J Agric Food Chem 48: 1637–1643, 2000.

104. KF Pocock, PB Hoj, KS Adams, MJ Kwiatkowski, EJ Waters. Combined heat and proteolytic enzyme treatment of white wines reduces haze formating protein content without detrimental effect. Austral J Grape Wine Res 9: 56–63, 2003.

105. V Moine-Ledoux, D Dubourdieu. An invertase fragment responsible for improving the protein stability of dry white wines. J Sci Food Agric 79: 537–543, 1999.

106. IV Dupin, BM McKinnon, C Ryan, M Boulay, AJ Markides, GP Jones, PJ Williams, EJ Waters. *Saccharomyces cerevisiae* mannoproteins that protect wine from protein haze: their release during fermentation and lees contact and a proposal for their mechanism of action. J Agric Food Chem 48: 3098–3105, 2000.

107. KJ Verstrepen, G Derdelinckx, H Verachtert, FR Delvaux. Yeast flocculation: what brewers should know. Appl Microbiol Biotechnol 61: 197–205, 2003.

108. K Ishida-Fujii, S Goto, H Sugiyama, Y Takagi, T Saiki, M Takagi. Breeding of flocculent industrial alcohol yeast strains by self-cloning of the flocculation gene *FLO1* and repeated-batch fermentation by transformants. J Gen Appl Microbiol 44: 347–353, 1998.

109. M Bony, P Barre, B Blondin. Distribution of the flocculation protein, Flop, at the cell surface during yeast growth: The availability of Flop determines the flocculation level. Yeast 14: 25–35, 1998.

110. KJ Verstrepen, G Derdelinckx, FR Delvaux, J Winderickx, JM Thevelein, FF Bauer, IS Pretorius. Late fermentation expression of *FLO1* in *Saccharomyces cerevisiae*. J Am Soc Brew Chem 59: 69–76, 2001.

111. H Alexandré, S Blanchet, C Charpentier. Identification of a 49–kDa hydrophobic cell wall mannoprotein present in velum yeast which may be implicated in velum formation. FEMS Microbiol Lett 185: 147–150, 2000.

112. TB Reynolds, GR Fink. Bakers' yeast, a model for fungal biofilm formation. Science 291: 878–881, 2001.

113. MG Lambrechts, IS Pretorius. Yeast and its importance to wine aroma. S Afr J Enol Vitic 21: 97–129, 2000.

114. P van Rensburg, IS Pretorius. Enzymes in winemaking: harnessing natural catalysts for efficient biotransformations. S Afr J Enol Vitic 21: 52–73, 2000.

115. E Laing, IS Pretorius. Co-expression of an *Erwinia chrysanthemi* pectate lyase encoding gene (*pel*E) and an *Erwinia carotovora* polygalacturonase-encoding gene (*peh*1) in *Saccharomyces cerevisiae*. Appl Microbiol Biotechnol 39: 181–188, 1993.

116. L González-Candelas, JV Gil, RM Lamuela-Raventos, D Ramon. The use of transgenic yeasts expressing a gene encoding a glycosyl-hydrolase as a tool to increase resveratrol content in wine. Int J Food Microbiol 59: 179–183, 2000.

117. M Vilanova, P Blanco, S Cortes, M Castro, TG Villa, C Sieiro. Use of a *PGU1* recombinant *Saccharomyces cerevisiae* strain in oenological fermentations. J Appl Microbiol 89: 876–883, 2000.

118. JA Pérez-González, R Gonzalez, A Querol, J Sendra, D Ramon. Construction of a recombinant wine yeast strain expressing β-(1,4)-endoglucanase and its use in microvinification processes. Appl Environ Microbiol 59: 2801–2806, 1993.

119. P van Rensburg, WH van Zyl, IS Pretorius. Overexpression of the *Saccharomyces cerevisiae* exo-β-1,3–glucanase gene together with the *Bacillus subtilis* endo-β-1,3–1,4–glucanase gene and the *Butyrivibrio fibrisolvens* endo-β-1,4–glucanase gene in yeast. J Biotechnol 55: 43–53, 1997.

120. C Chambon, V Ladeveze, A Oulmouden, M Servouse, F Karst. Isolation and properties of yeast mutants affected in farnesyl diphosphate synthetase. Curr Genet 18: 41–46, 1990.

121. AJ King, JR Dickinson. Biotransformation of monoterpene alcohols by *Saccharomyces cerevisiae*, *Torulaspora delbrueckii* and *Kluyveromyces lactis*. Yeast 16: 499–506, 2000.

122. AJ King, JR Dickinson. Biotransformation of hop aroma terpenoids by ale and lager yeasts. FEMS Yeast Res 3: 53–62, 2003.

123. PT Darriet, T Lavigne, V Boidron, J Dubourdieu, D. Identification of a powerful aromatic compound of *Vitis vinifera* L. var. Sauvignon wines: 4–Mercapto-4–methylpentan-2–one. Flavour and Fragrance Journal 10: 385–392, 1995.

124. T Tominaga, C Peyrot des Gachons, D Dubourdieu, D. A new type of flavour precursors in *Vitis vinifera* L. cv. Sauvignon Blanc: S-cysteine conjugates. J Agric Food Chem 46: 5215–5219, 1998.

125. T Fujii, N Nagasawa, A Iwamatsu, T Bogaki, Y Tamai, M Hamachi. Molecular cloning, sequence analysis, and expression of the yeast alcohol acetyltransferase gene. Appl Environ Microbiol 60: 2786–2792, 1994.

126. M Lilly, MG Lambrechts, IS Pretorius. Effect of increased yeast alcohol acetyltransferase activity on flavor profiles of wine and distillates. Appl Environ Microbiol 66: 744–753, 2000.

127. H Yoshimoto, T Fukushige, T Yonezawa, H Sone. Genetic and physiological analysis of branched-chain alcohols and isoamyl acetate production in *Saccharomyces cerevisiae*. Appl Microbiol Biotechnol 59: 501–508, 2002.

128. K Fukuda, N Yamamoto, Y Kiyokawa, T Yanagiuchi, Y Wakai, K Kitamoto, Y Inoue, A Kimura. Balance of activities of alcohol acetyltransferase and esterase in *Saccharomyces cerevisiae* is important for production of isoamyl acetate. Appl Environ Microbiol 64: 4076–4078, 1998.

129. JR Dickinson, LE Salgado, MJ Hewlins. The catabolism of amino acids to long chain and complex alcohols in *Saccharomyces cerevisiae*. J Biol Chem 278: 8028–8034, 2003.

130. A Eden, L van Nedervelde, M Drukker, N Benvenisty, A Debourg. Involvement of branched-chain amino acid aminotransferases in the production of fusel alcohols

during fermentation in yeast. Appl Microbiol Biotechnol 55: 296–300, 2001.

131. F Remize, J-L Roustan, J Sablayrolles, P Barre, S Dequin. Glycerol overproduction by engineered *Saccharomyces cerevisiae* wine yeast strains leads to substantial changes in by-product formation and to a stimulation of fermentation rate in stationary phase. Appl Environ Microbiol 65: 143–149, 1999.

132. F Remize, JM Sablayrolles, S Dequin. Re-assessment of the influence of yeast strain and environmental factors on glycerol production in wine. J Appl Microbiol 88: 371–378, 2000.

133. JM Eglinton, AJ Heinrich, AP Pollnitz, P Langridge, PA Henschke, M de Barros Lopes. Decreasing acetic acid accumulation by a glycerol overproducing strain of *Saccharomyces cerevisiae* by deleting the *ALD6* aldehyde dehydrogenase gene. Yeast 19: 295–301, 2002.

134. F Omura, Y Shibano, N Fukui, K Nakatani. Reduction of hydrogen sulfide production in brewing yeast by constitutive expression of *MET25* gene. J Am Soc Brew Chem 53: 58–62, 1995.

135. A Spiropoulos, LF Bisson. *MET17* and hydrogen sulfide formation in *Saccharomyces cerevisiae*. Appl Environ Microbiol 66: 4421–4426, 2000.

136. H Tezuka, T Mori, Y Okumura, K Kitabatake, Y Tsumura. Cloning of a gene suppressing hydrogen sulfide production by *Saccharomyces cerevisiae* and its expression in a brewing yeast. J Am Soc Brew Chem 50: 130–133, 1992.

137. H Park, AT Bakalinsky. *SSU1* mediates sulphite efflux in *Saccharomyces cerevisiae*. Yeast 16: 881–888, 2000.

138. JE Pérez-Ortin, A Querol, S Puig, E Barrio. Molecular characterization of a chromosomal rearrangement involved in the adaptive evolution of yeast strains. Genome Res 12: 1533–1539, 2002.

139. H Volschenk, M Viljoen, J Grobler, F Petzold, F Bauer, RE Subden, RA Young, A Lonvaud, M Denayrolles, HJJ van Vuuren. Engineering pathways for malate degradation in *Saccharomyces cerevisiae*. Nat Biotechnol 15: 253–257, 1997.

140. S Dequin, E Baptista, P Barre. Acidification of grape musts by *Saccharomyces cerevisiae* wine yeast strains genetically engineered to produce lactic acid. Am J Enol Vitic 50: 45–50, 1999.

141. CD Skory. Lactic acid production by *Saccharomyces cerevisiae* expressing a *Rhizopus oryzae* lactate dehydrogenase gene. J Ind Microbiol Biotechnol 30: 22–27, 2003.

142. A Smit, RR Cordero Otero, MG Lambrechts, IS Pretorius, P van Rensburg. Manipulation of volatile phenol concentrations in wine by expressing various phenolic acid decarboxylase genes in *Saccharomyces cerevisiae*. J Agric Food Chem 15: 4909–4915, 2003.

143. JVW Becker, GO Armstrong, MJ van der Merwe, MG Lambrechts, MA Vivier, IS Pretorius. The production of resveratrol by *Saccharomyces cerevisiae*. FEMS Yeast Research 4: 79–85, 2003.

144. K Kitamoto, K Oda, K Gomi, K Takahashi. Genetic engineering of a saké yeast producing no urea by successive disruption of arginase gene. Appl Environ Microbiol 57: 301–306, 1991.

145. MH Silla Santos. Biogenic amines: their importance in foods. Int J Food Microbiol 29: 213–231, 1996.

146. S Guerrini, S Mangani, L Granchi, M Vincenzini. Biogenic amine production by *Oenococcus oeni*. Curr Microbiol 44: 374–378, 2002.

147. A Lonvaud-Funel. Biogenic amines in wines: role of lactic acid bacteria. FEMS Microbiol Lett 199: 9–13, 2001.

148. LMT Dicks, F Dellaglio, MD Collins. Proposal to reclassify *Leuconostoc oenos* as *Oenococcus oeni* [corrig.] gen. nov, comb. nov. Int J Syst Bacteriol 45: 395–397, 1995.

149. D Wibowo, R Eschenbruch, CR Davis, GH Fleet, TH Lee. Occurrence and growth of lactic acid bacteria in wine: review. Am J Enol Vitic 36: 302–313, 1985.

150. J Ribérau-Gayon, D Dubourdieu, B Doneche, A Lonvaud-Funel. Lactic acid bacteria. in: J Ribérau-Gayon, A Maujean, D Dubourdieu (Eds.), Handbook of Enology: The Chemistry of Wine and Stabilization and Treatments. John Wiley & Sons, New York, 2000, pp 107–128.

151. LT Axelsson. Lactic acid bacteria: classification and physiology. in: S Salminen, A von Wright (Eds.), Lactic Acid Bacteria. Marcel Dekker Inc, New York, 1993, pp 1–63.

152. L Ze-Ze, R Teneiro, L Brito, MA Santos, H Paveia. Physical map of the genome of *Oenococcus oeni* PSU-1 and localization of genetic markers. Microbiology 144: 1145–1156, 1998.

153. L Ze-Ze, R Teneiro, H Paveia. The *Oenococcus oeni* genome: Physical and genetic map of strain GM and comparison with the genome of a 'divergent' strain, PSU-1. Microbiology 146: 3195–3204, 2000.

154. YX Zhang, K Perry, VA Vinci, K Powell, WP Stemmer, SB del Cardayre. Genome shuffling leads to rapid phenotypic improvement in bacteria. Nature 415: 644–646, 2002.

155. WP Stemmer. DNA shuffling by random fragmentation and reassembly: *in vitro* recombination for molecular evolution. Proc Natl Acad Sci USA 91: 10747–10751, 1994.

156. R Patnaik, S Louie, V Gavrilovic, K Perry, WP Stemmer, CM Ryan, S del Cardayre. Genome shuffling of *Lactobacillus* for improved acid tolerance. Nat Biotechnol 20: 707–712, 2002.

157. J Guzzo, M-P Jobin, F Delmas, C Divies. Study on physiology and molecular response to stress in the malolactic bacterium, *Oenococcus oeni*. Revue des Oenologues et des Techniques Vitivinicoles et Oenoloques 86: 26–28, 1997.

158. R Mira de Orduna, S Liu, ML Patchett, GJ Pilone. Ethyl carbamate precursor citrulline formation from arginine degradation by malolactic wine lactic acid bacteria. FEMS Microbiol Lett 183: 31–35, 2000.

159. R Mira de Orduna, S-Q Liu, ML Patchett, GJ Pilone. Kinetics of the arginine metabolism of malolactic wine lactic acid bacteria *Lactobacillus buchneri* CUC-3 and *Oenococcus oeni* Lo111. J Appl Microbiol 89: 547–552, 2000.

160. S-Q Liu, GG Pritchard, MJ Hardman, GJ Pilone. Citrulline production and ethyl carbamate (urethane) precursor formation from arginine degradation by wine lactic acid bacteria *Leuconostoc oenos* and *Lactobacillus buchneri*. Am J Enol Vitic 45: 235–242, 1994.

161. B Divol, T Tonon, S Morichon, E Gindreau, A Lonvaud-Funel. Molecular characterization of *Oenococcus oeni* genes encoding proteins involved in arginine transport. J Appl Microbiol 94: 738–746, 2003.

162. M McDaniel. Trained panel evaluation of Pinot Noir fermented with different strains of malolactic bacteria. Oregon Wine Advisory Board 2: 6, 1986.

163. W-L Deng, H-Y Chang, H-L Peng. Acetoin catabolism system of *Klebsiella pneumoniae* CG43: sequence, expression and organization of the *aco* operon. J Bacteriol 176: 3527–3535, 1994.

164. N Klijn, AH Weerkamp, WM de Vos. Identification of mesophilic lactic acid bacteria by using polymerase chain reaction-amplified variable regions of 16S rRNA and specific DNA probes. Appl Environ Microbiol 57: 3390–3393, 1991.

165. B Bojovic, G Djordjevic, A Banina, L Topisirovic. Mutational analysis of *cat-86* gene expression controlled by lactococcal promoters in *Lactococcus lactis* subsp. *lactis* and *Escherichia coli*. J Bacteriol 176: 6754–6758, 1994.

166. LJH Ward, JCS Brown, GP Davey. Detection of dairy *Leuconostoc* strains using the polymerase chain reaction. Lett Appl Microbiol 20: 204–208, 1995.

167. T Henick-Kling Malolactic fermentation. in: G Fleet (Ed.), Wine Microbiology and Biotechnology. Harwood Academic, Reading, 1993, pp 289–326.

168. E Coton, GC Rollan, A Lonvaud-Funel. Histinde carboxylase of *Leuconostoc oenos* 9204: purification, kinetic properties, cloning and nucleotide sequence of the *hdc* gene. J Appl Microbiol 84: 143–151, 1998.

169. C Le Jeune, A Lonvaud-Funel, B ten Brink, H Hofstra, JM van der Vossen. Development of a detection system for histidine decarboxylating lactic acid bacteria based on DNA probes, PCR and activity test. J Appl Microbiol 78: 316–326, 1995.

170. M Loessner, S Guenther, S Steffan, S Scherer. A pediocin-producing *Lactobacillus plantarum* strain inhibits *Listeria monocytogenes* in a multispecies cheese surface microbial ripening consortium. Appl Environ Microbiol 69: 1854–1857, 2003.

171. J Riberau-Gayon, E Penaud. Caracteres, transformations et traitements des vins. in: J Riberau-Gayon, E Penaud (Eds.), Traite d'Oenologie, Dunod, Paris, 1961.

172. CR Davis, D Wibowo, R Eschenbruch, TH Lee, GH Fleet. Practical implications of malolactic fermentation: a review. Am J Enol Vitic 36: 290–301, 1985.

173. B Martineau, T Henick-Kling. Performance and diacetyl production of commercial strains of malolactic bacteria in wine. J Appl Bacteriol 78: 526–536, 1995.

174. TM Cogan. Co-metabolism of citrate and glucose by *Leuconostoc* spp.: effects on growth, substrates and products. J Appl Bacteriol 63: 551–558, 1987.

175. A Ramos, JS Lolkema, WN Konings, H Santos. Enzyme basis for pH regulation of citrate and pyruvate metabolism by *Leuconostoc oenos*. Appl Environ Microbiol 61: 1303–1310, 1995.

176. A Ramos, H Santos. Citrate and sugar cofermentation in *Leuconostoc oenos*, a ^{13}C nuclear magnetic resonance study. Appl Environ Microbiol 62: 2577–2585, 1996.

177. M Gagiano, FF Bauer, IS Pretorius. The sensing of nutritional status and the relationship to filamentous growth in *Saccharomyces cerevisiae*. FEMS Yeast Res 2: 433–470, 2002.

178. E Bartowsky, P Costello, P Henschke. Management of malolactic fermentation — wine flavour manipulation. The Australian Grapegrower and Winemaker 461a: 7–12, 2002.

179. EJ Bartowsky, PA Henschke. Management of malolactic fermentation for the 'buttery' diacetyl flavour in wine. The Australian Grapegrower and Winemaker 438a: 58–67, 2000.

180. MJ Gasson, K Benson, S Swindell, H Griffin. Metabolic engineering of the *Lactococcus lactis* diacetyl pathway. Lait 76: 33–40, 1996.

181. D Garmyn, C Monnet, B Martineau, J Guzzo, J-F Cavin, C Divies. Cloning and sequencing of the gene encoding α-acetolactate decarboxylase from *Leuconostoc oenos*. FEMS Microbiol Lett 145: 445–450, 1996.

182. N D'Incecco, EJ Bartowsky, S Kassara, A Lante, P Spetolli, PA Henschke. Release of chardonnay glycosiducally bound flavour compounds by *Oenococcus oeni* during malolactic fermentation. Food Microbiol 21: 257–265, 2004.

183. G de Revel, N Martin, L Pripis-Nicolau, A Lonvaud-Funel, A Bertrand. Contribution to the knowledge of malolactic fermentation influence on wine aroma. J Agric Food Chem 47: 4003–4008, 1999.

184. F Sauvageot, P Vivier. Effects of malolactic fermentation on sensory properties of four Burgundy wines. Am J Enol Vitic 48: 187–192, 1997.

185. I Serageldin. Biotechnology and food security in the 21st century. Science 285: 387–389, 1999.

186. M Reiss. Labeling GM foods-the ethical way forward. Nat Biotechnol 20: 868, 2002.

187. L Sjoberg. Limits of knowledge and the limited importance of trust. Risk Anal 21: 189–198, 2001.

188. HA Kuiper, GA Kleter, HP Noteborn, EJ Kok. Assessment of the food safety issues related to genetically modified foods. Plant J 27: 503–528, 2001.

189. O Fiehn. Metabolomics—the link between genotypes and phenotypes. Plant Mol Biol 48: 155–171, 2002.

190. D Ferber. GM crops in the cross hairs. Science 286: 1662–1666, 1999.

191. H Daniell. Molecular strategies for gene containment in transgenic crops. Nat Biotechnol 20: 581–586, 2002.

192. FE Ahmed. Detection of genetically modified organisms in foods. Trends Biotechnol 20: 215–223, 2002.

193. EJ Kok, HJ Aarts, AM van Hoef, HA Kuiper. DNA methods: critical review of innovative approaches. J AOAC Int 85: 797–800, 2002.

194. E Garcia-Beneytez, MV Moreno-Arribas, J Borrego, MC Polo, J Ibanez. Application of a DNA analysis method for the cultivar identification of grape musts and experimental and commercial wines of *Vitis vinifera* L. using microsatellite markers. J Agric Food Chem 50: 6090–6096, 2002.

Part C

Food Analysis

41 Food Analysis: Basics

S. Suzanne Nielsen
Department of Food Science, Purdue University

CONTENTS

I. INTRODUCTION

Foods are analyzed for chemical composition and characteristics for a variety of reasons in the food industry, including nutrition labeling and quality control (1–5). The analyses may be performed continuously within the processing line, or samples are collected and analyzed in the quality control laboratory or sent to an outside analytical laboratory. In the latter two cases, samples must be properly selected and prepared for analysis, then analyzed and the data interpreted. Selecting the method of analysis depends on a variety of factors, including the objective of the testing, characteristics of the method and the food products, and needed accuracy and precision. Out of necessity, methods used during processing and on final products are typically rapid, while more time-consuming and accurate methods are specified to suppliers of raw ingredients and used for nutrition labeling of the final product. Whatever the method of analysis, data obtained must be handled appropriately and interpreted as the basis for decision-making. These basics of food analysis are necessary whether the method being utilized is wet chemistry, spectroscopy, chromatography, or some other method.

II. WHY ANALYSES ARE DONE

Demands of consumers, strong competition within the food industry, and government regulations and international standards all contribute to the need for analysis of food products and ingredients.

A. CONSUMERS

Safety, quality, nutrition, and good value are all important to consumers as they select their foods for purchase. It is increasingly a challenge for the food industry to meet the demands of consumers. Consumer interest in food safety has increased the testing for allergens and pesticide residues. Consumer concern about food materials that have been genetically modified using biotechnology has led to testing of foods and raw materials for such modification. Consumer interest in the relationship between diet and health has increased the importance of testing foods to allow for certain nutrient content claims (e.g., low fat) and health claims (e.g., dietary saturated fat and cholesterol, and the risk of coronary heart disease) (1).

B. FOOD INDUSTRY

To manage product quality, food companies must apply analytical methods across the entire food supply chain, from the raw ingredients to the final product (Table 41.1).

TABLE 41.1
Types of Samples Analyzed in a Quality Assurance Program for Food Products

Sample Type	Critical Questions
Raw materials	Do they meet your specifications?
	Do they meet required legal specifications?
	Will a processing parameter have to be modified because of any change in the composition of raw materials?
	Are the quality and composition the same as for previous deliveries?
	How does the material from a potential new supplier compare to that from the current supplier?
Process control samples	Did a specific processing step result in a product of acceptable composition or characteristics?
	Does a further processing step need to be modified to obtain a final product of acceptable quality?
Finished product	Does it meet the legal requirements?
	What is the nutritive value, so that label information can be developed? Or is the nutritive value as specified on an existing label?
	Does it meet product claim requirements (e.g., "low fat")?
	Will it be acceptable to the consumer?
	Will it have the appropriate shelf life?
Competitor's sample	What are its composition and characteristics?
	How can we use this information to develop new products?
Complaint sample	How do the composition and characteristics of a complaint sample submitted by a customer differ from a sample with no problems?

From: SS Nielsen, ed. Food Analysis, 3rd ed. New York: Kluwer Academic, 2003 (Ref. 1).

Analyzing various types of samples in the food processing system can help answer questions critical to the success of the business. Heavy emphasis is placed on the quality of raw ingredients, which reduces the need for extensive testing during processing and on the final product. Responsibility for ingredient testing has been shifted largely from the food companies to the ingredient suppliers. Most food companies have "select suppliers" who are given detailed ingredient specifications. These suppliers are asked to do the analytical testing and provide a "certificate of analysis" to show compliance with these specifications. Limited additional testing of ingredients may be done upon receipt by the food company. In some cases, a food company arranges to receive a small sample of the ingredient to check for particular characteristics before accepting a large shipment of the ingredient (1).

C. GOVERNMENT REGULATIONS

Government regulations dictate certain types of analyses (6). Three examples follow of food analysis required based on federal regulations in the U.S. First, nutrition labeling regulations in the U.S. are a major driver of the analysis of foods (Table 41.2). Chemical analysis of foods is required not only for the nutrition label itself, but also for making nutrient content claims that characterize the level of a nutrient (e.g., low fat, reduced sodium, high calcium) or health claims (e.g., folate and neural tube defects, soluble fiber from whole oats and coronary heart disease). Second, the U.S. Food and Drug Administration (FDA) has established standards of identity for certain food products. These standards often include which ingredients a food must contain, the maximum levels for inexpensive ingredients (e.g., water), the minimum levels for expensive ingredients (e.g., fat), and recommended analytical methods to determine the chemical composition. Table 41.3 summarizes food analysis-related information from the standard of identity for several food products. The recommended methods of analysis specified in standards of identity are typically from the *Official Methods of Analysis* of AOAC International (formerly known as the Association of Official Analytical Chemists, AOAC) (7). Third, grade standards established by the U.S. Department of Agriculture, while voluntary rather than mandatory, are used often as quality control tools. These grade standards classify products in a range from substandard to excellent in quality. This information is useful both to consumers (e.g., Grade A eggs) and to institutions (schools, hospitals, military) that purchase foods. Grade standards often include not only chemical composition characteristics (e.g., soluble solids and titratable acidity distinguish Grade A and B orange juice), but also sensory evaluation and visual appearance.

TABLE 41.2
Typical Methods Used for Nutrition Labeling Tests[a]

Item on Nutrition Label	Typical Analysis
Calories	Calculated from content of protein, total carbohydrate (or total carbohydrate less the amount of insoluble dietary fiber), and total fat (4, 4, and 9 calories per gram, respectively)
Calories from Fat	Calculated from total fat (9 calories per gram)
Total Fat	Extraction with petroleum or diethyl ether (e.g., Soxhlet or Goldfish methods), sometimes preceded by acid hydrolysis; Roese-Gottlieb or Mojonnier methods; Babcock; sum of fatty acid content by gas chromatography
Saturated Fat	Gas chromatography
Cholesterol	Gas chromatography
Sodium	Inductively coupled plasma-atomic emission spectroscopy, Atomic absorption spectroscopy, Mohr or Volhard titration, ion selective electrodes
Total Carbohydrate	Calculated as % Total carbohydrate = 100% − (% Moisture + % Protein + % Fat + % Ash)[b]
Dietary Fiber	Gravimetric-enzymatic method
Sugars	High performance liquid chromatography
Protein[c]	Kjeldahl, nitrogen combustion (Dumas)
Vitamin A	High performance liquid chromatography
Vitamin C	2, 6-Dichloroindophenol titration, microfluorometric assay
Calcium	Inductively coupled plasma-atomic emission spectroscopy, atomic absorption spectroscopy
Iron	Inductively coupled plasma-atomic emission spectroscopy, atomic absorption spectroscopy

[a]Nutrition labeling regulations of the United States Nutrition Labeling and Education Act of 1990.

[b]Moisture content may be determined by methods such as oven (e.g., forced draft oven, vacuum oven, rapid moisture analyzer), distillation, or Karl Fischer titration. Ash content for the purpose of calculating total carbohydrate content is usually done by dry ashing in a muffle furnace.

[c]Protein methods given are for determining content. If protein is expressed as a percent of the Daily Value, protein quality must be determined by either the Protein Efficiency Ratio method (foods for infants or children under four years of age) or the Protein Digestibility-Corrected Amino Acid Score method (foods other than for infants).

D. INTERNATIONAL STANDARDS

Many food companies must meet not only the regulations of individual governments, but also standards set by international organizations. For example, standards published in the *Codex Alimentarius* by the Codex Alimentarius Commission are intended to facilitate international trade of foods, ensure fair business practices, and protect the health of consumers. These standards make necessary the analysis of raw agricultural commodities and processed food products being imported or exported (6).

III. WHERE ANALYSES ARE DONE

The need continues for collecting samples from the processing line for analysis in the quality control laboratory or by an outside analytical laboratory, but there is increasing interest in continuously monitoring the quality characteristics of foods in line as they are being processed. Such analysis better ensures the quality of the final product and reduces the need for further testing of the final product before distribution. Infrared spectroscopy, one of the main tools used for this application (8), is described in more detail in Chapter 43, Spectroscopy Basics. However, briefly, infrared spectroscopy measures the absorption of radiant energy, in the near- or mid-infrared region of the electromagnetic spectrum, by molecules in foods. The frequency of energy absorbed depends on the functional groups of the molecules being measured, and the amount of energy absorbed is related to the concentration of the food constituent of interest. Other methods of analysis are being used and further studied for on-line analysis applications.

Samples collected from the processing line may be analyzed immediately using equipment stationed very near the processing line (e.g., rapid moisture analyzer to check moisture content of cereals; portable colorimeter to check color). However, often samples collected from the processing line are transported to an established quality control laboratory where generally rapid methods are used to test quality characteristics as part of the quality management plan. For less routine analysis and for nutrition labeling tests, collected samples may be sent to outside analytical laboratories. These analytical laboratories often are certified laboratories with highly trained and experienced personnel, and often are equipped with expensive analytical instrumentation. For example, a typical quality control laboratory would not be set up to do analyses for dietary fiber or certain vitamins, but samples for these analyses could be sent easily to an analytical laboratory.

IV. STEPS IN ANALYSIS

Analysis of foods involves three main steps: 1) selecting and preparing the sample, 2) performing the analysis, and 3) calculating and interpreting the results.

Collecting the sample and preparing it for analysis, which are covered in more detail in the next section, are much more difficult and important than they would appear. Non-homogeneity of food and ingredients, along with uneven distribution of certain constituents, make collecting a representative sample a challenge. Conditions of sample preparation and the instability of certain food constituents make it difficult to ensure that the composition and characteristics of the sample collected are identical to those of the sample subjected to the analytical procedure.

TABLE 41.3
Chemical Composition Requirements of Some Foods and Ingredients with Standards of Identity

Section in 21 CFR[1]	Food Product	Requirement	Number in 13th Ed.	AOAC METHOD[2] Number in 17th Ed.	Name/Description
131.125	Nonfat dry milk	Moisture $\geq$ 5% by wt.	16.192	927.05	Vacuum oven
		Milkfat $\leq$ 1.5% by wt.	16.199–16.200	932.06A, 932.06B	Roese-Gottlieb
145.110	Canned applesauce	Soluble solids $\geq$ 9%, expressed as % sucrose, °Brix	22.024	932.14A	Refractometer
168.20	Glucose syrup	Total solids $\leq$ 70%,mass/mass (m/m)	31.2088–941.14A, 941.14B 31.209		Vacuum oven, with diatomaceous earth
		Reducing sugar $\geq$ 20% m/m (dextrose equivalent, dry weight basis)	31.220(a)	945.66(a)	Lane-Eynon
		Sulfated ash $\leq$ 1% m/m, dry weight basis	31.216	945.63B	Dry ashing
		Sulfur dioxide $\leq$ 40 mg/kg	20.106–20.111	962.16A–963.20C	Modified Monier-Williams

[1]CFR, Code of Federal Regulations (2004).

[2]*Official Methods of Analysis* of the Association of Official Analytical Chemists (AOAC) International.

Each food or ingredient component or characteristic to be tested may require a unique assay. Descriptions of wet chemistry, spectroscopy, chromatography, and other methods for food analysis are given in subsequent chapters. However, for any particular assay, the analyst doing the assay needs to consult manuals, reference books, and articles for details on the necessary chemicals, reagents, equipment, and step-by-step instructions. It must be stressed that glassware and other labware used must be clean and equipment properly checked and calibrated.

The results obtained from performing the assay of food components and characteristics are utilized to make decisions and take action. A later section of this chapter deals in more detail with data handling and assessing its reliability. The analytical data obtained can be evaluated and integrated with other relevant information to address food quality-related problems. Such data are critical not only for quality assurance, but also in product formulation and process design.

V. SAMPLING AND SAMPLE PREPARATION

A. SAMPLE COLLECTION

Sample collection and sample reduction methods must be developed to ensure a representative sample is being subjected to analysis (9, 10). The choice of a sampling plan is affected by four factors: 1) purpose of the inspection, 2) nature of the product, 3) nature of the test method, and 4) nature of the population being investigated (11). Sampling plans are typically applied to heterogeneous (versus homogeneous) populations, for which it is more difficult to obtain a representative sample. Sampling plans are

designed to examine either attributes (i.e., to decide acceptability based on whether the sample possesses a certain characteristic, e.g., *Clostridium botulinum*) or variables (i.e., to estimate the amount of a substance or characteristic on a continuous scale, e.g., color). Variable sampling generally requires a smaller sample size than attribute sampling (12).

Three types of sampling plans exist: 1) single (one sample of a specified size, to allow accept/reject decisions), 2) double (select two samples, then make accept/reject decisions after testing one or both samples), and 3) multiple (reject low-quality lots and accept high-quality lots quickly; do further sampling of intermediate quality lots). No sampling plan is free of risks. The two types of risks associated with sampling are consumer risks and vendor risks. The consumer risk is the probability of accepting a poor quality product. The vendor risk is the probability of rejecting an acceptable product.

Sampling may be done manually by a person or continuously using some mechanical system. If operating properly, the continuous sampling should be less prone to human bias than is manual sampling.

Ideally the sampling method is statistically sound. However, sometimes nonprobability sampling is unavoidable. With such sampling, a representative sample of the population cannot be collected. Preferably one can do probability sampling, which has a statistically sound basis to obtain a representative sample and eliminate human error. Probability sampling ensures random samples, and allows calculation of sampling error and the probability of including any item of the population in the sample.

Samples collected for analysis must be clearly labeled in preparation for sample preparation and then analysis.

Samples collected for official or legal purposes must be sealed to protect from tampering, and the chain of custody must be clearly identified.

B. Preparation of Samples

The *Official Methods of Analysis* of AOAC International (7) gives detailed instructions on preparation of specific food samples for analysis, determined by the nature of the food and the type of analysis to be done. Such instructions include size of samples collected, particle size reduction, and storage of samples.

Samples that are too large in mass must be reduced. The mass can be reduced by spreading the sample on a clean surface, dividing into quarters, and collecting the two opposite quarters. The process can be repeated until a sample of manageable size is obtained. The method can be adapted to liquids by using four containers (9).

Grinding is used commonly to reduce particle size so more homogenous samples can be obtained and samples are suitable for analysis. Grinding procedures often specify the mesh size, meaning the number of openings per linear inch of mesh. A 40-mesh size, meaning very small particles, is used for assays that involve an extraction, such as lipid analysis. A 20-mesh size gives larger particles used for moisture or total protein analyses.

The various types of mills used for grinding differ in their mode of action and appropriate applications. A common concern in grinding is the loss of moisture due to air exposure or heating. Grinders are sometimes water cooled to reduce heating, and samples are sometimes ground frozen.

In addition to protecting samples from moisture loss during grinding, it is necessary to handle and store samples in such a way as to avoid several other potential problems. Enzymes naturally present in foods can degrade the food constituents to be analyzed. Enzyme action can be slowed or stopped by freezing, heat denaturation, or other means appropriate for the specific enzyme. Unsaturated lipids and some vitamins and pigments are especially sensitive to oxygen and light. This makes it necessary to store some samples under nitrogen in the dark, or analyzed as soon as possible after collection. Microbial growth in samples prior to analysis can change the chemical composition. Freezing, drying, and chemical preservatives may be used alone or in combination to prevent microbial problems.

VI. SELECTING THE METHOD AND DOING THE ASSAY

A. Objective

The objective of the measurement is a major factor in determining the choice of the method of analysis (1). For example, time-consuming, accurate, official methods are used for nutrition labeling purposes, while rapid, less accurate methods are applicable for on-line measurements. Well-equipped and well-staffed analytical laboratories are the best to utilize methods referred to as reference, definitive, official, or primary. The manufacturing floor in a food processing facility would more appropriately use rapid secondary or field methods. For example, results from the secondary, rapid refractive index method for sugar analysis used on the manufacturing floor can be correlated to the primary method of high performance liquid chromatography used in the analytical laboratory. Likewise, moisture analysis data from a time-consuming forced draft oven method can be related to that of a moisture balance unit used in a pilot plant.

B. Characteristics

The characteristics described and questions raised in Table 41.4 are useful in choosing a method of analysis for a particular application. The characteristics related to validity of the method (i.e., accuracy, precision, specificity, and sensitivity) are critical, and will be discussed further in the next section on data handling. The time, equipment, and personnel availability are major factors to consider. A careful assessment of advantages and disadvantages of methods for particular applications makes it easier to make an appropriate choice.

C. Food Matrix

Some analytical methods are very robust and can be applied to all food types, but most methods are not so widely applicable (13, 14). The major chemical components of a food, i.e., the food matrix, can affect the performance of many analytical methods. Fat, protein, and carbohydrate are the three major food components expected to have the strongest effect on analytical method performance. For example, the high fat or sugar content of certain foods can cause interferences in some assays. Extraction steps and digestion procedures can be necessary and specific, depending on the food matrix. Because food systems are quite complex and varied, one technique for analysis of a particular component cannot be applied to all foods. Rather, multiple techniques and procedures must be considered for application to any particular food matrix.

D. Official Methods

The availability of official methods has made easier the choice of methods for analyzing specific food components and characteristics (1). Such official methods have been carefully developed, standardized, and compiled by several nonprofit scientific organizations. Official methods make it possible to compare results between different laboratories that use the same procedure. These methods also provide a way to evaluate new and more rapid assays.

TABLE 41.4
Criteria for Choice of Food Analysis Methods

Characteristic	Critical Questions	Characteristic	Critical Questions
Inherent properties		• Equipment	Is the method very sensitive to slight or moderate changes in the reagents?
• Specificity/ Selectivity	Is the property being measured the same as that claimed to be measured, and is it the only property being measured? Are there interferences? What steps are being taken to ensure a high degree of specificity?		Do you have the appropriate equipment? Are personnel competent to operate equipment?
• Precision	What is the precision of the method? Is there within-batch, batch-to-batch, or day-to-day variation? What step in the procedure contributes the greatest variability?	• Cost *Usefulness* • Time required	What is the cost in terms of equipment, reagents, and personnel? How fast is it? How fast does it need to be?
• Accuracy	How does the new method compare in accuracy to the old or a standard method? What is the percent recovery?	• Reliability • Need	How reliable is it from the standpoints of precision and stability? Does it meet a need or better meet a need?
Applicability of method to laboratory		*Personnel*	Is any change in method worth the trouble of the change?
• Sample size	How much sample is needed? Is it too large or too small to fit your needs? Does it fit your equipment and/or glassware?	• Safety • Procedures	Are special precautions necessary? Who will prepare the written description of the procedures and reagents?
• Reagents	Can you properly prepare them? What equipment is needed? Are they stable? For how long and under what conditions?		Who will do any required calculations?

From: SS Nielsen, ed. Food Analysis, 3rd ed. New York: Kluwer Academic, 2003 (Ref. 1).

AOAC International is a volunteer organization dedicated to providing methods that perform with accuracy and precision under usual laboratory conditions. Members of AOAC International select published methods or develop new methods, then collaboratively test the methods in their own laboratories. The program to validate methods is carefully managed, with a specified number of laboratories involved, samples per level of analyte, controls, control samples, and the review process. If methods are found acceptable, they are adopted as official methods (initially as first action, and then as final action). Adopted methods are published in the *Official Methods of Analysis* (7), which is published about every four to five years and contains methods appropriate for a wide range of products and other materials (Table 41.5). New methods and revisions to current methods are published in supplements to the most recent edition of the book.

Other books of official methods of analysis related to foods and ingredients include the following:

1. *Approved Methods of Analysis*, published by the American Association of Cereal Chemists (AACC) (15); methods are mostly applicable to cereal products (e.g., tests for physical dough properties, baking quality, staleness/texture).

2. *Official Methods and Recommended Practices* published by the American Oil Chemists' Society (AOCS) (16); methods are applicable mostly to fat and oil analysis (e.g., vegetable oil, oilseed by-products, detergents, lecithin).

3. *Standard Methods for the Examination of Dairy Products*, published by the American Public Health Association (17); methods are applicable to milk and dairy products; chemical methods are for acidity, fat, lactose, moisture/solids, added water.

4. *Standard Methods for the Examination of Water and Wastewater*, published jointly by the American Public Health Association, American Water Works Association, and the Water Environment Federation (18).

5. *Food Chemicals Codex*, published by the Food and Nutrition Board of the National Research Council/National Academy of Sciences (19); contains methods for the analysis of food additives.

TABLE 41.5

Table of Contents of Official Methods of Analysis of AOAC International, 17th Edition (Ref. 7)

Chapter	Title	Chapter	Title
1	Agriculture liming materials	26	Distilled liquors
2	Fertilizers	27	Malt beverages and brewing materials
3	Plants	28	Wines
4	Animal feed	29	Nonalcoholic beverages and concentrates
5	Drugs in feeds	30	Coffee and tea
6	Disinfectants	31	Cacao bean and its products
7	Pesticide formulations	32	Cereal foods
8	Hazardous substances	33	Dairy products
9	Metals and other elements at trace levels in foods	34	Eggs and egg products
10	Pesticide and industrial chemical residues	35	Fish and other marine products
11	Waters; and salt	36	Flavors
12	Microchemical methods	37	Fruits and fruit products
13	Radioactivity	38	Gelatin, dessert preparations, and mixes
14	Veterinary analytical toxicology	39	Meat and meat products
15	Cosmetics	40	Nuts and nut products
16	Extraneous materials: isolation	41	Oils and fats
17	Microbiological methods	42	Vegetable products, processed
18	Drugs: Part I	43	Spices and other condiments
19	Drugs: Part II	44	Sugars and sugar products
20	Drugs: Part III	45	Vitamins and other nutrients
21	Drugs: Part IV	46	Color additives
22	Drugs: Part V	47	Food additives: Direct
23	Drugs and feed additives in animal tissues	48	Food additives: Indirect
24	Forensic sciences	49	Natural toxins
25	Baking powders and baking chemicals	50	Infant formulas, baby foods, and enteral products

E. CAUTIONS IN ANALYSIS

Basic guidelines for performing analytical methods appropriately caution the analyst with regard to proper use of blanks, sources of contamination, and other potential sources of error (e.g., equipment, analyst technique) (20). Problems with blanks, contamination, and other sources of error greatly affect the accuracy and precision and therefore the usefulness of data obtained.

A reagent blank is a sample that contains the reagents used in the sample analysis, in the appropriate quantities, but without any of the material being analyzed. For example, the reagent blank in the phenol-sulfuric acid method for total carbohydrate would contain sulfuric acid and phenol in the appropriate quantities, but water in place of any carbohydrate-containing sample. That reagent blank would be used to zero the spectrophotometer before reading the absorbance of the carbohydrate-containing samples. Use of a reagent blank is especially important in many mineral analyses to account for any mineral contamination in the reagents.

Contamination can be a source of error in many assays, but is especially a problem when the quantities of the compounds of interest in the food are very small. Such is the case in mineral analysis, because mineral levels in the food can be very low and since glassware and the water used can contain significant quantities of minerals. In the case of mineral analysis, any glassware used must be acid washed and reagents must be of the highest analytical grade possible.

Some of the sources of error in analytical methods are often overlooked. Especially when faced with a set of questionable data, the analyst or supervisor must do some problem solving and identify the factors that contributed to the problem. For example, one must ask if the sample analyzed was representative of the sample as a whole, and whether or not it may have been modified in composition and characteristics during sample preparation. Did the analyst follow in detail the analytical procedure? Was the equipment properly standardized and used? Table 41.6 gives a partial list of sources of error that can cause data gathered to be inaccurate and show low precision.

VII. VALIDITY OF METHOD

Validity of the data obtained using a specific analytical method can be assessed in multiple ways. As a first approach to evaluate the usefulness and validity of an analytical method being related to sensory characteristics,

TABLE 41.6
Sources of Laboratory Error

A. **Sample Collection and Handling**
　1. Representative
　2. Proper preparation
　3. Stability (time, temperature, light, oxygen)
　4. Identification throughout analysis

B. **Analytical Errors**
　1. Sample and reagent measurements (weighing, pipetting)
　2. Procedural steps (timing, mixing, order of reagents)
　3. Range and sensitivity limitation

C. **Reagents**
　1. Preparation; initial and periodic checking
　2. Conditions of use (temperature, mixing)
　3. Stability; storage conditions
　4. Contamination

D. **Instruments**
　1. Limitations
　2. Operation
　3. Routing checking

F. **Calibration**
　1. Blanks
　2. Linearity limits
　3. Standards

G. **Data Handling**

H. **Special Problems**
　1. Personal attitudes and techniques
　2. Laboratory water

one should ask a very practical question. How do the differences detected and the variability seen between samples by the analytical method compare to the detected differences and acceptability to a consumer? Also, how does the variability seen between samples by the analytical method compare to the variability of the specific characteristic inherent in processing of the food (1)?

A common test of validity is assessing the inherent characteristics of the method, including accuracy, precision, specificity, and sensitivity, as described in the next section. Of major assistance in assessing accuracy is the use of standard reference materials, which can be obtained from various organizations (e.g., in the United States from the National Institute of Standards and Technology). Control samples internal to the laboratory also can serve as a standard reference material. Such a sample can be prepared by careful selection of an appropriate type of sample (i.e., closely matching the matrix of the samples to be analyzed by a specific method). These control samples should be gathered in a large quantity,

mixed and prepared to ensure homogeneity, then packaged in small quantities and stored properly. The control samples can be analyzed routinely when test samples are analyzed. Besides standard reference materials, another test of method accuracy is using check samples (21). Organizations such as the AACC and AOCS offer check sample services, providing test samples to evaluate method reliability. Subscribing laboratories can check the accuracy of their data for specific types of check samples supplied, comparing their values against the statistical norm for those same samples obtained from other subscribing laboratories.

VIII. RELIABILITY OF ANALYSIS AND DATA HANDLING

A. ACCURACY AND PRECISION

Reliability of a method is judged largely on its accuracy and precision (22–24). How close the experimental measure is to the correct or true value is referred to as accuracy. How close replicate measures are indicates reproducibility, which is referred to as precision. Standard reference materials or internal control samples are very useful in assessing accuracy since they should provide the true value. The percent relative error is the value commonly used to assess accuracy, comparing the experimental mean to the true value.

$$\% \text{ Relative error} = [(\text{Experimental mean} - \text{True value})/\text{True value}] \times 100$$

Standard deviation (SD) measures the variability of the experimental values (x_i) around the mean ($\overline{x}$), and is the initial value calculated to assess precision:

$$\text{SD} = \frac{\sqrt{\Sigma(x_i - \overline{x})^2}}{n} \qquad (41.1)$$

With the mean and standard deviation, one can calculate the coefficient of variation, which relates the size of the standard deviation to the mean. This allows one to compare the precision of multiple sets of data for which the mean values differ.

$$\text{Coefficient of Variation (CV)} = \frac{\text{SD}}{\overline{x}} \times 100\% \qquad (41.2)$$

Other useful terms associated with precision and accuracy are confidence interval, standard error of the mean, and relative deviation from the mean.

B. SPECIFICITY

The specificity of a method is how well the method detects and measures the compound of interest, and only that compound. Some analytical methods are intended to be nonspecific (e.g., lipid extraction with organic solvents), and others very specific (e.g., enzyme test kit to measure glucose). Both types of methods can be very useful, when chosen appropriately for the particular application (22).

C. SENSITIVITY AND DETECTION LIMIT

Sensitivity of a method describes how small of a change can be made in the test material before we see a difference in readout from an instrument. This term relates the size of the change in the measuring device to the change in concentration of the compound of interest. Detection limit, a related but different term, describes the lowest possible increment or amount that we can detect with some degree of confidence. Below that lower limit, we cannot be sure if something is present. If one is working near the detection limit for a particular assay, it may be possible to concentrate the sample (22).

D. STANDARD CURVES

For analytical methods, two variables (e.g., concentration and absorbance) are commonly related to one another using a standard curve. The concentration of analyte in a sample is determined by the response measured, which is related to a known amount of standard. Usually a set of standards is prepared at several concentrations, subjected to the assay conditions, and the appropriate analytical measure is taken (e.g., absorbance, volume of titrant, chromatography peak area). Generally, the concentrations of the standards (the independent variable) are plotted on the x-axis, and the measured values (the dependent variable) are plotted on the y-axis, to generate a standard curve. The best-fit line of this relationship is mathematically determined using a mathematical procedure called linear regression, and the equation of the line can be determined. The equation of a straight line is described by $y = mx + b$, where y is the dependent variable, x is the independent variable, m is the slope of the line, and b is where the point on the line intercepts the y-axis (i.e., y-intercept). Ideally all the data points for a standard curve would fall exactly on a straight line, but various sources of error limit this possibility. Values called the correlation coefficient or coefficient of determination can be calculated to mathematically describe how well the data fit a straight line. The equation of that line can be used to calculate the concentration of an analyte of unknown concentration (x), once the measured value (y) for that sample has been determined (22).

E. REPORTING RESULTS

Results from analytical methods are commonly reported as a mean and the standard deviation (or some other measure of precision). To appropriately state the sensitivity of the assay and make the data meaningful, one must report the value with the correct number of significant figures. Detailed guidelines exist to help determine the appropriate number of significant figures to report. Rules also exist for rounding off numbers. Generally for analytical procedures, extra numbers are carried forward in the calculations, and the rounding is done on the final answer. Finally, mathematical tests exist for rejecting data obtained that do not match other data gathered. Rejecting data, and therefore excluding them in the final data calculations, must be very carefully considered. It is not the solution to a problem of consistently poor accuracy and precision (22, 24).

REFERENCES

1. SS Nielsen. Introduction to Food Analysis. In: SS Nielsen. ed. Food Analysis, 3rd ed. New York: Kluwer Academic, 2003, pp. 3–13.
2. WA Gould. Total Quality Assurance for the Food Industries. Lancaster, PA: Technomic, 1993.
3. J-L Multon. Analysis and Control Methods for Foods and Agricultural Products. Vol. 1. Quality Control for Foods and Agricultural Products. New York: John Wiley & Sons, 1995.
4. G Linden, WJ Hurst. Analysis and Control Methods for Foods and Agricultural Products. Vol. 2. Analytical Techniques for Foods and Agricultural Products. New York: John Wiley & Sons, 1996.
5. J-L Multon, WJ Stadleman, BA Watkins. Analysis and Control Methods for Foods and Agricultural Products. Vol. 4. Analysis of Food Constituents. New York: John Wiley & Sons, 1997.
6. SS Nielsen. United States Government Regulations and International Standards Related to Food Analysis. In: SS Nielsen. ed. Food Analysis, 3rd ed. New York: Kluwer Academic, 2003, pp. 15–33.
7. AOAC International. Official Methods of Analysis, 17th ed. Gaithersburg, MD: AOAC International, 2000.
8. RL Bradley, Jr. Moisture and Total Solids Analysis. In: SS Nielsen. ed. Food Analysis, 3rd ed. New York: Kluwer Academic, 2003, pp. 81–101.
9. A Proctor, J-F Meullenet. Sampling and Sample Preparation. In: SS Nielsen. ed. Food Analysis, 3rd ed. New York: Kluwer Academic, 2003, pp. 65–77.
10. DC Harris. Quantitative Chemical Analysis, 5th ed. New York: WH Freeman and Co., 1999.
11. SC Puri, D Ennis, K Mullen, 1979. Statistical Quality Control for Food and Agricultural Scientists. Boston, MA: GK Hall and Co., 1979.
12. W Horwitz. Sampling and preparation of samples for chemical examination. Journal of the Association of Official Analytical Chemists 71: 241–245, 1988.
13. AOAC International. A food matrix organizational system applied to collaborative studies. The Referee 17(7): 1, 6, 7, July 1993.

14. C Ellis, D Hite, H van Egmond. Development of methods to test all food matrixes unrealistic, says OMB. Inside Laboratory Management 1(8): 33–35, 1997.

15. AACC. Approved Methods of Analysis, 10th ed. St. Paul, MN: American Association of Cereal Chemists, 2000.

16. AOCS. Official Methods of Recommended Practices, 5th ed. (1999 and 2000/2001 Additions and Revisions). Champaign, IL: American Oil Chemists' Society, 1998.

17. HM Wehr, JF Frank, J.F. (Eds.), Standard Methods for the Examination of Dairy Products, 17th ed. Washington, D.C.: American Public Health Association, 2002.

18. LS Clesceri, AE Greenberg, AD Eaton (Eds.) Standard Methods for the Examination of Water and Wastewater. 20th ed. Washington, D.C.: American Public Health Association, 1998.

19. National Academy of Sciences. Food Chemicals Codex, 5th ed. Washington, D.C.: Food and Nutrition Board, National Research Council. National Academy Press, 2004.

20. CE Carpenter, DG Hendricks. Mineral Analysis. In: SS Nielsen, ed. Food Analysis, 3rd ed. New York: Kluwer Academic, 2003, pp. 189–203.

21. GW Latimer, Jr. Check sample programs keep laboratories in sync. Inside Laboratory Management 1(4): 18–20, 1997.

22. JS Smith. Evaluation of Analytical Data. In: SS Nielsen. ed. Food Analysis, 3rd ed. New York: Kluwer Academic, 2003, pp. 51–64.

23. DA Skoog, DM West, JF Holler, SR Crouch. Analytical Chemistry: An Introduction, 7th ed. Pacific Grove, CA: Brooks/Cole, 2000.

24. PC Meier, EZ Richard. Statistical Methods in Analytical Chemistry, 2nd ed. New York: John Wiley & Sons, 2000.

42 Analysis of the Chemical Composition of Foods

Eunice C. Y. Li-Chan
Food, Nutrition and Health Program, The University of British Columbia

CONTENTS

I. INTRODUCTION

The chemical composition of a food is of utmost importance from many standpoints, including nutrition and health, toxicology and safety, and stability to microbiological, chemical or physical changes. Analysis of these food components is required for regulatory purposes, to provide the data upon which nutrition labels and health claims are based, and for the information of health-conscious consumers. Food analysis is also used to monitor the stability or, conversely, the deterioration or reactivity of food components as a function of processing or storage conditions throughout the food distribution chain, which can influence decisions to control parameters for the purpose of quality assurance.

Foods are often characterized by the composition of their chemical components. However, a wide range in the precise levels of those constituents may in fact exist, due to intrinsic biological variability, multiplicity of cultivars and variants of each species, or as a result of geographical location, environmental and seasonal influences, or from the application of genetic engineering. Furthermore, the chemical composition of foods may also be influenced by natural or unintentional contaminants, by processing or upon storage. This potentially wide range of composition and characteristics leads to difficulty in defining the chemical composition of foods, and to issues of validating authenticity or detecting adulteration issues (1).

Given the fact that the constituents comprising foods are very large, both in number and diversity, it is not surprising that the analysis of the chemical composition of foods also encompasses a wide scope as well as a large number of techniques. Chapter 41 describes some key considerations for selecting the most appropriate method, including the objectives of the analysis, nature of the sample, and the available resources. The reported quantity of a food component may depend on the method used for its analysis. There is a need to develop standard specifications for food commodities, as well as more precise nomenclature and detailed description and classification of foods and their components (2), and identification of key foods for food composition research (3). The use of International Network of Food Data Systems (INFOODS)

tagnames has been proposed to provide clarity when describing the new nutrient variables (4). Examples of tagnames are described in Tables 42.1 A–D (5).

An overview of the chemical composition of foods can be obtained by conducting proximate analysis, which refers to the measurement of the major components of food, namely moisture, minerals or "ash," lipids, proteins, and carbohydrates. However, even within this simplified classification of food composition, the method of analysis is influential and should be clearly stated when reporting data, as illustrated in the tagnames for fat, protein, and carbohydrate (Tables 42.1 B–D, respectively.).

Further analysis of the composition is often conducted to meet the requirements for nutritional labeling, such as the contents of particular minerals and vitamins, cholesterol, saturated, monounsaturated and polyunsaturated fatty acids, simple sugars, and dietary fiber (6). Table 42.2 lists the nutrients in the United States Department of Agriculture's National Nutrient Database (7), while Table 42.3 shows the nutrients listed in the Canadian "Nutrition Facts Table Core Nutrition Information" as well as the methods of analysis used by the Canadian Food Inspection Agency (8).

More detailed analyses, usually preceded by fractionation and purification steps, are available to determine the precise nature of individual constituents. For example, rapid advances in proteomics have enabled sequence analysis of the multitudes of proteins naturally occurring in a cell, including isoforms or variants that may differ from each other by a single amino acid (9). Similarly, sophisticated instrumental analyses have been developed

TABLE 42.1A

Examples of INFOODS Tagnames Describing Moisture and Ash Contents and Energy Value of Foods

INFOODS Tagname	Component	Comments
\<DM\>	Dry matter	
\<WATER\>	Water Synonym: moisture	
\<ASH\>	Ash Synonym: minerals	
\<ENER\>	Energy, method of determination unknown Synonyms: kilojoules; kilocalories; calories; food energy	The tagname should be used if it is not known whether the energy value represents gross energy or total metabolizable energy. It should also be used if it is known that the energy value was calculated from the proximate components but the conversion factors used are unknown.
\<ENERA\>	Energy, gross; determined by direct analysis using bomb calorimetry Synonyms: kilojoules; kilocalories; Calories; food energy	
\<ENERC\>	Energy, total metabolizable; calculated from the energy-producing food components. Synonyms: kilojoules; kilocalories; calories; food energy	In addition to a value for the quantity of total metabolizable energy, includes a description or listing of the conversion factors used to calculate this energy value from the proximate quantities.

Source: Taken from "Tagnames for food components" on the INFOODS website at http://www.fao.org/infoods/tagnames_en.stm (accessed June 18, 2003), from Klensin et al. (5).

TABLE 42.1B

Examples of INFOODS Tagnames for Selected Food Components Related to Fat and Fatty Acids

INFOODS Tagname	Component	Comments
<FAT>	Fat, total; Synonym: total lipid	
<FATCE>	Fat, total; derived by analysis using continuous extraction	The Soxhlet method has often been used to analyze for total fat using continuous extraction. This method tends to underestimate the total fat value of a food.
<FATRN>	Fatty acids, total trans	
<FASAT>	Fatty acids, total saturated	
<FACID> ∶	Fatty acids, total	Two data items are required for tagname <FACID>: the total quantity of fatty acids and identification of the conversion factor used to calculate this value from the quantity of total fat.
<FADT>	Fatty acids, total double trans	Some countries are planning actions to limit these acids (not single trans) from foods, e.g., chocolate.
<FAESS>	Fatty acids, total essential	This value is the sum of linoleic acid, linolenic acid, and arachidonic acid.
<FAFRE>	Fatty acids, total free	
<FAMS>	Fatty acids, total monounsaturated	
<FAPU>	Fatty acids, total polyunsaturated	
<FAPUN3>	Fatty acids, total omega-3 polyunsaturated	

Source: Taken from "Tagnames for food components" on the INFOODS website at http://www.fao.org/infoods/tagnames_en.stm (accessed June 18, 2003), from Klensin et al. (5).

for the identification and quantitation of positional and geometric isomers of fatty acids in lipids (10, 11), and the nature of monosaccharide building blocks and their linkages in oligo- or polysaccharides (12).

It is beyond the scope of this chapter to describe all these aspects of food analysis. This chapter will primarily focus on methods for proximate analysis for the composition of major components of foods, and will briefly allude to some of the other components that are part of the nutrition facts listed on food labels in North America. An overview will be given of the principles and considerations behind official methods and some rapid methods of analysis, and some of the recent trends in analysis of chemical composition of foods will be explored.

The reader is encouraged to consult two excellent textbooks by Nielsen (13) and Pomeranz and Meloan (14) for more in-depth discussion on proximate analysis, and other methods of food analysis, as well as the principles behind some of the instrumental methods used in analysis. Primary literature sources such as the *Journal of Food Composition and Analysis* should be consulted for current trends and issues of interest in the analysis of chemical composition of foods. Detailed protocols for official methods of analysis have been compiled by various scientific organizations (e.g., AOAC International, the American Association of Cereal Chemists, the American Oil Chemists' Society, the International Dairy Federation), government agencies (e.g., the Food and Drug Administration in the United States, Health Canada and the Canadian Food Inspection Agency in Canada), and international bodies (e.g., the International Organization

for Standardization and the Codex Alimentarius Commission). In addition to publications about methods for analysis, most of these scientific organizations and government agencies have useful information on analysis of chemical composition of foods at their websites. As a good starting point, the reader is encouraged to browse the internet addresses provided in the chapters by Nielsen (15) and Nielsen and Metzger (6). The Compendium of Methods for Chemical Analysis of Foods on the Health Canada website (http://www.hc-sc.gc.ca/food-aliment/cs-ipc/fr-ra/e_chem_analysis_ foods.html) (16) is also a useful resource. Global standards are coordinated by the Codex Alimentarius Commission (for example, see references 17–19), and detailed information such as standards, the current meetings and deliberations of expert committees, etc. are described at its official website (http://www.codexalimentarius.net/index_en.stm#) (20).

II. PROXIMATE ANALYSIS

Pomeranz and Meloan (14) defined proximate analysis as "the determination of the major components (moisture, minerals, carbohydrates, lipids, and proteins)." The data from proximate analysis are typically included in standard tables of composition of foods, such as the U.S. Department of Agriculture Nutrient Database for Standard Reference (7). The following sections provide an overview on the methods that may be used for determining each of the major components in proximate analysis. Many of the methods cited here are official methods of AOAC International (21; accessible also on CD-ROM), and the reader is encouraged to refer to

TABLE 42.1C
Examples of INFOODS Tagnames Describing Protein and Nitrogen Contents of Foods

INFOODS Tagname	Component	Comments
\<NNP\>	Nitrogen, non-protein	
\<NPRO\>	Nitrogen, protein	
\<NT\>	Nitrogen, total	Determined by Kjeldahl method
\<PRO-\>	Protein, total; method of determination unknown	The \<PRO-\> tagname should be used for a total protein value when it is not known whether the value was the result of a direct analysis or whether it was calculated from total nitrogen, protein nitrogen, or amino nitrogen. The \<PRO-\> tagname should also be used if it is known that the total protein value was calculated from one of the nitrogen components, but the conversion factor used in the calculation is unknown.
\<PROA\>	Protein, total; determined by direct analysis	
\<PROCN\>	Protein, total; calculated from amino nitrogen	Two pieces of data are associated with the tagname \<PROCNA\>. The first is the quantity of total protein and the second is the conversion factor used to calculate total protein from amino nitrogen. Note: The total protein found in food tables is rarely calculated from amino nitrogen. \<PROCNT\> is the appropriate tagname for total protein in most cases.
\<PROCNP\>	Protein, total; calculated from protein nitrogen	Two pieces of data are associated with the tagname \<PROCNP\>. The first is the quantity of total protein and the second is the conversion factor used to calculate total protein from protein nitrogen. Note: The total protein found in food tables is rarely calculated from protein nitrogen. \<PROCNT\> is the appropriate tagname for total protein in most cases.
\<PROCNT\>	Protein, total; calculated from total protein nitrogen	Three pieces of data are associated with the tagname \<PROCNT\>. The first is the quantity of total protein; the second is a keyword which identifies the source of the conversion factor used to calculate the total protein from total nitrogen; and the third is the actual conversion factor used. If possible, all three pieces of data should be included with \<PROCNT\>. However, it is acceptable to include only the keyword or the conversion factor (rather than both) with the total protein value if one or the other is unknown. If the conversion factor used was generated from a source other than one of those identified by the available keywords, the conversion factor should be listed without any keyword information.

Source: taken from "Tagnames for food components" on the INFOODS website at http://www.fao.org/infoods/tagnames_en.stm (accessed June 18, 2003), from Klensin et al. (5).

these methods and the original references cited therein for more detail. The reader is also referred to other chapters in this handbook for descriptions of various spectroscopic techniques and other instrumental methods of analysis, as well as more detailed coverage of protein and fat analysis.

A. WATER (MOISTURE)

The moisture content of foods can range from 0 (e.g., for granulated sugar or vegetable oil) to over 90% (e.g., in raw watermelon or cucumbers) (22). The determination of the water or moisture content of a food and, conversely, of the dry matter or total solids (% solids = 100% − % moisture), is important not only to provide a basis for expressing the content of the other components on a wet- or

dry-basis, but also as an important factor in food stability and quality. Moisture assays can be one of the most important analyses performed on a food product and yet one of the most difficult in terms of obtaining adequate precision and accuracy (22).

1. Overview of and Considerations for Moisture Determination

Water may exist in foods in free form, as tightly adsorbed water, or as chemically bound water of hydration. The percentage of water that is actually measured is dependent on the method used for its analysis, and it is therefore important to always state the exact methodology used when reporting

TABLE 42.1D

Examples of INFOODS Tagnames for Selected Food Components Related to Total Carbohydrate, Fibre, Starch, and Sugars

INFOODS Tagname	Component	Comments
<CHO->	Carbohydrate, total; method of determination unknown	
<CHOCDF>	Carbohydrate, total; calculated by difference	This value is calculated using the following formula: 100 g minus total grams of water, protein, fat, and ash
<CHOCSM>	Carbohydrate, total; calculated by summation	This value is the sum of the sugars, starches, oligosaccharides, and carbohydrate dietary fibre.
<CHOAVL>	Carbohydrate, available	This value includes the free sugars plus dextrins, starch, and glycogen.
<CHOAVLM>	Carbohydrate, available; expressed in monosaccharide equivalents	This value includes the free sugars plus dextrins, starch, and glycogen.
<FIBAD>	Fibre; determined by acid detergent method	Includes cellulose, lignin, and some hemicelluloses
<FIBADC>.	Fibre, acid detergent method, Clancy modification	
<FIBC>	Fibre, crude	The crude fibre method of fibre analysis is obsolete
<FIBHEX>	Hexoses in dietary fibre	
<FIBINS>	Fibre, water-insoluble	Sum of insoluble components from the AOAC total dietary fibre method; includes primarily lignin, cellulose, and most of the hemicellulose Values for <FIBINS> may also be obtained by subtracting soluble fibre from total dietary fibre, i.e., by subtracting the value of <FIBSOL> from the value of <FIBTG>.
<FIBND>	Fibre; determined by neutral detergent method	Includes lignin, cellulose, and insoluble hemicellulose
<FIBSOL>	Fibre, water-soluble	Sum of soluble components from the AOAC total dietary fibre method; includes primarily algal polysaccharides, gums, pectins, and mucilages
<FIBTG>	Fibre, total dietary; determined gravimetrically by the AOAC total dietary fibre method	Sum of the water-soluble components and the water-insoluble components of dietary fibre; can be calculated by adding the values of <FIBSOL> and <FIBINS>; includes all non-starch polysaccharides and lignin
<FIBTS>	Fibre, total dietary; sum of non-starch polysaccharide components and lignin	Sum of the polysaccharide components of dietary fibre measured sequentially on the same sample (for example, by using the Southgate colorimetric procedure) plus lignin measured gravimetrically
<FIB->	Fibre; method of determination unknown	Note: Tagname <FIB-> is used to identify fibre values which represent unknown fibre components or which were obtained by unknown methods. Additional tagnames for fibre may be created to identify fibre components or specific methods of analysis that are not currently addressed in this listing.
<STARCH>	Starch, total	The sum of all polysaccharides yielding glucose after hydrolysis with suitable enzymes; includes amylose, amylopectin, glycogen, and dextrins
<STARCHM>	Starch, total; expressed in monosaccharide equivalents	The sum of all polysaccharides yielding glucose after hydrolysis with suitable enzymes; includes amylose, amylopectin, glycogen, and dextrins.
<STARES>	Starch, resistant Synonym: retrograded starch	
<SUGAR>	Sugars, total	Sum of free monosaccharides and disaccharides.

Source: Taken from "Tagnames for food components" on the INFOODS website at http://www.fao.org/infoods/tagnames_en.stm (accessed June 18, 2003), from Klensin et al. (5).

TABLE 42.2
Nutrients Listed in the USDA National Nutrient Database, Available Sorted Either by Food Description or in Descending Order by Nutrient Content in Terms of Common Household Measures

Nutrient
Moisture
Protein
Fat
Energy (Calories)
Carbohydrate (by difference)
Total dietary fiber
Total sugar
Calcium
Iron
Magnesium
Phosphorus
Potassium
Sodium
Zinc
Copper
Manganese
Selenium
Vitamin A (IU)
Vitamin A (RAE)
Vitamin E (alpha-tocopherol)
Vitamin K (phylloquinone)
Vitamin C
Thiamin
Riboflavin
Niacin
Pantothenic acid
Vitamin B-6
Vitamin B-12
Dietary folate equivalents
Cholesterol
Total saturated fatty acids
Total monounsaturated fatty acids
Total polyunsaturated fatty acids

Source: USDA 2004 (7).

moisture content. Methods for moisture determination include oven drying, distillation, and titration, as well as methods based on physical properties. Some of these methods are described in further detail in the following sections.

In addition to moisture content, water activity (a_w) is often measured and used as an indicator of the availability of water in food for chemical or enzymatic reactions or microbiological growth. Water activity is defined as the ratio of the partial pressure of water above a sample to the vapor pressure of pure water at the same temperature, and is commonly measured by sensors that measure the relative humidity of the sample atmosphere after equilibration, or by a variation of this method known as the chilled mirror technique (22).

It is important to bear in mind that some foods are prone to either gain moisture from or lose moisture to the surrounding atmosphere, depending on the nature of the food constituents, the relative humidity and temperature of the environment, and other parameters such as surface area. Detailed protocols for sampling and sample preparation have been described for different categories of foods (21), and should be followed to ensure that representative samples reflecting the composition of the food can be obtained for the analysis.

2. Oven Drying Methods

The principle of moisture determination by oven drying is based on evaporation of water from the sample, and calculation of moisture based on loss in weight. Oven drying methods are therefore considered as "indirect" methods, since moisture is not actually determined per se.

While the theory behind moisture determination by oven drying is simple, and routine simultaneous analysis of multiple samples is possible, in practice many factors must be considered. The amount of moisture removed during oven drying is influenced by many variables, including the time and temperature of drying, the type of oven used, and the type of sample.

Although the boiling point of pure water is 100°C, the presence of solutes raises the boiling point. This boiling point elevation continues throughout the drying process, as the sample becomes increasingly concentrated upon the removal of water. In theory, the higher the drying temperature, the more complete the moisture removal and the shorter the time required. It has been reported that a temperature of 250°C is required to obtain the true moisture content, assuming no adsorbed water present at the temperature in question (22). However, in practice, volatilization, deterioration, and chemical reactions of the constituents may occur at high temperatures, and it is prudent to use the minimum temperature that will allow moisture removal at an acceptable rate (14, 22). Drying in a vacuum oven may be preferred for some food samples since the boiling point is lower under vacuum, and the absence of air can minimize oxidative reactions especially of high fat samples during drying.

Using vacuum ovens and forced draft or convection ovens, the temperatures and times specified for various products typically range from 70–130°C and 1–16 hours, respectively. For example, the time-temperature combinations are 1 h at 130±3°C for solids (total) and moisture in flour (AOAC Official Method 925.10), 6 h at 70±1°C in a vacuum oven for moisture in dried fruits (AOAC Official Method 934.06), 16–18 h at 100–102°C in an air oven or 2–4 h at ca 125°C in a mechanical convection or gravity oven for moisture in meat (AOAC Official Method 950.46B(a) and (b)). More rapid drying, on the order of minutes, can be accomplished using infrared or microwave ovens for drying. Official methods stipulating different temperature-time combinations or oven types for the same food material have been approved for some

TABLE 42.3
Methods of Analysis Used by the Canadian Food Inspection Agency for the Nutrition Facts Table Core Nutrition Information

Nutrient	Method Reference	Technique
Calories	Atwater Method (Guide to Food Labelling and Advertising, section 6.4.1)	Application of Atwater factors to fat, carbohydrate and protein content
Fat (Sum of fatty acids expressed as triglycerides)	AOAC 996.06*	Capillary Gas Chromatography using SP2560 100m × 0.25mm, 0.2μm film column
Fatty acids: Saturates (all fatty acids that contain no double bonds) *trans* (unsaturated fatty acids that contain one or more isolated or non-conjugated double bonds in trans configuration)	AOAC 996.06*	Capillary Gas Chromatography using SP2560 100m × 0.25mm, 0.2μm film column
Cholesterol	AOAC 994.10*	Direct Saponification and Capillary Gas Chromatography
Carbohydrate (mono- and di-saccharides + starch+ fibre+sugar alcohols+ polydextrose)	By Difference (100-%ash-%moisture-%protein-%fat)	Determination by applicable AOAC method for Ash, Moisture, Protein, Fat
	HPB FA-78**, available carbohydrate, in special cases	Acid and enzymatic hydrolysis followed by redox titration
Fibre	AOAC 992.16* (Mongeau) or AOAC 985.29* (Prosky) (as in Guide to Food Labelling and Advertising 6.4.4.3)	Gravimetric determination after defatting and enzymatic hydrolysis of protein and carbohydrate (starch). (Results found non-compliant by Mongeau method should be confirmed by Prosky method)
Sugars (all monosaccharides and disaccharides)	AOAC 980.13* (modified HPLC column and mobile phase)	Aqueous food extraction followed by HPLC-RI
Protein	AOAC 981.10* AOAC 993.13*	Nitrogen by Kjeldahl or Combustion
Vitamin A (retinol and derivatives and beta carotene expressed as retinol equivalents, RE)	AOAC 992.04*	HPLC determination of vitamin A with UV detection
	(Method A-12 (version 3.0) 1993**) Determination of Vitamin A in milk, infant formula, and other complex food commodities. JAOAC. 76: 2, 1993	
	Method A-7** HPLC Determination of Vitamin A in margarine, milk, partially skimmed milk, and skimmed milk. JAOAC 63: 4, 1980	HPLC determination of vitamin A with UV detection
	Method LPFC-200** The fluorometric determination of Vitamin A in dairy products. J. Dairy Sci. 55:1077 (1992)	Fluorometric determination of vitamin A
Vitamin C (L-ascorbic acid and L-dehydroascorbic acid and their derivatives, calculated as mg equivalents L-ascorbic acid)	HPLC-C1 (1992)** Determination of vitamin C by HPLC. References: 1) Pelletier, O., and Brassard, R. Determination of Vitamin C in food by manual and automated methods. J. Food Sci., 42:1471–1477, 1977. 2) Behrens, W.A., and Madere, R. Ascorbic and Dehydroascorbic acid content of infant formula J. Food Comp. Anal., 2: 48–52, 1989. 3) Behrens, W. A., and Madere, R. Ascorbic and dehydroascorbic acid contents of canned food and frozen concentrated orange juice. J. Food Comp. Anal., 3: 3–8, 1990. 4) Behrens, W. A., and Madere, R. A Highly sensitive high-performance liquid chromatography method for the estimation of	HPLC determination of vitamin C with electrochemical detection

Continued

TABLE 42.3 *(Continued)*

Nutrient	Method Reference	Technique
	ascorbic and dehydroascorbic acid in tissues, biological fluids, and foods. Analytical Biochemistry 165:102–107, 1987.	
Iron	LPFC-137 **	Preparation of samples by calcination to determine different elements by Atomic Absorption Flame Spectroscopy
Calcium	LPFC-137**	Atomic Absorption Flame Spectroscopy
Sodium	LPFC-125** A rapid method for the determination of sodium and potassium.	Preparation of samples by aqueous extraction and flame emission spectroscopy.

* *Official Methods of Analysis of AOAC International* (Ed. W. Horowitz., AOAC International, Gaithersburg, Maryland.

** LPFC are laboratory procedures available from the CFIA or Health Canada websites.

Source: Canadian Food Inspection Agency 2002 (8).

foods, e.g., AOAC Official Methods 925.23, 990.19, and 990.20 for solids (total) in milk. The final choice of the appropriate method may depend on factors such as the need for speed, or further analyses using the dried material, or the availability of equipment. In order to determine the optimal temperature and time for drying of specific food products or using new equipment not described in the official methods published by scientific organizations, analysts should conduct their own trials and establish the appropriate conditions based on the resultant drying curves.

Additional steps conducted prior to oven drying are recommended for some types of samples. For example, a two-stage drying process involving a steam bath for pre-drying is frequently suggested for liquid products, while air-drying and grinding are performed prior to oven drying for samples such as bread or grain. Since surface area and porosity of the sample influence rate and efficiency of drying, and since surface crust formation, or case hardening, can impede moisture removal, sand or other inert material may be added prior to drying of food materials which have a tendency to lump together or to form a surface crust, such as dehydrated fruits or other foods high in sugar.

3. Distillation Methods

The moisture content of spices, nuts, oils and other foodstuff with relatively low moisture content can be measured directly through distillation methods (e.g., AOAC Official Methods 986.21 and 969.19 for spices and cheese, respectively). Water is co-distilled with an immiscible solvent with a high boiling point; the distilled water is condensed, collected, and measured in a collecting vessel or trap. Since direct measurement of water is involved, distillation methods can provide better accuracy and precision than oven drying methods based on weight loss,

especially for low-moisture samples. However, it should be noted that samples are still exposed to high temperatures during distillation, and therefore these methods are not suitable for analysis of heat-sensitive foods. In addition, distillation techniques are not easily amenable to routine testing of multiple samples.

4. Chemical Methods – Karl Fischer Titration

The Karl Fischer titration method is suitable for low-moisture foods that are sensitive to decomposition or volatilization under vacuum or high temperatures, such as dried fruits and vegetables (AOAC Official Method 967.19), candies and chocolates (AOAC Official Method 977.10), roasted coffee beans, oils and fats (AOAC Official Method 984.20). Several modifications of the original Karl Fischer method, which was based on the colorimetric detection of a stoichiometric reaction involving the reduction of iodine by sulfur dioxide in the presence of water, have been proposed over the years, leading to the commercial availability of titration units that automatically dispense the required proportions of reagents and titrants for conductometric or coulometric assay, and provide digital displays of the calculated moisture content.

5. Physical Methods

Physical methods of moisture determination are based on the measurement of various physical properties of food samples, such as dielectric constant, conductivity, specific gravity or density, refractive index, freezing point, or absorption of energy in the mid- or near-infrared spectrum, followed by comparison to the corresponding properties of standards with known moisture content (22). For example, hydrometry using a calibrated lactometer is applied to determine the total solids content of milk

(AOAC Official Method 925.23B), while refractometry is used to determine solids in syrups (AOAC Official Method 932.14C). Near-infrared spectrophotometry is used for water content in dried vegetables (AOAC Official Method 967.19), while mid-infrared spectroscopy forms the basis for using IRMA (Infrared Milk Analyzers) for proximate analysis of milk, including solids, fat, lactose, and protein (AOAC Official Method 972.16).

Physical methods often provide rapid analysis of large numbers of samples, but it is important to bear in mind that the relationship between the measured physical property and the moisture content of the specific food sample must be known, either by reference to published tables of standard composition for that food, or by construction of standard curves by the analyst.

B. ASH

Ash is defined as the inorganic material remaining after oxidation of organic matter, and is used to refer to the total minerals in food. The ash content of unprocessed fruits and vegetables typically ranges from about 0.4% in raw tomatoes (23) to 4% in beans (14). Pure fats and oils contain practically no minerals, while the ash content of salted butter is about 2.1%. Similarly, fresh meat and poultry contain about 1% ash, while dried and salted beef may contain as high as 12% ash (14). Milling of wheat yields white flour with 0.47% ash, or whole wheat flour with 1.60% ash (7). The determination of ash content may thus be used as an indicator of the extent of processing of a food commodity, or of the addition of salt to foods.

1. Overview of and Considerations for Ash Determination

Minerals in foods may occur as complexes with other minerals, or with macromolecules such as proteins. The incineration or oxidation of organic matter during ashing may result in volatilization of some minerals, or formation of new complexes of other minerals, as summarized by Pomeranz and Meloan (14). Both the amount and the composition of ash that remains after incineration or oxidation therefore depend on the nature of the food and the method of ashing. This is an important consideration in selection of the ashing method and conditions, especially if further analysis of specific minerals (e.g., Ca, Zn, Fe, and so on) is required (24).

Since minerals often constitute 1% or less of the total wet weight of a food sample, it is critical that contamination of the food with metals or their salts be avoided. Potential sources of trace metal contaminants include glassware, grinders or metal blades used for sample preparation, and the crucibles used to hold the samples during ashing.

The two main methods of ashing, which are termed dry ashing and wet ashing, are described in the following sections.

2. Dry Ashing

Dry ashing involves the incineration of samples in a muffle furnace at high temperatures ranging from 400–700°C and typically around 525 or 550°C for 12–18 hours, until a light gray or white powder remains (14). The residue after incineration is weighed as a direct measure of the ash content.

Some modifications of the basic dry ashing procedure are required depending on the sample. High fat or moisture content may cause smoking or spattering during ashing of samples. Therefore, liquid samples may be pre-dried, and fat from high fat samples should be extracted with a solvent, prior to ashing. In most cases, dry ashing can be performed using the solids remaining after oven-drying or solvent extraction conducted for moisture or fat determination, respectively. A few drops of ashless olive oil may be added to animal products, syrups, and spices, to allow steam to escape as a crust is formed on the product (23). Incomplete combustion, especially in high sugar samples, is manifested by the appearance of black or carbon residues in the ash, and requires re-suspension in water or acid, followed by re-ashing (e.g., see AOAC Official Method 900.02, for ash of sugars and syrups). Acceleration of dry ashing may be achieved by the addition of an ethanol solution of magnesium acetate. The magnesium acetate method for ash content of flour (AOAC Official Method 936.07) uses a temperature of 700°C for ashing, compared to 550°C for the direct method (AOAC Official Method 923.03). New microwave muffle furnaces with temperatures reaching up to 1200°C can also reduce ashing time to minutes instead of hours (23).

Dry ashing is simple in both theory and practice, and simultaneous analysis of many samples is feasible. However, as noted in the preceding section, the composition of the minerals in the residue is not usually identical to that in the original food sample, and it is assumed that losses due to volatilization or other causes are compensated by gains due to formation of new complexes such as oxides. Formation of fusion complexes between some minerals means that the dry ash is not usually suitable for further analysis of specific mineral content. To address this, a method of dry ashing of different categories of foods for determination of individual contents of Na, K, Ca, Mg, Fe, Zn, Cu, and Mn was established by the Health Protection Branch Laboratories of Health Canada (25). The protocol involves dry ashing at 450°C for 16 hours, followed by addition of water and nitric acid, evaporation to remove the acid, and re-ashing at 375°C for another hour. Lanthanum and cesium solutions are added as ionization suppressors, to allow determination of Ca, Mg and Na, K, respectively.

3. Wet Ashing

Wet ashing is also referred to as wet oxidation or wet digestion. It involves the oxidation or digestion of organic matter by heating in the presence of concentrated acids such as nitric acid, sulfuric acid (usually with hydrogen peroxide) or perchloric acid, either singly or in combination. A typical wet ashing procedure involves heating or boiling of the sample with concentrated sulfuric and nitric acids, at about 200°C, until white fumes from decomposing sulfuric acid are observed; additional nitric acid is then added, and boiling or ashing of the sample is continued until a clear or light yellow solution is obtained (23).

Due to the lower temperatures and shorter times involved in wet ashing, less volatilization or fusion of minerals occurs, compared to dry ashing. The minerals usually stay in solution after wet ashing, and further analysis of the composition of individual minerals may be performed, for example, using atomic absorption spectrophotometry or inductively coupled plasma emission spectrophotometry. Despite these advantages of wet ashing for specific mineral composition, wet ashing is not usually preferred over dry ashing as the method for total ash content determination. This is because of the dangers of using corrosive acids, especially perchloric acid which is potentially explosive, specifically in the presence of undigested biological components, and the relatively limited number of samples which can be analyzed at one time. Combination dry-wet ashing methods have been proposed, for example, for analysis of minerals in infant formula (AOAC Official Method 985.35). Specially designed microwave ovens have also been proposed for safer and quicker wet ashing of sample, using either open-vessel or closed-vessel digestion systems depending on the amount of sample and the temperatures required for digestion (23).

C. Fat

The term "fat" is often used synonymously with "lipid" or "oil" to represent food components that are insoluble in water but are soluble in organic solvents (14). The fat content of foods varies widely, from less than 1% in many fruits and vegetables, to almost 100% in lard, shortening, or vegetable oils (7).

1. Overview of and Considerations for Fat Determination

The methods for fat determination may be generally classified into (i) methods that involve solvent extraction of fat from the food, followed by gravimetric, volumetric, or other means of measurement of the fat, and (ii) instrumental methods that measure the fat content based on its physical properties in the food, in comparison to standards of known composition. Other methods involving extraction of fat without the use of solvents have also been developed.

Methods using solvent extraction in fat analysis are based on the functional definition of fats, as substances that are insoluble in water but soluble in organic solvents. However, this functional definition of fat does not give the true picture of its heterogeneity in terms of chemical composition. Fat in foods consists primarily of highly non-polar or hydrophobic molecules classified as triacylglycerols, with smaller amounts of di- and mono-acylglycerols, sterols, and the somewhat more polar molecules such as phospholipids and sphingolipids. Minor components such as fat-soluble vitamins, pigments, or hydrocarbons are also included as "fat" when defined by the property of solubility, whereas free fatty acids, especially the shorter chain fatty acids, may be water-soluble and therefore not included as fat.

In addition to heterogeneity in the type of molecule, further diversity of fat composition exists as a function of the chain length as well as saturation or degree of unsaturation of the hydrocarbon chain of fatty acid constituents of fats. Depending on the exact chemical composition, the constituents of "fat" in a particular food sample may encompass a wide range on the polarity scale. Consequently, the composition as well as the efficiency of extraction of these different components of fat from food are dependent on the polarity of the solvent used for extraction. Furthermore, fats in foods frequently occur in bound form, for example, as non-covalent complexes with proteins or carbohydrates, or as lipoproteins or glyco-lipids. Organic solvents do not usually extract the fat molecules in these bound forms, unless they are released prior to extraction by pre-treatment with mild acid, alkali, or enzymatic digestion. The fat content determined by direct extraction with non-polar solvents is usually termed "crude fat," while that determined by extraction after a pre-treatment may be referred to as "total lipids."

It is worth noting that the "total lipid (fat)" content reported in the USDA Nutrient Database, and identified as "nutrient 204," was determined for most foods by gravimetric methods such as those using ether or chloroform-methanol solvent extraction, or by acid hydrolysis (7). However, "Nutrient 204 may not be identical to the fat level declared on food labels under the Nutrition Labelling and Education Act of 1990 (NLEA). Under NLEA, fat is expressed as the amount of triglyceride that would produce the analytically determined amount of lipid fatty acids" (7). Similarly, the fat content reported in the "Nutrition Facts Table Core Nutrition Information" on food labels in Canada (Table 42.3) is also based on the sum of fatty acids, expressed as triglycerides, analyzed by capillary gas chromatography (AOAC Official Method 996.06).

2. Solvent Extraction Methods

Solvent extraction may be continuous (e.g., the Goldfish method), semi-continuous (e.g., the Soxhlet method for cereals AOAC Official Method 920.39C), or discontinuous (e.g., Mojonnier method for milk fat AOAC Official Method 989.05).

In the continuous method of solvent extraction, evaporating solvent from a boiling flask continuously condenses onto the dried sample held in a thimble. The solvent, carrying fat extracted as solvent drips through the sample, is collected back in the boiling flask. After completion of extraction, typically 4 hours to overnight (depending on the rate of solvent dripping through the sample), the solvent is evaporated from the extraction flask by air-drying overnight followed by brief oven drying, and the fat remaining in the flask is weighed. The semi-continuous solvent extraction method is similar except the extraction apparatus is constructed to allow solvent to remain with and soak the sample for 5–10 minutes, prior to returning to the boiling flask. In this manner, the sample is surrounded by solvent, thus avoiding channeling of solvent and providing for a more complete extraction of fat from the sample. For this reason, the semi-continuous methods, particularly the Soxhlet method, are often considered the standard methods for fat analysis of dried samples (26, 27).

For efficient extraction by both the Goldfish and the Soxhlet methods, it is important that samples are dried and ground to small particle size to maximize the surface area for extraction. Efficient extraction by organic solvents can only be achieved on dry samples, due to the inability of the organic solvents to penetrate the water phase of wet samples. Ethyl ether and petroleum ether are the most commonly used solvents for extraction by these methods. Ethyl ether is slightly more polar than petroleum ether and is a better solvent for fat. However, sample drying becomes essential to avoid extraction of non-fat components by ethyl ether; in addition, ethyl ether has a tendency to form peroxides and is more flammable than petroleum ether. Petroleum ether is cheaper, less dangerous and preferred over ethyl ether if a more selective solvent for hydrophobic lipids is desired (26).

The Roese-Gottlieb and the Mojonnier methods (AOAC Official Methods 905.02 and 989.05, respectively) are official methods for analysis of fat in milk, involving the release of bound fat by alkaline digestion with ammonium hydroxide, addition of ethanol, followed by sequential, discontinuous extraction of fat using ethyl ether and petroleum ether. The extractions are repeated three times and carried out in flasks designed to facilitate decanting of the fat-containing organic solvent (top layer) from the aqueous solution (bottom layer) during extraction. The fat-containing solvents from the repeated extractions are pooled, the solvent is removed by evaporation, and the weight of the fat is measured to determine the fat content. The Mojonnier method, using acid instead of alkali pre-treatment, has been modified for determination of fat content in flour (AOAC Official Method 922.06) and pet food (AOAC Official Method 954.02).

As an alternative method to gravimetric measurement (i.e., by weight), the measurement of refractive index has been proposed as a method to determine fat that has been extracted by solvent (14, 26). Fat is extracted using a discontinuous method with a solvent such as bromonaphthalene, which has a refractive index that is different from the fat to be extracted. The fat content is calculated by comparing the refractive index measured for the solvent containing the extracted fat, to the refractive index of solvent alone and that of the standard fat. The refractive index method has been reported to yield values of fat content comparable to the crude fat content measured gravimetrically.

For all of the solvent extraction-based methods, the content of fat analyzed depends on whether or not pre-treatments such as addition of acid or alkali to release bound fat have been performed, as well as the polarity of solvent used for extraction. For example, the content of "fat (crude) or ether extract in flour" (AOAC Official Method 920.85) would be expected to differ from that of "fat in flour – acid hydrolysis method" (AOAC Official Method 922.06). Many researchers have reported that the amounts of extracted lipid as well as non-lipid material increase with the polarity of solvents used for extraction. The binding of lipids to other molecules such as carbohydrates and proteins, and the differing abilities of solvent or solvent mixtures to solubilize lipid classes has led to the concept of "total lipid extract" and "extractable lipid" (28). Even with ammonia pretreatment to release bound lipids, the Roese-Gottlieb method was reported to grossly underestimate the total lipid content of samples such as chocolate powder, liquid milk, and eggs (28); this could be due to the use of relatively non-polar solvents, ethyl and petroleum ethers, for extraction after hydrolysis. More polar solvent mixtures such as dichloromethane-hexane (1:4) or acetone-hexane (1:4) have been suggested to improve the efficiency of extraction from dry solid samples using the Soxhlet method (28). For wet or liquid samples, specific ratios of chloroform and methanol are used in combination with water in the Bligh and Dyer method (29) and in AOAC Official Method 983.23 for determining "fat in foods" after enzymatic hydrolysis. In a modified Bligh and Dyer procedure, methanol is replaced by propan-2-ol, and chloroform is replaced by cyclohexane, with a ratio of 11:8:10 for water:propan-2-ol:cyclohexane; the modified procedure has the advantage that the extracted lipid is in the top (cyclohexane) layer of the extraction mixture, compared to the bottom layer when chloroform is used (28).

3. Non-Solvent Separation Methods

The Babcock method for milk fat (AOAC Official Methods 989.04 and 989.10) is the best-known example of a non-solvent wet extraction or separation method for fat analysis. Concentrated sulfuric acid (with specific gravity of 1.82–1.83 at 20°C) is added to a specified weight of milk sample in the Babcock bottle, digesting protein and generating heat, and thus releasing bound fat from the sample. The acid also functions to increase the density of the aqueous layer. Subsequent centrifugation at 55–60°C and addition of hot water at that temperature cause the fat layer to float on top of the aqueous layer into the calibrated neck of the Babcock bottle, where the percentage of fat content is read directly from the volumetrically calibrated markings.

The Babcock method has been adapted for determination of fat in other dairy products such as cream and cheese, as well as for essential oil in flavor extracts (AOAC Official Method 932.11) and fat in seafood (AOAC Official Method 964.12) (26). Similar to the Mojonnier method, the Babcock method can be applied to wet or liquid as well as dried samples, and includes a pre-treatment to release bound fat. However, it should be noted that fat components with high specific gravity, such as phospholipids, will not float to the top layer and therefore will not be included in the volumetric measurement for fat after centrifugation.

4. Instrumental Methods and Comparison to Standard Solvent Extraction Method

An automated turbidimetric method (AOAC Official Method 969.16) has been developed to determine fat in milk. In this method, EDTA is added to dilute the sample and to eliminate turbidity due to the casein protein. Homogenization is then used to form uniform fat globules, which may then be determined by measurement of turbidity, which is related to fat content through comparison to a standard curve.

Fat content of foods can also be analyzed using various other instrumental methods measuring such properties as density, nuclear magnetic resonance, x-ray absorption, dielectric constant, or infrared spectra (26). The differences in these properties between fat molecules and other food components form the basis for relating the measurement of these properties to the fat content. These methods are usually rapid and do not require extraction of fat from the food prior to analysis. However, it is important to construct standard curves for the specific food being analyzed, in order to determine the quantitative relationship between the particular physical property being measured by the instrumental method, and the fat content of standards with known composition, usually determined by solvent extraction methods such as the Soxhlet method.

Vogt et al. (27) compared four rapid methods to the standard Soxhlet extraction method for fat measurement in fish herring. The four methods were (i) the Torry Fatmeter based on dielectric properties of water, and intercorrelations between fish water and fat contents; (ii) microwave drying and calculation of fat from water content; (iii) near-infrared reflectance (NIR) spectroscopy with partial least-squares regression analysis; and (iv) fexIKA Soxhlet solvent extraction instrument modified to include filtration under reduced pressure. The NIR method gave the best prediction of the standard method (Soxhlet), while other methods gave lower fat content values. However, the NIR instrument is relatively

expensive. In comparison, the microwave method is low cost, requiring only a microwave oven, and the Torry meter is moderately priced. The Soxhlet and fexIKA were also both considered to have the disadvantages of being time-consuming and requiring solvents.

D. PROTEIN

Proteins are macromolecules composed of amino acids linked together through amide or peptide bonds to form polypeptide chains, which can range in molecular mass from a few thousand to over a million daltons. Proteins contribute to the nutritional value as well as textural and sensory properties of foods, and they also perform structural and biologically important functions. The protein content of foods ranges from less than 1–2% in fruits and vegetables, to 20–30% in meat, legumes, and dairy products (30).

1. Overview of and Considerations for Protein Determination

The most common official method for determination of protein content in food is based on measurement of total nitrogen content using the Kjeldahl method, followed by multiplication by a conversion factor to calculate the protein content. The Dumas (nitrogen combustion) method is also based on the principle of nitrogen determination and conversion to protein content. A number of other methods, mostly colorimetric or spectroscopic methods, are based on quantifying either the peptide bonds or particular side chains of the amino acid residues, and may be useful as rapid methods for quality control or research. These latter methods require calibration of the measured property, such as absorbance or color intensity, using standards of known composition, usually determined by nitrogen analysis, or sometimes by gravimetric analysis.

Many factors can affect the accuracy of analyzing protein content in food through measurement of its nitrogen content. Proteins are composed of amino acids whose chemical structures include hydrogen, carbon, nitrogen, oxygen, and sulfur atoms. Of these elements, nitrogen is considered most distinctive for proteins in comparison to other components considered in proximate analysis, since each of the twenty amino acid building blocks contains a nitrogen-containing amino (or imino) group. However, the side chains of these amino acids differ greatly, ranging from hydrocarbon chains containing primarily carbon and hydrogen atoms, to aromatic groups and polar or ionic groups that also contain sulfur, oxygen, or nitrogen atoms. Since proteins contain different combinations of the amino acids, each of which contains a different percentage of nitrogen in its chemical structure, the percentage of nitrogen can vary greatly between different proteins. Use of the correct conversion factor is required if an accurate estimation of protein is to be expected.

A nitrogen-to-protein conversion factor of 6.25 is commonly used to calculate the protein content of a food from the nitrogen content determined by Kjeldahl or combustion methods. This factor assumes an average of 16% (= 100 / 6.25) nitrogen content in proteins, i.e., 16 grams of nitrogen per 100 grams of protein. However, depending on the amino acid composition of the particular protein, the actual conversion factor may deviate from 6.25. For example, the conversion factors are 6.38, 5.70, and 6.25 for dairy products, wheat, and almonds, respectively (30), and 4.74, 5.3, 4.38, and 5.7 for chocolate and cocoa, coffee, mushrooms, and yeast, respectively (7). The conversion factor and source of information for the factor should be stated in listing protein content, as illustrated by some of the tagnames listed in Table 42.1C.

The presence of non-protein nitrogen in foods is another important consideration that may affect the accuracy of protein determination that is based on nitrogen measurement. Foods may contain varying levels of free amino acids or small peptides, ammonium salts, urea, uric acid, vitamins, amino sugars, nucleic acids, phospholipids or other constituents that contain nitrogen in their chemical structure. If unaccounted for, the contribution of nitrogen from these non-protein nitrogen sources will result in an over-estimation of protein content. Methods have therefore been established, using trichloroacetic acid or other protein precipitant, to enable distinction between protein and non-protein nitrogen. For example, AOAC Official Methods 991.20, 991.21, 991.22, and 991.23 describe methods for milk total nitrogen, non-protein nitrogen, protein nitrogen by direct method, and protein nitrogen by indirect method, respectively.

Due to the long period of time to perform Kjeldahl analysis and the necessity to determine the difference between non-protein nitrogen and total protein nitrogen, spectrophotometric or colorimetric methods for total proteins are commonly used as rapid methods suitable for research or quality control. However, there are potential interferences and other considerations that must be kept in mind when using these rapid methods (30–32).

An overview of the main methods for protein analysis based on total nitrogen analysis, and spectrophotometric, colorimetric, or other instrumental methods for protein analysis, are described in the following sections. For more details, the reader should refer to the chapter on protein analysis in this Handbook, and to an excellent book on this topic written recently by Owusu-Apenten (31).

2. Methods for Total Nitrogen Analysis

In the Kjeldahl method for total nitrogen analysis, the protein and other organic molecules in foods are digested by concentrated sulfuric acid in the presence of catalysts. The nitrogen is present in the acid digest in the form of ammonium sulfate, and may be analyzed either by an acid-base titration of the nitrogen after neutralization and distillation

of the resulting ammonia, or by other techniques including nesslerization or colorimetric reaction with a phenol hypochlorite reagent (30). The Kjeldahl method is described in AOAC Official Method 920.87 for protein (total) in flour or AOAC Official Methods 928.08 and 981.10 for nitrogen or crude protein, respectively, in meat. Various modifications of the original method have been proposed over the years, implementing copper as an alternative catalyst to mercury (AOAC Official Methods 984.13 and 2001.11), semi-automation or automation (AOAC Official Methods 976.05, 967.06, and 990.02), and analysis of microgram quantities of nitrogen (AOAC Official Method 960.52).

In the Dumas (also known as nitrogen combustion or pyrolysis) method, the samples are subjected to very high temperatures up to 1000°C. Nitrogen that is freed by pyrolysis and subsequent combustion at high temperature in pure oxygen, is then quantitated by gas chromatography and thermal conductivity. Official methods based on combustion have been established, for example, for animal feed, meats, cereal grains and oilseeds, and fertilizers (AOAC Official Methods 990.03, 992.15, 992.23, and 993.13, respectively).

Both the Kjeldahl and the combustion methods determine total nitrogen, so the correct nitrogen-to-protein conversion factor and the contribution of non-protein nitrogen to the total nitrogen content must be considered for an accurate determination of protein content. The analyte is referred to as "crude" protein in the AOAC Official Methods, when total nitrogen is determined without correcting for non-protein nitrogen. Combustion methods have the advantages of speed of analysis, and avoidance of corrosive and toxic reagents, compared to the Kjeldahl method, but the expenses of the equipment and high-purity oxygen must be considered.

3. Spectrophotometric Methods

Aromatic amino acids (tryptophan, tyrosine, and phenylalanine) and peptide bonds absorb electromagnetic radiation in the ultraviolet (uv) region near 257–280 nm and 190–205 nm, respectively (33). The intensity of uv absorbance can be related to the content of those groups and, therefore, to the protein content of a solution.

Spectrophotometric methods are simple in principle, but only applicable to samples that are non-turbid solutions of relatively pure protein composition. Since the content of aromatic amino acids differs between proteins, and since the extinction coefficient and wavelength of maximum absorbance are characteristic for each of the three aromatic amino acid types, this method for protein analysis requires standard curves or tables, such as those compiled by Fasman (33), relating the absorbance at a particular wavelength to the concentration of the specific protein. The uv absorbance of the peptide bond is less dependent on the nature of the amino acid side chains.

However, the absorbance of ultraviolet radiation in this wavelength region by other food components, such as organic acids, nucleic acids, triacylglycerols, etc., may result in considerable interference and inaccuracy in relating the absorbance directly to protein content in complex foodstuff.

4. Colorimetric Methods

A number of colorimetric methods have been established for determination of protein content, based on the development of color upon reaction with either the peptide bonds or with particular functional groups of the proteins. Colorimetric methods based on reaction with peptide bonds, such as the biuret, Lowry, and bicinchoninic acid (BCA) methods, show relatively low protein-to-protein variability in the relationship between colorimetric intensity (absorbance) and concentration for different proteins. Protein-to-protein variability is much greater for methods that are based on reaction with specific functional groups on the amino acid side chains, since the amino acid composition of the protein as well as the protein content will affect the resulting colorimetric response. The Bradford or Coomassie Brilliant Blue method is presently the most common example of the latter class of methods, although Acid Orange 12 and Amido Black 10B were established as official dye-binding methods for protein in milk in 1967 and 1975 (AOAC Official Methods 967.12 and 975.17, respectively).

The Bradford method is based on a change in the wavelength and intensity of absorbance (color) of the reagent dye Coomassie Brilliant Blue G-250, when it is bound to proteins, particularly at basic amino acid side chains and enhanced by hydrophobic interactions. The biuret method is based on the development of a blue color upon complex formation of cupric ions with peptide bonds in alkaline solution, while the Lowry method combines the biuret reaction with reduction of the Folin-Ciocalteau phenol reagent by tyrosine and tryptophan residues in proteins, and the BCA method involves the reduction of cupric to cuprous ions by peptide bonds under alkaline solution, followed by development of a purplish color upon formation of cuprous ion complexes with the BCA reagent. The absorbance is read at 595, 540, 700, or 562 nm for the Bradford, biuret, Lowry, and BCA reactions, respectively, and the protein content is determined using a standard curve. As noted above, due to protein-to-protein variability, the selection of the appropriate protein for the standard curve is important, especially in the case of the Bradford method. The Bradford, Lowry, and BCA methods have greater sensitivity and lower limit of detection than the biuret reaction. Selection of the most appropriate method depends on considerations with regard to potential interferences from other constituents in the sample, availability of the appropriate protein standard for calibration, and the sensitivity that is required (30, 31).

5. Infrared Spectroscopy

Infrared spectroscopy may be used to determine the protein content of foods by relating the absorption of infrared radiation at wavelengths assigned to the peptide bond of proteins. This technique is rapid, may be applied to solid as well as liquid samples in the presence of other food constituents, and is not affected by non-protein nitrogen or amino acid composition. However, calibration must be conducted using standard curves relating the infrared absorption to protein content. Examples of mid-infrared and near-infrared spectroscopy for protein content include the official methods for protein (crude) in forages (AOAC Official Method 989.03) and for protein in milk (AOAC Official Method 972.16).

E. CARBOHYDRATE

Carbohydrates in foods include monosaccharides (particularly D-glucose and D-fructose), disaccharides (e.g., sucrose, lactose, maltose), higher oligosaccharides (e.g., raffinose, stachyose and fructo-oligosaccharides) and polysaccharides (e.g., starch, food gums and hydrocolloids, pectin, hemicellulose, cellulose) (34, 35). The sugar alcohols, such as sorbitol, mannitol, xylitol, lactitol, and maltitol, are also considered as carbohydrates (34). Carbohydrates are important from a nutritional point of view, whereby metabolic energy is provided by digestible carbohydrates including simple sugars (monosaccharides, starch) while dietary fiber is obtained from the indigestible fraction. Polysaccharides also play a crucial role in textural properties of foods, while mono- and disaccharides may take part in reactions such as Maillard browning or caramelization, thereby imparting characteristic flavor and color to foods.

The total carbohydrate content of foods ranges from negligible (e.g., in chicken breast meat) to over 80% (e.g., in honey and breakfast cereals such as corn flakes) (35).

1. Methods and Considerations for Total Carbohydrate Determination

In proximate analysis for nutrition labeling, the total carbohydrate content of a food is usually calculated by subtracting the weights of moisture, ash, total fat, and crude protein from the total weight of the food (8, 35). When alcohol is present, it is also subtracted from the total weight in the calculation of carbohydrate by difference (7). It should be noted that protein calculated from total nitrogen, which may contain non-protein nitrogen, is used in determining carbohydrate by difference (7).

Although the calculation of carbohydrates by "difference" has a long history of usage as the method for determining total carbohydrates reported in food tables or nutrition labels, there are several problems with this approach (34). Firstly, it includes a number of non-carbo-hydrate components such as lignin, organic acids, tannins, waxes, and some Maillard browning products. Secondly, it incorporates the sum of all of the analytical errors from determination of the other analytes in proximate analysis. Thirdly, a single value for "total carbohydrates" is not very informative with regard to nutritional value, as it fails to distinguish between the distinct physiological properties of different classes of carbohydrates (34).

The phenol-sulfuric acid method may also be used to estimate total carbohydrates (35). Heating of carbohydrates in the presence of strong acids produces furan derivatives and their polymers, which condense with various phenolic substances, including phenol itself, to yield a yellow-orange color. The absorbance at 490–500 nm is related to the concentration of carbohydrate using a standard curve. Although the phenol-sulfuric acid method is applicable to different classes of carbohydrates from monosaccharides to polysaccharides, the relationship between absorbance and concentration, and even the wavelength of maximum color intensity, are dependent on the chemical composition of the carbohydrates. Therefore, accuracy is dependent on selecting the appropriate reference carbohydrate or carbohydrate mixtures to prepare the standard curve, which is a difficult task in reality since most foods are composed of complex mixtures of carbohydrates. Incorporation of additional sample purification steps such as selective precipitation may be helpful to address this problem (e.g., AOAC Official Method 988.12E for dextran in raw cane sugar).

Finally, rather than calculating total carbohydrates by "difference," or by chemical methods for total carbohydrate determination such as the phenol-sulfuric acid method, an alternative approach involves the direct measurement of the individual components, which are then combined to give a value for total carbohydrates (34). In addition to information on total carbohydrate content, the various classes or sub-classes of the individual components may be reported, such as total simple sugars, starch, dietary fiber, etc. Mono- and disaccharides may be analyzed specifically by enzymes, gas-liquid chromatography (GLC), or high performance liquid chromatography (HPLC). Polyols and oligosaccharides are also usually determined by GLC or HPLC methods. Starch analysis is based on enzymatic degradation, followed by determination of the liberated glucose. Non-starch polysaccharide-analysis involves removal of starch enzymatic hydrolysis products and other low-molecular-weight carbohydrates, followed by hydrolysis of the non-starch polysaccharides to its monomeric constituents for analyisis. Although a number of methods have been established in the past for determination of crude fiber, acid-detergent fiber, neutral detergent fiber, etc. (e.g., see Table 42.1D), it is recommended that dietary fiber be determined by the enzymatic-gravimetric methods of Prosky and co-workers or Lee and co-workers, or the enzymatic

chemical methods, such as that of Englyst and co-workers (34). Examples of the enzymatic-gravimetric method are AOAC Official Methods 985.29, 991.42, 991.43, and 993.19, for determining insoluble, soluble, and total dietary fiber.

III. OTHER COMPONENTS

As shown in Tables 42.2 and 42.3, in addition to conducting proximate analysis for the major food components described in Section II, further analysis is required to provide information on nutrition labels in the United States and Canada, respectively, and similar regulatory requirements are found in many countries internationally. This additional information includes the energy or caloric content, the contents of subclasses of fatty acids and carbohydrates, and the contents of a number of other components that may be minor in quantity but are of major importance as nutrients.

The specific methods recommended for analysis may vary between different countries. International standards are described in the FAO/WHO Codex Alimentarius Methods of Analysis and Sampling (19). The list of methods used by the Canadian Food Inspection Agency or CFIA (Table 42.3) to verify nutritional information is illustrative of the use of a combination of sources for the methods. As stated at the CFIA website: "The methods of analysis recommended are those published in the most recent version of the 'Official Methods of Analysis of AOAC International' wherever possible. Other collaboratively studied methods such as those published by the American Oil Chemists' Society, American Association of Cereal Chemists, ISO, etc. would also be considered appropriate. In house or journal methods with adequate method validation data are another possible option for method selection" (8). More detailed information on some of these methods is described in various chapters in this Handbook, including those on gas chromatography, HPLC, and mass spectrometry.

IV. TRENDS IN FOOD COMPOSITION ANALYSIS

Some of the trends in the analysis of chemical composition of food, with regard to methods validation, components analyzed, and new techniques, are outlined in the following sections.

A. VALIDATION OF METHODS OF ANALYSIS AND VALIDITY OF FOOD COMPOSITION DATA

Nutrient values in food composition databases may be collected from various sources of information generated by chemical analysis of food samples, by calculations, or by expert estimation or "imputation" (36). Furthermore, the analytical data may be obtained from chemical analysis of food samples from the food industry, from government agencies, from the scientific literature, or by analytical laboratories that may or may not be ISO-accredited. Since the data are gleaned from various sources and may be of uneven quality and detail of supporting documentation, it is crucial to assess whether or not the data are in fact reliable for inclusion in databases (36). For example, the USDA Nutrient Data Laboratory has been working to establish software for data acquisition, compilation, and dissemination, as well as to facilitate the evaluation of analytical data quality based on five categories – sampling plan, number of samples, sample handling, analytical method, and analytical quality control, leading to a combined rating represented by a quality index and confidence code (36).

There is a continuing need for reliable analytical methods that can be used to determine compliance with national regulations as well as international requirements in all areas of food quality and safety. Some form of validation procedure must be used to determine the reliability of a method. The Codex Alimentarius Commission, for example, requires that in order for a method of analysis to be included in a Codex commodity standard, certain method performance information should be available. This includes specificity, accuracy, precision (repeatability, reproducibility), limit of detection, sensitivity, applicability, and practicability, as appropriate. However, "It is not practical or necessary to require that all analytical methods used for food control purposes be assessed at the ideal level ... Limiting factors for completing ideal multi-laboratory validation studies include high costs, lack of sufficient expert laboratories available and willing to participate in such studies, and overall time constraints" (20).

A joint FAO/IAEA expert consultation on "Validation of Analytical Methods for Food Control" was held in Vienna, December 2–4, 1997, to review existing schemes for validation of international methods, to identify requirements for validation of methods for analysis of veterinary drug and pesticide residues, food additives, and environmental contaminants in food, and to recommend alternative approaches which would be practical, cost effective, and considerate of time and human resource constraints (18). Although a collaborative study conducted according to generally accepted international protocols is always the preferred validation procedure, in some cases it is not feasible to do so. In these circumstances, the evaluations may be done in one laboratory, provided they are conducted according to five principles addressing competence and third party review of the testing laboratory, appropriate criteria assessment of the analytical method, careful documentation in an expert validation report, and evidence of transferability (18).

B. THE IMPACT OF HEALTH ISSUES ON ANALYSIS OF CHEMICAL COMPOSITION

Increasing numbers of reports on the associations between consumption of certain foods or nutrients with improved health or reduced risk of disease, have led to an explosion of literature on food composition information on these nutrients, nutraceuticals, and functional foods. However, the validity of the measurements for specific bioactive analytes has not been adequately assessed in many cases. There is a need to apply the quality indices for methods validation described in Section IV.A., and to initiate an informatics approach to developing nutrient databases for these components. Recent trends in this direction include the initiation of a flavonoid database (37) and databases for several bioactive food components including carotenoids, six classes of flavonoids, omega-3 fatty acids, and plant sterols (38).

Increasing interest in the physiological roles of dietary fiber and resistant starch has also led to a renewed need to assess the methods for their determination. Resistant starch is considered to be that starch which resists digestion and absorption in the small intestine and escapes into the colon, where it may be fermented by bacterial microflora. The enzymatic-gravimetric and enzymatic-chemical methods for dietary fiber analysis include protocols for determining the content of resistant starch (35), but it has been reported that some data on resistant starch have only estimated retrograded amylose, which is only one of the 3 or 4 components of resistant starch in the diet (34). Similarly, data on dietary fibre intake around the world are difficult to compare because of methodology differences (34). In fact, a debate is ongoing at the present time on what should be included in the definition of dietary fiber. At the heart of the controversy is the issue of whether total fiber should be classified into dietary fiber (i.e. sources of fiber that are intrinsic or intact in plants) versus functional fiber (i.e., fiber that has been isolated and then incorporated as an ingredient in food products), with associated concerns of how these two classes of fiber might be analytically distinguished (39, 40).

C. TRENDS IN METHODOLOGY FOR FOOD ANALYSIS

There is a continuing need to explore the possibilities and limitations of rapid methods for analysis of food, and of equipment that will enable their successful application for quality control (41, 42). As reviewed by Ibañez and Cifuentes (43) in an excellent article, there have been many advances in applying new analytical techniques in food science, with an increasing focus on sophisticated techniques. These include nuclear magnetic resonance, capillary electrophoresis, mass spectrometry, and infrared spectroscopy, as well as coupled techniques and new approaches to sample preparation (43), mass spectrometry, and hyphenated mass-spectrometry techniques (44, 45) and the vibrational spectroscopic techniques of near-infrared, mid-infrared, and Raman spectroscopy (46). Other recent trends include the increased application of enzymes as indicators of food quality, biosensors, immunochemical techniques, DNA probes, the polymerase chain reaction (PCR), rapid methods for microbio-logical analysis, and authentication of foods using isotopic methods (1, 43). There has also been great interest in methods for the detection of genetically modified foods. For example, Dahinden et al. (47) described the application of real-time PCR technology for quantification of the genetically modified organism (GMO) content of soybean (Roundup Ready soybean-RRSoybean) or corn (Bt176, Bt11, Mon810, and T25), and for demonstrating the amplification capacity of DNA from corn (invertase) and soybean (lectin).

V. CONCLUSIONS

This chapter has provided an outline of the basic principles and considerations for proximate analysis of food, and briefly described the analysis of other constituents that are of interest from the viewpoint of nutrition and health. A multitude of techniques based on different principles are available or being developed for the analysis of the chemical composition of foods. Due to the diversity and heterogeneity of these food constituents, and the dependence of the measured content of each constituent on the method used for its analysis, it is imperative that reports on food composition be accompanied by sufficient description of the analytical methods used for obtaining those data, and that these methods have been validated by officially recognized associations. Only then can the data on chemical composition of food analyzed by different sources or agencies be meaningfully compared, interpreted, and applied.

REFERENCES

1. RS Singhal, PR Kulkarni, DV Rege. Handbook of Indices of Food Quality and Authenticity. Cambridge: Woodhead, 1997.
2. JD Ireland, A Møller. Review of international food classification and description. J Food Composition and Analysis 13:529–538, 2000.
3. DB Haytowitz, PR Pehrsson, JM Holden. The identification of key foods for food composition research. J Food Composition and Analysis 15:183–194, 2002.
4. SP Murphy. Dietary reference intakes for the U.S. and Canada: Update on implications for nutrient databases. J Food Composition and Analysis 15:411–417, 2002.
5. JC Klensin, D Feskanich, V Lin, AS Truswell, DAT Southgate. Identification of Food Components for INFOODS Data Interchange. Tokyo: United Nations University, 1989.
6. SS Nielsen, LE Metzger. Nutritional labeling. In: SS Nielsen (ed). Food Analysis. 3rd edition. New York: Kluwer Academic/Plenum Publishers, 2003, pp. 35–50.
7. USDA (United States Department of Agriculture, Agricultural Research Service). USDA National Nutrient Database for Standard Reference, Release 17. Nutrient Data Laboratory Home Page, 2003, http://www.nal.usda.gov/fnic/foodcomp (accessed May 17, 2005).
8. Canadian Food Inspection Agency. Nutrition Labelling, Nutrient Content Claims and Health Claims. A Compliance Test to Assess the Accuracy of Nutrient Values. Consultation Document. Appendix 4 – Laboratory Issues. 2002. http://www.inspection.gc.ca/english/ bureau/ labeti/nutricon/nutricon4e.shtml (accessed June 18, 2003); updated at http://inspection.gc.ca/engligh/ fssa/labeti/nutricon/nutriconapp4e.shtml (accessed May 11, 2005).
9. DC Liebler, JR Yates, III. Introduction to Proteomics. Tools for the New Biology. Totowa, NJ: Humana Press, 2002.
10. NK Andrikopoulos. Triglyceride species compositions of common edible vegetable oils and methods used for their identification and quantification. Food Reviews International 18:71–102, 2002a.
11. NK Andrikopoulos. Chromatographic and spectroscopic methods in the analysis of triacylglycerol species and regiospecific isomers of oils and fats. Critical Reviews in Food Science and Nutrition 42:473–505, 2002b.
12. DAT Southgate. Determination of Food Carbohydrates. London: Elsevier, 1991.
13. SS Nielsen (ed). Food Analysis. 3rd edition. New York: Kluwer Academic/Plenum Publishers, 2003.
14. Y Pomeranz, CE Meloan. Food Analysis Theory and Practice. 3rd ed. New York: Chapman Hall, 1994.
15. SS Nielsen. United States government regulations and international standards related to food analysis. In: SS Nielsen (ed). Food Analysis. 3rd edition. New York: Kluwer Academic/Plenum Publishers, 2003, pp 15–33.
16. Health Canada. The Compendium of Methods for Chemical Analysis of Foods. http://www.hc-sc.gc.ca/ food-aliment/cs-ipc/fr-ra/e_chem_analysis_foods.html (accessed August 18, 2003).
17. FAO/WHO (Food and Agriculture Organization of the United Nations World Health Organization). Understanding the Codex Alimentarius. Rome: FAO/ WHO, 1999.
18. FAO (Food and Agriculture Organization of the United Nations). Joint FAO/IAEA Expert Consultation on Validation of Analytical Methods for Food Control, 1997, Vienna, Austria. FAO Food and Nutrition Paper 68. Rome: Food and Agriculture Organization of the United Nations, 1998.
19. FAO/WHO (Food and Agriculture Organization of the United Nations World Health Organization). Codex Alimentarius Volume 13. Methods of Analysis and Sampling. Rome: FAO/WHO, 1994.
20. FAO/WHO (Food and Agriculture Organization of the United Nations World Health Organization). FAO/WHO Food Standards Codex Alimentarius.

http://www.codexalimentarius.net/index_en.stm (accessed June 18, 2003).

21. W Horowitz (ed.) Official Methods of Analysis of AOAC International. Volume I. Agricultural Chemicals; Contaminants; Drugs. Volume II. Food Composition; Additives; Natural Contaminants. 17th edition, Revision 1. Gaithersburg, MD: Aspen Publishers, 2002.

22. RL Bradley, Jr. Moisture and total solids analysis. In: SS Nielsen (ed). Food Analysis. 3rd edition. New York: Kluwer Academic/Plenum Publishers, 2003, pp. 81–101.

23. LH Harbers, SS Nielsen. Ash analysis. In: SS Nielsen (ed). Food Analysis. 3rd ed. New York: Kluwer Academic/Plenum Publishers, 2003, pp. 103–111.

24. CE Carpenter, DG Hendricks. Mineral Analysis. In: SS Nielsen (ed). Food Analysis. 3rd ed. New York: Kluwer Academic/Plenum Publishers, 2003, pp. 189–203.

25. Health Canada (Health Protection Branch Laboratories, Bureau of Nutritional Sciences). Sample preparation by dry ashing for the determination of various elements by flame atomic absorption spectroscopy. Laboratory Procedure LPFC-137, 1985 (available from Health Canada or at http://www.hc-sc.gc.ca/hpfb-dgpsa/onpp bppn/labelling-etiquetage/reg_preparation_dry_ashing_ e.pdf; accessed June 30, 2003).

26. DB Min, JM Boff. Crude fat analysis. In: SS Nielsen (ed). Food Analysis. 3rd edition. New York: Kluwer Academic/Plenum Publishers, 2003, pp. 113–129.

27. A Vogt, TR Gormley, G Downey, J Somers. A comparison of selected rapid methods for fat measurement in fresh herring (*Clupea harengus*). J Food Composition and Analysis 15:205–215, 2002.

28. P Manirakiza, A Covaci, P Schepens. Comparative study on total lipid determination using Soxhlet, Roese-Gottlieb, Bligh & Dyer, and modified Bligh & Dyer extraction methods. J Food Composition and Analysis 14:93–100, 2001.

29. EG Bligh, WJ Dyer. A rapid method of total lipid extraction and purification. Can J Biochem Physiol 37:911–917, 1959.

30. SKC Chang. Protein analysis. In: SS Nielsen (ed). Food Analysis. 3rd edition. New York: Kluwer Academic/ Plenum Publishers, 2003, pp. 131–141.

31. RK Owusu-Apenten. Food Protein Analysis. Quantitative Effects on Processing. New York: Marcel Dekker, 2002.

32. NKK Kamizake, MM Goncalves, CTBV Zaia, DAM Zaia. Determination of total proteins in cow milk powder samples: a comparative study between the Kjeldahl method and spectrophotometric methods. J Food Composition and Analysis 16:507–516, 2003.

33. G Fasman. Practical Handbook of Biochemistry and Molecular Biology. Boca Raton: CRC Press, 1992, pp. 77–85.

34. FAO/WHO (Food and Agriculture Organization of the United Nations World Health Organization). Carbohydrates in Human Nutrition. Report of a Joint FAO/WHO expert consultation 14–18 April 1997, FAO Food & Nutrition Paper 66. FAO/WHO: Rome, 1998.

35. JN BeMiller. Carbohydrate analysis. In: SS Nielsen (ed). Food Analysis. 3rd edition. New York: Kluwer Academic/Plenum Publishers, 2003, pp. 143–174.

36. JM Holden, SA Bhagwat, KY Patterson. Development of a multi-nutrient data quality evaluation system. J Food Composition and Analysis 15:339–348, 2002.

37. J Peterson, J Dwyer. An informatics approach to flavonoid database development. J Food Composition and Analysis 13:441–454, 2000.

38. JAT Pennington. Food composition databases for bioactive food components. J Food Composition and Analysis 15:419–434, 2002.

39. Institute of Medicine. Issues in defining dietary fiber. In: Dietary Reference Intakes: Proposed Definition of Dietary Fiber. Washington, D.C.: The National Academies Press, 2001, pp. 19–20.

40. AACC Dietary Fiber Technical Committee. All dietary fiber is fundamentally functional. Cereal Chemistry 48: 128–131, 2003.

41. R Matissek. Rapid methods for food analysis – possibilities and limits. In: W Baltes (ed). Rapid Methods for Analysis of Food and Food Raw Material. Lancaster, PA: Technomic Publishing, 1990, pp. 23–44.

42. KH Torkler. Rapid determination equipment for food quality control. In: W Baltes (ed). Rapid Methods for Analysis of Food and Food Raw Material. Lancaster, PA: Technomic Publishing, 1990, pp. 59–71.

43. E Ibañez, A Cifuentes. New analytical techniques in food science. Critical Reviews in Food Science and Nutrition 41:413–450, 2001.

44. M Careri, F Bianchi, C Corradini. Recent advances in the application of mass spectrometry in food-related analysis. J Chromatography A 970:3–64, 2002.

45. FA Mellon, R Self, JR Startin. Mass Spectrometry of Natural Substances in Food. Cambridge: Royal Society of Chemistry, 2000.

46. ECY Li-Chan, A Ismail, J Sedman, F van de Voort. Vibrational spectroscopy of food and food products. In: JM Chalmers, PR Griffiths (eds). Handbook of Vibrational Spectroscopy. Volume 5. Chichester: John Wiley & Sons Ltd, 2002, pp. 3629–3662.

47. I Dahinden, A Zimmermann, M Liniger, U Pauli. Variation analysis of seven LightCycler based real-time PCR systems to detect genetically modified products (RRS, Bt176, Bt11, Mon810, T25, lectin, invertase). In: U. Reischl, C. Wittwer, F. Cockerill (eds). Rapid Cycle Real-Time PCR Methods and Applications. Microbiology and Food Analysis. New York: Springer-Verlag, 2002, pp. 251–258.

43 Spectroscopy Basics

Christine H. Scaman
Food, Nutrition and Health Program, The University of British Columbia

CONTENTS

I.   INTRODUCTION TO SPECTROSCOPY

Spectroscopy is the study of the interaction of matter with electromagnetic radiation by absorption, emission, or scattering. Spectroscopic techniques are invaluable for obtaining both structural and quantitative information about atoms and molecules, and are used extensively in the analysis of foods and individual components.

Electromagnetic radiation has a dual nature and acts as if it is a particle (a photon) travelling through space with the characteristics of a wave, with oscillating electric and magnetic fields (Figure 43.1)(1). The energy of the radiation, E, is directly related to the frequency, v (the number of oscillations per second), by Planck's constant (h = 6.63×10^{-34} J-s),

$$E = h\,v \qquad (43.1)$$

The frequency, v, is inversely related to the wavelength, λ, by

$$v = c/\lambda \qquad (43.2)$$

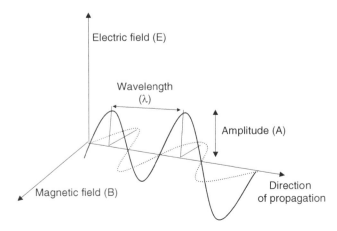

FIGURE 43.1   The characteristics of electromagnetic radiation, with electric and magnetic fields perpendicular to each other.

where c is the velocity of the radiation. The frequency of radiation is determined by the source, and does not change as the wave propagates through different media. However, the velocity, and therefore the wavelength, is affected by the medium. Wavelength is inversely related to energy, so ultraviolet radiation with short wavelengths has more energy than visible light. It should be noted that only those wavelengths that are visible to our eye, from about 400 to 800 nm, are referred to as light. Radiation is the general term used for electromagnetic radiation that ranges from cosmic rays with wavelengths of 10^{-12} m, to radio waves with wavelengths of 10^4 m.

The charged particles of matter, the nucleus and the electrons, can interact with specific wavelengths of radiation, and the energy from the radiation can be transferred to, or absorbed by, the material. This absorption of energy excites the atom or molecule from a lower energy state (often the ground state at room temperature) to a higher energy state, and is observed as an absorption spectrum. Alternatively, the emission of radiation when the atom or molecule moves from a higher energy state to a lower, more stable, energy state can be monitored as an emission spectrum. There are a limited number of discrete energy levels that a particular atom or molecule can achieve, based on its structure. Therefore, only wavelengths of radiation with the precise amount of energy that exists between two different energy states can be absorbed or emitted. This allows atoms and molecules to be identified by their unique absorption or emission spectra.

The absorption and emission spectra of atoms are less complicated than those of molecules. Atoms can undergo electronic energy transitions, in which electrons (usually valence electrons) move to higher or lower energy states. Electronic transitions associated with excitation of valence electrons can occur with the energy of ultraviolet or visible radiation. Molecules also undergo electronic transitions, but have rotational and vibrational motions as well. For each electronic state, there are several rotational states, and for each rotational state, there are several vibrational states (Figure 43.2). Vibrational motion occurs from the bending or stretching of bonds between nuclei. The energy required for vibrational motions is much smaller than for electronic transitions, and vibrational transitions are typically excited by infrared radiation. Rotational motion arises from movement of a molecule about its axes or center of gravity. Transitions between rotational states require even less energy than vibrational transitions, and can occur with the energy found in the far infrared to microwave regions of the electromagnetic spectrum.

In addition to absorption and emission, radiation can also be re-directed through scattering, reflection, or rotation due to its interaction with matter. This can occur with or without the transfer of energy, and therefore after interacting with a sample, the radiation may have a different or the same wavelength as the original radiation.

While many forms of spectroscopy are based on the interaction of electrons with electromagnetic radiation, the interaction of nuclei with radiation can also be detected under certain conditions. The nuclei of many elements have magnetic properties, and when they are placed in a strong external magnetic field, they will populate different magnetic states. If the nuclei are then exposed to radiation of an appropriate frequency, they will absorb the radiation and undergo transitions between magnetic states. The energy difference between these magnetic states varies with the strength of the external magnetic field and the chemical environment, but occurs in the radiowave region of the electromagnetic spectrum.

A summary of the spectroscopic techniques that will be explored in this chapter is given in Table 43.1. Spectroscopic techniques of fluorescence, infrared, and mass spectroscopy are discussed in other chapters of this book.

II. ULTRAVIOLET-VISIBLE SPECTROPHOTOMETRY

A. INTRODUCTION

Spectrophotometry is based on the ability of valence electrons of molecules to absorb specific frequencies of radiation, from the ultraviolet range (200 to 400 nm) through the visible range (400 to 800 nm). The absorption of the radiation can be detected using a spectrophotometer and will yield an absorption spectrum. Spectrophotometry can be used to obtain qualitative information regarding the compounds that are present in a sample extract, but it is not possible to obtain detailed structural information. In molecules, there are simultaneous transitions between different vibrational, rotational and electronic states, resulting in rather broad absorption bands. Spectrophotometry is more commonly used to quantitate the amount of a compound in solution. It is an extremely versatile technique, and spectrophotometric methods of detection and quantitation have been developed for hundreds of compounds. The technique can also be used to detect enzyme activity, and spectrophotometric detectors are commonly used for high performance liquid chromatography (HPLC). Some selected applications of spectrophotometry in food science are given in Table 43.2.

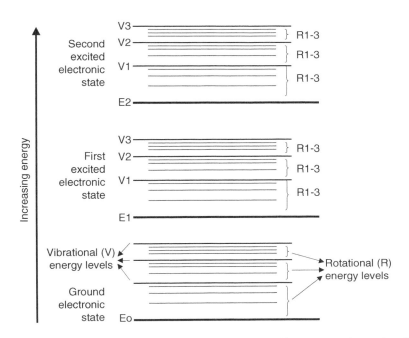

FIGURE 43.2 A partial energy diagram of a molecule, showing the relationship between electronic, vibrational, and rotational energy levels.

TABLE 43.1

Selected Characteristics of Some Spectroscopic Techniques

Spectroscopic Technique	Interacting Radiation	Transition	Interaction
Near Ultra-Violet Spectroscopy	200–400 nm	Valence electrons of molecules	Absorption
Visible Spectroscopy	400–800 nm	Valence electrons of molecules	Absorption
Tristimulus Colorimetry	400–800 nm	—	Reflection
Atomic Absorption Spectroscopy	160–900 nm	Valence electrons of atoms	Absorption
Atomic Emission Spectroscopy	160–900 nm	Valence electrons of atoms	Emission
Polarimetry/			
Optical Rotary Dispersion	200–800 nm Circularly Polarized	Valence electrons of molecules	Rotation
Circular Dichroism	170–700 nm Circularly Polarized	Valence electrons of molecules	Absorption
Nuclear Magnetic Resonance	Radiowaves > 1 mm	Nuclear spin transitions	Absorption and Emission

B. PRINCIPLES

The energy associated with ultraviolet and visible wavelengths of radiation varies from about 150 to 36 kcal mole^{-1} (15). Energy of this magnitude corresponds to the energy differences between electronic states of valence electrons of molecules. Therefore, electromagnetic radiation in this region absorbed by molecules can promote valence electrons to an excited orbital. The types of electronic transitions that occur with absorption of ultraviolet and visible radiation include sigma bonding (associated with single bonds) to sigma antibonding orbitals (σ-σ^*), non-bonding electrons to sigma antibonding orbitals (n-σ^*), or more commonly, pi bonding orbitals (formed by parallel overlap of p-orbitals) to pi antibonding orbitals (π-π^*) and non-bonding electrons to pi antibonding orbitals (n-π^*). The σ-σ^* and n-σ^* transitions require higher amounts of energy, and therefore

usually involve absorption of ultraviolet radiation below 200 nm. These transitions cannot be monitored in commonly used instruments. A π-π^* transition occurs with a carbon double bond and n-π^* transition requires a nitro or carbonyl group with a non-bonded electron as well as a double bond. The π-π^* and n-π^* transitions occur readily with the energy available in the ultraviolet and visible spectrum. Molecules in which these types of electron transitions occur are referred to as chromophores, from *chroma*, the Greek word for color, and *phoros* meaning producer. Many food colorants have these types of bonds, and therefore are capable of absorbing visible light, giving color to our foods. Some typical chromophoric groups are given in Table 43.3. An auxochrome is a compound that does not exhibit absorption itself, but alters the wavelength or the intensity of absorption of a chromophore. If a longer wavelength of radiation is absorbed, it is termed a bathochromic or red shift, while a shift to shorter wavelengths is referred to as a hypsochromic or blue shift.

In addition to excitation of valence electrons, absorption of radiation by a molecule can result in charge transfer reactions involving the movement of an electron from one atom to another. As well, transition metals, with unfilled d- or f-orbitals, can also absorb radiation in the ultraviolet-visible region of the spectrum, corresponding to transitions between different d- or f-electronic states.

TABLE 43.2

Selected Applications of Spectrophotometry

Application	Reference
Quantitation of chlorogenic acid in potatoes	2
Determination of protein and fat in milk	3
Determination of paraquat in food and other samples	4
Determination of sulfite in foods using HPLC and ultraviolet spectrophotometric detection	5
Ultraviolet spectra to assess oxidative stability of corn oils	6
Determination of vitamin C by visible spectrophotometry after derivatization with Folin reagent	7
Determination of histamine in fish meal using visible spectrophotometry	8
Determination of transglutaminase activity	9
Determination of allicin and alliinase activity	10
Derivative spectrophotometry to determine two food dyes simultaneously.	11
Derivative spectrophotometry for determination of *o*- or *p*-nitrophenol, as a marker for some pesticides	12
Derivative spectrophotometry to determine tryptophan in proteins	13
Estimation of specific growth rates and lag times of microbial cultures under different conditions	14

TABLE 43.3

Some Chromophoric Groups

Chemical Group	Structure	Transition
Acetylenic	- C ≡ C -	π-π^*
Amide	- CONH$_2$	π-π^*, n-π^*
Carbonyl	- C = O	π-π^*, n-π^*
Carboxylate	- COO$^-$	π-π^*, n-π^*
Ester	-COOR	π-π^*, n-π^*
Ethylenic	- C = C -	π-π^*
Nitro	- NO$_2$	π-π^*, n-π^*
Oxime	- C = N -	π-π^*, n-π^*

Source: Ref. 15.

To obtain the absorption spectrum of a sample, a beam of radiation is passed through the sample, and the power of the incident beam, P_o, is compared to the power of the radiation passing through the sample, P, the transmitted beam (Figure 43.3). The power of the transmitted beam will be reduced from the incident beam due to reflection at the cuvette and sample interfaces, scattering within the sample, and absorption by the analyte. The transmittance of the sample, T, is the ratio of the radiant power transmitted by a sample to the power of the incident beam,

$$T = P/P_o \qquad (43.3)$$

Transmittance values range from 0 to 1, or from 0–100% for percent transmission. There is a logarithmic relationship between transmission and concentration of a compound that makes it inconvenient to relate the two. Therefore, another term, absorbance, A, is used, defined as

$$A = \log(1/T) = -\log T \qquad (43.4)$$

The relationship between transmission and absorbance with concentration can be seen in Figure 43.4.

It was established, independently by Bouguer in 1729 and Lambert in 1760, that absorbance was directly proportional to the thickness of a sample, when concentration was constant, while Beer in 1852 determined that if the sample thickness was constant, the absorbance was proportional to concentration (15). These observations are combined to derive what is commonly referred to as the Beer-Lambert Law, or simply Beer's law, as

$$A = a \cdot d \cdot c \qquad (43.5)$$

where a is absorptivity, a proportionality constant for a molecule at a specific wavelength, d is the sample pathlength, and c is the concentration of absorbing molecules.

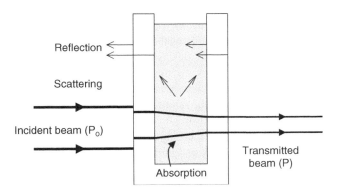

FIGURE 43.3 Attenuation of a beam of radiation by reflection at the cuvette and sample interfaces, scattering by particulates, and absorption by the analyte.

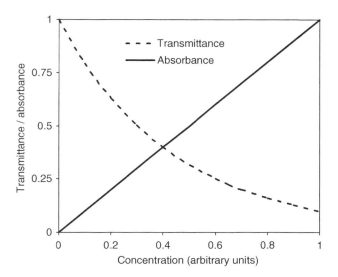

FIGURE 43.4 The relationship between transmittance, T, and absorbance, A, for a hypothetical compound.

The units of absorptivity vary, but reflect the units for concentration and sample pathlength. Molar absorptivity, or the molar extinction coefficient, ε, has units of $M^{-1}cm^{-1}$, while it is typical to give absorptivity constants of some compounds, such as proteins, in terms of a 1% solution at a specified wavelength and a 1 cm pathlength.

Beer's law is used in all absorptive spectroscopies, but is only valid if the following conditions are met: (1) the incident radiation is monochromatic, composed of a single frequency, since each wavelength will have its own absorptivity; (2) the solution is dilute enough that molecules absorbing the radiation act independently of each other; (3) the absorbing sample does not scatter or reflect the incident radiation (some unavoidable effects may be compensated by using a reference cell that contains all the sample components except the analyte); and (4) the absorption occurs in a uniform solution. Beer's law can also be applied to mixtures of molecules, as long as the components of the mixture do not chemically or physically interact. Therefore, absorbance of a mixture is additive, as follows,

$$A_{compounds\ 1-\iota} = \varepsilon_1 dc_1 + \varepsilon_2 dc_2 + ... = d\ \Sigma \varepsilon_\iota c_\iota \qquad (43.6)$$

C. EQUIPMENT

The basic elements of a spectrophotometer consist of a radiation source, a wavelength isolator, a sample container, and a detector.

1. Radiation Source

An ideal radiation source will produce stable, uniform, high intensity radiant energy over the wavelength spectrum of interest. A tungsten filament (or tungsten-halogen) lamp can be used from 320 nm into the infrared region to

2500 nm, but cannot be used in the ultraviolet region. The most common type of lamp for the ultraviolet region is a deuterium electrical discharge lamp with a quartz envelope, which can operate from about 180 to 370 nm.

2. Wavelength Isolator

A wavelength isolation device is an essential component of a spectrophotometer that enhances the selectivity of the analysis and the sensitivity of the instrument by eliminating most of the radiation that is not absorbed by the sample. The benefit of selecting radiation with a narrow range of wavelengths can be explained by the following example. Assume that a radiation source provides a constant 10 units of energy at *every* nm from 350 to 449 nm. A sample placed in the radiation beam absorbs 5 units of energy but only at 400 nm. If no wavelength isolation is used, the spectrophotometer must detect the difference between no sample (1000 units of radiation) and the sample (995 units), a 0.5% difference. However, if a crude wavelength isolation device is used which restricts the incident radiation to 10 nm around the wavelength of interest, 395–404 nm, the difference between the blank and the sample is now 100 versus 95 units of radiation. This is a difference of 5%, resulting in a 10-fold increase in sensitivity. A second important reason for using a wavelength isolation device is to enhance the selectivity of the analysis. If the radiation incident on the sample has a wide range of wavelengths, the observed absorption may be due to the interaction not only of the analyte of interest at the expected wavelength, but also from a contaminant which absorbs at another wavelength.

Using filters that only transmit radiation of certain wavelengths is one of the oldest methods of wavelength selection. Filters, however, have low selectivity and transmit relatively wide ranges of radiation. It is more common to use a monochromator, with a diffraction grating or a prism to separate wavelengths of radiation and focus them on the sample. The monochromator has an entrance slit to allow radiation to enter. The radiation is collected on a concave mirror and can be reflected to a prism or diffraction grating, which physically separates the different wavelengths of radiation. The diffraction grating is a reflective surface with 1200 to 1400 etched grooves per millimeter. The individual wavelengths of radiation are then reflected from another concave mirror to a focal plane aligned with the exit slit. By adjusting the exit slit, the desired wavelength of radiation is passed through the slit and can interact with the sample. In practice, it is not possible to select a single wavelength of radiation, but rather a narrow bandwidth of radiation, centered on the wavelength of interest, is obtained. Many instruments allow the entrance and exit slit widths to be varied, which affects the bandwidth of radiation selected. While a narrower exit slit results in a narrower bandwidth, the radiant power will be decreased. Usually, absorbance peaks in the ultraviolet-visible region are fairly broad, so a relatively wide bandwidth will give good results, and has the added advantage of giving a better signal to noise ratio.

3. Sample Holder

The sample holders used for spectrophotometric measurements are cuvettes. These are often sold in matched pairs that can be used in a dual beam spectrophotometer. Commonly used cuvettes have a pathlength of 1 cm, and may be constructed to hold either 4.5 or 1.5 mL volumes. Specialized cells are also available, with pathlengths varying from 1 mm to 10 cm, and volumes ranging from a few microliters to greater than 30 milliliters. Since the cuvette becomes part of the path that the radiation follows, it is critical that it does not contribute significantly to the absorption at the wavelengths of interest. The materials used for cuvettes vary depending on the wavelength of radiation that must be detected. For visible spectroscopy in the range from 340 nm to 800 nm, glass, quartz, polystyrene, or methacrylate cuvettes may be used. The polystyrene and methacrylate materials will give 75–90% transmission at the lower end of this range. For the ultraviolet region, only quartz or fused silica cuvettes must be used, as the other materials are opaque to ultraviolet radiation. It is important that the cuvette surface is free from scratches, material deposits, or other imperfections that can cause scattering or absorption of the incident radiation. Glass, quartz, or silica cuvettes can be cleaned periodically using 5M nitric acid or special detergents, designed to remove biological deposits, followed by rinsing with copious amounts of distilled-deionized, or reverse osmosis water. Ultrasonic baths for cleaning are not recommended by some manufacturers, as the cuvette may crack if it resonates with the bath frequency. Only lens paper or a soft cloth should be used to wipe the outer surface of the cuvette, as other papers with wood fibers can scratch the surface. The advantage of the plastic cuvettes is that they are inexpensive enough for single use, and therefore, maintenance is not an issue. An alternative to using cuvettes is to carry out analyses in microplates containing 96 wells. The absorbance of each well is obtained using a spectrophotometric reader designed specifically for such plates. Using this format, multiple assays can be performed quickly, with significant savings of precious samples or reagents since the volume of each well is only a few hundred microliters. However, the pathlength, and therefore the absorbance of the sample, varies with the total volume used for the assay and must be determined.

4. Detector

The radiation that is transmitted through a sample is quantified by conversion to an electrical signal by a detector. A common type of detector is a photomultiplier tube. The photomultiplier tube is made up of a photoemissive cathode, coated with an easily ionized material, and several dynodes in a vacuum. A voltage of 400 to 2500 V exists between the cathode and the anode. When a photon strikes the cathode, electrons are ejected and strike the first dynode and release multiple secondary electrons. These accelerate toward the next dynode, which again multiplies the electrons released in a cascade, with an eventual gain of 10^4 to 10^7. These gains are very useful in detecting low levels of radiation. The amplified electrical signal can be displayed on an analogue meter, through the position of a needle on a meter, or converted to a digital signal and manipulated by a computer and displayed on a numerical read-out.

5. Dispersive Instruments: Single-Beam and Double-Beam Optics

In a single-beam spectrophotometer, the radiation follows a path through a single cuvette to a detector. This type of instrument is calibrated for 0% T by completely blocking all radiation from the detector, and 100% T using a reference sample that, ideally, contains all the components except the analyte. Because the calibration for 0 and 100% T is carried out independent of the sample readings, random fluctuations in lamp intensity, electrical power, and drift over time may introduce error into the sample readings. Repeated calibrations can be used to compensate for instrumental drift over time.

A double-beam spectrophotometer has a design advantage over a single beam instrument in that the radiation emitted by the source is split into two beams of equal intensity (Figure 43.5). This can be accomplished by a rotating sector mirror (chopper), which rapidly focuses the radiation beam sequentially through the sample cell, and then the reference cell, as it rotates. A single detector can receive alternating signals from the sample and the reference cells or there may be separate detectors for the sample and reference. With either approach, any minor fluctuations or drift in the radiation will affect the reference and sample beam identically, and can be ignored. A disadvantage of the double beam configuration is that the power of the incident radiation on the sample is decreased by splitting the beam, and therefore, the signal to noise ratio may be lower than with single-beam optics.

6. Diode Array Instruments

Diode array spectrophotometers have a very different design from dispersive instruments (Figure 43.6). In this type of instrument, the radiation covering all the wavelengths of interest is collimated, passed through the sample, and then separated into its component wavelengths using a fixed grating. The radiation is then projected onto hundreds of diodes that are present on a silicon chip,

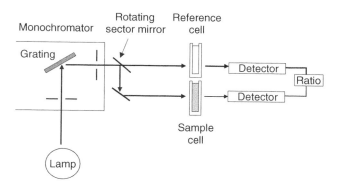

FIGURE 43.5 A schematic representation of a double-beam spectrophotometer.

termed the diode array. Each diode acts as a capacitor, and creates an electrical discharge proportional to the incident radiation. A photodiode is generally made up of a semiconductor and a capacitor to charge the semiconductor. As radiation hits the semiconductor, electrons flow through it, thereby lowering the charge on the capacitor. The intensity of radiation of the sample is proportional to the amount of charge needed to recharge the capacitor at predetermined intervals. This type of instrument allows an absorption spectrum to be obtained in less than a second, since each diode collects radiation at its unique wavelength at the same time; therefore, one of the major advantages of this type of instrument is the rapid analysis.

D. QUANTITATION

Quantitation is the most common use for spectrophotometry, and is typically carried out using a standard curve. A solution with a known concentration of the analyte is used to make up a series of dilutions. Then a plot of absorbance versus concentration at the appropriate wavelength is made. The slope of this plot can be used to determine the extinction coefficient of the compound. Alternatively, by knowing the extinction coefficient of the compound in the solvent, it is possible to calculate the concentration, using Beer's law, relating the concentration of an analyte in solution to the amount of absorbance of radiation.

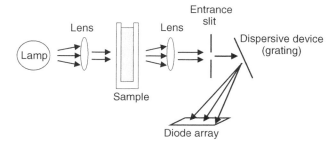

FIGURE 43.6 A schematic representation of a diode array spectrophotometer.

Care should be given to the selection of an appropriate reference sample. As noted above, the ideal reference sample contains all the sample components except the analyte. However, in practice, distilled water or even air is sometimes used to establish 100% transmission, which can cause erroneous absorbance measurements. If the refractive index of the reference and sample are not close, different amounts of reflective radiation loss will occur at the cuvette window. This failure to match the refractive index of the sample and reference can result in a shift of the baseline, with apparently greater than 100% transmission in the sample.

While many spectrophotometers are reported to give linear responses to 3 absorbance units, linearity of absorbance for any compound must be confirmed experimentally. At high concentrations of the analyte, one of the assumptions of Beer's law, the independence of the absorbing species, may not hold. At high concentrations, the analyte may interact with itself or other molecules, which can alter the absorption spectrum. As well, the design of the spectrophotometer dictates that the most accurate data will be obtained from absorbance values in the range from about 0.2–0.8 absorbance units. When sample concentration is very high, most of the radiation incident to the sample is absorbed, leaving only a small percentage traveling to the detector. Therefore, even a small error in determining the transmitted radiation power yields a large relative error, when compared to how much radiation is being detected. When the sample concentration is very low, on the other hand, most of the radiation falls on the detector. Again, a small error in radiation power at the detector translates into a large relative error in the amount of radiation absorbed by the sample.

Detection limits in spectrophotometry depend on the absorptivity of the compound being measured. A compound with a molar extinction coefficient of 10^4 to 10^5 $M^{-1}cm^{-1}$ can be detected in the micromolar concentration range. The wavelength of maximum absorbance (or minimum transmission) is the best to use for the analysis. This wavelength will yield the greatest sensitivity, with the greatest changes in absorbance as concentration changes. The accuracy and precision of a spectrophotometric assay depends on instrumental limitations, control over physical and chemical variables such as temperature, pH, and reagent purity, and operator skill.

In some analyses, the spectrum of the analyte of interest cannot be completely separated from interfering materials in the sample, or the baseline is shifted. In these cases, it may be beneficial to use the first, second, or higher order derivative for qualitative and quantitative analysis of absorption spectra (16). The derivatives can be easily calculated from the absorption spectra with the computers and programs that are standard with many modern instruments. The first derivative of a single peak spectrum is a plot of the gradient $dA/d\lambda$ versus wavelength, with a minimum that occurs at the λ_{max} and a maximum. The concentration of the analyte is proportional to the distance between these. The second derivative is $d^2A/d\lambda^2$ versus wavelength, and has two maxima with a minimum between them at the λ_{max}. The derivative spectra feature sharp bands, compared to the broader bands of the original spectra, which can enhance detection of minor spectral features. If Beer's law is valid for the original spectrum, then the derivative can be used for quantitation as

$$d^n A / d \lambda^n = d^n \varepsilon / d \lambda^n dc \qquad (43.7)$$

Another quantitative application of spectrophotometry is to determine reaction rates, rather than absolute absorbances. The rate of change in absorbance is determined just after mixing all the sample components and well before equilibrium is established. The concentration of the analyte is then proportional to the slope of absorbance as a function of time. Such procedures may be used for determining enzymatic activity. It should be noted that reaction rates can be very dependent on chemical and physical aspects of the reaction, such as pH and temperature, and these factors must be carefully controlled to obtain meaningful results.

Ultraviolet-visible absorption spectra can be used to qualitatively identify the presence of molecular species, by comparing the spectrum of an unknown with a library of possible compounds, or simply observing a characteristic absorption peak. Absorption is proportional to concentration, but spectra obtained at different concentrations can differ due to variations in absorptivity at different wavelengths, making comparisons difficult.

E. SAMPLE PREPARATION

Clear solutions are required for spectrophotometry. If the analyte is in a suspension with some turbidity, rather than a clear solution, then a significant amount of radiation will be scattered, rather than absorbed, violating one of the assumptions of the Beer-Lambert law. A wide variety of solvents with various additives can be used to enhance solubility of the analyte of interest. The only limitation is that the solvent and additives must not themselves exhibit a significant amount of absorption in the region where the analyte will be monitored. All common solvents are suitable for use in the visible range of the spectrum, while fewer are transparent at the lower end of the ultraviolet range (Table 43.4). For optimal results, the absorbance of the cuvette and solvent should be no more than 0.05 absorbance units.

Turbid suspensions are deliberately used for some specific applications, not involving absorption. Microbial cell growth curves can be determined by monitoring the decrease in transmission of radiation through a sample caused by scattering of radiation, and with a standard

TABLE 43.4
Ultraviolet Absorption Cut-Off of Some Solvents

Solvent	Ultraviolet Cut-Off (nm)
Acetonitrile	190
Cyclohexane	210
Ethane	210
Hexane	210
Methanol	210
Water	210
Glycerol	220
Ethyl ether	220
Chloroform	245
Ethyl acetate	260
Carbon tetrachloride	265
Benzene	280
Acetone	330

curve, microbial cell density in a solution can be estimated. Alternatively, an increase in transmission, as a result of a decrease in the scattering of radiation, of a bacterial suspension can be used as a qualitative indication of cell lysis.

III. TRISTIMULUS COLORIMETRY

A. INTRODUCTION

Tristimulus colorimetry is the measurement of the perceived color of objects, based on the reflection of visible light from an object. Three components influence colorimetry readings: the radiant energy spectrum of the light source impinging on the object, the characteristics of the object itself, and the sensitivity of the detector, the human eye (17). A change to any of these three interacting components usually results in a change of perceived color. Color is not a strictly physical characteristic of an object, but is a psychophysical characteristic, since it depends on human perception of light reflected from an object. There are many factors that influence color perception by an individual including the light source, the viewing angle, the background, the size of the object, surface texture, particle size, number of receptors in the eye, and even aging or yellowing of the lens in the eye. These factors, and the ability of the human eye to distinguish subtle color differences, make reproducible color description and color difference estimation by people very difficult. Instruments have been developed that standardize the radiation source, the viewing conditions, and the detector, so that reproducible color parameters can be obtained. This allows color to be unambiguously defined for an object, and color differences between objects to be measured. Colorimetry can be used to establish color standards or color tolerances that are used for quality assessment, to determine the effects of physical and chemical conditions on the color of a sample, and to establish color parameters

that can be used as rapid and non-destructive indices of other components in the sample, for example, the amount of a pigment in a sample or the loss of a reactive component. Applications of tristimulus colorimetry to foods are given in Table 43.5.

B. PRINCIPLES

Colorimetry has the ultimate objective of being able to provide color coordinates that will enable different people to describe and visualize a color unambiguously. This is most easily achieved with a uniform color space, so that the distance between two colors in three-dimensional space correlates with their visual color difference. Numerous color appearance models, or color space models have been developed, and one well-recognized system is the CIE[1] L*, a*, b* system, which provides a reasonably uniform color space (Figure 43.7). The L* value represents lightness and ranges from 0 (black) to 100 (white), the a* value represents red to green (positive to negative values), and the b* value represents blue to yellow (positive to negative values). These values can be manipulated to yield the hue and chroma of the object. Hue is the name given to a color, such as red, blue, or yellow, while chroma is the saturation, or intensity of the color, relative to a white object viewed under similar illumination. The absolute value of a* and b* values indicates the chroma of the object, and can be defined as

$$\text{Chroma} = (a^{*2} + b^{*2})^{0.5} \qquad (43.8)$$

while the hue is the angle defined by a point in color space joined to the origin and the positive a* axis. Hue can be calculated in positive degrees as

$$\text{Hue} = \tan^{-1}(b^*/a^*) \qquad (43.9)$$

TABLE 43.5
Selected Applications of Tristimulus Colorimetry

Application	Reference
Optimization of color stability of cured hams, determined from tristimulus color parameters	18
Tristimulus colorimetry to assess the color of honey	19
Tristimulus colorimetry to assess color changes in an oil in water emulsion due to Ostwald ripening	20
Tristimulus colorimetry to assess whitening ability of dairy products and coffee whiteners	21
Tristimulus colorimetry to assess relationship between color and flavor of roasted peanuts	22

---

[1] CIE, the International Commission on Illumination abbreviated from its French title Commission Internationale de l'Eclairage, is an international organization for research and exchange of information on matters relating to the science and art of lighting.

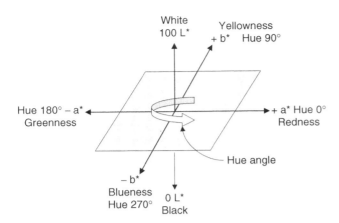

FIGURE 43.7 The CIE L*a*b* color appearance model. Hue is the positive angle calculated from a point in color space joined to the origin with the positive a* axis. Chroma (not shown) has a minimum at the intersection of the three axes and increases with distance from the origin.

C. EQUIPMENT

Tristimulus colorimeters use a light source with a defined energy spectrum, standardized illumination and viewing conditions, and sensors that simulate the way the human eye perceives color. While different instruments use different color appearance models, values from each model can be interconverted using appropriate equations. Tristimulus refers to the concept that most colors can be matched by addition of different amounts of the three primary color lights—red, green, and blue. The components of a tristimulus colorimeter include a light source, a sample holder, a set of filters, and a detector (Figure 43.8).

1. Light Source

The light source has a significant effect on the perceived color of an object, since the reflected light is dependent on the intensity of the incident light. It is a common experience to observe that the color of an object differs when viewed under different lighting conditions. There are two light sources that are commonly used in tristimulus colorimeters, Illuminant A and D65. Each is defined by the CIE. Illuminant A represents incandescent illumination. D65 mimics daylight, and is characterized by a correlated color temperature of 6500 K. The correlated color temperature of an illuminant is derived from the concept of a black body radiator, a theoretical light source, in which the quantity and wavelengths of energy emitted increase with the absolute temperature. Therefore, as correlated color temperature increases, the emitted radiation becomes more intense, with more blue (shorter) wavelengths. Although D65 is a commonly used illuminant, there are other D illuminates used in colorimeters with different correlated color temperatures.

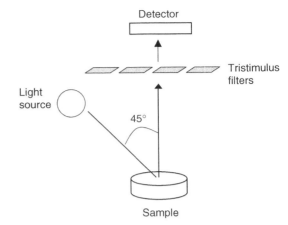

FIGURE 43.8 A tristimulus colorimeter with 45° illumination and 0° viewing geometry.

The angle that the light illuminates the object, coupled with the angle that the reflected light is viewed will also influence the perceived color. Therefore, the CIE has defined two sets of geometries for illumination and viewing that are commonly used in tristimulus colorimeters. In the first set, the sample is illuminated from all angles, using a sphere light source, and viewed at 0° to the surface. Alternatively, the sample can be illuminated at 0°, and the reflected light collected from all angles. Both of these configurations will yield the same tristimulus values. The second set of geometries includes illumination at 45° and viewing at 0° (shown in Figure 43.8), or alternatively, illumination at 0° and viewing at 45°. Again, both configurations will yield the same result. This design eliminates all components of gloss from the color parameters.

2. Filters and Detector

The filters used in a tristimulus colorimeter mimic the color sensitivity of an average person, based on the spectral responsiveness of the three types of cones in the human eye. The response curves are known as the standard observer curves. The concept can be understood as the amounts of red, green, and blue primary lights that are needed to match the colors of an equal energy spectrum by a person with average color vision. However, for calculation purposes, the red, blue, and green primary colors are mathematically converted to X, Y, and Z primaries, as some yellow hues cannot be matched by adding red, green, and blue light. Tristimulus colorimeters may use four filters, rather than three, for the same reason. Phototubes that monitor the light transmitted through each filter are used for detection.

An alternative system to the use of filters is a scanning spectrocolorimeter that uses a monochromator, coupled with diodes for detection. The reflectance data for every 5 or 10 nm are multiplied by the color-matching function of the standard observer curves, and then integrated across the spectrum to yield values for the color appearance model used by the instrument.

The specification of absolute color of an object requires careful calibration of the light source and detectors of a tristimulus colorimeter, and it is difficult to obtain identical readings between two different instruments. However, very reproducible results can be obtained from determinations of color differences between two objects, and this is a more common and reliable application of a colorimeter. It is important to remember that some color differences, measured instrumentally, may not be distinguished visually. Therefore, instrumental results must always be related to human perception.

D. SAMPLE PREPARATION

The ideal material for determining surface color is uniform in color, flat, smooth and does not exhibit gloss; however, few food materials have all of these characteristics. Therefore, the characteristics of each sample must be considered to obtain useful color information. Color measurements may be obtained on liquid, solid, or powder samples, and may require very little preparation prior to analysis. The main objective is to evaluate a sample as it would be normally viewed. Color parameters will vary with depth, surface characteristics, and particle size of the sample. Smaller particles will cause more scattering of light, and be perceived as brighter but less colorful than the same material with larger particles. Since color may vary within the sample, on the top or bottom, or depending on orientation, it may be appropriate to take several instrumental readings, turning or moving the sample between readings. The average color parameter can then be calculated. For translucent or transparent samples, a consistent sample depth must be used since color will change with the sample thickness. As well, some light may be transmitted through translucent or transparent samples, and therefore it is necessary to use a consistent background such as a white plate, and to avoid stray light that might be transmitted through the sides of the container holding the sample.

IV. ATOMIC ABSORPTION SPECTROSCOPY

A. INTRODUCTION

Atomic absorption spectroscopy (AAS) is a technique used to detect or quantitate the presence of elements, usually metals, at the sub part per million concentration. It can be used to detect elements in almost any solid, liquid, or gaseous sample, although most samples are converted into homogeneous solutions prior to analysis. Usually, only a single element is quantitated in each analysis. AAS is based on the absorption of radiation by ground state atoms, rather than molecules, but obeys the same general principles described for spectrophotometry. Two common types of AAS are flame AAS, and graphite furnace or electrothermal AAS. These methods differ in the way that ground state atoms are produced. Some applications of AAS to determine metals in food samples are given in Table 43.6.

B. PRINCIPLES

There are two key steps involved in AAS (27,28). The first step is the production of free atoms of the analyte from the sample material, produced by heating the sample using either a flame or a furnace. During heating of a sample, the solvent is evaporated, water of hydration is removed, oxides may be produced, and finally free atoms of the metal are generated. The second step is the excitation of the atoms to a higher electronic energy state, mediated by the absorption of radiation by the valence electrons. The energy associated with the absorbed radiation corresponds to the difference in energy between the ground state and an excited state of the valence electrons, and is characteristic of each atom. There are multiple excited states that an atom can achieve, and therefore the absorbance spectrum of an atom is composed of several absorption lines. However, the resonance transition state, from ground state to the first excited state, is the most intense and therefore used most often as it offers the best sensitivity. Alternative resonances may be used if there is interference at the wavelength of the first excited state. Absorption lines for the different elements occur in the wavelength range from about 160 to 900 nm. The lines of the atomic absorption spectrum are very narrow compared to the absorption spectrum of a molecule obtained in the ultraviolet and visible range because there are no vibrational or rotational transitions for free atoms.

C. EQUIPMENT

1. Flame Atomic Absorption Spectroscopy

The basic components of a flame AAS are the radiation source, flame atom cell with a burner, sample introduction system, monochromator, and the detection system (Figure 43.9). A computer is usually used for control of the instrument, and manipulation of the data.

TABLE 43.6
Selected Applications of Atomic Absorption Spectroscopy (AAS)

Application	Reference
Flame AAS to determine Cd, Cu, and Pb in samples	23
Graphite furnace AAS determination of vanadium in foods	24
Graphite furnace AAS determination of Pb in wine	25
Flame AAS simultaneous determination of Cu, Zn, Fe, and Mn, or Na, K, Ca, and Mg	26

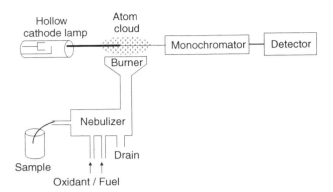

FIGURE 43.9 A schematic representation of a flame atomic absorption spectrometer.

a. Radiation source

The most common radiation source is the hollow cathode lamp (HCL), where the cathode is composed of the same metal as the analyte of interest. The HCL contains a glass envelope with a silica window for use in the ultraviolet spectrum. The glass envelope is filled with an inert gas such as neon or argon, at a low pressure between 1 to 5 torr. A voltage applied between the anode (positively charged) and the metal cathode causes the gas to ionize at the anode. The positive ions are accelerated toward the cathode, strike it, and cause some of the metal ions from the cathode to be released in an excited state. The excited ions produce an intense spectrum of radiation, characteristic of the metal when they return to the ground state. These metal atoms then diffuse back to the cathode or deposit on the glass envelope. Therefore, the HCL emits very narrow spectral lines of radiation, some of which are identical to the absorption lines of the analyte (Figure 43.10). The spectral width of atomic absorption lines is about 10^{-5} nm. There is some broadening of these lines to about 0.001–0.005 nm, but even these 'broader' absorption lines are much narrower than the resolution limits of the conventional spectral wave band selector. Therefore, the specific emission lines of the HCL eliminate a large background signal, and inherent loss of sensitivity, that would result from using a broad spectrum radiation source with a monochromator.

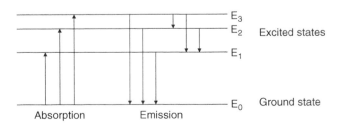

FIGURE 43.10 A comparison of the absorption and emission transitions corresponding to spectral lines for a hypothetical metal with three electronic excitation states. The emission transitions include those for absorption and additional transitions.

Typically, single element lamps are used but there are some multi-element lamps that can generate the absorption spectra of several metals simultaneously. However, usually one element is more volatile than the others, and tends to cover the surface of the other metals, reducing the intensity of radiation from these elements. The advantage of these multi-element lamps is that a single sample may be used to quantitate several elements, which is more time- and cost-efficient. An example of a multi-element lamp is the calcium and magnesium HCL, which has been used extensively for analysis of dairy products, plant extracts, and other samples.

b. Flame atom cell

The flame atom cell is where the sample is converted into free atoms by heating in a flame held in the burner. The flame therefore acts as the sample holder. A typical flame uses air as the oxidant and acetylene as the fuel. The ratio of oxidant and fuel can be varied to produce an oxidizing or reducing flame, which is optimized for each element. This flame is hot enough (~2500 K) to dissociate molecules of the sample into atoms for approximately 50 of the elements. However, there are approximately 10 to 20 elements that require a hotter flame, obtained using nitrous oxide-acetylene flame (~3200 K). These include elements that form very stable oxides such as aluminum, barium, and boron, and others such as lanthanum, the rare earth metals, molybdenum, silicon, and vanadium (29). A relatively long flame, several centimeters in length, is used to maximize the pathlength of the sample, and the amount of radiation absorbed by the atoms.

c. Sample introduction system

The sample is usually introduced into the flame as a fine mist with an ideal droplet size of 2 to 6 μm. The system should introduce the sample reproducibly, with no interferences, and no cross contamination between samples. Pneumatic nebulizers are the most common method of sample introduction. A jet of compressed air aspirates and nebulizes the solution. In a concentric nebulizer, the oxidant gas surrounds the sample as it emerges from a capillary tube, causing reduced pressure at the tip, and a suction of the sample solution from the container. The high velocity of the sample as it exits from the capillary tube creates a pressure reduction that causes the drop to break into a fine mist. Larger aerosol droplets are removed through a drain tube as the sample passes through an expansion chamber, and the remaining sample is mixed with the gases. Typically only 5 to 10% of the sample is nebulized and flows to the burner. Ultrasonic nebulizers, using high frequency sound between 0.1 to 10 MHz, have also been developed. These have a higher efficiency (~30%) than the pneumatic systems and can generate homogeneous aerosols with droplets smaller than 5 μm. They also allow the aerosol generation rate and gas flow rate to be varied independently. Because the sample is fed into the flame in a steady stream, a steady state signal is produced for each sample, depending on the flow rate.

d. Monochromator and detector

The monochromator is used to isolate the wavelength of interest. However, the inherent selectivity of the hollow cathode lamp means that only a low resolution monochromator is needed. A typical monochromator is composed of entrance and exit slits, and a prism, or gratings, similar to that used for a spectrophotometer. There has been some development of more complex optical systems for multi-element sensing. A photomultiplier tube, similar to those used in spectrophotometry, can be used for detection.

2. Graphite Furnace Atomic Absorption Spectroscopy

Furnace AAS differs from flame AAS in the way that atoms are generated and the sample is introduced into the system. Most designs are based on a heated graphite atomizer, commercially developed by the Perkin-Elmer Corporation. This system is a graphite tube, 50 mm long with a 10 mm diameter, heated by electrical resistance. An inert gas such as argon or nitrogen flows through the tube at a constant rate, and the system is enclosed in a water jacket. Discrete microlitre volumes of sample are deposited through an injection port onto a platform in the center of the tube, and are heated in three stages by applying a variable current. In the first stage, the solvent is evaporated, then the sample matrix is ashed, and finally the elements are atomized. The atom cloud then absorbs radiation from the HCL, and a single signal peak is produced from each sample application. Samples can be manually introduced to the graphite tube with micropipettes, but automatic sample introduction is also used. The technique requires from 2 to 200 µl volume, or a few milligrams of solid sample. While the technique is attractive because of the enhanced sensitivity and the small sample size, it is much more difficult to obtain reproducible results than with flame AAS. Furnace AAS is more prone to physical and chemical interferences that require more complex procedures to correct. As well, the instrumentation is more complex than flame AAS and requires more skill to operate and maintain.

D. QUANTITATION

Quantitation is achieved with a standard curve, where the relationship between signal intensity and the known concentration of analyte is determined. Usually, at least four concentrations of the analyte and a blank are used to establish the standard curve. The concentration of the unknown sample must fall within the upper and lower limits of the standard curve. The accuracy of the results will decrease, however, if atomization of analyte occurs differently in the standard solution compared to the samples. In cases where the matrix of the unknown cannot be matched with the standards, the method of standard addition may be used to compensate for interferences in the analysis. The signal from an unknown is determined, and then increasing amounts of the standard are added to the sample, and the signal is determined for each addition. The concentration of the original sample can then be determined by back extrapolation.

Flame atomic absorption produces a steady-state signal, depending on how rapidly the sample is introduced into the flame, and has a detection limit of 100 ppb for many elements. Graphite furnace AAS can have detection limits 10 to 100 times lower than flame AAS, achieving sub-ppb detection, and produces a transient signal, similar to a chromatographic peak. Therefore, peak area (recommended for more accurate results) or peak height may be used for quantitation.

E. SAMPLE PREPARATION

Almost any solid, liquid, or gas sample can be analyzed by AAS, with the appropriate pre-treatment to obtain a homogeneous solution. Liquid samples may be used directly, sometimes only with dilution to an appropriate metal concentration range. For flame AAS, solid samples are dissolved, or digested using a wet or dry ashing procedure, prior to analysis. Care must be taken to avoid losses of volatile metals during dry ashing. Solid samples may be analyzed directly by graphite furnace AAS. Metals can be extracted from a gas sample by passing the gas through a scrubber, followed by solvent extraction. Solvents and chemicals used to prepare the samples may be a source of contamination, so ultra-pure reagents should be used, and possible contamination must be accounted for by analyzing a blank. The actual measurement of a prepared sample may take approximately 10 seconds for flame AAS or 2 minutes for furnace AAS.

During AAS, there can be chemical or physical factors inherent in the sample that interfere with or enhance the production of atoms, causing errors in quantitation. A well-documented case of reduction in volatility occurs with calcium in the presence of phosphate. When these two metals are present together, calcium phosphate forms, reducing the atomization of calcium compared to that achieved from calcium chloride. Releasing agents, or ionization suppressors, are added to samples with this problem, to minimize interferences caused by incomplete or slow breakdown of a molecule to atoms or the formation of ions. Lanthanum and strontium are examples of release agents that release calcium from phosphate interference. Formation of complexes that enhance volatility are less common, although fluoride may have this effect.

V. ATOMIC EMISSION SPECTROSCOPY

A. INTRODUCTION

Atomic emission spectroscopy (AES) is used for the qualitative and quantitative analysis of metals, similar to atomic absorption spectrophotometry. While there are some common features between the two techniques, there are also important differences. Both techniques require the formation of atoms, followed by their excitation to a higher energy state. However, AES monitors the specific wavelengths of radiation emitted by excited atoms or ions, as the excited electrons fall back to lower states. Therefore, the *sample itself* creates the radiation signal in AES, and an external lamp is not required. Because a specific radiation source is not required, multiple elements can be detected in a single AES analysis. Examples of the application of AES to detect elements in food samples are given in Table 43.7.

B. PRINCIPLES

AES uses thermal energy to form free atoms from a sample matrix, and to promote valence electrons of the atoms into an excited state (28). When the electrons fall back to the ground state, the excess energy is emitted as radiation that can be detected and quantified. Similar to AAS, emission lines occur from about 160 to 900 nm, and are typically very narrow. Each ion or atom will emit a distinct set of spectral lines dependent on the electron structure of the material and the permitted energy states of the electrons that are used for identification. Qualitative analysis can be achieved by monitoring the presence of a spectral line with intensity greater than the background. The intensity of the spectral line is proportional to the concentration of the element, allowing for quantitative analysis.

The emission spectral lines are more complicated than the absorption spectral lines. With atomic absorption, the electronic transitions are usually from the ground state to the first excited state (the resonance transitions), while in atomic emission, more intermediate transitions are detected. However, because of the very narrow and characteristic emission lines from the gas-phase atoms, each element can be detected relatively free of interferences from other elements. Most elements exhibit several spectral lines that have reasonably similar sensitivities. Therefore, if one spectral line exhibits interference, an alternative may be chosen. There are several commonly used variations of atomic emission spectroscopy, depending on the energy source used to excite the samples, including flame AES (also termed flame photometry), arc/spark AES, and inductively coupled plasma (ICP) AES.

C. EQUIPMENT

The instrument used for AES requires an energy source to atomize and excite the analyte, a sample nebulizer and introduction system, a monochromator to select the emission wavelengths, a detector to record the radiation intensity, and data manipulation/readout device. Therefore, except for the radiation source (the HCL), the components are similar to those of an atomic absorption spectrometer (Figure 43.9), and some instruments can be used for both techniques. The liquid sample is aspirated into the energy source, using pneumatic or ultrasonic nebulizers, similar to those used for AAS. As previously described, only a small percentage of the sample reaches the energy source while the rest is lost through droplet condensation. In the energy source, the solvent is evaporated, the sample matrix (if present) is ashed, and the analyte is atomized and electronically excited. The emitted photons are passed through a narrow entrance slit, dispersed using a mono- or poly-chromator, and detected with a photomultiplier. The energy sources and the specific characteristics and applications of the different types of AES are described below.

1. Flame Atomic Emission Spectroscopy

Some of the flames used for flame AES include air-hydrogen (~2300 K), oxygen-hydrogen (~3000 K), and oxygen-acetylene (~3400 K). The flame must supply enough energy to atomize the analyte and to excite the atoms to higher energy states. The alkali metals and alkali earth metals (sodium, potassium, lithium, cesium, calcium, strontium, and barium) are easily excited and amenable to analysis by flame AES. The flame provides relatively low amounts of energy, however, and may result in low intensities of radiation for other metals that require more energy to reach higher excited states. Still, there are more than 70 elements, and some metal oxides, that can be detected and quantitated using flame AES. In theory, using a hotter flame should produce a stronger emission, but this is not always the case since atoms may ionize at higher temperatures. Ionization creates new spectral emission lines, reducing the intensity of the atomic lines.

TABLE 43.7
Selected Applications of Atomic Emission Spectroscopy (AES)

Application	Reference
Trace element (Ca, Cu, Fe, Mg, Mn, Zn, K, Na) food composition data for 32 different fruits by flame AAS and flame atomic emission spectroscopy	30
Selenoamino acids determined in garlic, onion, and broccoli using gas chromatography with atomic emission detection	31
ICP-AES to determine Al, As, B, Ba, Ca, Cd, Co, Cr, Cu, Fe, K, Mg, Mn, Mo, Na, Ni, P, Pb, Se, Sr, Tl, V, and Zn contents of food samples	32
ICP-AES of nickel, iron and copper in margarine samples	33
Simultaneous ICP-MS determination of 34 trace elements in the wines (Li, Be, Mg, Al, P, Cl, Ca, Ti, V, Mn, Fe, Co, Ni, Cu, Zn, As, Se, Br, Rb, Sr, Mo, Ag, Cd, Sb, I, Cs, Ba, La, Ce, Tl, Pb, Bi, Th, and U)	34
Double focusing ICP-MS analysis of Sr, Cd, Hg, and Pb, and Na, Al, Ca, Mg, Cr, Mn, Fe, Ni, Cu, Zn, and Se in milk whey	35

Because of the low energy flame, resonance spectral lines, arising from the transition between the first excited state and the ground state, are used for quantitation. However, at high concentrations, these spectral lines can self-absorb (i.e., atomic absorption occurs), causing a reduction in intensity and making it difficult to obtain reliable results. In addition, corrections to background emissions must be made for organic solvents which will yield spectral lines from products of complete or incomplete oxidation, and from the combustion fuel of the flame itself.

2. Arc/Spark Atomic Emission Spectroscopy

This type of AES utilizes an electrical discharge to excite the sample of interest. These sources can achieve temperatures of 4000 to 6000 K. Arc/spark emission spectroscopy has several advantages over flame AES. It is more universal in its application in that the higher temperature source can excite most elements, and therefore most metals can be analyzed. As well, the greater energy used in excitation causes transition beyond the first excited state, and allows transitions between two upper excited states to be used for analysis. This can improve quantitation since the number of atoms in the upper excited states is relatively low; therefore there is little self-absorption of these spectral lines, and a linear response between concentration and line intensity can often be obtained. Arc/spark AES is 10 to 1000 times more sensitive than flame AES. However, intense spectral lines that can cause interference can be produced from materials in the air near the electrical discharge.

3. Inductively Coupled Plasma Atomic Emission Spectroscopy (ICP-AES)

A plasma is an ionized gas that is neutral in charge. A plasma can be created starting with a stream of gas (typically argon) that flows through an open tube surrounded by a metal coil, such as copper. The coil transfers power from the radio frequency generator, acting as an inducer, and therefore the source is referred to as an inductively coupled plasma (ICP). The coil sets up an oscillating electromagnetic field. A few charged argon ions are introduced by an igniting device, and are caught in the oscillating field. These ions move rapidly with the field, generating more ions and free electrons from collisions with gas atoms. These secondary ions, in turn, create even more ions and free electrons, resulting in the plasma. Another stream of argon is used to carry the aerosol sample from the nebulizer into the plasma. The aerosol must be dried to remove the large amounts of solvent that would cool or extinguish the plasma. This is accomplished by passing the sample through a heated tube, and then a cooled condenser. When the atoms of the sample are introduced into the plasma, they collide with rapidly moving gas ions, become excited, and then relax to a lower energy state, emitting distinct spectral lines. The plasma source is extremely hot—estimates range from 6500 to 10,000 K—and therefore it is capable of breaking virtually all chemical bonds in the sample, resulting in independent ions and atoms. The method has high sensitivity since a large proportion of most elements will be excited, with little self-absorption and little chemical interference. Linearity can be achieved over four to six orders of magnitude. There are two configurations, radial and axial, for collecting radiation from the plasma. In the radial configuration, radiation is collected from the side of the plasma, across a narrow emitting central channel. An axial configuration views the plasma end-on. This configuration increases the pathlength of the sample, and increases the detection limits 5 to 10 times.

4. Detection Systems

An advantage of AES over AAS is that multiple elements can be detected in a single analysis. There have been several different detection systems designed to accommodate this characteristic (36).

a. Sequential spectrometers

Sequential instruments are the least expensive and most flexible types of emission spectrometers. Most include a single photomultiplier tube that receives wavelengths of emitted radiation in sequential order from a monochromator. This configuration is good to use when the metals to be determined, their concentration, and the sample matrices vary. The major disadvantages of the sequential instruments are the relatively long analysis times, since only one element may be determined at a time, and the greater sample volume required.

Two methods are used to obtain reproducible wavelength selection with this type of instrument. One approach is to rely on the analyte to produce the largest spectral line near the expected wavelength. This can result in selection of an erroneous line if an interfering element is present at relatively high concentrations. Alternatively, a known spectral line, such as the carbon line at 193 nm, can be used for reference, and the wavelength of interest is identified as a predefined number of steps from the reference. This method is less likely to lead to selection of the wrong spectral line, but increases analysis time.

b. Simultaneous spectrometers

Simultaneous spectrometers use multiple detectors, with one or more photomultiplier tubes for each analyte of interest, so that the instrument is configured for a set number of analytes, with known interferences. The radiation of different wavelengths emitted by the sample is dispersed through a monochromator onto the detectors. Because detectors and grating are stationary, there is no need for a peak search routine. Matrix-dependent interferences can be overcome by installing multiple detectors for a single element, and selecting the one that is most sensitive and interference free. The major disadvantage of these instruments is the lack of flexibility, as they are configured for specific spectral lines of analytes, and the installation of additional detectors after the instrument has been configured can be expensive.

c. Solid-state array detector spectrometers

To overcome the limitation of both the sequential and simultaneous instruments, charge-injection device (CID) or charge-coupled device (CCD) detectors have been introduced to give very high sensitivity and resolution. These detectors can monitor 250,000 or 5,000 spectral lines simultaneously, respectively. These instruments with a CID or CCD can be obtained for the same price as an instrument with a simultaneous configuration and 25 photomultiplier detectors, and therefore are likely to be the configuration of choice.

d. ICP-AES mass spectrometry

Mass spectrometry can be used in conjunction with ICP to detect the atoms and ions, rather than using the radiation they emit (28). The atoms and ions are produced by the plasma as previously described, extracted from the center channel of the plasma, and separated and detected using mass spectrometry, by their mass to charge ratio. The technique is extremely sensitive, with detection at the part per trillion level, and may require a clean room environment to eliminate background interferences. It is the only atomic absorption/emission technique that can separate and quantitate isotopes, but it is by far the most expensive type of AES.

D. QUANTITATION

AES can be used quantitatively, using a standard curve or by the method of standard addition, as described for AAS; however, careful calibration is required to obtain accurate results. Many different experimental variables affect the intensity of radiation emitted, including spectral line overlap from elements in the samples that cannot always be avoided. In these cases, correction factors are calculated, using pure solutions of each component.

Matrix effects are common for flame and arc/spark AES. If the matrix is more volatile than the analytes, it will cause the signal from the elements to be released over a longer time and with a lower intensity. Ideally, the matrix of the sample and the standards should be identical. If there are substantial differences in the matrix between the samples and standards, background correction must be used.

It is difficult to compare the different atomic absorption or atomic emission techniques for sensitivity and detection limits, since factors such as the equipment configuration, slit width, the sample matrix, and the spectral line used influence the signal obtained. For a particular

analysis, a literature search can be carried out to determine the best method. However, some general comparisons of the techniques can be made. Flame AES can detect elements at sub-ppm levels, while arc/spark-AES and ICP-AES have detection limits that are 10 to 1000 times lower, at sub-ppb to several hundred ppb. As mentioned above, ICP-AES mass spectroscopy has a detection limit that is several orders of magnitude lower than this, often at ppt to the sub-ppt level. In relationship to atomic absorption techniques, ICP-AES is between that of flame and furnace atomic absorption spectrophotometry, with flame AAS being the least sensitive method of detection.

E. SAMPLE PREPARATION

Sample preparation for AES is similar to that required for AAS. Only liquid samples can be applied to AES, and therefore solid samples must be solubilized in an appropriate solvent, and may require wet or dry ashing.

VI. POLARIMETRY

A. INTRODUCTION

Anisotropic materials, those that have a lack of symmetry in their molecular or crystalline structure, and non-racemic samples, those containing unequal concentrations of enantiomers of a chiral molecule, have the ability to rotate a plane of polarized radiation. Such substances are said to have optical activity. The measurement of the rotation of plane polarized radiation by an optically active material is called polarimetry. Polarimetry is a non-destructive technique that can be used for studying the structure of anisotropic materials, for checking the concentration and purity of chiral mixtures in solutions, and as an aid in identifying unknown compounds. Chemical or enzymatic reactions may be monitored by the change in optical rotation over time. The technique is used extensively for the analysis of carbohydrates in the sugar refining industry. Some selected applications of polarimetry in food science are given in Table 43.8.

B. PRINCIPLES

Linearly or plane polarized radiation is made up of equal intensities of left- and right-circularly polarized radiation (40). Optical rotation occurs because the electrical component of left- and right-circularly polarized radiation interact with the asymmetric centers of chiral molecules, differently. This differential interaction causes the two circularly polarized components to travel at different velocities. Therefore, they are not in phase when they exit the sample, and exhibit an overall rotation. Optical rotation occurs for both visible and ultraviolet radiation. The rotation is said to be dextrorotatory (d) if the radiation is rotated clockwise when viewed by an observer looking toward the radiation

TABLE 43.8

Selected Applications of Polarimetry

Application	Reference
Polarimetry in sugar analysis	37
Polarimetry as a quantitative tool for the determination of collagen content of isinglass finings	38
Laser-based polarimetry for the detection of gentamicin analogues separated by reverse phase ion pair chromatography in whole milk	39

source, and the enantiomer is given the (+) designation. Similarly, the enantiomer that rotates radiation to the left, or counterclockwise, is called the levorotatory (l) or the (−) enantiomer. It should be noted that the direction that polarized light will be rotated by a chiral compound cannot be predicted by its stereochemistry (designated R or S), and must be determined experimentally.

C. EQUIPMENT

The simplest polarimeter consists of a monochromatic radiation source, a polarizer, a sample cell, a second polarizer, which is called the analyzer, and a radiation detector (Figure 43.11). The analyzer is oriented 90° to the polarizer so that no radiation reaches the detector. When an optically active substance is present in the beam, it rotates the polarization of the radiation reaching the analyzer so that there is a component that reaches the detector. The angle that the analyzer must be rotated to regain the minimum detector signal is the optical rotation.

D. QUANTITATION

The amount of optical rotation depends on the number of optically active species, through which the radiation passes, and is therefore dependent on both the sample pathlength and the analyte concentration. Specific rotation, $[\alpha]$, accounts for these factors, and is defined as:

$$[\alpha]_\lambda = \alpha / (l \cdot d) \tag{43.10}$$

where α is the measured optical rotation in degrees, l is the sample pathlength in decimeters, and d is the density if the sample is a pure liquid, or the concentration if the sample is a solution. In either case, the units of d are g/cm^3. As well, optical rotation depends on the wavelength of radiation, λ,

and the temperature, t, so both are specified. A sodium lamp that has a spectral emission D-line at 589 nm is often used as a monochromatic source, and the specific rotation is designated as $[\alpha]_D$ to denote this. It can be noted that the specific rotation, $[\alpha]_\lambda$, and the measured optical rotation, α, of Equation 43.10 are analogous to the absorptivity, a, and the absorbance, A, respectively, of the Beer-Lambert law (Equation 43.5). Therefore, similar to spectrophotometry, the concentration of an analyte can be determined knowing the specific rotation of the compound, and determining the optical rotation at the specified wavelength and temperature. Alternatively, a standard curve relating optical rotation to concentration of a standard compound may be used for quantitation.

The optical rotatory dispersion (ORD) is the optical rotation as a function of wavelength. It is recorded using a spectropolarimeter, which has a broad-spectrum radiation source and a scanning monochromator. This technique has largely been replaced by circular dichroism spectroscopy. Additional information on ORD may be found in (40).

E. SAMPLE PREPARATION

Samples must be liquids or dissolved in an appropriate solvent for analysis by a polarimeter. The solvent used must be specified since it will affect the specific rotation of the analyte.

VII. CIRCULAR DICHROISM SPECTROSCOPY

A. INTRODUCTION

Circular dichroism (CD) can be observed when optically active matter both absorbs and rotates left- and right-handed circular polarized radiation slightly differently (40). If the left- and right-circularly polarized radiation has the same amplitude and wavelength, the resultant radiation is observed as plane polarized radiation. However, when the plane polarized radiation passes through a sample that absorbs the two circularly polarized components to different extents, the radiation rotates along an ellipsoid path (Figure 43.12). The difference in the left- and right-handed absorbance, $A(l)- A(r)$, is very small and will cause an ellipticity of the radiation, ψ, of a few 1/100ths to 1/10ths of a degree. This small ellipticity can be measured accurately, and recorded as a function of wavelength to yield a CD spectrum. CD spectroscopy can be a more informative method than ultraviolet-visible spectrophotometry since it reflects not only the absorption of radiation, but also the chiral centers of the analyte through features termed Cotton bands. CD spectroscopy can be used to establish the stereochemistry of a chiral molecule or confirm chiral purity, and is very useful for obtaining information about the secondary structure of chiral macromolecules such as proteins, peptides, polysaccharides, and nucleic acids. For example,

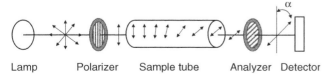

Lamp   Polarizer   Sample tube   Analyzer   Detector

FIGURE 43.11 A schematic representation of a polarimeter.

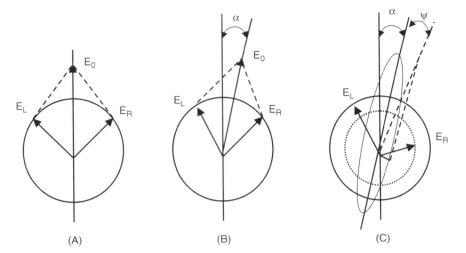

FIGURE 43.12 A. A sample that is not optically active does not preferentially interact or absorb left (E_L) or right (E_R) circularly polarized radiation. The radiation leaving the material is linearly polarized, with no rotation and ellipticity (E_O). B. The preferential interaction of one type of circularly polarized radiation passing through an optically active sample will cause a rotation in the detected radiation of α. C. The preferential absorption of one type of circularly polarized radiation will cause the transmitted radiation to follow an ellipse, with an ellipticity of ψ.

each of the three basic secondary structures of a polypeptide chain (helix, sheet, and coil) shows a characteristic CD spectrum from about 180 to 260 nm (41). Therefore, the spectrum of a protein will be the sum of the helix, sheet, and coil components, and can be deconvoluted to yield the proportion of the protein that is in each secondary structure. Examples of the application of CD spectroscopy in food analysis are given in Table 43.9.

B. PRINCIPLES

The CD spectrum is recorded in radians of ellipticity, ψ, as a function of wavelength, and can be expressed as

$$\psi = [2.303c \cdot d(\varepsilon_L - \varepsilon_R)] \quad (43.11)$$

TABLE 43.9
Selected Applications of Circular Dichroism (CD) Spectroscopy

Application	Reference
Conformation of wheat glutenin subunits under different chemical conditions	42
CD analysis of the effect of heating on beta-lactoglobulin A, B, and C	43
CD characterization of anthocyanin polymerization in wine liquid chromatographic fractions	44
CD analysis of ketoses, and application of the method to enzymatic hydrolysis and isomerization reactions, and chemical hydrolysis	45

where c is the concentration in mol/l, d is the optical pathlength in cm, ε_L and ε_R are the molar absorptivity coefficients of the sample for the left and right hand circularly polarized radiation at each wavelength. It is more convenient to convert ellipticity from radians to degrees, as

$$\theta = \psi(360/2\pi) = [32.09c \cdot d(\varepsilon_L - \varepsilon_R)] \quad (43.12)$$

Molar ellipticity, $[\theta]$, can then be calculated to obtain an intrinsic quantity, as

$$[\theta] = (\theta \cdot M)/(l \cdot c' \cdot 100) \quad (43.13)$$

where M is the molecular weight, l is the pathlength in decimeters, and c' is the analyte concentration in g/ml. For work with proteins, ellipticity is normalized to a mean residue ellipticity, $[\theta]_p$ with units of degree cm^2/decimol residue, to allow comparison between samples, calculated as

$$[\theta]_p = (\theta \cdot M)/(10 \cdot c \cdot d \cdot n_r) \quad (43.14)$$

where n_r is the number of residues in the protein.

C. EQUIPMENT

The components of a CD spectropolarimeter include a radiation source, a monochromator, a polarizer and modulator, a sample holder, and a detector (Figure 43.13). The radiation from the monochromator is first linearly polarized and then passed through a dynamic quarter wave plate that modulates it into left- and right-circularly polarized forms that pass through the sample. One type of quarter wave plate is an isotropic (uniform) crystal that is made to

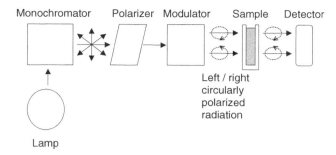

FIGURE 43.13 A schematic representation of a circular dichroism spectrometer.

be anisotropic through the application of an alternating current at high voltage. The signal intensity obtained in CD spectroscopy is small, and therefore the incident power of the radiation source must be high, and a 500 W xenon lamp is often used. As well, oxygen must be removed from the instrument by purging with pure nitrogen to eliminate the production of ozone that would interfere with absorbance at the lower wavelengths, since CD spectra are recorded from ~170 nm.

D. SAMPLE PREPARATION

The requirements for a compound to be amenable to CD spectroscopy are that it must have ultraviolet or visible absorption bands and be optically active. It should be remembered that a molecule that is chiral may not be optically active if it is present as a racemic mixture. As well, samples that are not optically active may be derivatized with a chiral material prior to analysis. The detection limits for CD spectroscopy can be around the ppm range. Unfolded protein and particulate matter act as scattering particles, and add significant noise to the CD spectrum. Therefore, passing sample solutions through a 0.45 to 0.2 µm filter may improve the signal to noise ratio.

The CD spectrum of a protein can typically be obtained using 20 to 50 µl of a 0.1 to 0.5 mg/ml protein in a low ionic strength buffer (5 to 10 mM), in a cuvette with a 0.1 to 1.0 mm pathlength. Protein concentration has a significant effect on the spectrum, and therefore accurate determination of protein concentration is required. Any compound that absorbs in the region of interest (190 to 250 nm), such as chloride ions, should be avoided, and only additives in the minimum concentration essential to maintaining the solubility of the protein should be present in the sample.

VIII. NUCLEAR MAGNETIC RESONANCE (NMR) SPECTROSCOPY

A. INTRODUCTION

Nuclear magnetic resonance (NMR) spectroscopy is one of the most powerful, non-destructive analytical tools. It uses low energy radio frequency radiation to induce transitions between different nuclear spin states of a sample in a magnetic field. A single type of nuclei (e.g., ^{1}H, ^{13}C, or ^{31}P) is observed in one analysis. The most common nuclei detected are protons, which have a high natural abundance, and high inherent sensitivity, and carbon-13, which has a low natural abundance (~1.1% of naturally occurring carbon) and a low sensitivity. However, other nuclei of potential interest in food systems, such as ^{14}N, ^{23}Na, and ^{43}Ca, can also be detected. The utility of NMR spectroscopy arises because the same nuclei in different chemical environments experience slightly different magnetic fields. This causes spin state transitions for the same nuclei in different functional groups to occur at slightly different resonance frequencies. NMR spectroscopy can be used for determining the detailed structural features of molecules, quantitative measurement of sample components, and for two- and three-dimensional imaging of solid materials (46). Some selected applications of NMR spectroscopy in food science are given in Table 43.10.

TABLE 43.10

Selected Applications of Nuclear Magnetic Resonance (NMR) Spectroscopy

Application	Reference
High resolution ^{1}H-NMR and MRI to monitor water-soluble and salt-soluble extracts from fish muscle during frozen storage	47
High resolution ^{1}H-NMR to determine the solution structure of *Escherichia coli* heat-stable enterotoxin b	48
High resolution ^{1}H- and ^{13}C-NMR spectroscopy analysis and characterization of carrageenan samples	49
Low resolution ^{1}H-NMR to determine crystallization kinetics of trehalose and trehalose-salt solutions	50
High resolution ^{2}H-NMR and ^{17}O-NMR to study water mobility in multicomponent model media	51
Solid-state ^{13}C cross-polarization, magic-angle spinning NMR to study the effect of post mortem changes on the quality of pork	52
Cross-polarization, magic angle spinning NMR to study glucose rotational mobility under different conditions	53
Site-specific natural isotope fractionation-NMR (SNIF-NMR) method of detection of maple syrup adulteration by beet or cane sugar addition	54
MRI to monitor lipid migration in chocolate confectionery	55
MRI to quantify extent of mixing in a non-reacting 2-component system	56
MRI to monitor the effects of compression on the structure of tomato	57
MRI used to validation thermal processing in food manufacture	58
^{23}Na-MRI to monitor the migration of sodium ions into pork during brining	59

B. PRINCIPLES

Nuclei with an odd number of protons, neutrons, or both will have an intrinsic nuclear angular momentum or nuclear spin (60). This causes the nucleus to have magnetic characteristics including a magnetic moment and a magnetic dipole. When such a nucleus is placed in a static magnetic field, B_0, the nuclear spin can align in the same direction as the external field, in a low energy state, or in the opposite direction as the external magnetic field, in a less favorable high energy state (Figure 43.14). The difference in energy (ΔE) between the two states increases with the strength of the magnetic field. When the nuclei are exposed to radio frequency radiation that has the same energy as the difference between the two states, they will absorb it and the population of the high energy state will increase slightly, by only a few nuclei for every 10^5 nuclei. This small excess of nuclei in the higher energy state accounts for the relatively low sensitivity of NMR compared to some other spectroscopic techniques. The frequency of radiation that causes the transition is referred to as the chemical shift, δ, and is expressed in parts per million (ppm), calculated relative to a reference signal as

$$\delta = [v_{signal} - v_{reference} / v_{reference}] \times 10^6 \quad (43.15)$$

Using chemical shift allows spectra obtained from instruments with different magnetic strengths to be compared directly. After absorbing energy, nuclei re-emit the radio frequency radiation and return to the lower energy state in a process termed relaxation. There are two types of relaxation, spin-lattice (T_1) that involves energy exchange with the environment, and spin-spin relaxation (T_2) that involves energy exchange between similar molecules. The relaxation times are a characteristic of the chemical and physical environment of the nuclei.

There are several parameters of the NMR spectrum that can yield information about the sample. Different chemical structures can be inferred from specific chemical shifts. Characteristic splitting patterns of the NMR signals known as spin-spin coupling that occur from interactions between nuclei close to each other and the size of the splitting, the J coupling constant, are also indicative of specific structures. The area under the NMR signal peaks is proportional to the number of nuclei causing the signal. As well, the relaxation times, T_1 and T_2, have been used to determine the mobility and physical state of sample components.

Low resolution NMR spectroscopy utilizes magnets with a field strength up to ~2.0 tesla (85 MHz)[2]. An advantage of this technique is the relatively low cost of the equipment, since the magnet strength is low and the magnetic field does not need to be extremely uniform. Low resolution

NMR spectroscopy can be used to determine the proportion of the sample that is moisture or lipid, the physical state of a component, and to follow chemical reactions such as crystallization, gel formation, or protein denaturation. It is not possible to obtain detailed structural information using low resolution NMR spectroscopy, as spin-spin coupling and the coupling constants may not be well resolved.

High resolution techniques use magnets of 2.3 to 21 tesla (100 to 900 MHz), with high magnetic field homogeneity. The more powerful the magnet, the greater the resolution between resonance signals. High resolution techniques are used to yield detailed structural information about molecules, and while not routine, it is possible to carry out structural analysis of macromolecules that are greater than 100 kDa (61). High resolution NMR spectroscopy has an advantage over other structure-determining techniques such as x-ray crystallography as the molecule can be analyzed in a more natural state, without the need for crystallization. High resolution NMR spectroscopy has also been used to detect sample adulteration by a technique known as site specific natural isotope fractionation (SNIF) that determines isotope ratios in specific chemical structures.

An extension of NMR spectroscopy is magnetic resonance imaging (MRI) (62). MRI yields two- and three-dimensional images of the internal structure of objects, using proton resonances. Linear radio frequency gradients are applied to the sample, in addition to the static magnetic field, B_0. This makes the resonance frequency of a nucleus dependent on its location in the gradient, and a position-dependent spectrum is obtained. By applying linear radio frequency gradients in several directions, an image based on proton density within a sample is obtained. MRI can be used to understand heat and mass transfer in a sample, water mobility, food stability, and processes such as ripening, drying, crystallization, and gelation.

C. EQUIPMENT

The basic components of a NMR spectrometer are a magnet and shim coils, the probe, the radio frequency receiver, and a computer (Figure 43.15). The magnet can be the most expensive component, and produces the principal magnetic field. Magnets greater than 4.7 tesla (200 MHz) are surrounded by liquid helium and liquid nitrogen to maintain the super-conducting conditions. There may be a number of shim coils to modify the magnetic field around the sample so that it is very homogenous, a requirement to obtain high resolution. The NMR probe is positioned in the shim coils, and generates the radio frequency radiation that causes the nuclear spin transitions. Radio frequency coils also act as the receiver to detect the relaxation signals from the sample. The sample is positioned within the radio frequency coil of the probe and is spun to minimize heterogeneity in the sample and the magnetic field. A computer is an integral part of NMR spectrometers, and controls the settings of the components, and data storage and manipulation.

---

[2] Although magnet strength is measured in tesla, it is common to refer to instruments in terms of the resonance frequency for a proton at the specified magnet strength, expressed in MHz.

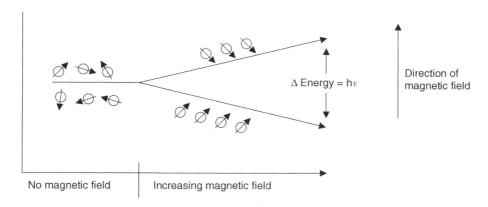

No magnetic field | Increasing magnetic field

Δ Energy $= h\nu$

Direction of magnetic field

FIGURE 43.14 A schematic illustration of nuclei with a magnetic moment in the absence or presence of an applied magnetic field. The energy difference between the magnetic states of the nuclei (ΔE) is related to the strength of the magnetic field, and is a function of the radiation frequency (ν) and Planck's constant (h).

Fourier transform spectrometers are the most common type of instrument. They emit a short pulse of radiation over a broad range of frequencies, so that the spin state of all the nuclei of interest (i.e., all the protons in a sample) is altered. All of the resulting relaxation signals are also received at the same time, and can be separated mathematically yielding the NMR spectrum. An alternate approach is the continuous wave instrument that emits the range of radio frequencies sequentially, and also received the signal sequentially. Therefore, data collection with a continuous wave instrument takes a significantly longer time.

D. SAMPLE PREPARATION

Solutions and solid samples may be analyzed by high resolution NMR spectroscopy. Pure samples are dissolved in an appropriate solvent (usually one in which all the hydrogens have been replaced with deuterium) to yield a homogeneous solution and filtered to remove particulate matter that will affect resolution. With the application of more powerful magnets, the resolution between the resonances increases and the amount of sample required for analyses decreases. A few micrograms to milligrams of sample may be required, depending on the instrument, and the molecular weight of the analyte. The ideal solid for high resolution NMR spectroscopy is a uniform powder compacted into a sample holder, that is subjected to 'magic-angle spinning'—a 54.44° angle between the sample spinning axis and the external magnetic field that is used to improve signal resolution.

For low resolution NMR applications, samples can be analyzed without extraction or solubilization because radio frequencies can penetrate solid materials. The sample must only be manipulated to fit in a sample tube. Therefore, valuable information relating to the intrinsic structure and composition of a sample can be determined based on the relaxation parameters, T_1 and T_2. Large samples with no modification can be monitored by MRI, the only limitation being the size of the probe cavity.

IX. CONCLUSION

This chapter has briefly highlighted the essential features of some commonly used spectroscopic techniques and provided examples of how each technique can be applied to food-related analyses. These techniques are fundamental analytical tools that have allowed us to better understand the individual components of food and foods as complex systems. They have played a key role in the maintenance of food quality and safety. Improvements in instrumentation and advances in the application of these techniques will continue to provide food scientists with more sensitive and informative methods of analysis.

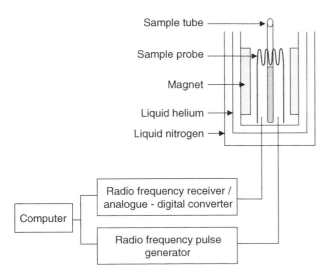

Sample tube

Sample probe

Magnet

Liquid helium

Liquid nitrogen

Radio frequency receiver / analogue - digital converter

Computer

Radio frequency pulse generator

FIGURE 43.15 A schematic representation of a nuclear magnetic resonance spectrometer.

REFERENCES

1. MH Penner. Basic principles of spectroscopy. In: SS Nielsen. ed. Food Analysis, 2nd ed. Gaithersburg, Maryland: Aspen Publishers Inc., 1998, pp 387–396.

2. L Dao, M Friedman. Chlorogenic acid content of fresh and processed potatoes determined by ultraviolet spectrophotometry. J Agric Food Chem 40:2152–2156, 1992.

3. E Gabor. Rapid simultaneous protein and fat content determination in milk by spectrophotometry. Nahrung 33:549–555, 1989.

4. MK Rai, DJ Vanisha, VK Gupta. A sensitive determination of paraquat by spectrophotometry. Talanta 45:343–348, 1997.

5. RF McFeeters, AO Barish. Sulfite analysis of fruits and vegetables by high-performance liquid chromatography (HPLC) with ultraviolet spectrophotometric detection. J Agric Food Chem 51:1513–1517, 2003.

6. TMFS Vieira, MAB Regitano-d'Arce. Ultraviolet spectrophotometric evaluation of corn oil oxidative stability during microwave heating and oven test. J Agric Food Chem 47:2203–2206, 1999.

7. SK Jagota, HM Dani. A new colorimetric technique for the estimation of vitamin C using Folin phenol reagent. Anal Biochem 127:178–182, 1982.

8. S Kose, G Hall. Modification of a colorimetric method for histamine analysis in fish meal. Food Res Int 33:839–845, 2000.

9. C Dinnella, MT Gargaro, R Rossano, E Monteleone. Spectrophotometric assay using *o*-phthaldialdehyde for the determination of transglutaminase activity on casein. Food Chem 78:363–368, 2002.

10. T Miron, A Rabinkov, D Mirelman, L Weiner, M Wilchek. A spectrophotometric assay for allicin and alliinase (Alliin lyase) activity: reaction of 2-nitro-5-thiobenzoate with thiosulfinates. Anal Biochem 265:317–325, 1998.

11. A Bozdogan, M Ustun-Ozgur, I Koyuncu. Simultaneous determination of Sunset Yellow and Ponceau 4R in gelatin powder by derivative spectrophotometry and partial least-squares multivariate spectrophotometric calibration. Anal Lett 33:2975–2982, 2000.

12. MI Toral, P Richter, M Cavieres, W Gonzalez. Simultaneous determination of o- and p-nitrophenol by first derivative spectrophotometry. Environ Mon Assess 54:191–203, 1999.

13. DJ Fletouris, NA Botsoglou, GE Papageorgiou, AJ Mantis. Rapid determination of tryptophan in intact proteins by derivative spectrophotometry. J Assoc Off Anal Chem 76:1168–1173, 1993.

14. P Dalgaard, K Koutsoumanis. Comparison of maximum specific growth rates and lag times estimated from absorbance and viable count data by different mathematical models. J Microbiol Meth 43:183–196, 2001.

15. JA Howell. Ultraviolet and visible molecular absorption spectrometry. In: FA Settle. ed. Handbook of Instrumental Techniques for Analytical Chemistry. Toronto: Prentice-Hall, Canada Inc., 1997, pp 481–506.

16. C Bosch Ojeda, F Sanchez Rojas, JM Cano Pavon Recent developments in derivative ultraviolet/visible absorption spectrophotometry. Talanta 42:1195–1214, 1995.

17. MD Fairchild. Color Appearance Models. Reading, MA, Addison Wesley Longman, Inc., 1997, pp 1–417.

18. JKS Moller, M Jakobsen, CJ Weber, T Martinussen, LH Skibsted, G Bertelsen. Optimisation of colour stability of cured ham during packaging and retail display by a multifactorial design. Meat Sci 63:169–175, 2003.

19. A Terrab, MJ DiezJ, FJ Heredia. Chromatic characterisation of Moroccan honeys by diffuse reflectance and tristimulus colorimetry-non-uniform and uniform colour spaces. Food Sci Technol Int 8:189–195, 2002.

20. J Weiss, DJ McClements. Color changes in hydrocarbon oil-in-water emulsions caused by Ostwald ripening. J Agric Food Chem 49:4372–4377, 2001.

21. W Kneifel, F Ulberth, E Schaffer. Evaluation of coffee whitening ability of dairy products and coffee whiteners by means of reflectance colorimetry. Milchwissenschaft 47:567–569, 1992.

22. W Kneifel, F Ulberth, E Schaffer. Comparison of peanut butter color determination by CIELAB L-*a-*b-* and Hunter color-difference methods and the relationship of roasted peanut color to roasted peanut flavor response. J Agric Food Chem 39:519–523, 1991.

23. AK Sella, AK Avila, RC Campos. The determination of Cd, Cu and Pb in potable water and plant material by flame-AAS after on-line preconcentration of DDTP-NH4 metal complexes on a C18 column. Anal Lett 32:2091–2104, 1999.

24. A Adachi, S Sawada, K Shida, E Nakamura, T Okano. Determination of vanadium in foods by atomic absorption spectrophotometry. Anal Lett 32:2327–2334, 1999.

25. PA Brereton, P Robb, CM Sargent, HM Crews, R Wood. Determination of lead in wine by graphite furnace atomic absorption spectrophotometry: interlaboratory study. J Assoc Off Anal Chem 80:1287–1297, 1997.

26. U Gottelt, G Henrion, R Kalaehne, M Stoyke. Simultaneous determination of the elements copper, zinc, iron and manganese as well as sodium, potassium, calcium and magnesium by flame atomic absorption spectrometry (F-AAS). Nahrung 40:313–318, 1996.

27. J Sneddon. Atomic absorption spectrometry. In: FA Settle. ed. Handbook of Instrumental Techniques for Analytical Chemistry. Toronto: Prentice-Hall, Canada Inc., 1997, pp 373–393.

28. JW Robinson. Atomic Spectroscopy, 2nd ed. New York: Marcel Dekker, Inc., 1996, pp 65–196, 219–386.

29. B Welz, M Sperling. Atomic Absorption Spectrometry, 3rd ed. Toronto: Wiley-VCH, 1999, pp 1–941.

30. NJ Miller-Ihli. Atomic absorption and atomic emission spectrometry for the determination of the trace element content of selected fruits consumed in the United States. J Food Compos Anal 9:301–311, 1996.

31. JC Xiao, E Block, PC Uden, BD Quimby, JJ Sullivan, Z Xing. Allium chemistry: identification of selenoamino acids in ordinary and selenium-enriched garlic, onion, and broccoli using gas chromatography with atomic emission detection. J Agric Food Chem 43:1754–1757, 1995.

32. SP Dolan, SG Capar. Multi-element analysis of food by microwave digestion and inductively coupled

plasma-atomic emission spectrometry. J Food Comp Anal 15:593–615, 2002.

33. Z Benzo, E Marcano, C Gomez, F Ruiz, J Salas, M Quintal, A Garaboto, M Murillo. Simultaneous determination of nickel, iron, and copper in margarine by inductively coupled plasma-atomic emission spectroscopy after sample emulsification. J Assoc Off Anal Chem 85:967–970, 2002.

34. VF Taylor, HP Longerich, JD Greenough. Multielement analysis of Canadian wines by inductively coupled plasma mass spectrometry (ICP-MS) and multivariate statistics. J Agric Food Chem 51:856–860, 2003.

35. A Rivero-Martino, ML Fernandez-Sanchez, A Sanz-Medel. Total determination of essential and toxic elements in milk whey by double focusing ICP-MS. J Anal Atomic Spectrosc 15:163–168, 2000.

36. AW Varnes. Inductively coupled plasma atomic emission spectroscopy. In: FA Settle. ed. Handbook of Instrumental Techniques for Analytical Chemistry. Toronto: Prentice-Hall, Canada Inc., 1997, pp 395–418.

37. B Trott. Polarimetry. Internat Sugar J 103(1230): 251–254, 1995.

38. RV Leather, M Sisk, CJ Dale, A Lyddiatt. Analysis of the collagen and total soluble nitrogen content of isinglass finings by polarimetry. J Inst Brew 100:331–334,1994.

39. K Ng, PD Rice, DR Bobbitt. Identification and quantitation of gentamicin in milk using HPLC separation and laser-based polarimetric detection. Microchem J 44:25–33, 1991.

40. P Schreier, A Bernreuther, M Huffer. Analysis of Chiral Organic Molecules. New York: Walter de Gruyter, 1995, pp 17–41.

41. NJ Greenfield. Methods to estimate the conformation of proteins and polypeptides from circular dichroism data. Anal Biochem 235:1–10, 1996.

42. S Fisichella, G Alberghina, ME Amato, M Fichera, D Mantarro, A Palermo, A Savarino, G Scarlata. Conformational studies of wheat flour high relative molecular mass glutenin subunits by circular dichroism spectroscopy. Biopolymers 65:142–147, 2002.

43. GA Manderson, LK Creamer, MJ Hardman. Effect of heat treatment on the circular dichroism spectra of bovine beta-lactoglobulin A, B, and C. J Agric Food Chem 47:4557–4567, 1999.

44. TV Johnston, JR Morris. Circular dichroism and spectroscopic studies of *Vitis vinifera* cv. Cabernet Sauvignon and *Vitis rotundifolia* cv. Noble red wine liquid chromatographic fractions. Am J Enol Vitic 47:323–328, 1996.

45. A Kimura, S Chiba. A simple and rapid determination of ketoses by circular dichroism. Carbohydr Res 175:17–23, 1988.

46. E Alberti, PS Belton, AM Gill. Applications of NMR to food science. Ann Rep NMR Spectrosc 47:109–148, 2002.

47. N Howell, Y Shavila, M Grootveld, S Williams. High-resolution NMR and magnetic resonance imaging (MRI) studies on fresh and frozen cod (*Gadus morhua*) and haddock (*Melanogrammus aeglefinus*). J Sci Food Agric 72:49–56, 1996.

48. M Sukumar, J Rizo, M Wall, LA Dreyfus, YM Kupersztoch, LM Gierasch. The structure of *Escherichia coli* heat-stable enterotoxin b by nuclear magnetic resonance and circular dichroism. Prot Sci 4:1718–1729, 1995.

49. F Van de Velde, SH Knutsen, AI Usov, HS Rollema, AS Cerezo. ^{1}H and ^{13}C high resolution NMR spectroscopy of carrageenans: application in research and industry. Trends Food Sci Technol 13:73–92, 2002.

50. A Gallo, MP Buera, ML Herrera. Crystallization kinetics of concentrated alpha,alpha-trehalose and alpha,alpha-trehalose/salt solutions studied by low-resolution ^{1}H-pulsed NMR. J Food Sci 67:1331–1336, 2002.

51. E Vittadini, LC Dickinson, JP Lavoie, P Xuyen, P Chinachoti. Water mobility in multicomponent model media as studied by ^{2}H and ^{17}O NMR. J Agric Food Chem 51:1647–1652, 2003.

52. HC Bertram, HJ Jakobsen, HJ Andersen, AH Karlsson, SB Engelsen. Post-mortem changes in porcine M. longissimus studied by solid-state ^{13}C cross-polarization magic-angle spinning nuclear magnetic resonance spectroscopy. J Agric Food Chem 51:2064–2069, 2003.

53. CP Sherwin, TP Labuza, A McCormick, C Bin. Cross-polarization/magic angle spinning NMR to study glucose mobility in a model intermediate-moisture food system. J Agric Food Chem 50:7677–7683, 2002.

54. YL Martin. Detection of added beet or cane sugar in maple syrup by the site-specific deuterium nuclear magnetic resonance (SNIF-NMR) method: collaborative study. J Assoc Off Anal Chem 84:1509–1521, 2001.

55. ME Miquel, LD Hall. Measurement by MRI of storage changes in commercial chocolate confectionery products. Food Res Int 35:993–998, 2002.

56. Y Lee, MJ McCarthy, KL McCarthy. Extent of mixing in a 2-component batch system measured using MRI. J Food Eng 50:167–174, 2001.

57. JJ Gonzalez, KL McCarthy, MJ McCarthy. MRI method to evaluate internal structural changes of tomato during compression. J Texture Stud 29:537–551, 1998.

58. JR Bows, ML Patrick, KP Nott, LD Hall. Three-dimensional MRI mapping of minimum temperatures achieved in microwave and conventional food processing. Int J Food Sci Technol 36:243–252, 2001.

59. TM Guiheneuf, SJ Gibbs, LD Hall. Measurement of the inter-diffusion of sodium ions during pork brining by one-dimensional ^{23}Na magnetic resonance imaging (MRI). J Food Eng 31:457–471, 1997.

60. TM Eads. Magnetic resonance. In: SS Nielsen. ed. Food Analysis, 2nd ed. Gaithersburg, Maryland: Aspen Publishers Inc., 1998, pp 455–484.

61. R Riek, G Wider, K Pervushin, K Wuthrich. Polarization transfer by cross-correlated relaxation in solution NMR with very large molecules. Proc Natl Acad Sci USA 96:4918–4923, 1999.

62. SJ Schmidt, X Sun, BJ Litchfield. Applications of magnetic resonance imaging in food science. Crit Rev Food Sci Nutr 36:357–385, 1996.

44 Infrared and Raman Spectroscopy in Food Science

Ashraf A. Ismail, Robert Cocciardi, Pedro Alvarez, and Jacqueline Sedman
Department of Food Science and Agricultural Chemistry, McGill University

CONTENTS

I. INTRODUCTION

Infrared (IR) and Raman spectroscopy provide detailed information about both the composition of foods and the molecular structure and the functionality of the components in food systems. Both techniques are based on molecular interactions with electromagnetic radiation that result in transitions between the vibrational energy levels of the ground electronic energy state of the molecule, corresponding to the excitation of various stretching and bending vibrations. However, the nature of these interactions is fundamentally different in these two types of vibrational spectroscopy, and hence they are regarded as complementary techniques. In general terms, as well as specifically in regard to applications to food systems, IR spectroscopy has found much more extensive use than Raman spectroscopy owing to the greater simplicity and

lower cost of the instrumentation as well as the greater utility of IR spectroscopy as a quantitative analysis tool. On the other hand, Raman spectroscopy offers certain advantages in relation to sample handling, the study of aqueous systems, and possibilities for on-line process monitoring. Thus, the selection of IR or Raman spectroscopy, or the combined use of both techniques, depends on the nature of the application. Near-infrared (NIR) spectroscopy combines the sample-handling advantages of Raman spectroscopy with the powerful multicomponent analysis capabilities of IR spectroscopy and thus has found widespread application for quality control and process monitoring in the food industry for several decades. However, by comparison with (mid-) IR and Raman spectra, NIR spectra are fairly uninformative, and NIR analysis is largely based on statistical treatment of the spectral data. Entire books have been devoted to NIR analysis of foods (1, 2) and NIR spectroscopy will not be considered in this chapter.

In the following sections, the principles of IR and Raman spectroscopy and the instrumentation and sample-handling techniques employed to acquire spectra will be briefly described. The utility of these two techniques for investigations of the individual components of food systems will then be illustrated by considering the information that can be extracted from the IR and Raman spectra of food proteins. Finally, a survey of the applications of IR and Raman spectroscopy in the analysis of foods will be presented.

II. FUNDAMENTAL PRINCIPLES OF IR AND RAMAN SPECTROSCOPY

IR and Raman spectroscopy are both based on the excitation of molecular vibrations by interaction with electromagnetic radiation. A nonlinear molecule made up of N atoms possesses $3N - 6$ vibrational modes, each of which has a specific frequency; the number of vibrational modes is reduced by one in the case of linear molecules. The factors determining the frequencies of molecular vibrations can be illustrated by considering the simplest case, a diatomic model AB, which has a single vibrational mode involving the stretching of the bond linking atoms A and B. The frequency at which this bond vibrates can be calculated from the model of a harmonic oscillator, whereby the restoring force (F) on the bond is given by Hooke's law:

$$F = -kx \qquad (44.1)$$

where k is the force constant of the bond and x is the displacement from the equilibrium internuclear distance. Under this approximation, the vibrational frequency, ν, is given by

$$\nu = (1/2\pi)(k/\mu)^{1/2} \qquad (44.2)$$

where μ is the reduced mass of the system, as defined by the following equation:

$$\mu = m_A \cdot m_B / (m_A + m_B) \qquad (44.3)$$

where m_A and m_B are the individual atomic masses of A and B. By convention, vibrational frequencies are given in wavenumbers ($\overline{\nu} = \nu/c$, where c is the speed of light), expressed in units of reciprocal centimeters (cm^{-1}), rather than in units of frequency (s^{-1}), although in older literature, band positions are often reported in units of wavelength (λ), i.e., microns (μ). The frequencies of molecular vibrations fall primarily in the mid-IR region of the electromagnetic spectrum (4000–400 cm^{-1}; 2.5–25 μm).

The quantum-mechanical treatment of molecular vibrations leads to modifications of the harmonic oscillator model as the vibrational energy levels are quantized:

$$E = (\nu + 1/2)h\nu \qquad (44.4)$$

where ν is the vibrational quantum number, h is Planck's constant, and ν is the fundamental vibrational frequency. The quantum-mechanical theory predicts that at room temperature, only transitions from the ground-state vibrational level ($\nu = 0$) to the first excited vibrational level ($\nu = 1$) will occur; however, experimentally this is not the case as weak overtone bands, corresponding to transitions to higher energy levels, can be observed, especially in the NIR spectral region.

IR spectroscopy is based on the measurement of molecular absorption of IR radiation of frequencies that match those of the molecular vibrations. However, all of a molecule's vibrational modes do not give rise to IR absorption bands because a vibration will only be IR-active if it results in a change in the dipole moment of the molecule. For example, the stretching vibration of a homonuclear diatomic molecule, such as N_2 or O_2, is not IR-active because the equal displacement of the two atoms from the center of mass does not change the dipole moment of the molecule. However, this is no longer the case when the two atoms in the diatomic molecule have different masses, and hence the stretching vibrations of molecules such as CO are IR-active. Similarly, the symmetric stretching vibration of the CO_2 molecule illustrated in Figure 44.1 is IR-inactive because of the molecule's linear geometry while the corresponding vibration of a nonlinear triatomic molecule such as H_2O is IR-active, as are the asymmetric stretching vibrations of both linear and nonlinear triatomics.

Raman spectroscopy is based on the inelastic scattering of light by the molecules in a sample rather than their absorption of IR radiation. When a sample is irradiated with light, most of the photons are elastically scattered; that is, the wavelength of the scattered photons is unchanged. However, a small fraction (~1 in 10^6 photons) will show a shift in wavelength from that of the incident light. This phenomenon was theoretically predicted by Adolf G. Smekal in 1923 but was first observed experimentally by Sir Chandrasekhara V. Raman in 1928 and hence is called

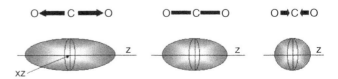

FIGURE 44.1   The symmetric stretch of the CO_2 molecule is a Raman-active but not an IR-active vibration because it results in a change in the molecule's polarizability but does not involve a change in its dipole moment.

the Raman effect. Detection of the inelastically scattered photons requires that the sample be irradiated with mono-chromatic (i.e., single-wavelength) light. Furthermore, since the Raman effect is very weak, an intense monochromatic light source is required. For these reasons, Raman spectroscopy only became practicable in the 1960s with the development of lasers and highly sensitive photon-counting devices, such as photomultiplier tubes.

In Raman spectroscopy, a sample is irradiated with a laser line of frequency $\overline{v}_0$, and the intensity of the scattered light as a function of frequency is then measured, yielding a Raman spectrum (Figure 44.2). Although most of the elastically scattered light is filtered out prior to reaching the detector, the spectrum is still predominated by a broad signal centered at the frequency of the incident light (referred to as the Rayleigh line). The remainder of the spectrum is composed of much weaker bands at lower frequencies, $\overline{v}_0 - \overline{v}_i$ (referred to as Stokes lines). The frequency shifts $\overline{v}_0 - \overline{v}_i$ (referred to as Raman shifts) are independent of $\overline{v}_0$, the frequency emitted by the excitation source, and correspond to the vibrational frequencies of the molecules in the sample. Even weaker bands occur at higher frequency, $\overline{v}_0 + \overline{v}_i$ (referred to as anti-Stokes lines). The Stokes and anti-Stokes lines are equally displaced from the Rayleigh line; however, the anti-Stokes lines are rarely observed owing to their very low intensity.

For a molecular vibration to be Raman-active (i.e., show a Raman effect), it must result in changes in the polarizability of the molecule, which is represented by an ellipsoid, and therefore must result in changes in the shape of the electron density cloud around the molecule. For example, as illustrated in Figure 44.1, in the symmetric stretching vibration of CO_2 the shape of the electron cloud is different between the minimum and maximum internuclear distances. Therefore, the polarizability of the molecule changes during the vibration and this vibrational mode is Raman-active. In the asymmetric stretch, the change in the polarizability ellipsoid as one of the bonds extends is cancelled by the opposite change due to the compression of the other bond, and hence there is no overall change in polarizability and the asymmetric stretch is Raman-inactive.

It is important to note that the criteria (referred to as "selection rules") for an IR-active vibration (i.e., a change in the dipole moment of the molecule) and a Raman-active vibration (i.e., a change in the polarizability of the molecule) are different. In fact, for any molecule that possesses a center of symmetry (such as the CO_2 molecule considered above), vibrations that are IR-active are Raman-inactive, and vice versa. In general, vibrations that give rise to weak IR bands often produce intense Raman bands, and vice versa. Hence, IR and Raman spectroscopy are complementary techniques, and it is usually necessary to apply both types of vibrational spectroscopy to obtain the full spectral profile of a sample.

III. INSTRUMENTATION

A. INFRARED SPECTROSCOPY

IR spectrometers essentially consist of a broad-band source of IR radiation, a means for resolving the IR radiation into

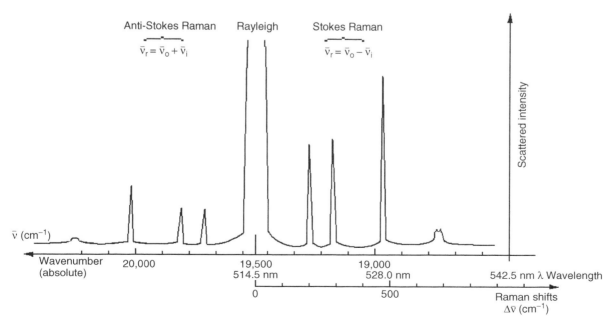

FIGURE 44.2 Schematic representation of a Raman spectrum excited with the 514-nm line of an argon ion laser. Most of the laser light is elastically scattered with the same frequency (v_0) as the incident light. However, a small proportion is inelastically scattered with frequencies of ($v_0 + v_i$) and ($v_0 - v_i$), where v_i is the frequency of one of the fundamental vibrations of the molecules in the sample.

its component wavelengths, and a detector. Generally speaking, an IR spectrum of a sample can be represented mathematically by the following equation:

$$T(\overline{v}) = I(\overline{v})/I_0(\overline{v}) \qquad (44.5)$$

where T is defined as transmittance, I is the intensity of IR radiation reaching the detector when it passes through the sample, I_0 is the intensity of IR radiation reaching the detector with no sample in the beam, and $\overline{v}$ is the wavenumber of the radiation. Usually, transmittance is converted to absorbance (A) using the following relationship:

$$A = -\log T \qquad (44.6)$$

In the early years of IR spectroscopy, prisms were used to resolve IR radiation from the source into its component wavelengths but they were subsequently replaced by diffraction gratings. In the 1970s, the field of IR spectroscopy was revolutionized when these dispersive IR spectrometers began to be replaced by Fourier transform infrared (FTIR) spectrometers. FTIR spectroscopy is based on interferometry and makes use of a beamsplitter to divide the IR radiation into two beams, with one beam being directed to a fixed mirror and the other to a moving mirror (Figure 44.3). When these two beams are reflected back to the beamsplitter and recombine, they undergo constructive and destructive interference due to the path difference between the two mirrors, yielding an interferogram. The path difference, known as retardation δ, is proportional to time t because the moving mirror travels at a constant velocity, v, i.e., $\delta = 2vt$. Through the use of a fast Fourier transform (FFT) algorithm, the time domain interferogram, $I(\delta)$, is converted into the frequency domain, $I(\overline{v})$, according to the following relationship:

$$I(\delta) = 0.5H(\overline{v})I(\overline{v})\cos 2\pi\overline{v}\delta \qquad (44.7)$$

where $H(\overline{v})$ is a single wavenumber-dependent correction factor that accounts for instrumental characteristics. The

interferogram decoded into the frequency domain is in the form of an energy curve called a single-beam spectrum (Figure 44.4). The ratio of the single-beam spectrum of the sample against a background single-beam spectrum recorded with no sample in the optical path results in a transmittance spectrum, in accordance with Equation [44.5], which is then normally converted into an absorbance spectrum by carrying out the mathematical transformation represented by Equation [44.6].

FTIR spectrometers have several advantages over conventional dispersive IR instruments, including a dramatic improvement in the signal-to-noise ratio (S/N) obtained by multiplexing (simultaneous detection of all frequencies), reduction in scan time, and higher energy throughput. Another important advantage is the excellent wavelength reproducibility of FTIR spectrometers, owing to the use of an internal reference laser, which allows spectral data manipulations such as spectral subtraction, addition, and ratioing to be performed with a very high degree of accuracy. The advancement of FTIR spectroscopy has been greatly assisted by the availability of increasingly powerful personal computers, which have facilitated the use of sophisticated software packages for both qualitative and quantitative applications.

B. RAMAN SPECTROSCOPY

The design of traditional dispersive Raman spectrometers differs markedly from that of IR instruments. However, FT-Raman spectrometers, which have become increasingly common in recent years, are similar in design to FTIR spectrometers, and combined FTIR/FT-Raman systems are available from most major FTIR vendors. In dispersive Raman spectroscopy, the source is a high-power laser emitting visible radiation at several discrete frequencies, with filters being employed to select a single laser line; commonly employed laser lines are the 488.0-nm (blue) and 514.5-nm (green) lines of an argon-ion laser. After this monochromatic radiation impinges on the sample, a portion of the scattered radiation is directed to a monochromator to resolve it into its component frequencies and then to a photomultiplier tube. The resulting signal as a function of frequency is plotted as intensity versus Raman shift, yielding a Raman spectrum.

The major drawbacks of traditional Raman spectrometers originate with the use of high-power visible lasers as excitation sources. Samples that are susceptible to either thermal or photochemical degradation may be destroyed by the laser radiation, although various experimental approaches can be taken to minimize such damage. However, a more pervasive problem is the fluorescence that results when species present in the sample are electronically excited by the visible laser radiation. Because the Raman effect is weaker than fluorescence by many orders of magnitude, even the fluorescence from a trace

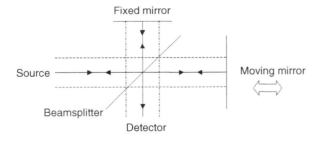

FIGURE 44.3 Schematic diagram of a Michelson interferometer. The IR radiation from the source is split into two beams by a beamsplitter and directed to the fixed and moving mirrors. The two IR beams recombine at the beamsplitter and are directed to the sample and the detector.

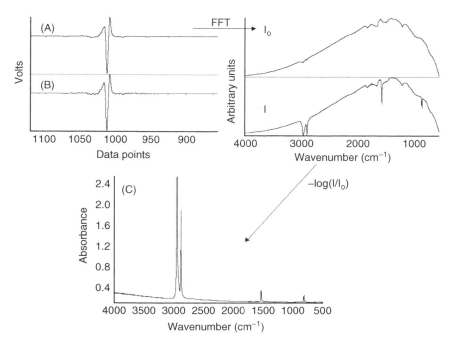

FIGURE 44.4 (A) Interferogram recorded with no sample in the path of the IR beam; (B) interferogram recorded with a thin film of polyethylene (PE) placed in the path of the IR beam. Fourier transformation of the interferogram A and B by a fast Fourier transform (FFT) algorithm yields, respectively, the open-beam spectrum (I_0) and the single-beam spectrum (I) of PE. (C) Absorbance spectrum of PE obtained by the mathematical transformation shown on the figure.

impurity can completely mask the Raman spectrum of the sample. In the past, this phenomenon severely restricted the scope of Raman spectroscopy, particularly in relation to samples of biological origin. However, it has been substantially alleviated by the use of laser excitation lines in the NIR instead of the visible region of the electromagnetic spectrum, such as the 1064-nm line emitted by neodymium-doped yttrium aluminum garnet (Nd:YAG) lasers. Because the use of NIR lasers as excitation sources in conventional dispersive Raman spectrometers is not technically feasible, this option only became practicable with the development of FT-Raman spectrometers (3), which, like FTIR spectrometers, are based on interferometry. In fact, FTIR spectrometers can be modified to acquire Raman spectra by incorporating a Nd:YAG laser and using beamsplitters and detectors appropriate for the NIR region. The availability of these dual-purpose instruments has greatly facilitated comprehensive vibrational spectroscopic studies, although their high cost remains a disadvantage.

IV. SAMPLING METHODS

A. INFRARED SPECTROSCOPY

Infrared sample-handling accessories include transmission cells, attenuated total reflectance (ATR) accessories (both multiple- and single-bounce crystals and fiber-optic probes), as well as diffuse reflectance infrared Fourier

transform (DRIFT) and photoacoustic spectroscopy (PAS). The latter two techniques, reviewed previously (4), will not be considered here, as they have had limited application in mid-IR food analysis, although DRIFT is widely used in NIR food analysis.

1. Transmission Mode

The transmission mode is the most common and oldest mode of IR sample analysis. The sample is placed in the optical path of the IR beam, and the amount of light transmitted through the sample is inversely proportional to the sample thickness, which can vary from meters for gas samples to microns for condensed-phase samples. The spectra of liquids and solutions are recorded in a transmission cell, composed of two optical windows separated by a spacer that determines the pathlength. The optical windows commonly employed are polished salt crystals (e.g., NaCl or KBr), because all materials containing covalent bonds, including glass, do not transmit IR radiation. There are also severe restrictions on the pathlength that can be employed because of the limited energy available from IR sources. For instance, aqueous solutions are typically measured in cells having pathlengths of 15–40 μm, owing to the intense absorption of IR radiation by water; beyond this thickness, virtually no IR radiation reaches the detector.

Transmission cells can be demountable or sealed, and the use of flow-through cells such as that shown in Figure 44.5 facilitates sample handling. Sealed transmission cells

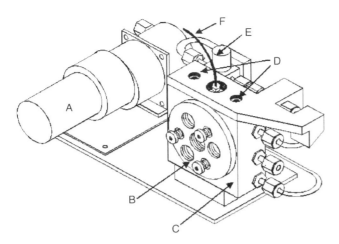

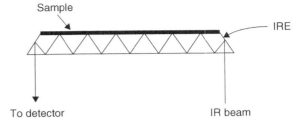

FIGURE 44.6 Schematic of a horizontal multiple-bounce attenuated total reflectance (MB-ATR) accessory.

FIGURE 44.5 Schematic diagram of a transmission flow-through cell: (A) micropump, (B) demountable cell insert (transmission cell), (C) cell block, (D) heat cartridges, (E) solenoid valve, (F) thermocouple. The accessory slides horizontally so that the cell can be moved out of the path of the beam to record an open-beam background spectrum.

are preferred for quantitative analysis because a constant pathlength is required to obtain reproducible results. However, if a demountable cell is used because the sample is too viscous to inject or pump through a sealed cell, or the cell cannot be effectively cleaned between samples by simply rinsing with a solvent or detergent solution, an internal standard with a distinct absorption band can be introduced into the sample to compensate for pathlength variations.

In the case of solid samples, light scattering effects are a problem when particle dimensions are comparable to or exceed the wavelengths of mid-IR radiation and, as such, particles must be ground to <3 μm prior to analysis. The sample can then be diluted with KBr, KCl, or NaCl and pressed to form a pellet. An alternative procedure for analyzing solid samples is to make a liquid dispersion using oils, such as mineral oil (Nujol) or paraffin oil. Both the pellet and the dispersion method have the disadvantage of destroying the sample.

2. Attenuated Total Reflectance

The restrictions on sample thickness and particle size imposed by the nature of transmission measurements represent major sample-handling limitations. Attenuated total reflectance (ATR) spectroscopy, developed in the 1960s, provides a more versatile sample-handling approach. ATR spectroscopy is based on total internal reflection of the IR beam in an ATR crystal, which is made of a high-refractive-index material and serves as an internal reflection element (IRE). Total internal reflection gives rise to an evanescent wave that emerges from the surface of the ATR crystal at each point of internal reflection and decays as it propagates away from the surface (Figure 44.6). The

evanescent wave is attenuated by the absorption of the IR radiation by species on or near the surface of the ATR crystal, and measurement of this attenuation as a function of wavenumber yields the IR spectrum of a sample placed on the surface of the ATR crystal.

The effective pathlength of an ATR accessory is calculated by multiplying the number of internal reflections by the depth of penetration (d_p), which is defined as the distance at which the intensity of the evanescent wave decays to $1/e$ of its value at the surface as given by the following equation:

$$d_p = \lambda/\{2\pi n_1[\sin^2\theta - (n_2/n_1)^2]^{1/2}\} \qquad (44.8)$$

where λ is the wavelength of IR radiation, n_1 is the refractive index of the IRE material, n_2 is the refractive index of the sample, and θ is the angle at which the IR radiation strikes the ATR crystal. Owing to the variation of the depth of penetration as a function of wavelength, the relative intensities of the bands in an ATR spectrum will differ from those in a conventional transmission spectrum, but this effect can be corrected for mathematically.

For a typical ATR accessory, the effective pathlength ranges from a few microns at the high-wavenumber end of the IR spectrum to several tens of microns at the low-wavenumber end. Thus, the ATR technique provides an inherently short effective pathlength without any physical restriction on the sample thickness, such that samples can be simply poured or spread on the surface of the ATR crystal and then wiped off after analysis. In addition, particle size in solid samples is not a concern as, unlike transmission spectra, ATR spectra are not affected by light scattering, and even the spectra of opaque samples can be recorded. The ATR technique is particularly advantageous for analyzing aqueous solutions, because the pathlength is sufficiently short and the common IRE materials (e.g., germanium and ZnSe) are water-insoluble, unlike most of the materials suitable for use as transmission cell windows.

The evident advantages of the ATR sample-handling technique are accompanied by certain disadvantages. The inherently short effective pathlength limits sensitivity. In addition, because the depth of penetration is on the micron scale, any surface contamination on the ATR crystal will make a major contribution to the spectrum. Furthermore, a spectrum representative of the entire sample will be obtained only if the sample is homogeneous on this scale. In the case of powdered and solid samples, intimate contact between the sample and the ATR crystal is required, and although various clamping devices are available to press the sample against the ATR crystal, it can be difficult to obtain reproducible spectra. Another drawback that limits the utility of ATR spectroscopy is the need for precise temperature control, because the depth of penetration is dependent on the refractive indices of the IRE material and the sample, which in turn are dependent on temperature.

Many of the disadvantages described can be alleviated by employing a single-bounce (SB-ATR) accessory because of the much smaller dimensions of the ATR crystal as compared to those in multiple-bounce (MB-ATR) accessories (Figure 44.7). Although such accessories were rarely employed in the past owing to their very short effective pathlengths, which severely limited sensitivity, improvements in the optical design of SB-ATR accessories in recent years have compensated for this limitation. Because of the small surface area of the ATR crystal, precise temperature control and good optical contact between solid samples and the crystal (particularly with diamond IREs, which can withstand a strong clamping force) can be more readily achieved than with MB-ATR accessories. In addition, only very small amounts of sample are required to cover the ATR crystal (e.g., for liquid samples, <50 μL), and thus cross-contamination between samples can be virtually eliminated by wiping the crystal with the next sample prior to applying it onto the crystal to record its spectrum, provided that the samples are miscible with each other. These advantages make this type of accessory very promising for quantitative analysis of foods, although potential applications are restricted by the short effective pathlength and hence limited sensitivity.

B. RAMAN SPECTROSCOPY

In terms of sample handling, Raman spectroscopy is a much more versatile and flexible method than IR spectroscopy because it does not suffer from restrictions on sample thickness (or pathlength), the need for specialized sample-handling accessories, or problems caused by light scattering. Thus, Raman spectra can be recorded directly from solid samples, even if opaque, with no sample preparation, and samples can be contained in ordinary glass vials. Thin glass capillaries are ideal for recording Raman

spectra of solids or liquids because the laser is a highly focused energy source, allowing spectra to be obtained from samples as small as 100 μm in diameter. The main sample-handling difficulty encountered in Raman spectroscopy is excessive heating of the sample if an intense visible laser is employed as an excitation source. To alleviate this problem, the laser beam may be defocused, or various accessories that are available to prevent heating of the sample may be employed; these range from devices that continuously rotate the sample, which can effectively reduce sample heating in the case of fluid samples, to expensive helium-cooled cryostats, which may be required to prevent burning in the case of thermally unstable solids. The need for such measures has been reduced, however, with the use of NIR lasers in FT-Raman spectroscopy.

V. IR AND RAMAN SPECTROSCOPY OF FOOD COMPONENTS AND FOODS

The vibrational spectra of foods are the superposition of the spectra of all the individual components present and are thus generally very complex. The IR spectra of aqueous systems are dominated by the intense absorptions of water (Figure 44.8A), which can obscure the spectral features of other components in broad regions of the spectrum, as illustrated by the transmission spectrum of milk in Figure 44.8B. Although the spectral contributions of water can be removed digitally by spectral subtraction (Figure 44.8C), information cannot be obtained from regions of intense IR absorption by water except when very short pathlengths are employed; this limitation is often addressed by taking advantage of the inherently short effective pathlengths of ATR accessories (Figure 44.9). This difficulty is absent in Raman spectroscopy because water is a weak Raman scatterer.

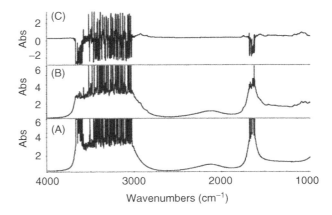

FIGURE 44.8 FTIR spectra of water (A) and milk (B) recorded using a 50-μm transmission cell and difference spectrum (C), obtained by subtraction of spectrum A from spectrum B.

FIGURE 44.7 Illustration of the relative sample dimensions in multiple- and single-bounce horizontal ATR accessories.

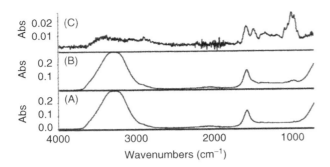

FIGURE 44.9 ATR/FTIR spectra of water (A) and milk (B) recorded using an SB-ATR accessory and difference spectrum (C), obtained by subtraction of spectrum A from spectrum B.

The other major components of foods—fats, proteins, and carbohydrates—give rise to strong bands in both IR and Raman spectra. Although many of the bands due to these individual components overlap with each other, fats, proteins, and carbohydrates each have certain characteristic bands that arise from particular functional groups. The band positions and assignments of some of the major bands of these components are summarized in Table 44.1. However, it should be noted that vibrational frequencies are sensitive to electrical effects, steric effects, the nature, size, and electronegativity of neighboring atoms, phase changes, hydrogen bonding, and solvent polarity. Although this sensitivity may complicate spectral interpretation, it also contributes to the high information content of vibrational spectra. Thus, IR and Raman spectroscopy are valuable techniques for the characterization of materials in terms of their chemical composition, detailed investigations of molecular structure and bonding, and studies of the interactions of molecules with their environment. Furthermore, IR and Raman spectra of substances serve as their "fingerprints," allowing for the identification of

substances with a high degree of specificity by comparison of their spectra with those in a spectral database or "library."

The powerful qualitative analysis capabilities of vibrational spectroscopy can be applied to complex samples, such as foods, for purposes of classification and authentication. For such applications, multivariate analysis techniques such as principal component analysis (PCA) are commonly used to reduce the dimensionality of the spectral data (5). Because an FTIR or FT-Raman spectrum is produced by Fourier transformation of an interferogram, as described in Section III.A, the spectra inherently consist of digital data. The dimensionality of the data depends on the spacing between data points, which is a function of the instrument resolution at which the spectra were collected and the level of zero filling employed in the calculation of the Fourier transform. For example, the FTIR spectra of condensed-phase samples are typically collected at 4-cm^{-1} resolution between 4000 and 400 cm^{-1} and thus, with one level of zero filling, each spectrum contains ~1800 data points. Each of these data points is a variable that contains the absorbance at a particular wavenumber, but many of these variables are highly correlated since (a) the inherent width of the bands is usually much greater than the resolution so that a given band contributes to several contiguous data points and (b) any given species present in the sample usually has multiple bands and the intensities of these bands thus change collinearly as a function of change in concentration. By using PCA, most of the variation in the data can be described by a few orthogonal principal components (PCs), or latent variables, which are linear combinations of the original variables. The data are characterized by scores, which are projections of the spectra onto each PC, and loadings, which represent the contributions of the variables to each PC. Cluster analysis based on PCA

TABLE 44.1
Selected Vibrational Bands of Major Food Components^a

Food Component(s)	Frequency (cm^{-1})	Band Assignment(s)
Water, carbohydrates	3600–3200	O-H stretching vibration; strong water IR absorption band
Fats	3012–3004	C-H stretching of *cis* double bonds
Fats, carbohydrates, and proteins	3000–2800	C-H stretching of CH_2 and CH_3 groups
Fats	1745–1725	C=O stretching, ester linkages in triacylglycerols
Proteins	1700–1600	Amide I band, peptide linkages of proteins
Fats^b	1678–1665	C=C stretching of *trans* double bonds
Fats	1662–1648	C=C stretching of *cis* double bonds
Water	1650	H-O-H bending vibration; strong IR absorption band
Proteins	1560–1520	Amide II band, peptide linkages of proteins
Proteins	1300–1190	Amide III band, peptide linkages of proteins
Carbohydrates	1250–800	C-O stretching and C-O-H bending vibrations
Fats^b	971–965	C=C-H bending of isolated *trans* double bonds

^{a} Compiled from a review of the literature.

^{b} Predominantly hydrogenated fats and oils.

scores may then be performed to group samples according to their degree of spectral similarity, which in turn reflects their degree of compositional similarity. Alternatively, with the application of supervised pattern recognition techniques (e.g., discriminant analysis), the PCA scores may be employed to assign samples to particular classes for purposes of authentication. The capability of distinguishing between different classes of samples on the basis of differences in their vibrational spectra has led to investigations of the potential utility of IR and Raman spectroscopy as a means of detecting adulteration of foods.

Both IR and Raman spectroscopy can also be employed for quantitative analysis. However, although Raman scattering intensity is directly related to concentration, quantitative analysis by Raman spectroscopy has generally been regarded as problematic, and relatively few applications in the area of food analysis have been reported. On the other hand, the scope of reported applications of quantitative IR spectroscopy in food analysis has increased substantially in recent years owing to the advantages of FTIR spectrometers and the new sample handling technologies available combined with the development of a range of sophisticated multivariate analysis methods. As in other types of absorption spectroscopy, IR quantitative analysis is based on the linear relationship between absorbance and concentration, as expressed by the Bouguer-Beer-Lambert law, commonly known as Beer's law:

$$A_\nu = \varepsilon_\nu bc \qquad (44.9)$$

where A_ν is the absorbance measured at frequency ν, ε_ν is the absorption coefficient of the absorbing species at the same frequency, b is the pathlength of the cell, and c is the concentration of the absorbing species. Therefore, a calibration curve can be developed by relating changes in absorbance to changes in concentration of a species at a fixed pathlength. It is important to note that IR spectroscopy is a secondary method of analysis, so the development of a calibration requires a set of standards of known composition, prepared gravimetrically or analyzed by a primary reference method. Once a calibration has been developed, it can be used to predict the concentrations of unknowns, provided that the spectra of the unknowns are recorded under the same conditions as the calibration standards and the spectra of the standards are representative of those of the unknowns in the spectral region(s) employed for quantitation. IR spectroscopy can also be employed to directly predict various physical properties and quality attributes of samples, provided that they are dependent on the chemical composition of the substance.

Although simple in theory, implementation of quantitative IR spectroscopy can be complicated by underlying absorptions due to other components as well as inter- and intramolecular interactions. However, these effects can usually be modeled by the application of multivariate analysis methods, such as multiple linear regression (MLR), partial-least-squares regression (PLS), or principal component regression (PCR). A full discussion of the mathematical basis of these multivariate analysis methods is available elsewhere (6) and is beyond the scope of this chapter.

A detailed review of IR and Raman spectroscopic studies of the major components of foods has recently been published (7). Thus, in the following section, the information that can be extracted from the IR and Raman spectra of individual food components will be illustrated by considering only a single class of food components, namely, proteins. In the subsequent section, reported applications of IR and Raman spectroscopy in the qualitative and quantitative analysis of various types of foods will be surveyed. This section will highlight the most significant research findings and practical applications and will focus mainly on IR spectroscopy, owing to its more widespread use in food analysis as well as the much larger amount of research activity in this area. However, certain specific applications for which Raman spectroscopy is particularly well suited will also be discussed.

A. IR AND RAMAN SPECTROSCOPY OF FOOD PROTEINS

IR and Raman spectroscopy have found extensive application in the study of proteins and are particularly useful techniques for the elucidation of protein secondary structure. The spectra of polypeptides and proteins exhibit nine amide bands that represent different vibrations of the peptide linkage. The wavenumber positions of these bands and their vibrational assignments are listed in Table 44.2 (8). Obtaining information pertaining to protein secondary structure from IR and Raman spectra is based on empirical correlations between the wavenumbers of certain of these bands and the various conformations adopted by the polypeptide chain. The amide I band (in the range of 1700–1600 cm^{-1}) is the most frequently employed in IR spectroscopy, and characteristic amide I band positions have been identified for α-helices, 3_{10}-helices, parallel or antiparallel β-sheets, turns, and unordered or irregular structures (Table 44.3). Using these band assignments, secondary structures of proteins can be deduced, although it is generally advisable to confirm the results with a second technique such as circular dichroism. The amide III band (in the range of 1300–1190 cm^{-1}) can similarly be employed for the estimation of the relative proportions of the secondary-structure components. However, in some cases, the amide III band can be overlapped by bands due to side-chain vibrations of particular amino acid residues—or absorptions from other biomolecules present, for example, in a food matrix—and consequently one must be cautious when assigning bands in this region. In IR spectra, the amide III band is much weaker than the amide I band and hence is much less frequently employed in secondary-structure investigations. However,

TABLE 44.2
Amide Bands of Proteins[a]

Designation	Nature of Vibration
A	N-H stretching
B	N-H stretching
I	80% C=O stretching; 10% C-N stretching; 10% N-H bending
II	60% N-H bending; 40% C-N stretching
III	30% C-N stretching; 30% N-H bending; 10% C=O stretching; 10% O=C=N bending; 20% other
IV	60% O=C-N bending; 60% other
V	N-H bending
VI	C=O bending
VII	C-N torsion

[a] Adapted from Ref. 8.

TABLE 44.3
Approximate Positions (cm⁻¹) of Amide I′ Band Components in IR Spectra of Proteins[a]

Secondary-Structure Component	Frequency (cm⁻¹)
Antiparallel β-sheet (intra- or intermolecular)	1695–1675
Loops and turns	1674–1662
α-Helix	1659–1646
Unordered structure (random coil)	1645–1641
3₁₀-Helix	1639–1637
Intramolecular parallel or antiparallel β-sheet[b]	1636–1625
Intermolecular antiparallel β-sheet[c]	1624–1614

[a] Compiled from a review of the literature. The band positions are for proteins in D_2O solution (by convention, termed amide I′ band components).
[b] Assigned to antiparallel β-sheet structure when it is accompanied by a high-wavenumber component (1695–1675 cm⁻¹); otherwise assigned to parallel (or extended) β-sheet structure.
[c] Indicative of protein aggregation.

TABLE 44.4
Approximate Positions (cm⁻¹) of Amide I and Amide III Band Components in Raman Spectra of Proteins[a]

Secondary Structure Component	Amide I (cm⁻¹)	Amide III (cm⁻¹)
α-Helix	1660–16	1300–1275
β-Sheet	1680–1665	1240–1230
Unordered structure (random coil)	1670–1660	1260–1240

[a] Adapted from Ref. 9.

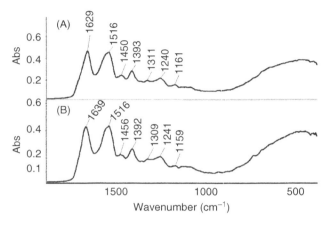

FIGURE 44.10 ATR/FTIR spectra of powdered β-lactoglobulin (A) and α-lactalbumin (B) recorded using an SB-ATR accessory. A pressure device was employed to ensure optical contact between the sample and the ATR crystal.

both the amide I and amide III bands are commonly employed in Raman spectroscopy (Table 44.4) (9), as their Raman intensities are comparable.

The IR spectra of proteins are most commonly recorded in aqueous solution in a transmission cell, although ATR accessories have also been employed to study the spectra of protein films and powdered samples (Figure 44.10). The Raman spectra of proteins can also be recorded in aqueous solution but the spectra obtained from solid samples are generally of much higher quality and exhibit sharper bands (Figure 44.11). For IR studies involving examination of the secondary-structure-sensitive amide I band, proteins are commonly dissolved in D_2O because H_2O has a strong band in the amide I region. Since D_2O has no absorptions that overlap with the amide I band (which, by convention, is termed the amide I′ band when D_2O is the solvent), the use of D_2O solutions allows the protein absorptions to be observed without the need

for subtraction of the spectrum of the solvent. More importantly, it also makes it permissible to use much longer pathlengths (40–80 μm vs. 10 μm for aqueous solutions), thereby yielding a higher signal-to-noise ratio. An additional advantage of dissolving proteins in D_2O is the resulting ability to study the rate at which the hydrogens of the amide groups exchange with the D_2O solvent due to the ~100-cm⁻¹ shift of the amide II band (from 1560–1520 to 1460–1420 cm⁻¹) that occurs upon H-D exchange. This rate is indicative of the compactness of the protein since amide groups exposed to the solvent undergo H-D exchange faster than those in the interior of the protein. Thus, increases in the rate of H-D exchange as a result of variations in physicochemical parameters such as pH, temperature, and pressure can be interpreted in terms of the extent of protein unfolding.

Because of the inherent overlap between the amide I′ band components of the various conformations of the polypeptide backbone, computational band-narrowing techniques such as Fourier self-deconvolution (FSD) and derivative spectroscopy are routinely employed. It should be noted that caution must be exercised in applying these techniques because they can distort the shapes of the

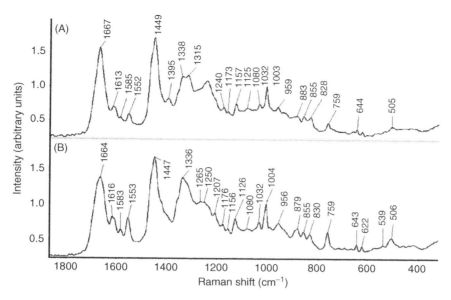

FIGURE 44.11 FT-Raman spectra of powdered β-lactoglobulin (A) and α-lactalbumin (B) in 1-mm glass capillaries recorded with 1064-nm excitation. (Nd:YAG laser). For band assignments, see Ref. 10.

bands and can also decrease the signal-to-noise ratio (11). Furthermore, the relative band intensities in derivative spectra are affected by the inherent widths of the bands, whereas deconvolution has the advantage of preserving the true relative band intensities (11). On the other hand, the results of deconvolution depend strongly on the values of the adjustable deconvolution parameters and are thus more subject to artifacts. For example, as illustrated in Figure 44.12, the selection of inappropriate deconvolution parameters that result in "overdeconvolution" amplifies the spectral noise, which may lead to spurious peaks. Similarly, atmospheric water vapor gives rise to very weak narrow peaks in the amide I region of IR spectra that can also be misinterpreted as amide I′ band components in deconvolved spectra. The latter pitfall is best avoided by thoroughly purging the spectrometer, including the optical compartment, with dry air or nitrogen. Other possible sources of artifacts are absorptions of buffers or contaminants in the protein solution (12).

Additional information about protein structure can be obtained from bands due to side-chain vibrations of amino acid residues, such as aspartic acid, glutamic acid, tyrosine, and tryptophan. For example, the ratio of the intensities of the Raman bands of tyrosine at 850 and 830 cm^{-1}, attributed to ring-breathing and out-of-plane bending vibrations, respectively, provides the following information about the polarity of the microenvironment of tyrosine residues (13):

- High I_{850}/I_{830} (>2.5): Tyr acts as H-bond acceptor
- Low I_{850}/I_{830} (<0.5): Tyr acts as H-bond donor
- I_{850}/I_{830} ~ 1: Tyr is exposed to an aqueous environment (i.e., Tyr near or at the protein surface)

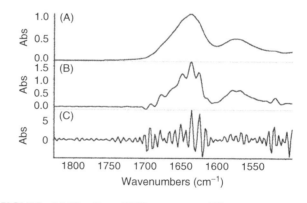

FIGURE 44.12 Raw FTIR spectrum (A), spectrum after Fourier self-deconvolution (FSD) (B), and "overdeconvolved" spectrum (C) of β-lactoglobulin in D$_2$O (5% w/v). FSD parameters: (B) bandwidth factor of w = 27 and resolution enhancement factor of k = 2.4; (C) w = 27 and k = 4.

Raman spectroscopy is also a very useful tool for probing the formation and rupture of disulfide linkages because the S-S and S-H stretching vibrations can be clearly discerned in the Raman spectra of proteins. The FT-Raman spectra of the amino acids L-cysteine and L-cystine are presented in Figure 44.13 and show, respectively, a band at 2552 cm^{-1} assigned to the S-H stretching vibration and a band at 498 cm^{-1} assigned to the S-S stretching vibration. In the Raman spectra of proteins, these bands are shifted to 2580–2550 and 550–500 cm^{-1}, respectively (14). The corresponding IR bands are not readily discernible, making Raman spectroscopy the technique of choice for the observation of disulfide linkages and examination of thiol-disulfide exchange. For example, in Figure 44.11, the higher content of disulfide linkages in α-lactalbumin as compared

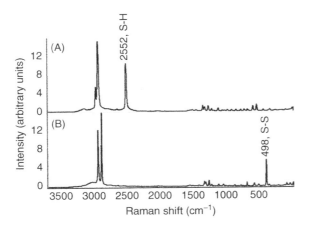

FIGURE 44.13 FT-Raman spectra of L-cysteine (A) and L-cystine (B). The spectra were recorded from solid samples in 1-mm glass capillaries, with 1064-nm excitation (Nd:YAG laser). Laser power was 500 mW; 1024 co-added scans were collected at 8-cm⁻¹ spectral resolution.

to β-lactoglobulin is evident from the stronger intensity of the v(S-S) band at ~ 505 cm⁻¹.

Although many of the proteins that have been studied by FTIR and Raman spectroscopy may be categorized as food proteins, such as whey, soy, and egg proteins, the majority of these studies have not been specifically concerned with the behavior of the proteins as food components. However, some detailed investigations of food proteins have been conducted to gain a better understanding of protein stability and structure-functionality relationships, with the overall objective of obtaining information that can assist the food industry in making more effective use of food proteins (7). Figure 44.14 shows an example from our studies on the thermal denaturation of whey proteins by variable-temperature FTIR spectroscopy (15–18). The spectra in the amide I region (Figure 44.14A) were recorded during heating of a 7% (w/v) solution of β-lactoglobulin in D₂O in a temperature-controlled transmission cell from 25 to 95°C and have been deconvolved by Fourier self-deconvolution. A plot of the changes in intensity of several of the amide I' band components as a function of temperature is shown in Figure 44.14B. The decreases in band intensity at 1648 (▲) and 1635 cm⁻¹ (●), assigned to α-helical and intramolecular β-sheet structures, respectively, and indicative of protein denaturation, occur prior to a sharp increase in the band intensity at 1618 cm⁻¹ (■), assigned to intermolecular β-sheet formation and characteristic of protein aggregation. Similar experiments have been performed with the use of a diamond-anvil high-pressure IR cell to monitor denaturation of whey proteins under conditions of applied hydrostatic pressure, similar to those utilized in high-pressure processing, and provided information on the nature of the differences between thermal and pressure-induced denaturation (19, 20). In addition,

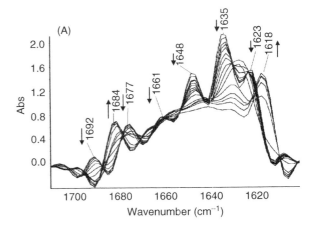

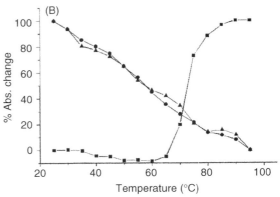

FIGURE 44.14 (A) Spectral overlay plot of the deconvolved amide I' band in the FTIR spectrum of β-lactoglobulin (7% w/v) as a function of increasing temperature (25–95°C). FSD parameters: w = 27 and k = 2.4. (B) Plot of changes in intensity at 1648 (▲), 1635 (●), and 1618 cm⁻¹ (■) as a function of increasing temperature.

multivariate analysis techniques have been employed to correlate FTIR spectral changes observed as a function of changes in physicochemical parameters, such as pH, ionic strength, temperature, and pressure, with rheological data collected under the same conditions (7). Such studies provide a better understanding of the structural changes at the molecular level that govern rheological behavior.

B. ANALYSIS OF FOODS BY FTIR AND RAMAN SPECTROSCOPY

1. Milk and Dairy Products

To date, the utility of IR spectroscopy in the quantitative analysis of foods has been most clearly exemplified by milk analysis. The determination of fat, protein, and lactose in milk by IR spectroscopy is an official method of the Association of Official Analytical Chemists (AOAC) and is used extensively as a basis for milk payment, dairy herd recording, and routine quality control in the dairy industry. High-volume automated instruments allow for the analysis of 100–500 samples per hour. Dispersive spectrometers and subsequently filter-based instruments were originally employed in commercial IR milk analyzers, but FTIR milk analyzers are now on the market (21). The accepted IR milk analysis methodology employs a 37-μm CaF_2 transmission flow cell, which is kept at a constant temperature (40 ± 0.1°C) to obtain reliable, stable, and accurate measurements. Typically, IR milk analyzers incorporate a high-pressure (150–200 kPa) homogenizer to reduce the size of the fat globules to <1 μm to avoid light scattering effects. The pressure is maintained in the system throughout the analysis to avoid formation of air bubbles in the cell, and the cell is flushed with the next sample at extremely high velocity (30 m/s), eliminating the need for rinsing of the cell. Whereas filter-based IR milk analyzers were restricted to the analysis of fat, protein, and lactose, because the filters employed were specifically selected for the measurement of these components, commercial FTIR milk analyzers can be calibrated to measure other components in a wide range of dairy products, such as infant formula, ice cream, yogurt, and whey and whey concentrates (21).

In transmission measurements of dairy products, light scattering by fat globules must be eliminated in order to obtain quantitative analytical results. In the case of fluid products, this requirement can be addressed, albeit at some cost, by the use of high-pressure homogenizers, as described above. Because ATR measurements are not affected by light scattering, ATR accessories would appear ideal for the analysis of dairy products, including non-fluid products such as butter and cheese. However, the presence of fat globules in dairy products is, in fact, highly problematic because it results in sample inhomogeneity on the scale of the depth of penetration, which is in the order of a few microns or less, and thus the spectrum obtained is not truly representative of the sample composition. In a study of the effect of fat globule size in cream on ATR/FTIR measurements, a nonlinear relationship was found between absorbance at 1744 cm^{-1} (commonly used as a measurement peak for fat) and fat content over the range of 0–48% (by volume) (22). The authors of this study proposed the use of a nonlinear calibration curve for samples having fat globules > 1 μm. In a study of assessing the feasibility of employing ATR/FTIR spectroscopy for fat, protein, and moisture determination in cheese (23), large variations in the ATR/FTIR spectra of replicate samples taken from the center of a cheese were observed owing to both variations in the diameter of the fat globules and inhomogeneous distribution of fat within the cheese. Based on the fairly poor accuracy of PLS calibrations that were developed for the determination of fat, protein, and moisture contents, the authors concluded that the utility of the ATR/FTIR method for the analysis of cheese was quite limited but might be improved by homogenization of the samples prior to analysis; however,

this requirement would significantly complicate the procedure. Another approach to overcoming the problem was employed in the development of a rapid FTIR quality control method for fat and moisture determination in butter employing an ATR sample-handling accessory (24). Samples were dissolved in 1-propanol and warmed to 40°C, thereby solubilizing the fat without causing separation of an aqueous phase, and applied to a heated ATR crystal (40°C) for spectral recording. A calibration was developed by employing gravimetrically prepared mixtures of anhydrous butterfat and water in 1-propanol as calibration standards. Analysis of 20 butter samples by this ATR/FTIR method yielded good agreement with reference values obtained by the Mojonnier method (24).

The speed of FTIR analysis (typically, <2 min/sample) is particularly advantageous in a processing environment since it allows the manufacturing process to be monitored and adjusted as it proceeds. A method for the simultaneous determination of sucrose, lactose, total solids, and fat in chocolate milk by FTIR spectroscopy for use in a production environment has been described (25). An ATR/FTIR method for fat and solids determination was developed for quality control purposes during manufacture of sweetened condensed milk (26). The ATR sample-handling technique is highly suitable for this type of viscous product, which would be very difficult to handle if a transmission cell were used, and highly reproducible results were obtained when samples were homogenized at 65°C prior to ATR/FTIR analysis. More recently, an SB-ATR/FTIR method has been developed for monitoring enzymatic hydrolysis of lactose during the production of lactose-reduced milk (27).

2. Beverages

Aside from milk analysis, numerous FTIR methods for the analysis of different types of beverages have been developed. Determination of sucrose, glucose, fructose, and total sugars in juices and soft drinks by ATR/FTIR spectroscopy was investigated by Rambla and co-workers (28, 29). Sinnaeve et al. analyzed apple juice using a 16-μm temperature-controlled transmission cell and successfully quantified malic acid, total sugars, glucose, fructose, sucrose, and specific gravity (30). Flow injection analysis coupled with transmission FTIR spectroscopy was used in the determination of sucrose in fruit juices (orange juice, apple juice, and sports drink) (31). Acetate buffer was used as the carrier solvent, and samples were passed through an enzyme reactor containing β-fructosidase prior to FTIR spectral acquisition. In another study, flow injection analysis/FTIR spectroscopy was employed to quantify malic acid, tartaric acid, and citric acid in juices and soft drinks using pH modulation to eliminate matrix effects (32). In a flow injection analysis/FTIR method for the determination of caffeine in soft drinks, caffeine was extracted by passing the samples through a solid-phase extraction column (C_{18}), using chloroform as the eluent (33). A rapid ATR/FTIR method was developed for the determination of caffeine in soft drinks without extraction (34). This method allowed caffeine quantitation in soft drinks at levels as low as 0.5 mg/100 mL and was found to produce results similar to, but slightly higher on average than, those obtained from the conventional ultraviolet (UV) method.

Various publications have described methods for ethanol determination in distilled liquors, wines, and beers. Dilution of beverages having ethanol contents of >15% (v/v) is often required for analysis in a transmission cell, but this step can be eliminated when an ATR accessory is employed (35). The use of ATR fiber-optic probes in the quantitation of alcohol in liqueurs has been reported (36).

Recently, commercial FTIR wine analyzers, employing a flow-through transmission cell similar to that incorporated in FTIR milk analyzers, have been marketed (21). Patz et al employed an FTIR wine analyzer to analyze for alcohol, tartaric acid, malic acid, lactic acid, total acidity, pH, volatile acidity, reducing sugars, fructose, glucose, total SO_2, total phenols, and glycerol (37). The calibration and test sets comprised 165 wine samples, preanalyzed by standard methods; because the concentration ranges for glycerol and volatile acidity in these samples were too narrow, standards prepared in water were added to the calibration set. The authors reported that results were acceptable for all parameters except total SO_2 and total phenols. Comparable results were obtained with a standard benchtop FTIR spectrometer equipped with an SB-ATR accessory in a similar study conducted by the McGill IR Group to demonstrate the feasibility of employing SB-ATR/FTIR spectroscopy for the routine analysis of distilled liquors and wines (27). Dubernet and Dubernet used a commercial FTIR wine analyzer to analyze for alcohol, reducing sugars, total acidity, pH, malic acid, tartaric acid, lactic acid, total phenols, volatile acidity, CO_2, glycerol, gluconic acid, and saccharose content in 200,000 wine samples (38). These authors reported that not all wines could be analyzed accurately using the same calibration due to matrix effects and therefore developed separate calibrations for dry and sweet wines as well as for wine musts. Because calibration development may require the accurate analysis of several hundred representative wines for multiple components, which is clearly a major undertaking, an alternative approach based on synthetically prepared mixtures of the major components present in wine has been investigated (39). It was demonstrated that the preparation of large numbers of calibration standards that are often required for multivariate calibration and the acquisition of their spectra may be automated by sequential injection, a form of flow injection analysis. However, when calibrations based on model solutions of nine common components as a substitute for preanalyzed wines were applied to the

analysis of wine samples, only limited agreement was obtained between the IR-predicted values for organic acids and sugars and results obtained by high-pressure liquid chromatography (HPLC) (39).

In a different type of application related to wine production, SB-ATR/FTIR spectroscopy in combination with PCA and cluster analysis was used to discriminate between phenolic extracts of different wine cultivars (40). Phenolic extracts were obtained by solid-phase extraction of the wine samples and subsequent elution of the phenols with methanol. Only 1 µL of the methanolic extract was required to cover the SB-ATR crystal and the methanol was allowed to evaporate prior to spectral recording. Almost complete discrimination of all cultivars investigated was achieved. SB-ATR/FTIR spectroscopy was also used in the analysis of white wine polysaccharide extracts to identify the type of wine-making process employed (must clarification versus maceration) based on the polysaccharides present (41).

3. Edible Oil Analysis

In the past decade, a large amount of work has been done on both FTIR and FT-Raman analyses of edible fats and oils. These included the development of both qualitative applications, involving the characterization and classification of oils, and numerous examples of quantitative analysis applications. The literature in this area has been surveyed in a recent review (42), and only selected applications will be highlighted in this section.

Typical FTIR and FT-Raman spectra of an edible oil are presented in Figure 44.15. The FTIR spectra of edible oils and premelted fats in their neat form can be recorded with the use of either a heated transmission flow cell or a heated ATR accessory, making these types of samples fairly ideal from a sample-handling perspective. On the other hand, dispersive Raman spectroscopy is generally unsuitable for the analysis of edible oils owing to background fluorescence arising from colored components present in oils. However, with the recent advent of FT-Raman instrumentation employing NIR excitation sources, the problem of background fluorescence has largely been eliminated, as can be seen from the high quality of the FT-Raman spectrum in Figure 44.15, and thus the potential for practical implementation of Raman analysis of fats and oils has been greatly enhanced.

The most noteworthy application of IR spectroscopy in the analysis of fats and oils is the determination of isolated *trans* isomers, which is an official method of the AOAC, the American Oil Chemists' Society (AOCS), and IUPAC. In the original IR *trans* analysis method, which was developed over 50 years ago with dispersive IR spectrometers, samples were dissolved in carbon disulfide before recording their spectra in a fixed-pathlength transmission cell (43). This dilution procedure was necessary

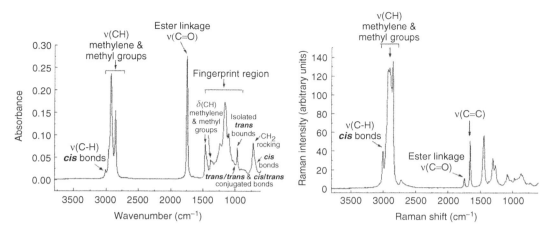

FIGURE 44.15 FTIR spectrum (left) and FT-Raman spectrum (right) of an edible oil. The spectra contain bands characteristic of *trans* double bonds because the sample is a partially hydrogenated oil.

because the analysis of oils in their neat form would require a cell pathlength of 10 μm or less due to the high absorptivity of the major absorption bands. With the development of FTIR spectrometers, however, it became possible to employ transmission cells with somewhat longer pathlengths (25–100 μm) or ATR accessories for the analysis of oils in their neat form. In 1996, Mossoba et al. described a rapid and simple ATR method for the determination of isolated *trans* isomers at levels down to 1% (44), and this method was subsequently adopted as an official method by both the AOAC and the AOCS. The use of an SB-ATR accessory for this analysis is advantageous because the small surface area of the ATR crystal allows for more precise temperature control and minimizes sample cross-contamination (45). Furthermore, the small volume of sample required (<50 μL) is advantageous in the analysis of fats extracted from foods, especially low-fat food products. This sample-handling technique was employed for the determination of *trans* content in hydrogenated vegetable oils in a collaborative study (46). The relative standard deviation between five labs was 1.62% for a sample having a *trans* content of 39.12% and 18.97% for a sample having a *trans* content of 1.95%. The relatively high error at low *trans* levels is attributable to the poor signal-to-noise ratio resulting from the very short effective pathlength of the SB-ATR accessory. Another factor limiting the accuracy of the method is the need for a *trans*-free reference oil that closely matches the fatty acid composition of the sample. If an appropriate reference oil is not available, as generally would be the case in the analysis of fats extracted from foods, the accuracy of the method may be poor, particularly at low *trans* levels (47).

The McGill IR Group extended the SB-ATR method for *trans* analysis to allow simultaneous determination of iodine value (IV), a measure of total unsaturation (45). Calibration models for the prediction of both IV and *trans* content were developed using PLS regression and a calibration set consisting of 9 pure triacylglycerols. Good agreement was obtained between the results obtained by gas chromatography (GC), the FTIR/PLS method, and the AOCS FTIR method for *trans* analysis and between a GC method and the FTIR/PLS method for IV determination (45). Much better precision and accuracy were achieved with the SB-ATR accessory than in previous work with an MB-ATR accessory (48). The McGill IR Group has also done extensive work on edible oil analysis using the custom-designed transmission flow-through cell shown in Figure 44.5, heated to 80°C to avoid fat crystallization during analysis (49). Methods have been developed for the determination of *trans* and *cis* content (50), free fatty acids (51), solid fat index (52), iodine value (53), saponification number (53), anisidine value (54), and peroxide value (PV) (55). While most of these methods are based on the spectral features of neat fats and oils, the PV method employs the stoichiometric reaction of triphenylphosphine with hydroperoxides to produce triphenylphosphine oxide, which has a strong absorption band at 542 cm^{-1} that is used for PV quantitation. Ruiz et al. automated this method through the application of flow injection analysis to allow on-line PV analysis, without the need for manual sample manipulation (56).

The complementary nature of IR and Raman spectroscopy is well illustrated by the spectra of edible fats and oils. By comparison of the spectra in Figure 44.15, it may be noted that the relative band intensities in the IR and Raman spectra differ markedly. Of particular significance in relation to the measurement of unsaturation is the 1700–1600 cm^{-1} region, in which strong C=C stretching absorptions are the dominant features in the Raman spectra of unsaturated oils whereas the corresponding bands in IR spectra are extremely weak. Because the C=C stretching absorptions of *cis* and *trans* double bonds are observed at different wavenumbers (1656 and 1670 cm^{-1}, respectively), Raman spectroscopy allows for the determination of both the degree and type of unsaturation (57, 58). Thus, the potential utility of Raman spectroscopy, in conjunction with fiber optics, to monitor hydrogenation processes has been suggested (59). Raman spectroscopy has also been reported to provide information about the relative proportions of saturated, monounsaturated, and polyunsaturated fatty acids in a variety of fats and oils of both plant and animal origin (60).

As reviewed in Ref. 42, there have also been many studies during the past decade on the classification of edible oils by vibrational spectroscopy. Although the spectra of most pure fats and oils appear fairly similar visually, they reflect the differences in fatty acid composition that exist among different types of fats and oils. Thus, with the use of chemometric techniques such as PCA and discriminant analysis, different types of oils can be distinguished on the basis of differences in their IR or Raman spectra. The powerful capabilities of these techniques are exemplified by the successful use of FTIR spectroscopy, in conjunction with discriminant analysis, to differentiate between extra virgin and refined olive oils, despite the strong similarities between the spectra of these two types of oils (61). In another study, SB-ATR/FTIR spectroscopy was employed to detect adulteration of sunflower oil in olive oil down to a level of 20 mL/L of extra virgin olive oil (62). Similarly, Raman spectroscopy was shown to allow for the detection of adulteration of virgin olive oil with hazelnut oil, a very chemically similar oil type, at levels down to 5% (63). These examples are illustrative of fairly extensive research that has demonstrated the potential utility of FTIR and Raman spectroscopy for the authentication of edible oils.

Another important qualitative analysis application involves the dynamic monitoring of oil oxidation by FTIR spectroscopy to evaluate the oxidative stability of oils. For example, by monitoring the FTIR spectra of a thin film of oil spread on the heated surface of an ATR sample-handling accessory (64, 65) or on a polymer film (66) and subtracting the fresh oil spectrum ($t = 0$) from those taken subsequently over time, the resulting differential spectra reveal subtle spectral changes that can be employed to track changes in oxidation via "indicator bands" such as the *cis*, isolated and conjugated *trans*, hydroperoxide, and aldehyde absorptions. This approach allows one to develop a "dynamic" oxidation profile (peak height vs. time) based on these indicator bands and evaluate the relative stability of oils in a simple and rapid manner.

4. Syrups and Semi-Solids

ATR/FTIR spectroscopy is particularly useful for the quantitative analysis of viscous samples that cannot be easily introduced into a sealed transmission cell. The potential utility of ATR/FTIR spectroscopy for continuous on-line process monitoring of the conversion of corn starch to corn syrup has been demonstrated (67). Another study used a ZnSe ATR accessory to determine dry substance (glucose,

maltose, and fructose) in glucose syrups after sample dilution (1 g/2 mL) (68). Determination of fruit content and detection of adulteration in strawberry jam by ATR/FTIR spectroscopy was investigated (69) but the accuracy of the method was limited by the overlapping of the 1725 cm^{-1} band used for fruit quantitation with the strong water absorption band at ~1650 cm^{-1}. In a later study, 36 jam samples were classified by ATR/FTIR spectroscopy according to their fruit content as "strawberry" or "non-strawberry," with a correct classification rate of 91% (70). In a similar but much larger study, 95% of over 1000 fruit puree samples were correctly classified as "raspberry" or "nonraspberry," and it was shown that adulteration with sucrose or with apple and plum could be detected at levels of 4% (w/w) and 20% (w/w), respectively (71). The detection of inverted cane sugar adulteration in honey (72) and beet and cane sugar adulteration in maple syrups (73) by ATR/FTIR spectroscopy has also been reported.

5. Solids

Classification and detection of adulteration of solid food products by ATR/FTIR spectroscopy has been investigated. Instant coffee samples were dissolved in distilled water at 50°C at a concentration of 30% (w/v) and applied onto the surface of a horizontal ATR accessory (74). Spectra were recorded immediately to avoid settling out of a small insoluble fraction. Discrimination of *Arabica* and *Robusta* instant coffees was achieved by applying linear discriminant analysis (LDA) to the scores obtained by PCA of the spectral data, and the composition of *Arabica* and *Robusta* blends was determined by multivariate analysis. A similar methodology was employed for the detection of adulteration of instant coffees with glucose, fructose, and xylose, and the carbohydrate profile was also successfully quantified (75). The capability to distinguish between minced chicken, pork and turkey meats as well as fresh and frozen-thawed samples by ATR/FTIR spectroscopy has also been described (76).

For quantitative analysis of solid samples, IR transmission measurements are unsuitable owing to light scattering effects whereas an ATR/FTIR spectrum may not be fully representative of the sample owing to inhomogeneity on the scale of the depth of penetration associated with ATR measurements. In a study of protein-starch mixtures (77), samples were prepared by mixing dry gluten and starch or casein and starch and then adding a gram of water per gram of sample to produce wet mixtures, which varied in consistency from a moist powder at high starch content to an elastic mass at high gluten content. These samples were spread evenly on the ATR crystal to ensure uniform coverage and a constant pressure was applied to achieve good optical contact between the ATR crystal and the sample. However, poor reproducibility was obtained, especially for the casein-starch mixtures due to large particle size of casein.

In general, IR quantitative analysis of solid food products with the use of transmission or ATR sample-handling techniques requires some prior sample preparation. For example, quantitative analysis of sugar powders (glucose, fructose, sucrose) by ATR/FTIR spectroscopy was performed by impregnating the powders with an organic solvent (acetone), thereby forming a film on the surface of the ATR crystal after evaporation of the acetone (78). Determination of total fat and protein in meat by FTIR spectroscopy was carried out on meat samples prepared by suspension in 0.1N NaOH solution at 67°C and homogenized using a high-pressure valve homogenizer, prior to injection into a 37-μm CaF_2 heated (65°C) flow-through cell (79). Total fat determination in food products by transmission FTIR spectroscopy has been performed by extracting the fat in a chloroform/methanol (2:1) solvent (80) or 1-propanol (81).

The need for such sample preparation steps can potentially be eliminated through the use of alternative sample-handling techniques. One technique that has been investigated is photoacoustic (PAS) spectroscopy, which is based on the detection of IR absorption by using sound (82, 83). However, PAS has poor S/N relative to transmission and ATR techniques because the efficiency of energy transfer (absorbance to sound) is poor, and thus it is a relatively insensitive technique. In addition, water vapor gives rise to strong photoacoustic signals, requiring that the sample be very dry during analysis. Finally, the photoacoustic signal is dependent on several factors, such as incident energy, absorption coefficient, surface morphology, and thermal diffusivity, which, in part, are sample dependent. Accordingly, PAS does not appear to have general applicability for quantitative food analysis.

Raman spectroscopy is better suited to the analysis of solid samples than IR spectroscopy. In the area of food analysis, this suitability is best illustrated by various studies on modified starches, in which the degrees of acetylation and succinylation were determined from the FT-Raman spectra of solid samples contained in glass capillary tubes (84). However, no examples of the use of Raman spectroscopy in the analysis of processed foods have been reported.

REFERENCES

1. P Williams, K Norris. Near-Infrared Technology in the Agricultural and Food Industries, 2nd ed. St. Paul, MN: American Association of Cereal Chemists, 2001.
2. BG Osborne, T Fearn, PH Hindle. Practical NIR Spectroscopy with Applications in Food and Beverage Analysis. Harlow, Essex: Longman, 1993.
3. T Hirschfeld, B Chase. FT-Raman spectroscopy: Development and justification. Appl Spectrosc 40:133–137, 1986.
4. PB Coleman, ed. Practical Sampling Techniques for Infrared Analysis. Boca Raton, FL: CRC Press, 2003.
5. IT Jolliffe. Principal Component Analysis. New York: Springer, 1986.
6. H Martens, T Naes. Multivariate Calibration, 2nd ed. Chichester, U.K.: John Wiley & Sons, 1989.
7. ECY Li-Chan, AA Ismail, J Sedman, FR van de Voort. Vibrational spectroscopy of food and food products. In: JM Chalmers, PR Griffiths, eds. Handbook of Vibrational Spectroscopy. New York: John Wiley & Sons, 2002, Vol 5, pp 3629–3662.
8. B Stuart. Biological Applications of Infrared Spectroscopy. Chichester, U.K.: John Wiley & Sons, 1997.
9. PR Carey. Biochemical Applications of Raman and Resonance Raman Spectroscopies. New York: Academic Press, 1982.
10. M Nonaka, ECY Li-Chan, S Nakai. Raman spectroscopic study of thermally induced gelation of whey proteins. J Agric Food Chem 41:1176–1181, 1993.
11. WK Surewicz, HH Mantsch. New insight into protein secondary structure from resolution-enhanced infrared spectra. Biochim Biophys Acta 952:115–130, 1988.
12. WK Surewicz, HH Mantsch, D Chapman. Determination of protein secondary structure by Fourier transform infrared spectroscopy: A critical assessment. Biochemistry 32:389–394, 1993.
13. MN Siamwiza, RC Lord, MC Chen, T Takamatsu, I Harada, H Matsuura, T Shimanouchi. Interpretation of the doublet at 850 and 830 cm^{-1} in the Raman spectra of tyrosyl residues in proteins and certain model compounds. Biochemistry 14:4870–4876, 1975.
14. ECY Li-Chan. The applications of Raman spectroscopy in food science. Trends Food Sci Technol 7:361–370, 1996.
15. JI Boye, AA Ismail, I Alli. Effect of physico-chemical factors on the secondary structure of β-lactoglobulin. J Dairy Res 63:97–109, 1996.
16. JI Boye, I Alli, AA Ismail. Interactions involved in the gelation of bovine serum albumin. J Agric Food Chem 44:996–1004, 1996.
17. JI Boye, I Alli, AA Ismail. Use of differential scanning calorimetry and infrared spectroscopy in the study of thermal and structural stability of α-lactalbumin. J Agric Food Chem 45:1116–1125, 1997.
18. JI Boye, CY Ma, AA Ismail, VR Harwalkar, M Kalab. Molecular and microstructural studies of thermal denaturation and gelation of β-lactoglobulins A and B. J Agric Food Chem 45:1608–1618, 1997.
19. T Hosseini-Nia, AA Ismail, S Kubow. Pressure-induced conformational changes of β-lactoglobulin by variable-pressure Fourier transform infrared spectroscopy. J Agric Food Chem 47:4537–4542, 1999.
20. T Hosseini-Nia, AA Ismail, S Kubow. Effect of high hydrostatic pressure on the secondary structures of BSA and apo- and holo-α-lactalbumin employing Fourier transform tnfrared spectroscopy. J Food Sci 67:1341–1347, 2002.
21. SK Andersen, PW Hansen, HV Andersen. Vibrational spectroscopy in the analysis of dairy products and wine. In: JM Chalmers, PR Griffiths, eds. Handbook of Vibrational Spectroscopy. New York: John Wiley & Sons, 2002, Vol 5, pp 1–10.

22. EK Kemsley, GP Appleton, RH Wilson. Quantitative analysis of emulsions using attenuated total reflectance (ATR). Spectrochim Acta A 50:1235–1242, 1994.

23. DH McQueen, RH Wilson, A Kinnunen, EP Jensen. Comparison of two infrared spectroscopic methods for cheese analysis. Talanta 42:2007–2015, 1995.

24. FR van de Voort, J Sedman, G Emo. A rapid FTIR quality control method for fat and moisture determination in butter. Food Res Int 25:193–198, 1992.

25. RA Cocciardi, AA Ismail, FR van de Voort, J Sedman. A rapid Fourier transform infrared quality control method for the determination of lactose, sucrose, fat and total solids in chocolate milk. Milchwissenschaft 57(2):90–93, 2002.

26. N Nathier-Dufour, J Sedman, FR van de Voort. A rapid ATR/FTIR quality control method for the determination of fat and solids in sweetened condensed milk. Milchwissenschaft 50:462–466, 1995.

27. RA Cocciardi, AA Ismail, FR van de Voort. Monitoring of lactose hydrolysis in milk by single-bounce attenuated total reflectance Fourier transform infrared spectroscopy. Milchwissenschaft 59:403–407, 2004.

28. FJ Rambla, S Garrigues, N Ferrer, M de la Guardia. Simple partial least squares-attenuated total reflectance Fourier transform infrared spectrometric method for the determination of sugars in fruit juices and soft drinks using aqueous standards. Analyst 123:277–281, 1998.

29. S Garrigues, FJ Rambla, M de la Guardia. Comparative study of reflectance cells for PLS-FTIR determination of sugars in soft drinks. Fresenius J Anal Chem 362:137–140, 1998.

30. G Sinnaeve, P Dardenne, R Agneessens, M Lateur, A Hallet. Quantitative analysis of raw apple juices using near infrared, Fourier-transform near infrared and Fourier-transform infrared instruments: A comparison of their analytical performances. J Near Infrared Spectrosc 5:1–17, 1997.

31. R Kellner, B Lendl, I Wells, PJ Worsfold. Comparison of univariate and multivariate strategies for the determination of sucrose in fruit juices by automated flow injection analysis with Fourier transform infrared detection. Appl Spectrosc 51:227–235, 1997.

32. MJ Ayora-Cañada, B Lendl. Sheath-flow Fourier transform infrared spectrometry for the simultaneous determination of citric, malic and tartaric acids in soft drinks. Anal Chim Acta 417:41–50, 2000.

33. Y Daghbouche, S Garrigues, MT Vidal, M de la Guardia. Flow injection Fourier transform infrared determination of caffeine in soft drinks. Anal Chem 69:1086–1091, 1997.

34. MM Paradkar, J Irudayaraj. Rapid determination of caffeine content in soft drinks using FTIR-ATR spectroscopy. Food Chem 78:261–266, 2002.

35. RA Cocciardi, AA Ismail, J Sedman. Investigation of the potential utility of single-bounce attenuated total reflectance Fourier transform infrared spectroscopy in the analysis of distilled liquors and wines. J Agric Food Chem 53:2803–2809, 2005.

36. EK Kemsley, RH Wilson, PS Belton. Potential of Fourier transform infrared spectroscopy and fiber optics for process control. J Agric Food Chem 40:435–438, 1992.

37. CD Patz, A David, K Thente, P Kurbel, H Dietrich. Wine analysis with FTIR spectrometry. Vitic Enol Sci 54(2–3):80–87, 1999.

38. M Dubernet, M Dubernet. Utilisation de l'analyse infrarouge à transformée de Fourier pour l'analyse oenologique de routine. Rev Fr Oenol 18:10–13, 2000.

39. R Schindler, R Vonach, B Lendl, R Kellner. A rapid automated method for wine analysis based upon sequential injection (SI)-FTIR spectrometry. Fresenius J Anal Chem 362:130–136, 1998.

40. A Edelmann, J Diewok, KC Schuster, B Lendl. Rapid method for the discrimination of red wine cultivars based on mid-infrared spectroscopy of phenolic wine extracts. J Agric Food Chem 49:1139–1145, 2001.

41. MA Coimbra, F Goncalves, AS Barros, I Delgadillo. Fourier transform infrared spectroscopy and chemometric analysis of white wine polysaccharide extracts. J Agric Food Chem 50:3405–3411, 2002.

42. FR van de Voort, J Sedman, T Russin. Lipid analysis by vibrational spectroscopy. Eur Lipid Sci Technol 103:815–826, 2001.

43. D Firestone, P LaBouliere. Determination of isolated *trans* isomers by infrared spectrophotometry. J Am Oil Chem Soc 48:437–443, 1965.

44. MM Mossoba, MP Yurawecz, RE McDonald. Rapid determination of the total *trans* content of neat hydrogenated oils by attenuated total reflection spectroscopy. J Am Oil Chem Soc 73:1003–1009, 1996.

45. J Sedman, FR van de Voort, AA Ismail. Simultaneous determination of iodine value and *trans* content of fats and oils by single-bounce horizontal attenuated total reflectance Fourier transform infrared spectroscopy. J Am Oil Chem Soc 77:399–403, 2000.

46. M Adam, M Chew, S Wasserman, A McCollum, RE McDonald, MM Mossoba. Determination of *trans* fatty acids in hydrogenated vegetable oils by attenuated total reflection infrared spectroscopy: Two limited collaborative studies. J Am Oil Chem Soc 75:353–358, 1998.

47. LH Ali, G Angyal, CM Weaver, JI Rader, MM Mossoba. Determination of total *trans* fatty acids in foods: Comparison of capillary-column gas chromatography and single-bounce horizontal attenuated total reflection infrared spectroscopy. J Am Oil Chem Soc 73:1699–1705, 1996.

48. FR van de Voort, J Sedman, G Emo, AA Ismail. Rapid and direct iodine value and saponification number determination of fats and oils by attenuated total reflectance/Fourier transform infrared spectroscopy. J Am Oil Chem Soc 69:1118–1123, 1992.

49. J Sedman, FR van de Voort, AA Ismail. Application of Fourier transform infrared spectroscopy in edible oil analysis In: RE McDonald, MM Mossoba, eds. New Techniques and Applications in Lipid Analysis. Champaign, IL: AOCS Press, 1997, pp 283–324.

50. FR van de Voort, AA Ismail, J Sedman. A rapid, automated method for the determination of *cis* and *trans* content of fats and oils by Fourier transform infrared spectroscopy. J Am Oil Chem Soc 72:873–880, 1995.

51. AA Ismail, FR van de Voort, G Emo, J Sedman. Rapid quantitative determination of free fatty acids in fats and oils by Fourier transform infrared spectroscopy. J Am Oil Chem Soc 70:335–341, 1993.

52. FR van de Voort, KP Memon, J Sedman, AA Ismail. Determination of solid fat index by Fourier transform infrared spectroscopy. J Am Oil Chem Soc 73:411–416, 1996.

53. J Sedman, FR van de Voort, AA Ismail, P Maes. Industrial validation of Fourier transform infrared *trans* and iodine value analyses of fats and oils. J Am Oil Chem Soc 75:33–39, 1998.

54. J Dubois, FR van de Voort, J Sedman, AA Ismail, HR Ramaswamy. Quantitative Fourier transform infrared analysis for anisidine value and aldehydes in thermally stressed oils. J Am Oil Chem Soc 73:787–794, 1996.

55. Kangming Ma, FR van de Voort, J Sedman, AA Ismail. Stoichiometric determination of hydroperoxides in fats and oils by Fourier transform infrared spectroscopy. J Am Oil Chem Soc 74:897–906, 1997.

56. A Ruiz, MJ Ayora-Cañada, B Lendl. A rapid method for peroxide value determination in edible oils based on flow analysis with Fourier transform infrared spectroscopic detection. Analyst 126:242–246, 2001.

57. GF Bailey, RJ Horvat. Raman spectroscopic analysis of the *cis/trans* isomer isomer composition of edible vegetable oils. J Am Oil Chem Soc 49:494–498, 1972.

58. H Sadeghi-Jorabchi, PJ Hendra, RH Wilson, PS Belton. Determination of the total unsaturation in oils and margarines by Fourier transform Raman spectroscopy. J Am Oil Chem Soc 67:483–486, 1990.

59. GL Johnson, RM Machado, KG Freidl, ML Achenbach, PF Clark, SK Reidy. Evaluation of Raman spectroscopy for determining *cis* and *trans* isomers in partially hydrogenated soybean oil. Org Process Res Dev 6:637–644, 2002.

60. V Baeten, P Hourant, MT Morales, R Aparicio. Oil and fat classification by FT-Raman spectroscopy. J Agric Food Chem 46:2638–2646, 1998.

61. YW Lai, EK Kemsley, RH Wilson. Potential of Fourier transform infrared spectroscopy for the authentication of vegetable oils. J Agric Food Chem 42:1154–1159, 1994.

62. A Tay, H Singh, SS Krishnan, JP Gore. Authentication of olive oil adulterated with vegetable oils using Fourier transform infrared spectroscopy. Lebensm-Wiss Technol 35:99–103, 2002.

63. EC Lopez-Diez, G Bianchi, R Goodacre. Rapid quantitative assessment of the adulteration of virgin olive oils with hazelnut oils using Raman spectroscopy and chemometrics. J Agric Food Chem 51:6145–6150, 2003.

64. FR van de Voort, AA Ismail, J Sedman, G Emo. Monitoring the oxidation of edible oils by FTIR spectroscopy. J Am Oil Chem Soc 71:243–253, 1994.

65. J Sedman, AA Ismail, A Nicodemo, S Kubow, FR van de Voort. Application of FTIR/ATR differential spectroscopy for monitoring oil oxidation and antioxidant efficiency. In: F Shahidi, ed. Natural Antioxidants. Champaign, IL: AOCS Press, 1996, pp 358–378.

66. TA Russin, FR van de Voort, J Sedman. Novel method for rapid monitoring of lipid oxidation by FTIR spectroscopy using disposable IR cards. J Am Oil Chem Soc 80:635–641, 2003.

67. MP Fuller, MC Gary, Z Stanek. An FTIR liquid analyzer. Am Lab 22:58–69, 1990.

68. F De Lene Mirouze, JC Boulou, N Dupuy, M Meurens, JP Huvenne, P Legrand. Quantitative analysis of glucose syrups by ATR/FT-IR spectroscopy. Appl Spectrosc 47:1187–1191, 1993.

69. RH Wilson, PT Slack, GP Appleton, L Sun, PS Belton. Determination of the fruit content of jam using Fourier transform infrared spectroscopy. Food Chem 47:303–308, 1993.

70. M Defernez, RH Wilson. Mid-infrared spectroscopy and chemometrics for determining the type of fruit used in jam. J Sci Food Agric 67:461–467, 1995.

71. EK Kemsley, JK Holland, M Defernez, RH Wilson. Detection of adulteration of raspberry purees using infrared spectroscopy and chemometrics. J Agric Food Chem 44:3864–3870, 1996.

72. S Sivakesava, J Irudayaraj. Prediction of inverted cane sugar adulteration of honey by Fourier transform infrared spectroscopy. J Food Sci 66:972–978, 2001.

73. MM Paradkar, S Sivakesava, J Irudayaraj. Discrimination and classification of adulterants in maple syrup with the use of infrared spectroscopic techniques. J Sci Food Agric 82:497–504, 2002.

74. R Briandet, EK Kemsley, RH Wilson. Discrimination of Arabica and Robusta in instant coffee by Fourier transform infrared spectroscopy and chemometrics. J Agric Food Chem 44:170–174, 1996.

75. R Briandet, EK Kemsley, RH Wilson. Approaches to adulteration detection in instant coffees using infrared spectroscopy and chemometrics. J Sci Food Agric 71:359–366, 1996.

76. O Al-Jowder, EK Kemsley, RH Wilson. Mid-infrared spectroscopy and authenticity problems in selected meats: a feasibility study. Food Chem 59:195–201, 1997.

77. PS Belton, AM Saffa, RH Wilson. Use of Fourier transform infrared spectroscopy for quantitative analysis: A comparative study of different detection methods. Analyst 112:1117–1120, 1987.

78. N Dupuy, M Meurens, B Sombret, P Legrand, JP Huvenne. Multivariate determination of sugar powders by attenuated total reflectance infrared spectroscopy. Appl Spectrosc 47:452–457, 1993.

79. B Dion, M Ruzbie, FR van de Voort, AA Ismail, JS Blais. Determination of protein and fat in meat by transmission Fourier transform infrared spectrometry. Analyst 119:1765–1771, 1994.

80. DA Cronin, K McKenzie. A rapid method for the determination of fat in foodstuffs by infrared spectrometry. Food Chem 35:39–49, 1990.

81. FR van de Voort, J Sedman, AA Ismail. A rapid FTIR quality-control method for determining fat and moisture in high-fat products. Food Chem 48:213–221, 1993.

82. CNG Scotter. Non-destructive spectroscopic techniques for the measurement of food quality. Trends Food Sci Technol 8:285–291, 1997.

83. DH McQueen, RH Wilson, A Kinnunen. Near- and mid-infrared photoacoustic analysis of principal components of foodstuffs. Trends Anal Chem 14:482–492, 1995.

84. DL Phillips, J Xing, CK Chong, H Liu, H Corke. Determination of the degree of succinylation in diverse modified starches by Raman spectroscopy. J Agric Food Chem 48:5105–5108, 2000.

45 Application of Gas Chromatography to the Identification of Foodborne Pathogens and Chemical Contaminants in Foods

Magdi M. Mossoba, Frederick S. Fry, Sufian F. Al-Khaldi,
Gregory O. Noonan, and Douglas G. Hayward
Center for Food Safety and Applied Nutrition, U.S. Food and Drug Administration

CONTENTS

I. INTRODUCTION

Gas chromatography (GC) has been widely used in various applications involving the qualitative and quantitative analyses of foods (1) for several decades. In order to improve food safety and quality, GC techniques and methods have been developed and evaluated for many diverse applications. GC has been an excellent tool for the separation and determination of trace level, thermally stable, volatile organic analytes in complex food matrices.

Many food matrices are analyzed by GC in order to determine nutritional and palatability needs, check food adulteration, engineer novel food products, or meet process-control, quality assurance, food labeling, or other requirements. The widely different components include natural constituents, contaminants, and additives of foods, as well as products that arise from natural reactions and/or industrial processing. Food constituents are primarily water, lipids, proteins, carbohydrates, vitamins, and minerals, and components such as fatty acids, sterols, alcohols, aroma components, and off-flavors, are determined by GC. Contaminants in food products include residues of pesticides, veterinary drugs, and industrial pollutants (such as polyhalogenated hydrocarbons and polycyclic aromatic hydrocarbons), as well as toxins from spoilage, vegetative bacteria, endospores, or fungi (mycotoxins). Additives usually consist of components that are added to food products (such as preservatives, colors, or flavors).

Auto-oxidation and food processing (for example, frying, catalytic hydrogenation, or irradiation) also lead to the production of components (such as cyclic or *trans* fatty acids, histamine, urethane, nitrosamines, or 2-alkylcyclobutanones irradiation markers) that can be identified by GC.

In the past decade, GC advances have been achieved including the development and/or optimization of GC instrumentation components (injectors, detectors) and of portable, miniaturized, high-speed GC systems in which retention times are very short due to high flow rates, short and narrow bore columns, low film thickness, increased diffusivity of a solute in the gas phase, and faster temperature programming. GC detectors with greater selectivity and sensitivity such as mass spectrometers (MS), pulsed flame photometric detectors, and halogen specific detectors proved to be advantageous in food-analysis applications. Fast-GC/MS analyses (1) have been carried out by using micro-bore columns with time-of-flight (TOF)-MS (2–4), low pressure (LP)-GC/MS (5–7), and supersonic molecular beam (SBM)-MS (8–10).

In this chapter, three different areas of research selected from a large field of issues related to food analysis by GC techniques are addressed. The sections describe the instrumentation and applications of fast-GC to the study of food contaminants, the application of high resolution (HR) GC to the analysis of polyhalogenated contaminants in foods, and the GC analysis of foodborne bacterial lipids. Reasons for selecting fast-GC include its future potential in the analysis of many GC-amenable food additives and contaminants. Polyhalogenated aromatic compound determination in foods provides an excellent example of the continued application of gas chromatography to one of the most intractable analytical problems with food analysis. Without the advances in column design, both size and phase, the isomer specific analysis of PCDD/Fs and PCBs would be a much longer and more difficult process. Finally, GC-based methodologies are important analytical chemical tools that have been used increasingly for the speciation of microorganisms.

II. FAST GAS CHROMATOGRAPHY AND FOOD ANALYSIS

A major breakthrough in gas chromatography occurred in 1957 with the introduction of open tubular columns (11). This was followed in 1962 by an infamous demonstration of very fast gas chromatography (12). Utilizing a 120 cm × 0.035 mm squalene-coated column, H_2 carrier gas, and a hammer to depress the syringe, Desty and coworkers (12) obtained near-baseline separation of 15 hydrocarbons and isomers in under 2 s. In addition to such demonstrations of very fast analysis times, early work in open tubular columns also led to the development of columns with extremely high plate numbers (10^6). In spite of these early

breakthroughs, open tubular columns were not rapidly accepted for chromatographic analysis. Small sample capacity, fragile, rigid glass capillaries, difficulty of incorporation into existing instruments and irreproducible column characteristics, attributed to slowing the implementation of open tubular columns. It was not until the late 1970s that the introduction of fused silica columns (13) and improvements in GC instrumentation led to the wider use of capillary columns.

The greater use of capillary columns was not accompanied by a large reduction in analysis time or sudden interest in fast chromatography. Instead, the greater efficiency of capillary columns was used to analyze and separate increasingly more complex mixtures. To ease in the transfer of methods from packed columns, developers chose capillary columns with large diameters, thick films, and excessive lengths. The concept of "killing it with plates" (14) and "over separating" (15) are often used to describe these early methods. Indeed, many of these methods became official or standard methods and the "over separation" still persists. Recently, with the increased cost of analysis, the interest in process control and the desire to develop rapid field-deployable test methods for environmental and security monitoring, there has been a renewed interest in rapid gas chromatographic analyses. The availability of fast chromatographic instrumentation (16) and method translation software will undoubtedly expand the use of the technique.

The terminology "fast gas chromatography" can be extremely subjective. If an analysis normally takes 70 minutes, then a 40-minute run time could be considered "fast." Dagan and Amirav first attempted to quantify the terminology used for Fast, Very Fast, and Ultra-Fast Gas Chromatography by identifying a "speed enhancement factor" (SEF) (17). SEF, the product of column length reduction factor and carrier gas linear velocity increase, constitutes a reduction factor in the flow time of the carrier gas compared to conventional GC. Dagan and Amirav defined a 30-m narrow bore column with a 1 ml/min gas flow rate (34 cm/s helium linear velocity) as the reference conditions for conventional GC-MS. Although SEF is quantitative in nature we find the classifications based on peak widths and total analysis time introduced by van Duersen et al. (1) to be more useful. According to the classification, "fast GC" separations happen in minutes and have peak widths of several seconds. "Very fast GC" describes seconds range separation with 30–200 ms peak widths and "ultra fast GC" is sub-second separations with 5–30 ms peak widths. Hinshaw (18) also "quantified" analysis speed by dividing methods into four levels based on relative speed, column dimensions, and inlet pressures. Hinshaw used the terminology of conventional, rapid, high-speed and very-high-speed for levels 1 through 4, respectively. This discussion will apply the van Duersen criteria for describing applications and will primarily focus on fast GC and the application in food analysis.

A. CHROMATOGRAPHIC THEORY

Prior to reviewing the practical aspects of fast gas chromatography, a brief review pertaining to resolution and efficiency in chromatographic separation is in order. It should be noted that the following discussion is a brief summary and is not intended as a thorough discussion of chromatographic theory. For the interested reader more in-depth and complete discussions of the equations and theory relating to sample introduction, speed of separation and detection in gas chromatographic analysis can be found in a number of sources (14,19–22).

In chromatographic analysis the goal is to separate the analytes of interest, denoted as the "critical pair," and to do so in the shortest amount of time. By definition, when the pair is separated, all of the peaks in the chromatogram will also be separated. The degree of separation is called the resolution (R_s), which is commonly defined by

$$R_s = \frac{\Delta t_R}{4\sigma_c} \qquad (45.1)$$

where Δt_R is the difference in retention time between a critical pair and σ_c is the standard deviation of chromatographic peak broadening. Baseline separation is achieved when peaks of equal size show a resolution of >1.5; however a resolution of > 1.0 is often sufficient. The number of theoretical plates required to produce a given resolution is expressed as:

$$N = 16R_S^2 \left[\frac{1+k}{k} \right]^2 \left[\frac{\alpha}{\alpha-1} \right]^2 \qquad (45.2)$$

where k is the solute capacity factor of the second eluting peak of the critical pair and α is the relative retention or selectivity factor for the two components.

Once resolution of the critical pair is achieved, the time for the chromatographic separation is minimized. The run time can be determined by the column length (L), average linear gas velocity ($\bar{\mu}$), and the solute capacity factor (k) of the last eluting peak using the following equation:

$$t_R = (L/\bar{\mu})(1 + k) \qquad (45.3)$$

where t_R is the retention time of the last eluting compound. Equation 45.3 exhibits the relationship between analysis time, column length, and linear gas velocity, but is more instructive when written in terms of the number of theoretical plates (N) and the height equivalent to a theoretical plate (H).

$$t_R = N(H/\bar{\mu})(1 + k) \qquad (45.4)$$

Equation 45.4 demonstrates the direct relationship between run time, plate number, and plate height. By combining equations 45.2 and 45.4 the relationship between analysis time and resolution becomes evident:

$$t_R = 16R_S^2 \left(\frac{\alpha}{\alpha+1} \right)^2 \frac{(1+k)^3}{k^2} \frac{H}{\bar{\mu}} \qquad (45.5)$$

B. REDUCTION OF CHROMATOGRAPHIC ANALYSIS TIME

Using narrow bore columns is one of the easiest and most common methods for reducing the analysis time, while maintaining resolution. Schutjes et al. (23), although not the first to utilize narrow bore columns, derived the expressions relating a decrease in column diameter to a decrease in analysis time. They also experimentally confirmed the relationships for isothermal and temperature programmed conditions using 30 and 50 μm diameter columns. Klee and Blumberg (13) report nearly a 10-fold increase in "relative speed" by reducing the column diameter from 530 to 100 μm, while keeping "separation power equivalent." These studies demonstrated that decreasing column diameter effectively increases the number of plates per unit length of column (24). However, there are practical limits to the column diameter, Schutjes et al. (23) used 30 and 50 μm columns in their studies; however, due to potential problems with sample capacity, inlet pressure limitations, and maintaining injection efficiency it has been recommended that columns with diameters ≥ 100 μm (13) and ≥180 μm (24) be used in routine analysis.

Along with reducing column diameter, the choice of carrier gas can also impact speed of analysis, without decreasing resolution. By switching from helium to hydrogen as a carrier a 30% reduction in analysis time can be achieved, while switching from nitrogen gives a >3-fold reduction in analysis time (25). Finally, reduced outlet pressures through vacuum-outlet conditions have also been shown to be a useful method for decreasing analysis time at constant resolution (26). However, under certain conditions Cramers et al. (26) did report a 12.5% reduction in column efficiency when using vacuum outlet conditions. Although vacuum outlet conditions are only applicable when utilizing mass spectrometric detectors, an understanding of the effects of high pressure drops is important when developing fast chromatographic methods. A thorough study of the effect of high pressure drop commonly seen in fast chromatography, performed by Blumberg (27–29) and summarized by Klee and Blumberg (13), shows the complex relationship of pressure drop, column efficiency, analysis speed, column length and diameter, and film thickness.

A number of methods are available to the analyst for shortening analysis time through a reduction in resolution. Many of these, shortening column length (30), adjusting carrier gas velocity, and increasing temperature program rates (30), are familiar options during traditional method development. However, as was mentioned previously, many of the current "official" methods are over separated, and some estimates suggest that up to 75% of the chromatogram contains no useful information (14). Even if that value overstates the extent of "lost time," the analyst should not overlook the ability to gain analysis speed through the optimization of resolution reducing parameters (14,19–21).

The reduction of peak widths and separation times achieved in fast chromatography begin to place stringent requirements on other instrumental parameters, often referred to as "extra-column sources." The Golay model (10), assumes that band broadening occurs only in the column, which is an accurate assumption when describing systems with long columns and low linear gas velocity. However, given the short column and/or high gas velocity in fast chromatography, this assumption is not always valid (20). Therefore, "extra-column sources" in general, and sample introduction specifically, can become an extremely important part of the analysis. The need to introduce the sample, without overloading the column or introducing band broadening, is critical to maintaining fast, highly resolved chromatograms. For fast chromatography conventional split/splitless injectors can be utilized, although the ratio or timing must be adjusted to avoid overloading column capacity (13). A number of other sample introduction systems have been developed for use in fast, very fast, and ultra-fast GC (21,22,31–33). The best method of introduction depends on the application of the chromatographic method.

As with sample introduction, sample detection mechanisms must maintain chromatographic efficiency by limiting band broadening. Additionally, detectors must have a sampling frequency fast enough to provide 15–20 data points across a peak (22). Many of the commonly used detectors including electron capture (EC), photoionization (PI), and thermal conductivity (TC), are sufficiently fast, but traditionally have large dead volumes, which leads to band broadening. The use of make-up gas to offset the large detector volume and limit band broadening leads to a loss of sensitivity with EC, PI, and TC detection (21). Small volume cells have been utilized to reduce band broadening and limit or eliminate the need for make-up gas (22). The use of mass-flow-sensitive detectors such as flame ionization, photometric, and thermionic detectors offer satisfactory data acquisition and sensitivity for use in fast GC (21). Along with the selection of a detection mechanism that has adequate sensitivity and maintains chromatographic efficiency, it is also beneficial to choose a selective detector that does not respond to co-extracted matrix components. Such selectivity will assist in shortening analysis time by reducing the need for increased chromatographic resolution. Perhaps the most common example is the use of mass spectrometric detectors to separate compounds not fully resolved by the chromatographic system (34). Wu and coworkers (35) utilized an element selective detector to assist in decreasing analysis time in their method. Additionally, Mastovska et al. (36) described the benefits in

using a flame photometric detector compared to FID when analyzing for organophosphate pesticides in wheat.

Column selectivity changes can also be used to alter the analysis and subsequently gain speed. The choice of stationary phase can have a profound effect on elution order and elution time. Additional changes in temperature rates, gas velocity, or column length can then be used to further increase analysis speed. An extension of the use of a selective stationary phase is the use of two columns (GC $\times$ GC) with different retention properties (14). Unfortunately, specialized instruments, data systems, and experience are required to utilize these methods.

C. APPLICATIONS OF FAST CHROMATOGRAPHY

In general, our interest in fast chromatography is not concentrated on a specific sub-discipline of the technique, but is in the overall potential benefits offered by the methods. As in any laboratory, the ability to analyze more samples in less time would represent a significant cost and time savings. Conversely, the shortened analysis time would enable us to investigate more samples in a given time period, allowing for a greater cross section of the food supply to undergo analysis. We are also intrigued by the application of fast chromatography to rapid field sampling. Such instrumentation would be useful in greater monitoring of the food supply, or in assisting manufacturers with process control as part of additional QA/QC procedures.

Although there has been an improvement in instrumentation and methods development associated with fast GC, food analysis can pose difficult challenges. Fortunately, the increase in interest in fast GC has produced a number of recent promising publications, which have application in our area of research. The research of Chen and coworkers (37) on the residual solvents is related to the work performed in our laboratories analyzing food and food packaging for volatile compounds (38–40). They were able to shorten the analysis of 40 organic solvents from 45 to less than 5 minutes using a short, narrow bore capillary column. Additional decreases in time were realized, by implementing temperature and pressure programming and limiting the list of analytes. Sample introduction was carried out by headspace analysis and direct injection. Although both showed acceptable reproducibility, the impact of the rapid method and sample introduction on detection limits was not evaluated.

Wang and Burleson (41) reported the development of a fast GC method used in the analysis of pyrolysis products from synthetic polymers. Pyrolysis GC has been shown to be useful in identifying low level additives in synthetic polymers (42) and a fast GC method could be useful in our analysis of polymer packaging materials (43,44). Wang and Burleson successfully transferred the traditional method to a fast GC, achieving a 10-fold increase in analysis speed. They also investigated the effect of head pressure and/or oven temperature on analysis time in conventional GC. Their findings indicate that pyrolysis-fast GC is a useful method for analyzing synthetic polymers in short time periods.

Although the applications mentioned above have direct implications in the analysis of food and food packaging, they do not represent the same challenges often encountered with direct food analysis. Food is an extremely complex matrix, with a variety of interferences, often at concentrations significantly higher than the analyte of interest. Therefore, the ability to analyze foods by fast GC represents a particular challenge. Reed and coworkers (45) used a 5 m × 330 μm column, combined with fast temperature programming, to analyze for 2,6-di-(tert-butyl)-4-methylphenol (BHT) in chewing gum, breakfast cereal, and granola bars. Realizing that the extraction of BHT is often the rate limiting step in these analyses, Reed et al. utilized microwave assisted extraction (MAE) to further increase the overall processing time (45). Chromatographic analysis of each of the three sample matrices was completed in about 3 minutes with acceptable resolution and reproducibility reported for all samples.

Sandra and David (46) reported a fast gas chromatographic method for the determination of polychlorinated biphenyls (PCBs) in food matrices, and the fatty acid composition (as fatty acid methyl esters, FAME). The method was developed in response to the need to analyze a large number of samples (4000) in as short a time as possible. Initial development and validation was carried out in side-by-side studies using the official method. For the PCB method a shorter, narrow bore column was implemented to achieve a 4-fold increase in analysis speed without sacrificing resolution. Sandra and David (46) also applied a splitless injection to the fast GC, improving the limits of detection. It should be noted that the splitless liner was replaced after every 100 samples. A shorter, narrow bore column was also used for the FAME analysis and it also produced a reduced analysis time. This study was extremely successful at demonstrating the utility of fast GC; additionally, it represents one of the most extensive uses of fast GC that has been reported to date.

Lloyd and Grimm (35) increased the temperature program rates in order to increase analysis speed for sugars and FAMEs in food. For the sugar analysis they report a >7-fold increase in speed, but do note a loss in chromatographic resolution. Such a loss in resolution is to be expected when using temperature program rates as the driving force behind faster separations (22). However, the resolution of the fast separation was still acceptable for this analysis. The FAME analysis showed an increase in speed similar to the sugar analysis; however, separation of several of the compounds was incomplete. The mass selective detector did help distinguish co-eluted analytes, except in the case of positional (*cis, trans*) isomers. Lloyd and Grimm concluded that fast GC was successful in reducing analysis time, but had reservations about the loss of resolution.

Mastovsak et al. (36) evaluated the impact of reducing column length and temperature program rates in their analysis of 15 organophosphate pesticides in wheat. They also compared the performance of conventional and fast GC with flash GC, a commercially available resistive heating device. By reducing the column length from 30 to 5 m, increasing their temperature program rate, but maintaining column diameter and film thickness, Mastovsak and coworkers were able to reduce their analysis time 10-fold. Splitless injections with different splitless timing were used for the conventional, fast, and flash analysis. The researchers found that the narrower peak widths produced in flash GC experiments produced better detection limits, despite the smaller quantities of analyte being introduced to the column. The comparison of fast GC and flash GC methods showed similar run times, but the flash GC produced better retention time reproducibility. Additionally, the flash GC runs had faster cooling rates, leading to faster overall analysis times. The only drawback of the fast and flash GC was the loss of some resolution and subsequent coelution of analytes. However, some of the lost resolution could be attributed to the less selective stationary phase used for the flash GC analysis.

D. METHOD TRANSLATION SOFTWARE

In creating methods for fast GC, the analyst has two choices; either redevelop the entire method or translate the method from traditional chromatography. Klee and Blumberg (13) offer an in-depth discussion of principles and practices of method translation. Method translation is often the easier of the two choices, especially if retention indices or "fingerprint" patterns need to be retained. To assist in the transfer, it is helpful to use method translation software, which is currently available on Agilent Technologies' internet site (www.chem.agilent.com/cag/servsup/usersoft/main.html#mxlator). A number of researchers (24,47) have evaluated the software's capabilities. David et al. (47) utilized the method translation software in transferring analysis of essential oils, bacterial fatty acids, and other complex mixtures from traditional to fast gas chromatography. By using a shorter, narrow bore column, and switching to hydrogen carrier gas they were able to analyze nutmeg and lemon oils in <13 min, a 6-fold decrease in analysis time. Additionally, the shorter analysis exhibited comparable retention indices and peak area ratios as the longer runs, allowing the "fingerprint pattern" of the separations to be maintained. Wool and Decker (24), by implementing a shorter, narrow bore column and using hydrogen as the carrier gas, observed a 50% reduction in time for analysis of 22 pesticides. Their conclusion was that "Method Translator should be a standard tool for analysts interested in speeding up the analyses done in their laboratories."

Fast gas chromatography is not a new concept, but the research and use appear to be undergoing a recent renaissance. This renewed interest is probably due to a number of factors, including cost of analysis, interest in field sampling, and availability of adequate instrumentation. Whatever the reasons it is clear from past and recent publications that there are real benefits in developing fast gas chromatographic methods. These benefits will apply to laboratory sampling, process control, and field sampling, and will have an impact on the analysis of food and food packaging.

III. HIGH RESOLUTION GC AND THE ANALYSIS OF CONTAMINANTS IN FOODS

A. SCOPE OF THE PROBLEM

This discussion will not be a review of the more than 25-year history of research involving high resolution gas chromatography (HRGC) and its application to the analysis of poly-halogenated contaminants. Rather than be a review, this treatment will examine the current approaches and future directions. The poly-halogenated contaminants of great interest in foods fall into several classes based on their carbon skeleton. A common feature of all the classes is the large number of isomers with similar physical and chemical properties, while conversely possessing widely varying effects on biological systems. These compounds exhibit very similar chemical properties to the analyst needing to detect and identify them, but nevertheless the individual isomers must be identified to determine their potential importance to a biological system. Table 45.1 lists some classes of poly-halogenated aromatic contaminant studied as a result of food contamination incidences or occupational exposures.

Table 45.2 provides a list of some of these classes along with a few chemical properties and their toxic equivalency factors (TEFs) values where known. Estimated toxicities often vary by many orders of magnitude for chemicals with fairly similar boiling points, melting points, vapor pressures, and octanol/water partitioning coefficients.

TABLE 45.1
Classes for Poly-Halogenated Aromatic Compounds, Synthetically and Environmentally Derived Contaminants

Chemical Class	Range(X)	Possible Congeners
Polychlorinated dibenzo-p-dioxins (PCDDs)	1–8(Cl)	75
Polychlorinated dibenzofurans (PCDFs)	1–8(Cl)	135
Polychlorinated naphthalenes (PCNs)	1–8(Cl)	75
Polychlorinated biphenyls (PCBs)	1–10(Cl)	209
Polybrominated biphenyls (PBBs)	1–10(Br)	209
Polybrominated diphenylethers (PBDEs)	1–10(Br)	209
Polychlorinated diphenylethers (PCDEs)	1–10(Cl)	209
Polybrominated dibenzo-p-dioxins (PBDDs)	1–8(Br)	75
Polybrominated dibenzofurans (PBDFs)	1–8(Br)	135

B. HRGC COLUMN STATIONARY PHASES

During the past 20 years, high resolution capillary GC columns have become the standard approach to separation difficulties presented by complex mixtures of polyhalogenated contaminants. Greater toxicological understanding of these chemicals has required increasing amounts of analytical data that report isomer-specific quantifications of these compounds in foods. Column lengths used in these procedures are typically at least 50 m, but most often 60 m, in length. PCDD/Fs provide a good example of separation difficulties with these compound classes. No single column could effectively separate all the isomers with largest TEFs from all others.

Ryan et al. (48) published the separations of all 136 tetrachloro- to octachloro-PCDD/Fs on nine different stationary phases and reported retention times on all the nine column phases. The column stationary phases covered a range of polarity from purely non-polar methyl silicone and the widely used 95% methyl, 5% phenyl polysiloxane (DB-5, RTX-5, equivalent, etc.) to the most polar 90% biscyanopropyl/ 10% 1:1 phenyl/ cyanopropyl polysiloxane (SP-2331) and 100% biscyanopropyl (CP-Sil-88) and the more recently introduced SB-smectic liquid crystalline methyl (80%) diphenyl carboxylic ester (20%) phase. Polar phases generally separated more of the 2,3,7,8-substituted isomers with the fewer numbers of congeners co-eluting, especially with 2,3,4,7,8-PeCDF and 2,3,7,8-TCDF, while leaving some HxCDFs or HxCDDs unresolved. Columns containing DB- 210 (50% methyl/ 50% trifluropropyl polysiloxane) or DB-225 (50% cyanopropylphenyl/50% methyl polysiloxane) equivalent phases are used for resolving the multiple co-elutions with 2,3,7,8-TCDF found on non-polar columns, but also produce co-elutions with 2,3,7,8-TCDD, 1,2,3,7,8-PeCDD, and certain HxCDFs such that they must be used with a second, usually non-polar, column.

Two medium polarity columns tested produced separations comparable or better to some more polar phases. A DB-17 column (50% phenyl/ 50% methyl polysiloxane) separated 2,3,7,8-TCDF completely and separated most other 2,3,7,8-substituted congeners except 1 isomer co-eluting with 2,3,7,8-TCDD, 1,2,3,7,8-PeCDF, and an incomplete separation of 1,2,3,6,7,8-HxCDF. An OV-17 column still contained an isomer co-eluting with 2,3,7,8-TCDF and with 1,2,3,7,8-PeCDD, while producing more complete separation for HxCDFs. While some column phases performed much better than others, a combination of at least two columns was needed to identify all isomers of the 2,3,7,8-chlorine substituted dibenzo-p-dioxin and –furan isomers in complex mixtures. The polar phases provide separation for all but a few of the 12 2,3,7,8-substituted tetrachloro-hexachloro-DD/Fs, but require hour-long GC run times leaving significant overlaps between chlorination levels. Often the performance of these polar phases

TABLE 45.2

Some Physical Properties for Poly-Halogenated Pollutants and Associated TEFs

Class or Member	MP [a]	BP [a]	VP	log(Kow)	TEF [b]
Polychlorinated Dibenzo-p-Dioxins (PCDDs)					
2,3,7,8-TetraCDD	305	412.2	1.4E–09	6.2–7.3	1
1,2,7,8-TetraCDD	–	–	–	–	0
1,2,3,7,8-PentaCDD	240	–	–	6.8	1
1,2,3,4,7,8-HexaCDD	–	–	–	–	0.1
1,2,3,6,7,8-HexaCDD	285–286	–	–	7.6	0.1
1,2,3,7,8,9-HexaCDD	243–244	–	–	7.6	0.1
1,2,3,4,6,7,8-HeptaCDD	–	–	–	–	0.01
1,2,3,4,6,8,9-HeptaCDD	140	–	–	–	0
1,2,3,4,6,7,8,9-OctaCDD	150	–	–	–	0.0001
Polychlorinated Dibenzofurans (PCDFs)					
2,3,7,8-TetraCDF	219–228	–	0.000002	5.8	0.1
2,3,4,8-TetraCDF	–	–	–	–	0
1,2,3,7,8-PentaCDF	225–227	–	–	–	0.05
2,3,4,7,8-PentaCDF	168–170	–	0.0000011	–	0.5
1,2,3,4,7,8-HexaCDF	226–227	–	–	–	0.1
2,3,4,6,7,8-HexaCDF	–	–	–	–	0.1
1,2,3,4,6,7,8-HeptaCDF	236–237	–	–	–	0.01
1,2,3,4,7,8,9-HeptaCDF	–	–	–	–	0.01
1,2,3,4,6,8,9-HeptaCDF	–	–	–	–	0
1,2,3,4,6,7,8,9-OctaCDF	–	–	–	–	0.0001
Polychlorinated Biphenyls (PCBs)					
Arochlor 1254 or 1260	–	275–420	7.7E–05 [d]	6.8	–
3,3',4,4'-TetraCB	–	–	1.1E–05 [d]	–	0.0005
3,3',4,4',5-PentaCB	–	–	2.1E–06 [d]	–	0.1
3,3',4,4',5,5'-HexaCB	–	–	4.0E–07 [d]	–	0.01
2,3,3',4,4'-PentaCB	–	–	5.3E–06 [d]	–	0.0001
2,3',4,4',5-PentaCB	–	–	7.2E–06 [d]	–	0.0001
2,3,4,4',5-PentaCB	–	–	3.3E–05 [d]	–	0.0005
2',3,4,4',5-PentaCB	–	–	6.8E–06 [d]	–	0.0001
2,3,3',4,4',5-HexaCB	–	–	5.5E–06 [d]	–	0.0005
2,3,3',4,4',5'-HexaCB	–	–	1.0E–06 [d]	–	0.0005
2,3',4,4',5,5'-HexaCB	–	–	1.4E–06 [d]	–	0.00001
2,3,3',4,4',5,5'-HeptaCB	–	–	1.08E–06 [d]	–	0.0001
2,2',3,3',4,4',5-HeptaCB	–	–	2.8E–06 [d]	–	0.0001
2,2',3,4,4',5,5'-HeptaCB	–	–	3.8E–06 [d]	–	0.00001
Polychlorinated Naphthalenes (PCNs)					
1,2,3,5,6,7/1,2,3,4,6,7-HexaCN	–	234/205	–	–	0.002(EROD) [c]
1,2,3,4,5,7/1,2,3,5,6,8-HexaCN	–	–	–	–	0.0002(EROD) [c]
1,2,3,5,7,8-HexaCN	–	148	–	–	0.002(EROD) [c]
1,2,4,5,6,8-HexaCN	–	153	–	0	0.000007(EROD) [c]
1,2,3,4,5,6,7-HeptaCN	–	–	–	–	0.003(EROD) [c]

[a] Ahlborg et al. (1994) (Ref. 94).
[b] EPA Study (1992) (Ref. 95).
[c] Hanberg et al. (1990) (Ref. 96).
[d] Holmes et al. (1993) (Ref. 97).

MP = melting point; BP = boiling point; VP = vapor pressure; Kow = octanol/water partitioning coefficient; TEF = toxic equivalency factor.

will deteriorate faster than non-polar ones which significantly alter the quality of the separation and increase maintenance time and costs. Some phases have been marketed specifically to produce a near-complete separation of the critical 12 2,3,7,8-substituted tetrachloro-through hexachloro-DD/Fs. The "DB-Dioxin" separates all 2,3,7,8-substituted congeners except for 1,2,3,4,7,8-HxCDF, although some congeners were not 100% resolved from other isomers.

Fraisse et al. (49) reported an improved separation using a non-polar phase initially developed for low bleed requirements of ion trap mass spectrometers. The "DB-5ms" phase used the same composition (95% methyl-5% phenyl polysiloxane) as a DB-5 or RTX-5 equivalent phase, but with phenyl groups pendant on as well as inserted as aryl inclusions in the polysiloxane chain. The resulting phase could easily separate 2,3,7,8-TCDD and 2,3,7,8-TCDF from the other 21 or 37 isomers, respectively, compared with an ordinary DB-5 which could not resolve 2,3,7,8-TCDF from 5 other isomers and produced only a slight separation of 2,3,7,8-TCDD from several closely eluting isomers. In addition, all the hexachlorinated isomers were also separated, except for a poor separation of 1,2,3,7,8,9-HxCDF, compared with separating only 4 of the 7 congeners on DB-5. The 1,2,3,7,8-PeCDD was still resolved well enough, but not to baseline as with DB-5. This column effects a separation for PCDD/Fs from food extracts with near-complete isomer specificity with a very durable high temperature column. There are almost no circumstances (e.g., an old DB-5 ms column measuring high levels of TCDF in a shellfish sample containing all TCDF isomers or where the cleanup was poor) where a second or alternative column is necessary for food analysis in a regulatory setting.

Isomer-specific PCB methods have recently focused on the unique GC separation and mass spectrometry determination of the PCB congeners with established TEFs (see Table 45.2). Frequently, the PCBs are fractionated before GC separations are attempted using non-polar columns (DB-5 equivalent, etc.). The separations greatly simplify the task of the GC so that a single non-polar capillary column with high durability can separate the remaining congeners. PCB congeners with no orthochlorine substitutions are isolated for analysis with the dioxins. Other PCB congeners are analyzed separately or further fractionated by the number of orthochlorine substitutions (e.g., mono-orthochloro and di-orthochloro-). Some methods attempt to determine all of the PCB congeners with TEFs with a single GC injection. EPA 1668 Rev. A has the purpose of separating PCBs 77, 81, 105, 114, 118, 123, 126, 156, 157, 167, 169, 189 from all other congeners in an environmental sample using an SPB-octyl column (Supelco 2-4218). This method requires retention time of decachlorobiphenyl to be greater than 55 minutes (quite long) and analyzes PCB 156 and 157 as a summed peak. The combination of the SPB octyl column and a DB-1 is reported in the method to uniquely separate 180 PCB congeners. Garrett et al. (50) reported that the SPB octyl column produced high bleed, producing unstable retention times within a few days. Some new columns could not meet the specifications of EPA 1668 Rev. A. An RTX-5 sil MS column was suggested as an alternative. Covaci et al. (98) reports separating PCBs in human adipose using a 50 m × 0.22 mm id HT-8 column made with 8% phenyl methyl silicone and dicarbaclosododecarborane that SGE has claimed will separate 192 of the 209 PCB congeners at least partially.

The separation and retention behavior of all 72 polychlorinated napthalenes isomers was investigated on six different HRGC columns phases by Järnberg et al. (51). No column could separate all congeners at any chlorination level from dichloro- to hexachloro-. A pair of hexachloronapthalene isomers (1,2,3,5,6,7 and 1,2,3,4,6,7) known to strongly bioaccumulate, were not separated on any phase. More recently, a complete separation of all 14 pentachloro- and 10 hexachloronapthalene isomers was demonstrated using a proprietary column phase made by Restek that used per-methylated β-cyclodextrin (52).

C. HRGC COLUMN DIMENSIONS

The efficient separation of isomeric mixtures has required relatively long columns (50 m or 60 m). Some better separations are accomplished on polar stationary phases with lower temperature maxima, further slowing the elution of highly chlorinated congeners. Hayward et al. (53,54) demonstrated that a shorter and narrower "minibore" 40 m × 0.18 mm ID DB-5 ms column could produce nearly identical separations as the wider and longer 60 m columns in 40 min and was durable enough for analysis of large numbers of food samples for PCDD/Fs. MacPherson et al. (55) optimized the conditions for PCDD/Fs, coplanar PCBs, and chlorinated pesticides on 40 m × 0.18 mm and 20 m × 0.1 mm DB-5 columns by adjusting temperatures ramps and using higher inlet pressures enabling comparable separations and quantifications using either 60 m, 40 m, or 20 m DB-5 columns. On 20 m columns, PCDD/Fs were eluted in as little as 14 min. This same approach using 20 m columns and fast temperature ramps was applied to a mixture of 56 PCBs and to PAH mixtures (56). Microbore columns have also been tested in dual column applications for determining target PCB congeners and dioxins in the same GC run. MacPherson et al. (57) recently reported the sequential acquisition by HRMS of mono-ortho PCBs (PCBs 105, 118, 156 etc.) eluting from a 20 m × 0.1 mm ID column while PCDD/Fs and non-ortho-PCBs 77, 81, 126, and 169 were being separated on a 40 m × 0.18 mm ID column in the same GC injected immediately after the injection on the 20 m column of the PCB fraction. This way separate PCB fractions could be determined with the same acquisition and into the same data file for processing. Worrall et al. (58) used a similar approach, but delay the injection of the PCDD/F containing fraction on the 40 m column for 2.4 min to help avoid co-determination of chlorinated diphenylethers that would be present in the mono-ortho PCB fraction eluting on the 20 m column.

Dimandja et al. (59) demonstrated a very fast separation of 38 PCBs found in human serum in 5 min using a short 15 m column using time-of-flight (TOF) mass spectrometry for detection. The high spectral acquisition rates inherent in TOF have been used to reduce the time of separations on standard sized columns allowing simultaneous PCB and pesticide determinations in as little as 9.5 min (60).

D. MULTI-DIMENSIONAL GC (GC²)

Multidimensional GC or GC² refers to the separation of chemicals using two or more independent migrations for a chemical during the same fixed distance (GC) experiment. Multidimensional separations increase the capacity and resolution of a given GC system. The concepts for multidimensional separations are aptly described by Giddings (61). Liu and Phillips (62) reported achieving two-dimensional gas chromatography through use of an on-column thermal modulator system. A narrow bore column of standard length (20 m) is connected through the modulator (short section of column rapidly heated and cooled) to a short (~0.5 m) microbore column that produces a second fast separation of components pulsed to it by modulator from the first column. Two dimensional gas chromatograms could be generated on complex mixes of hydrocarbons using this system. The same approach was reported for pesticides in human serum by Liu et al. (63). Rapid separations of pesticides, PCBs or PCDD/Fs require fast mass spectral acquisition of a TOF instrument for mass spectrometric detection. More recent work has focused on robust modulator designs. Vreuls et al. (64) compared the performance of 4 modulator systems and report separating 91 PCB congeners and all 17 2,3,7,8-PCDD/Fs with the GCxGC/microECD with an ultimate goal of using TOF for the determination of PCBs and dioxins.

IV. APPLICATION OF GC TO THE IDENTIFICATION OF FOODBORNE BACTERIA

Among the U.S. population, it is estimated that millions contract foodborne illnesses each year (65). Currently, there is active surveillance for laboratory-diagnosed cases of 10 foodborne diseases resulting from infection with *Campylobacter, Escherichia coli* O157, *Listeria monocytogenes, Salmonella, Shigella, Vibrio* spp., *Yersinia enterocolitica, Cryptosporidium parvum, Cyclospora cayetanensis,* and hemolytic uremic syndrome (HUS) (66). Since September 2001, there has been an additional need to identify select agents such as toxins (botulinum toxin and staphylococcal enterotoxin), chemical agents (sarin nerve gas and mustard gas), viruses, and particularly pathogenic bacteria including *Bacillus anthracis, variolla* (small pox), *Clostridium botulinum,* and *C. perfringens* (67). This requirement has led to a sudden surge in demand for routine rapid tests as well as fast and accurate microbiological assays and analytical methodologies for bacterial identification.

The most common techniques used for identifying bacteria include polymerase chain reaction (PCR), immunoassay biochemical reaction tests, and classical microscopy (67). Analytical chemical methods such as infrared spectroscopy (IR) (68–71), mass spectrometry (MS) (71,72), and gas chromatography (GC) (72–80) have been also used increasingly for bacterial speciation in research laboratories.

A. GAS CHROMATOGRAPHY AND CELLULAR MEMBRANE COMPONENTS

Early reports demonstrating that GC analysis of cellular fatty acid could be used successfully to identify bacteria were published in the 1960s (74,75). Whole bacterial cells are usually treated with sodium hydroxide and alcohol to cause hydrolysis and release of cellular membrane fatty acids. Sodium salts are formed and subsequently esterified. The resulting mixture of volatile fatty acid methyl esters (FAMEs) are separated by GC, identified and quantified. Derivatization increases volatility and improves chromatographic resolution. It was later recognized that further application of sophisticated multivariate statistical analyses to GC fatty acid profiles would facilitate the identification of microorganisms (75,76). The resulting new chemotaxonomy (75,76) based on multivariate statistical strategies such as principal component analysis differed from traditional microbial taxonomy that did not involve any statistical treatment.

The structures and names of cellular fatty acids are often complex (80). The structures of fatty acids can vary widely and include saturated, unsaturated, and branched fatty acids as well as those with hydroxy groups (e.g., 3-OH-C14:0) and rings. Branched fatty acids include the *iso* series, $(CH_3)_2CH(CH_2)_aCOOH$, and the *antiso* series, $CH_3CH_2CH(CH_3)(CH_2)_bCOOH$ or $CH_3(CH_2)_cCH(CH_3)(CH_2)_dCOOH$ with branching at a carbon in the middle of the fatty acid chain. Using a simplified nomenclature, examples include *iso*-C15:0, *antiso*-C15:0, and 10-Me-C19:0. An example of a fatty acid with a saturated 3-membered cyclopropane ring would be *cis*-11,12-methy- lene-octadecanoic acid (C19:0cyc11,12).

The primary source of cellular fatty acids is the lipid component of the cell membranes (including phospholipids) or the lipid A component of lipopolysaccharides in Gram-negative bacteria and lipoteichoic acid in Gram-positive bacteria (77). Most bacteria synthesize fatty acids with chain lengths having between 10 and 19 carbon atoms, and those with highest frequency are fatty acids with 16 to 18 carbons. Distinctive properties that allow identification of various microorganisms originate from differences in fatty acid composition, a characteristic that includes fatty acid distribution and quantity. Branched structures predominate in some Gram-positive bacteria, while cyclopropane-containing fatty acids and hydroxy fatty acids are often characteristic of lipopolysaccharides of Gram-negative bacteria. Gram-negative bacteria tend to have a greater proportion of saturated and monounsaturated fatty acids with an even number of carbon atoms than Gram-positive bacteria. The latter usually have a larger proportion of saturated branched-chain fatty acids with an odd number of carbon atoms and low levels of saturated straight-chain fatty acids.

With the advent of long fused silica capillary columns, the application of GC to the determination of cellular FAMEs has become more widely used since the 1980s. An automated commercial system, Microbial Identification System (MIS) (79), that applies a GC procedure with flame ionization detection (FID) and multivariate analysis to the profiling of fatty acids ranging in length from 9 to 20 carbon atoms has been used increasingly by research, government, and commercial laboratories because it offers a FAME database for more than 2000 bacteria. The generally recommended GC-FID procedure (79) is outlined below. GC procedures have been widely used to identify bacterial species and strains primarily from clinical, environmental, plant, and soil, but only to a limited extent from food matrices (80).

A full understanding of this chemical type of bacterial identification requires that analysts and researchers in different disciplines collaborate and/or acquire expertise in all three microbiological (bacterial growth), chemical/analytical (GC), and biometric/chemometric (multivariate analysis) techniques.

B. MICROBIOLOGICAL, GC-FID, AND MULTIVARIATE PROCEDURES

The analytical chemistry of bacterial identification depends on the comparison of the chemical composition of whole cells or their constituents (such as lipids or carbohydrates) that exhibit differences in microbiological characteristics. For the analysis to be reproducible, the various species and strains must be grown strictly under identical conditions to minimize variability.

Before any "fingerprinting" procedures can be used to analyze bacterial samples, the microorganisms must be cultured in order to produce sufficient biomass (*ca.* 40 mg) (79) for GC-FID analysis.

The accurate identification of unknown bacteria using a particular FAME database requires the use of microbiological conditions identical to those used to create that database. These conditions are primarily the temperature used in the cultivation of bacteria, the age of the culture, and the nature of the growth medium (79). It has been well documented (81) that differences in these factors will lead to large variations in the lipid content and composition of bacteria. Most aerobic bacteria are grown on trypticase soy broth agar (TSBA) medium that consists of 30 g trypticase soy broth and 15 g agar. Other common media are also used for aerobic bacteria and depend on the nature of the organism investigated. A temperature of 28°C would allow the growth of a wide range of microorganisms on TSBA. For anaerobic bacteria, agar cultures are grown at 35°C on brain heart infusion (BHI) with supplements. To minimize variability due to

age, broth cultures are harvested at a given turbidity, and plate cultures are grown for 24 (aerobes) or 48 hours (anaerobes). Longer incubation times may be used for slow-growing bacteria. Approximately 40 mg of the bacterial cells are needed per test sample. For plate cultures, the physiological age is usually standardized by selecting a particular sector from a quadrant-streaked plate. Bacterial colonies are harvested with a 4-mm loop (or spatula) from the third quadrant. For a slow-growing organism, other quadrants may be used. Oftentimes, more than one quadrant must be harvested to collect as much as 40 mg. The weighed cells are placed in a culture tube with a teflon-lined screw cap and their membranes are prepared for GC analysis.

The preparation of FAMEs from cellular membranes for GC analysis involves several steps that include saponification, methylation, and extraction (79,80). Lipids from approximately 40 mg (79) of bacterial cells are first saponified with 1 mL of a sodium hydroxide (NaOH) solution prepared from 45 mg NaOH, 150 mL H_2O, and 150 mL methanol. Tubes containing bacterial cells and NaOH solution are securely capped, vortexed for 5–10 sec, heated in a boiling water bath for approximately 5 min, vortexed for 5–10 sec again, and returned to the water bath for 25 min. The tubes are allowed to cool down to room temperature and the fatty acids are methylated with 2 mL of an acidic methanol stock solution prepared from 6N HCl (325 mL) and methanol (275 mL). The tubes are vortexed for 5–10 sec, recapped, carefully heated at 80°C $\pm$ 1°C for 10 $\pm$ 1 min, and rapidly cooled. The resulting FAMEs are poorly soluble in the aqueous phase and are extracted with 3 ml of a 1:1 solution of hexane:*tert*-butyl ether by gently shaking the tubes for 10 min. The lower aqueous phase is pipetted out and discarded. Sample clean up consists of washing the remaining organic phase with 3 mL NaOH solution prepared from 10.8 g NaOH in 900 mL H_2O. This is carried out by gently shaking the recapped tubes for 5 min. Two-thirds of the top organic phase is pipetted into a GC vial that is capped and saved for subsequent GC analysis.

The remaining analytical steps include computer-controlled automation (79). A GC autosampler allows test samples to be chromatographed unattended. GC separation is usually carried out on a 25-m and 0.2-mm-ID phenyl methyl silicone fused silica capillary column. A temperature program that consists of ramping the temperature from 170°C to 270°C at 5°C/min is followed. GC peaks are electronically integrated and fatty acid composition data are stored. GC-FID profiles of FAME test samples are compared to those in the MIDI commercial databases and analyzed by proprietary pattern recognition algorithms. Multivariate algorithms apply statistical techniques to reduce the dimensionality of multivariate data while preserving most of the variance (82).

C. Application of GC-FID Methodology to Foodborne Pathogens

While the vast majority of GC studies involve the identification of clinical, environmental, and other microorganisms (83–86), there is a paucity of publications on the analysis of fatty acid GC profiles of foodborne pathogens (87).

In a validation study (87), the performance of the GC-FID-based MIS was compared to four other commercially available automated microbial identification systems. These four microbial identification systems are based on substrate utilization and bacterial growth; these processes lead to changes in pH, which in turn trigger changes in the color of indicators. All five systems were evaluated for their ability to identify six of the most common foodborne pathogens. The sensitivities, specificities, and repeatabilities of the MIS, the MicroScan WalkAway 40 system (Dade Diagnostics Corp., Mississauga, Ontario, Canada), the MicroLog system (Biolog, Inc., Hayward, CA), the VITEK system (bioMerieux Vitek, Hazelwood, MO), and the Replianalyzer system (Oxoid Inc., Nepean, Ontario, Canada) were tested by identifying food isolates of *Bacillus cereus, Campylobacter jejuni, Listeria monocytogenes, Staphylococcus aureus, Salmonella* spp., and verotoxigenic *Escherichia coli* (VTEC).

In the GC validation study by Odumeru et al. (87), 40 reference positive isolates (RPIs) and 40 reference negative isolates (RNIs) of these six microorganisms were used. Of the 40 RPIs, 35 were obtained from food samples and 5 from the American Type Culture Collection (ATCC). Of the 40 RNIs, 5 were ATCC strains, and 35 were cultured from food, clinical, or environmental samples and consisted of laboratory isolates that were related to but not identical to the bacteria of interest; RNIs showed similarities regarding their biochemical reactions and Gram staining results to those of the microorganism of interest. Sensitivity was defined in this study as the proportion of the RPIs that were correctly identified with an acceptable identification confidence level specified by the system's manufacturer. Specificity was determined by the proportion of RNIs that were not identified as the pathogen of interest with an acceptable confidence rating. Repeatability tests consisted of performing replicate analyses for 20 randomly selected ATCC strains and laboratory isolates from the RPIs and RNIs. Repeatability of identification was defined as the proportion of replicate analyses that generated the same result at similar confidence levels.

Odumeru et al. (87) reported that the sensitivities of the five systems used for the identification of microorganisms ranged from 42.5 to 100%. In particular, the sensitivity of the MIS was 90% for *Listeria* spp., 47.5% for *S. aureus*, 55% for *B. cereus*, 72.5% for *C. jejuni*, 85% for *Salmonella* spp., and 52% for *E. coli*. The

authors attributed the lower sensitivities found for some of these pathogens with the MIS to the fact that they were based on fatty acid composition while the reference systems for these species were based on biochemical reactions. The specificities were usually close to 100%; those of the MIS were 100% for *Listeria* spp., 100% for *S. aureus*, 97.5% for *B. cereus*, 32.5% for *C. jejuni*, 100% for *Salmonella* spp., and 97.5% for *E. coli*. The repeatabilities of the MIS for the identification of test organisms were generally lower (30 to 90%) than those of the remaining four systems (60–100%). The repeatability of the MIS for RPIs was 30% for *Listeria monocytogenes*, 60% for *S. aureus*, 90% for *B. cereus*, 90% for *C. jejuni*, 90% for *Salmonella* spp., and 70% for *E. coli*, while the repeatability of the MIS for RNIs was 55% for *Listeria monocytogenes*, 90% for *S. aureus*, 80% for *B. cereus*, 75% for *C. jejuni*, 65% for *Salmonella* spp., and 65% for *E. coli*. According to Odumeru et al. (87), the selection of an automated system for the identification of foodborne bacteria depends on many factors including the nature of the available range of organisms in the system's database and the ability of the system to correctly identify the pathogen of interest.

In a GC-FID application study (88), the sources of *Bacillus cereus* in pasteurized milk were investigated. The MIS was used to determine the incidence and distribution of *B. cereus* vegetative cells and spores in raw and pasteurized milk. The presence of *B. cereus* in pasteurized milk is a concern for the dairy industry because it may lead to off-flavors, sweet curdling, and even outbreaks of food poisoning. *B. cereus* is a Gram-positive, spore-forming microorganism that can produce toxins in pasteurized milk at refrigeration temperatures. In pasteurized milk, *B. cereus* may originate from spores that are present in the raw milk or from the dairy plant environment.

In the study by Lin et al. (88), a total of 232 milk samples from sampling points along milk processing lines and 122 environmental swabs were collected in two dairy plants over several months. The fatty acid composition of each *B. cereus* isolate was determined by GC-FID. Using MIS, a database of *B. cereus* FAME profiles for 229 *B. cereus* isolates from milk samples and environmental swabs was created and used to determine the relationships between *B. cereus* isolate test samples.

Less than 10% of samples were positive for *B. cereus* vegetative cells in raw milk. The average *B. cereus* count in positive samples was less than 50 cfu per ml after enrichment at 8°C for 3 days. The incidence of *B. cereus* spores in raw milk samples was measured by the presence of *B. cereus* in heat-treated (75°C for 20 min) milk and was found to be very high. Of the heat-treated raw milk samples, more than 80% were found to contain *B. cereus,* and the average *B. cereus* count in positive samples was more than 1.1×10^5 cfu per ml after enrichment at 8°C for 14 days.

In pasteurized milk the incidence of *B. cereus* was high. After enrichment at 8°C for 14 days, 76–94% of these samples were contaminated with *B. cereus* and the average count reached 3.7×10^5 cfu per ml. Of the final products (pasteurized milk in cartons or plastic bags) more than 90% contained *B. cereus* and the average count reached 5.5×10^6 cfu per ml after enrichment. Most *B. cereus* isolates obtained from the pasteurized milk and final products belonged to the same sub-groups as the *B. cereus* strains germinated from spores in raw milk. Therefore, the authors (88) concluded that *B. cereus* spores in raw milk were the major source of *B. cereus* contamination in pasteurized milk.

The environmental swabs contained no *B. cereus* vegetative cells after enrichment at 8°C for 14 days. However, the heat-treated swabs had a low incidence (5%) of *B. cereus,* and the positive ones had a low average count for *B. cereus* of 30 cfu per ml after enrichment at 8°C for 14 days. According to Lin et al. (88), the presence of *B. cereus* in environmental swabs suggested that the dairy plant environment was a potential minor source of *B. cereus* in pasteurized milk.

Sundhein et al. (89) studied the contamination and spoilage of cold-stored chicken carcasses by *Pseudomonas* species. The shelflife of fish, red meat, and poultry in air is limited due to the presence of psychrotrophic pseudomonads that cause the formation of slime and production of off-odors. GC-FID traces of cellular FAMEs were analyzed by the MIS and used as an effective complementary technique to carbon source assimilation tests for the identification of pseudomonads from fresh and chill-stored chicken carcasses. Hundreds of bacterial strains were isolated from 18 chicken carcasses and based on results of carbon assimilation tests they were assigned to one of 17 defined groups of chicken pseudomonads. Isolates that had carbon assimilation patterns that could not be matched to any known species exhibited FAME profiles that corresponded to *P. fluorescens, P. lundensis* or *P. fragi*. The *P. fluorescens* biovars had greater levels of *cis* 9–16:1 (21–37%) and *cis* 9–18:1 (10–19%) relative to those of 17:0 cyclo (1–17%) and 19:0 cyclo (0–1%), while the opposite was found for *P. lundensis* and *P. fragi*. The authors concluded that none of the species was dominant and that the relative incidence of the various species may vary with flock or even individual birds.

D. OPTIMIZATION OF ANALYTICAL METHODOLOGIES

In research facilities, scientists have introduced minor refinements or major modifications to GC-FID analytical procedures, have added to existing commercial databases or created their own databases, and have applied and compared different analytical methodologies and pattern recognition algorithms.

A major drawback of using GC-based methods for fatty acid profiling is the requirement of laborious fatty acid derivatization procedures. To eliminate this manual step, researchers have used supercritical fluid derivatization/extraction and GC-MS (90), *in situ* thermal hydrolysis methylation (THM)-GC-MS (91), and *in situ* THM-MS (72) for the determination of cellular FAMEs. With *in situ* THM-MS, the 60-min extraction/methylation and the 20-min GC separation steps are eliminated, and this approach may potentially be amenable to rapid, single-step, automated analysis (72).

Muller et al. (86) used trimethylsulfonium hydroxide (TMSH) pyrolysis to complement the MIS procedure for the identification of FAMEs. This optimized TMSH procedure was used to transesterify bound fatty acids in phospholipids and triacylglycerol molecules to FAMEs in a rapid single step that can be carried out at room temperature. This reaction also released secondary alcohols and, for mycobacteria, mycolic acid cleavage products with chain lengths of C22 to C26 that were also amenable to GC-FID analysis. A pyrolysis-GC-atomic emission procedure (92) has also been used for identification of microorganisms.

Alternatively, the carbohydrate composition of bacterial cell hydrolysates may be analyzed by using a fully automated alditol acetate derivatization procedure and GC-MS and GC-MS-MS (78).

Selective detectors that require sophisticated instrumentation such as GC-MS/MS have provided high specificity and sensitivity in detecting trace amounts of chemical markers from clinical and environmental bacterial samples (78). However, the profiling of cellular fatty acids from vegetative cells and spores by GC-FID has been a more widely used analytical procedure (88,93). No single technique is suitable for all applications, and the full potential of analytical microbiological methodologies has yet to be reached.

REFERENCES

1. SJ Lehotay and J Hajslova. Application of gas chromatography in food analysis. Trends Anal Chem 21:686–697, 2002.
2. MM van Deursen, J Beens, HG Jansen, PA Leclercq, CA Cramers. Evaluation of time-of-flight mass spectrometric detection for fast gas chromatography. J Chromatogr A 878:205–213, 2000.
3. J Cochran. Fast gas chromatography-time-of-flight mass spectrometry of polychlorinated biphenyls and other environmental contaminants. J Chromatogr Sci 40:254–268, 2000.
4. J Dalluge, M van Rijn, J Beens, RJJ Vreuls, UA Th Brinkman. Comprehensive two-dimensional gas chromatography with time-of-flight mass spectrometric detection applied to the determination of pesticides in food extracts. J Chromatogr A 965:207–217, 2002.

5. J de Zeeuw, J Peene, HG Janssen, X Lou. A simple way to speed up separations by GC-MS using short 0.53 mm columns and vacuum outlet conditions. J High Res Chromatogr 23:677, 2000.

6. K Mastovska, SJ Lehotay, S Hajslova. Optimization and evaluation of low-pressure gas chromatography-mass spectrometry for the fast analysis of multiple pesticide residues in a food commodity. J Chromatogr A 926:291–308, 2001.

7. PA Leclercq, CA Cramers. High-speed GC-MS. Mass Spectrom Rev 17:37–49, 1998.

8. M Kochman, A Gordin, P Goldshlag, SJ Lehotay, A Amirav. Fast, high-sensitivity, multipesticide analysis of complex mixtures with supersonic gas chromatography-mass spectrometry. J Chromatogr A 974:185–212, 2002.

9. A Amirav, S Dagan, T Shahar, N Tzanani, SB Wainhaus. In EJ Karjalainen, Ed. Advances in Mass Spectrometry, Vol. 14. Amsterdam: Elsevier, 1998, 529–562.

10. A Dagan, A Amirav. Fast GC-MS. Int J Mass Spectrom Ion Process 133:187, 1994.

11. MJE Golay. Theory and practice of gas-liquid partition chromatography with coated capillaries. In VJ Coates, HJ Noebles, IS Ferguson, Eds. Gas Chromatography. New York: Academic Press, 1958, 1–13.

12. DH Detsy, A Goldup, WT Swanton. In N Brenner, JE Callen, MD Weis, Eds. Gas Chromatography. New York: Academic Press, 1962, 105.

13. RD Dandeneau, EH Zerenner. An investigation of glasses for capillary chromatography. J High Resol Chromatogr Chromatogr Commun 2:351–356, 1979.

14. MS Klee, LM Blumberg. Theoretical and practical aspects of fast gas chromatography and method translation. J Chromatogr Sci 40:234–247, 2002.

15. R Sacks, H Smith, M Nowak. High-speed gas chromatography. Anal Chem 70(1):29A–37A, 1998.

16. GA Eiceman. Instrumentation of gas chromatography. In RA Meyers, Ed. Encyclopedia of Analytical Chemistry. Chichester: John Wiley & Sons, 2000, 1–9.

17. S Dagan, A Amirav. Fast, very fast, and ultra-fast gas chromatography-mass spectrometry of thermally labile steroids, carbamates, and drugs in supersonic molecular beams. J Am Soc Mass Spectrom 7:737–752, 1996.

18. JV Hinshaw. How fast is fast enough. LCGC 19(2):170–177, 2001.

19. CA Cramers, PA Leclercq. Consideration on speed of separation, detection, and identification limits in capillary GC and GC/MS. CRC Crit Rev Anal Chem 20(2):117–147, 1988.

20. G Gaspar. High-speed gas chromatography: theoretical and practical aspects. J Chromatogr 556:331–351, 1991.

21. A van Es. High Speed Narrow Bore Capillary Gas Chromatography. Heidelberg: Huthig, 1992.

22. P Korytar, H-G Janssen, E Matisova, UAT Brinkman. Practical fast gas chromatography: methods, instrumentation and applications. Trends Anal Chem 21(9,10):558–572, 2002.

23. C PM Schutjes, EA Vermeer, JA Rijks, CA Cramers. Increased speed of analysis in isothermal and temperature-programmed capillary gas chromatography by reduction of the column inner diameter. J Chromatogr 253:1–16, 1982.

24. L Wool, D Decker. Practical fast gas chromatography for contract laboratory program pesticide analysis. J Chromatogr Sci 40:434–440, 2002.

25. CA Cramers, PA Leclercq. Strategies for speed optimization in gas chromatography: an overview. J Chromatogr Sci 40:434–440, 2002.

26. CA Cramers, GJ Scherpenzeel, PA Leclercq. Increased speed of analysis in directly coupled gas chromatography-mass spectrometry systems. Capillary columns at sub-atmospheric outlet pressures. J Chromatogr 203:201–216, 1981.

27. LM Blumberg. Theory of fast capillary gas chromatography. Part 1: column efficiency. J High Resol Chromatogr 20:597–604, 1997.

28. LM Blumberg. Theory of fast capillary gas chromatography. Part 2: speed of analysis. J High Resol Chromatogr 20:679–687, 1997.

29. LM Blumberg. Theory of fast capillary gas chromatography. Part 3: column performance vs gas flow rate. J High Resol Chromatogr 22:403–413, 1999.

30. M VanDuersen, J Beens, CA Cramers, H-G Janssen. Possible limitations of fast temperature programming as a route toward fast GC. J High Resol Chromatogr 22(9):509–513, 1999.

31. A van Es, J Janssen, C Cramers, J Rijks. Sample enrichment in high speed narrow bore capillary gas chromatography. J High Resol Chromatogr Chrom Commun 11:853–857, 1988.

32. BA Ewels, RD Sacks. Electrically heated cold trap inlet system for high-speed gas chromatography. Anal Chem 57(14):2774–2779, 1985.

33. AJ Borderding, CW Wilkerson. A comparison of cryofocusing injectors for gas sampling and analysis in fast GC. Anal Chem 68(17):2874–2878, 1996.

34. SW Lloyd, CC Grimm. Fast temperature programmed gas chromatography—mass spectrometry for food analysis. J Chromatogr Sci 40:309–314, 2002.

35. M Wu, Z Liu, PB Farnsworth, ML Lee. Comprehensive supercritical fluid extraction/gas chromatographic analysis of organic compounds in soil matrices with an element-selective radiofrequency plasma detector. Anal Chem 65(17):2185–2188, 1993.

36. K Mastovska, J Hajslova, M Godula, J Krivankova, V Kocourek. Fast temperature programming in routine analysis of multiple pesticide redidues in food matrices. J Chromatogr A 907:235–245, 2001.

37. TL Chen, JG Phillips, W Durr. Analysis of residual solvents by fast chromatography. J Chromatogr A 811:145–150, 1998.

38. TP McNeal, HC Hollifield. Determination of volatile chemicals released from microwave-heat-susceptor food packaging. J AOAC Int 76(6):1268–1275, 1993.

39. TP McNeal, PJ Nyman, GW Diachenko, HC Hollifield. Survey of benzene in foods by using headspace concentration techniques and capillary gas chromatography. J AOAC Int 76(6):1213–1219, 1993.

40. TP McNeal, HC Hollifield, GW Diachenko. Survey of trihalomethanes and other volatile chemical contaminants

in processed foods by purge-and-trap capillary gas chromatography with mass selective detection. J AOAC Int 78(2):391–397, 1995.

41. FC-Y Wang, AD Burleson. The development of pyrolysis-fast gas chromatography for analysis of synthetic polymers. J Chromatogr A 833:111–119, 1999.

42. FC-Y Wang, B Gerhart, CG Smith. Pyrolysis with a solvent trapping technique. Qualitative identification of acrylic acid and methacrylic acid in emulsion polymers. Anal Chem 67(20):3681–3686, 1995.

43. TH Begley, ML Gay, HC Hollifield. Determination of migrants in and migration from nylon food packaging. Food Addit Contam 12(5):671–676, 1995.

44. JE Biles, TP McNeal, TH Begley, HC Hollifield. Determination of Bisphenol-A in reusable polycarbonate food-contact plastics and migration to food-simulating liquids. J Agric Food Chem 45(9):3541–3544, 1997.

45. GL Reed, K Clark-Baker, HM McNair. Fast gas chromatography of various sample types using fast oven temperature programming. J Chromatogr Sci 37:300–305, 1999.

46. P Sandra, F David. High-throughput capillary gas chromatography for the determination of polychlorinated biphenyls and fatty acid methyl esters in food samples. J Chromatogr Sci 40:248–253, 2002.

47. F David, DR Gere, F Scanlan, P Sandra. Instrumentation and applications of fast high-resolution capillary gas chromatography. J Chromatogr A 842:309–319, 1999.

48. JJ Ryan, HBS Conacher, LG Panopio, B P-Y Lau, JA Hardy. Gas chromatographic separations of all 136 tetra to octa-polychlorinated dibenzo-p-dioxins and polychlorinated dibenzofurans on nine different stationary phases. J Chromatogr A 541:131–183, 1991.

49. D Fraisse, O Paisse, HI Nguyen, M.F Gonnord. Improvements in GC/MS Strategies and methodologies for PCDD and PCDF analysis. Fresenius J Anal Chem 348:154–158, 1994.

50. JH Garrett, TO Tiernan, JG Solch, GF VanNess, FL Rukunda, RK Gilpin. GC columns for the determination of specific polychlorinated biphenyl (PCB) congeners in environmental samples using U.S. EPA method 1668. Organohalogen Compounds 45:21–24, 2000.

51. U Jarnberg, L Asplund, E Jakobsson. Gas chromatographic retention behavior of polychlorinated naphthalenes on non-polar, polarizable, polar and smectic capillary columns. J Chromatogr A 683:385–396, 1994.

52. PA Helm, LMM Jantunen, TF Bidleman, FL Dorman. Complete separation of isomeric penta- and hexa-chloronaphthalenes by capillary gas chromatography. J High Resol Chromatogr 22:639–693, 1999.

53. DG Hayward, K Hooper, D Andrzejewski. Tandem-in-time mass spectrometry method for the sub-parts-per-trillion determination of 2,3,7,8-chlorine-substituted dibenzo-p-dioxins and –furans in high-fat foods. Anal Chem 71:212–220, 1999.

54. DG Hayward. Quadrupole Ion Storage Tandem Mass Spectrometry Application to the Analysis of all 2,3,7,8 substituted Chlorodibenzo-p-dioxins (dioxins) and Chlorodibenzofurans (furans) in Fruits, Vegetables, Beverages, High Sugar Foods, Pastas, Breads and Grains. Laboratory Information Bulletin No. 4203, Division of Food Science, Office of Regulatory Affairs, US Food and Drug Administration. Rockville, MD: US Food and Drug Administration, 2000.

55. KA MacPherson, R Brunato, T Chen, MA Bogard, EJ Reiner. Optimization of gas chlromatographic parameters for reduced analysis times of chlorinated organic compounds. Organohalogen Compounds 40:19–22, 1999.

56. EJ Reiner, KA MacPherson, R Brunato, T Chen, MA Bogard, AR Boden, G Ladwig. Analysis of persistent organic pollutants (POPS) using microbore columns. Organohalogen Compounds 45:17–20, 2000.

57. KA MacPherson, EJ Reiner, TM Kolie. Dual microbore column GC/HRMS analysis of polychlorinated dibenzo-p-dioxins (PCDDs), polychlorinated dibenzo-furans (PCDFs) and dioxin-like polychlorinated biphenyls (DLPCBs). Organohalogen Compounds 50:40–44, 2001.

58. K Worrall, E Aries, D Anderson, A Newton, R Rao. Method for the simultaneous analysis of PCDD/Fs and DLPCBs using dual microbore column GC/HRMS in sinter ash samples, allowing the determination of "totals" group concentrations. Organohalogen Compounds 55:171–174, 2002.

59. J-MD Dimandja, J Grainger, DG Patterson Jr. New fast single and multidimensional gas chromatography separations coupled with high resolution mass spectrometry and time-of-flight mass spectrometry for assessing human exposure to environmental toxicants. Organohalogen Compounds 40:23–26, 1999.

60. J-F Focant, E De Pauw, J Grainger, DG Patterson Jr., J-MD Dimandja. Time-compressed analysis of PCBs and persistent pesticides in biological samples by isotopic dilution gas chromatography/time-of-flight mass spectrometry. Organohalogen Compounds 50:25–28, 2001.

61. JC Giddings. Concepts and comparisons in multi-dimensional separation. J High Resol Chrom Comm 10:319–323, 1987.

62. Z Liu, JB Phillips. Comprehensive two-dimensional gas chromatography using an on-column thermal modulator interface. J Chromatogr Sci 29:227–231, 1991.

63. Z Liu, SR Sirmanne, DG Patterson, Jr., LL Needham, JB Phillips. Comprehensive two-dimensional gas chromatography for the fast separation and determination of pesticides extracted from human serum. Anal Chem 66:3086–3092, 1994.

64. R Vreuls, M Kristenson, UAT Brinkman, C Danielson, P Haglund, P Korytár, PEG Leonards, J de Boer. Modulator selection for comprehensive multi-dimensional GC of dioxins and PCBs. Organohalogen Compounds 55:127–130, 2001.

65. PS Mead, L Slutsker, V Dietz. Food-related illness and death in the U.S. Emerg Infect Dis 5:607–625, 1999.

66. CDC. Preliminary FoodNet Data on the incidence of foodborne illnesses—selected sites, U.S. 2001. MMWR Weekly 51(15):325–329, 2002.

67. JR Jordan. Analyzing bioterrorism. Inside Laboratory Management, AOAC International Jan/Feb 19–23, 2002.

68. K Maquelin, C Kirschner, L Choo-Smith, N van den Braak, H Endtz, D Naumann, G Puppels. Identification of medically relevant microorganisms by vibrational spectroscopy. J Microbiol Meth 51:255–271, 2002.

69. MM Mossoba, FM Khambaty, FS Fry. Novel application of a disposable optical film to the analysis of bacterial strains. A chemometric classification of mid-infrared spectra. Appl Spect 56:732–736, 2001.

70. MM Mossoba, SF Al-Khaldi, A Jacobson, LI Segarra Crowe, FS Fry. Application of a disposable transparent filtration membrane to the infrared spectroscopic discrimination among bacterial species. J Microbiol Meth 55:311–314, 2003.

71. R Goodacre, B Shann, RJ Gilbert, E Timmins, AC McGovern, BK Alsberg, DB Kell. Detection of the dipiclonic acid biomarker in Bacillus spores using curie-point pyrolysis mass spectrometry and Fourier transform infrared spectroscopy. Anal Chem 72:119–127, 2000.

72. M Xu, KJ Voorhees, TL Hadfield. Repeatability and pattern recognition of bacterial fatty acid profiles generated by direct mass spectrometric analysis of in situ thermal hydrolysis/methylation of whole cells. Talanta 59(3):577–589, 2003.

73. AT James. Qualitative and quantitative determination of the fatty acids by gas-liquid chromatography. Meth Biochem Anal 8:1–59, 1960.

74. K Abel, H deDchmerting, JI Peterson. Classification of microorganisms by analysis of chemical composition. I. Feasibility of utilizing gas chromatography. J Bacteriol 85:1039–1044, 1963.

75. I Brondz, I Olsen, M Sjostrom. Multivariate analysis of quantitative chemical and enzymatic characterization data in classification of Actinobacillus Haemophilus and Pasteurella spp. J Gen Microbiol 136:507–513, 1990.

76. I Brondz, J Carlsson, M Sjostrom, G Sundquist. Significance of cellular fatty acids and sugars in defining the genus Porphyromonas. Int J Syst Bacteriol 39(3):314–318, 1989.

77. DF Welch. Applications of cellular fatty acid analysis. Clin Microbiol Rev 4(4):422–438, 1991.

78. A Fox. Carbohydrate profiling of bacteria by gas chromatography-mass spectrometry and their trace detection in complex matrices by gas chromatography-tandem mass spectrometry. J Chrom A 843:287–300, 1999.

79. M Sasser, Identification of bacteria by gas chromatography of cellular fatty acids. MIDI Technical Note #101. Newark, DE: MIDI Inc., May 1990, Revised Feb 1997.

80. I Brondz. Development of fatty acid analysis by high-performance liquid chromatography, gas chromatography, and related techniques. Anal Chim Acta 465:1–37, 2002.

81. J Asselineau. The Bacterial Lipids (Chemistry of Natural Products series, E Lederer, ed.). San Francisco, CA: Holden-Day, 1966.

82. B Kowalski. Chemometrics: Mathematics in Statistics and Chemistry. In NATO, Vol 138. Series C. Mathematical and Physical Sciences. Boston, MA: D. Reidel Publishing Co., 1983, 479 pp.

83. C Dees, D Ringelberg, TC Scott, TJ Phelps. Characterization of the cellulose-degrading bacterium NCIMB 10462. Appl Biochem Biotechnol 51(2):263–274, 1995.

84. A Vongraevenitz, V Punter, E Gruner, GE Pfyffer, G Funke. Identification of coryneform and other Gram-positive rods with several methods. APMIS 102(5):381–389, 1994.

85. YW Tang, NM Ellis, MK Hopkins, DH Smith, DE Dodge, Comparison of phenotypic and genotypic techniques for identification of unusual aerobic pathogenic Gram-negative bacilli DH Persing. J Clin Microbiol 36(12):3674–3679, 1998.

86. KD Muller, EN Schmid, RM Kroppenstedt. Improved identification of mycobacteria by using the microbial identification system in combination with additional trimethylsulfonium hydroxide pyrolysis. J Clin Microbiol 36(9):2477–2480, 1998.

87. JA Odumeru, M Steele, L Fruhner, C Larkin, J Jiang, E Mann, WB McNab. Evaluation of accuracy and repeatability of identification of food-borne pathogens by automated bacterial identification systems. J Clin Microbiol 37(4):944–949, 1999.

88. S Lin, H Scraft, JA Odumeru, MW Griffiths. Identification of contamination sources of Bacillus cereus in pasteurized milk. Int J Food Microbiol 43:159–171, 1998.

89. G Sundheim, A Sletten, RH Dainty. Identification of pseudomonads from fresh and chill-stored chicken carcasses. Int J Food Microbiol 39:185–194, 1998.

90. AA Ghoraibeh, KJ Voorhees. Characterization of lipid fatty acids in whole-cell microorganisms using in situ supercritical fluid derivatization/extraction and gas chromatography/mass spectrometry. Anal Chem 68:2805–2810, 1996.

91. JP Dworzanski, L Berwald, HL Meuzelaar. Pyrolytic methylation-GC of whole bacterial cells for rapid profiling of cellular fatty acids. Appl Environ Microbiol 56:1717–1724, 1990.

92. S Voisin, FNR Renaud, J Freney, M de Montclos, R Boulier, D Derauz. Pyrolysis-gas-liquid chromatography with atomic emission detection for the identification of Corynebacterium species. J Chrom A 863:243–248, 1999.

93. Y Song, R Yang, Z Guo, M Zhang, X Wang, F Zhou. Distinctness of spore and vegetative cellular fatty acid profiles of some aerobic endospore-forming bacilli. J Microbiol Meth 39:225–241, 2000.

94. UG Ahlborg, GC Becking, LS Birnbaum, A Brouwer, HJGM Derks, M Feeley, G Golor, A Hanberg, JC Larsen, AKD Liem, SH Safe, C Schlatter, F Waern, M Younes, E Yrjänheikki. Toxic equivalency factors for dioxin-like PCBs. Chemosphere 28:1049–1067, 1994.

95. United States Environmental Protection Agency, National Study of Chemical Residues in Fish, Volume 2. Office of Science and Technology (WH-551) Washington, D.C., EPA 823-r-92–008b.

96. A Hanberg, F Wern, L Asplund, E Haglund, S Safe. Swedish dioxin survey: determination of 2,3,7,8-TCDD

toxic equivalent factors for some polychlorinated biphenyls and naphthalenes using biological tests. Chemosphere 20:1161–1164, 1990.

97. DA Holmes, BK Harrison, J Dolfing. Estimation of Gibbs free energies of formation for polychlorinated biphenyls. Environ Sci and Technol 27:725–731, 1993.

98. A Covaci, J de Boer, JJ Ryan, S Voorspoels, P Schepens. Determination of polybrominated diphenyl ethers and polychlorinated dephenyls in human adipose tissue by large-volume injection-narrow-bore capillary gas chromatography/electron impact low-resolution mass spectrometry. Anal Chem 74:790–798, 2002.

46 Modern Thin-Layer Chromatography in Food Analysis

Bernd Spangenberg
Umweltanalytik Fachhochschule Offenburg

CONTENTS

I. INTRODUCTION

Thin-layer chromatography (TLC) is a well-established and widely used separation technique. Most undergraduate students of chemistry or food science used TLC as a primitive separation tool, which does not need more than small pieces of TLC plates, a glass jar and some solvents. TLC has evolved from a simple separation method of the past into an instrumental technique that offers automation, reproducibility and accurate quantification for a wide variety of applications [1]. The use of modern 10*10 cm TLC plates with narrow particle size distribution is called high performance thin layer chromatography (HPTLC), to distinguish the method from the use of traditional 20 × 20 cm TLC plates.

Numerous applications of TLC in the areas of food analysis, especially food composition, artificial additives, and contaminants have been reported. An excellent overview of modern thin layer chromatography is given by C. F. Poole [1,2], Sz. Nyiredy [3], J. Sherma and B. Fried [4], and also by N. Grinberg [5]. TLC analysis methods of agricultural products, foods, beverages, and plant constituents is comprehensively reviewed by J. Sherma for the period 1995–2000 [6].

There is strong competition among the different separation systems in food analysis. Widely used are GC (gas chromatography), IC (ion chromatography), and CE (capillary electrophoreses). HPLC (high performance liquid chromatography), which is often called the direct competitor of TLC [7], is especially common. The question here is not whether we need TLC beside HPLC but whether it is necessary to discuss how far thin-layer chromatography can be employed as a pilot technique. It is important to determine to what extent TLC can be used for optimization of separation selectivity. New developments show that TLC is not obsolete but has its niche in separation science and that niche is even still expanding. In this sense TLC and HPLC are competitors (S. Ebel from [7]).

II. THEORY OF TLC

HPLC and TLC separations are similar because nearly identical stationary and mobile phases are used. In HPLC reversed phase separations are preferred whereas in TLC the normal phase conditions dominate (the mobile phase is more lipophilic than the stationary phase). TLC has often been used as a pilot method for HPLC because TLC with various mobile phases can be performed much faster. Thin-layer chromatography in general has the advantage of higher sample throughput by performing separation in parallel. TLC can handle cruder extracts than column techniques because the separation medium is used only once. The experience of the analyst is important in TLC separations because some steps have to be performed by hand. HPLC, in contrast, is fully automated with regard to the sample application, separation, and detection. But nevertheless, pre-cleaning of the analyte is mostly done by hand.

There are principal differences in TLC compared to commonly used column techniques like HPLC, GC, CE, or IC. In all the column techniques mobile and stationary phases have to be in equilibrium conditions before samples are injected. In TLC the sample is applied on the dry plate before the solvent contact starts the separation. It is worth noting that the solvent used in TLC is not identical with the mobile phase of the separation. The mobile phase arises from the equilibrium formation between solvent and TLC plate. When a plate is immersed under capillary flow-controlled conditions in a tank containing a few milliliters of the solvent, the distance moved by the solvent front z_f is related to time by the following equation:

$$z_f = \sqrt{\chi t} \tag{46.1}$$

$$\chi = 2k_0 d_b \frac{\gamma}{\eta} \cos\delta \tag{46.2}$$

t = separation time
χ = velocity constant
k_0 = permeability constant
d_b = particle diameter
γ = surface tension
η = viscosity of the solvent
δ = contact angle

To increase layer efficiency, high performance thin layer plates have been commercially available since the mid-1970s. The layers of these plates consist of fine particles with a very narrow particle distribution [8]. Assuming a narrow particle-size distribution, the velocity constant increases linearly with the average particle size. For coarse-particle layers of TLC plates the solvent front velocity is greater than for HPTLC layers. The velocity of the solvent front depends linearly on the ratio of surface tension and viscosity of the mobile phase. Although for silica gel layers the contact angle of all common solvents is close to zero, for reversed-phase layers containing bonded lipophilic groups the contact angle of the solvent increases rapidly with increasing water content of the mobile phase and $\cos(\delta)$ will become very small, even zero. In this case the solvent is virtually unable to ascend the plate surface.

The nature of the sorbents, which is fixed as a layer of 100 μm to 250 μm thickness on glass, aluminum, or plastic plates, crucially influences the kind of separation. In TLC

mainly strong polar sorbents like silica gel or Al_2O_3 are used. These sorbents have active centers, where sample molecules can be reversibly fixed. During the separation, an equilibrium is established between sample molecules, active centers of the stationary phase, and the solvent. If molecules remain primary in the stationary phase, they will move less than molecules staying mainly in the mobile phase.

The definition of the relative spot movement in comparison to the movement of the solvent front is given by the following formula:

$$R_f = \frac{z_S}{z_f - z_0} \tag{46.3}$$

R_f = retardation factor
z_S = movement distance of the sample spot
z_f = movement distance of the solvent front
z_0 = difference between starting position of solvent and spot

Two extreme situations are possible. If the sample does not pass into the mobile phase, it will not move. The R_f-value of this sample will be $R_f = 0$. If the sample stays constantly in the mobile phase, it will move with the solvent front and will not have any interchange with the stationary phase. In this case the R_f-value will be 1. It is obvious that a sample spending the same time adsorbed at the stationary phase as dissolved in the mobile phase will show an R_f-value of 0.5. If k is the equilibrium factor (often call the capacity factor), which represents the distribution probability between stationary and mobile phase, the expression (1) is valid.

$$R_f = \frac{m_m}{m_s + m_m} = \frac{1}{k+1} \tag{46.4}$$

m_s = mass of sample in the stationary phase
m_m = mass of sample in the mobile phase
k = capacity factor

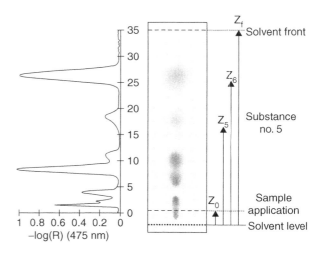

FIGURE 46.1 Separation of a dye mixture (CAMAG dye III, Switzerland) with densitogram (left).

If a sample stays at the point of application, obviously no separation can have taken place. The same situation is valid when all samples move with the solvent front. A sample separation is only possible if the samples change phases to different extents. In formulas, the appropriate k-values of substances must be different for them to separate. Chromatography is a separation technique where molecules can be separated because of their distinctive attraction to mobile and stationary phase. During the time of separation, all molecules in the mobile phase show a randomized diffusion movement. This diffusion causes a gaussian shaped peak with the variance σ_S. Diffusion effects are responsible for peak-broadening, which can be described with the following expression:

$$N' = \left(\frac{z_S - z_0}{\sigma_S} \right)^2 = NR_f' \qquad (46.5)$$

σ_S = variance of the sample spot (peak width)
N' = number of measurable plates
N = number of theoretical plates
R_f' = average R_f-value of all separated substances

The number of theoretical plates (N) is be corrected by an averaged R_f-value of all separated spots, because not all sample spots will, like in column separations, move over the same distance. The product of the theoretical plates number and the averaged R_f-value of all separated substances is a measure for layer efficiency. The basic evidence of the formula is that the squared quotient of the passed distance and the peak width is a constant value for all separated spots.

The baseline width (W_B) of a peak is virtually the spot diameter and this is easy to measure on the plate. In contrast, the peak width at half peak height in a densitogram is much easier to determine than the baseline peak width. The baseline width of a chromatographic peak can be assumed as $W_B = 4\sigma_S$ and the peak width at half peak

height ($W_{1/2}$) is $W_{1/2} = 2.354\sigma_S$. For this, the chromatographic law can be expressed as follows:

$$N' = 16\left(\frac{z_S - z_0}{W_B} \right)^2 = 5.545\left(\frac{z_S - z_0}{W_{1/2}} \right)^2 \qquad (46.6)$$

W_B = baseline peak width
$W_{1/2}$ = peak width at half peak height
N' = number of measurable plates

It is worth mentioning that increasing separation distances are gained proportional to the square root of time. To double the separation distance it needs four-fold time! Unfortunately, diffusion is a matter of time and will increase over-proportionally with increasing distance. This is a definite disadvantage of TLC in comparison to column techniques, where the flow velocity is constant. This disadvantage of planar chromatography strongly affects the separation of two substances. The resolution (R_S) of two neighbourhood peaks is defined as the distance between both peak maximums and the averaged baseline width of the peaks.

$$R_S = \frac{z_{S2} - z_{S1}}{\frac{w_{B1} + w_{B2}}{2}} = 2\frac{z_{S2} - z_{S1}}{w_{B1} + w_{B2}} \qquad (46.7)$$

The resolution can be expressed in terms of capacity factors, the number of effective plates, and the R_f-value.

$$R_S = \frac{1}{4} \sqrt{N'}(1 - R_{f2})\left(\frac{k_1}{k_2} - 1 \right) \qquad (46.8)$$

$N'(1 - R_{f2})^2$ = number of effective plates
R_{f2} = retardation factor of peak 2
k_1, k_2 = capacity factors of peak 1 and peak 2

The change in resolution of two closely migrated spots as a function of different R_f values is shown in Figure 46.3. Resolution increases only by square root of measurable plate number, which is a measure of layer quality and

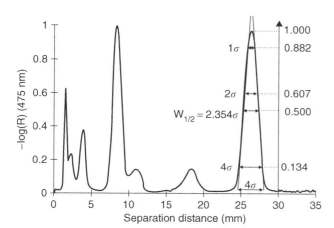

FIGURE 46.2 Gaussian peak of dye no. 6 in a densitogram of several dye spots.

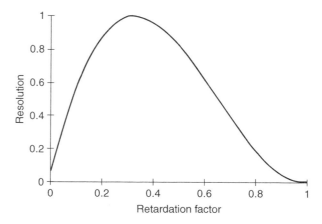

FIGURE 46.3 The plot shows the change in resolution of two peaks, plotted as a function of R_f-values.

efficiency. The influence of peak position on resolution is the opposite behavior to that of the layer quality. At larger values of R_{f2} the term $(1 - R_{f2})$ decreases and in the case of $R_{f2} = 1$ the resolution will become zero [9]. This is reasonable and agrees with the statement that phase changes are essential for separation. Figure 46.3 indicates that a resolution optimum of two closely migrating peaks can be observed at a R_f value of 0.33.

In summary, the selectivity $(k_1/k_2 - 1)$ can easily be increased by a factor of 10 or even 50 by solvent/sorbent changes, while it is difficult to change the layer quality factor $\sqrt{N'}$ by more than 2–3. Therefore, for resolution enhancement it is most rewarding to invest time in solvent optimization and to a lesser extent in sorbent optimization and least in the improvement of layer quality [10].

If the separation system is perfectly chosen, baseline separation of the desired substance can be done even on a few centimeters. In Figure 46.4 the separation of caffeine is shown, separated over a distance of only 11 mm. Samples from coffee, tea, or even strong sugar-containing beverages can be applied without further cleaning steps directly on the plate, after removal of CO_2.

The separation power of TLC or HPTLC plates is normally not sufficient to separate more than ten spots in one run. For the separation of more complicated mixtures, more than one solvent system must be used. However, the planar chromatographic separation power can be increased if a two-dimensional separation mode is used. Several AOAC (Association of Official Analytical Chemistry) methods, for instance, recommend a two-dimensional separation of aflatoxin samples to avoid overlapping spots [80]. For a two-dimensional HPTLC separation, samples have to be spotted at all four edges of a 10×10 cm HPTLC plate and four standards are also spotted on each of the four plate sides exactly between the

sample spots. After simultaneous development from both plate sides to a distance of 45 mm the plate is dried and, after a turn of 90°, developed once again to a distance of 45 mm by use of a different mobile phase. The separation in two directions using different mobile phases extends the TLC separation power dramatically. A separation of a dye mixture in two dimensions is plotted in Figure 46.5.

In Figure 46.5 a dye mixture consisting of six dyes is shown, which can be separated only by two-dimensional separation using different solvent phases. One spot in the two-dimensional separation is not in a rectangular position between the two single separations. This indicates a compound, which changed its chemical property during the separation. Two-dimensional developments can be beneficially used to check sample decomposition during the separation.

III. STATIONARY PHASES

TLC and HPLC plates are commercially available as pre-coated layers supported on glass, plastic sheets, or aluminum foil. The classic TLC plates are 20×20 cm in size whereas the modern HPTLC plates are smaller (10×10 cm or 10×20 cm). Compared with TLC, HPTLC-phases provide better separation efficiency, faster separations over shorter distances, and lower detection limits. In Table 46.1 the parameters of both plate types are listed.

The choice of the layer and the development solvent depends on the nature of the sample. In general, more than 75% of all HPTLC separations are done using silica gel as the stationary phase [5]. Silica gel, silica, or kiesel gel are various names for a polycondensation product of orthosilicic acid. It is prepared from silica solution by precipitation with acids. The improvements of HPTLC-plates are still under development. Macherey-Nagel company (Düren, Germany) developed especially hard and waterproof silica gel plates. These materials are commercially available

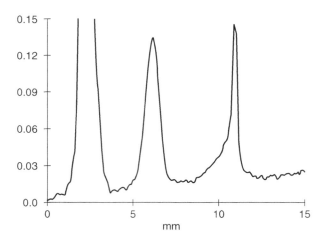

FIGURE 46.4 Plotting the caffeine peak at 6 mm from a well-known sparkling and sugar-containing black beverage. The solvent system isopropanol-cyclohexane-aqueous NH_3 (25%) (7+2+1) has been used in combination with a Si_{60} plate [11].

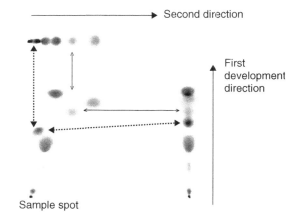

FIGURE 46.5 The plot shows a two-dimensional HPTLC separation of a dye mixture, with two one-dimensional standard separations right and on top.

TABLE 46.1

Comparison of Conventional TLC and Modern HPTLC Parameters

Parameter	TLC	HPTLC
Plate size (cm)	20×20	10×10
Layer thickness (µm)	100–250	100
Particle size (µm)	20	5–15
Sample volume (µl)	1–5	0.1–5
Application distance from plate side (mm)	10–15	5–10
Solvent migration distance (cm)	6–15	3–7
Starting spot diameter (mm)	3–6	1–1.5
Time of development (min)	30–200	3–20
Detection limits in remission (ng)	10–50	5–50
Fluorescence (pg)	500–1000	20–100

under the labels DurasilR and Nano-DurasilR. Merck (Darmstadt, Germany) sells HPTLC-plates with regular, ball-like particles under the name LiChrospher^R. The company claims a shorter developing time and better resolution in comparison to irregular articles. The use of Al_2O_3 as a stationary phase is restricted to mainly pesticide separations. Aluminia and silica gel plates form typical normal phase adsorption systems in retaining substances by active centers of the stationary phase.

Cellulose phases are more often used as aluminia, especially for amino acid separations and basic reacting substances like nucleotides. Polyamides as stationary phases are not often used. This very interesting material is well suited for the separation of acid-reacting substances like phenols, nucleotides, or dansyl derivatives. Bonded phases, based on silica gel, are becoming increasingly important in food analysis. These sorbents are typical for reversed phase separations. HPTLC is mostly performed on chemical bonded C-18, C-8, C-2, C-NH$_2$, C-CN, and C-CHOHCH$_2$OH (diol phase) material. Cellulose and chemical bonded stationary phases are typical materials for distribution chromatography.

The flexibility of planar chromatography is a consequence of the absence of restrictions on the choices of mobile and stationary phases. Usually, TLC and HPTLC plates are obtained from commercial suppliers, but home-made layers are recommended for special purposes. Plates containing silver ions, for example, are able to separate compounds differing only in the position of one double bond [12]. The plates are difficult to store and are made by hand, mostly for research purposes. Other customers prefer home-made plates.

Although TLC is an inexpensive separation method, industrial produced plates must be purchased or may not be available everywhere. In developing countries cost and

availability might be strong reasons to be independent of plate suppliers. A versatile TLC-layer can be made by mixing 27 g of corn starch with 3 g gypsum in 20 mL water and 10 mL ethanol. Nada Perišić-Janjić et al. [13] published the determination of organic acids like malic acid, citric acid, tartaric acid, and ascorbic acid in fruit juice using the solvent mix ethanol-n-butanol-water-conc. ammonia (40+30+15+15) in combination with the TLC-layer just described. A separation of amino acids with the solvent system 2-propanol-formic acid-water (40+2+10) is also possible as well as the separation of fat-soluble vitamins. For the separation of vitamin E and D$_2$ a solvent system containing acetone-conc. acetic acid (3+2) was used. Fructose, glucose, sucrose, and galacturonic acid are perfectly separated with the solvent system n-propanol-benzylalcohol-water-formic acid-dioxan-benzene (10+27+5+4+10+20) and anthocyanins from fresh cherries and cherry juice were separated on this unconventional layer using n-butanol-glacial acid-water-benzene (30+20+10+0.5).

IV. MOBILE PHASES

In planar chromatography the mobile phase is not restricted to a special kind of solvent. This makes it possible to separate a wide range of different analytes using only a single plate layer. In HPLC solvents are restricted to substances with low absorption values because analyte and mobile phase both have to pass the on-line detector. In planar chromatography even strong light absorbing solvents can be used because the mobile phase is removed before plate scanning. Nevertheless carcinogenic substances should be avoided. In the older literature (and even modern methods) benzene is often recommended as a solvent, but in this case toluene should be used.

Sometimes it is necessary to use chlorinated substances like chloroform or CH$_2$Cl$_2$. The leftover solvents should be collected separately to protect the environment. The mobile phase in planar chromatography is commonly chosen by trial and error, guided by literature descriptions of similar separations. On the basis of a sufficient substance movement in the R_f-range between 0.2 and 0.8, fine-tuning of the mobile phase should be done using different solvent mixtures with nearly the same solvent strengths (P'). The solvent strengths of a mixture can be calculated as the sum of the appropriate solvent strengths of the different mixture shares. A change in selectivity can be achieved if solvents with various selectivity parameters (x_e, x_d, x_n) are used. In Table 46.2 the most important solvents for planar chromatography are listed.

To create a new solvent system, one solvent should be tested from at least each selectivity class. While the velocity of the solvent front depends linearly on the ratio of surface tension and viscosity, this quotient should also be taken into account. Small values indicate fast separations, little peak diffusion, and therefore narrow peaks.

TABLE 46.2
Solvent Parameters for Different Solvents (the Values in Brackets Refer to RP Conditions; the Polarity Index (P') Refers to the R_f-Value, Whereas (x_e, x_d, x_n) Influences the Selectivity of a Separation ($+ \gamma/\eta[m/s]$))

Solvent	P'-Value	x_e	x_d	x_n	Group	$\gamma/\eta(25°)^+$
n-Hexane	0.1	–	–	–	0	56
n-Pentane	0.1	–	–	–	0	67
Cyclohexane	0.2	–	–	–	0	28
Dibuthylether	2.1	0.44	0.18	0.38	I	91
Diisopropylether	2.4	0.48	0.14	0.38	I	91
Toluol	2.4	0.25	0.28	0.47	VII	48
Triethylamin	1.9	0.56	0.12	0.32	I	52
Methyl-t-Butylether	2.7	0.49	0.14	0.37	I	72
Diethylether	2.8	0.53	0.13	0.34	I	71
Methylenchlorid	3.1	0.29	0.18	0.53	V	62
1,1-Dichlorethane	3.5	0.30	0.21	0.49	V	41
2-Propanol	3.9	0.55	0.19	0.27	II	8.7
n-Butanol	3.9	0.56	0.19	0.25	II	8.3
THF	4.0 (4.4)	0.38	0.20	0.42	III	56
1-Propanol	4.0	0.54	0.19	0.27	II	11
t-Butanol	4.1	0.56	0.20	0.24	II	7.3
CHCl$_3$	4.1	0.25	0.41	0.34	VIII	47
Ethanol	4.3 (3.6)	0.52	0.19	0.29	II	19
Ethylacetat	4.4	0.34	0.23	0.43	VIa	52
Methylethylketon	4.7	0.35	0.22	0.43	VIa	57
Dioxan	4.8	0.36	0.24	0.40	VIa	26
Chinolin	5.0	0.41	0.23	0.36	III	26
Aceton	5.1 (3.4)	0.35	0.23	0.42	VIa	74
Methanol	5.1 (3.0)	0.48	0.22	0.31	II	38
Pyridin	5.3	0.41	0.22	0.36	III	39
Methoxyethanol	5.5	0.38	0.24	0.38	III	18
Acetonitril	5.8 (3.1)	0.31	0.27	0.42	VIb	75
Acetic acid	6.0	0.39	0.31	0.30	IV	21
DMF	6.4	0.39	0.21	0.40	III	40
Ethylenglycol	6.9	0.43	0.29	0.28	IV	2.3
DMSO	7.2	0.39	0.23	0.39	III	2.4
Formamid	9.6	0.37	0.33	0.30	IV	17
Water	10.2 (0.0)	0.37	0.37	0.25	VIII	73

Sample Pre-Treatments, Application and Plate Development. In food analysis a pre-treatment step prior to separation is usually necessary. The pre-cleaned analyte is then applied on the plate, separated, and either visually detected or scanned by use of appropriate items. The determination of α-solanine and α-chaconine in potatoes is a typical example of a complete HPTLC determination. Solanines are toxic substances because they inhibit cholinesterases and cause gastrointestinal necrosis. An undamaged potato tuber contains 20–150 mg/Kg total solanines. Exposure to light or mechanical damage can increase the content. A routine analytical method to determine solanines is useful [14].

For preparation of potato samples 2 g dehydrated potatoes were extracted with three 15 mL portions of boiling methanol-acetic acid (95+5). The solution is filtered and evaporated under vacuum. The residue is dissolved in 4 mL methanol-acetic acid (99+1). In modern methods very often pre-columns, containing a stationary phase, are used in pre-cleaning. The analyte is accumulated on the stationary phase, cleaned by washing with appropriate solvents, and eluted by a solvent with high solvent strength. This pre-treatment increases the analyte concentration and removes contamination.

The sample application for qualitative purposes is mostly done by use of glass capillaries. If the same capillary is used, even quantitative measurements are possible. Glass capillaries in the size 0.5 μm, 1.0 μm, 2.0 μm, and 5.0 mm are commercially available. The disadvantage of this kind of application is the rather large spot diameter of the starting spots, which restrict the chromatographic resolution. For better resolution an automated application item should be used which is able to bring the sample bandwise on the plate. If a band length of 7 mm is chosen, even 20 µl analyte can be applied on an HPTLC-plate. In general, an automated application is recommended if low measurement uncertainties are desired. Prior to separation the plates should be pre-washed by development at best with the mobile phase. In the case of solanine separation, the authors recommend pre-washing with methanol, pre-equilibration with the separation solvent for 1 h in a twin-trough chamber, and development up to a distance of 85 mm [14]. The separation conditions are very important, especially with respect to the vapor phase to obtain reproductive results [10]. The use of vapor dry chambers without mobile phase pre-equilibration should be avoided, and therefore the use of twin chamber or a linear chamber is recommended. The linear chamber for sandwich developments (Figure 46.6) is ready to use without time-consuming pre-equilibration because the very small vapor volume, in contrast to trough chambers, is responsible for reliable development conditions. If TLC plates are to be used, the separation distance should not be above 15 cm. For HPTLC-plates the separation optimum is 4.5 cm.

After solanine separation the plate is dried and dipped in a modified Carr-Price reagent containing 70 g antimony (III) chloride in 280 mL acetic acid-CH_2Cl_2 (1+3). After dipping the plate is subsequently heated for 5 min at 105°C [14]. One of the most important advantages of planar chromatography is the huge number of different staining systems [15], which makes planar chromatography very specific. The Carr-Price system, for example, reacts most specifically and sensitivly with the double bond of steroids. If staining is recommended, the plate should be automatically dipped for a defined time instead of spraying with reagent because sprayed plates are useless for quantification purposes.

The solanine peaks are quantified by densitometric reflectance measurement at 507 nm. The range of linearity for α-solanine is 100–2000 ng per spot. The limit of detection (LOD) is 50 ng and the limit of quantification (LOQ) is 100 ng. The LOD is the smallest quantity of the target substance that can be detected as peak, but not precisely quantified in the sample. The LOQ is the smallest quantity of the target substance in the sample that can be assayed under experimental conditions with well-defined precision and accuracy. The analytical precision is determined by measuring the repeatability at different concentrations. The repeatability for 5 determinations within 3 days for 500 ng α-solanine is 3.2%. Accuracy is a measure of agreement between a conventionally accepted value or a reference value and a mean experimental value. The extraction recovery for 900 ng α-solanine is calculated to 98.9% [14]. All these data are necessary to present a complete TLC or HPTLC method in food analysis.

Separations without complicated pre-cleaning steps are superior to those which need a lot of practical work prior to detection. The application of "dirty" samples on the separation medium is only possible in planar chromatography because disposable plates are used. This is a real advantage in comparison to HPLC because the pre-cleaning is simplified and the overall precision can be increased. C. F. Pool and co-workers [16] describe an elegant method to quantify vanillin in chocolate. Although chocolate is a difficult matrix it is only necessary to extract 5–8 g chocolate with 15 ml 70% ethanol in an ultrasonic bath for 15 minutes. After extraction the sample is centrifuged and separated on silica gel HPTLC-plates with chloroform-ethyl acetate-1-propanol (94+2+4) to a distance of 6 cm. Quantification is done by remission measurements at 280 nm.

V. DENSITOMETRIC MEASUREMENTS

In situ densitometry offers a simple way of quantifying by measuring the optical density of the separated spots directly on the plate [17]. During densitometric measurements the illuminating light is either absorbed or scattered. Only the scattered light is reflected from the plate and this light provides the desired information. This reflected light is called remission light. Quantitative evaluation of thin-layer chromatograms by optical methods is based on a differential measurement of light, emerging from the sample-free and sample-containing zones of the plate, although the relationship between detector response and sample concentration is not simple [18–20]. At first approximation a parallel light beam with the intensity I is used for illuminating the HPTLC-plate. To get a lamp-independent spectrum it is recommended to use the quotient of the sample spectrum and the spectrum of the clean HPTLC-plate. Usually the remission values (I_{rem}) are

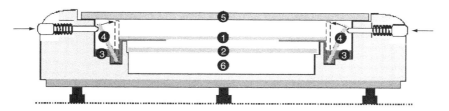

FIGURE 46.6 Sketch of a linear chamber. 1. HPTLC plate; 2. counterplate used only for sandwich development; 3. troughs for eluents; 4. glass strip to regulate eluent flow; 5. covering glass plate. (Reproduced with permission from CAMAG, Switzerland.)

calculated from the measurement values of the HPTLC-track divided by reference values (I_0).

$$R(\lambda) = \frac{I_{rem}(\lambda)}{I_0(\lambda)} \qquad (46.9)$$

$R(\lambda)$ = corrected remission light spectrum
$I_{rem}(\lambda)$ = remission light spectrum
$I_0(\lambda)$ = reference spectrum

The proper choice of the reference spectrum $I_0(\lambda)$ is a very effective method for baseline corrections. A convenient way to transform remission data into mass-dependant signals is to use the folowing formula:

$$A(I_{rem}, \lambda) = -\ln R(\lambda) \qquad (46.10)$$

The logarithm expression sets all intensities smaller than I_0 to positive values. Theoretical predictions indicate that the Kubelka/Munk-equation is the only transformation formula which shows linearity between the remission data and the sample mass (m) [11].

$$KM(I_{rem}, \lambda) = \frac{(1 - R(\lambda))^2}{2R(\lambda)} = const.m \qquad (46.11)$$

In principle, all light absorbing substances are detectable because a modern diode-array TLC-scanner covers the range from 200 nm to 1100 nm. In Figure 46.7 a typical contour-plot of a dye mixture is shown, which comprises 450 single spectra, evaluated with Equation (46.10). Within less than 1 minute the diode-array scanner measures the track over the distance of 45 mm in the wavelength range of 200 to 600 nm with a spatial resolution of 0.1 mm.

There are numerous examples for *in situ* densitometric determination in food matrices. For example, the quantification of methyl and propyl parabens, benzoic acid, and sorbic acid at 228 nm and 254 nm are published in [21]. Fruit juices and jams are extracted and separated on silica gel TLC-plates, using the solvent mix ethanol-NH_3 aqueous-ethyl acetate-acetone (1+3+3+28) for the parabens and ethyl acetate-acetic acid-hexane (1+4+16) for both acids. The AOAC Official Method Polycyclic Aromatic Hydrocarbons (PAHs) and Benzo[a]pyrene in Food, describes a PAH separation using isooctane on cellulose plates. After separation the spots have to be scraped out and measured externally in UV [22]. In contrast, a modern TLC-scanner can separate 16 PAHs in one run, using the different absorption maxima of the PAHs spectra for quantification. Even spots not separated on the plate can be quantified, because spots can be spectrally distinguished [20].

The Kubelka/Munk equation is the only theoretically founded expression describing all remission processes. If a substance absorbs more light than the clean part of a

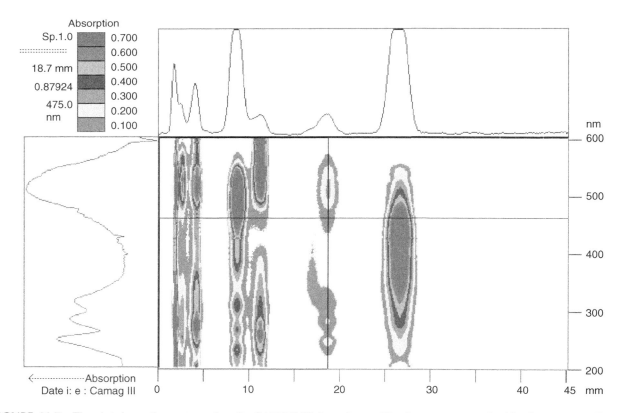

FIGURE 46.7 The plot shows the contour-plot of a CAMAG-III dye mixture. The dyes are separated with toluene over a distance of 45 mm. The spectrum at 18.7 mm (peak 5) is plotted left and the densitogram, taken at 475 nm, is shown on top.

plate, the comparison of sample and reference spectrum using Equation (46.10) or (46.11) can be used for quantification purposes. If the spot emits more light than the reference, the sample shows fluorescence. The fluorescence spectrum is derived from sample and reference spectrum using either Equation (46.11) or Equation (46.12).

$$F(I_{rem}, \lambda) = [I_{rem}(\lambda) - I_0(\lambda)]/1000 \qquad (46.12)$$

Quinine is a fluorescent compound which emits light which was absorbed below 380 nm. In Figure 46.8 the densitogram of a beverage sample, applied undiluted on a silica gel HPTLC-plate, is plotted. The mobile phase (the same as shown in Figure 46.4) cannot separate quinine completely from sugars. The absorption densitogram (lower plot in Figure 46.8, evaluated using Equation (46.10) shows an irregular baseline and the quinine signal cannot be used for quantitative determination. If the same data set is evaluated using Equation (46.12) (upper plot in Figure 46.8), the quinine peak can be easily integrated [11].

The AOAC Official Method No. 969.27 [23] describes the separation of the non-nutritive sweeteners calcium cyclamate, sodium saccharin, and dulcine in non-alcoholic beverages on silica-gel plates using n-butanol-alcohol-NH_3-H_2O (40+4+1+9). Saccharin ($R_f = 0.5$) shows fluorescence at shortwave UV and can be quantified using the fluorescence mode of a diode-array scanner. In the AOAC method, color reagents for cyclamat and dulcine are recommended. These substances are detectable by direct remission measurements.

TLC scanners for *in situ* remission measurements are modern computer-controlled, high-sensitivity instruments that measure absorption and fluorescence. Modern diode-array TLC scanners are able to measure simultaneously at different wavelengths. They allow quick peak identification and peak purity investigation, using the registered spectra. Furthermore, the simultaneous registration at different wavelengths opens the way for chemo metric evaluations,

like peak purity monitoring, to improve accuracy and reliability in HPTLC analysis. Diode-array scanners make fluorescent measurements possible without use of edge-filters or other facilities. Even a separate run for fluorescent measurements is not necessary, because the required information can be extracted from the remission data [11, 17–20].

VI. SUGAR ANALYSIS AND SEPARATION OF DYES AND FOOD LIPIDS

Planar chromatography offers a wide range of different reagents for specific staining of analytes. The recommended handling of mostly hazard reagents eliminated many TLC methods from official method collections. To avoid plate dipping with mostly hazard reagents, specific plate coatings can be used for staining purposes. In the past, sugars had to be transformed into colored products by use of 4-aminobenzoic acid in glacial acetic or similar reagents [24]. The AOAC official method for glucose in honey or fructose starch sirup in honey recommends sugar detection by spraying with aniline/diphenylamine reagent after separation with n-butanol-acetic acid-water (2+1+1) on silica gel [25, 26]. In modern HPTLC amino phases are used for sugar separation [27, 28]. The separation is possible by using CH_3CN-H_2O solvent systems. After separation the amino plates are placed at 150°C for 15 minutes. All carbonyl-group containing substances will react with the NH_2-group to form colored, strong fluorescent products. Sample pre-treatments usaully are not necessary. In Figure 46.9 the separation of the artificial sweeter Sucralose® after amino plate derivation is shown. The detection limit is 10 ng/spot of Sucralose® [29], which is a typical value for what is termed thermochemical activation in sugar analysis.

Dye separation is one of the basic TLC applications because no scanner and staining reagent are necessary. Companies like CAMAG sell dye mixtures to check the layer quality of TLC and HPTLC plates. In [30] a rapid clean-up procedure for FD&C color additives in foods by use of reverse phase C_{18} cartridges is given. The color additives are separated on silica gel G TLC plates with n-butanol-methyl ethyl ketone-NH_4OH-H_2O (5+3+1+1). Similar systems are used to quantify colours from non-alcoholic and alcoholic beverages [31] and from raw sausages [32]. Detection of natural pigments from red pepper, paprika, and tomato is performed by using different hexane-aceton solvents or by using a mixture of CH_2Cl_2-ethyl ether (9+1) on silica gel [33].

Beside dyes, food lipids are a classic field of TLC analysis. A review of planar chromatography separations of food lipids is given in [34]. An AOAC official method describes the separation of some fatty acids in oils and fats. Erucic acid, cetolic acid, and trans-isomers of docosenoic acid are converted to methyl ester and separated by use of silver impregnated silica gel TLC plates.

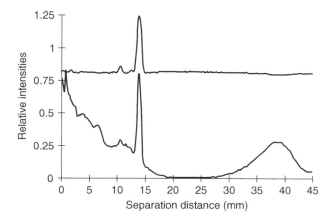

FIGURE 46.8 Densitogram of a bitter lemon sample in absorption (lower graph) and fluorescent mode (upper graph).

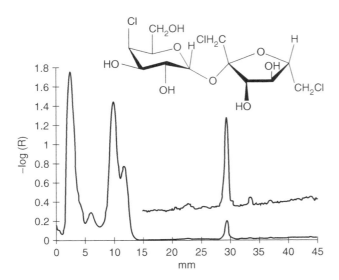

FIGURE 46.9 Densitogram of a "Cola" type softdrink in the absorption mode (1 µl spotted) containing 48 mg/L Sucralose® (peak at 29 mm). The upper signal line is plotted 5-fold enhanced.

The development of the plates is performed at $-22°C$ with toluene-n-hexane (9+1) as mobile phase [35]. For spot visualization the plate is dipped in sulfuric acid-ethanol-hexane (1+35+64) for 2 seconds and then heated to 110°C for 45 min. This treatment turns lipids into fluorescent compounds [36]. Animal fat in vegetable fats and oil is identified by analyzing cholesterol with ether-petrol-ether (1+1) on silical gel. In the AOAC official method, cholesterol is scraped off at R_f: 0.2–0.3 and quantified by use of GC [37]. Charring with 50% sulfuric acid can be used to visualize cholesterol as well as all carbon-containing substances [38]. In this sense sulfuric acid acts as a universal detector in planar chromatography. To visualize oils and fats, plates are often sprayed (or dipped) in 2'7'-dichlorofluorescein reagent (0.5 g/L in 50% aqueous methanol), because the fluorescence in a lipophilic surrounding is mostly enhanced. This can either be used to visualize fats with fluorescing substances, or to enhance fluorescent intensity by dipping in non-polar reagents like Triton-X or parafine.

VII.   DRUGS IN FOOD AND FEED

TLC or HPTLC methods are widely used in the screening of drugs in food and feed. The following examples show that in planar chromatography quantification can be done without a special column pre-cleaning. Coccidostats like aklomide or buquinolate are incorporated in the broiler feed as additives to prevent coccidiosis in poultry. To check the legal limits of aklomide in feeds [39] the sample is extracted with methanol and separated on a silica gel G TLC plate in ether [39]. The plate is sprayed with 1 ml

20% $TiCl_3$ to 25 ml p-(dimethyl-amino)cinnamaldehyde (DMC) (0.1 g in 100 ml 1.0 N HCl) solution. Aklomide forms reddish pink spots. Buquinolate can be identified after extraction from feeds with $CHCl_3$, concentrated and separated by TLC with $CHCl_3$ as mobile phase. Busquinolate shows fluorescence under short wavelength UV light with excitation at 265 nm and emission wavelength at 375 nm (R_f: 0.4–0.6) [40]. For quantification purposes the busquinolate TLC zone is transferred to a vial, extracted with 80% alcohol and measured with a spectrophotofluorometer [40]. The busquinolate fluorescence makes the method very specific.

Invermectin is a highly potent antiparasitic drug that is active at extremely low dosage against a wide variety of nematodes and arthropod parasites. The drug is widely used for antiparasitic control in cattle, horses, sheep, and swine. An HPTLC method using UV detection after reaction with acetic anhydride in pyridine was able to detect 5 µg/Kg in cattle blood or plasma [41]. With an improved derivative step (fluoroacetic anhydride instead of acetic anhydride) and a separation on silica gel HPTLC Si60 plates using $CHCl_3$-ethyl acetate (75+25) as the solvent, a visual fluorescence detection of the drug in liver, muscle, and fat as low as 5 µg/Kg was achieved [41]. AOAC methods in particular, often prefer visual detection to keep the method simple. For qualification the spot color and R_f-values are accepted as sufficient. Quantification is done by comparison of sample and standard spot intensity or zone transfer to spectrometric devices. By use of a diode-array scanner, food and feed additives can be easily identified and quantified using *in situ* measured UV/vis-spectra in combination with spectral libraries. Time-consuming transfer steps can be avoided. If fluorescence signals can be used, HPTLC methods are very specific and show detection limits comparable to HPLC.

There are several official AOAC methods for sulfonamide residues in animal tissues. The screening method for sulfabromomethazine, sulfadimethoxine, sulfamethazine, sulfapyridine, sulfaquinoxaline, and sulfathiazole recommends a tissue extraction with ethyl acetate after addition of sulfapyridine as internal standard and a cleanup step by seperating organic and aqueous solvents. Spotting zones on silica gel TLC-plates are focused by developing 1 cm in ethanol followed by 2 developments, 6 cm and 12 cm, in $CHCl_3$-tert-Butanol (8+2). Compounds are derived by dipping the plate in fluorescamine solution (25 mg fluorescame in 250 ml acetone) and scanned in UV [42]. To identify sulfamethazine the plate is sprayed with 1% sodium nitrite, dried at 100°C, and sprayed with NEDA (0.4% 1-naphthyl-ethyl-endimine in methanol) to form pink spots [43]. The AOAC method for trisulfapyrimidines determination in drugs recommends separation with $CHCl_3$-methanol-NH_4OH (30+12+1) on silica gel. The substances are located under shortwave UV [44]. A simple HPTLC method to quantify thiamphenicol in bovine plasma has been published by P. Corti. Different phases like NH_2, CN-, and Si_{60} plates are used to increase determination specificity. A detection limit of 180 µg/Kg thiamphenicol is achieved whereas the HPLC detection limit is calculated to 70 µg/Kg [45].

The multiclass and multiresidue qualitative detection of chloramphenicol, nitrofuran, and sulfonamide residues in animal muscle was published by J.-P. Abjean [46]. The identification is done with the help of a specific reaction either with pyridine to identify nitrofurans or with fluorescamine to identify chloramphenicol and sulfonamides. Furans appear as blue spots on Si_{60} plates and were visually quantified. The limit used by the U.S. Food and Drug Administration for enforcement purposes for nitrofurans in 1989 was 100 µg/Kg. The expected limit of sensitivity with the method described is 1 µg/Kg [46]. The HPTLC method allows screening of residues in food with a sample throughput of about 20 samples per analyst per day without requiring expensive apparatus.

The identification and determination of oxytetracycline, tiamulin, lincomycin, and spectinomycin in veterinary preparations separated by two solvent systems is described in [47]. After separation on TLC silica gel aluminum sheets the absorption spectra of the separated substances were recorded by densitometry. The spots are visualized with Ehrlich's reagent (1 g 4-dimethylaminobenzaldehyde in 36% HCl-ethanol, 25+75) or 16% sulfuric acid and heated at 105°C for 10 min. The stained spots were scanned again to confirm the identification. Quantitative analysis achieved quantification limits per spot of 40 ng for tiamulin, 200 ng for lincomycin, 280 ng for oxytetracycline, 500 ng for spectinomycin, and 630 ng for oxytetracycline [47]. All antibiotic determination methods mentioned use specific post-separation reactions, which can be easily performed on the plate. Nearly all compounds can be identified using the R_f-values in combination with appropriate staining reactions. Hundreds of different staining reactions have been published and all act as specific TLC detectors [15].

Most specific is the use of enzymes for detection purposes. Oxytetracycline and chlortetracycline hydrochloride are antibiotics incorporated into feeds, either individually or in combination with other drugs, at concentrations ranging from 10 mg/Kg to 500 mg/Kg [48]. P. K. Markakis developed a simple, reliable, and precise TLC method for both these tetracyclines in animal feeds in the presence of other drugs. He used HPTLC Si_{60} plates and $CHCl_3$-methanol (10+1) as the developing solvent. After separation the appropriate HPTLC-zones were scraped out and the material was incubated for 11 h at 30°C in the presence of *Bacillus subtilis*. A detection limit of 0.625 mg/Kg for chlortetracycline hydrochloride and 1.25 mg/Kg for oxytetracycline was achieved, using the diameter of *Bacillus subtilis* inhibition zones for quantification [48].

The combination of TLC and very specific biology detection shows the great flexibility of planar chromatographic methods; nevertheless, scraping the TLC plate and incubation are time-consuming preparation steps that are difficult to automate. Much more elegant is the paper by H. E. Hauck [49] where an *in situ* bioautography of antibiotics is presented. Methanolic extracts of foods and feeding stuffs are subjected to HPTLC plates und separated using different solvents. After separation the plate is dipped in a bacteria culture (*Bacillus subtilis*) and incubated at room temperature for 19 h. The plate is sprayed with a tetrazonium salt as a reagent to detect active bacteria as purple color. The inhibition zones are recorded with a video system. Detection limits down to 100 µg/Kg were obtained [49]. This kind of detection is useful not on special compounds but on special attributes, for example, antibiotic quality. Attribute identification is also used to identify free radical scavenger capacity (RSC) of foodstuff [50]. Extracts of samples were separated on silica gel plates and after separation the plates were stained with a methanolic solution of 2,2-diphenyl-1-picrylhydrazyl radical. Dots of separated foodstuff extracts with RSC turn yellow, with color intensity depending on the RSC compounds present in the extract. This test is sensitive enough to detect differences of RSC between varieties and brands of water- or methanol-soluble products [50].

VIII. PESTICIDES

Attribute analysis is particularly useful for pesticides which inhibit the enzyme cholinesterase. This is the case for all organophosphates and carbamates [51]. For quantification, pre-cleaned samples were separated on Si60 HPTLC plates using tetrahydofurane-hexane (7+25) as a solvent. The plates were dipped in a solution containing cholinesterase, 1-naphthyl acetate, and Fast Blue salt B. If the enzyme is not inhibited, it will cleave the acetate to 1-naphthyl phenol. The substance will react on the plate surface with Fast Blue salt B to form a violet color. The inhibition spots of organophosphates and carbamates become visible as white zones on a violet background. The spots can be quantified by reflectance spectrometry at 535 nm. Detection limits for different substances were in the range of 13–800 pg per spot [51].

The AOAC standard test to detect organochlorine pesticide contaminations like aldrin, DDT, dieldrin, chlordane, strobane, and toxaphen [52] recommends n-hexane as the solvent and silica gel as the stationary phase. The stationary phase is either mixed with $AgNO_3$ or dipped in 0.1% aqueous $AgNO_3$ after separation. When the plate is radiated with shortwave UV in the presence of chlorine substances, AgCl will be formed, which reacts with light to elementary silver. Reduced silver forms black spots, which can be used for a very sensitive chlorine pesticide screening.

For determination of carbaryl pesticide residues in apple and spinach the samples are extracted with CH_2Cl_2 and separated on Al_2O_3 TLC plates with aceton-benzene (1+4) [53]. The plate is sprayed with 1.0 N alcoholic KOH and then with a solution of diethylene glycol-alcohol solution (1+9) with p-nitrobenzene-diazonium fluoborate (25 mg/100 mL). The diazonium salt forms blue spots in the R_f-range between 0.52–0.6. For semi-quantitative estimation size and intensity of sample and standard spots have to be compared. For the determination of biphenyl pesticide residues in citrus fruits [54] no derivation step is necessary. Biphenyl is extracted from blended peel or pulp by steam liquid-liquid extraction. The extract is separated on a silica gel TLC plate with heptane. Viewed under UV light, biphenyl appears as a blue spot on a yellow background.

TLC or HPTLC is in general well suited to separate a few compounds from a complicated matrix. The resolution in TLC becomes maximal for R_f-values around 0.3. If a special phase system separates substances in the optimal R_f-range of 0.1 and 0.8, only compounds with k-values between 9 and 0.25 will move (4). This is a very narrow polarity window. All other substances outside this window will stay at the point of application or will move with the solvent front. Therefore, only few substances of similar polarity can be separated in one run. But in samples like water or food, pesticides of a wide polarity range can be present. To cover a wide range of polarity a special gradient mode, the automated multiple development (AMD) technique, can be exploited using a great variety of solvents [54, 55]. The principle of AMD is simple. The TLC plate is developed at first only over a very short distance using a solvent of great elution strengths to move all substances. After plate drying another separation step takes place, but now the solvent strength is slightly reduced whereas the separation distance is slightly increased. During the first separation cycle all substances of the sample will move because the highest elution power of the solvent is working. When the solvent front reaches a sample spot the sample will be concentrated in a narrow band because the molecules in the sample zone start their upward moving earlier than those in the upper part of the spot. During every cycle the zones will be concentrated to a narrow band if the substances are moving. Between the developments the solvent is completely removed from the developing chamber and the plate is dried under vacuum. For the next development the layer is conditioned with the vapor phase of the next solvent. Cycle for cycle, the solvent strength is reduced and more and more substances will remain at their plate positions. At the end of the last cycle only the compound with the largest mobility will move. Usually the number of cycles is between 10 and 40 for a separation distance of not more than 8 cm. All the steps in AMD are computer controlled and fully automated. A development of 40 cycles needs between 2 and

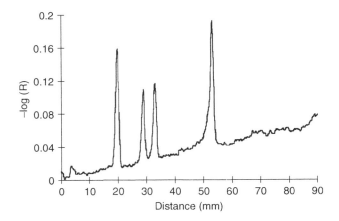

FIGURE 46.10 AMD separation of four pesticides, separated by use of a "universal" gradient [56]. Separated are 2,4-D (Aryloxyalkanoic acid), Methoxuron, Atrazine, and Parathion-ethyl.

4 h. The AMD technique brings substances of a large polarity range to move and compresses substances in very narrow zones. This technique, like all gradient developments, increases the chromatographic resolution dramatically. It should be mentioned that a commercially available AMD system is able to separate more than 40 samples in parallel.

The AMD technique is especially suited for pesticide monitoring because several pesticides can be simultaneously determined in the same sample [55–57]. An overview of AMD methods for the determination of pyrethrin and pyrethroid pesticide residues in crops, foods, and environmental matrices is given by Z.-M. Chen [57]. The combination of AMD and diode-array TLC-scanner is a powerful tool especially for pesticide monitoring because the photodiode array technique substantiates the analytical result by providing spectral confirmation for the appropriate substances.

IX. MYCOTOXINS

Mycotoxins are fungal metabolites, which are of great concern as toxic contaminants in food and feeds. Among a number of other techniques, planar chromatography is still very popular in the determination of certain mycotoxins. Sample preparation is necessary and is mostly an extraction step to clean up the sample and to concentrate the mycotoxins is proposed. In general, TLC can cope better with more crude extracts than HPLC where the clean-up step is more important to save the column. An important feature of TLC is its off-line operating principle. For instance, Leming Lin et al. [58] employed two development systems for the determination of zeraleone and patulin in maize. In the first step the lipids in the sample were isolated, and the second development is used to separate the mycotoxins. For mycotoxin visualization on plate two different methods are frequently applied: the examination under UV light if the mycotoxins show naturally fluorescence and the spraying or dipping with chemical reagents that produce colored or fluorescent products. The spot colors and the R_f-values in combination with *in situ* measured spectra are used for mycotoxin identification. The natural fluorescence of aflatoxins, citrinin, and ochratoxin A makes its identification much more certain. A review from 1998 sums up more than 10 different mycotoxin TLC methods compared with other techniques [59]. The high sample throughput of TLC and HPTLC makes it the most cost-effective analytical technique for mycotoxins screening routine. A drawback of TLC in comparison with HPLC is its untapped potential for automation.

Ochratoxin A is a mycotoxin with nephrotoxic, carcenogenic, teratogenic, and immunosuppressive properties. A review of chromatographic methods for determination of ochratoxin A is given by H. Valenta [60]. The official AOAC method for ochratoxin determination in barley [61] recommends silica gel plates and the solvent mix benzene-methanol-acetic acid (18+1+1) [61]. The solvent system toluene-ethyl acetate-formic acid (5+4+1) can be used as well [62]. The blue-green fluorescence of the ochratoxin A, brought out by long-wave UV light, is used for detection. For densitometric fluorescence measurements an exication wavelength range from 310–340 nm and an emission range from 440–475 nm should be used. A detection limit of 25 µg/Kg rice is achieved [63, 64], whereas the quantification limit for HPLC is 0.2 µ/Kg [61, 63, 64].

A review of the chromatographic determination of patulin in fruits and fruit juices is given by G. S. Shepard [65]. Patulin has no teratogenic or carcenogenic effects but shows embryo toxicity accompanied by maternal toxicity. The official AOAC method of patulin determination in apple juice [66] is that the juice is extracted with ethyl acetate and cleaned up on silica gel column. The silica gel TLC plate is developed with toluene-ethyl acetate-90%-formic acid (5+4+1) and sprayed with 3-methyl-2-benzothiazolinone hydrazone-HCl solution (0.5 g in 100 ml H_2O) before the plate is heated for 15 min to 130°. Patulin appears as yellow brown spots at R_f 0.5 with a detection limit of 20 µg/L whereas HPLC methods show a detection limit of 0.5 µg/L [67] and a quantification limit of 5 µg/Kg [64]. The quantification limit for patulin in HPTLC is 50 µg/Kg [64].

The AOAC official method for zearalenone in [68] corn recommends $CHCl_3$-acetone (9+1) as the mobile phase for separation on a Si_{60} HPTLC plate with a quantification limit of 100 µg/Kg and an overall recovery of 97% [64, 67–69]. The appropriate HPLC quantification limit is 35 µg/Kg [64]. The separation of deoxynivalenol (DON) in wheat on silica gel 60 TLC plates with the mobile phase $CHCl_3$-acetone-isopropanol (8+1+1) is published in [70]. The developed plates have to be sprayed with $AlCL_3$ solution and heated

7 min to 120° to see blue fluorescent spots under long-wave UV at R_f 0.6. The detection limit is 37.5 mg/Kg for TLC [71] and 20 µg/Kg for HPLC [72]. Using toluene-ethyl acetate-formic acid (6+3+1) nephrotoxic citrinin and ochratoxin A can be separated and viewed under UV [73]. Citrinin can be separated from patulin and aflatoxin B_1, B_2, G_1, and G_2 in one run, using oxalic acid impregnated silica gel TLC plates. A limit of detection of 35 µg/Kg for citrin is achievable [74].

Fumonisins B_1, B_2, and B_3 were isolated in 1988 from corn and have been associated with cases of leucoencephalomalacea in equines, pulmonary oedema in swine, and hepatic cancer in rats [75]. A great majority of reports on fumonisin determinations use fluorescent derivatives for sensitive detection [76]. Using an immunoaffinity column for extract purification and an RP-18 HPTLC plate with 4% aqueous KCL-methanol (2+3) as the mobile phase, a fluorescamine derivation detection limit of 2 ng per spot is achievable [74]. This is an overall detection limit of 100 µg/Kg. The appropriate detection limit for HPLC is 10 to 500 µg/Kg [75].

Aflatoxins are considered to play an important role in the high incidence of human hepatocellular carcinoma in certain areas of the world [77]. There are official AOAC methods for aflatoxins in peanut products, corn, milk and cheese, liver, green coffee, and cotton seed. Mostly these methods refer to the TLC separation method for peanuts and peanut products using silica gel TLC plates and the solvent mixture acetone-$CHCl_3$ (9+1) [78]. Due to the natural fluorescence of all aflatoxins the overall detection limit for TLC methods is 5 µg/Kg [79] or better [80]. The HPLC overall detection limit for all four aflatoxins is published as better than 1 µg/Kg [59]. Quantification limits for aflatoxin B_1 are specified with 5 µg/Kg in corn [64] in comparison to 3 µg/Kg (in corn also) for HPLC [66]. Dell et al. [81] reports that for the aflatoxin determination in peanut butter the TLC method was more precise than HPLC. Tosch et al. compared TLC and HPLC methods and showed that TLC appeared to be equivalent to HPLC [82] with respect to precision, accuracy, sensitivity, recovery, and linearity of response.

One of the major advantages of TLC analysis is the simplicity of the separation step, which makes the method very cost effective. If densitometric quantifications are recommended, costs will arise. An interesting method to keep the analytical costs in densitometry low has been published by E. Anklam et al. [83, 84]. A simplified densitometer for the detection of aflotoxins was developed using a low-cost UV-light emitting diode (UV-LED) with a peak emission wavelength of 370 nm [83]. The resulting signal was further amplified by means of a commonly used operational amplifier integrated circuit and directly converted into a digital signal with a simple analogue-digital converter. The signal was recorded at the signal port (RS232) of a portable PC and processed with a widely used spreadsheet program.

The same working group developed a modified computer scanner by substitution of the scanner light tube with a black light tube and additional inclusion of a UV-filter. The modified scanner in combination with a personal computer can be used to determine aflatoxins at low nanogram levels, which, when used in combination with an appropriate TLC method, enables monitoring of the compounds in food and feed at the levels stipulated in European legislation [84]. Both systems are available for less than 2000 Euro and both methods can be expanded in combination with the appropriate TLC system to all mycotoxins that show long-wave UV fluorescence.

TLC is a well-established, easy-to-perform, fast, routine, cost-effective, and suitable method for analysis of a wide range of mycotoxins [59]. TLC will continue to play an important role in mycotoxin analysis because of the worldwide requirement for fungal metabolite control. Mycotoxins occurring in a matrix are usually very low quantity levels and the analysis method must be very sensitive. In general, all mycotoxin TLC methods show detection limits or quantification limits 10-fold higher than HPLC values. Nevertheless the FDA regulatory level for aflatoxin in human food and for feed for immature livestock is 20 µg/Kg. The appropriate value for deoxynivalenol is 1000 µg/Kg. HPTLC is able to check these levels in feed and food as well as HPLC. The advantage of HPTLC methods has been described by B. Renger [85]. An assay and purity testing of phospholipids HPTLC is only 38% of the HPLC costs, a value that can surely be adapted to TLC food analysis.

X. FUTURE OF PLANAR CHROMATOGRAPHY

What is the future of TLC and HPTLC? First of all, TLC methods that are able to check official regulatory levels without using technical equipment will of course remain in use. This simple and inexpensive way of doing analysis is too effective to discontinue. It must also be kept in mind that not all countries have or will have the resources to check official regulatory levels using expensive methods like HPLC. A low-cost flat-bed scanner in combination with a personal computer for documentation and quantification purposes will be used. HPTLC methods are strong in screening and will play an increasing role in the field of pesticides and drug monitoring in feed and food. The combination of AMD and diode-array scanner technology, using spectral libraries for sample identification and checking of regulatory levels, will increase in importance. The quantification ability of HPLC will be used for the determination of critical analyts like sugars, the quantification of which can be easily performed by NH_2 layers. The simple pre-cleanings of caffeine, quinine, and sucralose® in beverages or vanillin in chocolate will probably be used for quantification purposes to keep the overall standard deviation low. All in all, TLC and HPLC methods will find niches where the chromatography is more cost-effective than other methods or the performance is so outstanding that no other assays will show comparable results.

LITERATURE

1. C. F. Poole and S. K. Poole, "Instrumental Thin-Layer Chromatography," Anal. Chem. 66 (1994), 27A–37A.
2. C. F. Poole, "Planar chromatography at the turn of the century," J. Chromatogr. A 856 (1999), 399–427.
3. Sz. Nyiredi (editor), Planar Chromatography. A Retrospective View for the Third Millennium, Springer, Budapest, 2001.
4. J. Sherma and B. Fried (editors), Handbook of Thin-Layer-Chromatography, Second Edition, Chromatographic Science Series Volume 71, Marcel Dekker, New York, 1996.
5. N. Grinberg (editor), Modern Thin-Layer Chromatography, Chromatographic Science Series Volume 52, Marcel Dekker, New York, 1990.
6. J. Sherma, "Thin-layer chromatography in food and agricultural analysis," J. Chromatogr. A 880 (2000), 129–147.
7. H. Jork, "Thin-layer chromatography — liquid-column chromatography: partners or competitors?" Fresenius Anal. Chem. 318 (1984), 177–178.
8. A. Zlatkis and R. E. Kaiser (editors), HPTLC- High Performance Thin-Layer Chromatography, Elsevier, Amsterdam, 1977, 15–38.
9. C. F. Poole and S. K. Poole, "Modern thin-layer chromatography," Anal. Chem. 15 (1989), A1257–1269.
10. F. Geis, Fundamentals of Thin Layer Chromatography, Huetig-Verlag, New York, 1987.
11. B. Spangenberg, P. Post and S. Ebel, "Fiber optical scanning in TLC by use of a diode-array detector — linearization models for absorption and fluorescence evaluation," J. Planar Chromatogr. 15 (2002), 88–93.
12. C. B. Barrett, M. S. Dallas and F. B. Padley, "The quantitative analysis of triglyceride mixtures by thin layer chromatography on silica impregnated with silver nitrate," J. Amer. Oil Chem. Soc. 40 (1963), 580–584.
13. N. Perišić-Janjić and Bizerka Vujićić, "Analysis of some food components by thin-layer chromatography on unconventional layers," J. Planar Chromatogr. 10 (1997), 447–452.
14. P. Bodart, Ch. Kabengera, A. Noirfalise, P. Hubert and L. Angenot, "Determination of α-chaconine and α-solanine in potatoes by high-performance thin-layer chromatography/densitometry," J. Assoc. Off. Anal. Chem. 83 (2000), 1468–1473.
15. H. Jork, W. Funk, W. Fischer and H. Wimmer, Thin Layer Chromatography Reagents and Detection Methods, Vols. 1a and 1b, Wiley, New York, 1994.
16. S. K. Poole, S. L. Daly and C. F. Poole, "A thin layer chromatographic method for determining the authenticity of natural vanilla extracts," J. Planar Chromatogr. 6 (1993), 129–137.

17. B. Spangenberg and K.-F. Klein, "Fibre optical scanning with high resolution in thin-layer chromatography," J. Chromatogr. A 898, 2000, 265–269.

18. J. Stroka, B. Spangenberg and E. Anklam, "New approaches in TLC densitometry," J. Liq. Chrom. & Rel. Technol. 25, 2002, 1497–1513.

19. B. Spangenberg, B. Ahrens and K.-F Klein, "TLC-analysis in forensic sciences using a diode-array detector," Chromatographia 53, 2001, 438–441.

20. B. Spangenberg and K.-F. Klein, "New Evaluation Algorithm in Diode-Array Thin-Layer Chromatography," J. Planar Chromatogr. 14, 2001, 260–265.

21. A. El-Bayoumi, M. S. Tawakkol and J. M. Diab, "In situ spectrodensitometric determination of methyl and propyl parabens, benzoic and sorbic acid in bulk powder, food, and pharmaceutical formulations," Spectrosc. Lett. 30 (1997), 355–366.

22. Official Methods of Analysis of AOAC International (1995) 16th Ed., Method 973.73.

23. Official Methods of Analysis of AOAC International (1995) 16th Ed., Method 969.27.

24. G. Vaccari, G. Lodi, E. Tamburini, T. Bernardi and S. Tosi, "Detection of oligosaccharides in sugar products using planar chromatography," Food Chem. 74 (2001), 99–110.

25. Official Methods of Analysis of AOAC International (1995) 16th Ed., Method 979.22B.

26. Official Methods of Analysis of AOAC International (1995) 16th Ed., Method 979.22.

27. R. Klaus, W. Fischer and H. E. Hauck, "Use of a new adsorbent in the separation and detection of glucose and fructose by HPTLC," Chromatographia 28, 1989, 364–366.

28. R. Klaus, W. Fischer and H. E. Hauck, "Application of a thermal in situ reaction for fluorimetric detection of carbohydrates on NH_2-Layers," Chromatographia 29, 1990, 467–472.

29. B. Spangenberg, J. Stroka, I. Aranz and E. Anklam, "Simple and reliable working HPTLC quantification method for sucralose," J. Liq. Chrom. & Rel. Technol. 26(16/2003), 2729–2739.

30. Official Methods of Analysis of AOAC International (1995) 16th Ed., Method 988.13.

31. S. M. Anderton, C. D. Incarvito and J. Sherma, "Determination of natural and synthetic colours in alcoholic and non-alcoholic beverages by quantitative HPTLC," J. Liq. Chromatogr. Relat. Technol. 20 (1997), 101–110.

32. R. Brockmann, "Detection of natural colorants in raw sausages. Results of a collaborative test," Fleischwirtschaft 78 (1998), 143–145.

33. M. I. Minguez-Mosquera, D. Hornero-Mendez and G. Fernandez, "Detection of bixin, lycopene, canthaxanthin, and β-apo-8'-carotenal in products derived from red pepper," J. Assoc. Off. Anal. Chem. 78 (1995), 491–496.

34. N. U. Olsson, "Advances in planar chromatography for separation of food lipids," J. Chromatogr. A 624 (1992), 11–19.

35. Official Methods of Analysis of AOAC International (1995) 16th Ed., Method 985.20.

36. M. J. Kurantz, R. J. Maxwell, R. Kwoczak and F. Taylor, "Rapid and sensitive method for the quantitation of nonpolar lipids by high-performance thin-layer chromatography and fluorodensitometry," J. Chromatogr. A 549 (1991), 387–399.

37. Official Methods of Analysis of AOAC International (1995) 16th Ed., Method 970.51.

38. J. C. Touchstone and D. Rogers (editors), Thin Layer Chromatography: Quantitative Environmental and Clinical Applications, John Wiley & Sons, New York, 1980.

39. Official Methods of Analysis of AOAC International (1995) 16th Ed., Method 969.54.

40. Official Methods of Analysis of AOAC International (1995) 16th Ed., Method 967.34.

41. J.-P. Abjean and M. Gaugin, "Planar chromatography for screening of ivermectin residues in swine and cattle tissue," J. Assoc. Off. Anal. Chem. 78 (1995), 1141–1144.

42. Official Methods of Analysis of AOAC International (1995) 16th Ed., Method 983.31.

43. Official Methods of Analysis of AOAC International (1995) 16th Ed., Method 982.40.

44. Official Methods of Analysis of AOAC International (1995) 16th Ed., Method 973.73.

45. E. Dreassi, G. Corbini, V. Ginanneschi, P. Corti and S. Furlanetto, "Planar chromatographic and liquid chromatographic analysis of thiamphenicol in bovine and human plasma," J. Assoc. Off. Anal. Chem. 80 (1997), 746–750.

46. J.-P. Abjean, "Planar chromatography for the multiclass, multiresidue screening of chloramphenicol, nitrofuran and sulfonamide residues in pork and beef," J. Assoc. Off. Anal. Chem. 80 (1997), 737–740.

47. J. Krzek, A. Kwiecien, M. Starek, A. Kierszniewska and W. Rzeszutko, "Identification and determination of oxytetracycline, tiamulin, lincomycin and spectinomycin in veterinary preparations by thin-layer chromatography/densitometry," J. Assoc. Off. Anal. Chem. 83 (2000), 1502–1506.

48. P. K. Markakis, "Determination of tetracyclines in animal feeds in the presence of other drugs by thin-layer chromatography and microbiological method," J. Assoc. Off. Anal. Chem. 79 (1996), 375–379.

49. R. Eymann and H. E. Hauck, "Bioautography of antibiotics," CLB Chem. Labor. Biotech. 51 (2000), 204–206.

50. C. Soler-Rivas, C. J. Espin and H. J. Wichers, "An easy and fast test of compare total free radical scavenger capacity of foodstuffs," Phytochem. Anal. 11 (2000), 330–338.

51. C. Weins and H. Jork, "Toxicological evaluation of harmful substances by in situ enzymatic and biological detection in high-performance thin-layer chromatography," J. Chromatogr. A 750 (1996), 403–407.

52. Official Methods of Analysis of AOAC International (1995) 16th Ed., Method 972.05.

53. Official Methods of Analysis of AOAC International (1995) 16th Ed., Method 968.26.

54. Official Methods of Analysis of AOAC International (1995) 16th Ed., Method 968.25.

55. S. Butz and H.-J. Stan, "Screening of 265 pesticides in water by thin-layer chromatography with automated multiple development," Anal. Chem. 67 (1995), 620–630.

56. G. E. Morlock, "Analysis of pesticide residues in drinking water by planar chromatography," J. Chromatogr. A 754 (1996), 423–430.

57. Z.-M. Chen and Y.-H. Wang, "Chromatographic methods for the determination of pyrethrin and pyrethroid pesticide residues in crops, foods and environmental samples," J. Chromatogr. A 754 (1996), 367–395.

58. L. Lin, J. Zhang, K. Sui and W. Song, J. Planar. Chromatogr. 6 (1993), 274.

59. L. Lin, J. Zhang, P. Wang, Y. Wang and J. Chen, "Thin-layer chromatography of mycotoxins and comparison with other chromatographic methods," J. Chromatogr. A 815 (1998), 3–20.

60. H. Valenta, "Chromatograhic methods for the determination of ochratoxin A in animal and human tissues and fluids," J. Chromatogr. A 815 (1998), 75–92.

61. Official Methods of Analysis of AOAC International (1995) 16th Ed., Method 973.37.

62. M. Dawlatana, R. D. Coker, M. J. Nagler and G. Blunden, "A normal-phase HPTLC method for the quantitative determination of ochratoxin A in rice," Chromatographia 42 (1996), 25–28.

63. B. Hald, G. M. Wood, A. Boenke, B. Schurer and P. Finglas, "Ochratoxin A in wheat: an intercomparison of procedures," Anal. Lett. 26 (1993), 1831–1845.

64. J. Gilbert and E. Anklam, "Validation of analytical methods for determining mycotoxins in foodstuffs," Trends Anal. Chem. 21 (2002), 468–486.

65. G. S. Shephard and N. L. Legott, "Chromatographic determination of the mycotoxin patulin in fruit and fruit juces," J. Chromatogr. A 882 (2000), 17–22.

66. Official Methods of Analysis of AOAC International (1995) 16th Ed., Method 974.18.

67. L. M. Lin, Z. Jun, S. Kai and W. B. Sung, "Simultaneous thin-layer chromatographic determination of zeralenone and patulin in maize," J. Planar Chromatogr. 6 (1993), 274–277.

68. Official Methods of Analysis of AOAC International (1995) 16th Ed., Method 976.22.

69. N. M. Quiroga, I. Sola and E. Varsavsky, J. AOAC Int. 77 (1994), 939–941.

70. Official Methods of Analysis of AOAC International (1995) 16th Ed., Method 986.17.

71. L. Czerwiecki and H. Giryn, "Thin-layer chromatographic determination of trichothecenes in cereals," Rocz. Panstw. Zakl. Hig. 40 (1989), 284–290.

72. F. Kotal and Z. Radova, " A simple method for determination of Deoxynivalenol in cereals and flours," Czech. J. Food Sci. 20 (2002), 63–68.

73. A. K. Sinha and K. S. Ranjan, "Report of mycotoxin contamination in Bhutanese cheese," J. Food Sci. Technol. 28 (1991), 398–399.

74. A. Gimeno and M. L. Martins, "Rapid thin-layer chromatographic determination of patulin, citrin and aflatoxin in apples and pears, and their juices and jams," J. Assoc. Off. Anal. Chem. 66 (1983), 85–91.

75. R. A. Preis and E. A. Vargas, "A method for determining fumonisin B_1 in corn using immunoaffinity clean-up and thin layer chromatography/densitometry," Food Additives and Contaminants 17 (2000), 463–468.

76. G. S. Shephard, "Chromatographic determination of the fumonisin mycotoxins," J. Chromatogr. A 815 (1998), 31–39.

77. A. E. Cespedes and G. J. Diaz, "Analysis of aflatoxins in poultry and pig feeds and feedstuffs used in colombia," J. Assoc. Off. Anal. Chem. 80 (1997), 1215–1219.

78. Official Methods of Analysis of AOAC International (1995) 16th Ed., Method 968.22, 982.24, 982.25 and 978.15.

79. F. H. El-Tahan, M. H. El-Tahan and M. A. Shebl, "Occurrence of aflatoxins in cereal grains from four Egyptian governorates," Nahrung 44 (2000), 279–280.

80. V. P. DiProssimo and E. G. Malek, "Comparison of three methods for determining aflatoxins in melon seeds," J. Assoc. Off. Anal. Chem. 79 (1996), 1330–1335.

81. M. P. K. Dell, S. J. Haswell, O. G. Roch, R. D. Coker, V. F. P. Medlock and K. Tomlins, "Analytical methodology for the determination of aflatoxins in butter: comparison of high-performance thin-layer chromatography, enzyme-linked immunosorbent assay and high-performance liquid chromatography." Analyst 115 (1990). 1435–1439.

82. D. Tosch, A. E. Waltking and J. F. Schlesier, "Comparison of liquid chromatography and high-performance thin-layer chromatography for determination of aflatoxin in peanut products," J. Assoc. Off. Anal. Chem. 67 (1984), 337–339.

83. J. Stroka and E. Anklam, "Development of a simplified densitometer for the determination of aflatoxins by thin-layer chomatography," J. Chromatogr. A 904 (2000), 1263–268.

84. J. Stroka, T. Peschel, G. Tittelbach, G. Weidner, R. van Otterdijk and E. Anklam, "Modification of an office scanner for the determination of aflatoxins after TLC separation," J. Planar Chromatogr. 14 (2001), 109–112.

85. B. Renger, "Benchmarking HPLC and HPTLC in pharmaceutical analysis," J. Planar Chromatogr. 12 (1999), 58–62.

47 High Performance Liquid Chromatography

Antoine-Michel Siouffi
Université Paul Cezanne, Campus St. Jerôme

CONTENTS

I. GENERAL

According to the IUPAC definition (1) chromatography is a physical method of separation in which the components to be separated are distributed between two phases, one of which is stationary (the stationary phase) while the other (the mobile phase) moves in a definite direction.

The mobile phase is a fluid which percolates through or along the stationary bed. Chromatography is a differential migration technique where the flux of solutes to separate is perpendicular to the displacement of the mobile phase (2).

Three types of fluid are in current use: liquid, gas, or supercritical. Chromatography is named principally by the nature of the fluid. We can distinguish liquid, gas, or supercritical fluid chromatography.

The stationary phase may be a solid or a liquid. The combination of mobile and stationary phases unambiguously names the chromatographic mode.

Mobile phase	Gas	Liquid	Supercritical
Stationary	Liquid	Liquid	Liquid
Phase	Solid	Solid	Solid

Gas-liquid chromatography (GC) and liquid-solid chromatography are by far the most popular types. A special type of stationary phase consists of bonding chemical moieties onto a solid surface by covalent bonds. It is a bonded phase. Liquid chromatography with alkyl (or any other) bonded phases is considered liquid-solid. Use of liquid-liquid chromatography is rapidly declining and reports on the technique in recent years are scarce.

According to the nature of the stationary phase a chromatographic mode is often named by the chemical species which governs the retention mechanism.

We can thus distinguish in liquid chromatography (LC):

Adsorption chromatography, often referred to as normal phase mode (NP)

Reversed phase chromatography (on alkyl bonded silica) (RP)
Ion chromatography (IC)
Affinity chromatography
Size exclusion chromatography (SEC)
Chiral chromatography
Micellar liquid chromatography

High performance liquid chromatography (HPLC) is a well-established method in modern analysis. The method is simple, robust, and applicable to the majority of components to be analyzed. Low efficiency and small peak capacity are of HPLC when complex mixtures have to be separated. In contrast to GC the diffusion coeficient of the analytes is small and that is the biggest obstacle to efficient separations.

II. BASIC CHROMATOGRAPHIC INSTRUMENTATION

The heart of the separation is the column. Solutes are injected onto the column where they partition between the mobile and the stationary phase. When a solute is flowing off the column it is eluted.

Typically a chromatograph is depicted as follows:

Solutes to separate are placed in an injector, they are driven to the separation column; when they elute, they are monitored by a detector.

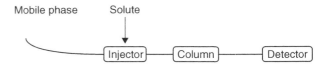

There are two ways to perform chromatography: analytical mode and preparative mode. We shall only consider the analytical mode in which solutes are infinitely diluted.

Molecules of solute which do not interact with stationary phase are not retained. Molecules of solute that can partition between both phases are retained. Detection and recording of separated solutes yield a chromatogram (Figure 47.1). On the chart solutes appear as peaks, the shape of which is nearly gaussian.

III. DEFINITIONS

The column volume is Vcol; the volume of the stationary phase inside the column is Vs; the volume of the mobile phase is V_M, which can be divided in extraparticular volume Ve and intraparticular volume Vi according to the type of the packing; and the porosity is $\varepsilon = V_M / Vcol$.

t_M is the mobile phase hold-up time; this is not the same as the retention time of the unretained solute, written as t_0. In fact, t_0 and t_M are not equal (especially in packed columns) and the nature of the unretained (or inert) solute should be mentioned in any reported experimental conditions. t_{Ri} is the retention time of the solute i.

The volume of the mobile phase required to elute an unretained solute is called V_0.

$$t_0 = \frac{V_0}{F}$$

where F is the mobile phase flow rate. $F = u_o \, \varepsilon \, S$ where u_o is the linear velocity of the liquid; ε is the porosity; and S is the cross section of the column. $t_0 = L/u_o$. Similarly, V_{Ri} is the retention volume of solute i.

The mobile phase must flow through the column. In packed columns Darcy's law (3) is written

$$u_0 = B_0 d_p^2 \, \Delta P \,/\eta \, L$$

B_0 is the permeability of the column packed with particles of average size d_p; ΔP is the pressure difference between inlet and outlet of the column; η is the viscosity of the mobile phase; and L is the column length.

The retention factor is

$$k_i = \frac{(t_{Ri} - t_0)}{t_0} = \frac{(V_{Ri} - V_0)}{V_0} = \frac{(d_{Ri} - d_0)}{d_0}$$

where d_0, d_R are retention distances measured on the recording chart.

The retention factor is also equal to the ratio of amounts of a sample component in the stationary and mobile phases, respectively, at equilibrium.

$$k = \frac{\text{Number of solute molecules in stationary phase}}{\text{number of solute molecules in mobile phase}}$$

$k = K(Vs/V_M)$ where K is the partition coefficient and Vs/V_M is the phase ratio.

The adjusted retention time is $t'_{Ri} = t_{Ri} - t_0$ and $k = t'_{Ri}/t_0$. Similarly,

$$V'_{Ri} = V_{Ri} - V_0$$

$$d'_{Ri} = d_{Ri} - d_0$$

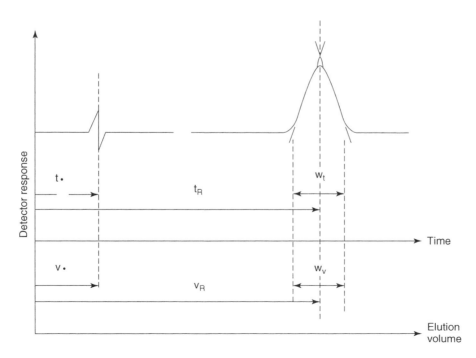

FIGURE 47.1 A chromatogram.

In analytical mode, peaks are presumed to be gaussian and retention parameters are taken at maximum peak heights.

When peaks are not truly gaussian, it is necessary to use statistical moments. The zero moment

$$M_0 = \int_b^a h(t) \cdot dt$$

where h(t) is the peak height at time t yields the peak area.

The first moment $M_1 = (1/M_0) \int_b^a t \cdot h(t) \cdot dt$ expresses the true retention time as it corresponds to the elution time of the center of gravity of the peak.

$$M_2 = \text{peak variance}$$

$$M_3 = \text{peak skew}$$

When two consecutive (i, j) gaussian peaks are close, the

$$\text{resolution is } Rs = 2 \, (t_{rj} - t_{ri})/(\omega_i + \omega_j)$$

ω is the peak width in time units (see Figure 47.2).

When peaks are gaussian $\omega = 4\sigma$ (σ is the standard deviation).

When two peaks are well resolved then $Rs \geq 1.25$ (see Figure 47.2).

Resolution can be written $Rs = (\overline{\sqrt{N/4}})(\Delta u/\overline{u})$ where Δu is the difference in velocity between two solutes i and j, $\overline{u}$ is the average velocity, and N is the efficiency.

Assymetry is determined by the A/B ratio (Figure 47.3).

Selectivity a is defined as $\alpha = k_j/k_i$. In this way $\alpha \geq 1$; when $\alpha = 1$ no separation occurs.

When solutes are late-eluting it is convenient to use gradient elution. The gradient retention factor is

$$k^* = t_G F/\Delta\%B V_M S$$

where t_G is the gradient time in min, F is the flow-rate in ml/min, Δ%B is the gradient range (e.g., Δ%B = 0.80 for a 20–100% gradient), V_M is the column volume in ml, and S is a constant for a given compound (see below).

Sharp peaks are indicative of the efficiency of the chromatographic process since the variance is small. Efficiency is also called plate number.

$$N = \left[\frac{t_R}{\sigma_t}\right]^2 = \left[\frac{V_R}{\sigma_V}\right]^2 = \left[\frac{d_R}{\sigma_d}\right]^2$$

When peaks are gaussian $N = 16(t_R/\omega)^2$:

$$N = 5.54 \left[\frac{t_R}{\delta}\right]^2$$

δ is the peak width at mid-height. When peak tailing occurs, it is convenient to use the Dorsey-Foley equation (4) from an exponentially modified gaussian equation.

The area of a gaussian peak is a function of its standard deviation and peak height according to the equation

$$A = \sqrt{2\pi}\sigma h_p, \quad h_p \text{ is the peak height}$$

$$\text{From } N = \left[\frac{t_r}{\sigma}\right]^2$$

and rearranging

$$N = \frac{2\pi(h_p t_r)^2}{A^2}$$

The plate height H is the column length divided by the plate number N = L/H

$$\text{Number of effective plates } N_{eff} = 16\left[\frac{t_R'}{\omega}\right]^2$$

The above equations can be combined. If $\overline{k} = \dfrac{(k_i + k_j)}{2}$ and assuming peaks are close enough,

$$Rs = \frac{\alpha - 1}{\alpha + 1} \frac{\overline{k}}{1 + \overline{k}} \frac{\sqrt{N}}{4}$$

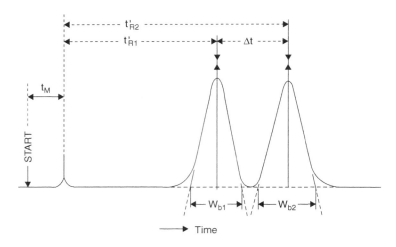

FIGURE 47.2   Resolution between two gaussian peaks: t is retention time, ω is peak width.

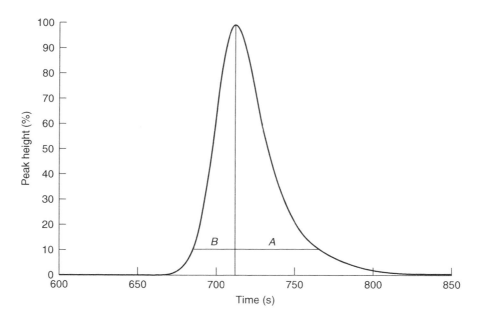

FIGURE 47.3 Asymmetry factor by determination of A/B ratio at 10% height.

A slightly different equation is written as

$$N = 16 \, Rs \left[\frac{\alpha}{\alpha - 1} \right]^2 \left[\frac{1 + \overline{k}}{\overline{k}} \right]^2$$

The equation permits us to determine the number of plates required to achieve the separation between two solutes of retention factors k_i and k_j, respectively, with a given Rs.

There are three factors in this equation which together determine the chromatographic resolution. The overall resolution is affected (assuming that the column length L is constant) by the selectivity term ($\alpha/\alpha - 1$), the retention term factor ($k/1 + k$), and the plate height H. Larger k values may lead to an increase in resolution at the expense of longer run times and wider bands. It is best to set k values between 1 and 6. The resolution power is the number of plates necessary to separate two solutes of relative retention α with a resolution Rs.

$$\alpha = [1 - 4Rs/\sqrt{N}.1 + k/k]^{-1}$$

The height equivalent to a theoretical plate (HETP) is dependent on the flow rate of the mobile phase. A slightly different equation from the well-known Van Deemter Equation (5) is valid in LC, the Knox Equation (6).

$$h = A\nu^{1/3} + B/\nu + C\nu$$

where h is the reduced plate height $h = H/d_p$; ν is the reduced velocity, $\nu = u_0 d_p/D_m$ where D_m is the diffusion coefficient of the solute in the mobile phase; and d_p is the average particle diameter.

The peak capacity is the number of peaks which can be observed on a chromatogram with baseline resolution (sometimes with unit resolution) assuming the constant N.

$$n_p = 1 + \frac{\sqrt{N}}{4} \log \frac{t_{Rz}}{t_{r1}}$$

In this equation t_{Rz} is the retention time of the last eluted solute. t_{r1} is the retention time of the first eluted solute.

Capacity of a column is the maximum amount of sample that can be injected into a column before significant peak distortion occurs.

Peak distortion is measured by either peak skew or by asymmetry factor.

IV. INSTRUMENTATION

Despite the trend towards miniaturization, most instruments are "conventional." A scheme of a LC instrument is displayed in Figure 47.4.

It consists of:

Solvent reservoirs
A solvent delivery system
An injection device
The column
A detector
A data acquisition system.

A. SOLVENT RESERVOIRS

Solvent reservoirs are usually made of glass. They should be equipped with degassing device. Degassing with helium is usually performed but it may form slugs of helium in the tubing.

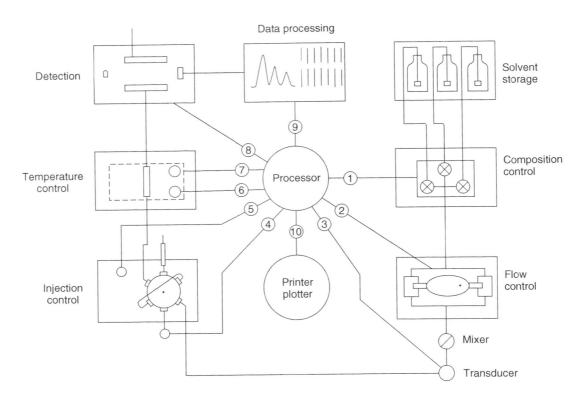

FIGURE 47.4   A scheme of a LC instrument.

Solvents are mixed in a mixing chamber. To account for the desired composition solenoid valves are actuated. Solvents should be HPLC grade. Careful attention should be paid to water and preparation of buffers.

B. SOLVENT DELIVERY SYSTEM

Reciprocating pumps are almost exclusively utilized with conventional columns. They exhibit large column back pressure compensation abilities, flow rates in the 0.1–10.0 ml range with high precision. Precise control of flow rate is of primary importance to ensure reproducibility of retention times. In some cases titanium or ceramic head pumps ensure biocompatibility. With open tubular columns, split flow techniques are probably best. Flow splitting devices are based on the microflow processor concept.

At present, most commercially available pumping units for conventional HPLC are the single or multihead reciprocating piston type. There is a trend towards very high pressures (up to 1200 bar) but that is achieved by modifying a commercially available pump.

Requirements for solvent delivery systems are as follows:

Flow rate stability
Flow rate accuracy (usually ± 0.3%)
Flow rate reproducibility
Large flow rate range (from 0.1 to 10 ml/min in HPLC)

Compatibility with any liquid
Standing with high pressures

In capillary LC, syringe-style, positive-displacement, continuous delivery design delivers solvent at the low-microliter flow rates that are optimal for micro-LC-MS but eluent compressibility and mixing of microflows are serious drawbacks.

1. Gradient Formation

Increasing the solvent strength permits us to achieve elution of highly retained solutes. Moreover, optimization procedures such as Drylab G make use of two gradients.

Two methods can generate binary solvent gradients: low pressure mixing or high pressure mixing. Some manufacturers display both. In the low mixing method, two solvent reservoirs and one single pump are used. In high pressure mixing mode two pumps separately deliver the required volumes of solvents.

The most critical points are the electronic control units and the mixing chamber.

Linear or curved shape gradients are possible but linear gradients are used by the vast majority of chromatographers. There is obviously a time delay between the solvent composition programmed and the actual composition at the column inlet due to the dwell volumes. Gradient delay and rounding are observed. Blank runs are carried out with the injector directly connected to a UV detector. Mobile phase

A is UV transparent and mobile phase B contains a slight proportion of UV absorbing solvent (1% acetone in methanol, for example). The gradient is performed and the delay time is determined. This is of primary importance to obtain reliable retention times.

Gradient delay volume is the volume between the start of the gradient and the top of the column.

Gradient delay time is the time elapsed between the start of the gradient and the time it reaches the top of the column.

C. COLUMN

Most commercially available columns are 4.6 mm inside diameter P (i.d.). They are made of stainless steel and the inner wall of the tubing is electropolished. Stainless steel tubing is easily machined and compression fittings can be affixed readily to ensure high pressure seals. Among the alternatives are polytetrafluoroethylene (PTFE)-lined stainless steel, polyetheretherketone (PEEK), hasteloy, and titanium. Metal-free systems are desirable for ion chromatography and the analysis of trace metals by ion exchange. Variable lengths are available (10-cm-long columns are most popular). Columns or cartridges can be serially connected to increase the plate number. Columns are packed with 3 μm or 5 μm particles either spherical or irregular shaped. Particles are either porous or non-porous. Silicagel is still the mainstay base material for most HPLC packings. Silicagel is rigid, provides excellent efficiency, is reasonably priced, and can be functionalized by virtue of the reactive silanols (SiOH). Most commercial silica-based analytical HPLC materials are made of ultra-pure monodisperse silica. In a porous particle solutes transfer from the moving mobile phase outside the particle into the stagnant mobile phase within the pores to interact with the stationary phase. The slow rate of mass transfer into and out of the porous particles is a major source of band broadening. The non-porous packings are less and less in use due to the limited sample capacity; on the one hand the thin layer allows faster mass transfer; on the other hand, the back pressures are high. Superficially porous packings (e.g., Poroshell from Agilent) are recommended for large biomolecules. Polymeric materials are used by approximately 15–20% of liquid chromatographers. Similar to silicagel, polymeric packings are also available with a variety of particle diameters. Polystyrene-divinylbenzene (PS-DVB) is the most popular with polymethacrylates. The PS-DVB polymers have a wide pH range, high cross-linking, withstand average pressure, and have no silanols to interact with the basic compounds. Conversely, the efficiency provided cannot compare with silica-based material since the rate of mass transfer is slower.

Copolymers of organofunctional silanes and tetraethoxysilane are a new means to synthesize of HPLC packings.

Zirconia provides some interesting features since it can be produced in monodisperse porous spherical particles, withstand a pH of 14, and has no silanols. However, it exhibits hard Lewis acid sites and consequently has a strong affinity towards Lewis bases (hydroxyls, phosphate). To overcome this drawback the analyst must use a competing anion or, even better, a polymer-coated, zirconia-based stationary phase.

Manufacturers provide a test chromatogram and ensure reproducibility from batch to batch.

An increase in column performances can be achieved by increasing the column permeability. The use of monolithic columns is a convenient way to overcome the drawback of the back pressure generated by small particles (see Darcy's equation above). Moreover, in the search for new stationary phase configurations with enhanced mass-transfer properties, the concept of monolithic stationary phases was established in which the separation medium consists of a continuous rod that has no interstitial volume but only internal porosity consisting of micro- and nanopores. Four approaches have been utilized to prepare continuous beds: polymerization of an organic monomer with additives, formation of a silica-based network using a sol-gel process, fusing the porous particulate packing material in a capillary by a sintering process, and organic hybrid materials. Polymer-based monolithic chromatographic supports are usually prepared by the *in situ* polymerization of suitable monomers and porogens within a tube that acts as a mold. Polymer monoliths are Polystyrene-divinyl benzene, polyacrylamide, or polymethacrylate (7–9). Silica-based monoliths were pioneered by Nakanishi and coworkers (10–12). Silica-based monolithic columns were released in 2000 by Merck. They consist of a single rod of silica-based material embedded in a PEEK tubing (13, 14). The new sorbent material consists of monolithic cylindrically shaped rods of highly porous metal-free silica. The defined homogeneous bimodal pore structure, produced during the manufacturing process, means that the columns possess a unique combination of a large internal surface area, over which quick chemical adsorption can take place, together with a significantly higher total porosity.

The pressure drop is dramatically decreased and longer columns can be used. These monolithic columns possess about 15% higher porosity as compared to particulate ones. Monolithic columns are 10 cm long and can be connected in series.

To reduce solvent consumption, there is a trend towards microcolumns, minicolumns, or true capillary columns.

Columns which exhibit internal diameter in the range 0.5–1.0 mm are called microcolumns (they were formerly called microbore). Good efficient microcolumns can be produced at the present time because the packing procedure has been optimized.

Capillary LC columns are of 10–500 μm internal diameter. It seems that 50 μm i.d. packed with 8 μm particles exhibit the best performances.

From theoretical papers published in the 1980s, open tubular columns in LC can only match performances of packed columns if the diameter of the column is of the same order of magnitude of the particle diameter in conventional columns. This conclusion has led to nanoscale LC with 5–11 μm i.d. open tubular columns which are used in research laboratories but not yet available for routine use.

The current trend of lab on a chip will result in new packing materials. Packing a stationary phase in microchannels looks impossible but microfabrication by ablation is promising (15).

Guard columns (1 cm long) must be connected to the analytical column to increase the lifetime, especially when dealing with complex samples. Guard columns, which fit between the injector and the analytical column, collect debris and stongly retained components. Two types of guard columns are available: those that are separate with their own holders and those that are integrated with the analytical column. A recent improvement is the use of guard discs that can be replaced periodically.

D. INJECTION

For manual and automated injection, the majority of the injection systems consist of injection valves. Sample loops are usually 10 μL for injection with a conventional column. In LC the analyst can increase the volume of injection without disturbing the separation efficiency. Conversely, the analyst must prevent any mass overloading. If so, partition of the solute is not performed in the linear portion of the isotherm with the consequence of peak tailing. Autosamplers are time-saving devices; design and associated problems were thoroughly discussed by Dolan (16,17).

E. DETECTORS

Some requirements of a LC detector are that it be of such a design that the separated components are not remixed while passing through the detector cell; have a low drift and noise level; have a fast response time; have a wide dynamic range; be relatively insensitive to changes in mobile phase flow rates and temperature; and be easy to operate and reliable.

There are three different types of detector noise: short-term noise, long-term noise, and drift.

1. Photometric Detectors

They rely on Beer's law. The Beer Lambert law is expressed as
where

$$A = \varepsilon \cdot l \cdot c$$

ε = molar absorptivity of the solute
l = path length through the sample
c = concentration of solute
A = absorbance

a. UV-VIS

These detectors measure changes in absorbance of light in the 190–350 nm region or 350–700 nm region.

Basic instrumentation includes a mercury lamp with strong emission lines at 254, 313, and 365 nm, cadmium at 229 and 326 nm, and zinc at 308 nm. Deuterium and xenon lamps exhibit a continuum in the 190–360 nm region which requires the use of a monochromator. A filter or grating is used to select a specific wavelength for measurement. Cut-off filters pass all wavelengths of light above or below a given wavelength. Band-pass filters pass light in a narrow range (e.g., 5 nm). In the single beam mode, the energy from the source lamp passes through the sample flow cell to a photocell via some wavelength selection device. The double beam system is preferred.

The flow cell is typically 8 μL with a 10-mm path length.

The photodiode array (see below) is currently the best sensor.

According to Beer's law, the higher the path length, the higher the transmitted light. For that purpose most cells are Z shaped.

With capillaries such as LC capillaries or CE capillaries there is only limited path length. A free portion of capillary is brought into the light path of a UV absorbance detector. When the aperture of the source is adjusted to the inside diameter of the capillary the effective light path is

$$l_{eff} = 1/2\pi r$$

where r is the radius of the capillary.

To improve the transmitted light a ball is placed after the capillary to focus the beams.

The limit of detection is highly dependent on the molar absortivity of the solutes ε (see Beer's law). UV-VIS detectors must be checked for wavelength accuracy, absorption accuracy, scattered light, and spectral resolution. Derivative spectra are obtained by differentiating the absorbance (A) spectra of the sample with respect to wavelength.

First, second, or higher-order derivatives may be generated. All the derivatives emphasize the features of the original spectra by enhancing small changes in slope.

Derivative spectra are generated optically, electronically, or mathematically. The usual optical method utilizes the wavelength modulation technique where wavelength of incident radiation is rapidly modulated over a narrow wavelength range. Electrically, derivatives are performed by analog resistance capacitance devices. Mathematical methods are obviously the best performing. The Savitsky Golay algorithm generates derivatives with a variable degree of smoothing.

Derivatives are used to

Enhance spectral differences
Enhance resolution
Selective substraction.

A photodiode array (PDA) is shown in Figure 47.5.

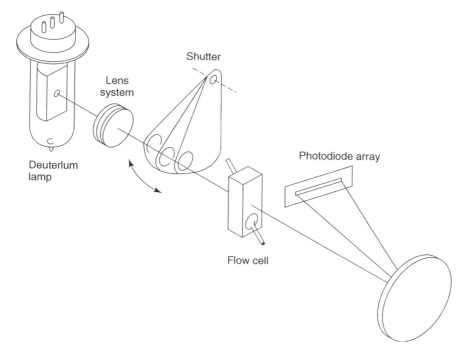

FIGURE 47.5   A photodiode array.

The detection of structurally similar impurities eluting simultaneously with the analytes of interest is a problem. The analyst must detect the existence of peaks of interest, determine the extent of their purity, and confirm their identity.

Photodiode operation relies on the photovoltaic effect. In the typical photodiode there are two components of semiconductor called P and N. P is a very pure silicon with low levels of three valent impurities such as boron or gallium. Each impurity atom can accept an electron from the valence bonds, giving rise to a hole that can take part in the electrical conduction process and an immobile negatively charged impurity ion. Since the hole is positively charged such a material is a P (positive) silicon crystal. If the impurity added is a pentavalent atom (As) the atoms behave as donors of electrons that can move through the entire silicon crystal. It is thus a N (negative) type. A photon of wavelength less than 1.1 nm is able to break a covalent bond between the silicon atoms. The free electron formed is free to move with the missing electron in the broken valence bond which induces electrical conduction by repeated replacement. The PDA detector passes the total light through the flow cell and disperses it with a diffraction grating. The dispersed light is measured by an array of photosensitive diodes. The array of photodiodes is scanned by the microprocessor (16 times a second is usual). The reading for each diode is summed and averaged. A PDA detector can simultaneously measure the absorbance of all wavelength versus time. The amount of data storage is a key feature in PDA. A run can easily take several megabytes of data storage. The dynamic range is usually 0.5 mAU–2.0 AU. Each pixel spans 1.25 nm.

Noise is around + or − $1.5*10^{-5}$ absorbance units (AU) with a 2 sec time constant.

Peak purity is based on the proprietary spectral contrast algorithm which converts spectral data into vectors that are used to compare spectra mathematically. This comparison is expressed as a purity angle. The purity angle is derived from the combined spectral contrast angles between the peak apex spectrum and all other spectra within that peak. To determine peak purity, the purity angle is compared to the purity threshold. For a pure peak the purity angle will be less than the purity threshold.

Spectral deconvolution techniques are used when two peaks co-elute.

Identification of peaks is performed by comparison with spectra contained in a library of standards.

b.   Fluorescence detection

The quantum yield ϕ is a fundamental molecular property that describes the ratio of a number of photons emitted to the number of photons absorbed.

$$\phi = \frac{k_f}{k_f + \Sigma k_d}$$

k_f is the rate constant for fluorescence emission. Σk_d is the sum of the rate constants for all the nonradiative processes which can depopulate S_1.

The signal intensity I_f is given by Beer's law:

$$I_f = I_o(1 - e^{\varepsilon l C})\phi k$$

When sample absorbance is small this expression is reduced to

$$I_f = I_0 \cdot 2 \cdot 3 \cdot \varepsilon \cdot 1 \cdot C \cdot \phi k$$

k is the instrumental efficiency for collecting the fluorescence emission. I_0 is the intensity of the incident radiation.

Fluorescence emission provides more selectivity and increased sensitivity compared to UV absorption. Attomole detection is possible. Xenon lamps are far superior to Hg lamps or D_2 lamps as light sources. Selection of excitation or emission wavelength is done by a monochromator.

Laser-induced fluorescence is in current use. Various lasers are utilized (He-Cd diode, Argon ion). The diode laser seems the best choice. Due to the highly collimating nature of lasers most scattering sources are eliminated. Increased detection is carried out with pre- or post-column derivatization. A three-dimensional spectrofluorometer incorporating a charge-coupled-device has been described (18) that made possible the collection of fluorescence excitation-emission intensity data of polycyclic aromatic hydrocarbons in a flow stream in 0.05 s with ng/milliter limits of detection.

Chiroptical detection provides additional qualitative and quantitative information for photometric detection since only chiral compounds are monitored. A detector provides both the differential absorbance of the circular dichroism and the absorbance of the UV mode simultaneously as a function of time (19).

c. Chemiluminescence method

Oxidative combustion of nitrogen-containing compounds produce nitric oxide. Nitric acid when in contact with ozone produces a metastable nitrogen dioxide molecule

$$NO + O_3 \longrightarrow NO_2^* + O_2$$

which relaxes to a stable state by emitting at a wavelength of 700–900 nm

$$NO_2^* \longrightarrow NO_2 + h\nu$$

Chemiluminescence is used for specific detection of nitrogen.

d. Derivatization

Many solutes do not exhibit UV absorption or fluorescence; they can be converted into UV absorbing or fluorescent derivatives by pre- or post-column derivatization. When precolumn derivatization is carried out the chromatographic system is obviously different fom the one selected for the non-derivatized solutes. A large volume of literature deals with post-column reactions. They can be carried out in coils, in packed bed reactors, or by photolysis. The main requirement is not the completion of the reaction but the reproducibility. Reaction vessels should not produce excessive band broadening. Table 47.1 displays some derivatizing reagents for the fluorescence labeling of functional groups.

2. Electrochemical Detection

a. Conductivity

The detection method is based on the application of an alternative voltage E to the cell electrodes. The cell current is directly proportional to the conductance G of the solution between the electrodes by Ohm's law.

$$G = \frac{1}{k} = \frac{i}{E}$$

The measured conductivity is the sum of individual contribution to the total conductivity of all the ions in solution. Kohlrausch's law states that

$$k = \frac{\Sigma_i \lambda_i^0 C_i}{1000}$$

C_i is the concentration of each ion i, and λ_i^0 is the limiting equivalent conductivity which is the contribution of an ion to the total conductivity divided by its concentration extrapolated to infinite dilution.

Kohlrausch's law is only valid in dilute solutions (chromatography or electrophoresis). The magnitude of the signal is greatest for small high mobility ions with a multiple charge such as sulphate. The conductivity detector was the breakthrough in ion chromatography (IC).

Early IC systems detected ions eluted by strong eluents from high capacity ion exchange columns by measuring changes in conductivity. To achieve reasonable sensitivity, it was necessary to suppress the conductivity of eluent prior to detection in order to enhance the overall conductance of the analyte and lower the background conductance of the eluent. This was achieved by a "suppressor" column in which counter ions were exchanged with H^+ or OH^-. Due to excessive band-broadening column suppressors are no longer in use. Membrane based devices are utilized. The membrane suppressor incorporates two semi-permeable ion exchange membranes sandwiched between sets of screens. The eluent passes through a central chamber. Regenerant flows in a counter-current direction over the outer surfaces of the membranes providing constant regeneration. Electrolysis of water produces hydrogen or hydroxide ions required for regeneration. There is no contamination with carbonate (Figure 47.6).

In conductivity detectors the change in conductivity Δk depends on the concentration of the injected ion (A) and its equivalent ionic conductivity λ_A compared with that of the eluent ion λ_E.

$$\Delta k = (A) \cdot (\lambda_A - \lambda_E)$$

Conductivity detectors usually operate at 10 kHz; scale ranges are 0.01 to 5000 µS in 12 steps.

TABLE 47.1

Derivatizing Reagents for the Fluorescence Labeling of Functional Groups

Reagent	Abbreviation	Functional Group
Aminoethyl-4-dimethylaminonaphthalene	DANE	Carboxyl
4-(Aminosulfonyl)-7-fluoro-2,1,3-benzoxadiazole	ABD-F	Thiol
Ammonium-7-fluorobenzo-2-oxa-1,3,diazole-4-sulfonate	SBD-F	Thiol
Anthracene isocyanate	AIC	(Amine), hydroxyl
9-Anthryldiazomethane	ADAM	Carboxyl (and other acidic groups)
Bimane, monobromo-	mBBr	Thiol
Bimane, dibromo-	bBBr	Thiol
Bimane, monobromotrimethylammonio-	qBBr	Thiol
4-Bromo-methyl-7-acetoxycoumarin	Br-Mac	See Br-Mmc
4-Bromo-methyl-7-methoxycoumarin	Br-Mmc	Carboxyl,imide, phenol, thiol
N-Chloro-5-dimethylaminonaphthalene-1-sulfonamide	NCDA	Amine (prim., sec.), thiol
9-(Chlormethyl)anthracene	9-CIMA	See Br-Mmc
7-Chloro-4-nitrobenzo-2-oxa-1,3-diazole	NBD-Cl	Amino (prim., sec.), phenol
2-p-Chlorosulfophenyl-3-phenylindone	DIS-Cl	Amino acids, amino sugars
9,10-Diaminophenanthrene	9,10-DAP	Carboxyl
2,6-Diaminopyridine-Cu^{2+}	2,6-DAP-Cu	Amines (prim. aromatic)
4-Diazomethyl-7-methoxycoumarin	DMC	See ADAM
5-Di-n-butylaminonaphthalene-1-sulfonyl chloride	Bns-Cl	See Dns-Cl
Dicyclohexylcarbodiimide	DCC	Carboxyl
N,N'-Dicyclohexyl-O-(7-methoxycoumarin-4-yl)methylisourea	DCCl	Carboxyl
N,N'-Diisopropyl-O-(7-methoxycoumarin-4-yl)methylisourea	DlCl	Carboxyl
4-Dimethylaminoazobenzene-4'-sulfonylchloride	Dbs-Cl	See Dns-Cl
N-(7-Dimethylaminoazobenzene-4'-methyl-3-coumarinylmaleimide	DACM	Thiol
5-Dimethylaminonaphthalene-1-sulfonyl-aziridine	Dns-aziridine	Thiol
5-Dimethylaminonaphthalene-1-sulfonylchloride	Dns-Cl	Amino (prim., sec., tert.), (hydroxyl), imidazole, phenol, thiol
5-Dimethylaminonaphthalene-1-sulfonyl-hydrazine	Dns-hydrazine	Carbonyl
4-Dimethylamino-1-napthoylinitrile	DMA-NN	Hydroxyl
9,10-Dimethoxyanthracene-2-sulfonate	DAS	Amine (sec., tert.)
2,2'-Dithiobis (1-aminonaphthalene)	DTAN	Aromatic aldehydes
1-Ethoxy-4-(dichloro-s-triazinyl)naphthalene	EDTN	Amine, hydroxyl (prim.)
9-Fluorenyl-methylchloroformate	FMOCCl	Amine (prim., sec.)
7-Fluoro-4-nitrobenzo-2-oxa-1,3-diazole	NBD-F	Amine (prim., sec.), phenol, thiol
4'-Hydrazino-2-stilbazole	—	α-Oxo acids
4-Hydroxymethyl-7-methoxycoumarine	Hy-Mmc	Carboxyl
4-(6-Methylbenzothiazol-2-yl)-phenyl-isocyanate	Mbp	Amine (prim., sec.), hydroxyl
N-Methyl-1-naphthalenemethylamine	—	Isocyanates (aliphatic, aromatic)
1,2-Naphthoylenebenzimidazole-6-sulfonyl chloride	NBl-SO2Cl	See Dns-Cl
2-Naphthylchloroformate	NCF	Amine (tert.)
Naphthyl isocyanate	NlC	(Amine), hydroxyl
Ninhydrin	—	Amine (prim.)
4-Phenylspiro(furan-2(3H), 1'-phthalan)-3,3'-dione (fluorescamine)	Flur	Amine (prim., sec.), hydroxyl, (thiol)
o-Phthaldialdehyde (o-phthalaldehyde)	OPA	Amine (prim., sec.), thiol
N-(1-Pyrene)maleimide	PM	Thiol

(Reproduced from Journal of Planar Chromatogarphy. With permission.)

b. Amperometric

Electrochemical detection is a concentration-sensitive technique. In amperometric mode compounds undergo oxidation or reduction reaction through the loss or gain, respectively, of electrons at the working electrode surface. The working electrode is kept at the constant potential against a reference electrode. The electrical current from the electrons passed to or from the electrode is recorded and is proportional to the concentration of the analyte present.

A thin layer cell is displayed in Figure 47.7.

A thin gasket with a slot cut in the middle is sandwiched between two blocks: one contains the working electrode, the other contains the counter electrode. The slot in the gasket forms the thin layer channel. The reference electrode is placed downstream from the working electrode.

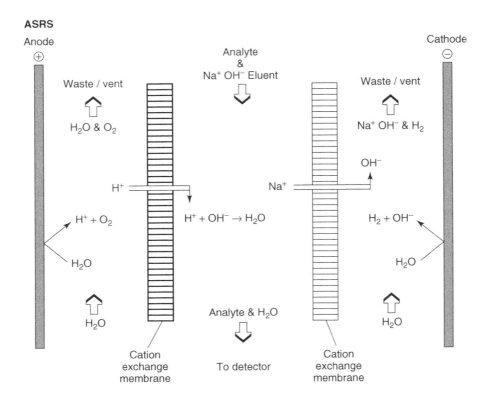

FIGURE 47.6 Anion self-regenerating suppressor for ion chromatography. (Courtesy of Dionex.)

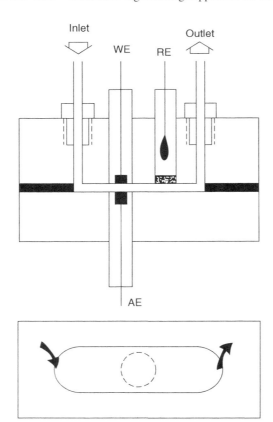

FIGURE 47.7 Electrochemical detector: a thin layer cell. WE: working electrode; AE: auxiliary electrode; RE: reference electrode.

The thin layer design produces high mobile phase linear velocity which in turn produces high signal magnitude.

The intensity of the current is

$$i = f \cdot n \cdot F \cdot u^{1/2} \cdot C \cdot D^{2/3} \cdot A$$

n = the number of electrons
F = the Faraday constant
u = the linear velocity of the mobile phase
C = the analyte concentration
D = the diffusion coefficient of the solute
A = the electrode surface
f = the geometrical constant of the cell

The quality of the sample clean-up procedure often determines the detection limits. The instability of the reference electrode is the source of voltage noise.

A parallel dual electrode may be used for a number of reasons.

i. With one electrode at a positive and one electrode at a negative potential, oxidizable and reducible compounds can be detected in one single chromatographic run.

ii. When two solutes with different redox potentials co-elute from the column, the potential of one electrode can be selected such that only the most easily oxidized (or reduced) compound is detected while on the other electrode both compounds are converted. The concentration of the second compound is evaluated by subtraction of the signal.

Series dual electrodes are set up in that one electrode is in oxidative and the other is in reductive mode. The downstream electrode measures the products of the upstream electrode. The second electrode only responds to compounds which are converted reversibly. The redox product is more selectively detected.

Voltammetric analysis is performed by scanning the potential or by applying triangular potential wave form to the electrode. Co-eluting peaks are distinguished if their voltagrams are significantly different.

3. Refractive Index Detector (RI)

This is one of very few universal detectors available. An RI detector monitors both the eluent and the analyte. The output reflects the difference in refractive index between a sample flow cell and a reference flow cell. The measured RI response is determined by the volume fraction of the analyte in the flow cell (x) and the volume fraction of the eluent in the other flow cell $(1 - x)$.

$$\eta - \eta_2 = v_1 (\eta_1 - \eta_2)$$

where

v_1 = volume fraction of the analyte
η_1 = refractive index of pure analyte
η_2 = refractive index of pure solvent (contained in a reference cell)
η = refractive index of solution in sample cell.

$$\text{RI signal} = K_{RI} \cdot dn/dc \cdot C$$

where K_{RI} is an instrument constant, dn/dc is the refractive index increment, and C, the concentration.

There are four types of RI detectors.

– The deflection type is by far the most popular; it relies on Snell's law which governs the angles of incidence and refraction at an interface:

$$\eta_1 \sin \theta_1 = \eta_2 \sin \theta_2$$

where θ_1 is the angle of the beam with respect to the normal of the interface in the medium with RI of η_1.

– The eflection type according to Fresnel's law of reflection; measurement of Δn is a measure of change in reflectivity
– The interference type (utilized in capillary LC)
– The Christiansen effect type

The refractive index is very sensitive to temperature and pressure. For that reason the reference and the measurement cell are close since the difference in temperature

between them is critical. Specifications of a RI detector are: refractive index range, linearity range, cell volume, maximum pressure in cell, and temperature control.

$$\frac{d\eta}{dt} \cdot 10^{-4} = 0.67 \text{ for water}$$
$$= 6.84 \text{ for dichloromethane}$$

$$\frac{d\eta}{dp} \cdot 10^5 = 1.53 \text{ for water}$$
$$= 6.84 \text{ for dichloromethane}$$

He/Ne laser-based RI detection has been developed for nanoscale LC.

4. Light Scattering Detector

The principle of operation is a three-step process. The effluent of the LC column is vaporized in a nebulizer by means of a gas. The droplets pass through a drift tube at a temperature of 40–50°C, and the only particles left are the analyte and the solvent impurities. A laser (typically 1 mV He/Ne) irradiates the particles, and the scattered light is collected by a glass rod and transmitted to a photomultiplier tube (Figure 47.8). The light measured is proportional to the amount of sample in the light scattering chamber.

Parameters affecting the response are particle size, degree of nebulization (most critical), and nature of the solvent. When an LSD detector is used to detect thermally labile compounds the temperature used to evaporate the mobile phase is critical. If the temperature is too high, the compounds of interest can be thermally decomposed and reduce the sensitivity of the assay. The temperature range of the nebulizer is 40°–220°. The design of the evaporation tube is critical. The amount of scattered light depends strongly on the molar absorptivity of the solute. The light-scattering detector is universal detector but not a mass detector. Its response is nonlinear and the calibration curve is log-log. It can easily be used with a gradient. The benefits are low temperature evaporation of the mobile phase, and gradients can be used since the mobile phase is removed. The detector is suited for lipids and sugars. The signal of a light-scattering detector is proportional to the molecular weight of polymers.

V. HYPHENATION

Combining a chromatographic separation system on-line with a spectroscopic detector in order to obtain structural information on the analytes present in a sample has become the most important approach for the identification or confirmation of identity of target and unknown chemical species. In most instances, such hyphenation can be accomplished by using commercially available instruments. For most trace-level analytical problems the LC-MS combination is the accepted approach. However, more information is retrieved from concatenation of LC-MS with FTIR or NMR.

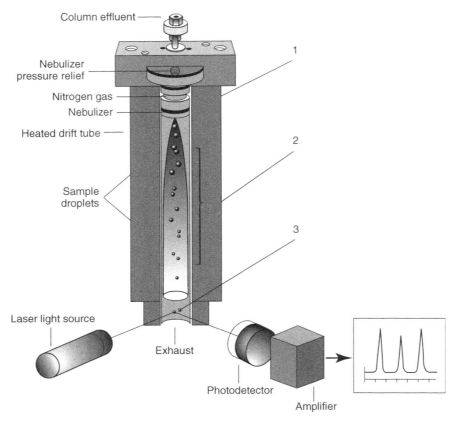

FIGURE 47.8   Light scattering detector: 1: nebulization; 2: mobile phase evaporation; 3: detection. (Courtesy of Alltech.)

The LC-UV-NMR-MS (hypernation) is the best example (Figure 47.9).

A.   LC-MS

The mass spectrometer is becoming the detector of choice for many LC methods. In this case it is important in RPLC to select buffers that are MS-compatible such as 0.1% trifluoroacetic acid (pH $\cong$ 1.9) and ammonium formate for applications at higher pH values.

Interfaces have been developed to solve the problem of handling high LC flow rates (1 mL/min) and the high vacuum required by mass spectrometers.

The mass spectrometer is a mass flow sensitive detector. The enrichment factor is the ratio of the analyte concentration in the MS flow and that in the LC flow. The transfer yield is

$$Y = Q_m/Q_l$$

Q_m is the amount of solute transferred in MS and Q_l is the amount of solute from LC column.

LC is not nearly as compatible with MS as in GC.

Hyphenating LC and MS requires overcoming some difficulties.

- Conventional packed columns are operated at 1 mL/min; to overcome this drawback microbore columns are more and more frequently utilized.

- LC separations make use of non-volatile mobile phases and very often buffer solutions.
- Ionization of non-volatile or thermally labile solutes is difficult. However, difficulties have been overcome and LC-MS has become a robust and routinely applicable tool in environmental laboratories.

Electrospray (ESI), atmospheric pressure chemical ionization (APCI), and atmospheric-pressure photoionization (APPI) are today the ionization techniques enabling robust interfacing of LC to (tandem) MS. Nowadays LC-MS-MS instruments are marketed within the chromatographic community as a laboratory workhouse requiring only basic knowledge about mass spectrometry from the analyst. A wide variety of atmospheric pressure ionization (API) source designs are available from the instrument manufacturers.

1.   Ionization

a.   Electrospray ionization(ESI)
A typical LC-MS with ESI interface is displayed in Figure 47.10. In ESI the ionization occurs in the liquid phase (in the spray) where ions might already be present or are created by application of a high electrical potential (3–5kV) to the sprayer tip. Evaporation of the liquid is assisted by

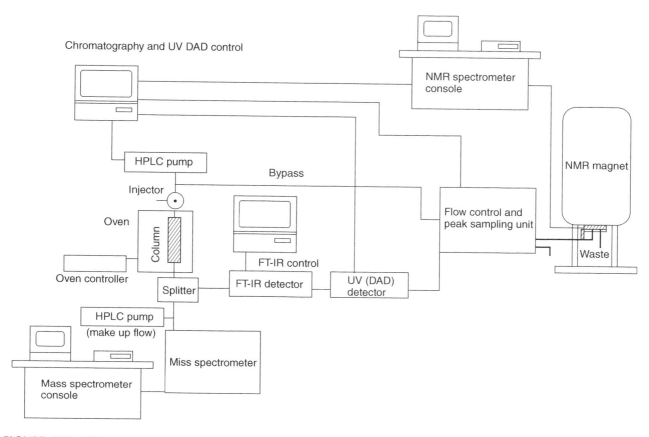

FIGURE 47.9 Hypernation: set up for LC-[DAD UV] –FTIR NMR/MS. (Reproduced from Journal of Chromatography A, Vol. 1000, p. 350. With permission from Elsevier.)

pneumatic pressure and by heat. Orthogonal spray orientation keeps the capillary and ion optics cleaner. The standard ESI sources cover the range from 0.1 to 2 mLmin^{-1} and are therefore compatible with the average flow rate (1 mL/min) from 4.6 mm i.d. columns. ESI is a soft technique well suited to thermally labile molecules. The drawback is the occurrence of matrix effects. ESI is concentration dependent. A great deal of effort is focused on miniaturization of the system.

Two mechanisms have been proposed for the formation of ions by electrosray. The first is ion evaporation, which results in analyte ion desorption from a droplet due to high-field strength generated by charged droplets (20,21) The other relies on Rayleigh fissions to form very small charged droplets followed by solvent evaporation to result in a gas phase analyte ion (22). One characteristic of ESI instrumentation is the large pressure differential which is necessary for the combination of ionization at atmospheric pressure with the low pressures required for mass analysis and ion detection. The pressure differential is usually achieved either with a sampling cone/skimmer or capillary/skimmer arrangements. As the gas expands through the sampling cone into the lower pressure region, it forms a supersonic jet. The position of the skimmer in the source relative to the cone or capillary is extremely

important for ensuring minimal ion losses in this region. Potentials applied between the skimmer and the cone/capillary serve both to focus the ion beam through the skimmer orifice and to accelerate ions through the intermediate pressure region.

Most manufactured electrospray interfaces attempt to negate the effects of the charged residues by using off-axis nebulizers, have an arrangement of off-axis skimmers or skimmer capillary sampling orifices, or use a shield in front of the sampling orifice. The disadvantage of ESI is its low tolerance to buffer salts. Nano ESI is more and more in use in protein analysis.

b.   Sonic spray ionization (SSI)
In this technique (Figure 47.11), a sample solution is sprayed from a sample introduction capillary by a high speed nitrogen gas flow that is coaxial to the capillary, and ions of the chemical in the solution as well as charged droplets are produced at room temperature and atmospheric pressure. An electric field is applied to the solution in the capillary to increase the charge density of produced droplets, so that multiply charged ions are produced. The most important feature of SSI is that it does not require a heated nebulizer or the application of a high voltage to the sprayer. The range of solution flow rates in SSI is under

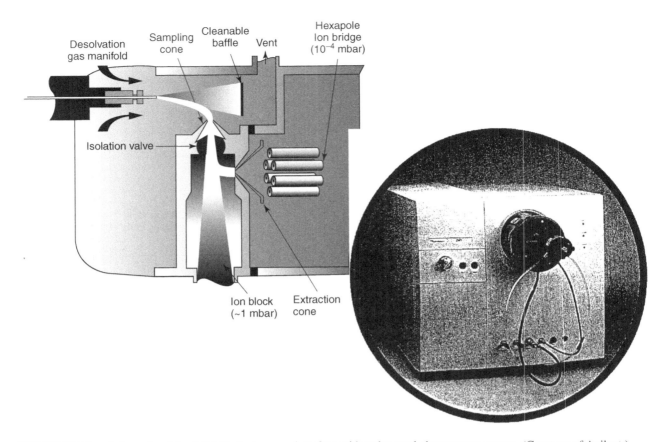

FIGURE 47.10   Schematic of the LC-MS electrospray interface with orthogonal electrospray system. (Courtesy of Agilent.)

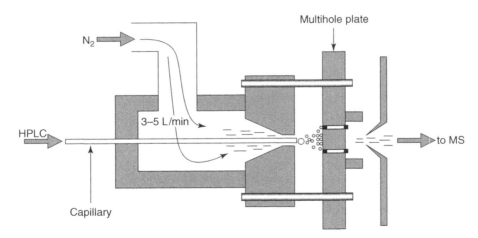

FIGURE 47.11   Schematic of a sonic spray ionization source. (Courtesy of Hitachi.)

0.2 mL/min; SSI is useful for semi-micro LC-MS but not well suited for conventional flow rates of 1mL/min.

c. Atmospheric pressure chemical ionization (APCI)

Atmospheric pressure chemical ionization (APCI) is a three-step process: the liquid flow from the LC is sprayed and rapidly evaporated by a coaxial nitrogen stream and heating the nebulizer to high temperature (350°–500°).

Additional ionization is achieved by means of a corona discharge (3–6 keV) producing primary ions (N_2^+ and O_2^+ in positive mode). Interface consists of a concentric pneumatic nebulizer and a heated large-diameter, quartz tube. The primary ions react immediately with the solvent molecules of the mobile phase with the formation of reagent ions (e.g., H_3O^+, $CH_3OH_2^+$ in positive mode). The reagent ions react (e.g., proton transfer) with solute molecules yielding $[M+H]^+$ in positive ion mode or

$[M-H]^-$ in negative ion mode. Processes are separated in APCI which allows the use of some unfavorable solvents. Ionization occurs in the gas phase whereas it occurs in the liquid phase in ESI. APCI is mass dependent and less prone to matrix effects. APCI can withstand high flow rates but miniaturization is more difficult than with ESI.

d. Atmospheric-pressure photoionization (APPI)

Photoionization is induced by means of a xenon lamp (10 eV). A dopant species, with the ionization potential of <10 eV, such as toluene, is utilized. Covaporized dopant molecules are ionized by UV radiation. Photoions thus produced initiate ion molecule reactions with the solute molecules, yielding $[M+H]^+$ and M^+ by proton transfer or charge transfer. The solvents in the mobile phase must have a ionization potential >10 eV to prevent ionization from the xenon lamp with a resulting increase in background signal.

e. Maldi

Matrix-assisted laser desorption ionization (MALDI) is well suited for macromolecules such as peptides, proteins, oligosaccharides, and oligonucleotides. In a Maldi experiment a proper organic matrix (e.g., glycerol) is required for mixing with the analyte in a ratio typically 500/1. The mixture is dried and inserted in a MS. A laser beam will desorb and ionize the matrix species, thus ionizing the analyte. Most Maldi-MS systems are based on time of flight (TOF) mass analyzers. Ions produced by the laser beam are extracted from the source and expelled to the flight tube.

B. MASS ANALYZERS

The resolving power of a mass spectrometer is a measure of its ability to distinguish between two neighboring masses. Resolution is $\Delta amu/amu$ (atomic mass unit). Spectrometers easily perform resolutions of 50,000 (i.e., distinguish $\Delta amu = 0.01$ when M = 500). Resolution is often written in ppm, $\Delta amu *10^6/M$.

The quadrupole mass filter consists of four parallel hyperbolic rods in a square array (Figure 47.12). The inside radius (field radius) is equal to the smallest radius curvature of the hyperbola. Diagonally opposite rods are electrically connected to radio frequency/direct current voltages. For a given radio frequency/current voltage ratio, only ions of a dedicated m/z value are transmitted to the filter and reach the detector. Ions with a different m/z ratio are deflected away from the principal axis and strike the rods. To scan the mass spectrum, the frequency of the radio frequency voltage and the ratio of the ac/dc voltages are held constant while the magnitudes of ac and dc voltages are varied. The transmitted ions of m/z are then linearly dependent on the voltage applied to the quadrupole producing m/z scale which is linear with time. A triple quadrupole instrument uses two quadrupole MS analyzers for the actual MS experiments and a third

quadrupole in RF mode which transmits all incoming ions from MS1 to MS2.

For quadrupole mass spectrometers, selected ion monitoring (SIM) yields significantly enhanced detection limits compared with scanning MS operation because of the greater dwell time for signal acquisition at each selected m/z values.

Ionization steps and ion separation are space separated in a quadrupole system whereas they are time spaced in ion traps. An ion trap (Figure 47.13) is a linear quadrupole bent to a close loop. Typically, three electrodes are a common design of an ion trap: a ring electrode and two end cap electrodes. The outer rods form a ring and the inner rod is reduced to a mathematical point in the center of the trap. End electrodes exhibit a hole in their center to allow for introduction of ions and ejection of these ions towards the detecting device. A radio frequency is applied to the ring electrode and consequently, a quadrupole field is produced which traps ions. Each ion is submitted to an oscillating motion, the amplitude of which depends on the RF and the m/z ratio. Ions of different masses are stored together in the trap and released one at a time by scanning the applied voltages. They can be ejected through the end caps and detected by applying a RF voltage with a frequency corresponding to the characteristic frequency of the ion moving through the ion trap or by scanning the amplitude of the applied RF voltage. With a reduced pressure of gas (He)(10^{-3} torr) the motion of ions in the trap is dampened and the ions move closely around the center of the trap. Ion traps are a powerful tool in elucidating fragmentation mechanisms since it allows stepwise and controlled fragmentation in multistage MS. Ion traps are small benchtop instruments.

Linear two-dimensional ion traps are now commercially available (23).

1. Time of Flight

A scheme is displayed below:

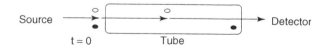

Heavy ions (slow) : ○
Light ions (fast) : ●

A small number of ions is extracted from the source in a few μseconds, accelerated with few kV, and directed to a tube. The process can be repeated 100,000 times per second. Kinetic energy is similar for every ion and ions with higher velocities (light ions) will reach the end of the tube before heavy ions. Instruments have two tubes with a mirror in the middle and resolution may reach 5000. A schematic diagram of an instrument is displayed in Figure 47.14.

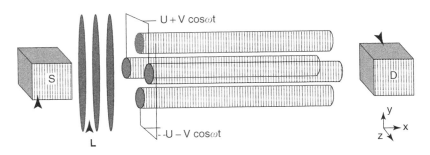

FIGURE 47.12   Scheme of a quadrupole instrument. (Coustesy of Micromass.)

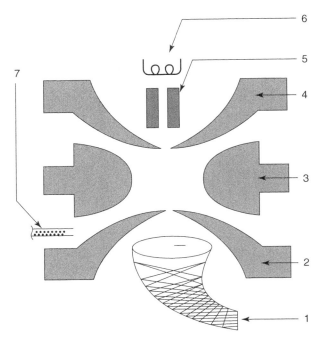

FIGURE 47.13   An ion trap. 1 = channeltron detection; 2 = cap electrode; 3 = ring electrode; 4 = cap electrode, 5 = electron gate; 6 = eletron emitting device; f = column. (Courtesy of Agilent.)

In a tube L the time of flight t is connected to the velocity v

$$t = L/v$$

Ions get a kinetic energy $E_k = 1/2\ mv^2 = 2V$ where V is the voltage, then $t = L[m/2Vz]^{1/2}$. The time of flight is proportional to the square root of the ion mass which allows discrimination according to the m/z ratio.

As an example, if 300V are used to accelerate the ions in the flight tube, an ion with m/z = 1000 needs about 200 μs to reach the detector.

The hybrid quadrupole time of flight mass spectrometer (Q-TOF) was introduced as a mass spectrometer capable of tandem MS with particular emphasis on its applicability for protein and peptide analysis. Key components of the instrument are the quadrupole, hexapole collision cell, and the reflectron-TOF analyzer. In normal mode, the quadrupole region and hexapole collision cell, are operated in a non-mass discriminative wide-band pass mode allowing all ions

to pass unperturbed in the pusher of the TOF analyzer. Like all TOF analyzers, the m/z measurement is based on the amount of time required for an ion to travel the distance from the source of entry (pusher on a Q-TOF) to the multi-channel plate (MCP) detector. The signal detected by the MCP is integrated over an unspecified period of time and each integrated spectrum is written to disk.

The electronics of the detector must record the complete mass spectrum within the flight time of the ions (1–100 μs range) with peak widths in the ns range. This is possible since high scan rate (up to 20,000 scans/s) allows for the detection of narrow chromatographic peaks. There is virtually no limit on mass range and no ion loss. The use of time-dependent accelerating fields can improve the resolution of TOF instruments. The technique involves the introduction of an appropriate time-delay between the ion formation and ion acceleration. During this time, ions disperse with their individual kinetic energies. Since the accelerating potential varies linearly with the position of the ions

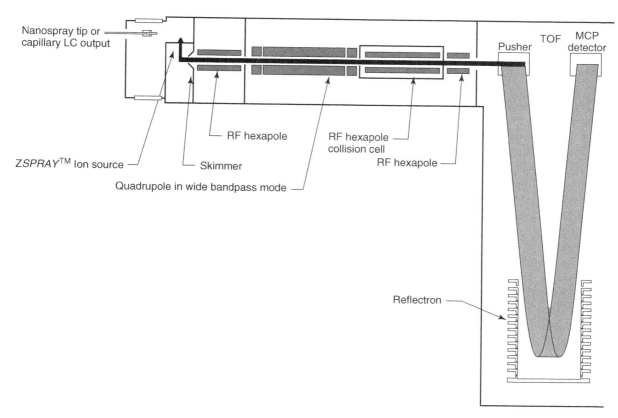

FIGURE 47.14 Schematic of a quadrupole time of flight (Q-TOF) mass spectrometer shown operating in MS mode. (Courtesy of Micromass.)

in the source region, ions with the same m/z ratio but different positions are accelerated through different acceleration voltages. In this way, correction for the initial ion velocity distribution is achieved.

TOF-MS has to a large extent replaced high resolution double-focusing magnetic sector instruments for LC-MS applications. With the fast acquisition capacity of the TOF instrument (>10 spectra/sec), the effluents from four HPLC columns are continuously electrosprayed.

C. ICP-MS

Inductively coupled plasma mass spectrometry is highly selective in ultra-trace-level metal detection technique. Interfacing HPLC to ICP-MS can be achieved with relative ease by means of a length of PEEK tubing connecting the HPLC column to the nebulizer of the ICP-MS. Performances are strongly dependent on the type of nebulizer utilized as the sample introduction device. HPLC-isotope dilution-ICPMS offers considerable potential for speciation studies.

D. NMR

On-line coupling of HPLC with nuclear magnetic resonance spectroscopy (NMR) has proved useful for a wide range of applications. The shortcoming of suppression of eluent signals can be circumvented by use of a capillary separation technique. Capillary concentration techniques are important to take advantage of the miniaturized rf coils. In this mode detection cells with internal volumes in the nanoliter scale and miniaturized probe heads have been developed by Albert and colleagues in Tübingen (24). The system can be used in either HPLC, CE, or CEC and consists of a capillary inserted into a 2.5 or 2.0 mm NMR microprobe equipped with a Helmholtz coil. In experiments a capillary tube of 315 μm can create a detection volume of 900 nL. The flow rate of the capillary HPLC-NMR can be adjusted to 3 μL/min with the help of a T piece inserted between the HPLC pump and the capillary device. The polyimide coating was removed over the length of the NMR coil directly after the outlet frit of the capillary packing. In another design the packed capillary LC column is placed directly below the cryomagnet. With the help of a transfer capillary (400*50 μm) the eluate is transferred to the detection capillary with an internal diameter of 180 μm. The NMR detection volume is thus 200 nL. For example, assignment of vitamin E structures is possible.

VI. PERFORMANCES

The HETP equation with packed columns has been devised by Knox (6) and is written in reduced variables:

$$h = A \nu^{1/3} + B/\nu + C\nu$$

where A stands for the anisotropy of flow rate, B is the molecular diffusion, and C is the mass transfer term. With good columns A = 1, B = 2, and C is around 0.01. h is the reduced plate height (h/d_p with packed columns, h/d_c in open tubular columns), and ν is the reduced velocity $\nu = ud_p/Dm$. Small particles yield HETP curves with negligible C term. In this mode, HETP does not vary too much when flow rates are increasing beyond the minimum but back pressures dramatically increase. It must be pointed out that the Van Deemter equation H = A + B/u + Cu applies with monolithic columns.

The pressure used to pack a column can have a dramatic effect on the performance characteristics of the column.

Recorded peak width is the sum of column and extra-column contributions to band spreading. The instrument contribution comes from the injector, connecting tubings, column frits, detector, and data-handling. Since residence times of the solute in all these parts are independent, variances are additive and thus:

$$\sigma^2 = \sigma^2_{injector} + \sigma^2_{column} + \sigma^2_{detector} + \sigma^2_{connecting\ tubes}$$
$$= \sigma^2_{column} + \sigma^2_{extra\ column}$$

There are two methods to obtain the extra column band broadening of the chromatographic system: a linear extrapolation method using σ^2_{peak} as a function of retention time; and a zero length column method where the column is removed from the system and replaced by a capillary.

In the linear extrapolation $N_{th} = (t_r/\sigma_{column})^2$; hence $\sigma^2_{column} = t_r^2/N_{th}$.

A plot of σ^2_{peak} versus t_r^2 will be linear with a slope determined by N_{th} and an intercept value on the vertical σ^2_{peak} axis representing $\sigma^2_{extra\ column}$.

Column performance is expressed as the number of theoretical plates per unit of time, N/t or per meter N/m or by separation impedance, E = $\Delta Pt_0/N^2\eta$ where ΔP is the pressure drop, t_0 the retention time of the inert solute, N the plate count, and η the mobile phase velocity. N is around 100,000 plates/m. A new monolith column can produce 38,000 plates/25 cm.

Recently, temperature has attracted attention from LC chromatographers since the eluent viscosity is reduced. The contribution of temperature to the retention is mainly given by the enthalpy term of the Van't Hoff equation

$$Lnk = -\Delta H/RT + \Delta S/R + \log\beta$$

where ΔH is the enthalpy change associated with the transfer of the solutes between phases, ΔS is the corresponding entropy change, R is the molar gas constant, T is the absolute temperature, and β is the phase ratio of the column. Plots of Lnk versus 1/T are usually called Van't Hoff plots and the slope of the curve yields ΔH. Most studies are related to reverse phase systems. When dealing with small solutes that experience hydrophobic interactions, lower selectivity is observed with elevated temperatures. Solutes with basic groups or ionizable compounds experience increased selectivity at high mobile phase pHs. In the Knox equation the A term is not affected by temperature, the C term is reduced, but the B term increases. The stability of silica-based C18 stationary phases is questionable over 80°C but PS-DVB are resistant up to 220°C. It must be pointed out that the dielectric constant of water is reduced at elevated temperatures giving it some characteristics of an organic solvent. A discussion on temperature effects can be found in (25).

Zhu et al. (26, 27) studied the combined effects of solvent gradients and temperature.

VII. OPTIMIZATION

When dealing with complex samples column switching is the method of choice to focus on solutes of interest. The method is rather simple; it uses two columns packed with different supports but the compatibility of eluent with the two phases is not straightforward.

The best chromatogram is the one which provides the complete resolution (Rs ≅ 1.25) of all solutes in a minimum time. The large number of chromatographic parameters and the relationships between them rules out the possibility of empirical optimization by trial and error. Many methods have been developed to optimize parameters of interest. These methods were reviewed by Siouffi (28). The analyst either selects a response function (most often the resolution Rs) or tries to predict retention. There are roughly two types of approaches: the chemometrics approach and methods based on models. Because most useful variables in RPLC reside in the mobile phase, they are generally referred to as mobile phase optimization.

Full or fractional factorial designs are useful for screening the effects of a large number of parameters. One does not need to know the retention mechanism. Data from a Central Composite Design can be evaluated and plotted as a response surface which provides a graphical representation of the data over the range of the key parameters to study. It allows us to check the influence of a parameter but it is not predictive. Experimental retention data can be used to train an artificial neural network to enable it to predict the effects of changes in experimental variables.

Softwares and method development in LC separations are readily and widely available. Such products rely on the input of two or more pilot runs to calibrate a retention model. The Drylab computer simulation approach is widespread (29–31). The retention data of two initial gradient runs are used to adjust the steepness and the range of the gradient. In Chromsword from Galushko (32), a molecule must be translated into volume fragments and bond dipoles

$$Lnk = a(\Sigma Vi)^{2/3} + b(\Sigma Ge \cdot sj_{H_2O})$$

where Vi are the increments of the partial molar volumes of fragments in water, $Ge \cdot sj_{H_2O}$ are the increments of energy of interaction of bond dipoles with water, and a, b, and c are the parameters of the RP system and the column (polarity, column ratio, etc.).

Baczek et al. (33) performed a comparison of the two softwares. The Prisma optimization model was developed by Nyiredy (34) for the purpose of TLC optimization and was extended to HPLC. It is a three-dimensional geometrical design which correlates the solvent strength with the selectivity of the mobile phase. A software package called Virtual Column enables simulation and optimization of ion chromatography separations (35).

The linear Solvation Energy Relationship advocated by Abraham (36) and extensively studied by Carr and Poole (37,38) relies on the following equation

$$Lnk = LnK_0 + rR_2 + vV_x + s\pi^2_H + a\Sigma\alpha^2_H + b\Sigma\beta^2_H$$

where R_2 is an excess molar refraction of the analyte, V_x is its molar volume (in $cm^3 \cdot mol^{-1}/100$) according to the MacGowan algorithm, π^2_H is the solute dipolarity/polarizability descriptor, $\Sigma\alpha^2_H$ is the analytes ability to donate hydrogen bonds, $\Sigma\beta^2_H$ is the measure of hydrogen bond accepting capability. Lnk_0, r, s, a, and b are fitting coefficients which reflect the difference in specific bulk property between the mobile and stationary phases. The solvation parameter model is a useful tool for evidencing the contribution of defined intermolecular interactions to retention of neutral molecules (or polar but not ionized molecules) in chromatographic systems. The retention process is the sum of the *differential* interactions of a solute with the mobile phase and the stationary phase.

In general, the solute size and the basicity are the most important solute descriptors governing retention.

VIII. DIFFERENT MODES OF LC

A. ADSORPTION OR NPLC (NORMAL PHASE LIQUID CHROMATOGRAPHY)

In this mode the stationary phase is polar. Since only silicagel and alumina were utilized at the beginning of liquid chromatography and hydrophobic alkyl bonded phases were developed later, this mode is called normal phase.

Stationary phases: Bare silicagel and alumina are declining but bare silica is still widely used in thin layer chromatography. Polar bonded phases are now widely used.

Synthesis of bonded silica is performed either by surface modification or bulk modification.

Diol phase $Si—O—Si—(CH_2)_3—O—CH_2—CH(OH)—CH_2OH$

is very similar to bare silica but less retentive.

$$Si—O—Si—(CH_2)_3NH_2$$
– Amino phase

acts by the lone pair of electrons on the nitrogen atom.

– Cyano phase $Si—O—Si—(CH_2)_3CN$

is less polar and has been advocated in some optimization procedures as the unique phase since it may be used with any solvent.

Other polar phases are available but less often advocated.

Mobile phases: Theoretically any solvent is convenient.

Extensive work has been carried out on adsorption theory and retention mechanism since the pioneering work of Snyder (39). In this chromatographic mode physical adsorption of solute occurs. That means weak interactions with the stationary phase. Adsorption of the solutes occurs via donor acceptor mechanism (hydrogen bonding, charge transfer, etc.). According to Snyder's displacement model a solute S takes place of n molecules of previously adsorbed mobile phase solvent molecules M.

$$nM_S + S_m \overset{K}{\Leftrightarrow} S_s + nM_m$$

The subscripts s and m refer to stationary phase and mobile phase, respectively.

$$K = \frac{(S)_s}{(S)_m} \frac{(M_m)^n}{(M_s)^n}$$

From this starting equilibrium the Snyder-Soczewinski equation (40) yields the retention equation

$$Ln\,k = Ln\frac{V_aW}{Vm} + \alpha(\varepsilon^0 - S^0A_s) + \Sigma\,secondary\,effects$$

V_aW is the volume of solvent forming a monolayer coverage on the absorbent surface.

When a solute is strongly adsorbed, eluent must exhibit a strong affinity towards the stationary phase to displace the solute. ε^0 represents the dimensionless energy of solvent adsorption. Ranking ε^0 gives a scale of adsorption strength. It is obvious that n alkanes exhibit weak affinity towards polar stationary phases. Conversely, silicagel and alumina are hygroscopic and exhibit strong affinity towards water. Ranking ε^0 constitutes the eluotropic strength scale (Table 47.2).

Fine retention tuning is somewhat difficult with a single solvent. Mixtures of solvents most often constitute the eluent. Binary mixtures are a blend of apolar diluent (A) and polar modifier (B). Direct calculation of the eluting strength is possible through a formula derived by Snyder (39). The plot of ε^0 versus % of B is displayed in Figure 47.15. These plots are readily available in most manufacturers' softwares. Three (or more) solvent mixtures as eluent are difficult to handle and reproduce. With a binary mixture retention is given by

$$Ln\ k = Ct - n\ Ln\ (X_B)$$

where X_B is the molar fraction of modifier B and Ct is a constant.

Continuous increase of X_B is gradient elution (see below).

Normal phase chromatography is well adapted to separation of polar or moderately polar compounds. NPLC is well suited for the separation of structural isomers.

B. REVERSED PHASE LC (RPLC)

In this mode the stationary phase is hydrophobic (apolar) and to maximize the difference between the nature of both stationary and mobile phases, the former is hydrophobic, the latter is highly polar. Retention in RPLC is described in terms of free energy change

$$\Delta G^\circ = RT\ Log\ K + Log\ \varphi$$

$$Log\ K = -\Delta H^\circ/RT + \Delta S^\circ/R + log\ \varphi$$

where T is the absolute temperature, R is the gas constant, φ is the phase ratio, and ΔH° and ΔS° are enthalpy and entropy, respectively, associated with the transfer of a solute from an aqueous mobile phase to a non-polar stationary phase.

TABLE 47.2
Eluotropic Series for Different Adsorbents

Solvent	Solvent Strength Parameter					
	Alumina	Silica	Carbon	Aminopropyl	Cyanopropyl	Diol
Pentane	0.00	0.00				
Hexane	0.01	0.01	0.13–0.17			
Carbon tetrachloride	0.17	0.11		0.069		
1-Chlorobutane	0.26	0.20	0.09–0.14			
Benzene	0.32	0.25	0.20–0.22			
Methyl-tert. butyl ether	0.48		0.11–0.124	0.049–0.085	0.071	
Chloroform	0.36	0.26	0.12–0.20	0.13–0.14	0.106	0.097
Dichloromethane	0.40	0.30	0.14–0.17	0.13	0.120	0.096
Acetone	0.58	0.53			0.14	
Tetrahydrofurane	0.51	0.53	0.09–0.14	0.11		
Dioxane	0.61	0.51	0.14–0.17			
Ethyl acetate	0.60	0.48	0.04–0.09	0.113		
Acetonitrile	0.55	0.52	0.01–0.04			
Pyridine	0.70					
Methanol	0.95	0.70		0.00	0.24	

Buffering Ranges

Buffer	pK$_a$	Range
Phosphate	201	1.1–3.1
	7.2	6.2–8.2
Acetate	4.8	3.8–5.8
Citrate	3.1	2.1–4.1
	4.7	3.7–5.7
	5.4	4.4–6.4

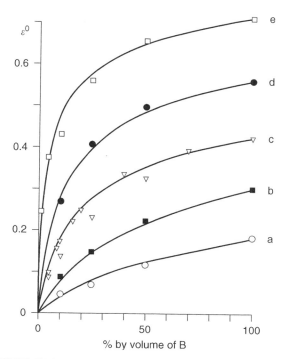

FIGURE 47.15 1 Plot of eluent strength versus the % of modifier in a binary mixture (A: diluent; B: polar modifier) in NPLC. (a) carbon tetrachloride, (b) propyl chloride, (c) methylene chloride, (d) acetone, (e) pyridine. (reproduced with permission from Edinburgh University Press, (Scotland.)).

Stationary phases: More than 600 reversed phase columns are commercially available and every year new phases are released (see the annual review in LC-GC magazine). Most are silica bonded of the C_8 or C_{18} type.

$$Si—O—Si—C_{18} \quad or \quad C_8$$

In spite of many shortcomings silica backbone is still the material of choice and is considered as unsurpassed by other inorganic oxides such as zirconia or polymers, e.g., polystyrene/divinyl benzene. Hydrophilic solutes are more retained on porous graphite packings than on C_{18} bonded silica. Small, monodisperse, spherical particles are available in a variety of particle diameters (1.5–10.0 μm) and pore sizes (60–4000 Å). Differences exist between type of silica, type of ligand, end capping, bonding density, residual silanols, etc. Selection of the proper packing among the available types from manufacturers is not simple. The overall retention behavior of packed columns depends on the physico-chemical properties of the silica (specific surface area, packing density), the chemical surface properties (type and concentration of surface silanols, surface concentration of metal oxides), the bonding procedure (whether mono, di, or tri alkoxy or

chlorosilanes have been used), the surface concentration of bonded groups achieved, and end capping or not. In many cases the manu-facturer's description is insufficient to characterize the stationary phases. ^{29}Si and ^{13}C NMR provide information on ligand attachment to substrate surface.

From the carbon content, %C and the specific surface area Sp the surface concentration (Sco) of the bonded phase is

$$Sco = \%C/(100nC*12Sp)(1-\%C/100*Ml-1/nC*12)$$

Where nC is the number of carbon atoms (typically 8 or 18), Ml is the molecular mass of the ligand. Bonding density is expressed as μmoles/m². Silicagel has a maximum silanol density of 8.0 μmoles/m² but only part of them can react. With stationary phases with alkyl group surface concentrations below 3.8 μmoles/m², silanophilic interactions contribute to retention producing asymmetric peak shapes of basic solutes. At surface coverages of 4.24 μmoles/m², ca 85% of the silanol groups are blocked. To ensure that the minimum silanols are remaining manufacturers perform a further reaction with a small size silane (e.g., Trimethyl chloro silane). This is called end capping. Another procedure is to shield silanols with t-butyl groups, for example.

RP phases should be tested for

Efficiency expressed by N/m (plates per meter)
Hydrophobic properties
Steric selectivity
Silanophilic properties
Metal content

The majority of column characterization procedures can be divided into empirical methods, thermodynamically based methods, and model-based methods. A good chromatographic method for the characterization of a RP packing should attempt to measure several parameters. Many tests have been descibed in the literature. In Engelhardt's test (41), toluene, ethylbenzene, phenol, benzoic acid, aniline, NN-dimethylaniline, and p-ethylaniline are injected in methanol/water (49/51) eluent; the retention of toluene and ethylbenzene are measures of the hydrophobicity of a packing while the retention and the tailing factor of the bases are measures of the silanophilic interaction. Hydrophobic properties depend on the level of the surface coverage.

Hydrophobicity, which is usually considered as the ratio of the retention factors of successive homologues (e.g., pentylbenzene/butylbenzene), is a good guide to the carbon content of the column. The measured hydrophobicity is dependent on the mobile phase composition and temperature of the column (42).

All tests give good agreement on the hydrophobic retention, which is proportional to the carbon content per unit column volume, whereas hydrophobic selectivity, i.e., separation potential of two analytes differing for one methylene group, hardly shows differences between the various column types. Manufacturers who provide carbon content should also provide the specific surface area. In Tanaka's test (43) the analyst is able to measure the hydrophobic retentivity of the packing, the steric selectivity, the hydrogen bonding, and the ion exchange properties of the packing. Shape selectivity of RPLC phases refers to the ability of a packing to discriminate between conformational differences between molecules; however, it must be kept in mind that the majority of the evaluation methods for HPLC columns have been developed specifically for narrow pore phases using small molecular probes. Silanol activity is checked from the peak shape of benzylamine and phenol. Kele and Guiochon (44) extensively published on the reproducibility and performances of RP phases. Claessens (45) published a review of RP phases' characterization. McCalley (46) evaluated the performance of RP columns for the analysis of basic compounds.

Stationary phases especially developed for the analysis of basic compounds are phases in which the ionic interaction between basic analytes and silanols are minimized. In this mode various approaches of stationary phase manufacturing have been described: high purity silica, end capping procedures, polymer encapsulation, shielding of silanols, bidentate, or surface-modified silica. Polar-embedded phases provide good peak shapes of basic analytes and good compatibility towards highly aqueous mobile phases. To overcome the contamination by metal traces, silica is prepared by a sol-gel method which does not guarantee metal-free silica. It has been observed that basic analytes exhibit variable retention on RP packings; there may be partial or total exclusion effects giving rise to detrimental loss of resolution. At pH 7, which is often used to increase the retention of hydrophilic bases, poor peak shapes are obtained on many phases. The properties of RP columns also substantially depend on the actual eluent pH; addition of organic modifier to an aqueous buffer causes a shift which can be as high as one pH unit in the actual pH of the eluent. According to Neue (47), the pH needs to be controlled to better than 0.01 units, the mobile phase composition to better than 0.1% and the temperature to better than 0.1% if one wants to get reliable data on the batch to batch reproducibility of a packing. Classification and ranking of RP phases can be performed through principal component analysis (48).

Silica bonded phases are not stable over the whole pH range; low pH (≤ 2) or high pH (≥ 9) may damage the siloxane bond, and phosphate buffers lead to fast degradation. To overcome this drawback polymeric phases of the polystyrene divinylbenzene (PS-DVB) type have been developed. With a high degree of cross linking they are mechanically stable and can withstand high pressures. Porous glassy carbons (PGC) are pH stable as well but the number of published separations with this support is small compared to silica bonded supports.

On these hydrophobic supports, hydrophilic solutes are not retained and by consequence water is the weakest eluent. The eluotropic strength is thus exactly the reverse of the one observed in NPLC.

Mobile phases are typically water + organic modifier mixtures. Methanol, acetonitrile, and tetrahydrofuran (THF) are the usual organic modifiers.

The mechanism of retention has been a matter of dispute. The volume of "definitive" papers on the topic is impressive. Partition mechanism is generally accepted but some deviations from this mechanism may be observed. A low organic modifier content causes the collapse of the bonded chains that are brought together by the intermolecular C_{18} dispersive interactions while they tend to exclude water. A high organic modifier content induces the rupture of the C_{18} intermolecular interactions via chain solvation by the modifier and the formation of a brush-like structure.

Two features are important in RPLC. In an homologous series (n-alkanols, saturated fatty acids, etc.) linear plots of Ln k versus carbon number of the solutes are observed. Increasing the volume percentage of organic modifier in the mobile phases decreases retention according to

$$Ln\ k = a - b\phi - c\phi^2$$

where ϕ is the volume percentage of the modifier in a binary mixture water-organic modifier.

Curvature of the quadratic plot of Ln k versus ϕ is highly dependent on the nature of the solute (Figure 47.16). In a more or less limited range of the volume %, the above equation can be written as

$$Ln\ k = Ln\ k_w - S\phi$$

where Ln k_w is the retention with pure water as mobile phase. Values of k_w are obtained by extrapolation to $\phi = 0$.

S is the slope of the regression and is characteristic of the solute.

Discrepancy can occur when methanol, acetonitrile, or tetrahydrofurane (THF) is used as a modifier. k_w has often been considered the hydrophobicity of the solute. It comes from the correlation plot of Ln k_w versus Log P octanol-water. Like correlation plots, some discrepancies can occur, depending on the number of solutes in the plot and correlation coefficient values.

Slope (S) of the Ln k_w versus ϕ plot is typical of the solute considered. When considering, for example, two solutes, two situations can occur: either the two solutes have the same S, and in this case, selectivity remains constant whatever the ϕ value, or the two solutes exhibit S_1 and S_2 values which means that slope are different and consequently there exists a ϕ value where no separation occurs.

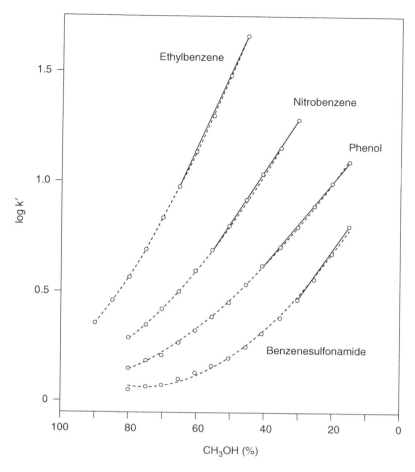

FIGURE 47.16   Plots of solute retention on C_{18} stationary phase (as logk) versus the volume fraction of modifier in RP. The solid line shows the linear region, the dotted line shows the quadratic region. (Reproduced from Chromatographia with permission from Vieweg.)

Beyond this value the order of retention is reversed. Peak crossover occurs when scanning the φ values range.

Selection of organic modifier is often achieved through trial and error. Experienced chromatographers are well aware of solute-solvent interactions. Snyder (49) has provided a useful selectivity triangle of solvent where dipole-dipole, proton donor, and proton acceptor interactions are the three apices (Figure 47.17). Solvents are gathered in eight groups. Solvents in a single group exhibit similar interactions. When considering the triangle, it is obvious that acetonitrile and methanol, for example, will interact differently. When solutes are eluted according to the sole hydrophobicity (for example, an homologous n alkanol series) use of either methanol or acetonitrile does not change the order of retention. Conversely, when very different chemical species are separated use of methanol or acetonitrile will yield different retention and selectivities and reversal of retention order is possible. In the same way chloroform and dichloromethane (two modifiers very often advocated in NPLC) may yield different retentions. A discussion on solvent classification has been published by Siouffi (50).

Gradient elution is performed when solutes are strongly retained. To decrease the t_r of these late eluting peaks modifier (stronger eluent) is incrased. From the above linear equation a linear increase in φ will result in a linear decrease in Ln k. This is called LSS (linear solvent strength).

The general approach is based on the solution of the basic differential equation $dV = k \cdot dVo$ where dV is the differential increase in the volume of mobile phase that has passed through the column, dVo is a differential fraction of the column hold up Vo, and k is the retention factor that is assumed constant during the migration of the solute band by an infinitely small distance corresponding to dVo. In binary gradients a "weaker" eluent (or diluent) A is associated with a "strong" eluent B. In linear gradient $\varphi = a + bt$ where a is the initial concentration φ of the solvent B in the mobile phase at the start of the gradient, and b is the steepness (slope) of the gradient per time or per volume unit of the eluate. Snyder (51) and Jandera (52) extensively published on gradient and derived equations which can be used for optimization of separation.

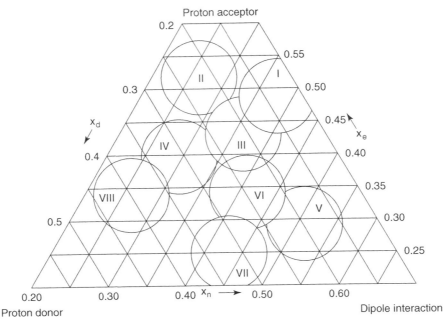

FIGURE 47.17   Selectivity triangle for solvents (Ref. 49). (Reproduced with permission from Preston Publications.)

Classificaiton of solvent selectivity according to snyder

Group Designation	Solvents
I	Aliphatic ethers, *mehtyl t-butyl ether*, tetramethylguanidine, hexamethyl phosphoric acid amide (trialkylamines)
II	Aliphatic alcohols, *methanol*
III	Pyridine derivatives, *tetrahydrofuran*, amides (except formamide), glycol ethers, sulfoxides
IV	Glycols, benzyl alcohol, *acetic acid*, *formamide*
V	Ethylene chloride
VI	a) Tricresyl phosphate, aliphatic ketones and esters, *dioxane*, polyesters b) Sulfones, nitriles, acetonitrile, propylene carbonate
VII	Aromatic hydrocarbons, *toluene*, halosubstituted aromatic hydrocarbons, nitro compounds, *methylene chloride*, aromatic ethers
VIII	Fluoroalcohols, m-cresol, water, (*chloroform*)

Gradient runs can be used to predict either isocratic or gradient separations. First, software was developed for RP separations. The model has been extended to other types. The selection of initial instrument parameters and separation mode are left to the user. Binary systems were first proposed. Extension to ternary mobile phase in RPLC permits a fine selectivity tuning.

RP phases allow a wide range of separation. They are well suited for polar organic solutes soluble in water. A rule of thumb is that retention order is similar to solubility in water or water modifier mixture. Apolar solutes such as polycyclic aromatic hydrocarbons are well separated on C_{18} phases according to their hydrophobicity.

In micellar liquid chromatography the mobile phase consists of surfactants at concentrations above their critical micelle concentration (CMC) in an aqueous solvent with an alkyl bonded phase. Micelles act as a mobile phase modifier. Retention behavior is controlled by solute partitioning from the bulk solvent into micelles and into the stationary phase as well as on direct transfer from the micelles in the mobile phase into the stationary phase. Reference (53) gives a broad overview of the method.

C. IONIZABLE SOLUTES

Separation of ionic or ionogenic solutes can be performed with three fundamental methods: ion pair formation, ion exchange, and ion exclusion.

a). Assume a weak acid AH. The dissociation equilibrium is

$$AH \Leftrightarrow A^- + H^+ \quad \text{with the dissociation constant } k_A$$

At low pH in a buffered solution only AH exists. Separation with a RP system is thus possible provided that the acid is not too strong. Alkyl sulfonic acids, for example, may exhibit very low pK_A. Separation of acids in RP occurs according to the degree of hydrophobicity. Knowledge of the analyte pKa can greatly assist in achieving a desired mobile phase pH. A requirement is that the buffer should be soluble in the amount of the organic modifier. This is particularly relevant in the case of gradient methods especially with methanol and phosphate buffer. For UV detection, the buffer must be sufficiently transparent at the wavelength selected. LC-MS confers its own set of considerations regarding buffer concentration, buffer volatility, and ionization suppression. Ammonium acetate is better suited for LC-MS. Table 47.3 displays some characteristics of common buffers. Conversely, if pH solution is raised, A^- and H^+ are the only existing species. A^- can be chromatographed on an anion exchanger. Another method is ion pairing or ion interaction.

b). Ion pairing

In this technique a reversed phase column (most often RP8) is utilized with a mobile phase consisting of an aqueous organic mixture to which an ion pairing agent is added.

An ion pairing agent may form with analyte an ion pair with increased lipophilicity and consequently is retained on the RP stationary phase. Since the ion pairing agent is continuously fed onto the column it is most often advocated that the ion pairing agent induces a dynamic modification of the surface of the RP stationary phase. The lipophilic part of the ion pairing agent coats the surface, leaving the ionic part to interact with counter ions.

Retention can occur via

   i. Retention of the ion pair formed between the cations (or the anions) of the analyte and the anion (or the cation) of the ion pairing agent. The ion pair itself is adsorbed onto the stationary phase.
   ii. The analyte is retained through an ion pair complex formed with an amphiphilic ion previously absorbed onto the surface of the hydrophobic material.
   iii. The analyte is retained through ion exchange reactions with the adsorbed pair reagent.

Retention increases as concentration of the ion pairing agent increases but decreases beyond a certain concentration; pH is a key parameter.

Ion pair reagents are most often either nitrogen (+) or sulfonate (−) species, e.g., cetyl trimethyl ammonium bromide, diamino dodecane, tributyl ammonium chloride, cetyl pyridinium chloride; sodium dodecyl sulfate, Chap:3-[(3 cholamidoproyl) dimethyl ammonio]-1propane sulfonate, Tris: tris-(hydroxymethyl) aminomethane.

TABLE 47.3
Buffering Ranges

Buffer	pKa	Range
Phosphate	2.1	1.1–3.1
	7.2	6.2–8.2
Acetate	4.8	3.8–5.8
Citrate	3.1	2.1–4.1
	4.7	3.7–5.7
	5.4	4.4–6.4

c). Ion chromatography (IC)

IC is the modern version of the well-known ion exchange chromatography. IC is able to separate any ion when the appropriate column is utilized: bromide, chloride, fluoride, nitrite, phosphate, sulphate, etc. It is able to speciate oxidation states of several metals such as Fe(II) and Fe(III). The challenge to IC comes from capillary electrophoresis.

Instrumentation required for IC simply comprises a metal-free HPLC system and conductivity detection. Since conductivity is a common property of ions this method is universal and quite sensitive.

In IC both mobile and stationary phases are ionic.

a. Ion exchange

Principle of operation: ion exchangers are insoluble solid materials which contain exchangeable cations or anions. These ions can be exchanged for a stoechiometrically equivalent amount of other ions present in an electrolyte solution.

Exchange reactions are written as (for example, in cation exchange)

$$R—H^+ + Na^+ \Leftrightarrow R—Na^+ + H^+$$

R— is the matrix of ion exchanger.

The thermodynamic equilibrium constant is

$$K_{H^+}^{Na^+} = \frac{(R–Na^+) \cdot (H^+)}{(Na^+) \cdot (R–H^+)}$$

Assume E^+ is a monovalent element cation, and M^{n+} is a sample metal ion

$$R–nE^+ + M^{n+} \Leftrightarrow R–M^{n+} + nE^+$$

$$K_{E/M} = \frac{(M^{n+}Rn) \cdot (E^+)^n}{(E^+-R)^n \cdot (M^{n+})}$$

At low loading of sample ions, the term (E^+-R) is equal to the exchanger capacity Q.

$$K_D = \frac{(M^{n+}Rn)}{(M^{n+})}$$

is proportional to k, the retention factor

and

$$k = K_{E/M} \cdot \frac{(Q)^n}{(E^+)^n}$$

More generally,

$$Ln\, k_A = \frac{1}{y} \cdot Ln\, K_{A/E} + \frac{x}{y} \cdot Ln\, \frac{Q}{y} + Ln\, \frac{W}{V_M}\, \frac{x}{y}\, Ln(E_m{}^y)$$

$$Ln\, k = Constant - \frac{x}{y} Log\, (E_m{}^y)$$

k_A is the retention factor for a solute A^x

$K_{A/E}$ is the ion exchange coefficient for solute A and eluent E

Q   is the ion exchange capacity of the stationary phase

W   is the weight of the stationary phase used in the column

V_M is the volume of mobile phase

x   is the charge of the solute anion

E_m^y is the concentration of the element ion in the mobile phase.

In IC low capacity ion exchange columns are utilized. Eluents are in the range 1–10 mmol.

Stationary Phases. In ion exchange we can distinguish

SCX: strong cation exchangers (functional group SO_3^-); in the H^+ form they represent "solid" acids.

WCX: weak cation exchangers (functional group COO^-)

SAX: strong anion exchangers or strong base (functional group alkanol quaternary amine)

WAX: weak anion exchanger (functional group amino)

Amphoteric ion exchangers contain anionic and cationic exchange sites.

Chelating ion exchange groups are: iminodiacetate, 8-hydroxyquinolinol, β diketone, triphenyl methane dyes, carbamates, EDTA, PAR [(4–2 pyridyl-azo)resorcinol]. New packings are compiled in the annual review which appears in LC/GC magazine.

Base materials

i.   The majority of stationary phases are agglomerated or pellicular materials consisting of a monolayer of charged latex particles which are electrostatically attached to a functionalized internal core particle. Polystyrene Divinylbenzene (PS-DVB) with different degrees of cross linking is the substrate. Particle diameters are typically in the range of 5–25 μm while adsorbed latex particles are 0.1 μm. This material exhibits very good pH stability and excellent mass transfer properties. For example, analysis of oligosaccharides from honey is performed at pH 11–12.

ii.   Microporous methacrylate-based materials are mainly used for anion exchange because of their resistance to high pH eluents.

iii. Silica-based materials are produced by grafting organic moieties according to the procedure utilized in producing reversed phase silica: aminopropyl bonded silica or functionalized silicas such as sulphonate are available. An advantage of silica-based materials is the low probability of secondary interactions between the solute ions and the silica substrate. Use of

Silica-based materials is rapidly declining due to their poor hydrolytic stability.

iv.   Electrostatic agglomerated films on ultra-wide-pore substrates (1000–3000 A) have been widely used. Wide pores accommodate a coating of ion exchange colloid on the interior or exterior surfaces. Another means of producing base material is the polymer coating of silica material. A layer of polybutadiene-maleic acid (PBDMA) is deposited on silica and then cross linked by peroxide-initiated radical chain reaction.

Mobile phases

Any ion in solution can be used that can compete with the analyte for the fixed ions on the stationary phase. In anion analysis hydroxyde eluents have distinct advantages over the carbonate eluents. These advantages include a wider linear working range for analyte conductivity, increased sensitivity, and the capacity to effectively elute highly retained ionic analytes using gradient capabilities. Conversely, carbonate is a divalent anion that possesses strong pushing properties in comparison to hydroxide eluents. In the EG 40™ eluent generator from Dionex, deionized water is pumped through the KOH generation chamber and a DC current is applied between the anode and the cathode of the cartridge (Figure 47.18). Under the applied field, the electrolysis of water occurs while hydronium ions generated at the anode displace K+ ions in the electrolyte reservoir. The displaced K+ ions migrate across the ion exchange connector into the KOH generation chamber and combine with OH− ions generated at the cathode to produce a KOH solution.

Factors influencing retention and selectivity are: hydration enthalpy, hydration entropy, polarizability, charge, and size and structure of both eluent and solute ions. Concentration of eluent ion (or ionic strength) and pH also play important roles.

A secondary equilibrium occurs according to the nature of the sorbent matrix. Hydrophobic interaction markedly influences retention (a typical example is the well-known aminoacid sequence on cation exchanger which does not follow the pKa sequence). With inorganic ions the perchlorate (ClO_4^-) effect is also well established. Non-ionic eluent modifiers are often used to change the ion exchange affinity of hydrophobic ions.

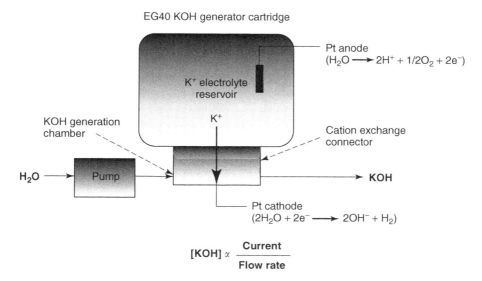

FIGURE 47.18   The EG 40 generator cartridge. (Courtesy of Dionex.)

Gradient elution starts with an eluent of low ionic strength for the resolution of the most weakly retained species. The dependence of the analyte retention on the eluent concentration is a straight line with slope given by the ratio of charges of analyte and eluent. Column switching permits the separation of both inorganic and organic anions in one run. Simultaneous analysis of ions is possible; column switching is configured for anion analysis in column A and cation analysis in column B.

Separation selectivity depends on the degree of electrostatic forces. With a SCX phase the binding force decreases with decreasing diameter.

$$H^+ < Li^+ < Na^+ < NH^{4+} < K^+ < Ag^+ < Be^{2+} < Mg^{2+} < Ca^{2+} < Sr^{2+} < Ba^{2+}$$

With SAX material a selectivity series with respect to binding force also exists:

$$F^- < OH^- < CH_3COO^- < Cl^- NO_2^- < CN^- < NO_3^- < SO_4^{2-}$$

b.   Ion exclusion

Ion exclusion relies upon Donnan equilibrium. The main parameter in this mode is the electrostatic interaction of the solute with the charged functional groups on the surface of the stationary phase.

The stationary phase can be considered as a charged membrane separating the flowing mobile phase from the static, occluded mobile phase trapped in the pores of the exchanger. Ionic solutes are rejected because of their inability to penetrate inside the pores and so are eluted at the void volume of the column. Conversely, non-ionic substances may partition between the occluded liquid phase and the flowing mobile phase. The degree of partition determines the extent of the retention. Sample anions are excluded

from the resin phase by the fixed charges of the sulfonate groups of the cation exchange resin.

Separations by ion exclusion are usually performed on a cation exchange column with a PS-DVB resin. The solute retention volume is

$$V_R = V_o + K_D \cdot V_i$$

where

V_o is the interstitial volume of eluent (eluent outside the resin beads)

V_i is the occluded volume within the resin beads

K_D is the distribution constant of the solute

When a very large solute or ion cannot enter the stationary phase K_D is 0; when the solute is free to enter $K_D = 1$.

The range of retention volumes is rather small and consequently, ion exclusion columns are rather long.

Acids are found to elute in decreasing order of their acid dissociation constants; the stronger acids elute first.

D.   Chiral Stationary Phases

The food and beverage industry is becoming increasingly concerned with the analysis of enantiomers which can affect flavor, fragrance, age, and even the adulteration of products. Most efforts have been directed towards resolution of amino acids either native or derivatized.

In chiral chromatography, an enantioselective molecule (selector) is either immobilized on a surface support as a stationary phase or present as an additive to the mobile phase.

When a chiral selector is used as the stationary phase, the primary retention mechanism is complexation with the surface immobilized chiral selector. For 1:1 solute-selector complexation, the equilibrium constant (Kcomp) is related to the retention factor k by

$$Kcomp = \frac{[solute\text{-}selector]}{[solute]\ [selector]} = \frac{k}{\varphi[selector]}$$

where [solute-selector], [solute], and [selector] represent the equilibrium concentrations of solute selector, free solute, free selector and respectively, and φ is the phase ratio.

Enantioselective ligand exchange chromatography was suggested by Davankov et al. (54) in the late 1960s for the resolution of racemic compounds into stereoisomers of amino acids, amino alcohols, and diamines. Such molecules exhibit a pair of heteroatoms which can form labile chelate type coordination complexes with Cu(II), Zn (II), or Ni(II). A chiral bidentate ligand such as hydroxyproline was attached to a support. Copper (II) was added to the mobile phase and coordinated with both the chiral selector on the stationary phase and the free amino acids in solution, to form a transient diastereomeric complex. This approach is limited to specific chiral molecules which can coordinate with the copper (II).

A discussion of the mixed-ligand ternary complexes between the chiral selector and the enantiomers to be separated can be found in Ref. 55.

The only commercially successful chiral stationary phase for thin layer chromatography is based on the ligand exchange approach (56).

The use of cyclodextrins as chiral selectors has grown rapidly in recent years. Cyclodextrins are cyclic oligosaccharides composed of D-glucose units connected through the 1 and 4 positions by α linkages (Figure 47.19). Those containing 6, 7, and 8 glucose units (i.e., α cyclodextrin, β cyclodextrin, γ cyclodextrin) are most common and available commercially. Cyclodextrins are usually described and depicted as toroidal molecules (conical cylindrical); they exhibit a relatively hydrophobic cavity in the middle and a relatively hydrophilic surface on the outside. They can form host-guest complexes with a variety of molecules. Since the internal cavity of the cyclodextrin tends to be more hydrophobic than either its exterior most non-polar or weakly polar molecules can penetrate and reside in the cavity. Cyclodextrins can be used as a mobile phase additive but the selectivity of covalently bonded cyclodextrins on a support is larger. There are many commercially available "cyclodextrin" stationary phases. Various moieties are utilized to functionalize the cyclodextrins and a huge amount of literature is available on the topic. Commercially available cyclodextrin derivatives are: acetylated, hydroxypropylether, naphtylethyl carbamate, or 3,5 diphenyl carbamate. The various moieties used to functionalize cyclodextrins can alter the enantioselectivity. It is possible to suppress the inclusion complexation by using a non-hydrogen bonding, polar organic solvent such as acetonitrile as the main component of the mobile phase. The acetonitrile occupies the cyclodextrin cavity and enhances hydrogen bonding between the hydroxyl groups on the cyclodextrin and any hydrogen bonding groups on the chiral analyte.

Macrocyclic glycopeptide antibiotics are multimodal as they can be used in the reverse phase mode, normal phase mode, or polar organic mode. The most successful are avoparcin, teicoplanin, ristocetin A, or vancomycin. They exhibit an aglycon "basket" made of fused macrocyclic rings and pendant carbohyhydrate moieties (Figure 47.20). Vancomycin and teicoplanin are the the most interesting. Teicoplanin, for example, (Mw1877) exhibits 2″ stereogenic centers; it has a hydrophobic acyl side chain attached to a 2-amino-2-deoxy-β-D-glycopyranosyl moiety. Teicoplanin has been used successfully in a number of applications (57); it can be used with no buffer in the mobile phase which greatly facilitates the LC/MS.

Protein LC columns have the least capacity of any chiral stationary phases. α1-acid glycoprotein, (AGP), ovomucoid, human serum albumin (HSA), or bovine serum albumin (BSA) are used in the reversed phase mode with aqueous buffers or hydro-organic solvents. HSA-based columns usually present the problem of a significant variation of the chromatographic performances, depending not only on the immobilization procedure but also on the origin of the anchored protein. Recombinant HSA can overcome the problem. AGP is one of the most used protein phases to separate enantiomeric amines. Reversal of elution order is not unusual in RPLC when working with protein-based enantioselective columns.

Historically, cellulose or starch components were the first to be used as chromatographic chiral selectors.

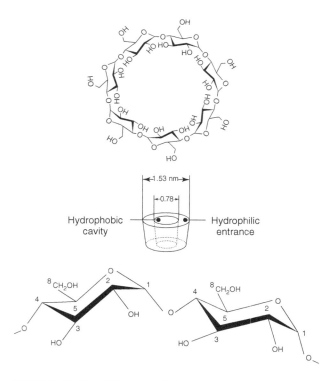

FIGURE 47.19 Schematic of the various cyclodextrins.

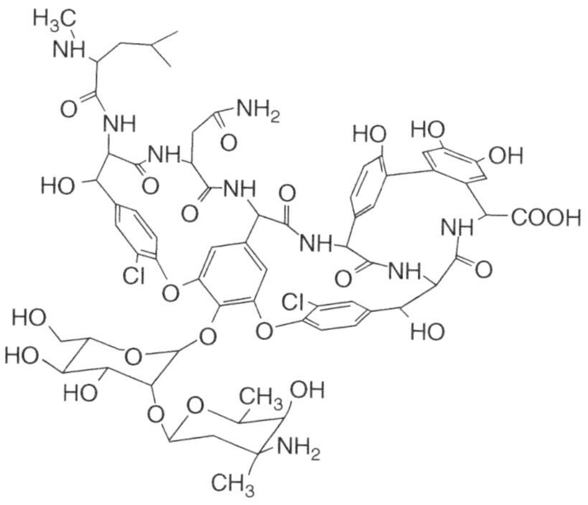

FIGURE 47.20 Structures of Vancomycin, Teicoplanin, and Ristocetin A.

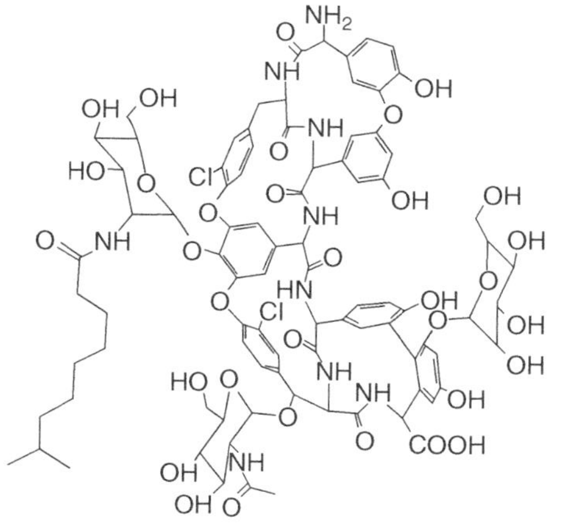

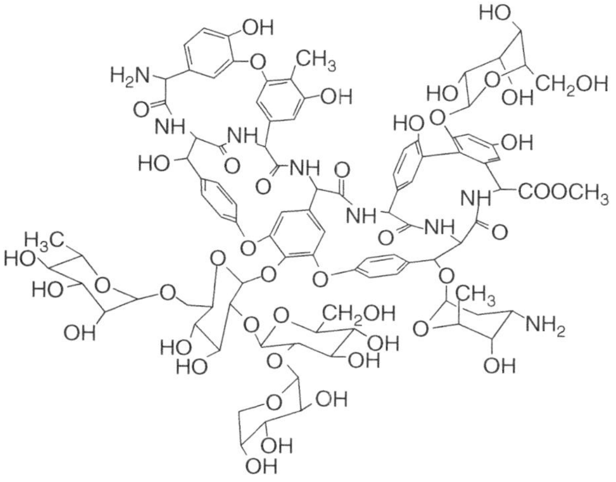

Cellulose and amylose are the most accessible naturally occurring optically active polymers. These polysaccharides themselves show chiral recognition, but do not afford practical chiral stationary phases. Their derivatization brings about practically useful CSPs. Cellulose esters or phenylcarbamates, amylose phenylcarbamates are not covalently attached to the support, but rather are coated on wide pore silica that has first been silanized. Polysaccharide-derived CSPs supported on silica are classically prepared by reaction of the polysaccharide with a benzoyl chloride or a phenyl isocyanate in homogeneous conditions; these derivatives are coated from a solution onto a macroporous γ-aminopropylsilica matrix by evaporation of the solvent. They have good capacity in the normal phase mode. Among the various kinds of cellulose esters, cellulose tribenzoate and its derivatives show high chiral recognition abilities when adsorbed onto macroporous silica. The optical resolving ability of the benzoate or carbamate derivatives are dependent on the substituents on the phenyl group (58).

Francotte (59) has demonstrated that many polymeric chains are involved in the chiral recognition mechanism. The supramolecular effect depends on the dissolution solvent which predetermines the geometry of chiral centers. A compilation of enantiomer separation by such phases can be found in Reference 60.

Pirkle and coworkers (61) first employed the concept of reciprocity of chiral recognition in designing effective chiral selectors. The reciprocity of chiral recognition states that if a chiral stationary phase (CSP) derived from an optically pure compound A can discriminate each isomer of compound B, then a CSP derived from an optically pure B may discriminate each enantiomer of compound A. Many CSP were synthesized. Some contain either a π acid or π base moiety (or even both). However, simultaneous interactions must be present, too (hydrogen bonding, dipolar interactions).

Molecular imprinted polymers (MIPs) can selectively recognize the template molecule used in the imprinting process. In molecular imprinting, monomers, such as methacrylic acid and styrene, are first assembled around the template molecule. This arrangement of monomers is fixed on polymerization. After polymerization, the polymer is dried, ground, and sieved, the linker bond is chemically cleaved, and the templates are freed from the polymer matrix, leaving cavities that are complementary to the template in shape and spatial configuration. For a review, see Reference 62.

Chirbase provides comprehensive structural, experimental, and bibliographic information on successful or unsuccessful chiral separations which have been obtained on CSPs. Data mining and pattern recognition with a decision tree leads to a more rational choice of the CSP or of the mobile phase to a given CSP (63).

E. SIZE EXCLUSION

In this mode, the stationary phase is a porous solid support, the mobile phase is the most eluting one e.g. porous silica and water. All molecules are eluted in the void volume. Large molecules cannot enter the pores and travel in the external volume only, they are excluded; small molecules can penetrate into the pores and they travel through both external and internal volumes; by consequence their velocity is lower than the one of large molecules. The relevant retention parameter is the radius of gyration of the molecule which can be obtained by light scattering detection at several angles. Since there is no partition, the entropy is of paramount importance and the column temperature should be thoroughly controlled. The column set is calibrated using a series of polymer standards to determine a relationship between logM and the retention time of the standards. Calibration is typically performed using well-characterized standards (polystyrene, dextrans).

For any polymer, $Hv = M[\eta]$ where Hv is the hydrodynamic volume, M is the molecular weight (Mw), and $[\eta]$ is intrinsic viscosity. The intrinsic viscosity is the value of the reduced specific viscosity at infinite dilution $[\eta] = \lim c \to 0 \; \eta_{sp}/c$. The Mark Houwink equation relates intrinsic viscosity and molecular weight for a given polymer/solvent combination.

$[\eta] = K \, M^{\alpha}$ where K and α are the Mark Houwink constants.

A triple detection (differential refractometry, viscosimetry, and light scattering detector) is often used which yields an accurate response and allows the determination of branching distribution of polyolefins, for example.

The number-average M_n, the weight-average M_w, molecular mass values, and polydispersity are defined by

$$M_n = \Sigma n_i M_i / n_i$$

$$M_w = \Sigma n_i M^2 / n_i M_i$$

Polydispersity $= M_w/M_n$ where n_i represents the number of oligomer molecules having a mass of M_i, M_n is the number-average molecular mass, and M_w is the weight-average molecular mass.

IX. SAMPLE PREPARATION

A sample preparation step is often necessary to isolate the components of interest from a sample matrix. Sample preparation is often the major source of error in analytical procedures as practitioners are often required by law to use traditional methods.

Ideal sample preparation technique should be simple, solvent free, efficient, and inexpensive. EPA method 3600C gives general guidance on the selection of clean-up methods that are appropriate for various target analytes.

A sample pretreatment will:

   i. Improve accuracy
  ii. Improve detectability
 iii. Improve selectivity by removal of interfering matrix

A result is reproducible if the sample to be analyzed is fully representative of the material to be tested. That means that the samples taken can be equated with the entire batch.

We can distinguish off-line and on-line procedures.

A. LYOPHILIZATION

Relatively large samples containing water-soluble analytes are frozen in a dry ice-acetone bath or in liquid nitrogen. Subsequently, the frozen samples are placed in the freeze dryer where water is removed by vacuum sublimation. After freeze drying, the residues can be dissolved in a suitable organic solvent.

B. ULTRAFILTRATION

Ultrafiltration involves the use of specialized membranes that allow rapid and gentle concentration or removal of molecules based on their molecular weight. Ultrafiltration membranes consist of a very thin and dense layer on top of a macroporous support that has progressively larger open spaces on the downstream side of the membrane. Substances that pass through the membrane will also pass easily through the macroporous support. Concentration can be accomplished because molecules smaller than the molecular weight cut-off of the membrane flow through. Molecules larger than the membrane cut-off will be retained on the sample side of the membrane. Performances are affected by pressure. As the pressure increases so does the flow rate but there is a resistance from the concentrated layer on the surface of the membrane. This phenomenon is called concentration polarization.

Membranes are usually made out of cellulose or polysulfone.

Porosity of membrane determines the size of molecules concentrated. In the supported liquid membrane device analytes are extracted in a flow system from an aqueous sample through a hydrophobic membrane liquid into a second aqueous solution. The impregnated membrane is clamped between two circular PTFE blocks. Two types of transport mechanisms across the membrane are in use: pH gradient or ion pairing formation.

C. DIALYSIS

Dialysis is a method used to separate molecules through a semi-permeable membrane separating two chambers. The concentration gradient of the components across the membrane drives the separation. Dialysis is used for removal of excess low-molecular-weight solutes. Analytes small enough to diffuse through the pores of the membrane are collected.

Microdialysis probes are implanted into the area of interest and slowly perfused with a solution usually matching the fluid outside. The probe is equipped with a membrane through which substances pass due to the concentration gradient. It can be coupled on line to liquid chromatography (HPLC), capillary electrophoresis (CE), or mass spectrometry.

The flux through a dialysis membrane is described by Fick's law:

$$I = -D \cdot A/\tau * dc/dx$$

where
I   is the flux (mol/s)
D   is the solute diffusion coefficient (m^2/s)
A   is the membrane area (m^2) τ: is the tortuosity of the membrane
dc/dx   is the concentration gradient across the membrane mol/m^4
D   is obtained from the Stocke Einstein equation,

$$D = k \cdot T / 6\pi \eta r$$

k   is the Boltzmann's constant
T   is the absolute temperature ($^\circ K$)
η is the viscosity of the medium
r   is the radius of the molecule

The smaller the molecule, the larger the diffusion coefficient and the higher the flux. The relative recovery or the dialysis factor is the ratio of the dialysate (analyte in the outgoing liquid) to the concentration outside the membrane.

There are three modes of conducting a microdialysis experiment:

Perfusion and stirring are continuous over the monitoring period

Perfusion is carried out only during sampling but the stirring is maintained
Perfusion and stirring are carried out during sampling only

D. LIQUID/LIQUID EXTRACTION (LLE)

This sample pretreatment is mainly devoted to organic compounds which can be removed from an aqueous solution by extracting them into a water-immiscible solvent. Chelation or ion pairing between large and poorly hydrated ions and chelating agent may form neutral compounds which can be extracted by organic solvents.

When two immiscible solvents are placed in contact, any substance soluble in both of them will distribute or partition between the two phases in a definite proportion. According to the Nernst partition isotherm, the following relationship for a solute partitioning between two phases a and b is

$$\frac{(A)_a}{(A)_b} = K_d \quad K_d \text{ is the partition coefficient}$$

$$(A)_a \Leftrightarrow (A)_b \quad \text{very often} \quad (A)_{aq} \Leftrightarrow (A)_{org}$$

It assumes that no significant solute-solute interactions or strong specific solute-solvent interaction occurs. The K_d value is constant when the distributing substance does not chemically react in either phase and temperature is kept constant.

The fraction extracted R is related to K_d by

$$\frac{C_o V_o}{C_o V_o + C_w V_w} = K_d V/1 + K_d V$$

C_o and C_w represent the solute concentration in organic (o) and water (w) phases, respectively. V_o and V_w are volumes of organic and aqueous phases $V = V_o / V_w$.

It is possible to increase the extent of extraction with a given K_d by increasing the phase volume ratio. When performing micro LLE the analyst works with an extreme ratio of extracting solvent/extracted liquid (for example, 1/800). Another way is to carry out a second and a third extraction. After n extractions the final concentration of the compound in the aqueous phase is

$$Cw_n = C_w \left[\frac{Vw^n}{V_w + K_d V_0} \right]$$

An extraction process is more efficient if it is performed with several small portions of solvents.

Solubility increases as the values of solubility parameter δ of the solute and the solvent are close.

$$Ln \, K_d = \frac{\overline{V_s}}{RT} [(\delta_s - \delta_i)^2 - (\delta_j - \delta_s)^2]$$

$\overline{V}_s$ is the molar volume of the distributing solute, δ_s is its solubility parameter, and δ_i and δ_j are the solubility parameters of the pair of immiscible solvents.

It must be kept in mind that some species may exist under different forms in aqueous media. An acid, for example, must be written in this form:

$$HA \Leftrightarrow A^- + H^+$$

$$K_d = \frac{(HA)_0}{(HA)_w} = \frac{(HA)_0}{(HA)_{aq} + (A^-)_{aq}}$$

P_{ow} is the partition coefficient of a solute between octanol and water. It is a common measure of hydrophobicity. The usual measurement for Log P_{ow} is the shake flask method where a compound is shaken in an octanol-water mixture. After equilibrium the concentration is measured in one or both phases. Reversed phase HPLC has also been extensively used. Correlation plots of Log P_{ow} against retention time or capacity factors are drawn.

High values of Log P_{ow} give guidelines for extraction.

The single drop extraction is a micro LLE method in which a single drop of organic solvent is contained at the end of a PTFE rod. The procedure is as follows: 2 microliters of organic solvent are drawn into a microsyringe; the needle of the microsyringe is passed through the sample via valve and immersed in the aqueous sample; the syringe plunger is depressed to expose the solvent to the sample; the drop is drawn back into the syringe; and the needle is removed from the sample vial. Usually the needle is inserted into the hot injector of a GC instrument (64).

Microporous membrane liquid-liquid extraction (MMLLE) is a continuous liquid-liquid extraction proceeding via a hydrophobic membrane. The microporous membrane is sandwiched between two immiscible liquid phases: one aqueous and the other an organic solvent. The

membrane is wetted with a suitable organic solvent that fills the pores of the membrane. The mass transfer process takes place between the two phases via the pores of the membrane (65).

E. SOLID-PHASE EXTRACTION (SPE)

This is the most widely used method. Analytes (mainly organics) are trapped by a suitable sorbent by passing through a plastic cartridge containing an appropriate support. A selective organic solvent is used to wash out the target analytes. SPE is rapid and relies upon chromatographic retention and Log Pow. It can be easily automated. Off-line procedures are inexpensive. On-line devices are readily available from many companies.

1. Off-Line Methods

A typical SPE cartridge is displayed in Figure 47.21.

Sorbents are very similar to the liquid chromatography stationary phase. The analyst can take advantage of:

i. Non-polar interactions (hydrophobic): typically octadecyl modified silica, polystyrene, -divinyl benzene copolymers, or carbon-based sorbent.
ii. Polar interactions through hydrogen bond, for example. In this mode sorbents are: bare silica, polar-bonded silica, or polyamide.
iii. Ion exchange: benzene sulphonic acid (cation exchange) quaternary amine (anion exchange).
iv. Immuno sorbents: the lack of selective sorbents to trap organic analytes in water is certainly the most significant weakness of the SPE technique.

The most popular format is the cartridge filled with 40–60 μm d_p packing materials. The most second popular format is the disk which allows higher flow rates without channeling effects. One format devoted to high throughput

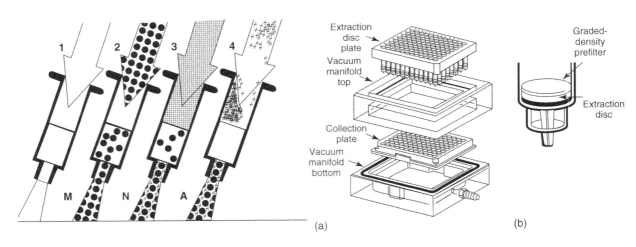

(a)   (b)

FIGURE 47.21   A SPE cartridge (far left), a 96 well plate format (a), and an extraction disk (b).

applications is the 96 well plate format (Figure 47.21) designed to fit automated plate handling systems.

The SPE technique procedure is as follows: conditioning, sample application, washing, and elution.

The adsorbent must be wetted. With bare silica no problem generally occurs but problems may occur with hydrophobic sorbents. In this case adsorbent must be treated with a suitable solvent. Methanol is preferred for most applications; however, other solvents which are miscible with water such as isopropanol, tetrahydrofuran, or acetonitrile are convenient as well. Conditioning is achieved with about 2–3 column volumes of solvent. Then 1–2 column volumes of the sample solvent are poured through the column. After this step the phase must not run dry. After adsorption of the sample molecules the phase may run dry through either a water jet pump or flushing with inert gas.

Elution is then performed with a strong solvent to elute with the lowest possible volume.

Capacity is the quantity of sample molecules retained per unit quantity of adsorbent. Capacity depends on solute size. It lies in the range of 4 to 60 mg/g of packing.

Breakthrough of solutes occurs when they are no longer retained by the sorbent. Overloading beyond the sorbent capacity may also lead to breakthrough of analytes. The breakthrough volume can be measured from the breakthrough curve obtained by monitoring the signal of the effluent from the extraction column (Figure 47.22).

V_b is usually defined at 1% of the initial absorbance and corresponds to the sample volume that can be handled without breakthrough.

V_r is the retention volume of the analyte.

V_m is defined at 99% of the initial absorbance.

The method is time consuming. Another method is proposed: a small volume spiked with a trace concentration (μg/L) level of all the analytes is percolated through the cartridge and peak areas are recorded. The first volume is selected so that breakthrough does not occur for any solute. The sample volume is then increased and the concentration decreased in order to have a constant amount of analytes in the percolated samples. In this mode peak areas remain constant. The breakthrough volume of an analyte is calculated when the peak area begins to decrease and the corresponding recovery can be also calculated by dividing the peak area obtained for the sample volume by the constant peak area obtained for sample volumes before breakthrough.

Prediction of breakthrough volume is important for selecting a convenient sorbent and consequently the amount of sorbent (66).

i. Hydrophobic sorbents: n alkyl silicas are by far the most utilized. A large number of applications on such sorbents has been published. The drawbacks (as with every bonded silica) are the poor stability in very acidic or basic media, the relatively low capacity for polar solutes, and the low recovery of basic analytes.

From liquid chromatography we know that in reversed phase mode

$$\text{Ln } k = \text{Ln } k_w - S \phi$$
$$\text{or Ln } k = \text{Ln } k_w - b\phi - a\phi^2$$

where ϕ is the organic modifier volume percent in the binary mobile phase (water/modifier).

Ln k_w can be estimated by a graphical extrapolation to zero modifier content. Ln k_w represents the hypothetical capacity factor of the solute with pure water as eluent. Since Ln k_w is very often correlated with Log P octanol/water, it is often taken as a hydrophobicity constant. Values of Ln k_w may be as high as 3–4 which means that large sample volumes with trace amount of solutes can be handled.

Styrene Divinyl Benzene copolymers (PS-DVB), either porous or rigid, are stable over the whole pH range. Calculated Ln k_w values on these sorbents are higher than those on C_{18}. Consequently, moderately polar compounds which are not retained by C_{18} silica are more

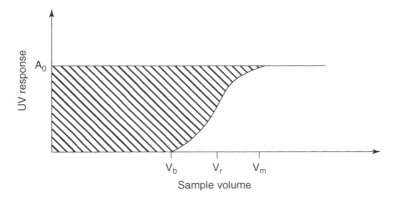

FIGURE 47.22 Breakthrough curve.

readily concentrated on these sorbents. Carbon-based sorbents are gaining acceptance since the availability of porous graphitic carbon. Data obtained with this support demonstrate that it exhibits high retention for apolar compounds but some differences with PS-DVB and C$_{18}$ bonded silica are observed. Hydrophilic-lipophilic polymers do not require equilibration prior to extraction of the analytes.

Selection of eluting solvent is performed through knowledge of eluting strength ε^0 of the solvent in the chromatographic mode.

ii. Use of polar adsorbents is less advocated. Behavior of solutes is well understood since a lot of chromatographic data can be retrieved from TLC (thin layer chromatography) experiments. Flash chromatography is often a new version of silica-based cartridges. Flash chromatography is utilized for laboratory-scale separation. The apparatus is a sintered funnel partially filled with the sorbent (mostly bare silica or reverse phase silica). The mixture of compounds to be purified is adsorbed on the top of the sorbent and the funnel is connected to a flask under vacuum. The vacuum is maintained while the solvent is added to the surface of the column. The solvent is sucked through and collected in the flask.

iii. By pH adjusting many solutes can be ionized (e.g., carboxylic acids) and trapped on ion exchangers. Owing to pH stability resins are widely used. The drawback comes from high amounts of inorganic ions which easily overload the capacity of the sorbent. SPE products of the mixed mode type are gaining acceptance. Most of them are a mixture of hydrophobic and ion exchange materials.

iv. Classical SPE sorbents suffer from a lack of selectivity. Many compounds present in the sample and belonging to the same range of polarity as the target analytes are co-extracted, thus making difficult the determination of analytes of interest. A biological approach consists of developing antibodies against a target molecule. These antibodies are immobilized onto a solid phase to produce an immunosorbent. The most common approach involves covalent bonding of the antibodies onto activated silica or sepharose. Another method is the sol-gel one, which consists of encapsulating antibodies in the pores of a hydrophilic glass matrix. As usual, there are two procedures: off-line and on-line. Main requirements are cross reactivity (affinity towards compounds with a structure similar to the antigen), capacity (defined as the total number of immobilized active antibodies), and extraction recovery. It is now possible to produce antibodies against some target compounds including some small molecules such as pesticides. For example an immunosorbent made with polyclonal anti-isoproturon antibodies covalently bound to a silica sorbent is able to concentrate several phenylureas. Due to the high selectivity, phenylureas can be detected at 0.1 μg/L level in waste waters (67).

2. On-Line Methods

On-line coupling SPE to either LC or GC is easily performed. In the simplest way a precolumn is placed in the sample loop position of a six port switching valve. After conditioning, sample application, and cleaning via a low-cost pump the precolumn is coupled to an analytical column by switching the valve into the inject position. The solutes of interest are directly eluted from the precolumn to the analytical column by an appropriate mobile phase.

The sequence can be fully automated, for example, in the Prospekt system (69).

F. Solid-Phase Micro Extraction (SPME)

This process uses a 1 cm length of focused silica fiber, coated on the outer surface with a stationary phase and bonded to a stainless steel plunger holder that looks like a modified microliter syringe (68). The fused silica fiber can be drawn into a hollow needle by using the plunger. In the first process, the coated fiber is exposed to the sample and the target analytes are extracted from the sample matrix into the coating. The fiber is then transferred to an instrument for desorption (Figure 47.23). Miniaturized SPME devices were recently designed by Millipore. These Zip Tips™ are used with Maldi –TOF.

G. Clean-Up

Extracts obtained from either LLE or SPE contain analytes and other compounds which may interfere in the chromatographic separation. A clean-up is required. The most widely used is fractionation by LC. Extract is loaded onto a chromatographic column packed with an appropriate sorbent (silica, alumina, florisil, bonded silica), and step elution with solvents is carried out. Each fraction is collected and submitted to chromatography. Derivatization prior to fractionation is sometimes performed.

Coupling two sorbents in SPE procedure, for example, hydrophobic sorbent and ion exchange in series, is efficient.

A chart on sample preparation is available upon request from LC-GC International.

X. VALIDATION

Evaluation and validation of analytical methods and laboratory procedures are of paramount importance since the quality of produced chemical information must be

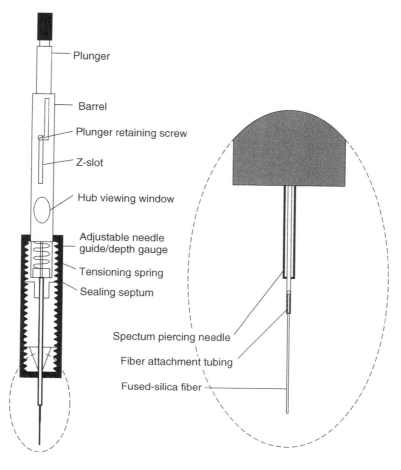

FIGURE 47.23 SPME system.

acknowledged by the customer as the end user of this information. A recognition of quality demands is achieved through accreditation or certification based on international quality standards as issued for example by ISO or OECD. The ideal validated method for food control was defined by the FAO, Food and Nutrition Paper 68, Validation of Analytical Methods for Food Control, Report of FAO/IAEA Expert Consultation FAO/UN Rome, 1998. The ideal validated method is one that has progressed fully through a collaborative study in accordance with internationally harmonized protocols for the design, conduct, and interpretation of method performance studies. This usually requires a study design involving a miniumum of five test materials, the participation of eight laboratories reporting valid data, and most often includes blind replicates or split levels to assess within laboratory repeatability parameters.

Validation begins at the vendor's site, in the structural validation stage. During this stage, the analytical instrument and software are developed, designed, and produced according to Good Laboratory Practice (GLP) and/or the International Organization for Standardization (ISO) guidelines. The FDA has published draft guideline 21 CFR Part 11, which focuses on software validation of computer systems (Draft Guidance for Industry: 21 CFR Part 11

Electronic Records; Electronic Signatures, Validation, U.S. Food and Drug administration, August 2001.

21 CFR Part11 has specific requirements that involve back-up and recovery of chromatographic data.

Calibration is a set of operations that establish, under specified conditions, the relationship between values of quantities indicated by a measuring instrument or measuring system, or values represented by a material measure or a reference material and corresponding values realized by standards. Calibration constitutes the link between materials and analyzed samples that is necessary for traceability of analytical results.

A. DETECTION

Dynamic range is that range of concentrations of the test substance over which a change in concentration produces a change in detector signal.

The lower limit of the dynamic range is defined as the concentration producing a detector output signal equal to a specified multiple of the detector short-term noise level.

The upper limit of the dynamic range is the concentration at the point where the slope of the curve obtained by plotting detector response as a function of concentration becomes zero.

Linear range is that range of concentrations over which the sensitivity (S) is constant to within a defined tolerance (Figure 47.24).

Limit of detection (LOD) is defined as the lowest concentration of an analyte in a sample, below which the analytical method cannot reliably detect a response.

A widely used detection limit technique is the 3 σ approach which is mandated for EPA testing. The standard deviation in concentration units is calculated by computing the standard deviation of blank replicates (≥7) and dividing by the slope of the calibration curve. The number is multiplied by the appropriate value of the Student's t for the chosen α and for n−1 degrees of freedom. The method used to determine LOD should be documented and defined.

Limit of quantification (LOQ) is the smallest quantity of compound to be determined in given experimental conditions with defined reliability and accuracy. A signal to noise ratio of ten is adequate.

$$\text{Limit of detection} = (3Sx/y)/b$$

$$\text{Limit of quantification} = (10Sx/y)/b$$

where b = slope of best fit regression line and Sx/y = estimate of residual standard deviation.

Both LOD and LOQ are affected by chromatographic conditions. Peak height is proportional to the solute concentration in the sample and to the injected volume. If one wants to improve the plate count of the column he or she may lose sensitivity.

Detector's noise is short-term noise in the maximum amplitude of response for all random variations of the detector signal of a frequency greater than 1 cycle per minute. Long-term noise is similar to short-term noise except that the frequency range is between 6 and 60 cycles

per hour. Drift is the measure of the amplitude of the deviation of detector response within 1 hour.

B. REPEATABILITY (ISO 3534)

Qualitative means the closeness of agreement between the results obtained by the same method on identical test material under the same conditions (same operator), same laboratory, same apparatus, and short interval of time (same day).

Quantitative is the value below which the absolute difference between two single test results obtained under the above conditions may be accepted to lie with a specified probability (usually 95%).

It is generally assessed by a minimum of nine determinations over the prescribed range for the procedure, e.g., at three concentrations, three replicates each, or by a minimum of six determinations at 100% of the test concentration.

C. REPRODUCIBILITY (ISO 3531)

Reproducibility expresses the precision between laboratories.

Qualitative means the closeness of agreement between individual results obtained with the same method on identical test material but under different conditions (different operators, different apparatus, different times, interday).

Quantitative is the value below which the absolute difference between two single test results on individual material obtained by operators in different laboratories using the standardized test method may be expected to lie within a specific probability (usually 95%).

D. SELECTIVITY

Selectivity is a measure of the extent to which the method is able to determine a particular compound in the matrices

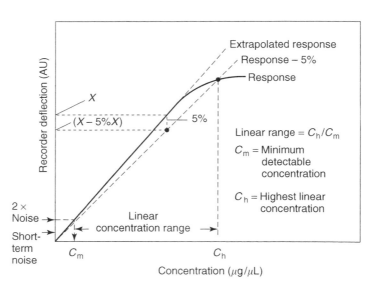

FIGURE 47.24   A calibration curve.

without interference from matrix components. Specificity is often used instead of selectivity.

E. LINEARITY

Linearity of analytical procedure it is the ability of the method to elicit test results that are directly proportional to analyte concentration (or mass) within a given range.

The analyst must determine:

- linear slope
- y intercept
- correlation coefficient
- relative standard deviation
- normalized intercept/slope.

F. ACCURACY

Accuracy measures the difference between the true value and the mean value obtained from repeated analysis. Accuracy can be assessed by analyzing a sample of known concentration (reference material) and comparing the measured value to the true value. One can compare test results from the new method with results from an existing method. Another procedure is to spike the analyte in blank matrices or to perform standard additions. Analysis of variance (ANOVA) estimates the within run precision and the between run precision.

G. PRECISION

Precision is the measure of the degree of repeatability of an analytical method under normal operation and is normally expressed as the percent relative standard deviation (RSD) for a statistically significant number of samples.

H. RELIABILITY

Reliability means the probability that the results lie in the interval defined by two selected limits. It gives a rigorous method for evaluating the correctness of a method of analysis in relation to two limits for error.

I. RUGGEDNESS

Ruggedness is the capacity of an analytical method to produce accurate data in spite of small changes in experimental conditions (for example, small flow-rate variations in HPLC). The robustness of the method is evaluated by varying method parameters such as percent of organic modifier, pH of the buffer, column temperature, flow rate, etc.

J. EXTRACTION RECOVERY

Percentage recovery of the extraction is determined by comparing the detector response of an extracted sample with that of a directly injected standard.

K. INTERNAL STANDARD

Mostly used in chromatography and capillary electrophoresis, the internal standard monitors the behavior of sample solutes to be analyzed and quantitatively determined.

Internal standard must fulfill some requirements:

- It must exhibit retention behavior similar to the solutes.
- It must exhibit chemical functionalities and structure similar to the solute.
- If a derivatization step is involved in the method, the same reaction must be applied to the internal standard.
- If a sample pretreatment is required, it is better to submit the internal standard to the sample pretreatment and check recovery.

Analysis procedure

A standard solution contains the sample and the internal standard at concentrations C_T and C_E, respectively.

$$m_T = C_T * V_T = K_T \cdot A_T$$

$$m_E = C_E * V_E = K_E \cdot A_E$$

V_T, V_E are the injected volume of the sample and the internal standard. K_T is the response coefficient of the sample and A_T the peak area. K_E is the response coefficient and A_E the peak area of the internal standard. Usually $V_T = V_E$

The concentration ratio is kept constant whatever the injection volume. A sample solution contains the substance to quality at concentration C_X. Internal standard is added at the same C_E concentration as in the previous standard solution. We thus can write:

$$m_X = C_X \cdot V_{inj} = K_X \cdot A_X$$

$$m_E = C_E \cdot V_{inj} = K_E \cdot A'_E$$

$A'_E \neq A_E$ since two injections are performed. V_{inj} is constant.

$$\frac{C_X}{C_E} = \frac{K_X}{K_E} = \frac{A_X}{A'_E}$$

$$\frac{K_X}{K_E} = \frac{K_T}{K_E}$$

then

$$\frac{C_X}{C_E} = \frac{C_T \cdot A_E}{C_E \cdot A_T} = \frac{K_X}{K_E}$$

$$\frac{C_X}{C_E} = \frac{C_T}{C_E} \cdot \frac{A_X}{A_T} = \frac{K_X}{K_E}$$

$$C_X = C_T \cdot \frac{A_E}{A_T} \cdot \frac{A_X}{A'_E} \text{ if } C_E \text{ is kept constant}$$

It is necessary to check the detector response. Standard solutions are prepared.

$$C_{1T} + C_E \longrightarrow A_{1T} + A'_E$$

$$C_{2T} + C_E \longrightarrow A_{2T} + A''_E$$

$$C_{3T} + C_E \longrightarrow A_{3T} + A'''_E$$

Sample solution $\quad C_X + C_E \longrightarrow A_E + A_E$

XI. CONCLUSIONS

The large volume of available literature on HPLC is highly indicative of the wide use of the technique. Columns are being constantly improved and are highly reproducible. Progress in instrumentation is based on the hyphenation with mass spectrometry which can be considered as *the* detector. Looking for a separation, one is 99% sure that it has been carried out previously. The drawback is that the published separation generally does not fit the analyst's purpose since it has been performed on standards or another matrix, but it is of great help. Analysts should not forget that selectivity is cheaper to achieve than efficiency.

The reader can find more information on chromatography in Refs. 70 to 73; on mass spectrometry in Refs. 74 to 77; and on sample preparation in Refs. 78 and 79.

ABBREVIATIONS AND ACRONYMS

%	Percent (parts per hundred)
A	Absorbance ($A = \log [1/T]$)
AAS	Atomic absorption spectrometry
ACN	Acetonitrile
amu	Atomic mass unit
APCI	Atmospheric pressure chemical ionization
API	Atmospheric pressure ionization
AU	Absorbance units
AUFS	Absorbance units full scale
CCD	Charge-coupled device
CE	Capillary electrophoresis
CEC	Capillary electrochromatography
CL	Chemiluminescence
CLND	Chemiluminescent nitrogen detection
CMC	Critical micelle concentration
CSP	Chiral stationary phase
DAD	Diode-array detection
ESI	Electrospray ionization
FTIR	Fourier transform infrared
GC	Gas chromatography
GLP	Good laboratory practice
HETP	Height equivalent to a theoretical plate
HPLC	High performance liquid chromatography
IC	Ion chromatography

ICP	Inductively coupled plasma
IEC	Ion-exchange chromatography
IR	Infrared
IS	Internal standard
ISO	International Organization for Standardization
LDR	Linear dynamic range
LIF	Laser-induced fluorescence
LIFD	Laser-induced fluorescence detection
LLE	Liquid liquid extraction
LSC	Liquid-solid chromatography
LSD	Light scattering detector
LSS	Linear solvent strength
MALDI	Matrix assisted laser desorption ionization
MCP	Multi channel plate
MIP	Molecular imprinted polymer
MMLLE	Micro membrane liquid liquid extraction
MS	Mass spectrometer or mass spectroscopy
MW	Molecular weight (also mol wt, M)
NMR	Nuclear magnetic resonance
NP	Normal phase
NPC	Normal phase chromatography
PDA-UV	Photodiode-array UV
PS-DVB	Polystyrene-divinylbenzene
Q-TOF	Quadrupole time of flight
RI	Refractive index
RP	Reversed phase
RP-HPLC	Reversed-phase high performance liquid chromatography
SAX	Strong anion exchanger
SCX	trong cation exchanger
SIM	Selected ion monitoring
SPE	Solid-phase extraction
SPME	Solid-phase microextraction
SSI	Sonic spray ionization
TLC	Thin layer chromatography
TOF	Time of flight
UV	Ultraviolet
UV-VIS	Ultraviolet-visible

REFERENCES

1. L. S. Ettre, Pure Appl. Chem. 65:819 (1993).
2. J. C. Giddings, Unified Separation Science, Wiley-Interscience, New York, 1991.
3. H. P. G. Darcy, Les fontaines publiques de la ville de Dijon, Victor Dalmont, Ed. Paris, 1856.
4. J. P. Foley, J. G. Dorsey, Anal. Chem. 55:730 (1983).
5. J. J. Van Deemter, H. J. Zinderweg, A. Klinkenberg, Chem. Eng. Sci. 55:271 (1956).
6. J. H. Knox, J. Chromatogr. Sci. 15:352 (1977).
7. F. Svec, E. C. Peters, D. Sykora, J. M. J. Frechet, J. Chromatogr. A 887:3 (2000).

8. F. Svec, T. Tennikova, Z. Deyl, Monolithic Materials, Elsevier, Amsterdam (2003).

9. K. Branovicacute, A. Buchacher, M. Barut, S. Jaksa, M. Zigon, A. Strancar, J. Chromatogr. A 903:21 (2000).

10. K. Nakanishi, H. Minakuchi, N. Soga, N. Tanaka, J. Sol-Gel Sci. Technol. 13:163 (1998).

11. N. Tanaka, H. Koyabashi, N. Ishizuka, H. Minakuchi, K. Nakanishi, K. Hosoya, T. Ikegami, J. Chromatogr. A 965:35 (2002).

12. N. Tanaka, H. Koyabashi, K. Nakanishi, H. Minakuchi, N. Ishizuka, Anal. Chem. 74:421A (2001).

13. K. Cabrera, G. Wieland, D. Lubda, K. Nakanishi, N. Soga, H. Minakuchi, K. K. Unger, TrAC 17:50 (1998).

14. D. Lubda, K. Cabrera, W. Kraas, D. Schaefer, D. Cunningham, LC-GC Int. 14:730 (2001).

15. Buig He, N. Tait, F. Regnier, Anal. Chem. 70:3750 (1998).

16. J. W. Dolan, LC-GC Int. 14:75 (2001).

17. J. W. Dolan, LC-GC Int. 14:276 (2001).

18. S. Setford, S. Saini, J. Chromatogr. A 867:93 (2000).

19. F. Brandl, N. Pustet, A. Mannschreck, Int. Laboratory 29:10C (1999).

20. B. A. Thompson, J. V. Iribarne, J. Chem. Phys. 71:4451 (1979).

21. J. B. Fenn, J. Am. Soc. Mass Spectrom. 4:525 (1993).

22. P. Kebarle, H. Yeungshaw, in Electrospray Ionization Mass Spectrometry, Fundamentals, Instrumentation and Applications, R. B. Cole, Ed., John Wiley & Sons, New York, 1997, pp. 1–63.

23. W. Hager, Rapid Commun. Mass Spectrom. 16:512 (2002).

24. K. Albert, J. Chromatogr. A 856:(1999).

25. T. Greibrokk, T. Andersen, J. Sep. Sci. 24:899 (2001).

26. P. L. Zhu, J. W. Dolan, L. R. Snyder, D. W. Hill, L. Van Heukelem, T. Waeghe, J., Chromatogr. A 756:51 (1996).

27. P. L. Zhu, J. W. Dolan, L. R. Snyder, N. M. Djorjevic, D. W. Hill, J. T. Lin, L. C. Sander, L. Van Heukelem, J. Chromatogr. A 756:63 (1996) and references therein.

28. A-M. Siouffi, R. Phan Tan Luu, J. Chromatogr. A 892:75 (2000).

29. Drylab Chromatogr. Ref. Guide, LC Resources Inc. 1998.

30. J. W. Dolan, D. C. Lommen, L. R. Snyder, J. Chromatogr. 485:91 (1989).

31. T. H. Jupille, J. W. Dolan, L. R. Snyder, I. Molnar, J. Chromatogr. A 948:35 (2002).

32. S. V. Galushko, Chromsword for Windows 95 and NT, Software for Method Development in LC, Manual for Program Version 1. 1, Merck KgA.

33. T. Baczek, R. Kaliszan, H. A. Claessens, M. A. Van Straten, LC-GC Eur. 14:304 (2001).

34. S Nyiredy, K. Dallenbach-Tolke, O. Sticher, J. Planar Chromatogr. 1:336 (1988).

35. J. E. Madden, N. Avadalovic, P. R. Haddad, J. Havel, J. Chromatogr. A 910:173–179 (2001).

36. M. H. Abraham, Chem. Soc. Rev. 22:73 (1993).

37. D. Bolliet, C. F. Poole, Chromatographia 46:381 (1997).

38. L. C. Tan, P. W. Carr, J. Chromatogr. A 799:1 (1998).

39. L. R. Snyder, Principles of Adsorption Chromatography, Marcel Dekker, New York, 1968.

40. E. Soczewinski, Anal. Chem. 41:179 (1969).

41. H. Engelhardt, M. Jungheim, Chromatographia 29:59 (1990).

42. M. Czok, H. Engelhardt, Chromatographia 27:5 (1989).

43. K. Kimata, K. Iwaguchi, S. Onishi, K. Jinno, R. Eksteen, K. Osoya, N. Tanaka, J. Chromatogr. Sci. 27:721 (1990).

44. M. Kele and G. Guiochon, J. Chromatogr. A 960:19 (2002) and references therein.

45. H. A. Claessens, TrAC 37:563 (2001).

46. D. V. McCalley, J. Chromatogr. A 769:169 (1997).

47. U. D. Neue, B. A. Aden, T. H. Walter, J. Chromatogr. A 849:101 (1999).

48. M. R. Euerby, P. Petersson, LC-GC Europe, 13:665 (2000).

49. L. R. Snyder, J. Chromatogr. Sci. 16:223 (1978).

50. A-M Siouffi in Planar Chromatography, A Retrospective View for the Millenium, SZ Nyiredy, Ed., Springer, Budapest, 2003, p. 47.

51. M. A. Quarry, R. L. Grob, L. R. Snyder, Anal. Chem. 58:917 (1986).

52. P. Jandera, J. Chromatogr. A 845:133 (1999).

53. Micelles as Separation Media, J. Chromatogr. 780 (1997).

54. V. A. Davankov, I. Chromatogr. A 666:55 (1994).

55. A. Kurganov, J. Chromatogr. A 906:51 (2001).

56. K. Gunther, J. Martens, M. Schickedanz, Angew. Chem. 96:514 (1984).

57. F. Hui, K. H. Ekborg-Ott, D. W. Armstrong, J. Chromatogr. A 906:91–103 (2001).

58. Y. Okamoto, E. Yashima, Angew. Chem. Int. Ed 37:1021–1043(1998), T. Nakano, Chem. Rev. 94:349 (1994).

59. E. Francotte, Chem. Anal. Series 142:633(1997).

60. E. Yashima, J. Chromatogr. A 906:105–125 (2001).

61. W. H. Pirkle, T. C. Pochadsky, Chem. Rev. 89:347 (1989).

62. L. I. Andersson, J. Chromatogr. B Biomed. Sci. Appl. 745:3 (2000).

63. P. Piras, C. Roussel, J. Pierrot-Sanders, J. Chromatogr. A 906:443–458 (2001).

64. M. A. Jeannot, F. F. Cantwell, Anal. Chem. 68:2236 (1996).

65. T. Hyotylainen, L. Riekkola, LC-GC Europe 15:298 (2002).

66. M. C. Hennion J. Chromatogr. 856:3 (1999).

67. M. C. Hennion, V. Pichon, J. Chromatogr. A 1000:29 (2003).

68. J. Pawliszyn, Solid Phase Microextraction, Theory and Practice, New York, Wiley, 1997.

69. J. A. B. Ooms, G. J. M. Van Gils, A. R. Duinkerken, O. Halmingh, Intern. Lab. 30:18 (2000).

70. E. Katz, R. Eksteen, P. Schoenmakers, N. Miller, Ed. Handbook of HPLC, Marcel Dekker, New York, 1998.

71. L. R. Snyder, J. J. Kirkland and J. L. Glajch, Practical HPLC Development, 2nd Ed., Wiley, New York, 1997.

72. P. R. Haddad and P. E. Jackson, Ion Chromatography (IC) in Ion Chromatography: Principles and Applications, Journal of Chromatography Library, Vol 46, Elsevier, Amsterdam, 1990.

73. C. F. Poole, The Essence of Chromatography, Elsevier, Amsterdam, 2003.

74. R. B. Cole, Electrospray Mass Spectrometry, Fundamentals, Instrumentation and Applications, Wiley-Interscience, New York, 1996.

75. E. De Hoffman, J. Charrette, V. Stroobant, Mass Spectrometry, Principle and Applications, John Wiley & Sons, New York, 1996.

76. W. M. A. Niessen, R. D. Voyksner (Eds.), Current Practice of Liquid Chromatography-Mass Spectrometry, Elsevier Science, New York, 1998.

77. Special Issue of LC-GC Europe, December 2001.

78. R. M. Smith, J. Chromatogr. A 1000:1 (2003).

79. J. Pawliszyn, Solid Phase Microextraction, Theory and Practice, Wiley, New York, 1997.

48 The Use of Mass Spectrometry in Food Analysis

*Sherri B. Turnipseed**
Animal Drug Research Center, U.S. Food and Drug Administration

CONTENTS

Mass spectrometry (MS) is a powerful modern analytical technique which provides detailed structural information for molecules. This capability, and the fact that it easily interfaces with commonly used chromatographic techniques, makes it a very useful tool for food analysis. MS can be used to characterize food composition or to monitor adulteration of foods by residues or other extraneous substances. A recent review by Careri et al. [1] is an excellent reference that demonstrates the wide scope of MS in the analysis of food, including the analysis of natural and xenobiotic substances as well as metals in food products. An earlier review by Careri et al. [2] described the use of LC/MS for residue analysis in food.

This chapter is not meant to be an exhaustive list of all references pertaining to the use of MS for food analysis, but rather is intended to further illustrate the many different applications in which MS has been used to characterize food. First, the types of modern instruments and experiments that may be used to perform MS on food samples are briefly described. An overview of how MS has been used to determine the natural components of food is followed by a description of the use of MS to determine residue level contaminants such as pesticides, animal drugs, mycotoxins, and packaging materials in foods. Further illustration of how MS has been used to study foods for a variety of purposes is given using examples of specific commodities (bovine milk and berries). Finally, some of the emerging trends in the analysis of food by MS are discussed.

I. MASS SPECTROMETRY (MS): INSTRUMENTS AND TECHNIQUES

The MS experiment consists of forming ions, separating those ions based on differences in their mass/charge (m/z) ratio, and detecting (counting) the number of ions at each m/z value. Although MS has changed dramatically in the past few decades, this basic process applies to modern techniques as well as those performed with more traditional MS instruments. A complete review of the fundamentals of MS theory is beyond the scope of this chapter, but many such resources are available [3, 4].

MS is an important modern analytical technique for the analysis of food because of the type of detailed information that is obtained. Traditionally, using an electron impact (EI) ion source, the analyte is introduced in the gas phase into an evacuated chamber and is bombarded with an electron beam of 70 eV. As a result of this interaction, the compound loses an electron and becomes a positively charged radical cation. In addition, the amount of energy used is generally enough to break bonds in the molecule and provide ionized fragments. The resulting fingerprint of ions at different m/z values with varying intensities can be used to determine a probable identity of the original analyte. This process of interpreting mass spectra to deduce molecular structure from EI experiments has been well studied and described [5].

In addition to collision with a high energy electron beam, there are many other methods of ionizing compounds so that they can be analyzed by MS. For example,

---

* The opinions expressed are those of the author and do not necessarily reflect the official views of the U.S. FDA.

positive ion chemical ionization (CI) transfers a proton from an ionized reagent gas, such as methane or isobutane, to an analyte with higher proton affinity to form a protonated (ionized) compound. Alternatively, a highly electronegative compound can capture thermalized (slower) electrons to form a negative ion when a reagent gas is present in the ion source. Desorption from high energy sources such as a lasers, fast atoms, high fields, etc. can also be used to form and eject ions from solids or liquids into the lower pressure region of an MS instrument. Matrix assisted laser desorption ionization (MALDI) has become a very popular method for introducing large biomolecules such as proteins into a mass spectrometer and has helped revolutionize the study of these compounds in many biological applications.

The introduction of two interfaces, electrospray ionization and atmospheric pressure chemical ionization, has allowed LC/MS to become widely used and commercially available. In electrospray ionization (ESI) the effluent from an LC is sprayed, usually pneumatically assisted with nitrogen gas, into a high electric field (3–5 kV) at atmospheric pressure. This process creates a stream of charged droplets that become smaller as they are accelerated into the field. Charged particles in the solution are ejected as the droplets evaporate or are released when the droplets explode as the surface forces become too high. The ionized molecules can then be sampled and accelerated through small orifices into a high vacuum region of the instrument where they can be separated and detected. One advantage of ESI is that multiply charged ions can be formed (e.g., on proteins with multiple sites available for protonation). This allows compounds with very high molecular weight to be analyzed with MS instruments utilizing traditional mass range (m/z 1000–2000) ion separators. With atmospheric pressure chemical ionization (APCI), the LC effluent is again sprayed into an atmospheric pressure chamber with nitrogen gas. However, in this case the LC mobile phase (water, methanol, etc.) is vaporized and ionized by a corona discharge. The ionized mobile phase can then act as a chemical ionization reagent gas and perform proton transfer reactions with the analyte to generate charged molecules. The bulk of the mobile phase must then be thermally vaporized before entering the lower pressure region of the MS instrument.

In contrast to electron ionization, the alternative ionization methods of CI, ESI, and APCI are relatively soft (low energy) ionization techniques. Therefore, not as many fragment ions are formed by the breaking of chemical bonds during these processes. As a result, the mass spectrum obtained may only consist of one peak, the protonated (or deprotonated) molecular ion. While these data give valuable information regarding the molecular weight of an analyte, structural ions are not available. For this reason, tandem MS or "MS/MS" is often used in conjunction with these ionization techniques to yield additional

structural details. In the MS/MS experiment, one ion is isolated from all other ions, and a secondary energy source (such as bombardment with energized argon or helium gas) is introduced to break that ion into fragment ions. A second stage of ion separation is then performed to yield another mass spectrum consisting of only ions created from the collision induced dissociation of the initial parent ion. This secondary spectrum is referred to as a product ion spectrum and contains more information regarding fragments of the original molecule. For example, one common MS/MS instrument used is the triple quadrupole. After an ion is formed and introduced into the MS, it can be isolated from others using a quadrupole ion filter. A second quadrupole, which uses only RF frequency, acts as a collision cell, where the ion is impacted with argon. The third quadrupole can then be used to separate ions formed in the collision cell. This instrument can be used in other modes, but this is a common method to obtain structural information for a specific analyte. An ion trap separation device can also be used to obtain information-rich product ion spectra from molecular ions created from soft ionization techniques.

Mass spectrometers can be programmed to optimize for selectivity, specificity and sensitivity for any given compound. For example, when looking for a specific analyte in a complex mixture, an MS method can be programmed to scan for only one ion or set of ions (selected ion monitoring, or SIM). With an MS/MS instrument, specific ion transitions or parent-product ion pairs can be acquired (selective or multiple reaction monitoring, SRM or MRM). These techniques can greatly improve detection and confirmation limits for residues in food. Another valuable MS experiment that has been used in food analysis, for component characterization as well as residue analysis, is the measurement of the exact mass of molecules of interest using high resolution instruments. Time-of-flight analyzers have been used to obtain exact mass information for large biomolecules; these are often coupled to a MALDI MS source.

The commodities included for consideration under the category of food analysis represent a wide variety of complex matrices of plant and animal origin. In order to analyze a specific compound in a food product by MS, extensive sample preparation and analyte isolation is often required. Examples of some of the approaches used to accomplish this are liquid-liquid extraction, solid-phase extraction, and immunoaffinity techniques. The goal of these procedures is to remove as many matrix components as possible, while concentrating the analyte of interest. Often there is a trade-off between maximum recovery of the residue and the time and effort required to perform the analysis. This becomes more of an issue as requirements for high sample throughput increases.

Regardless of the sample preparation and extraction procedures used, a chromatographic separation step is usually applied prior to MS analysis when analyzing components or residues in food. If the compounds of interest are sufficiently volatile and thermally stable, GC/MS is the preferred technique. Electron ionization is the most common MS technique used with GC because it gives structurally rich spectra. Chemical ionization with either positive or negative ion detection, is also possible with GC/MS. The most common LC/MS methods involve the use of a reverse-phase LC system interfaced to an electrospray or APCI MS source. Tandem MS can then be used to obtain additional structural ions. Often many compounds of interest in food analysis can be ionized using either ESI or APCI, and the best interface for each analyte may have to be determined empirically. Helpful resources detailing many more of the practical aspects for implementation of successful LC/MS analyses are also available [4].

II. MS ANALYSIS FOR DETERMINATION OF FOOD COMPOSITION

MS has been used to characterize the natural composition of food products. Specifically, this can be used to describe the profile of major components in a food product, to differentiate between similar products, or to measure small amounts of naturally occurring substances which are believed to be either beneficial or deleterious. The type of MS analysis used for the characterization of food components depends on the nature of the analytes. Many of the articles cited below are reviews and should serve as a guide to the reader looking for a specific type of analysis or food product.

Several reviews cover MS analysis of major components in foods including proteins and peptides [6, 7]. The analysis of peptides and proteins requires the use of technique that is designed for large non-volatile molecules such as electrospray ionization or MALDI. MS can be used in protein studies to characterize conformational changes or post-translational modifications such as glycosylation or phosphorylation. The information obtained by MS can then be used to help determine how these factors affect food qualities such as flavor, texture and nutritional value. The effect of processing (pasteurization, hydrolysis, etc.) on the structure and function of food proteins can also be examined using MS techniques. Analyses of the proteins associated with milk (casein, whey components lactalbumin and lactoglobulin), cereal (globulins, albumins, glutenins, prolamins), and eggs (ovalbumin, conalbumin, lyzozyme) have been performed using MS. One study characterized the different gluten proteins that are unique to various grains (wheat, rye, barley and oats) in cereal mixtures using MALDI time-of-flight (TOF) MS [8]. A few studies of meat proteins have been performed using MS. In one report, LC/MS using electrospray was used to study the polypeptides from whole and ground meat and how that profile changed during storage of the meat products [9].

The analysis of fatty foods (lipids, oils, fatty acids, etc.) can be accomplished using either GC/MS or LC/MS methods. In one study, GC/MS was used to determine the types and amounts of free fatty acids produced in the ripening of ewe milk cheese [10]. In this study, solid phase microextraction (SPME) was used to extract the fatty acids from the food matrix and the amount of butanoic, hexanoic, octanoic and decanoic acids were measured at part-per-million levels using GC/MS. Alternatively, a direct infusion electrospray MS method was developed to study different nut and vegetable oils and to determine if additional (adulterant) oils were added to olive oil [11]. Razzazi-Fazeli et al. [12] published a determination of cholesterol oxides in processed foods such as butter, lard, and egg powder using LC/MS with APCI and selected ion monitoring.

Characterizing the carbohydrate composition in food is also important. These compounds are difficult to analyze using traditional methods as they are nonvolatile, thermally unstable, and generally do not have a strong UV chromophore. In one food application, the saccharide profiles of caramel from different sources were evaluated using GC/MS after forming trimethylsilyl derivatives. Specific compounds were identified as possible indicators of the authenticity of the caramel product [13]. The carbohydrates found in human milk have been studied after derivatization with 2-aminoacridone using MALDI-TOF and electrospray MS, in addition to spectrofluorimetry [14]. The changes that occur to carbohydrates after processing can also by studied by MS methods. For instance, the starch components in treated potato starch were analyzed using anion exchange chromatography coupled to electrospray MS after enzymatic hydrolysis of the starch polymer [15]. In addition to studying carbohydrate profiles, MS is often used to characterize compounds such as peptides or flavonoids that may also include one or more sugar molecules.

Minor components of food products can also be characterized by MS analysis. Flavor and fragrance components tend to be inherently volatile and thermally stable organic compounds such as ketones, aldehydes, alcohols, and terpenes. GC/MS is the preferred MS analysis technique for these compounds. Isolation from the food product is often accomplished by head-space sampling techniques such as purge and trap or solid phase micro extraction methods [16, 17]. Examples of how these MS techniques are used in flavor analysis for specific food commodities, bovine milk and berries, are illustrated later in this chapter.

Recently there has been a great deal of interest in minor components of foods that may have high nutritional or nutraceutical value. Vitamins such as tocopherols and folates can be measured in food using MS techniques. For example, a method to determine alpha-tocopherol in infant foods (milk and cereal) was developed using

LC/MS (single quadrupole) with an APCI interface [18]. Deuterium- labeled tocopherol was used as an internal standard and detection limits of 2.5 ng/mL were achieved. A LC/fluorescence method for folic acid and 5-methyl-tetrahydrofolic acid in a variety of foods was validated using a complementary electrospray LC/MS method [19].

Flavanoids, including anthocyanins, may have beneficial antioxidant properties. The identification and quantification of these compounds in different foods is an important aspect of the research to determine the effects these chemicals may have on human health. There are many recent examples of how MS is being used in this emerging area of food analysis including the characterization of anthocyanins in food using LC/MS and capillary electrophoresis [20]. The oxidative phenolic compounds in artichokes have been characterized using electrospray LC/MS [21]. Flavonoid glycosides, such as kaempferol glucoside and others, were studied in almonds [22] using MALDI-TOF MS and in tomatoes using electrospray LC/MS/MS [23]. The distribution of anthocyanins, flavonols, and carbohydrates in different layers of red onion was also studied using electrospray LC/MS [24].

Some minor components in food products are thought to be deleterious and the characterization of these is also important. For example, the health effects of acrylamide residues that can be formed in various fried and baked foods have recently been questioned and can be monitored by LC/MS/MS [25]. Another area of interest is the presence of known cancer causing agents such as polycyclic aromatic hydrocarbons (PAHs) and heterocyclic aromatic amines that may occur in food treated in certain ways, such as frying or smoking. These compounds can also be monitored using MS analysis [26]. In one study, polyaromatic hydrocarbons in liquid smoke flavorings were analyzed by GC/MS, and a higher proportion of lower molecular weight PAHs were found; benzo(a)pyrene was present in a few samples, but at fairly low concentrations [27]. The determination of heterocyclic amines in lyophilized meat extracts was performed using LC/MS with an APCI source and ion trap MS/MS detection. Low part-per-billion levels could be detected [28]. Volatile nitrosamines in dry sausages were also monitored using an APCI LC/MS/MS method [29].

III. MS ANALYSIS IN THE DETECTION OF CONTAMINANTS AND RESIDUES IN FOOD

MS in also used to detect, measure, and identify foreign compounds such as pesticide or drug residues and environmental contaminants in food products. Several types of experiments can be performed when using MS to analyze food commodities for residues including screening, determinative or confirmatory analyses. Historically MS, often in conjunction with GC or LC, has been used for confirmatory analysis to positively identify a residue of concern. Mass spectrometry is the ideal tool to confirm the identity of a residue due to its inherent sensitivity and selectivity. There are established guidelines that define how closely the mass spectrum of an unknown or suspect residue must match that of a standard in order to be considered confirmed [30, 31]. MS methods can also be used to quantitate the amount of residue present. Traditionally, this has been more widespread with GC/MS, but is becoming more standard practice with LC/MS as well [32]. Care must be taken to use appropriate internal standards. If available, isotopically labeled analogues are the preferred internal standard because their response and fragmentation will most closely match that the analyte of interest. Because of its universal nature, MS can also be a powerful tool for screening for multiresidues or even multiclass residues in food analysis, and this application is becoming more common as MS is used more routinely.

Antibiotics are the most common type of drugs given to food animals. These are given both therapeutically and subtherapeutically to prevent disease and increase feed efficiency. The possibility of drug residues remaining in the edible product and the potential human health problems associated with exposure to these residues is a concern with widespread drug use in food animals. Mass spectrometry is commonly used to analyze antibiotic residues in foods [33, 34]. MS was traditionally used as a confirmatory analysis method to identify illegal residues in food. Many of the drugs of concern are polar nonvolatile compounds, so while it used to be more common to analyze derivatized residues by GC/MS, many recent reports utilize LC/MS methods. There are many examples of this including beta-lactam and sulfonamides residues in milk [35, 36], tetracycline residues in various foods [37], and fluoroquinolones and phenicols in aquacultured products [38], as well as many others. In addition to antibiotics, other animal drugs such as hormones can be monitored by MS. An example is a method that uses GC/MS not only to confirm, but also to quantitate anabolic steroids in bovine muscle tissue [39]. An upcoming trend is to use the universal response of the mass spectrometer, along with the capability of LC/MS/MS to provide diagnostic information, to screen for many types of residues with a generic extraction procedure [38, 40].

There is a long record of using MS for the determination and identification of pesticide residues in food products, especially in produce commodities. Historically pesticide residues could be monitored by GC/MS analysis only after extensive sample preparation using large sample sizes and liquid-liquid extraction procedures. Because many pesticides are volatile and thermally stable GC/MS is still the technique of choice for many of these compounds. The use of time-dependent selected ion monitoring GC/MS programs allows for the screening, determination and confirmation of a large number of pesticides from a single analysis. This technique has been used to determine pesticides containing nitrogen, sulfur, or oxygen in a variety of foods [41]. Alternatively, the analysis of pesticides using GC/MS/MS with an ion trap detector to obtain product ion spectra can yield a very selective and sensitive method for a large number of compounds [42]. A new trend in the analysis of pesticides by GC/MS is the use of more rapid extraction methods. One report describes the use of automated solid phase extraction to isolate organochlorine and pyrethroid residues from a variety of fruits for analysis by GC with electron capture and confirmation by GC/MS [43]. In another example solid phase micro extraction (SPME) coupled directly to GC/MS has been used for the analysis of chlorpropham in potatoes and amitraz in honey at ppb levels [44]. Another innovation in this area is to use low-pressure fast GC coupled to MS for pesticide analysis [45]. In this approach a shorter, wider bore GC column with a thicker film was operated at fast flow rates and low pressure allowing for faster analysis, increased injection sample size and reduced thermal degradation.

Some classes of pesticides are not as amenable to GC/MS due to limitations of volatility or thermal stability, and LC/MS may be the technique of choice for these analytes [46]. For example, the determination of aldicarb and its metabolites in various food extracts has been reported using LC-APCI [47]. Carbamates are another class of pesticides that can be best analyzed by LC/MS. One report describes the isolation of thirteen carbamates from orange, grape, onion and tomatoes by matrix solid-phase dispersion with analysis by LC/MS [48]. These authors determined that both electrospray and APCI were suitable for the analysis of these compounds with similar sensitivity (ppb) and structural information obtained.

Dioxins are a class of compounds that create a particular analytical challenge. Formed as breakdown products from industrial chemicals, these compounds are extremely toxic and have a very long residence time in the environment. Because of this, the potential of very low, yet possibly still toxic, amounts of dioxins entering the food supply is a real concern. Analytical methods must therefore be able to detect part-per-trillion (and sub-ppt) amounts of these compounds in a wide variety of environmental and food matrices. Another challenge is that dioxins exist in many similar forms, or congeners. These compounds may have closely related molecular structure but different toxicological properties. Historically, extensive extraction methods (Soxlet, multi-stage column chromatography, etc.) using relatively large sample sizes were coupled with GC/MS detection [49]. The MS instruments used may need to have high enough resolution to distinguish between compounds with the same nominal molecular weight. Magnetic sector or high-resolution ion trap instruments typically have been employed for this purpose. Recently some of the newer MS techniques have been

applied to dioxin analysis including the use of time-of-flight instruments and isotopic dilution quantitation [50].

The formation of mycotoxins is a prevalent problem in foods such as grains and peanuts. The use of MS, especially LC/MS, has allowed for much more efficient monitoring of these toxins. For example, the analysis of aflatoxin can be performed with great sensitivity and selectivity by LC/MS. One recent reference describes the use of MS to identify individual peanuts with high levels of aflatoxin in a processing stream by dipping the nuts into an extraction fluid and analyzing the fluid by MS/MS [51]. Other methods describe the optimized LC/MS APCI conditions for the determination of A-trichothecene mycotoxins in grains such as oats, maize, barley and wheat [52]. Mycotoxins can also occur in fruits and their juice products. LCMS and GC/MS have been used for the analysis of the mycotoxins alternariol and patulin in apples and other fruit [53, 54].

Several acute human illnesses can result from the consumption of shellfish containing marine toxins including diarrhetic shellfish poisoning, amnesic shellfish poisoning and azaspiracid poisoning. Diarrhetic shellfish poisoning is caused by compounds such as okadaic acid, dinophysistoxin, pectenotoxin, yessotoxin, dinophysistoxins, among others. MS has played an important role in the analysis of these compounds, as well as the initial characterization of newly discovered compounds [55, 56]. Domoic acid is a toxin which causes amnesic symptoms. Determination and confirmation of this compound can also be achieved using LC/MS methodology [57]. A series of related toxins, the azaspiracids, can also results in human illness after consumption of affected shellfish. These compounds have been characterized by electrospray LC/MS using an ion trap instrument and a method to quantitate the azaspiracids in mussel tissues has been developed [58, 59].

A recent concern involving packaged food products is that potentially harmful substances from the packaging material may migrate into the food and be consumed. MS can be used to characterize possible contaminants from processing or packaging materials or the degradation of those substances. For example the amount of styrene or styrene oxide or other volatile organic compounds from polystyrene containers and the factors affecting the rate of migration into the food commodity using GC/MS have been reported [60]. Plasticizers in food have also been determined by GC/MS with ion trap detection [61]. Bisphenols, which are breakdown products from canned food coating material, have been measured in a wide range of different canned foods including soup, fruit, infant formula, and meat products using GC/MS methods [62].

The potential threat for adulteration of food by deliberate tampering, either at the manufacturing facility, the retail outlet, or by individual consumers, has always been a concern and has become more so in recent years. MS can be a very valuable tool for determining what foreign compound may have been added to a product, as well as the possible source of the contamination. Due to the sensitive nature of this work and possible legal and regulatory implication, there are not many references on this subject in the published literature. A few references include the determination of a rodenticide in consumer products [63] and the identification of cocaine in fruit (and syringes found at the same location) in a supermarket tampering case [64].

IV. SPECIFIC APPLICATIONS OF MS IN FOOD ANALYSIS

The use of MS to analyze two common food commodities, bovine milk and berries, is examined in more detail. The major components of bovine milk have been characterized by MS methods. The triacylglycerols in milk have been characterized by LC/MS using APCI as well as by GC/MS [65] after initial prefractionation using both TLC and gel permeation chromatography. LC/MS alone could not resolve the complicated mixture of triacylglycerols, and interpretation was difficult because many compounds shared common fragment ions. Fractions of the mixture were separated using either TLC or gel permeation and subsequent analysis of these portions was used to identify individual triacylglyceraols. GC/MS was also performed on the majority of the fractions and yielded complementary data to assist in the identification of individual components. Using these techniques, 120 triacylglycerols were identified. The whey proteins derived from milk have also been better described using LC/MS with an electrospray interface and time-of-flight MS detection [66]. This study found that the principle proteins in whey (lactalbumin and lactaglobulins) can be extensively modified by glycosylation and oxidation upon processing.

The more volatile compounds in foods or beverages often determine their flavor. The use of SPME coupled to GC/MS has become the method of choice to sample the volatile compounds present in milk [67, 68]. For a more rapid analysis, the GC column can be omitted and the compounds can be analyzed directly by electron impact MS. In this case, a short fused silica transfer line can take the place of an analytical GC column. The MS then acts as an "electronic nose" and pattern recognition techniques are required to distinguish significant differences in milk samples [69].

Phytoestrogens, which include isoflavones, lignans, and coumestans, are a class of compounds that are often a minor naturally occurring component of milk. These compounds can potentially act as endrocrine disruptors and are passed into bovine milk from injestion of compounds present in animal feed. A method was developed to analyze phytoestrogens in milk using LC/MS/MS [70]. An electrospray interface (using both positive and negative

ionization) was used along with a triple quadrupole MS operated in the selected reaction monitoring mode. Identification limits for these compounds using this method was determined to be less than 1 µg/L. Analysis of milk samples confirmed the presence of the hydroxylated isolflavones genistein and daidzein and also higher amounts of the metabolite equol.

Potential residual compounds that could be present in milk include industrial compounds, mycotoxins, pesticides and animal drugs. Examples of industrial chemicals that have been analyzed in milk using MS include polycyclic aromatic hydrocarbons [71] and polychlorinated biphenyls [72]. Cyclopiazonic acid is a mycotoxin produced by *Aspergillus* and *Penicillium* genuses in milk. This compound has been analyzed using negative ion electrospray LC/MS with ion trap detection [73]. The authors were able to quantitate over three orders of magnitude with a detection limit of 5 ng/mL. Twenty milk samples were analyzed for cyclopiazonic acid by this method, and three of those samples were found to be contaminated at detectable levels.

Multiresidue methods for pesticide residues in milk have been developed. A method for detection, quantitation, and confirmation of over 100 pesticides using GC with ion trap MS/MS was developed and applied to several different types of foods including milk [42]. The advantage of using the ion trap as a detector, in this method or any other application, is the ability to achieve additional selectivity and sensitivity. This is demonstrated in this method by the ability to obtain very clean traces for individual compounds using specific individual acquisition parameters in very complex food matrices. Another method developed more specifically for milk uses GC/MS (single quadrupole detection) as well as GC with flame photometric detection to quantitate several classes of pesticides including organophosphorous compounds, organochlorine compounds, methylcarbamates, as well as others [74]. Residues were confirmed using high-resolution GC/MS and GC/MS-MS with a hybrid magnetic sector/quadrupole instrument.

Residues of animal drugs can be a potential problem in bovine milk because dairy cows may be treated for illness such as mastisis or respiratory disease. Some drugs are approved for treatment of affected dairy cattle, but they may result in violative residues if appropriate drugs, dosages, and withdrawal times are not used. Antibiotics are the most common drug residues found in milk, and MS has been used extensively to monitor for these residues. MS methods for residues in milk include sulfonamides [36, 75], tetracyclines [76], penicillins and related compounds [35, 77], aminoglycosides [78], and many others [33]. Other types of animal drugs that can be analyzed for in milk by MS methods include anthelmintics such as bendazoles [79].

Berries are another type of food product that have been extensively analyzed and characterized using MS methods. One primary focus of analytical methods using berries as a matrix is understanding which chemical compounds give the fruit the best flavor and odor characteristics. A thorough study of the volatile components that define the aroma and flavor characteristics of strawberries has been reported [80]. This method employed SPME headspace analysis combined with thermal desorption GC/MS to identify and quantitate 23 different compounds. Statistical techniques were then utilized to classify and compare the different varieties of berries. GC/MS with headspace sampling was also used in a study [81] that compared the aroma components, primarily aliphatic esters, of strawberries grown in different conditions.

Another aspect of berry chemistry that has received a great deal of attention is the presence of anthocyanins, procyanidins, and flavanols in these fruits. These compounds are thought to have potential beneficial value due to their antioxidant properties. The flavonal components quercetin, myricetin and kaempferol were studied in 25 berries including cranberries, currants, whortleberries, blueberries and strawberries [82]. A LC/UV method was used to quantitate the amounts of those compounds in the various berries and electrospray LC/MS along with diode array data were used to identify the various compounds. In another study, an MS method using MALDI-TOF was compared to a traditional LC method to measure the amount of anthocyanin in blueberries [83]. While both techniques gave comparable profile results, the MS method was faster and also provided confirmatory information, although the LC method provided better information on isomeric compounds.

The chemical residues in berries that are of most concern are pesticide residues. One report describes the analysis of organochlorine and chlorobenzene pesticide residues in strawberries using GC/MS [84]. The residues were extracted from the fruit using the novel techniques accelerated solvent extraction, SPME, or stir bar sorptive extraction. Detection limits of 1–10 μg/kg were reported. This method was used to monitor contamination of strawberries in an industrial region. Another paper also reports on the use of SPME in conjunction with GC/MS (using selected ion monitoring) for a wide variety of pesticides and fungicides in strawberries [85]. In an alternative approach, capillary electrophoresis using an electrospray interface and selected ion monitoring was used to measure the fungicides procymidone and thiabendazole in strawberries as well as other fruits [86]. A survey of consumer samples using this method found that these residues are present in real samples more than 50% of the time.

V. EMERGING TRENDS IN THE MS ANALYSIS OF FOODS

MS should remain an important analytical tool in the characterization of food, and the application of new technologies will continue to expand. The flexibility of the new MS/MS instruments will allow multi-component methods to be developed with performance (in terms of sensitivity and selectivity) that was previously only possible for single compounds. Just as the advent of practical and commercially available LC/MS/MS instruments has had a great effect on food analysis, the introduction of time-of-flight and other high resolution instruments will also have a great impact. The use of exact mass measurements to identify and confirm food components or residues should increase.

Innovations from other areas of analytical chemistry and biology can be borrowed and adapted for food analysis. For example, the advances made in the area of drug discovery in terms of rapid throughput of compounds (multiplexing, robotics, etc.) should lead to the ability to screen a large number of food samples using some of the same technological advances. The use of MS, as well as other means of structural elucidation, to study a wide variety of proteins has exploded in recent years, giving rise to the whole field of proteomics. Researchers in this area are applying their knowledge to a wide variety of biological systems and disease mechanisms. The same analytical techniques should be able to be applied to food matrices as well, leading to better ways to distinguish species or varieties of commodities. Identification of bacterial food pathogens using MS is already an area of increasing development [87].

In the future, MS will likely become a valuable tool in determining not only what components are present in any given food, but also what role a particular compound may play in the food's esthetic quality, nutritional value, and perhaps even in its ability to mitigate or prevent disease.

REFERENCES

1. Careri, M., F. Bianchi, C. Corradini. 2002. Recent advances in the application of mass spectrometry in food-related analysis. J. Chromatogr. A 970:3–64.
2. Careri, M., A. Mangia, M. Musci. 1996. Applications of liquid chromatography-mass spectrometry interfacing systems in food analysis: pesticide, drug and toxic substance residues. J. Chromatogr. A 727:153–184.
3. De Hoffman, E., V. Stroobant. 2001. *Mass Spectrometry: Principles and Applications, 2nd Edition.* John Wiley & Sons, New York.
4. Ardrey, R.E. 2003. *Liquid Chromatography-Mass Spectrometry: An Introduction.* John Wiley & Sons, New York.
5. McLafferty, F.W. 1996. *Interpretation of Mass Spectra, Fourth Edition.* University Science Books, Mill Valley, CA.
6. Alomirah, H.F., I. Alli, Y. Konishi. 2000. Applications of mass spectrometry to food proteins and peptides. J. Chromatogr. A. 893:1–21.
7. Leonil, J., V. Gagnaire, D. Molle, S. Pezennec, S. Bouhallab. 2000. Application of chromatography and

mass spectrometry to the characterization of food proteins and derived peptides. J. Chromatogr. A 881:1–21.

8. Camafeita, E., J. Solis, P. Alfonso, J.A. Lopez, L. Sorell, E. Mendez. 1998. Selective identification by matrix-assisted laser desorption/ionization time-of-flight mass spectrometry of different types of gluten in foods made with cereal mixes. J. Chromatogr. A 823:299–306.

9. Alomirah, H.F., I. Alli, B.F. Gibbs, Y. Konishi. 1998. Indentification of proteolytic products as indicators of quality in ground and whole meat. J. Food Quality 21:299–316.

10. Pinho, O., I.M. Ferreira, M.A. Ferreira. 2002. Solid-phase microextraction in combination with GC/MS for quantification of the major volatile free fatty acids in ewe cheese. Anal. Chem. 74:5199–5204.

11. Goodacre, R., S. Vaidyanathan, G. Bianchi, D.B. Kell. 2002. Metabolic profiling using direct infusion electro-spray ionization mass spectrometry for the characterization of olive oils. Analyst 127:1457–1462.

12. Razzazi-Fazeli, E., S. Kleineisen, W. Luf. 2000. Determination of cholesterol oxides in processed food using high-performance liquid chromatography-mass spectrometry with atmospheric pressure chemical ionization. J. Chromatogr. A 896:321–334.

13. Ratsimba, V., J. M. Garcia Fernandez, J. Defaye, H. Nigay, A. Voilley. 1999. Qualitative and quantitative evaluation of mono- and disaccharides in D-fructose, D-glucose and sucrose caramels by gas-liquid chromatography-mass spectrometry. Di-D-fructose dianhydrides as tracers of caramel authenticity. J. Chromatogr. A 844:283–293.

14. Charlwood, J., D. Tolson, M. Dwek, P. Camilleri. 1999. A detailed analysis of neutral and acidic carbohydrates in human milk. Anal. Biochem. 273:261–277.

15. Richardson, S., A. Cohen, L. Gorton. 2001. High performance anion-exchange chromatography electrospray MS for investigation of the substituent distribution in hydryoxylpropylated potato amylopectin starch. J. Chromatogr. A 917:111–121.

16. Rouseff, R., K. Cadwallader. 2001. Headspace techniques in foods, fragrances and flavors: an overview. Adv. Exp. Med. Biol. 488:1–8.

17. Jung, D.M., S.E. Ebeler. 2003. Headspace solid-phase microextraction method for the study of the volatility of selected flavor compounds. J. Agric. Food Chem. 51:200–205.

18. Kalman, A., C. Mujahid, P. Mottier, O. Heudi. 2003. Determination of alpha-tocopherol in infant foods by liquid chromatography combined with atmospheric pressure chemical ionization mass spectrometry. Rapid Commun. Mass Spectrom. 17:723–727.

19. Pawlosky, R.J., V.P. Flanagan, R.F. Doherty. 2003. A mass spectrometric validated high-performance liquid chromatography procedure for the determination of folate in foods. J. Agric. Food Chem. 51:3726–3730.

20. da Costa, C. T., D. Horton, S.A. Margolis. 2000. Analysis of anthocyanins in foods by liquid chromatography, liquid chromatography-mass spectrometry and capillary electrophoresis. J. Chromatogr. A 881:403–410.

21. Wang, M., J.E. Simon, I.F. Aviles, K. He, Q.Y. Zheng, Y. Tadmor. 2003. Analysis of antioxidative phenolic compounds in artichoke. J. Agric. Food Chem. 51:601–608.

22. Frison, S., P. Sporns. 2002. Variation in the flavanol glycoside composition of almond seedcoats as determined by MALDI-TOF mass spectrometry. J. Agric. Food Chem. 50:6818–6822.

23. Le Gall, G., M.S. DuPont, F.A. Mellon, A.L. Davis, G.J. Collins, M.E. Verhoeyen, J.J. Colquhoun. 2003. Characterization and content of flavonoid glycosides in genetically modified tomato (Lycopersicon esculentum) fruits. J. Agric. Food Chem. 51:2438–2446.

24. Gennaro, L., C. Leonardi, F. Esposito, M. Salucci, G. Maiani, G. Quaglia, V. Fogliano. 2002. Flavonoid and carbohydrate contents in Tropea red onions: effects of homelike peeling and storage. J. Agric. Food Chem. 50:1904–1910.

25. Tareke, E., P. Rydberg, P. Karlsson, S. Eriksson, M. Tornqvist. 2002. Analysis of acrylamide, a carcinogen formed in heated foodstuffs. J. Agric. Food Chem. 50: 4998–5006.

26. Pais, P., M.G. Knize. 2000. Chromatographic and related techniques for the determination of aromatic heterocyclic amines in foods. J. Chromatogr. B Biomed. Sci. Appl. 747:139–169.

27. Guillen, M.D., P. Sopelana, M.A. Partearroyo. 2000. Determination of polycyclic aromatic hydrocarbons in commercial liquid smoke flavorings of different compositions by gas chromatography-mass spectrometry. J. Agric. Food Chem. 48:126–131.

28. Toribio, F., E. Moyano, L. Puignou, M.T. Galceran. 2002. Ion-trap tandem mass spectrometry for the determination of heterocyclic amines in food. J. Chromatogr. A 948:267–281.

29. Eerola, S., I. Otegui, L. Saari, A. Rizzo. 1998. Application of liquid chromatography-atmospheric pressure chemical ionization mass spectrometry and tandem mass spectrometry to the determination of volatile nitrosamines in dry sausages. Food Addit. Contam. 15:270–279.

30. U.S FDA. 2003. *Guidance for Industry: Mass Spectrometry for Confirmation of the Identity of Animal Drug Residues.* Final Guidance #118. Federal Register 68:25617.

31. André, F., K.K.G. De Wasch, H.F. De Brabander, S.R. Impens, L.A.M. Stolker, L. van Ginkel, R.W. Stephany, R. Schilt, D. Courtheyn, Y. Bonnaire, P. Gowik, G. Kennedy, T. Kuhn, J.-P. Moretain, M. Sauer. 2001. Trends in the identification of organic residue and contaminants: EC regulations under revision. Trends Anal. Chem. 20:435–445.

32. Balizs, G., A. Hewitt. 2003. Determination of Veterinary Drug Residues by Liquid Chromatography and Tandem Mass Spectrometry. Anal. Chim. Acta 492: 105–131.

33. Kennedy, D.G., R.J. McCracken, A. Cannavan, S.A. Hewitt. 1998. Use of liquid chromatography-mass spectrometry in the analysis of residues of antibiotics in meat and milk. J. Chromatogr. A 812:77–98.

34. Di Corcia, A., M. Nazzari. 2002. Liquid chromatographic-mass spectrometric methods for analyzing

antibiotic and antibacterial agents in animal food products. J. Chromatogr. A 974:53–89.

35. Holstege, D.M., B. Puschner, G. Whitehead, F.D. Galey. 2002. Screening and mass spectral confirmation of beta-lactam antibiotic residues in milk using LC-MS/MS. J. Ag. Food Chem. 50:406–411.

36. Volmer, D.A. 1996. Multiresidue determination of sulfonamide antibiotics in milk by short-column liquid chromatography coupled with electrospray ionization tandem mass spectrometry. Rapid Commun. Mass Spectrom. 10:1615–1620.

37. Oka, H., Y. Ito, Y. Ikai, T. Kagami, K. Harada. 1998. Mass spectrometric analysis of tetracycline antibiotics in foods. J. Chromatogr. A 812:309–319.

38. Turnipseed, S.B., J.E. Roybal, A.P. Pfenning, P.J. Kijak. 2003. Use of liquid chromatography-ion trap mass spectrometry to screen and confirm drug residues in aquacultured products. Anal. Chim. Acta 483:373–386.

39. Daeseleire, E., R. Vandeputte, C. Van Peteghem. 1998. Validation of multi-residue methods for the detection of anabolic steroids by GC/MS in muscle tissues and urine samples from cattle. Analyst 123:2595–2598.

40. Rose, M.D., J. Bygrave, G.W. Stubbings. 1998. Extension of multi-residue methodology to include the determination of quinolones in food. Analyst 123:2789–2796.

41. Mercer, G.E., J.A. Hurlbut. 2004. A multiresidue pesticide monitoring procedure using gas chromatography/mass spectrometry and selected ion monitoring for the determination of pesticides containing nitrogen, sulfur, and/or oxygen in fruits and vegetables. J. AOAC Int. 87:1224–1236.

42. Sheridan, R.S., J.R. Meola. 1999. Analysis of pesticide residues in fruits, vegetables, and milk by gas chromatography/tandem mass spectrometry. J. AOAC Int. 82:982–990.

43. Colume, A., S. Cardenas, M. Gallego, M. Valcarcel. 2001. Multiresidue screening of pesticides in fruits using an automatic solid-phase extraction system. J. Agric. Food Chem. 49:1109–1116.

44. Volante, M., M. Cattaneo, M. Bianchi, G. Zoccola. 1998. Some applications of solid phase micro extraction (SPME) in the analysis of pesticide residues in food. J. Environ. Sci. Health B 33:279–292.

45. Mastovska, K., S.J. Lehotay, J. Hajslova. 2001. Optimization and evaluation of low-pressure gas chromatography-mass spectrometry for the fast analysis of multiple pesticide residues in a food commodity. J. Chromatogr. A 926:291–308.

46. Pico, Y., G. Font, J.C. Molto, J. Manes. 2000. Pesticide residue determination in fruit and vegetables by liquid chromatography-mass spectrometry. J. Chromatogr. A 882:153–173.

47. Nunes, G.S., R.M. Alonso, M.L. Ribeiro, D. Barcelo. 2000. Determination of aldicarb, aldicarb sulfoxide and aldicarb sulfone in some fruits and vegetables using high-performance liquid chromatography-atmospheric pressure chemical ionization mass spectrometry. J. Chromatogr. A 888:113–120.

48. Fernandez, M., Y. Pico, J. Manes. 2000. Determination of carbamate residue in fruits and vegetables by matrix solid-phase dispersion and liquid chromatography-mass spectrometry. J. Chromatogr. A 871:43–56.

49. Firestone, D. 1991. Determination of dioxins and furans in foods and biological tissues: Review and update. J. Assoc. Off. Anal. Chem. 74:375–384.

50. Eljarrat, E., D. Barcelo. 2002. Congener-specific determination of dioxins and related compounds by gas chromatography coupled to LRMS, HRMS, MS/MS and TOFMS. J. Mass Spectrom. 37:1105–1117.

51. Schatzki T.F., W.F. Haddon. 2002. Rapid, non-destructive selection of peanuts for high aflatoxin content by soaking and tandem mass spectrometry. J. Agric. Food Chem. 50:3062–3069.

52. Razzazi-Fazeli, E., B. Rabus, B. Cecon, J. Bohm. 2002. Simultaneous quantification of A-trichothecene mycotoxins in grains using liquid chromatography-atmospheric pressure chemical ionization mass spectrometry. J. Chromatogr. A 968:129–142.

53. Lau, B.P., P.M. Scott, D.A. Lewis, S.R. Kanhere, C. Cleroux, V.A. Roscoe. 2003. Liquid chromatography-mass spectrometry and liquid chromatography-tandem mass spectrometry of the Alternaria mycotoxins alternariol and alternariol monomethyl ether in fruit juices and beverages. J. Chromatogr. A 998:119–131.

54. Roach, J.A., A.R. Brause, T.A. Eisele, H.S. Rupp. 2002. HPLC detection of patulin in apple juice with GC/MS of patulin identity. Adv. Exp. Med. Biol. 504:135–140.

55. Ito, S., K. Tsukada. 2002. Matrix effect and correction by standard addition in quantitative liquid chromatographic-mass spectrometric analysis of diarrhetic shellfish poisoning toxins. J. Chromatogr. A 943:39–46.

56 Draisci, R., L. Lucentini, L. Giannetti, P. Boria, K.J. James, A. Furey, M. Gillman, S.S. Kelly. 1998. Determination of diarrheic shellfish toxins in mussels by micro liquid chromatography-tandem mass spectrometry. J. AOAC Int. 81:441–447.

57. Hess, P., S. Gallacher, L.A. Bates, N. Brown, M. A. Quilliam. 2001. Determination and confirmation of the amnesic shellfish poisoning toxin, domoic acid, in shellfish from Scotland by liquid chromatography and mass spectrometry. J. AOAC Int. 84: 1657–1667.

58. Moroney, C., M. Lehane, A. Brana-Magdalena, A. Furey, K.J. James. 2002. Comparison of solid-phase extraction methods for the determination of azaspiracids in shellfish by liquid chromatography-electrospray mass spectrometry. J. Chromatogr. A 963:353–361.

59. James, K.J., M.D. Sierra, M. Lehane, A. Brana Magdalena, A. Furey. 2003. Detection of five new hydroxyl analogues of azaspiracids in shellfish using multiple tandem mass spectrometry. Toxicon 41:277–283.

60. Nerin, C., C. Rubio, J. Cacho, J. Salafranca. 1998. Part-per-trillion determination of styrene in yoghurt by purge-and-trap gas chromatography with mass spectrometry detection. Food Addit. Contam. 15:346–354.

61. Lau, O., S.K. Wong. 1996. Determination of plasticizers in food by gas chromatography-mass spectrometry with ion-trap mass detection. J. Chromatogr. A 737:338–342.

62. Goodson, A., W. Summerfield, I. Cooper. 2002. Survey of bisphenol A and bisphenol F in canned foods. Food Addit. Contam. 19:796–802.

63. Mesmer, M.Z., R. A. Flurer. 2001. Determination of bromethalin in commercial rodenticides found in consumer product samples by HPLC-UV-vis spectrophotometry and HPLC-negative-ion APCI-MS. J. Chromatogr. Sci. 39:49–53.

64. Tomlinson, J.A., J.B. Crowe, N. Ranieri, J.P. Kindig, S.F. Platek. 2001. Supermarket tampering: Cocaine detected in syringes and in fruit. J. Forensic Sci. 46:144–146.

65. Mottram, H.R., R.P. Evershed. 2001. Elucidation of the composition of bovine milk fat triacylglycerols using high-performance liquid chromatography-atmospheric pressure chemical ionization mass spectrometry. J. Chromatogr. A 926:239–253.

66. Hau, J., L. Bovetto. 2001. Characterisation of modified whey protein whey protein in milk ingredients by liquid chromatography coupled to electrospray ionization mass spectrometry. J. Chromatogr. A 926:105–112.

67. Contarini, G., M. Povolo. 2002. Volatile fraction of milk: Comparison between purge and trap and solid phase microextraction techniques. J. Agric. Food Chem. 50:7350–7355.

68. Toso, B., G. Procida, B. Stefanon. 2002. Determination of volatile compounds in cows' milk using headspace GC-MS. J. Dairy Res. 69:569–577.

69. Marsili, R.T. 1999. SPME-MS-MVA as an electronic nose for the study of off-flavors in milk. J. Agric. Food Chem. 74:648–654.

70. Antignac, J.P, R. Cariou, B. Le Bizec, J.P. Cravedi, F. Andre. 2003. Identification of phytoestrogens in bovine milk using liquid chromatography/electrospray tandem mass spectrometry. Rapid Commun. Mass Spectrom. 17:1256–1264.

71. Grova, N., C. Feidt., C. Crepineua, C. Laurent, P.E. Lafargue, A. Hachimi, G. Rychen. 2002. Detection of polycyclic aromatic hydrocarbon levels in milk collected near potential contamination sources. J. Agric. Food Chem. 50: 4640–4642.

72. Llompart, M., M. Pazos, P. Landin, R. Cela. 2001. Determination of polychlorinated biphenyls in milk samples by saponification-solid-phase microextraction. Anal. Chem. 73:5858–5865.

73. Losito, I., L. Monaci, A. Aresta, C.G. Zambonin. 2002. LC-ion trap electrospray MS-MS for the determination of cyclopiazonic acid in milk samples. Analyst 127:499–502.

74. Bennett, D.A., A.C. Chung, S.M. Lee. 1997. Multiresidue method for analysis of pesticides in liquid whole milk. J. AOAC Int. 80:1065–1077.

75. Van Rhijn, J. A., J.J. Lasaroms, B.J. Berendsen, U.A. Brinkman. 2002. Liquid chromatographic tandem mass spectrometric determination of selected sulphonamides in milk. J. Chromatogr. A 960:121–133.

76. Bruno, F., R. Curini, A.D. Corcia, M. Nazzari, M. Pallagrosi. 2002. An original approach to determining traces of tetracycline antibiotics in milk and eggs by solid-phase extraction and liquid chromatography/mass spectrometry. Rapid Commun. Mass Spectrom. 16:1365–1376.

77. Daeseleire, E., H. De Ruyck, R. Van Renterghem. 2000. Confirmatory assay for the simultaneous detection of penicillins and cephalosporins in milk using liquid chromatography/tandem mass spectrometry. Rapid Commun. Mass Spectrom. 14:1404–1409.

78. Carson, M.C., D.N. Heller. 1998. Confirmation of spectinomycin in milk using ion-pair solid-phase extraction and liquid chromatography-electrospray ion trap mass spectrometry. J. Chromatogr. B Biomed. Sci. Appl. 718:95–102.

79. De Ruyck, H., E. Daeseleire, H. De Ridder, R. Van Renterghem. 2002. Development and validation of a liquid chromatographic-electrospray tandem mass spectrometric multiresidue method for antihelmintics in milk. J. Chromatogr. A 976:181–194.

80. Urruty, L., J.L. Giraudel, S. Lek, P. Roudeillac, M. Montury. 2002. Assessment of strawberry aroma through SPME/GC and ANN methods. Classification and discrimination of varieties. J. Agric. Food Chem. 50:3129–3136.

81. Loughrin, J.H., M.J. Kasperbauer. 2002. Aroma of fresh strawberries is enhanced by ripening over red versus black mulch. J. Agric. Food Chem. 50: 161– 165.

82. Hakkinen, S.H., S.O. Karenlampi, I. M. Heinonen, H.M. Mykkanen, A.R. Torronen. 1999. Content of the flavonols quercetin, myricetin, and kaempferol in 25 edible berries. J. Agric. Food Chem. 47:2274–2279.

83. Wang, J., W. Kalt, P. Sporns. 2000. Comparison between HPLC and MALDI-TOF MS analysis of anthocyanins in highbush blueberries. J. Agric. Food Chem. 48:3330–3335.

84. Wennrich, L., P. Popp, G. Koller, J. Breuste. 2001. Determination of organochlorine pesticides and chlorobenzenes in strawberries by using accelerated solvent extraction combined with sorptive enrichment and gas chromatography/mass spectrometry. J. AOAC Int. 84:1194–1201.

85. Hu, R., B. Hennion, L. Urruty, M. Montury. 1999. Solid phase microextraction of pesticide residues from strawberries. Food Addit. Contam. 16:111–117.

86. Rodriguez, R., Y. Pico, G. Font, J. Manes. 2002. Analysis of thiabendazole and procymidone in fruits and vegetables by capillary electrophoresis-electrospray mass spectrometry. J. Chromatogr. A 949:359–366.

87. Lay, J.O. Jr. 2001. MALDI-TOF mass spectrometry of bacteria. Mass Spectrom. Rev. 20:172–194.

49 Food Analysis: Other Methods

Manoj K. Rout and Ching-Yung Ma
Department of Botany, The University of Hong Kong

CONTENTS

I. INTRODUCTION

There is considerable demand in the food industry for analytical methods to quantitatively measure various components in raw materials and finished food products, and to monitor physicochemical changes during and after food processing. This chapter describes a number of classical and newly developed methods for food analysis not covered in other chapters. These techniques have wide application in the food industry due to their simplicity and potential applications to a wide variety of food materials.

II. POTENTIOMETRY

Potentiometry is one of the two main categories of electroanalytical techniques, being classified as voltammetry at zero current. The basic principle of potentiometry involves the use of an electrolytic cell composed of two electrodes dipped into a test solution. A voltage (electromotive force, EMF) develops, which is related to the ionic concentration of the solution. This EMF is measured under conditions such that an infinitesimal current (10^{-12} amperes or less) is drawn during measurement. Hence, the classification voltammetry at zero current is used in potentiometry. When an appreciable current is drawn, changes in solution concentration surrounding the electrodes will be produced, and the measured potential corresponds to a system different from the original. In addition, irreversible changes may occur in either of the two electrodes.

A. ELECTRODE POTENTIAL

When an electrode is placed in a solution, it tends to send ions into the solution (electrolytic solution pressure), reacting with the electrode (activity). These two factors, the electrode pressure and the activity of the solution ions, combine to produce an electrode potential. At a given external pressure and temperature, the potential is a constant characteristic of the metal in solution.

The pH meter is a good example of a potentiometer. pH is defined as the logarithm of the reciprocal of hydrogen ion concentration. It may also be defined as the negative logarithm of the molar concentration of hydrogen ions. The four major parts of the pH meter system are: (1) reference electrode, (2) indicator electrode (pH sensitive), (3) voltmeter or amplifier that is capable of measuring small EMF differences in a circuit of very high resistance, and (4) the sample being analyzed.

Hydrogen ion concentration (activity) is determined by the voltage developed between the two electrodes. The Nernst equation relates the electrode response to the activity:

$$E = E° + 2.3 \frac{RT}{NF} \log A$$

Where E = actual electrode potential; E° = a constant, the sum of several potentials in the system; R = universal gas constant, 8.313 joules/degree/g mole; F = Faraday constant, 96,490 coulombs per g equivalent; T = absolute temperature (Kelvin); N = charge of the ion; and A = activity of the ion being measured.

At 25°C, the relationship of 2.3RT/F can be calculated as:

$$\frac{23 \times 8\,316 \times 298}{96,490} = 0.0591 \text{ volts}$$

Thus, the voltage produced by the electrode system follows a linear function of the pH, with the electrode potential being +60 millivolts for each change of one pH unit. At neutrality (pH 7), the electrode potential is zero millivolt. The above relationship of millivolt versus pH exists only at 25°C.

B. REFERENCE ELECTRODES

1. Standard Hydrogen Electrode

The universally adopted primary standard reference electrode is the standard hydrogen electrode (SHE). It consists of a platinum wire or foil coated with platinum black, immersed in a hypothetical solution of unit hydrogen ion activity and in equilibrium with hydrogen gas at unit partial pressure. The potential of this standard electrode by convention is defined as zero millivolt at all temperatures. The standard hydrogen electrode is the international standard, but is seldom used for routine work because more convenient electrodes and reliable calibration buffers are available.

2. Saturated Calomel Electrode

The saturated calomel electrode is the most common reference electrode. It is based on the following reversible reaction:

$$Hg_2Cl_2 + 2e^- \rightleftharpoons 2Hg + 2Cl^-$$

Thus, the potential is dependent upon the chloride ion concentration, which is easily regulated by the use of saturated KCl solution in the electrode. A calomel reference electrode has three principal parts: (1) a platinum wire covered with a solution of calomel (Hg_2Cl_2), (2) a filling solution (saturated KCl), and (3) a permeable junction through which the filling solution slowly migrates into the sample being measured. Junctions are made of ceramic material or fibrous material. A sleeve junction may also be used. Because these junctions tend to clog up, causing a slow, unstable response and inaccurate results, one electrode manufacturer has introduced a free-flowing junction wherein electrolyte flowing from a cartridge is introduced at each measurement. The calomel electrode is unstable above 80°C or in strongly basic samples (pH >9), and should be replaced by a silver-silver chloride electrode.

3. Silver-Silver Chloride Electrode

The silver-silver chloride electrode is very reproducible and is based on the reversible reaction:

$$AgCl (s) + e^- \rightleftharpoons Ag(s) + Cl^-$$

The internal element is a silver-coated platinum wire with the surface silver being converted to silver chloride by hydrolysis in hydrochloric acid. The filling solution is a mixture of 4 M KCl saturated with AgCl used to prevent the AgCl surface of the internal element from dissolving. The permeable junction is usually of the porous ceramic type. Due to the relative insolubility of AgCl, this electrode tends to clog more readily than the calomel reference electrode. However, it is possible to obtain a double-junction electrode in which a separate inner body holds the Ag/AgCl internal element, electrolyte, and ceramic junction. An outer body containing a second electrolyte and junction isolates the inner body from the sample.

C. Indicator Electrodes

The indicator electrode most commonly used in measuring pH is referred to as the glass electrode. Prior to its development, the hydrogen electrode and the quinhydrone electrode were used. The history of the glass electrode goes back to 1875, when it was suggested by Lord Kelvin that glass was an electrical conductor. The glass electrode potential was discovered 30 years later when it was observed that a thin glass membrane placed between two aqueous solutions exhibited a potential sensitive to changes in acidity. Subsequently, the reaction was shown to be dependent upon hydrogen ion concentration. These observations were of great importance in the development of the pH meter.

The glass electrode has three principal parts: (1) a silver-silver chloride electrode with a mercury connection needed as a lead to the potentiometer, (2) a buffer solution consisting of 0.01N HCl, 0.09N KCl, and acetate buffer used to maintain a constant pH, and (3) a small pH–sensitive glass membrane whose potential varies with the pH of the test solution. Conventional glass electrodes are suitable for measuring pH in the range of 1–9. These electrodes are sensitive to higher pH, especially in the presence of sodium ions. Thus, modern glass electrodes developed are usable over the entire pH range of 0–14, and feature a very low sodium ion error, typically <0.01 pH unit at 25°C.

D. Ion-Selective Electrodes

The glass electrode is generally considered useful only in measuring pH, but if the composition of the glass membrane is changed, this type of electrode can be quite sensitive for detecting other cations. In recent years, much attention has been given to this potential. Many electrodes have been developed for the direct measurement of various cations and anions, such as bromide, calcium, chloride, fluoride, potassium, sodium, and sulfide. There are even electrodes available for measuring dissolved gases, such as ammonia and carbon dioxide. While some of these methods are limited in their application due to interference from other ions, the problem can be overcome by pH adjustment, reduction of the interfering ions, and removal of these ions by complexing or precipitation.

Varying the composition of the glass in a glass electrode is one means of changing the sensitivity of the glass membrane to different ions. For example, an electrode membrane containing 71% SiO_2, 11% Na_2O, and 18% Al_2O_3 is sensitive to potassium.

1. Precipitate Impregnated Membrane Electrodes

According to Rechnitz (1), the success of glass membranes as cation-selective electrodes rests largely on the fact that the hydrated glass lattice contains anionic 'sites' that are attractive to cations of appropriate charge-to-size ratio. It is quite easy to construct ion-exchange membranes that permit exchange of either cations or anions; the difficulty is that these membranes show insufficient selectivity among anions and cations of a given charge to be satisfactorily used as practical electrodes. The problem is to find an anion-exchange material that displays appreciable selectivity among anions of the same charge, and also possesses suitable properties to permit its processing into a membrane electrode. In this case silicone rubber has been found to be the most effective material.

An inert, semi-flexible matrix (silicone rubber) is used to hold an active precipitate phase (AgI for an iodide electrode) in place. Such membranes are called heterogeneous or precipitate impregnated membranes. Fisher and Babcock (2) used radioactive tracer materials to show that the electrode potential is determined by the electrical charge on the surface of the inorganic precipitate particles, and that the current is carried by the transport of the counter ions through the membrane. The main advantage of membrane type electrodes over the older metal-metal halide electrodes is their insensitivity to redox interferences and surface poisoning. Electrodes sensitive to chloride, bromide, iodide, sulfide, sulfate, phosphate, and hydroxide ions have been developed.

2. Solid-State Electrodes

The active membrane portion of a solid-state electrode consists of a single inorganic crystal doped with a rare earth. For example, the Orion fluoride electrode is crystalline lanthanum fluoride that has been doped with europium to lower its electrical resistance and to facilitate ionic charge transport. This electrode has approximately tenfold higher selectivity for fluoride than hydroxide, and at least 1000-fold higher selectivity for fluoride over chloride, bromide, iodide, hydrogen carbonate, nitrate, sulfate, and monohydrogen phosphate. The fluoride electrode does not require pre-conditioning or soaking prior to use. Solid-state electrodes are available for detecting the anions Cl^-, Br^-, I^-, and S^{2-}, and the cations Cd^{2+}, Co^{2+}, Pb^{2+}, and As^{3+}.

3. Liquid-Liquid Membrane Electrodes

The range of selective ion-exchange materials could be greatly extended if such materials could be used in electrodes in their liquid state. Liquid ion-exchange materials that possess high selectivity for specific ions may be tailored by appropriate chemical adjustment of the exchanger on the molecular level. The main problems hindering the development of successful liquid-liquid electrodes are mechanical. It is necessary, for example, that the liquid ion-exchanger be in electrolytic contact with the sample solution, yet actual mixing of the liquid phases must be minimal. Electrodes of this type are available for Ca^{2+}, Mg^{2+}, Cu^{2+}, Cl^-, ClO_3^-, and NO_3^-.

E. Enzyme Electrodes

Enzyme electrodes are used to determine certain uncharged molecules. This type of electrode contains an enzyme that can convert the molecule to be measured into an ion that can be detected with a conventional electrode. For example, urea can be determined by coating the end of an ammonium ion electrode with uricase imbedded in a gel. As urea in a sample penetrates the gel, it reacts with the enzyme, which converts part of the urea to ammonia. The ammonia, in the presence of water, becomes ammonium ion which is then detected by an ammonium ion electrode.

An enzyme electrode can be prepared by placing a piece of nylon stocking over the end of an electrode. A thin film of polyacrylamide gel containing the specific enzyme is polymerized onto this network. The gel is then covered with a film of clear plastic such as Saran wrap. Both the stocking and plastic membrane can be held in place with a rubber band placed around the neck of the electrode.

F. Applications

The measurement of pH has many uses in the food industry. The safety of many foods is pH-dependent, and the desired flavor of a food is often determined by the $[H^+]$ concentration. Thus, pH measurements are routinely conducted in both the laboratory and the processing plant.

The chloride and fluoride contents in several types of cheese have been determined by potentiometric titration with silver using ion-selective electrodes (3). The chloride and calcium contents of milk fats were measured by potentiometric titration to detect adulteration (4). A portable meter was developed by Dracheva (5) to determine nitrate in fruits and vegetables.

D-Fructose dehydrogenase was immobilized on an electrode and used for the selective determination of fructose (6). Glucose oxidase was immobilized on an electrode surface and found to be sufficiently fast and reliable to determine sucrose in flow injection systems (7). Sugar beet pulp precipitated with acetone was examined and found to be a suitable biocatalytic layer for a tyrosine tissue-based membrane electrode (8).

III. RADIOACTIVITY AND COUNTING TECHNIQUES

A. Radioactivity and High-Energy Particles

Radioactivity is a general term applied to the emission of high energy particles (e.g., alpha and beta particles) and electromagnetic radiation emanating from the unstable and excited nuclei of atoms. The main advantage of radioanalytical methods is their high sensitivity, allowing determinations to the nanogram (10^{-9}g), pictogram (10^{-12}), and sometimes fantogram (10^{-15}) range. These methods have high specificity and can be used to determine most inorganic elements including trace elements, and organic compounds such as amino acids, fatty acids, vitamins, and hormones.

Alpha particles are helium nuclei moving at high speeds (on the average, 1×10^7 cm/min) emitted from unstable nuclei having large atomic numbers. All alpha particles from a given isotope have the same energy, nearly identical penetration ranges which are very short, and produce about 25,000 ion pairs/cm while they last. Beta particles are distinguishable from simple electrons only by the fact that they originate in the nucleus and are usually moving at high speed. A beta spectrum is continuous, having energies varying from a few thousand electron-volts to several million electron-volts. An average beta particle produces about 60 ion pairs/cm.

Following nuclear transformation, the formed nucleus is often found in an excited state. When the excited nucleus falls back to its ground state, electromagnetic radiations called gamma rays are emitted. Many equations have been developed to describe the various parts of the radioactive process, but the most widely used is the half-life equation:

$$t_{1/2} = 0.693/\lambda$$

where λ is the radioactive decay constant (sec^{-1}). If A is the count rate and A_0 is the number of counts at zero time then the above equation becomes:

$$A = A_0 \exp(-0.693 \, t/t_{1/2})$$

B. COUNTING DEVICES

Although the radiations mentioned previously have high energies in bulk, individually the energies are not sufficient, by a factor of about one million, to permit direct observation and measurement. Detection and measurements are therefore done indirectly by utilizing the effects of interactions produced by these radiations as they traverse matters.

1. Geiger–Muller Counter

The Geiger–Muller (GM) counter or tube is very sensitive to alpha and beta particles (98% efficient) compared to gamma rays (2% efficient). The GM counter is relatively inexpensive and simple to operate, but it does not discriminate between the types of radiation and it has a finite lifetime. It is being steadily replaced by proportional and scintillation counters.

When a ray of radiation comes through the mica window of a GM tube and strikes an argon atom, the argon atom is ionized to produce a positive argon ion and an electron. The positive ion moves toward the cathode at a speed about 1000 times slower than the movement of the electron toward the anode. The electron, attracted by the high potential of the anode, is rapidly accelerated. It has sufficient energy that when it collides with an argon atom another ion and electron can be produced. The two electrons accelerating toward the anode produce 4, then 8, and 16, etc. electrons. The net result is called the Townsend avalanche. Thousands of electrons can reach the anode and a small current is produced and the pulse signal is measured.

In addition, some of the electrons striking the anode may have high enough energy to knock electrons from the anode. These electrons will immediately be re-attracted to the anode and they in turn can knock other electrons loose. This is known as photon spread. The total time it takes for this signal to build up is known as the rise time (t_r) and is usually 2–5 μsec in duration.

While electrons are moving toward the anode, the positive ions move slowly toward the cathode as a positive space charge. If they strike the cathode with their full energy, more photoelectrons will be generated, more than the tube can handle. The net result is that the counter will burn out. Something is needed to dissipate this energy and from photon spread. Molecules, with their many energy levels, are used for this purpose, and ethanol and chlorine are the favorites. The ionized argon atoms will transfer their energy to these molecules which may form ions or free radicals or simply absorb the energy. The energy is so spread out that the cathode has little affinity for these particles, and no photoelectrons are thus produced. Since there is a limit to the amount of quenching gas that can be added to this type of counter, the counter will only work as long as quenching gas is present.

What happens if a second ray of radiation enters the counter before the first ray has completed its reaction? If the second ray ionizes an argon atom at a point between the cathode and the positive space charge, then the electron produced will not "see" the anode but will combine with the argon ion instead. The net result is that the ray of radiation was not counted.

2. Proportional Counters

Geiger–Muller tubes are limited to about 15,000 counts per minute (cpm) because of their long dead time. If the voltage applied to the anode of a GM tube is reduced to a value at which the anode can collect electrons but not produces photon spread, the output pulse is proportional to the energy of the initial ionization, since the number of secondary electrons now depends only on the number of primary ion pairs produced initially. A device operated in this manner is called proportional counter.

The dead times of proportional counters are very short, of the order of 1 μsec, and they can therefore count up to 200,000 cpm. The pulse signal is much weaker than that with a GM tube and better amplification system is needed. It is not possible to make a proportional counter out of a GM tube by simply lowering the anode voltage.

Proportional counters can operate at atmospheric pressure, so the quenching gas can be added continuously. Hence, a proportional counter can count indefinitely. Proportional counters are very good for detecting alpha and beta particles, and because of their ionization efficiency, these counters can easily distinguish the two types of particles.

3. Scintillation Counters

The basic principle behind the operation of the scintillation counter is that an energetic particle incident upon a luminescent material (a phosphor) excites the material, and the photons created in the process of de-excitation are collected at the photocathode of the photomultiplier tube causing the ejection of electrons. The electrons ejected are then led to impinge upon other electrodes, each approximately 100V higher in potential than the previous one. During acceleration from dynode to dynode, more electrons are ejected and a large amplification is obtained.

It would be expected that the greater the energy of the incident particle, the greater the number of electrons is produced. Thus the scintillation counter could be used to measure the energy of the particle. In a scintillation counter, advantage is not taken of the proportional properties of the scintillation process. However, a scintillation spectrometer uses these proportional characteristics to good advantage.

The liquid scintillation counter is particularly convenient for the counting of beta emitters with very low energy, such as tritium, carbon-14, and sulfur-35. The pulses of light emitted by the scintillating solution (caused by the particles in the radioactive decay process) are observed with a photomultiplier tube and counted. It is common practice to cool the photomultipliers to lower their noise, caused in part by thermal emission from the photocathode.

4. Semiconductor Detectors

Germanium, a semi-conducting material, can be made sensitive to gamma radiation by placing small amounts of an impurity, such as lithium, into the germanium crystal structure. When a gamma ray interacts in the crystal, an electrical charge is produced. The charge is collected and amplified to produce a voltage pulse whose height is proportional to the amount of energy deposited in the crystal by the gamma ray.

A single crystal of semiconductor material, such as silicon or germanium, will not make a suitable counter because of the direct current in the crystal. Random variations of this current may produce pulses similar to the radiation-induced pulses. To reduce this current, a p-n (positive-negative) junction in reverse bias is used.

C. Applications

Radioactivity techniques are widely applied in the food industry due to their high sensitivity. A wide variety of food components can be detected and quantified. Positron lifetime spectroscopy has been used to study the structural changes of water in the presence of dissolved sugar molecules such as sucrose, D-glucose, and D-fructose (9). Proton-induced X-ray and radioisotope-induced X-ray fluorescence methods were used to determine trace elements in beef, mutton, and chicken (10). Radioactivity

tracing of anthocyanins has been carried out in food and beverages (e.g., red wine) where products are difficult to isolate and analyze (11). Variations in cell wall polysaccharides of ready-to-use grated carrots after treatment with ionizing gamma radiation and $CaCl_2$ were demonstrated (12). Calcium did not modify the polysaccharide composition or the effects of the ionizing radiation. The gamma radiolysis of phenylalanine in aqueous solution has been studied as a model for the formation of o-tyrosine in irradiated food containing phenylalanine (13). Several methods have been developed to detect irradiated foods, including the thermoluminescence technique which appears to originate from mineral contamination in food materials which have a natural thermoluminescence (14).

IV. ENZYMATIC METHODS

Enzymes are protein molecules that catalyze various metabolic reactions in living organisms (15). Enzymes are capable of very high specificity and reactivity under physiological conditions. Enzymatic analysis is the measurement of compounds with the aid of added enzymes or the measurement of endogenous enzyme activity to give an indication of the state of a biological system including foods. The fact that enzyme catalysis can take place under relatively mild conditions allows for the measurement of unstable compounds not amenable to some other techniques. In addition, the specificity of enzyme reactions can allow for measurement of components in complex mixtures without the need of complicated and expensive chromatographic separation.

A. Enzyme Kinetics

Enzymes are biological catalysts which increase the rate (velocity) of a thermodynamic reaction. An enzyme does not modify the equilibrium constant of the reaction and is not consumed in the reaction. To measure the rate of an enzyme-catalyzed reaction, the enzyme is mixed with the substrate under specified conditions (pH, temperature, ionic strength, etc.) and the reaction is monitored by measuring the disappearance of the substrate. An enzyme-catalyzed reaction is represented as:

$$S + E \rightleftharpoons ES \rightarrow P + E$$

where S = substrate, E = enzyme, ES = enzyme-substrate complex and P = product. The formation of the enzyme-substrate complex is very rapid (in millisecond scale) and is not normally seen in the laboratory. The time course of an enzyme-catalyzed reaction is illustrated in Figure 49.1 (15). The brief time in which the enzyme-substrate complex is formed is called the pre-steady state period. The slope of the linear portion of the curve following the pre-steady state period gives the initial velocity (V_0).

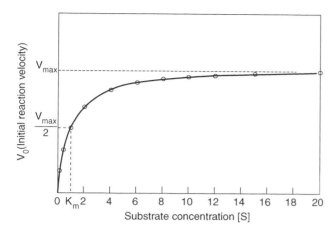

FIGURE 49.1 Effect of substrate concentration on the rate of an enzyme-catalyzed reaction plotted according to the Michaelis-Menten equation.

The rate of the enzyme-catalyzed reactions depends on the concentration of both the enzyme and the substrate. With a fixed enzyme concentration, increasing substrate concentration will result in increased velocity. As the substrate concentration increases further, increase in velocity slows, and at very high substrate concentration, the maximum velocity (V_{max}) of the reaction is reached and no further velocity increase is noted. The substrate concentration at which one-half V_{max} is observed is defined as the Michaelis constant or K_m which is an important characteristic of an enzyme. It is an indication of the relative binding affinity of the enzyme for a particular substrate. The lower the K_m, the greater is the affinity of the enzyme for the substrate.

The Michaelis-Menten equation is derived from a simplified enzyme-catalyzed reaction as:

$$E + S \underset{k_{-1}}{\overset{k_1}{\rightleftharpoons}} ES \overset{k_2}{\to} E + P$$

where k_1, k_{-1}, k_2 are reaction rate constants.

B. MEASUREMENT OF ENZYME ACTIVITY

A wide variety of methods is available to follow enzyme reactions, including spectrophotometry, fluorimetry, manometric methods, titration, and isotope and viscosity measurements. The review by Whitaker (16) provides a comprehensive guide to enzyme methods applicable to foods.

C. APPLICATIONS

There are several applications of enzyme analyses in food science and technology. In several instances, enzyme activity is a useful measure for adequate processing of a food product. For example, peroxidase activity is used as a measure of adequacy of blanching of vegetable products. Enzyme activity assays are also used by the food

technologists to assess potency of enzyme preparations used as processing aids.

Enzymatic analysis is currently being used more often in the determinations of various substrates and enzymes in food products, such as beverages, milk (lactose), fats (cholesterol), and meats (pyrophosphates, creatine, creatinine, gluconate). A few examples of enzymatic analysis of food components are shown.

1. Sulfite

Sulfite is a food additive that can be measured by several techniques, including titration, gas chromatography, and colorimetric analysis. Sulfite can also be specifically oxidized to sulfate by the commercially available enzyme sulfite oxidase (SO). The H_2O_2 product can be measured by several methods, including the use of the enzyme NADH-peroxidase. The reactions are shown as follow:

$$SO_3^= + O_2 + H_2O \xrightarrow{SO} SO_4^= + H_2O_2$$

$$H_2O_2 + NADH + H^+ \xrightarrow{NADH\text{-peroxidase}} 2H_2O + NAD^+$$

The amount of sulfite in the system is equal to the NADH oxidized, which is determined by the decrease in absorbance at 340 nm. Ascorbic acid can interfere with the assay but can be removed by using ascorbic acid oxidase (17).

2. Glucose

Glucose in food can be measured by a colorimetric method using glucose oxidase and peroxidase (18). Glucose is preferentially oxidized by glucose oxidase to produce gluconolactone and hydrogen peroxide. In the presence of peroxidase, hydrogen peroxide and o-dianisidine react to produce a yellow colored dye that absorbs at 420 nm:

$$\beta\text{-D-glucose} + O_2 \xrightarrow{glucose\ oxidase} \delta\text{-gluconolactone} + H_2O_2$$

$$H_2O_2 + o\text{-dianisidine} \xrightarrow{peroxidase} H_2O + \text{oxidized dye (colored)}$$

3. Starch/Dextrin

Starch and dextrin contents in food can be determined by enzymatic hydrolysis using amyloglucosidase, an enzyme that cleaves α-1,4 and α-1,6 bonds of starch, glycogen and dextrins, liberating glucose. The glucose formed can be subsequently determined enzymatically.

V. SEROLOGY, IMMUNOCHEMISTRY AND IMMUNOELECTROPHORESIS

Immunology is both a fundamental medical science and a technology. As a technology it has engendered the development of a whole ensemble of techniques based on the antigen-antibody (*Ag-Ab*) reaction, categorized under the term *immunochemistry*. These techniques have been highly developed in other domains of biology to seek, identify, quantify, and even purify various molecules or associations of molecules (such as microorganisms) using antibodies.

A. ANTIGENS AND ANTIBODIES

An antigen is any substance that, when introduced into a living organism, is susceptible to inducing the production of antibodies that are able to recognize it. Antigens can be molecules (proteins, polysaccharides, etc.) or associations of molecules (viruses, bacteria, etc.). All antigenic molecules are constituted of an assortment of determinants or antigenic sites called epitopes, each possessing a molecular component that is recognized by an antibody. A given antigen can have several identical or different epitopes, with the latter introducing a set of different antibodies. Thus, microorganisms that possess a variety of antigens contain a large number of epitopes.

Antibodies are substances produced by an animal in response to the introduction of a foreign substance (antigen). They react specifically with the antigens that induced their formation. These antibodies (or immunoglobulins) are produced by the B lymphocytes and are present in the blood. There are five classes of immunoglobulins, IgG, IgM, IgA, IgD, and IgE. Immunoglobulins are composed of a pair of long polypeptide heavy chains and a pair of short polypeptide light chains. Both inter- and intra-chain disulfide bonds are present. The heavy chains of different immunoglobulin classes differ chemically, while the light chains are of two types, kappa (*K*) and lambda (λ). All immunoglobulin classes contain either type of light chain. Each immunoglobulin molecule, therefore, consists of a pair of heavy chains specific for its class and a pair of either kappa or lambda light chains (Figure 49.2) (15).

All immunoglobulin molecules have a constant carboxyl-terminal end and a variable amino-terminal end. The amino-terminal end is the "antibody active site" or the "antigen combining site" with an amino acid sequence that varies to correspond with the configuration of challenging antigens. The specificity of antibodies formed in response to an antigen varies. Although antibodies generally react only with the antigen used, cross reactions due to structural similarities between antigens may occur. For example, antibodies to horse serum protein also react with donkey serum protein, and ovalbumin from duck eggs also reacts with antibodies to hen egg albumin. Serum albumins of different mammalian species are antigenically similar, though not identical. The more closely related any two species are, the greater the serological likeness of their corresponding proteins.

The structure of antibodies resembles a "Y" constituted of four polypeptide chains (Figure 49.2) (15). Each

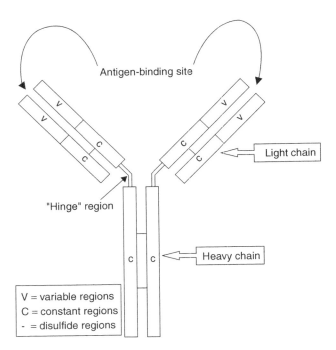

FIGURE 49.2 Diagram of the IgG tetrachain monomer.

branch of the "V" shaped section (or F_{ab} fragment) carries an active site that is complementary to an epitope. Thus, each antibody molecule can bind to two antigenic molecules with identical epitopes. The tail of the "Y" (or the F_c fragment) does not directly participate in binding with the antigen, but can fix to specific cells and activates the complement. Each lymphocyte descendant produces only one type of antibody that recognizes only one type of epitope.

1. Polyclonal Antibodies

After injecting an animal with antigen, antibodies appear fairly rapidly in its blood, and their concentration increases to a maximum and then decreases, constituting the primary response. When the same antigen is then re-injected (booster injection), antibody production is accelerated to higher levels and diminishes more slowly than the first time, constituting the secondary response. This production can be maintained at a relatively high level by re-injecting the antigen at regular intervals. Rabbit is often chosen, but other animals (mice, goats, sheep, etc.) can also be used. Immunization protocols are varied, and the injection can be intravenously (when working with bacteria), intramuscularly, or subcutaneously with the antigen preferably in suspensions (or emulsions) rather than in solution. The quantity of antigen injected (a few μg to a few mg) depends on the nature of the antigen, the animal, and its size.

2. Monoclonal Antibodies

Even if the antigen used to inoculate the animal is pure, the immunoserum collected is composed of a mixture of antibodies directed against different epitopes. A more recent development involves obtaining a cellular clone that produces only one antibody with a well-defined specificity, known as monoclonal antibody. Kohler and Milstein in 1975 first developed the techniques for the production of monoclonal antibody.

B. IMMUNODIFFUSION

Several methods based on specific precipitation of antigen and antibody in agarose gels have been developed (19), and are called immunodiffusion. Single diffusion is a technique in which only one of the two reactants (generally the antigens) migrates in the agarose gel, and double diffusion techniques involve both components migrating simultaneously toward each other. The precipitate forms at a location where the concentrations of the two reactants reach equivalence, leaving a limited precipitation zone for each antigen.

1. Tube Precipitin Test

Qudin (20) devised a method by which complex antigen-antibody systems could be analyzed by allowing them to react in a capillary tube filled with agar. The antibody solution is mixed with warm agar, which is then allowed to harden in the tube. When an antigen solution is added, the antigen reacts with the antibody, forming a precipitation zone. The number of such zones is less than or equal to the number of independent precipitation systems (i.e., antigen-antibody reactions) present in the mixture.

2. Single Radial Diffusion

Mancini (21) developed this method, in which agarose containing the antibody is poured onto a transparent plate. The antigen solutions are deposited in circular wells cut in the gel. The antigens diffuse around the well and form a precipitation ring or halo, and the square root of the inner diameter is proportional to their concentrations. The quantity of antigen contained in the unknown sample is determined by comparing with a range of reference values. The sensitivity threshold is about 3 μg/ml.

3. Double-Diffusion

The double-diffusion method was developed by Ouchterlony (22). It permits both antigen and antibody to diffuse into an agar-filled glass dish that initially contains neither reagents. A few drops each of antigen and antibody solutions are placed separately in small wells in the agar. Antigen and antibody diffuse toward each other at a rate related to their concentrations and their diffusion coefficients. A precipitate line is formed where an antigen interacts with its antibody. Because of differences in diffusion rates, the lines are distinctly separated. The clean

separation of lines on these Ouchterlony plates makes it possible to distinguish more reactions than with Qudin tubes. Consequently the plates are more useful in studying complex systems. The line of precipitation formed by an individual reaction can be identified if either the antigen or the antibody is available in relatively pure form.

C. IMMUNOENZYMOLOGY

The technique of immunoenzymology was first applied to histochemistry and only assumed its present form as ELISA (Enzyme Linked Immunosorbent Assay) in 1971 simultaneously in France, Sweden, and Holland. The most commonly used enzyme markers are catalase, glucose oxidase, β-galactosidase, alkaline phosphatase, and peroxidase. The enzymatic reaction that allows detection is in the last step of the procedure. The technique involves the addition of a substrate which produces a colored product that can be read visually, or by a simple adapted colorimeter when micro-titration plates are used. The diverse substrates that can be used depend on the enzymes. The most common substrates for peroxidase are orthophenyldiamine (OPD) and 2,2'-di (ethyl 3-benzothiazoline-sulfonic-6) acid (BTSA) coupled to H_2O_2. With certain enzymes, substrates that produce fluorescent or luminescent products can also be used to increase sensitivity, but special measuring devices are required.

ELISA is a heterogeneous assay requiring washing between each step to remove unbound reagents. Widely used enzyme labels include alkaline phosphatase, glucose oxidase, and horseradish peroxidase. These enzymes catalyze reactions that cause substrates to degrade, forming colored products that can be read visually or spectrophotometrically. Depending on the format, either antibody or antigen is adsorbed onto a solid phase, which can be polystyrene tubes, polystyrene microtiter wells, or membranes (nitrocellulose and nylon) (23).

D. IMMUNOELECTROPHORESIS

To improve the resolution and interpretation of the double-diffusion method, immunoelectrophoresis was developed by Grabar (24).

1. Classical Immunoelectrophoresis

Classical immunoelectrophoresis (25) is performed in two steps. First, there is a classical electrophoresis of the antigen mixture deposited in wells, in which the antigens are separated into small spots as a function of their charge. Customarily, two runs are done in parallel on the same gel, one with the sample mixture, and the other with a standard for comparison (Figure 49.3) (26). Then there is a double diffusion, in which antibodies placed in a central groove between the antigen spots migrate toward the antigens. This produces one or more precipitation lines

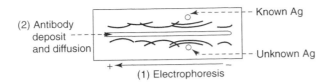

FIGURE 49.3 Classical immunoelectrophoresis (*Source*: From Ref. 26).

depending on whether each electrophoretically separated antigen spot is pure, or is constituted of several antigens that have the same charge. This method is sensitive, reproducible and qualitative in nature (26).

2. Rocket Immunoelectrophoresis

Rocket immunoelectrophoresis is a quantitative technique directly derived from radial immunodiffusion by applying an electric current to the gel (27). The antibodies are distributed evenly throughout the gel, and the sample (antigen) is placed in a small well at one end. As the antigen moves toward the positive electrode, it diffuses outward and reacts with the antibody, forming a precipitate. During migration, the antigen meets more antibodies, but since the antigen is now less concentrated, it will diffuse slower and the line of precipitate is less far away from the center of migration. Eventually, all antigens will have moved forward and reacted, and the resulting shape looks like a rocket (Figure 49.4) (26). The length or the area of the rocket is measured and correlated with standards for quantification.

3. Crossed Immunoelectrophoresis

Crossed immunoelectrophoresis is a two-dimensional separation technique (28, 29). The antigen mixture placed in the well is subjected to simple electrophoresis. The gel band is cut out and placed on a plate, and agarose gel containing antibodies is poured. A second electrophoresis is run perpendicularly to the first. The antigen migrates in the second gel, and produces one or several lines or peaks. This technique is more sensitive than simple immunoelectrophoresis.

E. APPLICATIONS

The application of immunochemical methods in food analysis has been reviewed by Hitchcock (30). Sinnell and Mentz (31) described the use of electroimmunodiffusion methods for quantitative determination of non-meat proteins added to meat products. Kurth and Shaw (32) reviewed the identification of the species of origin of meat by immunochemical methods. Griffith et al. (33) recommended the use of a commercial ELISA system to measure levels of soya protein in meat. The presence of the major food allergen ovomucoid in human milk was studied

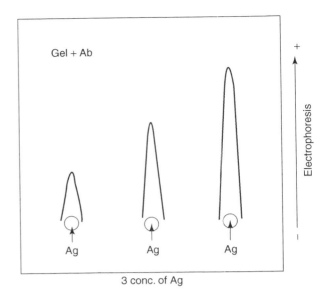

FIGURE 49.4 Rocket immunoelectrophoresis (*Source*: From Ref. 26).

using ELISA (34). ELISA-based methodologies were applied to detect and quantify allergenic proteins in peanut, soy, egg, milk, tree nuts, and crustacea (35).

VI. NUCLEIC ACID-BASED METHODS

Nucleic acids are high-molecular-weight macromolecules that form the genetic material of all living organisms. Two types of nucleic acids are generally encountered, deoxyribonucleic acid (DNA) and ribonucleic acid (RNA). DNA serves as the repository for genetic information for both prokaryotes and eukaryotes. RNA serves a functional role in the conversion of genetic information into cellular proteins, and in the case of some viruses RNA serves as the genetic material as well.

Nucleic acids can be considered polymers of deoxyribo- or ribonucleotides. Each nucleotide unit is composed of a nitrogenous heterocyclic base, a sugar residue, and a phosphate group. The heterocyclic bases are either six-membered pyrimidine rings or nine-membered purine rings. Two types of purines and two types of pyrimidines are found in nucleic acids. Both DNA and RNA contain the purines adenine and guanine. DNA contains the pyrimidines cytosine and thymine, whereas RNA contains the pyrimidines cytosine and uracil. The heterocyclic bases are linked to the sugar via an N-glycosyl bond. The resulting compound is called a nucleoside. The nucleoside units in nucleic acids are joined through the 3'-hydroxyl group of one sugar and the 5'-hydroxyl group of the next sugar via a phosphodiester bond. This 3'-5' internucleotide bond is found in both DNA and RNA. The double-helix model of DNA structure was first deduced in 1953 by James Watson and Francis Crick.

A. BASIC METHODOLOGY

One of the landmark events in molecular biology was the development in 1975 by Edwin Southern of a DNA:DNA hybridization technique (36). This technique can detect rare DNA sequences in complex populations of DNA fragments generated by restriction enzymes. Nucleic acid strands having complementary base sequences can form double-stranded helices. The process of duplex formation is generally referred to as nucleic acid hybridization. Hybridization can occur between single strands of DNA and RNA or between complementary strands of DNA and RNA. Hybridization also includes the formation of complexes between single-stranded nucleic acids and complementary oligonucleotides. These reactions can be carried out in solution or with the nucleic acid immobilized on solid matrices such as nitrocellulose, nylon, or gels. Hybridization in solution is used to study the sequence complexity of cellular or viral DNA. Radioactively labeled nucleic acid probes (37) or probes capable of being tagged with fluorescent antibodies are used to search for and identify nucleic acid sequences (38). In this case the immobilized nucleic acid on nitrocellulose is bathed in a solution containing the probe.

1. Southern Analysis

Southern analysis is among the most powerful methods for DNA analysis. The first step in Southern analysis is the electrophoresis of DNA. DNA fragments digested with restriction enzymes are fractionated on agarose gels (0.7% to 1%) no more than 6 mm thick to allow for efficient transfer of the separated DNA to the filter membrane. The total amount of DNA loaded per lane of gel is dependent upon the relative abundance of the target sequence that is probed during hybridization.

Prior to transfer, the DNA is usually fragmented into smaller pieces and then denatured. This process can be divided into depurination, denaturation, and neutralization steps. The DNA is then transferred to the membrane using one of several methods: capillary, vacuum-assisted, pressure-assisted, or electrophoretic transfer. The DNA is then hrybridized with a probe.

2. Northern Analysis

Northern analysis involves a three-stage process: gel electrophoresis, gel blotting and hybridization to a labeled probe. Gel electrophoresis separates molecules of RNA on the basis of their size and conformation. Molecular size is the main determinant of migration speed, with smaller molecules moving through the matrix faster than larger molecules. Compact molecules also migrate faster than extended molecules of the same size. However, since RNA aggregation may occur, it is necessary to use denaturing gels to determine the actual size of RNA in the absence of conformational factors, aggregation, and nicks in the RNA. The choice of denaturing conditions depends on the nature of the gel and electrophoretic conditions. Formaldehyde is perhaps the most commonly used denaturant. A fact worthy of consideration during experimental design is that nonlinear RNA migrates more slowly than would be expected from its size since it cannot pass through the pores as easily as linear RNA.

The blotting of gels onto membranes can be achieved by capillary action or by electrophoresis. Nucleic acid transferred to a membrane is fixed into position by baking or UV crosslinking to the membrane. Subsequent hybridization of DNA probes to the bound RNA is carried out under stringent conditions to ensure that only complementary sequences hybridize.

B. POLYMERASE CHAIN REACTION

The polymerase chain reaction (PCR) was discovered in 1983 by Kary Mullis. PCR is an *in vitro* method for the enzymatic synthesis of specific DNA sequences, using two oligonucleotide primers that hybridize to opposite strands and flank the region of interest in the target DNA. The standard PCR has three steps defined by temperature: denaturation, annealing and primer extension. The first step, denaturation, occurs when the reaction mixture is heated to 92–96°C. At this temperature the template DNA is single-stranded and the enzyme *Taq* (thermostable DNA polymerase isolated from *Thermus aquaticus*) has no measurable synthetic activity and is not denatured by the near-boiling temperature. Successful amplification is dependent upon complete denaturation of the template DNA during this step.

The middle step of the PCR cycle results in the annealing of the oligonucleotide primers to the template DNA. The temperature for this step varies from 45°C to 65°C depending upon the homology of the primers for the target sequence as well as the base composition of the oligonucleotide. The primers hybridize to their target sequences at an annealing rate several orders of magnitude faster than the target DNA duplex can reform. The ideal temperature for annealing oligonucleotides to the target template is 2–5°C below the melting temperature (T_m) for the primers. If the two primers used for a reaction have different T_m, this 2–5°C rule applies for the one with the lower T_m.

The final step is the primer-dependent DNA synthesis by the *Taq* polymerase. This portion of the cycle is carried out at 72°C. The thermal activation of *Taq* is complemented by the use of Tris buffers since *Taq* has a broad pH optimum, with maximum activity at pH 7.3. The pH of the Tris buffer drops from 8.3 at room temperature to 7.3 at 72°C. The increase in temperature leads to maximum enzyme activity. The published rate of DNA synthesis by this highly processive enzyme 72°C is 60 nucleotides per second (39).

A repetitive series of cycles involving template denaturation, primer annealing, and extension of the annealed primers by DNA polymerase results in the exponential accumulation of a specific fragment whose termini are defined by the 5′ ends of the primers. Because the primer extension products synthesized in one cycle can serve as a template in the next, the number of target DNA copies approximately doubles at every cycle. The simplest detection method of amplified product is the standard agarose ethidium bromide stained gel electrophoresis.

C. APPLICATIONS

Due to recent advances in these nucleic acid-based techniques, numerous food applications have been developed. DNA probes offer an exciting new approach to the highly specific detection of cells in any given environment such as microorganisms in foods. The concept of hybridization and DNA probes, as well as potential applications, have been reviewed (40, 41). The rapid development of biotechnology enables the launching of products and ingredients derived from genetically modified organisms (GMOs) into the food market. Information availability and transparency are essential for the acceptance of these new products by the consumers. A key factor in this issue is the availability of methods to distinguish between GM foods and their traditional counterparts. PCR has been found to be the method of choice for the detection of GMOs in food. PCR methods for the detection of GMOs were developed that can be used for screening purposes and for specific detection of glyphosate–tolerant soybean and insect-resistant maize in foods (42).

REFERENCES

1. GA Rechnitz. Ion selective electrodes. Chem Eng News 12: 146–158, 1967.
2. RB Fisher, RF Babcock. Effects on aging of reagent solutions on the particle size of precipitants – electrodes consisting of membranes of precipitates. Diss Abstr 19: 428, 1958.
3. MA Gonzalez, AJ Aller, R Pardo, E Barrado, L Deban. Fluoride and chloride determination in cheese with ion selective electrodes. Electroanalysis 3: 439–442, 1991.
4. E Tschaeer. Detection of whey in milk fat. Milchwirtsch Ber Bundesanst Wolfpassing Rotholz 107: 61–65, 1991.
5. LV Dracheva. Portable nitrate meter. Pishch Prom-St (Moscow) 5: 73–75, 1991.
6. X Xie, S Kuan, G Guilbault. A simplified fructose biosensor. Biosen Bioelectron 6: 49–54, 1991.
7. W Schuhmann, R Kittsteiner-Eberle. Evaluation of polypyrrole/glucose oxidase electrode in flow injection systems for sucrose determinations. Biosen Bioelectron 6: 263–273, 1991.
8. Y Fang, R Cai, Y Zhang, J Wu, J Deng. Sugar beet acetone pulp as biocatalyst for the tyrosine electrode. Fenxi Huaxue 19: 891–894, 1991.
9. K Suvegh, F Mohos, A Vertes. Investigation of aqueous solutions of sucrose, D-glucose, and D-fructose with positron lifetime spectroscopy. Acta Aliment 20: 3–10, 1991.
10. SA Tarafdar, M Ali, A Islam, AH Khan. Level of some minor and trace elements in Bangledeshi meat products. J Radioanal Nucl Chem 152: 3–9, 1991.
11. A Zimman, AL Waterhouse. Enzymatic synthesis of (3′-O-methyl-3H) malvidin-3-glucoside from petunidin-3-glucoside. J Agric Food Chem 50: 2429–2431, 2002.
12. A Baron, P Massiot, C Prioult, N Marnet. Variation of cell wall polysaccharides of ready to use grated carrots after ionizing radiation and/or calcium treatment. Sci Aliment 11: 627–639, 1991.
13. D Wang, C Von Sonntag. Radiation induced oxidation of phenylalanine. Comm European Communities (REP) EUR 13331: 207–212, 1991.
14. S Pinnioja, T Autio. Identification of irradiated foods by thermoluminescence. Proc 7th Tihany Symp Radiat Chem, 1991, pp 469–470.
15. RL Switzer, LF Garrity. Experimental Biochemistry, 3rd ed. New York: W. H. Freeman & Company, 1999.
16. JR Whitaker. Analytical uses of enzymes in food analysis: Principles and techniques. In: D Gruenwedel and JR Whitaker, eds. Biological Techniques, Vol. 3. New York: Marcel Dekker, 1985.
17. H Beutler. A new enzymatic method for determination of sulphite in food. Food Chem 15: 157, 1984.
18. E Raabo, TC Terkildsen. On the enzyme determination of blood glucose. Scand J Clin Lab Invest 12: 402, 1960.
19. AJ Crowle. Immunodiffusion. New York: Academic Press, 1961.
20. J Qudin. Immunochemical methods of analysis involving selective precipitation in solidified media. Compt Rend Acad Sci 22: 115–116, 1946.
21. G Mancini, AO Carbonora, JF Heremans. Immunochemical quantitation of antigens by single radial immunodiffusion. In: Immunochemistry. Oxford: Pergamon Press, 1965, pp 235–254.
22. O Outcherlony. Antigen antibody reaction in gels. Acta Pathol Microbiol Scand 26: 507–515, 1949.
23. RH Burdon, PH Van Knippenberg. Practice and Theory of Enzyme Immunoassays, Vol. 15. New York: Elsevier, 1985.
24. P Grabar. Immunochemistry. Annu Rev Biochem 19: 453–486, 1950.
25. P Grabar, CA Williams. Methode permettant letude conjuguee des proprietes electrophoretiques et immunochimiques d'un mélange de proteines. Application au serum sanguine. Biochim Biophys Acta 10: 193–194, 1953.
26. G Linden. Analytical Techniques for Foods and Agricultural Products. New York: VCH Publishers, Inc., 1996.
27. CB Laurell. Quantitative estimation of electrophoresis in agarose gel containing antibodies. Anal Biochem 15: 45–52, 1966.
28. N Ressler. Two dimensional electrophoresis of protein antigens with antibody containing buffer. Clin Chem Acta 5: 795–800, 1960.

29. CB Laurell. Antigen antibody crossed electrophoresis. Anal Biochem 10: 358–361, 1965.

30. CHS Hitchcock. Immunological methods. In: GG Birch and KJ Parker, eds. Control of Food Quality and Food Analysis. London: Elsevier Applied Science, 1984, pp 117–133.

31. HJ Sinnell, I Mentz. Use of electroimmunodiffusion for quantitative determination of nonmeat proteins added to meat products. Folia Vet Latina 7: 41–54, 1977.

32. L Kurth, FD Shaw. Identification of the species of origin of meat by electrophoretic and immunological methods. Food Technol Aust 35: 328–331, 1983.

33. M Griffith, MJ Billington, AA Crimes, CHS Hitchcock. An assessment of commercially available reagents for an enzyme-linked immunosorbent assay (ELISA) of soya proteins in meat products. J Sci Food Agric 35: 1255–1260, 1984.

34. J Hirose, S Ito, N Hirata, S Kido, N Kitabatake, H Narita. Occurrence of the major food allergen, ovomucoid, in human breast milk as an immune complex. Biosci Biotech Biochem 65: 1438–1440, 2001.

35. JM Yeung, RS Applebaum, R Hildwine. Criteria to determine food allergen priority. J Food Protect 63: 982–986, 2000.

36. EM Southern. Detection of specific sequences among DNA fragments separated by gel electrophoresis. J Mol Biol 98: 503–517, 1975.

37. KL Agarwal, J Brunstedt, BE Noyes. A general method detection and characterization of a mRNA using an oligonucleotide probe. J Biol Chem 256: 1023–1028, 1984.

38. W Langer, DC Ward. Enzymatic synthesis of biotin-labeled polynucleotides: Novel nucleic acid affinity probes. Proc Natl Acad Sci USA 78: 6633–6637, 1984.

39. MA Innis, KB Myambo, DH Gelfand, MAD Brow. DNA sequencing with *Thermus aquaticus* DNA polymerase and direct sequencing of polymerase chain reaction-amplified DNA. Proc Natl Acad Sci USA 85: 9436–9440, 1988.

40. A Klausner, T Wilson. Gene detection technology opens doors for many industries. Bio/Technology 1: 471–478, 1983.

41. J Meinkoth, G Wahl. Hybridization of nucleic acids immobilized on solid supports. Anal Biochem 138: 267–284, 1984.

42. S Vollenhofer, K Burg, J Schmidt, H Kroath. Genetically modified organisms in food-screening and specific detection by Polymerase Chain Reaction. J Agric Food Chem 47: 5038–5043, 1999.

Part D

Food Microbiology

50 Microbiology of Food Systems

Joseph D. Eifert, Fletcher M. Arritt III, and David Kang
Department of Food Science and Technology, Virginia Polytechnic Institute and State University

CONTENTS

I. INTRODUCTION: MICROORGANISMS IN FOODS

Microbiology is the study of living organisms that are so small that they can only be observed with the aid of a powerful microscope. In food microbiology, the organisms of concern are usually classified as bacteria, fungi (yeasts and molds), viruses, and parasitic protozoa. Bacteria are single-celled microorganisms found in nearly all environments. Bacterial cells are often classified by their outward appearance, including their size, shape, and arrangement.

Some bacteria have the ability to form spores. Spores can typically withstand adverse environmental conditions better than the vegetative form of the bacteria. For example, spores can be highly resistant to boiling water or chemical sanitizers. Bacterial spores are not a means of reproduction. Fungi include organisms as small as a single cell or as large as a mushroom. True fungi produce large masses of filamentous hyphae that form a mycelium. Yeasts, along with bacteria, reproduce by fission. Other fungi typically reproduce by spores carried on fruiting structures. Viruses are extremely small parasites. They require living cells of plants, animals, or bacteria for growth. The virus is mainly a packet of genetic material which must be reproduced by the host cells. Protozoa are single-celled organisms that can cause disease in humans and animals. Their cell structure is more complex than that of bacteria.

The presence of microorganisms in foods may have adverse or beneficial effects. Some microorganisms may hasten the spoilage of foods, thereby reducing sensory quality and shelf-life. Other organisms may be pathogenic, or could cause human illness. Some species of bacteria, yeast, and molds can be used to ferment foods or to produce desirable changes in quality, especially in taste and texture. These organisms can be intentionally used to process a wide variety of plant or animal foods.

II. HISTORY OF FOOD MICROBIOLOGY

Microorganisms have always been closely related to food and food systems. Authorities believe that approximately 8,000 to 10,000 years ago, humans began to have problems associated with food poisoning and food spoilage. The importance of one's ability to produce and preserve food was recognized early. Both livestock and salt had monetary value and could be compared to today's currency. Wealth and social status in many cases was based upon the amount of success one had at producing in times of plenty and preserving what could not be consumed immediately for times of hardship. Many early religious laws prohibiting the consumption of "impure" or "unclean" foods were based on hygiene, and were similarly seen in countries not conforming to the same religious beliefs.

The first individual to describe microorganisms was Kircher in 1658 who reported "worms" that were undetectable to the naked eye on several decomposing items. Shortly thereafter the theory of spontaneous generation, later known as abiogenisis, became widely accepted. In 1683, Leeuwenhoek's superior knowledge of lens design allowed him to be the first to observe and record yeast cells using a primitive microscope. Spallanzani sought to disprove spontaneous generation in 1765 when his beef broth did not spoil after being boiled in a sealed container for an hour. Critics, however, disagreed, believing his process was void of oxygen, a vital ingredient to spontaneous generation. In 1785, the French government offered a prize to anyone who could develop a practical method to preserve food. In 1809, Nicholas Appert was successful by preserving meats that had been boiled in water in corked glass bottles. At the time, he was unaware of the microbiological logic behind this process. Louis Pasteur, however, was the first to understand the role of microorganisms in food. He was most noted for his heat pasteurization process to destroy deleterious organisms in beer and wine. Pasteur's process was later commercialized in 1867. He also proved that microorganisms caused souring milk. Some other examples of important dates in food microbiology history include:

1825 - U.S. patent issued for food preservation in tin cans.
1840 - Fresh fruit and fish were first canned.
1857 - Milk identified as a vector for typhoid fever.
1874 - Use of ice for transport of meat at sea was widespread.
1880 - Milk pasteurization began in Germany.
1888 - *Salmonella enteriditis* isolated from meat in a food poisoning outbreak.
1895 - First bacteriological study of canning.
1906 - U.S. Congress passed the Federal Food and Drug Act.
1928 - Controlled atmosphere was commercially used for storage of apples.
1929 - Frozen foods introduced into retail markets.
1967 - United States was the first to design a commercial irradiation facility.
1976 - In California infant botulism was identified.
1981 - First outbreak of foodborne listeriosis occurred in the U.S.
1986 - The first diagnosis of Bovine Spongiform Encephalopathy (BSE).

III. SOURCES OF CONTAMINATION: ANIMAL, PLANT, PROCESSING, FOOD HANDLERS

Foods or their ingredients may harbor a wide variety of microorganisms. Some of these microorganisms may be a part of the natural microbiota of raw foods of plant and animal origin, while others may be introduced during production, processing, and preparation for consumption. Microbial contamination refers to the presence or added presence of pathogenic or spoilage microorganisms that were not originally present in or on the food. Microbial cross-contamination refers to the situation where microorganisms are transferred from one surface or food to another food or food contact surface.

Raw and processed foods can be contaminated with many types of bacteria, yeast, or molds prior to consumption. Contamination may occur during all steps of food processing. These steps may include: harvest, slaughter, transportation, processing, packaging, storage, and preparation for consumption. Prior to crop harvest or food animal slaughter, raw agricultural commodities may become contaminated with pathogenic and spoilage organisms from soil, irrigation water, animal feces, insects, manure, and wild or domestic animals. During transport and processing, foods can be contaminated by harvesting and transport equipment. Furthermore, contamination by sorting, packing, cutting, packaging, or other further processing equipment may occur. Also, process water, air or dust, and worker contact may further contaminate food products. Processed or packaged foods can become contaminated by food handlers, including foodservice and retail employees and consumers. Cross-contamination of raw and ready-to-eat foods can occur due to improper sanitation of food contact surfaces or equipment or when raw and ready-to-eat foods are poorly separated during preparation.

Prevention of contamination or cross-contamination by unwanted microorganisms is a critical element for ensuring the safety and quality of raw and processed foods. At the farm level, biosecurity programs can enhance prevention of microbial contamination. At the processing level food manufacturers can practice regular cleaning and sanitizing of equipment and facilities. Cleaning requires removing visible soil or food residue from equipment, utensils, floors, and walls. Subsequent sanitizing must reduce the number of microorganisms to a very low or safe level. Also, good employee hygiene practices such as handwashing, protective clothing, and prohibiting food and drink consumption in work areas can limit opportunities for microbial contamination of foods and ingredients. During food preparation, workers or consumers should frequently wash their hands and work surfaces. Hands or utensils should not touch raw food prior to ready-to-eat food without washing. Food contact surfaces and utensils must be regularly cleaned and sanitized.

IV. MICROBIAL GROWTH

Microorganisms can grow and reproduce at different rates over time. When bacteria are in a rapid growth phase they may be able to double their population in just 20–30 minutes. Prior to achieving a rapid or exponential growth rate, organisms may need time to adjust to their environment. During food processing, microbes may need time to adjust to changing conditions of acidity, temperature, oxygen level, nutrient levels, or available moisture. The population of bacteria may only marginally increase during the time that the organisms are adjusting to a new environment. After this lag phase of growth, the bacteria may enter into a rapid growth phase that greatly increases their numbers. Eventually the growth rate will slow as a key nutrient becomes exhausted or environmental conditions act to limit growth. When the population or the growth rate is plotted against time, a sigmoid or s-shaped curve often expresses how the growth changes over time. In these plots, a lag phase is followed by a (exponential) growth phase, a stationary phase, and a die-off phase (Figure 50.1).

Microorganism growth rates are influenced by many environmental factors. Similar to other living organisms, they need water and nutrients to grow. Temperature is also a very important factor affecting microbial growth. The time that microorganisms need to grow and reproduce can vary greatly depending on the environmental temperature. Other important factors affecting growth include pH, atmospheric gas concentrations, and available water for growth.

Water is necessary for growth, but microbes cannot grow in pure water. While all foods contain some water,

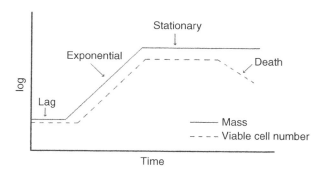

FIGURE 50.1 Bacterial growth curve.

some of this water is not available to the bacteria. Often the water in foods is bound with some of the molecules of the food such as the proteins, fats, and carbohydrates. The bound water may not be accessible to microorganisms to use for growth. Water activity, or a_w, is a measure of the water available to microorganisms in foods. Water activity is measured on a scale of zero to one (pure water). For growth, most bacteria require a a_w of at least 0.90. Yeasts and molds can tolerate a lower water activity, perhaps as low as 0.7. A water activity of less than 0.85 in food will suppress the growth of organisms of public health significance.

Microorganisms can generally grow over a wide range of temperatures, but their growth rate at different temperatures can vary greatly. Organisms grow fastest at an optimal temperature. The optimum growth temperature for most organisms is near room temperature or body temperature (25–35°C). However, microorganisms may still be able to grow over a temperature range of 10–45°C. Foodborne microorganisms can survive temperatures of 0°C, but typically will not grow at this temperature.

Acidity can be measured with the pH scale where 0 is strongly acidic, 7 is neutral, and 14 is strongly basic. Many bacteria multiply more rapidly when the pH of their surroundings is near neutral, but may be able to grow when the pH ranges from 4 to 9. Yeasts and molds are more tolerant of low pH (high acidity) than bacteria. Many foods have a pH value between 4 and 7 which favors the growth of most pathogenic and spoilage microorganisms. As microorganisms reproduce, their metabolic by-products may alter the pH of their surroundings.

Just as microbial temperature and pH requirements can vary, microbial oxygen requirements can also differ greatly. Bacteria that require oxygen for growth are commonly called aerobes. Anaerobic bacteria do not grow in the presence of oxygen, but can grow in vacuum-packed foods. Some organisms can grow with or without oxygen and are referred to as facultative anaerobes. Finally, some organisms grow favorably under a low oxygen atmosphere. These microaerophiles grow optimally when the oxygen concentration in the atmosphere is 5–10% whereas the concentration in air is 18–20%.

V. MICROBIAL INACTIVATION, SURVIVAL, AND DEATH

Often a correlation exists between the rate and amount of treatment applied during the preserving process and the rate of microbial inactivation, survival, and death. In using heat processing to preserve foods, the temperature denatures proteins, which destroys enzyme activity and enzyme-controlled metabolism in microorganisms. The rate of microbial inactivation follows the first order reaction, by which when the product is heated to a temperature that is high enough to destroy contaminates, the same percentage die in a given time interval regardless of the numbers present initially. This is known as the logarithmic order of death and is described by a death rate curve (Figure 50.2). Microbial inactivation, survival, and death rate of the microorganism can be extrapolated from this curve.

The decimal reduction time, also known as the D-value, is defined as the time in minutes to achieve a $1-\log_{10}$ reduction in a specific microorganism at a specific temperature in a specific growth medium. D-values are variables for different microbial species and a higher D-value indicates greater heat resistance. Since microbial destruction occurs logarithmically, it is theoretically impossible to destroy all cells. The heating process therefore aims to reduce the number of surviving microorganisms by a pre-determined amount, depending on the type of microorganisms that is expected to contaminate the raw product. Usually, foods are processed to ensure at least a $12D$ reduction for *Clostridium botulinum* in low acid foods. This organism is targeted due to its importance in the food industry as well as its spore-forming abilities.

If the destruction of microorganisms is determined by temperature, cells die more rapidly at higher temperatures. The z-value characterizes the change in temperature required to achieve a $1-\log_{10}$ change in the D-value. This gives an indication of the temperature dependency of the heat resistance of an organism. Most heat-resistant spores have a z-value of 10°C.

The thermal death time (F-value) is used as a basis of comparing heat sterilization techniques. The F-value is defined as the equivalency in minutes at a given temperature, of all things considered, with respect to its capacity to destroy spores or vegetative cells of a particular organism. It can also be considered as the time needed to reduce the microbial numbers by a multiple of the D-value. When plotted, it is a bell-shaped curve, which is affected by product type, container size, container shape, and method of load of the unit for heat process. $F = D (\log n_1 - \log n_2)$, where n_1 = initial number of microorganisms and n_2 = final number of microorganisms.

VI. DETECTION OF MICROORGANISMS

Food microbiologists examine foods for the presence, types, and numbers of microorganisms and/or their products. Sampling techniques as well as the enumeration of the affected food product or surface are crucial in obtaining an accurate analysis. In spite of its importance, the enumeration methods used commonly permit only the estimation of microorganisms in a food product or their surrounding environment. Although some analytical methods are more sensitive and more rapid than others, every method has certain inherent limitations associated with its use.

A. SAMPLING FROM FOODS OR THE ENVIRONMENT

Many methods exist for sampling the environment of the food plant as well as the foods and air for the presence and relative numbers of microorganisms. Some commonly used methods are described below.

1. Gravimetric and volumetric sampling: Defined portions of food or water samples can be collected and analyzed by numerous microbiological methods. For liquids a volumetric sample of 10–100 mL is typically analyzed. For solids, a gravimetric or weighed sample of approximately 10–50 grams is analyzed. Solid foods may need to be diluted with one of several aqueous solutions during an analysis. In these cases, microbial concentrations can be reported as "per volume of diluent."
2. Swab sampling: Swabbing is the oldest and most prevalently used method for the microbiologic surface examination not only in the food and dairy industries but also in hospitals and restaurants. With this method, surface areas can be sampled corresponding to the size of the

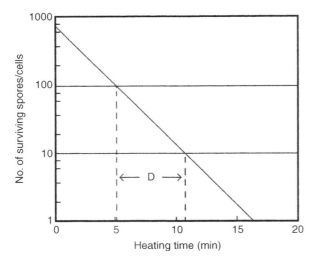

FIGURE 50.2 Death rate curve.

surface with the use of a sterile template. A moistened swab is used to thoroughly rub the exposed surface. After exposure, the swab is returned to its holder containing a suitable diluent which can contain selective media and neutralizers for sanitation chemicals, if necessary. After proper dislodging from the swab, the organisms are then examined by enumeration or qualitative analysis. The swab method is best suited for flexible, uneven, and heavily contaminated surfaces. The ease of removal of the microorganism is dependent on the texture of the surface and the nature and type of flora.

3. Contact plate: The replicate organism direct agar contact (RODAC) method consists of a raised agar surface on the petri plate. When the plate is inverted, the agar surface makes direct contact with the surface. Once exposed, the plate is then covered, incubated, and enumerated for viable colonies. With this method, foods surfaces as well as environmental surfaces can be examined. In testing a surface that may have been cleaned with certain compounds, it may be necessary to add a neutralizer in the medium. This method, however, is not effective for enumerating heavily contaminated surfaces.

4. Air sampling: Numerous methods exist for the sampling of air in food plants for the presence and relative numbers of the microorganism. The most commonly used methods are impingement in liquids, impaction on solid surfaces, and sedimentation. Impingers are advantageous in that a specific quantity of air can be sampled. Filtration, centrifugation, electrostatic precipitation, and thermal precipitation may be used in air sampling. The simplest of air sampling techniques is to open pre-poured petri dishes for specific periods of time in the area to be assessed. The results obtained are influenced by size of particles and speed and direction of air flow.

B. ISOLATION AND IDENTIFICATION

Isolation and identification of microorganisms can be as simple as performing isolation streaks for a colony and gram stains to much more sophisticated procedures using immunologic assays, chemical assays, and physical assays. Many microbiological analytical methods require that samples be immersed into an enrichment media to encourage growth of the target organism and to discourage growth of other naturally occurring organisms. Subsequent transfers to other microbiological media are used to purify food extract and isolate specific bacterial species. Additional confirmatory tests can be used to identify microbial species and biotypes. Selection and use of any microbiological methods should depend on resources available, analysis time, cost, sensitivity, specificity, technical expertise required, etc. In this chapter, it is not possible to go into detail about all of the procedures that may be used to identify microorganisms in foods. Some of these methods are briefly described below.

1. Nucleic acid (DNA) probes: DNA probes have been prepared for a number of foodborne microorganisms such as *salmonellae*, *listeriae*, staphylococcal enterotoxins, *Clostridium perfringens* enterotoxin, *Entamoeba histolytica*, and enterotoxigenic *E. coli*. A DNA probe, which is usually labeled with a radioisotope, consists of the DNA sequence of an organism of interest that can be used to detect homologous DNA or RNA sequences. The probe DNA must hybridize with that of the strain to be sought. Ideally, the DNA sequence that contains the genes that code for a specific contaminant is used.

2. PCR: An increasingly popular and highly reliable method for identification is DNA amplification – polymerase chain reaction (PCR) method. This method is a powerful, rapid system for detecting the presence of foodborne pathogens. This technique, performed in a very clean work environment, employs thermostable DNA polymerase and $5'$ and $3'$ specified oligonucleotide primers. It enables amplification of a single molecule of DNA to 10^7 molecules after a series of amplification cycles, typically from 20 to 50. The amplified DNA is then detected by use of either agarose gels or Southern hybridization employing a radiolabeled probe. Most PCR reagents now come in kit form.

3. Immunoassays: These methods are based on the interaction of antibodies, and consist of a wide range of rapid detection methods that are relatively simple to detect and identify contaminants associated with food products. Many are readily available in kits. Examples of immunoassays used in the food industry include the use of fluorescent antibodies, immunoaffinity columns, enrichment serology, enzyme-linked immunosorbent assay (ELISA), radioimmunoassay, and hemagglutination. The technique of radioimmunoassay (RIA) consists of adding a radioactive label to an antigen, allowing the antigen to react with its specific antibody, and measuring the amount of antigen that combined with the antibody by the use of a

counter to measure radioactivity. Using this method, detection and identification of bacterial cells can be achieved. RIA is used for identifying and enumerating staphylococcal enterotoxins, *V. cholerae* that produce cholera toxin, aflatoxins, and other mycotoxins. Multibacterial species can be detected in one operation when mixtures of homologous antibodies are used. The RIA method can also be used to identify biological hazards such as endotoxins and paralytic shellfish toxins in foods examined.

The ELISA method is similar to that of the RIA but rather than employing a radioactive isotope, it uses an enzyme coupled to antigen. A typical ELISA is performed with a solid phase (e.g., beads, test wells, or dipstick) coated with antigen and incubated with antiserum. Following incubation and washing, an enzyme-labeled preparation of anti-immunoglobulin is added. After gentle washing, the amount of enzyme remaining in the tube or microtiter well is measured colorimetrically. The color change reveals the presence or absence of the contaminant as well as estimation on enumeration. There are many variations of ELISA.

C. ENUMERATION

Many procedures exist for estimating a microbial population. Ideally, the method used should be accurate, rapid, inexpensive, and standardized. Methods should be selected based on the use of the information that is obtained. Examples of systems used in estimating the number of microorganisms in foods are listed in Table 50.1. The basic methods used in quantitative analysis include standard plate counts (SPC) for viable cells, the most probable number (MPN) method as a statistical determination of viable cells, dye-reduction techniques to estimate numbers of viable cells that possess reducing capacities, and direct microscopic count (DMC) for both viable and non-viable cells.

1. Plate Counts for Viable Cells

The most widely used and basic technique used for enumeration of microorganisms is the standard plate count (SPC). It is relatively simple and consists of plating appropriate dilutions by transferring an aliquot for either pour plating (pouring molten agar onto plate) or spread plating (evenly transferring the aliquot onto a hardened agar surface). The plates are incubated at an appropriate temperature/time and the colonies are enumerated. Use of spiral plates and use of selective media in the agar further enhance this procedure. SPC is considered one of the most precise methods for determining microorganisms such as bacteria and yeast that will grow in an agar medium.

TABLE 50.1
Systems Used in Enumeration of Microorganisms in Foods

Direct microscopic count (DMC)	Electrical
Breed clump count	Conductance
Electronic particle count	Impedance
Howard mold counts	Capacitance
	Voltage drop
Pour plate	Spectrophotometric (optical density)
Spread plate	Adenosine triphosphate (ATP)
Spiral plate	Reductase tests
Drop plate	Easicult-TTC
Plate loop	Immuno-affinity columns
Roll tube	Respiration rates
Oval tube	*Limulus* amoebocyte lysate (LAL)
Burri strip/slant	Chemical indicators
Restriction fragment length	(decomposition products)
polymorphism (RFLP)	
Little plate	pH
Tube dilution	Agar droplets
Most probable number	Millipore sampler
Membrane filter	Bactoscan
Hydrophobic grid (HGMF)	Microcalorimetry
Direct epifluorescent filter	Flow cytometry
technique (DEFT)	Gas chromatography
Microcolony-DEFT	Radioimmunoassay (RIA)
Agar droplets	Thermostable nuclease
Microtiter-Spot plate	Fluorescent antibody
Dry rehydratable film	Enzyme-linked immunosorbent
Petri film	assay (ELISA)

2. Total Cell Counts

Some methods do not differentiate between viable and non-viable cells, giving total cell counts. These methods are appropriate for use when evaluating the microbial content of a food and/or evaluating the number of body cells in milk such as the detection for mastitis in cows. The value of total cell counts is limited to samples with high cell loads. Total cell counts are useful in determining the quality of pasteurization and recontamination of foods, and are a rapid method to estimate the bacterial load. Examples of total cell counts are direct microscopic count (DMC), spectrophotometric assay, and electronic particle count. In DMC, a suspension of the sample is stained and observed using a counting chamber or spread over a prescribed area on a glass slide and the number of cells calculated per area. Using this method, cell morphology can be seen and it lends itself to fluorescent probes for improved efficiency. However, since it is a microscopic analysis, it is fatiguing to the analyst, and food particles are not always distinguishable from the bacteria.

A rapid method to estimate total cell count is the spectrophotometric analysis. A suspended sample is analyzed by a spectrophotometer, where a light of a specified wavelength is passed through the sample. The amount of absorbance and percentage of transmittance of the light can then be correlated to an estimated cell count. However, using this method, no selectivity is made to the microorganism or debris in the sample such as food particles. Clumping of cells may also lead to a miscued estimation. Due to the various size of contaminates, adjustments may have to be made to the readings as well as the wavelength used.

Many more methods exist for the enumeration of viable organisms in foods. Most of the basic systems for enumeration of viable organisms are based on the plate count or the tube dilution method. Selective media or environmental conditions are often used if a specific contaminant is targeted. More advanced assays for rapid analysis are based on the metabolic activity of the contaminant on given substrates, measurements of growth response, or the immunologic responses to the microorganism.

Use of nitrocellulose or hydrophobic grid membranes to filter the sample solution through pores that retain bacteria or mycobacterium (usually 0.45 μm) but allow for the suspension to flow through is especially suited for assays when the microbial count of the sample is expected to be relatively low. Following the collection of the contaminant upon filtering a given volume, the membrane is placed on a hardened growth media and incubated at an appropriate temperature. To improve microbial yield and decrease background particles on the filter such as food and sediments, use of prefilters, surfactants and enzymes, and stains are incorporated into the assay. Analysis of the samples can be made after 2–4 hours with a microscope or 24–48 hours similarly to plate counts after incubation.

3. Most Probable Number (MPN) Methods

To estimate a low concentration of organisms in a sample, the most probable number (MPN) method can be used. Several tubes are prepared from consecutive ten-fold sample dilutions and recorded as either positive or negative for growth. In some instances, MPN is easier and simpler to perform than the plate count. It is particularly useful for samples with only a few organisms and can be used to detect organisms in samples larger than 1 g. The relationship between positive and negative tubes has been determined mathematically and tables have been developed for convenient estimations of cell concentrations.

The adenosine triphosphate (ATP) bioluminescence measurement system is relatively simple and rapid, with its results being reliable and acceptable for food and water analysis. The method for determining ATP is based on the reaction of luciferin and luciferase, which when reacted with ATP in the presence of magnesium ions causes a light emission. By using a photometer to measure the light emission when bacterial ATP reacts with the luciferin-luciferase system, quantitative analysis is made of the microbial load.

Limitation to the analysis is that, since the luciferin-luciferase system accounts for all ATP in the sample, non-bacteria ATP must be removed prior to analysis.

D. INDICATOR ORGANISMS

The first use of indicator organisms probably occurred in 1892, when Schardinger tested water for *E. coli* in search of *Salmonella typhi*. He theorized that, while it is difficult to detect *S. typhi* in a water supply, the presence of *E. coli* would indicate that there might have been contamination from sewage and that *Salmonella* or other coliforms might be present. Certain criteria are used to determine the value of an indicator organism in instances where specific pathogens such as fecal coliforms are targeted. Exclusive association with contamination and specificity with the pathogen should be seen. The usual source of the indicator and the significance of it should be known. The indicator should not be present as a natural contaminant of the material being analyzed. Moreover, detection, differentiation from background microorganisms, and enumeration of the indicator should be rapid and accurate. It is also beneficial if a standardized test for detection and enumeration exists. In using indicator organisms to determine product quality or shelf life, it is ideal that the indicator organism used possess qualities such as: presence and detection in all foods to assess quality growth and numbers have a direct correlation with product quality (in spoilage, the indicator organisms can be a natural contaminant of the material being analyzed) detection; and enumeration should be relatively easy, quick, and distinguishable from background microorganisms; growth of indicator microorganisms are not affected adversely by other components of the food flora.

VII. FOOD SAFETY

Ensuring safe food is an important public health priority for our nation. An estimated 76 million illnesses, 323,914 hospitalizations, and 5,194 deaths are attributable to foodborne illness in the United States each year. The estimated cost of foodborne illness is $10–$83 billion annually. For some consumers, foodborne illness results only in mild, temporary discomfort or lost time from work or other daily activity. For others, especially pre-school age children, older adults, and those with impaired immune systems, foodborne illness may have serious long-term consequences or may even be life threatening. The risk of foodborne illness is of increasing concern due to changes in the global market, aging of our population, increasing numbers of immunocompromised and immunosuppressed individuals, and changes in food production practices.

Numerous biological agents other than bacteria are known to cause foodborne illness. Many of these organisms or substances, such as the toxins produced by some fungi, were identified and confirmed as a causative agent of foodborne illness several decades ago. Others, especially prions and some of the parasitic protozoa, have only been studied during the past 20 years. The etiology of foodborne disease outbreaks is changing and can be a subject of great debate. The majority of illnesses or deaths due to food consumption are grossly underreported worldwide. The ability to link particular food sources, and food production, processing and preparation practices to foodborne illness is a challenge for epidemiologists. In the U.S., fewer than 1 in 1,000 estimated cases of foodborne illness are confirmed. Bacteria are the causative agents in approximately half of the confirmed cases of foodborne illness in the U.S. The remainder are attributed primarily to viruses or to other chemical agents or parasites. In the future, we should expect the proportion of confirmed cases and outbreaks of foodborne illness to increase as improved diagnostic tools are developed and surveillance for foodborne diseases improves.

Over the past two decades, microbiological food safety has received greater attention from regulatory authorities, researchers, public health officials, and consumers. We are continually learning more about the sources of microbial foodborne safety problems and how to prevent them. For several reasons, we may discover new food safety problems that may shift our current priorities for control of microbial foodborne illnesses. For example, we may be able to more easily detect and quantify microbial disease agents due to advances in laboratory methodologies. Also, we may discover new or emerging pathogenic organisms. Many microbial species have been shown to become more or less virulent over time. And, increased global food trade and international travel can lead to rapid transmission of foodborne pathogens around the world.

VIII. SPOILAGE BY MICROORGANISMS

Many species of microorganisms are known to cause spoilage of some foods. Spoiled foods are generally considered unacceptable to eat because of a poor odor, flavor, texture or appearance. Microbiological food spoilage occurs when the growth of bacteria, yeast, or mold leads to the production of microbial metabolic byproducts which make the food product unacceptable to eat.

The shelf life of a food refers to its useful storage life. At the end of shelf life, foods may be perceived as significantly different or unacceptably different from fresh quality. In foods, the shelf life of a perishable item is greatly affected by the initial microbial load present. Generally, if a food contains a large population of spoilage organisms, it will have a shorter shelf life than the same food containing fewer numbers of the same spoilage organisms. Excessive growth of spoilage microorganisms in a food can lead to changes in its composition or structure which may ultimately render the food

unacceptable to consumers. For example, many microorganisms produce enzymes that can cause fats or proteins to breakdown into aromatic compounds that can diminish sensory qualities and consumer acceptance. The breakdown of food components may also change the texture or water holding capacity of the food, especially near the surface. High temperature storage of these products can accelerate the rate that these enzymes promote changes in food quality.

Microbiological food spoilage can occur when bacteria, yeast, or mold grows to a sufficient level leading to the production of metabolic by-products that ultimately make the food unacceptable for consumption. Generally, many foods are considered spoiled or at the end of their typical shelf life when their total bacterial concentration is approximately 10^7 per g or per mL. Also, foods may be at the end of their shelf life if the yeast concentration is 10^5 per g or per mL, or if visible mold is present. Since bacteria, yeast, and molds are typically present in some foods and proliferate under different environmental conditions, spoilage of particular foods is usually caused by specific species of bacteria, yeast, or mold.

Generally, spoilage of foods can be delayed by appropriate processing, packaging, and storage of these products. Food processors can also delay microbiological spoilage by using quality raw materials with low microbial loads. Also, strict adherence to industry current Good Manufacturing Practices or processing under sanitary conditions will also prevent the introduction or growth of spoilage microorganisms in processed foods. The processing and packaging techniques used to inactivate or inhibit pathogenic microorganisms may also inhibit spoilage-causing microorganisms.

Microorganisms that may cause spoilage can replicate to unacceptably high concentrations in foods that are stored at higher temperatures and for longer times than recommended. After processing, most foods have optimum or prescribed storage conditions including time, temperature, and humidity. Processors, retailers, and consumers should follow proper storage recommendations for raw and processed foods to ensure optimal product quality.

IX. FOOD PRESERVATION

From the first stage of processing, the quality of food can deteriorate over time. The shorter the amount of time it takes a product or ingredient to be transformed or transported to its final destination, the consumer, the more advantageous. For this reason many foods are kept "alive" and "healthy" as long as possible. Once a food is no longer "alive" the quality decreases at varying rates dependant on the product and its environment. Degradation begins on many physical and chemical levels. This may be caused by microbiological, enzymatic, chemical, or physical means. Environmental conditions that may increase or decrease the quality of a product include temperature, humidity, handling, packaging, transport, and, of course, time. Product water activity (Table 50.2), pH, amino acid content, fatty acid content, vitamin content, and naturally occurring enzymes may also affect the quality of a product. Atmospheric modification, acidification, temperature reduction, thermal processing, reduction of water activity (Table 50.2), fermentation, and the addition of antimicrobials can combat naturally occurring microbiological processes.

The two major categories of food preservation are chemical methods and physical methods. Chemical methods are chemical preservatives, which include antimicrobials, antioxidants, and anti-browning agents. Physical methods of preservation include low temperature preservation, high temperature preservation, radiation, modified atmosphere packaging, and drying.

A. ANTIMICROBIALS AND PRESERVATIVES

Many antimicrobials are bacteriostatic or fungistatic and can only be added to certain levels within strict accordance with established regulations. Therefore, preservation of the quality of the food will not last indefinitely. Oftentimes use is in conjunction with other methods of preservation in order to provide a "multiple hurdle" defense against microorganisms. Occasionally, preservatives are added to foods for one purpose, but they may also indirectly act as antimicrobials. For many antimicrobials the exact mechanism or component that the chemical affects on the microorganism's cellular level is unknown. In general, particular cellular components such as the cell wall, cell membrane, metabolic processes, and genetic material are targeted for disruption, causing cell death or inhibition. No antimicrobial is the "silver bullet" for all microorganisms. Some may affect several types of microorganism but with only a limited effect; therefore, several different antimicrobials may be applied to help control the multiple microbiological concerns of a single product. A list of several common antimicrobials is provided in Table 50.3.

B. LOW TEMPERATURE PRESERVATION

The ability of low temperatures to preserve foods is based on the principal that all biological systems are controlled by enzymatic reactions including those that control microorganisms and cause quality degradation. The rate of these reactions is directly related to temperature. With a rise or fall in temperature the enzymatic rate of reaction increases or decreases, respectively. In biological systems, for each rise in temperature of 10°C there is approximately a two-fold increase in the enzymatic rate of reaction. Keep in mind that the temperature range and increase must be within appropriate parameters for that particular enzymatic function. Most microorganisms are significantly slowed at temperatures ranging from 0–7°C and many will not replicate with the exception of psychrotrophic organisms that will cause spoilage at these temperatures. Below 0°C all microbiological activity ceases; however, some enzymatic activity may still occur.

TABLE 50.2
Water Activity of Microorganisms and Select Foods

Food	Minimal a_w
Fresh fruits, vegetables, meat, and fish	0.98
Cooked meat	0.98–0.95
Cured meat products, cheeses	0.95–0.91
Sausages, syrups	0.91–0.87
Most bacteria can grow	0.91
Most yeasts can grow	0.88
Flours, rice, beans, peas	0.87–0.80
Most molds can grow	0.80
Jams	0.80–0.75
Halophilic bacteria can grow	0.75
Xerotolerant molds can grow	0.71
Dried fruits	0.65–0.60
Spices, milk powder	0.60–0.20

TABLE 50.3
Chemical Food Preservatives

Preservatives	Maximum Tolerance	Organisms Affected	Foods
Propionic acids	0.32%	Molds	Bread, cakes, cheeses
Sorbic acid	0.2%	Molds	Hard cheeses, syrups, salad dressings
Benzoic acid	0.1%	Yeasts and molds	Margarine, pickle, relishes, soft drinks, salad dressings
Parabens	0.1%	Yeasts and molds	Bakery products, soft drinks, pickles
Sulfites	200–300 ppm	Insects, microorganisms	Molasses, dried fruits, wines
Ethylene/propylene oxides	700 ppm	Yeasts, molds	Fumigant for spices, nuts
Sodium diacetate	0.32%	Molds	Bread
Nisin	1%	Lactis, clostridia	Pasteurized cheese
Dehydroacetic acid	65 ppm	Insects	Pesticide on strawberries, squash
Sodium nitrite	120 ppm	Clostridia	Meat-curing preparations

C. HIGH TEMPERATURE PRESERVATION

Two common types of high temperature preservation are pasteurization and sterilization. These processes are successful due to the general destruction of microorganisms at elevated temperatures. Pasteurization employs a technique of heating a substance, usually a liquid, to temperatures high enough to destroy most bacteria, including pathogens, without major chemical alteration of the product. The organisms that survive fit into either thermoduric or thermophilic categories. Thermoduric organisms, including the genus *Lactobacillus*, can withstand relatively high temperatures but are non-spore forming. Thermophiles, including the genera *Bacillus* and *Clostridium*, are sporeformers that require high temperatures for regular metabolic activity. The complete elimination of all microorganisms is referred to as sterilization. No viable organisms can be detected after this process.

D. RADIATION PRESERVATION

Radiation can be defined as the emission of radiant energy in the form of particles or waves. The food industry uses four major forms of radiation, including ultraviolet light, gamma radiation, electron beam radiation, and microwave radiation. The first three types depend on disruption at a molecular level causing lethal mutations in the microorganism's genetic code to destroy microorganisms. Ultraviolet light is most destructive at a range between 240 nm and 280 nm. Gram-negative bacteria are most affected by this kind of radiation. Gamma radiation is radiation emitted from Cobalt or Cesium sources. Electron beam radiation has a lower penetration power and requires a higher dose. Electron beam and gamma radiation are referred to as cold sterilization, achieving no increase in heat to produce to the required bactericidal effect. These methods can, however, cause undesirable color changes in the product at higher dosages. Microwaves use the friction of oscillating molecules to produce heat and thereby destroy microorganisms. Depending upon the radiation source, dose, product, presence or absence of oxygen, condition of food, target organism, microbial load, packaging, and surface cleanliness the effect of radiation varies widely.

In using radiation to preserve foods, the reactive ions produced by irradiating foods injure or destroy microorganisms by altering the cell membrane structure and affecting metabolic enzyme activity. More importantly, the DNA and RNA molecules in cell nuclei, which are essential for growth and replication, are affected. Analogous to heat processing, the rate of destruction of individual cells depends on the rate at which ions are produced and interreact with DNA, whereas the reduction in cell numbers depends on the total dose of radiation received. The rate of reduction is expressed as the D-value, in which the units

are expressed in kiloGrays (kGy). A Gray (Gy) is the absorbed dose where 1Gy is the absorption of 1 J of energy per kilogram of food. Like thermal processing, irradiation is a first-order reaction, in which theoretically, a logarithmic reduction in microbial numbers with increasing dose is expected.

E. DRYING PRESERVATION

Microorganisms and enzymes require water in order to be active. Low-moisture foods, including freeze-dried foods, and intermediate-moisture foods are the two categories of shelf stable dried food preservation. To be defined as a low-moisture food, the product cannot contain more than 25% moisture and has to achieve a_w less than 0.60. If the product contains between 15–50% moisture and a a_w of between 0.60 and 0.85 it is defined as an intermediate moisture food. During drying a wet hot heat causes more damage to microbial cells than dry heat. Freeze drying employs a vacuum sublimation of the ice content. The lowered a_w and moisture levels produced through these processes are capable of inhibiting any spoilage or pathogenic organisms.

F. MODIFIED ATMOSPHERE PACKAGING

Modified atmosphere packaging (MAP) is any package that contains a gas composition deviant from atmospheric air. Typically this is achieved by varying the amounts of oxygen, carbon dioxide, and nitrogen, in effect to increase the amount of CO_2. Carbon dioxide has been known to extend the shelf life of food products for over 100 years. The reduction or removal of atmospheric air does not provide an environment conducive for growth of typical spoilage organisms. Occasionally, as in the case with vacuum packaging, a product may begin with little atmospheric oxygen, which is consumed and converted to CO_2 by normal aerobic microflora. The concentration of CO_2 may reach as high as 30%. Most of the time a known concentration of CO_2 is added to a high barrier plastic film in order to achieve a preservation effect. Many different variations of this general principle are used to achieve the proper effect for different products. Another way to manipulate the atmosphere of a package is to employ the use of different types of plastics for packaging. Depending upon the molecular composition of the plastic and how it is formed the rate at which molecules of oxygen, carbon dioxide, and water vapor pass through it vary. These are referred to as the oxygen transmission rate (OTR), carbon dioxide transmission rate (CO_2TR), and the water vapor transmission rate (WVTR). The units for these measurements are $cc/m^2/24$ h at 70°F. Transmission rates are also proportional to the thickness of the film. Some plastics may possess a low OTR but a high WVTR; therefore, many manufacturers use several combinations of plastics added in layers to achieve the desired film. No plastic has a zero transmission rate; therefore, a food package, no matter how well constructed, may start with one type of atmosphere which will change over time.

Unfortunately, there are some problems associated with MAP. Pathogenic organisms compete for nutrients with spoilage organisms. Usually, the consumer would reject a food before pathogenic organisms are in high enough concentrations to cause harm. In the MAP environment the normal spoilage organisms are not there to compete with pathogens. What develops is a food product that smells and looks edible but is in fact riddled with pathogenic organisms. Due to the fear of *Clostridium botulinum* the FDA has recently increased the minimum recommended OTR to 10,000 $cc/m^2/24$ h at 70°F. An increase in CO_2 also causes some physiological changes such as the exudative loss of water. The binding of CO_2 to moisture in the product forms carbonic acid ultimately changing the pH. This can lead to off-flavors and consumer rejection.

G. OTHER PROCESSES FOR FOOD PRESERVATION

Other methods of preservation are increasingly used by researchers and are commercially available to a limited extent. Destruction of microorganisms through the use of high-power ultrasound has been attempted but thus far has not been made economically feasible. High-intensity pulsed light using high-intensity xenon arc lamps on quick short bursts utilizing a UV affect is currently being studied. Finally, high hydrostatic pressure (300 to 1,000 MPa) is used with products that are liquid or mostly consisting of liquid. The underlying mechanism hinges on the destruction of non-covalent bonds, which in turn disrupt the target organism's cellular function causing deactivation.

X. FERMENTATION

Fermentation is probably the oldest form of food preservation and can be defined as the breakdown of carbohydrates under anaerobic conditions. Fermented foods do not always fall under this strict definition and many times are produced from the breakdown of carbohydrates and carbohydrate-like components under aerobic and anaerobic conditions. Most fermentations, however, seldom break down only carbohydrates. These foods are products of microbial and enzymatic actions affecting many food constituents including fats, carbohydrates, proteins, and many others, each of which contributes to the final product.

Most forms of spoilage are undesirable. Conversely, fermentative spoilage produces favorable benefits of increased shelf life and added flavor. This beneficial spoilage is encouraged by the promotional growth of selected microorganisms for their unique end products and metabolic processes. Most forms of food preservation

try to reduce or inhibit growth of microorganisms. Essentially, fermentation is a controlled spoilage using many variables such as atmosphere, temperature, salt content, and starter cultures.

Fermented foods can also be microbiologically safe as well as more nutritious. Many organisms used for fermentation produce acid as a by-product of their metabolic processes. As these organisms increase in number, the amount of acid produced increases, ultimately accumulating in the food and lowering the total pH of the product. Many pathogenic bacteria such as *Clostridium botulinum* cannot proliferate in low acid environments; therefore, the product remains microbiologically safe for extended periods of time. These same organisms can synthesize growth factors and vitamins, release nutrients from indigestible materials, and enzymatically break down indigestible sugars such as hemicellulose into usable sugar derivatives.

A list of several common fermented products, their substrates, and the microorganisms involved can be found in Table 50.4. One classic fermented product is beer. In this fermentation carbohydrates are broken down by the yeast *Saccharomyces cerevisae*, producing alcohol and carbon dioxide as by-products. Dairy fermentations are also very common whereby cheeses, yogurt, buttermilk, and sour cream are produced. For most common cheeses such as blue, cheddar, cottage, and gouda as well as buttermilk and sour cream *Lactococcus lactis* subsp. *cremoris/lactis* are the primary acid producers with a wide variety of secondary microflora.

Vegetable fermentation is also a major industry for food production. Cabbage (sauerkraut), cucumbers (pickles), olives (green olives), and soybeans (soy sauce) are but a few examples of vegetable fermentation. The three major types of vegetable fermentation include lactic acid,

TABLE 50.4
Fermented Food Products

Fermentation Product	Substrate	Microorganism
Cocoa beans	Cacao fruit	*Candida krusei, Geotrichum* spp.
Coffee beans	Coffee cherries	*Erwinia dissolvens, Saccharomyces* spp.
Miso	Soybeans	*Aspergillus oryzae*
Olives	Green olives	*Leuconostoc mesenteroides, Lactobacillus plantarum*
Pickles	Cucumbers	*Lactobacillus plantarum*
Sauerkraut	Cabbage	*Leuconostoc mesenteroides*
Soy sauce	Soybeans	*Rhizopus oligosporus*
Beer and ale	Cereal wort	*Saccharomyces cerevisae*
Bourbon whiskey	Corn, rye	*Saccharomyces cerevisae*
Cider	Apples	*Saccharomyces* spp.
Sake	Rice	*Saccharomyces sake*
Vinegar	Cider, wines	*Acetobacter* spp.
Wines	Grapes	*Saccharomyces* spp.

acetic acid, and alcoholic fermentation. Lactic acid may be produced in fermented vegetables by species including *Leuconostoc mesenteroides*, *Lactobacillus plantarum*, *Lactobacillus bavaricus*, and *Lactobacillus casei*. Other bacterial species, including *Acetobacter hansenii* and *Gluconobacter oxydans*, may produce acetic acid or vinegar during fermentation. Fermentations that result in alcoholic products may be produced by microbial species including *Saccharomyces cerevisae*, *Kluveromyces marxianus*, and *Aspergillus oryzae*. Meat, fish, and poultry can also be fermented to produce desirable products. For example, meats can be fermented to produce products such as pepperoni and sausage. Although the origins of fermentation may be ancient, the processes are still used today to provide a rich variety of safe and shelf stable foods.

XI. OTHER USES OF MICROORGANISMS IN FOOD PRODUCTION AND PROCESSING

Many bacteria are beneficial and essential to human health. At any time numbers of bacteria on and in a human body outnumber human body cells. Areas that contain consistently large numbers of microflora are the nose, throat, and gastrointestinal tract. When certain amounts of these beneficial bacteria, typically in the live state, are consumed or applied certain health benefits may be experienced. Generally, these microbial cocktails may contain one or many different strains in addition to viable cells, dead cells, and/or certain cellular components, and are loosely defined as probiotics. Prebiotics are indigestible components that influence certain numbers of targeted bacteria in the colon stimulating their activity and/or growth to benefit the host. Synbiotics are prebiotic and probiotic components combined.

Some dairy products contain probiotic bacteria, most commonly from the genera *Bifidobacterium* and *Lactobacillus*. When these harmless types of bacteria establish themselves in the gastrointestinal tract they occupy available space, thereby aiding in the inhibition of colonization of pathogenic bacteria. This concept has been expanded to an on-farm strategy called competitive exclusion. Young animals are given cocktails of nonpathogenic bacteria at a young age to colonize the gut in an attempt to prevent the infection of certain pathogenic strains. It has been successfully achieved in poultry with a combination of 29 species of bacteria and proven effective in cattle with one *Proteus mirabilis* strain and 17 strains of *E. coli*. In addition to reduced numbers of pathogenically infected animals, these treatments allow for faster growth and weight gain. If further developed, probiotic use may ultimately reduce the need for extensive antibiotic treatments for farm animals and aid in the reduction of the appearance of antibiotic-resistant strains of bacteria.

All the benefits from probiotic treatments are not currently known; however, successful treatments do increase the immune response and disrupt metabolic pathways for detrimental flora in the gastrointestinal tract. It is difficult to draw conclusions because key aspects of the studies (i.e., type and amount of cultures used, initial participant health, age, and resident flora) all vary greatly. As we learn more about the intricate relationship between nonpathogenic, pathogenic bacteria, and host response, this new technology will provide a healthier food system.

REFERENCES

1. N. N. Potter, J. H. Hotchkiss. Food Science. Fifth ed. Gaithersburg, MD: Aspen Publishers Inc., 1998.
2. P. A. Hartman. 2001. The evolution of food microbiology. In: M. P. Doyle, L. R. Beuchat, T. J. Montville. Eds. Food Microbiology: Fundamentals and Frontiers. 2nd ed. Washington, D.C.: ASM Press, 2001.
3. J. M. Jay. Modern Food Microbiology. New York: Van Nostrand Reinhold, 1992.
4. G.J. Banwart. Basic Food Microbiology. New York: Van Nostrand Reinhold, 1989.
5. P. Fellows. Food Processing Technology. Abingdon, England: Woodhead Publishing Ltd., 2000.
6. D. N. McSwane, R. Linton. Essentials of Food Safety and Sanitation. Upper Saddle River. NJ: Prentice Hall, 1998.
7. M. P. Doyle, L.R. Beuchat, T.J. Montville, eds. Food Microbiology Fundamentals and Frontiers. 2nd ed. Washington, D.C.: ASM Press, 2001.
8. U.S. Food and Drug Administration. Bacteriological Analytical Manual, 8th edition, Revision A. Gaithersburg, MD: AOAC International, 1998.

51 Microbial Food Spoilage

Lone Gram
Danish Institute for Fisheries Research, Technical University of Denmark

CONTENTS

I. INTRODUCTION

Descriptions of the potentially negative influence of microorganisms on food quality often focus on describing potential disease-causing organisms. Typically, many reviews or books on food microbiology contain many sections or chapters describing different pathogenic agents, and often spoilage of all foods is dealt with in a briefer manner. Although microbial spoilage of foods may somehow not be as spectacular as the intriguing behaviour of pathogenic agents, the problem must not be underestimated. Thus, microbial growth and metabolism, which is the major cause of *post-harvest* spoilage of foods, causes an estimated loss of 10–50% of all raw agricultural commodities produced globally (1). In some cases (fruits, vegetables, nuts), spoilage processes may also be initiated *pre-harvest*.

In the context of the present chapter, spoilage will describe changes in a product which render it unaccceptable for the consumer from a sensory perspective. Spoilage is product specific; for instance, formation of ammonia is a sign of spoilage in fresh, chill-stored fish but may be a desired quality in Camembert cheese.

Reactions or events other than microbial growth may lead to spoilage (sensory rejection). This includes phenomena such as lipid oxidation or discolouration, which will not be dealt with in this chapter.

II. CONCEPTS IN MICROBIAL FOOD SPOILAGE

Foods constitute a range of different ecosystems. Some foods are "alive" (fruits, vegetables, grains, nuts) and contain defense systems which microorganisms need to overcome when growing. Other "dead" foods (meat, fish) are typically preserved by manipulating the physical and chemical environment by cooling, acidifying, salting, etc. (2). Microbial spoilage is almost always a consequence of growth of the spoiling organism to high numbers. Hence, a primary assessment of the microorganisms potentially involved in spoilage of a particular product can be done by matching the growth characteristics of different microorganisms with the preserving characteristics of the product. Although this will not identify the exact cause of spoilage, it will narrow the spectrum of potential culprits.

Microbial spoilage is detectable in many forms: as gas formation causing bombage, as slime formation due to production of extracellular polymers or the degradation of food matrixes, as visible colonial growth, or as off-flavours and off-odours arising from the microbial metabolism of food components. Mostly, growth of microorganisms to high numbers ($>10^5$ yeast cfu/g or $>10^7$–10^8 bacteria cfu/g) is required for spoilage to be noticable. In a few products, enzymes produced by microorganisms may remain active after inactivation of the microorganisms and cause spoilage during storage.

The microbiota on raw foods is very varied but a few species typically become dominant during storage. These are the ones capable of tolerating the specific preservation conditions used. The microbiota on freshly processed foods is also heterogenous and is a function of the microorganisms found on raw materials, on ingredients, and in the processing environment. Logically, the food processing steps, such as heat treatment or acidification, also have a major influence.

The concepts in microbial food spoilage have been outlined (3): the microbiota present when the product is spoiled is called the spoilage association or the spoilage microbiota. To determine the importance of the different microorganisms in the spoilage process, pure cultures are isolated from spoiled foods and tested for their ability to produce the sensory (and chemical) changes associated with the naturally spoiling product. Microorganisms with these abilities are said to posess a spoilage potential. However, it is crucial for the understanding of the spoilage process that quantitative considerations are included. Hence, for each organism with a spoilage potential, it must be evaluated if it is capable of growing in the "spoiling" product and if it reaches cell numbers in the spoiling product that are sufficient for the sensory and chemical changes to take place. Organisms that both qualitatively and quantitatively are linked to the spoiling product are said to have a spoilage activity. Verifying that these organisms are indeed the causative agents of spoilage requires trials with food systems. Thus, the identification of specific spoilage organism(s) of a product will require a combination of sensory, chemical, and microbiological analyses (4). The term spoilage domain is used to describe the range of conditions

under which a specific spoilage organism is capable of influencing the spoilage process.

Using such approaches the specific spoilage microorganisms of several food products have been determined (Table 51.1). Gram-negative psychrotrophic bacteria such as pseudomonads are important spoilage agents of most fresh foods. As preservation "pressure" increases, e.g., by adding salt and acid, lactic acid bacteria and other fermentative organisms take over. Filamentous fungi and yeast are the spoilage agents of many products with low water activity or products such as citrus fruits where the fungi tolerate the specific defense components of the food (5). Although the same organisms may be the spoiling agent of different food products, the reactions leading to spoilage can be very different. Thus, pseudomonads are the main spoilage agents of fresh, chilled, aerobically packed meat where they degrade amino acids producing spoilage off-odours (4). In vegetables, where *Pseudomonas* spp. are also identified as one of the main spoilage organisms, they typically degrade the polymer (pectin) by pectinolytic acitivity, leaving a soft rotting liquified product (6).

Different organisms may, as single species, be the cause of spoilage. Hence, both Enterobacteriaceae (mostly *Erwinia* species) and *Pseudomonas* spp. may cause soft rot of vegetables. In some products, it may be difficult identifying one organism as the specific agent of spoilage and here mixtures of organisms may be responsible for spoilage. Examples of such metabiotic relationships include the combination of Enterobacteriaceae and lactic acid bacteria, which in vacuum-packed meat or cold-smoked salmon only produce spoilage metabolites similar to the spoiling products when both groups are present (7–10).

III. EXAMPLES OF SPECIFIC SPOILAGE ORGANISMS

Although many different types of microorganisms grow in different food products, several groups or species often are involved in the spoilage process. The sections below provide examples of the involvement of different microorganisms in food spoilage.

A. PSEUDOMONADS, SHEWANELLA, PHOTOBACTERIUM, PSEUDOALTEROMONAS

The psychrotrophic, Gram-negative, non-fermentative bacteria belonging to *Pseudomonas* spp. or identified as *Shewanella* spp. are very often identified as specific spoilage organisms. *Pseudomonas* spp. are the spoilage agents of vegetables where they degrade pectin (6), of aerobically packed meat where they degrade amino acids to volatile compounds such as sulfides (4), and of aerobically stored iced freshwater fish (11) and iced crustaceans where they produce esters and sulphydryl compounds (12). Also, extracellular hydrolytic enzymes of

TABLE 51.1

Typical Spoilage Organisms of Food Products

Organism	Vegetables	Chilled Meat			Chilled Fish			Milk	Flavoured Yogurt	Egg	Fruit	Soft Drinks	Beer	Bakery Goods	Oil-Based
		Fresh	Packed	Cured	Fresh	Packed	Cured								
Pseudomonas	+	+			+			+		+					
Shewanella					+	+									
Photobacterium						+	+								
Enterobacteriaceae	+		+	+			+	+							+
Lactic acid bacteria															
Leuconostoc			+	+			+						+		
Brochothrix				+										+	
Bacillus								+							
Clostridium			+												
Acyclobacillus															
Anaerobes													+		
Halophiles															
Yeasts							+		+			+	+	+	+
Filamentous fungi	+										+	+		+	

pseudomonads may be the cause of milk spoilage where lipolytic and proteolytic activity contributes to off-flavour formation and clotting (13). *Pseudomonas* spp. are also the main cause of rotting in eggs (14) where they cause pink rot (*P. fluorescens*) or fluorescent green rot (*P. putida*) (15). *Pseudomonas* spp. are strict respiratory organisms and are most important in products where oxygen is available.

Psychrotolerant *Shewanella* species are often involved in spoilage of marine products. Their ability to reduce the odourless trimethyl amine oxide (TMAO) to trimethylamine (TMA), which has a fishy smell, and to produce hydrogen sulphide involves them in spoilage of iced marine fish and shellfish. Psychrotrophic *Shewanella* spp. are sensitive to low pH and are not normally associated with spoilage of meat. However, they have been identified as a cause of off-odour in high-pH meat (16) and in chicken (17). The H_2S formation by *Shewanella* spp. in high-pH meat may also cause greening of the meat. Although strictly respiratory, *Shewanella* spp. are capable of utilizing several compounds as electron acceptors in an anaerobic respiration and they are therefore also associated with spoilage of vacuum-packed foods. The type strain of *Shewanella putrefaciens* was originally isolated from tainted butter (18).

In CO_2-packed marine fish, respiratory bacteria are inhibited and a marine, psychrotolerant bacterium *Photobacterium phosphoreum* is selected (19). The organism belongs to the Vibrionaceae family and produces large amounts of TMA (19).

Recently, another marine bacterium, *Pseudoalteromonas,* was identified as part of the spoilage microbiota of iced squid (20). These bacteria are capable of degrading urea, which occurs in high concentrations in squid, and they may be contributing to spoilage through ammonia formation.

B. ENTEROBACTERIACEAE

In classical food microbiology, members of the Enterobacteriaceae family are enteric mesophilic organisms and their presence in food products is an indication of hygienic failure. However, the family also covers psychrotrophic environmental strains that may occur in the environment of food raw materials and that may grow on chill-stored products. *Erwinia* species are common spoilage organisms of vegetables where, due to pectinolytic and proteolytic activity, they cause extensive soft rot spoilage (21, 22). Organisms like *Serratia, Enterobacter, Rahnella,* and *Hafnia* are often isolated in high numbers from fresh proteinaceous products such as milk, meat, or fish. Enterobacteraiceae may spoil liquid milk products during prolonged storage (23, 24) due to formation of off-odours or proteases causing "sweet curdling." Their interactive behaviour with lactic acid bacteria has been suggested to play a role in the spoilage process of vacuum-packed meat (7–9) and cold-smoked salmon (10).

C. LACTIC ACID BACTERIA AND *BROCHOTHRIX*

Lactic acid bacteria (LAB) covers a conglomerate of many bacteria. LAB grow well under vacuum-packing and have a relatively high tolerance towards salt and acid. Hence, they must be considered when evaluating spoilage of packed and/or preserved products. Yeasts, as will be discussed below, tolerate many of the same preservation parameters and are often selected in the same products where LAB dominate. Many of the LAB have no effect on food quality and, for instance, some *Carnobacterium* spp. may grow to numbers of $10^8–10^9$ cfu/g with no adverse effects on quality (25). Some may even have a preserving effect on the product. However, some species are potent spoilage organisms producing sour off-odours (26, 27), gas (28, 29), or exopolysaccharides (30, 31). Some species (e.g., *L. saké* or *L. curvatus*) are able to produce hydrogen sulphide (32, 33), causing sulphorous off-odours. The green discolouration which may sometimes be seen on meats can be caused by LAB due to hydrogen peroxide oxidation of meat pigment (33). Greening may also be explained by the formation of sulfmyoglobin caused by Gram-negative H_2S-producing bacteria, typically *Shewanella* (34). LAB have also been identified as spoilage organisms of beer and soft drinks. Some species of LAB, such as *Lactobacillus curvatus* and *Lactobacillus saké*, are potent producers of hydrogen sulphide whereas other species produce acid and/or CO_2 in large amounts, causing souring or bombage of the product. Some homofermentative *Lactobacillus* may also form so-called ropy slime due to exopolymer production (9).

If allowed to grow to high numbers, *Leuconostoc* species are often associated with spoilage. They may produce off-odours and off-flavours as well as bombage. However, their most prominent characteristic is their ability to produce slime (exo-polysaccharides), which can be a spoilage sign of cured meat products (9, 35).

Brochothrix thermosphacta is a Gram-positive, catalase-negative bacterium which is capable of growing in chilled, packed products. In vacuum-packed, high-pH meat, *B. thermosphacta* is able to grow (36) and its metabolism (carbohydrate fermentation and lipolytic ability) gives rise to compounds like acetoin and diacetyl, both of which are off-odourous. Acetoin requires glucose as substrate whereas other carbohydrates may be metabolized to, e.g., diacetyl (37). *B. thermosphacta* is also typical of spoilage of cured, packed meat products where it grows to high numbers producing off-odours and then dies off as *Lactobacillus* species become dominant (38). Although *B. thermosphacta* can often be isolated from aerobic packed meat, pseudomonads will eventually dominate and spoil the product (39). In contrast, *B. thermosphacta* is often isolated from meats packed in CO_2-containing atmosphere (40) but does require a limited amount of oxygen to produce spoilage off-odours (41).

D. Sporeformers

Gram-negative, spore-forming organisms, *Clostridium* and *Bacillus*, have been identified as the specific spoilage organisms of several food commodities. Clostridia are typically involved in spoilage of packed (anaerobic) products due to their intolerance to oxygen, whereas *Bacillus* spp. tolerate oxygen and can grow also in non-packed products. Psychrotrophic clostridia have been involved in spoilage of chilled, vacuum-packed raw or cooked meats. Spoilage of vacuum-packed meat may sometimes present itself as a "blown pack" and *Clostridium* species have been identified as the causative agent (42, 43). Several clostridia produce both CO_2, hydrogen, or butyric acid, which can explain the blowing (43) but CO_2 and hydrogen are probably the main causes (44). It appears that several different psychrotrophic clostridia may cause spoilage, including *Cl. gasigenes, Cl. estertheticum* (45), and *Cl. frigidicarnis* (46). Similarly, outgrowth of *Cl. butyricum* can cause so-called late-blowing of cheese (especially hard cheeses) due to fermentation of lactate (47). Sugar-salted, barrel-stored herring may spoil due to growth of clostridial species (48).

Bacillus species spoil different food products which typically have been heat treated as part of processing; hence, spores survive and grow. "Rope" formation in bread is caused by growth of *Bacillus* (49) and "sweet curdling," e.g., clotting, of milk can be caused by *Bacillus* where exoproteases degrade the casein micelles of the milk (50). "Ropiness" is caused by the enzymatic degradation of the bread crumbs and the parallel production of exopolysaccharides by the bacilli (51, 52). *Bacillus stearothermophilus* is a thermophilic organism which may cause a so-called flat-sour spoilage of evaporated milk (53) or some canned products (54).

A unique kind of spoilage has been found in heat-treated fruit juices, where an acid-requiring, spore-forming organism, *Alicyclobacillus acidoterrestris*, has been identified as the cause of a disinfectant taint (2,6 dibromophenol and 2,6 dichlorophenol) (55, 56). The kinetics of spoilage are not completely understood as it appears that very low levels of spores are sufficient to cause spoilage (55).

E. Yeasts

Yeasts are involved in spoilage of a wide array of food products where they are detected due to visible colonial growth, the formation of gas, or production of off-odour (57). A range of pickled products (mayonnaises, ketchups, salad dressings) are preserved with low pH and, often, addition of preservatives. This eliminates most microorganisms but lactic acid bacteria and yeasts may grow. Yeast cells are typically much larger than bacterial cells and hence a lower cell number is required to cause spoilage. Several of the *Zygosaccharomyces* yeasts in particular, and some isolates

of *Saccharomyces cerevisiae* are spoilage agents in foods high in sugar, low in pH, and/or containing food preservatives. Also, alcohol-containing products are prone to yeast spoilage. The most important are *Z. rouxii, Z. bailii,* and *Z. bisporus* (58). Foods with low a_w (e.g., high in sugar) are often spoiled by *Z. rouxii* or *Z. mellis* which has been identified in spoiled bakery products (59) and sugars and syrups.

Zygosaccharomyces bailii and, to some extent also *Z. bisporus*, have been involved in spoilage of mayonnaises, ketchups, and salad dressings. *Z. bailii* grows at low pH in acetic acid and salt (60) and may adapt to food preservatives such as sorbate and benzoate. *Z. bailii* is also associated with wine spoilage. At lower temperatures *Z. lentus* is also a spoilage agent in preserved products (61).

Saccharomyces cerevisiae are commonly isolated as wild yeasts in breweries and are potential spoilage organisms (62, 63). Fermented foods may spoil due to yeast metabolism of lactate and acetate or the production of CO_2 and ethanol. Several *Saccharomyces* species have been isolated from spoiled fermented products (64).

Various species of yeast (*Candida, Yarrowia*) have been detected at levels up to 10^5 cfu/g in chilled spoiling poultry; however, a role in spoilage has not been elucidated (65, 66).

F. Filamentous Fungi

Filamentous fungi (moulds) may grow in many different types of food products and it is estimated that 5–10% of foods are lost *post-harvest* due to growth of filamentous fungi (2). They may affect sensory quality of the products in several ways: through visible filamentous growth, through production of exo-enzymes which degrade the product, or through production of small off-odourous compounds, such as geosmin (5). They may be involved in spoilage of a very broad range of food commodities but are commonly involved in spoilage of low water activity products (grains, nuts, dried fish, cheeses, fermented meats, bread and bakery products) and in spoilage of fruits and vegetables. Although the production of mycotoxins by filamentous fungi is a food safety issue, companies encountering food spoilage often wish to determine whether mycotoxin production may also have occurred. This often requires specialist advice (5, 67).

Foods spoiled by filamentous fungi are divided into two categories: living products such as fresh fruits and vegetables, cereals and nuts before harvest, and stored, processed, or preserved products (i.e., dried cereals, nuts, meat and fish, bread, bakery products, cheese, juice and beverages) (2).

Living plant foods rely on natural defense mechanisms to prevent microbial growth. Fruits have skins which require penetration, while cereals and nuts may produce phytoalexins or other natural antifungal material. Fresh animal foods are more liable to spoilage by bacteria than fungi. Stored processed and dried products must rely on classical food preservation techniques such as drying of cereals, nuts, meat, and fish, or heat processing and/or the use of preservatives for juices and beverages. The genera *Aspergillus, Penicillium, Fusarium, Alternaria, Botrytis, Rhizopus*, and *Eurotium* are common causes of food spoilage. Although many species within each genera may have a spoilage potential, only 2–12 species seem to be important in spoilage (5) and for many types of living food, only 1–2 species are of major importance. For instance, some fungi (e.g., *Rhizopus*) have specific enzymes allowing skin penetration whereas others (e.g., *Pencillium*) have mechanisms for overcoming the specific antifungal defenses (2). Although many fungi may potentially spoil citrus fruits, the primary spoilage fungi are *Pen. italicum* and *Pen. digitatum* (2, 5).

An overview of the spoilage mycobiota of different foods is presented in Table 51.2.

G. OTHERS

Several of the groups/species of spoilage organisms described above are involved in spoilage of several foods or products. However, in some products it appears that one single species appears and is involved in spoilage of only one specific product. This may of course just be a matter of understanding the ecology and metabolism of a particular organism to predict if it will have spoilage activity in other products. One such example is the spoilage of flavoured bottled water by species of the aerobic Gram-negative bacteria, *Gluconobacter*, which produces sour off-odours (68, 69). This organism is closely related to the acetic acid bacteria and proliferates at very low pH values (e.g., pH 3.5) (69), hence being adapted to these particular products.

IV. SPOILAGE PATTERNS OF FOODS

A summary of examples of typical spoilage substrates and metabolites is presented in Table 51.3.

A. VEGETABLES

Vegetables have a high water content (80–90%) and their texture is built by pectins or other carbohydrate polymers such as starch. They typically contain low amounts of protein and simple carbohydrates and many are rich in pigments. pH is around 6 (5.5–7). In some countries, vegetables are distributed at chill temperatures. Increasingly, vegetables are sold processed into ready-to-eat salads (70). Spoilage of vegetables is primarily caused by microorganisms capable of degrading the polymers of the product. The main spoiling organisms are *Pseudomonas* spp., Enterobacteriaceae (mostly *Erwinia*), and filamentous fungi. The bacterial spoilage is evident when high numbers ($>10^8$ cfu/g) are reached. Typically, these organisms are pectinolytic and hence cause softening of the tissue, known as soft-rot. Also, during degradation off-flavours and off-odours are formed. In some bacteria, spoilage is enhanced by proteolytic capability (22), probably because proteolysis causes an increase in pH and some pectate lyases have a higher activity at high pH (8–9) (71).

The expression of hydrolytic enzymes (proteases, pectinases, cellulases) in the plant-pathogenic *Erwinia carotovora* subsp. *carotovora* is regulated in a quorum

TABLE 51.2
Associated Spoilage Mycobiota of Different Foods (Modified from References 2, 5)

Product	\[Genera Involved in Spoilage\] *Penicillium*	*Alternaria*	*Fusarium*	*Cladosporium*	*Aspergillus*	*Eurotium*	*Botrytis*	*Rhizopus*
Citrus fruits	+	+						
Pome fruits	+						+	
Stone fruits		+						+
Onions	+				+			
Leafy green vegetables		+					+	+
Potato tubers			+					
Yam tubers	+							
Grain, in field		+	+					
Grain, stored	+				+	+		
Maize			+					
Peanuts					+			
Rye bread	+						+	
Cheese	+			+				
Processed meat products	+						+	
Salted, dried fish					+			
Jams	+						+	

TABLE 51.3

Examples of Typical Spoilage Substrates and Metabolites Found in Microbiologically Spoiled Foods (160)

Sensory Impression	Spoilage Product	Spoilage Substrate	Food Product	Specific Spoilage Organism	Reference
Slime	EPS (dextran)	Sucrose	Kimchi	*Leuconostoc*	31
			Turkey breast	*Leuconostoc*	35
		Sugars	Wine	*Pediococcus damnosus*	29
		Sugars	Bread	*Bacillus*	49
Slime	Hydrolysed polymer	Pectin	Vegetables	*Erwinia, Pseudomonas*	70
Fishy off-odour	Trimethylamine (TMA)	Trimethylamine oxide (TMAO)	Fish	*Shewanella putrefaciens*	161
				P. phosphoresum	19
				Aeromonas spp.	96
Ammonia, putrid	NH$_3$	Amino acids	Proteinaceous foods	Many microorganisms	
	Biogenic amines	Amino acids	Meat	*Enterobacteriaceae* and LAB	7
			Fish[1]	*Enterobacteriaceae*, LAB	10
			Fish[1]	*P. phosphoreum*	10
Sulhidy off-odour	H$_2$S	Cysteine	Fish, meat	*S. putrefaciens*	98, 162
				Enterobacteriaceae	4
				Lb. saké, Lb. curvatus	
Greening	H$_2$S	Cysteine	Meat	*Lb. plantarum*	33
Sulphydryl off-odours	(CH$_3$)$_2$S$_2$	Methionine	Fish, meat	*Pseudomonas* spp.	163
				Enterobacteriaceae	164
Acid off-odour	Acetic acid	Glucose, ribose, other CHO	Meat	LAB	165
	L,D-lactic acid				
"Sweet curdling"	Proteinaceus fat particles	Phospholipid	Milk	*Bacillus cereus*	166
Fruity off-odour	Esters		Fish	*Ps. fragi*	167
			Milk	*Ps. fragi*	84
				Ps. putida and *Y. intermedia*	85
Cheesey off-odour	Acetoin, diacetyl, 3-methylbutanoyl	Glucose	Meat	*B. thermosphacta*	4
				Enterobacteriaceae	
				Homofermentative LAB	
Medicine off-odour	2-methoxy-phenol, sediment	Sugars	Juice	*Alicyclobacillus acidoterrestris*	55
Musty odour	Trichloroanisol	2,4,6 Trichlorophenol	Wine	*Penicillium brevicompactum Aspergillus flavus*	5

[1] Biogenic amines may not be the cause of spoilage but can serve as a spoilage index (10).

sensing dependant way. The bacterium produces small hormone-like signal molecules (acylated homoserine lactones, AHLs) that allow the bacterial population to sense its own density (72). Expression of hydrolytic enzymes is up-regulated at high densities. Interestingly, the production of pectin-degrading enzymes in an onion spoiling *Burkholderia* (73) and the production of protease and cellulase in a bean sprout spoiling *Serratia* (22) are regulated also by AHLs. Hence, AHL-negative mutants have a lower spoilage activity.

In vegetables high in simple carbohydrates, such as sugar beets which contain high concentrations of sucrose, levan (slime) formation may cause both spoilage and technical problems during further processing (74).

The spoilage of potatoes is caused by different organisms including *Pseudomonas*, *Streptomyces*, and a range of filamentous fungi (75). Spoilage may present itself as soft-rot, dry-rot, wilt, and blight. It may be initiated pre-harvest but the causative organisms can also attack during storage.

B. FRESH PROTEINACEOUS FOODS (MILK, MEAT, FISH)

Liquid milk consists of water, protein (casein), carbohydrate (lactose), salts, and lipids in varying proportions. Water activity is high, the pH is between 6 and 7 and preservation parameters include pasteurisation and chill storage. Pasteurised liquid milk products undergo different types of spoilage. Typically, spoilage results from action of *Bacillus*, *Pseudomonas*, or Enterobacteriaceae (76, 77) and is evident when high numbers ($> 10^7$ cfu/ml) are reached (13). Sometimes, degradative enzymes which survive pasteurisation cause spoilage during storage with no bacterial growth (78). Spoilage by *Pseudomonas* and Enterobacteriaceae is the result of post-pasteurisation contamination (79, 80) whereas spores of *Bacillus* may survive pasteurisation and grow during storage. Several types of psychrotrophic *Bacillus* have been involved in spoilage of chill-stored, liquid milk (81, 82). At normal chill storage temperatures, *Pseudomonas* spp. will typically become the dominant spoilage organism (83). Spoilage is characterized by bitter, sour, or fruity off-flavours (76) and/or by clotting ("sweet curdling"). The bitter off-flavours can be caused by proteolytic action of pseudomonads (78) and protelytic degradation of the casein-micelles leads to clotting of milk. Rancid off-flavours may be caused by lipoytic activity of, for instance, *Pseudomonas* spp. (13), whereas fruity off-flavours arise from esters produced by *Pseudomonas* spp. or Enterobacteriaceae (84, 85).

Water is the main constituent of red meat and poultry. It contains protein, lipid, and several non-protein nitrogen-containing compounds such as amino acids and creatine. Carbohydrates are present as glycogen, glucose, and lactate. In non-stressed animals, pH will decrease significantly (to approx. 5.5) in red meat *post mortem* due to glycogen metabolism. Glycogen depots are depleted in stressed animals *pre mortem* and pH after slaughter reaches 6.0–6.5. These differences can have a profound impact on the spoilage microbiology of vacuum-packed meats since the hydrogen sulphide-producing bacteria *Shewanella putrefaciens* may grow in packed, high-pH meat and cause rapid spoilage (4). The *Shewanella* spoilage is characterised by sulphidy off-odours and H_2S may cause greening of the meat due to conversion of myoglobin to sulfmyoglobin (33, 34). *S. putrefaciens* will not grow at pH 5.0–5.5 and hence packed, normal pH meat has a much longer shelf life. Greening of cured meat is caused by lactic acid bacteria (86) where H_2O_2 converts myoglobin to a green iron (III) complex (87).

"Meat" covers muscle tissue from a range of different animals: beef, veal, lamb, poultry (fatty, lean). Whole meat is typically more stable than ground meat. In aerobic atmosphere, whole meat has a shelf life of approximately 1 week at 5°C whereas ground meat will spoil in 1–2 days depending on the initial bacterial count. The bacterial counts of ground meats are, in general, higher than on non-comminuted meats. Typically, gound meat contains trimmings and has a much greater surface-to-volume ratio allowing a more rapid spoilage (88). Packaging extends shelf life and the atmosphere of packaging will have a marked influence on the extension. Vacuum-packing can extend storage life of beef (held at 0°C) from 2–4 weeks to more than 15 (41). Packing in 100% CO_2 may extend shelf life at 4–5°C to 8–12 weeks (4). Many packaging atmospheres do contain oxygen as this allows retainment of the red oxygenated myoglobin colour.

The microflora on fresh meat is a mixture of many different species originating from hides, environment, and the gastro-intestinal tract. During aerobic storage, psychrotrophic pseudomonads become dominant (4). After 1–2 weeks, counts of 10^8–10^9 are reached and spoilage is detectable as slime and off-odours. Vacuum-packing or CO_2-packing (in O_2-impermeable films) eliminate pseudomonads and the microflora becomes dominated by lactic acid bacteria belonging to *Lactobacillus*,

Leuconostoc, and *Carnobacterium* (35, 89). Enterobacteriaceae and *Brochothrix thermosphacta* are often present in quite high proportions reaching 10^3–10^7 cfu/g (4, 9). Depending on the level of oxygen addition to the modified atmosphere packaging, shelf life (at 5°C) may be increased to 3–12 weeks.

Metabolism of glucose and amino acids supports bacterial growth. Off-odours in aerobically packed meat are not detected as long as glucose is metabolised; however, off-odours and spoilage of aerobically packed meat become evident when glucose is depleted and amino acids are metabolised (90). During glucose metabolism, the sweet, fruity off-odours of incipient spoilage are caused by ethyl esters produced by *Ps. fragi*. Degradation of amino acids is the cause of production of sulphur-containing compounds giving the putrid off-flavours in the advanced stages of spoilage.

Packed meats are typically characterised by sour off-odours being produced by the dominant lactic acid bacteria. The so-called cheesey off-odour often detected in vacuum-packed meat products is caused by acetoin and di-acetyl which are produced by *Br. thermosphacta* in packed (high pH) meats (4, 9).

Fresh fish is rich in water, protein and, for some species, lipids. Fish muscle also contains free amino acids, nucleotides and, in some species, trimethylamine oxide (TMAO) (11). TMAO, which is an odourless compound, is typically accumulated in marine fish species, especially the gadoid species, but may also be detected in fish from fresh waters (91). Some bacteria can use the oxygen in TMAO in anaerobic respiration and this reduction results in the formation of trimethylamine (TMA) which has the characteristic "fishy" flavour. As opposed to meat from mammalian animals, fish do not accumulate glycogen and pH therefore does not decrease *post mortem*. As in high-pH meat, this allows psychrotolerant *Shewanella* to grow during storage. Fish are cold-blooded animals and the microorganisms on newly caught fish from temperate waters are adapted to low temperatures. This combination of several factors explains why fish is a very perishable product and should be stored at low temperatures, preferably in melting ice (0°C). The shelf life of iced fish varies from 2 weeks (cod-like fish) to 4 weeks (fish from tropical waters). Some fatty fish species such as herring and mackerel have short shelf lives if left unpacked due to lipid oxidation and development of rancid off-flavours.

During storage of fish in ice, psychrotrophic pseudomonads, shewanellae, and *Neisseria* species become dominant (92–95). *Pseudomonas* spp. spoil freshwater fish when counts reach 10^8–10^9 cfu/g (96). Spoilage is typically characterised by sweet, sulphydryl, rotten off-odours. In contrast, the sensory impression of spoilage of marine fish is characterised as putrid, rotten, fishy due to formation of TMA and H_2S by psychrotrophic *Shewanella* species (97, 98). The off-odourous compounds are typically formed by bacterial metabolism of low-molecular-weight compounds (99). Spoilage proceeds very rapidly (12–48 hours) if fish is left at ambient temperature and mesophilic *Vibrio* and *Aeromonas* species are causing the spoilage. Packing of fish from marine waters causes selection of the CO_2-resistant, psychrotolerant *Photobacterium phosphoreum* which is the dominat spoilage organism of CO_2 packed fish (19, 100). Fish from fresh waters and fish from tropical waters probably do not harbour this organism and organisms such as lactic acid bacteria become dominant in these products.

C. CURED OR PROCESSED PROTEINACEOUS FOODS

A wide range of "cured" milk products are produced world-wide. This covers yogurts, soft unripened cheeses, and an enormous range of hard or ripened soft cheeses. Some of these products are acidified by fermenting microorganisms (mostly lactic acid bacteria); in others the curdling is caused by addition of protelytic enzymes (rennet) which degrade the casein-micelles and allow a curd to be formed. Pasteurization, acidification, and, often, chilling, are effective preservation hurdles; however, spoilage of the acidified products can be caused by yeasts and filamentous fungi. In particular flavoured yogurts, where sugar/fruit is added, are good substrates for yeast spoilage organisms (101, 102) and spoiling filamentous fungi (103).

The most important spoilage organisms of hard, semi-hard, and soft cheeses are the filamentous fungi; especially *Pencicillium* species (5, 104, 105). In some cheeses, the development of fungi is part of the processing; however, growth of other filamentous fungi is a sign of spoilage. Fresh, unripened cheeses such as cottage cheese, may also spoil because of bacterial growth and especially *Pseudomonas* spp. and psychrotrophic Enterobacteriaceae produce visible colonies on the surface and cause development of off-odours (106). Bacterial gas formation may be the cause of spoilage of cheeses. So-called "early blowing" can be caused by a range of bacteria producing CO_2 from lactose (107). "Late blowing" is specifically caused by growth and production of butyric acid by clostridia during storage and ripening of hard cheeses (47).

Meat is processed/cured to produce an enormous range of products including bacon, sausages, cooked and sliced product. Raw cured products (ham, fermented sausages) are preserved to an extent where bacteria do not grow well and hence spoilage is typically caused by yeasts or filamentous fungi. Bacterial spoilage by Enterobacteraiceae or clostridia may occur during processing before the salt concentration is high enough (108, 109). Cooked, perishable products include frankfurters and luncheon meat products. *Pseudomonas* are the main spoilage agent of such product-stored aerobically, whereas vacuum or modified atmosphere packaging selects for the same types of organisms as described under fresh meats. The spoilage organisms typically include lactic acid bacteria, *Br. thermosphacta* and

Enterobacteriaceae (9, 90, 110). Spoilage may be detectable as slime formation (111) as sour off-odours (26), or as the cheesey off-odours produced by *Br. thermosphacta*.

As meat products, fish are preserved using salting, acidifying, and heat treatments. Lightly preserved products, e.g., cold-smoked fish, typically spoil due to growth and metabolism of lactic acid bacteria and Gram-negative bacteria, either Enterobacteriaceae or *P. phosphoreum* (112–114). *Br. thermosphacta* also may be detected in levels between 10^3 and 10^7 cfu/g (115) and in pure culture it does produce rotten off-odours (116). Growth and spoilage by Gram-negative bacteria are inhibited in semi-preserved products which are salted, lightly acidified, and kept at chill temperatures. Spoilage is caused by growth of lactic acid bacteria or yeasts and may involve souring or gas formation (28). Packed and heated products which are distributed at chill temperatures may spoil due to growth of Gram-positive, spore-forming organisms (117). Heavily salted fish products may spoil due to growth of strictly halophilic bacteria which cause discolouration (red colour) due to their own pigmentation (118) and rotten off-odours due to protelytic degradation. In heavily salted fish which is re-hydrated, bacterial growth resumes and *Psychrobacter* spp. producing musty odours have been identified as spoilage organisms (119). Shelf life of dried fish species may be limitied by fungal growth (2).

D. FRUITS

Fruits contain high amounts of easily digestible sugars and the water content of fruits is high. However, bacteria do not grow well because the pH is low (in the range of 2–5) and most bacteria are inhibited under these conditions, so spoilage is caused by filamentous fungi (120). Spoilage manifests itself in many ways as spots, scabs, soft rot, or dry rot. Cucumber, capsicum, and tomatoes are fruits with a pH closer to neutral and spoilage is also often caused by growth of Gram-negative, pectin-degrading bacteria, (*Pseudomonas* spp. or *Erwinia* spp.) (21, 120).

E. DRESSINGS, KETCHUP, AND HIGH FAT PRODUCTS

Foods dealt with in this section are typically highly preserved using mayonnaise-based dressings and/or low levels of water activity and/or high levels of preservatives. Typical examples are coleslaw, ketchup, and various dressings. Most Gram-negative bacteria and many Gram-positive bacteria are effectively inhibited by the preserving parameters, and typical spoilage organisms are lactic acid bacteria and yeasts (121, 122). Their spoilage is detected as sour off-odours or swelling of the product (123). Off-odour or slime formation may also characterise the spoilage (124). Many of these types of product contain acetic acid and only organisms resistant to this acid are involved in spoilage. Several types of *Lactobacillus* have been isolated from spoiled products (124, 125).

Products such as margarine and butter which are low in water activity and high in fat/lipid content are typically stable products but may spoil due to growth of yeasts or filamentous fungi. Thus, *Penicillium* species have commonly been isolated from spoiled margarine (104). Filamentous fungi (e.g., *Chrysosporium* species) have been the cause of chocolate spoilage (126).

F. BEVERAGES

Fruit juices and most soft drinks are high in sugar and typically have a low pH. Hence, yeasts, fungi, and acid-tolerant bacteria can grow in the products and some will ultimately cause spoilage. *Saccharomyces* and *Zygosaccharomyces* strains are common spoilage organisms (127). Also, some lactic acid bacteria have been identified as spoilers of soft drinks (128) and the acid-tolerant, spore-forming *Alicyclobacillus acidoterrestris* has been detected as the cause of medicinal off-odour in pasteurised fruit juices (55).

Wines are typically preserved by the dominance of the fermenting organism and the subsequent production of alcohol. Lactic acid bacteria and yeasts are the major causes of spoilage (57, 63) although strictly anaerobic Gram-negative bacteria have also been the cause of off-odour (129, 130). Beer spoilage organisms may be wild yeasts present in the brewery (63) and can be transferred to the product where they grow and spoil the product (57). Alcohol and hop components are inhibitory to most bacteria. However, several beer-spoiling microorganisms have the ability to grow in hop which will inhibit most microorganisms (129, 131). Sluggish or stuck wine fermentations have sometimes been linked to growth of lactic acid bacteria which may inhibit growth of the desired fermenting organisms (132). Growth of spoilage microorganisms may cause a range of off-odours or may be visible as slime formation (30).

G. BAKERY GOODS

Filamentous fungi are the most prominent spoilage organisms of bakery products (2, 5, 133). The combination of their ability to grow at low water activities and the easy spreading of spores in the dry baking environment gives them a selective advantage. Another typical spoilage problem is the so-called ropiness caused by *Bacillus* species, especially *B. subtilis* (49, 134).

V. CHEMICAL ANALYSIS OF SPOILAGE

As defined at the beginning of this chapter, "spoilage" is any change in sensory properties that renders a product unacceptable for the consumer. Sensory methods can be developed to a very high degree of standardization using trained panels (135, 136). Using multivariate statistics, sensory analysis may be combined with chemical analysis to determine which compounds are causing specific odours and flavours. Specific electronic chemical gas sensors (so-called "electronic noses") may be used to profile the odours (137) and so-called "electronic tongues" to detect flavours (138).

Gas chromatographic separation followed by mass spectrometry is often used for profiling odours of spoiled foods. Examples include GC-MS studies of bacterial spoilage of prawns (12), cold-smoked salmon (116, 139), and chilled chicken (140). GC-MS analysis also has been used to determine mycological quality of barley grains (141).

Recently attempts have been made to combine nondestructive chemical methods with statistical analyses of complex patterns derived to correlate with spoilage and/or shelf life. An example of such studies include use of sophisticated techniques to determine well-known indicators of spoilage, such as the use of ion mobility spectrometry to determine biogenic amines (142). Sometimes such compounds are indeed only indicative (143) and may not necessarily be the ones responsible for the off-odours and off-flavours. The volatile compounds developing during spoilage of packed, chilled meat were analysed using a so-called electronic nose sensitive to several volatiles (144). Subsequently, multivariate analyses were used to correlate the magnitude of the "nose signals" with sensory impressions. Whilst this allowed an expression correlated to the quantitative degree of spoilage, no information on individual spoilage components was obtained. A somewhat similar approach was described by Ellis et al. (145) that used Fourier transformed infrared spectroscopy data to evaluate spoilage of meat. Different spectra were found in fresh and spoiling meat and peaks indicative of spoilage were identified.

VI. PRESERVATION STRATEGIES

Food preservation in ancient times relied on experience with treatments that ensured lack of spoilage. Examples are heavily dried or salted products and a range of fermented products. Development of more modern food preservation allowed the use of processes eliminating microorganisms, for example pasteurisation or autoclaving, or processes preventing growth completely, for example by freezing. The trend towards so-called milder preservation techniques typically combines a variety of parameters that allow growth to be controlled but not completely abolished. Examples include packaging, chill-storage, mild salting, etc.

Currently a range of new preservation procedures is under investigation. This includes physical treatments such as high hydrostatic pressure which is a promising non-thermal treatment allowing inactivation similar to heat treatments (146). The high hydrostatic pressure affects the bacterial membrane (147). Other inactivation processes include high-voltage electrical discharges and high-magnetic-field pulses (148).

The use of live bacterial cultures (149) or the antimicrobial peptides (bacteriocins) produced by lactic acid bacteria (150) has been intensively studied, in particular with the purpose of inhibiting pathogenic bacteria. Also, natural antimicrobial enzyme systems (151) or naturally occurring antimicrobials (152–154) are being tested as food preservatives.

Several biopreservation techniques have been assessed for their inhibition of spoilage microorganisms. For instance, Pepe et al. (52) demonstrated that lactic acid bacteria could inhibit rope-producing *Bacillus* in bread. The delay/control of ropiness was seen both when lactic acid bacteria were added to bread inoculated with *Bacillus* and, more importantly, when lactic acid bacteria were used as a starter during dough preparation. Also, a bacteriocin-producing lactic acid bacterium (*Leconostoc* spp.) allowed control of spoilage of vacuum-packed beef by a sulfide-producing lactic acid bacteria (155).

VII. MODELLING GROWTH OF SPOILAGE MICROORGANISMS AND PREDICTION OF SHELF LIFE

Modern "predictive microbiology" was in some ways born with mathematical descriptions of spoilage as a function of, for instance, temperature (156) but has increasingly focused on determining, modelling, and predicting the growth or survival of food-borne pathogenic organisms as a function of changing environmental factors.

Modelling of growth of spoilage bacteria as a function of environmental and preservative parameters allows (i) determination of the range of products in which the particular organism may be imporant (e.g., will have the ability to grow) and (ii) prediction of remaining shelf life of a particular product in which the number of spoilage organisms can be determined in the fresh product. Results as obtained in (i) may reduce the number of challenge trials required to determine shelf life of new products with altered preservation profiles.

For instance, the growth of the soft-drink spoilage organism *Gluconobacter oxydans* under different pH, acidity, sugar, and benzoate concentrations was determined and modelled (157) allowing the effect of change in each parameter on growth to be quantified. Membre and Kubaczka (158) not only modelled the growth of a vegetable juice spoilage bacterium but also described how the actual spoilage process (kinetics of pectin compound degradation) evolved. Parts of the "seafood spoilage predictor" may exemplify (ii) from above. This software includes models for growth of specific spoilage organisms

and allows relative rates of spoilage to be predicted based on temperature profiles (159).

VIII. CONCLUDING REMARKS AND PERSPECTIVES

Our understanding of microbial food spoilage is, for a range of products, very detailed. The organisms, their spoilage metabolites, and the conditions under which spoilage is important are known for several product types. This is particularly true for products where one specific organism is important, for instance the spoilage of packed marine fish (from temperate waters) by *P. phosphoreum*. In contrast, our understanding of more complex spoilage processes where several organisms are involved is less developed. Although we have identified the spoilage microbiota and may have some indication of which organisms contribute to the spoilage, we need to further our understanding of these products. In particular, products where "mild" combinations of preservation parameters are used allow the growth of several organisms. These products are often delicatessen products and understanding their spoilage would allow science-based quality indices to be developed and would allow prediction and labelling with appropriate shelf lives.

The evolution of such understanding will be facilitated and must run in parallel with development of methods for specific enumeration of spoilage microorganisms. Very sensitive methods are needed, especially for shelf life predictions based on numbers of specific spoilage organisms. Finally, the understanding of food spoilage and the spoilage process should enable design of more targeted food preservation methods where only the unwanted organisms or their unwanted metabolism is inhibited.

ACKNOWLEDGMENTS

Comments and suggestions from Jesper B. Bruhn on the complete chapter and from Dr. John Pitt on sections dealing with filamentous fungi have been most helpful.

REFERENCES

1. TC Baird-Parker. The production of microbiologically safe and stable foods. In: BM Lund, TC Baird-Parker, GW Gould, eds. The Microbiological Safety and Quality of Food. Aspen Publishers, New York, 2000, pp 3–18.
2. J Pitt, A Hocking. Fungi and Food Spoilage. 2nd ed. Blackie Academic and Professional, London, 1997.
3. L Gram, P Dalgaard. Fish spoilage bacteria – problems and solutions. Curr Op Biotechnol 13:262–266, 2002.
4. RH Dainty, BM Mackey. The relationship between the phenotypic properties of bacteria from chill-stored meat and spoilage processes. J Appl Bacteriol Symp Suppl 73:103S–144S, 2002.

5. O Filtenborg, JC Frisvad and U Thrane. Moulds in food spoilage. Int J Food Microbiol 33:85–102, 1996.

6. BM Lund. The effect of bacteria on post-harvest quality of vegetables and fruits, with particular reference to spoilage. Soc Appl Bacteriol Symp Ser 10:133–153, 1982.

7. RA Edwards, RH Dainty, CM Hibbard. Putrescine and cadaverine formation in vacuum packed beef. J Appl Bacteriol 58:13–19, 1985.

8. RH Dainty, RA Edwards, CM Hibbard, SV Ramantanis. Bacterial sources of putrescine and cadaverine in chill stored vacuum-packaged beef. J Appl Bacteriol 61:117–123, 1986.

9. E Borch, M-L Kant-Muermans, Y Blixt. Bacterial spoilage of meat and cured meat products. Int J Food Microbiol 33:103–120, 1996.

10. LV Jørgensen, HH Huss, P Dalgaard. The effect of biogenic amine production by single bacterial cultures and metabiosis on cold-smoked salmon. J Appl Microbiol 89:920–934, 2000.

11. L Gram, HH Huss. Fresh and processed fish and fish products. In: BM Lund, TC Baird-Parker, GW Gould, eds. The Microbiological Safety and Quality of Food. Aspen Publishers, New York, 2000, pp 472–506.

12. HN Chinivasagam, HA Bremner, AF Wood, SM Nottingham 1998. Volatile components associated with bacterial spoilage of tropical prawns. Int J Food Microbiol 42:45–55, 1998.

13. B Dogan, KJ Boor 2003. Genetic diversity and spoilage potential among Pseudomonas spp. isolated from fuid milk products and dairy processing plants. Appl Environ Microbiol 69:130–138, 2003.

14. J Bruce, EM Drysdale. Trans-shell transmission. In: RG Board, R Fuller, eds. Microbiology of the Avian Egg. Chapman and Hall, London, 1994, pp 63–91.

15. RG Board. Eggs and egg products. In: BM Lund, TC Baird-Parker, GW Gould, eds. The Microbiological Safety and Quality of Food. Aspen Publishers, New York, 2000, pp 590–619.

16. RA Edwards, RH Dainty. Volatile compounds associated with the spoilage of normal and high pH vacuum-packed pork. J Sci Food Agric 38:57–66, 1987.

17. SM Russel, Dl Fletcher, NA Cox. Spoilage bacteria of fresh broiler chicken carcasses. Poultr Sci 74:2041–2047, 1995.

18. H Derby, B Hammer B. Bacteriology of butter. IV. Bacteriological studies on surface taint butter. Iowa Exp Sta Res Bull 145:389–416, 1931.

19. P Dalgaard, L Gram, HH Huss. Spoilage and shelf life of cod fillets packed in vacuum or modified atmosphere. Int J Food Microbiol 19:283–294, 1993.

20. T Paarup, JA Sanchez, A Moral, H Christensen, M Bisgaard, L Gram. Sensory, chemical and bacteriological changes during storage of iced squid (Todaropsis eblanae). J Appl Microbiol 92:941–950, 2002.

21. C Nguyen-the, F Carlin. Fresh and processed vegetables. In: BM Lund, TC Baird-Parker, GW Gould, eds. The Microbiological Safety and Quality of Food. Aspen Publishers, New York, 2000, pp 620–663.

22. M Rasch, JB Andersen, KF Nielsen, LR Flodgaard, H Christensen, M Givskov, L Gram. Involvement of

bacterial quorum sensing signals in spoilage of bean sprouts. Appl Environ Microbiol 71: in press.

23. Å Eneroth, A Christiansson, J Brendehaug, G Molin. Critical contamination sites in the production line of pasteurised milk with reference to the psychrotrophic spoilage flora. Int Dairy J 8:829–834, 1998.

24. HM Craven, BJ Macauley. Microorganisms in pasteurized milk after refrigerated storage 1. Identification of types. Aust J Dairy Technol 47:38–45, 1992.

25. C Paludan-Müller, P Dalgaard, HH Huss, L. Gram. Evaluation of the role of Carnobacterium piscicola in spoilage of vacuum- and modified-atmosphere-packed cold-smoked salmon stored at 5°C. Int J Food Microbiol 39:155–166, 1998.

26. ES Pexara, J Metaxopoulos, EH Drosinos. Evaluation of shelf life of cured, cooked, sliced turkey fillets and cooked pork sausages – 'piroski' – stored under vacuum and modified atmosphere at +4 and +10°C. Meat Sci 62:33–43, 2002.

27. H Korkeala, KJ Bjorkroth. Microbiological spoilage and contamination of vaccum-packaged cooked sausages. J Food Prot 60:724–731, 1997.

28. U Lyhs, H Korkeala, P Candamme, J Björkroth. Lactobacillus alimentarius: a specific spoilage organism in marinated herring. Int J Food Microbiol 64:355–360, 2001.

29. JL Leisner, G Rusul, BW Wee, HC Boo, K Muhammed. Microbiology of chili-bo, a popular Malaysian food ingredient. J Food Prot 60:1235–1340, 1997.

30. E Walling, E Gindreau, A Lonvaud-Funel. La biosynthèse e'exopolysaccharide par des souches de Pediococcus damnosus isolées du vin: mise au point d'outils moléculaires de détection. Lait 81:289–300, 2001.

31. B-J Kim, B-H Min, J Kim, H-U Han. Isolation of dextran-producing Leuconostoc lactis from kimchi. J Microbiol 39:11–16, 2001.

32. V Stohr, JJ Joffraud, M Cardinal, F Leroi. Spoilage potential and sensory profile associated with bacteria isolated from cold-smoked salmon. Food Res Int 34:797–806, 2001.

33. BH Lee, RE Simard. Evaluation of methods for detecting the production of H₂S, volatile sulfides and greening by lactobacilli. J Food Sci 49:981–983, 1984.

34. DJ Nicol, MK Shaw, DA Ledward. Hydrogen sulfide production by bacteria and sulfmyoglobin formation in prepacked chilled beef. Appl Microbiol 937–939, 1970.

35. J Samelis, A Kakouri, J Rementzis. The spoilage microflora of cured, cooked turkey breasts prepared commercially with or without smoking. Int J Food Microbiol 56: 133–143, 2000.

36. SM Jiménez, MS Salis, MC Tiburzi, RC Rafaghelli, MA Tessi, VR Coutaz. Spoilage microflora in fresh chicken breasts stored at 4°C: influence of packaging methods. J Appl Microbiol 83:613–618, 1997.

37. RH Dainty, CM Hibbard. Aerobic metabolism of Brocothrix thermosphacta growing on meat surfaces and in laboratory media. J Appl Bacteriol 48:387–396, 1980.

38. DL Collins-Thompson, G Rodriquez Lopez. Influence of sodium nitrite, temperature, and lactic acid bacteria on

the growth of *Brochothrix thermosphacta* under anaerobic conditions. Can J Microbiol 26:1416–1421, 1980.

39. CO Gill, KG Newton. The development of aerobic spoilage flora on meat stored at chill temperatures. J Appl Bacteriol 43:189–195, 1977.

40. CD Gill, G Molin. Modified atmospheres and vacuum packaging. In NJ Russell, GW Gould, eds. Food Preservatives. Blackie, London, 1991, pp 172–199.

41. CO Gill. The control of spoilage. In AM Pearson, TR Dutson, eds. Advances in Meat Research. Volume 2. Meat and Poultry Microbiology. AWI Publishing Company, Westport, CT, 1986, pp 49–88.

42. RH Dainty, RA Edwards, CM Hibbard. Spoilage of vacuum-packed beef by a *Clostridium* sp. J Sci Food Agric 49:473–486, 1989.

43. DM Broda, KM De Lacy, RG Bell, TJ Braggins, RL Cook. Psychrotrophic *Clostridium* spp. associated with 'blown pack' spoilage of chilled vacuum-packed red meats and dog rolls in gas-impermeable plastic casings. Int J Food Microbiol 29:335–352, 1996.

44. DM Broda, DJ Saul, PA Lawson, RG Bell, DR Musgrave. *Clostridium gasigenes* sp. nov., a psychrophile causing spoilage of vacuum-packed meat. Int J System Evol Microbiol 50:107–118, 2000.

45. DM Broda, JA Boerema, RG Bell. PCR detection of psychrophilic *Clostridium* spp. causing 'blown pack' spoilage of vacuum-packed chilled meats. J Appl Microbiol 94:515–522, 2003.

46. DM Broda, PA Lawson, RG Bell, DR Musgrave. *Clostridium frigidicarnis* sp. nov., a psychrotolerant bacterium associated with 'blown pack' spoilage of vacuum-packed meats. Int J System Bacteriol 49:1539–1550, 1999.

47. N Klijn, FFJ Nieuwenhof, JD Hollwerf, CB Vanderwaals, AH Weerkamp. Identification of *Clostridium butyricum* as the causative agent of late blowing in cheese by species-specific PCR amplification. Appl Environ Microbiol 61:2919–2914, 1995.

48. S Knøchel, HH Huss. Ripening and spoilage of sugar salted herring with and without nitrate. 1. Microbiological and related chemical changes. J Food Technol 19:203–213, 1984.

49. JM Thompson, WM Waites, CER Dodd. Detection of rope spoilage in bread caused by *Bacillus* species. J Appl Microbiol 85:481–486, 1998.

50. HI Abo-Elnaga, FZ Hegazi, IG Abo-Elnaga. Spore-forming rods surviving boiling of the raw milk and implicated in the later spoilage of the product. Arch Lebensmittelhyg 53:86–89, 2002.

51. JM Thompson, WM Waites, CER Dodd. Spoilage of bread by *Bacillus*. Int Biodet Biodegr 32:55–66, 1993.

52. O Pepe, G Blaiotta, G Moschetti, T. Greco, F Villani. Rope-producing strains of *Bacillus* spp. from wheat bread and strategy for their control by lactic acid bacteria. Appl Environ Microbiol 69:2321–2329, 2003.

53. D Kalogridou-Vassiliadou. Biochemical activities of *Bacillus* species isolated from flat-sour evaporated milk. J Dairy Sci 75:2681–2686, 1992.

54. FE Feeherry, DT Munsey, DB Rowley. Thermal inactivation and injury of *Bacillus stearothermophilus* spores. Appl Environ Microbiol 53:365–370, 1987.

55. I Walls, R Chuyate. Spoilage of fruit juices by *Alicyclobacillus acidoterrestris*. Food Aust 52:286–288, 2000.

56. N Jensen, FB Whitfield. Role of *Acyclobacillus acidoterrestris* in the development of a disinfectant taint in shelf-stable fruit juice. Lett Appl Microbiol 36:9–14, 2003.

57. G Fleet. Spoilage yeasts. Crit Rev Biotechnol 12:1–44, 1992.

58. M Mollapour, PW Pipier. Targeted gene delection in *Zygosaccharomyces bailii*. Yeast 18:173–186, 2001.

59. J-M Membré, M Kubaczka, C Chéne. Combined effects of pH and sugar on growth rate of *Zygosaccharomyces rouxii*, a bakery product spoilage yeast. Appl Environ Microbiol 65:4921–4925, 1999.

60. P Jenkins, PG Poulos, MB Cole, MH Vandeven, JD Legan. The boundary for growth of *Zygosaccharomyces bailii* in acidified products described by models for time to growth and probability of growth. J Food Prot 63:222–230, 2000.

61. H Steels, SA James, IN Roberts, M. Stratford. Sorbic acid resistance: the inoculum effect. Yeast 16:1173–1183, 2000.

62. A van der Kuhle, L Jespersen. Detection and identification of wild yeasts in lager breweries. Int J Food Microbiol 43:205–213, 1998.

63. L Jespersen, M Jakobsen. Specific spoilage organisms in breweries and laboratory media for their detection. Int J Food Microbiol 33:139–155, 1996.

64. T Savard, C Beaulieu, NJ Gardner, CP Champagne. Characterization of spoilage yeasts isolated from fermented vegetables and inhibition by lactic, acetic and propionic acids. Food Microbiol 19:363–373, 2002.

65. SAS Ismail, T Deak, HA Abd El-Rahman, MAM Yassien, LR Beuchat. Presence and changes in populations of yeasts on raw and processed poultry products stored at refrigeration temperature. Int J Food Microbiol 62:113–121, 2000.

66. A Hinton Jr, JA Cason, KD Ingram. Enumeration and identification of yeasts associated with commercial poultry processing and spoilage of refrigerated broiler carcasses. J Food Prot 65:993–998, 2002.

67. H Girardin. Detection of filamentous fungi in foods. Sci des Ali 17:3–19, 1997.

68. FEMJ Sand. Gluconobacter, still drinks and plastic containers. Soft Drinks Trad J 29:371–373, 1975.

69. JE Moore, J Xu, N Heaney, BC Millar. Spoilage of fruit-flavoured bottled water by *Gluconobacter sacchari*. Food Microbiol 19:399–401, 2002.

70. C Nguyen-The, JP Prunier. Involvement of pseudomonads in deterioration of 'ready-to-eat' salads. Int J Food Sci Technol 24:47–58, 1989.

71. C-H Liao, J Sullivan, J Grady, L-JC Wong. Biochemical characterization of pectate lyases produced by flourescent pseudomonads associated with spoilage of fruits and vegetables. J Appl Microbiol 83:10–16, 1997.

72. S Jones, B Yu, NJ Bainton, M Birdsall, BW Bycroft, SR Chhabra, AJR Cox, P Golby, PJ Reeves, S Stephens, MK Winson, GPC Salmond, GSAB Stewart,

P Williams. The *lux* autoinducer regulates the production of exoenzyme virulence determinants in *Erwinia carotovora* and *Pseudomonas aeruginosa*. EMBO J 12:2477–2482, 1993.

73. C Aguilar, I Bertani, V Venturi 2003. Quorum-sensing system and stationary-phase sigma factor (rpoS) of the onion pathogen *Burkholderia cepacia* genomovar I type strain, ATCC 25416. Appl Environ Microbiol 69:1739–1747, 2003.

74. AH Tallgren, U Airaksinen, R von Weissenberg, H Ojamo, J Kuusisto, M Leisola. Exopolysaccharide-producing bacteria from sugar beet. Appl Environ Microbiol 65:862–864, 1999.

75. CH Doan, PM Davidson. Microbiology of potatoes and potato products: A review. J Food Prot 63:668–683, 2000.

76. HC Deeth, T Khusniati, N Datta, RB Wallace. Spoilage patterns of skim and whole milk. J Dairy Res 69:227–241, 2002.

77. A Ternstrøm, A-M Lindberg, G Molin. Classification of the spoilage flora of raw and pasteurized bovine milk with special reference to *Pseudomonas* and *Bacillus*. J Appl Bacteriol 75:2–34, 1993.

78. T Sørhaug, T Stepaniak. Psychrotrophs and their enzymes in milk and dairy products: Quality aspects. Review. Trends Food Sci Technol 8:35–41, 1997.

79. RD Ralyea, M. Wiedmann, KJ Boor. Bacterial tracking in a dairy production system using phenotypic and ribotyping methods. J Food Prot 61:1336–1340, 1998.

80. Å Eneroth, S Ahrné, G Molin. Contamination routes of Gram-negative spoilage bacteria in the production of pasteurised milk, evaluated by randomly amplified polymorphic DNA (RAPD). Int Dairy J 10:325–331, 2000.

81. RR Meer, J Baker, FW Bodyfelt, MW Griffiths. Psychrotrophic *Bacillus* spp. in fluid milk products – a review. J Food Prot 54: 969–979, 1991.

82. SJ Cromie, TW Dommett, D Schmidt. Changes in the microflora of milk with different pasteurization and storage conditions and aseptic packaging. Aust J Dairy Technol 44: 74–77, 1989.

83. JF Frank. Milk and dairy products. In: MP Doyle, LR Beuchat, T Montville, eds. Food Microbiology. Fundamentals and Frontiers. ASM Press, Washington, D.C., 1997, pp 101–116.

84. F Cormier, Y Raymond, CP Champagne, A Morin. Analysis of odor-active volatiles from *Pseudomonas fragi* grown in milk. J Agric Food Chem 39:159–161, 1991.

85. FB Whitfield, N Jensen, KJ Shaw. Role of *Yersinia intermedia* and *Pseudomonas putida* in the development of fruity off-flavours in pasteurized milk. J Dairy Res 67:561–569, 2000.

86. MD Peirson, TY Guan, RA Holley. Aerococci and carnobacteria cause discoloration on cooked cured bologna. Food Microbiol 20:149–158, 2003.

87. CP Baron, LH Skibsted, HJ Andersen. Prooxidative activity of myoglobin species in linoleic acid emulsions. J Agric Food Chem 45:1704–1710, 1997.

88. JM Jay. Modern Food Microbiology. Van Nostrand Reinhold Company, New York, 1986.

89. CK Yost, FM Nattress. The use of multiplex PCR reactions to characterize populations of lactic acid bacteria

associated with meat spoilage. Lett Appl Microbiol 31:129–133, 2000.

90. CO Gill. Substrate limitation of microbial growth at meat surfaces. J Appl Bacteriol 41:401–410, 1976.

91. U Anthoni, T Børresen, C Christophersen, L. Gram PH Nielsen. Is Trimethylamine oxide is a reliable indicator for the marine origin of fishes?–Comp Biochem Physiol 97B:569–571, 1990.

92. JM Shewan, G Hobbs, W Hodgkiss. The Pseudomonas and Achromobacter groups of bacteria in the spoilage of marine white fish. J Appl Bacteriol 23:463–468, 1960.

93. A Gelman, L Glatman, V Drabkin, S Harpaz. Effects of storage temperature and preservative treatment on shelf life of the pond-raised freshwater fish, silver perch (*Bidyanus bidyanus*). J Food Prot 64:1584–1591, 2001.

94. M Gennari, S. Tomaselli. Changes in aerobic microflora of skin and gills of Mediterranean sardines (*Sardinus pilchardus*) during storage in ice. Int J Food Microbiol 6:341–347, 1988.

95. P Tryfinopoulou, E Tsakalidou, G-JE Nychas. Characterization of *Pseudomonas* spp. associated with spoilage of gilt-head sea bream stored under various conditions. Appl Environ Microbol 68:65–72, 2002.

96. L Gram, C Wedell-Neergaard, HH Huss. The bacteriology of spoiling Lake Victorian Nile perch (*Lates niloticus*). Int J Food Microbiol 10:303–316, 1990.

97. R Adams, L Farber, P. Lerke. Bacteriology of spoilage of fish muscle. II. Incidence of spoilers during spoilage. Appl Microbiol 12:277–279, 1964.

98. T Chai, C Chen, A Rosen, RE Levin. Detection and incidence of specific species of spoilage bacteria on fish. II. Relative incidence of *Pseudomonas putrefaciens* and fluorescent pseudomonads on haddock fillets. Appl Microbiol 16:1738–1741, 1968.

99. P Lerke, L Farber, R Adams. Bacteriology of spoilage of fish muscle. Appl Microbiol 15:770–776, 1967.

100. J Emborg, BG Laursen, T Rathjen, P Dalgaard. Microbial spoilage and formation of biogenic amines in fresh and thawed modified atmosphere-packed salmon (*Salmo salar*) at 2°C. J Appl Microbiol 92:790–799, 2002.

101. C Caggia, C Restuccia, A Pulvirenti, P Giudici. Identification of *Pichia anomala* isolated from yoghurt by RFLP of the ITS region. Int J Food Microbiol 71:71–73, 2001.

102. BC Viljoen, A Lourens-Hattingh, B Ikalafeng, G Peter. Temperature abuse initiating yeast growth in yoghurt. Food Res Int 36:193–197, 2003.

103. F Cappa, PS Cocconcelli. Identification of fungi from dairy products by means of 18S rRNA analysis. Int J Food Microbiol 69:157–160, 2001.

104. AD Hocking. Fungal spoilage of high-fat foods. Food Aust 46:30–33, 1994.

105. CF Kure, Y Wasteson, J Brendehaug, I Skaard. Mould contamination on Jarslberg and Norvegia cheese blocks from four factories. Int J Food Microbiol 70:21–27, 2001.

106. TF Brocklehurst, BM Lund. The effect of pH on the initiation of growth of cottage cheese spoilage bacteria. Int J Food Microbiol 6:43–49, 1988.

107. ICMSF (International Commission for the Microbiological Specification for Foods). Microorganisms in Foods 6. 2nd edition. in press.

108. GA Gardner. Microbial spoilage of cured meats. in TA Robers and FA Skinner, eds. Food Microbiology: Advances and Prospects. The Society for Applied Bacteriology Symposium Series. Academic Press, New York, 1983, pp 179–202.

109. C Garcia, A Marin, ML Timon, JJ Cordoba. Microbial populations and volatile compounds in the 'bone taint' spoilage of dry cured ham. Lett Appl Microbiol 30:61–66, 2000.

110. EA Davies, CF Milne, HE Bevis, RW Potter, JM Harris, GC Williams, LV Thomas, J Delves-Broughton. Effective use of nisin to control lactic acid bacterial spoilage in vacuum-packed bologna-type sausage. J Food Prot 62:1004–1010, 1999.

111. J Björkroth, H Korkeala. Ropy slime-producing *Lactobacillus sake* strain possess a strong competitive ability against a commercial biopreservative. Int J Food Microbiol 38:117–123, 1997.

112. L Truelstrup Hansen, HH Huss. Comparison of the microflora isolated from spoiled cold-smoked salmon from three smokehouses. Food Res Int 31:703–711, 1998.

113. L Truelstrup Hansen, S Drewes Røntved, HH Huss. Microbiological quality and shelf life of cold-smoked salmon from three different processing plants. Food Microbiol 15:137–150, 1998.

114. U Lyhs, J Brörckroth, E Hyytiä, H Korkeala. The spoilage flora of vacuum-packaged, sodium nitrite or potassium nitrate treated, cold-smoked rainbow trout stored at 4°C or 8°C. Int J Food Microbiol 45:135–142, 1998.

115. F Leroi, JJ Joffraud, F Chevalier, M Cardinal. Research of quality indices for cold-smoked salmon using a stepwise multiple regression of microbiological counts and physico-chemical parameters. J Appl Microbiol 90:578–587, 2001.

116. JJ Joffraud, F Leroi, C Roy, JL Berdagué. Characterisation of volatile compounds produced by bacteria isolated from the spoilage flora of cold-smoked salmon. Int J Food Microbiol 66:175–184, 2001.

117. PK Ben Embarek. Microbial safety and spoilage of sous vide fish products. Ph.D. thesis, Technological Laboratory of the Danish Ministry of Agriculture and Fisheries & the Royal Veterinary and Agricultural University, Copenhagen, 1994.

118. MM Prasad, CCP Rao. Storage studies on dry salt cured fish with special reference to red discolouration. Fish Technol 31:162–166, 1995.

119. I Bjørkevoll, RL Olsen, OT Skerdal. Origin and spoilage potential of the microbiota dominating genus *Psychrobacter* in sterile rehydrated salt-cured and dried salt-cured cod (*Gadus morhua*). Int J Food Microbiol 84:175–187, 2003.

120. BM Lund, Al Snowdon. Fresh and processed fruits. In: BM Lund, TC Baird-Parker, GW Gould, eds. The Microbiological Safety and Quality of Food. Aspen Publishers, New York, 2000, pp 738–758.

121. PJ Delaquis, HS Graham, R Hocking. Shelf-life of coleslaw made from cabbage treated with gaseous acetic acid. J Food Proc Pres 21:129–140, 1997.

122. TF Brocklehurst, CA White, C Dennis. The microflora of coleslaw and factors affecting the growth of spoilage yeasts in coleslaw. J Appl Bacteriol 55:57–63, 1983.

123. KJ Bjorkroth, H Korkeala. *Lactobacillus fructivorans* spoilage of tomato ketchup. J Food Prot 60:505–509, 1997.

124. MJM Michels, W Koning. Mayonnaise, dressings, mustad, mayonnaise-based salads, and acid sauces. In: BM Lund, TC Baird-Parker, GW Gould, eds. The Microbiological Safety and Quality of Food. Aspen Publishers, New York, 2000, pp 807–835.

125. RB Smittle, RS Flowers. Acid tolerant microorganisms involved in the spoilage of salad dressings. J Food Prot 45:977–983, 1982.

126. JL Kinderlerer. *Chrysosporium* species, potential spoilage organisms of chocolate. J Appl Microbiol 83:771–778, 1997.

127. M Stratford, PD Hofman, MB Cole. Fruit juices, fruit drinks and soft drinks. In: BM Lund, TC Baird-Parker GW Gould, eds. The Microbiological Safety and Quality of Food. Aspen Publishers, New York, 2000, pp 836–869.

128. W Back, I Bohak, M Ehrmann, T Ludwig, B Pot, KH Shleifer. *Lactobacillus perolens* sp. nov., a soft drink spoilage bacterium. Syst Appl Microbiol 22:354–359, 1999.

129. SY Lee, MS Mabee, NO Jangaard, EK Horiuchi. *Pectinatus,* a new genus of bacteria capable of growth in hopped beer. J Inst Brew 86:28–30, 1980.

130. R Satokari, R Juvonen, K Mallison, A von Wright, A Haikara. Detection of beer spoilage bacteria *Megasphaera* and *Pectinatus* by polymerase chain reaction and colorimetric microplate hybridization. Int J Food Microbiol 45:119–127, 1998.

131. K Sakamoto, A Margolles, HW van Veen, WN Konings. Hop resistance in the beer spoilage bacterium *Lactobacillus brevis* is mediated by the ATP-binding casette multidrug trasporter HorA. J Bacteriol 183:5371–5375, 2001.

132. Y-C Huang, CG Edwards, JC Peterson, KM Haag. Relationship between sluggish fermentations of grape juice and the antagonism of yeast by lactic acid bacteria. Am J Enol Viticult 47:1–10, 1996.

133. G Keshri, P Voysey, N Magan. Early detection of spoilage moulds in bread using volatile production patterns and quantitative enzyme assays. J Appl Microbiol 92:165–172, 2002.

134. RGK Leuschner, MA O'Callaghan, EK Arendt. Bacilli spoilage in part-baked and rebaked brown soda bread. J Food Sci 63:915–918, 1998.

135. D Pal, S Schdeva, S Singh. Methods for determination of sensory quality of foods – a critical appraisal. J Food Sci Technol Mysore 32:357–367, 1995.

136. JR Piggott, EA Hunter. Evaluation of assessor performance in sensory analysis. Ital J Food Sci 11:289–303, 1999.

137. E Schaller, JO Bosset, F Escher. "Electronic noses" and their application to food. Food Sci Technol – Lebenswiss Technol 31:305–316, 1998.

138. G Roy, JT McDevitt. In vitro sensors: Technology and applications. Chemistry of Taste: Mechanisms, Behaviours, and Mimics. ACS Symp Ser 825:262–275, 2002.

139. LV Jørgensen, HH Huss, P Dalgaard. Significance of volatile compounds produced by spoilage bacteria in vaccum-packed cold-smoked salmon (*Salmo salar*) analyzed by GC-MS and multivariate regression. J Agric Food Chem 49:2376–2381, 2001.

140. SD Senter, JW Arnold, V Chew. APC values and volatile compounds formed in commerically processed, raw chicken parts during storage at 4 and 13 degrees C and under simulated temperature abuse. J Sci Food Agric 80:1559–1564, 2000.

141. J Olsson, T Borjesson, T Lundstedt, J. Schnurer. Volatiles for mycological quality grading of barley grains: determinations using gas chromatography-mass spectrometry and electronic nose. Int J Food Microbiol 59:167–178, 2000.

142. Z Karpas, B. Tilman, R. Gdalevsky, A. Lorber. Determination of volatile biogenic amines in muscle food products by ion mobility spectrometry. Anal Chim Acta 463:155–163, 2002.

143. G Vinci, ML Antonelli. Biogenic amines: quality index of freshness in red and white meat. Food Control 13:519–524, 2002.

144. Y Blixt, E. Borch. Using an electronic nose for determining the spoilage of vacuum-packed beef. Int J Food Microbiol 46:123–134, 1999.

145. DI Ellis, D. Broadhurst, DB Kell, JJ Rowland, R Goodacre. Rapid and quantitative detection of the microbial spoilage of meat by Fourier transformed infrared spectroscopy and machine learning. Appl Environ Microbiol 68:2822–2828, 2002.

146. MF San Martin, GV Barbosa-Canovas, BG Swanson. Food processing by high hydrostatic pressure. Crit Rev Food Sci Nutr 42:627–645, 2002.

147. NJ Russell. Bacterial membranes: the effects of chill storage and food processing: an overview. Int J Food Microbiol 79:27–34, 2002.

148. GW Gould. Symposium on 'nutritional effects of new processing technologies.' New processing technologies: an overview. Proc Nutr Soc 60:463–474, 2001.

149. FK Lucke. Utilization of microbes to process and preserve meat. Meat Sci 56:105–115, 2000.

150. J Cleveland, TJ Montville, IF Nes, ML Chikindas. Bacteriocins: safe, natural antimicrobials for food preservation. Int J Food Microbiol 71:1–20, 2001.

151. WH Holzapfel, R Geisner, U Schillinger. Biological preservation of foods with reference to protective cultures, bacteriocins and food-grade enzymes. Int J Food Microbiol 24:343–362, 1995.

152. S. Brul, P. Coote. Preservative agents in foods. Mode of action and microbial resistance mechanisms. Int J Food Microbiol 50:1–17, 1999.

153. S Roller, N Covill. The antimicrobial properties of chitosan in mayonnaise and mayonnaise-based shrimp salads. J Food Prot 63:202–209, 2000.

154. EA Davies, CF Milne, HE Bevis, RW Potter, JM Harris, GC Williams, LV Thomas, J Delves-Broughton. Effective use of nisin to control lactic acid bacterial spoilage in vacuum-packed bologna-type sausage. J Food Prot 62:1004–1010, 1999.

155. JL Leisner, GG Greer, ME Stiles. Control of beef-spoilage by a sulfide-producing *Lactobacillus sake* strain with bacteriocinogenic *Leuconostoc gelidum* UAL187 during anaerobic storage at 2 degrees C. Appl Environ Microbiol 62:2610–2614, 1996.

156. TA McMeekin, T Ross. Predictive microbiology: providing a knowledge-based framework for change management. Int J Food Microbiol 78:133–153, 2002.

157. AS Battey, DW Schaffner. Modelling bacterial spoilage in cold-filled ready to drink beverages by *Acinetobacter calcoaceticus* and *Gluconobacter oxydans*. J Appl Microbiol 91:237–247, 2001.

158. JM Membre, M Kubaczka. Degradation of pectic compounds during pasteurised vegetable juice spoilage by *Chryseomonas luteola*: a predictive microbiology approach. Int J Food Microbiol 42:159–166, 1998.

159. P Dalgaard, P Buch, S Silberg. Seafood spoilage predictor – development and distribution of a product specific application. Int J Food Microbiol 73:343–349, 2002.

160. L Gram, L Ravn, M Rasch, JB Bruhn, AB Christensen, M Givskov. Food spoilage – interactions between food spoilage bacteria. Int J Food Microbiol 78:79–97, 2002.

161. BG Shaw, JM Shewan. Psychrophilic spoilage bacteria of fish. J Appl Bacteriol 31:89–96, 1968.

162. RA Herbert, JM Shewan. Roles played by bacterial and autolytic enzymes in the production of volatile sulphides in spoiling North Sea cod (*Gadus morhus*). J Sci Food Agric 27:89–94, 1976.

163. RA Herbert, JM Shewan. Precursors of the volatile sulphides in spoiling North Sea cod (*Gadus morhua*). J Sci Food Agric 26:1195–1202, 1975.

164. W Segal, RL Starkey. Microbial decomposition of methionine and identity of the resulting sulfur products. J Bacteriol 98:908–913, 1969.

165. PS Nassos, AD King, Jr, AE Stafford. Relationship between lactic acid concentration and bacterial spoilage in ground beef. Appl Environ Microbiol 46:894–900, 1983.

166. IDF. International Dairy Federation. *Bacillus cereus* in milk and milk products. Bull Int Dairy Fed No 272, Brussels, Belgium, 1992.

167. A Miller III, RA Scanlan, JS Lee, LM Libbey. Identification of the volatile compounds produced in sterile fish muscle (*Sebastes melanops*) by *Pseudomonas fragi*. Appl Microbiol 25:952–955, 1973.

52 Microbiology of Land Muscle Foods

Konstantinos P. Koutsoumanis
Department of Food Science and Technology, Aristotle University of Thessaloniki

Ifigenia Geornaras and John N. Sofos
Department of Animal Sciences, Colorado State University

CONTENTS

I. INTRODUCTION

Meat and poultry products are highly perishable foods since they support growth of microorganisms associated with spoilage. In addition, by their very nature and origin they may be implicated in the spread of microbial food-borne diseases. During the past twenty years, the increasing consumer demand for a wider variety of convenient products of high quality and safety along with the producers' desire for economies of scale in production have led to dramatic changes in the processing, storage, distribution and packaging of meat and poultry products. As a consequence, the important areas of meat and poultry microbiology have also changed. Since the vast subject of meat and poultry microbiology has been discussed extensively in various books, book chapters and review papers (1–5), this chapter focuses on recent research interests and matters of current practice used within the meat and poultry production and distribution chain. The topics include sources, type and extent of microbial contamination including spoilage and pathogenic organisms, microbial changes during storage, methods for controlling microorganisms in meat and meat products, and management of processes for the microbiological safety of these foods.

II. MICROBIAL CONTAMINATION OF MEAT FROM LAND ANIMALS

A. GENERAL

In general, the muscle tissues of healthy animals and birds, before slaughter, can be considered sterile. Exceptions to this generalization are the lymph nodes and some organs that may carry limited microbial contamination. In contrast, surfaces of the animal exposed to the environment such as hide, pelt, feathers, fleece, the mouth and the gastrointestinal tract may be heavily contaminated (6–8). These parts of the animal are the major sources of meat and poultry carcass contamination. The extent of contamination transfer from the above sources to the carcass is greatly dependent on the conditions under which animals are reared, slaughtered and processed (4,6–8). Hygienic practices, sanitation procedures, product handling and processing procedures, and conditions of storage and distribution are the most important factors that determine the microbiological quality of the final meat and poultry products. Consequently, variations in facilities, raising methods and practices of slaughtering and processing operations may lead to significant differences in the type and extent of meat contamination (4). Sources of contamination during processing, and the factors affecting the type and extent of contamination are discussed in the following sections.

B. SOURCES OF MICROBIAL CONTAMINATION

1. Red Meat

a. Live animal

It is generally agreed that the majority of microorganisms on red meat carcasses originate from the live animals, which also serve as sources of environmental and water contamination. These sources introduce contamination in animal products or other foods through cross-contamination and

through contamination of equipment and utensils. Contamination from surfaces exposed to the environment is transferred to the underlying sterile carcass tissue during animal slaughter and dressing. The hide of the animal is the most significant contamination source (7,9). During the raising of cattle, pigs and sheep, large numbers of spoilage and pathogenic microorganisms, mainly originating from soil, pastures and feces, can be found on the hides of the animals. For example, the total microflora of cattle hides may reach 10^{12} cfu/100 cm^2 (10), while an incidence of greater than 10% of *Escherichia coli* O157:H7 has been reported for cattle hides in the U.S. (11). The part of the hide with the highest incidence rate of pathogens is the brisket, followed by the flank and the rump (12). In a similar study, however, the part of the hide with the highest incidence of shiga-toxigenic *E. coli* O157 was found to be the back, followed by the neck, flank, ventrum and hock, in decreasing order (13).

A number of factors associated with the type, prevalence and extent of animal hide contamination have been identified in recent years including climate, season of the year, geographic location, and raising, transportation and holding methods (14). Animals raised in feedlots may carry more bacteria of fecal origin while soil microorganisms are usually more common on animals raised in pastures (4,15). During transport from farm to slaughter, animals may be exposed to further fecal, and therefore, pathogen contamination in the transport vehicles. In addition, animal-to-animal transfer of contamination can occur during transport, either directly via body contact or indirectly via contact with contaminated surfaces. Transportation of cattle from the feedyard to a commercial packing facility was found to result in a 14-fold increase in *Salmonella* prevalence on hides, and a 2-fold increase in fecal *Salmonella* levels (16).

Although it may be assumed that the cleanliness of the animals prior to slaughter is a crucial factor that determines the microbiological quality and safety of carcasses after processing, studies have shown this not to be the case (17,18). For example, no association was found between tag (mud, bedding and feces) on the hides of beef cattle and bacterial counts of carcasses (17). Furthermore, preharvest management practices (wool length, use of bedding and wet versus dry pens) appeared to have no effect on the microbiological quality of lamb carcasses (18). However, evaluation of microbial contamination of the stock presented for slaughter may be beneficial for adjustment of the speed of processing lines or the separate processing of highly contaminated animals (19,20).

b. Slaughter and dressing

During the slaughtering process bacteria can enter the tissues through the bloodstream from contamination of the sticking knife. However, bacteria introduced into the bloodstream do not survive for long in the tissues due to the defense mechanisms of the animal that continue for at least 1 h after death (6). Thus, if high levels of contamination from slaughter instruments are avoided by reasonable hygienic precautions, carcass contamination from this source should not be a problem.

Most of the bacterial contamination of the carcass is acquired during the dressing process. Knife incisions for the removal of cattle and sheep hides introduces microorganisms from the hide onto the underlying tissue. Further bacterial transfer may occur from contact of the hide with exposed carcass tissue or from aerosols, dust, wool and hair from the hide or fleece (7). Unlike cattle and sheep, the skin of pigs is usually not removed during the dressing procedure, although certain facilities process skinned pork carcasses. After slaughter, pigs are scalded to loosen the attachment of the hair to the skin before dehairing (7). Although the scalding operation reduces the number of microorganisms on the skin, recontamination may occur during dehairing due to the high level of contamination of dehairing equipment (21). The numbers of such contaminants can be reduced by the singeing process used to burn hair remaining on the carcass. However, as the singeing of the surface is usually uneven, significant numbers of bacteria, including both spoilage and pathogenic types, can persist on some areas of the carcass or be introduced or spread during carcass polishing operations (8,22,23).

Other significant sources of contamination during the dressing process are the mouth and the viscera of the animals. The mouth harbors large numbers of bacteria including pathogens such as pathogenic *E. coli* and *Salmonella* (13,24). If other areas of the carcass are handled by workers after handling the throat and the tongue, then carcasses may be heavily contaminated with bacteria from the mouth. During evisceration, contamination can occur if the intestinal tract is pierced or if fecal material is released from the rectum during removal of abdominal contents. Careful handling of the head and viscera as well as the use of plastic bags to enclose the head and the end of the cut bung of animals reduces contamination from these sources.

In addition to the hide, head and viscera, bacteria may be introduced onto the carcass during the dressing process from the processing environment such as floors, walls, contact surfaces, knives and workers' hands. Thus, hygienic conditions and sanitation procedures are important factors affecting the microbiological quality of the dressed carcasses.

c. Chilling

Before fabrication, carcasses need to be chilled to adequately low deep muscle temperatures in order to avoid microbial proliferation during and following fabrication (15). Most carcass cooling processes are operated so as to reduce deep muscle temperatures to 7°C or lower within a 12–24 h period (25). However, due to their size, commercial chilling of beef carcass sides requires 18–36 h for temperatures of <7°C to be reached. Traditionally, carcasses

were chilled by exposure to a flow of cold air only, which, due to the evaporation of water, resulted in drying of the carcass surface (26). Experimental studies have shown that depending on the temperature, humidity and air velocity, this type of chilling may result in increases, decreases or no changes in total numbers of aerobic bacteria of carcasses (6). Drying of the carcass surface, however, results in loss of carcass weight, which in turn leads to economic losses (27). Hot carcass weight losses of at least 2% during the first 24 h of air chilling have been reported for beef (28,29), pork (30) and lamb (31). In order to circumvent this, most packing plants in North America use intermittent spraying of carcasses with chilled water, especially during the initial stages of chilling, which facilitates carcass temperature decreases without loss of surface moisture. Spray chilling results in carcass weights that are slightly less than those of carcasses entering the chilling process (8). The practice of spray chilling is uncommon outside North America, partly due to concerns that the prevention of drying of the carcass surface would allow growth of pathogenic bacteria (26). Experimental studies, however, have shown that as for traditional air chilling of carcasses, microbial levels on carcasses can increase, decrease or remain unchanged by adjusting air temperatures and speeds, as well as the frequency, intensity and duration of spraying (32–34). The incorporation of chlorine (35,36), acetic and lactic acids (37,38) in the spray chilling process have been evaluated as a means of sanitizing beef carcasses during the chilling process.

d. Fabrication

The chilling process is followed by cutting (fabrication) of the carcass into primal and sub-primal cuts, and trimmings. The meat receives extensive handling during these operations and high levels of cross-contamination may occur by contact of freshly cut meat surfaces with work surfaces, hands and equipment. Factors affecting the extent of contamination during fabrication include temperature of the boning room, the time duration that meat is held there, and the cleanliness of fabrication equipment. Equipment such as cutting tables, conveyor belts, saws and knives can carry high numbers of spoilage and pathogenic bacteria (21,39). In order to minimize cross-contamination and spreading of contamination during fabrication, adequate cleaning of the plant and equipment as well as sanitation practices to prevent microbial contamination and biofilm formation are required. Proper control of the above conditions may maintain bacterial densities on meat after the fabrication process to as close to initial levels of contamination as possible.

2. Poultry

a. Live bird

Although freshly laid eggs rarely contain microorganisms, eggs and ultimately the developing embryo can be contaminated through two possible routes; by vertical (transovarial) or horizontal transmission of microorganisms. Transovarial transmission occurs when bacteria infect the hen's ovaries or oviducts resulting in possible contamination of the egg during its formation (7,40,41). Of major concern is the vertical transmission of *Salmonella* Enteritidis (42). The more common route of microbial contamination of eggs, however, is via horizontal transmission. This occurs when the natural defenses of the egg, which include the cuticle layer, shell, and outer and inner membranes, are penetrated resulting in contamination of the internal contents of the egg (43,44). Microorganisms contaminating the egg after it has been laid originate from the intestines when the egg passes through the cloaca, nest materials, litter or incubator surfaces (42,45,46).

Newly hatched chicks from uninfected eggs are microbiologically sterile but are readily contaminated with microorganisms present in their environment, for example, from contaminated eggshells, fecal matter, fluff from infected newly hatched chicks, and walls and floors of the incubator (47,48). Healthy chickens carry millions of microorganisms in their intestines and on their skin (49). Sources of microorganisms on the rearing farms are contaminated feed and water, soil, litter, dust and air. Insects, rodents, wild birds, reptiles and other small animals may also act as reservoirs and vectors of microorganisms (41).

During transportation of birds from growing houses to slaughter facilities, contamination and cross-contamination with fecal material may occur. Stress conditions during transport may lead to more frequent excretion of fecal material and cecal contents (50,51), and thus an increase in the level of contamination. Since transport crates become heavily contaminated with fecal material, they need to be thoroughly cleaned and disinfected before being reused to prevent cross-contamination of other flocks (52).

b. Slaughter and processing

Incoming birds are the principal source of most microorganisms found on poultry carcasses. Similar to red meat animals, healthy birds carry extensive microbial contamination on their feathers, skin and intestinal tract (3,49,53). In general, transfer of this contamination to the carcasses occurs during all processing steps including stunning, bleeding, scalding, defeathering, evisceration, washing and chilling (50).

As birds are hung and bled, the flapping of wings may generate dust and aerosols which distribute contamination onto nearby birds or carcasses. After bleeding, poultry carcasses are scalded by submerging in a warm waterbath (scald tank) at temperatures between 50 and 60°C. The accumulation and survival of microorganisms in the scald tank is influenced by the temperature of water and the rate at which fresh water is added (54). The pH of the scalding water and the presence of organic matter are also important

for bacterial survival since they affect the rate of inactivation of microorganisms (55). It is obvious that from a hygienic point of view scalding is a hazardous operation. Attempts to avoid the use of immersion scalding have led to the development of alternative methods including spraying systems and division of the scald tank into several smaller ones (56). Although under experimental conditions these methods improve the hygiene of the scalding process, their commercial implementation is, however, limited because most of them have yet to be fully adapted to commercial requirements.

After scalding, the carcasses pass through a series of mechanical plucking machines which remove the feathers. The defeathering process may spread contamination between carcasses or from the defeathering equipment (56). The level of cross-contamination during defeathering is very high since one contaminated bird can cross-contaminate hundreds of others as they pass through the pluckers (50).

Evisceration of poultry carcasses is carried out in several stages including head removal, opening of the body cavity, removal of intestines and cleaning of the carcass. As with red meat animals this process is associated with contamination of the carcass with microorganisms originating from intestines, including pathogens. Contamination during evisceration may occur by bacterial transfer from carcass to carcass by knives, eviscerating implements and worker's hands. The automated transfer of carcasses to the different stages of the evisceration process significantly reduces product handling and potential cross-contamination. However, contamination may still occur due to improper cleaning of the machines involved in the process.

Poultry carcasses are washed and chilled immediately after evisceration. Washing of carcasses removes the organic matter and some of the contaminating microorganisms. Chilling aims to limit multiplication of spoilage bacteria and restrict the growth of pathogens. The two most common chilling methods for poultry carcasses are water (immersion) and air chilling. Carcasses destined for the frozen market are normally water chilled, while fresh, non-frozen carcasses can either be water or air chilled and marketed as 'wet' or 'dry,' respectively (56). Water chilling is almost exclusively used in the U.S. poultry industry, while European processors commonly use air chilling. Water chilling has a washing effect on the carcasses, but if not properly maintained and operated, has the potential for allowing cross-contamination of carcasses with spoilage bacteria, indicator organisms and pathogens. In-plant chlorination of the chiller water at levels >25 ppm reportedly controls or reduces cross-contamination of carcasses with Gram-negative spoilage bacteria and salmonellae (57). Chlorine levels do not normally exceed 50 ppm, and at this level, microbial loads on carcasses are only reduced by 1 log unit (58). Factors affecting the efficacy of chlorine include the initial bacterial load of the water, the water level, organic load, temperature, pH and trace minerals in the water (59). In some European countries, chlorine addition to the chiller water is prohibited because of the theoretical link to carcinogenesis (60). Other chemicals used or tested in the poultry processing industry to reduce microbial contamination of carcasses during washing and water chilling steps of processing include chlorine dioxide, trisodium phosphate, acidified sodium chlorite, organic acids (lactic and acetic acids), ozone, cetylpyridinium chloride and hydrogen peroxide (59). These are discussed in more detail in a subsequent section of the chapter.

Air chilling of poultry carcasses is basically a dry process, where cold air is circulated, either in a chill room or air-blast tunnel, to chill the carcasses. In order to enhance cooling, the chilling process may be combined with evaporative chilling, which involves the intermittent spraying of carcasses with water, so that the water absorbs heat as it evaporates (61). The latter process is said to minimize carcass weight loss, which contrasts with the weight gains resulting from water chilling (60). In a U.K. study where these three poultry chilling systems were compared, water chilling resulted in a reduction of microbial contamination of carcasses, while air chilling had little effect on microbial numbers recovered from the skin. Microbial levels of the body cavity, however, were reduced by approximately 1 log unit when the dry chilling process was used. Conversely, evaporative cooling through the use of water sprays that were not in-plant chlorinated led to a large (1–2 log units) increase of pseudomonads in the body cavity of the carcasses (61).

After chilling, carcasses are either packaged whole, or are cut into portions, placed in bags or on trays, weighed, and chilled, or more often frozen. The product is thus exposed to extensive cross-contamination through handling and contact with equipment surfaces such as knives, conveyor belts, and weighing and packaging equipment.

C. TYPE AND EXTENT OF CONTAMINATION

1. Red Meat

The type and extent of meat carcass and product contamination depends on sanitation, hygienic practices and handling during harvesting and processing, and conditions of storage and distribution. Red meat carcass contamination after processing is usually variable and may consist of 10^1–10^7 aerobic mesophiles per cm^2 (Table 52.1) depending on plant, carcass and site on the carcass sampled (62,63). In general, contamination of pork carcasses is higher than beef (Table 52.1). A nationwide baseline carcass contamination study carried out by the Food Safety and Inspection Service (FSIS) of the United States Department of Agriculture (USDA) found the mean level of aerobic plate counts of carcasses after chilling to be 3.69 log cfu/cm^2 for market hogs, 3.05 log cfu/cm^2 for cows and bulls and 2.68 log cfu/cm^2 for steers and heifers (64–66). In an additional study incorporating seven U.S. beef packing plants (four steer and heifer; three cow and bull), mean aerobic plate counts of carcasses after 24 h of chilling was 2.55 log cfu/cm^2 (67). Baseline carcass contamination data from Australia showed mean total viable counts of 2.4 log cfu/cm^2 for beef carcasses (68) and 3.6 log cfu/cm^2 for sheep carcasses (69).

The microflora of fresh red meat carcasses usually consists of Gram-negative rods and micrococci including *Pseudomonas* spp., Enterobacteriaceae, *Acinetobacter* spp., *Alcaligenes* spp., *Moraxella* spp., *Flavobacterium* spp., *Aeromonas* spp., *Staphylococcus* spp., *Micrococcus* spp., coryneforms and fecal streptococci (49,70). In addition, lactic acid producing bacteria, *Brochothrix thermosphacta*, *Bacillus* and *Clostridium* spores, and enteric viruses may be present in lower numbers (49,70). Yeasts and molds rarely contribute to the microflora of fresh meat, and, generally, may be detected only during extended storage and when the surface of the meat becomes dry, which limits

TABLE 52.1
Aerobic Plate Count Distribution on Raw Beef and Pork Carcasses

Range (cfu/cm²)	Steers and Heifers		Cows and Bulls		Hogs	
	Number of Samples	Percent of Total	Number of Samples	Percent of Total	Number of Samples	Percent of Total
<1	25	1.2	8	0.4	0	0
1–10¹	41	2.0	13	0.6	0	0
10¹–10²	415	19.9	261	12.4	18	0.9
10²–10³	990	47.4	856	40.5	501	23.7
10³–10⁴	474	22.7	651	30.8	954	45.2
10⁴–10⁵	103	4.9	244	11.6	461	21.8
10⁵–10⁶	32	1.5	68	3.2	130	6.2
10⁶–10⁷	9	0.4	9	0.4	43	2.0
>10⁷	0	0	2	0.1	5	0.2
Total	2,089	100	2,112	100	2,112	100

Source: Refs. 64–66.

bacterial growth and allows yeasts and molds to dominate. They include *Torulopsis, Trichosporon, Candida, Rhodotorula, Cryptococcus, Penicillium, Aspergillus, Geotrichum, Mucor, Rhizopus, Monillia, Alternaria, Thamnidium* and *Chaeotostylum* (6,70–72).

The prevalence and levels of pathogenic bacteria on red meat carcasses depends on a number of factors including the origin of the animal, sanitation procedures and hygienic practices employed during handling and processing of the product, application of decontamination interventions, and conditions of storage. Based on baseline data collected by FSIS, 14.6% of steers and heifers and 27.2% of cows and bulls are contaminated with one to three different pathogenic bacteria (Table 52.2) (64,65). The baseline data also showed that the prevalence of pathogens on pork carcasses was higher since 52.4% of market hogs were contaminated with one to five different pathogenic bacteria (Table 52.2) (66). The most important pathogens associated with red meat included salmonellae,

Staphylococcus aureus, verotoxigenic *E. coli, Clostridium perfringens, Campylobacter jejuni/coli, Listeria monocytogenes, Yersinia enterocolitica* and *Aeromonas hydrophila* (Figure 52.1). Depending on the factors mentioned above the concentration of pathogens on meat carcasses can vary from 1 to >30 most probable number (MPN)/cm² (Figures 52.2 and 52.3). Some of these pathogens are more commonly associated with meat from one animal species rather than another. For example, *Y. enterocolitica* (73) and *C. jejuni/coli* (66) are more commonly associated with pork carcasses. In the U.S., the reported prevalence of *C. jejuni/coli* on beef carcasses is ten times less than on pork carcasses (Figure 52.1). *E. coli* O157:H7, on the other hand, is more commonly associated with beef carcasses since cattle and other ruminants have been identified as major reservoirs of this pathogen (11,74,75). The prevalence of pathogens can also differ within the same species. For example, the prevalence of *Salmonella* for cow and bull carcasses is reportedly higher

TABLE 52.2
Number of Raw Meat Samples Containing One or More Species of Pathogenic Bacteria

	Steers and Heifers		Cows and Bulls		Hogs	
Number of Pathogens[a]	Number of Samples	Percent of Total	Number of Samples	Percent of Total	Number of Samples	Percent of Total
0	1,785	85.4	1,538	72.8	1,006	47.6
1	278	13.4	484	22.9	754	35.7
2	23	1.1	82	3.9	265	12.6
3	3	0.1	8	0.4	70	3.3
4	0	0	0	0	15	0.7
5	0	0	0	0	2	0.1

[a] *C. perfringens, S. aureus, L. monocytogenes, C. jejuni/coli, E. coli* O157:H7, *Salmonella* spp.

Source: Refs. 64–66.

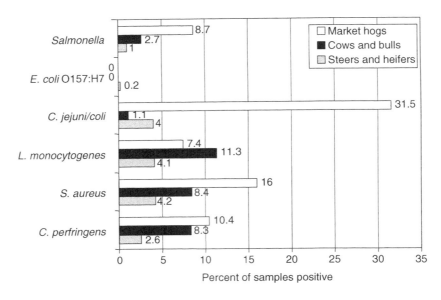

FIGURE 52.1 Prevalence of selected pathogenic microorganisms of raw beef and pork carcass surface samples. (From Refs. 64–66.)

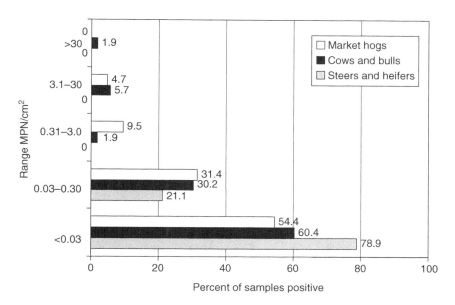

FIGURE 52.2 *Salmonella* distribution on enumerated positive raw beef and pork carcass surface samples. (From Refs. 64–66.)

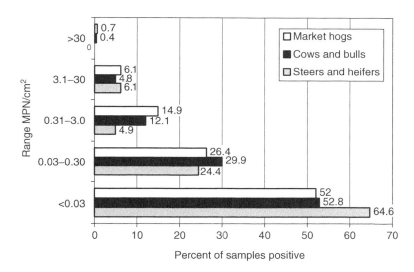

FIGURE 52.3 *Listeria monocytogenes* distribution on enumerated positive raw beef and pork carcass surface samples. (From Refs. 64–66.)

than for steer and heifer carcasses (67,76,77). The season of the year can also affect the prevalence of pathogens on carcasses. Studies carried out on cattle in North America have shown an increased prevalence of *E. coli* O157 during the summer and early fall (11,78).

The extent of contamination and the variety of contaminant types increase with product handling and comminution (70). Comminuted meats present a higher contamination than carcass meat due to an increase in the level of cross-contamination from grinders and utensils, spreading of contamination, and the greater surface area of the trimmings. The mean level of total aerobic mesophiles of ground beef reported in the U.S. during the years 1993–1994 was 3.90 log cfu/g (Table 52.3) (79) compared to 2.68 log cfu/cm² reported for beef carcasses.

2. Poultry

The microbial contamination associated with poultry carcasses at the end of processing is a combination of the natural population found on the carcass skin, the transient population that is associated with the skin and feathers at the time of slaughter and the population that is acquired as a result of processing (41). The microbiological condition (numbers and types of microorganisms) of poultry carcasses immediately after processing is thus dependent on factors such as the level of contamination on the live incoming birds, the efficiency of the processing methods, the level of cross-contamination during processing, temperature control, and sanitary and hygienic practices in the abattoir (80). Typically, the number of aerobic mesophilic bacteria associated with

TABLE 52.3

Estimated Prevalences and Mean Levels of Selected Bacteria in Raw Ground Beef

Microorganism	Prevalence %	SE	Mean Log in Positive Samples	SE
Direct enumeration (cfu/g)				
Aerobic plate count	100	NA[a]	3.90	0.12
Total coliforms	92.0	3.9	1.98	0.10
Escherichia coli (Biotype I)	78.6	5.9	1.73	0.13
C. perfringens	53.3	8.7	1.83	0.10
S. aureus	30.0	8.7	1.49	0.06
MPN enumeration (MPN/g)				
L. monocytogenes	11.7	4.1	0.46	0.43
C. jejuni/coli	0.002	0.003	NA	NA
E. coli O157:H7	0.0	NA	NA	NA
Salmonella	7.5	3.1	−1.29	0.89

[a] Not applicable.

Source: Ref. 79.

TABLE 52.4

Aerobic Plate Count Distribution in Chicken Broiler and Turkey Carcass Rinse Fluids

Range (cfu/ml)	U.S. Percent of Total Chicken Broilers	Turkey	Canada Percent of Total Chicken Broilers	Turkey
<1	0	0.2	0	0.2
1–10^1	0	2.5	0	3.3
10^1–10^2	0.5	29.9	2.7	40.7
10^2–10^3	32.3	53.6	53.4	40.5
10^3–10^4	58.9	13.3	39.7	11.3
10^4–10^5	7.8	0.5	3.7	4.0
10^5–10^6	0.5	0.1	0.5	0.0

Source: Refs. 81–83.

carcasses at the end of processing range from 10^3 to 10^5 cfu/cm^2 (49). Studies in the U.S. and Canada during the last decade showed that the total aerobic mesophiles of chicken and turkey carcasses ranged from 10^2 to 10^6 and from 10^0 to 10^6, respectively (Table 52.4). The reported mean total aerobic mesophile levels on chicken and turkey carcasses were 2.60 log cfu/cm^2 and 2.47 log cfu/cm^2, respectively, in the U.S. and 2.32 log cfu/cm^2 and 2.20 log cfu/cm^2, respectively, in Canada (81–83). Bacterial populations associated with carcasses at the end of processing are predominantly Gram-negative, and include *Acinetobacter/Moraxella* spp., Enterobacteriaceae, *Flavobacterium* spp. and *Pseudomonas* spp. (84–88).

Human pathogens that are associated with poultry carcasses are *Salmonella* serotypes, *C. jejuni*, *S. aureus*, *L. monocytogenes*, *C. perfringens*, non-O157:H7 Shiga-like toxin-producing *E. coli*, *Aeromonas* spp. and *Y. enterocolitica*

(Figure 52.4) (41,89–94). Poultry meat represents the single most important source of foodborne salmonellosis, with the most common serotypes implicated in outbreaks being *S.* Enteritidis and *S.* Typhimurium (70,95,96). Prevalence levels of *Salmonella* associated with poultry carcasses at the end of processing or at the retail market are reportedly as high as 100% (57,97). The level of *Salmonella* contamination on live birds entering the processing plant is reportedly low, but subsequent cross-contamination during processing procedures results in an increase in the *Salmonella* contamination of carcasses. In a FSIS study, a *Salmonella* incidence level of 3 to 5% was found on live birds entering a processing plant, which increased to 36% on carcasses at the end of processing (98). During the period 1998–2002, the prevalence of *Salmonella* in broiler carcass samples from federally inspected establishments in the U.S. was reduced from a baseline prevalence of 20.0%, to 10.9% (available at: http://www.fsis.usda.gov/OPHS/haccp/ salm5year.htm).

III. MICROBIAL EFFECTS IN MEAT AND MEAT PRODUCTS

A. SPOILAGE

Only 10% of the microorganisms present initially on a muscle food will grow at refrigeration temperatures, and only a fraction of those will eventually spoil the product by means of their biochemical attributes (99,100). A muscle food is characterized as spoiled when it exhibits an offensive appearance and/or has an off-odor or off-flavor. Off-odors are detected first when bacterial numbers exceed 10^7 cells/cm^2, while bacterial slime becomes evident when numbers reach 10^8 cells/cm^2 (101); bacterial colonies coalesce to form slime when the water activity of the product is approximately 0.99 (41). The spoilage microflora that develops during storage is determined by the initial number and types of microorganisms contaminating the product, the processing the product may undergo, the storage temperature and gaseous atmosphere, and composition of the product (102). The types of bacteria that are normally involved in the spoilage of meat and poultry products are *Pseudomonas* spp., psychrotrophic Enterobacteriaceae (*Serratia liquefaciens*, *Hafnia alvei*, *Enterobacter agglomerans*), *Brochothrix thermosphacta*, lactic acid bacteria (*Lactobacillus*, *Carnobacterium*, *Pediococcus*, *Streptococcus*, *Lactococcus* and *Leuconostoc* spp.), *Moraxella* spp., *Psychrobacter* spp., *Acinetobacter* spp., *Aeromonas* spp. and *Shewanella putrefaciens* (70,101). Yeast and mold spoilage of muscle foods can also occur but only under conditions where bacterial competition is reduced (103), such as exposure to ionizing radiation, reduced water activity, the presence of preservatives or antimicrobial treatments (104).

Microbiological spoilage occurs in the aqueous phase of meat (105). Spoilage microorganisms within this phase

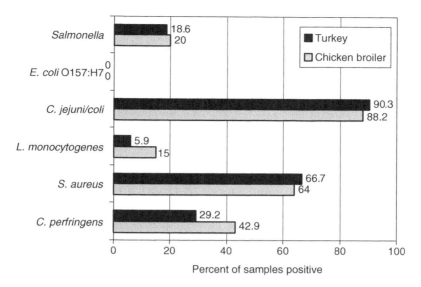

FIGURE 52.4 Prevalence of selected pathogenic microorganisms in chicken broiler and turkey carcass rinse fluids in the U.S. and Canada. (From Refs. 81–83.)

TABLE 52.5
Substrates Used for Growth by Major Meat Spoilage Microorganisms[a]

Microorganism	Substrates Used for Growth[a]	
	Aerobic	Anaerobic
Pseudomonas spp.	Glucose[1], glucose-6-P, D, L-lactic acid[2], pyruvate, gluconate, gluconate 6-P, amino acids[2], creatine, creatinine, citrate, aspartate, glutamate	Glucose[1], acetic acid[1], pyruvate, gluconate, amino acids (glutamate)
Acinetobacter/Moraxella	Amino acids[1], lactic acid[2], glucose[1], amino acids[1,2]	Glucose[1], amino acids[1,2]
Shewanella putrefaciens	Glucose, lactic acid, pyruvate, gluconate, propionate, ethanol, acetate, amino acids (serine)	Formate
Brochothrix thermosphacta	Glucose[1], amino acids[2] (glutamate, L-valine, L-leucine, *iso*-leucine), ribose, glycerol	Glucose[1]
Enterobacter spp.	Glucose[1], glucose-6-P[2], amino acids[3] (lysine, arginine, threonine), lactic acid[4]	Glucose[1], glucose-6-P[2], amino acids[3]
Lactobacillus spp.	Glucose[1]	Glucose[1], lactic acid[2], amino acids[2]

[a] The number in superscript indicates the order of utilization of this substrate.

Source: Ref. 412.

catabolize glucose, lactic acid, certain amino acids, nucleotides, urea and water-soluble proteins (106–108). Table 52.5 shows the substrates utilized by some of the predominant spoilage bacteria and the order in which they are attacked, under aerobic and anaerobic conditions. Spoilage of meat and meat products packaged in air or under modified atmosphere is discussed in the following sections.

1. Spoilage under Aerobic Conditions

Organoleptic changes brought about by aerobic spoilage microorganisms include green, brown or gray discolorations, off-odors and off-flavors, surface slime and taint. Off-odors and slime production may be detected after 10

or 5 days of storage at 0 or 5°C, respectively (109). Off-odors have been described as dairy/buttery/fatty/cheesy at levels of 10^8 bacteria/g, and as sweet/fruity and putrid at levels of $>10^9$ bacteria/g (110).

Meat and meat products stored under aerobic, chill conditions generally succumb to spoilage by strictly aerobic, Gram-negative bacteria, which exhibit faster growth rates under these conditions. *Pseudomonas* spp., and specifically *P. fragi*, *P. fluorescens* and *P. lundensis*, usually predominate (normally >50%) on meat stored at chill temperatures. The pseudomonads preferentially metabolize glucose, resulting in organoleptically innocuous end products. When, however, the diffusion gradient of glucose from the underlying tissue to the surface of the meat can no longer meet the demands of the large numbers of spoilage bacteria ($>10^8$ cfu/g), amino acids (cysteine, cystine and methionine) and proteins are degraded which result in the formation of ammonia, amines (cadaverine, putrescine, spermidine, spermine, histamine and tyramine) and sulfides (hydrogen sulfide, methylsulfide and dimethylsulfide) (111,112).

Facultative anaerobes belonging to the family of Enterobacteriaceae can also form part of the aerobic spoilage microflora. Like the pseudomonads, these bacteria preferentially metabolize glucose, and some utilize glucose-6-phosphate followed by amino acids. The slower growth rates of the Enterobacteriaceae under chill conditions, however, prevent them from predominating on aerobically stored muscle foods (111). The Gram-positive, facultative anaerobe, *B. thermosphacta*, also usually forms a minor component of the spoilage microflora on aerobically stored meat. Psychrotrophic Enterobacteriaceae and *B. thermosphacta*, however, seem to be more prevalent on lamb and pork, especially on the fat surfaces, and when the meat is stored at 5°C and not 1°C (101,113). Other bacterial groups implicated in the spoilage of meat under aerobic conditions are *Acinetobacter* spp., *Psychrobacter* spp. and *Moraxella* spp. These strict aerobes tend to form a higher proportion of the spoilage microflora on meat of higher ultimate pH (pH >5.8), or when the meat is stored at ambient temperature (114). Unlike pseudomonads, most of these strict aerobic bacteria do not metabolize hexoses, but attack amino acids directly (102).

Meat of high ultimate pH (pH >6.0) and low glucose concentration, like dark, firm, dry (DFD) meat, undergoes spoilage more rapidly than meat of normal pH (pH 5.5 to 5.8). Dark, firm, dry beef stored aerobically at 6°C produced off-odors after 2 days of storage while beef of normal pH produced off-odors after 4 days (115). *Pseudomonas* spp. degrade amino acids on DFD meat without delay and thus onset of spoilage is simply dependent on the time required to accumulate bacterial metabolites responsible for off-odors; this occurs at bacterial levels of $>10^6$ cells/cm^2 (116).

2. Spoilage under Vacuum

The predominant spoilage organisms of meat stored under vacuum and refrigeration conditions are lactic acid bacteria, which are able to metabolize glucose to produce lactic, isobutanoic, isopentanoic and acetic acids (100,117). *Carnobacterium* spp., *Lactobacillus* spp. and *Leuconostoc* spp. are reportedly the dominant lactic acid bacteria isolated from meat and meat products, where levels of 10^7/cm^2 may be reached (118,119). Spoilage is normally characterized by a sour/acid/cheesy odor (101). Growth of *B. thermosphacta*, *Pseudomonas* spp. and Enterobacteriaceae may also occur at levels of 10^3–10^6/cm^2, but is dependent on the oxygen permeability of the packaging film, storage temperature, pH and initial contamination levels (120,121). Higher numbers

of *B. thermosphacta* and Gram-negative bacteria are more commonly found on vacuum packaged pork and lamb than on vacuum packaged beef (113,122). The shelf life of vacuum packaged pork and lamb is also reportedly a few weeks shorter than that of beef. Blixt and Borch (123) compared the shelf life of vacuum packed, cold-stored minced pork and beef and found high correlations between intrinsic factors of the two types of meat, such as initial pH values, fat and L-lactate, respectively, and the rate of spoilage. Almost 70% of the variation in the rate of spoilage was explained by changes in the pH and concentrations of L-lactate and glucose-6-phosphate during storage, and not by whether the meat was pork or beef.

Spoilage of vacuum packaged DFD meat occurs within 3 to 6 weeks of storage at 0°C and is characterized by an offensive putrid odor (115,124). The spoilage flora is dominated by *S. putrefaciens*, Enterobacteriaceae and species of *Lactobacillus*. spp. *Shewanella putrefaciens* causes a characteristic green discoloration of vacuum packaged DFD meat which results from the production of hydrogen sulfide from cysteine or glutathione. The green pigment (sulfmyoglobin) is formed by the hydrogen sulfide reacting with the meat myoglobin (125,126).

Certain psychrophilic and psychrotrophic species of *Clostridium* have been characterized as spoilage organisms of vacuum packed meat (beef, lamb, venison and dog rolls) that was stored between -1.5 to 2°C and that exhibited extensive gas production and gross pack distension within 4 to 6 weeks of storage (127–129). Species linked to 'blown pack' spoilage include *C. laramie*, *C. gasigenes*, *C. frigidicarnis*, *C. estertheticum* and *C. estertheticum*-like strains (128–132). Using restriction fragment length polymorphism analysis of the 16S rDNA genes and 16S–23S rDNA internal transcribed spacer analysis, Broda et al. (132) showed that the source of these organisms on chilled vacuum packed venison was most likely soil particles attached to the hide or present in the feces of the animals.

3. Spoilage in Modified Gas Atmospheres

Lactic acid bacteria and/or *B. thermosphacta* are the predominant spoilage flora of beef, pork and lamb stored in modified atmospheres (133–138). Enterobacteriaceae and *Pseudomonas* spp. reportedly compete more effectively under modified atmosphere packaging conditions than in vacuum packed meat, especially pork that is stored at approximately 5°C and has undergone prior conditioning in air (101). A CO_2 concentration of 100% can be used to extend the storage life of meat of normal and high pH to more than 3 months when stored at 0 to 1°C (101). Pork stored at 0 and 4°C reached total bacterial populations of 10^6 to 10^7 per cm^2 and exhibited off-odors in 119 and 40 days, respectively, with *Lactobacillus* spp. dominating at both temperatures (139).

4. Spoilage of Processed Meats

Chilled comminuted products, including ground meats, burger-type products and raw sausages, in general, have a short aerobic shelf life of 3 to 5 days at 2 to 4°C, due to high initial loads of bacteria (140). The spoilage flora of ground beef stored in air or under modified atmosphere (20% CO_2/80% O_2) is composed of *Pseudomonas* spp., lactic acid bacteria, *B. thermosphacta*, Enterobacteriaceae and yeasts; however, under aerobic conditions *Pseudomonas* spp. are dominant, while under modified atmosphere lactic acid bacteria and *B. thermosphacta* dominate (141,142). The dominant spoilage flora of fresh sausages is dependent on the meat type, storage temperature, gaseous environment, and the presence of preservatives, but in general, it resembles that of ground meat (100).

In general, spoilage of cooked, uncured meat products (whole and restructured joints and poultry, and ready-to-eat meals) is a result of post-processing contamination (100). Gram-negative psychrotrophic bacteria are the main spoilage organisms of aerobically chill-stored sliced cooked meat, while lactic acid bacteria and *B. thermosphacta* predominate on vacuum packed and modified atmosphere packed products (41). Spoilage of meat pies is a result of molds, including *Mucor*, *Penicillium*, *Rhizopus* and *Aspergillus* spp., which usually contaminate the product during cooling (49).

Microbial spoilage of raw, cured meats, like Wiltshire-style bacon, is characterized by surface slime, discoloration, off-odors and off-flavors (143). Major spoilage populations associated with these products are Micrococcaceae, halophilic *Vibrio* spp., lactic acteria, coryneforms and yeasts, which are tolerant to salt and sodium nitrite (113,143). Factors influencing the composition of the spoilage flora are concentration of additives (salt, nitrite and nitrate), temperature, pH and water activity (100).

Cooking of cured meat products inactivates vegetative bacteria but recontamination occurs during post-cooking steps, like slicing, portioning or skinning. Spoilage of these products (cooked ham, corned beef, emulsion-type sausages, luncheon meats) stored at cold temperatures and packed under vacuum or modified atmosphere is predominantly by lactic acid bacteria (99,144–146). *Lactobacillus* spp. (*Lactobacillus sake* and *Lactobacillus curvatus*) and *Leuconostoc* spp. are the main spoilage organisms of cooked, cured meats (99,146–148). Spoilage is characterized by a sour odor and flavor, greening, gas production and slime formation (99,149). The growth rates and identity of the spoilage lactic flora are found to differ depending on the product composition (salt content, nitrite concentration, pH and water activity), processing method, storage temperature and gaseous atmosphere (99,150). The growth of lactic acid bacteria was more delayed in smoked meats (pork loin, bacon, pariza,

mortadella and frankfurters) than in non-smoked, boiled whole meats (cooked ham and turkey fillets) (146). Furthermore, characterization of the predominant spoilage lactic acid bacteria showed that the *Lactobacillus sake/curvatus* group predominated on the smoked meats, whereas *Leuconostoc mesenteroides* subsp. *mesenteroides* predominated on the cooked ham and turkey fillets (146).

Canning or commercial sterilization of uncured and cured meats results in a shelf stable product due to the complete elimination of microorganisms. Spoilage rarely occurs due to underprocessing, loss of package integrity and leakage of microorganisms into the package post-processing (4).

Molds are generally responsible for the spoilage of unsmoked, air-dried fermented sausages, some of which may have the ability to produce mycotoxins while growing on the sausage. Furthermore, molds have been reported to grow on the surface of frozen meat stored at temperatures as low as −8 to −10°C (113).

5. Spoilage of Poultry

Poultry spoilage follows the same principles as those involved in the spoilage of red meat products. The bacterial groups most frequently implicated as the main causes of spoilage of refrigerated poultry are *Pseudomonas* spp., and to a lesser extent, *Acinetobacter* spp., *Moraxella* spp. and *S. putrefaciens* (85,151). The *Pseudomonas* population reportedly may increase from <10% before storage to 93% of the total carcass bacterial population at the time of spoilage, following storage at 1 to 5°C (84,85,152). The type of spoilage bacteria as well as their growth rate is affected by the numbers and types of spoilage microorganisms present on carcasses at the end of processing, the type of packaging material and the composition of the atmosphere surrounding the packaged product, the storage temperature and the muscle type and pH (85). Poultry leg muscle has a pH of 6.4 to 6.7 while that of breast muscle is 5.7 to 5.9 (153). Spoilage populations of the breast muscle are thus essentially the same as those found on red meat of normal ultimate pH, while populations of the leg muscle mimic those found on DFD meat (126). Poultry leg meat thus spoils more rapidly than breast meat (41).

B. Foodborne Illness

Current estimations indicate that microbially contaminated food causes approximately 76 million illnesses, 325,000 hospitalizations and 5,000 deaths in the U.S., per year. Bacterial agents are responsible for 30% of these illnesses, while viruses and parasites cause 67% and 3% of the illnesses, respectively. The total percentage of deaths caused by each of these agents, however, is the highest for foodborne illnesses caused by bacteria (*ca.* 72%), followed by those of parasitic (*ca.* 21%) and viral (*ca.* 7%) origin (154).

The U.S. Centers for Disease Control and Prevention (CDC) Emerging Infections Program Foodborne Diseases Active Surveillance Network (FoodNet) collects data on 10 foodborne diseases in nine U.S. site areas, equivalent to 37.4 million people. According to preliminary data for 2002, 16,580 laboratory-diagnosed cases were identified, with *Salmonella* (16.1 cases/100,000 population), *Campylobacter* (13.4 cases/100,000 population) and *Shigella* (10.3 cases/100,000 population) having the highest incidence (155). An equivalent network in Australia (OzFoodNet), consisting of seven sites and encompassing 68% (12.9 million) of the Australian population, and monitoring eight foodborne diseases, reported a total of 22,999 cases of foodborne infections for the year 2001, with *Campylobacter* (125.0 cases/100,000), *Salmonella* (34.1 cases/100,000) and *Shigella* (2.6 cases/100,000) again having the highest incidence (156).

During the period of 1993–1997, a total of 2,751 outbreaks of foodborne disease were reported to the CDC, causing a reported 86,058 persons to become ill (157). Bacterial pathogens were responsible for the largest percentage of cases (86%); however, 68% of the reported outbreaks were of unknown etiology (157). Foodservice establishments (restaurants, cafeterias and delicatessens) were responsible for the highest percentage (43%) of the outbreaks, followed by private residences (21%). Contributing factors to the outbreaks during this period were improper holding temperatures (34.1%), poor personal hygiene (17.8%), contaminated equipment (14.5%), inadequate cooking (10.0%) and food from an unsafe source (5.6%) (157). Beef, chicken, turkey, other/unknown meat, pork, ham and sausage accounted for 6.8, 3.1, 2.3, 2.3, 1.4, 1.2 and 0.2%, respectively, of the total number of outbreaks where the vehicle of transmission was known (967 outbreaks). The respective percentage of cases where the vehicle of transmission was known (58,908 cases) for each of the above meat products was 5.4, 1.9, 1.3, 1.1, 1.1, 0.5 and 0.1%, respectively (157). These products thus accounted for 17.3% of the total outbreaks and 11.4% of the total cases of known etiology during the period of 1993–1997. Bacterial pathogens that were involved in the outbreaks through consumption of meat and meat products during this 5-year period were *Bacillus cereus*, *Campylobacter*, *C. botulinum*, *C. perfringens*, pathogenic *E. coli*, *Salmonella*, *Shigella*, *S. aureus* and *Y. enterocolitica* (Table 52.6) (157).

Other documented or suspected bacterial pathogens of potential concern in meat and meat products are *L. monocytogenes* and *Aeromonas hydrophila*, as well as *Arizona hinshawii*, *Bacillus anthracis*, *Brucella* spp., *Chlamydia psittaci*, *Coxiella burnetii*, *Erysipelothrix rhusopathiae*, *Francisella tularensis*, *Leptospira* spp., *Mycobacterium* spp., *Pseudomonas* spp. and *Streptococcus* spp. (158). As it is beyond the scope of this chapter to go into extensive

TABLE 52.6
Number of Reported Foodborne Disease Outbreaks for Meat and Meat Products by Etiology and Vehicle of Transmission – United States (Includes Guam, Puerto Rico, and the U.S. Virgin Islands), 1993–1997

Etiology	Beef	Pork	Chicken	Turkey	Ham	Sausage	Other/ Unknown Meat
Bacterial							
Bacillus cereus	-	1	1	-	-	-	1
Campylobacter	-	1	-	-	-	-	-
Clostridium botulinum	-	-	-	-	-	-	2
Clostridium perfringens	11	1	-	2	-	-	2
Pathogenic *Escherichia coli*	21	-	-	-	-	-	2
Salmonella	14	4	6	6	1	-	6
Shigella	-	-	1	-	-	-	-
Staphylococcus aureus	4	1	1	4	7	-	-
Yersinia enterocolitica	-	2	-	-	-	-	-
Other bacterial	2	-	-	-	-	-	1
Parasitic							
Trichinella spiralis	-	-	-	-	-	-	1
Viral							
Other viral	-	-	1	-	-	-	-
Confirmed etiology	52	10	10	12	8	-	15
Unknown etiology	14	4	20	10	4	2	7
Total 1993–1997	66	14	30	22	12	2	22

Source: Ref. 157.

detail about each of the etiologic agents involved in food-borne illness (159), a few of the important bacterial agents have been chosen and are discussed briefly. They have been separated into common and emerging bacterial pathogens.

1. Common Bacterial Pathogens

FoodNet data for the year 2002 showed that *Salmonella* was responsible for causing the highest total number of cases of gastrointestinal illness among the bacterial agents (155). The *Salmonella* genus comprises two species: *Salmonella enterica*, which is divided into seven sub-species groups (I, II, IIIa, IIIb, IV, VI and VII), and *Salmonella bongori* (160). There are approximately 2,600 serotypes of *Salmonella*, of which *S.* Typhimurium and *S.* Enteritidis are the most prevalent in the U.S. These serovars cause disease in humans, cattle, poultry, sheep, pigs, horses and wild rodents (161). The emergence of the multi-drug-resistant strain, *S.* Typhimurium DT104, has been the cause of widespread concern regarding the use of antimicrobial agents in agriculture (162). Raw meat, and especially poultry, is frequently contaminated with *Salmonella*, which originates from the intestinal tract or fecal material found on the hair, feathers, feet and skin of the animals. Processed meats and ground products reportedly have the highest prevalence of *Salmonella* (162).

Staphylococcal intoxication is one of the most common types of foodborne disease worldwide caused by the ingestion of food contaminated with one or more preformed heat-resistant enterotoxins produced by *S. aureus* (163). This organism is ubiquitous in nature and can be found in the nasal passages, throat and skin of humans and most warm-blooded animals, including food animals; in fact, 30–50% of humans are carriers of *S. aureus* (163,164). The primary source of contamination of foods implicated in foodborne illness are food handlers. Foods are normally contaminated post-processing and then stored at warm temperatures for adequate time to allow for significant growth and production of enterotoxin by the organism (163,164).

Clostridium perfringens forms part of the normal flora of the gastrointestinal tract of humans and animals. Ingestion of $>10^8$ vegetative cells of this organism followed by the production of enterotoxins during sporulation in the small intestine leads to a toxicoinfection (165,166). Cooked meat and poultry that have been cooled over a long period of time at ambient or warm temperatures are common vehicles of foodborne illness (166).

Clostridium botulinum produces neurotoxins which are considered to be the most toxic of all natural substances (164). Seven types (A through G) of *C. botulinum* are currently recognized, based on the antigenic specificity of the toxins. The organism is further divided into four distinct groups based on their DNA homology and reactions to specific substrates (167). Group I includes all of type A and the proteolytic strains of types B and F;

Group II includes the nonproteolytic strains of types B and F, and all of type E strains, all of which are able to grow at refrigeration (3.3°C) temperatures; Group III includes all the strains of type C and D; Group IV includes all the strains of type G, which based on their biochemical properties are proposed to form a new species, *C. argentinense* (167,168). The spores of the proteolytic strains (Group I) are more heat resistant than those of the nonproteolytic strains, a fact that led to the development of the 'botulinum process' or '12-D cook' for low acid canned foods (167).

Different types of *C. botulinum* appear to predominate in different parts of the world; for example, the main cause of *C. botulinum* outbreaks in the U.S., China and Argentina is type A, while in central Europe, type B is responsible for most outbreaks. Furthermore, type A is mainly associated with vegetables, while type B is often linked with meats (169). There are different clinical forms of botulism; foodborne, infant, wound and a fourth classification currently called 'adult infectious botulism.' In foodborne botulism, illness is caused due to ingestion of food that has been undercooked or improperly stored or reheated, resulting in toxin production due to growth of the organism (170). With regards to infant and adult infectious botulism, spores that are ingested or inhaled germinate, in the absence of competition in the intestine, resulting in toxin production (167).

2. Emerging Bacterial Pathogens

Outbreaks involving *C. jejuni* are relatively uncommon (157). However, this organism is believed to be one of the most commonly diagnosed causes of sporadic cases of gastroenteritis in the U.S. and other industrialized countries. *Campylobacter jejuni* and other *Campylobacter* spp. are estimated to cause an annual 14.2% of the total foodborne illnesses in the U.S. (154). The infectious dose of *C. jejuni* is low, ranging from 500 to 1000 cells (171). The main vehicle of foodborne illness by *Campylobacter* is poultry, either due to handling raw or eating undercooked poultry, and especially through cross-contamination of other foods. Other sources include raw milk, water, pork, beef, lamb and seafood (172). Of great recent concern is the emergence of fluoroquinolone-resistant strains of *C. jejuni* isolated from patients in Western Europe, shortly after the approval of fluoroquinolones for veterinary use (173).

Escherichia coli is the dominant Gram-negative facultative anaerobe in the gastrointestinal tract of humans and other warm-blooded animals and is generally considered harmless (174). Pathogenic strains of *E. coli*, however, also exist which can cause distinct syndromes of diarrheal disease (159). Currently, at least six categories of pathogenic *E. coli* are recognized; they include enteropathogenic *E. coli* (EPEC), enterotoxigenic *E. coli* (ETEC), enteroinvasive *E. coli* (EIEC), enterohemorrhagic *E. coli*

(EHEC), enteroaggregative *E. coli* (EAEC) and diffusely adherent *E. coli* (DAEC) (175–177). Unlike most foodborne pathogens, diarrheagenic *E. coli* are tolerant to acidic environments and have been shown to be resistant to acetic, citric and lactic acids applied at concentrations as high as 1.5% (159). More information about each of these diarrheagenic groups can be found in book chapters and reviews by Levine (175), Doyle and Padye (176), ICMSF (164), Donnenberg and Nataro (178), Fratamico et al. (177) and Bacon and Sofos (159).

Enterohemorrhagic *E. coli* causes the majority of the most severe outbreaks associated with pathogenic *E. coli* in the U.S. and other developed countries (177). This group includes *E. coli* serotypes that share the same clinical, pathogenic and epidemiologic features as *E. coli* O157:H7, which is responsible for the greatest proportion of *E. coli*-associated diarrheal disease cases in North America and the U.K. *E. coli* O157:H7 is estimated to cause approximately 73,000 cases of foodborne illness in the U.S. each year (154). Serotypes belonging to the EHEC group produce Shiga toxins, otherwise known as Shiga-like toxins, verotoxins or verocytotoxins, and are associated with hemorrhagic colitis and hemolytic uremic syndrome. Non-O157:H7 EHEC serotypes seem to be more important in some countries in the southern hemisphere like Argentina, Australia, Chile and South Africa (174). *E. coli* O157:H7 was first identified as a pathogen in 1982 when it was epidemiologically linked to the consumption of undercooked ground beef in the U.S. (179). Since then numerous outbreaks associated with this serotype have been documented in Canada, Japan, the U.K. and the U.S. (180). The largest reported outbreak occurred in Japan in 1996, with a total of 9,578 reported cases and 11 deaths, which were linked to the consumption of radish sprouts (181).

Cattle have been identified as a major reservoir of *E. coli* O157:H7. It has been isolated from the oral cavity (13), rumen contents (182), the hide (11,13) and feces (11,13,183,184) of cattle. A study conducted in the U.S. showed that *E. coli* O157:H7 is present in 28% of fecal samples taken from cattle in slaughterhouses during the summer months (11). It is therefore not surprising that undercooked ground beef is implicated in a large number of the cases linked to *E. coli* O157:H7 infection. The FSIS has declared *E. coli* O157:H7 as an adulterant in ground and other non-intact beef products. Results from a FSIS testing program to enforce this regulation showed that 0.78 to 0.86% out of 6,374 to 7,026 samples tested during the period of 2000 to 2002 were positive for this pathogen. Besides foods of bovine origin, outbreaks due to *E. coli* O157:H7 have been linked to raw milk, water, apple cider, mayonnaise, cantaloupe and lettuce (178).

Listeria monocytogenes is the causative agent of approximately 0.02% of all foodborne illnesses in the U.S., annually. Its associated illness, listeriosis, however, accounts for approximately 28% of deaths due to foodborne illness (154). There are two variants of the disease: invasive and non-invasive listeriosis. The invasive form mainly affects specific segments of the population, including the elderly, neonates, pregnant women and immunocompromised individuals (185,186). The non-invasive variant has been recently described and causes febrile gastroenteritis. Among the foods identified as causes of non-invasive listeriosis are cold corn salad, tuna fish and cold-smoked rainbow trout (187,188).

Listeria monocytogenes is widely distributed in nature, including soil, decaying vegetation, animal and human feces, sewage, silage and water. It is a psychrotroph and can grow at temperatures as low as $-0.4°C$ and up to $45°C$. Furthermore, it can grow at pH levels of 4.4 to 9.4, a_w levels of >0.92 and NaCl levels of 10% (189). Survival of the pathogen, however, has also been reported at levels of 25.5% NaCl in trypticase soy broth for 24 days at $22°C$ and >132 days at $4°C$ (190). Furthermore, *L. monocytogenes* can survive freezing and drying, as well as low or oxygen-free and elevated carbon dioxide atmospheres encountered in MAP (189).

Foods implicated in outbreaks of listeriosis include milk and dairy products, seafood products, vegetables, coleslaw and ready-to-eat meat products (186,191). According to a FSIS monitoring program for ready-to-eat products conducted at FSIS-inspected establishments during the period of 1990 to 1999, *L. monocytogenes* prevalence rates were 5.16% for sliced ham and luncheon meats, 3.56% for small diameter cooked sausages such as franks, 3.25% for fermented sausages (data were only collected from 1997 and onwards), 3.09% for cooked beef, roasted beef or cooked, corned beef, 3.03% for salads and spreads, 2.12% for cooked poultry products, 1.31% for large diameter cooked sausage, and 0.52% for jerky (192). In a more recent study, analysis of 31,705 samples belonging to eight different categories of ready-to-eat foods from retail markets in Maryland and California showed the prevalence of *L. monocytogenes* to be 1.82%, with prevalences ranging from 0.17 to 4.7% among the product categories (193). Furthermore, Wallace et al. (194) found 1.6% of 32,800 packages of frankfurters to be positive for the pathogen. Contamination of ready-to-eat products with *L. monocytogenes* occurs primarily during post-processing steps like slicing, dicing and packaging. Of particular concern is the establishment of virulent strains of the pathogen in the food processing environment which can potentially contaminate multiple lots of product over days or months of production (191). For example, the strain involved in the 2000 multistate outbreak of listeriosis in the U.S. (serotype 1/2a), where turkey deli meat products were implicated, reportedly had persisted in the processing environment for more than 10 years (186,195). Of the 13 serotypes of *L. monocytogenes* that can cause disease, three serotypes (4b, 1/2a and 1/2b) account for 89 to 96% of the sporadic and outbreak cases of human listeriosis that occur worldwide (196). The most publicized outbreaks in the past 20 years in North America and Europe have involved serotype 4b (186).

In view of the high mortality rate of *L. monocytogenes* (154), as well as outbreaks associated with the consumption of contaminated ready-to-eat meat and poultry products (195,197,198), the FSIS has published an interim final rule to control this pathogen in these products (199). Briefly, according to this regulation, establishments that produce ready-to-eat meat or poultry products that support growth of the pathogen and are exposed to the environment after lethality treatments are required to include in their HACCP plans, or in their sanitation operating procedures or other prerequisite programs, one or more validated measures that prevent product adulteration with *L. monocytogenes*. Three alternative methods to prevent or control *L. monocytogenes* during post-lethality exposure of products are proposed in the regulation: (i) application of both a post-lethality treatment and an antimicrobial agent or process; (ii) application of either a post-lethality treatment or an antimicrobial agent or process; and (iii) require no application of a post-lethality treatment or process, but instead require the combination of a sanitation program with microbiological testing of food contact surfaces to hold products when positive results are obtained (199).

Bacillus cereus causes two types of intoxications: one is diarrheal and the other emetic. In Japan, the occurrence of the emetic syndrome is reportedly ten times that of the diarrheal syndrome. Conversely, in North America and Europe, the diarrheal type is more common (200). Foods usually implicated in the diarrheal syndrome are meats, vegetables, sauces and puddings, while foods containing rice are associated with the emetic syndrome (201). The number of cells of the organism needed to cause illness is $>10^5$/g.

Yersinia enterocolitica is an infrequent cause of foodborne illness; however, it can cause severe foodborne infection and pseudoappendicitis (4,159). Pigs are regarded to be the main reservoir of *Y. enterocolitica* bioserotypes that are pathogenic to humans (164). The most common bioserotypes involved in foodborne illness are O:3, O:8, O:9 and O:5, 27. *Y. enterocolitica* is a psychrotroph and is able to proliferate at temperatures of 0 to 45°C (159). Storage of food at refrigeration temperatures, therefore, should not be considered an effective way to control this pathogen.

3. Viruses and Parasites

Foodborne transmission of viruses has in recent years been recognized as an important cause of foodborne illness. More than 9 million cases of viral foodborne illness of known etiology are estimated to occur annually in the U.S. (154). According to data collected in the U.S., however, outbreaks of viral foodborne illness due to the consumption of land muscle foods are rare (157). Viruses reported to cause foodborne illness include, among others, hepatitis A, Norwalk and Norwalk-like (now known as norovirus), rotavirus, astroviruses and enteroviruses (159,202). In general, transmission of these viruses occurs due to inadequately cooked foods, cross-contamination before consumption and poor sanitation (4,159).

Parasitic agents, on the other hand, are estimated to result in more than 350,000 cases of foodborne illness of known etiology in the U.S. annually (154). Parasites of concern in foods of meat origin include, among others, *Toxoplasma gondii*, *Sarcocystis* spp., *Trichinella* spp. and *Taenia* spp. (203). Treatments that inactivate parasites in foods include proper cooking, freezing, salt, chemicals and ionizing radiation (4,159).

IV. METHODS FOR CONTROL OF MICROORGANISMS IN MEAT AND MEAT PRODUCTS

A. GENERAL

Meat and poultry products are highly perishable foods, and, if not properly handled, processed and preserved, may support growth of spoilage and pathogenic microorganisms (4). The major technologies that are employed to preserve the quality and microbiological safety of these and other food products include (204):

a) Procedures that prevent or minimize the access of microorganisms to the product.
b) Procedures that reduce initial contamination by removal or inactivation of microorganisms which have gained access.
c) Procedures that inactivate microorganisms on products.
d) Procedures that prevent or slow down growth of viable microorganisms which have gained access and have not been inactivated.

Procedures that restrict the access of microorganisms include mainly sanitation and hygienic procedures or packaging technologies such as the aseptic packaging of thermally processed foods. Procedures that reduce initial levels of microorganisms, which have gained access to the food, include decontamination technologies such as washing, application of hot water, steam, acids or other chemicals, and their combinations. Procedures that inactivate microorganisms remaining on products include heat or thermal processing, ionizing radiation, high hydrostatic pressure and electric shock treatments. Despite their ability to remove or inactivate the microorganisms, some of the above technologies may also result in the inhibition of microbial growth during storage. Preservation technologies that slow down or prevent the growth of viable microorganisms rely on the control of factors affecting microbial growth. Microbial growth on meat and poultry products, or other foods, is affected by the type and extent of initial contamination and by factors intrinsic or extrinsic to the product (70). Among these, the most important ones, especially for fresh products, are extrinsic factors such as storage temperature and gas atmosphere, while intrinsic factors such as pH, water activity and antimicrobials become more important in processed products. Major preservation technologies based on the inhibition of microbial growth include temperature control, decreased water activity (curing, drying), acidification, vacuum and modified atmosphere packaging, fermentation-biopreservation, and addition of preservatives. In addition to the extreme modification of a single factor, inhibition of microbial growth is often achieved with a combination of preservation technologies at individually sublethal levels that interact to yield the multiple 'hurdle' effect (205–207). In the next paragraphs the most important traditional and emerging preservation technologies applied to meat and poultry carcasses or products are discussed. The discussion is focused on current technologies and new developments of decontamination and preservation methods including animal carcass decontamination (physical, chemical and combinations), emerging decontamination or preservation technologies (irradiation, high hydrostatic pressure, pulsed-field electricity, ultrasonic energy, UV light, oscillating magnetic fields, controlled instantaneous decompression), preservative packaging (modified atmosphere packaging, active packaging) and biopreservation. Traditional processing and preservation technologies are briefly discussed.

B. DECONTAMINATION TECHNOLOGIES

Highly publicized outbreaks of foodborne disease associated with meat and poultry have increased consumer concerns and interest in the safety of these products. In response, the industry is implementing decontamination interventions to improve the microbiological quality of fresh meat and poultry (4,20,208–210). Decontamination treatments can roughly be divided into three types (208): chemical, physical and combinations of the two. Physical treatments are based on the use of knives for removal, by cutting of visually soiled tissue, cold or hot water (wash, rinse, spray), vacuum and/or steam, high hydrostatic pressure, irradiation, pulsed-field electricity, ultrasonic energy and UV light (the latter technologies apply more to processed products than animal carcasses). Chemical decontamination includes treatments with chlorine, organic acids, inorganic phosphates, bacteriocins, organic preservatives and oxidizers. Decontamination treatments may be applied at different stages of production and processing including animal (before slaughter), carcass, primal cuts and final product.

1. Animal Cleaning

As has been mentioned, live animal contamination, in addition to environmental plant contamination, is considered as the most significant source of carcass and meat contamination. One approach to potentially reduce the external animal contamination and subsequently carcass contamination is to clean or wash the hide of the animal with water or chemical solutions before slaughter. There are, however, concerns related to preslaughter washing of animals since fecal material and the microorganisms associated with it may be more readily spread through wet animals. Bell (211) indicated that carcass contamination resulting from contact with a clean hide (i.e., a hide with no visible evidence of fecal contamination) was appreciably lower than that following contact with a fecally soiled hide that had undergone preslaughter washing. Furthermore, a higher contamination level was found on lamb carcasses derived from preslaughter washed animals than on unwashed animals (212,213). In another study carried out in Ireland, it was shown that preslaughter washing of pigs with cold water did not lead to significant changes in total viable counts of the live animals, but *Salmonella* incidence was reduced from 27% on live animals prior to transport to the abattoir to 10% after washing (214). Furthermore, a significant reduction of hide fecal contamination with *E. coli* O157:H7 was obtained on cattle that were washed with a power-hose for 3 min before the slaughter process; a lower recovery of the organism was also found on the resultant carcasses (215). In general, the effectiveness of animal cleaning and washing on the microbiological quality of the carcasses have been variable, while application of these procedures is often difficult due to climate, type of animal and the availability of facilities (20). Preslaughter animal washing has been applied for sheep in New Zealand (212), and for cattle in Australia and by some plants in the U.S., especially in recent years. A means of minimizing accidental transfer of contamination from the exterior of animals that have undergone preslaughter washing to the carcass surface and plant environment is to reduce slaughter speeds, and to modify the steps or the equipment involved in hide removal (15,216,217).

An additional hide decontamination process is chemical dehairing; a patented process (218) for cattle early during slaughter to remove hair, mud, manure and other external contaminants and thus, to minimize carcass and plant contamination from these sources (15,20,217). Application of this process to artificially contaminated beef hide samples resulted in significant reductions of inoculated meat pathogens such as *E. coli* O157:H7, *Salmonella* and *L. monocytogenes* (219,220), and in 1995, FSIS approved commercial trials for testing of the chemical dehairing process. Schnell et al. (221) studied a commercial application of chemical dehairing in a beef slaughterhouse. Although these authors reported that chemical dehairing resulted in a reduction of the visible contamination of cattle compared to the conventional process, the microbial loads were not significantly different between the two processes. It needs to be noted, however, that in the latter study both dehaired and nondehaired animals were processed in the same facility during the same day and thus the weak effectiveness of chemical dehairing could be attributed to the contamination of the plant environment by the nondehaired animals. In an additional study carried out in a commercial beef slaughtering facility, however, chemical dehairing was found to significantly reduce bacterial levels of carcasses immediately after hide removal (pre-evisceration) by approximately 2 logs (222). Furthermore, carcasses that had undergone chemical dehairing had a significantly lower prevalence of *E. coli* O157:H7 (1%) than carcasses that had not received the chemical treatment (50%) (222).

2. Carcass Decontamination

In general, carcass decontamination technologies in the U.S. are applied immediately after hide removal but before evisceration, as well as at the end of the dressing process, before carcass chilling. Decontamination technologies are based on treatments with water of various temperatures and pressures and other chemical solutions. The effectiveness of these treatments in reducing microbial contamination is affected by a number of factors including water pressure, temperature, chemicals used and their concentration, time duration of exposure (which depends on speed of slaughter and length of the application chamber), method of application and time or stage of application during slaughter and processing (20,217). Decontamination technologies that have been proposed, applied or tested for their effectiveness on the reduction of carcass microbial loads include treatments with water or steam (hot water, steam pasteurization, steam-vacuum), and chemical solutions, mostly organic acids (lactic, acetic and citric), as well as chlorine and chlorine dioxide, trisodium phosphate, acidified sodium chlorite, peroxyacetic acid, cetylpyridinium chloride, hydrogen peroxide, ozone, sodium bisulfate, sodium hydroxide, sodium chloride, and protein compounds such as lactoferrin (15,20,208,210). Today, in the U.S., decontamination systems are approved by FSIS if the agents used: i) are 'Generally Recognized as Safe' (GRAS), ii) do not create an 'adulterant' situation, iii) do not create labeling issues (i.e., added ingredients), and iv) can be supported with scientific studies as being effective (15). Among the agents that have been approved for use in foods by FSIS are acetic, lactic, peroxyacetic, citric, malic, propionic and tartaric acid, chlorine, trisodium phosphate, acidified sodium chlorite, hydrogen peroxide, ozonated water and lactoferrin (available at: http://www.fsis.usda.gov/OPPDE/rdad/ FR Pubs/88-026F.htm; http://www.fsis.usda.gov/OPPDE/

rdad/FSISDirectives/7120.1.htm). Some of these are extensively used in commercial plants in the U.S. In contrast, no chemical or physical treatments of meat and poultry carcasses are allowed by European Union regulations (208).

a. Spot carcass and pre-evisceration decontamination

Under the 'zero tolerance' policy of the U.S., knife-trimming is required to remove visible contamination on carcasses before any washing or other decontamination treatment is allowed. As an alternative, in 1996, FSIS approved the use of steam-vacuuming for removal of fecal and ingesta contamination spots of <2.5 cm in diameter on carcasses, through the use of a hand-held piece of equipment. This method uses hot water and/or steam to loosen soil and inactivate bacteria, followed by removal of the contaminants through application of a vacuum; this process, thus, has a combined effect of removing and/or inactivating surface contamination (15,20,223,224). Kochevar et al. (224) reported that application of steam-vacuuming to beef carcasses resulted in reductions of 1.7–2.0 log cfu/cm^2 in aerobic plate counts and 1.7–2.2 log cfu/cm^2 in total coliform counts. After the approval of the two commercially available steam-vacuuming systems, and as a result of their relatively low cost, steam-vacuuming units became very popular in U.S. slaughterhouses as an alternative method to knife-trimming to remove accidental visible carcass decontamination (20). However, the effectiveness of both knife-trimming and steam-vacuuming in reducing carcass contamination depends on employee diligence of application and the operational status of the equipment (20).

As soon as the hide is removed, whole carcasses are sprayed with water and possibly organic acid solution to remove microbial contamination that may have been acquired during the hide removal stage. In general, water and acid treatments applied soon after slaughter (before evisceration) appear to be effective since bacteria have not yet become firmly attached to the muscle (225–227). This is supported by a study by Cabedo et al. (227), where it was found that the number of bacteria removed or inactivated by the application of different spray-washing treatments decreased, as the length of time between contamination of beef carcass tissue and application of the treatments increased. Pre-evisceration washing of carcasses may also reportedly lead to an alteration of the surface physical characteristics (e.g., contact angle and surface free energy) of the carcass tissue, resulting in less attachment of microorganisms (228). Final washing and decontamination of carcass sides with water, organic acids and other treatments are discussed in the following sections.

b. Water
Water sprays of various pressures are used to remove bone dust and to clean and wash carcasses that have passed the

'zero tolerance' for visible soil inspection at the end of the dressing process in the U.S. Water is also used as a carrier of chemical or physical energy when carcasses are decontaminated with chemical solutions, hot water or steam. The use of hot water as a meat decontamination technology has been studied extensively during the last 30 years. Both laboratory scale and commercial plant evaluation studies have found hot water (74°C) to be an effective method of carcass decontamination (223,224,229–231). The application of hot water for meat decontamination may involve immersion or dipping, deluging, rinsing at low pressures and spraying at higher pressures. Each of these approaches has advantages and disadvantages (20). In all cases, however, the effectiveness of the method is strongly dependent on water temperature. Davey and Smith (232) found a linear relationship between water temperature and *E. coli* numbers on beef carcasses decontaminated with hot water by spraying. In general, effective temperatures exceed 74°C and become more effective as they approach 80–85°C (232,233). Gorman et al. (234) reported that spraying of beef carcasses with hot water at 74°C resulted in higher microbial reductions compared to chemical interventions, while at lower temperatures (16–35°C) chemical decontamination was more effective than water treatment.

Another form of hot water decontamination involves exposure of carcasses to pressurized steam (223,235,236). Davidson et al. (235) reported that exposure of whole and cut-up chicken meat to steam at 180–200°C for 20 sec resulted in 1–3 log reductions in aerobic plate counts and in 50% reduction in *Salmonella* contamination. Morgan et al. (236) applied an ultra-high temperature, ultra-short time steam pasteurization process on beef, pork and chicken samples and found a 4 log reduction in inoculated *Listeria innocua*. A patented steam pasteurization process for carcass decontamination developed by Frigoscandia and Cargill, Inc. (The Frigoscandia Steam Pasteurization System™) has been approved for use in the U.S. (237). Phebus et al. (238) and Nutsch et al. (239) evaluated the Steam Pasteurization System™ using *cutaneus truncii* muscles from steers and beef sides, respectively, and reported significant reductions in aerobic plate counts, *E. coli*, coliforms and Enterobacteriaceae, and inoculated *L. monocytogenes, E. coli* O157:H7 and *S.* Typhimurium. The advantages of using steam rather than water for decontamination purposes are the efficiency of heat transfer, lack of residues, and the reduced water and energy usage (20). However, steam pasteurization requires a major capital investment and may present difficulties in application in a continuous production process.

c. Organic acids

In recent years the use of organic acids such as acetic and lactic, for meat and poultry decontamination, has received considerable attention mainly due to their antimicrobial properties and their characterization as GRAS substances

(15,217,226,240–242). Decontamination with organic acid solutions of 1–2% may significantly reduce the bacterial load of meat and poultry carcasses (208,224,243). In addition to the immediate microbial reduction, acid decontamination results in a residual antimicrobial effect during storage, which has been attributed to the residual acids remaining on the meat after treatment as well as the sublethal injury of bacteria caused by the acid treatment (244–246). The effectiveness of acid decontamination can be augmented by increasing the temperature of the solution and the time of application. The stage of processing selected for the application is also important, as mentioned previously. The efficacy of the acid treatments may be further influenced by the type of surfaces to which the bacteria are attached. For example, acid treatment of lean meat surfaces results in higher microbial reductions than on fatty tissues (247).

Organic acid decontamination of carcasses has also been shown to reduce pathogen populations (246,248–250). Decontamination of beef surfaces with 2% lactic or acetic acid resulted in 2–3 log cfu/cm^2 reductions of *S.* Typhimurium DT104 and *E. coli* O157:H7 (250). *Salmonella* is generally more sensitive to organic acid decontamination than *E. coli* O157:H7 (251). This was also shown in a study by Samelis et al. (252), where *S.* Typhimurium DT 104 was found to die off after 2 days incubation, at 4 or 10°C, in lactic acid (pH 2.4) and acetic acid (pH 3.1) fresh beef decontamination runoff fluids (washings), while *E. coli* O157:H7 and *L. monocytogenes* survived in lactic acid washings for at least 2 days, and in acetic acid washings for at least 7 and 4 days, respectively, with better survival at 4 than at 10°C (252). Although decontamination with organic acids has been shown to reduce prevalence and concentration of *E. coli* O157:H7 on meat carcasses (251,253), the potential increase in the acid resistance of the pathogen remains an important concern (254–258), and is discussed in a subsequent section. The potential ability of *E. coli* O157:H7 to resist acidity (254,259) has been attributed, among other mechanisms, to binding of the pathogen to collagen of the meat tissue (260). Recent studies have shown that the latter problem may be reduced by spraying the carcass with a non-ionic surfactant such as Tween 20 prior to spraying with the organic acid (261).

In addition to the microbiological point of view, another important issue regarding the use of acid decontamination on meat and poultry is its effect on the quality of the products. Depending on the concentration and intensity of application, acid treatments may sometimes result in undesirable effects in color and/or flavor of the products. Such effects, however, should be only slight and reversible at acid concentrations below 2% (262,263). Discoloration problems can also be prevented by using buffered acids (264). In general, organic acid (lactic or acetic) spraying finds extensive use as a beef carcass treatment after hot water or steam decontamination.

d. Other chemical solutions

Several non-acid chemical solutions have been tested, and in some instances approved and used in the decontamination of meat and poultry (15,20,208,210,217). Chlorine is a common sanitizing agent used in process water during meat and poultry processing. Application of chlorine (20 ppm) reduced *Salmonella* contamination on chicken carcasses (265,266) while chlorine spray-washing (800 ppm) of beef carcass tissue resulted in a mean reduction of 1.3 log cfu/cm^2 of *E. coli* O157:H7 (267). Chlorine dioxide (ClO$_2$) has been proposed as an alternative to traditional chlorine sanitizing agents. However, the use of ClO$_2$ (1.33 mg/l) to control *Salmonella* in poultry chiller water did not result in any significant reduction (<0.5 logs) in bacterial counts on the poultry skin (268). Similar results have been reported by Cutter and Dorsa (1995) who found that spraying beef tissue with ClO$_2$ (20 ppm) for 10 sec at 520 kPa was no more effective in reducing fecal contamination than spraying with water alone. Mullerat et al. (270) applied Salmide®, a commercial complex mixture of chlorine-based components, and reported that it can reduce the levels of *Salmonella* on poultry skin. Although chlorine has been approved for meat and poultry decontamination in many countries, there are some safety concerns regarding its use related to corrosion of metals and formation of harmful chemical reaction products with organic residue materials (20).

Trisodium phosphate (TSP) has also been approved for treatment of beef and poultry carcasses in the U.S. A patented solution of TSP (AvGard™, Rhone-Poulenc, France) has been shown to reduce both spoilage and pathogenic bacteria including *Salmonella, L. monocytogenes, E. coli* O157:H7, *S. aureus* and pseudomonads on meat and poultry tissues (234,271–274). Cabedo (275) reported that TSP may inhibit bacterial attachment and thus allow easier bacterial removal by washing. Studies on the effect of TSP on the sensory characteristics of beef and chicken samples have indicated that a 10–12% solution of TSP does not cause any undesirable sensory effects that are detectable by consumers (276–278).

Acidified (citric acid activated) sodium chlorite (ASC) is another antimicrobial that has received approval from the U.S. federal government for use in beef carcass decontamination systems. Spraying of beef carcass surfaces with ASC, at a concentration of 1,200 mg/l, in combination with a water wash, resulted in a 4.5 log cfu/cm^2 reduction of inoculated (5.5 log cfu/cm^2) *E. coli* O157:H7, compared to a 2.3 log cfu cm^2 reduction obtained with a water wash only (279).

Hydrogen peroxide and ozonated water are also among the chemical agents proposed and tested for meat and poultry decontamination (20), and have recently received approval by FSIS for use on meat and poultry products. The antimicrobial effect of hydrogen peroxide is mainly based on the formation of radicals that damage nucleic acids, proteins and lipids. Treatment of beef and lamb carcass tissue with a hydrogen peroxide solution (5%) has been shown to reduce mean bacteria counts by 1–2 logs (224,227,234). Similar microbial reductions have been observed after spray-washing of beef carcasses with ozonated water (227,230,234). As in the case of chlorine, the use of hydrogen peroxide and ozone, despite their bactericidal effect, may be of concern due to their oxidizing effects on fat and muscle pigments.

Decontamination with cetylpyridinium chloride (CPC) has been shown to be effective in reducing levels of pathogens on meat and poultry carcass tissues. Kim and Slavik (280) reported that CPC spraying or immersion of poultry skin reduced the numbers of *Salmonella* by 0.9–1.7 logs and 1.0–1.6 logs, respectively. Cutter et al. (281) showed that spray washing of beef fat with 1% CPC resulted in significant reductions of *E. coli* O157:H7 and *S.* Typhimurium. In an additional study, 0.5% CPC was shown to reduce *E. coli* O157:H7 levels by 4.8 and 2.1 log cfu/cm^2 on beef carcass surfaces and lean tissue, respectively (282). In a study on the effect of CPC on the sensory characteristics of beef trimmings, the authors indicated that treatments with 0.5% CPC did not affect instrumental color or other sensory characteristics of the samples (278).

Peroxyacetic acid has been recently recognized as an effective chemical agent for meat decontamination. A commercial peroxyacetic acid-based solution (Inspexx 200™, Ecolab Company, St. Paul, MN) for pre-chilling application of carcasses has been approved in the U.S. Ransom et al. (282) reported that 0.02% peroxyacetic acid was effective in reducing the bacterial load of beef samples; however, under the conditions of that study, which did not reflect those recommended by the manufacturer, it was found less effective compared to lactic acid (2%; heated to 55°C).

Naidu and Bidlack (283) reported that lactoferrin, an iron binding protein, presents strong antimicrobial activity and can be used as an alternative to other chemical antimicrobial agents. Activation of bovine lactoferrin, which can be extracted in commercial quantities from skim milk or whey, yields a potent bactericidal peptide that has been shown to inhibit and/or inactivate a wide range of meat pathogenic and spoilage bacteria including *L. monocytogenes, Salmonella, Campylobacter* spp., *Pseudomonas* spp. and *Klebsiella* spp. (284). The patented process of producing activated lactoferrin involves immobilization of milk lactoferrin, via its N-terminus region, on a food-grade glycosaminoglycan (e.g., galactose-rich polysaccharide or carrageenan), solubilized in a precalibrated citrate/bicarbonate buffer system containing sodium chloride and an excess of unbound lactoferrin (284). The resultant activated lactoferrin reportedly acts as a microbial blocking agent that is able to (i) interfere with the adhesion or colonization of microorganisms to biological surfaces (ii) detach viable or non-viable cells from biological surfaces, (iii) inhibit microbial growth, and (iv) neutralize the activity of endotoxins (284). The U.S. Food and Drug Administration (FDA) recently accepted activated lactoferrin as GRAS while FSIS approved the compound for use on fresh beef (284).

A variety of other chemical compounds such as polyphosphates, benzoates and propionates, sodium hydroxide, sodium bisulfate, etc. have been tested with various rates of success for the decontamination of meat and poultry (15,20,208,210,217). Application of these or other chemicals as meat and poultry decontaminants in the future will depend on their efficacy, safety, effects on quality and cost (20).

e. Carcass decontamination with multiple processes

The use of more than one treatment may lead to synergistic or additive decontamination effects (20) and could be considered as a multiple hurdle approach (206). In fresh meat decontamination, the multiple hurdle decontamination approach may involve the simultaneous application of treatments (e.g., warm acid solutions) or the sequential application of treatments (e.g., hide cleaning, steam-vacuuming, pre-evisceration washing, hot water or steam treatment, organic acid rinsing). Several studies on the comparison between the effectiveness of single and multiple decontamination treatments have reported that the latter result in significantly higher microbial reductions (Table 52.7) (10,285,286). Bacon et al. (10) studied multiple-sequential decontamination interventions including carcass washing, steam-vacuuming, hot water and organic acid rinsing before and after evisceration in commercial beef slaughter facilities. The authors reported that E. coli counts were reduced from an initial range of 2.6–5.3 log cfu/cm^2 to a final range of 0.9–1.3 log cfu/cm^2 after carcass chilling. Graves Delmore et al. (287) used various technologies and interventions to decontaminate beef adipose tissue samples and reported that a higher reduction in E. coli counts was achieved by a series of four processes including pre-evisceration washing, warm-water washing and two steps of acetic acid rinsing. In addition to the number and intensity, the sequence of treatments can be very important in a multiple decontamination process (Table 52.7). For example, Castillo et al. (286) reported

that a lactic acid rinse, following hot water washing, was more effective than their use in the opposite order. Overall, when the appropriate number and sequence of hurdles are selected, the multiple hurdle decontamination approach can be a very effective tool for improving the safety of meat and poultry carcasses, and may minimize the potential for resistance development and cross protection (258).

f. Concerns of decontamination technologies

Despite the generally accepted effectiveness of decontamination technologies in reducing numbers and prevalence of pathogenic and/or spoilage bacteria on meat and poultry carcasses, there are a number of concerns associated with their use. Application of spraying/rinsing treatments to carcasses may lead to spreading and redistribution of bacteria over the carcass or penetration into the tissue (20). These problems, however, can be avoided by appropriate selection and adjustment of the factors affecting the efficacy of the decontamination treatment. For example, the issue of bacterial redistribution may be addressed by using decontamination interventions that may inactivate (hot water, steam, chemical solutions) rather than remove contamination. As mentioned previously, the period of time before decontamination has an important effect on bacterial attachment and biofilm formation; thus, decontamination treatments applied before evisceration will be more effective since bacterial attachment is still weak.

Another important concern associated with the use of decontamination technologies is the potential development of stress-resistant pathogens (20,242,252,258,288). Heat or acid resistance are important physiological characteristics that may contribute significantly to the behavior of pathogenic microorganisms during meat processing, cooking or in host systems (gastric secretions, phagocytosomal vacuoles) where acidity is the final barrier that the pathogen must overcome before pathogenesis. The potential concern for development of stress-resistant pathogens can be attributed to the 'stress hardening' phenomenon which refers to the increased tolerance of a pathogen to a specific lethal stress after adaptation to the same or a different sublethal stress environment (258,289). Several studies have demonstrated that adaptation of pathogenic bacteria such as L. monocytogenes, E. coli O157:H7 and Salmonella to a mild

---

TABLE 52.7

Mean Log Reduction (log cfu/cm^2) of *Salmonella* Typhimurium, *E. coli* O157:H7, Aerobic Plate Count (APC), Total Coliforms and Enterobacteriaceae on Beef Carcass Surfaces as Affected by the Type of Decontamination Treatment

Treatment	*Salmonella* Typhimurium	*Escherichia coli* O157:H7	APC	Total coliforms	Enterobacteriaceae
Water wash	2.3	2.4	1.6	1.8	1.7
Water wash + hot water	4.2	4.0	3.2	4.0	3.8
Water wash + lactic acid	>4.9	4.6	4.6	4.5	4.3
Water wash + hot water + lactic acid	>4.5	4.9	3.6	>4.6	>4.7
Water wash + lactic acid + hot water	4.4	4.4	4.1	>5.0	>4.9

Source: Ref. 286.

stress environment results in increased survival under stress conditions that would be lethal for non-adapted cells (288–293). In addition to increased stress resistance, adaptation may lead to mutations with enhanced virulence (294) since microorganisms may sense the unfavorable conditions as a signal for the expression of virulence factors (295). It needs to be noted, however, that the majority of the studies on the 'stress hardening' phenomenon have been performed in laboratory media and thus more research is needed on the investigation of stress adaptation in actual foods. Nevertheless, an evaluation of the contribution of decontamination interventions to food safety improvement should take into account the potential development of stress-resistant pathogens. It should be stressed, however, that irrespective of potential stress adaptation inducement on survivors, decontamination treatments are highly effective in reducing microbial contamination of carcasses and thus, allowing meat operations to meet regulatory performance standards and industry specifications (15,20,217,258). Proposed strategies to control stress resistance of bacteria involve the continued application of lethal levels of preservatives, or optimization of decontamination interventions, in type, intensity and sequence, to maximize microbial destruction and minimize resistance development (258,296).

C. MEAT PROCESSING AND PRESERVATION

Processing and preservation technologies involving physical, chemical and biological factors are used by food processors to ensure the safety and stability of foods by inactivating or inhibiting growth of spoilage and pathogenic microorganisms. Physical preservation methods include refrigeration, freezing, heating, drying, smoking, packaging and irradiation. Addition of antimicrobial agents or preservatives to meat products, including sorbates, benzoates and lactates, or curing agents such as sodium nitrite or salt, as well as treatment of products with acidifying agents like acetic and lactic acid, all constitute methods of chemical preservation. An example of biological preservation, or biopreservation, is fermentation where lactic acid bacteria may be used to inhibit the growth of spoilage and pathogenic microorganisms by the production of inhibitory metabolites by the lactic acid bacteria (297). Details of these processing and preservation methods are excellently reviewed by Claus et al. (298), van Laack (299) and Pearson and Gillett (300). Combination of these preservation technologies, applied individually at sublethal levels (hurdle technology), can result in a product that is more microbiologically stable and safe, as well as of higher nutritive and sensory quality (207).

Before discussing some of these technologies, however, another important aspect that can greatly affect the quality and safety of the final product is the cleaning and sanitation operations of a food-processing establishment.

1. Cleaning and Sanitation

During food processing procedures, equipment surfaces and the surrounding environment inevitably become soiled and require cleaning. Failure to effectively remove the soil from these surfaces may result in the soil becoming a niche for microorganisms. These organisms then have the potential to attach to the surface and form biofilms, which upon detachment may cross-contaminate foods. An effective sanitation program includes cleaning and disinfection; however, to ensure good sanitation and to maximize the effectiveness of the cleaning operation, the design and layout of the processing area and food plant are of primary concern (301). The importance of factory design and food processing equipment are described by Forsythe and Hayes (302). According to the same authors, there are three steps involved in cleaning and two steps in disinfection (sanitation). Cleaning involves removal of gross soil or dirt, removal of residual soil with detergent, and rinsing of the cleaned surface to remove detergent and soil; while sanitation, which often follows cleaning, involves the use of an antimicrobial agent to inactivate microorganisms, followed by rinsing off of these agents. Removal of soil normally involves the use of hot or cold water and cleaning aids such as brush bristles. The type of detergent used is important and ideally should be able to disperse insoluble materials, emulsify and saponify fats, rinse well, remove or inactivate calcium and magnesium salts dissolved in hard waters, and should not be corrosive to equipment surfaces (301,302). Detergents may be classified into inorganic alkalis (e.g., sodium hydroxide, sodium carbonate), inorganic and organic acids (e.g., phosphoric and citric acids, respectively), surface-active agents (e g., synthetic detergents which are either anionic, cationic, non-ionic or amphoteric), and sequestering agents (e.g., sodium polyphosphates and EDTA). Modern detergent formulations contain a mixture of different chemicals, each of which contributes to the desired properties of the detergent (302).

Application of the sanitizer follows rinsing of the detergent from the surfaces. The sanitizer should ideally be able to rapidly inactivate Gram-negative and Gram-positive bacteria, be stable in the presence of organic residues, be able to work in a wide pH range, water hardness, and temperatures, and should be readily soluble in water and readily rinsable. Sanitizers used in the food industry can be classified into chlorine releasing compounds, quaternary ammonium compounds, iodophors and amphoteric compounds (301,302).

2. Processing for Microbial Destruction

Application of heat, or thermal processing, is one of a few preservation methods that result in the inactivation of microorganisms, with time and temperature of cooking determining the number of organisms destroyed. Furthermore, thermal inactivation of microorganisms is dependent on the level, type and heat resistance of the organisms, as well as the environment (moisture and fat content, pH, salt, nitrite) (298,299). Most spoilage and pathogenic bacteria are sensitive to heat and are destroyed due to inactivation of bacterial enzymes, protein denaturation and increased membrane permeability (299). Most heat labile organisms, like micrococci, pseudomonads and Enterobacteriaceae are inactivated after several minutes at 65°C; destruction of certain spores, however, may require heating to at least 115.6°C for extended periods of time (298). Thermal processing may be classified as 'pasteurization' or 'sterilization,' based on the level of destruction of bacteria and spores. Pasteurization results in the destruction of vegetative cells of pathogenic bacteria; however, heat-resistant spoilage organisms and spores may survive during this process. Commercially sterile products are processed to be free of detectable microbial contaminants, but may contain spores of thermophilic bacteria that do not germinate below 43°C (299). The internal temperature reached in commercially sterile meat products is generally at least 107.2°C, but depending on the salt and nitrite content of the product, the temperature can be as low as 101.7°C (300). These products remain stable and safe even after long-term storage at ambient temperatures in temperate climates.

Other processing technologies that result in inactivation of microorganisms include irradiation and high hydrostatic pressure, and are discussed in a subsequent section.

3. Processing for Microbial Inhibition

As mentioned previously, preservation technologies that inhibit the growth of microorganisms in foods rely on the control of one or more factors affecting microbial growth (e.g., temperature, water activity, pH, antimicrobials). The most important means of preserving fresh unfrozen meat and other perishable meat products is refrigeration at temperatures between −2 and 5°C (299). Although growth of most mesophilic bacteria at these temperatures is prevented, growth of psychrotrophic and psychrophilic bacteria, including pathogens like *L. monocytogenes*, *A. hydrophila* and *Y. enterocolitica*, is only delayed (due to increased lag times and reduced growth rates) (303). Freezing of meat products, however, results in inhibition of microbial growth with some reduction of microbial levels during freezing, and potential increases during thawing (41,299). Preservation of food by drying is brought about by a reduction in the water activity of the product to a level that prevents growth of microorganisms. Drying methods include hot air drying, refrigerated air-drying, freeze-drying and brine-process drying (299,303). Water activity is also reduced with addition of humectants (e.g., salt, sugar) and by freezing. Smoking is also regarded as a preservation method. Many cured meats are smoked, and this process is either carried out directly from smoldering hardwood or hardwood sawdust, or in liquid form that is produced from natural smoke precipitated in water or oil (304). Smoke is composed of many different compounds including alcohol, carbonyls, hydrocarbons and gases; however, the antimicrobial properties of smoke are due to phenols and acids present in the smoke, as well as the heat that is associated with wood smoking (300). Foodborne pathogens, including pathogenic *E. coli* and *S. aureus*, are reportedly inactivated by commercially available liquid smoke products used in processed meats (297).

The use of salt as a preservative serves to inhibit microbial growth by reducing the water activity and increasing the osmotic pressure of the food (70,305). Salt is also the major ingredient, by weight, of curing mixtures; the active curing agent, however, is nitrite, and to a limited extent, nitrate. These curing agents function to stabilize the color of lean tissues, impart the characteristic flavor of cured meat, retard development of rancidity and provide microbial stability by inhibiting the growth of microorganisms, including *Acinetobacter/Moraxella*, *Flavobacterium*, *Pseudomonas*, *Enterobacter*, and *Escherichia* spp., as well as the pathogen *C. botulinum* (49,300,306). The antibotulinal effect of nitrite, however, occurs only in combination with heat, as is the case with canned products. Furthermore, the inhibitory effect of nitrite is reportedly pH dependent, with an approximate tenfold increase of its inhibitory effect for every one pH unit reduction (299).

Addition of antimicrobial agents in meat products is a widely used method of preservation. The use of antimicrobial agents in ready-to-eat meat and poultry products is, in fact, one of the alternatives given to the U.S. food industry by FSIS, as a means to control *L. monocytogenes* in these products (199). Numerous studies have shown the antilisterial effect of GRAS chemical compounds in ready-to-eat meats, including potassium lactate (307,308), sodium lactate and sodium acetate (309–311), sodium diacetate (310,311), and acetic and lactic acid (312). The most widely used chemical preservatives used by the industry, however, are sodium or potassium lactate and sodium diacetate, alone or in combination, at levels of 2% sodium or potassium lactate (on a dry weight basis) and 0.1 to 0.15% sodium diacetate (191). The other alternatives of the final rule for control of *L. monocytogenes* in ready-to-eat meat and poultry products are post-lethality treatments, which may be applied pre-packaging or post-packaging (e.g., radiant heat, hot water or steam pasteurization, high hydrostatic pressure) (313–316) and sanitation measures (199).

4. Preservative Packaging

a. Modified atmosphere packaging

Modified atmosphere packaging can be defined as the enclosure of food products in high gas barrier material, in which the gaseous environment has been changed in order to reduce microbial growth and retard enzymatic spoilage, with the intent of extending shelf life (317).

Among the factors limiting the shelf life of meat and poultry products, oxygen can be considered as one of the most important. Consequently, a logical barrier to extend the shelf life of these products is to modify the gaseous atmosphere surrounding them, which is the principle behind modified atmosphere packaging (MAP). A comprehensive list of different gas mixtures and packaging materials with different oxygen transmission rates that have been used to extend the shelf life of different meat types at specific storage temperatures, and the predominant spoilage bacteria isolated from those products can be found in Stanbridge and Davies (138). Four types of MAP can be differentiated by the manner in which spoilage organisms are inhibited (318): (i) in vacuum packaging, the inhibition of aerobic organisms is based on the removal of oxygen from the in-pack environment and the CO_2 production; (ii) In high oxygen MAP, growth of aerobic organisms is inhibited, but not suppressed by moderate concentrations of CO_2; (iii) In low oxygen MAP the low concentrations of O_2 inhibit the growth of aerobic species while the concentration of CO_2 may be sufficiently high to slow down the growth of both aerobic and anaerobic organisms; and (iv) in oxygen-free controlled atmosphere packaging, the absence of oxygen prevents growth of aerobic organisms, while high concentrations of CO_2 inhibit growth of aerobes and organisms tolerant to anaerobic conditions.

b. Vacuum packaging

Vacuum packaging is widely used for shelf-ready retail packs of meat products and for primal cuts of raw meat in wholesale storage. Vacuum packaging is not commonly used for display packs of raw meats because the anoxic environments results in a dull, purple color of native myoglobin, which is considered unattractive to the consumers (317,319). The shelf life extension of primal cuts achievable by vacuum packaging can be as long as two- to fivefold compared with aerobic storage depending on their pH, size and film permeability (318,320,321). Beef of pH 5.6 to 5.8, vacuum packaged with film of low oxygen permeability and stored at 0 to 1°C, may have a shelf life of 10 to 12 weeks (144). Growth of *Pseudomonas* under these conditions, where the CO_2 and O_2 concentrations are approximately 20% and <1% (v/v), respectively, is inhibited.

Vacuum packaging is also applied to cured and other cooked meat (322,323). The major disadvantage associated with the application of vacuum packaging to these products is that both package and meat are subjected to mechanical strain. This may cause product deformations, exudation and even puncture of the pack if bone is present (321). These problems, however, may be overcome with improvements in packaging techniques such as the use of appropriate packaging material, shrink packs, surface sealing and skin packs (4).

c. High oxygen modified atmosphere packaging

In high oxygen MAP the gaseous composition is approximately 70% O_2, 30% CO_2 and 0–20% N_2 (318). This type of packaging is used mainly for red meats and it has been introduced to extend color stability and delay microbial spoilage of products on display (319,324). The high oxygen concentration preserves a desirable color by extending the depth of the surface layer of oxygenated muscle tissue while the 30% CO_2 is sufficient to reduce the growth rate of pseudomonads, which dominate the spoilage flora. In general, the storage life of meats in high oxygen MAP can be twice that of meat stored under aerobic conditions. However, spoilage changes of foods stored in high oxygen MAP are comparable to those stored in air, since pseudomonads remain the responsible spoilage organisms.

d. Low oxygen modified atmosphere packaging

In low oxygen MAP, the atmosphere is composed almost exclusively of CO_2 and N_2. The exact level of residual oxygen depends on the procedure of air replacement. Without evacuation, oxygen may remain at levels of up to 10% while with evacuation the residual oxygen is about 1% (318). Low oxygen MAP is not commonly used for red meats due to the rapid discoloration of the product. Such packaging is usually applied when product color is not critically dependent on the oxidation state of myoglobin and thus it is more useful for poultry products. The extension of product shelf life achieved with low oxygen MAP can vary significantly depending on the initial atmosphere established in the pack and the extent to which the gaseous composition changes during storage. The spoilage process of low oxygen MAP meats is generally similar to that observed in vacuum packed products since in both cases the limited oxygen concentration inhibits growth of aerobic organisms, and species tolerant to anaerobic conditions dominate the microflora.

e. Oxygen-free controlled atmosphere packaging

Oxygen-free controlled atmosphere packaging is based on the complete elimination of oxygen from the package. The strictly anoxic environment may prevent meat discoloration and microbial shelf life may be greatly extended when the air is completely replaced with CO_2 in a controlled-atmosphere package (319). Scientists in New Zealand developed an oxygen-free controlled atmosphere packaging system (Captech system), which is in commercial use with lamb primal cuts and whole carcasses (319,325). The system involves packaging of cuts in heat-shrunk, air-permeable bags, which are then put in a larger pack of highly impermeable film that is flushed with carbon dioxide and sealed. The permeability of the inside packs allows penetration of carbon dioxide during storage and shipment, as well as oxygen after removal from the external pack and during display for formation of oxymyoglobin, which results in a bright red color. The storage life of such products can be 8–15 times longer than those stored in air depending on their initial contamination, pH and storage temperature. For example, shelf life may be substantially shorter when highly contaminated, high pH products are stored at temperatures above 0°C (318). The success of the packaging method also requires effective evacuation equipment and totally impermeable packaging materials made from aluminium foil laminate with good sealing and puncture-resistant properties. The extended product stability achieved by this type of packaging is likely to ensure its future commercial use with a wide range of meat products.

f. Factors that influence the effectiveness of modified atmosphere packaging

In addition to gas concentration and composition, the packaging material, the storage temperature and the time of MAP application are important factors influencing the shelf life extension conferred by MAP technology (318,321,326–328). Packages are mainly constructed of plastic films, the majority of which are permeable to gases. The extent of gas transmission through a plastic material depends on a number of factors such as type of plastic, thickness of the plastic layer, temperature, humidity and contamination of the plastic material with food components such as fat (318). Thus, proper selection of the plastic film in order to maintain the essential balance of the flushed gaseous atmosphere in the headspace of the pack is crucial. Bacterial inhibition by MAP is also affected by storage temperature. The solubility of CO_2 is inversely proportional to storage temperature and thus low temperatures have a synergistic affect upon its action (327). In addition, the multiple hurdle application (CO_2 and low temperature) leads to a higher inhibition of meat spoilage bacteria (329).

The time of MAP application is another important factor affecting the storage life of the product. If MAP is applied to fresh meat when the spoilage bacteria are still in the lag phase, shelf life may be extended by 50% compared to products stored aerobically, while MAP application during the exponential phase of the spoilage bacteria reduces the shelf life extension to 30% (326). In addition, the effectiveness of MAP is influenced by the extent of contamination at the time of application since high microbial populations result in an increased probability of the presence of some bacteria which are more resistant to the antimicrobial effect of the gaseous atmosphere. In general, the effectiveness of MAP is enhanced with earlier application and lower initial contamination levels.

g. Safety concerns of modified atmosphere packaging

Given that MAP is capable of extending the shelf life of meat products, the major safety concern is whether MAP can inhibit sensory changes by spoilage microorganisms, which ordinarily would warn consumers, while either allowing or promoting the growth of pathogens by limiting the competition with the spoilage flora (321). The impact of MAP on the microbiological safety of meats is not very well defined especially with respect to C. botulinum. For example, in sausages and meat sandwiches inoculated with C. botulinum (types A and B) and stored at 26°C, toxin was detected at 6 days for aerobically stored sandwiches and at 4 days for anaerobically stored samples (330). The most important observation in the latter study was that anaerobic samples were found organoleptically acceptable when toxic, while the aerobic were not. In a study by Silliker and Wolfe (331), pork cubes inoculated with C. botulinum spores and stored at 27°C under MAP were found to contain toxin by day 1 while aerobic samples were toxic by day 2. It is clear that C. botulinum may find atmospheric microenvironments allowing growth at highly abusive temperatures and thus the combination of MAP with strict temperature control is of great importance. Even at low storage temperatures, however, it is known that cold-tolerant pathogens such as Y. enterocolitica, L. monocytogenes and A. hydrophila are able to grow on vacuum-packaged, high pH raw meat (332).

The majority of the available information on the safety of meat and poultry packaged in modified atmospheres is based on traditional inoculation studies. Such data, however, cannot lead to reliable estimations of MAP safety risks since they are not statistically predictive and ignore the relationship between spoilage and pathogenicity. Thus, there is a need for further research information including risk assessment studies in which MAP will be compared against the current distribution and retail practices by taking into account the effect of factors such as temperature, time, pH and atmosphere as well as the relationship between growth of spoilage and pathogenic organisms. Such studies would lead to a better understanding of the action and interaction of the above factors in MAP and identify the potential need for additional antimicrobial hurdles to assure predictable safety.

h. Active packaging

Active packaging is one of the innovative concepts of food packaging that have been introduced as a response to the increasing consumer demands and the continuous changes in market trends. Major active packaging concepts include the use of substances that absorb oxygen, ethylene, carbon dioxide, flavors/odors and substances that release carbon dioxide, antimicrobial agents, antioxidants and flavors (333). Antimicrobial packaging has been characterized as a promising preservation concept for intact meat and poultry products mainly due to the fact that microbial contamination of these products occurs primarily on the surface (334).

The antimicrobial packaging concept is based on the incorporation of antimicrobial agents with polymeric packaging materials or biodegradable films and coatings. Compared to direct surface application of antimicrobial agents by spraying or dipping, antimicrobial packaging could be more efficient due to the slow release of the agent from the packaging material to the surface of the product, which helps to maintain high concentrations where they are needed. In addition, a long migration period of the antimicrobial agent may extend its activity into all stages of the food chain including transport, storage and distribution.

Non-edible antimicrobial packaging systems may contain different types of food grade additives in their packaging materials. Among compounds that have been proposed and tested in meat and poultry products are organic acids such as sorbate (335), propionate (336) and benzoate (337) or their respective anhydrides, bacteriocins including nisin and pediocin (338,339), enzymes such as lysozyme (340), and natural antimicrobial compounds from aromatic plants (341) (Table 52.8). The antimicrobial activity of triclosan incorporated plastic (TIP) has been recently investigated and the results showed a satisfactory inhibition against both spoilage and pathogenic bacteria associated with meat and poultry products such as *B. thermosphacta*, *S.* Typhimurium, *S. aureus* and *E. coli* (342). Triclosan is a tasteless, odorless and orally non-toxic bacteriostatic agent (343) and its use for food applications has been recently allowed in EU countries. Another interesting application of antimicrobial packaging is the use of polymers with modified surface composition by electron irradiation in such a way that the surface would contain amine groups with antimicrobial activity (344). These surface-bound amine groups have been proven active against pathogenic and spoilage bacteria (345).

Edible coatings and films prepared from polysaccharides, proteins and lipids and supplemented with antimicrobial agents can be considered as another type of antimicrobial packaging application. In this case, however, selection of the active agents is limited to edible compounds. Edible coatings and films with antimicrobial compounds present the following benefits to the meat and poultry industry: (i) inhibit the growth of spoilage and pathogenic bacteria and lead to products with low safety risk and extended shelf life; (ii) help alleviate the problem of moisture loss that leads to texture, flavor and color changes and weight losses; (iii) hold in juices and enhance product presentation; and (iv) reduce the rate of rancidity and brown discoloration caused by lipid and myoglobin oxidation (346). An additional advantage of this application is that the development of films and coatings can be based on the biopolymer by-products of the meat and poultry industry such as gelatin, blood protein and feather keratin.

5. Biopreservation

Biopreservation refers to extended storage life and enhanced safety of foods using their natural or controlled microflora and/or their antibacterial metabolic end products (347,348). In meats, lactic acid bacteria (LAB) constitute a part of the initial microflora which develops easily during fermentation processing, chill storage or packaging under vacuum or modified atmosphere conditions. Lactic acid bacteria growth in meat can cause interference against spoilage and pathogenic bacteria through several mechanisms including nutrient and oxygen depletion, and production of a wide range of inhibitory metabolic substances such as lactic and acetic acid, acetoin, diacetyl, hydrogen peroxide, reuterin and bacteriocins.

Biopreservation may be applied to food and meat systems by four basic methods (348–350):

a) Adding a pure culture of LAB. This is an indirect way of incorporating the antimicrobial metabolites of LAB (e.g., bacteriocins) in a food product. The success of the method depends on the ability of the culture to grow and produce the metabolites under the environmental and technological conditions of the product (temperature, pH, a_w, additives, etc.).

b) Adding a crude metabolite-preparation obtained by growing the LAB culture on a complex substrate in order to avoid the use of a purified compound.

c) Adding purified or semi-purified antagonistic substances. By using this method the dosage of the antimicrobial metabolite is more accurate and thus more predictable. However, application of this method is limited due to regulations concerning food additives.

d) Adding mesophilic LAB as a protective culture to be activated in the event of potential storage temperature abuse. In this case LAB should remain at low levels in cold environments while under temperature-abuse conditions they should grow competitively with pathogens and thus reduce the safety risk of the product.

TABLE 52.8
Applications of Antimicrobial Packaging Tested in Meat and Poultry Products

Product-Substrate	Antimicrobial Agent	Packaging Material
Bologna, cooked ham, pastrami	Acetic acid	Chitosan
Beef muscle	Lactic acid	Alginate
Bologna, cooked ham, pastrami	Propionic acid	Chitosan
Chicken breast	Potassium sorbate	Starch/glycerol
Beef tissue	Lysozyme	Silicon coating
Broiler drumstick skin	Nisin	Polyethylene
Cooked meats	Pediocin	Cellulose

Source: Ref. 334.

a. Lactic acid bacteria

The use of LAB as starter cultures in fermented meat products shortens the fermentation time, ensures product safety, extends shelf life and results in products with desirable, distinct and consistent quality (351,352). In addition to their inhibitory activity against meat spoilage and pathogenic bacteria, the production of lactic acid by LAB denatures meat proteins and affects product texture. Protein denaturation also results in the decrease of a_w which leads to the microbial stabilization of the transformed product.

The starter cultures used predominantly in fermented meat products include strains of *Pediococcus acidilactici*, *Pediococcus pentosaceus*, *Lactobacillus plantarum*, *Lactobacillus sake* and *Lactobacillus curvatus*. Other bacteria such as *Micrococcus* (*Micrococcus varians*) and coagulase-negative staphylococci are also used, mostly in Europe, and mainly due to their ability to reduce nitrate to nitrite and the production of specific flavors and catalase, which decomposes hydrogen peroxide and prevents quality defects.

In addition to fermented meat products, the use of LAB is permitted in bacon produced with minimal nitrite levels to reduce formation of nitrosamine during frying; the LAB grow and reduce the pH to inhibit *C. botulinum* growth in the absence of higher nitrite levels if the product is temperature abused (353). Inoculation of selected strains of LAB on fresh meat may suppress other LAB that degrade amino acids to undesirable compounds such as sulfides or biogenic amines (354,355) and contribute to the control of meat pathogens such as *L. monocytogenes* (356).

Addition of LAB to meat products, however, may also impart quality or safety problems. For example, heterofermentative LAB can produce undesirable compounds such as diacetyl, hydrogen sulfide and hydrogen peroxide gases, which affect product flavor and color. In addition, the ability of some LAB to decarboxylate the amino acid, histidine, may result in high levels of histamine, which has been associated with several outbreaks of foodborne illness (357). Thus, starter cultures should be screened for absence of metabolic products that cause quality or safety problems.

b. Bacteriocins

Bacteriocins are ribosomally produced polypeptides or proteins that produce, in their mature form, an antibacterial effect against a narrow spectrum of closely related bacteria (358,359). Bacteriocins exert their inhibitory action by formation of pores in the cytoplasmic membrane of sensitive cells. They are effective inactivators or inhibitors of various Gram-positive bacteria including pathogens, while Gram-negative bacteria are protected by their outer membrane, which prevents bacteriocins from reaching the cytoplasmic membrane (360).

Although several meat-borne LAB have been described as bacteriocin producers (Table 52.9) only a few have been studied as biopreservatives in meat systems. The production

TABLE 52.9
Bacteriocins Characterized from Lactic Acid Bacteria

Lactic Acid bacteria	Bacteriocin
Carnobacterium piscicola	Carnocin U149
	Carnobacteriocin (A and B)
Lactococcus lactis	Nisin (A and Z)
	Lacticin 481
	Diplococcin
	Lactococcin (A, B and M)
Lactobacillus sake	Lactocin S
	Sakacin (A and P)
Lactobacillus curvatus	Curvacin A
Lactobacillus johnsonii	Lactacin F
Leuconostoc gelidum	Leucocin A-UAL-187
Enterococcus faecium	Enterocin 1146
Pediococcus acidilactici	Pediocin (AcH and PA-1)

Source: Ref. 413.

and antimicrobial activity of certain bacteriocins in laboratory media does not imply their effectiveness in a food system. Bacteriocin activity may be reduced by the binding of bacteriocin molecules to meat components, by the action of proteases and other enzymes or by an uneven distribution in the food matrix (361). In addition, bacteriocins are not only of narrow activity among microorganisms, but there is also strain variation and their activity in foods may be reduced with storage time. Thus, when evaluating a bacteriocin for meat biopreservation, the influence of the product formulation and processing technology on the antimicrobial performance of the bacteriocin needs to be assayed.

The most studied bacteriocins in meat and meat products include nisin A, A, P and K, leucocin A and pediocin PA-1/AcH (350); nisin, however, is the only bacteriocin approved for use in certain food products. Sprayed nisin has been effective for the decontamination of meat surfaces while its combination with nitrite was effective on *Clostridium* and other Gram-positive pathogens such as *L. monocytogenes* and *S. aureus* in frankfurters, pork slurries and raw meat (362,363). In fermented American-style sausages, pediocin production prevented *L. monocytogenes* growth (364). The activity of pediocin PA-1 was not affected by fat or proteins present in the product while a synergistic effect was observed between the effect of bacteriocin and lactic acid.

6. Emerging Preservation Technologies

a. Irradiation

Food irradiation is generally defined as the process in which foods are exposed to ionizing energy from radioactive sources such as cobalt 60 or with machine sources such as high energy electron beams or X-rays. The role of irradiation as an alternative method to ensure hygienic quality of meat and poultry products is increasingly advocated and used in some countries (365–367). By properly adjusting the irradiation process it is possible to achieve a specific reduction of the level of microbial contamination commonly found on meat and poultry. Depending on the product and conditions of the process, irradiation treatments at doses of 3–7 kGy can effectively eliminate vegetative cells of pathogens including *Salmonella, S. aureus, Campylobacter, L. monocytogenes* and *E. coli* O157:H7 (368,369). The number of cells that are killed by irradiation depends on various factors such as type of microorganism, type of food, irradiation dose, temperature,

oxygen presence and water content (368–372). Table 52.10 provides examples of decimal reduction radiation doses (radiation D_{10} values) which have been determined for various non-spore-forming pathogenic bacteria in meat and poultry products (366). In addition to microbial inactivation, sublethal damage to microorganisms taking place during irradiation can increase their sensitivity to other preservative factors and thus synergistic effects of irradiation and other processes applied in food technology can be encountered (373). Among the benefits of irradiation is its applicability to frozen foods without having to thaw them,

TABLE 52.10
Irradiation D_{10} Values of Some Pathogenic Bacteria in Non-Frozen Meat and Poultry Products

Bacterium	Product	Temp. (°C)	Atmosphere	D_{10} (kGy)
Campylobacter jejuni	Ground pork	NS	Vacuum	0.19±0.01
	Filet americain	18–20	Micro-aeroph.	0.08–0.11
	Ground beef	18–20	Micro-aeroph.	0.14–0.16
	Ground beef	0–5	Air	0.161
	Ground beef	30±10	Air	0.174
	Ground turkey	0–5	Air	0.186
	Ground turkey	30±10	Air	0.162
Escherichia coli O157:H7	Mech. deboned chicken	0	Air	0.26±0.01
	Mech. deboned chicken	0	Vacuum	0.27±0.01
	Ground beef	0	Vacuum	0.27±0.03
	Ground beef (low fat)	4±1	Air	0.241
	Ground beef (high fat)	4±1	Air	0.251
Listeria monocytogenes	Minced chicken	NS	Air	0.417–0.553
	Mech. deboned chicken	2–4	Air	0.27–0.77
	Minced pork	10	Air	0.573–0.648
	Minced pork	10	CO_2:N_2(1:3)	0.602–0.709
	Ground pork	4	Air	0.422–0.447
	Roast beef	NS	Air	0.644±0.061
	Ground beef (low fat)	4±1	Air	0.578–0.589
	Ground beef (high fat)	4±1	Air	0.507–0.574
Salmonella Typhimurium	Filet americain	18–20	Air	0.37
	Ground beef	18–20	Air	0.55
	Ground beef (low fat)	2	Air	0.59
	Minced pork	10	Air	0.403–0.860
	Minced pork	10	CO_2:N_2(1:3)	0.394–0.921
	Roast beef	NS	Air	0.569±0.067
	Mech. deboned chicken	20	Air	0.52–0.56
	Mech. deboned chicken	20	Vacuum	0.52–0.56
	Minced chicken	4	Air	0.436–0.502
	Minced chicken	4	CO_2	0.436–0.502
	Minced chicken	4	N_2	0.550–0.662
Staphylococcus aureus	Minced chicken	4	Air	0.419
	Minced chicken	4	CO_2	0.411
	Minced chicken	4	Vacuum	0.398
	Minced chicken	4	N_2	0.371
	Roast beef	NS	Air	0.387±0.056
	Ground beef (low fat)	4±1	Air	0.437–0.453
	Ground beef (high fat)	4±1	Air	0.443–0.448
	Ground beef (low fat)	2	Air	0.57

NS = Not stated.
Source: Ref. 366.

and in packed products as a terminal treatment, eliminating the possibility of recontamination before consumption.

The main limitations of radiation decontamination are the effect of the process on the nutritional and sensory characteristics of the product (374) and the consumer acceptability of the process. Irradiation of meat and poultry may result in nutrient losses and changes in product odor, flavor and color depending on the radiation dose, dose rate, temperature, packaging and atmosphere during the process (375). Threshold irradiation doses at which detectable sensory changes occur in meat and poultry products are shown in Figure 52.5 (376). However, irradiation at low doses under low or no oxygen, or in the cured and frozen states for low fat products, has no notable sensory effects. A disadvantage of using irradiation at low doses is that bacterial spores, viruses and microbial toxins are not inactivated. Thus, as with other processed foods, irradiated products must be handled in accordance with good manufacturing practices and require appropriate temperature control.

Irradiation treatment of packaged products as a final processing step is a special case since this may cause cross-linking between the packaging material and the food. Irradiation may result in the decomposition of package components to lower-molecular-weight entities with increased migration characteristics (377). Therefore, the FDA requires that packaging that holds food during irradiation complies with specific regulations (21 CFR 179.45) based on appropriate testing.

The safety and effectiveness of irradiation as a method of food processing/preservation have been recognized by the Codex Alimentarius Commission (378). The FDA and FSIS approved a petition from industry to allow radiation decontamination of poultry and non-frozen and frozen red meats with maximum doses of 3 kGy, 4.5 kGy and 7.0 kGy, respectively (379,380). Despite this legislation, however, only a small fraction of the total amount of meat and poultry products produced in the U.S. is irradiated (381). Production of irradiated meat and poultry products is also limited in the EU, where no agreement has been reached on guidelines for regulating food irradiation (381). The limited application of irradiation of foods could be attributed to the widely held opinion of some national authorities and the food industry that consumers would be apprehensive about foods treated with irradiation because of the perceived association with radioactivity (365). Proper information about the safety and the benefits of irradiated foods could increase the level of understanding and acceptance of irradiated products by consumers and lead to a wider application of the process by the food industry (382). Furthermore, problems with the undesirable sensory effects of irradiation as well as investigations on the appropriate packaging materials for irradiated foods need to be addressed before this technology can be extensively used.

b. High hydrostatic pressure

High hydrostatic pressure (HHP) is an emerging non-thermal processing technology whereby foods are subjected to high hydrostatic pressure, generally in the range of 100–600 MPa, at low or moderate temperatures. It has been characterized as a very promising technology for the preservation of sliced cooked and cured meat products mainly due to its potential for the innovative development of new products of low safety risk with a relatively low energy consumption (383). High pressure application is of special interest in food processing technology since pressure represents an alternative to thermal processing, especially for foods such as meat and poultry whose nutritional and sensorial characteristics are thermosensitive. Indeed, HHP can reduce microbial contamination without markedly altering the taste and flavor or the nutrient content of foods (384–386). However, pressure processing also presents some disadvantages since it induces protein denaturation and texture modifications (385,386).

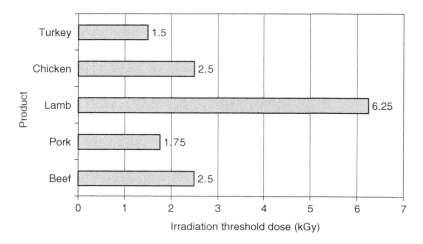

FIGURE 52.5 Irradiation threshold doses of meat and poultry products resulting in detectable sensory changes. (From Ref. 376.)

The mechanisms of inactivation of high hydrostatic pressure can be grouped into cell envelope-related effects, pressure-induced cellular changes, biochemical aspects and effects on genetic mechanisms (available at: http://vm.cfsan.fda.gov/~comm/ift-hpp.html). It has been established that cellular morphology is altered by pressure, and that cell division slows with the application of increasing pressures.

Bacterial spores are the most pressure-resistant life forms known. Thus, unless high hydrostatic pressures in excess of 800 MPa are used, heat in conjunction with HPP is a requirement for effective elimination of bacterial endospores (available at: http://vm.cfsan.fda.gov/~comm/ift-hpp.html). It is well established that the most pressure-resistant pathogen is *C. botulinum*. Spore suspensions of *C. botulinum* strains 17B and Cap 9B tolerated exposures of 30 min to 827 MPa and 75°C (available at: http://vm.cfsan.fda.gov/~comm/ift-hpp.html). Consequently, *C. botulinum* heads the list of most dangerous organisms faced by HPP. Among the vegetative cells, as in the case of other environmental stresses, Gram-positive bacteria are more resistant to pressure than vegetative cells of Gram-negative bacteria. However, there appears to be a wide range of pressure sensitivity among the pathogenic Gram-negative bacteria. Patterson et al. (387) have studied a clinical isolate of *E. coli* O157:H7 that possesses extremely high resistance to HHP.

Microbial inactivation through HHP application on fresh or processed meat has been studied in the last decade (388,389). The results have shown that pressure treatments at 200–600 MPa and 10–25°C for 10–20 min reduced, by at least 5–7 log cycles, the populations of both spoilage and pathogenic bacteria including pathogenic vegetative strains of *E. coli*, *C. jejuni*, *Pseudomonas aeruginosa*, *Y. enterocolitica*, *S.* Typhimurium, *S. aureus* and *Pseudomonas fluorescens*. The extent of inactivation, however, depends on several parameters such as the type of microorganism, the pressure level, the process temperature and time, and the pH and composition of the product. For example, pressure resistance of vegetative organisms increases at high (35 or 50°C) or low (4°C) temperatures and with decreasing water activity (386,390). Furthermore, the endogenous meat microflora, including *Pseudomonas* spp., appeared to be more resistant to pressure than the artificially inoculated organisms (390). The effect of HHP on microbial inactivation can be increased by combining it with other preservation treatments such as moderate heating or cooling, pH modifications, use of additives or various pretreatments. It may also be of special interest to apply HHP to ready-to-eat, packed products, as a terminal treatment in order to reduce microbial contamination originating from portioning, slicing or comminuting (386).

Other issues related to the application of HHP to meat products are associated with the effect of pressure on meat enzymes and proteins. For example, meat pressurization soon after slaughter usually results in a rapid pH decrease and an intense contraction. This greater rate of pH decrease has been related to changes in the activity of key meat enzymes involved in the regulation of glycogen breakdown. The above issues are considered significant since they may change important quality characteristics such as meat tenderness and structure. The effect of HHP on enzyme activity and meat proteins is extensively discussed in the study by Cheftel and Culioli (386).

Clearly, the benefits of HHP in terms of safety, storage life and quality can be applied to many high-value and heat-sensitive meat products and meat-based, ready-to-eat meals. At present, commercial HHP finds some applications in processed meat products for control of post-processing contamination with *L. monocytogenes*. The high cost of HHP technology and its limitation in terms of capacity could lead to the conclusion that HHP will not replace the conventional preservation and processing technologies. In the future, however, HHP is expected to find its position in the growing market of high-quality, high-priced foods (391).

c. Other technologies

Processing treatments with possible application in the meat industry include pulsed-field electricity, ultrasonic energy, UV light, oscillating magnetic fields (ohmic heating, dielectric heating, microwaves) and controlled instantaneous decompression (208,383,392,393, available at: http://vm.cfsan.fda.gov/~comm/ift-hpp.html). Pulsed field electricity, which is currently used in the meat industry for the electrostimulation of beef carcasses, can also lead to a reduction in the microbial load and extension of the lag phase of bacterial growth (392,394). Ultrasonic energy can be applied to small carcasses such as poultry when they are immersed in water. Research has shown that sonication can reduce the microbial contamination of the carcass especially when combined with appropriate adjustment of pH and temperature or with chlorination (395,396). The use of UV light in meat storage rooms and processing areas may control the bacterial load of the atmosphere (208).

All the above technologies aim at energy saving and being environmentally friendly. They have the same goal of being mild for food and reducing pathogenic and spoilage microorganisms. However, in most countries, these technologies are not approved and thus their application is limited at the present time.

V. MANAGEMENT OF PROCESSES FOR THE MICROBIOLOGICAL SAFETY OF MUSCLE FOODS

Traditionally, the microbiological safety of foods was heavily reliant on end product testing to determine the presence of a pathogen in a batch of product, and in so doing, determine the acceptance or rejection of a specific food lot (397). Limitations are, however, associated with finished product testing since foodborne pathogens may be distributed sporadically and unpredictably and/or occur at a low incidence within the product (397,398). Thus, the number of samples tested from a specific lot may be insufficient to provide meaningful information, and furthermore, the results obtained may provide a false sense of security (399). A more effective means of ensuring food safety than end product testing is the implementation of food safety management systems that incorporate the principles of good manufacturing practices (GMP), prerequisite programs and hazard analysis critical control point (HACCP) (400–403). To develop an effective HACCP system, a systematic approach is used to identify, evaluate and control food safety hazards. GMP, however, constitute the foundation needed before implementation of HACCP is possible in a food processing operation (403). Prerequisite programs and GMP differ from HACCP in that the former deal indirectly with food safety and are, in general, applicable to the whole processing plant. On the other hand, the sole purpose of HACCP *is* food safety and is product- or line-specific (404). Since its inception, many food industries have adopted HACCP. Countries like the U.S., EU, Canada, Australia and New Zealand have made HACCP compliance mandatory in some or all of their food sectors (405,406). The seafood (since 1997), meat and poultry (phasing in began in 1998), and juice (effective in 2002) industries are currently mandated to implement HACCP in the U.S. (404).

A relatively new concept recommended for adoption into food safety management systems by the International Commission on Microbiological Specifications for Foods, is the food safety objective (FSO) (403,407). The FSO is proposed as a tool to link information from risk assessment and risk management processes with the implementation of measures to control the identified risk(s) (403,407). The FSO refers to the maximum level of a microbiological hazard in a food considered acceptable for consumer protection (403). Once it has been determined that the FSO is technically achievable through the application of HACCP and GMP, the next step is to develop and document strategies to satisfy the FSO, including quantifiable and verifiable performance, process or end product criteria (403). Microbiological criteria differ from FSOs in that they determine the acceptability of a specific food lot. These criteria specify the microorganisms of concern and/or their toxins or metabolites, the sampling plan to be used (number of samples, method of sampling and handling, size of analytical unit), the analytical method to be used, microbiological limits and the number of analytical units required to conform to the limits (403). Sampling plans should be based on statistical probability, and in so doing, provide confidence during interpretation of the results (408).

Microbiological testing programs are thus a necessary part of food safety management systems. The main purpose of testing in a properly implemented HACCP system is to identify hazards and critical control points, and to validate and verify process control measures, and not as a means to assure the microbial safety of the final end product (397–399,401,409,410). As mentioned previously, testing for pathogens during meat and poultry processing operations provides very little information of use for the implementation and maintenance of HACCP systems, since they are generally found infrequently, unpredictably and in low numbers on the animals, and are usually detected rather than enumerated (397). A negative result for the presence of the pathogen could, therefore, be due to process control or simply due to the pathogen being absent at that particular time in that particular sample of product. Testing for pathogens that are found at a low frequency would require larger sample numbers and would thus be costly, and still would not guarantee the safety of the product. Testing for indicator microorganisms, which are indicative of process control, may be more appropriate, as it is generally assumed that the absence or low numbers of an indicator microorganism is a sign of process control and thus a lower likelihood of the presence of the pathogen, with which the indicator microorganism is associated (397,403). Examples of indicator microorganisms that have been used to assess meat plant processes include aerobic bacteria, coliforms, Enterobacteriaceae and *E. coli* biotype I (397,403,411). It should be noted, however, that no microorganisms that can serve as direct indices for pathogens are known. In the U.S., the Pathogen Reduction-HACCP System's Final Rule issued by FSIS in 1996 (400) requires meat and poultry slaughter establishments to conduct microbial testing for generic (biotype I) *E. coli* at regular intervals. Microbial testing for *E. coli* biotype I aims to verify that the establishments' HACCP-based process controls are adequate in preventing and removing fecal contamination, which is also the primary route of contamination of meat and poultry with pathogenic bacteria, like *E. coli* O157:H7, *Salmonella*, and *Campylobacter* spp. (400). Another requirement of the Final Rule is for establishments that produce raw ground products to meet pathogen reduction performance standards for *Salmonella*. These performance standards were issued in order to verify that plant HACCP systems are effective in reducing contamination with pathogenic microorganisms (400). It is expected that improvements in process control that lead to reductions in *Salmonella* will also result in reductions of other enteric pathogens of concern. Reasons for selecting *Salmonella* as the target organism include that it is a major pathogen of concern in the meat and poultry industry, and furthermore, is present in detectable numbers which can be easily tested for with current methodologies, on all types of raw products. Performance standards set by FSIS are based on the most recent U.S. baseline prevalence levels for *Salmonella* (400). Thus, by implementing the requirements of the 1996 Final Rule (sanitation, standard operating procedures, HACCP-based process control, microbial testing and pathogen reduction standards), meat and poultry establishments are expected to significantly reduce contamination of their products with pathogenic bacteria, which ultimately will reduce the risk of foodborne illness.

REFERENCES

1. MH Brown. Meat Microbiology. London: Applied Science Publishers, 1982.
2. AM Pearson, TR Dutson. Advances in Meat Research, vol. 2, Meat and Poultry Microbiology. Westport: AVI Publishing Company Inc., 1986.
3. FE Cunningham, NA Cox. The Microbiology of Poultry Meat Products. New York: Academic Press, 1987.
4. JN Sofos. Microbial growth and its control in meat poultry and fish. In: AM Pearson, TR Dutson. eds. Quality Attributes and their Measurements in Meat, Poultry and Fish Products. London: Blackie Academic & Professional, 1994, pp 359–403.
5. A Davies, R Board. The Microbiology of Meat and Poultry. London: Blackie Academic & Professional, 1998.
6. PM Nottingham. Microbiology of carcass meats. In: MH Brown. ed. Meat Microbiology. London: Applied Science Publishers, 1982, pp 13–65.
7. FH Grau. Microbial ecology of meat and poultry. In: AM Pearson, TR Dutson. eds. Advances in Meat Research, vol. 2, Meat and Poultry Microbiology. Westport: AVI Publishing Company Inc., 1986, pp 1–47.
8. CO Gill. Microbiological contamination of meat during slaughter and butchering of cattle, sheep and pigs. In: A Davies, R Board. eds. The Microbiology of Meat and Poultry. London: Blackie Academic & Professional, 1998, pp 118–157.
9. JA Lahr. Beef carcass microbial contamination-post slaughter numbers of bacteria, sources of contamination and variability of data. In: Proceedings of the 49th Annual Reciprocal Meat Conference, Provo, Utah, American Meat Science Association, Chicago, Illinois, 1996, pp 132–137.
10. RT Bacon, KE Belk, JN Sofos, RP Clayton, JO Reagan, GC Smith. Microbial populations of animal hides and beef carcasses at different stages of slaughter in plants employing multiple-sequential interventions for decontamination. J Food Prot 63:1080–1086, 2000.
11. RO Elder, JE Keen, GR Siragusa, GA Barkocy-Gallagher, M Koohmaraie, WW Laegreid. Correlation of enterohemorrhagic *Escherichia coli* O157 prevalence in feces, hides, and carcasses of beef cattle during processing. Proc Natl Acad Sci USA 97:2999–3003, 2000.
12. CA Reid, A Small, SM Avery, S Buncic. Presence of food-borne pathogens on cattle hides. Food Control 13:411–415, 2002.
13. JE Keen, RO Elder. Isolation of shiga-toxigenic *Escherichia coli* O157 from hide surfaces and the oral cavity of finished beef feedlot cattle. J Am Vet Med Assoc 220:756–763, 2002.
14. MH Davies, PJ Hadley, PJ Stocic, SD Webster. Production factors that influence the hygienic condition of finished beef cattle. Vet Record 146:179–183, 2000.

15. JN Sofos, KE Belk, GC Smith. Processes to reduce contamination with pathogenic microorganisms in meat. Proceedings of the 45th International Congress of Meat Science and Technology, Yokohama, Japan, 1999, pp 596–605.
16. AR Barham, BL Barham, AK Johnson, DM Allen, JR Blanton JR, MF Miller. Effects of the transportation of beef cattle from the feedyard to the packing plant on prevalence levels of *Escherichia coli* O157 and *Salmonella* spp. J Food Prot 65:280–283, 2002.
17. J van Donkersgoed, KWF Jericho, H Grogan, B Thorlakson. Preslaughter hide status of cattle and the microbiology of carcasses. J Food Prot 60:1502–1508, 1997.
18. EA Duffy, SB LeValley, KE Belk, JN Sofos, GC Smith. Pre-harvest management practices, good manufacturing practices during harvest, and microbiological quality of lamb carcasses. Dairy Food Environ Sanit 20:753–762, 2000.
19. F Bager, HD Emborg, LL Sorensen, C Halgeerd, PT Jensen. Control of *Salmonella* in Danish pork. Fleischwirtschaft 75:1000–1001, 1995.
20. JN Sofos, GC Smith. Non-acid meat decontamination technologies: model studies and commercial applications. Int J Food Microbiol 44:171–188, 1998.
21. CO Gill, T Jones. The presence of *Aeromonas*, *Listeria* and *Yersinia* in carcass processing equipment at two pig slaughtering plants. Food Microbiol 12:135–141, 1995.
22. CO Gill, J Bryant. The contamination of pork with spoilage bacteria during commercial dressing, chilling and cutting of pig carcasses. Int J Food Microbiol 16:51–62, 1992.
23. CO Gill, J Bryant. The presence of *Escherichia coli*, *Salmonella* and *Campylobacter* in pig carcasses dehairing equipment. Food Microbiol 10:337–344, 1993.
24. CO Gill, LP Baker. Assessment of the hygienic performance of a sheep carcass dressing process. J Food Prot 61:329–333, 1998.
25. SJ James, C Bailey. Chilling systems for foods. In: TR Gormley. ed. Chilled Foods: The State of the Art. London: Elsevier Applied Science, 1990, pp 159–182.
26. CO Gill, J Bryant. Assessment of the hygienic performances of two beef carcass cooling processes from product temperature history data or enumeration of bacteria on carcass surfaces. Food Microbiol 14:593–602, 1997.
27. AJ Gigiel, P Collett, SJ James. Fast and slow beef chilling in a commercial chiller and the effects of operational factors on weight loss. Int J Refrig 12:338–349, 1989.
28. SDM Jones, WM Robertson. The effect of shrouding on the appearance of spray-chilled beef carcasses. Can Inst Food Sci Technol J 21:112–114, 1988.
29. SDM Jones, WM Robertson. The effects of spray-chilling carcasses on the shrinkage and quality of beef. Meat Sci 24:177–188, 1988.
30. SDM Jones, AC Murray, WM Robertson. The effects of spray chilling pork carcasses on the shrinkage and quality of pork. Can Inst Food Sci Technol J 21:102–105, 1988.
31. T Brown, KN Chourouzidis, AJ Gigiel. Spray chilling of lamb carcasses. Meat Sci 34:311–325, 1993.

32. GG Greer, SDM Jones, BD Dilts, WM Robertson. Effects of spray chilling on the quality, bacteriology and case life of aged carcasses and vacuum packaged beef. Can Inst Food Sci Technol J 23:82–86, 1990.

33. CL Hippe, RA Field, B Ray, WC Russell. Effect of spray-chilling on quality of beef from lean and fatter carcasses. J Anim Sci 69:178–183, 1991.

34. PE Strydom, EM Buys. The effects of spray–chilling on carcass mass loss and surface associated bacteriology. Meat Sci 39:265–276, 1995.

35. Swift and Company. Carcass chilling process. U.S. patent number 1380891, 1973.

36. EF Heitter. Chlor-chil. Proceedings of the Meat Industry Research Conference, p 31, 1975.

37. PL Hamby, JW Savell, GR Acuff, C Vanderzant, HR Cross. Spray-chilling and carcass decontamination systems using lactic and acetic acid. Meat Sci 21:1–14, 1987.

38. JS Dickson. Control of *Salmonella typhimurium*, *Listeria monocytogenes*, and *Escherichia coli* O157:H7 on beef in a model spray chilling system. J Food Sci 56:191–193, 1991.

39. CO Gill, LP Baker, T Jones. Identification of inadequately cleaned equipment used in a sheep carcass-breaking process. J Food Prot 62:637–643, 1999.

40. G Froning, A Izat, G Riley, H Magwire. Eggs and egg products. In: C Vanderzant, DF Splittstoesser. eds. Compendium of Methods for the Microbiological Examination of Foods, 3rd ed. Washington, D.C.: American Public Health Association, 1992, pp 857–873.

41. ICMSF (International Commission on Microbiological Specifications for Foods). Microorganisms in Foods. vol. 6. Microbial Ecology of Food Commodities. London: Blackie Academic & Professional, 1998.

42. TJ Humphrey. Contamination of egg shell and contents with *Salmonella enteritidis*: a review. Int J Food Microbiol 21:31–40, 1994.

43. M Padron. *Salmonella typhimurium* penetration through the eggshell of hatching eggs. Avian Dis 34:463–465, 1990.

44. H Wang, MF Slavik. Bacterial penetration into eggs washed with various chemicals and stored at different temperatures and times. J Food Prot 61:276–279, 1998.

45. JE Williams, LH Dillard, GO Hall. The penetration patterns of *Salmonella typhimurium* through the outer structures of chicken eggs. Avian Dis 12:445–466, 1968.

46. RG Board. Microbiology of the hen's egg. Adv Appl Microbiol 11:245–281, 1969.

47. JE Williams. Paratyphoid infection. In: MS Hofstad, HJ Barnes, WM Reid HW Yoder. eds. Diseases of Poultry Ames: Iowa State University Press, 1984, pp 91–129.

48. JS Bailey, NA Cox, ME Berrang. Hatchery-acquired salmonellae in broiler chicks. Poult Sci 73:1153–1157, 1994.

49. ICMSF (International Commission on Microbiological Specifications for Foods). Microbial Ecology of Foods. vol. 2. Food Commodities. New York: Academic Press, 1980.

50. GC Mead. Microbiology of poultry and game birds. In: MH Brown. ed. Meat Microbiology. London: Applied Science Publishers, 1982, pp 67–101.

51. RWAW Mulder. Impact of transport on the incidence of human pathogens in poultry. World Poultry 12:18–19, 1996.

52. FL Bryan. Foodborne diseases in the United States associated with meat and poultry. J Food Prot 43:140–150, 1980.

53. FE Cunningham. Microbiological aspects of poultry and poultry products—an update. J. Food Prot. 45:1149–1164, 1982.

54. MF Slavik, JW Kim, JT Walker. Reduction of *Salmonella* and *Campylobacter* on chicken carcasses by changing scalding temperature. J Food Prot 58:689–691, 1995.

55. TJ Humphrey. The effects of pH and levels of organic matter on the death rates of salmonellas in chicken scald-tank water. J Appl Bacteriol 51:27–39, 1981.

56. NM Bolder. The microbiology of the slaughter and processing of poultry. In: A Davies, R Board. eds. The Microbiology of Meat and Poultry. London: Blackie Academic and Professional, 1998, pp 159–173.

57. NACMCF (National Advisory Committee on Microbiological Criteria for Foods). Generic HACCP application in broiler slaughter and processing. J Food Prot 60:579–604, 1997.

58. WO James, RL Brewer, JC Prucha, WO Williams, DR Parham. Effects of chlorination of chill water on the bacteriologic profile of raw chicken carcasses and giblets. J Am Vet Med Assoc 200:60–63, 1992.

59. DE Conner, MA Davis, L Zhang. Poultry-borne pathogens: plant considerations. In: AR Sams. ed. Poultry Meat Processing. Boca Raton, FL: CRC Press, 2001, pp 137–158.

60. AR Sams. First processing: slaughter through chilling. In: AR Sams. ed. Poultry Meat Processing. Boca Raton, FL: CRC Press, 2001, pp 19–34.

61. VM Allen, JEL Corry, CH Burton, RT Whyte, GC Mead. Hygiene aspects of modern poultry chilling. Int J Food Microbiol 58:39–48, 2000.

62. GL Nortje, RT Naude. Microbiology of beef carcass surfaces. J Food Prot 44:355–358, 1981.

63. FJM Smulders, CHJ Woolthuis. Influence of two levels of hygiene on the microbiological condition of veal as a product of two slaughtering/processing sequences. J Food Prot 46:1032–1035, 1983.

64. FSIS (Food Safety and Inspection Service). Nationwide beef microbiological baseline data collection program: steers and heifers. Washington, D.C.: U.S. Department of Agriculture, 1994.

65. FSIS (Food Safety and Inspection Service). Nationwide beef microbiological baseline data collection program: cows and bulls. Washington, D.C.: U.S. Department of Agriculture, 1996.

66. FSIS (Food Safety and Inspection Service). Nationwide pork microbiological baseline data collection program: market hogs. Washington, D.C.: U.S. Department of Agriculture, 1996.

67. JN Sofos, SL Kochevar, GR Bellinger, DR Buege, DD Hancock, SC Ingham, JB Morgan, JO Reagan, GC Smith. Sources and extent of microbiological contamination of beef carcasses in seven United States slaughtering plants. J Food Prot 62:140–145, 1999.

68. D Phillips, J Sumner, JF Alexander, KM Dutton. Microbiological quality of Australian beef. J Food Prot 64:692–696, 2001.

69. D Phillips, J Sumner, JF Alexander, KM Dutton. Microbiological quality of Australian sheep meat. J Food Prot 64:697–700, 2001.

70. JM Jay. Modern Food Microbiology, 6th ed. Gaithersburg: Aspen Publishers, 2000.

71. AW Kotula, BW Berry, BS Emswiler-Rose. Microbiology of restructured meat and poultry products. In: AM Pearson, TR Dutson. eds. Advances in Meat Research, vol. 3, Restructured Meat and Poultry Products. New York: Van Nostrand Reinhold, 1987, pp 161–220.

72. VM Dillon, RG Board. Yeasts associated with red meats: a review. J Appl Bacteriol 71:93–108, 1991.

73. H Fukushima, K Maruyama, I Omori, K Ito, M Iorihara. Contamination of pigs with Yersinia at the slaughter-house. Fleischwirtsch Int 70:1300–1302, 1990.

74. PA Chapman, CA Siddons, AT Cerdan Malo, MA Harkin. A 1-year study of Escherichia coli O157:H7 in cattle, sheep, pigs and poultry. Epidemiol Infect 119:245–250, 1997.

75. MA Rasmussen, TA Casey. Environmental and food safety aspects of Escherichia coli O157:H7 infections in cattle. Crit Rev Microbiol 27:57–73, 2001.

76. JN Sofos, SL Kochevar, JO Reagan, GC Smith. Incidence of Salmonella on beef carcasses relating to the U.S. meat and poultry inspection regulations. J Food Prot 62:467–473, 1999.

77. BE Rose, WE Hill, R Umholtz, GM Ransom, WO James. Testing for Salmonella in raw meat and poultry products collected at federally inspected establishments in the United States, 1998–2000. J Food Prot 65:937–947, 2002.

78. PA Chapman, CA Siddons, AT Cerdan Malo, MA Harkin. A one year study of Escherichia coli O157 in raw beef and lamb products. Epidemiol Infect 124:207–213, 2000.

79. FSIS (Food Safety and Inspection Service). Nationwide federal plant raw ground beef microbiological survey. Washington, D.C.: U.S. Department of Agriculture, 1996.

80. JS Bailey, JE Thomson, NA Cox. Contamination of poultry during processing. In: FE Cunningham, NA Cox. eds. The Microbiology of Poultry Meat Products. Orlando: Academic Press, Inc., 1987, pp 193–211.

81. FSIS (Food Safety and Inspection Service). Nationwide broiler chicken microbiological baseline data collection program. Washington, D.C.: U.S. Department of Agriculture, 1996.

82. FSIS (Food Safety and Inspection Service). Nationwide young turkey microbiological baseline data collection program. Washington, D.C.: U.S. Department of Agriculture, 1998.

83. CFIA (Canadian Food Inspection Agency). Canadian microbiological baseline survey of chicken broilers and young turkey carcasses, 2000.

84. EM Barnes, MJ Thornley. The spoilage flora of eviscerated chickens stored at different temperatures. J Food Technol 1:113–119, 1966.

85. EM Barnes. Microbiological problems of poultry at refrigerator temperatures—a review. J Sci Food Agric 27:777–782, 1976.

86. CJ Thomas, TA McMeekin. Contamination of broiler carcass skin during commercial processing procedures: an electron microscopic study. Appl Environ Microbiol 40:133–144, 1980.

87. I Geornaras, GA Dykes, A von Holy. Microbial populations associated with refrigerated poultry. S Afr J Sci 90:579–582, 1994.

88. I Geornaras, AE de Jesus, E van Zyl, A von Holy. Bacterial populations associated with poultry processing in a South African abattoir. Food Microbiol 13:457–465, 1996.

89. E de Boer, BJ Hartog, J Oosterom. The occurrence of Yersinia enterocolitica in poultry products. J Food Prot 45:322–325, 1982.

90. M Samadpour, JE Ongerth, J Liston, N Tran, D Nguyen, TS Whittam, RA Wilson, and PI Tarr. Occurrence of Shiga-like toxin-producing Escherichia coli in retail fresh seafood, beef, lamb, pork and poultry from grocery stores in Seattle, Washington. Appl Environ Microbiol 60:1038–1040, 1994.

91. FL Bryan, MP Doyle. Health risks and consequences of Salmonella and Campylobacter jejuni in raw poultry. J Food Prot 58:326–344, 1995.

92. I Geornaras, A de Jesus, E van Zyl, A von Holy. Microbiological survey of a South African poultry processing plant. J Basic Microbiol 35:73–82, 1995.

93. AL Waldroup. Contamination of raw poultry with pathogens. World Poult Sci J 52:7–25, 1996.

94. M Akan, A Eyigor, KS Diker. Motile aeromonads in the feces and carcasses of broiler chickens in Turkey. J Food Prot 61:113–115, 1998.

95. NH Bean, PM Griffin, JS Goulding, CB Ivey. Foodborne disease outbreaks, 5-year summary, 1983–1987. J Food Prot 53:711–728, 1990.

96. C Soumet, G Ermel, V Rose, N Rose, P Drouin, G Salvat, P Colin. Identification by a multiplex PCR-based assay of Salmonella Typhimurium and Salmonella Enteritidis strains from environmental swabs of poultry houses. Lett Appl Microbiol 29:1–6, 1999.

97. AS Abu-Ruwaida, WN Sawaya, BH Dashti, M Murad, HA Al-Othman. Microbiological quality of broilers during processing in a modern commercial slaughterhouse in Kuwait. J Food Prot 57:887–892, 1994.

98. SS Green. Results of a national survey. Salmonella in broilers and overflow chill tank water 1982–1984. United States Department of Agriculture, Food Safety and Inspection Service, Science, Washington, D.C., 1987.

99. E Borch, M-L Kant-Muermans, Y Blixt. Bacterial spoilage of meat and cured meat products. Int J Food Microbiol 33:103–120, 1996.

100. ML García-López, M Prieto, A Otero. The physiological attributes of Gram-negative bacteria associated with spoilage of meat and meat products. In: A Davies, R Board. eds. The Microbiology of Meat and Poultry. London: Blackie Academic & Professional, 1998, pp 1–34.

101. RH Dainty, BM Mackey. The relationship between the phenotypic properties of bacteria from chill-stored meat

and spoilage processes. J Appl Bacteriol Symp Suppl 73:103S–114S, 1992.

102. CO Gill. Meat spoilage and evaluation of the potential storage life of fresh meat. J Food Prot 46:444–452, 1983.

103. HW Walker, JC Ayres. Yeasts as spoilage organisms. In: AH Rose, JS Harrison. eds. The Yeasts, vol. 3, Yeast Technology. London: Academic Press, 1970, pp 463–527.

104. VM Dillon. Yeasts and moulds associated with meat and meat products. In: A Davies, R Board. eds. The Microbiology of Meat and Poultry. London: Blackie Academic & Professional, 1998, pp 85–117.

105. GJE Nychas, PA Gibbs, RG Board, JJ Sheridan. Improving the safety and quality of meat and meat products by modified atmosphere and assessment by novel methods. FLAIR proposal No 89055, Contract No AGRF/0024 (SCP), Final Report, EU, DGXII, Brussels, Belgium, 1994.

106. CO Gill. Substrate limitation of bacterial growth at meat surfaces. J Appl Bacteriol 41:401–410, 1976.

107. GJ Nychas, VM Dillon, RG Board. Glucose, the key substrate in the microbiological changes occurring in meat and certain meat products. Biotechnol Appl Biochem 10:203–231,1988.

108. EH Drosinos. Microbial associations of minced lamb and their ecophysiological attributes. Ph.D. thesis, University of Bath, U.K., 1994.

109. DE Hood, GC Mead. Modified atmosphere storage of fresh meat and poultry. In: RT Parry. ed. Principles and Applications of Modified Atmosphere Packaging of Food. London: Blackie Academic & Professional, 1993, pp 269–298.

110. RH Dainty, RA Edwards, CM Hibbard. Time course of volatile compound formation during refrigerated storage of naturally contaminated beef in air. J Appl Bacteriol 59:303–309, 1985.

111. CO Gill, KG Newton. The development of aerobic spoilage on meat stored at chill temperatures. J Appl Bacteriol 43:189–195, 1977.

112. CO Gill, KG Newton. The ecology of bacterial spoilage of fresh meat at chill temperatures. Meat Sci 2:207–217, 1978.

113. AF Egan, TA Roberts. Microbiology of meat and meat products. In: JR Norris, GL Pettipher. eds. Essays in Agricultural and Food Microbiology. New York: John Wiley & Sons, 1987, pp 167–197.

114. CO Gill, KG Newton. Effect of lactic acid concentration on growth on meat of gram-negative psychrotrophs from a meatworks. Appl Environ Microbiol 43:284–288, 1982.

115. Z Bem, H Hechelmann, L Leistner. Mikrobiologie des DFD-Fleisches (The bacteriology of DFD meat). Fleischwirtschaft 56:985–987, 1976.

116. KG Newton, CO Gill. Storage quality of dark, firm, dry meat. Appl Environ Microbiol 36:375–376, 1978.

117. BJ Hitchener, AF Egan, PJ Rogers. Characteristics of lactic acid bacteria isolated from vacuum-packaged beef. J Appl Bacteriol 52:31–37, 1982.

118. BG Shaw, CD Harding. A numerical taxonomic study of lactic acid bacteria from vacuum-packed beef, pork lamb and bacon. J Appl Bacteriol 56:25–40, 1984.

119. E Borch, G Molin. Numerical taxonomy of psychrotrophic lactic acid bacteria from prepacked meat and meat products. Antonie van Leeuwenhoek 54:301–323, 1988.

120. KG Newton, WJ Rigg. The effect of film permeability on the storage life and microbiology of vacuum-packed meat. J Appl Bacteriol 47:433–441, 1979.

121. R Dainty, BG Shaw, TA Roberts. Microbial and chemical changes in chill-stored red meats. In: TA Roberts, FA Skinner. eds. Food Microbiology: Advances and Prospects. London: Academic Press, 1983, pp 151–178.

122. BG Shaw, CD Harding, AA Taylor. The microbiology and storage stability of vacuum packed lamb. J Food Technol 15:397–405, 1980.

123. Y Blixt, E Borch. Comparison of shelf life of vacuum-packed pork and beef. Meat Sci 60:371–378, 2002.

124. AA Taylor, BG Shaw. The effect of meat pH and package permeability on putrefaction and greening in vacuum packed beef. J Food Technol 12:515–521, 1977.

125. DJ Nicol, MK Shaw, DA Ledward. Hydrogen sulphide production by bacteria and sulfmyoglobin formation in prepacked chilled beef. Appl Microbiol 19:937–939, 1970.

126. KG Newton, CO Gill. The microbiology of DFD fresh meats: a review. Meat Sci 5:223–232, 1981.

127. RH Dainty, RA Edwards, CM Hibbard. Spoilage of vacuum-packed beef by a *Clostridium* sp. J Sci Food Agric 49:473–486, 1989.

128. N Kalchayanand, B Ray, MC Johnson. Characteristics of psychrotrophic *Clostridium laramie* causing spoilage of vacuum-packaged refrigerated fresh and roasted beef. J Food Prot 56:13–17, 1989.

129. DM Broda, KM DeLacy, RG Bell, TJ Braggins, RL Cook. Psychrophilic *Clostridium* spp. associated with 'blown pack' spoilage of chilled vacuum-packed red meats and dog rolls in gas-impermeable plastic casings. Int J Food Microbiol 29:335–352, 1996.

130. MD Collins, UM Rodrigues, RH Dainty, RA Edwards, TA Roberts. Taxonomic studies on a psychrophilic *Clostridium* from vacuum-packed beef: description of *Clostridium estertheticum* sp. nov. FEMS Microbiol Lett 96:235–240, 1992.

131. DM Broda, PA Lawson, RG Bell, DR Musgrave. *Clostridium frigidicarnis* sp. nov., a psychrotolerant bacterium associated with 'blown pack' spoilage of vacuum-packed meats. Int J Syst Bacteriol 49:1539–1550, 1999.

132. DM Broda, RG Bell, JA Boerema, DR Musgrave. The abattoir source of culturable psychrophilic *Clostridium* spp. causing 'blown pack' spoilage of vacuum-packed chilled venison. J Appl Microbiol 93:817–824, 2002.

133. KG Newton, JCL Harrison, KM Smith. The effect of storage in various gaseous atmospheres on the microflora of lamb chops held at −1°C. J Appl Bacteriol 43:53–59, 1977.

134. I Erichsen, G Molin. Microbial flora of normal and high pH beef stored at 4°C in different gas environments. J Food Prot 44:866–869, 1981.

135. MO Hanna, C Vanderzant, GC Smith, JW Savell. Packing of beef loin steaks in 75% O_2 plus 25% CO_2. II. Microbiological properties. J Food Prot 44:928–933, 1981.

136. AA Taylor, NF Down, BG Shaw. A comparison of modified atmosphere and vacuum skin packing for the storage of red meats. Int J Food Sci Technol 25:98–109, 1990.

137. JA Ordóñez, B de Pablo, BP de Castro, MA Asensio, B Sanz. Selected chemical and microbiological changes in refrigerated pork stored in carbon dioxide and oxygen enriched atmospheres. J Agric Food Chem 39:668–672, 1991.

138. LH Stanbridge, AR Davies. The microbiology of chill-stored meat. In: A Davies, R Board. eds. The Microbiology of Meat and Poultry. London: Blackie Academic & Professional, 1998, pp 175–219.

139. E Blickstad, G Molin. Carbon dioxide as a controller of the spoilage flora of pork, with special reference to temperature and sodium chloride. J Food Prot 46:756–763, 1983.

140. JP Sutherland, A Varnam. Fresh meat processing. In: MH Brown. ed. Meat Microbiology. London: Applied Science Publishers, 1982, pp 103–128.

141. A von Holy, WH Hozapfel. The influence of extrinsic factors on the microbiological spoilage pattern of ground beef. Int J Food Microbiol 6:269–280, 1988.

142. KA Lambropoulou, EH Drosinos, GJE Nychas. The effect of glucose supplementation on the spoilage microflora and chemical composition of minced beef stored aerobically or under a modified atmosphere at 4°C. Int J Food Microbiol 30:281–291, 1996.

143. GA Gardner. Microbial spoilage of cured meats. In: TA Roberts, FA Skinner. eds. Food Microbiology: Advances and Prospects. London: Academic Press, 1983, pp 179–202.

144. AF Egan. Lactic acid bacteria of meat and meat products. Antonie van Leeuwenhoek 49:327–336, 1983.

145. HJ Korkeala, KJ Björkroth. Microbiological spoilage and contamination of vacuum-packaged cooked sausages. J Food Prot 60:724–731, 1997.

146. J Samelis, A Kakouri, J Rementzis. Selective effect of the product type and the packaging conditions on the species of lactic acid bacteria dominating the spoilage microbial association of cooked meats at 4°C. Food Microbiol 17:329–340, 2000.

147. GA Dykes, TE Cloete, A von Holy. Taxonomy of lactic acid bacteria associated with vacuum-packaged processed meat spoilage by multivariate analysis of cellular fatty acids. Int J Food Microbiol 28:89–100, 1995.

148. J Samelis, A Kakouri, KG Georgiadou, J Metaxopoulos. Evaluation of the extent and type of bacterial contamination at different stages of processing of cooked ham. J Appl Microbiol 84:649–660, 1998.

149. WH Holzapfel. The Gram-positive bacteria associated with meat and meat products. In: A Davies, R Board. eds. The Microbiology of Meat and Poultry. London: Blackie Academic & Professional, 1998, pp 35–84.

150. GF Grant, AR McCurdy, AD Osborne. Bacterial greening in cured meats: a review. Can Inst Food Sci Technol 21:50–56, 1988.

151. I Arnaut-Rollier, L De Zutter, J van Hoof. Identities of the *Pseudomonas* spp. in flora from chilled chicken. Int J Food Microbiol 48:87–96, 1999.

152. G Sundheim, A Sletten, RH Dainty. Identification of pseudomonads from fresh and chill-stored chicken carcasses. Int J Food Microbiol 39:185–194, 1998.

153. EM Barnes, CS Impey. Psychrophilic spoilage bacteria of poultry. J Appl Bacteriol 31:97–107, 1968.

154. PS Mead, L Slutsker, V Dietz, LF McCaig, JS Bresee, C Shapiro, PM Griffin, RV Tauxe. Food-related illness and death in the United States. Emerg Infect Dis 5:607–625, 1999.

155. CDC (Centers for Disease Control and Prevention). Preliminary FoodNet data on the incidence of foodborne illnesses—selected sites, United States, 2002. Morbid Mortal Wkly Rep 52:340–343, 2003.

156. CDI (Communicable Disease Intelligence). Enhancing foodborne disease surveillance across Australia in 2001: the OzFoodNet Working Group. Commun Dis Intell 26:375–406, 2002.

157. CDC (Centers for Disease Control and Prevention). Surveillance for foodborne-disease outbreaks—United States, 1993–1997. Morbid Mortal Wkly Rep 49 (SS-1):1–51, 2000.

158. FL Bryan. Miscellaneous pathogenic bacteria in meat and poultry products. In: AM Pearson, TR Dutson, eds. Advances in Meat Research. Westport, CT: AVI Publishing, 1986, pp 241–275.

159. RT Bacon, JN Sofos. Characteristics of biological hazards in foods. In: RH Schmidt, GE Rodrick. eds. Food Safety Handbook. New York: John Wiley & Sons, 2003, pp 157–195.

160. F García-Del Portillo. Molecular and cellular biology of *Salmonella* pathogenesis. In: JW Cary, JE Linz, D Bhatnagar. eds. Microbial Foodborne Diseases: Mechanisms of Pathogenesis and Toxin Synthesis. Lancaster, PA: Technomic Publishing, 2000, pp 3–49.

161. AJ Bäumler, RM Tsolis, TA Ficht, LG Adams. Evolution of host adaptation in *Salmonella enterica*. Infect Immun 66:4579–4587, 1998.

162. JT Gray, PJ Fedorka-Cray. *Salmonella*. In: DO Cliver, HP Riemann. eds. Foodborne Diseases. San Diego: Academic Press, 2002, pp 53–68.

163. ACL Wong, MS Bergdoll. Staphylococcal food poisoning. In: DO Cliver, HP Riemann. eds. Foodborne Diseases, 2nd ed. San Diego: Academic Press, 2002, pp 231–248.

164. ICMSF (International Commission on Microbiological Specifications for Foods). Microorganisms in Foods 5: Microbiological Specifications of Food Pathogens. London: Blackie Academic & Professional, 1996.

165. PE Granum. *Clostridium perfringens* toxins involved in food poisoning. Int J Food Microbiol 10:101–112, 1990.

166. RG Labbe, VK Juneja. *Clostridium perfringens*. In: DO Cliver, HP Riemann. eds. Foodborne Diseases, 2nd ed. San Diego: Academic Press, 2002, pp 119–126.

167. NG Parkinson, K Ito. Botulism. In: DO Cliver, HP Riemann. eds. Foodborne Diseases, 2nd ed. San Diego: Academic Press, 2002, pp 249–259.

168. K Oguma, Y Fujinaga, K Inoue, K Yokota. Mechanisms of pathogenesis and toxin synthesis in *Clostridium botulinum*. In: JW Cary, JE Linz, D Bhatnagar. eds. Microbial Foodborne Diseases: Mechanisms of

Pathogenesis and Toxin Synthesis. Lancaster, PA: Technomic Publishing, 2000, pp 273–293.

169. C Bell, A Kyriakides. *Clostridium botulinum*. Malden: Blackwell Science, 2000.

170. H Sugiyama, JN Sofos. Botulism. In: RK Robinson. ed. Developments in Microbiology—4. Amsterdam: Elsevier, 1988, pp 77–120.

171. SF Altekruse, DL Swerdlow. *Campylobacter jejuni* and related organisms. In: DO Cliver, HP Riemann. eds. Foodborne Diseases, 2nd ed. San Diego: Academic Press, 2002, pp 103–112.

172. W Jacobs-Reitsma. *Campylobacter* in the food supply. In: I Nachamkin, MJ Blaser. eds. *Campylobacter*, 2nd ed. Washington, D.C.: ASM Press, 2000, pp 467–481.

173. HP Endtz, GJ Ruijs, B van Klingeren, WH Jansen, T van der Reyden, RP Mouton. Quinolone resistance in *Campylobacter* isolated from man and poultry following the introduction of fluoroquinolones in veterinary medicine. J Antimicrob Chemother 27:199–208, 1991.

174. JP Nataro, JB Kaper. Diarrheagenic *Escherichia coli*. Clin Microbiol Rev 11:142–201, 1998.

175. MM Levine. *Escherichia coli* that cause diarrhea: enterotoxigenic, enteropathogenic, enteroinvasive, enterohemmorrhagic, and enteroadherent. J Infect Dis 155:377–389, 1987.

176. MP Doyle, VV Padye. *Escherichia coli*. In: MP Doyle. ed. Foodborne Bacterial Pathogens. New York: Marcel Dekker, 1989, pp 235–281.

177. PM Fratamico, JL Smith, RL Buchanan. *Escherichia coli*. In: DO Cliver, HP Riemann. eds. Foodborne Diseases, 2nd ed. San Diego: Academic Press, 2002, pp 79–101.

178. MS Donnenberg, JP Nataro. The molecular pathogenesis of *Escherichia coli* infections. In: JW Cary, JE Linz, D Bhatnagar. eds. Microbial Foodborne Diseases: Mechanisms of Pathogenesis and Toxin Synthesis. Lancaster, PA: Technomic Publishing, 2000, pp 87–130.

179. LW Riley, RS Remis, SD Helgerson, HB McGee, JG Wells, BR Davis, RJ Hebert, ES Olcott, LM Johnson, NT Hargrett, PA Blake, ML Cohen. Hemorrhagic colitis associated with a rare *Escherichia coli* serotype. N Engl J Med 308:681–685, 1982.

180. PM Griffin, RV Tauxe. The epidemiology of infections caused by *Escherichia coli* O157:H7, other enterohemorrhagic *E. coli*, and the associated hemolytic uremic syndrome. Epidemiol Rev 13:60–98, 1991.

181. H Michino, K Araki, S Minami, S Takaya, N Sakai, M Miyazaki, A Ono, H Yanagawa. Massive outbreak of *Escherichia coli* O157:H7 infection in schoolchildren in Sakai City, Japan, associated with consumption of white radish sprouts. Am J Epidemiol 150:787–796, 1999.

182. J van Donkersgoed, T Graham, V Gannon. The prevalence of verotoxins, *Escherichia coli* O157:H7 and *Salmonella* in the faeces and rumen of cattle at processing. Can Vet J 40:332–338, 1999.

183. PA Chapman, CA Siddons, DJ Wright, P Norman, J Fox, E Crick. Cattle as a possible source of verocytotoxin-producing *Escherichia coli* O157 infections in man. Epidemiol Infect 119:439–447, 1993.

184. AE Heuvelink, FLAM van den Biggelaar, E de Boer, RG Herbes, WJG Melchers, JHJ Huis in't Veld, LAH

Monnens. Isolation and characterization of verocytotoxin-producing *Escherichia coli* O157 strains from Dutch cattle and sheep. J Clin Microbiol 36:878–882, 1998.

185. E Borch, P Arinder. Bacteriological safety issues in red meat and ready-to-eat meat products, as well as control measures. Meat Sci 62:381–390, 2002.

186. S Kathariou. *Listeria monocytogenes* virulence and pathogenicity, a food safety perspective. J Food Prot 11:1811–1829, 2002.

187. MK Miettinen, A Siitonen, P Heiskanen, H Haajanen, KJ Björkroth, HJ Korkeala. Molecular epidemiology of an outbreak of febrile gastroenteritis caused by *Listeria monocytogenes* in cold-smoked rainbow trout. J Clin Microbiol 37:2358–2360, 1999.

188. G Franciosa, S Tartaro, C Wedell-Neegaard, P Aureli. Characterization of *Listeria monocytogenes* strains involved in invasive and non-invasive listeriosis outbreaks by PCR-based fingerprinting techniques. Appl Environ Microbiol 67:1793–1799, 2001.

189. LJ Harris. *Listeria monocytogenes*. In: DO Cliver, HP Riemann. eds. Foodborne Diseases, 2nd ed. San Diego: Academic Press, 2002, pp 137–150.

190. M Shahamat, A Seaman, M Woodbine. Survival of *Listeria monocytogenes* in high salt concentrations. Zbl Bakt Mikr Hyg A 246:506–511, 1980.

191. RB Tompkin. Control of *Listeria monocytogenes* in the food-processing environment. J Food Prot 65:709–725, 2002.

192. P Levine, B Rose, S Green, G Ransom, W Hill. Pathogen testing of ready-to-eat meat and poultry products collected at federally inspected establishments in the United States, 1990 to 1999. J Food Prot 64:1188–1193, 2001.

193. DE Gombas, Y Chen, RS Clavero, VN Scott. Survey of *Listeria monocytogenes* in ready-to-eat foods. J Food Prot 66:559–569, 2003.

194. FM Wallace, JE Call, ACS Porto, GJ Cocoma, The ERRC Special Projects Team, JB Luchansky. Recovery rate of *Listeria monocytogenes* from commercially prepared frankfurters during extended refrigerated storage. J Food Prot 66:584–591, 2003.

195. CDC (Centers for Disease Control and Prevention). Multistate outbreak of listeriosis—United States, 2000. Morbid Mortal Wkly Rep 49:1129–1130, 2000.

196. JM Farber, PI Peterkin. *Listeria*. In: BM Lund, AC Baird-Parker, G Gould. eds. The Microbiology of Food. London: Chapman and Hall, 2000, pp 1178–1232.

197. CDC (Centers for Disease Control and Prevention). Multistate outbreak of listeriosis, United States, 1998. Morbid Mortal Wkly Rep 47:1085–1086, 1998.

198. CDC (Centers for Disease Control and Prevention). Public Health Dispatch: Outbreak of listeriosis—Northeastern United States, 2002. Morbid Mortal Wkly Rep 51:950–951, 2002.

199. FSIS (Food Safety and Inspection Service). Control of *Listeria monocytogenes* in ready-to-eat meat and poultry products; final Rule. Fed Regist 68:34208–34254, 2003.

200. MW Griffiths, H Schraft. *Bacillus cereus* food poisoning. In: DO Cliver, HP Riemann. eds. Foodborne Diseases, 2nd ed. San Diego: Academic Press, 2002, pp 261–270.

201. JM Kramer, RJ Gilbert. *Bacillus cereus* and other *Bacillus* species. In: MP Doyle. ed. Foodborne Bacterial Pathogens. New York: Marcel Dekker, 1989, pp 21–70.

202. M Koopmans, C-H von Bonsdorff, J Vinjé, D de Medici, S Monroe. Foodborne viruses. FEMS Microbiol Rev 26:187–205, 2002.

203. JP Dubey, KD Murrell, JH Cross. Parasites. In: DO Cliver, HP Riemann. eds. Foodborne Diseases, 2nd ed. San Diego: Academic Press, 2002, pp 177–190.

204. GW Gould. New Methods of Food Preservation. London: Blackie Academic & Professional, 1995.

205. L Leistner. Shelf-stable products and intermediate moisture foods based on meat. In: LB Rockland, LR Beuchat. eds. Water Activity: Theory and Applications to Foods. New York: Marcel Dekker, 1987, pp 295–327.

206. L Leistner. Principles of hurdle technology. In: GW Gould. ed. New Methods of Food Preservation. London: Blackie Academic & Professional, 1995, pp 1–21.

207. L Leistner. Combined methods for food preservation. In: M Shafiur Rahman. ed. Handbook of Food Preservation. New York: Marcel Dekker. 1999, pp 457–485.

208. NM Bolder. Decontamination of meat and poultry carcasses. Trends Food Sci Technol 8:221–227, 1997.

209. JN Sofos, GC Smith. Animal, carcass and meat hygiene to enhance food safety. EOLSS Encyclopedia, Oxford: EOLSS Publishers Ltd, 1999.

210. RD Huffman. Current and future technologies for the decontamination of carcasses and fresh meat. Meat Sci 62:285–294, 2002.

211. RG Bell. Distribution and sources of microbial contamination on beef carcasses. J Appl Microbiol 82:292–300, 1997.

212. ME Biss, SC Hathaway. Microbiological and visible contaminants of lamb carcasses according to preslaughter presentation status: Implications for HACCP. J Food Prot 58:776–783, 1995.

213. ME Biss, SC Hathaway. Effect of pre-slaughter washing of lambs on the microbiological and visible contamination of the carcasses. Vet Record 138:82–86, 1996.

214. DJ Bolton, RA Pearce, JJ Sheridan, IS Blair, DA McDowell, D Harrington. Washing and chilling as critical control points in pork slaughter hazard analysis and critical control point (HACCP) systems. J Appl Microbiol 92:893–902, 2002.

215. CM Byrne, DJ Bolton, JJ Sheridan, DA McDowell, IS Blair. The effects of preslaughter washing on the reduction of *Escherichia coli* O157:H7 transfer from cattle hides to carcasses during slaughter. Lett Appl Microbiol 30:142–145, 2000.

216. PJ Hadley, JS Holder, MH Hinton. Effects of fleece soiling and skinning method on the microbiology of sheep carcasses. Vet Record 140:570–574, 1997.

217. JN Sofos. Approaches to pre-harvest food safety assurance. In: FJM Smulders, JD Collins. eds. Food Safety Assurance and Veterinary Public Health. vol. 1. Food Safety Assurance in the Pre-harvest Phase. Wageningen: Wageningen Academic Publishers, 2002, pp 23–48.

218. RA Bowling, RP Clayton. Method for dehairing animals. U.S. Patent 5,149,295, 1992.

219. LR Graves Delmore, JN Sofos, GR Schmidt, GC Smith. Inactivation of pathogenic bacteria by the chemical dehairing process proposed for use on beef carcasses before slaughter. Presented at the 50th Reciprocal Meat Conference, June 29 to July 2, Iowa State University, Ames, Iowa. Chicago: American Meat Science Association, Chicago, 1997.

220. A Castillo, JS Dickson, RP Clayton, LM Lucia, GR Acuff. Chemical dehairing of bovine skin to reduce pathogenic bacteria and bacteria of fecal origin. J Food Prot 61:623–625, 1998.

221. TD Schnell, JN Sofos, VG Littlefield, JB Morgan, BM Gorman, RP Clayton, GC Smith. Effects of postexsanguination dehairing on the microbial load and visual cleanliness of beef carcasses. J Food Prot 58:1297–1302, 1995.

222. X Nou, M Rivera-Betancourt, JM Bosilevac, TL Wheeler, SD Shackelford, BL Gwartney, JO Reagan, M Koohmaraie. Effect of chemical dehairing on the prevalence of *Escherichia coli* O157:H7 and the levels of aerobic bacteria and *Enterobacteriaceae* on carcasses in a commercial beef processing plant. J Food Prot 66:2005–2009, 2003.

223. WJ Dorsa, CN Cutter, GR Siragusa, M Koohmarie. Microbial decontamination of beef and sheep carcasses by steam, hot water spray washes and a steam-vacuum sanitizer. J Food Prot 59:127–135, 1996.

224. SL Kochevar, JN Sofos, SB LeValley, GC Smith. Effect of water temperature, pressure and chemical solution on removal of fecal material and bacteria from lamb adipose tissue by spray-washing. Meat Sci 45:377–388, 1997.

225. PL Hamby, JW Savell, GR Acuff, C Vanderzant, HR Cross. Spray chilling and carcass decontamination systems using lactic and acetic acid. Meat Sci 21:1–14, 1987.

226. JS Dickson, ME Anderson. Microbiological decontamination of food animal carcasses by washing and sanitizing systems: a review. J Food Prot 55:133–140, 1992.

227. L Cabedo, JN Sofos, GC Smith. Removal of bacteria from beef tissue by spray washing after different times of exposure to fecal material. J Food Prot 59:1284–1287, 1996.

228. JS Dickson. Susceptibility of preevisceration washed beef carcasses to contamination by *Escherichia coli* O157:H7 and salmonellae. J Food Prot 58:1065–1068,1995.

229. CO Gill, DS McGinnis, J Bryant, B Chabot. Decontamination of commercial polished pig carcasses with hot water. Food Microbiol 12:143–149, 1995.

230. JO Reagan, GR Acuff, DR Buege, MJ Buyck, JS Dickson, CL Kastner, JL Marsden, JB Morgan, R Nickelson, GC Smith, JN Sofos. Trimming and washing of beef carcasses as a method of improving the microbiological quality of meat. J Food Prot 59:751–756, 1996.

231. LR Graves Delmore, JN Sofos, GR Schmidt, GC Smith. Decontamination of inoculated beef with sequential spraying treatments. J Food Sci 63:890–893, 1998.

232. KR Davey, MG Smith. A laboratory evaluation of a novel hot water cabinet for the decontamination of beef sides. Int J Food Sci Technol 24:305–316, 1989.

233. KR Davey. Theoretical analysis of two hot water cabinet systems for decontamination of beef sides. Int J Food Sci Technol 24:291–304, 1989.

234. BM Gorman, JN Sofos, JB Morgan, GR Schmidt, GC Smith. Evaluation of hand-trimming, various sanitizing agents and hot water spray-washing as decontamination interventions of beef brisket adipose tissue. J Food Prot 58:899–907, 1995.

235. CM Davidson, JY D'Aoust, W Allewell. Steam decontamination of whole and cut-up raw chicken. Poult Sci 64:765–767, 1985.

236. AI Morgan, ER Radewonuk, OJ Scullen. Ultra high temperature, ultra short time surface pasteurization of meat. J Food Sci 61:1216–1218, 1996.

237. FSIS (Food Safety and Inspection Service). Comparison of methods for achieving the zero tolerance standards for fecal, ingesta and milk contamination of beef carcasses: Notice of Conference. Fed Regist 60:49553–49564, 1995.

238. RK Phebus, AL Nutsch, DE Schafer, RC Wilson, MJ Riemann, JD Leising, CL Kastner, JR Wolf, RK Prasai. Comparison of steam pasteurization and other methods for reduction of pathogens on surfaces of freshly slaughtered beef. J Food Prot 60:476–484, 1997.

239. AL Nutsch, RK Phebus, MJ Riemann, JS Kotrola, RC Wilson, JE Boyer, TL Brown. Steam pasteurization of commercially slaughtered beef carcasses: evaluation of bacterial population at five anatomical locations. J Food Prot 61:571–577, 1998.

240. GR Acuff, C Vanderzant, JW Savell, DK Jones, DB Griffin, JG Ehlers. Effect of acid decontamination of beef subprimal cuts on the microbiological and sensory characteristics of steaks. Meat Sci 19:217–226, 1987.

241. ME Anderson, RT Marshall. Reducing microbial populations on beef tissues: Concentration and temperature of an acid mixture. J Food Sci 55:903–905, 1990.

242. J Samelis, JN Sofos. Organic acids. In: S Roller. ed. Natural Antimicrobials for the Minimal Processing of Foods. Cambridge: Woodhead Publishing Limited, 2003, pp 98–120.

243. FJM Smulders, GG Greer. Integrating microbial decontamination with organic acids in HACCP programmes for muscle foods: prospects and controversies. Int J Food Microbiol 44:149–169, 1998.

244. DAA Mossel, P van Netten. Harmful effects of selective media on stressed microorganisms: nature and remedies. In: MHE Andrew, AD Russell. eds. The Revival of Injured Microorganisms. London: Academic Press, 1984, pp 329–369.

245. ME Anderson, HE Huff, HD Naumann, RT Marshall. Counts of six types of bacteria on lamb carcasses dipped or sprayed with acetic acid at 25°C or 55°C and stored vacuum packaged at 0°C. J Food Prot 51:874–877, 1988.

246. JS Ikeda, J Samelis, PA Kendall, GC Smith, JN Sofos. Acid adaptation does not promote survival or growth of *Listeria monocytogenes* on fresh beef following acid and nonacid decontamination treatments. J Food Prot 66:985–992, 2003.

247. GG Greer, BD Dilts. Lactic acid inhibition of the growth of spoilage bacteria and cold tolerant pathogens on pork. Int J Food Microbiol 25:141–151, 1995.

248. P van Netten, JHJ Huis in't Veld, DAA Mossel. The immediate bactericidal effect of lactic acid on meat-borne pathogens. J Appl Bacteriol 77:490–496, 1994.

249. WJ Dorsa, CN Cutter, GR Siragusa. Effects of acetic acid, lactic acid and trisodium phosphate on the microflora of refrigerated beef carcass surface tissue inoculated with *Escherichia coli* O157:H7, *Listeria innocua*, and *Clostridium sporogenes*. J Food Prot 60:619–624, 1997.

250. CN Cutter, M Rivera-Betancourt. Interventions for the reduction of *Salmonella* Typhimirium DT104 and non O157:H7 enterohemorrhagic *Escherichia coli* on beef surfaces. J Food Prot 63:1326–1332, 2000.

251. MD Hardin, GR Acuff, LM Lucia, JS Oman, JW Savell. Comparison of methods for decontamination from beef carcass surfaces. J Food Prot 58:368–374, 1995.

252. J Samelis, JN Sofos, PA Kendall, GC Smith. Fate of *Escherichia coli* O157:H7, *Salmonella* Typhimurium DT 104, and *Listeria monocytogenes* in fresh meat decontamination fluids at 4 and 10°C. J Food Prot 64:950–957, 2001.

253. CN Cutter, GR Siragusa. Efficacy of organic-acids against *Escherichia coli* O157:H7 attached to beef carcass tissue using a pilot scale model carcass washer. J Food Prot 57:97–103, 1994.

254. J Lin, MP Smith, KC Chapin, HS Baik, GN Bennett, JW Foster. Mechanisms of acid resistance in enterohemorrhagic *Escherichia coli*. Appl Environ Microbiol 62:3094–3100, 1996.

255. P van Netten, A Valentijn, DAA Mossel, JHJ Huis in't Veld. The survival and growth of acid-adapted mesophilic pathogens that contaminate meat after lactic acid decontamination. J Appl Microbiol 84:559–567, 1998.

256. ED Berry, CN Cutter. Effects of acid adaptation of *Escherichia coli* O157:H7 on efficacy of acetic acid spray washes to decontaminate beef carcass tissue. Appl Environ Microbiol 66:1493–1498, 2000.

257. M Uyttendaele, E Jozwik, A Tutenel, L de Zutter, J Uradzinski, D Pierard, J Debevere. Effect of acid resistance of *Escherichia coli* O157:H7 on efficacy of buffered lactic acid to decontaminate chilled beef tissue and effect of modified atmosphere packaging on survival of *Escherichia coli* O157:H7 on red meat. J Food Prot 64:1661–1666, 2001.

258. J Samelis, JN Sofos. Strategies to control stress-adapted pathogens. In: AE Yousef, VK Juneja. eds. Microbial Stress Adaptation and Food Safety. Boca Raton, FL: CRC Press, 2003, pp 303–351.

259. DE Conner, JS Kotrola. Growth and survival of *Escherichia coli* O157:H7 under acidic conditions. Appl Environ Microbiol 61:382–385, 1995.

260. PM Fratamico, FJ Schultz, RC Benedict, RL Buchanan, PH Cooke. Factors influencing attachment of *Escherichia coli* O157:H7 to beef tissues and removal using selected sanitizing rinses. J Food Prot 59:453–459, 1996.

261. M Calicioglu, CW Kaspar, DR Buege, JB Luchansky. Effectiveness of spraying with Tween 20 and lactic acid in decontaminating inoculated *Escherichia coli* O157:H7 and indigenous *Escherichia coli* biotype I on beef. J Food Prot 65:26–32, 2002.

262. FJM Smulders, CHJ Woolthuis. Immediate and delayed microbiological effects of lactic acid decontamination of calf carcasses—influence on conventionally boned

versus hot-boned and vacuum-packaged cuts. J Food Prot 48:838–847, 1985.

263. FJM Smulders, P Barendsen, JG van Logtestijn, DAA Mossel, GM van der Marel. Review: Lactic acid: considerations in favour of its acceptance as a meat decontaminant. J Food Technol 21:419–436, 1986

264. AAM Zeitoun, JM Debevere. Decontamination with lactic acid/sodium lactate buffer in combination with modified atmosphere packaging effects on the shelf life of fresh poultry. Int J Food Microbiol 16:89–98, 1992.

265. JS Bailey, JE Thomson, NA Cox, AD Shackelford. Chlorine spray washing to reduce bacterial contamination of poultry processing equipment. Poult Sci 65:1120–1123, 1986.

266. AL Waldroup. Summary of work to control pathogens in poultry processing. Poult Sci 72:1177–1179, 1993.

267. CN Cutter, GR Siragusa. Application of chlorine to reduce populations of Escherichia coli on beef. J Food Safety 15:67–75, 1995.

268. GP Thiessen, WR Usborne, HL Orr. The efficacy of chloride dioxide in controlling Salmonella contamination and its effect on product quality of chicken broiler carcasses. Poult Sci 63:647–653, 1984.

269. CN Cutter, WJ Dorsa. Chlorine dioxide spray washes for reducing fecal contamination on beef. J Food Prot 58:1294–1296, 1995.

270. J Mullerat, NA Klapes, BW Sheldon. Efficacy of Salmide®, a sodium chlorite-based oxy-halogen disinfectant, to inactivate bacterial pathogens and extend shelf-life of broiler carcasses. J Food Prot 57:596–603, 1994.

271. JS Dickson, CGN Cutter, GR Siragusa. Antimicrobial effects of trisodium phosphate against bacteria attached to beef tissue. J Food Prot 57:952–955, 1994.

272. G Salvat, PP Coppen, JC Allo, P Collin. Efficiency of some decontamination treatments on the microbiological flora of broilers. In Proceedings FLAIR 6/Cost 906:14, Hygiene in poultry production chain, JD Collind, MH Hinton, RWAW Mulder. eds. Beekbergen, the Netherlands: The Institute for Animal Science and Health, 1994, pp 105–112.

273. BM Gorman, SL Kochevar, JN Sofos, JB Morgan, GR Schmidt, GC Smith. Changes on beef adipose tissue following decontamination with chemical solution or water of 35°C or 74°C. J Muscle Foods 8:185–197, 1997.

274. CA Morris, LM Lucia, JW Savell, GR Acuff. Trisodium phosphate treatmant of pork carcasses. J Food Sci 62:402–405, 1997.

275. L Cabedo. Attachment, removal or growth of spoilage bacteria and the pathogens Listeria monocytogenes, Escherichia coli O157:H7 on beef. Ph.D. Dissertation. Colorado State University, Fort Collins, 1995.

276. R Hollender, FG Bender, RK Jenkins, CL Black. Consumer evaluation of chicken treated with a trisodium phosphate application during processing. Poult Sci 72:755–759, 1993.

277. R Capita, C Alonso-Calleja, M Sierra, B Moreno, M del Camino Garcia-Fernandez. Effect of trisodium phosphate solutions on the sensory evaluation of poultry meat. Meat Sci 55:471–474, 2000.

278. JR Jimenez-Villarreal, FW Pohlman, ZB Johnson, AH Brown JR. Effects of chlorine dioxide, cetylpyridinium chloride, lactic acid and trisodium phosphate on physical, chemical and sensory properties of ground beef. Meat Sci 65:1055–1062, 2003

279. A Castillo, LM Lucia, GK Kemp, GR Acuff. Reduction of Escherichia coli O157:H7 and Salmonella Typhimurium on beef carcass surfaces using acidified sodium chlorite. J Food Prot 62:580–584, 1999.

280. JW Kim, MF Slavik. Cetylpyridinium chloride (CPC) treatment on poultry skin to reduce attached Salmonella. J Food Prot 59:322–326, 1996.

281. CN Cutter, WJ Dorsa, A Handie, S Rodriguez-Morales, X Zhou, PJ Breen, CM Compadre. Antimicrobial activity of cetylpyridinium chloride washes against pathogenic bacteria on beef surfaces. J Food Prot 63:593–600, 2000.

282. JR Ransom, KE Belk, JD Stopforth, JN Sofos, JA Scanga, GC Smith. Comparison of intervention technologies for reducing Escherichia coli O157:H7 on beef cuts and trimmings. Food Prot Trends 23:24–34, 2003.

283. AS Naidu, WR Bidlack. Milk lactoferrin-natural microbial blocking agent (MBA) for food safety. Environ Nutrit Interactions 2:35–50, 1998.

284. AS Naidu. Activated lactoferrin-a new approach to meat safety. Food Technol 56:40–45, 2002.

285. CN Cutter, WJ Dorsa, GR Siragusa. Parameters affecting the efficacy of spray washes against Escherichia coli O157:H7 and fecal contamination of beef. J Food Prot 60:614–618, 1997.

286. A Castillo, LM Lucia, KJ Goodson, JW Savell, GR Acuff. Comparison of water wash, trimming and combined hot water and lactic acid treatments for reducing bacteria of fecal origin on beef carcasses. J Food Prot 61:823–828, 1998.

287. LR Graves Delmore, JN Sofos, GR Schmidt, GC Smith. Evaluation of multiple hurdles for beef carcass decontamination. Presented at the 50th Reciprocal Meat Conference, June 29–July 2, Iowa State University, Ames, Iowa. Chicago: American Meat Science Association: 1997.

288. J Samelis, JN Sofos, PA Kendall, GC Smith. Influence of the natural microbial flora on the acid tolerance response of Listeria monocytogenes in a model system of fresh meat decontamination fluids. Appl Environ Microbiol 67:2410–2420, 2001.

289. YQ Lou, AE Yousef. Adaptation to sublethal environmental stresses protects Listeria monocytogenes against lethal preservation factors. Appl Environ Microbiol 63:1252–1255, 1997.

290. IS Lee, JS Lin, HK Hall, B Bearson, JW Foster. The stationary-phase sigma-factor σ^S (RpoS) is required for a sustained acid tolerance response in virulent Salmonella typhimurium. Mol Microbiol 17:155–167, 1995.

291. CGM Gahan, B O'Driscoll, C Hill. Acid adaptation of Listeria monocytogenes can enhance survival in acidic foods and during milk fermentation. Appl Environ Microbiol 62:3128–3132, 1996.

292. JH Ryu, LR Beuchat. Changes in heat tolerance of Escherichia coli O157:H7 after exposure to acidic environments. Food Microbiol 16:317–324, 1999.

293. L Phan-Thanh, F Mahouin, S Alige. Acid responses of *Listeria monocytogenes*. Int J Food Microbiol 55:121–126, 2000.

294. B O'Driscoll, CGM Gahan, C Hill. Adaptive acid tolerance response in *Listeria monocytogenes*: Isolation of an acid-tolerant mutant which demonstrates increased virulence. Appl Environ Microbiol 62:1693–1698, 1996.

295. JJ Mekalanos. Environmental signals controlling expression of virulence determinants in bacteria. J Bacteriol 174:1–7, 1992.

296. C Shadbolt, T Ross, TA McMeekin. Differentiation of the effects of lethal pH and water activity: food safety implications. Lett Appl Microbiol 32:99–102, 2001.

297. Y Lou, AE Yousef. Characteristics of *Listeria monocytogenes* important to food processors. In: ET Ryser, EH Marth. eds. *Listeria*, Listeriosis and Food Safety, 2nd ed. New York: Marcel Dekker Inc., 1999, pp 131–224.

298. JR Claus, J-W Colby, GJ Flick. Processed meats/poultry/seafood. In: DM Kinsman, AW Kotula, BC Breidenstein. eds. Muscle Foods: Meat, Poultry and Seafood Technology. New York: Chapman & Hall, Inc., 1994, pp 106–162.

299. RLJM van Laack. Spoilage and preservation of muscle foods. In: DM Kinsman, AW Kotula, BC Breidenstein. eds. Muscle Foods: Meat, Poultry and Seafood Technology. New York: Chapman & Hall, Inc., 1994, pp 378–405.

300. AM Pearson, TA Gillett. Processed Meats. 3rd ed. New York: Chapman & Hall, 1996.

301. JH Giese. Sanitation: the key to food safety and public health. Food Technol 45:74–80, 1991.

302. SJ Forsythe, PR Hayes. Food Hygiene, Microbiology and HACCP. 3rd ed. Gaithersburg: Aspen Publishers, 1998.

303. CF Niven, JR. Microbiology and parisitology of meat, part 1, microbiology. In: JF Price, BS Schweigert. eds. The Science of Meat and Meat Products. 3rd eds. Westport: Food & Nutrition Press, Inc., 1987, pp 217–263.

304. RE Rust. Sausage products. In: JF Price, BS Schweigert. eds. The Science of Meat and Meat Products. 3rd ed. Westport: Food & Nutrition Press, Inc., 1987, pp 457–485.

305. WM Urbain, JF Campbell. Meat preservation. In: JF Price, BS Schweigert. eds. The Science of Meat and Meat Products. 3rd ed. Westport: Food & Nutrition Press, Inc., 1987, pp 371–412.

306. JN Sofos, FF Busta, CE Allen. Botulism control by nitrite and sorbate in cured meats: review. J Food Prot 42:739–770, 1979.

307. ACS Porto, BDGM Franco, ES Sant'anna, JE Call, A Piva, JB Luchansky. Viability of a five-strain mixture of *Listeria monocytogenes* in vacuum-sealed packages of frankfurters, commercially prepared with and without 2.0 or 3.0% added potassium lactate, during extended storage at 4 and 10°C. J Food Prot 65:308–315, 2002.

308. FK Stekelenburg. Enhanced inhibition of *Listeria monocytogenes* in frankfurter sausage by the addition of potassium lactate and sodium diacetate mixtures. Food Microbiol 20:133–137, 2003.

309. H Blom, E Nerbrink, R Dainty, T Hagtvedt, E Borch, H Nissen, T Nesbakken. Addition of 2.5% lactate and 0.25% acetate controls growth of *Listeria monocytogenes* in vacuum-packed, sensory-acceptable servelat sausage and cooked ham stored at 4°C. Int J Food Microbiol 38:71–76, 1997.

310. GK Bedie, J Samelis, JN Sofos, KE Belk, JA Scanga, GC Smith. Antimicrobials in the formulation to control *Listeria monocytogenes* postprocessing contamination on frankfurters stored at 4°C in vacuum packages. J Food Prot 64:1949–1955, 2001.

311. J Samelis, GK Bedie, JN Sofos, KE Belk, JA Scanga, GC Smith. Control of *Listeria monocytogenes* with combined antimicrobials after postprocess contamination and extended storage of frankfurters at 4°C in vacuum packages. J Food Prot 65:299–307, 2002.

312. J Samelis, JN Sofos, ML Kain, JA Scanga, KE Belk, GC Smith. Organic acids and their salts as dipping solutions to control *Listeria monocytogenes* inoculated following processing of sliced pork bologna stored at 4°C in vacuum packages. J Food Prot 64:1722–1729, 2001.

313. RY Murphy, LK Duncan, ER Johnson, MD Davis, RE Wolfe, HG Brown. Thermal lethality of *Salmonella* Senftenberg and *Listeria innocua* in fully cooked and packaged chicken breast strips via steam pasteurization. J Food Prot 64:2083–2087, 2001.

314. RY Murphy, LK Duncan, KH Driscoll, JA Marcy, BL Beard. Thermal inactivation of *Listeria monocytogenes* on ready-to-eat turkey breast meat products during postcook in-package pasteurization with hot water. J Food Prot 66:1618–1622, 2003.

315. PM Muriana, W Quimby, CA Davidson, J Grooms. Postpackage pasteurization of ready-to-eat deli meats by submersion heating for reduction of *Listeria monocytogenes*. J Food Prot 65:963–969, 2002.

316. N Gande, P Muriana. Prepackage surface pasteurization of ready-to-eat meats with a radiant heat oven for reduction of *Listeria monocytogenes*. J Food Prot 66:1623–1630, 2003.

317. LL Young, RD Reviere, AB Cole. Fresh red meats: a place to apply modified atmospheres. Food Technol 42:65–69, 1988.

318. CO Gill, G Molin. Modified atmospheres and vacuum packaging. In: NG Russel, GW Gould. eds. Food Preservatives. London: Blackie, 1991, pp 172–199.

319. CO Gill. Controlled atmosphere packaging of chilled meat. Food Control 1:74–78, 1990.

320. DL Seman, KR Drew, PA Clarken, RP Little-John. Influence of packaging method and length of chilled storage on microflora, tenderness and colour stability of venison loins. Meat Sci 22:267–282, 1988.

321. AD Lambert, JP Smith, KL Dodds. Shelf life extension and microbiological safety of fresh–meat—a review. Food Microbiol 8:267–297, 1991.

322. TP Carr, JA Marchello. Microbial changes of precooked beef slices as affected by packaging procedure. J Food Prot 49:534–536, 1986.

323. ML Anderson, JT Keeton, GR Acuff, LM Lucia, C Vanderzant. Microbiological characteristics of pre-cooked,

vacuum-packaged uncured beef and pork. Meat Sci 25:69–79, 1989.

324. CO Gill. The solubility of carbon dioxide in meat. Meat Sci 22:65–71, 1988.

325. CO Gill. Packaging meat for prolonged chilled storage: The Captech process. Bit Food J 91:11–15, 1989.

326. CO Gill, KH Tan. Effect of carbon dioxide on meat spoilage bacteria. Appl Environ Microbiol 39:317–319, 1980.

327. C Genigeorgis. Microbial and safety implications of the use of modified atmospheres to extend the storage life of fresh meat and fish. Int J Food Microbiol 1:237–251, 1985.

328. E Tsigarida, GJE Nychas. Ecophysiological attributes of a *Lactobacillus* sp. and a *Pseudomonas* sp. on sterile beef fillets in relation to storage temperature and film permeability. J Appl Microbiol 90:696–705, 2001.

329. CO Gill, JCL Harrison. The storage life of chilled pork packaged under carbon dioxide. Meat Sci 26:313–324, 1989.

330. DA Kautter, RK Lynt, T Lilly JR, HM Solomon. Evaluation of the botulism hazard from nitrogen-packed sandwiches. J Food Prot 44:59–61, 1981.

331. JH Silliker, SK Wolfe. Microbiological safety considerations in controlled atmosphere storage of meats. Food Technol 34:59–63, 1980.

332. CO Gill, MP Reichel. Growth of the cold-tolerant *Yersinia enterocolitica*, *Aeromonas hydrophila* and *Listeria monocytogenes* on high-pH beef packaged under vacuum or carbon dioxide. Food Microbiol 6:223–230, 1989.

333. L Vermeirein, F Devlieghere, M van Beest, N de Kruijf, J Debevere. Developments in the active packaging of foods. Trends Food Sci Technol 10:77–86, 1999.

334. S Quintavalla, L Vicini. Antimicrobial food packaging in meat industry. Meat Sci 62:373–380, 2002.

335. A Cagri, Z Ustunol, ET Ryser. Antimicrobial, mechanical and moisture barrier properties of low pH whey protein-based edible films containing p-aminobenzoic or sorbic acids. J Food Sci 66:865–870, 2001.

336. B Quattara, RE Simard, G Piette, A Begin, RA Holley. Diffusion of acetic and propionic acids from chitosan-based antimicrobial packaging films. J Food Sci 65:768–773, 2000.

337. YM Weng, MJ Chen. Sorbic anhydride as antimycotic additive in polyethylene food packaging films. Food Sci Technol 30:485–487, 1997.

338. X Ming, GH Weber, JW Ayres, WE Sandine. Bacteriocins applied to food packaging materials to inhibit *Listeria monocytogenes* on meats. J Food Sci 62:413–415, 1997.

339. GR Siragusa, CN Cutter, JL Willett. Incorporation of bacteriocin in plastic retains activity and inhibits surface growth of bacteria on meat. Food Microbiol 16:229–235, 1999.

340. T Padgett, IY Han, PL Dawson. Incorporation of food-grade antimicrobial compounds into biodegradable packaging films. J Food Prot 61:1330–1335, 1998.

341. PN Skandamis, GJE Nychas. Preservation of fresh meat with active and modified atmosphere packaging conditions. Int J Food Microbiol 79:35–45, 2002.

342. CN Cutter. The effectiveness of triclosan-incorporated plastic against bacteria on beef surfaces. J Food Prot 62:474–479, 1999.

343. HN Bhargava, PA Leonard. Triclosan: applications and safety. American J Inf Control 24:209–218, 1996.

344. JD Cohen, CW Erkenbrecher, SL Haynie, MJ Kelley, H Kobsa, AN Roe, MH Scholla. Process for preparing antimicrobial polymeric materials using irradiation. U.S. patent 5,428,078, 1995.

345. JS Paik, M Dhanasekharan, MJ Kelly. Antimicrobial activity of UV-irradiated nylon film for packaging applications. Packaging Technology and Science 11:179–187, 1998.

346. A Gennadios, MA Hanna, LB Kurth. Application of edible coatings on meats, poultry and seafoods: a review. Lebensm Wiss Technol 30:337–350, 1997.

347. C Hill. Bacteriocins: natural antimicrobials from microorganisms. In: GW Gould. ed. New Methods of Food Preservation. London: Blackie Academic & Professional, 1995, pp 22–39.

348. ME Stiles. Biopreservation by lactic acid bacteria. Antonie van Leeuwenhoek 70:331–345, 1996.

349. LGM Gorris. Bacteriocins: potential applications in food preservation. In: Food Preservation by Combined Processes. Final report. FLAIR Concerted Action No. 7 UE. DGXII. pp 79–86, 1997.

350. M Hugas. Bacteriocinogenic lactic acid bacteria for the biopreservation of meat and meat products. Meat Sci 49:S139–S150, 1998.

351. JL Smith, SA Palumbo. Microorganisms as food additives. J Food Prot 44:936–955, 1981.

352. JL Smith, SA Palumbo. Use of starter cultures in meat. J Food Prot 46:997–1006, 1983.

353. N Tanaka, L Meske, MP Doyle, E Traisman, DW Thayer, RW Johnston. Plants trials of bacon made with lactic acid bacteria, sucrose and lowered sodium nitrite. J Food Prot 48:679–686, 1985.

354. U Schillinger, FK Lucke. Lactic acid bacteria on vacuum packaged meat and their influence on shelf life. Fleischwirtschaft 67:1244–1248, 1987.

355. JJ Leisner, GG Greer, ME Stiles. Control of beef spoilage by a sulfide-producing *Lactobacillus sake* strain with bacteriocinogenic *Leuconostoc gelidum* UAL187 during anaerobic storage at 2°C. Appl Environ Microbiol 62:2610–2614, 1996.

356. U Schillinger, M Kaya, and FK Lucke. Behavior of *Listeria monocytogenes* in meat and its control by a bacteriocin-producing strain of *Lactobacillus sake*. J Appl Bacteriol 70:473–478, 1991.

357. SL Taylor. Histamine food poisoning: toxicology and clinical aspects. Crit Rev Toxicol 17:91–128, 1986.

358. RW Jack, JR Tagg, B Ray. Bacteriocins of Gram-positive bacteria. Microbiol Rev 59:171–200, 1995.

359. RD Joerger. Alternatives to antibiotics: bacteriocins, antimicrobial peptides and bacteriophages. Poult Sci 82:640–647, 2003.

360. T Abee, L Krockel, C Hill. Bacteriocins: mode of action and potential in food preservation and control of food poisoning. Int J Food Microbiol 28:169–185, 1995.

361. U Schillinger, R Geisen, WH Holzapfel. Potential of antagonistic microorganisms and bacteriocins for the biological preservation of foods. Trends Food Sci Technol 7:158–164, 1996.

362. K Rayman, N Malik, A Hurst. Failure of nisin to inhibit outgrowth of *Clostridium botulinum* in a model cured meat system. Appl Environ Microbiol 46:1450–1452, 1983.

363. K Chung, JS Dickson, JD Crouse. Effects of nisin on growth of bacteria attached to meat. Appl Environ Microbiol 55:1329–1333, 1989.

364. PM Foegeding, AB Thomas, DH Pilkington, TR Klaenhammer. Enhanced control of *Listeria monocytogenes* by in-situ produced pediocin during dry fermented sausage production. Appl Environ Microbiol 58:884–890, 1992.

365. P Loaharanu. Food irradiation: current status and future prospects. In: GW Gould. ed. New Methods of Food Preservation. London: Blackie Academic & Professional, 1995, pp 90–109.

366. J Farkas. Irradiation as a method for decontaminating food: a review. Int J Food Microbiol 44:189–204, 1998.

367. RA Molins, Y Motarjemi, FK Kaferstein. Irradiation: a critical control point in ensuring the microbiological safety of raw foods. Food Control 12:347–356, 2001.

368. DW Thayer. Use of irradiation to kill enteric pathogens on meat and poultry. J Food Safety 15:181–192, 1995.

369. DW Thayer, G Boyd, JB Fox, L Lakritz, JW Hampson. Variations in radiation sensitivity of foodborne pathogens associated with the suspending meat. J Food Sci 60:63–67, 1995.

370. DW Thayer, G Boyd. Effect of ionizing radiation, temperature and atmosphere on the survival of *Salmonella typhimurium* in sterile, mechanically deboned chicken meat. Poult Sci 70:381–388, 1991.

371. DW Thayer, G Boyd. Radiation sensitivity of *Listeria monocytogenes* on beef as affected by temperature. J Food Sci 60:237–240, 1995.

372. DW Thayer, G Boyd, JB Fox, Jr, L Lakritz. Effects of NaCl, sucrose and water content on the survival *Salmonella typhimurium* on irradiated pork and chicken. J Food Prot 58:490–496, 1995.

373. M Szczawinska. Radiation resistance of *Salmonella* in meat. Food Irradiat Newsl 7:4–5, 1983.

374. WM Urbain. Food Irradiation. Orlando: Academic Press, 1986.

375. DG Olson. Irradiation of food. Food Technol 52:56–62, 1998.

376. S Sudarmadji, WM Urbain. Flavor sensitivity of selected raw animal protein foods to gamma radiation. J Food Sci 37:671–672, 1972.

377. KM Morehouse. Food Irradiation—US regulatory considerations. Radiation Physics and Chemistry 63:281–284, 2002.

378. CAC (Codex Alimentarius Commission). Codex General Standard for Irradiated Foods and Recommended International Codex Practice for the Operation of Radiation Facilities used for the Treatment of Food. CAC/Vol. XV.-Ed.1. FAO, Rome, 1994.

379. FDA (Food and Drug Administration). Irradiation in the production, processing and handling of food. U.S. Food and Drug Administration. Fed Regist 62:64102–64121, 1997.

380. FSIS (Food Safety and Inspection Service). Ingredients and sources of radiation listed or approved for use in the production of meat and poultry products final rule, Food Safety and Inspection Service, United States Department of Agriculture, Washington, D.C. Fed Regist 64:72167–72194, 1999.

381. FE DeRuiter, J Dwyer. Consumer acceptance of irradiated foods: dawn of a new era? Food Service Technol 2:47–58, 2002.

382. CM Bruhn. Strategies for communicating the facts on food irradiation to consumers. J Food Prot 58:213–216, 1995.

383. M Hugas, M Garriga, JM Monfort. New mild technologies in meat processing: high pressure as a model technology. Meat Sci 62:359–371, 2002.

384. JC Cheftel. Effects of high hydrostatic pressure on food constituents: an over-review. In: C Balny, R Hayashi, K Heremans, P Masson. eds. High pressure and Biotechnology, London: Colleque INSERM/John Libbey Eurotext Ltd., 1992, pp 195–209.

385. A Carlez, T Veciana-Nogues, JC Cheftel. Changes in colour and myoglobin of minced beef meat due to high pressure processing. Lebensm-Wiss Technol 28:528–538, 1995.

386. JC Cheftel, J Culioli. Effects of high pressure on meat: a review. Meat Sci 46:211–236, 1997.

387. MF Patterson, M Quinn, R Simpson, A Gilmour. Sensitivity of vegetative pathogens to high hydrostatic pressure treatment in phosphate buffered saline and foods. J Food Prot 58:524–529, 1995.

388. T Shigehisa, T Ohmori, A Saito, S Taji, R Hayashi. Effects of high hydrostatic pressure on characteristics of pork slurries and inactivation of microorganisms associated with meat and meat products. Int J Food Microbiol 12:207–216, 1991.

389. A Carlez, JP Rosec, N Richard, JC Cheftel. High pressure inactivation of *Citrobacter freundii*, *Pseudomonas fluorescens* and *Listeria innocua* in inoculated minced beef muscle. Lebensm-Wiss Technol 26:357–363, 1993.

390. A Carlez, JP Rosec, N Richard, JC Cheftel. Bacterial growth during chilled storage of pressure-treated minced meat. Lebensm-Wiss Technol 27:48–54, 1994.

391. B Mertens. Hydrostatic pressure treatment of food: equipment and processing. In: GW Gould. ed. New Methods of Food Preservation. London: Blackie Academic & Professional, 1995, pp 135–158.

392. DW Bawcom, JD Thompson, MF Miller, CB Ramsey. Reduction of microorganisms on beef surface utilizing electricity. J Food Prot 58:35–38, 1995.

393. J Dunn, T Ott, W Clark. Pulsed-light treatment of food and packaging. Food Technol 49:95–98, 1995.

394. Y Li, JT Walker, MF Slavik, H Wang. Electrical treatment of poultry chiller water to destroy *Campylobacter jejuni*. J Food Prot 58:1330–1334, 1995.

395. HS Lillard. Decontamination of poultry skin by sonication. Food Technol 48:72–73, 1994.

396. RG Earnshaw, J Appleyard, RM Hurst. Understanding physical inactivation processes: Combined preservation

opportunities using heat, ultrasound and pressure. Int J Food Microbiol 28:197–219, 1995.

397. MH Brown, CO Gill, J Hollingsworth, R Nickelson II, S Seward, JJ Sheridan, T Stevenson, JL Sumner, DM Theno, WR Usborne, D Zink. The role of microbiological testing in systems for assuring the safety of beef. Int J Food Microbiol 62:7–16, 2000.

398. JE Kvenberg, D Schwalm. Use of microbial data for hazard analysis and critical control point verification-food and drug administration perspective. J Food Prot 63:810–814, 2000.

399. AMSA (American Meat Science Association). The role of microbiological testing in beef food safety programs: consensus of the 1999 symposium. Kansas City: AMSA, 1999.

400. FSIS (Food Safety and Inspection Service). Pathogen reduction: hazard analysis critical control point (HACCP) systems; final rule. Fed Regist 61:38806–38989, 1996.

401. NACMCF (National Advisory Committee on Microbiological Criteria for Foods). Hazard analysis and critical control point principles and application guidelines. J Food Prot 61:762–775, 1998.

402. RJ Delmore, Jr, JN Sofos, KE Belk, WR Lloyd, GL Bellinger, GR Schmidt, GC Smith. Good manufacturing practices for improving the microbiological quality of beef variety meats. Dairy Food Environ Sanit 19:742–752, 1999.

403. ICMSF (International Commission on Microbiological Specifications for Foods). Microorganisms in Foods 7: Microbiological Testing in Food Safety Management. New York: Kluwer Academic/Plenum Publishers, 2002.

404. BP Quinn, NG Marriott. HACCP plan development and assessment: a review. J Muscle Foods 13:313–330, 2002.

405. K Ropkins, AJ Beck. Evaluation of worldwide approaches to the use of HACCP to control food safety. Trends Food Sci Technol 11:10–21, 2000.

406. L Unnevehr, T Roberts. Food safety incentives in a changing world food system. Food Control 13:76–76, 2002.

407. M van Schothorst. Principles for the establishment of microbiological food safety objectives and related control measures. Food Control 9:379–384, 1998.

408. DE Conner, MA Davis, L Zhang. Poultry-borne pathogens: plant considerations. In: AR Sams. ed. Poultry Meat Processing. Boca Raton, FL: CRC Press, 2001, pp 137–158.

409. CAC (Codex Alimentarius Commission). Joint FAO/WHO Food Standards Programme, Codex Committee on Food Hygiene. Food Hygiene, Supplement to Volume 1B-1997. Principles for the Establishment of and Application of Microbiological Criteria for Foods. CAC/GL 21–1997. Secretariat of the Joint FAO/WHO Food Standards Programme. Rome: Food and Agriculture Organization of the United Nations, 1997.

410. KMJ Swanson, JE Anderson. Industry perspectives on the use of microbial data for hazard analysis and critical control point validation and verification. J Food Prot 63:815–818, 2000.

411. CO Gill, JC McGinnis, M Badoni. Use of total or *Escherichia coli* counts to assess the hygienic characteristics of a beef carcass dressing process. Int J Food Microbiol 31:181–196, 1996.

412. G-JE Nychas, EH Drosinos, RG Board. Chemical changes in stored meat. In: A Davies, R Board. eds. The Microbiology of Meat and Poultry. London: Blackie Academic & Professional, 1998, pp 288–326.

413. L De Vuyst, EJ Vandamme. Nisin, an antibiotic produced by *Lactococcus lactis* subsp. *lactis*: properties, biosynthesis, fermentation and applications. In: L De Vuyst, EJ Vandamme. eds. Bacteriocins of Lactic Acid Bacteria. Glasgow: Blackie Academic & Professional, 1994, pp 151–221.

53 Microbiology of Marine Muscle Foods

Paw Dalgaard
Danish Institute for Fisheries Research, Technical University of Denmark

CONTENTS

I. INTRODUCTION

This chapter discusses the microbiology of finfish, crustaceans with a chitinous exoskeleton, and molluscan shellfish with a calcareous shell. Bivalve (two-shelled) molluscs are filter-feeding and during this process they concentrate microorganisms from water, which may lead to specific safety issues. Marine muscle foods, or seafood, are produced from a large number of aquatic species that live in habitats as differrent as (i) permanently cold seawater with 3–4% NaCl, e.g., in polar or deep-sea regions, (ii) warm shallow or surface seawaters in the tropics, (iii) estuarine waters or (iv) freshwater of different temperatures. In addition, aquatic animals are captured or reared by different methods and this also influence the microflora of seafoods. The majority of the microorganisms on aquatic animals have no recognized importance in marine muscle foods but spoilage and disease, i.e., infection or intoxication are caused by specific microorganisms.

Spoilage can be considered as any change that renders seafood unacceptable from a sensory point of view. Degradation of lipids by enzymatic hydrolysis or chemical oxidation can result in spoilage of fresh fatty fishes, frozen and dried products as well as fish-oil containing products. However, microbial activity is responsible for spoilage of most fresh and lightly preserved seafood. Globally, the post-harvest losses of food have been estimated to be as high as ~25% due to microbial activity alone (1). At the same time, the world's annual production in capture fisheries has not increased but remained at ~90 million tonnes during the last decade. Only aquaculture production in marine and particularly in fresh water has increased; if reached 35 million tonnes in 2000 (2). Despite the limited increases in fisheries production, international trade in seafood has increased and optimal utilization of available aquatic food resources and prevention of losses during distribution are more important than ever. Historically, seafood spoilage has been inhibited by processes like salting, drying and smoking, developed without knowledge about the microorganisms present in the aquatic raw materials. Today, the interest in fresh and lightly preserved foods is increasing (3) and this represents a challenge where detailed information about microorganisms in seafoods becomes important to reduce losses due to spoilage and to ensure products are safe at the time of consumption.

This chapter describes the microflora and microbial spoilage of marine muscle foods. The concept of specific spoilage organisms (SSO) is presented and it is shown how it can be applied to determine, predict and extend the shelf life of fresh and lightly preserved seafood. Several previous overview articles concerned the microbiology and microbial spoilage of seafoods. Shewan (4–6) summarized early studies on microbial spoilage, particularly of chilled and aerobically stored fresh fish. Later, Shewan (7) and Liston (8) reviewed the microflora of seafood from different geographical regions. Ashie et al. (9) summarized information on shelf-life extension whereas Dalgaard (10) described the SSO concept and its application with modified atmosphere packed (MAP) seafood. Gram et al. 2002 (11) discussed the importance of microbial interaction in food spoilage. Compared to previous reviews this chapter includes new information on the occurrence and importance of luminous bacteria in marine muscle foods.

Consumption of seafood can result in food-borne human diseases but the more exact numbers of outbreaks and cases are uncertain. In fact, it has been estimated that as little as 1% of the actual cases of food-borne diseases is reported; see (12). The U.S. and the U.K. have well-established reporting systems and some of their epidemiological data from the 1990s are included here to illustrate the importance of marine muscle foods in food-borne disease. In the U.S. finfish and shellfish were responsible, respectively, for 5.1% and 1.7% of the outbreaks and 0.8% and 2.2% of the cases of food-borne disease. For cases due to finfish, the main etiological agents were histamine fish poisoning (47%), ciquatera fish poisoning (24%), salmonellae (18%), *Clostridium botulinum* (3%), *Vibrio cholerae* (2%), *Cl. perfringens* (2%) and viruses (2%). The corresponding agents and figures for molluscan shellfish were viruses (66%), *Vibrio parahaemolyticus* (22%), salmonellae (6%), paralytic shellfish poisoning (3%) and *Cl. perfringens* (2%). In the U.K. cases due to finfish were caused by histamine fish poisoning (70%), salmonellae (16%) and viruses (4%) whereas cases due to molluscan shellfish resulted from viruses (91%) and salmonellae (4%) (12–15). Compared to amounts consumed and relative to other foods the number of cases of seafood-borne disease is high and should be reduced.

This chapter presents information about histamine fish poisoning, *Vibrio* species, *Clostridium botulinum*, *Listeria monocytogenes*, *Salmonella* and viruses. Recent overview articles concerning safety of seafood include (12, 16–18) and these or other chapters in the present volume should be consulted for information about aquatic biotoxins, parasites, toxic algae, and veterinary drugs as well as industrial and environmental contaminants which are hazards of importance in some marine muscle foods but not included in this chapter, which focuses on microbiology.

II. MICROFLORA OF AQUATIC ANIMALS FROM DIFFERENT HABITATS

The microflora of finfish, crustaceans and molluscs depends to a large extent on the microflora of the water in which they live. Microorganisms are found on outer surfaces (e.g., skin, gills and intestine) whereas the muscle tissue of healthy animals is sterile. The concentration of culturable microorganisms is variable and in general $10^2–10^5$ cfu/cm^2 are found on skin, $10^3–10^7$ cfu/g in gills and $10 – >10^8$ cfu/g in the intestinal content. The variable concentrations of intestinal microorganisms is related to the aquatic animal's intake of food (8, 19, 20). Higher temperatures typically correspond to higher concentrations of culturable microorganisms in water and on aquatic animals. For example, shrimps from cold water harbored $10–10^3$ cfu/g, whereas shrimps from warm water had 10^6 cfu/g (8). Similarly, in Japan, seasonal temperature changes had some effect on the total concentration of microorganisms in river, lake and seawater (21–23) and in the intestinal content of wild salmon but no effect was observed for cultured salmon (21). Water salinity has little effect on the total concentration of microorganisms but influences the composition of microbial species in aquatic animals, as discussed in the following section. Organic matter, particularly sewage and land run-off, increases the load of microorganisms, including potentially pathogenic species in water and aquatic animals. Finally, catching methods have an effect; for example, trawled finfish may have 10–100 times higher concentration of microorganisms on skin and gills than similar fishes caught by long line (5).

Heat-labile and sodium-requiring microorganisms are common in sea- and brackish waters as well as on seafood. Thus, for enumeration of microorganisms pour plating with ~45°C hot agar must be avoided as this procedure may kill a major part of the microflora (10). The concentration of microorganisms in deep-water pink shrimp (*Parapenaeus longirostris*) was, for example about twenty times higher when determined by spread plating as compared to pour plating (24). In this respect it may be relevant to note that even in tropical regions where surface seawater is above 25°C, psychrotolerant and heat-labile microorganisms like *Photobacterium phosphoreum* can be present in seawater and aquatic animals at depths below 50–100 m (25–28). Microorganisms on seafood frequently require sodium for growth and although standard plate count agar without NaCl is recommended for many foods this medium is obviously inappropriate for seafood. In addition, bacteria on marine fishes may be fastidious (29) and rich enumeration media are required. For various fresh and lightly preserved seafoods spread plating on pre-chilled plates of Long & Hammer's agar, modified to contain 1% NaCl, and incubated aerobically during 5–7 days at 15°C have been appropriate for enumeration of the dominant microflora (10, 30). Strictly anaerobic microorganisms are found in low concentrations on skin and gills of newly caught aquatic animals but in some cases these or not-yet-cultured microorganisms dominated the intestinal microflora of marine and freshwater fishes (31–35). In contrast, direct microscopy and both aerobic and anaerobic techniques determined similar concentrations of microorganisms in the intestine of several commercially important fish species (30). Although they may only be important in specific situations, anaerobic or not-yet-cultured microorganisms in the intestinal content of aquatic animals merits further study using culture-independent techniques as increasingly applied within microbial ecology in general.

A. MICROFLORA ON SKIN, SHELL AND GILLS

The genera or groups of microorganisms found on skin, outer shell and in gills of newly caught or harvested finfish, crustaceans and shellfish have been determined in numerous studies and summarized in several overview articles (8, 17, 19, 20, 31, 36). The dominant groups of Gram-negative bacteria were (i) *Acinetobacter*, *Moraxella* and *Psychrobacter*, (ii) *Pseudomonas* and *Shewanella*, (iii) *Flavobacterium* and *Cytophaga*, (iv) *Vibrio* and *Photobacterium*, (v) *Aeromonas* and (vi) Enterobacteriaceae. The dominant groups of Gram-positive bacteria were cocci primarily *Micrococcus*, coryneforms and rods including *Bacillus*, *Clostridium* and lactic acid bacteria. In some studies the percentage distribution of bacteria in seawater corresponded to the distribution of species on the surface of fish (31). Nevertheless, when data from many studies are compared (8, 17, 19, 20, 31, 36) surprisingly little can be concluded about the effect of water temperature and salinity or about the type of animal, for example dermersal or pelagic on the percentage distribution of genera/groups of microorganisms. However, for animals in freshwater the sodium-requiring species of *Vibrio* and *Photobacterium* are very rarely present whereas *Aeromonas* and Enterobacteriaceae are relatively more important in those habitats. Also, the *Flavobacterium-Cytophaga* group seems less dominant in marine animals. Furthermore, the percentages of *Bacillus*, *Micrococcus* and Enterobacteriaceae tend to be higher in tropical than in temperate regions. Greater differences between the microflora on aquatic animals from warm and cold water could be expected and, as noted by Liston (8), fungi are common on plankton but rarely found on the surface of fishes. Aquatic animals may prevent growth or attachment of microorganisms by antimicrobials like lysozyme in their surface slime, but this area remains little studied. However, the apparent lack of difference between groups of microorganisms on aquatic animals from various habitats may also result from the use of

simple identification schemes relying on relatively few phenotypic characteristics. In an attempt to elucidate this problem this chapter will focus on the occurrence of bioluminescent bacteria. Due to a unique ability to glow, these microorganisms have been enumerated and identified in aquatic animals even when they did not quantitatively dominate the microflora. In addition, simple keys for identification of several species of luminous bacteria have been available since about 1970 (37, 38). Luminous bacteria can dominate the microflora in the intestinal content of many aquatic animals; therefore they are discussed in detail in the following section.

B. INTESTINAL MICROFLORA AND LUMINOUS BACTERIA

Seafood can be produced from gutted or whole ungutted animals, e.g., products of herring, mussels, oysters, sardines and shrimps. Due to the high concentration of intestinal microorganisms, contamination of seafood during processing of both gutted and ungutted animals is practically impossible to eliminate and the gut microflora has a very direct influence on the microbiology of many seafoods.

Intestinal microorganisms are mainly found in the gut content, although some may be attached to epithelial cells, and concentrations can be orders of magnitude higher than in water, food, skin and gills. This indicates microbial growth within the time it takes food to pass through the digestive tract and under conditions with acid in the stomach and bile, low oxygen and possibly elevated carbon dioxide concentrations in the gut (39, 40). Data from several studies (19, 20, 41) showed Enterobacteriaceae, *Aeromonas* and *Pseudomonas* dominated in the intestinal content of freshwater species, whereas *Vibrio/Photobacterium*, *Pseudomonas* and Enterobacteriaceae dominated in marine species. However, *Acinetobacter/Moraxella*, lactic acid bacteria, yeast and strictly anaerobic microorganisms, including *Bacterioides* and *Clostridium*, can occur in high concentrations. In addition, a *Mycoplasma* phenotype was recently determined in salmon by a culture-independent approach relying on extraction and amplification of 16S rDNA (31, 34, 42–44).

It has been debated if fish has a specific intestinal microflora as found in warm-blooded animals. Sera and Ishida (45) suggested marine fish with a developed digestive tract have a specific gut microflora consisting of marine vibrios, i.e., sodium-requiring species of *Vibrio* and *Photobacterium*, whereas fish with a simple digestive tract, including immature individuals, have more complex intestinal flora that reflect the microflora in water and food. Salmon that return from seawater with an intestinal microflora dominated by marine vibrios can retain this dominating microflora even after three months in freshwater (46) or after migrating 1228 km away from the marine environment up the Yukon River in Alaska (47).

Thus, marine vibrios are either associated with the gut or growing so fast that they avoid 'wash-out.'

In Japan, luminous and non-luminous marine vibrios dominated the intestinal flora of ten commercially important marine fish species including mackerels and tunas (48). In fact, marine vibrios, particularly luminous species of *Vibrio* and *Photobacterium*, frequently dominate the intestinal microflora of marine aquatic animals. The luminous or bioluminescent bacteria are fascinating and they have been extensively studied, but controversy remains about the influence of luminous bacteria on eating quality, shelf-life and safety of marine muscle foods. For example, J. M. Shewan from Torry Research Station in Scotland concluded in an overview manuscript that luminous bacteria were "...of little real importance to the practical fish technologist..." (6) and the opinion that luminous bacteria do not compromise the safety or eating quality of seafood is common. However, it has now been shown that luminous bacteria are responsible for spoilage of different marine muscle foods and due to biogenic amine production may cause histamine fish poisoning (see Sections III and IV).

The luminous marine bacteria occur in light organs in symbiosis with host animals, in seawater and on skin, shell and gills of animals, but, quantitatively, the major habitat is the intestinal content of marine animals where from <10 to $>10^8$ cfu/g can be found (38, 49). At least thirteen species of bacteria contain luminous variants, but only some are important in seafoods. *Photobacterium phosphoreum* and *Vibrio logei* are psychrotolerant bacteria growing at $0°C$ and are typically inactivated above $25–30°C$. *P. leiognathi* and *V. fischeri* grow between ~$4°C$ and $35–37°C$, whereas *V. harveyi* grow from $5–10°C$ and up to ~$40°C$. Other luminous bacteria include *V. orientalis*, *V. splendidus* biotype I, *V. cholerae*, *V. vulnificus*, *V. salmonicida*, *Shewanella hanedai*, *Sh. woodyi* and the terrestrial insect pathogen *Photorhabdus luminescens*, but these are less common in seafood (50–53). *P. phosphoreum* dominate in the intestinal content of aquatic animals in cold seawater at ~$0°C$ to ~$15°C$ (28, 29, 54). In coastal waters in California, *V. fischeri* was the dominating luminous bacteria in gut content and in seawater of ~$15°C$; however, between June and October the water temperature was ~$20°C$ and *V. harveyi* became dominant in both habitats. Interestingly, these studies showed the intestinal microflora of a single fish species in a given location to be dominated by *V. harveyi*, *V. fischeri* or *P. phosphoreum* depending on changes in the water temperature (55, 56). *V. harveyi*-like and *P. leiognathi*-like luminous bacteria dominated in the intestinal flora of a large number of fish species from the Gulf of Oman (57). In the same way, *P. leiognathi*, *V. harveyi* and *V. fischeri* were present in high concentrations and dominated the gut microflora of commercially important crabs from India (58). *V. harveyi* (75–80%) and *V. fischeri* (20–25%) also dominated the intestinal flora of fladhead mullet and sea catfish from India, but the luminous bacteria disappeared when water salinity decreased from 2.17–3.23% to 1.7–1.8% during the monsoon (59). It seems luminous bacteria in aquatic animals are selected by temperature and salinity. Thus, species of luminous bacteria are not specifically associated with intestines of aquatic animals in general, but all luminous marine vibrios are chitinolytic and may contribute to the digestion of the chitin-containing exoskeleton of crustaceans eaten by various marine animals (59–61). Species of non-luminous microorganisms are likely also to be selected by temperature and salinity and the apparent similarity of the dominant microflora of seafoods from different habitats (discussed in section II A) may reflect identification of major groups of microorganisms like *Acinetobacter/Moraxella* or Enterobacteriaceae rather than specific species.

Contamination of seafood with luminous bacteria from the intestinal content is difficult to avoid during processing. *V. harveyi* (80–90%) and *V. fischeri* (10–20%) dominated the luminous microflora on the surface of white seabream caught in the Mediterranean Sea in July but during aerobic storage at $5°C$ the dominant luminous microflora became *P. phosphoreum* and *V. fischeri* (62). Luminous variants of *P. phosphoreum* and *V. logei* can grow to high concentrations during normal chilled storage of fish and squid from different parts of the world (62–66). In a few studies it has been attempted to measure the light produced by luminous bacteria on seafood. At $10°C$ and $25°C$ changes in bioluminescence may be used as an indication of product spoilage, but at $5°C$ and below bioluminescence in fresh fish was too weak to be useful as an indicator of spoilage (62, 63). From 1989 to 1998 the U.S. Food and Drug Administration (FDA) registered and evaluated 23 luminous seafoods. The majority of the products were cooked and peeled shrimps and imitation crab or lobster meats but glowing red snapper fillet, raw Pacific rockfish, raw herring and raw shrimps were also reported. The dominant luminous bacteria isolated from these products were *P. phosphoreum* and *V. logei* (67). Both *P. phosphoreum* and *V. logei* are heat labile and their presence in cooked seafood must be a result of recontamination. However, bioluminescence of *P. phosphoreum* and *V. logei* is stimulated by the low level of NaCl typically added to cooked shrimps and imitation shellfish products [see Figure 53.1 (38)] and this may explain why processed products have been reported luminous more often than raw fish. In any case, light produced by bacteria in marine muscle food is weak and only visible in a dark room where electric and sunlight are excluded. Thus, common use of refrigerators with inferior electric lights probably masks the bioluminescence of many seafoods. Nevertheless, when glowing seafood is observed it should not be consumed as it is likely to be of poor sensory quality and may be toxic due to histamine formed by luminous bacteria (see Sections III and IV). Finally, when discussing the

Light from flash   Bioluminescence produced by the bacteria

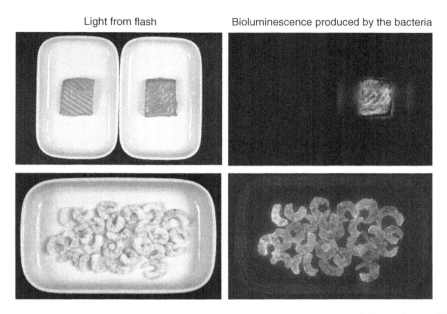

FIGURE 53.1 Bioluminescence by *Photobactrerium phosphoreum* in two pieces of salmon (*Salmo salar*) and in cooked and peeled shrimps (*Pandalus borealis*). Samples were inoculated, incubated aerobically during three days at 5°C and photographed with artificial light (left) and without artificial light (right). One of the two pieces of raw salmon was supplemented with 2% NaCl (w/w) to illustrate how this stimulates bioluminescence. The cooked and peeled shrimps contained 1.5% NaCl which is typical for this product (71).

occurrence and importance of luminous marine bacteria it must be mentioned that non-luminous variants exist for all species of luminous bacteria and the importance of these species of bacteria may be underestimated by enumeration of luminous bacteria only (30, 38, 68–70).

C. MICROFLORA OF FARMED AQUATIC ANIMALS

The microflora of cultured finfish, crustaceans and shell-fish does not as such differ from those of wild aquatic animals. However, cultured aquatic animals are closer to land and human activities than those in the wild and this may influence their environment and microflora. *Listeria monocytogenes,* a psychrotolerant bacteria pathogenic to humans, is absent from clean open waters but found in decaying plant material and indigenous to the general environment. Thus, animals reared in near-shore areas can be contaminated by run-off waters from land and must be expected to contain low levels of *L. monocytogenes* (12). Particularly in Southeast Asia ponds used for shrimp farming may be fertilized by animal excreta and this may result in contamination with *Salmonella, Escherichia coli* and viruses. In warm tropical water the bacteria may persist or even grow and shrimps from some, but not all, areas in Southeast Asia have been contaminated with bacteria potentially pathogenic to humans (72). Mortality of cultured aquatic animals can be a major problem and various diseases are due to bacterial infections. To overcome these problems, antibiotics can be used therapeutically to cure diseases or, on a daily basis, to prevent diseases. Use of antibiotics, particularly prophylatic use in sub-therapeutic

concentrations, is problematic because various bacteria develop resistance and the resistance may be transferred by plasmids to other bacteria and thereby reduce efficacy of antibiotic treatment for human and animal diseases. *Vibrio* and *Aeromonas* species, pathogenic to different aquatic animals, have been resistant to several antibiotics and this can make it impossible to control disease in cultured aquatic animals. In Southeast Asia, infection of farmed shrimps by antibiotic-resistant *V. harveyi* has caused so-called luminous vibrioses resulting in significant economic losses during the last 10–20 years. Antibiotic-resistant potential human pathogens, including *Salmonella, V. cholerae, Aeromonas hydrophila* and *Plesiomonas shigelloides*, have also been reported in relation to aquaculture production. Human infections by antibiotic-resistant pathogens are most problematic and changes in the use of antibiotics in some aquaculture-producing regions are required. In salmon farming, the use of antibiotics has to a large extent been replaced by vaccination. However, for crustaceans and shellfish with less-developed immune systems, this may not be possible (72–74).

III. MICROBIAL SPOILAGE OF MARINE MUSCLE FOODS

Newly caught fish and shellfish typically have a species-specific flavor that disappears after a few days of chilled storage. Further storage results in development of off-flavors which are often ammonia-like, sulphurous, malt-like or rancid. The off-flavors are typically caused by microbial metabolites and they increase in intensity during storage resulting in spoilage as determined by sensory methods. The importance of microbial activity in seafood spoilage has been established by comparing off-flavor development in muscle pieces that were (i) sterile, (ii) inoculated with specific microorganisms or (iii) naturally contaminated. Knowledge about spoilage microorganisms facilitates the development of methods to determine, predict and extend product shelf-life and this is particularly important due to the short and variable shelf-life of seafood (10, 75). The short shelf-life of many seafoods is explained by some unique product properties. First, many aquatic animals live in cold waters and their natural microflora include psychrotolerant species able to grow in chilled seafood at temperatures above −2°C. To illustrate the importance of this, it can be mentioned that shelf-life of tropical white-fleshed fish typically is 18–35 days at 0°C, whereas similar coldwater fish spoil after 12–18 days. Second, many finfish, crustaceans and molluscs contain trimethylamine-oxide (TMAO) that stimulates microbial growth and activity. In general, animals from freshwater contain less TMAO than those from seawater, but considerable variation exists between species in both habitats (76, 77). *Aeromonas, Alteromonas,* most Enterobacteriaceae, *Shewanella* and *Vibrionaceae,* including all marine luminous bacteria, reduce TMAO to trimethylamine (TMA) and this anaerobic respiration facilitates their growth under oxygen-limiting conditions, e.g., in vacuum-packed or modified atmosphere-packed products (69, 78–80). TMA contributes to the typical ammonia-like and fishy off-odors in spoiled seafoods, particularly in products with pH above ~6.5 (10). Third, the *post rigor* pH of finfish, crustaceans and molluscs is high compared to beef and pork. White-fleshed dermesal finfish and crustaceans have pH of ~6.5 to above 7, whereas pelagic, dark-fleshed fish like tuna, mahi-mahi, mackerel and garfish, have pH as low as ~5.8. Molluscs have pH similar to finfish, but contain much more carbohydrate (2.5–5.0%) compared to <0.5% for finfish and crustaceans. Consequently, a fermentative type of spoilage with decreasing pH is typical for molluscs but most unusual in other seafoods unless carbohydrates are added (16, 81–84). Finally, high concentrations of free amino acids are present in seafoods and metabolized by spoilage microorganisms, e.g., arginine in shrimps and histidine in dark-fleshed pelagic finfish (85, 86).

Only some of the numerous species of microorganisms in seafoods are important for spoilage and during storage a pattern of microbial growth and activity is frequently observed (Figure 53.2). This pattern is known as the specific spoilage organism (SSO) concept (10). On newly processed, fresh or lightly preserved seafood the SSO are usually present in very low concentrations and constitute only a minor part of the total microflora. During storage and at particular conditions of temperature, atmosphere,

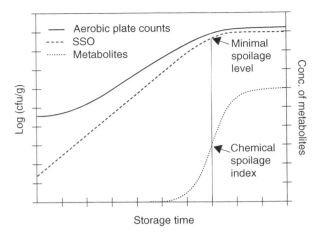

FIGURE 53.2 Specific spoilage organism (SSO) concept. Typical changes in aerobic plate counts, specific spoilage organisms (SSO) and metabolites produced by SSO during storage of fresh seafood (87).

NaCl, a_w, preservatives, etc., SSO, which is often a single microbiological species, grow faster than the remaining microflora, produce metabolites responsible for off-flavors, and finally cause sensory product rejection (Figure 53.2). SSO are typically present in levels of about 10^7 cfu/g when products become sensory spoiled. The importance of an SSO is closely related to its spoilage domain, i.e., the range of environmental parameters within which it is responsible for product spoilage. In contrast to SSO, the spoilage microflora, i.e., the microflora found at the time a product becomes sensorily rejected, can be a mixture of many microbial species, some of which are not important for spoilage.

Identification of an SSO relies on comparison of spoilage characteristics for a naturally contaminated product with those of isolates from the spoilage microflora. Initially, spoilage potential is frequently determined qualitatively as the ability of isolates to produce off-odors and metabolites, e.g., ammonia, TMA or H_2S. This screening technique has been used for decades to separate isolates from spoiled products into potential "spoilers" and "non-spoilers" (88). Isolates of *Shewanella putrefaciens* and *Pseudomonas fragi* often have a strong spoilage potential in seafood. To evaluate if the actual concentration of a microorganism in a product at the time of sensory rejection enables this microorganism to cause spoilage, a quantitative evaluation is required, i.e., determination of the spoilage activity. Yield factors can be used to evaluate if the concentration of cells and metabolites in a seafood corresponds to the spoilage activity of an isolate from the spoilage microflora, i.e., if the isolate is likely to be the SSO (69, 89, 90). The yield factor approach was used to identified *P. phosphoreum* as the SSO in chilled MAP cod fillets and showed this SSO to produce 10–100 times more TMA/cell than *Shewanella putrefaciens*. Despite a strong spoilage

TABLE 53.1
Specific Spoilage Organisms (SSO) in Groups of Fresh and Lightly Preserved Seafoods

Seafood	Typical SSO	Metabolites Produced	Selected References
Fresh chilled products stored in air:			
Various species, particularly those containing TMAO and with pH above ~6;	*Shewanella putrefaciens*-like[a]	TMA, H$_2$S and other sulphur compounds, hypoxanthine	(97–99)
various species, including some with little or no TMAO and low pH ~6	*Pseudomonas* spp.	NH$_3$, esters, sulphur compounds but not H$_2$S	(86, 90, 100, 101)
Fresh, chilled products in modified atmosphere packaging:			
TMAO containing species from seawater at temperatures below ~15°C;	*Photobacterium phosphoreum*	TMA, hypoxanthine, alcohols and ketones	(24, 69, 92)
species from warmer waters, particularly species with little or no TMAO;	Lactic acid bacteria and *Brochothrix thermosphacta*[b]	Acetic acid, NH$_3$, tyramine, acetoin, diacetyl, H$_2$S	(102, 103)
species from tropical freshwater	*Aeromonas* spp.	?	(104)
Fresh and lightly preserved products stored at ambient temperature	*Aeromonas* spp.	TMA, sulphur compounds, biogenic amines	(105, 106)
	Vibrio spp./*Photobacterium* spp.		
	Enterobacteriaceae *Enterococcus faecalis*	NH$_3$, acetic acid, acetoin, diacetyl, tyramine	(107)
Lightly preserved and chilled products: Brined, spiced/gravad and smoked products including fish roe	Lactic acid bacteria[c] and *Brochothrix thermosphacta*	Acetic acid, NH$_3$, tyramine, acetoin, diacetyl, sulphur compounds	(89, 108–113, 130)
	P. phosphoreum, Vibrio and Enterobacteriaceae[d]	TMA, biogenic amines, alcohols, aldehydes, sulphur compounds	

[a] *Shewanella putrefaciens, Shewanella baltica* and other closely related H$_2$S-producing Gram-negative bacteria.
[b] *Brochothric thermosphacta* is important for products in oxygen-containing modified atmospheres.
[c] Include *Lactobacillus curvatus, Lactobacillus sake* and *Leuconostoc* spp.
[d] Include *Enterobacter agglomerans, Hafnia alvei,* and *Serratia liquefaciens.*

potential, *S. putrefaciens* had low spoilage activity and was not important in sensory rejection of MAP cod fillets (Table 53.1). Furthermore, SSO in seafood may be identified by comparison of (i) the profiles of metabolites produced in naturally contaminated products with similar profiles produced by isolated microorganisms and (ii) by evaluating the effect on spoilage when growth of a suspected SSO is specifically inhibited in a seafood (91, 92).

It is well established that many microorganisms from seafoods, including bacteria, yeasts and several SSO (Table 53.1), produce extracellular proteolytic enzymes (93, 94). Nevertheless, seafood spoilage microorganisms typically produce off-flavors from substrates in muscle extractives and proteolytic activity is not important for spoilage of fresh and lightly preserved seafoods (95, 96). The importance of microbial proteolytic enzymes was primarily evaluated for fresh fish, and further research, including lightly and semi-preserved seafoods, seems justified.

A. SPECIFIC SPOILAGE ORGANISMS (SSO) IN GROUPS OF SEAFOODS

Spoilage of fresh chilled and aerobically stored seafood is primarily caused by *Shewanella putrefaciens*-like species and *Pseudomonas* spp. This is well established (Table 53.1), but the taxonomy of these Gram-negative

and non-fermentative rods has been changing (114–116). Frequently, *Pseudomonas* were not identified at the species level, but strains similar to *Ps. fragi, Ps. fluorescens* and *Ps. putida* seem common in seafood and recently *P. lundensis* dominated the spoilage microflora of chilled aerobically stored marine fish from Greece (114, 117, 118). *Pseudomonas* spp. are unable to reduce TMAO and growth is considerably reduced under oxygen-limited conditions. As an example, *P. fragi* spoiled different species of warm water shrimps stored in ice but spoilage was due to *S. putrefaciens*-like species when shrimps from the same lots were kept in an ice/water slurry (86, 101). Other bacteria may also influence spoilage of fresh chilled and aerobically stored seafood. Lipolytic *Psychrobacter immobilis* can dominate the spoilage microflora in both marine and freshwater fish and, despite a low spoilage potential, they may increase the rancid spoilage of sardines (119, 120). In 1974, van Spreekens (30) suggested *P. phosphoreum* was important for TMA production in iced cod and whiting. More recently, *P. phosphoreum* dominated the spoilage microflora of gutted saithe and plaice (70) and seemed responsible for TMA formation in iced cod fillets and squid (66, 121).

For fresh seafood in modified atmosphere packaging (MAP) with CO$_2$, luminous and non-luminous variants of *P. phosphoreum* are important spoilage microorganisms

(Table 53.1). Not all studies have detected this SSO in fresh MAP seafoods and in some studies inappropriate enumeration methods and experiments with previously frozen raw material are likely reasons why luminous and non-luminous variants of *P. phosphoreum* were not observed. *P. phosphoreum* is rapidly inactivated by freezing and absent in thawed products (92, 122). The relative importance of *P. phosphoreum* and *Shewanella putrefaciens*-like species in vacuum-packed fresh chilled seafoods probably depends on the initial concentration of the two spoilage bacteria. For shucked bivalve molluscs, i.e., mollusc meat removed from the shells, spoilage is fermentative when stored under vacuum or otherwise with reduced access to oxygen, but the microorganisms responsible remain to be identified (81, 84, 123). Spoilage of chilled MAP seafood from freshwater or products without TMAO need further study, e.g., with respect to identification of lactic acid bacteria and the importance of *Aeromonas* spp. (Table 53.1). High concentrations of *Aeromonas* spp. were found in chilled MAP seafood from tropical regions and they are likely to be the SSO (Table 53.1).

Low dose irradiation changes the spoilage microflora of chilled seafood and *Moraxella* spp. become dominant and probably responsible for spoilage (124). For sous vide cooked and chilled cod fillets, *Clostridium sardiniense*, an anaerobic spore-forming bacteria, caused a most unpleasant type of spoilage due to production of different volatile sulphur compounds (10).

Spoilage of chilled lightly preserved seafoods has been extensively evaluated within the last decade (Table 53.1). In general, lactic acid bacteria seemed to be the most important group of spoilage microorganisms. However, identification of the SSO responsible for spoilage has been complicated and variation in product characteristics, including the initial microflora, NaCl, pH, smoke components, chemical preservatives and packaging, is probably responsible for the various spoilage patterns observed. Thus, the spoilage domain of SSOs identified in several chilled lightly preserved seafood is unclear (Table 53.1), although, with sun-dried tropical fish, the spoilage domains of *Staphylococcus xylosus*, *Halobacterium salinarium* and molds were suggested as a function of temperature and water activity (125). For fermented and semi-preserved seafoods little is known about SSOs, but lactic acid bacteria, yeasts, molds and strict anaerobes seem important in some products.

The SSO concept embodies the hypothesis that in any given product a single species/group of microorganisms is responsible for spoilage. Microorganisms in seafoods interact in several ways, including substrate competition and metabolite inhibition. When the dominating microflora in food reach their maximum population density, i.e., inhibit their own growth, then other groups of microorganisms are frequently inhibited. This has been named the Jameson effect irrespective of the underlying mechanism being substrate competition, bacteriocins,

siderophores or other metabolites (126). There is no conflict between the simple SSO hypothesis (Figure 53.2) and the Jameson effect as long as the SSO reaches a high concentration and causes product spoilage before it is inhibited by the dominant microflora. This is typically the case with fresh seafood (Table 53.1). The metabolism of one group of microorganisms may also stimulate the activity of another group and this so-called metabiosis can limit the usefulness of the simple SSO concept for evaluation of microbial seafood spoilage. In cold-smoked salmon, putrescine production by arginine deiminase/decarboxylase negative Enterobacteriaceae increased 10–15 times by co-culturing with arginine deiminase positive lactic acid bacteria. The Enterobacteriaceae and the formed putrescine, however, had little influence on product spoilage (89). In contract, Joffraud et al. (111) found mixtures of spoilage isolates from different microbial species formed stronger off-odors and higher concentration of specific metabolites than mixtures of strains from individual species. The importance of such interactions on spoilage and shelf-life of seafood merits further study.

B. DETERMINATION, PREDICTION AND EXTENSION OF SHELF-LIFE

Indices of freshness or spoilage of seafood have been extensively studied and it is generally accepted that there is a poor correlation between remaining shelf-life, as determined by sensory methods, and aerobic plate counts. However, much closer correlations have been observed between remaining shelf-life and concentration of SSOs in different products. Data have been summarized for (i) H_2S-producing bacteria, e.g., *S. putrefaciens*, in different chilled and aerobically stored fish, (ii) *P. phosphoreum* in chilled MAP cod fillets and (iii) *B. thermosphacta* in chilled MAP red mullet and sea bream from Greece. Correlation coefficients between −0.929 and −0.975 were obtained in all cases (102, 127, 128). For several chilled lightly preserved seafoods a close correlation between remaining shelf-life and concentration of any specific group of microorganisms or any specific metabolite has not been determined. Nevertheless, Jørgensen et al. (129) identified a multiple compound quality index (MCQI) to relate sensory quality of sliced and vacuum packed cold-smoked salmon (SVP-CSS) with the product's pH and cadaverine, histamine, putrescine and tyramine content. Furthermore, Leroi et al. (130) related remaining shelf-life of SVP-CSS at 5°C with the products concentration of *Lactobacillus* spp. and concentration of total volatile nitrogen (TVN). Microbiological criteria relying on mesophilic aerobic bacteria in concentrations between 10^5 and 10^6 cfu/g are included in EU Directives [(12), pp. 195–203]. Due to the frequent dominance of heat-labile spoilage bacteria in seafood, it must not be expected that such criteria correspond to sensory spoilage.

Increased transportation of seafood at both national and international levels makes shelf-life prediction important to prevent rejections of products and disappointed consumers. Kinetic models can be used to predict the effect of product characteristics and storage conditions on growth of SSO, but the range of the environmental factors in the models must be within the spoilage domain of the SSO. In fresh seafoods, SSOs often grow without a lag phase and this facilitates shelf-life prediction (Figure 53.2). In fact, kinetic models to predict growth of *B. thermosphacta*, *P. phosphoreum*, psychrotolerant *Pseudomonas* spp. and *S. putrefaciens* as a function of temperature or both temperature and CO_2 concentration in MAP seafoods have been developed. In addition, the models have been incorporated in user-friendly application software and thus the effect of product temperature profiles can be evaluated by electronic time-temperature integration [see (75) for a review or www.dfu.min.dk/micro/sssp/ where the Seafood Spoilage and Safety Predictor (SSSP) software is available]. Other microorganisms, including species of *Aeromonas*, Enterobacteriaceae, lactic acid bacteria and *Vibrio*, are also important in seafood spoilage (Table 53.1) and for these SSO, kinetic models remain to be developed and/or validated in relevant seafoods. Kinetic models are available for some species of Enterobacteri-aceae and lactic acid bacteria (131), but evaluation and validation, particularly with lightly preserved seafood, is lacking. Predictive microbiology is an active research area and in the near future it is likely that more extensive kinetic models can be developed from different existing models and from easily accessible results collected in databases like ComBase (www.combase.cc). Clearly, evaluation of these models' ability to predict growth in specific seafoods will become important. Another and more ambitious future challenge is to predict the species of microorganisms that become SSOs when (i) new product are formulated, (ii) seafoods are processed by a new technology or (iii) seafoods are stored under conditions not previously evaluated. Data obtained within the last decades (Table 53.1) clearly demonstrate that knowledge about the microbial ecology in seafood has been insufficient to make such predictions.

Developments in classical and emerging technologies to extend shelf-life of seafood are numerous and only the effect of a few aspects will be mentioned here. The targeted inhibition of SSOs is interesting as product shelf-life may be extended by mild preservation methods, selected depending on properties of a particular SSO. Mesophilic motile *Aeromonas* spp. spoil Nile perch at ambient temperature and experiments in liquid media showed this SSO could be inhibited by combinations of NaCl, sorbate and smoke components. Relying on this information, a lightly preserved fish product with marked shelf-life extension was developed (132). Other examples include inhibition of *P. phosphoreum* in chilled MAP cod fillet by oregano essential oil (133) or inactivation of this SSO by freezing (92, 122).

IV. MICROBIOLOGY AND SAFETY OF MARINE MUSCLE FOODS

The safety records and etiological agents vary considerably between groups of seafood and between products from different geographical regions. This section includes information concerning the effect of raw material origin, processing, product characteristics, storage conditions and seafood preparation prior to consumption, which are the most important hazards (Table 53.2).

A. HISTAMINE, BIOGENIC AMINES AND HISTAMINE FISH POISONING (HFP)

HFP is a mild disease that occurs rapidly after intake of seafood containing above 500–1000 ppm of histamine. The toxic effect of histamine is probably potentiated by other biogenic amines in seafood, i.e., agmatine, cadaverine, phenylethylmine, putrescine, spermidine, spermine and tyramine. Alone, tyramine may cause migraine headaches in susceptible individuals. Symptoms of HFP can be cutaneous (e.g., rash or inflammation), gastrointestinal (nausea, vomiting, diarrhoea), neurological (e.g., headache, burning or itching) or circulatory (hypotension). Once formed in seafood, biogenic amines are heat stabile and will not be destroyed by cooking, baking or even canning (135–138).

Not all seafoods cause HFP and it has long been know that a high content of free histidine, growth of histidine decarboxylase-producing microorganisms to high concentrations and high activity of microbial histidine decarboxylases are prerequisites for histamine production in significant amounts and thereby HFP. Fish with a sufficient content of free histidine to cause HFP include anchovy, bluefish, bonito, herring, mackerel, mahimahi/dolphinfishes, marlin, saury/garfish, swordfish, tuna and yellowtail (135–137). Storage temperature is important for histamine formation and, as a general rule, little histamine is formed below 5–7°C whereas above 7–10°C toxic concentrations are frequently produced. However, toxic concentration of histamine have been observed at 0–4°C, e.g., in mackerel (139), saury (139), sardines (139–141) and tunas (142).

Numerous microorganisms produce histamine but only some species of Enterobacteriaceae, *Vibrionaceae*, and lactic acid bacteria (LAB) can grow to above ~10^7 cfu/g and produce toxic concentrations of histaming in seafood. Some Enterobacteriaceae are strong histamine producers, e.g., *Enterobacter aerogenes*, *E. cloacae*, *Morganella morganii*, *Proteus vulgaris* and *Raoultella planticola*. It seems *Klebsiella* spp. do not produce histamine and that, e.g., strains of *Klebsiella pneumoniae* and *K. oxytoca* previously reported to do so may subsequently have been identified as *Raoultella* spp. (143, 144). Below 7–10°C Enterobacteriaceae did not produce toxic concentrations of histamine (145) but histidine decarboxylase

TABLE 53.2
Seafood Associated Hazards and their Prevention;

Hazard	Safety Concern	Preventive Measures
Histamine and biogenic amines	Microbial formation of >500 ppm histamine in products; of primary concern are Enterobacteriaceae in temperature-abused seafoods and *P. phosphoreum* and possible other bacteria in chilled products	Reduce microbial growth and activity by storage of fresh seafood at <2°C and lightly preserved products at <5°C; critical histamine formation may precede sensory spoilage and storage times should be established accordingly (134)
Vibrio species, primarily hemolysin producing *V. parahaemolyticus*, cholera toxin producing *V. cholerae* and *V. vulnificus*	Growth to high levels in live molluscs, in fresh seafood from warmer waters and in cross-contaminated, ready-to-eat products	Avoid storage of live molluscs and fresh seafood at abusive temperature conditions and avoid consumption of improperly cooked seafood, particularly bivalve molluscs
Clostridium botulinum Group I: Proteolytic, particularly toxin type A and B	Growth and toxin formation in products	Inactivate bacteria and spores by canning (>2.4 min. at 121°C) or prevent growth by chilling (<10°C), acidification (pH <4.5) or salt curing (>10% NaCl)
Group II: Non-proteolytic and psychrotolerant, particularly toxin type E	Growth and toxin formation in ready-to-eat (hot-smoked and fermented) products from temperate or cold regions	3.5% water phase salt prevents toxin formation during 4 weeks storage at 4–5°C
Listeria monocytogenes	Growth in ready-to-eat seafoods	Limit contamination by good hygiene practices, reduce growth through controlled product characteristics and limited product shelf-life
		L. monocytogenes is inactivated by normal cooking
Salmonella spp.	Contamination, even by low levels	Avoid direct or indirect faecal contamination of products; inactivate the bacteria by normal cooking
Viruses, primarily Norwalk-like virus (Noroviruses group I and II) and hepatitis A virus	Presence in seafood particularly in bivalve molluscan shellfish consumed raw or lightly cooked	Avoid harvest of bivalve molluscan shellfish from contaminated waters; avoid consumption of improperly cooked seafood, particularly bivalve molluscs

produced at ≥10°C may remain active after chilling to 0–5°C (146, 147). The quantitative effect of this merits further study in seafoods. Mesophilic *Vibrionaceae*, including *Vibrio alginolyticus* and *Plesiomonas shigelloides*, produce histamine but not in important amounts in seafood. In contrast, the psychrotolerant *P. phosphoreum* (previously N-group bacteria and gut-group vibrios) and the mesophilic *Photobacterium damselae* subsp. *damselae* (previously *P. histaminum* and C-group bacteria) have been important in chilled and temperature-abused seafood, respectively (139). *P. phosphoreum* can produce toxic histamine concentrations at 0–4°C [(148) and unpublished data from the laboratory of the author]. However, the temperature history of seafood causing outbreaks of HFP and the microorganisms responsible for histamine formation typically are not known. Further research, and particularly quantitative studies, e.g., including yield factors (89), are needed to determine the importance of psychrotolerant histamine-producing microorganisms and the risk of HFP from appropriately chilled seafoods. LAB do not produce toxic concentrations of histamine in chilled seafood, whereas formation of tyramine is common, e.g., by *Carnobacterium* spp. (149). A mesophilic LAB, *Tetragenococcus muriaticus*, occurs in salt-fermented fish sauce. At 30°C and with 5–15% NaCl it produced >400 ppm of histamine and the production was markedly

increased when pH was reduced from 7.6 to 5.8 and by growth under oxygen-limiting conditions (150). At 20°C, *Lactobacillus buchneri* formed >500 ppm of histamine in herring and tuna salad (151). Interestingly, the optimum pH for histamine production by Enterobacteriaceae, *Vibrionaceae*, and LAB is 5–6, which is much lower than their pH optimum for growth, but similar to the pH in many of the dark-fleshed fish where toxic concentrations of histamine are formed.

EU regulations indicate histamine concentrations in specific seafoods must not exceed 100–200 ppm, whereas the U.S. FDA uses a defect action level of 50 ppm. These relatively low values reflect the fact that histamine concentrations in seafood vary considerably and that a low concentration in one sample suggests a toxic concentration may be present in a different sample from the same lot (137, 152). To control histamine formation in seafood, chilling and storage time are the most important factors (Table 53.2). Freezing can inactivate histamine-producing bacteria but histidine decarboxylase is active during frozen storage and products of dubious freshness should not be frozen. Recently, molecular methods were suggested to identify and detect histamine-producing microorganisms (144, 153). However, quantitative, sensitive and robust methods to enumerate histamine-producing microorganisms in seafood are lacking. This is also the case for methods to predict histamine formation, although a few simple models to assess the effect of time and temperature on histamine formation in skipjack tuna are available (154, 155) and a semi-quantitative risk assessment tool has been suggested (156).

B. VIBRIO SPECIES

Within this genus, the most important seafood-borne human pathogenic species are *Vibrio parahaemolyticus*, *V. vulnificus* and *V. cholerae*, but *V. alginolyticus*, *V. fluvialis*, *V. hollisae* and *V. mimicus* have also caused seafood-borne gastrointestinal disease. In Japan, Asian countries and the U.S. outbreaks are common, whereas they are rare in Europe. Disease is primarily due to consumption of temperature-abused raw or inadequately cooked seafood (Table 53.2). Raw fish like sushi and sashimi is increasingly consumed in Europe but this has not yet resulted in outbreaks caused by *Vibrio* spp. Analysis of *Vibrio* spp. is important in Europe and their occurrence has been a major reason to reject seafood imported into the EU (12, 18). As for the luminous vibrios discussed in Section II, occurrence of mesophilic human pathogenic species in water and aquatic animals depends on temperature and salinity. Both their concentration in seawater and outbreaks of seafood-borne disease are highest during in the warmer months of the year. *V. parahaemolyticus* and *V. vulnificus* are typical marine vibrios that grow optimally with 2.0–2.5% NaCl, whereas *V. cholerae* does not require NaCl and growth is optimal with 0.2–0.5%, corresponding to its natural habitat in estuarine waters (12, 157–159).

V. parahaemolyticus causes a gastrointestinal disease characterized by diarrhoea abdominal cramps, nausea, vomiting and headache. Antibiotics, e.g., tetracyclines, can reduce prolonged infections. For clinical isolates, >95% produce a thermostable direct hemolysin (TDH) (causing a positive Kanagawa reaction) or a TDH-related hemolysin (TRH). For seafood isolates, <1–5% contain genes for TDH and/or TRH and the large majority of *V. parahaemolyticus* in seafoods are non-pathogenic (159–161). Pathogenic variants of *V. parahaemolyticus* can be detected by molecular methods, including various PCR approaches, and further development in this area can be expected also for other pathogenic *Vibrio* species (161–164). The infectious dose for *V. parahaemolyticus* is ~10^6 pathogenic cells and growth in seafood is required for disease to occur. In relation to risk assessment activities, there have been attempts to model the effect of water temperature and salinity on the concentration of *V. parahaemolyticus* in live oysters. Furthermore, inactivation in chilled and growth in temperature-abused live oysters have been quantified (157). For processed seafoods, a mathematical model is available to predict the effect of product storage temperature and water activity on growth of *V. parahaemolyticus* (165).

V. vulnificus is an invasive species that may cause septicemia. Symptoms include high fever, chills, nausea and hypotension. The disease can be fatal, with mortality rates as high as 50%, and prompt antibiotic treatment is required. Individuals with liver disorder are particularly at risk and they should never consume raw seafood. Virulence factors and infectious dose remain uncertain for *V. vulnificus* and in contrast to *V. parahaemolyticus*, a high percentage of *V. vulnificus* isolates from oysters seems to be pathogenic (166). *V. vulnificus* is particularly associated with oysters in seawater at above 15°C and models to predict the effect of water temperature and salinity on the concentration in live oysters at harvest and growth at high distribution temperatures post-harvest have been suggested (157, 167, 168).

V. cholerae causes the notorious gastrointestinal disease cholera with severe watery diarrhoea that results in dehydration and can be fatal. For *V. cholerae*, the two serotypes O1 (including the biotype O1 El Tor) and O139 produce cholerae toxin (CT) and they have been responsible for epidemics. However, *V. cholerae* non-O1/non-O139 have also caused sporadic cases of milder gastrointestinal disease and 10–17% of environmental *V. cholerae* non-O1/non-O139 isolates has been found to contain genes for CT production (169). The infectious dose of *V. cholerae* is ~10^6 cells depending on the food matrix (160). Water contaminated with sewage is the major reason for *V. cholerae* O1/O139 in seafood and improved sanitation is the key to solving the problem. *V. cholerae* non-O1/non-O139, however, occur naturally in estuarine waters. In the U.S. 14% of freshly harvested oysters were contaminated with *V. cholerae* non-O1 (18) and *V. cholerae* non-O1/non-O139 were found, e.g., in French mussels (170). In South America, *V. cholerae* O1 was not reported until a major outbreak in the early 1990s caused >400,000 cases and 4,000 deaths. A lightly preserved seafood *ceviche* consisting of raw fish, lime juice, vegetables and salt, was a possible vehicle for *V. cholerae* O1 (171).

Depuration of oysters may not reduce concentrations of pathogenic *Vibrio* spp. and above ~20°C they may even grow. Fortunately *Vibrio* spp. are sensitive to many types of seafood preservation including chilling at 0–5°C, resulting in slow inactivation, and freezing, which inactivates the bacteria more rapidly. The pathogenic *Vibrio* species are heat sensitive and inactivated by normal cooking (12). Recently, high-pressure processing at 250–300 MPa has been used commercially to inactivate *Vibrio* spp. in sucked oysters and concentrations of *V. parahaemolyticus*, *V. vulnificus* and *V. cholerae* were found to be efficiently reduced (83, 172, 173).

C. CLOSTRIDIUM BOTULINUM

Cl. botulinum is a botulinum neurotoxin (BoNT) producing Gram-positive, anaerobic spore-forming bacteria.

After consumption of seafood with BoNT, symptoms of botulism initially include nausea and vomiting, later double vision, inability to focus, difficulty swallowing and speaking and loss of muscular coordination that can lead to death by respiratory paralysis or cardiac arrest. Onset of symptoms after 12–36 hours is typical and without treatment death after 3–6 days is likely. In fact, mortality has been as high as 50–75%, but treatment with antisera and respiratory aid has reduced mortality to 10–15% (174, 175).

The biochemical and phylogenic variability of *Cl. botulinum* isolates does not correspond to a single microbial species (176) and strains have been divided into four groups (I–IV). Based on antigenic properties, seven types of BoNTs have been identified (types A to G). *Cl. botulinum* group I are proteolytic, halotolerant and mesophilic with minimum growth temperature ~10°C. They produce heat-resistant spores ($D_{121°C} = 0.21$ min) and BoNTs of type A, B and F. Group II consist of non-proteolytic and psychrotolerant strains with minimum growth temperature as low as ~ 3°C. They produce spores that are relatively heat sensitive ($D_{82.2°C} = 0.4$–2.4 min) and BoNTs of types B, E and F. *Cl. botulinum* group III and IV are not related to food-borne disease, but some strains of *Cl. butyricum* produce BoNT type E and may cause food-borne disease. BoNTs have a very low lethal dose and they are resistant to low pH and NaCl. Fortunately, the proteins are sensitive to heat and pH above 7–7.5 and can be inactivated by 20 min at 79°C or by 5 min. at 85°C (12, 174). BoNTs can be detected by mouse bioassays or enzyme-linked immunosorbent assays (ELISA), whereas enrichment procedures, selective plating media and PCR methods are available for detection of vegetative cells and spores of *Cl. botulinum* (174, 177). *Cl. botulinum* group I occurs frequently in soil, but is also found on aquatic animals, primarily in warm waters. In contrast, group II is found frequently in sediments, water and aquatic animals from freshwater and seawater environments in temperate or cold regions. In agreement with this, numerous studies have found low concentrations of spores of particularly *Cl. botulinum* type E in newly caught or processed seafood. Typically <0.1 spore/g was found, but higher concentrations have been found for pond-raised freshwater fishes. Although seafood is frequently contaminated with *Cl. botulinum*, outbreaks of botulism have primarily been associated with fermented/salted and hot-smoked products (174, 175).

For fresh seafood stored aerobically, vacuum-packed (VP) or modified-atmosphere-packed (MAP) growth and toxin formation by *Cl. botulinum* have been extensively studied. Below ~10°C products become spoiled before toxin can be detected, but with substantial temperature abuse toxin formation is more critical and these storage conditions must be avoided. In general, oxygen delays toxin formation by *Cl. botulinum*, but aerobic storage or modified atmospheres with oxygen cannot totally prevent toxin formation as anaerobic microenvironments are formed in the products (17, 178). Cooking prior to consumption can, to some extent, inactivate BoNT and this may have contributed to the excellent botulinum safety record of fresh seafood irrespective of its storage atmosphere.

The psychrotolerant and non-proteolytic *Cl. botulinum* (group II) is able to grow and produce toxin at ~3°C, with <5% NaCl and at pH > 5.0, but combinations of these parameters are inhibitory, which is most important for the safety of several lightly preserved seafoods. It is generally accepted that 3.5% water phase salt (WPS) is sufficient to prevent toxin formation in seafood during 4 weeks at 4–5°C (175). However, BoNT formation in some seafood was inhibited by considerably lower NaCl concentrations. From a sensory point of view, less than 3.5% WPS is often desirable and further studies to identify product characteristics that may contribute to inhibition of BoNT formation in chilled lightly preserved seafoods is relevant. Mathematical models have been developed to predict the effect of temperature, NaCl, pH, CO_2 and spore concentration on growth or BoNT formation by *Cl. botulinum*. These models may assist in identification of safe storage conditions for some types of seafoods (131). Proteolytic *Cl. botulinum* are much more NaCl resistant than the non-proteolytic, but conditions to prevent their growth and BoNT formation in seafood by heating, salt curing or acidification are well established [Table 53.2 (12)]. In fact, recent association of botulism with seafoods has resulted from poorly managed heat treatment or fermentation conditions (174).

D. LISTERIA MONOCYTOGENES

Occurrence of *L. monocytogenes* in seafood is a considerable problem with respect to trade, but fortunately it is very rare that seafood consumption results in listeriosis. *Listeria* is Gram-positive, non-spore-forming, motile rods that biochemically resemble lactic acid bacteria. *L. monocytogenes* is typically invasive and causes disease in people who are elderly, pregnant or have predisposing health conditions like organ transplants, diabetes or AIDS. The incubation time can be long (weeks to months) and this complicates tracing of sporadic outbreaks back to the implicated foods. *L. monocytogenes*, however, may also cause a non-invasive febrile gastroenteritis in otherwise healthy people. If diagnosed, listeriosis can be treated with antibiotics, e.g., ampicillin but mortality rates of untreated listeriosis have been high (~30%) and this is a major reason for the extensive studies of *L. monocytogenes* during the last 20 years.

As mentioned in Section II.C, *L. monocytogenes* is indigenous to the general environmant and frequently found in low concentrations on newly caught aquatic animals and in fresh and lightly preserved seafoods (12, 179). Low concentrations of *L. monocytogenes* in seafood are not an important risk to human health and the main safety concern is growth in ready-to-eat products [Table 53.2, (180)]. More than 1000 *L. monocytogenes* per gram or ml have been found in foods that caused listeriosis (181). Despite this fact, some countries, including the U.S., require absence of *L. monocytogenes* in 25-g samples of products. This zero tolerance is a frequent reason for import refusal of seafood by the U.S. FDA (12).

L. monocytogenes is able to grow between ~0°C and ~40°C, with <10% NaCl corresponding to $a_w > 0.92$, at pH above ~4.5 and it is problematic to control growth in some types of seafoods. In fact, a recent risk assessment found smoked seafood and cooked ready-to-eat crustaceans to be of high risk on a "per serving basis" and of moderate risk when evaluated per annum for the total U.S. population (180).

Models to predict the effect of, e.g., temperature, $NaCl/a_w$, pH, organic acids, nitrite, smoke components, atmosphere and microbial interaction on growth, survival or inactivation of *L. monocytogenes* have been extensively studied. Some models are included in application software to facilitate prediction of growth in foods (131, 182). However, predictive models developed in liquid laboratory media may not be appropriate for use with seafoods. Thus, users of models should verify that a model has been successfully validated for seafoods with microbial ecology similar to the product to which it will be applied.

L. monocytogenes is inactivated by normal cooking of seafood ($D_{60°C} = 2$–4.5 min) and inhibited by the high concentrations of acetic acid (~2.5%) used in several semi-preserved seafoods, like marinated herring. However, processing of a number of ready-to-eat seafoods, including cold-smoked products, does not include critical control points for *L. monocytogenes*. To prevent growth to high concentrations the following parameters are of major importance: (i) good hygiene practices with careful cleaning and sanitation of known or likely niches in the processing environment, (ii) controlled product characteristics and (iii) limited shelf-life at specified temperature conditions. Modified atmosphere packing with CO_2-containing atmospheres reduces but does not prevent growth of *L. monocytogenes*. The combined effect of 1–2% lactate and 0.1–0.2% diacetate reduces growth of *L. monocytogenes* in different meat products and use of these organic acids in seafood deserves further study. Addition of lactic acid bacteria can to inhibit *L. monocytogenes* in lightly preserved seafood (183, 184), but this type of biopreservation has not yet been used at industrial scale.

E. SALMONELLA

Salmonella is responsible for a significant number of the cases of disease caused by finfish and shell-fish, both in the U.S. and in the U.K. (see Section I). In contrast to the etiological agents discussed above, *Salmonella* originate from the human/animal reservoir and therefore good hygienic practices, with focus on clean water and personal hygiene, are essential to control occurrence in seafood.

Salmonella is a mesophilic member of the Enterobacteriaceae family that grows at above ~5°C, pH > 3.8 and with <6% NaCl. The genus consists of only two species: *Sal. enterica* and *Sal. bongori*. The former is divided into six subspecies and the genus includes more than 2400 serovars (185). The infectious dose of *Salmonella* is frequently ~10^6 cells, but it can be much lower (10–100 cells) when the bacteria is protected against stomach acid, e.g., by fat (12). Typhoid and paratyphoid strains can lead to enteric fever syndrome salmonellosis with watery diarrhoea, fever, abdominal pain, headache and nausea occurring 7 to 28 days after intake of the strains. In contrast, symptoms caused by nontyphoid strains appear rapidly after exposure (8–72 hours) and include nausea, abdominal cramps, diarrhoea, fever and vomiting (185). When symptoms disappear, people continue to excrete *Salmonella* for up to several months and this is a potential risk for seafood contamination during processing.

Salmonella is rare in temperate waters, but can be found in tropical estuaries and coastal waters as well as in aquatic animals from these habitats. Compared to other types of foods, seafood has caused relatively few, and no major, outbreaks of salmonellosis, but occurrence of *Salmonella* in seafood has been a major reason to reject products at port of entry into both the EU and the U.S. (12, 185).

Mathematical models to predict growth or inactivation of *Salmonella* as a function of temperature, NaCl, pH and essential oils are available (131) and can be used to facilitate assessment and management of the risk caused by the pathogen in seafoods. *Salmonella* is heat labile ($D_{60°C}$ of 1–3 min) and inactivated by normal cooking and, for example, hot-smoking. Thus, focus on post-processing contamination and reduced consumption of raw seafood are important to limit salmonellosis in seafoods (Table 53.2).

F. VIRUSES

Viruses cause a higher number of seafood-borne diseases than any other microbial hazard. This is particularly due to filterfeeding molluscan shellfish consumed as raw or lightly cooked products. Seawater contains numerous indigenous viruses in high concentrations but seafood-borne diseses are caused by human enteric viruses and particularly Norwalk-like virus (NLV, also referred to as Noroviruses group I and group II) and to a lesser extent hepatitis A virus (HAV). NLV and HAV do not grow in the environment and the main concerns with respect to seafoods are (i) sewage or faecal contamination of aquatic habitats, particularly shellfish growing areas, where molluscan shellfish through their filtration of water to obtain food can accumulate viruses from the water to concentrations that are infectious to humans and (ii) fecal contamination of seafood during processing as a result of poor personal hygiene (186, 187). Seafood-borne disease due to virus in molluscan shellfish is much more frequent than due to virus in finfish (Section I), suggesting contamination of aquatic habitatsis relatively more important than contamination during processing.

NLV is a genetically diverse group of virus strains divided into two genogroups (188). NLV causes gastroenteritidis with diarrhoea, vomiting and possibly abdominal pain, nausea and fever. Incubation time is ~24 hours and duration of symptoms ~2 days. The infectious dose is estimated to be low but lack of sensitive enumeration methods has prevented more exact determination (186). Recently, oysters with >1000 virions each were shown by a most-probable-number-reverse-transcriptase-PCR approach to cause an outbreak (189). HAV causes infectious hepatitis with jaundice (yellow coloring of skin and eyes), fever, headace, nausea, malaise/vomiting, diarrhoea and abdominal pian. The disease is occasionally fatal. The incubation period is 2–6 weeks and symptoms can last 2 months (186). Both NLV and HAV contain RNA genomes and a protein cover (capsid).

Viruses, in contrast to bacteria, cannot be cultured in simple laboratory media and NLV and HAV from seafood cannot even grow in cell cultures. In faeces, where high concentrations are precent, virus can be detected by electron microscopy and immunoassays, but the detection limit of these techniques is too high for enumeration of NLV and HAV in seafood. Lack of sensitive methods for detection and enumeration have greatly limited our understanding of the occurrence and ecology of viruses in seafoods. However, application of molecular methods including various PCR approaches is now changing this situation (186, 190–192). Further developments, particularly of sensitive and quantitative PCR-based methods, must be expected in the near future although the genetic variability of NLV and the specific detection of active viruses that cause disease represent challenges. Difficulties with virus detection are reasons why both U.S. and EU use legislative standards for live shellfish that rely on enumeration of faecal coliforms or *Escherichia coli*. In fact, numerous studies have found poor correlation between contamination of shellfish with virus and the coliform indicators of faecal contamination and there is a need for updated standards (186, 191).

To control the presence of human enteric viruses in seafood several options are available. Preventing harvest in contaminated waters is an obvious but not always easy solution. If, e.g., a shellfish harvesting area is contaminated by sewage after heavy rainfall, the virus can remain for a long time in seawater. The decimal reduction time of HAV is 671 days at 4°C and 25 days at 25°C (193). However, overboard disposal of faeces by personnel working in a shellfish harvesting area caused an outbreak of NLV disease. This type of contamination should be easy to prevent (186). Depuration of shellfish by circulation of non-contaminated water for 1–7 days is common and can reduce virus concentrations in the animals but faecal coliforms are

eliminated more rapidly and virus removal may require weeks (186, 194). To prevent virus contamination during seafood processing it is important that NLV is shed by a person two days after onset disease whereas HAV is shed in faeces ~2 weeks prior to symptoms and 1–2 weeks after of the disease. In appropriate periods after NLV, and HAV-related disease, seafood industry personnel should not handle products.

RNA has limited stability but viruses seem relatively resistant in seafood although the resistance of pathogenic strains in the low concentrations actually found in seafood merits further study. 90°C during 1.5 min has been recommended for inactivation of virus in seafood (186). High-pressure processing of oysters at 250–300 MPa may reduce levels of NLV but will probably have little effect on HAV (195).

V. CONCLUDING REMARKS

Many aspects of the microbiology of marine muscle foods have been extensively studied and the information obtained has been valuable in the management of product quality and safety. However, occurrence of microbial seafood spoilage and seafood-borne disease remains unacceptably high and further research is needed to improve this situation.

The development and distribution of antibiotic-resistant microorganisms in aquatic animals and seafood needs further study. Concerning SSOs, research is particularly needed for lightly/semi-preserved and fermented seafoods where combinations of several preserving parameters influence microbial growth and activity. It is also relevant to evaluate spoilage caused by mixed groups of microorganisms (metabiosis) and to evaluate how information about SSOs can be used to determine, predict and extend the shelf-life of lightly and semi-preserved seafoods. As a part of this work development of sensitive, specific and rapid methods to detect SSOs is relevant and it seems appropriate to evaluate quantitative PCR approaches. Concerning seafood-borne disease, more precise information is needed to understand the occurrence and inactivation of viruses in seafood. The importance of psychrotolerant histamine-producing microorganisms is not yet completely understood. Finally, improved methods to control the growth of *L. monocytogenes* in lightly preserved seafoods are required.

REFERENCES

1. Anonymous. An Evaluation of the Role of Micro-biological Criteria for Foods and Food Ingredients. Food and Nutrition Board, National Research Council. Washington, D.C.: National Academic Press, 1985. p. 46.
2. FAO (Food and Agriculture Organization). The State of World Fisheries and Aquaculture (www.fao.org/docrep/005/y7300e00.htm, accessed October 2003). Rome, Italy: FAO, 2002.

3. GW Gould. Methods for preservation and extension of shelf life. Int J Food Microbiol 33: 51–64, 1996.

4. GA Reay, JM Shewan. The spoilage of fish and its preservation by chilling. Adv Food Res 2: 343–398, 1949.

5. J Shewan. The microbiology of seawater fish. In: G Borgstrøm, ed. Fish as a Food, Vol I. London: Academic Press, 1961, pp. 487–560.

6. JM Shewan. The microbiology of fish products — a progress report. J Appl Bact 34: 299–315, 1971.

7. JM Shewan. The bacteriology of fresh and spoiling fish and the biochemistry changes induced by bacterial action. In: Proceedings of the Conference on the Handling, Processing and Marketing of Trobical Fish. London: Tropical Products Institute, Ministry of Over-Seas Development, 1977, pp. 51–66.

8. J Liston. Microbiology in fishery science. In: JJ Connell, ed. Advances in Fish Science and Technology. London: Fishing News Books Ltd., 1980, pp. 138–157.

9. INA Ashie, JP Smith, BK Simpson. Spoilage and shelf-life extension of fresh fish and shellfish. Cri Rev Food Sci Nutr 36: 87–121, 1996.

10. P Dalgaard. Fresh and lightly preserved seafood. In: CMD Man, AA Jones, eds. Shelf-Life Evaluation of Foods. London: Aspen Publishers, Inc., 2000, pp. 110–139.

11. L Gram, L Ravn, M Rasch, JB Bruhn, AB Christiansen, M Givskov. Food spoilage — interactions between food spoilage bacteria. Int J Food Microbiol 78: 79–97, 2002.

12. HH Huss, L Ababouch, L Gram. Assessment and Management of Seafood Safety and Quality. Rome, Italy: FAO, 2003, pp. 1–230.

13. SJ Olsen, LC MacKinnon, JS Goulding, NH Bean, L Slutsker. Surveillance for foodborne-disease outbreaks — United States, 1993–1997. CDC Surveillance Summaries. MMWR 49: 1–62, 2000.

14. CSPI (Center for Science in the Public Interest). Outbreak Alert. Closing the Gaps in our Federal Food-Safety Net. Washington, D.C.: CSPI, 2001.

15. IA Gillespie, GK Adak, SJ O'Brien, MM Brett, FJ Bolton. General outbreaks of infectious intestinal disease associated with fish and shellfish, England and Wales, 1992–1999. Comin Dis Public Health 4: 117–123, 2001.

16. ICMFS (International Commission on Microbiological Specifications for Foods). Fish and fish products. In: TA Roberts, JJ Pitt, J Farkas, FH Grau, eds. Microorganisms in Foods 6. Microbial Ecology of Food Commodities. London: Blackie Academic & Professional, 1998, pp. 130–189.

17. L Gram, HH Huss. Fresh and processed fish and shellfish. In: BM Lund, TC Baird-Parker, GW Gould, eds. The Microbiological Safety and Quality of Food. Gaithersburg: Aspen Publishers, Inc., 2000, pp 472–506.

18. F Feldhausen. The role of seafood in bacterial food-borne diseases. Microb Infec 2: 1651–1660, 2000.

19. RW Horsley. A review of the bacterial flora of teleosts and elasmobranchs, including methods for its analysis. J Fish Biol 10: 529–553, 1977.

20. MM Cahill. Bacterial flora of fishes: A review. Microb Ecol 19: 21–41, 1990.

21. M Yoshimizu, K Kamiyama, T Kimura, M Sakai. Studies on the intestinal microflora of salmonids — IV. The intestinal microflora of fresh water salmon. Bull Jap Soc Sci Fish 42: 1281–1290, 1976.

22. M Okuzumi, M Awano. Seasonal variations in numbers of psychrophilic and halophilic histamine-forming bacteria (N-group bacteria) in seawater and on marine fishes. Bull Jap Soc Sci Fish 49: 1285–1291, 1983.

23. R Yoguchi, M Okuzumi, T Fujii. Seasonal variation in numbers of mesophilic and halophilic histamine-forming bacteria in inshore of Tokyo Bay and Sagami Bay. Nippon Suisan Gakkaishi 56: 1467–1472, 1990.

24. ME López-Caballero, A Goncalves, ML Nunes. Effect of CO_2/O_2-containing modified atmosphere on packed deepwater shrimp (Parapenaeus longirostris). Eur. Food Res Technol 214: 192–197, 2002.

25. EG Ruby, EP Greenberg, JW Hastings. Planktonic marine luminous bacteria: Species distribution in the water column. Appl Environ Microbiol 39: 302–306, 1980.

26. N Ramaiah, D Chandramohan. Distribution of luminous bacteria and bacterial luminescence in the equatorial region of the Indian Ocean. Microbiological 11: 243–254, 1988.

27. N Ramaiah, D Chandramohan. Distribution and species composition of planktonic luminous bacteria in the Arabian Sea. Indian J Mar Sci 16: 139–142, 1987.

28. GA Vydryakova, AM Kuznetsov, GA Primakova, YV Chugaeva, AM Fish. Luminescent bacterial symbionts and commensals of luminescent and non-luminescent marine animals of the Indian Ocean. Microbiology 64: 589–592, 1995.

29. J Liston. The occurrence and distribution of bacterial types on flatfish. J Gen Microbiol 16: 205–216, 1957.

30. KJA van Spreekens. The suitability of a modification of Long and Hammer's medium for the enumeration of more fastidious bacteria from fresh fishery products. Arch Lebensmittelhyg 25: 213–219, 1974.

31. JM Shewan. The bacteriology of fresh and spoiling fish and some related chemical changes. Rec Adv Food Sci 167–193, 1962.

32. JR Matches, J Liston, D Curran. Clostridium perfringens in the environment. Appl Microbiol 28: 655–660, 1974.

33. H Sugita, C Miyajima, Y Deguchi. The vitamin B_{12}-producing ability of the intestinal microflora of fresh-water fish. Aquaculture 92: 267–276, 1991.

34. WE Holben, P Williams, M Saarinen, LK Särkilahti, JHA Apajalahti. Phylogenetic analysis of intestinal microflora indicates a novel Mycoplasma phylotype in farmed and wild salmon. Microb Ecol 44: 175–185, 2002.

35. I Huber, B Spanggaard, J Nielsen, KF Appel, T Nielsen, L Gram. Phylogenetic analysis and in situ identification of the intestinal microbial community of rainbow trout (Onchorhynchus mykiss, Walbaum). J Appl Microbiol 96: 117–132, 2004.

36. I Karunasagar, I Karunasar. Harvest and post-harvest microbiology of fishes. Indian J Microbiol 31: 211–229, 1991.

37. JL Reichelt, P Baumann. Taxonomy of the marine, luminous bacteria. Arch Microbiol 94: 283–330, 1973.

38. KH Nealson, JW Hastings. The luminous bacteria. In: A Balows et al., eds. The Procaryotes. New York: Springer-Verlag, 1992, pp. 625–639.

39. H Sera, Y Ishida, H Kadota. Bacterial flora in the digestive tract of marine fish — IV. Effect of H$^+$ concentration and gastric juices on the indigenous bacteria. Bull Jap Soc Sci Fish 38: 859–863, 972.

40. A Ramesh, VK Venugopalan. Response of enteric luminous bacteria to environmental conditions in the gut of the fish. J Appl Bact 66: 529–533, 1989.

41. E Ringø, E Strøm, J-A Tabachek. Intestinal microflora of salmonids: a review. Aquac Res 26: 773–789, 1995.

42. M Yoshimizu, T Kimura, M Sakai. Studies on the intestinal microflora of salmonids — V. The intestinal microflora of the anadromous salmon. Bull Jap Soc Sci Fish 41: 1291–1298, 1976.

43. E Ringø, F-J Gatesoupe. Lactic acid bacteria in fish: a review. Aquaculture 160: 177–203, 1998.

44. B Spanggaard, I Huber, J Nielsen, T Nielsen, KF Appel, L Gram. The microflora of rainbow trout intestine: a comparison of traditional and molecular identification. Aquaculture 182: 1–15, 2001.

45. H Sera, Y Ishida. Bacterial flora in the digestive tract of marine fish — III. Classification of isolated bacteria. Bull Jap Soc Sci Fish 38: 853–858, 1972.

46. M Yoshimizu, B Kimura. Study on the intestinal microflora of salmonids. Fish Pathol 10: 243–259, 1976.

47. KJ Budsberg, CF Wimpee, JF Braddock. Isolation and identification of Phosphoreum phosphoreum from an unexpected niche: migrating salmon. Appl Environ Microbiol 69: 6938–6942, 2003.

48. M Okuzumi, S Horie. Studies on the bacterial flora in the intestine of various marine fish. Bull Jap Soc Sci Fish 35: 93–100, 1969.

49. EN Harvey. Bioluminescence. New York: Academic Press, 1952.

50. A Ramesh, BG Loganathan, K Venkateswaran. Ecological dynamics of marine luminous bacteria. J Basic Microbiol 30: 689–703, 1990.

51. LM Palmer, RR Colwell. Detection of luciferase gene sequence in nonluminescent Vibrio cholerae by colony hybridization and polymerase chain reaction. Appl Environ Microbiol 57: 1286–1293, 1991.

52. JD Oliver, DM Roberts, VK White, MA Dry, LM Simpson. Bioluminescence in a strain of the human pathogenic bacterium Vibrio vulnificus. Appl Environ Microbiol 52: 1209–1211, 1986.

53. PM Fidopiastic, H Sørum, EG Ruby. Cryptic luminescence in the cold-water fish pathogen Vibrio salmonicida. Arch Microbiol 171: 205–209, 1999.

54. J Liston. A group of luminous and non-lumonous bacteria from the intestine of flatfish. J Gen Microbiol 12: XII, 1955.

55. EG Ruby, KH Nealson. Seasonal changes in the species composition of luminous bacteria in nearshore seawater. Limnol Oceanogr 23: 530–533, 1978.

56. EG Ruby, JG Morin. Luminous enteric bacteria of marine fishes: a study of their distribution, densities, and dispersion. Appl Environ Microbiol 38: 406–411, 1979.

57. JC Makemson, GV Mermosa. Luminous bacteria cultured from fish guts in the Gulf of Oman. Luminescence 14: 161–168, 1999.

58. K Venkateswaran, S Sethuramalingam, R Natarajan. Gut microflora of some edible crabs from Porto Novo coast. Indian J Mar Sci 10: 399–401, 1981.

59. A Ramesh, VK Venugopalan. Luminous microflora associated with the fishes Mugil cephalus and Tachysurus arius. FEMS Microbiol Ecol 53: 27–34, 1988.

60. NL MacDonald, JR Stark, B Austin. Bacterial microflora in the gastro-intestinal tract of Dover sole (Solea solea L.), with emphasis on the possible role of bacteria in the nutrition of the host. FEMS Microbiol Lett 35: 107–111, 1986.

61. A Ramesh, VK Venugopalan. Role of luminous bacteria in chitin degradation in the intestine of fish. MICREN Journal 5: 55–59, 1989.

62. M Barak, S Ulitzur. Bacterial bioluminescence as an early indication of marine fish spoilage. Eur J Appl Microbiol 10: 155–165, 1980.

63. H Morii, DC Cann, LY Taylor, CK Murray. Formation of histamine by luminous bacteria isolated from scomboid fish. Bull Jap Soc Sci Fish 52: 2135–2141, 1986.

64. H Morii, DC Cann, LY Taylor. Histamine formation by luminous bacteria in mackerel stored at low temperatures. Nippon Suisan Gakkaishi 54: 299–305, 1988.

65. T Paarup, JA Sanchez, C Peláez, A Moral. Sensory, chemical and bacteriological changes in vacuum-packed pressurised squid mantle (Todaropsis eblanae) stored at 4°C. Int J Food Microbiol 74: 1–12, 2002.

66. T Paarup, JA Sanchez, A Moral, H Christensen, M Bisgaard, L Gram. Sensory, chemical and bacteriological changes during storage of iced squid (Todaropsis eblanae). J Appl Microbiol 92: 941–950, 2002.

67. P. N. Sado, Glowing Seafood, U.S. Food and Drug Administration. Seafoods Products Research Center. (Accessed January 2003 at: vm.cfsan.fda.gov/~ear/esa-glow.html), 1998.

68. U Simidu, E Kaneko. A numerical taxonomy of Vibrio and Aeromonas from normal and diseased marine fish. Bull Jap Soc Sci Fish 39: 689–703, 1973.

69. P Dalgaard. Qualitative and quantitative characterization of spoilage bacteria from packed fish. Int J Food Microbiol 26: 319–333, 1995.

70. P Dalgaard, O Mejlholm, TJ Christiansen, HH Huss. Importance of Photobacterium phosphoreum in relation to spoilage of modified atmosphere-packed fish products. Lett Appl Microbiol 24: 373–378, 1997.

71. P Dalgaard. Luminous bacteria — occurrence and importance in seafoods (in Danish). Fisk & Hav 56: 48–54, 2003.

72. L Gram, E Ringø. Prospects of fish probiotics. In: W Holzapfel, PJ Naughton, eds. Microbal Ecology of the Growing Animal. Elsevier, 2004, in press.

73. DJ Alderman, TS Hastings. Antibiotic use in aquaculture: development of antibiotic resistance — potential for consumer health risks. Int J Food Sci Technol 33: 139–155, 1998.

74. K Holmström, S Gräslund, A Wahlström, S Poungshompoo, B-E Bengtsson, N Kautsky. Antiobiotic use in shrimp farming and implications for environmental impacts and human health. Int J Food Sci Technol 38: 255–266, 2003.

75. P Dalgaard. Modelling and prediction the shelf-life of seafood. In: HA Bremner, ed. Safety and quality issues in fish processing. Cambridge, England: Woodhead Publishing Ltd., 2002, pp. 191–219.

76. CE Hebard, GJ Flick, RE Martin. Occurrence and significance of trimethylamine oxide and its derivatives in fish and shellfish. In: RE Martin, GJ Flick, CE Hebard, DR Ward, eds. Chemistry and biochemistry of marine food products. Westport: AVI Publishing Company, 1982, pp. 149–304.

77. HH Huss. Quality and quality changes in fresh fish. Rome: FAO Fisheries Technical Paper No. 348, 1995.

78. R Spencer. The taxonomy of certain luminous bacteria. J Gen Microbiol 13: 111–118, 1955.

79. EL Barret, HS Kwan. Bacterial reduction of trimethylamine oxide. Annu Rev Microbiol 39: 131–149, 1985.

80. LM Proctor, RP Gunaslus. Anaerobic respiratory growth of *Vibrio harveyi*, *Vibrio fischeri* and *Photobacterium leiognathi* with trimethyle N-oxide, nitrate and fumarate: ecological implications. Environ Microbiol 2: 399–406, 2000.

81. HA Bremner, JA Statham. Spoilage of vacuum-packed chill-stored scallops with added lactobacilli. Food Technol 35: 284–287, 1983.

82. ME López-Caballero, M Pérez-Mateos, P Montero, AJ Borderías. Oyster preservation by high-pressure treatment. J Food Prot 63: 196–201, 2000.

83. H He, RM Adams, DE Farkas, MT Morrissey. Use of high-pressure processing for oyster shucking and shelf-life extension. J Food Sci 67: 640–645, 2002.

84. A Vasakou, K Vareltzis, JG Bloukas. Effect of sodium lactate and potassium sorbate on quality characteristics and shelf-life of Mediterranean mussel (*Mytilus galloprovincialis*) meat during chilled storage in pouches with water. Ital J Food Sci 15: 359–370, 2003.

85. H Abe. Distribution of free L-histidine and its related compounds in marine fishes. Bull Jap Soc Sci Fish 49: 1683–1687, 1983.

86. HN Chinivasagam, HA Bremner, AF Wood, SM Nottingham. Volatile compounds associated with bacterial spoilage of tropical prawns. Int J Food Microbiol 42: 45–55, 1998.

87. P Dalgaard. Evaluation and Prediction of Microbial Fish Spoilage (Ph.D. thesis). Lyngby, Denmark: Technological Laboratory, Danish Ministry of Fisheries, 1993.

88. CH Castell, GW Anderson. Bacteria associated with spoilage of cod fillets. J Fish Res Bd Canada 7: 370–377, 1948.

89. LV Jørgensen, HH Huss, P Dalgaard. The effect of biogenic amine production by single bacterial cultures and metabiosis on cold-smoked salmon. J Appl Microbiol 89: 920–934, 2000.

90. K Koutsoumanis, G-JE Nychas. Application of a systematic experimental procedure to develop a microbial model for rapid fish shelf life prediction. Int J Food Microbiol 60: 171–184, 2000.

91. P Dalgaard, LG Munoz, O Mejlholm. Specific inhibition of *Photobacterium phosphoreum* extends the shelf life of modified-atmosphere-packed cod fillets. J Food Prot 61: 1191–1194, 1998.

92. J Emborg, BG Laursen, T Rathjen, P Dalgaard. Microbial spoilage and formation of biogenic amines in fresh and thawed modified atmosphere packed salmon (*Salmo salar*) at 2°C. J Appl Microbiol 92: 790–799, 2002.

93. V Venugopal. Extracellular proteases of contaminant bacteria in fish spoilage: A review. J Food Prot 53: 341–350, 1990.

94. M Kobatake, NJW Kreger-van Rij, TLC Plácido, N van Uden. Isolation of proteolytic psychrotrophic yeasts from fresh raw seafoods. Lett Appl Microbiol 14: 37–42, 1992.

95. P Lerke, L Farber, R Adams. Bacteriology of spoilage of fish muscle: IV. Role of protein. Appl Microbiol 15(4): 770–776, 1967.

96. G Karnop. Die Rolle der Proteolyten beim Fischverderb. II. Verkommen und Bedeutung der Proteolyten als bakterielle Verderbsindikatoren. Arch Lebensmittelhyg 33: 61–66, 1982.

97. T Chai, C Chen, A Rosen, RE Levin. Detection and incidence of specific species of spoilage bacteria on fish. Appl Microbiol 16: 1738–1741, 1968.

98. RA Herbert, JM Shewan. Roles played by bacterial and autolytic enzymes in the production of volatiles sulphides in spoiling North Sea cod (*Gadus morhua*). J Sci Food Agric 27: 89–94, 1976.

99. KJA van Spreekens. Characterization of some fish and shrimp spoiling bacteria. Antonine van Leewenhoek 43: 283–303, 1977.

100. A Miller, RA Scanlan, JS Lee, LM Libbey. Identification of the volatile compounds produced in sterile fish muscle (*Sebastes melanops*) by *Pseudomonas fragi*. Appl Microbiol 25: 952–955, 1973.

101. HN Chinivasagam, HA Bremner, SJ Thrower, SM Nottingham. Spoilage pattern of five species of Australian prawns: Deterioration is influenced by environment of capture and mode of storage. J Aquat Food Prod Technol 5: 25–50, 1996.

102. K Koutsoumanis, P Taoukis, ES Drosinos, GJE Nychas. Lactic acid bacteria and *Brochothrix thermosphacta* — the dominant spoilage microflora of Mediterranean fresh fish stored under modified atmosphere packaging conditions. In: G Ólafsdóttir et al., eds. Methods to Determine the Freshness of Fish in Research and Industry, Paris, France, Int. Inst. Refrig. 1998, pp 158–165.

103. D López-Gálvez, L de la Hoz, JA Ordóñez. Effect of carbon dioxide and oxygen enriched atmospheres on microbiological and chemical changes in refrigerated tuna (*Thunnus alalunga*) steaks. J Agric Food Chem 43: 483–490, 1995.

104. TK Srinivasa Gobal, VN Nambiar, SK Bhattacharyya. Modified atmosphere storage of fresh water fish fillets (*Catla catla*). In: Proceedings from Commission C2 meeting, International Institute of Refrigeration, Aberdeen, UK. Refrig Sci Technol 173–177, 1990.

105. J Liston. Bacterial spoilage of seafood. In: HH Huss, M Jacobsen, J Liston, eds. Quality assurance in the fish industry. Amsterdam: Elsevier, 1992, pp. 93–105.

106. M Okuzumi, I Fukumoto, T Fujii. Changes in bacterial flora and polyamines contents during storage of horse mackerel meat. Nippon Suisan Gakkaishi 56: 1307–1312, 1990.

107. P Dalgaard, LV Jørgensen. Cooked and brined shrimps packed in a modified atmosphere have a shelf-life of >7 months at 0°C, but spoil at 4–6 days at 25°C. Int J Food Sci Technol 35: 431–442, 2000.

108. L Truelstrup Hansen, HH Huss. Comparison of the microflora isolated from spoiled cold-smoked salmon from three smokehouses. Food Res Int 31: 703–711, 1998.

109. F Leroi, JJ Joffraud, F Chevalier, M Cardinal, Study of the microbial ecology of cold-smoked salmon during storage at 8°C. Int J Food Microbiol 39: 111–121, 1998.

110. M Basby, VF Jeppesen, HH Huss. Characterization of the microflora of lightly salted lumpfish (*Cyclopterus lumpus*) roe stored at 5°C. J Aquat Food Prod Technol 7: 35–51, 1998.

111. JJ Joffraud, F Leroi, C Roy, JL Berdagué. Characterization of volatile compounds produced by bacteria isolated from the spoilage flora of cold-smoked salmon. Int J Food Microbiol 66: 175–184, 2001.

112. LV Jørgensen, HH Huss, P Dalgaard. Significance of volatile compounds produced by spoilage bacteria in vacuum-packed cold-smoked salmon (*Salmo salar*) analysed by GC-MS and multivariate regression. J Agric Food Chem 49: 2381, 2001.

113. V Stohr, JJ Joffraud, M Cardinal, F Leroi. Spoilage potential and sensory profile associated with bacteria isolated from cold-smoked salmon. Food Res Int 34: 797–806, 2001.

114. I Stenstrøm, G Molin. Classification of the spoilage flora of fish, with special reference to *Shewanella putrefaciens*. J Appl Bact 68: 601–618, 1990.

115. F Ziemke, M Höfle, J Lalucat, R Rosselló-Mora. Reclassification of *Shewanella putrefaciens* Owen's genomic group II as *Shewanella baltica* sp. nov. Int J Syst Bacteriol 48: 179–186, 1998.

116. K Venkateswaran, DP Moser, ME Dollhopf, DP Lies, DA Saffarini, BJ MacGregor, DB Ringelberg, DC White, M Nishijima, H Sano, J Burghardt, E Stackebrandt, KH Nealson. Polyphasic taxonomy of the genus *Shewanella* and description of *Shewanella oneidensis* sp. nov. Int J Syst Bacteriol 49: 705–724, 2000.

117. NC Gillespie. A numerical taxonomic study of *Pseudomonas*-like bacteria isolated from fish in southeastern Queensland and their association with spoilage. J Appl Bact 50: 29–44, 1981.

118. P Tryfinopoulou, E Tsakalidou, G-JE Nychas. Characterization of *Pseudomonas* spp. associated with spoilage of Gilt-Head Sea Bream stored under various conditions. Appl Environ Microbiol 68: 65–72, 2002.

119. M Gennari, S Tomaselli, V Cotrona. The microflora of fresh and spoiled sardines (*Sardina pilchardus*) caught in Adriatic (Mediterranean) Sea and stored in ice. Food Microbiol 16: 15–28, 1999.

120. CJ González, JA Santos, M-L García-López, A Otero. Psychrobacter and related bacteria in freshwater fish. J Food Prot 63: 315–321, 2000.

121. E Larsen, G Hyldig, P Dalgaard, AC Bech, C Østerberg. Consumers and experts responses to fresh cod fillets. In: JB Luten, J Oehlenschlager, G Ólafsdóttir, eds. Quality of Fish from Catch to Consumer. Wageningen, the

Netherlands: Wageningen Academic Publishers, 2003, pp. 345–360.

122. HS Guldager, N Bøknæs, C Østerberg, J Nielsen, P Dalgaard. Thawed cod fillets spoil less rapidly than unfrozen fillets when stored under modified atmosphere at 2°C. J Food Prot 61: 1129–1136, 1998.

123. Y-M Kim, H-D Paik, D-S Lee. Shelf-life characteristics of fresh oysters and ground beef as affected by bacteriocin-coated plastic packaging film. J Sci Food Agric 82: 998–1002, 2002.

124. KJA van Spreekens, L Toepoel. Quality of fishery products in connection with the psychrophillic and psychotrophic bacterial flora. In: TA Roberts, G Hobbs, JHB Christian, N Skovgaard, eds. Psychrotrophic Microorganisms in Spoilage and Pathogenicity. London: Academic Press, 1981, pp. 283–294.

125. PE Doe, E Heruwati. A model for the prediction of the microbial spoilage of sun-dried tropical fish. J Food Eng 8: 47–72, 1988.

126. T Ross, P Dalgaard, S Tienungoon. Predictive modelling of the growth and survival of *Listeria* in fishery products. Int J Food Microbiol 62: 231–245, 2000.

127. C Capell, P Vaz-Pires, R Kirby. Use of counts of hydrogen sulphide producing bacteria to estimate remaining shelf-life of fresh fish. In: G Ólafsdóttir et al., eds. Methods to Determine the Freshness of Fish in Research and Industry. Paris, France: Int. Inst. Refrig. 1998, pp. 175–182.

128. P Dalgaard. Photobacterium phosphoreum — a microbial parameter for prediction of remaining shelf life in MAP cod fillets. In: G Ólafsdóttir et al., eds. Methods to Determine the Freshness of Fish in Research and Industry. Paris, France: Int. Inst. Refrig., 1998, pp. 166–174.

129. LV Jørgensen, P Dalgaard, HH Huss. Multiple compound quality index for cold-smoked salmon (*Salmo salar*) developed by multivariate regression of biogenic amines and pH. J Agric Food Chem 48: 2448–2453, 2000.

130. F Leroi, JJ Joffraud, F Chevalier, M Cardinal. Research of quality indices for cold-smoked salmon using a stepwise multiple regression of microbiological counts and physico-chemical parameters. J Appl Microbiol 90: 578–587, 2001.

131. T Ross, P Dalgaard. Secondary models. In: Modeling Microbial Responses in Foods. Boca Raton, FL: CRC Press, 2004, pp. 63–150.

132. L Gram. Inhibition of mesophilic spoilage by *Aeromonas* spp. on fish by salt, potassium sorbate, liquid smoke, and chilling. J Food Prot 54: 436–442, 1991.

133. O Mejlholm, P Dalgaard. Antimicrobial affect of essential oils on the seafood spoilage micro-organism *Photobacterium phosphoreum* in liquid media and fish products. Lett Appl Microbiol 34: 27–34, 2002.

134. GC Fletcher, G Summers, RV Winchester, RJ Wong. Histamine and histidine in New Zealand marine fish and shellfish species, particularly Kahawai (*Arripis trutta*). J Aquat Food Prod Technol 4: 53–74, 1995.

135. SL Taylor. Histamine food Poisoning: toxicological and clinical aspects. CRC Critical Reviews in Toxicology 17: 91–128, 1986.

136. L Lehane, J Olley. Histanine fish poisoning revisited. Int J Food Microbiol 58: 1–37, 2000.

137. GJ Flick, MP Oria, L Douglas. Potential hazards in cold-smoked fish: Biogenic amines. J Food Sci Supplement to Vol. 66: S-1088–S-1099, 2001.

138. JE Perkin, J Hartje. Diet and migraine: A review of the literature. J Am Diet Assoc 83: 459–463, 1983.

139. M Okuzumi, S Okuda, M Awano. Occurrence of psychrophilic and halophilic histamine-forming bacteria (N-group bacteria) on/in red meat fish. Bull Jap Soc Sci Fish 48: 799–804, 1982.

140. L Ababouch, ME Afilal, H Benabdeljelil, FF Busta. Quantitative changes in bacteria, amino acids and biogenic amines in sardine (Sardina pilchardus) stored at ambient temperature (25–28°C) and in ice. J Food Sci Technol 26: 297–306, 1991.

141. LH Ababouch, L Souibri, K Rhaliby, O Ouahdi, M Battal, FF Busta. Quality changes in sardines (Sardina pilchardus) stored in ice and at ambient temperature. Food Microbiol 13: 123–132, 1996.

142. CCG Silva, DJB Da Ponte, MlN Enes Dapkevicius. Storage temperature effect on histamine formation in Big Eye tuna and Skipjack. J Food Sci 63: 644–647, 1998.

143. M Kanki, T Yoda, T Tsukamoto, T Shibata. Klebsiella pneumoniae produces no histamine: Raoultella planticola and Raoultella ornithinolytica strains are histamine producers. Appl Environ Microbiol 68: 3462–3466, 2002.

144. H Takahashi, B Kimura, M Yoshikawa, T Fujii. Cloning and sequencing of the histidine decarboxylase genes of Gram-negative, histamine-producing bacteria and their application in detection and identification of these organisms in fish. Appl Environ Microbiol 69: 2568–2579, 2003.

145. SH Arnold, RJ Price, WD Brown. Histamine formation by bacteria isolated from Skipjack tuna, Katsuwonus pelamis. Bull Jap Soc Sci Fish 46: 991–995, 1980.

146. Y Sakabe. Studies on allergy-like food poisoning. 2. Studies on the relation between storage temperature and histamine production. J Nara Med Assoc 24: 257–264, 1973.

147. NK Klausen, HH Huss. Growth and histamine production by Morganella morganii under various temperature conditions. Int J Food Microbiol 5: 147–156, 1987.

148. M Kanki, T Yoda, M Ishibashi, T Tsukamoto. Photobacterium phosphoreum caused a histamine fish poisoning incident. Int J Food Microbiol 92: 79–87, 2004.

149. JJ Leisner, JC Millan, HH Huss, LM Larsen. Production of histamine and tyramine by lactic acid bacteria isolated from vacuum-packed sugar-salted fish. J Appl Bact 76: 417–423, 1994.

150. B Kimura, Y Konagaya, T Fujii. Histamine formation by Tetragenococcus muriaticus, a halophilic lactic acid bacterium isolated from fish sauce. Int J Food Microbiol 70: 71–77, 2001.

151. RGK Leuschner, WP Hammes. Formation of biogenic amine in mayonnaise, herring and tuna fish salad by lactobacilli. Int J Food Sci Nut 50: 159–164, 1999.

152. PA Lerke, SB Werner, SL Taylor, LS Guthertz. Scombroid poisoning. West J Med 129: 381–386, 1978.

153. S-H Kim, H An, KG Field, C Wei, JB Velazquez, B Ben-Gigirey, MT Morrissey, RJ Price, TP Pitta. Detection of Morganella morganii, a prolific histamine former, by the polymerase chain reaction assay with 16S rDNA-targeted primers. J Food Prot 66: 1385–1392, 2003.

154. HA Frank, DH Yoshinaga, IP Wu. Nonograph for estimating histamine formation in skipjack tuna at elevated temperatures. Mar Fish Rev 45(4–6): 40–44, 1983.

155. HA Frank, DH Yoshinaga. Table for estimating histamine formation in Skipjack tuna, Katsuwonus pelamis, at low nonfreezing temperatures. Mar Fish Rev 49: 67–70, 1987.

156. T Ross, J Sumner. A simple, spreadsheet-based, food safety risk assessment tool. Int J Food Microbiol 77: 39–53, 2002.

157. FAO/WHO, Hazard identification, exposure assessment and hazard characterization of Vibrio spp. in seafood. (Accessed November 2003 at: www.fao.org/es/ESN/food/risk_mra_riskassessment_en.stm), 2002.

158. FDA-CFSAN, Draft risk assessment on the public health impact of Vibrio parahaemolyticus in raw molluscan shellfish (Accessed in November 2002 at: vm.cfsan.fda.gov/~dms/vprisk.html), 2001.

159. DW Cook, P O'Leary, JC Hunsucker, EM Sloan, JC Bowers, RJ Blodgett, A DePaola. Vibrio vulnificus and Vibrio parahaemolyticus in U.S. retail shell oysters: A national survey from June 1998 to July 1999. J Food Prot 65: 79–87, 2002.

160. CA Kaysner. Vibrio species. In: BM Lund, TC Baird-Parker, GW Gould, eds. The Microbiological Safety and Quality of Food. Gaithersburg: Aspen Publishers, Inc., 2000, pp. 1336–1362.

161. A Robert-Pillot, A Guénolé, J Lesne, R Delesmont, J-M Fournier, M-L Quilici. Occurence of the tdh and trh genes in Vibrio paraharmolyticus isolates from waters and raw shellfish collected in two French coastal areas and from seafood imported into France. Int J Food Microbiol 91: 319–325, 2004.

162. C-Y Lee, G Panicker, AK Bej. Detection of pathogenic bacteria in shellfish using multiplex PCR followed by CovaLink™ NH microwell plate sandwich hybridization. J Microbiol Methods 53: 199–209, 2003.

163. GM Blackstone, JL Nordstrom, MCL Vickery, MD Bowen, RF Meyer, A DePaola. Detection of pathogenic Vibrio parahaemolyticus in oyster enrichments by real time PCR. J Microbiol Methods 53: 149–155, 2003.

164. WJ Lyon. TaqMan PCR for detection of Vibrio cholerae O1, O139, non-O1 and non-O139 in pure cultures, raw oysters, and synthetic seawater. Appl Environ Microbiol 67: 4685–4693, 2000.

165. DW Miles, T Ross, J Olley, TA McMeekin. Development and evaluation of a predictive model for the effect of temperature and water activity on the growth rate of Vibrio parahaemolyticus. Int J Food Microbiol 38: 133–142, 1997.

166. A DePaola, JL Nordstrom, A Dalsgaard, A Forslund, J Oliver, T Bates, KL Bourdage, PA Gulig. Analysis of Vibrio vulnificus from market oysters and septicemia cases from virulence markers. Appl Environ Microbiol 69: 4006–4011, 2003.

167. TA Lorca, MD Pierson, GJ Flick, CR Hackney. Levels of *Vibrio vulnificus* and organoleptic quality of raw shellstock oysters (*Crassostrea virginica*) maintained at different storage temperatures. J Food Prot 64: 1716–1721, 2001.

168. ML Tamplin, GM Casper. Persistence of *Vibrio vulnificus* in tissues of Gulf Coast oysters, *Crassostrea virginica*, exposed to seawater disinfection with UV light. Appl Environ Microbiol 58: 1506–1510, 1992.

169. S Jiang, W Chu, W Fu. Prevalence of cholera toxin genes (*ctxA* and *zot*) among non-O1/O139 *Vibrio cholerae* strains from Newport Bay, California. Appl Environ Microbiol 69: 7541–7544, 2003.

170. D Hervio-Heath, RR Colwell, A Derrien, A Robert-Pillot, J-M Fournier, M Pommepuy. Occurrence of pathogenic vibrios in coastal areas of France. J Appl Microbiol 92: 1123–1135, 2002.

171. MR Torres-Vitela, A Castillo, LM Ibarra-Velazquez, V Navarro-Hidalgo, MO Rodríguez-García, NE Martínez-Gonzáles, JA Pérez-Montaño. Survival of *Vibrio cholerae* O1 in ceviche and its reduction by heat pretreatment of raw ingredients. J Food Prot 63: 445–450, 2000.

172. H Calik, MT Morrissey, PW Reno, H An. Effect of high-pressure processing on *Vibrio parahaemolyticus* strains in pure culture and Pacific oysters. J Food Sci 67: 1506–1510, 2002.

173. DW Cook. Sensitivity of *Vibrio* species in phosphate-buffered saline and in oysters to high-pressure processing. J Food Prot 66: 2276–2282, 2003.

174. BM Lund, MW Peck. *Clostridium botulinum*. In: BM Lund, TC Baird-Parker, GW Gould, eds. The Microbiological Safety and Quality of Food. Gaithersburg: Aspen Publishers, Inc., 2000, pp. 1057–1109.

175. L Gram. Potential hazards in cold-smoked fish: *Clostridium botulinum* type E. J Food Sci 66: S-1082–S-1087, 2001.

176. MD Collins, AK East. Phylogeny and taxonomy of the food-borne pathogen *Clostridium botulinum* and its neurotoxins. J Appl Microbiol 84: 17, 1998.

177. B Kimura, S Kawasaki, H Nakano, T Fujii. Rapid, quantitative PCR monitoring of growth of *Clostridium botulinum* Type E in modified-atmosphere-packed fish. Appl Environ Microbiol 67: 206–216, 2001.

178. I Dufresne, JP Smith, NL Jiun, I Tarte. Effect of headspace oxygen and film of different oxygen transmission rate on toxin production by *Clostridium botulinum* type E in rainbow trout stored under modified atmospheres. J Food Safety 20: 157–175, 2000.

179. JM Farber, PI Peterkin. *Listeria monocytogenes*. In: BM Lund, TC Baird-Parker, GW Gould, eds. The Microbiological Safety and Quality of Food. Gaithersburg: Aspen Publishers, Inc., 2000, pp. 1178–1232.

180. FDA-CFSAN. Quantitative Assessment of the Relative Risk to Public Health from Foodborne *Listeria monocytogenes* Among Selected Categories of Ready-to-Eat (Accessed in December 2003 at: http://www.foodsafety.gov/~dms/lmr2-toc.html). FDA/Center for Food Safety and Applied Nutrition, USDA/Food Safety and Inspection Service, Centers for Disease Control and Prevention, 2003.

181. RB Tompkin. Control of *Listeria monocytogenes* in the food-processing environment. J Food Prot 65: 709–725, 2002.

182. BC Giménez, P Dalgaard. Modelling and predicting the simultaneous growth of *Listeria monocytogenes* and spoilage microorganisms in cold-smoked salmon. J Appl Microbiol 96: 96–109, 2004.

183. F Duffes, C Corre, F Leroi, X Dousset, P Boyaval. Inhibition of *Listeria monocytogenes* by in situ produced and semipurified bacteriocins of *Carnobacterium* spp. on vacuum-packed refrigerated cold-smoked salmon. J Food Prot 62: 1394–1403, 1999.

184. L Nilsson, L Gram, HH Huss. Growth control of *Listeria monocytogenes* on cold-smoked salmon using a competitive lactic acid bacteria flora. J Food Prot 62: 336–342, 1999.

185. J-Y D'Aoust. *Salmonella*. In: BM Lund, TC Baird-Parker, GW Gould, eds. The Microbiological Safety and Quality of Food. Gaithersburg: Aspen Publishers, Inc., 2000, pp 1233–1299.

186. D Lees. Viruses and bivalve shellfish. Int J Food Microbiol 59: 81–116, 2000.

187. M Koopmans, C-H von Bonsdorff, J Vinjé, D de Medici, S Monroe. Foodborne viruses. FEMS Microbiol Rev 26: 187–205, 2002.

188. K Katayama, H Shirato-Horikoshi, S Kojima, T Kageyama, T Oka, FB Hoshino, S Fukushi, M Shinohara, K Uchida, Y Suzuki, T Gojobori, N Takeda. Phylogenic analysis of the complete genome of 18 Norwalk-like viruses. Virology 299: 225–239, 2002.

189. FS Le Guyader, FH Neill, E Dubois, F Bon, F Loisy, E Kohli, M Pommepuy, RL Atmar. A semiquantitative approach to estimate Norwalk-like virus contamination of oysters implicated in an outbreak. Int J Food Microbiol 87: 107–112, 2003.

190. F Le Guyader, L Haugarreau, L Miossec, E Dubois, M Pommepuy. Three-year study to assess human enteric viruses in shellfish. Appl Environ Microbiol 66: 3241–3248, 2000.

191. JL Romalde, E Area, G Sánchez, C Ribao, I Torrado, X Abad, RM Pintó, JL Barja, A Bosch. Prevalence of enterovirus and hepatitis A virus in bivalve molluscs from Galicia (NW Spain): inadequacy of the EU standards of microbiological quality. Int J Food Microbiol 74: 119–130, 2002.

192. C Beuret, A Baumgartner, J Schluep. Virus-contaminated oysters: a three-month monitoring of oysters imported to Switzerland. Appl Environ Microbiol 69: 2292–2297, 2003.

193. C Gantzer, E Dubois, J-M Crance, S Billaudel, H Kopecka, L Schwartzbrod, M Pommepuy, F Le Guyader. Influence of environmental factors on the survival of enteric viruses in seawater. Oceanol Acta 21: 983–992, 1998.

194. DH Kingsley, GP Richards. Persistence of hepatitis A virus in oysters. J Food Prot 66: 331–334, 2003.

195. DH Kingsley, DG Hoover, E Papafragkou, GP Richards. Inactivation of hepatitis A virus and a calicivirus by high hydrostatic pressure. J Food Prot 65: 1605–1609, 2002.

54 Microbial Analysis of Foods

Mieke Uyttendaele and Johan Debevere
Department of Food Technology, Chemistry, Microbiology and Human Nutrition,
Ghent University

CONTENTS

I. INTRODUCTION

Microbial analysis of foods is important in food safety control. It can be done for many reasons (legislation, trend analysis, outbreak analysis, etc.) and by many participants (governmental agencies, food processors, etc.) (1). An overview of the various categories of microbial testing is given in Table 54.1.

TABLE 54.1
Microbial Testing in Food Microbiology

Categories of Microbial Testing	Definition	User/Purpose
Acceptance/rejection testing	Testing for presence/absence of pathogens in defined amount of sample or determination of plate counts of indicator organisms based on agreed specifications and sampling plans (3)	International trade
End product testing	To document that a batch of food meets legal or internal quality standards	Food producer
Trend analysis	Accumulate data to measure changes in the product rather than in the batch, to verify that the application of HACCP keeps the process under control	Food producer
Statutory testing	To control whether a batch of food meets the legal requirements; duplicate samples are made available for independent analysis by the food producer/outlet	Control authorities
Investigative sampling	To determine the source of contamination of a product by pathogens or spoilage organisms	Food producer
Outbreak analysis	To determine the food which could have caused a problem of food-borne illness	Control authorities
Environmental and hygiene monitoring	To determine the hygienic status of the food plant: swabs or scrapings and agar contact plates from food production infrastructure and equipment	Food producer

The major incentive for testing is legislation. Microbial analyses of end-products are specified and mandatory for specific food categories, especially for foods of animal origin. End-product testing is performed by control authorities to check whether a batch of food meets the legal requirements for such food. Although the limitations of end-product testing of foods at the port-of-entry or elsewhere in the food chain to ensure microbiological safety was recognized, numerous end-product testing is still widely performed. However, the overall framework for microbiological testing and interpretation of results is slowly changing. End-product testing has shifted to a system where the focus is verification of preventive approaches based on the use of good manufacturing practices (GMP) in combination with the Hazard Analysis Critical Control Points (HACCP) systems as more reliable means of assuring product safety in the modern food industry (2). In contrast to original expectations, introduction of HACCP did not lead to a reduction of the number of microbial analyses performed. Effective implementation of HACCP requires knowledge on the incidence of pathogenic bacteria in foods, and the organism's response to conditions in foods. Microbial testing programs have been elaborated by manufacturers to acquire in-house knowledge on the prevalence, persistence and behavior of pathogens in a specific food commodity/production site. In addition, the microbiological analysis of ingredients, half-fabricates and end-products as well as of environmental samples are often part of the monitoring program. Although microbiological analyses included in legislation are especially directed towards investigation of pathogenic bacteria and/or indicator organisms, microbial testing of foods is not restricted to these groups of microorganisms. Microbial analysis is an economically relevant parameter. Many food commodities have a limited shelf life because of microbial proliferation during storage. Microbial analysis to determine the composition and the level of the initial microbial flora is essential to predict typical spoilage patterns and to monitor shelf life in foods.

The present chapter will give an overview of the problems associated with microbial food testing, the classical culture-based methodology available for enumeration, detection and identification of food- and water-borne microorganisms, the microbial parameters under consideration for microbial testing and the conventional applied methodology. For discussion of rapid analysis techniques in food microbiology, the reader is referred to Chapter 55 of this handbook.

II. PROBLEMS ASSOCIATED WITH FOOD ANALYSIS

A. SAMPLING PLANS

The quality and safety of a food product cannot be guaranteed by end-product control. While acceptance or rejection of a food is ideally decided by inspection of 100% of the items of a lot, this is too laborious, time-consuming, costly and destroys the lot. Testing of representative samples has to be undertaken instead. When a batch of food is composed from separate units, a selection of units has to be taken from this lot at random. The sample units so drawn will, after examination, yield results which are compared with defined criteria to reach a decision as to whether the entire lot should be accepted or rejected. The particular choice of sampling procedure and the decision criteria is called the 'sampling plan.' A sampling plan states the number of units required to be randomly collected from a lot and lists the acceptance and rejection criteria. As an example, consider that a lot $N > 1000$ units is to be analyzed for coliforms per gram and a unit is to be called defective if it has ≥ 100 coliforms per gram (rejection criterion) and to be called acceptable or nondefective if it has < 100 coliforms per gram (acceptance criterion). A sampling plan is necessary to define the number of units (n) to sample where the number of defectives (c) equals zero. A sampling plan of $n = 30$ and $c = 0$ may be chosen, however, unless all units are sampled there is always a probability that a 'bad' lot, when offered, will be falsely accepted (consumer's risk). For each sampling plan (definition of n and c) the probability of lot acceptance in relation to lot quality (usually expressed as percent defective units) can be calculated. Using the above mentioned sampling plan (n = 30, c = 0) the chance (consumer's risk) of accepting a lot with one defective unit out of 40 will be about 50%. With regard to food-borne pathogens, large numbers of samples must be found free of target organisms before any significance can be attached to negative results. No feasible sampling plan can ensure complete absence of a particular organism, e.g., if 60 samples were taken and analyzed there is still one chance in two of being accepted for lots in which 1% of the sample units carry a pathogen. Moreover, the above calculation is based on the assumption that the organisms sought are homogenously distributed in the food. In the vast majority of foods, microorganisms are randomly distributed. This makes clear that end-product control alone cannot control the production process but can only help in verification of the good functioning of the preventive modern quality assurance systems, including HACCP. For more information on specific proposals for sampling and sampling plans the reader is referred to the ICMSF publication (3) or to the website www.dfst.csiro.au/icmsf/publications.htm.

B. DYNAMIC BIOLOGICAL POPULATION

Microbial populations of foods have a dynamic character. Often there is an increase or decrease in numbers of viable cells during processing, storage and distribution. The outcome of a microbiological analysis or a typing method reflects the microbial quality of the food or the type of pathogen present at that particular time of sampling. The microbial condition of the product should not change during sampling. Appropriate measures should be taken to prevent any contamination of the sample units and any microbial growth or death within the sample units during collection, transport to the laboratory and subsequent storage and handling of the samples. Sampling should be performed in an aseptic way using clean, dry, sterile materials. Microbiologically unstable products should be transported and stored at a temperature below 4°C and, in general, the period between sampling and analysis should not exceed six hours. Specific rules for the preparation of test samples are to be found in the ISO 6887 series.

C. SUB-LETHAL DAMAGE AND THE RESUSCITATION OF DAMAGED POPULATIONS

Microorganisms occurring in foods are frequently impaired by sub-lethal injury as a result of having been exposed to adverse conditions. This may be due to processing by mild heat treatment or non-thermal inactivation methods.

Exposure to adverse intrinsic conditions including low a_w and pH, or to extrinsic factors such as low temperature, oxidizing agents and modified atmospheres may also lead to sub-lethal injury. Such cells may pose problems of detection because they fail to grow on selective media. An increased lag phase duration in injured cells and difficulty in isolating especially low numbers of stressed cells have been demonstrated (4, 5). However, these sub-lethally injured organisms may be capable of repair in certain food products and may possess the potential for pathogenicity, thus posing a potential public health risk. New improved protocols have been proposed for recovery of injured cells. For enumeration procedures some authors have included a resuscitation step on a solid non-selective medium for a few hours, plates being then overlaid with selective agar. For detection procedures, enrichment broths differed significantly in the ability to detect injured cells. The addition of various components to the media, including sugars, yeast extracts, egg yolk, salt, osmoprotectants, cations, reducing agents and antioxidant enzymes (6), may aid in the recovery of sub-lethally damaged cells.

However, one of the main problems remains the dilemma of promoting resuscitation of injured cells whilst avoiding overgrowth by the competitive microflora. In microbiological food control laboratories the use of sufficiently selective media may even be necessary and give better recovery results when food contains high levels of competing background flora.

D. THE NEED FOR HIGHLY SELECTIVE PROCEDURES

Raw food products harvested or processed under GMP and under applications of well-functioning quality assurance systems such as HACCP are in general of good microbial quality calling for methods allowing assessment of levels of the order of 100 per gram for indicator organisms to 10^4–10^6 per gram for total viable count depending upon the type of product. Several food-borne pathogens are highly infective and often low numbers of pathogens (0.1–10 cfu per g) are present in a ratio of 10^{-4} amongst physiologically similar organisms. These low numbers may not go undetected in these foods. An example is the enforcement of detection of one to ten colony forming units (cfu) of salmonellae amongst some 10^4–10^5 other Enterobacteriaceae. The detection of low numbers of pathogens amongst high numbers of background flora demands highly selective enrichment and isolation procedures. If the presence of injured cells is suspected prior incubation under non- or less selective conditions may be necessary.

III. MICROBIOLOGICAL BASIC ENUMERATION TECHNIQUES

For more information on basic microbial techniques and modifications thereof the reader is referred to the

Compendium of Methods for the Microbiological Examination of Foods published by the American Public Health Association (7).

A. THE COLONY COUNT METHOD

In the colony count method the total number of bacteria in a product is determined by inoculating dilutions of suspensions of the sample onto the surface of a growth medium that has been solidified by agar-agar (spread-plate method) or by mixing the test portion with the liquefied agar medium in Petri dishes (pour plate method). Enumeration is performed after incubation for fixed periods at temperatures varying from 7 to 55°C in an aerobic, microaerophilic or anaerobic atmosphere. During incubation each individual cell will multiply into a colony that is visible to the naked eye. If several cells are physically connected (e.g., by adsorption to a particle of suspended matter) this will also result in one colony. The result of the viable count technique is therefore expressed as the number of cfu per unit volume. Appropriate dilutions of the food samples should have been made in order to enable counts reported from plates in the range of 25–250 colonies for pour plates and 15–150 colonies for spread plates. The principle of microbial enumeration by the conventional culture-based method is illustrated in Figure 54.1.

B. CULTURE MEDIA

The culture medium used to cultivate microorganisms contains all necessary components for the growth of the microorganisms. Each medium consists of the following components: water, nitrogen compounds (peptones, amino-acids, etc), an energy source (carbohydrates, proteins, anorganic salts) and sometimes additional growth factors (yeast extract, vitamins, etc.) for nutritionally demanding microorganisms.

By addition or removal of certain components a medium can be made selective. Selective compounds frequently employed in culture media are antibiotics, chemicals (bile salts, azide, selenite, tellurite) and dyes (brilliant green, crystal violet) (Table 54.2). In addition certain extrinsic factors, e.g., increase or decrease of temperature or changes in redox potential can often be used to enhance the selectivity (8).

Designing adequate selectivity into a medium becomes more difficult as the proportion of interfering organisms increases and almost impossible when the background association is more robust than the organisms to be counted or detected. Shigellae, for example, are easily overgrown by other bacteria present in the food. Many of the enterococci are also resistant to many inhibitors used in selective culture media and may pose a seriously interfering background flora. It is often necessary, therefore, to use so-called diagnostic or elective media. Using these, the organisms sought can be distinguished from the background flora on the basis of a specific metabolic activity, e.g., dissimilation of lactose visualized by the incorporation of a pH indicator monitoring acid production, dissimilation of aesculine to aesculitin, iron salts which result in a black precipitate upon production of H_2S by the target organism from a sulphate-containing substrate. For more information on the composition of culture media and their selective and diagnostic agents the reader is referred to the catalogues of the suppliers of these media.

1. Semi-Solid Media

Semi-solid media are media which differentiate microorganisms on the basis of their motility. Due to the low incidence of non-motile *Salmonella* strains, the use of motility enrichment has been found effective for rapid detection and isolation of *Salmonella* (9). As a combined enrichment-isolation medium for *Salmonella*, modified semi-solid Rappaport-Vassiliadis (MSRV) medium compares favorably with standard protocol using RV broth followed by isolation on a selective agar and gives results

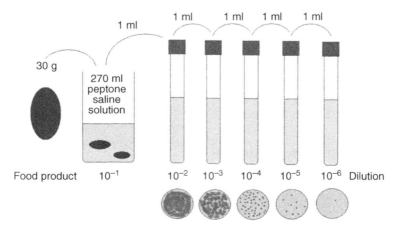

FIGURE 54.1 Lay-out of the conventional procedure for a colony count method.

TABLE 54.2
Review of Selective Agents used in Selective Culture Media

Category of Selective Agent	Examples	Inhibitory Towards	Example of Application in Culture Media (Microbial Parameter)
Dyes	Brilliant green	Gram-positives	Brilliant green agar (*Salmonella*)
	Crystal violet	Gram-positives	Violet red bile glucose agar (Enterobacteriaceae)
Surface active agents	Bile salts	Non-enteros	Violet red bile glucose agar (Enterobacteriaceae)
	Tergitol-7	Gram-positives	Tergitol-7 agar (coliforms)
Inorganic salts	Potassium tellurite	Gram-negatives	Baird-Parker agar (*Staphylococcus aureus*)
	Lithium chloride	Enterococci	(demi)-Fraser broth, Oxford agar (*Listeria monocytogenes*)
Antibiotics	Acriflavine	Gram positive cocci	(demi)-Fraser broth, PALCAM agar (*Listeria monocytogenes*)
	Cycloserine	Broad spectrum	TSC (*Clostridium perfringens*)
	Novobiocin	Gram positives	DIASALM, MSRV (*Salmonella*)
	Oxytetracycline	Broad spectrum	OGY (yeast and molds)
	Polymyxin	Gram negatives	MYP (*Bacillus cereus*)
	Ticarcilline	Broad spectrum	ITC (*Yersinia enterocolitica*)
Anti-fungal agents	Cycloheximide	Moulds	Preston broth, Karmali agar (*Campylobacter*)
	Amphotericin	Moulds	Bolton broth, mCCDA (*Campylobacter*)

one day earlier. Diagnostic semi-solid (DIASALM) agar uses a saccharose/bromocresol purple indicator to observe migrating salmonellae as a pink zone within a green medium. Addition of nitrofurantoin to DIASALM agar favors the isolation of *Salmonella* Enteritidis from poultry samples. In a typical application, three drops of pre-enriched BPW are inoculated in one spot into the center of a semi-solid medium. After incubation, plates are examined for a motility zone. A loopful of the motile zone which is the farthest from the sample inoculum is subsequently subcultured and confirmed as *Salmonella*.

2. Chromogenic and Fluorogenic Media

Chromogenic and fluorogenic media are culture media which have the ability to detect the presence of a specific exclusive enzyme using suitable substrates, a fluorogenic or chromogenic enzyme substrate. The introduction of these media has led to development of improved methods for the identification of microorganisms even in primary isolation media.

Chromogenic and fluorogenic media are well established for detection of indicator organisms but have recently also been accepted in standard methods for detection of food-borne pathogens such as *Escherichia coli* O157:H7 and *Listeria monocytogenes*.

The definition of coliforms is the possession of the β-D-galactosidase gene which is responsible for the cleavage of lactose into glucose and galactose by the enzyme β-D-galactosidase. The determination of β-D-galactosidase can be accomplished by using the chromogenic substrates o-nitrophenyl-β-D-galactopyranoside (ONPG), 6-bromo-3-indolyl-β-galactopyranoside (Salmon-Gal), 5-bromo-4-chloro-3-indolyl-β-D-galactopyranoside (X-Gal). The β-D-galactosidase cleaves the chromogenic substrate and the released chromophore causes distinct and easy-to-read colored colonies, respectively, yellow, red and blue colonies for ONPG, Salmon-Gal and X-Gal.

The new generation of media use β-D-glucuronidase (GUD) as an indicator for *E. coli*. GUD activity is measured by using different chromogenic and fluorogenic substrates such as p-nitrophenyl-β-D-glucuronide rendering yellow colonies or 5-bromo-4-chloro-3-indolyl-β-D-glucuronide (X-Gluc or BCIG) rendering blue colonies. TBX agar is a modification of Tryptone Bile agar to which the substrate BCIG is added. TBX agar complies with the ISO standard 16649 for the enumeration of *E. coli* in food and animal feeding stuffs. The fluorogenic substrate 4-methylumbelliferyl-β-D-glucuronide (MUG) has been incorporated into various liquid media for most probable number detection of *E. coli*. MUG is hydrolyzed by GUD yielding 4-MU, which shows blue fluorescence when irradiated with long-wave UV-light (366 nm).

Commercially available media have been developed which permit rapid simultaneous enumeration of *E. coli* and coliforms in water and foods by their distinctive coloration. These media contain a variety of enzyme substrates for detection of β-D-galactosidase (presence of coliforms) and β-D-glucuronidase (presence of *E. coli*).

For more information on the development in chromogenic and fluorogenic media the reader is referred to Ref. 10.

C. MODIFICATIONS OF THE COLONY COUNT METHOD

Modifications to the format of colony count techniques have been introduced in order to decrease the detection limit (membrane filtration, most probable number method), to decrease the workload (Petrifilm™, spiral plate method) or to monitor environmental contamination (surface contact methods).

1. Membrane Filter Method

For liquid foods, the membrane filtration method enables testing of large volumes by passing them through a bacteriological membrane filter (usually of 0.45 μm pore size) and placing the filter on the growth medium. The method is especially useful for samples that contain low numbers of bacteria. Membrane filtration is the basis of the standard methods for indicator organisms in water analysis.

2. Most Probable Number (MPN) Methods

In this method dilutions of food samples are prepared as for the plate count method. Three serial aliquots or dilutions are then transferred into 9 or 15 tubes of appropriate medium for the three- or five-tube method, respectively. Specific groups of organisms can be determined by use of appropriate selective and differential media. After incubation, the number of positive tubes for each dilution is counted. To confirm the growth in questionable tubes, a loopful of the medium from the tube is transferred to an appropriate culture medium and incubated. On the basis of the number of positive tubes for each dilution a MPN in the original sample is determined by use of standard MPN tables and taking into account the dilution factor. The method was introduced by McGrady in 1915. It is statistical in nature. Unlike the viable count, the MPN does not provide a direct measure of the bacterial count. In addition, the MPN is more variable than the viable count and tends to yield a higher result. Nevertheless, it produces estimates of bacterial concentrations that are below the detectability of most current direct measurement microbiological methods. MPN methods are often the method of choice for detection of low numbers of indicator organisms or pathogens in foods (11).

3. Hydrophobic Grid Membrane Filter (HGMF)

The HGMF can be used to enumerate all or specific microorganisms from a variety of foods. The method employs a specially constructed filter that consists of 1,600 wax grids on a single membrane filter that restricts growth and colony size to individual grids. On one filter, from 10 to 9×10^4 cfu can be enumerated by an MPN procedure, and enumeration can be automated. The procedure consists of pre-filtering homogenized food samples, which traps food particles larger than 5 μm. The sample is then filtered through the membrane followed by placing the filter on a suitable agar medium for incubation, to allow colonies to develop. The grids that contain colonies are enumerated and the MPN is calculated. The method has been given AOAC approval for total coliforms, faecal coliforms, salmonellae and yeast and molds (12, 13).

4. Petrifilm™ Plate Method

An alternative to plating to agar-agar media in Petri dishes is the Petrifilm™ plate method (3M). The Petrifilm™ plate count consists of two plastic films. The bottom film is coated with adhesive, powdered standard methods nutrients, and a dehydrated cold water-soluble gelling agent. The upper film is permeable and fosters oxygen diffusion, although it retains gas formed by, e.g., coliforms during lactose fermentation. An indicator dye, triphenyltetrazolium chloride (TTC), is included. The major advantage of Petrifilm™ is that colony counts can be taken on these small and sample-ready Petrifilm™ plates, without the need for the preparation of culture media. The indicator stains the colonies red and facilitates counting. The Petrifilm™ plate occupies small volume for storage, incubation and disposal and is a user-friendly method to control the microbiological quality of foods (14). The Petrifilm™ plate Aerobic Count method for the enumeration of aerobic bacteria in foods and dairy products has regulatory approval, certification or official recognition in a number of countries. Petrifilm™ products are also available for yeast and mold counts, coliforms, *Escherichia coli*.

5. Spiral Plate Method

Traditional colony count methods are laborious and do not allow for efficient management of numerous samples. The spiral plate method is a variation of an agar spread plate method which automates the sample dilution and agar inoculation steps and provides savings in time and effort. A known volume of sample is dispensed onto a rotating agar plate in an Archimedes spiral. The amount of sample decreases as the spiral moves out toward the edge of the plate. A modified counting grid, which relates the area of the plate to sample volume, is used to count colonies on an appropriate area of the plate and enables the colony count for the sample to be calculated. The primary advantage of this method is that one inoculation can enumerate bacterial densities of, for example, 500–500,000 cfu/ml, depending on the manufacturer. Within that range no additional dilutions are needed and thus savings on materials (pipettes, Petri dishes) can be made. The biggest disadvantage of the spiral plate method is the tendency of food particulates to plug the inoculation stylus. The small volume of sample plated also limits the sensitivity of the method. The spiral plate count is accepted for total enumeration by the U.S. Food and Drug Administration and is an AOAC International Official Method for food testing. The spiral plate method has also been used to test milk samples (15).

6. Surface Contact Methods

An environmental monitoring program may be necessary to assess the microbial contamination of the processing equipment and the plant itself (16) and to verify the effectiveness of cleaning and disinfection cycles. Swab procedures and replicate organism direct agar contact (RODAC) plates are the methods of choice for sampling of surfaces (17).

Swab techniques should be used for flexible, uneven and potentially heavily contaminated surfaces on equipment and utensils. The swab will be more effective than the RODAC plate in recovering organisms from these sites. The swab methods use either cotton or calcium alginate swabs. If one wishes to examine given areas of surfaces, templates may be prepared. The sterile template is placed over the surface, and the exposed area is rubbed thoroughly with a moistened swab. The exposed swab is returned to a test tube containing a suitable diluent and stored under refrigeration until plated. Sponge swab procedures are useful for sampling large areas of food processing equipment and environmental surfaces.

The RODAC procedure should be used only on flat, firm and nonporous surfaces that are relatively easy to clean and disinfect. The RODAC method employs special Petri plates which are poured with an appropriate plating medium resulting in a raised agar surface. When the plate is inverted, the solidified agar makes direct contact with the surface. Plates are incubated under the appropriate time and temperature regime for the microorganism in question and enumerated. Samples taken from heavily contaminated areas will result in overgrowth of the plates.

IV. METHODS FOR IDENTIFICATION AND CHARACTERISATION OF FOOD BORNE MICROORGANISMS

A. IDENTIFICATION BASED ON MORPHOLOGICAL, PHYSIOLOGICAL AND BIOCHEMICAL CHARACTERISTICS

Isolates obtained from a food product can be broadly categorized to a group depending on characteristics such as Gram stain, colony characteristics (pigmentation, mucoid colonies, swarming or pin-point), cell morphology (shape, size, motility and flagellar patterns, endospore formation, inclusion bodies), relation to oxygen (aerobic, facultatively anaerobic, anaerobic, microaerophilic), catalase activity, oxidase activity, ability to dissimilate glucose and the type of metabolism (oxidative or fermentative). Most often further identification is based on a number of diagnostic characteristics (18):

- Physiological features such as growth at different temperatures, pH values, salt concentrations, growth in the presence of various substances such as antimicrobial agents
- Biochemical features such as activity of various enzymes, metabolism of carbohydrates

It is essential to start from a pure culture for identification of an organism. Determination of phenotypic characteristics is prone to experimental error. Rigorous standardization of phenotypic methods is of the outmost importance to obtain reproducible results. The results of physiological and biochemical tests may vary depending upon the size of the inoculum, the incubation temperature, length of the incubation period, composition of the medium and the criteria used to define a "positive" or "negative" reaction. Therefore it is advisable to include reference strains, available from culture collections for comparison with, when using a phenotypic identification scheme in order to check the performance of the test under the conditions employed in one's own laboratory.

Several commercial identification kits have been developed to simplify and automate the identification of individual microorganisms, e.g., API galeries (bioMérieux, Marcy-l'Etoile, France), Biolog microplates (Biolog Inc., Hayward, CA, U.S.A.), the BBL Crystal ID system (Becton Dickinson, Meylan Cedex, France). In microbial analysis of foods often a complete identification is not required but only a confirmation of the suspected colony based on a restricted number of typical characteristics which are easily determinable and enable good differentiation between competitive closely related strains. However, miniaturized identification systems are increasingly used because the saving in time (e.g., media preparation, ease of reading) is significant and results are comparable to conventional tests.

B. IDENTIFICATION BASED ON CHEMOTAXONOMIC AND GENETIC METHODS

Phenotypic testing is often insufficient for correct identification of species especially if the taxonomy of the organism is complex, e.g., *Bacillus* spp., lactic acid bacteria. Also the paucity of phenotypic characteristics, in particular bacterial groups, can cause problems for identification, e.g., thermophilic campylobacters.

Chemotaxonomy is the application of chemical and physical techniques to elucidate the chemical composition of whole bacterial cells or parts of cells (19). Amongst the techniques, which can be applied for identification of these difficult taxonomic groups, are comparisons of the fatty acid methyl ester content (FAME) or comparison of the whole-cell protein patterns obtained by highly standardized sodium dodecyl-sulfate-polyacrylamide gel electrophoresis (SDS-PAGE). These techniques are based on the comparison of patterns/fingerprints with a database. FAME makes use of the variability in chain length, double-bond position and substituent groups of the cellular lipids and lipopolysaccharides and has proven to be very useful for the characterization of bacteria, e.g., *Aeromonas* species (20) and *Bacillus* species (21). The comparison of SDS-PAGE profiles has proven to be extremely reliable for comparing and grouping large numbers of closely related strains, e.g., lactic acid bacteria and campylobacters (22, 23) SDS-PAGE yields discriminative information at or below the species level.

The accumulation of bacterial DNA sequences and the introduction of user-friendly PCR protocols provide the tools for the use of molecular techniques in bacterial diagnostics. For a well-studied genus or species, genus or species-specific primers from the 16 S rDNA sequence may be selected to construct a PCR for identification purposes with the advantage that it is feasible to examine many strains and acquire a rapid reliable identification. PCR assays are useful for correct identification of *Listeria monocytogenes* (24) and thermotolerant *Campylobacter* species (25). Ultimately, identification of strains may be performed by partial or complete sequencing of the 16 S rRNA gene using comparative sequence software and a database. Strains sharing more than 97% of 16S rRNA sequence homology belong to the same species.

For more information on identification of bacteria based on phenotypic and genetic characteristics the reader is referred to Uyttendaele et al. (26).

C. TYPING OF FOOD-BORNE MICROORGANISMS

Discrimination of strains below the species level is performed in academic and governmental research institutes to assemble epidemiological data on the transmission routes and distribution of food-borne pathogens (27). Moreover, typing of food-borne pathogens is essential to establish the role of a contaminated food as the responsible agent for a food-borne outbreak (28). Typing in microorganisms may also assist in the identification of critical control points of a food manufacturing process by tracking down the sources of product contamination during processing of the food in the manufacturing plant (29).

The relatedness of bacterial isolates may be determined by testing for one or several phenotypic markers using methods such as serotyping, phage typing, biotyping, antibiotic susceptibility testing, bacteriocin typing. These are still the conventional methods for typing of the major food-borne pathogens such as *Salmonella*, *Escherichia coli* 0157, *Listeria monocytogenes* and thermotolerant campylobacters. However, the analysis of DNA by molecular typing methods offers advantages over traditional techniques. DNA can always be extracted from bacteria, thus all bacteria should be typeable. In addition, the discriminatory power of DNA-based methods is greater than that of phenotypic methods. These methods do not require specialized reagents and can be readily performed in molecular biology laboratories (30). Several types of molecular typing techniques can be distinguished: typing techniques based on chromosomal restriction fragment length polymorphism such as PFGE (pulsed field gel electrophoresis) and ribotyping, PCR mediated typing techniques such as RAPD (random amplified polymorphic DNA) and typing techniques combining restriction digestion with selective amplification such as AFLP (amplified fragment length polymorphism). The various molecular typing techniques differ in their simplicity of performance, their reproducibility and their resolution; the latter are sometimes pathogen-dependent. The techniques,

which are characterized by their high reproducibility and resolution, are largely also the most complex and laborious ones (PFGE, AFLP). They also tend to be more expensive (cost of reagents and specialized equipment). On the other hand, RAPD is a rapid and simple technique with a good discriminatory power (if a suitable RAPD primer is found) but it often lacks reproducibility (inter- and intra-laboratory). Ribotyping is open to automation and reproducible patterns with a reasonable number of fragments are obtained but it is not as discriminatory as some of the newer molecular methods.

For more information of molecular typing of food-borne pathogens the reader is referred to Heyndrickx et al. (31).

D. TOXIN DETECTION

Apart from establishing the presence of pathogens in foods, it is of concern to determine whether bacterial toxins are produced in the food or if the pathogen is a potential toxin-producing strain. The major food intoxications are caused by *Staphylococcus aureus*, *Bacillus cereus*, *Clostridium perfringens* and *Clostridium botulinum*. The characteristics and detection of the major bacterial toxins are reviewed in Table 54.3. The immunological methods are still the method of preference for detection of the enterotoxins of *S. aureus*, *Cl. perfringens* and *B. cereus* in foods (Table 54.4) (32). The ELISA (enzyme-linked immuno-sorbent assay) methods use a solid support to which the antibodies are attached. The samples (which may contain the toxin serving as an antigen) are put into contact with the solid support and allowed to react with the antibodies. After the reaction the samples are removed and the plate or strip is washed. The enzyme-antibody conjugate is added and allowed to react with the enterotoxin-antibody complex. The plate or strip is again washed before the substrate is added and subsequently the colorimetric or chemiluminescent reaction is measured. RPLA (Reversed Passive Latex Agglutination) tests are also available. The RPLA technique involves the use of sensitized (antiserum to enterotoxin-treated) latex beads that are exposed to serial dilutions of the extracted enterotoxin. The agglutination titer is determined after overnight incubation. Enterotoxin controls and blanks are included in the test kits. Some kits allow the identification of the type of enterotoxin present, others are limited to demonstration of the presence of enterotoxin (without further indicating the type). For the emetic toxin (cereulide) of *Bacillus cereus* no immunological method is available (no antigenic property assigned to the small cereulide molecule). Cell cultures (33) or a boar spermatozoa test (cytotoxicity) are used to assess the presence of the enterotoxin (34). As an alternative, animal assays may be applied. The mouse lethality assay is still employed as the reference method for botulinal toxins in foods. Immunological

TABLE 54.3
Characteristics and Detection of Toxins Produced by *S. aureus*, *B. cereus*, *Cl. perfringens* and *Cl. botulinum*

Staphylococcus	*Staphylococcus aureus* Emetic Toxin	*Bacillus cereus* Diarrheal Toxin	*Bacillus cereus* Diarrheal Toxin	*Clostridium perfringens* Neurotoxin	*Clostridium botulinum*
Toxin type	Enterotoxin (single chain polypeptide, with cystine-lus) MW 26–34 kDa	Enterotoxin Cereulide (cyclic dodecapsipeptide)	Enterotoxin a) Haemolysin BL: tripartite protein complex B, L₁, L₂ b) Non-haemolytic tripartite protein complex	Enterotoxin Single chain protein with MW 36 kDa	Neurotoxin Protein with MW 150–170 kDa complex with non-toxic proteins
Formation of toxin	In the food, during vegetative growth	In the food during the late exponential or stationary phase	During vegetative growth in the food or in the intestines after ingestion of high numbers of cells	In the intestines after ingestion of high number of cells; toxin formed during sporulation	In the food during vegetative growth
Effect of proteolysis	Resistant	Resistant	Activity loss	Increased activity after treatment with trypsin	Activation
Heat stability	Resistant to 100–120°C	Resistant to 90 min at 121°C	Inactivation by 5 min at 56°C	Inactivation by 15 min at 60°C	Inactivation by a few minutes at 75–80°C
Symptoms	Nausea, vomiting (sometimes diarrhea)	Nausea, vomiting	Cramps, diarrhea	Cramps, diarrhea	Gastro-enteritis, trouble vision and finally paralysis
Incubation period	1–5 h (recovery after 24–48 h)	1–5 h (recovery after 6–24 h)	8–16 h (recovery after 12–24 h)	8–24 h (recovery after 24–48 h)	12–36 h (deceased after 3–6 days)
Toxicity (LD₅₀)	LD₅₀ (monkeys): 25 µg/kg dose causing symptoms in humans: 100–200 ng	Unknown	100 × more toxic than *Cl. perfr.*	1.5 µg for a 20 g mouse	25 pg for a 20 g mouse
Detection methods	Immunological detection (Oxoïd BCET RPLA, Vidas (Biomérieux), Tecria immunoassay)	No immunological detection method Cytotoxicity Animal feed trials	Oxoïd BCET RPLA (L₂ component Haemolysin BL) Tecra immunoassay (Non-haemolytic protein complex) Cytotoxicity	RPLA en ELISA	Mouse bio-assay ELISA

TABLE 54.4
Present Status of ISO Standards for Indicator Organisms in Food and Animal Feeding Stuffs and Water

ISO Standard	Product Group	Title
DIS 21528-1:2003	Horizontal	Detection and enumeration of Enterobacteriaceae – Part 1: most probable number technique with pre-enrichment
DIS 21528-2:2003	Horizontal	Detection and enumeration of Enterobacteriaceae – Part 2: colony-count method
5552:1998	Meat (products)	Detection and enumeration of Enterobacteriaceae without resuscitation – most probable number technique and colony-count technique
7402:1993	Horizontal	Enumeration of Enterobacteriaceae without resuscitation – most probable number technique and colony-count technique
8523:1991	Horizontal	Detection of Enterobacteriaceae with pre-enrichment
4831:1991	Horizontal	Enumeration of coliforms – most probable number technique
4832:1991	Horizontal	Enumeration of coliforms – colony count technique
5541-1:1986	Milk (products)	Enumeration of coliforms – colony count technique at 30°C
5541-2:1986	Milk (products)	Enumeration of coliforms – most probable number technique at 30°C
9308-1:2000	Water	Detection and enumeration of *Escherichia coli* and bacteria of the coli- group – Part 1: membrane filtration
16649-1:2001	Horizontal	Enumeration of β-D glucuronidase-positive *Escherichia coli* – Part 1: colony count at 44°C by membrane filtration
16649-2:2001	Horizontal	Enumeration of β-D glucuronidase-positive *Escherichia coli* – Part 2: colony count technique at 44°C
CD16649-3:2001	Horizontal	Enumeration of β-D glucuronidase-positive *Escherichia coli* – Part 3: most probable number technique
6391:1997	Meat (products)	Enumeration of *Escherichia coli* – colony count technique at 44°C using membranes
11866-1:1997	Milk (products)	Enumeration of presumptive *Escherichia coli* – Part 1: most probable number technique
11866-2:1997	Milk (products)	Enumeration of presumptive *Escherichia coli* – Part 2: most probable number technique using 4-methylumbelliferyl-β-D-glucuronide (MUG)
11866-3:1997	Milk (products)	Enumeration of presumptive *Escherichia coli* – Part 3: colony-count technique at 44°C using membranes
DIS 7251:2002	Horizontal	Enumeration of presumptive *Escherichia coli* – most probable number technique
7899-2:2000	Water	Detection and enumeration of enterococci – Part 2: membrane filtration

Modified from de Boer (7).

methods have been reported for the botulinal toxin but seem to lack sensitivity in comparison to the mouse bioassay. PCR methods targeting the toxin genes have also been developed.

V. MICROBIAL PARAMETERS IN FOOD ANALYSIS

The bacteriological examination of food products falls into one or more of the following categories: total viable count, indicator organisms, specific spoilage organisms, functional flora and food-borne pathogens.

A. "TOTAL" BACTERIAL (COLONY) COUNT

The total bacterial count or, better, "colony count," is an attempt to measure the total number of viable microorganisms present in a food sample as an indication of the overall microbial quality of the food product. "Total" is often associated with microscopic counts which also include dead cells, whereas these procedures are actually based on the assumption that each viable microbial cell will form a visible, separate colony when mixed with an agar and permitted to grow.

Since microorganisms in foods represent various populations with many different growth requirements, the optimum conditions for determining the total viable count may vary from one food to another. The conventional aerobic plate count for examining frozen, chilled, precooked or prepared foods uses pour plates of Plate Count Agar (PCA) and incubates plates for 72 h at 30°C (35) or 48 h at 35°C (36). For analysis of milk and milk products PCA can be supplemented with milk powder in order to favor growth of nutritional fastidious organisms such as lactic acid bacteria. Generally, the lactic acid bacteria show delayed growth and smaller colony size (pin point colonies) in normal PCA. On the other hand, when high numbers of a functional flora are expected, as is the case in fermented foods, a nutritional poor agar medium such as peptone agar may be used to suppress the growth of this competing functional flora.

For the determination of the colony count of thermophilic and mesophilic bacteria in, for example, canned food, Dextrose Tryptone agar is recommended incubated respectively, for 48 h at 55°C and 72 h at 30°C. Flat sour bacteria (e.g., *Bacillus stearothermophilus*) which are important spoilers in these types of product are on this agar medium typically surrounded by a yellow zone because of acid production in contrast to the purple medium (pH indicator is bromocresol purple) (7).

For enumeration of psychrotrophs, the predominant spoilage flora of refrigerated minimal processed foods, incubation for 10 days at 7°C for pour plates has been described. Incubation conditions using shorter times at higher temperatures have included 25 h at 21°C for raw and pasteurized milk using Plate Count Milk agar. Under the assumption that most psychrotrophs are Gram-negative bacteria, a selective medium was recommended that contains crystal violet and triphenyl tetrazolium chloride and is incubated for 5 days at 22°C (7).

Aerobic plate counts of water uses pour plates with Yeast Extract agar incubated either for 48 h at 37°C or for 72 h at 22°C (37).

Anaerobic plate count methods use a medium to favor growth of anaerobic organisms. Although thioglycollate is widely used in anaerobic media to lower the redox potential, it has been reported to be inhibitory to some anaerobes. Shaedler anaerobe agar contains cysteine hydrochloride and glucose as reducing substances and has been shown to successfully recover obligate anaerobes under anaerobic incubation (38).

The mesophilic bacterial spore count is determined by previously heating the primary suspension for 10 minutes at 80°C in order to eliminate vegetative cells and subsequently plating on, respectively, PCA (39) and Reinforced Clostridial Agar with incubation under, respectively, aerobic and anaerobic conditions for 48 h at 37°C for the aerobic and anaerobic spore count. A heat treatment for 30 minutes at 100°C is applied before plating and incubation at 55°C for 48 h to determine the thermophilic bacterial spore count (7).

There is no single set of conditions that will allow growth of the whole spectrum of microorganisms present in a natural sample. Nevertheless, in all of the above-mentioned methods, the selectivity is unintentional and merely a consequence of the choice of time, temperature, atmosphere or nutritional composition of the medium. They all aim to maximize the number of bacteria that may be found in a food product. However, once a procedure for a given food is determined, it should be respected and can be very useful for routine microbial analysis of the food.

B. INDICATOR ORGANISM COUNT

Specific organisms are sought indicating the standard of hygiene used in the manufacture, storage and handling of the food products. The presence of indicator organisms in given numbers points to failure to comply with appropriate GMP.

The use of Enterobacteriaceae as indicator organisms has gained acceptance now in several countries. In the monitoring of foods processed for safety, e.g., by heat or by a chemical process like chlorination, Enterobacteriaceae are the indicators of choice since all member of the

Enterobacteriaceae are known to be eliminated by these treatments. In the case of milk and dairy products, because of the selection of lactose-positive types by the high levels of lactose in the environment, the coli-aerogenes group or coliform bacteria have been used successfully for safeguarding pasteurized products. However, taxonomically, the coliform bacteria are a rather ill-defined group. In general, all Gram-negative bacteria capable of growing on bile salts-containing media, and which produce acid from lactose, are included in the coliform count. In addition, coliforms are not a good indicator in foods where lactose-negative bacteria dominate the microbial ecology of a food.

The entire group of Enterobacteriaceae is of limited use in the examination of foods that have been possibly involved in outbreaks of disease: tests for properly selected pathogens are required here. There is also very limited scope for using the complete taxon of Enterobacteriaceae as an indicator of faecal contamination as not all genera of the Enterobacteriaceae are of faecal origin. The use of an Enterobacteriaceae test on a large number of samples offers considerable advantages for trend analysis in assessment of the overall hygiene during food processing, however, only on the day of production. When raw meats and poultry or vegetables are examined for Enterobacteriaceae in the frame of hygiene monitoring at sampling times during the shelf life, the psychrotrophic types (which grow during refrigerated storage of these products) should not be included in these counts. An alternative approach is to rely on the thermotrophic population fraction of the Enterobacteriaceae also referred to as the 'faecal coliform' group. However, the 'faecal coliform' group is ill-defined as the coliform bacteria having the ability to grow at 44°C and include coliform bacteria which are not of faecal origin and therefore this is also not an absolute marker of faecal contamination. To demonstrate that faecal pollution in a food may have occurred, *Escherichia coli* should be used as the marker organism. It is a well-defined taxonomic unit and ecological investigations have substantiated that *E. coli* originates from the intestinal tract of man and warm-blooded animals.

The Enterococcus group (formerly Lancefield-Group D Streptococci) can be used as an enteric marker organism in specific situations. All streptococci of this group occur in faecal niches. Nevertheless, enterococci possess a high extra-enteric resistance whereas *E. coli* declines quite rapidly in some non-enteric environments, particularly under conditions of reduced a_w. Streptococci are useful marker organisms in certain foods (dry foods, cooked foods) to demonstrate the elimination of the more resistant pathogens (e.g., *Listeria monocytogenes*), an assurance which cannot be provided by the absence of the more fragile Enterobacteriaceae.

Test methods for indicator organisms are also of the utmost importance in water quality assessment. Under European legislation, treated waters should contain (per

100 ml) no coliforms, no faecal coliforms/ *E. coli* and no enterococci. For more information on the use of indicator organisms the reader is referred to Mossel et al. (40).

Violet red bile glucose agar for Enterobacteriaceae and violet red bile lactose agar for coliforms have been widely used in the last 20–30 years for counting and isolating Enterobacteriaceae and coliforms. Enterobacteriaceae and coliforms are determined by incubation at 37°C, faecal coliforms by incubation at 44°C. In fact no new developments in solid media for these bacteria have appeared recently (Table 54.4). Standardized methods for detection and enumeration of *E. coli* comprise a MPN technique, a membrane filtration method and a direct plate count (Table 54.4). The MPN technique comprises, using lauryl sulphate tryptose broth incubated at 37°C and isolation on a chromogenic medium, namely tryptone bile agar with X-glucuronide agar (TBX-agar), and a substrate for β-D-glucuronidase (GUD) and incubated at 44°C. The membrane filtration procedure uses cellulose membranes on minerals modified glutamate agar incubated for 4h at 37°C for resuscitation and subsequent transfer to TBX-agar and incubation at 44°C for enumeration. If high numbers are present, direct enumeration on TBX agar incubated at 44°C can be performed. The introduction of chromogenic media has enabled detection of β-D glucuronidase-positive *E. coli* without the necessity of colony confirmation steps. Over 95% of *E. coli* strains are positive for GUD. The older methodology for detection of *E. coli* relied on used lauryl sulphate trypose broth and subsequent selective enrichment in EC broth (MPN technique) or isolation on tryptone bile agar (membrane filtration method) or violet red bile lactose agar (enumeration) incubated at 44°C and subsequent confirmation of *E. coli* as the only true faecal coliform by indole production from tryptophan at 44°C (41).

Enterococci are enumerated on Slanetz and Bartley agar medium incubated at 37°C for 24–48 h. Kanamycin aesculin azide medium may be used as an alternative (42).

C. DETECTION OF SPECIFIC SPOILAGE ORGANISMS/FUNCTIONAL FLORA

Spoilage organisms are usually associated with taints and off-flavours in stored products. They are the major factor in determining the shelf-life of microbiological unstable food products and are considered to be of more relevance than total viable counts to indicate the microbial quality of the product. For prediction of the shelf-life it is of interest to focus microbial analysis on a selected fraction of the microbial community that contributes to the spoilage of the food defined as the specific spoilage group or organism. This microflora is a function of the raw material flora, the processing, preservation and storage conditions. For more information of the spoilage flora associated with different food products is referred to Chapter? The following microbial parameters are often involved in microbial analyses of

foods in order to determine the shelf-life of a particular food product: lactic acid bacteria, yeast and moulds, osmophilic yeasts, lipolytic microorganisms, proteolytic microorganisms, sulfide producing spoilers, thermoduric flat sour bacteria, *Pseudomonas* species, *Clostridium tyrobutyricum*, etc. However, this is not a restrictive list.

In contrast to provoking deterioration of the food product, microorganisms (mainly lactic acid bacteria), are sometimes added as deliberate starters or take part in the fermentation processes as a result of their being natural contaminants of the starting substrates. In addition, lactic acid bacteria, predominantly *Bifidobacterium* spp. and *Lactobacillus acidophilus*, are increasingly used in dairy products as probiotic organisms. Microbial analyses may be performed to determine whether the claimed starter of probiotic cultures is, indeed, present in the quantities claimed (43, 44).

Intentionally selective methods have been elaborated to quantify this defined sub-set of the microbial population. Media formulation for the important group of the lactic acid bacteria and the yeasts and moulds is provided beneath. For description of the culture media and incubation conditions of other spoilers used as an indication of the microbial quality of foods the reader is referred to specialized literature.

1. Lactic Acid Bacteria

The MRS formulation was developed by de Man, Rogosa and Sharpe to encourage the growth of lactic acid bacteria which includes species of the following genera: *Lactobacillus, Streptococcus, Pediococcus* and *Leuconostoc*. The MRS medium is a complex medium with an acid pH (6.2) and includes high concentrations of glucose and the essential growth factors magnesium and manganese. MRS supports rapid growth of the fastidious lactic acid bacteria resulting in a rapid decrease in pH to 5.0 or less because of the lactic acid production thus further enhancing the selectivity of the medium. Growth of lactic acid bacteria is considerably enhanced by micro-aerophilic conditions. MRS is commonly incubated with an agar overlay for 72 h at 30°C. Selection for lactobacilli can be made by pH adjustment. Acidified MRS to pH 5.4 with acetic acid is, for example, used for enumeration of *Lactobacillus bulgaricus* in yoghurt. Vancomycin and thallium acetate can be added to enhance the selectivity towards *Leuconostoc*. Addition of sorbic acid in combination with low pH inhibits growth of competitive yeasts and moulds. However, upon addition a compromise between the combinations and concentrations of substances used has to be reached between selectivity and productivity of the organism sought (38).

2. Yeasts and Moulds

For determination of yeast and moulds several media are available. In general, an antibacterial compound is added to the culture medium (oxytetracycline, chloramphenicol) or pH of the medium is lowered (pH 5.7) although the latter approach also allows growth of acidophilic bacteria. Dichloran or rose bengal may be added to inhibit spreading and restrict the colony size (45).

VI. DETECTION OF FOOD-BORNE PATHOGENS

Food infection is caused by consumption of food contaminated with the etiological agent, in other words, the pathogenic microorganism. The pathogen develops in the gastro-intestinal system, accompanied or not by toxin production, causing food infection. Food infection can be caused by low numbers of the pathogen. Low numbers can be expected in foods that are correctly processed for safety and not recontaminated or recolonised subsequently. Often detection of single cell in 25 g is required. Virtually all pathogens in foods are sub-lethally stressed. Therefore the detection method of infectious agents encompasses four subsequent steps (46):

- A *resuscitation* procedure or *pre-enrichment* lasting between a few hours to overnight incubation in a non- or half-selective medium to enable recovery and limited outgrowth (10^2–10^4 cfu/ml) of the stressed target organism. Stressed cells are often particularly susceptible to reactive oxygen metabolites. Thus, anaerobic incubation or the addition of free radical quenching agents may be highly effective in resuscitation. Often incubation for a few hours at a more optimum reduced temperature is applied before exposure to the higher selective temperature of incubation (47).
- A period of *enrichment* in a selective medium to suppress the competitive flora and enabling multiplication of the target organism to attain detectable levels of the order 10^5–10^7/ml (48).
- *Isolation* of the pathogen on a selective differential agar medium. Selective agars are streaked with a loopful of enrichment broth and incubated under appropriate conditions. It must be stressed that the ability to grow on specific selective media does not mean that the organism growing is that for which the medium was developed. Differentiation of typical colonies must be regarded as presumptive and confirmatory tests are required.
- Purification of typical colonies and confirmation using a number of morphological, biochemical, and physiological tests.

A few remarks should be made to this general procedure:

- Enrichment is applied where pathogenic microorganisms are present only in small numbers, particularly if large numbers of competing spoilage microorganisms are present. It is not normally applied where the organism is a common contaminant of foods in low (and harmless) numbers, such as the bacterial food intoxicants *Bacillus cereus*, *Staphylococcus aureus*, and *Clostridium perfringens*. These food borne pathogens are tolerated in the order of 100 cfu/ml or g and only pose a health hazard in numbers above 10^5 cfu/ml or g. In the latter case selective media are used for direct plating without prior enrichment and enumerations may be made.

- Although in many cases enrichment media are used in conjunction with selective plating media, they may be used to enumerate specific microorganisms or groups of microorganisms using the MPN technique. In such circumstances, it is necessary to incorporate a diagnostic (differential) reaction to distinguish the organism being enumerated from other microorganisms, which are able to grow under the imposed conditions. Examples are lactose fermentation in media for 'coliforms' and the 'sulphide' reaction in media for clostridia. Further confirmatory tests are required where reactions are positive.

- The use of culture media with selective agents and the incorporation of an elective system to differentiate the target organism has been discussed above. Numerous selective media are available for the isolation of specific food borne pathogens, and development of media and modification of existing media is a continuous process in microbial food analysis. The choice of media should take into consideration factors such as selectivity and sensitivity of the medium as well as the ease of use. However, another important factor is the type of food for analysis. Food borne pathogens from specific foods may be unusually sensitive to selective agents or competing microorganisms from specific foods may be unusually resistant to selective agents. For example *Listeria monocytogenes* may be sub-lethally stressed and selective agents in enrichment media may interfere with the process of repair in such cells. Consequently, the isolation of stressed *Listeria monocytogenes* from particular types of cheese benefit from a partially non-selective pre-enrichment compared to the completely selective pre-enrichment and enrichment procedure conventionally used (49).

An overview of the recommended procedure according to ISO for detection of the most important pathogenic bacteria implied in food analysis namely *Salmonella* spp.,

Listeria monocytogenes, *Campylobacter* spp. and *Escherichia coli* O157 is shown in Figure 54.2 (a–d). A description of the selective media and recommended confirmation tests for detection of the food-borne intoxicating *Bacillus cereus*, *Staphylococcus aureus* and *Clostridium perfringens* is given in Table 54.5.

For more information on approved protocols for the detection of food-borne pathogens the reader is referred to the different national and international standard organizations.

VII. STANDARD METHODS, VALIDATION OF METHODS AND QUALITY ASSURANCE IN MICROBIOLOGY

Microbiological tests are important in governmental food inspection to enforce legal regulations, in international trade to determine compliance with a microbiological standard, in commercial relationships between trade partners to control on agreed microbiological specifications, in the food industry to maintain quality control and process requirements, in

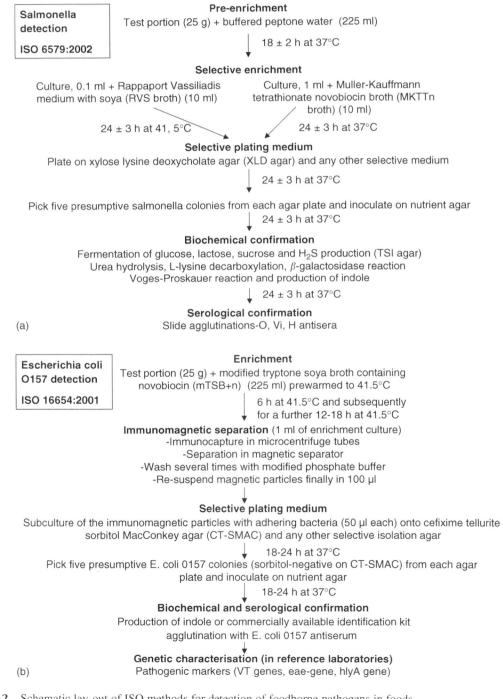

FIGURE 54.2 Schematic lay-out of ISO methods for detection of foodborne pathogens in foods.

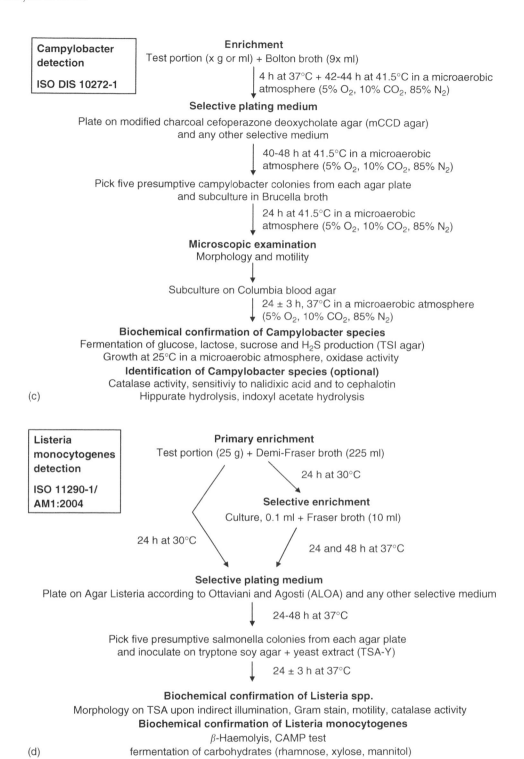

FIGURE 54.2 Continued.

academic laboratories for conducting research, and in reference laboratories to confirm the analyses of another laboratory and to provide surveillance data. The results of these tests should be reliable. It is required that performance characteristics of the method are determined. Apart from these technical characteristics, it is important that all parties involved agree with and accept the methods employed.

Mutual recognition of test methods in international trade relations facilitates commerce and exchange of results.

A. STANDARD METHODS

Standard methods have been elaborated by international, national or trade organizations such as ISO (International

TABLE 54.5

Overview of the Standard Media Used for Enumeration of *Staphylococcus aureus*, *Clostridium perfringens* and *Bacillus cereus* in Foods

	Coagulase-Positive Staphylococci (*Staphylococcus aureus* and Other Species)	*Clostridium perfringens*	Presumptive *Bacillus cereus*
Selective media	Baird-Parker agar medium with egg yolk tellurite emulsion (spread plate)	Egg-yolk-free tryptose-sulfite-cycloserine agar (poured plate + overlay)	Mannitol Egg Yolk Polymyxin agar
Incubation conditions	Aerobic incubation for 48 h at 37°C	Anaerobic incubation for 20 h at 37°C	24–48 h 30°C
Growth promoting compounds	Sodium pyruvate		
Selective compounds	Glycine, tellurite, lithium	D-cycloserine anaerobic incubation	Polymyxin B
Diagnostic compounds	Reduction of tellurite results in gray-black shiny colonies		
	Egg yolk emulsion renders medium yellow and opaque; clear zones around colonies produced by proteolytic action; most strains also form opaque haloes around colonies because of lipase activity	Sodium metabisulphite and ammonium ferric citrate indicate sulphite reduction and produce black colonies	Most strains produce phospholipase C and hydrolyze lecithine in egg yolk resulting in a white precipitate surrounding the colony
			Failure of *B. cereus* to use mannitol induces alkaline color of the pH indicator phenol red rendering violet/pink background to the rough/dry colonies
Confirmation tests	Coagulase test	Lactose fermentation and gelatine hydrolysis, motility and nitrate reduction	Haemolysis on sheep blood agar and motility
Remarks	Rabbit Plasma Fibrinogen agar (incorporation of rabbit plasma in the basal medium enables direct detection of coagulase-positive staphylococci)	Confirmation in lactose sulfite medium when incubated at 46°C is very specific	
Reference	ISO 6888-1:1999 and ISO 6888-2:1999	ISO/DIS 7937:2002	ISO 7932:1993 and ISO 7392/A1:2002

Standards Organization), AOAC International (formerly Association of Official Analytical Chemists), CEN (Comité Européen de Normalisation), NMKL (Nordisk Metodik-komitté för Livsmeddel), AFNOR (Association Fran-çaise de Normalisation), NNI (Nederlands Normalisatie Instituut), DIN (Deutsches Institut für Normung), IDF (International Dairy Federation), etc. (50).

These standard methods for detection of microbiological contaminants in foods are usually conventional cultural methods. Primarily because the intention is to provide the users of these methods with a reliable and internationally accepted method which enables them to obtain equivalent results in different laboratory settings without having exclusivity of materials related to one manufacturer. Although in essence these standard methods serve only as guidelines for reliable microbial analysis of foods, historically in many countries governmental agencies and trading agencies recommend or accept them as official methods for detection or enumeration of microorganisms in foods (51, 52) they may also recommend their own established methods, e.g., the U.S. FDA

compiles its recommended methods in a Bacteri-ological Analytical Manual (US FDA-BAM) (36).

B. VALIDATION OF METHODS

The confidence in the results produced by a microbiological analytical procedure depends on the reliability of the analytical method. Determination of the performance characteristics of a method by validation will facilitate it to gain acceptance of the test results by international, national or regional regulators and trade partners. Standard methods, which are published by international, national or regional standardization organizations or trade organizations, are considered as validated. In this case the laboratory implementing a new standard method has to demonstrate that criteria for validation indicated in the standard can be achieved. This is done by a systematic research on specific analytical parameters. However, only recently the performance characteristics of six ISO methods, namely *Bacillus cereus* (enumeration), *Listeria monocytogenes* (detection and enumeration), *Staphylococcus aureus* (enumeration), *Clostridium perfringens* (enumeration) and *Salmonella* (detection), were determined and published in the corresponding ISO methods (53–55). In the present situation, laboratories will have to show that they are capable of performing the standard method of choice correctly on experiments with their own range of samples. This is preferably referred to as a method verification study because it is not a validation study *sensu strictu*. Validation of a method is a formidable collaborative research task that so-called rapid, modern methods are subjected to before they are accepted and will be discussed in Chapter 55. Methods are most effectively assessed with specially designed experiments. Routine analyses usually lack a plan or replications that is are prerequisites for method verification.

For quantitative methods (enumeration) this method verification study should focus on establishment of the trueness (bias) and the precision of the method.

Trueness (bias) is defined as the closeness of agreement between the true value or, if not known, the accepted reference value and the mean result which is obtained when the experimental procedure is applied a large number of times (= systematic error) (56, 57). The trueness can be obtained by the analysis of certified reference materials (CRMs), derived from a certifying body (e.g., the Community Bureau of Reference (BCR) of the European Commission (EC)). However, only a limited number of CRMs or stable reference materials from other sources are available for microbiological purposes. The analysis of spiked materials (recovery studies) can be performed as an alternative. Participation in proficiency testing schemes can also help in assessing the laboratory performance for the parameter of trueness.

Precision is defined as the closeness of agreement between independent test results obtained by applying the experimental procedure several times on the same sample under stipulated conditions (= random error) (57, 58). The measure of precision is usually expressed in terms of imprecision and calculated as a standard deviation of the test results. Less precision is reflected by a larger standard deviation. Checks of precision in routinely used methods should be made to ensure that the result does not change with time as a result of changes in reagents, equipment, staff, etc. Distinction is made between:

- Repeatability: indicates the variability observed within a laboratory, over a short time, using a single operator, the same apparatus on identical test material.
- Reproducibility: inter-laboratory reproducibility indicates the variability observed when different laboratories analyse the same sample by use of the same method and may be estimated directly by inter-laboratory study. Intra-laboratory reproducibility relates to the variation in results observed when one or more factors,

such as time, equipment and operator, are varied within a laboratory.

For qualitative methods (presence/absence testing) the method verification study should focus on establishment of the detection limit and the specificity and sensitivity of the method.

The *detection limit* is defined as the smallest number of culturable microorganisms that can be reliably detected in the sample. For qualitative methods it can be defined as the smallest number of culturable microorganisms that can be detected on 50% of occasions by the reference method (56).

Both *sensitivity and specificity* relate to the degree to which a method responds uniquely to the specified target organism or group of organisms and relate to the number of false positives and false negatives results that are found with the validated method. Various definitions for sensitivity and specificity are proposed, includig the following (58).

The sensitivity of a method is the proportion of target organisms that can be detected; it can be calculated with the following equation:

$$\text{Sensitivity (\%)} = \frac{\text{number of true positives (P)}}{P + \text{number of false negatives}} \times 100$$

A failure to detect the target when present is a false negative result and will lower the sensitivity of a test. In food microbiology only a very low frequency of false-negative results can be tolerated for safety reasons.

The specificity of a method is the ability to discriminate between the target organism and other organisms; it can be calculated with the formula:

$$\text{Sensitivity (\%)} = \frac{\text{number of true negatives (N)}}{N + \text{number of false positivies}} \times 100$$

A positive result in the absence of the target is a false-positive result and will lower the specificity of a method. For rapid screening methods, a higher false-positive frequency may be acceptable, as positive screening tests are followed by confirmation tests.

In addition to the specificity and sensitivity as described above, the inclusivity and exclusivity of a qualitative method also may be determined, inclusivity being the ability of the validated method to detect a wide range of strains belonging to the target organism, exclusivity being the lack of detection with the validated method of a relevant range of non-target strains (56).

A number of issues need to be addressed in the preparation of a solid method verification scheme. These are listed in Table 54.6.

TABLE 54.6

Considerations in the Preparation of an Experimental Design for Method Verification

Number of food types to be tested	If the method is to be validated for all foods, usually five categories of foods are included
	Food categories are predominantly determined by the origin of the product, e.g., meat products, dairy, fruits and vegetables, etc.
	The modes of processing to increase shelf life may further be used to select food types within a category, e.g., raw, heat-treated, etc.
	The types of food chosen should be relevant to the type of target organism(s) sought and the scope of the laboratory
Number of samples to be analyzed	A sufficient number of samples should be analyzed in order to generate sufficient data to allow the use of appropriate statistics for interpretation
Naturally contaminated food samples versus artificially contaminated food samples	Whenever possible naturally contaminated samples should be used. These represent best real-life encountered samples with the target organism(s) present as a minority (if pathogenic bacteria) in a vast majority of other bacteria and in a non-optimal (stressed) conditions
	When artificially contaminated samples are used, the levels of inoculation and the preparation of the inoculants to achieve this should be similar to those expected to be found in naturally contaminated samples; the background flora also should be representative
The source and number of inoculum strains	Strains that have been isolated from the same type of food product are preferred; if not possible, then inoculants should be fully characterized (reference) cultures
	Cover the recognized range of the target and non-target organism with respect of the geographical distribution, incidence and diversity of the identification characteristics it is biochemical activity, serotype, phage type, etc.

TABLE 54.7

Requirements of the ISO 17025:1999 for the Accreditation of Testing Laboratories

Management requirements	Technical Requirements
Organisation	Personnel
Quality system	Accommodation and environmental conditions
Document control	
Review of requests, tenders and contracts	Test methods and validation, measurement of uncertainty
Subcontracting of tests and calibrations	
Purchasing services and supplies	Equipment
Service to the client, complaints	Measurement of traceability, control of data
Corrective and preventive actions	Sampling
Control of records	Reporting of results
Iternal audits, management review	

By method verification insight is obtained into the possibilities and limitations of the test method under the laboratory's own conditions in the area typically served by the laboratory.

C. QUALITY ASSURANCE IN MICROBIOLOGY

The performance characteristics of a method are closely related to analyst performance, the equipment and, more generally, the competence of the laboratory to provide accurate, reliable and repeatable test results under controlled conditions. Accreditation of laboratories carrying out microbiological food analysis provides to those relying upon its services the assurance of the reliability of

the test results. Accreditation of a laboratory is the formal approval given by a national authorized body (linked by the European co-operation for Accreditation of Laboratories (EAL)) that the laboratory is competent to carry out specific methods of analysis and has a commitment to quality assurance in the lab (59). A detailed account of the requirements that testing labs have to meet is described in ISO 17025:2000 (60) and reviewed in Table 54.7.

It is clear that, to comply with the requirements of the ISO17025:1999, the laboratory should use validated methods which are documented in standard operating procedures and must have a systematic approach of quality control. Of equal importance is the execution of the method by qualified staff with well-maintained and properly functioning equipment and utensils.

REFERENCES

1. NF Lightfoot, EA Maier. Microbiological analysis of food and water: Guidelines for quality assurance. Dordrecht: Elsevier Science, 1998.
2. ICMSF. HACCP in Microbiological Safety and Quality. London: Blackwell Scientific Publications, 1998.
3. ICMSF. Microorganisms in Foods 2. Sampling for Microbiological Analysis: Principles and Specific Applications. London: Blackwell Scientific Publications, 1986.
4. PJ Stephens, JA Joynson, KW Davies, R Holbrook, HM Lappin-Scott, TJ Humphrey. The use of an automated growth analyser to measure recovery times of single heat-injured Salmonella cells. J Appl Microbiol 83: 445–455, 1997.
5. L Restaino, EW Frampton, H Spitz. Repair and growth of heat- and freeze-injured *Escherichia coli* O157:H7 in selective enrichment broths. Food Microbiol 18:617–629, 2001.

6. NG Besse. Influence of various environmental parameters and of detection procedures on the recovery of stressed *Listeria monocytogenes*: a review. Food Microbiol 19:221–234, 2002.

7. FP Downes, K Ito. Compendium of Methods for the Microbiological Examination of Foods. Washington, D.C.: American Public Health Association, 2001.

8. FJ Bolton. Strategies in the development of media for the detection of food-borne pathogens. Int J Food Microbiol 45:29–34, 1998.

9. E De Boer. Update on media for isolation of *Enterobacteriaceae* from foods. Int J Food Microbiol 45:43–53, 1998.

10. M Manafi. New developments in chromogenic and fluorogenic media. Int J Food Microbiol 60:205– 218, 2000.

11. R Capita, C Alonso-Calleja. Comparison of different most-probable-number methods for enumeration of Listeria in poultry. J Food Prot 66(1):65–71, 2003.

12. P Entis, I Lerner. Enumeration of beta-glucuronidase-positive Escherichia coli in foods by using the ISO-GRID method with SD-39 agar. J Food Prot 61(7):913–916, 1998.

13. P Entis. Two-day hydrophobic grid membrane filter method for yeast and mold enumeration in foods using YM-11 agar: collaborative study. J AOAC Int 79(5): 1069–1082, 1996.

14. R Priego, LM Medina, R Jordano. Evaluation of petri-film series 2000 as a possible rapid method to count coliforms in foods. J Food Prot 63(8):1137–1140, 2000.

15. MR García-Armesto, A Otero, J Rúa, B Moreno, ML García-Lopez. Evaluation of the spiral plating system for the routine assessment of indicator microorganisms in taw ewe's milk. J Food Prot 65(8):1281–1286, 2002.

16. WG Eisel, RH Linton, PM Muriana. A survey of microbial levels for incoming raw beef, environmental sources, and ground beef in a red meat processing plant. Food Microbiol 14(3):273–282, 1997.

17. S Salo, A Laine, T Alanko, AM Sjoberg, G Wirtanen. Validation at the microbiological methods Hygicult dip-slide, contact plate, and swabbing in surface hygiene control: a Nordic collaborative study. J AOAC Int 83(6): 1357–1365, 2000.

18. P Vandamme, B Pot, M Gillis, P De Vos, K Kersters, J Swings. Polyphasic taxonomy, a consensus approach to bacterial systematics. Microbiol Rev 60(2):407–438, 1996.

19. D Jones, NR Krieg. Serology and chemotaxonomy. In: PHA Sneath, NS Mair, ME Sharpe, JG Holt. Eds. Bergey's Manual of Systematic Bacteriology, Volume 2. Baltimore: Williams & Wilkins, 1986, pp 311–335.

20. G Huys, M Vancanneyt, R Coopman, P Janssen, E Falsen, M Altwegg, K Kersten. Cellular fatty acid composition as a chemotaxonomic marker for the differentiation of phenospecies and hybridization groups in the genus *Aeromonas*. Int J Syst Bacteriol 44(4):651–658, 1994.

21. P Kämpfer. Limits and possibilities of total fatty acid analysis for classification and identification of *Bacillus* species. Syst Appl Microbiol 17:86–98, 1994.

22. JJ Leisner, M Vancanneyt, G Rusul, B Pot, K Lefebvre, A Fresi, LK Tee. Identification of lactic acid bacteria constituting the predominating microflora in an acid-fermented condiment (tempoyak) popular in Malaysia. Int J Food Microbiol 63(1–2):149–157, 2001.

23. HI Atabay, F Aydin, K Houf, M Sahin, P Vandamme. The prevalence of *Arcobacter* spp. on chicken carcasses sold in retail markets in Turkey, and identification of the isolates using SDS-PAGE. Int J Food Microbiol 81(1):21–28, 2003.

24. RE Levin. Application of the polymerase chain reaction for detection of *Listeria monocytogenes* in foods: a review of methodology. Food Biotechnol 17(2):99– 119, 2003.

25. EO Engvall, B Brändström, A Gunnarsson, T Mörner, H Wahlström, C Fermer. Validation of a polymerase chain reaction/restriction enzyme analysis method for species identification of thermophilic campylobacters isolated from domestic and wild animals. J Appl Microbiol 92:47–54, 2002.

26. M Uyttendaele, J Debevere. The use of applied systematics to identify foodborne pathogens. In: T McMeekin. Ed. Detecting Pathogens in Food, Cambridge, U.K.: Woodhead Publishing Ltd, 2003.

27. B Swaminathan, TJ Barett, SB Hunter, RV Tauxe. PulseNet: The molecular subtyping network for food-borne bacterial disease surveillance, United States. Emerging Infect Dis 7(3):382–389, 2001.

28. JM Farber, EM Daley, MT Mackie, B Limerick. A small outbreak of listeriosis potentially linked to the consumption of imitation crab meat. Lett Appl Microbiol 31(2):100–104, 2000.

29. K Aarnisalo, T Autio, AM Sjoberg, J Lunden, H Korkeala, ML Suihko. Typing of *Listeria monocytogenes* isolates originating from the food processing industry with automated ribotyping and pulsed-field gel electrophoresis. J Food Prot 66(2):249–255, 2003.

30. JM Farber. An introduction to the hows and whys of molecular typing. J Food Prot 59(10):1091–1101, 1996.

31. M Heyndrickx, N Rijpens, L Herman. Molecular detection and typing of food borne bacterial pathogens: a review. In: A Durieux, JP Simon. Eds. Applied Microbiology. Dordrecht, the Netherlands: Kluwer Academic Publishers, 2001, pp 193–238.

32. YC Su, ACL Wong. Current perspectives on detection of staphylococcal enterotoxins. J Food Prot 60(2):195–202, 2002.

33. SH Beattie, AG Williams. Detection of toxigenic strains of *Bacillus cereus* and other *Bacillus* spp. with improved cytotoxicity assay. Lett Appl Microbiol 28(3):221–225, 1999.

34. MA Andersson, R Mikkola, J Helin, MC Andersson, M Salkinoja-Salonen. A novel sensitive bioassay for detection of Bacillus cereus emetic toxin and related depsipeptide ionophores. Appl Environ Microbiol 64: 1338–1343, 1998.

35. International Standards Organisation (ISO) ISO 4833:2003. Horizontal method for the enumeration of microorganisms – Colony count technique at 30°C. Geneva, 2003.

36. LJ Maturin, JT Peeler. Food and Drug Administration, Bacteriological Analytical Manual online, www.cfsan.fda.gov/~ebam.html, 2001.

37. International Standards Organisation (ISO) ISO 6222:1999. Water quality. Enumeration of culturable microorganisms. Colony count by inoculation in a nutrient agar culture medium. Geneva, 1999.

38. Oxoid Manual online, www.oxoid.com.

39. MC Tegiffel, RR Beumer, J Hoekstra, FM Rombouts. Germination of bacterial-spores during sample preparation. Food Microbiol 12(4):327–332, 1995.

40. DAA Mossel, JEL Corry, CB Struijk, RM Baird. Essentials of the Microbiology of Foods, Chichester, U.K.: John Wiley & Sons, 1995.

41. E de Boer. Update on media for isolation of Enterobacteriaceae from foods. Int J Food Microbiol 45(1):43–53, 1998.

42. KJ Domig, HK Mayer, W Kneifel. Methods used for the isolation enumeration, characterisation and identification of Enterococcus spp. 1. Media for isolation and enumeration. Int J Food Microbiol 88(2–3):147–164, 2003.

43. N Thamaraj, NP Shah. Selective enumeration of Lactobacillus delbrueckii spp bulgaricus, Streptococcus thermophilicus, Lactobacillus acidophilus, bifidobacteria, Lactobacillus casei, Lactobacillus rhamnosus, and propionibacteria. J Dairy Sci 86(7):2288–2296, 2003.

44. D Roy. Media for the isolation and enumeration of bifidobacteria in dairy products. Int J Food Microbiol 69(3):167–182, 2001.

45. LR Beuchat. Media for detecting and enumerating yeasts and molds. Int J Food Microbiol 17(2):145–158, 1992.

46. AH Varnam, MG Evans. Foodborne Pathogens. An Illustrated Text. England: Manson Publishing Ltd, 1996, pp 27–29.

47. NG Besse. Influence of various environmental parameters and of detection procedures on the recovery of stressed L-monocytogenes: a review. Food Microbiol 19(2–3):221–234, 2002.

48. AD Hitchins, RE Duvall. Feasibility of a defined microflora challenge method for evaluating the efficacy of foodborne Listeria monocytogenes selective enrichments. J Food Prot 63(8):1064–1070, 2000.

49. N Rijpens, L Herman. Comparison of selective and nonselective primary enrichments for the detection of Listeria monocytogenes in cheese. Int J Food Microbiol Accepted for publication, 2003.

50. PA Bertram-Drogatz, F Wilborn, P Scheu, A Pardigol, C Koob, C Grönewald, M Fandke, K Berghof. PCR-based commercial tests for pathogens. In: RK Robinson, CA Batt, PD Patel. eds. Encyclodedia of Food Microbiology. London: Academic Press, 2000, pp 1688–1640.

51. AD Hitchins. The International Dairy Federation's procedure for the validation of microbiological analytical methods for dairy foods. Food Control 7(1): 13–18, 1996.

52. C Lahellec. Development of standard methods with special reference to Europe. Int J Food Microbiol 45:13–16, 1998.

53. SM Schulten, PH in 't Veld, NJD Nagelkerke, S Scotter, ML De Buyser, P Rollier, C Lahellec. Evaluation of the ISO 7932 standard for the enumeration of Bacillus cereus in foods. Int J Food Microbiol 57(1–2):53–61, 2000.

54. SL Scotter, S Langton, B Lombard, S Schulten, NJD Nagelkerke, PH in 't Veld, P Rollier, C Lahellec. Validation of ISO method 11290 Part 1. Detection of Listeria monocytogenes in foods. Int J Food Microbiol 64:295–306, 2001.

55. SL Scotter, S Langton, B Lombard, C Lahellec, S Schulten, NJD Nagelkerke, PH in 't Veld, P Rollier. Validation of ISO method 11290 Part 2. Enumeration of Listeria monocytogenes in foods. Int J Food Microbiol 70:121–129, 2001

56. International Standards Organisation (ISO) ISO 16140:2003. Microbiology of food and animal feeding stuffs – protocol for the validation of alternative methods. Geneva, 2003.

57. SLR Ellison, M Rosslein, A Williams. Quantifying uncertainty in analytical measurement, London: Eurachem/CITAC, 2000.

58. S Notermans, R Beumer, F Rombouts. Detecting foodborne pathogens and their toxins: conventional versus rapid and automated methods. In: P Doyle, LR Beuchat, TJ Montville. Eds. Food Microbiology Fundamentals and Frontiers. Washington, D.C.: ASM Press, 1997, pp 705–708.

59. C Bowles. Laboratory management accreditation schemes. In: RK Robinson, CA Batt, PD Patel. eds. Encyclopedia of Food Microbiology. London: Academic Press, 2000, pp 1128–1133.

60. International Standards Organisation (ISO) ISO 17025:2000. General requirements for the competence of testing and calibration laboratories. Geneva, 2000.

55 Rapid Methods in Food Diagnostics

Mieke Uyttendaele and Johan Debevere
Department of Food Technology, Chemistry,
Microbiology and Human Nutrition, Ghent University

CONTENTS

I. INTRODUCTION

The classical procedures for enumeration or detection of microorganisms in foods (Chapter 54) are labor-intensive and time-consuming. Several days are needed to obtain confirmed results. To shorten analysis time, new methods have been developed that can rapidly enumerate or detect low numbers of microorganisms in foods. In this chapter, the term 'rapid' will be used to describe methods which are able to give results within a 24–48 h timeframe, whereas results within 0.5–4 h are considered extremely rapid. In order to allow for immediate corrective action during food manufacturing processes, 'real-time' or 'on-line' detection of microorganisms in foods is sought by manufacturers.

The lack of sensitivity or lack of robustness of most new technologies, however, makes 'real-time' detection in solid foods difficult to obtain. Water and beverages are easier to manipulate and, therefore, more amenable for application of 'on-line' methodology.

A number of instrumental methods have been developed for rapid detection of pathogens using various principles of detection. Direct microscopic methods like DEFT (Direct Epifluorescent Filter Technique) or flow cytometry (FCM) are based on the detection of the actual cells. Indirect methods detect growth and metabolic activity (e.g., conductimetry/impedance) or cellular components (e.g., ATP bioluminescence). Immunological methods have been and still are popular in different formats for rapid detection of pathogens. More recently, nucleic acid-based methods like PCR (Polymerase Chain Reaction) have been advancing rapidly and are promising for rapid screening of foods for presence of pathogens. Finally, the development of biosensors opens new perspectives for 'real-time' or 'on-line' detection of pathogens. Because there are many manufacturers supplying commercially available options for the rapid detection methods discussed and the format in which these techniques are available changes rapidly, no listing of these commercial assays is included. For an up-to-date overview the reader is referred to the internet sites of the manufacturers, or to comprehensive information websites such as http://www.foodhaccp. com or http://www.rapid-microbiology.com. The present chapter aims to discuss the potential and pitfalls of each of the above-mentioned techniques as a rapid detection method of either spoilage organisms or pathogens in foods. For a discussion of the modified and automated traditional culture-based methods, e.g., spiral plater, chromogenic media, commercial identification kits, etc. the reader is referred to Chapter 54.

II. BENEFITS AND LIMITATIONS OF RAPID METHODS IN FOOD MICROBIOLOGY

Some distinguishing features of both traditional culture-based methods and alternative rapid methods for microbiological analyses of foods are listed in Table 55.1.

Alternative rapid methods are especially cost-effective if large numbers of samples need to be screened for a defined parameter in a short period of time. The reliability of the results is related to the intrinsic performance characteristics of the method and the degree to which operators are trained and familiar with the execution and interpretation of the methods.

Although rapid methods have become increasingly popular in recent years, they also have their limitations:

- Often rapid methods are developed for a specific scope of application (e.g., a defined product group) and linked to strict protocols in order to obtain good performance. They are less

TABLE 55.1
Significant Distinguishing Features of Traditional and Rapid Methods

Traditional Culture-Based Methods	Alternative Rapid Methods
Labor-intensive	User-friendly, amenable to automation
Time-consuming	Rapid results
Low investment in apparatus and materials	Often expensive apparatus and consumables needed
Subjective interpretation (linked to personnel observation)	Objective interpretation (print-out)
Moderate reproducible (depends on quality-assurance program in the laboratory)	Better reproducible (quality-controlled reagents, meticulously standardized protocols)

flexible than traditional methods which are most of the time horizontal methods that are more amenable to modification depending on the food product to be analyzed.

- Rapid methods may, in many cases, only be able to indicate the presence or absence of target organism(s) but they do not provide an isolated colony, the availability of which may be desirable for epidemiological purposes.

- Novel rapid methods measure parameters (antigen-antibody response, DNA or RNA sequences, metabolic activity) distinct from the classically accepted ones (phenotypic traits). This may complicate the problem of interpretation of the results in comparison studies of the methods.

- Rapid methods that work remarkably well with pure cultures of target organisms fail sometimes when applied to real food specimens which may include inhibitory components. The effect of these may be overcome by previous concentration and purification of target organisms, although at the expense of ease of use and rapid results.

- Often rapid methods still make partial use of the traditional culture-based method. For example, ELISA methods and PCR methods both employ a one- or two-day culture enrichment step to resuscitate sub-lethally damaged cells and enable multiplication of low numbers of pathogens to the intrinsic detection limit of the proper ELISA (10^4–10^6 cfu/ml) or PCR assay (ca 10^2 cfu/ml). As such, these methods do not entirely replace traditional culture-based methods but rather are complementary to the traditional methods in overcoming their lack of speed in reporting results. This also implies that the reliability of the outcome of the ELISA or

PCR assay not only depends on the assay as such but also on the effectiveness of the enrichment procedure to provide sufficient numbers of the target organism.

III. MICROSCOPIC METHODS

Due to the necessity of incubation to enable multiplication of cells to become visual colonies, the traditional culture-based methods cannot be classified as rapid. Truly rapid methods are based on the detection of target organisms at the single cell level by use of microscopy. In order to visualize cells for microscopical examination, coloring agents are used to provide information on the total level of microorganisms (e.g., acridine orange staining) or specific types of microorganisms (e.g., fluorescent labeled antibodies). In combination with different pre-treatments (e.g., pre-filtration to remove solid particles, enrichment to enhance the number of cells) and detecting principles (epifluorescent microscopy or flow cytometry), microscopic methods have developed into promising rapid methodologies for microbial analysis of particular food categories such as dairy products and beverages.

A. DEFT

DEFT stands for Direct Epifluorescent Filter Technique, a microscopic cell counting method. Originally developed for the determination of total bacterial counts in raw milk, this technique also found application in the fields of meat and fish microbiology. The DEFT procedure consists of four main steps: homogenization and pre-treatment of samples with detergents and proteolytic enzymes, filtration of an aliquot of the sample over a polycarbonate membrane, fluorescent staining of the bacteria retained on the filter and the subsequent microscopic counting of the cells under a fluorescent microscope. This detection can be automated by linking the microscope to an image analyzing system. DEFT differs from conventional light microscopy in that different fluorogenic labels can provide different types of information. Originally, the nucleic acid stain acridine orange was used as the labeling reagent for total bacterial counts. Although it has been said to label viable cells orange and to render dead or impaired cells green, intermediate colors can occur and a clear distinction cannot always be obtained. Alternative fluorescent probes, such as nucleic acid stains like DAPI ($4'$,6-diamidino-2-phenylindol), indicate total number of bacteria present irrespective of metabolic activity. Viability labels have also been developed, including fluorescein derivatives that are cleaved into intensely green products by viable (metabolically active) cells. Although the actual staining and counting takes less than 0.5–1 h, the total detection time is seriously lengthened by sample pre-treatment steps. The intrinsic detection limit of DEFT is around 10^4–10^5 cells

per ml of original sample, and so concentration techniques and enrichment steps usually have to be included in the protocol (1). The inherent lack of specificity in conventional DEFT methodology is a serious drawback in terms of specific pathogen detection. All the above-mentioned fluorescent stains are "universal" ones, incapable of demonstrating specific pathogens. Consequently, fluorescent labeled antibodies are used for specific pathogens in the so-called antibody-DEFT (Ab-DEFT) approach. A protocol using Ab-DEFT has been described for detection of E. coli O157:H7 in beef (2).

A novel way of cellular staining in combination with conventional DEFT methodology has been described recently and is termed "oligo-DEFT." It uses the combination of FISH (Fluorescent In Situ Hybridisation) with a highly specific oligonucleotide probe for the 16S rRNA, and DEFT. It has been used for the detection of E. coli in water, beverages and sprouts (detection limit: 1 CFU per ml) (3).

To conclude, DEFT in se allows a near on-line detection of microorganisms, but its practical applicability in food analysis is seriously hampered by the need for sample pre-treatment and concentration/isolation steps. As a result, the 30-min assay time in model systems takes more than 20 h when specific pathogens have to be detected in real food samples.

B. FLOW CYTOMETRY

Flow cytometry (FCM) is an optically based method for analyzing individual cells. It comprises the suspension of target cells in a fluid, injection of an aliquot in the detection system (flow cytometer) and the automated real-time analysis by the instrument. Basically, the cells, which can be labeled with a fluorogenic compound prior to the assay, pass a laser beam and scattering of light occurs. The extent and the nature of the light scatter reflects bacterial number, size and shape, and the fluorescence is measured as well by a system of lenses and optical cells (Figure 55.1). The sensitivity of the technique is very high: as few as 10^2 yeast cells and about 10^2–10^3 bacterial cells per ml can be detected with results being obtained in less than 30 minutes. However, as is the case for DEFT, the application in the field of food microbiology is limited by the fact that a homogenous suspension, free of interfering particles, is needed to be injected in the system. This necessitates an appropriate sample preparation method (e.g., enzymatic clearing). As a consequence the application of FCM in food microbiology is mostly limited to the enumeration of total viable counts (TVC) or yeast cells in milk and beverages (4). Flow cytometry is often used in conjunction with the commercially available LIVE/DEAD®BacLight™ bacterial viability kit. The kit was developed to differentiate live and dead bacteria based on plasma membrane permeability. The staining mechanism using LIVE/DEAD kit on bacterial cells is based on the attachment of the non-fluorescent

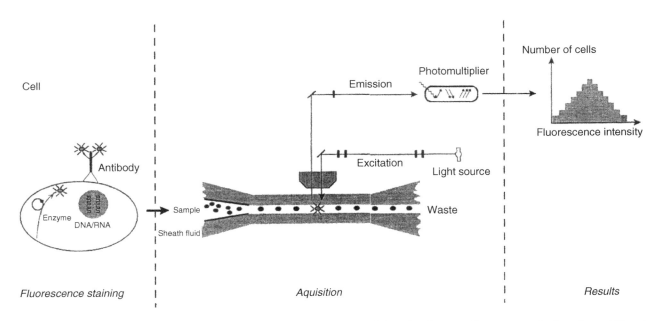

FIGURE 55.1 The principle of flow cytometric analysis. (Ph.D. thesis of C.N. Jacobsen on flow cytometric detection of *Listeria monocytogenes*, courtesy of M. Jakobsen, Dept. Dairy and Food Science, Royal Veterinary and Agricultural University, Denmark.)

agents on nucleic acids. Once the DNA-dye complex is formed fluorescence can be measured. The kit consists of two fluorochromes, which have distinct fluorescent behavior in terms of emission of wavelengths and membrane permeability. The first component is the membrane-permeant stain SYTO9®, which fluoresces green at 530 nm upon excitation at 488 nm. It stains all cells, thus acting as total cell stain. During cell death, accompanied by membrane damage, the second, membrane-impermeant, dye propidium iodide (PI) penetrates into cells and quenches the green SYTO9® fluorescence. PI is able to excite at 488 nm as well and emit red fluorescence at 620 nm. When used in combination, intact cells are labeled green and cells with damaged membranes are labeled red. Raw milk data using LIVE/DEAD staining showed good agreement between FCM and standard plate count methods. The detection limit of the FCM assay was $\leq 10^4$ bacteria per ml of milk. However, this limit is below the level of detection required to satisfy legislation in many countries (5). Sensitivity may be improved by flow cytometry using fluorescein labeled antibodies, or by using immunomagnetic separation as the specific step in combination with a less specific staining such as viability staining for flow cytometric detection of the separated cells (6).

IV.   METABOLISM

To permit routine in-process measurements in a production setting to monitor critical control points very rapid methods are needed. ATP bioluminescence and impedance are two methodologies which emerged about a decade ago and

that have been extensively evaluated, especially in the dairy and meat industry for fast and reliable microbiological screening of raw material on arrival at the processing plant. Both methods rely on monitoring the metabolic activity of microorganisms. Often, the major drawback of these methods is that the detection limit requires high numbers of bacteria (10^4–10^5 cfu/ml) present in the food matrix because the moment a signal can be measured or detected is in a limited time interval.

A.   ATP BIOLUMINESCENCE

ATP bioluminescence acts by measuring ATP levels in bacterial cells in order to calculate the number of cells. ATP bioluminescence is a natural phenomenon which is responsible for the glowing of fireflies. When the enzyme luciferase and the substrate D-luciferin are added in excess amounts, the light generated is proportional to the ATP present, according to the following reaction.

$$\text{Luciferin} + \xrightarrow[\text{Mg}^{2+}]{\text{Luciferase}} \text{Oxyluciferin} + \\ \text{ATP} + O_2 \qquad\qquad \text{AMP} + CO_2 + PPi +$$

ATP measurements take about 10–15 minutes. There are two major fields for the application of the ATP bioluminescence in the context of food diagnostics (7):

- Measurement of microbial ATP to determine microbial cell counts
- Measurement of total ATP to test the efficiency of cleaning procedures

1. Measurement of Microbial ATP to Determine Microbial Cell Counts

The problem with ATP bioluminescence is that ATP is the primary energy source of all living cells and the food samples themselves (fat cells in milk, blood, muscle cells) will also contain large amounts of this energy source which have to be destroyed before microbial ATP can be measured. An initial step (enzymatic, physical) for the release and destruction of any somatic cell's ATP should be included before bacterial ATP can be measured.

The use of ATP bioluminescence has been evaluated for the counting of microorganisms present in raw milk (8) or on the surface of raw meat (9, 10) upon delivery to the processing plant. In order to predict CFU values from relative light units (RLU) a correlation needs to be established (Figure 55.2) (8), imposing the necessity of an extensive standardization. This correlation is not universal and should be performed 'in-house.' Indeed the RLU that are measured depend on the actual experimental conditions (type of food matrix) and the type of luminometer for ATP measurement. In general, ATP bioluminescence is not recommended for accurate enumeration of CFU but better suited for a good bacteriological grading of the samples. Each interval of RLU may be considered as a cut-off level, an arbitrary boundary that separates defined levels of microbiological quality. ATP bioluminescence can only be used to control microbial contamination when the food to be tested is expected to have a total viable count above the detection limit of 10^4 cfu/g or cm^2. ATP readings only allow conclusions on the levels of bacterial cells present and not on the composition of the microflora. No correlation can be established between ATP readings and the presence of pathogens.

2. Measurement of Total ATP to Test the Efficiency of Cleaning Procedures

Because of the problems described with non-microbial ATP, the measurement of ATP bioluminescence is probably best suited to detect contaminated surfaces on equipment associated with food production. Residues of ATP (microbial or non-microbial) on equipment and working surfaces which have already undergone cleaning procedures suggest insufficient cleaning. As the corresponding tests can be carried out on site with portable luminometers and as results are available within 5 minutes, corrective measures can be taken immediately. Application of ATP determination for hygiene monitoring again necessitates the establishment of cut-off values to be linked to a hygienic standard (dirty, unsatisfactory, tolerable, clean) (Table 55.2) (11). As criteria differ according to the product (e.g., fat remaining in the deep reliefs of the surfaces may produce high RLUs) and kind of surface (e.g., plastic surface yielded higher RLU values than a stainless steel surface), each plant should set its own limits (11).

B. CONDUCTIMETRY/IMPEDANCE

Conductimetry or impedance measurements are based on the detection of electrical current during microbial growth. Changes are caused by bacteria that metabolize uncharged macromolecules in the medium (proteins, carbohydrates, lipids) to mostly charged particles (amino acids, lactate, acetate, etc.), increasing the conductivity of the medium and causing a decrease in electrical impedance. Specially developed media are required for these methods. During the incubation period of the inoculated broth in the instrument, changes in conductance/impedance are measured at regular time intervals. The time taken to reach the threshold value for detection is related to the number of target organisms inoculated in the medium and their subsequent growth. Detection time is inversely related to the bacterial number: the lower the initial content, the longer the detection time (up to 16 h for low numbers ($\pm 10^2$/ml)) (Figure 55.3). The results are presented as a conductance/impedance curve, which is compared with a previously generated calibration curve to estimate the numbers of bacteria. The systems most commonly used to estimate total viable count or indicator organisms include the Bactometer (bioMérieux), Malthus (Malthus Instruments), RABIT (Don Whitley Scientific Ltd.) and Bactrac (Sy-lab). They are fully automated to enable continuous monitoring of changes in electrical current in several samples at the same time. A drawback of

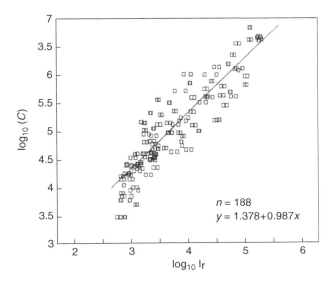

FIGURE 55.2 Relation between relative light intensity, Ir, with an improved ATP filtration method and numerical value of number concentration of bacteria in ml-1, both log-transformed, in 206 raw milk samples. Orthogonal linear regression line calculated for samples with a plate count ≥ 10000 ml-1 (n = 188). (From Reference 8.)

TABLE 55.2
Hygienic Standard of Cleaned and Disinfected Surfaces in Meat Cutting Plants (11)

Material	Dirty RLU/20 cm³	Unsatisfactory RLU/20 cm³	Tolerable RLU/20 cm³	Clean RLU/20 cm³
Stainless steel	>1000	1000-200	199-55	<55
Plastic	>2000	2000-600	599-190	<190

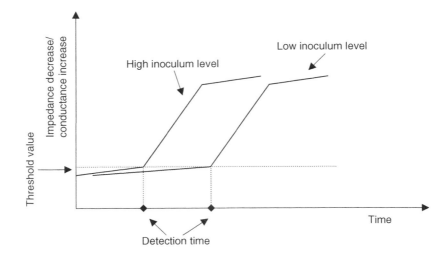

FIGURE 55.3 Graphic presentation of impedance readings, threshold value and detection time.

these electrical measurements is that the food matrix and the degree of sub-lethal stress to which the microflora is exposed may influence the analysis, which necessitates the determination of calibration curves for each food matrix examined.

Indirect conductimetry is based on the production of carbon dioxide by growing microorganisms. The carbon dioxide is absorbed into an alkaline solution and the reduction of conductivity of the solution is measured. This method is suitable for food products with low contamination levels such as juices and beverages, since carbon dioxide formation can be detected much earlier. Specific growth media are not necessary.

Detection of pathogenic bacteria such as *Salmonella* may also be done by the conductance method but usually pre-enrichment is required. Immunomagnetic separation (IMS) to capture and concentrate salmonellae from pre-enriched broth prior to inoculating the impedance medium has been evaluated. Additionally, a reduced pre-enrichment period was proposed since salmonellae from a 6-h pre-incubation period were detected in 5–7 h by impedance. Under these conditions the impedance method can be classified as a rapid method for detection of *Salmonella*.

For more information on the impedance systems available and their use as a rapid method in food microbiology the reader is referred to the reviews of Silley and Forsythe (12) and Wawerla et al. (13).

V. BACTERIAL BIOLUMINESCENCE/ REPORTER BACTERIOPHAGE ASSAYS

Bacterial bioluminescence is a specific bioluminescent assay which shows promise for rapid detection of food-borne pathogens. Many marine microorganisms like *Vibrio* spp. or *Photobacterium* spp. are capable of emitting light due to the presence of so-called *lux*-genes. The introduction of these *lux*-genes into highly specific bacteriophages by genetic engineering has resulted in the development of rapid and sensitive methodologies for pathogens in food-stuffs. Bacteriophages are highly specific for bacteria, usually to the genus level, and as they need host cell machinery to multiply they are good indicators of bacterial viability, too. In the luminescent phage test concept, bacteriophages possessing *lux*-genes infect target bacteria. This infection results in expression of the light-emitting genes which renders the bacteria luminescent upon the addition of an exogenous substrate. Luminescent bacteriophage assays have been developed to detect *Escherichia coli*, *Salmonella* spp. and *Listeria monocytogenes* (14). Loessner et al. (15) described the luciferase reporter bacteriophage A511: *luxAB* to detect viable *L. monocytogenes* in foods, where, without prior enrichment, as few as 500 cells were detected. The presence of less than one cfu/g could be detected within 24 h. Additionally, the assay could detect *L. monocytogenes* cells from naturally contaminated foods, including meat, poultry and various cheeses (16).

Apart from bioluminescent reporter genes, other reporter genes have been implicated in reporter bacteriophage assays. The ability of the *ina*-genes to confer ice nucleation activity on bacteria previously unable to produce ice nuclei, is the basis of a commercially available assay known as the Bacterial Ice Nucleation Diagnostic (BIND) (17). This test uses a genetically modified *Salmonella*-specific phage carrying an *ina*-gene. Due to the synthesis of an ice-nucleating protein *Salmonella*-positive samples will freeze while uncontaminated samples remain in a supercooled liquid state (temperature lowered to −9.3°C or below). It enables the detection of less than 10 *Salmonella* cells per g of food within 2–6 h (18).

The use of reporter bacteriophage assays for the rapid detection of food-borne pathogens is a powerful technique with a strong potential for future applications. Despite this, the technology has not been widely accepted. One potential problem may be the fact that an individual bacteriophage may not possess the host range required to detect all isolates of a bacterial species (14).

VI. IMMUNOLOGICAL METHODS

Over the past two decades, immunological techniques have been developed in a number of different formats for application as rapid confirmation tests (agglutination), as improvements for currently available enrichment and isolation methods (immunomagnetic separation), or as rapid detection methods (ELISA) of food-borne pathogens and their toxins. Immunoassays are based on the specific reaction of an antigen (a specific lipopolysaccharide on the outer cell wall, a protein on the flagella of motile bacteria, or a toxin) with its antibody. Sensitivity and specificity of immunoassays are mainly determined by the antibody used. In this respect the use of well-selected monoclonal antibodies can be of advantage. Each immunoassay may be sensitive to non-specific reactions, for example, *Escherichia hermanni* is known to cross-react with *Escherichia coli* O157 in specific immunoassays. Recognition of false positive results is necessary and supplementary tests such as biochemical tests are recommended to confirm the presence of the target organism.

A. HOMOGENOUS IMMUNOASSAYS

1. Latex Agglutination

Traditional agglutination tests rely on the interaction between soluble antibody (in an antiserum) and a particulate antigen such as a bacterial cell, resulting in visual clumping (agglutination). Agglutination is often used to confirm the serological identity of a pathogenic isolate and is a common test in case of detection of *E. coli* O157 or *Salmonella*.

Latex agglutination uses latex particles to amplify antigen:antibody agglutination reactions. The latex particle

is coated with antibody for detection of antigen such as a toxin or a component of a bacterial cell. Upon reaction, cross-linking of the latex particles results in the formation of a lattice structure which is visible to the naked eye as agglutination. If the target antigen is absent or below the detection limit of the test, the lattice structure does not form and the coated latex particles form a homogenous suspension. Latex agglutination for toxins is referred to as Reversed Phase Latex Agglutination (RPLA). Oxoid Ltd (Basingstoke, Hampshire, England) is one manufacturer that provides a range of RPLA kits for the detection of different bacterial toxins.

2. Immunochromatography

Lateral flow immunochromatographic devices were originally introduced, and are now widespread, in clinical diagnosis. They are now being applied for rapid detection of food-borne pathogens. A sample of enrichment culture is added to the sample port of the device. The liquid migrates by capillary diffusion along the surface of a solid support. During this flow, any target organism present reacts with a conjugate (antibody linked to a chromogen) contained in the device. The resulting complex proceeds to move and migrate towards the capture binding protein where it becomes immobilized and forms a visible line in a viewing window (Figure 55.4). For the test to be valid a control line should form in a second viewing window. In an evaluation of rapid methods for detecting *E. coli* O157 on beef carcasses three immunochromatographic methods were compared to the conventional culture method. These assays were all simple and rapid to use, giving a result at least 24 h earlier than culture. However, although one of the assays compared favorably with culture, both other assays lacked the sensitivity of culture and this finding seriously limits their usefulness (19). This was already

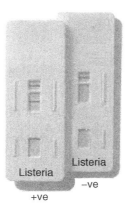

FIGURE 55.4 Example of a rapid Listeria test (Clearview™) based on immunochromatography showing test and control lines in the viewing window. (Courtesy of Oxoid, Basingstoke, Hampshire, England.)

mentioned in the study of Johnson et al. (20) who found 18 of the 107 culture-confirmed samples negative with the immunochromatography method for *E. coli* O157. False negatives spanned both high- and low-inoculum subsets.

B. HETEROGENEOUS IMMUNOASSAYS

The most widely used tests for rapid detection of pathogens, in particular *Salmonella, E. coli* O157 and *Listeria,* in foods are enzyme-linked immunosorbent assays (ELISA) using a sandwich configuration (Figure 55.5). The word 'sandwich' indicates that the assay uses two antibodies which trap or sandwich the target antigen. They use a capturing antibody immobilized on a solid matrix (strip, microtitre tray, dipstick) and enzyme labeling of the secondary antibody to make the primary antigen-antibody reaction detectable. Colorimetric or chemiluminescent substrates are used to visualize the antibody-antigen-antibody sandwich. A range of commercial immunological tests are available in different formats for the common food-borne pathogens. These tests normally require enrichment of the target bacterium to the level of the assay's detection limit (generally 10^4–10^6 CFU per ml). Their dependence on conventional cultural enrichment still remains the most important limiting feature of the majority of these immunoassays. In most cases, a presumed positive result is obtained in approximately 54 h. The magnitude of the resulting reaction will be proportional to the number of bacteria in the broth. However, results are usually converted to a dichotomous scale: results at or above a chosen cut-off value are regarded as positive and results below as negative. A high

cut-off value will decrease sensitivity and increase specificity and vice versa. False-positive or false-negative results can be significantly reduced by appropriate antibody selection and preparation. ELISAs are of considerable use in situations where the value of a negative result is high, for example, if a negative is required before a product can be released for distribution or further processing. This explains why these tests are extremely popular for routinely screening food samples following enrichment. In case of a positive ELISA the sample will need to be subjected to further conventional cultural testing to confirm the presence of the pathogen. Many of the ELISAs require the elaboration of a number of steps: capture of the 'target' antigen to the antibody absorbed to the solid phase, washing steps to remove 'non-target' antigens, capture of the secondary labeled antibody (=conjugate), washing to remove excess conjugate, addition of enzyme substrate and reaction which makes the procedure labor-intensive. The introduction of automated plate washers and readers can decrease the hands-on time. Typically these assays take between 1–2 hours, depending upon the format of the test and number and length of incubation steps (21, 22).

Automated immunoassays have also been developed. Vidas (bioMérieux, Marcy-l'Etoile, France) is an automated enzyme-linked immunofluorescent assay (ELFA) based on the detection of specific pathogens using specific antibodies coated on the inner surface of a tip-like disposable pipette which is introduced into the Vidas system along with the Vidas pathogen-specific reagent strip containing the boiled enrichment culture (Figure 55.6). A chemiluminescent substrate is used to visualize the antibody-antigen-antibody sandwich (23, 24). The Vidas system enables high-throughput and rapid screening of large

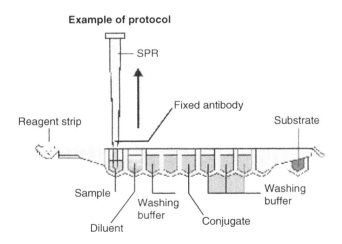

FIGURE 55.5 Principle of ELISA: capturing antibody immobilized in the well of a microtitre tray (a) interacts with target antigen in the sample and enzyme-labeled secondary antibody (conjugate) makes the primary antigen-antibody detectable (b). Washing steps are include to remove unbound conjugate and non-specific sample components (c). Colorimetric or chemiluminescent substrates are used to make the primary antigen-antibody reaction detectable (d).

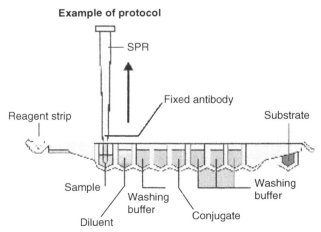

FIGURE 55.6 The Vidas system: an automated ELFA method based on the detection of pathogen-specific antibodies coated on the inner surface of a tip-like disposable pipette which is automatically transferred in the Vidas strip in which the test sample is introduced and which holds the necessary ELISA reagents. (Courtesy of bioMérieux, Marcy-l'Etoile, France.)

number of samples for presence of pathogens. The VIDAS is available for detection of *Salmonella*, *Listeria* spp., *Listeria monocytogenes*, *Campylobacter* spp., *E. coli* O157 and *Staphylococcus aureus* toxins.

C. IMMUNOMAGNETIC SEPARATION (IMS)

IMS, which employs paramagnetic particles coated with specific antibodies, promises to be a useful tool to remove small food particles from a sample and to selectively enrich and concentrate target bacterial cells by altering the ratio of target to non-target organisms in favor of the target organism. IMS techniques are nowadays widespread in food diagnostics (25). The efficiency and specificity of IMS depends upon the type of magnetic beads, the choice of the antibodies, the target organism, the numbers of the competitive flora and the food matrix. The sensitivity of the IMS technique varies from 10^2–10^4 CFU per ml. In most cases IMS after 24 h pre-enrichment results in an increase in the isolation of the pathogen with concomitant reduction in the number of competitive flora. Thus the use of IMS improves the sensitivity of microbiological tests and eliminates the need for a secondary 24h enrichment, thus reducing the total test time. IMS can be of significant value in conjunction with a number of endpoint detection techniques (Figure 55.7). IMS was shown to improve the sensitivity of ELISA, PCR and both used in conjunction enabled detection of *Salmonella* and *E. coli* O157 in foods within 24 h. As such, IMS is an important contribution to the development of a rapid and facile preliminary screening method of food for the presence of pathogens. IMS has become an integral part of the conventional as well as some rapid methods for *E. coli* O157. The use of IMS was shown to increase the isolation rate of *E. coli* O157. The IMS procedure has now been automated (BeadRetriever™, Dynal Biotech Ltd. Wirral, U.K.). Automated immuno-magnetic separation in combination with an enzyme immunoassay complements the conventional culture approach to produce more timely results for the detection of pathogens without significantly increasing the workload of the laboratory (26).

IMS methodology has been coupled to electrochemiluminescence (ECL) detection for rapid detection of *E. coli* O157 or *Salmonella typhimurium* with a commercial immunomagnetic (IM)-ECL sensor. Like other chemiluminescence techniques, ECL offers high signal-to-background ratios and is comparable in sensitivity to radioisotopic methods but has the advantage over other chemiluminescent techniques of being initiated by a voltage potential and thus providing better-controlled luminescence. ECL can be accomplished by heavy metal chelates such as ruthenium(II) trisbipyridal [Ru(bpy)$_3$$^{2+}$] chelate. Following IMS, [Ru(bpy)$_3$$^{2+}$]-labeled antibodies were added and after a short incubation period magnetic beads were captured and ECL was measured. The IM-ECL assays were capable of detecting less than 2000 CFU per ml in various food samples (27). The IM-ECL approach proved to be at least 100 times more sensitive than the current ELISA assays and enabled rapid detection (within 24 h) of low numbers (0.05 CFU per g) of *E. coli* O157:H7 in ground beef (28).

An alternative format for IMS, ImmunoFlow, has recently been developed to capture bacteria and eliminates an enrichment step to allow bacteria to be concentrated directly in food and water samples in 30 minutes. ImmunoFlow uses a high-flow-rate fluidized bed with large beads to capture and concentrate bacteria and is volume-independent. Specific antibody is covalently linked to the beads and large beads (>3 mm) are used to prevent sample clogging when testing food samples. Detection of bound targets is done using conventional ELISA protocols. This protocol enabled detection of 10 cells independent of the sample volume (29).

VII. NUCLEIC ACID-BASED METHODS

The application of molecular biological techniques to food microbiology has increased tremendously in recent years. These techniques represent a new generation of rapid methods, based on the primary information contained in the nucleic acid sequences of a particular organism. Indeed, nowadays a bacterial species is defined on

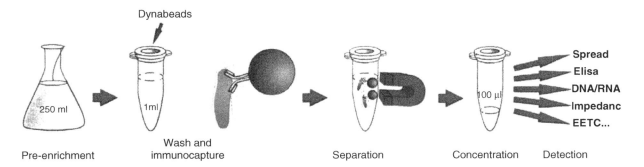

FIGURE 55.7 Immunomagnetic separation uses paramagnetic particles with specific antibodies to selectively concentrate bacterial cells. IMS can be of significant value in conjunction with a number of end-point detection techniques. (Courtesy of Dynal, Oslo, Norway.)

the basis of genetic information combined with a phenotypic description. Detection of pathogens based on specific DNA or RNA sequences thus goes back to the basis of classification of unknown organisms.

A. OLIGONUCLEOTIDE PROBES

With the classical DNA probe hybridization assay, microorganisms are collected on a filter, cells are lysed and the liberated DNA or RNA is immobilized in single-stranded form. The nucleic acid is identified by hybridization with radioactively or non-radioactively labeled specific DNA probes. For many pathogens rRNA genes are targeted in hybridization assays. The rRNA gene contains very conserved parts but also variable regions in which specific probes for a certain species can be chosen. In addition, rRNA is present in high numbers in the bacterial cell ($>10^4$/cell). Although all these DNA probes offer good specificity, they are limited in sensitivity. Typically, these assays need about 10^5–10^6 CFU per ml to obtain a reliable result. There are two types of user-friendly nucleic acid probe tests commercially available in routine food laboratories for several pathogens, e.g., *Salmonella, Listeria* spp., *Listeria monocytogenes*, etc. The Gene-Trak system (Neogen, Lansing, MI, U.S.A.) uses a dipstick format with a colorimetric detection and is generally applied after 48-h enrichment of the food sample. The AccuProbe test (Gen-Probe Inc., San Diego, CA, U.S.A.) is a chemiluminescent homogenous DNA probe system based on the principle of DNA hybridization protection. It is recommended as a culture confirmation test applied to purified colonies from isolation media, thus providing qualitative results (30).

Recently, PNA probes were developed as an alternative to DNA probes. Peptide nucleic acid (PNA) is a pseudo-peptide that binds strongly and specifically to nucleic acids. PNA consists of a non-charged polyamide backbone to which the different nucleo-bases are attached. The neutral PNA backbone confers unique properties on the molecule, relative to oligonucleotides. These include faster hybridization kinetics and the ability to use more stringent hybridization conditions that favor the disruption of the target structure while still promoting strong hybridization of PNA. PNA probes can be used for rapid detection and identification of specific microorganisms (31).

B. POLYMERASE CHAIN REACTION

1. Principle and Applications in Food Microbiology

A significant factor in the application of molecular techniques for rapid detection of pathogens lies in the development of the polymerase chain reaction (PCR). Conventional PCR assays incorporate a pair of oligonucleotide primers to amplify by use of the Taq DNA polymerase, a specific gene

that is then detected using agarose gel electrophoresis. PCR is based on repetitive cycles of DNA denaturation, primer annealing if they meet a complementary target DNA sequence, and elongation of the primers according to the complementary base sequence given by the target DNA by a thermostable DNA polymerase (Figure 55.8). This results in duplication of the target DNA after each cycle. Thus, during thermocycling, exponential amplification of target DNA occurs. PCR has become an important tool in microbial diagnostics because of the potential for detecting less than 10 copies of a specific gene within a complex sample. However, its sensitivity is also the greatest potential weakness of the method. Cross-contamination with external DNA or carry-over contamination of target DNA produced during prior amplification assays may give false results very easily. Technical improvements (real-time PCR instrumentation, enzymatic decontamination systems), the adherence to careful laboratory procedures and the use of dedicated materials and pre-aliquoted reagents may solve this problem. The reliable identification due to the use of specific DNA or RNA sequences and the intrinsic sensitivity of PCR shows tremendous promise for rapid detection of pathogens in foods. Specific primer sets were developed for almost all established and emerging pathogens in food microbiology (32, 33). Target genes involved for PCR detection of pathogens are numerous:

- rRNA genes or the spacer region between 16 S rRNA and 23 S rRNA genes.
- Virulence genes and toxin genes. Some virulence genes are located on plasmid DNA. A chromosomal location is preferred because of the instability of plasmid during subculturing. By targeting virulence genes (*hlyA*-gene for *L. monocytogenes*, *invA*-gene for *Salmonella*, *eae*-gene for *E. coli* O157:H7, *ail*-gene for *Y. enterocolitica*, etc.) or toxin genes (*vt*-genes for VTEC, *lt*-genes and *st*-genes for ETEC, *ct*-genes for *Vibrio cholera*, BoNT for *Cl. botulinum*, etc.), potential pathogenic strains can be discriminated from non-pathogenic strains belonging to the same species.
- A specific sequence with a known function, e.g., flagellin genes for *Campylobacter*, beta-D-glucuronidase gene for *E. coli*, IS 200 element for *Salmonella*, etc.
- A specific sequence with an unknown function, often derived from species-specific bands in DNA fingerprinting patterns.

Multiplex PCR uses multiple primer sets to amplify two or more target loci in a single reaction. It was described for simultaneous detection of *Listeria* spp. and *Listeria monocytogenes* in poultry products and dairy samples, *Salmonella* spp. and *Shigella* spp. in mussels, *Salmonella* strains and *Escherichia coli* O157 in meat,

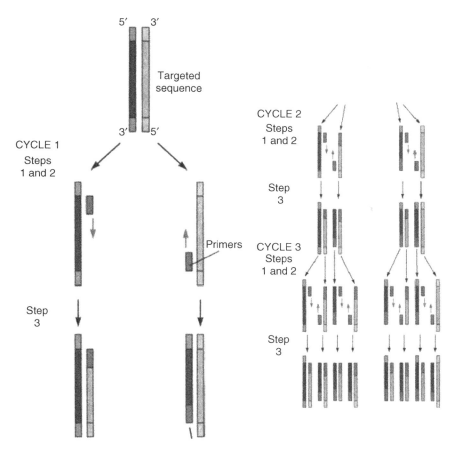

FIGURE 55.8 Principle of PCR. PCR is based on repetitive cycles of DNA denaturation and primer annealing if they meet a complementary target DNA sequence (steps 1 and 2), and elongation of the primers according to the complementary base sequence given by the target DNA by a thermostable DNA polymerase (step 3). This results in duplication of the target DNA after each cycle.

Campylobacter jejuni and *Arcobacter butzleri* in a range of food products (1).

PCR methods are of particular importance in two areas in the field of food microbiology:

1. In the context of rapid detection of food-borne pathogens.

   In accordance with immunoassays, PCR provides a rapid screening method for the presence of pathogens. If a specific primer set is chosen, amplification conditions well optimized, appropriate sampling protocols are applied and proper controls are included, PCR assays may be developed that are highly specific and provide a reliable detection of pathogens in the food sample under examination in a 24-h time period.

2. As a complementary technique in the identification of pathogens where the conventional cultural methodology lacks accuracy.

   Usually, phenotypic characteristics such as morphological, physiological and biochemical features are applied as confirmation tests for food-borne pathogens. However, sometimes the development of simple and restricted confirmation schemes may not be feasible to provide a reliable identification of the pathogenic organism, especially for particular genera or species with a difficult taxonomic position, e.g., identification of *Bacillus cereus senso stricto* being part of the *B. cereus* group including *B. cereus*, *B. anthracis*, *B. mycoides* and *B. thuringiensis* may be accomplished by a PCR method based on the *gyr*B-gene. In the case of emerging pathogens, e.g., pathogenic strains of *Escherichia coli* for which pathogenicity is associated with the presence or absence of certain virulence genes, PCR is an essential part of the full characterization of the strain. For the genus *Campylobacter*, which is characterized by its biochemical inertness, detection of the hippuricase gene by PCR provides a more useful test for confirmatory identification of *C. jejuni* because wrong identification may occur due to non-expression of the gene when only relying on the hippurate hydrolysis phenotypic confirmation test (34).

Although user-friendly PCR formats are available now, the technique still requires a significant amount of labor with regard to sample preparation and subsequent detection of PCR amplicons.

2. The Necessity of Sample Preparation in PCR-Based Pathogen Detection Systems

Any PCR-based detection system, while potentially very sensitive, must still confront a number of challenges inherent with sampling complex substrates such as food samples. PCR is an *in vitro* enzymatic reaction which only takes place under well-defined conditions of pH and ionic strength and is very susceptible to interfering factors which may be co-extracted from the food sample. If the complexity of the samples adversely impacts the assay, causing reduced amplification efficiency or complete inhibition of the enzymatic reaction, then a negative result may in fact be caused by lack of sensitivity to detect a given pathogen at the minimum concentration that is known to cause health risk. Thus sample preparation needs to be well designed: how much sample is processed, the efficiency of pathogen isolation, the efficiency of nucleic acid extraction, and the effect of co-factors that inhibit PCR. In the context of food diagnostics the following points need to be considered:

1. The PCR technique has the intrinsic sensitivity to achieve the required detection limit for pathogens in food (approximately 5–10 CFU per PCR reaction). However, direct detection of the pathogen in food samples by PCR presents a number of technical difficulties. The relative low levels of pathogens are present in a large amount of food (1–30 g used for food analysis) while only a small sample size (normally one ml of food homogenate) is used for nucleic acid isolation and only a small portion of the DNA extracted (2–10 μl) can be used in the PCR reaction. The pathogen may also be non-uniformly distributed in the food product (35).

2. Several studies indicated the presence of PCR-inhibitory factors in milk (calcium ions), soft cheeses (proteins and fats), red meat (coagulated blood) and various other foods (36, 37). The inclusion of proper controls makes it possible to develop and apply PCR methods for reliable and rapid detection of pathogens in routine laboratories. A positive control (in a separate tube) should be taken along in each PCR run and preferentially an internal control is co-amplified with the target DNA in each PCR tube to check on inhibitory compounds in the sample.

3. From a food safety point of view, care must be taken in interpreting results generated by PCR analysis since this technique cannot distinguish between viable and non-viable organisms. The precise correlation of cell viability with detection of DNA was shown to be poor, with DNA persisting in actively killed cells for significant periods of time (38). The detection of dead cells has to be considered.

The above-mentioned problems can be solved by the execution of PCR after a short enrichment period. Most commonly, the food sample is homogenized in a broth and the number of bacteria is increased *in vivo* by enrichment in order to obtain a sufficient number in a small volume while at the same time diluting out inhibitory components of the food. In addition, previous culture also ensures that only DNA from viable cells is detected (39). Prior enrichment also enables the use of rapid and simple protocols for lysis of bacterial cells and DNA purification. The commercially available PCR systems, the BAX™-assay (DuPont Qualicon, Wilmington, DE, U.S.A.) (20), the Probelia™ assay and its real-time format, the iQ Check PCR assay (Bio-Rad Laboratories, Marnes-la-Coquette, France) (40, 41) and the Taqman™ assay (Applied Biosystems, Foster City, CA, U.S.A) (42) all recommend the application of PCR after a 16–24 h pre-enrichment step.

The use of a shortened pre-enrichment (4–12 h) should be carefully evaluated. In contrast to fully viable pathogenic bacteria used for artificial contamination, bacterial cells in naturally contaminated foods are subjected to stress. The enrichment time needed for a positive PCR detection of stressed cells will be adversely affected. In this state, the microorganisms require a period of recovery before they regain full growth potential and limitation of the enrichment time could lead to an underestimation of the contamination of the food products (43). Often a technical intervention for further concentration of the bacteria is performed after enrichment to increase the sensitivity of the PCR assay and eliminate interfering food components. These include filtration, centrifugation, buoyant density centrifugation, immunomagnetic separation (IMS), surface adhesion or selective adsorption to metal hydroxides, etc. (1, 44). At present several protocols combining a short enrichment, subsequent bacterial concentration, DNA extraction and PCR analysis for rapid (within 24 h) detection of low numbers of pathogenic bacteria in various foods are described (Table 55.3) (20, 40, 42, 45–55). To reduce the time needed for a PCR result the direct application (without prior enrichment) to food is preferred. It must be considered that for application in routine microbiological analysis the complexity of the procedures should be limited. For fluid food products such as milk a single concentration step such as centrifugation or filtration allowed the detection of 1–10 CFU of *L. monocytogenes* per 25 ml

TABLE 55.3

Some Examples of Nucleic Acid Amplification Protocols for Rapid Detection (within 24 h) of Pathogens in Foods

Micro-Organism	Period of Enrichment	Sample Preparation	Detection	Food Types	Ref.
Escherichia coli O157:H7	6–11 h	InstaGene™ Matrix (Bio-Rad laboratories)	PCR + Molecular Beacon based detection	Pasteurized apple juice and milk (I)	Fortin et al. 2001 (45)
Salmonella	16–20 h	InstaGene™ Matrix (Bio-Rad laboratories) EnviroAmp Kit (PE Applied Biosystems)	Taqman PCR assay	Raw meat and shrimp (I +NC)	Kimura et al. 1999 (42)
Salmonella	16–20 h	Multiple protocols	Taqman PCR assay	Chicken carcass rinses, raw meat, raw milk (I+NC)	Chen et al. 1997 (46)
Salmonella	16–20 h	InstaGene™ Matrix (Bio-Rad laboratories)	Probelia™ PCR assay	Various foods (I + NC)	Fach et al. 1999 (40)
Escherichia coli O157:H7	20 h	BAX lysis reagent	PCR + agarose gel detection	Ground beef (I)	Johnson et al. 1998 (20)
Campylobacter spp.	6–24 h	Surface adhesion to a polycarbonate membrane + phenol:chloroform extraction	PCR + agarose gel detection	Meat and poultry (I+NC)	Cloak et al. 2001 (47)
Salmonella spp.	16 h	IMS + heat treatment	PCR + agarose gel detection	Dairy and egg products (I)	Rijpens et al. 1999 (48)
Escherichia coli O157:H7	6 h	Buoyant density centrifugation + boiling	PCR + agarose gel detection	Raw meat (I + NC)	Lindqvist 1997 (49)
Campylobacter jejuni	24 h	GuSCN lysis + silica-based extraction	NASBA + internal enzyme labeled detection probe	Various foods (I), poultry (NC)	Uyttendaele et al. 1995, 1996 (50, 51)
Escherichia coli O157:H7	0 h	Adsorption to titanium hydroxides + GuSCN lysis and phenol-chloroform extraction	PCR + Molecular Beacon based detection	Skim milk (I)	McKillip and Drake 2000 (52)
Listeria monocytogenes	0 h	Centrifugation + IMS + phenol: chloroform extraction	PCR +agarose gel detection	Ham (I)	Hudson et al. 2001 (53)
Campylobacter jejuni	0 h	Mechanical disruption in the presence of DNAzol	PCR+ agarose gel detection	Chicken carcass rinses (I)	Englen and Kelley 2000 (54)
Miscellaneous	0 h	FTA filters	PCR +agarose gel detection	Fresh produce (I), beef (I), apple cider (I)	Lampel et al. 2000 (55)

I = artificially inoculated, NC=naturally contaminated

(56, 57). To obtain this detection limit the filtration step was combined with a complex DNA-purification protocol.

3. Detection of PCR Amplicons/Real-Time PCR

The location of the primers in the selected gene determines the length of the amplification fragment. The detection of the amplicon is usually performed by agarose gel electrophoresis combined with an intercalating dye (e.g., ethidium bromide) and UV light. Electrophoresis makes it possible to estimate the length of the PCR product and length often serves as a proxy for product identification. However, production of non-specific PCR products is known to occur sometimes as the result of priming at loci that share homology with the target sequence or because of primer artefacts. Confirmation of the identity of the amplification product is recommended either by

- Hybridization with a probe internal to the amplification primers (Southern blots or dot-blots)
- Digestion of the amplicon with a restriction endonuclease
- Generation of an internal fragment using nested or semi-nested PCR
- Sequencing to identify the PCR product

In addition to testing the specificity of the product, hybridization with an internal probe or nested PCR can also improve the sensitivity of the assay system.

The application of fluorescent probes to the detection of PCR amplicons, together with suitable instrumentation capable of combining amplification and detection, has led to the development of real-time PCR methodologies. These assays eliminate the need for gel-based detection and yield data amenable to storage and retrieval in an electronic database. Fluorescent real-time detection uses either the SYBR Green fluorescent dye that binds to double-stranded DNA or specific hybridization of fluorescence-labeled probes to the amplicon (44, 58). For the latter approach three different chemistries are predominantly applied in food microbiology: Taqman probes (Applied Biosystems, Foster City, CA, U.S.A.), molecular beacons (Bio-Rad Laboratories, Marnes-la-Coquette, France) and the LightCycler hybridisation system (Roche Molecular Diagnostics, Basel, Switzerland). These systems are commercially available for routine detection of pathogens in foods. The application of each of these fluorescent real-time PCR techniques is linked to dedicated suitable instrumentation.

a. SYBR Green DNA binding dyes

SYBR Green binds specifically to double-stranded DNA (dsDNA). The unbound dye exhibits little fluorescence in solution in the presence of denatured DNA, but during elongation increasing amounts of dye bind to the nascent dsDNA. When fluorescence is monitored in real time in every cycle at the end of the elongation step, an increase is observed in fluorescence as the PCR progresses and target DNA is exponentially amplified. This method obviates the need for target-specific fluorescent probes, but its specificity is determined entirely by the choice of specific primers. Thus this assay is no more specific than conventional PCR with agarose gel detection. Additional specificity and PCR product verification should be achieved by the generation of melting curves following amplification. Melting curves are generated by slowly ramping the temperature of the sample to a denaturing level (95°C). As the dsDNA denatures, the dye becomes unbound from the DNA duplex, and the fluorescent signal decreases. This change in fluorescence can be plotted against temperature to yield a melting curve waveform. A characteristic melting peak at the melting temperature (T_m) of the amplicon will distinguish it from amplification artefacts.

b. Taqman probes

The Taqman assay utilizes the 5'-nuclease activity of the DNA polymerase to hydrolyse a hybridization probe bound to its target DNA. This probe (the Taqman probe) contains a fluorescent reporter dye at its 5'-end, the emission of which is quenched by a second dye at its 3'-end when the reporter and quencher dye are close to each other. Intact Taqman probes do not generate fluorescence. During the annealing both the primers and the Taqman probe will anneal to its complementary sequence of the target DNA. However, during elongation, when the Taq DNA polymerase is adding bases to the synthesize specific dsDNA, it will degrade the Taqman probe on its way by its 5'-nuclease activity, the quencher and reporter dye will separate from each other and fluorescence will occur (Figure 55.9). By measuring fluorescence in the PCR tube every cycle, the PCR reaction can be followed up in real time.

c. Molecular beacons

Molecular beacons are DNA hybridization probes that form a stem-and-loop structure; the loop portion of the molecule is complementary to the target nucleic acid molecule and the stem is formed by the annealing of complementary arm sequences on the ends of the probe. On one end of the probe a fluorophore is attached and on the other end a quencher of the fluorophore (Figure 55.10). In the absence of the target PCR product the beacon is in a hairpin shape and there is no fluorescence. However, during PCR reactions and the generation of target PCR products, the beacons will attach to the PCR products and cause the hairpin to unfold. As the quencher moves away from the fluorophore, fluorescence will occur and this can be measured. The measurement can be done every cycle of the PCR during the annealing step as the PCR is in progression allowing real-time detection of target PCR products and thus the presence of the target pathogen in the sample. By using molecular beacons containing different fluorophores, one can detect different PCR products in the same reaction tubes, which enables one to perform multiplex tests of several pathogens.

d. The Light Cycler hybridization system

This method uses two hybridization probes. One of the probes carries at its 3'-end a fluorescent donor which emission spectrum overlaps the excitation spectrum of an acceptor fluorophore that is attached to the 5'-end of the probe. Excitation of the donor results in fluorescence resonance energy transfer (FRET) to the acceptor and thus fluorescence. In solution the two dyes are apart, and because FRET depends on the spacing between the two dye molecules, only background fluorescence occurs. During the annealing step, both probes hybridize to their complementary sequence, specific target DNA, in a head-to-tail confirmation. This brings the two dyes in close proximity to one another, promoting FRET and fluorescence is measured. Increasing amounts of fluorescence are measured proportional to the amount of specific target DNA synthesized during the PCR reaction.

There are three competing instruments on the market to perform real-time PCR: the ABI PRISM® Instruments (Applied Biosystems), the iCycler (Bio-Rad Laboratories) and the LightCycler (Roche Diagnostics). All three are run as closed-tube systems requiring no post-amplification manipulations for detection of amplicons. This avoids problems of carry-over contamination. The entire PCR process is amenable to automatization and can handle large amounts of samples making real-time PCR suited for high-throughput screening applications. Although real-time PCR allows quantification, automated fluorescent PCR methods are predominantly used for qualitative pathogen testing (presence/absence in the food sample). However, the real-time monitoring of PCR reactions by tracking a fluorescent signal at every cycle during PCR thermal cycling demonstrates positive results more rapidly (at the cycle at which fluorescence exceeds the statistically determined fluorescence background threshold) thus decreasing the time to detect a positive sample.

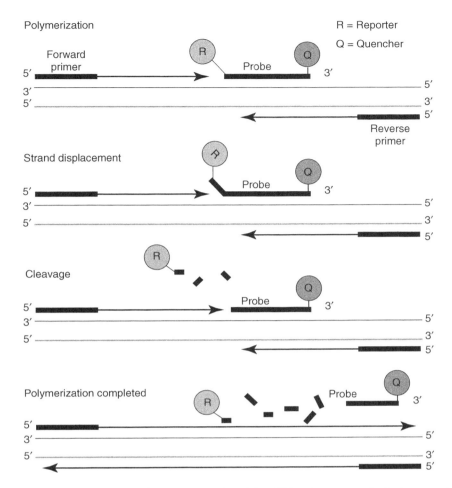

FIGURE 55.9 The Taqman assay utilizes the 5′-nuclease activity of the DNA polymerase to hydrolyze a probe bound to its target DNA. Subsequently, the quencher and reporter dye at the ends of the probe will separate from each other and fluorescence will occur. (Courtesy of Applied Biosystems, Foster City, California, U.S.A.)

4. Quantitative PCR

During real-time PCR, fluorescence values are recorded during every cycle and represent the amount of product amplified to that point in the amplification reaction. The more amplified product appears during PCR amplification, the more fluorescence intensity increases due to hybridization of the fluorescent probe to the PCR product. The instrument-associated software plots automatically during the amplification the RFU (Relative Fluorescent Unit) versus number of cycle which allows the detection in real-time of the PCR product. In the software a baseline for the RFU is calculated as a function of fluorescence noise. When adjusting the graph to have log RFU in Y-axis versus the cycle number in the X-axis it should be verified that the threshold cycle Ct (the cycle at which the fluorescence rises appreciably above background) is located in the linear part of the graph (corresponding to the PCR exponential phase since the scale is in logarithmic units). The combination of a sample preparation method for direct PCR (without cultural enrichment step) with a PCR method using a real-time monitoring fluorescent PCR amplicon detection system allows rapid quantification of pathogens. Quantification is based on the threshold cycle. The higher the level of pathogenic bacteria present in the sample, the higher the input of pathogenic target DNA in the PCR reaction and the faster the threshold cycle is reached. Quantification is performed by an external standard correlating the time to detection to the initial number of pathogens or DNA material used as an input (Figure 55.11). As the real-time quantitative PCR does not use an internal standard but is based on an external scale, quantification demands a good reproducibility of isolation/concentration of bacteria, DNA extraction and PCR. Quantification of *Salmonella, Campylobacter jejuni* and *Escherichia coli* O157 in pure cultures using real-time PCR was reported (59–61). Evaluation of a quantitative real-time PCR for rapid enumeration of *Listeria monocytogenes* showed that log differences in the pathogen added to cabbage could be reliably distinguished. The method produced a linear response over 7 log cycles from 10^2 to 10^9 cfu in 25 g of cabbage (62).

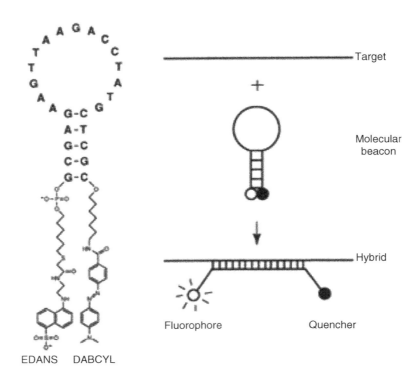

FIGURE 55.10 Molecular beacons are DNA probes that form a stem-and-loop structure. During PCR reactions, the beacons will attach to the PCR products and cause the hairpin structure to unfold. As the quencher moves away from the fluorophore, fluorescence will occur.

5. Microarrays

The recently developed nucleic acid microarray (oligonucleotide microchip) technology has been introduced to enhance the detection capabilities of PCR. In this context, microarrays serve as a system for rapid detection of multiple amplicons resulting from a multiplex PCR. DNA microarrays are in fact a series of reverse dot-blots for which sequence-specific short oligonucleotide-probes are attached to a substrate in a lattice pattern. Probes appear as "spots" in the final image where each spot represents a unique probe sequence. PCR products can deposit on the surface and if these PCR products specific hybridize to complementary probes, it can be visualized using some type of reporter molecule (either a fluorescent label or biotin that permits subsequent detection with a secondary label). This system enables simultaneous detection of the presence of distinct PCR products based on inter-product DNA sequence differences. Multiplex PCR in combination with microarrays have been used for the detection and genotyping (identification of various virulence factors) of enterohemorrhagic *E. coli*. The microarray technology has great potential for use in diagnostic microbiology, by combination of DNA amplification with a universal primer pair with an oligonucleotide microchip with specific probes for several pathogens (63).

6. RNA Amplification Systems

DNA was also demonstrated to persist in a PCR-detectable form in culture negative samples. However, the presence of intact DNA sequences does not give an indication of cell viability. RNA is chemically and biologically more labile than DNA. The type of target RNA, the primer choice, the inoculum level, the inactivation treatment and the holding conditions of the inactivated culture influence the half-life of the target RNA and as a consequence its (in)ability to be amplified. The longer half-life of rRNA and its variable retention following a variety of bacterial stress treatments make rRNA, under many conditions, a less accurate indicator of viability than mRNA. Studies investigating messenger RNA as a target for amplification showed genes with inducible expression (e.g., the *hlyA*-gene of *L. monocytogenes*) not to be suitable; because of the inducible expression, the extraction efficiency of the transcript is variable. The use of housekeeping genes (e.g., the elongation factor) seems a better target as an indicator for viability.

The most commonly used amplification techniques for detecting mRNA are RT-PCR (reverse transcriptase-PCR) or NASBA (nucleic acid sequence-based amplification). RT-PCR is a two-stage process, in which a target messenger RNA sequence is first transcribed into a complementary DNA (cDNA) sequence, either using random hexanucleotide primers or sequence-specific primers. The

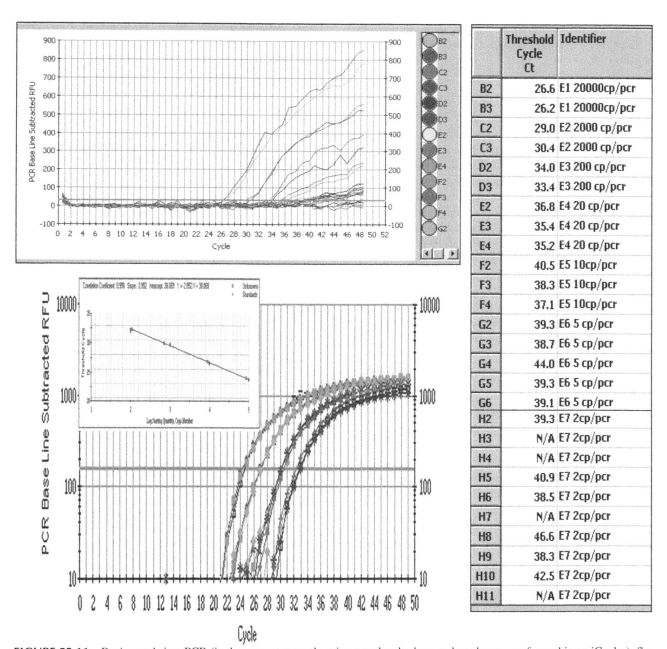

	Threshold Cycle Ct	Identifier
B2	26.6	E1 20000cp/pcr
B3	26.2	E1 20000cp/pcr
C2	29.0	E2 2000 cp/pcr
C3	30.4	E2 2000 cp/pcr
D2	34.0	E3 200 cp/pcr
D3	33.4	E3 200 cp/pcr
E2	36.8	E4 20 cp/pcr
E3	35.4	E4 20 cp/pcr
E4	35.2	E4 20 cp/pcr
F2	40.5	E5 10cp/pcr
F3	38.3	E5 10cp/pcr
F4	37.1	E5 10cp/pcr
G2	39.3	E6 5 cp/pcr
G3	38.7	E6 5 cp/pcr
G4	44.0	E6 5 cp/pcr
G5	39.3	E6 5 cp/pcr
G6	39.1	E6 5 cp/pcr
H2	39.3	E7 2cp/pcr
H3	N/A	E7 2cp/pcr
H4	N/A	E7 2cp/pcr
H5	40.9	E7 2cp/pcr
H6	38.5	E7 2cp/pcr
H7	N/A	E7 2cp/pcr
H8	46.6	E7 2cp/pcr
H9	38.3	E7 2cp/pcr
H10	42.5	E7 2cp/pcr
H11	N/A	E7 2cp/pcr

FIGURE 55.11 During real-time PCR (in the present example using a molecular beacon-based assay performed in an iCycler), fluorescence intensity increases due to hybridization of the fluorescent probe to the PCR product. When adjusting the graph to have log RFU in Y-axis versus the cycle number in the X-axis the threshold cycle Ct (the cycle at which the fluorescence rises appreciably above background) can be derived. Quantification is performed by an external standard correlating the time to detection to the initial number of pathogens or DNA material used as an input. (Courtesy of Bio-Rad, Hercules, California, U.S.A.)

cDNA sequence may then serve directly as a template for PCR. NASBA is a transcription-based amplification reaction that utilizes three enzymes (avian myeloblastosis virus reverse transcriptase (AMV-RT), ribonuclease H (Rnase H) and T7 RNA polymerase) acting together to mimic retroviral replication. A major advantage of NASBA over RT-PCR is that NASBA is performed isothermally which avoids amplification of double-stranded DNA and enables amplification of RNA from a pool of total nucleic acid.

Both methods have been applied for detection of microbial pathogens in food and water samples. NASBA accomplished rapid detection of food-borne pathogens (*Listeria monocytogenes, Campylobacter jejuni*) in foods after a preceding 24-48 h enrichment period. RT-PCR has been applied for detection of viable *Listeria monocytogenes* in beef and eggs and *Salmonella* Enteritidis in beef (64, 65) (Table 55.3).

RNA amplification methods offer in many instances the best means of detecting food-borne enteric viruses (hepatitis A virus, rotaviruses, Norwalk-like virus); other methods such as ELISA or cell culture are too inefficient or slow (66, 67).

7. International Acceptance

Despite rapid advances in the field of molecular-based methods, there is no doubt that the complexity of the food samples will continue to challenge further these rapid detection methodologies. Nucleic acid-based diagnostics, such as PCR, are very young compared to traditional detection methods and although well-established in research laboratories, still need to gain general acceptance as reliable methods in routine food diagnostics. However, it is considered that PCR can be established as a routine reference method, alongside traditional techniques within the next decade. Currently, there are international collaborative efforts to produce PCR-based methods for foodborne pathogens which are suitable for standardization, and thereafter adoption as routine diagnostic procedures. The framework of these efforts is based on three principal steps: demonstration of primer specificity, evaluation of the method through collaborative trial and, finally, proposal to an international standardization body such as CEN (Commission Europeén de Normalisation) (68). At the same time ISO Technical Specifications are under development to formulate some general definitions and recommendations on the requirements for sample preparation, the performance criteria for thermocyclers, and the requirements for amplification and detection in order to control the overall reliability of the PCR methods executed in food diagnostic laboratories.

VIII. BIOSENSORS

Biosensors are defined as analytical devices which combine biospecific recognition systems with physical or electrochemical signalling. The architecture of a generic system comprises three components: the biospecific reaction, the signal emitted when the target is bound, and the platform, which transduces the binding reaction into a machine-readable output signal. Recently new concepts have begun to yield biosensors aimed at addressing pathogen detection in the food industry. They consist of immobilized biologically active material (e.g., enzymes, antibodies or antigens, nucleic acids) in close proximity to a receiving transducer unit. Target recognition results in the generation of an electrical, optical or thermal signal which is proportional to the concentration of target molecules. However, the application of biosensors to the on-line detection of food pathogens is seriously hampered by problems of stability, sterilizability, sensitivity and matrix interferences. Some current papers have reported the detection of common food-borne pathogens like *E. coli*, *Salmonella* or *Listeria* in model systems within minutes.

Only very few papers, however, deal with their direct detection in food samples. Given the complexity of the different types of biosensors and their limited application in food pathogen testing, we refer to excellent reviews by Ivnitski et al. (69) and Hall (70) for further reading.

IX. VALIDATION OF ALTERNATIVE (RAPID) METHODS

In the past, different countries have developed different validation schemes. Several standardization organizations such as AOAC, IDF, AFNOR, NMKL, etc. have expanded their activities and started up a validation protocol for alternative methods. This has frustrated kit manufacturers, as they have to undertake a number of different validations in different countries, in order to get widespread acceptance of their test. There is a need for harmonization in validation schemes. In 2002, the European Standard "Protocol for the Validation of Alternative Methods" was accepted by the CEN. Through the CEN/ISO "Vienna agreement," this European Standard will also be adopted as an ISO standard (ISO 16140) and agreements have been made with AOAC International for mutual recognition of the different validation schemes. A European certification organization named MicroVal for independent validation and approval of alternative methods based on the European standard is set up and pilot validation studies are ongoing. The proposed ISO 16140 standard for validation of alternative methods describes a technical protocol for the validation of qualitative methods and a technical protocol for the validation of quantitative methods which both include a method comparison study and an interlaboratory study. Specific recommendations are given relating to the experimental setup of the measurement protocol and the calculation and interpretation of the data obtained using appropriate statistics. Nevertheless, the acceptance criteria are not clearly defined in the protocol. Results of the alternative method should be 'comparable' to those of the reference method. The actual criteria will depend upon the type of method and the circumstances under consideration.

In the U.S. but also worldwide, AOAC International, which has a long tradition in validation of methods, is the expert organization for validation of alternative (rapid) methods. The collaborative study forms the essence of the AOAC validation process. In this study, competent, experienced analysts, working independently in different laboratories, use a specified method to analyze homogeneous samples for a particular microorganism. An Associate Referee, under the guidance of the General Referee and assisted by a statistical consultant, is responsible for the actual development of the protocol for the collaborative study which should be approved through the Methods Committee on Microbiology and Extraneous Materials. The Associate Referee also conducts ruggedness testing and a pre-collaborative study to determine the applicability of the method for detection of the target organism(s) in a wide range of food matrices and conditions. The Associate Referee is required to be an expert in a particular target organism or a particular type of method or a food matrix or a combination of these. The General Referee must be a recognized authority in the field of interest (71). For the parameters taken into consideration to evaluate the performance of alternative (rapid) methods the reader is referred to Chapter 54.

X. CONCLUSIONS

Improvements in the field of instrumentation and data processing, immunology and molecular biology have led to the development of rapid (within 24–48 h) methods for the detection of food-borne pathogens. The introduction of these methods for 'real-time' detection of specific bacteria is hampered by the complexity of the food matrix and the low numbers of pathogens present in the sample. One of the most challenging problems is sample preparation. More research is needed on techniques for separating microorganisms from the food matrix and for concentrating them before detection. The potential of combining different methods should be further exploited. Results obtained from alternative (rapid) methods should be carefully interpreted because positive tests are not necessarily linked to biological activity and should be supported by classical cultural methods which are still the reference methods whereas negative test results are only representative for the absence of the pathogen in the sample taken at that time. Anyhow, it should be kept in mind that microbiological monitoring of foods as such cannot control entirely microbiological quality or food safety. It is only a tool to verify the well functioning of preventive measures taken to eliminate, reduce or prevent the contamination from spoilage or pathogenic microorganisms.

ACKNOWLEDGMENTS

Mieke Uyttendaele is indebted to the Fund for Scientific Research, Flanders, for a position as a postdoctoral research assistant.

REFERENCES

1. E D'Haese, HJ Nelis, M Uyttendaele, J Debevere. Real-time detection of pathogenic bacteria in foods. In: BW Blais. ed. Current Challenges in Food Microbiology. Kerala: Research Signpost, 2003, pp 111–134.

2. ML Tortorello, D Stewart. Antibody-direct epifluorescent filter technique for rapid, direct enumeration of *Escherichia coli* O157:H7 in beef. Appl Environ Microbiol 60:3553–3559, 1994.

3. ML Tortorello, KF Reineke. Direct enumeration of *scherichia coli* and enteric bacteria in water, beverages and sprouts by 16S rRNA in situ hybridisation. Food Microbiol 17:305–313, 2000.

4. P Attfield, T Gunasekera, A Boyd, D Deere, D Veal. Applications of flow cytometry to microbiology of food and beverage industries. Australasian Biotechnology 9:159–166, 1999.

5. TS Gunasekera, PV Attfield, DA Veal. A flow cytometry method for rapid detection and enumeration of total bacteria in milk. Appl Environ Microbiol 66:1228–1232, 2000.

6. CN Jacobsen, J Rasmussen, M Jacobsen. Viability staining and flow cytometric detection of *Listeria monocytogenes*. J Microbiol Methods 28:35–43, 1997.

7. R Tholen, R Stephan, F Untermann. The application of ATP bioluminescence to the meat industry. In: Proceedings of a Concerted Action CT 94–1456 meeting "Microbial control in the meat industry": Factors affecting the microbial quality of meat. 4. Microbial methods for the meat industry. MH Hinton and C Rowlings. Eds. Bristol, U.K.: University of Bristol Press, 1997, pp. 75–82

8. W Reybroeck, E Schram. Improved ATP filration method to assess bacteriological quality of raw milk based on bioluminescence of adenosine triphosphate. Neth Milk Dairy J 49:1–14, 1995.

9. DA Bautista, JP Vaillancourt, RA Clarke, S Renwick, MW Griffiths. M.W Rapid assessment of microbiological quality of poultry carcasses using ATP bioluminescence. J Food Prot 58:551–554, 1995.

10. GR Siragusa, CN Cutter, WJ Dorsa, M Koohmaraie. Use of a rapid microbial ATP bioluminescence assay to detect contamination on beef and pork carcasses. J Food Prot 58:770–775, 1995.

11. H Poggemann, J Baumgart. Hygiene monitoring by ATP-determination with the HY-LITE™ system. Fleischwirtschaft 76:272–273, 1996.

12. P Silley, S Forsythe. Impedance microbiology – a rapid change for microbiologists. J Appl Bacteriol 80:233–243, 1996.

13. M Wawerla, A Stolle, B Schalch, H Eisgruber. Impendance microbiology: applications in food hygiene. J Food Prot 62:1488–1496, 1999.

14. L Goodridge, M Griffiths. Reporter bacteriophage assays as a means to detect foodborne pathogenic bacteria. Food Res Int 35:863–870, 2002.

15. MJ Loessner, CED Rees, GSAB Stewart, S Scherer. Construction of luciferase reporter bacteriophage A511::luxAB for rapid and sensitive detection of viable *Listeria* cells. Appl Environ Microbiol 62:1133–1140, 1996.

16. MJ Loessner, M Rudolf, S Scherer. Evaluation of luciferase reporter bacteriophage A511::luxAB for detection of *Listeria monocytogenes* in contaminated foods. Appl Environ Microbiol 63:2961–2965, 1997.

17. PK Wolber, RL Green. Detection of bacteria by transduction of ice nucleation genes. Trends Biotechnol 8:276–279, 1990.

18. P Irwin, A Gehring, SI Tu, J Brewster, J Fanelli, E Ehrenfeld. Minimum detectable level of *Salmonellae* using a binomial-based bacterial ice nucleation detection assay (BIND) J AOAC Int 83:1087–1095, 2000.

19. PA Chapman, R Ashton. An evaluation of rapid methods for detecting *Escherichia coli* O157 on beef carcasses. Int J Food Microbiol 87(3):279–285, 2003.

20. JL Johnson, CL Brooke, SJ Fritschel. Comparison of the BAX for screening/*E.coli* O157 method with conventional methods for detection of extremely low levels of *Escherichia coli* O157:H7 in ground beef. Appl Environ Microbiol 64:4390–4395, 1998.

21. RR Beumer, E Brinkman, FM Rombouts. Enzyme-linked immunoassays for the detection of *Salmonella* spp. – a comparison with other methods. Int J Food Microbiol 12:363–374, 1991.

22. S Notermans, K Wernars. Immunological methods for detection of foodborne pathogens and their toxins. Int J Food Microbiol 12:91–102, 1991.

23. M Keith. Evaluation of an automated enzyme-linked fluorescent immunoassay system for the detection of Salmonellae in foods. J Food Prot 60:682–685, 1997.

24. MS Curiale, V Gangar, C Gravens. VIDAS enzyme-linked fluorescent immunoassay for detection of *Salmonella* in foods: collaborative study. J AOAC Int 80:491–504, 1997.

25. I Safarik, M Safarikova, SJ Forsythe. The application of magnetic separations in applied microbiology. J Appl Bacteriol 78:575–585, 1995.

26. P Duncanson, DRA Wareing, O Jones. Application of an automated immunomagnetic separation-enzyme immunoassay for the detection of *Salmonella* spp. during an outbreak associated with a retail premises. Lett Appl Microbiol 37:144–148, 2003.

27. H Yu, JG Bruno. Immunomagnetic-electrochemiluminescent detection of *Escherichia coli* O157 and *Salmonella* Typhimurium in foods and environmental water samples. Appl Environ Microbiol 62:587–592, 1996.

28. CG Crawford, D Wijey, P Fratamico, SI Tu, J Brewster. Immunomagnetic-electrochemiluminescent detection of *E. coli* O157:H7 in ground beef. J Rapid Meth Automat Microbiol 8:249–264, 2000.

29. BC Weimer, MK Walsh, C Beer, R Koka, X Wang. Solid-phase capture of proteins, spores and bacteria. Appl Environ Microbiol 67:1300–1307, 2001.

30. MJ Wolcott. DNA-based rapid methods for the detection of foodborne pathogens. J Food Prot 54:387–401, 1991.

31. H Perry-O'Keefe, H Stender, A Broomer, K Oliveira, J Coull, JJ Hyldig-Nielsen. Filter-based PNA in situ hybridisation for rapid detection, identification and enumeration of specific microorganisms. J Appl Microbiol 90:180–189, 2001.

32. JE Olsen, S Aabo, W Hill, S Notermans, K Wernars, PE Granum, T Popovic, H Rasmussen, O Olsvik. Probes and polymerase chain reaction for detection of foodborne bacterial pathogens. Int J Food Microbiol 28:1–78, 1995.

33. PM Schue, K Berghof, U Stahl. Detection of pathogenic and spoilage microorganisms in food with the polymerase chain reaction. Food Microbiol 15:13–31, 1998.

34. M Uyttendaele, J Debevere. The use of applied systematics to identify foodborne pathogens. In: T. McMeekin. Ed. Detecting pathogens in food. Cambridge, England: Woodhead Publishing Limited, 2003, pp. 332–359.

35. M Uyttendaele, J Debevere. Nucleic acid based methods for detection and typing of foodborne pathogens. De Ware(n) Chemicus 28:19–23, 1998.

36. IG Wilson. Inhibition and facilitation of nucleic acid amplification. Appl Environm Microbiol 63:3741–3745, 1997.

37. P Lantz, R Knutsson, Y Blixt, WA Al-Soud, E Borch, P Radström. Detection of pathogenic *Yersinia enterocolitica* in enrichment media and pork by a multiplex PCR: a study of sample preparation and PCR-inhibitory components. Int J Food Microbiol 45:93–105, 1998.

38. CI Masters, JA Shallcross, BM Mackey. Effect of stress treatments on the detection of *Listeria monocytogenes* and enterotoxigenic *Escherichia coli* by the polymerase chain reaction. J Appl Bacteriol 77:73–79, 1994.

39. U Candrian. Polymerase chain reaction in food microbiology. Int J Food Microbiol 23:89–103, 1995.

40. P Fach, F Dilasser, J Grout, J Tache. Evaluation of a polymerase chain reaction-based test for detecting *Salmonella* spp. in food samples: Probelia™ *Salmonella* spp. J Food Prot 62:1387–1393, 1999.

41. M Uyttendaele, K Vanwildemeersch, J Debevere. Evaluation of real-time PCR versus automated ELISA and a conventional cultural method using a semi-solid medium for detection of *Salmonella*. Lett Appl Microbiol 37(5):386–391, 2003.

42. B Kimura, S Kawasaki, T Fujii, J Kusunoki, T Itoh, SJA Flood. Evaluation of a Taqman™ PCR assay for detecting *Salmonella* in raw meat and shrimp. J Food Prot 62:329–335, 1999.

43. M Uyttendaele, C Grangette, F Rogerie, S Pasteau, J Debevere, M Lange. Influence of cold stress on the preliminary enrichment time needed for detection of enterohemorrhagic *Escherichia coli* in ground beef by PCR. Appl Environm Microbiol 64:1640–1643, 1998.

44. N Rijpens, L Herman. Molecular methods for identification and detection of bacterial food pathogens. J AOAC Int 85:984–995, 2002.

45. NY Fortin, A Mulchandani, W Chen. Use of real-time polymerase chain reaction and molecular beacons for the detection of *Escherichia coli* O157:H7. Analyt Biochem 289:281–288, 2001.

46. S Chen, A Yee, M Griffiths, KY Wu, CN Wang, K Rahn, SA De Grandis. A rapid, sensitive and automated method for detection of *Salmonella* species in foods using AG-9600 AmpliSensor analyser. J Appl Microbiol 83:314–321, 1997.

47. OM Cloak, G Duffy, JJ Sheridan, IS Blair, McDowell. A survey on the incidence of *Campylobacter* spp. and the development of a surface adhesion polymerase chain reaction (SA-PCR) assay for the detection of *Campylobacter jejuni* in retail meat products. Food Microbiol 18:287–298, 2001.

48. N Rijpens, L Herman, F Vereecken, G Jannes, J De Smedt, L De Zutter. Rapid detection of stressed *Salmonella* spp. in dairy and egg products using immunomagnetic separation and PCR. Int J Food Microbiol 46:37–44, 1999.

49. R Lindqvist. Preparation of PCR samples from food by a rapid and simple centrifugation technique evaluated

by detection of *Escherichia coli* O157:H7. Int J Food Microbiol 37:73–82, 1997.

50. M Uyttendaele, R Schukkink, B Van Gemen, J Debevere. Detection of *Campylobacter jejuni* added to foods by using a combined selective enrichment and nucleic acid sequence-based amplification (NASBA). Appl Environ Microbiol 61:1341–1347, 1995.

51. M Uyttendaele, R Schukkink, B Van Gemen, J Debevere. Comparison of the nucleic acid amplification system NASBA^R and agar isolation for detection of pathogenic campylobacters in naturally contaminated poultry. Food Prot 59:683–687, 1996.

52. JL McKillip, M Drake. Molecular beacon polymerase chain reaction detection of *Escherichia coli* O157:H7 in milk. J Food Prot 63:855–859, 2000.

53. JA Hudson, RJ Lake, MG Savill, P Scholes, RE McCormick. Rapid detection of *Listeria monocytogenes* in ham samples using immunomagnetic separation followed by polymerase chain reaction. J Appl Microbiol 90:614–621, 2001.

54. MD Englen, LC Kelley. A rapid DNA isolation procedure for the identification of *Campylobacter jejuni* by the polymerase chain reaction. Lett Appl Microbiol 31:421–426, 2000.

55. KA Lampel, PA Orlandi, L Kornegay. Improved template preparation for PCR-based assays for detection of food-borne bacterial pathogens. Appl Environ Microbiol 66:4539–4542, 2000.

56. MAB Starbuck, PJ Hill, GSAB Stewart. Ultra sensitive detection of *Listeria monocytogenes* in milk by the polymerase chain reaction. Lett Appl Microbiol 15:248–252, 1992.

57. L Herman, JHE De Block, RJB Moermans. Direct detection of *Listeria monocytogenes* in 25 milliliters of raw milk by two-step PCR with nested primers. Appl Environ Microbiol 61:817–819, 1995.

58. SA Bustin. Absolute quantification of mRNA using real-time reverse transcription polymerase chain reaction assays. J Endocrinol 25:169–193, 2000.

59. HK Novga, D Lillehaug. Detection and quantification of *Salmonella* in pure cultures using 5′ nuclease polymerase chain reaction. Int J Food Microbiol 51:191–196, 1999.

60. HK Novga, A Bergh, A Holck, K Rudi. Application of the 5′ nuclease PCR assay in evaluation and development of methods for quantitative detection of *Campylobacter jejuni*. Appl Environ Microbiol 66:4029–4036, 2000.

61. MA Ibekwe, PM Watt, CM Grieve, VK Sharma, SR Lyons. Multiplex fluorogenic real-time PCR for detection and quantification of *Escherichia coli* O157:H7 in dairy wastewater wetlands. Appl Environ Microbiol 68:4853–4862, 2002.

62. AJ Hough, SA Harbison, MG Savill, LD Melton, G Fletcher. Rapid enumeration of *Listeria monocytogenes* in artificially contaminated cabbage using real-time polymerase chain reaction. J Food Prot 65:1329–1332, 2002.

63. DR Call, MK Borucki, FJ Loge. Detection of bacterial pathogens in environmental samples using DNA microarrays. J Microbiol Meth 53:235–243, 2003.

64. PG Klein, VK Juneja. Sensitive detection of viable *Listeria monocytogenes* by reverse transcription-PCR. Appl Environ Microbiol 63:4441–4448, 1997.

65. EA Szabo, BM Mackey. Detection of Salmonella Enteritidis by reverse transcription-polymerase chain reaction. Int J Food Microbiol 51:113–122, 1999.

66. N Cook. The use of NASBA for the detection of microbial pathogens in food and environmental samples. J Microbiol Meth 53:165–174, 2003.

67. JT Keer, L Birch. Molecular methods for the assessment of bacterial viability. J Microbiol Meth 53:175–183, 2003.

68. B Malorny, PT Tassios, P Radstrom, N Cook, M Wagner, J Hoorfar. Standarization of diagnostic PCR for the detection of foodborne pathogens. Int J Food Microbiol 83:39–48, 2003.

69. D Ivnitski, I Abdel-Hamid, P Atanasov, E Wilkins. Biosensors for detection of pathogenic bacteria. Biosens Bioelectron 14:599–624, 1999.

70. RH Hall. Biosensor technologies for detecting microbiological foodborne hazards. Microbes Infect 4:425–432, 2002.

71. J Debevere, M Uyttendaele. Validating detection techniques. In: T. McMeekin. ed. Detecting pathogens in food. Cambridge: Woodhead Publishing Limited, 2003, pp 69–92.

#0145 - 271017 - C0 - 276/216/58 - PB - 9781574445510